FUNDAMENTALS OF INDUSTRIAL HYGIENE

6ᴛʜ EDITION

BARBARA A. PLOG, MPH, CIH, CSP
EDITOR IN CHIEF

PATRICIA J. QUINLAN, MPH, CIH
EDITOR

National Safety Council
Itasca, IL

Editor-in-Chief: Barbara A. Plog, MPH, CIH, CSP
Editor: Patricia J. Quinlan, MPH, CIH
Project Editor: Carolyn Chmiel
Cover Design, Interior Design, and Composition: Jennifer Villarreal
Executive Director, Publications: Suzanne Powills
Cover Photos: ©2012 Hemera, iStockphoto, and Comstock collections/Thinkstock, photo
courtesy of MSA – The Safety Company, and photo courtesy of Draeger

Copyright © 1971, 1979, 1988, 1996, 2002, 2012 by the National Safety Council
All Rights Reserved
Printed in the United States of America
18 17 16   12 11 10

Library of Congress Cataloging-in-Publication Data

Fundamentals of industrial hygiene / Barbara A. Plog, editor in chief ; Patricia J. Quinlan, editor.
  p. cm.
 Includes bibliographical references and index.
 ISBN 978-0-87912-312-3 (hardcover) -- ISBN 978-0-87912-313-0 (compact disc) --
ISBN 978-0-87912-314-7 (hardcover + compact disc)
 1. Industrial hygiene. I. Plog, Barbara A. II. Quinlan, Patricia, 1951-
RC967.F85 2012
613'.5--dc23

2012024308

2.5M1016   NSC Press Product Number: 15149-0000

Contents

Preface

This edition of *Fundamentals of Industrial Hygiene* presents original new chapters on Particulate Matter (Chapter 8), Ionizing Radiation (Chapter 11), Personal Protective Equipment (Chapter 23), Environmental Health and Safety (Chapter 28), Government Regulations (Chapter 30), and International Developments in Occupational Safety and Health (Chapter 31). All other chapters have been extensively updated and revised.

The primary purpose of this book is to provide a reference for those who have either an interest in or a direct responsibility for the recognition, evaluation, and control of occupational health hazards. Thus, it is intended to be of use to industrial hygienists, industrial hygiene students, physicians, nurses, safety personnel from labor and industry, labor organizations, public service groups, government agencies, and manufacturers. Others who may find this reference helpful include consultants, engineers, architects, lawyers, and allied professional personnel who work with those engaged in business, industry, and agriculture. It is hoped that this book will be of use to those responsible for planning and carrying out programs to minimize occupational health hazards.

Fundamentals of Industrial Hygiene is also intended to be used either as a self-instructional text or as a text for an industrial hygiene fundamentals course, such as the ones offered by the National Safety Council, various colleges and universities, and professional organizations.

The increase in the number and complexity of substances found in the workplace—substances that may spill over into the community environment—makes imperative the dissemination, as efficiently and conveniently as possible, of certain basic information relating to occupational health hazards and resultant occupational diseases.

We would like to gratefully acknowledge the work of the contributors to this book. They are all highly skilled and expert occupational health professionals.

I would like to very gratefully acknowledge the work of editor Patricia J. Quinlan whose professional knowledge, organizational prowess, and dogged determination helped us finish this edition. And I also so thankfully acknowledge the work of project editor Carolyn Chmiel. She is new to our team, jumped in after the project began, and her professionalism and tireless attention to technical detail has helped to produce the best edition yet.

Barbara A. Plog, MPH, CIH, CSP
Editor in Chief
July 2012

Dedication

This book is dedicated in loving memory to:
Doris J. Plog, medical secretary and dedicated backbone of the kidney transplant unit
at the Tucson Veterans Administration Hospital
Henry J. Plog, airplane mechanic at Davis Monthan AFB and firefighter for the Tucson Fire Department

and

Edward W. Quinlan, retired U.S. Army Lt. Colonel and budget analyst for the
Federal Reserve Bank of New York
Lillian M. Quinlan, wonderful mother and tireless volunteer in her church and community

Contributors

Michael S. Andrew, MS, CIH, CSP, LEED AP, has over ten years of experience in occupational and environmental health and safety. Currently, Mr. Andrew serves as the Asia Operations Director of Sumerra, an environmental health & safety and corporate social responsibility (CSR) consulting company. He has conducted hundreds of evaluations worldwide to evaluate physical, biological, and chemical hazards in both occupational and community environments. Mr. Andrew regularly provides training on occupational & environmental health and safety issues such as risk assessment and prioritization, root cause analysis, proper chemical management and handling, personal protection equipment, conducting exposure assessments, and forensic assessments of contamination/damage. Mr. Andrew is both a Certified Industrial Hygienist and a Certified Safety Professional. Additionally, Mr. Andrew is a Leadership in Energy and Environmental Design Accredited Professional. Mr. Andrew has a Master of Science degree from the Environmental Engineering department of the Georgia Institute of Technology.

Karen Andrews, MLS, is a professional librarian with 16 years of experience in the field. She has served as the librarian for the Labor Occupational Health Program at the University of California-Berkeley for 12 of those years. In addition, she has served as a reference librarian for the Sheldon Margen Public Health Library at the University of California-Berkeley for 11 of those years. Ms. Andrews has extensive experience in searching for literature on occupational safety and health issues for the LOHP staff, answering occupational safety and health queries from unions, labor/management groups, community organizations, worker centers, small businesses, schools, academia, government agencies, and the general public, and assisting the students and faculty of the University of California-Berkeley School of Public Health to find and organize the research literature they need for their projects. Previously, Ms. Andrews served as a librarian for the Woodbridge Town Library in Woodbridge, CT, where she provided reference services for teens and adults, oversaw the adult and children's programs, wrote press releases, and assisted with materials selection. She has a BA degree from the University of Iowa and a MLS from the State University of New York at Albany.

John R. Balmes, MD, is a Professor of Medicine at the University of California-San Francisco (UCSF) where he is the Chief of the Division of Occupational and Environmental Medicine at San Francisco General Hospital (SFGH) and an Attending Physician on the Pulmonary/Critical Care Service at SFGH. He leads an active research program involving controlled human exposure studies of the respiratory effects of ambient air pollutants in his Human Exposure Laboratory at the UCSF Lung Biology Center. Dr. Balmes is also Professor of Environmental Health Sciences in the School of Public Health at the University of California-Berkeley where he is Director of the Northern California Center for Occupational and Environmental Health. He leads and/or collaborates on several epidemiological projects involving the effects of exposure to occupational or environmental agents on respiratory health.

Sean Barry, RBP, is a Registered Biosafety Professional with over 35 years of experience in biological research and biological safety. He has been the Biological Safety Officer at the University of California-Davis campus for the past seven years, and is the chair of the University of California Systemwide Biological Safety Working Group, an affiliate of the American Biological Safety Association. Mr. Barry has broad experience in biological safety including Biosafety Level 3 laboratory development and management, select agent research, recombinant DNA program administration, and agricultural pathogen program management. Before working in the University of California-Davis biological safety program, Mr. Barry was a Staff Researcher at University of California-Davis and an independent environmental consultant. Mr. Barry has BS and MS degrees from the University of California-Davis.

Thomas E. Bernard, PhD, CIH, joined the University of South Florida faculty in 1989 and is now Professor and Chair of the Department of Environmental and Occupational Health. He offers classes in the industrial hygiene and safety programs. His active research programs involve the evaluation of heat stress and strain, the role of clothing in heat stress assessment, and ergonomics. Dr. Bernard also promotes the practice of industrial hygiene through active participation in professional associations.

Paul W. Brigandi has been working in the area of Hazard Communication for the past 21 years. He has served as the Hazard Communication subject matter expert for CGI Technologies and Solutions Inc. in Fairfax, VA, for the past 12 years. Mr. Brigandi has extensive experience in the area of international hazard communication regulations and represented industry during the development of the Globally Harmonized System (GHS) for the Classification and Labeling of Chemicals. More recently, Mr. Brigandi has led the requirement, design, and implementation phases of projects to deliver commercial software supporting compliance with GHS, REACH, and EPA's new Chemical Data Reporting (eCDR) requirements. Prior to working at CGI Technologies and Solutions Inc., Mr. Brigandi was a Senior Product Safety Advisor at Mobil Oil Corporation in Paulsboro, NJ, providing support for the planning and implementation of global product safety compliance programs. He has a BA from Rutgers University.

Barbara J. Burgel, RN, PhD, COHN-S, FAAN, is a Professor of Clinical Nursing and Adult Nurse Practitioner in the Department of Community Health Systems at the University of California-San Francisco School of Nursing. Dr. Burgel has taught in the Occupational Health Nursing graduate program since 1981 and is conducting research exploring health and safety concerns of taxi drivers.

Susan Caskey is a Senior Member of the Technical Staff in the International Chemical Threat Reduction Program at Sandia National Laboratories. Currently, she is the project lead for the analytical projects focusing on threat prioritization models and risk assessment models and tools. She also leads efforts for the International Biological Threat Reduction department on Biological threat prioritization and risk assessments. Ms. Caskey has degrees in Biology and Computer Science, specializing in information management, risk and decisional analysis, and security. She is certified in network security architecture and has designed and implemented secure information management systems worldwide. She designs methodologies for performing risk assessments and has conducted numerous risk assessments of biological agents and bioscience facilities. In addition, Ms. Caskey has designed and implemented network-based disease surveillance systems for humans and animals. She designed and developed the model and software for the two BioRAM tools (Biosafety RAM and Biosecurity RAM), including the backend database and communication components. She performs statistics-based risk assessments, audits and secures inventory systems, and conducts security assessments including reviewing the physical security, information security, personnel reliability, and safety of facilities worldwide.

Richard Cohen, MD, MPH, is a Clinical Professor of Medicine at the University of California-San Francisco. Dr. Cohen is board certified in both Occupational Medicine and General Preventive

Medicine. He has been a member of the CAL/OSHA PEL Advisory Committee and is a Fellow in the American College of Occupational and Environmental Medicine. He provides expertise in industrial toxicology and occupational medicine to industry, particularly in the pharmaceutical, biotechnology, and electronics sectors.

Craig E. Colton, CIH, is a Division Scientist in the Technical Service and Regulatory Affairs group of the 3M Occupational Health and Environmental Safety Division with 34 years of experience specializing in respiratory protection. His responsibilities as a Division Scientist include conducting workplace protection factor studies on 3M respirators, monitoring and responding to regulatory affairs related to respiratory protection, serving on various American National Standards Institute (ANSI) and International Standard Organization (ISO) respiratory protection standard committees, and providing technical assistance to respirator users. Before joining the 3M staff, Mr. Colton was an instructor at the OSHA Training Institute where he was course chair for respiratory protection and quantitatively fit tested OSHA personnel. Mr. Colton teaches continuing education courses for the University of North Carolina. He is a past chair of the AIHA Respiratory Protection Committee and Americas' Section of the International Society for Respiratory Protection and was a member of the ANSI Z88.10 subcommittee for Respirator Fit Testing Methods. He is currently a member of the ANSI Z88 Committee for respiratory protection, ANSI Z88.2 Subcommittee for respiratory protection selection and use, and ISO standard committee TC94 SC15 for respiratory protection.

Marjorie De Groot, MS, received her Master's Degree in Audiology from the University of Colorado in 1985. She has worked in various medical settings performing both diagnostic and rehabilitative audiology. Currently Ms. De Groot is employed as Director of the Hearing Conservation Program for the City and County of San Francisco. She is certified as Course Director with the Council for Accreditation in Occupational Hearing Conservation. She is a member of the American Academy of Audiology and the National Hearing Conservation Association.

Dorothy Dougherty, MS, is the Director of the Directorate of Standards and Guidance. Ms. Dougherty joined OSHA 18 years ago as a Supervisory Safety and Occupational Health Specialist. Since joining OSHA, she has held a variety of positions in OSHA's National Office.

Ms. Dougherty began her career with OSHA in 1992 as a Chief of the Compliance and Technical Guidance Division for the Office of Federal Agency Programs. She has worked as an Agency Liaison Officer in the Office of the Secretary; an Executive Assistant for the OSHA Assistant Secretary; a Deputy Director in the Directorate of Health Standards Programs; a Deputy Director in the Directorate of Standards and Guidance; and in October 2006 was named the Director for the Directorate of Standards and Guidance. Before coming to OSHA, Ms. Dougherty worked for Mine Safety and Health Administration for 9 years as an Industrial Hygienist and Coal Mine Inspector.

Amanda L. Edens, MSPH, currently serves as the Deputy Director for the Directorate of Standards and Guidance for OSHA where she oversees the Agency's development of safety and health standards and guidance. She joined OSHA in 1985 as an Industrial Hygienist in the standard setting division where she worked on a number of rulemaking projects, including asbestos, methylene chloride, cadmium, glycol ethers, lead, bloodborne pathogens, and tuberculosis. From 2002 to 2007 she served as the Director for the Office of Chemical Hazards-Metals where she led the agency's efforts on beryllium and hexavalent chromium. Ms. Edens received her Masters of Science in Public Health from the University of North Carolina in Chapel Hill.

Matt A. Fragala, MS, CIH, is a Certified Industrial Hygienist with more than 12 years of experience in the field of industrial hygiene. He is currently a Senior Scientist at Environmental Health

& Engineering and is the Environmental Health and Safety Practice Leader for the Building Science and Forensics Division. Mr. Fragala has extensive experience coordinating all aspects of industrial hygiene project work, including measurement and evaluation of worker exposure to contaminants and physical stressors in almost any occupation environment. Mr. Fragala works with a diverse range of organizations, including large corporations, government agencies, research hospitals, universities, and professional athletics. He has BS and MS degrees from the University of Massachusetts-Amherst.

Jennifer Gaudioso, PhD, is the Manager of the International Biological Threat Reduction program at Sandia National Laboratories in Albuquerque, NM. This program enhances U.S. and international security by promoting safe, secure, and responsible use of dangerous biological agents. Dr. Gaudioso and her Sandia team have worked extensively and internationally in laboratory biosafety, biosecurity, biocontainment, and infectious disease diagnostics and control. They have organized many international conferences, trainings, and workshops on these topics. In the past five years, the team has visited biocontainment laboratories in more than 40 countries, specifically to consult on laboratory biorisk management issues. Dr. Gaudioso and her Sandia team work with international partners, such as the World Health Organization, on the development of international laboratory biorisk guidelines and standards. She has served on the National Academies' Committees for "Education on Dual Use Issues in the Life Sciences" and "Anticipating Biosecurity Challenges of the Global Expansion of High Containment Biological Laboratories." She is author of numerous journal articles and has presented her research at national and international meetings. She also coauthored the *Laboratory Biosecurity Handbook,* published by CRC Press. Dr. Gaudioso serves on Sandia's Institutional Biosafety Committee, and is an active member of the American Biological Safety Association. She earned her PhD at Cornell University.

Elizabeth Gross, MA, MS, CIH, is Director of Environmental Health and Safety at the Whitehead Institute for Biomedical Research in Cambridge, as well as a Consulting Safety Officer for Safety Partners, a consulting firm providing contract environmental health and safety (EH&S) services to small and medium-sized biotechnology companies. She also serves as an independent consultant to several biotechnology firms.

Prior to working at Whitehead, Ms. Gross was EH&S Director at Dana-Farber Cancer Institute in Boston for 22 years. Prior to that, she was Assistant Industrial Hygienist at Harvard University. In both capacities, she has evaluated and helped control a broad range of potential exposures to workers.

Until 2011, Ms. Gross was a Visiting Lecturer at Harvard School of Public Health, and until 2005, at Boston University School of Public Health, where she lectured on Fundamentals of Industrial Hygiene and Laboratory, Hospital, and Office Health and Safety. She has also been an active participant in the American Industrial Hygiene Association, the Harvard School of Public Health Industrial Hygiene Program Advisory Board, the American Board of Industrial Hygiene, the Academy of Industrial Hygiene, and the Joint Industrial Hygiene Ethics Education Committee. She is a CIH and has an MS in Industrial Hygiene from Harvard School of Public Health, an MA from the University of California-Berkeley, and a BA from the University of Michigan.

S. Katharine Hammond, PhD, CIH, is Professor and past Head of Environmental Health Sciences at the University of California, Berkeley, School of Public Health, where she also directs the industrial hygiene program. She is a chemist, and her research focuses on exposure assessment for epidemiological studies. Dr. Hammond has developed new methods for collecting and analyzing chemicals in the workplace as well as assessing exposures without airborne measurements. Among her major research projects are studies of the relationship between diesel exhaust and lung cancer among railroad workers; the rates of spontaneous abortion among women who work in wafer fabricating clean rooms and their exposures to a variety of chemical, physical, and ergonomic agents; respiratory health effects of automobile assembly work; methods to reduce workers' exposure to lead during bridge rehabilitation; unintended consequences of environmental regulations on occupational exposures; and secondhand tobacco smoke exposure in the workplace and elsewhere. Currently, Dr. Hammond heads the Bay Area Solvent Study, which is examining neurologic, visual, neuropsychological, and reproductive effects of hexane and other solvents on automobile technicians. She is also studying the cardiovascular effects of particulate matter exposure among workers in the aluminum industry and in the automobile manufacturing industry.

Bob Hashimoto, MS, CBSP, is currently the Biosafety Officer at the University of California-Berkeley. He spent twelve years as a biosafety officer at the University of California-Los Angeles, the University of California-San Francisco, and Stanford University.

Mr. Hashimoto received his BS and MS degrees in Biology from the University of San Francisco. He is a member of the American Biological Safety Association and has earned his certification in his profession as a Certified Biosafety Professional through ABSA and the American Society for Microbiology. He also has commented on the rulemaking process for the Laboratory Hood Standard and Airborne Transmissible Disease Standard in the State of California. In 2008, Mr. Hashimoto received the ABSA Everett Hanel Jr. Award for career achievements in biosafety.

Theodore J. Hogan, PhD, CIH, is an Assistant Professor at Northern Illinois University where he conducts research on nanomaterial exposures and teaches industrial hygiene courses, including air sampling. He is a Member Candidate of the ACGIH TLV® Chemical Substances Committee and previously was on the ACGIH national board. Dr. Hogan has been a consultant to over 400 companies since 1990. In the 1980's he was corporate head of safety and industrial hygiene for Commonwealth Edison.

Michael J. Horowitz, MS, CIH, is currently a Senior Safety Engineer/Industrial Hygienist for Cal/OSHA's Research and Standard's Development Unit. His 23 years of work for the Cal/OSHA program include many years as a field compliance enforcement officer and as manager of district enforcement offices. He is proud to be a second-generation industrial hygienist.

Sarah Jewell, MD, MPH, is board-certified in Internal Medicine and Occupational/Environmental Medicine and a Clinical Professor of Medicine at the University of California-San Francisco. She is currently leader of the scientific strategy office at the German Center for Neurodegenerative Diseases in Bonn, Germany.

Rick Kelly, MS, CIH, is the Facilities and Environmental Health & Safety Manager for the Materials Sciences Division including the Molecular Foundry and Joint Center for Artificial Photosynthesis at the Lawrence Berkeley National Laboratory, University of California. In a long career with the university, Mr. Kelly previously served in several positions at the Lawrence Livermore National Laboratory and as Supervisor of Industrial Hygiene and Safety at the University of California-Berkeley. He was also the founder of an EPA grant-initiated health and safety training program at the University of California-Berkeley Extension.

Ben Kollmeyer, MPH, CIH, holds a Masters of Public Health from University of California-Berkeley and is a Certified Industrial Hygienist. He has extensive experience in the environmental health arena, conducting investigations involving a variety of physical, chemical, and biological hazards in occupational and community settings. He routinely consults in both the public and private sector, performing field investigations and developing prevention and management programs. With experience on a multitude large and high-profile building investigations, Mr.

Kollmeyer is frequently called upon to provide forensic analysis as an expert witness and to manage risk communication issues with stakeholder groups. In his role as Chief Technical Officer for Forensic Analytical, he is responsible for ensuring technical consistency and integrity throughout all consulting operations.

David L. Lee, PhD, OTR/L, is a Research Scientist at University of California at San Francisco, Department of Medicine, and University of California at Berkeley, Department of Bioengineering, UC Ergonomics Program. He has more than 10 years of experience in the field of ergonomics. Dr. Lee has extensive experience in the areas of prevention of upper extremity musculoskeletal disorders, human-computer interaction, input device design, occupational and office ergonomics, and rehabilitation. Dr. Lee's primary research expertise is in investigating the effect of input device and tool design on upper extremity motor control and physiology, particularly in the medical, dental, and human-computer interaction fields. He is also a registered and licensed occupational therapist. Dr. Lee received his PhD in Ergonomics and Injury Prevention (with minors in Biomechanics and Biostatistics) from Harvard University.

Andrew Levinson, MPH, is the Director of the Office of Biological Hazards in OSHA's Directorate of Standards and Guidance. Mr. Levinson works on emergency response and preparedness, infectious disease, and protective clothing and equipment issues. Prior to joining the Agency, he worked on emergency responder health and safety matters at the International Association of Fire Fighters and on safety and environmental compliance at Anheuser-Busch's Brewery in Cartersville, GA. Mr. Levinson received his Master's in Public Health from the Emory University's Rollins School of Public Health and is a graduate of the University of Michigan-Ann Arbor.

Janet Macher, ScD, MPH, is an air pollution research specialist with the California Department of Health Services. She has a master's degree from the University of California and doctorate from Harvard University with emphasis on industrial hygiene, public health, and microbiology. Dr. Macher studies engineering measures to control airborne infectious and hypersensitivity diseases, evaluates methods to collect and identify airborne biological material, and participates in investigations of bioaerosol-related illnesses in the state of California.

Howard Maibach, MD, is Professor of Dermatology at University of California-San Francisco. He has numerous publications, articles and books, on occupation dermatology. Dr. Maibach instituted the Occupational Dermatology clinic in 1963 and continues to work there.

H.J. (Hank) McDermott CIH, CSP, PE, currently is the President of H.J. McDermott, Inc., an occupational safety and health consulting firm. He has more than 40 years of safety and industrial hygiene experience in industry and the U.S. Air Force, where he served as a bioenvironmental engineering officer. He has a BS in Civil Engineering from the University of Delaware, an MS in Civil Engineering from Northwestern, and an MA in Public Administration from the University of New Mexico. He is the author of the *Handbook of Ventilation for Contaminant Control*, 3rd ed., published by the American Conference of Governmental Industrial Hygienists, and *Air Monitoring for Toxic Exposures*, 2nd ed., published by Wiley Inter-Science. He is a member of the California Occupational Safety and Health Standards Board, and is a Fellow of the American Industrial Hygiene Association.

Bruce Arthur Millies, JD, CIH, is a Certified Industrial Hygienist with more than 20 years of experience in the comprehensive practice of industrial hygiene. He formerly practiced law and has experience in workers' rights, environmental legislation, and hazardous materials regulation. He served for more than 15 years on the staff of the Safety and Health Department of the International Brotherhood of Teamsters, where he developed curriculum and trained worker-trainers to present training programs in hazardous materials, hazardous waste, construction safety, and radiological safety and hazard communication. He is a former Assistant Professor of Industrial Hygiene and Safety at the Harry Van Arsdale Jr. School of Labor Studies, Empire State College, State University of New York, and former Deputy General Counsel of the Massachusetts Department of Public Health. He has developed and presented safety and health workshops and classes for union members and government safety and health inspectors in Chile, Venezuela, Mexico, and Costa Rica. He is currently an Affiliate Assistant Professor in the Department of Environmental and Occupational Health Sciences of the University of Washington, and an Instructor for the OSHA Region X Education and Training Center. He has a BA from the University of Massachusetts, JD from Northeastern University, and an MS from the University of Washington.

Linda Morse, MD, is Board Certified in Occupational Medicine and former Chief of Occupational Health Services for Kaiser Permanente San Francisco. She is a Fellow of the American College of Occupational and Environmental Medicine and co-editor of Occupational Injuries—Evaluation, Management and Prevention, published by Mosby in 1995. Dr. Morse has lectured and written widely on diverse topics including firefighter health and safety, cumulative trauma disorders of the neck and upper extremity, and the role of the treating physician in the workers compensation system. She is also an Assistant Clinical Professor of Medicine at the University of California, San Francisco, Medical Center.

Jill Niland, MPH, has more than 30 years of experience in industrial hygiene and occupational health. She currently is the training director at Frontline Healthcare Workers Safety Foundation, where she develops and administers biosafety training programs for high containment laboratories through the National Biosafety and Biocontainment Training Program, sponsored by the National Institute of Allergy and Infectious Diseases. Previously she was principal consultant and partner in CDIC Chicago, an occupational safety and health consulting firm focused on training, auditing, and program development. Prior to 2000, Ms. Niland was occupational health programs manager and senior industrial hygiene consultant at the National Safety Council in Itasca, IL, where she was also an associate editor of the 4th edition of *Fundamentals of Industrial Hygiene*. In prior positions at Zurich American Insurance and at Alexander and Alexander, an insurance broker, she provided industrial hygiene services to clients in a wide variety of industries. Ms. Niland received a BA from Cornell University, Ithaca, NY, and an MPH from the School of Public Health at the University of Illinois at Chicago.

Elsa Nimmo, MS, CHP, is a Certified Health Physicist with over 30 years of experience in radiation safety program development and implementation in manufacturing, research, and academic organizations. She is currently the Acting Radiation Safety Officer for the University of California, Berkeley. In past years, she served on the subcommittees responsible for updating the ANSI standards *Sealed Source Classification* and *Classification of Industrial Ionizing Radiation Gauging Devices*. Elsa Nimmo has an MS in Medical Physics from the University of Wisconsin-Madison and a BS in Physics and Chemistry from the University of Redlands.

Elise Pechter, MAT, MPH, CIH, is a Certified Industrial Hygienist who works for the Occupational Health Surveillance Program at the Massachusetts Department of Public Health (MDPH). In this capacity she coordinates intervention activities in response to work-related asthma, teen injuries, and acute chemical poisonings, and works to integrate occupational health into public health activities. A member of ACGIH, NEAIHA, and APHA, Ms. Pechter chairs the Health/Technical committee of MassCOSH, and the adult asthma committee of the Massachusetts Asthma Action Partnership. In addition, she works on several other projects: the Toxics Reduction Taskforce for state purchasing of environmentally preferable products, supervising physicians in public health rotations at MDPH during their Occupational and Environmental Training, participating on the joint labor management health and safety committee for MDPH, and promoting occupational health and safety prevention in public health endeavors.

William Perry, CIH, is Deputy Director of the Directorate of Standards and Guidance, OSHA, where he is responsible for directing technical analysis and scientific research to develop standards and guidance materials on a variety of occupational safety and health topics. Since he began his Federal career at OSHA in 1994, Mr. Perry served on several project teams to develop standards for butadiene, respiratory protection programs, and updates for selected permissible exposure limits, ergonomics, and working conditions on shipyards. His contributions included developing health and risk assessments for both cancer and noncancer health effects and evaluating the effectiveness of alternative exposure control approaches. Prior to joining OSHA, Mr. Perry was Vice President of a consulting firm that assisted OSHA for over 10 years in conducting health and risk assessments, control technology evaluations, and economic impact studies for several OSHA standards including cadmium, asbestos, benzene, ethylene oxide, air contaminants update, and lead.

Mr. Perry graduated from the University of Maryland in 1975 with a Bachelor of Science degree in Microbiology, and earned a Master's degree in Microbiology in 1978. He has been certified in the Comprehensive Practice of Industrial Hygiene since 1990.

Barbara A Plog, MPH, CIH, CSP, is a Certified Industrial Hygienist and a Certified Safety Professional and has been in the field of occupational health for 32 years. She is the Director of the Continuing Education Program of the Center for Occupational and Environmental Health (COEH) at the University of California-Berkeley School of Public Health. COEH is a NIOSH Education and Research Center. Ms. Plog is a Lecturer in the School of Public Health's industrial hygiene program and an associate clinical professor at the University of California-San Francisco School of Nursing's Occupational Health Nursing program. She teaches Industrial Hygiene and Occupational Safety to graduate students in industrial hygiene and occupational health nursing.

Ms. Plog holds a Masters of Public Health Degree in Industrial Hygiene from the University of Illinois School of Public Health. Before coming to the University of California-Berkeley in 1987, she was manager of Occupational Health at the National Safety Council for five years. She is editor-in-chief of the 1,000-plus page textbook, *Fundamentals of Industrial Hygiene,* 3rd, 4th, 5th, and 6th editions.

Patricia Quinlan, MPH, CIH, is a Certified Industrial Hygienist in the Division of Occupational and Environmental Medicine at the University of California-San Francisco and Deputy Director of the Northern California Center for Occupational and Environmental Health at the University of California-Berkeley. She also holds an appointment as Clinical Professor in the Department of Community Health Systems, School of Nursing, University of California-San Francisco. Ms. Quinlan has been active in the field of industrial hygiene for 30 years, since her graduation with a Masters degree in Public Health in Industrial Hygiene from the University of California-Berkeley in 1982. She has served on a number of committees of the AIHA and APHA Occupational Health Section and has been a member of the California OSHA Airborne Contaminants Advisory Committee. She currently serves on the Institute of Medicine's Committee on Personal Protective Equipment, the California OSHA Statewide Advisory Committee, and is on the Board of Directors for Worksafe.

Susan Raterman, CIH, is the founder and President of The Raterman Group, Ltd., an industrial hygiene and environmental hazard consulting firm. The Raterman Group, Ltd. specializes in the areas of comprehensive industrial hygiene consulting, asbestos and lead hazard assessments and remediation oversight, indoor air quality evaluations, green/healthy building practices, and infection control. Ms. Raterman provides management and technical expertise in industrial hygiene and environmental health to clients in the commercial, industrial, health care, and public sectors. Additionally, she provides compliance program development and training, and expert testimony and litigation support to clients on environmental issues. Ms. Raterman is certified in the Comprehensive Practice of Industrial Hygiene by the American Industrial Hygiene Association, and is an Illinois Environmental Protection Agency Licensed Industrial Hygienist. She is also an Illinois Department of Public Health licensed Asbestos Building Inspector/Management Planner and Asbestos Project Designer. She attained a Master of Science Degree in Environmental Health Engineering from Northwestern University in Evanston, IL, and a Bachelor of Arts in Biology from St. Louis University in St. Louis, MO. Ms. Ratermanan active member of the American Industrial Hygiene Association, the American Board of Industrial Hygiene, the International Facility Management Association, the Indoor Air Quality Association, and the Association for Professionals in Infection Control.

David Rempel, MD, MPH, CP, is Professor of Medicine at the University of California at San Francisco, Professor of Engineering at University of California-Berkeley, and Director of the Ergonomics Graduate Training Program at University of California-Berkeley. His research focuses on understanding how tendons, muscles, and nerves are injured at work and how workplace tools, workstations and tasks can be designed to prevent musculoskeletal disorders. From 1985 to 1990 he was a medical epidemiologist responsible for occupational medicine and ergonomics for the California Department of Public Health. Dr. Rempel is board certified in internal medicine, occupational medicine, and ergonomics. He received his MD from the University of California-San Francisco in 1982 and his MPH in Epidemiology from the University of California-Berkeley in 1981. The publications of his group and a description of research projects are at http://ergo.berkeley.edu/.

Pete Rice, CIH, CSP, REHS, has 35 years of experience in developing, implementing, and supervising environmental and occupational safety and industrial hygiene programs, both domestic and international. He has participated in the recognition, evaluation, and control of safety and health practices and procedures on hundreds of various industrial, construction, and waste cleanup projects involving chemical, physical, biological, ergonomic, and safety hazards. In addition, Mr. Rice has been partly responsible for developing Cal/OSHA health standards for respiratory protection, ventilation, hazard communication, and asbestos. Mr. Rice currently serves as the Director for Environmental, Health, and Safety Programs for Ahtna Inc. and for ClickSafety (www.clicksafety. com), a leader in distance occupational safety and health learning, Mr. Rice teaches industrial hygiene and safety at the university level (University of California-Berkeley) and has trained numerous industrial hygienists and safety professionals. He formerly acted as the senior technical industrial hygienist, safety professional, and chief training officer for Cal/OSHA. Additionally, Mr. Rice has published numerous articles and book chapters, provided expert opinions and supported volunteer organizations in pursuit of improved occupational and environmental health and safety in both the business world and public health. He is Certified Industrial Hygienist, American Board of Industrial Hygiene 1981, No. 2156; Certified Safety Professional, Board of Certified Safety Professionals 1984, No. 7287; Registered Environmental Health Specialist, California 1977, No. 4265; California Community College Instructor Credential; MS, Environmental and Occupational Health and Safety, California State University, Northridge, 1977; BS, Environmental Health and Biology, California State University, Northridge, 1976.

Marc Roe, MS, CIH, is a certified industrial hygienist with more than 6 years of experience in the field of industrial hygiene. He serves as a Technical Service Specialist supporting powered and supplied air respiratory systems at 3M Company, St. Paul, MN, with previous experience as an Environmental Health and Safety Engineer. He is past-chair of the American Industrial Hygiene

Association's Real-Time Detection Systems Committee. Mr. Roe has a BA in biochemistry from St. John's University, and an MS in industrial hygiene from University of Minnesota-School of Public Health.

Jennifer Silk is an occupational safety and health consultant, and a training advisor to the United Nations Institute for Training and Research. She is retired OSHA, where she was the Deputy Director of Standards and Guidance. Jennifer was the team leader for development of the original Hazard Communication Standard. She represented the U.S. Government in negotiations to develop the Globally Harmonized System of Classification and Labeling of Chemicals, chaired the international coordinating group that managed development of the GHS, and served as the U.S. expert to the United Nations Subcommittee of Experts on the GHS.

Philip Smith, PhD, CIH, is a graduate of Brigham Young University (BS, Zoology, 1984), and the University of California, Berkeley (MPH, Environmental Health Science, 1987). He has been engaged in field industrial hygiene since 1987 when he began his career as an Industrial Hygiene Officer in the U.S. Navy. He has been a Certified Industrial Hygienist since 1993, and completed requirements for the PhD degree in toxicology at Utah State University in 1998. He served as a full-time faculty member in the graduate program at the Uniformed Services University of the Health Sciences in Bethesda, MD, between 1998 and 2003, and again from 2007 to 2010. While there he directed the research work of a number of doctoral and masters degree students, and participated in the successful reaccreditation of the university's MSPH degree program by ABET. He also worked with the U.S. Marine Corps Chemical Biological Incident Response Force to develop methods to rapidly detect and identify chemical warfare agents and degradation products using gas chromatography-mass spectrometry in the field, and delivered training to the unit's mobile laboratory operators to complete this mission. After completing more than 23 years of service in the Navy, Dr. Smith joined the U.S. Department of Labor as a member of the OSHA Health Response Team in 2010. He has authored or coauthored more than 40 peer-reviewed papers or book chapters related to his academic interests, which include laboratory methods and real-time detection techniques that provide high-certainty information to protect human health and the environment, including gas chromatography, mass spectrometry, and field-friendly sampling and analysis methods such as solid phase microextraction and thermal desorption. He has served twice as the chair of the AIHA Real-Time Detection Systems Committee.

Jack Standard, CIH, CSP, is a private consultant who worked for the majority of his career as an instructor and curriculum developer at OSHA's Directorate of Training and Education. He developed curriculum and instructed in many OSHA Training Institute courses in subject areas including industrial hygiene, safety standards for compliance officers, noise, hazardous materials, and respiratory protection. Mr. Standard continues to be the principal instructor in OSHA's Industrial Noise course. Prior to his career at OSHA, he was a noise control engineer in private industry.

Mr. Standard is a Certified Industrial Hygienist, Certified Safety Professional, and Noise Control Engineer. He graduated from the University of Illinois with a BS and MS in Mechanical Engineering and a Master of Public Health degree.

James H. Stewart, PhD, CIH, CSP, received his PhD in Environmental Health/Toxicology (minor in Epidemiology) from the University of Massachusetts-Amherst. He also holds a Master's degree in Chemistry and a Bachelor's degree in Public Health. He has served as a Plant, Division, and Corporate Director/Manager of Environmental Health and Safety for large multinational semiconductor/electronics companies, and Director of Environmental Health and Safety for Harvard University. Prior to these positions, Dr. Stewart was employed as a Compliance Officer with U.S. Department of Labor/OSHA. Dr. Stewart is Director of the Building Science and Forensics Division of Environmental Health and Engineering, Inc., a large consulting firm in Needham, MA. His work focuses on exposure assessment, exposure reconstruction, and forensic industrial hygiene.

Dr. Stewart is certified in Comprehensive Practice of Industrial Hygiene and is also a Certified Safety Professional. He has 37 years of experience as an active member of the environmental health and safety profession. He is the author of professional articles and several books in the area of industrial hygiene, safety, risk assessment of carcinogens, mathematical modeling, and management of environmental health and safety programs. Dr. Stewart has served on two National Academy Committees as an industrial hygiene and safety expert. He has also served as a testifying and consulting expert in litigation for both defendants and plaintiffs.

Dr. Stewart is an Instructor in the Harvard University School of Public Health's Occupational Hygiene Program, where he teaches graduate classes/courses in industrial hygiene, semiconductor health and safety, industrial hygiene management and mathematical modeling of exposures and conducts research in exposure assessment.

Victor Toy, MPH, CIH, CSP, is Director of Global Transformation and Strategy, Integrated Health Services, for the IBM Corporation. He is involved with managing health, safety, and industrial hygiene programs including policy setting and organizational transformation. He has over 25 years of diverse industrial hygiene experience in government and industry. He is a Certified Industrial Hygienist, as well as a Certified Safety Professional and holds a Bachelor's degree in Environmental Sciences from University of California-Berkeley and a Masters of Public Health in Industrial Hygiene from the University of Michigan. He's been a guest lecturer for San Jose State University and the University of California-Berkeley Labor Occupational Health Program. Mr. Toy is a frequent presenter and instructor at major conferences and is active in the industrial hygiene profession, including Vice Chair of the ANSI Z10 Committee on Occupational Health and Safety Management Systems. He is a Fellow member of the American Industrial Hygiene Association and a Past-president of the Academy of Industrial Hygiene.

Michael Yost, MS, PhD, is a Professor in the Department of Environmental and Occupational Health Sciences at the University of Washington, as well as the Director of the Exposure Sciences program. His interests include optical remote sensing of chemicals in the environment, and physical agents, such as noise, vibration, and nonionizing radiation, in the workplace. Prior to joining the University of Washington in 1993, Dr. Yost was a Research Industrial Hygienist and a Lecturer in the School of Public Health at the University of California, Berkeley. He also served as a Reader at University of California-Berkeley's Department of Electrical Engineering. Dr. Yost's current research projects focus on developing novel tools for environmental and occupational exposure assessment.

Allison S. Zaum, OD, MPH, is an optometrist in private practice in Mountain View, CA. Before becoming an optometrist, she worked for many years as an industrial hygienist in the pharmaceutical and semiconductor industries and for Stanford University. She was ABIH certified in comprehensive practice from 1985 to 1997. Dr. Zaum's undergraduate degree in Biology was from Brandeis University. She received an MPH in Environmental Health Sciences from the University of California-Berkeley School of Public Health, and her OD degree from the University of California-Berkeley School of Optometry.

PART I
History and Development

CHAPTER 1

Overview of Industrial Hygiene

by Barbara A. Plog, MPH, CIH, CSP

Industrial hygiene is the science and art devoted to the anticipation, recognition, evaluation, and control of those environmental factors or stresses arising in or from the workplace that may cause sickness, impaired health and well-being, or significant discomfort among workers or among the citizens of the community. Industrial hygienists are occupational health professionals who are concerned primarily with the control of environmental stresses or occupational health hazards that arise as a result of or during the course of work. The industrial hygienist recognizes that environmental stresses may endanger life and health, accelerate the aging process, or cause significant discomfort.

The industrial hygienist, although trained in engineering, physics, chemistry, environmental sciences, safety, or biology, has acquired through postgraduate study or experience a knowledge of the health effects of chemical, physical, biological, and ergonomic agents. The industrial hygienist is involved in the monitoring and analysis required to detect the extent of exposure, and the engineering and other methods used for hazard control.

Evaluation of the magnitude of work-related environmental hazards and stresses is done by the industrial hygienist, aided by training, experience, and quantitative measurement of the chemical, physical, ergonomic, or biological stresses. The industrial hygienist can thus give an expert opinion as to the degree of risk the environmental stresses pose.

Industrial hygiene includes the development of corrective measures to control health hazards by either reducing or eliminating the exposure. These control procedures may include the substitution of harmful or toxic materials with less dangerous ones, changing of work processes to eliminate or minimize work exposure, installation of exhaust ventilation systems, good housekeeping (including appropriate waste disposal methods), *and the provision of proper personal protective equipment.*

An effective industrial hygiene program involves the anticipation and recognition of health hazards arising from work operations and processes, evaluation and measurement of the magnitude of the hazard, and control of the hazard.

Occupational health hazards may mean conditions that cause legally compensable illnesses, or may mean any conditions in the workplace that impair the health of employees enough to make them lose time from work or cause significant discomfort. Both are undesirable. Both are preventable. The correction of such hazards is properly a responsibility of management.

PROFESSIONAL ETHICS

The American Board of Industrial Hygiene (ABIH) is a voluntary, nonprofit professional credentialing organization located in Lansing, Michigan. It was founded in 1980. ABIH administers the Certified Industrial Hygienist (CIH) program. Earning the CIH requires that candidates meet rigorous education and experience requirements, pass an examination, and recertify every five years by fulfilling certification maintenance requirements designed to enhance the ongoing knowledge and skills of the CIH. More than 6,500 industrial hygienists currently hold the CIH and Certified Associate Industrial Hygienist (CAIH) designations.

The Board discontinued the CAIH examination program in 2006 because of low demand. However, many CAIHs have chosen to continue to maintain their CAIH designation. The ABIH continues to administer the CAIH certification maintenance program.

Once the CIH or CAIH credential is obtained, the Diplomate can apply their knowledge in many different situations, some broad scope and comprehensive, and some narrow scope as the person specializes. The domains of practice often differ and change many times during the course of a career. Thus, ABIH places no restrictions or qualifications on the career paths of a CIH or CAIH as long as the person meets the on-going requirements in the certification maintenance program and adheres to the professional, enforceable Code of Ethics (Figure 1–1).

The Occupational Health and Safety Team

The chief goal of an occupational health and safety program in a facility is to prevent occupational injury and illness by anticipating, recognizing, evaluating, and controlling occupational health and safety hazards. The medical, industrial hygiene, and safety programs may have distinct, additional program goals, but all programs interact and are often considered different components of the overall health and safety program. The occupational health and safety team consists, then, of the industrial hygienist, the safety professional, the occupational health nurse, the occupational medicine physician, the employees, senior and line management, and others depending on the size and character of the particular facility. All team members must act in concert to provide information and activities, supporting the other parts to achieve the overall goal of a healthy and safe work environment. Therefore, the separate functions must be administratively linked in order to effect a successful and smoothly run program.

The first vital component to an effective health and safety program is the commitment of senior management and line management. Serious commitment is demonstrated when management is visibly involved in the program both by management support and personal compliance with all health and safety practices. Equally critical is the assignment of the authority, as well as the responsibility, to carry out the health and safety program. The health and safety function must be given the same level of importance and accountability as the production function.

The function of the industrial hygienist has been defined above. (Also see Chapter 24, The Industrial Hygienist.) The industrial hygiene program must be made up of several key components: a written program/policy statement, hazard recognition procedures, hazard evaluation and exposure assessment, hazard control, employee training, employee involvement, program evaluation and audit, and record-keeping. (See Chapter 29, The Industrial Hygiene Program, for further discussion.)

The safety professional must draw upon specialized knowledge in the physical and social sciences. Knowledge of engineering, physics, chemistry, statistics, mathematics, and principles of measurement and analysis is integrated in the evaluation of safety performance. The safety professional must thoroughly understand the factors contributing to accident occurrence and combine this with knowledge of motivation, behavior, and communication in order to devise methods and procedures to control safety hazards. Because the practice of the safety professional and the industrial hygienist are so closely related, it is rare to find a safety professional who does not practice some traditional industrial hygiene and vice versa. At times, the safety and industrial hygiene responsibilities may be vested in the same individual or position. (See Chapter 25, The Safety Professional.)

The occupational health nurse (OHN) is the key to the delivery of comprehensive health care services to workers. Occupational health nursing is focused on the promotion, protection, and restoration of workers' health within the context of a safe and healthy work environment. The OHN provides the critical link between the employee's health status, the work process, and the determination of

The Mark of Professionalism

American Board of Industrial Hygiene Code of Ethics

Introduction

The American Board of Industrial Hygiene (ABIH) is a voluntary, non-profit, professional credentialing organization. ABIH certifies qualified industrial hygienists engaged in the practice of industrial hygiene, and who have met the professional knowledge standards established by the Board of Directors. Regardless of any other professional affiliation, the ABIH Code of Ethics (Code) applies to: each individual certified by the ABIH as a Certified Industrial Hygienist (CIH) or a Certified Associate Industrial Hygienist (CAIH) (certificants); and, each individual seeking ABIH certification (candidates). The Code serves as the minimal ethical standards for the professional behavior of ABIH certificants and candidates.

The Code is designed to provide both appropriate ethical practice guidelines and enforceable standards of conduct for all certificants and candidates. The Code also serves as a professional resource for industrial hygienists, as well as for those served by ABIH certificants and candidates.

Preamble/General Guidelines

The ABIH is dedicated to the implementation of appropriate professional standards designed to serve the public, employees, employers, clients and the industrial hygiene profession. First and foremost, ABIH certificants and candidates give priority to health and safety interests related to the protection of people, and act in a manner that promotes integrity and reflects positively on the profession, consistent with accepted moral, ethical and legal standards.

As professionals in the field of industrial hygiene, ABIH certificants and candidates have the obligation to: maintain high standards of integrity and professional conduct; accept responsibility for their actions; continually seek to enhance their professional capabilities; practice with fairness and honesty; and, encourage others to act in a professional manner consistent with the certification standards and responsibilities set forth below.

I.   **Responsibilities to ABIH, the profession and the public.**

    A.   Certificant and candidate compliance with all organizational rules, policies and legal requirements.

        1.   Comply with laws, regulations, policies and ethical standards governing professional practice of industrial hygiene and related activities.

        2.   Provide accurate and truthful representations concerning all certification and recertification information.

        3.   Maintain the security of ABIH examination information and materials, including the prevention of unauthorized disclosures of test information.

        4.   Cooperate with ABIH concerning ethics matters and the collection of information related to an ethics matter.

        5.   Report apparent violations of the ethics code by certificants and candidates upon a reasonable and clear factual basis.

        6.   Refrain from public behavior that is clearly in violation of professional, ethical or legal standards.

Figure 1–1. The American Board of Industrial Hygiene Code of Ethics, May 2007. *(Reprinted with permission of the American Board of Industrial Hygiene.)*

II.   **Responsibilities to clients, employers, employees and the public.**

    A.   Education, experience, competency and performance of professional services.

        1.   Deliver competent services with objective and independent professional judgment in decision-making.

        2.   Recognize the limitations of one's professional ability and provide services only when qualified. The certificant/candidate is responsible for determining the limits of his/her own professional abilities based on education, knowledge, skills, practice experience and other relevant considerations.

        3.   Make a reasonable effort to provide appropriate professional referrals when unable to provide competent professional assistance.

        4.   Maintain and respect the confidentiality of sensitive information obtained in the course of professional activities unless: the information is reasonably understood to pertain to unlawful activity; a court or governmental agency lawfully directs the release of the information; the client or the employer expressly authorizes the release of specific information; or, the failure to release such information would likely result in death or serious physical harm to employees and/or the public.

        5.   Properly use professional credentials, and provide truthful and accurate representations concerning education, experience, competency and the performance of services.

        6.   Provide truthful and accurate representations to the public in advertising, public statements or representations, and in the preparation of estimates concerning costs, services and expected results.

        7.   Recognize and respect the intellectual property rights of others and act in an accurate, truthful and complete manner, including activities related to professional work and research.

        8.   Affix or authorize the use of one's ABIH seal, stamp or signature only when the document is prepared by the certificant/candidate or someone under his/her direction and control.

    B.   Conflict of interest and appearance of impropriety.

        1.   Disclose to clients or employers significant circumstances that could be construed as a conflict of interest or an appearance of impropriety.

        2.   Avoid conduct that could cause a conflict of interest with a client, employer, employee or the public.

        3.   Assure that a conflict of interest does not compromise legitimate interests of a client, employer, employee or the public and does not influence or interfere with professional judgments.

        4.   Refrain from offering or accepting significant payments, gifts or other forms of compensation or benefits in order to secure work or that are intended to influence professional judgment.

    C.   Public health and safety.

        1.   Follow appropriate health and safety procedures, in the course of performing professional duties, to protect clients, employers, employees and the public from conditions where injury and damage are reasonably foreseeable.

Effective Date: May 25, 2007

Figure 1–1. Continued.

employee ability to do the job. Knowledge of health and safety regulations, workplace hazards, direct care skills, counseling, teaching, and program management are but a few of the key knowledge areas for the OHN, with strong communication skills of the utmost importance. OHNs deliver high-quality care at worksites and support the primary prevention dictum that most workplace injuries and illnesses are preventable. If injuries occur, OHNs use a case-management approach to return injured employees to appropriate work on a timely basis. The OHN often functions in multiple roles within one job position, including clinician, educator, manager, and consultant. (See Chapter 27, The Occupational Health Nurse.)

The occupational medicine physician has acquired, through graduate training or experience, extensive knowledge of cause and effect relationships of chemical, physical, biological, and ergonomic hazards, the signs and symptoms of chronic and acute exposures, and the treatment of adverse effects. The primary goal of the occupational medicine physician is to prevent occupational illness and, when illness occurs, to restore employee health within the context of a healthy and safe workplace. Many regulations provide for a minimum medical surveillance program and specify certain mandatory tests and procedures.

The occupational medicine physician and the occupational health nurse should be familiar with all jobs, materials, and processes used. An occasional workplace inspection by the medical team enables them to suggest protective measures and aids them in recommending placement of employees in jobs best suited to their physical capabilities.

Determining the work-relatedness of disease is another task for the occupational medicine physician. The industrial hygienist provides information about the manufacturing operations and work environment of a company to the medical department as well. In many cases it is extremely difficult to differentiate between the symptoms of occupational and nonoccupational disease. The industrial hygienist supplies information on the work operations and their associated hazards and enables the medical department to correlate the employee's condition and symptoms with potential workplace health hazards. (Also see Chapter 26, The Occupational Medicine Physician.)

The employee plays a major role in the occupational health and safety program. Employees are excellent sources of information on work processes and procedures and the hazards of their daily operations. Industrial hygienists benefit from this source of information and often obtain innovative suggestions for controlling hazards.

The safety and health committee provides a forum for securing the cooperation, coordination, and exchange of ideas among those involved in the health and safety pro-

gram. It provides a means of involving employees in the program. The typical functions of the safety and health committee include, among others, to examine company safety and health issues and recommend policies to management, conduct periodic workplace inspections, and evaluate and promote interest in the health and safety program. Joint labor–management safety and health committees are often used where employees are represented by a union. The committee meetings also present an opportunity to discuss key industrial hygiene program concerns and to formulate appropriate policies.

FEDERAL REGULATIONS

Before 1970, government regulation of health and safety matters was largely the concern of state agencies. There was little uniformity in codes and standards or in the application of these standards. Almost no enforcement procedures existed.

On December 29, 1970, the Occupational Safety and Health Act, known as the OSHAct, was enacted by Congress. Its purpose was to "assure so far as possible every working man and woman in the nation safe and healthful working conditions and to preserve our human resources." The OSHAct sets out two duties for employers:

- Each employer shall furnish to each employee a place of employment, which is free from recognized hazards that are causing or are likely to cause death or serious harm to their employees.
- Each employer shall comply with occupational safety and health standards under the Act.

For employees, the OSHAct states that "Each employee shall comply with occupational safety and health standards and all rules, regulations, and orders issued pursuant to the Act which are applicable to his own actions and conduct."

The Occupational Safety and Health Administration (OSHA) came into official existence on April 28, 1971, the date the OSHAct became effective. It is housed within the Department of Labor. The OSHAct also established the National Institute for Occupational Safety and Health (NIOSH), which is housed within the Centers for Disease Control and Prevention (CDC). The CDC is part of the Public Health Service.

OSHA was empowered to promulgate safety and health standards with technical advice from NIOSH. OSHA is empowered to enter workplaces to investigate alleged violations of these standards and to perform routine inspections. Formal complaints of standards violations may be made by employees or their representatives. The OSHAct also gives OSHA the right to issue citations and penalties, provide for employee walkarounds or interview of employees during the inspection, require employers to maintain accurate records of exposures to potentially hazardous materials, and to inform employees of the monitoring results. OSHA is also empowered to provide up to 50/50 funding with states that wish to establish state OSHA programs that are at least as effective as the federal program. As of this date, there are 25 approved state plans and approved plans from Puerto Rico and the Virgin Islands.

NIOSH is the principal federal agency engaged in occupational health and safety research. The agency is responsible for identifying hazards and making recommendations for regulations. These recommendations are called Recommended Exposure Limits (RELs). NIOSH also issues criteria documents and health hazard alerts on various hazards and is responsible for testing and certifying respiratory protective equipment.

Part of NIOSH research takes place during activities called Health Hazard Evaluations. These are on-the-job investigations of reported worker exposures that are carried out in response to a request by either the employer or the employee or employee representative. In addition to its own research program, NIOSH also funds supportive research activities at a number of universities, colleges, and private facilities.

As of this writing, NIOSH has training grant programs in colleges and universities across the nation. These are located at designated Education and Research Centers (ERCs). ERCs train occupational medicine physicians, occupational health nurses, industrial hygienists, safety professionals, ergonomists, and others in the safety and health field. They also provide continuing professional education for practicing occupational health and safety professionals. The future of the ERCs is unclear at this writing. The program has been slated for budgetary elimination in the first version of the 2013 federal budget. (See Chapter 30, Government Regulations, for a full discussion of federal agencies and regulations.)

ENVIRONMENTAL FACTORS OR STRESSES

The various environmental factors or stresses that can cause sickness, impaired health, or significant discomfort in workers can be classified as chemical, physical, biological, or ergonomic.

Chemical hazards. These arise from excessive airborne concentrations of mists, vapors, gases, or solids in the form of dusts or fumes. In addition to the hazard of inhalation, some of these materials may act as skin irritants or may be toxic by absorption through the skin.

Physical hazards. These include excessive levels of nonionizing radiation (see Chapter 10), ionizing radiation (see Chapter 11), noise (see Chapter 9), vibration, and extremes of temperature (see Chapter 12) and pressure.

Ergonomic hazards. These include improperly designed tools, work areas, or work procedures. Improper lifting or reaching, poor visual conditions, or repeated motions in an awkward position can result in accidents or illnesses in the occupational environment. Designing the tools and the job to fit the worker is of prime importance. Engineering and biomechanical principles must be applied to eliminate hazards of this kind (see Chapter 13).

Biological hazards. These are any living organism or its properties that can cause an adverse response in humans. They can be part of the total environment or associated with a particular occupation. Work-related illnesses caused by biological agents have been widely reported, but in many workplaces their presence and resultant illness are not well recognized. It is estimated that the population at risk for occupational biohazards may be several hundred million workers worldwide (see Chapter 14).

Exposure to many of the harmful stresses or hazards listed above can produce an immediate response as a result of the intensity of the hazard, or the response can result from longer exposure at a lower intensity.

In certain occupations, depending on the duration and severity of exposure, the work environment can produce significant subjective responses or strain. The energies and agents responsible for these effects are called environmental stresses. An employee is most often exposed to an intricate interplay of many stresses, not to a single environmental stress.

Chemical Hazards

The majority of occupational health hazards arise from inhaling chemical agents in the form of vapors, gases, dusts, fumes, and mists, or by skin contact with these materials. The degree of risk of handling a given substance depends on the magnitude and duration of exposure. (See Chapter 15, Evaluation, for more details.)

To recognize occupational factors or stresses, a health and safety professional must first know about the chemicals used as raw materials and the nature of the products and by-products manufactured. This sometimes requires great effort. The required information can be obtained from the Safety Data Sheet (SDS), formerly known as the Material Safety Data Sheet (MSDS). The SDS must be supplied by the chemical manufacturer or importer for all hazardous materials under the OSHA Hazard Communication Standard (HCS).

The Safety Data Sheet is a summary of the important health, safety, and toxicological information on the chemical or the mixture ingredients. Other stipulations of the Hazard Communication Standard require that all containers of hazardous substances in the workplace be labeled with appropriate warning and identification labels. As this book goes to press, OSHA has just published a revision of the Hazard Communication Standard that aligns the United States with the Globally Harmonized System (GHS) for Classification and Labeling of Chemicals that is in use in Canada and European Union countries. In addition to new pictogram labels, signal words, and hazard class designations and categories, a new SDS format will be required with 16 required sections (Table 1–A). (See Chapter 31, International Developments in Occupational Safety and Health for a full discussion of the GHS.) As the standard was published in the Federal Register on March 26, 2012, it goes into effect 60 days later. It is effective in phases until full implementation in 2016.

If the SDS or the label does not give complete information but only trade names, it may be necessary to contact the manufacturer to obtain this information.

Many industrial materials such as resins and polymers are relatively inert and nontoxic under normal conditions of use, but when heated or machined, they may decompose to form highly toxic by-products. Information about these hazardous products and by-products must also be included in the company's hazard communication program.

Inhalation of some materials can irritate the upper respiratory tract or the terminal passages of the lungs and the air sacs, depending upon the solubility of the material. Contact of irritants with the skin surface can produce various kinds of dermatitis.

TABLE 1–A   GHS Safety Data Sheet Sections

1. Identification
2. Hazard(s) identification
3. Composition/information on ingredients
4. First-aid measures
5. Fire-fighting measures
6. Accidental release measures
7. Handling and storage
8. Exposure controls/personal protection
9. Physical and chemical properties
10. Stability and reactivity
11. Toxicological information
12. Ecological information
13. Disposal considerations
14. Transport information
15. Regulatory information
16. Other information

The presence of excessive amounts of biologically inert gases can dilute the atmospheric oxygen below the level required to maintain the normal blood saturation value for oxygen and disturb cellular processes. Other gases and vapors can prevent the blood from carrying oxygen to the tissues or interfere with its transfer from the blood to the tissue, thus producing chemical asphyxia or suffocation. Carbon monoxide and hydrogen cyanide are examples of chemical asphyxiants.

Some substances may affect the central nervous system and brain to produce narcosis or anesthesia. In varying degrees, many solvents have these effects. Substances are often classified, according to the major reaction they produce, as asphyxiants, systemic toxins, pneumoconiosis-producing agents, carcinogens, irritant gases, and so on.

Solvents

This section discusses some general hazards arising from the use of solvents; a more detailed description is given in Chapter 7, Gases, Vapors, and Solvents.

Solvent vapors enter the body primarily by inhalation, although some skin absorption can occur. The vapors are absorbed from the lungs into the blood and are distributed mainly to tissues with a high content of fat and lipids, such as the central nervous system, liver, and bone marrow. Solvents include aliphatic and aromatic hydrocarbons, alcohols, aldehydes, ketones, chlorinated hydrocarbons, and carbon disulfide.

Occupational exposure can occur in many different processes, such as the degreasing of metals in the machine industry, the extraction of fats or oils in the chemical or food industry, dry cleaning, painting, and the plastics industry.

The widespread industrial use of solvents presents a major problem to the industrial hygienist, the safety professional, and others responsible for maintaining a safe, healthful working environment. Getting the job done using solvents without hazard to employees or property depends on the proper selection, application, handling, and control of solvents and an understanding of their properties.

A working knowledge of the physical properties, nomenclature, and effects of exposure is absolutely necessary in making a proper assessment of a solvent exposure. Nomenclature can be misleading. For example, benzine is sometimes mistakenly called benzene, a completely different solvent. Some commercial grades of benzine may contain benzene as a contaminant.

Use the information on the SDS or the manufacturer's label for the specific name and composition of the solvents involved.

The severity of a hazard in the use of organic solvents and other chemicals depends on the following factors:

- how the chemical is used
- type of job operation, which determines how the workers are exposed
- work pattern
- duration of exposure
- operating temperature
- exposed liquid surface
- ventilation rates
- evaporation rate of solvent
- pattern of airflow
- concentration of vapor in workroom air
- housekeeping

The hazard is determined not only by the toxicity of the solvent or chemical itself, but by the conditions of its use (who, what, how, where, and how long). The health and safety professional can obtain much valuable information by observing the manner in which health hazards are generated, the number of people involved, and the control measures in use.

After the list of chemicals and physical conditions to which employees are exposed has been prepared, determine which of the chemicals or agents may result in hazardous exposures and need further study. Dangerous materials are chemicals that may, under specific circumstances, cause injury to persons or damage to property because of reactivity, instability, spontaneous decomposition, flammability, or volatility. Under this definition, we will consider substances, mixtures, or compounds that are explosive, corrosive, flammable, or toxic. Explosives are substances, mixtures, or compounds capable of entering into a combustion reaction so rapidly and violently as to cause an explosion. Corrosives are capable of destroying living tissue and have a destructive effect on other substances, particularly on combustible materials; this effect can result in a fire or explosion. Flammable liquids are liquids with a flash point of 100°F (38°C) or less, although those with higher flash points can be both combustible and dangerous. Toxic chemicals are gases, liquids, or solids that, through their chemical properties, can produce injurious or lethal effects on contact with body cells. Oxidizing materials are chemicals that decompose readily under certain conditions to yield oxygen. They may cause a fire in contact with combustible materials, can react violently with water, and when involved in a fire can react violently. Dangerous gases are those that can cause lethal or injurious effects and damage to property by their toxic, corrosive, flammable, or explosive physical and chemical properties.

Storage of dangerous chemicals should be limited to one day's supply, consistent with the safe and efficient operation of the process. The storage should comply with applicable local laws and ordinances. An approved storehouse should be provided for the main supply of hazardous materials.

For hazardous materials, SDSs can be consulted for toxicological information. The information is useful to the medical, purchasing, managerial, engineering, and health and safety departments in setting guidelines for safe use of these materials. This information is also very helpful in an emergency. The information should cover materials actually in use and those that may be contemplated for early future use. Possibly the best and earliest source of information concerning such materials is the purchasing agent. Thus, a close liaison should be set up between the purchasing agent and health and safety personnel so that early information is available concerning materials in use and those to be ordered, and to ensure that SDSs are received and reviewed for all hazardous substances.

Toxicity versus Hazard

The toxicity of a material is not synonymous with its hazard. Toxicity is the capacity of a material to produce injury or harm when the chemical has reached a sufficient concentration at a certain site in the body. Hazard is the probability that this concentration in the body will occur. This degree of hazard is determined by many factors or elements. (See Chapter 6, Industrial Toxicology.)

The key elements to be considered when evaluating a health hazard are as follows:

- What is the route of entry of the chemical into the body?
- How much of the material must be in contact with a body cell and for how long to produce injury?
- What is the probability that the material will be absorbed or come in contact with body cells?
- What is the rate of generation of airborne contaminants?
- What control measures are in place?

The effects of exposure to a substance depend on dose, rate, physical state of the substance, temperature, site of absorption, diet, and general state of a person's health.

Physical Hazards

Problems caused by such things as noise, temperature extremes, ionizing radiation, nonionizing radiation, and pressure extremes are physical stresses. It is important that the employer, supervisor, and those responsible for safety and health be alert to these hazards because of the possible immediate or cumulative effects on the health of employees.

Noise

Noise (unwanted sound) is a form of vibration conducted through solids, liquids, or gases. The effects of noise on humans include the following:

- psychological effects (noise can startle, annoy, and disrupt concentration, sleep, or relaxation)
- interference with speech communication and, as a con-

sequence, interference with job performance and safety
- physiological effects (noise-induced hearing loss, or aural pain when the exposure is severe)

Damage risk criteria. If the ear is subjected to high levels of noise for a sufficient period of time, some loss of hearing may occur. A number of factors can influence the effect of the noise exposure:
- variation in individual susceptibility
- total energy of the sound
- frequency distribution of the sound
- other characteristics of the noise exposure, such as whether it is continuous, intermittent, or made up of a series of impacts
- total daily duration of exposure
- length of employment in the noise environment

Because of the complex relationships of noise and exposure time to threshold shift (reduction in hearing level) and the many contributory causes, establishing criteria for protecting workers against hearing loss is difficult. However, criteria have been developed to protect against hearing loss in the speech-frequency range. These criteria are known as the Threshold Limit Values for Noise. (See Chapter 9, Industrial Noise.)

There are three nontechnical guidelines to determine whether the work area has excessive noise levels:
- If it is necessary to speak very loudly or shout directly into the ear of a person to be understood, it is possible that the exposure limit for noise is being exceeded. Conversation becomes difficult when the noise level exceeds 70 decibels (dBA).
- If employees say that they have heard ringing noises in their ears at the end of the workday, they may be exposed to too much noise.
- If employees complain that the sounds of speech or music seem muffled after leaving work, but that their hearing is fairly clear in the morning when they return to work, they may be exposed to noise levels that cause a partial temporary loss of hearing, which can become permanent with repeated exposure.

Permissible levels. The criteria for hearing conservation, required by OSHAct in 29 CFR 1910.95, establishes the permissible levels of harmful noise to which an employee may be subjected. The permissible decibel levels and hours (duration per day) are specified. For example, a noise level of 90 dBA is permissible for eight hours, 95 dBA for four hours, etc. (See Chapter 9, Industrial Noise, for more details.)

The regulations stipulate that when employees are subjected to sound that exceeds the permissible limits, feasible administrative or engineering controls shall be used. If such controls fail to reduce sound exposure within permissible levels, personal protective equipment must be provided and used to reduce sound levels to within permissible levels.

According to the Hearing Conservation Amendment to 29 CFR 1910.95, in all cases when the sound levels exceed 85 dBA on an eight-hour time-weighted average (TWA), a continuing, effective hearing conservation program shall be administered. The Hearing Conservation Amendment specifies the essential elements of a hearing conservation program. (See Chapter 9, Industrial Noise, for a discussion of noise and OSHA noise regulations.) Administering a hearing conservation program goes beyond the wearing of earplugs or earmuffs. Such programs can be complex, and professional guidance is essential for establishing programs that are responsive to the need. Valid noise exposure information correlated with audiometric tests results is needed to help health and safety and medical personnel to make informed decisions about hearing conservation programs.

The effectiveness of a hearing conservation program depends on the cooperation of employers, employees, and others concerned. Management's responsibility in such a program includes noise measurements, initiation of noise control measures, provision of hearing protection equipment, audiometric testing of employees to measure their hearing levels (thresholds), and information and training programs for employees. The employee's responsibility is to properly use the protective equipment provided by management, and to observe any rules or regulations on the use of equipment in order to minimize noise exposure.

Extremes of Temperature

Probably the most elementary factor of environmental control is control of the thermal environment in which people work. Extremes of temperature, or thermal stress, affect the amount of work people can do and the manner in which they do it. In industry, the problem is more often high temperatures rather than low temperatures. (More details on this subject are given in Chapter 12, Thermal Stress.)

The body continuously produces heat through its metabolic processes. Because the body processes are designed to operate only within a very narrow range of temperature, the body must dissipate this heat as rapidly as it is produced if it is to function efficiently. A sensitive and rapidly acting set of temperature-sensing devices in the body must also control the rates of its temperature-regulating processes.

Heat stress is a common problem, as are the problems presented by a very cold environment. Evaluation of heat stress in a work environment is not simple. Considerably more is involved than simply taking a number of air-temperature measurements and making decisions on the basis of this information. One question that must be asked is whether the temperature is merely causing discomfort or whether continued exposure will cause the body temperature to fall below or rise above safe limits. It is difficult for a person with only a clipboard full of data to interpret how another person actually feels or is adversely affected.

People function efficiently only in a very narrow body temperature range, a core temperature measured deep inside the body, not on the skin or at body extremities. Fluctuations in core temperatures exceeding 2°F below or 3°F above the normal core temperature of 99.6°F (37.6°C), which is 98.6°F (37°C) mouth temperature, impair performance markedly. If this five-degree range is exceeded, a health hazard exists. The body attempts to counteract the effects of high temperature by increasing the heart rate. The capillaries in the skin also dilate to bring more blood to the surface so that the rate of cooling is increased. Sweating is an important factor in cooling the body.

Heatstroke is caused by exposure to an environment in which the body is unable to cool itself sufficiently. Heatstroke is a much more serious condition than heat cramps or heat exhaustion. An important predisposing factor is excessive physical exertion or moderate exertion in extreme heat conditions. The method of control is to reduce the temperature of the surroundings or to increase the ability of the body to cool itself, so that body temperature does not rise. In heatstroke, sweating may cease and the body temperature can quickly rise to fatal levels. It is critical to undertake emergency cooling of the body even while medical help is on the way. Studies show that the higher the body temperature on admission to emergency rooms, the higher the fatality rate. Heatstroke is a life-threatening medical emergency.

Heat cramps can result from exposure to high temperature for a relatively long time, particularly if accompanied by heavy exertion, with excessive loss of salt and moisture from the body. Even if the moisture is replaced by drinking plenty of water, an excessive loss of salt can cause heat cramps or heat exhaustion.

Heat exhaustion can also result from physical exertion in a hot environment. Its signs are a mildly elevated temperature, pallor, weak pulse, dizziness, profuse sweating, and cool, moist skin.

Environmental Measurements

In many heat stress studies, the variables commonly measured are work energy metabolism (often estimated rather than measured), air movement, air temperature, humidity, and radiant heat. (See Chapter 12, Thermal Stress, for illustrations and more details.)

Air movement is measured with some type of anemometer, and the air temperature is measured with a ther-

mometer, often called a dry bulb thermometer. Humidity, or the moisture content of the air, is generally measured with a psychrometer, which gives both dry bulb and wet bulb temperatures. Using these temperatures and referring to a psychrometric chart, the relative humidity can be established. The term wet bulb is commonly used to describe the temperature obtained by having a wet wick over the mercury-well bulb of an ordinary thermometer. Evaporation of moisture in the wick, to the extent that the moisture content of the surrounding air permits, cools the thermometer to a temperature below that registered by the dry bulb. The combined readings of the dry bulb and wet bulb thermometers are then used to calculate percent relative humidity, absolute moisture content of the air, and water vapor pressure. Radiant heat is a form of electromagnetic energy similar to light but of longer wavelength. Radiant heat (from such sources as red-hot metal, open flames, and the sun) has no appreciable heating effect on the air it passes through, but its energy is absorbed by any object it strikes, thus heating the person, wall, machine, or whatever object it falls on. Protection requires placing opaque shields or screens between the person and the radiating surface. An ordinary dry bulb thermometer alone will not measure radiant heat. However, if the thermometer bulb is fixed in the center of a metal toilet float that has been painted dull black, and the top of the thermometer stem protrudes outside through a one-hole cork or rubber stopper, radiant heat can be measured by the heat absorbed in this sphere. This device is known as a globe thermometer.

Heat loss. Conduction is an important means of heat loss when the body is in contact with a good cooling agent, such as water. For this reason, when people are immersed in cold water, they become chilled much more rapidly and effectively than when exposed to air of the same temperature.

Air movement cools the body by convection: the moving air removes the air film or the saturated air (which is formed very rapidly by evaporation of sweat) and replaces it with a fresh air layer capable of accepting more moisture from the skin.

Heat stress indices. The methods commonly used to estimate heat stress relate various physiological and environmental variables and end up with one number that then serves as a guide for evaluating stress. For example, the effective temperature index combines air temperature (dry bulb), humidity (wet bulb), and air movement to produce a single index called an effective temperature.

Another index is the wet bulb globe temperature (WBGT). The numerical value of the WBGT index is calculated by the following equations.

Indoors or outdoors with no solar loads:

$$WBGT_{in} = 0.7\ T_{nwb} + 0.3\ T_{gt}$$

Outdoors with solar load:

$$WBGT_{out} = 0.7\ T_{nwb} + 0.2\ T_{gt} + 0.1\ T_{db}$$

where T_{nwb} = natural wet bulb temperature
T_{gt} = globe temperature
T_{db} = dry bulb temperature

In its *Criteria Document on Hot Environments* (see Bibliography), NIOSH states that when impermeable clothing is worn, the WBGT should not be used because evaporative cooling would be limited. The WBGT combines the effects of humidity and air movement, air temperature and radiation, and air temperature. It has been successfully used for environmental heat stress monitoring at military camps to control heat stress casualties. The measurements are few and easy to make; the instrumentation is simple, inexpensive, and rugged; and the calculations are straightforward. It is also the index used in the *ACGIH® Threshold Limit Values (TLVs®) for Chemical Substances and Physical Agents and Biological Exposure Indices (BEIs®)*.

The ACGIH recommends TLVs for continuous work in hot environments as well as when 25, 50, or 75 percent of each working hour is at rest. Regulating allowable exposure time in the heat is a viable technique for permitting necessary work to continue under heat-stress conditions that would be intolerable for continuous exposure. The NIOSH criteria document also contains a complete recommended heat stress control program including work practices.

Work practices include acclimation periods, work and rest regimens, distribution of work load with time, regular breaks of a minimum of one per hour, provision for water intake, protective clothing, and application of engineering controls. Experience has shown that workers do not stand a hot job very well at first, but develop tolerance rapidly through acclimation and acquire full endurance in a week to a month. (For more details, see Chapter 12, Thermal Stress, and NIOSH, *Criteria Document on Hot Environments*.)

Cold Stress

Generally, the answer to a cold work area is to supply heat where possible, except for areas that must be cold, such as food storage areas.

General hypothermia is an acute problem resulting from prolonged cold exposure and heat loss. If an individual becomes fatigued during physical activity, he or she will be more prone to heat loss, and as exhaustion approaches, sudden vasodilation (blood vessel dilation) occurs with resultant rapid loss of heat.

Cold stress is proportional to the total thermal gradient between the skin and the environment because this gradient determines the rate of heat loss from the body by radiation and convection. When vasoconstriction (blood vessel constriction) is no longer adequate to maintain body heat balance, shivering becomes an important mechanism for increasing body temperature by causing metabolic heat production to increase to several times the resting rate.

General physical activity increases metabolic heat. With clothing providing the proper insulation to minimize heat loss, a satisfactory microclimate can be maintained. Only exposed body surfaces are likely to be excessively chilled and frostbitten. If clothing becomes wet either from contact with water or as a result of sweating during intensive physical work, its cold-insulating property is greatly diminished.

Frostbite occurs when the skin tissues freeze. Theoretically, the freezing point of the skin is about 30°F (1°C); however, with increasing wind velocity, heat loss is greater and frostbite occurs more rapidly. Once started, freezing progresses rapidly. For example, if the wind velocity reaches 20 mph, exposed flesh can freeze within about 1 minute at 14°F (-10°C). Furthermore, if the skin comes in direct contact with objects whose surface temperature is below the freezing point, frostbite can develop at the point of contact despite warm environmental temperatures. Air movement is more important in cold environments than in hot because the combined effect of wind and temperature can produce a condition called *windchill*. The windchill index should be consulted by everyone facing exposure to low temperature and strong winds. (See Chapter 12, Thermal Stress.)

Ionizing Radiation

A brief description of ionizing radiation hazards is given in this section; for a complete description, see Chapter 10, Ionizing Radiation.

To understand a little about ionization, recall that the human body is made up of various chemical compounds that are in turn composed of molecules and atoms. Each atom has a nucleus with its own outer system of electrons.

When ionization of body tissues occurs, some of the electrons surrounding the atoms are forcibly ejected from their orbits. The greater the intensity of the ionizing radiation, the more ions are created and the more physical damage is done to the cells.

Light consisting of electromagnetic radiation from the sun that strikes the surface of the earth is very similar to x-rays and gamma-radiation; it differs only in wavelength and energy content. (See description in Chapter 11, Nonionizing Radiation.) However, the energy level of sunlight at the earth's surface is too low to disturb orbital electrons, so sunlight is not considered ionizing, even though it has enough energy to cause severe skin burns over a period of time.

The exact mechanism of the manner in which ionization affects body cells and tissue is complex. At the risk of oversimplifying some basic physical principles and ignoring others, the purpose of this section is to present enough information so the health and safety professional will recognize the problems involved and know when to call on health physicists or radiation safety experts for help.

At least three basic factors must be considered in such an approach to radiation safety:

- Radioactive materials emit energy that can damage living tissue.
- Different kinds of radioactivity present different kinds of radiation safety problems. The types of ionizing radiation we will consider are alpha-, beta-, x-ray, and gamma-radiation, and neutrons.
- Radioactive materials can be hazardous in two different ways. Certain materials can be hazardous even when located some distance away from the body; these are external hazards. Other types are hazardous only when they get inside the body through breathing, eating, or broken skin. These are called internal radiation hazards.

Instruments are available for evaluating possible radiation hazards. Meters or other devices are used for measuring radiation levels and doses.

Kinds of radioactivity. The five kinds of radioactivity that are of concern are alpha, beta, x-ray, gamma, and neutron. The first four are the most important because neutron sources usually are not used in ordinary manufacturing operations.

Of the five types of radiation mentioned, alpha-particles are the least penetrating. They do not penetrate thin barriers. For example, paper, cellophane, and skin stop alpha-particles.

Beta-radiation has considerably more penetrating power than alpha radiation. A quarter of an inch of aluminum can stop the more energetic betas. Virtually everyone is familiar with the penetrating ability of x rays and the fact that a barrier such as concrete or lead is required to stop them.

Gamma-rays are, for all practical purposes, the same as x rays and require the same kinds of heavy shielding materials.

Neutrons are very penetrating and have characteristics that make it necessary to use shielding materials of high hydrogen atom content rather than high mass alone.

Although the type of radiation from one radioactive material may be the same as that emitted by several other different radioactive materials, there may be a wide variation in energies.

The amount of energy a particular kind of radioactive material possesses is defined in terms of million electron volts (MeV); the greater the number of MeV, the greater the energy. Each radioactive material emits its own particular kinds of radiation, with energy measured in terms of MeV.

External versus internal hazards. Radioactive materials that emit x rays, gamma rays, or neutrons are external hazards. In other words, such materials can be located some distance from the body and emit radiation that produces ionization (and thus damage) as it passes through the body. Control by limiting exposure time, working at a safe distance, use of barriers or shielding, or a combination of all three is required for adequate protection against external radiation hazards.

As long as a radioactive material that emits only alpha-particles remains outside the body, it will not cause trouble. Internally, it is a hazard because the ionizing ability of alpha particles at very short distances in soft tissue makes them a veritable bulldozer. Once inside the body—in the lungs, stomach, or an open wound, for example—there is no thick layer of skin to serve as a barrier and damage results. Alpha-emitting radioactive materials that concentrate as persisting deposits in specific parts of the body are considered very hazardous.

Beta-emitters are generally considered an internal hazard although they also can be classed as an external hazard because they can produce burns when in contact with the skin. They require the same precautions as do alpha-emitters if there is a chance they can become airborne. In addition, some shielding may be required.

Measuring ionizing radiation. Many types of meters are used to measure various kinds of ionizing radiation. These meters must be accurately calibrated for the type of radiation they are designed to measure.

Meters with very thin windows in the probes can be used to check for alpha-radiation. Geiger-Mueller and ionization chamber-type instruments are used for measuring beta-, gamma-, and x-radiation. Special types of meters are available for measuring neutrons.

Devices are available that measure accumulated amounts (doses) of radiation. Film badges are used as dosimeters to record the amount of radiation received from beta-, x-ray, or gamma-radiation and special badges are available to record neutron radiation.

Film badges are worn by a worker continuously during each monitoring period. Depending on how they are worn, they allow an estimate of an accumulated dose of radiation to the whole body or to just a part of the body, such as a hand or arm.

Alpha-radiation cannot be measured with film badges because alpha-particles do not penetrate the paper that must be used over the film emulsion to exclude light. (For more details on measurement and government regulations for ionizing radiation, see Chapter 10, Ionizing Radiation.)

Nonionizing Radiation

This is a form of electromagnetic radiation with varying effects on the body, depending largely on the wavelength of the radiation involved. In the following paragraphs, in approximate order of decreasing wavelength and increasing frequency, are some hazards associated with different regions of the nonionizing electromagnetic radiation spectrum. Nonionizing radiation is covered in detail by OSHAct regulations 29 CFR 1910.97, and in Chapter 11, Nonionizing Radiation.

Low frequency. Longer wavelengths, including powerline transmission frequencies, broadcast radio, and shortwave radio, can produce general heating of the body. The health hazard from these kinds of radiation is very small, however, because it is unlikely that they would be found in intensities great enough to cause significant effect. An exception can be found very close to powerful radio transmitter aerials.

Microwaves are found in radar, communications, some types of cooking, and diathermy applications. Microwave intensities may be sufficient to cause significant heating of tissues.

The effect is related to wavelength, power intensity, and time of exposure. Generally, longer wavelengths produce a greater penetration and temperature rise in deeper tissues than shorter wavelengths. However, for a given power intensity, there is less subjective awareness to the heat from longer wavelengths than there is to the heat from shorter wavelengths, because of the absorption of the longer wavelength radiation beneath the body's surface.

An intolerable rise in body temperature, as well as localized damage to specific organs, can result from an exposure of sufficient intensity and time. In addition, flammable gases and vapors can ignite when they are inside metallic objects located in a microwave beam.

Infrared radiation does not penetrate below the superficial layer of the skin, so its only effect is to heat the skin and the tissues immediately below it. Except for thermal burns, the health hazard of exposure to low-level conventional infrared radiation sources is negligible. (For information on possible damage to the eye, consult Chapter 11, Nonionizing Radiation.)

Visible radiation, which is about midway in the electromagnetic spectrum, is important because it can affect both the quality and accuracy of work. Good lighting conditions generally result in increased product quality with less spoilage and increased production.

Lighting should be bright enough for easy and efficient sight, and directed so that it does not create glare. Illumination levels and brightness ratios recommended for manufacturing and service industries are published by the Illuminating Engineering Society. (See Chapter 11, Nonionizing Radiation, for further information.)

One of the most objectionable features of lighting is glare (brightness in the field of vision that causes discomfort or interferes with seeing). The brightness can be caused by either direct or reflected light. To prevent glare, the source of light should be kept well above the line of vision or shielded with opaque or translucent material.

Almost as problematic is an area of excessively high brightness in the visual field. A highly reflective white paper in the center of a dark, nonreflecting surface or a brightly illuminated control handle on a dark or dirty machine are two examples. To prevent such conditions, keep surfaces uniformly light or dark with little difference in surface reflectivity. Color contrasts are acceptable, however. Although it is generally best to provide even, shadow-free light, some jobs require contrast lighting. In these cases, keep the general (or background) light well diffused and glareless and add a supplementary source of light that casts shadows where needed.

Ultraviolet radiation in industry can be found around electrical arcs, and such arcs should be shielded by materials opaque to ultraviolet. The fact that a material can be opaque to ultraviolet has no relation to its opacity to other parts of the spectrum. Ordinary window glass, for instance, is almost completely opaque to the ultraviolet in sunlight although transparent to the visible wavelengths. A piece of plastic dyed a deep red-violet may be almost entirely opaque in the visible part of the spectrum and transparent in the near-ultraviolet spectrum.

Electric welding arcs and germicidal lamps are the most common strong producers of ultraviolet radiation in industry. The ordinary fluorescent lamp generates a good deal of ultraviolet inside the bulb, but it is essentially all absorbed by the bulb and its coating.

The most common exposure to ultraviolet radiation is from direct sunlight, and a familiar result of overexposure—one that is known to all sunbathers—is sunburn. Most people are familiar with certain compounds and lotions that reduce the effects of the sun's rays, but many are unaware that some industrial materials, such as cresols, make the skin especially sensitive to ultraviolet rays. After exposure to cresols, even a short exposure in the sun usually results in severe sunburn.

Lasers emit beams of coherent radiation of a single color or wavelength and frequency, in contrast to conventional light sources, which produce random, disordered light wave mixtures of various frequencies. The laser (an acronym for light amplification by stimulated emission of radiation) is made up of light waves that are nearly parallel to each other, all traveling in the same direction. Atoms are "pumped" full of energy, and when they are stimulated to fall to a lower energy level, they give off radiation that is directed to produce the coherent laser beam.

The maser, the laser's predecessor, emits microwaves instead of light. Some companies call their lasers *optical masers*. Because the laser is highly collimated (i.e., has a small divergence angle), it can have a large energy density in a narrow beam. Direct viewing of the laser source or its reflections should be avoided. The work area should contain no reflective surface (such as mirrors or highly polished furniture) because even a reflected laser beam can be hazardous. Suitable shielding to contain the laser beam should be provided. The OSHAct covers protection against laser hazards in its construction regulations.

Biological effects. The eye is the organ that is most vulnerable to injury by laser energy because the cornea and lens focus the parallel laser beam on a small spot on the retina. The fact that infrared radiation of certain lasers may not be visible to the naked eye contributes to the potential hazard.

Lasers generating in the ultraviolet range of the electromagnetic spectrum can produce corneal burns rather than retinal damage, because of the way the eye handles ultraviolet light. Other factors that affect the degree of eye injury induced by laser light are as follows:

- pupil size (the smaller the pupil diameter, the less laser energy reaches the retina)
- the ability of the cornea and lens to focus the incident light on the retina
- the distance from the source of energy to the retina
- the energy and wavelength of the laser
- the pigmentation of the eye of the subject
- the location on the retina where the light is focused
- the divergence of the laser light
- the presence of scattering media in the light path

A discussion of laser beam characteristics and protective eyewear can be found in Chapter 11, Nonionizing Radiation, and Chapter 23, Personal Protective Equipment.

Extremes of Pressure

It has been recognized from the beginning of caisson work (i.e., work performed in a watertight structure) that people working under pressures greater than normal atmospheric pressure are subject to various health effects. Hyperbaric (greater than normal pressure) environments are also encountered by divers who work under water, whether by holding the breath while diving, breathing from a self-contained underwater breathing apparatus (SCUBA), or by breathing gas mixtures supplied by compression from the surface.

Occupational exposures occur in caisson or tunneling operations, where a compressed gas environment is used to exclude water or mud and to provide support for structures. Humans can withstand large pressures if air has free access to lungs, sinuses, and the middle ear. Unequal distribution of pressure can result in barotrauma, a kind of tissue damage resulting from expansion or contraction of gas spaces within or adjacent to the body, which can occur either during compression (descent) or during decompression (ascent).

The teeth, sinuses, and ears are often affected by pressure differentials. For example, gas spaces adjacent to tooth roots or fillings may be compressed during descent. Fluid or tissue forced into these spaces can cause pain during descent or ascent. Sinus blockage caused by occlusion of the sinus aperture by inflamed nasal mucosa prevents equalization of pressures.

Under some conditions of work at high pressure, the concentration of carbon dioxide in the atmosphere can be considerably increased so that the carbon dioxide acts as a narcotic. Keeping the oxygen concentration high minimizes this condition, but does not prevent it. The procedure is useful where the carbon dioxide concentration cannot be kept at a proper level.

Decompression sickness, commonly called the bends, results from the release of nitrogen bubbles into the circulation and tissues during decompression. If the bubbles lodge at the joints and under muscles, they cause severe cramps. To prevent this, decompression is carried out slowly and by stages so that the nitrogen can be eliminated slowly, without forming bubbles.

Deep-sea divers are supplied with a mixture of helium and oxygen for breathing, and because helium is an inert diluent and less soluble in blood and tissue than is nitrogen, it presents a less formidable decompression problem.

One of the most common troubles encountered by workers under compressed air is pain and congestion in the ears from inability to ventilate the middle ear properly during compression and decompression. As a result, many workers subjected to increased air pressures suffer from temporary hearing loss; some have permanent hearing loss. This damage is believed to be caused by obstruction of the eustachian tubes, which prevents proper equalization of pressure from the throat to the middle ear.

The effects of reduced pressure on the worker are much the same as the effects of decompression from a high pressure. If pressure is reduced too rapidly, decompression sickness and ear disturbances similar to the diver's conditions can result.

Ergonomic Hazards

Ergonomics literally means the study or measurement of work. It is the application of human biological science in conjunction with the engineering sciences to achieve the optimum mutual adjustment of people to their work, the benefits being measured in terms of human efficiency and well-being. The topic of ergonomics is covered briefly here. (For more details, see Chapter 13, Ergonomics.)

The ergonomics approach goes beyond productivity, health, and safety. It includes consideration of the total physiological and psychological demands of the job on the worker. In the broad sense, the benefits that can be expected from designing work systems to minimize physical stress on workers are as follows:

- reduced incidence of repetitive motion disorders
- reduced injury rate
- more efficient operation
- fewer accidents
- lower cost of operation
- reduced training time
- more effective use of personnel

The human body can endure considerable discomfort and stress and can perform many awkward and unnatural movements for a limited period of time. However, when awkward conditions or motions are continued for prolonged periods, they can exceed the worker's physiological limitations. To ensure a continued high level of performance, work systems must be tailored to human capacities and limitations.

Ergonomics considers the physiological and psychological stresses of the task. The task should not require excessive muscular effort, considering the worker's age, sex, and state of health. The job should not be so easy that boredom and inattention lead to unnecessary errors, material waste, and accidents. Ergonomic stresses can impair the health and efficiency of the worker just as significantly as the more commonly recognized environmental stresses.

The task of the design engineer and health and safety professional is to find the happy medium between easy and difficult jobs. In any human–machine system, there are tasks that are better performed by people than by machines and, conversely, tasks that are better handled by machines.

Ergonomics deals with the interactions between humans and such traditional environmental elements as atmospheric contaminants, heat, light, sound, and tools and equipment. People are the monitoring link of a human–machine environment system. In any activity, a person receives and processes information, and then acts on it. The receptor function occurs largely through the sense organs of the eyes and the ear, but information can also be conveyed through the senses of smell, touch, or sensations of heat or cold. This information is conveyed to the central mechanism of the brain and spinal cord, where the information is processed to arrive at a decision. This can involve the integration of the information, which has already been stored in the brain, and decisions can vary from automatic responses to those involving a high degree of reasoning and logic.

Having received the information and processed it, the individual then takes action (control) as a result of the decision, usually through muscular activity based on the skeletal framework of the body. When an individual's activity involves the operation of a piece of equipment, the person often forms part of a *closed-loop servosystem,* displaying many of the feedback characteristics of such a system. The person usually forms the part of the system that makes decisions, and thus has a fundamental part to play in the efficiency of the system.

Biomechanics–Physical Demands

Biomechanics can be a very effective tool in preventing excessive work stress. Biomechanics means the mechanics of biological organisms. It deals with the functioning of the structural elements of the body and the effects of external and internal forces on the various parts of the body.

Cumulative effects of excessive ergonomic stress on the worker can, in an insidious and subtle manner, result in physical illnesses and injuries such as *trigger finger,* tenosynovitis, bursitis, carpal tunnel syndrome, and other cumulative trauma disorders.

Cases of excessive fatigue and discomfort are, in many cases, forerunners of soreness and pain. By exerting a strong distracting influence on a worker, these stresses can render the worker more prone to major accidents.

Discomfort and fatigue tend to make the worker less capable of maintaining the proper vigilance for the safe performance of the task.

Some of the principles of biomechanics can be illustrated by considering different parts of the human anatomy, such as the hand. (Also see the TLV for hand activity level.)

Hand anatomy. The flexing action in the fingers is controlled by tendons attached to muscles in the forearm. The tendons, which run in lubricated sheaths, enter the hand through a tunnel in the wrist formed by bones and ligaments (the carpal tunnel) and continue on to point of attachment to the different segments, or phalanges, of the fingers (Figure 1–2).

When the wrist is bent toward the little finger side, the tendons tend to bunch up on one side of the tunnel through which they enter the hand. If an excessive amount of force is continuously applied with the fingers while the wrist is flexed, or if the flexing motion is repeated rapidly over a long period of time, the resulting friction can produce inflamma-

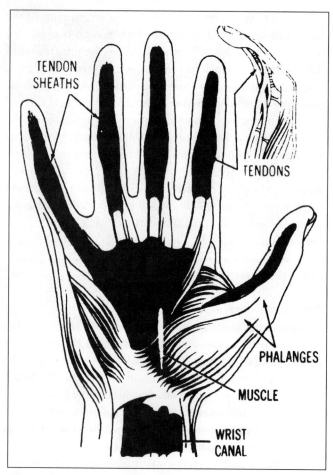

Figure 1–2. Diagram of hand anatomy.

tion of the tendon sheaths, or tenosynovitis. This can lead to a disabling condition called *carpal tunnel syndrome.*

The palm of the hand, which contains a network of nerves and blood vessels, should never be used as a hammer or subjected to continued firm pressure. Repetitive or prolonged pressure on the nerves and blood vessels in this area can result in pain either in the palm itself or at any point along the nerve pathways up through the arm and shoulder. Other parts of the body, such as the elbow joints and shoulders, can become painful for similar reasons.

Mechanical vibration. A condition known to stonecutters as *dead fingers* or *white fingers* (Raynaud's phenomenon) occurs mainly in the fingers of the hand used to guide the cutting tool. The circulation in this hand becomes impaired, and when exposed to cold the fingers become white and without sensation, as though mildly frostbitten. The white appearance usually disappears when the fingers are warmed for some time, but a few cases are sufficiently disabling that the victims are forced to seek other types of work. In many instances both hands are affected.

The condition has been observed in a number of other occupations involving the use of vibrating tools, such as the air hammers used for scarfing metal surfaces, the air chisels for chipping castings in the metal trades, and the chain saws used in forestry. The injury is caused by vibration of the fingers as they grip the tools to guide them in performing their tasks. The related damage to blood vessels can progress to nearly complete obstruction of the vessels.

Prevention should be directed at reducing the vibrational energy transferred to the fingers (perhaps by the use of padding) and by changing the energy and frequency of the vibration. Low frequencies, 25–75 hertz, are more damaging than higher frequencies. There are also TLVs for segmental and whole body vibration.

Lifting. The injuries resulting from manual handling of objects and materials make up a large proportion of all compensable injuries. This problem is of considerable concern to the health and safety professional and represents an area where the biomechanical data relating to lifting and carrying can be applied in the work layout and design of jobs that require handling of materials. (For more details, see Chapter 13, Ergonomics, and the Application Manual for the Revised NIOSH Lifting Equation. Also see the current TLV for Lifting.)

The relevant data concerning lifting can be classified into task, human, and environmental variables.
- *Task variables*
  - location of object to be lifted
  - size of the object to be lifted
  - height from which and to which the object is lifted
  - frequency of lift
  - weight of object
  - working position
- *Human variables*
  - gender of worker
  - age of worker
  - training of worker
  - physical fitness or conditioning of worker
  - body dimensions, such as height of the worker
- *Environmental variables*
  - extremes of temperature
  - humidity
  - air contaminants

Static work. Another very fatiguing situation encountered in industry, which unfortunately is often overlooked, is static, or isometric, work. Because very little outward movement occurs, it seems that no muscular effort is involved. Often, however, such work generates more muscular fatigue than work involving some outward movement. A cramped working posture, for example, is a substantial source of static muscular loading.

In general, maintaining any set of muscles in a rigid, unsupported position for long periods of time results in muscular strain. The blood supply to the contracted muscle is diminished, a local deficiency of oxygen can occur, and waste products accumulate. Alternating static and dynamic work, or providing support for partial relaxation of the member involved, alleviates this problem.

Armrests are usually needed in two types of situations. One is the case just mentioned—to relieve the isometric muscular work involved in holding the arm in a fixed, unsupported position for long periods of time. The second case is where the arm is pressed against a hard surface such as the edge of a bench or machine. The pressure on the soft tissues overlaying the bones can cause bruises and pain. Padded armrests have solved numerous problems of both types (see Figure 1–3).

Workplace Design

Relating the physical characteristics and capabilities of the worker to the design of equipment and to the layout of the workplace is another key ergonomic concept. When this is done, the result is an increase in efficiency, a decrease in human error, and a consequent reduction in accident frequency. However, several different types of information are needed: a description of the job, an understanding of the kinds of equipment to be used, a description of the kinds of people who will use the equipment, and the biological characteristics of these people.

In general, the first three items—job, equipment, and users—can be defined easily. The biological characteristics of the users, however, can often be determined satisfactorily only from special surveys that yield descriptive data on human body size and biomechanical abilities and limitations.

Anthropometric data. Anthropometric data consist of various heights, lengths, and breadths used to establish the minimum clearances and spatial accommodations, and the functional arm, leg, and body movements that are made by the worker during the performance of the task.

Behavioral Aspects—Mental Demands

One important aspect of industrial machine design directly related to the safety and productivity of the worker is the design of displays and controls.

Design of displays. Displays are one of the most common types of operator input; the others include direct sensing and verbal or visual commands. Displays tell the operator what the machine is doing and how it is performing. Problems

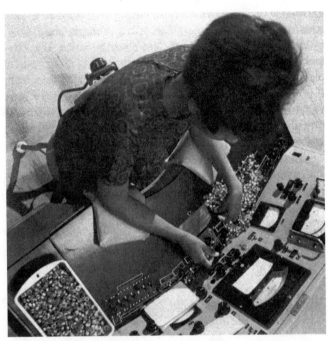

Figure 1–3. Worker uses pads to keep her forearm off the sharp table edge.

of display design are primarily related to the human senses.

A machine operator can successfully control equipment only to the extent that the operator receives clear, unambiguous information when needed on all pertinent aspects of the task. Accidents, or operational errors, often occur because a worker has misinterpreted or was unable to obtain information from displays. Displays are usually visual, although they also can be auditory (for example, a warning bell rather than a warning light), especially when there is danger of overloading the visual sensory channels.

Design of Controls. An operator must decide on the proper course of action and manipulate controls to produce any desired change in the machine's performance. The efficiency and effectiveness—that is, the safety with which controls can be operated—depend on the extent to which information on the dynamics of human movement, or biomechanics, has been incorporated in their design. This is particularly true whenever controls must be operated at high speed, against large resistances, with great precision, or over long periods of time.

Controls should be designed so that rapid, accurate settings easily can be made without undue fatigue, thereby avoiding many accidents and operational errors. Because there is a wide variety of machine controls, ranging from the simple on–off action of pushbuttons to very complex mechanisms, advance analysis of the task requirements must be made. On the basis of considerable experimental evidence, it is possible to recommend the most appropriate control and its desirable range of operation.

In general, the mechanical design of equipment must be compatible with the biological and psychological characteristics of the operator. The effectiveness of the human–machine combination can be greatly enhanced by treating the operator and the equipment as a unified system. Thus, the instruments should be considered as extensions of the operator's nervous and perceptual systems, the controls as extensions of the hands, and the feet as simple tools. Any control that is difficult to reach or operate, any instrument dial that has poor legibility, any seat that induces poor posture or discomfort, or any obstruction of vision can contribute directly to an accident or illness.

Biological Hazards

Approximately 200 biological agents, such as infectious microorganisms, biological allergens, and toxins, are known to produce infections or allergenic, toxic, or carcinogenic reactions in workers. Most of the identified biohazardous agents belong to these groups:

- microorganisms and their toxins (viruses, bacteria, fungi, and their products) resulting in infection, exposure, or allergy
- arthropods (crustaceans, arachnids, insects) associated with bites or stings resulting in skin inflammation, systemic intoxication and transmission of infectious agents, or allergic response
- allergens and toxins from higher plants, producing dermatitis, rhinitis, or asthma
- protein allergens (such as urine, feces, hair, saliva, and dander) from vertebrate animals

Other groups with the potential to expose workers to biohazards include lower plants other than fungi (lichen, liverworts, ferns) and invertebrate animals other than arthropods (parasites such as protozoa, Schistosoma) and roundworms (Ascaris).

Workers engaging in agricultural, medical, and laboratory work have been identified as most at risk to occupational biohazards but many varied workplaces present the potential for such exposure. For example, at least 24 of the 150 zoonotic diseases known worldwide are considered to be a hazard for agricultural workers in North America. Risk of infection varies with the type and species of animal and geographic location. Disease may be contracted directly from animals, but more often it is acquired in the workplace environment. Controls include awareness of specific hazards, use of personal protective equipment, preventive veterinary care, worker education, and medical monitoring or prophylactic therapy, where appropriate.

The potential for exposure to occupational biohazards

exists in most work environments. The following are but a few examples in very diverse workplaces:

- Workers maintaining water systems can be exposed to *Legionella pneumophila* and *Naegleria spp.*
- Workers associated with birds (parrots, parakeets, pigeons) in pet shops, aviaries, or on construction and public works jobs near perching or nesting sites can be exposed to *Chlamydia psittaci.*
- Workers in wood processing facilities can be exposed to endotoxins, allergenic fungi growing on timber, and fungi causing deep mycoses.
- Sewage and compost workers can be exposed to enteric bacteria, hepatitis A virus, infectious or endotoxin-producing bacteria, parasitic protozoa, and allergenic fungi.
- Health care workers, emergency responders, law enforcement officers, and morticians may be exposed to such bloodborne pathogens as hepatitis B (HBV), hepatitis C (HCV), and the human immunodeficiency virus (HIV) in addition to other biological hazards. (See Chapter 14, Biological Hazards.)

Building-Related Illnesses due to Biological Hazards

The sources of biological hazards may be fairly obvious in occupations associated with the handling of microorganisms, plants, and animals and in occupations involving contact with potentially infected people. However, recognizing and identifying biological hazards may not be as simple in other situations, such as office buildings and nonindustrial workplaces. Building-related illness (BRI) is a clinically diagnosed disease in one or more building occupants, as distinguished from sick-building syndrome (SBS), in which building occupants' nonspecific symptoms cannot be associated with an identifiable cause. Certain BRI, such as infectious and hypersensitivity diseases, are clearly associated with biological hazards, but the role of biological materials in SBS is not as well understood.

The conditions and events necessary to result in human exposure to bioaerosols are the presence of a reservoir that can support the growth of microorganisms or allow accumulation of biological material, multiplication of contaminating organisms or biological materials in the reservoir, generation of aerosols containing biological material, and exposure of susceptible workers. (See Chapter 14, Biological Hazards, for a full discussion.)

Industrial Sanitation—Water Supply

The requirements for sanitation and personal facilities are covered in the OSHAct safety and health regulations 29 CFR 1910, Subpart J—General Environmental Controls. The OSHAct regulations for carcinogens require special personal health and sanitary facilities for employees working with potentially carcinogenic materials.

Potable water should be provided in workplaces when needed for drinking and personal washing, cooking, washing of foods or utensils, washing of food preparation premises, and personal service rooms.

Drinking fountain surfaces must be constructed of materials impervious to water and not subject to oxidation. The nozzle of the fountain must be located to prevent the return of water in the jet or bowl to the nozzle orifice. A guard over the nozzle prevents contact with the nozzle by the mouth or nose of people using the drinking fountain.

Potable drinking water dispensers must be designed and constructed so that sanitary conditions are maintained; they must be capable of being closed and equipped with a tap. Ice that comes in contact with drinking water must be made of potable water and maintained in a sanitary condition. Standing water in cooling towers and other air-moving systems should be monitored for legionella bacteria. (See Chapter 14, Biological Hazards, for details.)

Outlets for nonpotable water, such as water for industrial or firefighting purposes, must be marked in a manner that indicates clearly that the water is unsafe and is not to be used as drinking water. Nonpotable water systems or systems carrying any other nonpotable substance should be constructed so as to prevent backflow or backsiphonage.

HARMFUL AGENTS—ROUTE OF ENTRY

In order to exert its toxic effect, a harmful agent must come into contact with a body cell and must enter the body via inhalation, skin absorption, or ingestion.

Chemical compounds in the form of liquids, gases, mists, dusts, fumes, and vapors can cause problems by inhalation (breathing), absorption (through direct contact with the skin), or ingestion (eating or drinking).

Inhalation

Inhalation involves airborne contaminants that can be inhaled directly into the lungs and can be physically classified as gases, vapors, and particulate matter including dusts, fumes, smokes, aerosols, and mists.

Inhalation, as a route of entry, is particularly important because of the rapidity with which a toxic material can be absorbed in the lungs, pass into the bloodstream, and reach the brain. Inhalation is the major route of entry for hazardous chemicals in the work environment.

Absorption

Absorption through the skin can occur quite rapidly if the skin is cut or abraded. Intact skin, however, offers a reasonably good barrier to chemicals. Unfortunately, there are many compounds that can be absorbed through intact skin.

Some substances are absorbed by way of the openings for hair follicles and others dissolve in the fats and oils of the skin, such as organic lead compounds, many nitro compounds, and organic phosphate pesticides. Compounds that are good solvents for fats (such as toluene and xylene) also can be absorbed through the skin.

Many organic compounds, such as trinitrotoluene (TNT), cyanides, and most aromatic amines, amides, and phenols, can produce systemic poisoning by direct contact with the skin.

Ingestion

In the workplace, people can unknowingly eat or drink harmful chemicals. Toxic compounds can be absorbed from the gastrointestinal tract into the blood. Lead oxide can cause serious problems if people working with this material are allowed to eat or smoke in work areas. Thorough washing is required both before eating and at the end of every shift.

Inhaled toxic dusts can also be ingested in hazardous amounts. If the toxic dust swallowed with food or saliva is not soluble in digestive fluids, it is eliminated directly through the intestinal tract. Toxic materials that are readily soluble in digestive fluids can be absorbed into the blood from the digestive system.

It is important to study all routes of entry when evaluating the work environment—candy bars or lunches in the work area, solvents being used to clean work clothing and hands, in addition to airborne contaminants in working areas. (For more details, see Chapter 6, Industrial Toxicology.)

TYPES OF AIRBORNE CONTAMINANTS

There are precise meanings of certain words commonly used in industrial hygiene. These must be used correctly to understand the requirements of OSHAct regulations, effectively communicate with other occupational health professionals, recommend or design and test appropriate engineering controls, and correctly prescribe personal protective equipment. For example, a fume respirator is worthless as protection against gases or vapors. Too often, terms (such as gases, vapors, fumes, and mists) are used interchangeably. Each term has a definite meaning and describes a certain state of matter.

States of Matter

Matter is divided into dusts, fumes, smoke, aerosols, mists, gases, and vapors. These are discussed in the following sections.

Particulate Matter (Dusts)

Dusts are solid particles generated by handling, crushing, grinding, rapid impact, detonation, and decrepitation (breaking apart by heating) of organic or inorganic materials, such as rock, ore, metal, coal, wood, and grain.

Dust or particulate matter (PM) is a term used in industry to describe airborne solid particles that range in size from 0.001 µm (1 nm) to 100 µm. To clarify, µm refers to micron. Nm is nanometer. To compare sizes relatively, 0.1–25 µm in diameter (1 µm = 0.0001 cm or 1/25,400 in.). Dusts more than 5 µm in size usually do not remain airborne long enough to present an inhalation problem.

Engineered nano particles, (ENPs) are particles that are intentionally made to be very small, well under a micrometer in diameter. While no perfect definition of *engineered nanoparticle* has arisen, ENP materials typically include four specific characteristics:

1. They are very small, generally less than 100 nm in at least two dimensions
2. They are either free independent particles with no strong bonds to a larger substrate, or, if they are attached to a substrate, they are readily displaced.
3. They are novel, that is, only recently used or studied.
4. They are made intentionally as a product.

While engineered nanoparticles are finding rapidly growing uses in manufacturing today, they are also presenting their own unique levels of toxicity, measuring difficulty, and problems of control. (See Chapter 8, Particulate Matter, for a full discussion of this subject).

Dust can enter the air from various sources, such as when a dusty material is handled (as when lead oxide is dumped into a mixer or talc is dusted on a product). When solid materials are reduced to small sizes in processes such as grinding, crushing, blasting, shaking, and drilling, the mechanical action of the grinding or shaking device supplies energy to disperse the dust.

Evaluating dust exposures properly requires knowledge of the chemical composition, particle size, dust concentration in air, how it is dispersed, and many other factors described here. Although in the case of gases, the concentration that reaches the alveolar sacs is nearly like the concentration in the air breathed, this is not the case for aerosols or dust particles. Large particles, more than 10 µm aerodynamic diameter, can be deposited through gravity and impaction in large ducts before they reach the very small sacs (alveoli). Only the smaller particles reach the alveoli. (See Chapter 2, The Lungs, for more details.)

Except for some fibrous materials, dust particles must usually be smaller than 5 µm in order to penetrate to the alveoli or inner recess of the lungs.

A person with normal eyesight can detect dust particles as small as 50 µm in diameter. Smaller airborne particles can be detected individually by the naked eye only when strong light is reflected from them. Particles of dust of respirable size (less than 10 µm) cannot be seen without the aid of a microscope, but they may be perceived as a haze.

Most industrial dusts consist of particles that vary widely in size, with the small particles greatly outnumbering the large ones. Consequently (with few exceptions), when dust is noticeable in the air near a dusty operation, probably more invisible dust particles than visible ones are present. A process that produces dust fine enough to remain suspended in the air long enough to be breathed should be regarded as hazardous until it can be proved safe.

There is no simple one-to-one relationship between the concentration of an atmospheric contaminant and duration of exposure and the rate of dosage by the hazardous agent to the critical site in the body. For a given magnitude of atmospheric exposure to a potentially toxic particulate contaminant, the resulting hazard can range from an insignificant level to one of great danger, depending on the toxicity of the material, the size of the inhaled particles, and other factors that determine their fate in the respiratory system.

Fumes

Fumes are formed when the material from a volatilized solid condenses in cool air. The solid particles that are formed make up a fume that is extremely fine, usually less than 1.0 µm in diameter. In most cases, the hot vapor reacts with the air to form an oxide. Gases and vapors are not fumes, although the terms are often mistakenly used interchangeably.

Welding, metalizing, and other operations involving vapors from molten metals may produce fumes; these may be harmful under certain conditions. Arc welding volatilizes metal vapor that condenses as the metal or its oxide in the air around the arc. In addition, the rod coating is partially volatilized. These fumes, because they are extremely fine, are readily inhaled.

Other toxic fumes, such as those formed when welding structures that have been painted with lead-based paints or when welding galvanized metal, can produce severe symptoms of toxicity rather rapidly unless fumes are controlled with effective local exhaust ventilation or the welder is protected by respiratory protective equipment.

Fortunately, most soldering operations do not require temperatures high enough to volatilize an appreciable amount of lead. However, the lead in molten solder pots is oxidized by contact with air at the surface. If this oxide, often called dross, is mechanically dispersed into the air, it can produce a severe lead-poisoning hazard.

In operations when lead dust may be present in air, such as soldering or lead battery-making, preventing occupational poisoning is largely a matter of scrupulously clean housekeeping to prevent the lead oxide from becoming dispersed into the air. It is customary to enclose melting pots, dross boxes, and similar operations, and to ventilate them adequately to control the hazard. Other controls may be necessary as well.

Smoke

Smoke consists of carbon or soot particles less than 0.1 µm in size, and results from the incomplete combustion of carbonaceous materials such as coal or oil. Smoke generally contains droplets as well as dry particles. Tobacco, for instance, produces a wet smoke composed of minute tarry droplets.

Aerosols

Aerosols are liquid droplets or solid particles of fine enough particle size to remain dispersed in air for a prolonged period of time.

Mists

Mists are suspended liquid droplets generated by condensation of liquids from the vapor back to the liquid state or by breaking up a liquid into a dispersed state, such as by splashing, foaming, or atomizing. The term mist is applied to a finely divided liquid suspended in the atmosphere. Examples are the oil mist produced during cutting and grinding operations, acid mists from electroplating, acid or alkali mists from pickling operations, paint spray mist in painting operations, and the condensation of water vapor to form a fog or rain.

Gases

Gases are formless fluids that expand to occupy the space or enclosure in which they are confined. They are a state of matter in which the molecules are unrestricted by cohesive forces. Examples are arc-welding gases, internal combustion engine exhaust gases, and air.

Vapors

Vapors are the volatile form of substances that are normally in the solid or liquid state at room temperature and pressure. Evaporation is the process by which a liquid is changed into the vapor state and mixed with the surrounding atmosphere. Solvents with low boiling points volatilize readily at room temperature.

In addition to the definitions concerning states of matter that are used daily by industrial hygienists, terms used to describe degree of exposure include the following:

- ppm: parts of vapor or gases per million parts of air by volume at room temperature and pressure
- mppcf: millions of particles of a particulate per cubic foot of air
- mg/m3: milligrams of a substance per cubic meter of air
- f/cc: fibers of a substance per cubic centimeter of air

The health and safety professional recognizes that air contaminants exist as a gas, dust, fume, mist, or vapor in the workroom air. In evaluating the degree of exposure, the measured concentration of the air contaminant is compared to limits or exposure guidelines that appear in the published standards on levels of exposure (see Appendix B).

Respiratory Hazards

Airborne chemical agents that enter the lungs can pass directly into the bloodstream and be carried to other parts of the body. The respiratory system consists of organs contributing to normal respiration or breathing. Strictly speaking, it includes the nose, mouth, upper throat, larynx, trachea, and bronchi (which are all air passages or airways) and the lungs, where oxygen is passed into the blood and carbon dioxide is given off. Finally, it includes the diaphragm and the muscles of the chest, which perform the normal respiratory movements of inspiration and expiration. (See Chapter 2, The Lungs.)

All living cells of the body are engaged in a series of chemical processes; the sum total of these processes is called metabolism. In the course of its metabolism, each cell consumes oxygen and produces carbon dioxide as a waste product.

Respiratory hazards can be broken down into two main groups:

1. Oxygen deficiency, in which the oxygen concentration (or partial pressure of oxygen) is below the level considered safe for human exposure
2. Air that contains harmful or toxic contaminants

Oxygen-Deficient Atmospheres

Each living cell in the body requires a constant supply of oxygen. Some cells are more dependent on a continuing oxygen supply than others. Some cells in the brain and nervous system can be injured or die after 4–6 min without oxygen. These cells, if destroyed, cannot be regenerated or replaced, and permanent changes and impaired functioning of the brain can result from such damage. Other cells in the body are not as critically dependent on an oxygen supply because they can be replaced.

Normal air at sea level contains approximately 21 percent oxygen and 79 percent nitrogen and other inert gases. At sea level and normal barometric pressure (760 mmHg or 101.3 kPa), the partial pressure of oxygen would be 21 percent of 760 mm, or 160 mm. The partial pressure of nitrogen and inert gases would be 600 mm (79 percent of 760 mm).

At higher altitudes or under conditions of reduced barometric pressure, the relative proportions of oxygen and nitrogen remain the same, but the partial pressure of each gas is decreased. The partial pressure of oxygen at the alveolar surface of the lung is critical because it determines the rate of oxygen diffusion through the moist lung tissue membranes.

Oxygen-deficient atmospheres may exist in confined spaces as oxygen is consumed by chemical reactions such as oxidation (rust, fermentation), replaced by inert gases such as argon, nitrogen, and carbon dioxide, or absorbed by porous surfaces such as activated charcoal.

Deficiency of oxygen in the atmosphere of confined spaces can be a problem in industry. For this reason, the oxygen content of any tank or other confined space (as well as the levels of any toxic contaminants) should be measured before entry is made. Instruments are commercially available for this purpose. (See Chapter 16, Air Sampling; Chapter 17, Direct-Reading Instruments for Gases, Vapors, and Particulates; and Chapter 22, Respiratory Protection, for more details.)

The first physiological signs of an oxygen deficiency (anoxia) are an increased rate and depth of breathing. A worker should never enter or remain in areas where tests have indicated oxygen deficiency without a supplied-air or self-contained respirator that is specifically approved by NIOSH for those conditions.

Oxygen-deficient atmospheres can cause an inability to move and a semiconscious lack of concern about the imminence of death. In cases of abrupt entry into areas containing little or no oxygen, the person usually has no warning symptoms, immediately loses consciousness, and has no recollection of the incident if rescued in time to be revived. The senses cannot be relied on to alert or warn a person of atmospheres deficient in oxygen.

Oxygen-deficient atmospheres can occur in tanks, vats, holds of ships, silos, mines, or in areas where the air may be diluted or displaced by asphyxiating levels of gases or vapors, or where the oxygen may have been consumed by chemical or biological reactions.

Ordinary jobs involving maintenance and repair of systems for storing and transporting fluids or entering tanks or tunnels for cleaning and repairs are controlled almost entirely by the immediate supervisor. The supervisor should be particularly knowledgeable of all rules and precautions

to ensure the safety of those who work in such atmospheres. Safeguards should be meticulously observed.

For example, there should be a standard operating procedure for entering tanks. Such procedures should be consistent with OSHAct regulations and augmented by in-house procedures, which may enhance the basic OSHAct rules. The American National Standards Institute (ANSI) lists confined space procedures in its respiratory protection standard and NIOSH has also issued guidelines for work in confined spaces including a criteria document for working in confined spaces (see Bibliography). Even if a tank is empty, it may have been closed for some time and developed an oxygen deficiency through chemical reactions of residues left in the tank. It may be unsafe to enter without proper respiratory protection.

The Hazard of Airborne Contaminants

Inhaling harmful materials can irritate the upper respiratory tract and lung tissue, or the terminal passages of the lungs and the air sacs, depending on the solubility of the material.

Inhalation of biologically inert gases can dilute the atmospheric oxygen below the normal blood saturation value and disturb cellular processes. Other gases and vapors may prevent the blood from carrying oxygen to the tissues or interfere with its transfer from the blood to the tissue, producing chemical asphyxia.

Inhaled contaminants that adversely affect the lungs fall into three general categories:

1. Aerosols (particulates), which, when deposited in the lungs, can produce either rapid local tissue damage, some slower tissue reactions, eventual disease, or physical plugging
2. Toxic vapors and gases that produce adverse reactions in the tissue of the lungs
3. Some toxic aerosols or gases that do not affect the lung tissue locally, but pass from the lungs into the bloodstream where they are carried to other body organs or have adverse effects on the oxygen-carrying capacity of the blood cells

An example of an aerosol is silica dust, which causes fibrotic growth (scar tissue) in the lungs. Other harmful aerosols are fungi found in sugar cane residues, producing bagassosis.

An example of the second type of inhaled contaminant is hydrogen fluoride, a gas that directly affects lung tissue. It is a primary irritant of mucous membranes, even causing chemical burns. Inhalation of this gas causes pulmonary edema and direct interference with the gas transfer function of the alveolar lining.

An example of the third type of inhaled contaminant is carbon monoxide, a toxic gas passed into the bloodstream without harming the lung. The carbon monoxide passes through the alveolar walls into the blood, where it ties up the hemoglobin so that it cannot accept oxygen, thus causing oxygen starvation. Cyanide gas has another effect—it prevents enzymatic utilization of molecular oxygen by cells.

Sometimes several types of lung hazards occur simultaneously. In mining operations, for example, explosives release oxides of nitrogen. These impair the bronchial clearance mechanism so that coal dust (of the particle sizes associated with the explosions) is not efficiently cleansed from the lungs.

If a compound is very soluble—such as ammonia, sulfuric acid, or hydrochloric acid—it is rapidly absorbed in the upper respiratory tract and during the initial phases of exposure does not penetrate deeply into the lungs. Consequently, the nose and throat become very irritated.

Compounds that are insoluble in body fluids cause considerably less throat irritation than the soluble ones, but can penetrate deeply into the lungs. Thus, a very serious hazard can be present and not be recognized immediately because of a lack of warning that the local irritation would otherwise provide. Examples of such compounds (gases) are nitrogen dioxide and ozone. The immediate danger from these compounds in high concentrations is acute lung irritation or, possibly, chemical pneumonia.

There are numerous chemical compounds that do not follow the general solubility rule. Such compounds are not very soluble in water and yet are very irritating to the eyes and respiratory tract. They also can cause lung damage and even death under certain conditions. (See Chapter 6, Industrial Toxicology.)

THRESHOLD LIMIT VALUES

The ACGIH Threshold Limit Values (TLVs®) are exposure guidelines established for airborne concentrations of many chemical compounds. The health and safety professional or other responsible person should understand something about TLVs and the terminology in which their concentrations are expressed. (See Chapter 15, Evaluation; Chapter 6, Industrial Toxicology; and Appendix B for more details.)

TLVs are airborne concentrations of substances and represent conditions under which it is believed that nearly all workers may be repeatedly exposed, day after day, without adverse effect. Control of the work environment is based on the assumption that for each substance there is some safe or tolerable level of exposure below which no significant adverse effect occurs. These tolerable levels are called Threshold Limit Values. In its Introduction, the *ACGIH Threshold Limit Values (TLVs®) for Chemical Substances and Physical Agents and Biological Exposure Indices (BEIs®)* states that because individual susceptibility varies widely, a small percentage of workers may experience discomfort from some substances at concentrations at or below the threshold limit. A smaller percentage may be affected more seriously by aggravation of a preexisting condition or by development of an occupational illness. Smoking may enhance the biological effects of chemicals encountered in the workplace and may reduce the body's defense mechanisms against toxic substances.

Hypersusceptible individuals or those otherwise unusually responsive to some industrial chemicals because of genetic factors, age, personal habits (smoking and use of alcohol or other drugs), medication, or previous exposures may not be adequately protected from adverse health effects of chemicals at concentrations at or below the threshold limits.

These limits are not fine lines between safe and dangerous concentration, nor are they a relative index of toxicity. They should not be used by anyone untrained in the discipline of industrial hygiene.

The copyrighted trademark Threshold Limit Values refers to limits published by ACGIH. The TLVs are reviewed and updated annually to reflect the most current information on the effects of each substance assigned a TLV.

The data for establishing TLVs come from animal studies, human studies, and industrial experience, and the limit may be selected for several reasons. As mentioned earlier in this chapter, the TLV can be based on the fact that a substance is very irritating to the majority of people exposed, or the fact that a substance is an asphyxiant. Still other reasons for establishing a TLV for a given substance include the fact that certain chemical compounds are anesthetic or fibrogenic or can cause allergic reactions or malignancies. Some additional TLVs have been established because exposure above a certain airborne concentration is a nuisance.

The amount and nature of the information available for establishing a TLV varies from substance to substance; consequently, the precision of the estimated TLV continues to be subject to revision and debate. The latest documentation for that substance should be consulted to assess the present data available for a given substance.

In addition to the TLVs set for chemical compounds, there are limits for physical agents such as noise, radio frequency/microwave radiation, segmental vibration, lasers, ionizing radiation, static magnetic fields, light, near-infrared radiation, subradiofrequency ($\leq$ 30 kHz) magnetic fields, subradiofrequency and static electric fields, ultraviolet radiation, cold stress, and heat stress. Under Ergonomics there are TLVs for lifting, hand activity levels, and segmental and whole body vibration. There are also biological exposure indices (BEIs).

The ACGIH periodically publishes a documentation of TLVs in which it gives the data and information on which the TLV for each substance is based. This documentation can provide health and safety professionals with insight to aid professional judgment when applying the TLVs.

The most current edition of the *ACGIH Threshold Limit Values (TLVs®) for Chemical Substances and Physical Agents and Biological Exposure Indices (BEIs®)* should be used. When referring to an ACGIH TLV, the year of publication should always preface the value, as in "the 2012 TLV for nitric oxide was 25 ppm." Note that the TLVs are not mandatory federal or state employee exposure standards, and the term TLV should not be used for standards published by OSHA or any agency except the ACGIH.

Three categories of TLVs are specified as follows:

Time-Weighted Average

The time-weighted average limit (TLV-TWA) is the time-weighted average concentration for a conventional eight-hour workday and 40-hour workweek, to which it is believed that nearly all workers may be repeatedly exposed, day after day, without adverse effect.

Short-Term Exposure Limit

The short-term exposure limit (TLV-STEL) is the concentration to which it is believed workers can be exposed continuously for a short period of time without suffering from
- irritation;
- chronic or irreversible tissue damage; or
- narcosis of sufficient degree to increase the likelihood of accidental injury, impair self-rescue, or materially reduce work efficiency and provided that the daily TLV–TWA is not exceeded.

A STEL is a 15-minute TWA exposure that should not be exceeded at any time during a workday, even if the eight-hour TWA is within the TLV-TWA. Exposures above the TLV-TWA up to the STEL should not be longer than 15 minutes and should not occur more than four times per day. There should be at least 60 minutes between successive exposures in this range.

The TLV–STEL is not a separate, independent exposure limit; it supplements the TWA limit when there are recognized acute effects from a substance that has primarily chronic effects. The STELs are recommended only when toxic effects in humans or animals have been reported from high short-term exposures.

Note: None of the limits mentioned here, especially the TWA–STEL, should be used as engineering design criteria.

Ceiling

The ceiling limit (TLV-C) is the concentration that should not be exceeded during any part of the working exposure. To assess a TLV–C if instantaneous monitoring is not feasible, the conventional industrial hygiene practice is to sample during a 15-minute period, except for substances that can cause immediate irritation with short exposures.

For some substances (such as irritant gases), only one category, the TLV–C, may be relevant. For other substances, two or three categories may be relevant, depending on their physiological action. If any one of these three TLVs is exceeded, a potential hazard from that substance is presumed to exist.

Limits based on physical irritation should be considered no less binding than those based on physical impairment. Increasing evidence shows that physical irritation can initiate, promote, or accelerate physical impairment via interaction with other chemical or biological agents.

The amount by which threshold limits can be exceeded for short periods without injury to health depends on many factors: the nature of the contaminant; whether very high concentrations, even for a short period, produce acute poisoning; whether the effects are cumulative; the frequency with which high concentrations occur; and the duration of such periods. All factors must be considered when deciding whether a hazardous condition exists.

Skin Notation

A number of the substances in the TLV list are followed by the designation Skin. This refers to potential significant exposure through the cutaneous route, including mucous membranes and the eyes, either by contact with vapors or, of probably greater significance, by direct skin contact with the substance. Vehicles, such as certain solvents, can alter skin absorption. This designation is intended to suggest appropriate measures for the prevention of cutaneous absorption.

Mixtures

Special consideration should be given in assessing the health hazards that can be associated with exposure to mixtures of two or more substances.

Federal Occupational Safety and Health Standards

The first compilation of the health and safety standards promulgated by OSHA in 1970 was derived from the then-existing federal standards and national consensus standards. Thus, many of the 1968 TLVs established by the ACGIH became federal standards or permissible exposure limits (PELs). Also, certain workplace quality standards known as ANSI maximal acceptable concentrations were incorporated as federal health standards in 29 CFR 1910.1000 (Table Z–2) as national consensus standards.

In adopting the ACGIH TLVs, OSHA also adopted the concept of the TWA for a workday. In general:

$$TWA = \frac{C_a T_a + C_b T_b + \ldots + C_n T_n}{8}$$

where T_a = the time of the first exposure period during the shift

C_a = the concentration of contaminant in period a

T_b = another time period during the shift

C_b = the concentration during period b

T_n = the nth or final time period in the shift

C_n = the concentration during period n

This simply provides a summation throughout the workday of the product of the concentrations and the time periods for the concentrations encountered in each time interval and averaged over an eight-hour standard workday.

EVALUATION

Evaluation can be defined as the decision-making process resulting in an opinion on the degree of health hazard posed by chemical, physical, biological, or ergonomic stresses in industrial operations. The basic approach to controlling occupational disease consists of evaluating the potential hazard and controlling the specific hazard by suitable industrial hygiene techniques. (See Chapter 15, Evaluation, for more details.)

Evaluation involves judging the magnitude of the chemical, physical, biological, or ergonomic stresses. Determining whether a health hazard exists is based on a combination of observation, interviews, and measurement of the levels of energy or air contaminants arising from the work process, as well as an evaluation of the effectiveness of control measures in the workplace. The industrial hygienist then compares environmental measurements with hygienic guides, TLVs, OSHA PELs, NIOSH RELs, or reports in the literature.

Evaluation, in the broad sense, also includes determining the levels of physical and chemical agents arising out of a process in order to study the related work procedures and to determine the effectiveness of a given piece of equipment that is used to control the hazards from that process.

Anticipating and recognizing industrial health hazards involve knowledge and understanding of the several types of workplace environmental stresses and the effects of these stresses on the health of the worker. Control involves the reduction of environmental stresses to values that the worker can tolerate without impairment of health or productivity. Measuring and quantitating environmental stress

are the essential ingredients for modern industrial hygiene, and are instrumental in conserving the health and well-being of workers.

Basic Hazard-Recognition Procedures

There is a basic, systematic procedure for recognizing and evaluating environmental health hazards, which includes the following questions:
- What is produced?
- What raw material is used?
- What materials are added in the process?
- What equipment is involved?
- What is the cycle of operations?
- What operational procedures are used?
- Is there a written procedure for the safe handling and storage of materials?
- What about dust control, cleanup after spills, and waste disposal?
- Are the ventilating and exhaust systems adequate?
- Does the facility layout minimize exposure?
- Is the facility well-equipped with safety appliances such as showers, masks, respirators, and emergency eyewash fountains?
- Are safe operating procedures outlined and enforced?
- Is a complete hazard communication program that meets state or federal OSHA requirements in effect?

The industrial hygienist must understand the industrial process well enough to see where contaminants are released. For each process, the following should be performed:
- For each contaminant, find the OSHA PEL or other safe exposure guideline based on the toxicological effect of the material.
- Determine the actual level of exposure to harmful physical agents.
- Determine the number of employees exposed and length of exposure.
- Identify the chemicals and contaminants in the process.
- Determine the level of airborne contaminants using air-sampling techniques.
- Calculate the resulting daily average and peak exposures from the air-sampling results and employee exposure times.
- Compare the calculated exposures with OSHA standards, the TLV listing published by the ACGIH, the NIOSH RELs, the hygienic guides, or other toxicological recommendations.

All of the above are discussed in detail in the following chapters.

Information Required

Detailed information should be obtained regarding types of

hazardous materials used in a facility, the type of job operation, how the workers are exposed, work patterns, levels of air contamination, duration of exposure, control measures used, and other pertinent information. The hazard potential of the material is determined not only by its inherent toxicity, but also by the conditions of use (who uses what, where, and how long?).

To recognize hazardous environmental factors or stresses, a health and safety professional must first know the raw materials used and the nature of the products and by-products manufactured. Consult Safety Data Sheets for the substances.

Any person responsible for maintaining a safe, healthful work environment should be thoroughly acquainted with the concentrations of harmful materials or energies that may be encountered in the industrial environment for which they are responsible.

If a facility is going to handle a hazardous material, the health and safety professional must consider all the unexpected events that can occur and determine what precautions are required in case of an accident to prevent or control atmospheric release of a toxic material.

After these considerations have been studied and proper countermeasures installed, operating and maintenance personnel must be taught the proper operation of the health and safety control measures. Only in this way can personnel be made aware of the possible hazards and the need for certain built-in safety features. The operating and maintenance people should set up a routine procedure (at frequent, stated intervals) for testing the emergency industrial hygiene and safety provisions that are not used in normal, ordinary facility or process operations.

Degree of Hazard

The degree of hazard from exposure to harmful environmental factors or stresses depends on the following:

- nature of the material or energy involved
- intensity of the exposure
- duration of the exposure

The key elements to be considered when evaluating a health hazard are how much of the material in contact with body cells is required to produce injury, the probability of the material being absorbed by the body to result in an injury, the rate at which the airborne contaminant is generated, the total time of contact, and the control measures in use.

Air Sampling

The importance of the sampling location, the proper time to sample, and the number of samples to be taken during the course of an investigation of the work environment cannot be overstressed.

Although this procedure might appear to be a routine, mechanical job, actually it is an art requiring detailed knowledge of the sampling equipment and its shortcomings. The person taking the sample(s) needs to know where and when to sample; and how to weigh the many factors that can influence the sample results, such as ambient temperature, season of the year, unusual problems in work operations, and interference from other contaminants. The sample must usually be taken in the breathing zone of an employee.

The air volume sampled must be sufficient to permit a representative determination of the contaminant to properly compare the result with the TLV or PEL. The sampling period must usually be sufficient to give a direct measure of the average full-shift exposure of the employees concerned. The sample must be sealed and identified if it is to be shipped to a laboratory so that it is possible to identify positively the time and place of sampling and the individual who took the sample.

Area samples, taken by setting the sampling equipment in a fixed position in the work area, are useful as an index of general contamination. However, the actual exposure of the employee at the point of generation of the contaminant can be greater than is indicated by an area sample.

To meet the requirement of establishing the TWA concentrations, the sampling method and time periods should be chosen to average out fluctuations that commonly occur in a day's work. If there are wide fluctuations in concentration, the long-term samples should be supplemented by samples designed to catch the peaks separately.

If the exposure being measured is from a continuous operation, it is necessary to follow the particular operator through two cycles of operation, or through the full shift if operations follow a random pattern during the day. For operations of this sort, it is particularly important to find out what the workers do when the equipment is down for maintenance or process change. Such periods are often also periods of maximum exposure. (See Chapter 16, Air Sampling.)

As an example of the very small concentrations involved, the industrial hygienist commonly samples and measures substances in the air of the working environment in concentrations ranging from 1 to 100 ppm. Some idea of the magnitude of these concentrations can be appreciated when one realizes that 1 inch in 16 miles is 1 part per million; 1 cent in $10,000, 1 ounce of salt in 62,500 pounds of sugar, and 1 ounce of oil in 7,812.5 gallons of water all represent 1 part per million.

OCCUPATIONAL SKIN DISEASES

Some general observations on dermatitis are given in this chapter, but more detailed information is given in Chapter 3,

The Skin and Occupational Dermatoses. Occupational dermatoses can be caused by organic substances, such as formaldehyde; solvents or inorganic materials, such as acids and alkalis; and chromium and nickel compounds. Skin irritants are usually either liquids or dusts.

Types

There are two general types of dermatitis: primary irritation and sensitization.

Primary Irritation Dermatitis

Nearly all people suffer primary irritation dermatitis from mechanical agents such as friction, from physical agents such as heat or cold, and from chemical agents such as acids, alkalis, irritant gases, and vapors. Brief contact with a high concentration of a primary irritant or prolonged exposure to a low concentration causes inflammation. Allergy is not a factor in these conditions.

Sensitization Dermatitis

This type results from an allergic reaction to a given substance. The sensitivity becomes established during the induction period, which may be a few days to a few months. After the sensitivity is established, exposure to even a small amount of the sensitizing material is likely to produce a severe reaction.

Some substances can produce both primary irritation dermatitis and sensitization dermatitis. Among them are organic solvents, chromic acid, and epoxy resin systems.

Causes

Occupational dermatitis can be caused by chemical, mechanical, physical, and biological agents and plant poisons.

Chemical agents are the predominant causes of dermatitis in manufacturing industries. Cutting oils and similar substances are significant because the oil dermatitis they cause is probably of greater interest to industrial concerns than is any other type of dermatitis.

Detergents and solvents remove the natural oils from the skin or react with the oils of the skin to increase susceptibility to reactions from chemicals that ordinarily do not affect the skin. Materials that remove the natural oils include alkalis, soap, and turpentine.

Dessicators, hygroscopic agents, and anhydrides take water out of the skin and generate heat. Examples are sulfur dioxide and trioxide, phosphorus pentoxide, strong acids such as sulfuric acid, and strong alkalis such as potash.

Protein precipitants tend to coagulate the outer layers of the skin. They include all the heavy metallic salts and those that form alkaline albuminates on combining with the skin, such as mercuric and ferric chloride. Alcohol, tannic acid,

formaldehyde, picric acid, phenol, and intense ultraviolet rays are other examples of protein-precipitating agents.

Oxidizers unite with hydrogen and liberate nascent oxygen on the skin. Such materials include nitrates, chlorine, iodine, bromine, hypochlorites, ferric chloride, hydrogen peroxide, chromic acid, permanganates, and ozone.

Solvents extract essential skin constituents. Examples are ketones, aliphatic and aromatic hydrocarbons, halogenated hydrocarbons, ethers, esters, and certain nitro compounds.

Allergic or anaphylactic proteins stimulate the production of antibodies that cause skin reactions in sensitive people. The sources of these antigens are usually cereals, flour, and pollens, but can include feathers, scales, flesh, fur, and other emanations.

Mechanical causes of skin irritation include friction, pressure, and trauma, which may facilitate infection with either bacteria or fungi.

Physical agents leading to occupational dermatitis include heat, cold, sunlight, x rays, ionizing radiation, and electricity. The x rays and other ionizing radiation can cause dermatitis, severe burns, and even cancer. Prolonged exposure to sunlight produces skin changes and may cause skin cancer.

Biological agents causing dermatitis can be bacterial, fungal, or parasitic. Boils and folliculitis caused by staphylococci and streptococci, and general infection from occupational wounds, are probably the best known among the bacterial skin infections. These can be occupationally induced infections.

Fungi cause athlete's foot and other types of dermatitis among kitchen workers, bakers, and fruit handlers; fur, hide, and wool handlers or sorters; barbers; and horticulturists. Parasites cause grain itch and often occur among handlers of grains and straws, and particularly among farmers, laborers, miners, fruit handlers, and horticulturists.

Plant poisons causing dermatitis are produced by several hundred species of plants. The best known are poison ivy, poison oak, and poison sumac. Dermatitis from these three sources can result from bodily contact with any part of the plant, exposure of any part of the body to smoke from the burning plant, or contact with clothing or other objects previously exposed to the plant.

Physical Examinations

Preplacement examinations help identify those especially susceptible to skin irritations. The examining physician should be given detailed information on the type of work for which the applicant is being considered. If the work involves exposure to skin irritants, the physician should determine whether the prospective employee has deficiencies or characteristics likely to predispose him or her to dermatitis (see Chapter 26, The Occupational Medicine Physician, for more details).

Preventive Measures

Before new or different chemicals are introduced in an established process, possible dermatitis hazards should be carefully considered. Once these hazards are anticipated, suitable engineering controls should be devised and built into the processes to avoid them.

The type, number, and amount of skin irritants used in various industrial processes affect the degree of control that can be readily obtained, but the primary objective in every case should be to eliminate skin contact as completely as possible. The preventive measures discussed in Chapter 18, Methods of Control, can be adapted to control industrial dermatitis.

CONTROL METHODS

With employment in the United States shifting from manufacturing to the service sector, many workplaces today present nontraditional occupational health hazards. Industrial hygienists need to possess the skills to implement control methodology in both industrial settings and in workplaces such as laboratories, offices, health care facilities, and environmental remediation projects. Hazards can change with time as well, so that hazard control systems require continual review and updating.

Control methods for health hazards in the work environment are divided into three basic categories:

1. Engineering controls that are used to engineer out the hazard, either by initial design specifications or by applying methods of substitution, isolation, enclosure, or ventilation. In the hierarchy of control methods, the use of engineering controls should be considered first.
2. Administrative controls that reduce employee exposures by scheduling reduced work times in contaminant areas, or during cooler times of the day for heat stress exposure, for example. Also included here is employee training that includes hazard recognition and specific work practices that help reduce exposure. This type of training is required by law for all employees exposed to hazardous materials in the course of their work.
3. Personal protective equipment that employees wear to protect them from their environment. Personal protective equipment includes anything from gloves to full body suits with self-contained breathing apparatus, and can be used in conjunction with engineering and administrative controls. Engineering controls should be used as the first line of defense against workplace hazards wherever feasible. Such built-in protection, inherent in the design of a process, is preferable to a method that depends on continual human implementation or intervention. The federal regulations, and their interpreta-

tion by the Occupational Safety and Health Review commission, mandate the use of engineering controls to the extent feasible; if they are not sufficient to achieve acceptable limits of exposure, the use of personal protective equipment and other corrective measures may be considered.

Engineering controls include ventilation to minimize dispersion of airborne contaminants, isolation of a hazardous operation or substance by means of barriers or enclosures, and substitution of a material, equipment, or process to provide hazard control. Although administrative control measures can limit the duration of individual exposures, they are not generally favored by employers because they are difficult to implement and maintain. For similar reasons, control of health hazards by using respirators and protective clothing is usually considered secondary to the use of engineering control methods. (See Chapter 18, Methods of Control.)

Engineering Controls

Substituting or replacing a toxic material with a harmless one is a very practical method of eliminating an industrial health hazard. In many cases, a solvent with a lower order of toxicity or flammability can be substituted for a more hazardous one. In a solvent substitution, it is always advisable to experiment on a small scale before making the new solvent part of the operation or process.

A change in process often offers an ideal chance to improve working conditions as well as quality and production. In some cases, a process can be modified to reduce the hazard. Brush painting or dipping instead of spray painting minimizes the concentration of airborne contaminants from toxic pigments. Structural bolts in place of riveting, steam-cleaning instead of vapor degreasing of parts, and airless spraying techniques and electrostatic devices to replace hand-spraying are examples of process change. When buying individual machines, the need for accessory ventilation, noise and vibration suppression, and heat control should be considered before the purchase.

Noisy operations can be isolated from the people nearby by a physical barrier (such as an acoustic box to contain noise from a whining blower or a rip saw). Isolation is particularly useful for limited operations requiring relatively few workers or where control by any other method is not feasible.

Enclosing the process or equipment is a desirable method of control because it can minimize escape of the contaminant into the workroom atmosphere. Examples of this type of control are glove box enclosures and abrasive shot blast machines for cleaning castings.

In the chemical industry, isolating hazardous processes in closed systems is a widespread practice. The use of a closed system is one reason why the manufacture of toxic substances can be less hazardous than their use.

Dust hazards often can be minimized or greatly reduced by spraying water at the source of dust dispersion. *Wetting down* is one of the simplest methods for dust control. However, its effectiveness depends on proper wetting of the dust and keeping it moist. To be effective, the addition of a wetting agent to the water and proper and timely disposal of the wetted dust before it dries out and is redispersed may be necessary.

Ventilation

The major use of exhaust ventilation for contaminant control is to prevent health hazards from airborne materials. OSHA has ventilation standards for abrasive blasting, grinding, polishing and buffing operations, spray finishing operations, and open-surface tanks. (For more details, see Chapter 19, Local Exhaust Ventilation, and Chapter 20, Dilution Ventilation of Industrial Workplaces.)

A local exhaust system traps and removes the air contaminant near the generating source, which usually makes this method much more effective than general ventilation. Therefore, local exhaust ventilation should be used when exposures to the contaminant cannot be controlled by substitution, changing the process, isolation, or enclosure. Even though a process has been isolated, it still may require a local exhaust system.

General or dilution ventilation—removing and adding air to dilute the concentration of a contaminant to below hazardous levels—uses natural or forced air movement through open doors, windows, roof ventilators, and chimneys. General exhaust fans can be mounted in roofs, walls, or windows. (See Chapters 19 and 20 for more details.)

Consideration must be given to providing replacement air, especially during winter. Dilution ventilation is feasible only if the quantity of air contaminant is not excessive. It is particularly effective if the contaminant is released at a substantial distance from the worker's breathing zone. General ventilation should not be used where there is a major, localized source of contamination, especially highly toxic dusts and fumes. A local exhaust system is more effective in such cases.

Air conditioning does not substitute for air cleaning. Air conditioning is mainly concerned with control of air temperature and humidity and can be accomplished by systems that accomplish little or no air cleaning. An air-conditioning system usually uses an air washer to accomplish temperature and humidity control, but these air washers are not designed as efficient air cleaners and should not be used as such. (See Chapter 21, General Ventilation of Nonindustrial Occupancies.)

Processes in which materials are crushed, ground, or transported are potential sources of dust dispersion, and should be controlled either by wet methods or enclosed and ventilated by local exhaust ventilation. Points where conveyors are loaded or discharged, transfer points along the conveying system, and heads or boots of elevators should be enclosed as well as ventilated. (For more details, see Chapter 19, Local Exhaust Ventilation.)

Personal Protective Equipment

When it is not feasible to render the working environment completely safe, it may be necessary to protect the worker from that environment by using personal protective equipment. This is considered a secondary control method to engineering and administrative controls and should be used as a last resort.

Where it is not possible to enclose or isolate the process or equipment, ventilation or other control measures should be provided. Where there are short exposures to hazardous concentrations of contaminants and where unavoidable spills may occur, personal protective equipment must be provided and used.

Personal protective devices have one serious drawback: They do nothing to reduce or eliminate the hazard. They interpose a barrier between worker and hazard; if the barrier fails, immediate exposure is the result. The supervisor must be constantly alert to make sure that required protective equipment is worn by workers who need supplementary protection, as may be required by OSHA standards. (See Chapter 22, Respiratory Protection, and Chapter 23, Personal Protective Equipment.)

Administrative Controls

When exposure cannot be reduced to permissible levels through engineering controls, as in the case of air contaminants or noise, an effort should be made to limit the employee's exposure through administrative controls. Examples of some administrative controls are

- arranging work schedules and the related duration of exposures so that employees are minimally exposed to health hazards and
- transferring employees who have reached their upper permissible limits of exposure to an environment where no further additional exposure will be experienced.

Where exposure levels exceed the PEL for one worker in one day, the job can be assigned to two, three, or as many workers as needed to keep each one's duration of exposure within the PEL. In the case of noise, other possibilities may involve intermittent use of noisy equipment.

Administrative controls must be designed only by knowledgeable health and safety professionals, and used cautiously and judiciously. They are not as satisfactory as engineering controls and have been criticized by some as a means of spreading exposures instead of reducing or eliminating the exposure.

Good housekeeping plays a key role in occupational health protection. Basically, it is a key tool for preventing dispersion of dangerous contaminants and for maintaining safe and healthful working conditions. Immediate cleanup of any spills or toxic material, by workers wearing proper protective equipment, is a very important control measure. Good housekeeping is also essential where solvents are stored, handled, and used. Leaking containers or spigots should be fixed immediately, and spills cleaned promptly. All solvent-soaked rags or absorbents should be placed in airtight metal receptacles and removed daily.

It is impossible to have an effective occupational health program without good maintenance and housekeeping. Workers should be informed about the need for these controls. Proper training and education are vital elements for successful implementation of any control effort, and are required by law as part of a complete federal or state OSHA hazard communication program. (See Chapter 18, Methods of Control.)

SOURCES OF HELP

Specialized help is available from a number of sources. Every supplier of products or services is likely to have competent professional staff that can provide technical assistance or guidance. Many insurance companies that carry workers' compensation insurance provide industrial hygiene consultation services, just as they provide periodic safety inspections.

Professional consultants and privately owned laboratories are available on a fee basis for concentrated studies of a specific problem or for a facilitywide or companywide survey, which can be undertaken to identify and catalog individual environmental exposures. Lists of certified analytical laboratories and industrial hygiene consultants are available from the AIHA.

Many states have excellent industrial hygiene departments that can provide consultation on a specific problem. Appendix A, Additional Resources, contains names and addresses of state and national health and hygiene agencies. NIOSH has a Technical Information Center that can provide information on specific problems. Scientific and technical societies that can help with problems are listed in Appendix A. Some provide consultation services to nonmembers; they all have much accessible technical information. A list of organizations concerned with industrial hygiene is included in Appendix A.

SUMMARY

No matter what health hazards are encountered, the approach of the industrial hygienist is essentially the same. Using methods relevant to the problem, he or she secures qualitative and quantitative estimates of the extent of hazard. These data are then compared with the recommended exposure guidelines. If a situation hazardous to life or health is shown, recommendations for correction are made. The industrial hygienist's recommendations place particular emphasis on effectiveness of control, cost, and ease of maintenance of the control measures.

Anticipation, recognition, evaluation, and control are the fundamental concepts of providing all workers with a healthy working environment.

BIBLIOGRAPHY

American Conference of Governmental Industrial Hygienists. *Threshold Limit Values (TLVs®) for Chemical Substances and Physical Agents and Biological Exposure Indices (BEIs®)*. Cincinnati, OH: ACGIH, published annually.

American Conference of Governmental Industrial Hygienists. *Guide to Occupational Exposure Values, 2012.* Cincinnati, OH: ACGIH, 2012.

American Conference of Governmental Industrial Hygienists. *Air Sampling Instruments*, 9th ed. Cincinnati, OH: ACGIH, 2001.

American Conference of Governmental Industrial Hygienists. *Industrial Ventilation: A Manual of Recommended Practice for Design,* 27th ed. Lansing, MI: ACGIH, 2010.

American Conference of Governmental Industrial Hygienists. *Industrial Ventilation: A Manual of Recommended Practice for Operation and Maintenance,* 27th ed. Lansing, MI: ACGIH, 2007.

American Conference of Governmental Industrial Hygienists. *Documentation of Threshold Limit Values,* 7th ed., 2011 Supplement. Cincinnati, OH: ACGIH, 2011.

Balge MZ, Krieger GR, eds. *Occupational Health & Safety,* 3rd ed. Itasca, IL: NSC Press, 2000.

Bingham E, Cohrssen B, Powell C, eds. *Patty's Toxicology,* 5th ed. Vols. 1-9. New York: John Wiley & Sons, Inc., 2001.

Burgess WA. *Recognition of Health Hazards in Industry: A Review of Materials and Processes,* 2nd ed. New York: John Wiley & Sons, Inc., 1995.

Clayton GD, Clayton FE, Cralley LJ, et al., eds. *Patty's*

Industrial Hygiene and Toxicology, 4th ed. Vols. 1A–B, 2A–F, 3A–B. New York: John Wiley & Sons, Inc., 1991–1995.

Harber P, Schenker M, Balmes JR. *Occupational & Environmental Respiratory Diseases.* St. Louis, MO: Mosby, 1995.

Hathaway GJ, Procter NH. *Proctor and Hughes Chemical Hazards of the Workplace,* 5th ed. Hoboken, NJ: John Wiley & Sons, Inc., 2004.

Levy BS, Wegman DH. *Occupational Health: Recognizing and Preventing Work-Related Disease,* 6th ed. New York: Oxford University Press, 2011.

McDermott HJ. *Handbook of Ventilation for Contaminant Control,* 3rd ed. Cincinnati, OH: ACGIH Worldwide, 2001.

National Institute for Occupational Safety and Health, USDHHS Division of Safety Research. *Application Manual for the Revised NIOSH Lifting Equation* (NIOSH Pub. no. 94–110). Cincinnati, OH: NIOSH Publications, 1994.

National Institute for Occupational Safety and Health, USDHHS Division of Safety Research. *Criteria for a Recommended Standard: Working in Confined Spaces* (NIOSH Pub. no. 80–106). Cincinnati, OH: NIOSH Publications Dissemination, 1979.

National Safety Council. *Accident Prevention Manual for Business & Industry: Administration & Programs,* 13th ed. Itasca, IL: NSC Press, 2009.

National Safety Council. *Accident Prevention Manual for Business & Industry: Engineering & Technology,* 13th ed. Itasca, IL: NSC Press, 2009.

National Safety Council. *Accident Prevention Manual for Business & Industry: Environmental Management,* 2nd ed. Itasca, IL: NSC Press, 2000.

National Safety Council. *Accident Prevention Manual for Business & Industry: Security Management,* 2nd ed. Itasca, IL: NSC Press, 2010.

National Safety Council. *Protecting Workers' Lives: A Safety and Health Guide for Unions,* 3rd ed. Itasca, IL: NSC Press, 2007.

National Safety Council. *Safety Through Design.* Itasca, IL: NSC Press, 1999.

Rose VE, Cohrssen B, eds. *Patty's Industrial Hygiene,* 6th ed., Vols. 1-4. Hoboken, NJ: John Wiley & Sons, Inc., 2011.

Zenz C, Dickerson OB, Horvath EP, eds. *Occupational Medicine,* 3rd ed. St. Louis, MO: Mosby-Year Book Medical Publishers, 1994.

PART II

Anatomy, Physiology, and Pathology

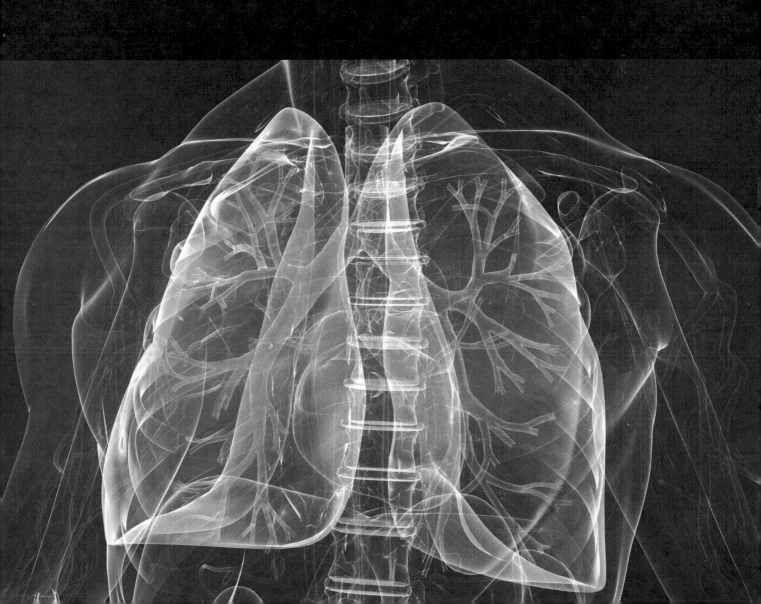

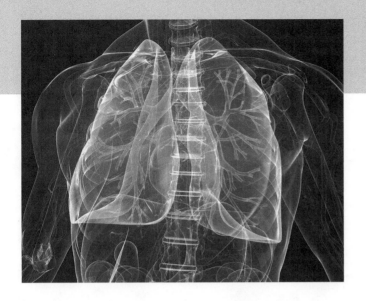

CHAPTER 2

The Lungs

by John Balmes, MD

The material in this chapter on human respiration is intended primarily for engineers and health and safety professionals who must evaluate and control industrial health hazards.

Establishing an effective industrial hygiene program calls for an understanding of the anatomy and physiology of the human respiratory system. The respiratory system is a quick and direct avenue of entry for toxic materials into the body because of its intimate association with the circulatory system and the constant need to oxygenate human tissue cells. Anything affecting the respiratory system, whether it is insufficient oxygen or contaminated air, can affect the entire human organism.

Humans can survive for weeks without food and for days without water, but for only a few minutes without air. Air must reach the lungs almost constantly so oxygen can be extracted and distributed via the blood to every body cell. The life-giving component of air is oxygen; oxygen constitutes a little less than one-fifth of the volume of air.

All living cells of the body are engaged in a series of chemical processes. The total of these processes is metabolism. In the course of the body's metabolism, each cell consumes oxygen and produces carbon dioxide as a waste substance.

Each living cell in the body requires a constant supply of oxygen. Some cells, however, are more vulnerable than others; cells in the brain and heart may die after 4–6 minutes without oxygen. These cells can never be replaced, and permanent changes result from such damage. Other cells in the body are not so critically dependent on an oxygen supply because they are replaceable.

Thus, the respiratory system by which oxygen is delivered to the body and carbon dioxide removed is a very important part of the body. The respiratory system consists of all the organs of the body that contribute to normal respiration or breathing. Strictly speaking, it includes the nose, mouth, upper throat, larynx, trachea, and bronchi, which are all air passages or airways. It includes the lungs, where oxygen is passed into the blood and carbon dioxide is given off. Finally, it includes the diaphragm and the muscles of the chest, which permit normal respiratory movements (Figure 2–1).

ANATOMY

The human respiratory system includes the nose, the pharynx, the larynx, the trachea, the bronchi, and the lungs. Each is discussed in the following sections.

Nose

The nose consists of an external and an internal portion. The external portion of the nose protrudes from the face and is highly variable in shape. The upper part of this triangular structure is held in a fixed position by the supporting nasal bones that form the bridge of the nose. The lower portion is movable because of its pliable framework of fibrous tissue, cartilage, and skin.

The internal portion of the nose lies within the skull between the base of the cranium and the roof of the mouth, and is in front of the nasopharynx (the upper extension of the throat). The skull bones that enter into the formation of the nose include the frontal, the sphenoid, the ethmoid,

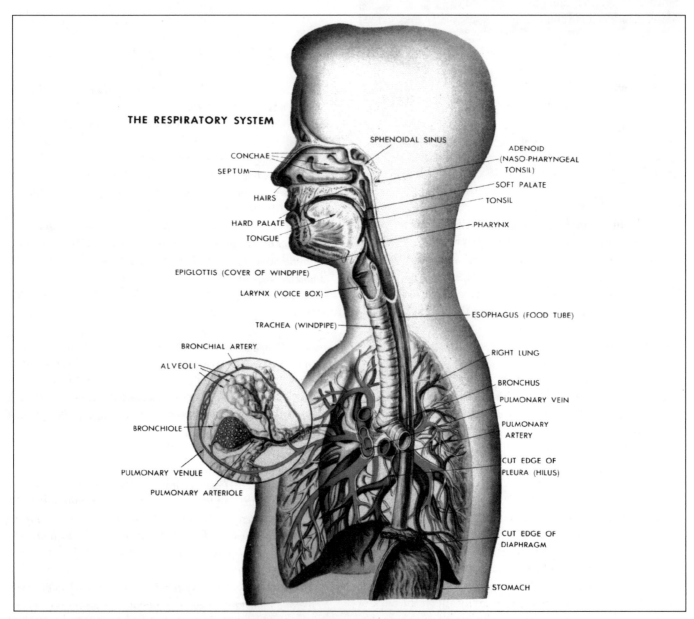

Figure 2–1. Schematic drawing of the respiratory system. *(Copyright 1971. American Medical Association. All Rights Reserved. Reprinted with permission.)*

the nasal, the maxillary, the lacrimal, the vomer, and the palatine and inferior conchae.

The nasal septum is a narrow partition that divides the nose into right and left nasal cavities. In some people the nasal septum is markedly deflected to one side, causing the affected nasal cavity to be almost completely obstructed; this condition is called a deviated nasal septum.

The nasal cavities are open to the outside through the anterior nares (or nostrils); toward the rear, they open into the nasopharynx by means of the posterior nares, or conchae. The vestibule of each cavity is the dilated portion just inside the nostril. Toward the front, the vestibule is lined with skin and presents a ring of coarse hairs that serve to trap dust particles. Toward the rear, the lining of the vestibule changes from skin to a highly vascular ciliated mucous membrane, called the nasal mucosa, which lines the rest of the nasal cavity.

Extending into the nasal cavity from the base of the skull are large nerve filaments, which are part of the sense organ for smell. From these filaments, information on odors is relayed to the olfactory nerve, which goes to the brain.

Turbinates

Near the middle of the nasal cavity and on both sides of the septum are a series of scroll-like bones called the conchae, or turbinates. The purpose of the turbinates is to increase the amount of tissue surface within the nose so that incoming air has a greater opportunity to be conditioned before it continues to the lungs.

Respiration begins with the nose, which is specially designed for the purpose, although there are times when you breathe through the mouth as well. When you perform any vigorous activity and begin to puff and pant, you are breathing rapidly through the mouth to provide the blood with the extra oxygen needed.

However, the mouth is not designed for breathing. On cold days, people make a deliberate effort to keep their mouths tightly closed, because if air is taken in through the mouth, its coldness can be felt. Cold air passing through the mouth has no chance to become properly warmed. But cold as the air may be, people can breathe comfortably through the nose.

Air enters through the nares or nostrils, passes through a web of nasal hairs, and flows posteriorly toward the nasopharynx. The air is warmed and moistened in its passage and partially depleted of particles. Some particles are removed by impaction on the nasal hairs and at bends in the air path, and others by sedimentation.

In mouth breathing, some particles are deposited, primarily by impaction, in the oral cavity and at the back of the throat. These particles are rapidly passed to the esophagus (food tube) by swallowing.

Mucus

The surfaces of the turbinates, like the rest of the interior walls of the nose, are covered with mucous membranes. These membranes secrete a fluid called mucus. The film of mucus is produced continuously and drains slowly into the throat. The mucus gives up heat and moisture to incoming air and serves as a trap for bacteria and dust in the air. It also helps dilute any irritating substances in the air.

The common cold involves an inflammation of the mucous membrane of the nose. It is characterized by an acute congestion of the mucous membrane and increased secretion of mucus. It is difficult to breathe through the nose because of the swelling of the mucous membrane and the accumulated secretions clogging the air passageway.

In cold weather, the membranes can increase the flow of mucus. If the atmosphere is unusually dry, as in an improperly heated building, the mucus may lose its moisture too rapidly and the membrane may become dry and irritated.

Cilia

In addition to the mucus, the membrane is coated with cilia, or hairlike filaments, that move in coordinated waves to propel mucus and trapped particles toward the nostrils. The millions of cilia lining the nasal cavity help the mucus clean the incoming air. When breathing through the mouth, the protective benefits of the cilia and mucus are lost.

In summary, the nose serves not only as a passageway for air going to and from the lungs but also as an air conditioner/filter and as the sense organ for smell. The importance of breathing through the nose is obvious as it moistens, filters, and warms or cools the air that is on its way to the lungs (Figure 2–2).

Throat

From the nasal cavity, air moves into the pharynx, or throat. Seven tubes enter the pharynx: the two from the nasal cavity, the eustachian tubes (which lead to the ears), the mouth cavity, the opening of the esophagus, and the opening of the trachea (windpipe).

Pharynx

The pharynx, or throat, is a tubular passageway attached to the base of the skull and extending downward behind the nasal cavity, the mouth, and the larynx to continue as the esophagus. Its walls are composed of skeletal muscle and the lining consists of mucous membrane. The nasal passage joins the esophagus just behind the mouth. The union of the two passageways at this point makes it possible to breathe with reasonable comfort through the mouth when the nasal passages are blocked because of a cold or allergy.

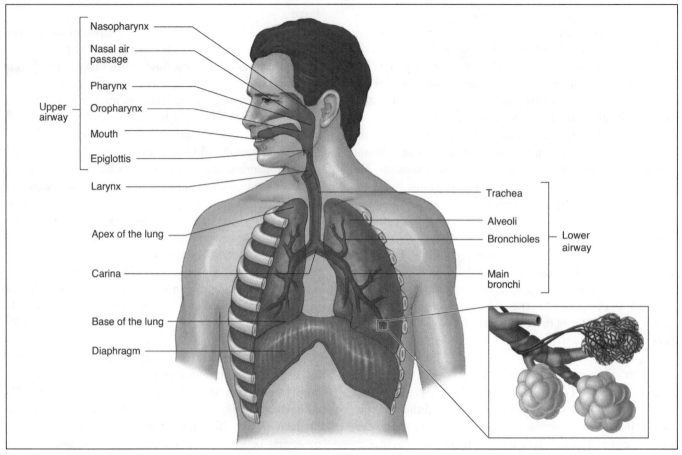

Figure 2–2. Parts of the human respiratory system. Air enters through the mouth and nose, then passes down the trachea and into the lungs. *(Reprinted with permission from Pollack AN, ed.* Emergency Care and Transportation of the Sick and Injured, *10th ed. Rosemont, IL: American Academy of Orthopaedic Surgeons, 2011.)*

Nasopharynx

The nasopharynx is the superior portion of the pharyngeal cavity; it lies behind the nasal cavities and above the level of the soft palate. This portion of the upper respiratory tract serves as a major defense against infectious organisms. Its ciliated mucosal lining is continuous with that of the nasal cavities. Immediately beneath the mucosa are collections of lymphoid tissue, the adenoids. The adenoids and tonsils, lower down in the throat, are part of the immune system and serve as a first defense against infectious organisms.

Esophagus and Trachea

At the bottom of the throat are two passageways: the esophagus behind and the trachea in front. Food and liquids entering the pharynx pass into the esophagus, which carries them to the stomach. Air and other gases enter the trachea to go to the lungs.

Epiglottis

Guarding the opening of the trachea is a thin, leaf-shaped structure called the epiglottis (Figure 2–3). This structure helps food glide from the mouth to the esophagus.

Everyone is aware that swallowing food and breathing cannot take place at the same time without danger of choking. But nature has devised a way for food and air to use the same general opening, the pharynx, with only an occasional mix-up.

The incoming air travels through the nasal cavity and through the larynx by crossing over the path used by food on its way to the stomach. Similarly, food crosses over the route of air. When food is swallowed, the larynx rises against the base of the tongue to help seal the opening.

If food accidentally starts down the wrong way, into the lungs rather than the stomach, there are explosive protests from the lungs. Any contact of a sizable liquid or solid particle with the trachea sets off a cough, an explosive expulsion of air that blows it out again. A cough can be a very powerful force. A slight breathing in, closing of the glottis, buildup of pressure, and a sudden release of the trapped air are involved. Also, stimulation of the larynx can cause spasm of the vocal cords, with total obstruction of breathing.

Normally, swallowing blocks off the glottis, halts

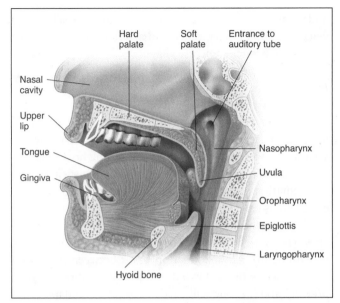

Figure 2–3. The anatomy of the mouth and neck: including the epiglottis, larynx, vocal cords, trachea, and esophagus. *(Reprinted with permission from Pollack AN, ed.* Emergency Care and Transportation of the Sick and Injured, *10th ed. Rosemont, IL: American Academy of Orthopaedic Surgeons, 2011.)*

breathing briefly, and ensures correct division of air and food. However, an unconscious person may lack this automatic response, and if a drink is given, it may proceed straight into the lungs.

The diaphragm is sometimes subject to periodic spasms of contraction that enlarge the lung cavities and lead to a quick inrush of air. The vocal cords come together to stop the flow, and the air, so suddenly set into motion and so suddenly stopped, makes the sharp noise called the hiccup. Hiccups may be due to indigestion, overloaded stomach, irritation under the surface of the diaphragm, too much alcohol, or many other possible causes, including heart attacks.

Larynx

The larynx, or voice box, serves as a passageway for air between the pharynx and the trachea. It lies in the midline of the neck, below the hyoid bone and in front of the laryngopharynx. The unique structure of the larynx enables it to function somewhat like a valve on guard duty at the entrance to the windpipe, controlling air flow and preventing anything but air from entering the lower air passages. Exhalation of air through the larynx is controlled by voluntary muscles; thus, the larynx is the organ of voice.

The larynx is a triangular box composed of nine cartilages joined together by ligaments and controlled by skeletal muscles. The larynx is lined with ciliated mucous membrane (except the vocal folds), and the cilia move particles upward to the pharynx.

Vocal Cords

The larynx is at the top of the windpipe, or trachea, which takes air to the lungs. Although incoming air passes through the boxlike larynx, it is actually air expelled from the lungs that makes voice sounds. In the front of the larynx, two folds of membranes, the vocal cords, are attached and held by tiny cartilages. Muscles attached to the cartilages move the vocal cords, which are made to vibrate by air exhaled from the lungs.

During ordinary breathing, the vocal cords are held toward the walls of the larynx so that air can pass without being obstructed. During speech, the vocal cords swing over the center of the tube and muscles contract to tense the vocal cords.

Speech

Sounds are created as air is forced past the vocal cords, making them vibrate. These vibrations make the sound. You can feel these vibrations by placing your fingers lightly on your larynx (Adam's apple) while speaking.

The vibrations are carried through the air upward into the pharynx, mouth, nasal cavities, and sinuses, which act as resonating chambers. The greater the force and amount of air from the lungs, the louder the voice. Pitch differences result from variations in the tension of the cords. The larger the larynx and the longer the cords, the deeper the voice. The average man's vocal cords are about 0.75 in. (1.9 cm) long. Shorter vocal cords give women higher-pitched voices. Words and other understandable sounds are formed by the tongue and muscles of the mouth.

Infections of the throat and nasal passages alter the shape of the resonating chambers and change the voice, roughening it so that it sounds hoarse. When the membranes of the larynx themselves are affected (laryngitis), speech may be reduced to a whisper. In whispering, the vocal cords are not involved; sound is produced by tissue folds, sometimes called false vocal cords, which lie just above the vocal cords themselves.

Trachea

The trachea, or windpipe, is a tube about 4.5 in. (11.5 cm) long and 1 in. (2.5 cm) in diameter, extending from the bottom of the larynx through the neck and into the chest cavity. At its lower end, the trachea divides into two branches, the right and left bronchi.

Rings of cartilage hold the trachea and bronchi open. If the head is tilted back, the tube can be felt as the fingers run down the front of the neck. The ridges produced by the alternation of cartilage and fibrous tissue are also felt, giving the tube a feeling of roughness.

The windpipe wall is lined with mucous membrane and

with many hairlike cilia fanning upward toward the throat, moving dust particles that have been caught in the sticky membrane away from the lungs.

The path of the esophagus, which carries food to the stomach, runs immediately behind the trachea. It is at the point behind the middle of the breastbone, where the aorta arches away from the heart, that the trachea divides into the right and the left bronchi.

Bronchi

The trachea divides into the right and left main stem bronchi under the sternum (breastbone), approximately where the second and third ribs connect to the sternum. Each bronchus enters the lung of its own side through the hilus (an opening through which vessels or nerves enter or leave an organ).

The right main stem bronchus is wider and shorter than the left. Its direction is almost identical to that of the trachea. That is why most aspirated material enters the right lung.

Each bronchus leads to a separate lung, and in doing so divides and subdivides into increasingly smaller, finer, and more numerous tubes, something like the branches of a tree; the whole structure is sometimes called the bronchial tree. In the larger branches there also is stiffening by rings of cartilage, but as the branches get smaller the cartilage diminishes to small plates and finally disappears.

The smaller branches of the bronchial tree are called bronchioles. These fine subdivisions of the conducting airways are lined by circular muscles, which through contraction or relaxation can alter the diameter of the passageway, or lumen, thus helping to control the flow of air through the lungs. Sometimes, as a result of infection or an allergic reaction to some foreign substance, there is spasmodic contraction of the small muscles and welling of the mucous membrane of the bronchioles. This causes a narrowing of the airways and airflow is reduced.

Inflammation of the trachea, bronchi, or bronchioles is called tracheitis, bronchitis, or bronchiolitis, respectively.

Lungs

There are two lungs, one on each side of the thoracic cage (Figure 2–4). The lungs are suspended within the thoracic cage by the trachea, by the arteries and veins running to and from the heart, and by pulmonary ligaments.

The lungs extend from the collarbone to the diaphragm, one on the right side of the body and one on the left. Taken together, they fill almost the entire thoracic cavity. The two lungs are not quite mirror images of each other. The right lung, slightly larger than the left, is partially divided into three lobes; the left lung is divided into only two.

The mediastinum is the compartment between the left

and right lungs. It contains the heart, great vessels (aorta, vena cava, pulmonary veins, and arteries), nerves, trachea, main stem bronchi, and esophagus.

Pleura

The lungs are covered by a double membrane, called the pleura. One part of the pleural membrane lies over the lungs; the other lines the chest cavity (Figure 2–5). They are separated by a thin layer of fluid that, during breathing, prevents the two membranes from rubbing against each other. Inflammation of the pleura can cause sharp chest pain; this condition is called pleurisy.

The potential intrapleural space (between the two pleural layers) has a negative atmospheric pressure during inspiration (breathing in). An introduction of air between the pleural layers (pneumothorax) will decrease or disrupt this negative pressure and the lung will partially or totally collapse.

The tendency to collapse is counteracted by a pull in the opposite direction; the chest wall wants to spring outward. The lung surface is held tenaciously to the chest wall not by physical bonds, but by the negative pressure of the intrapleural space. Normally, this negative pressure acts somewhat like a suction cup to pull the lung against the chest wall and keep it expanded.

Alveoli

After many divisions of the conducting airways come the acini, or terminal lung units that are supplied by a termi-

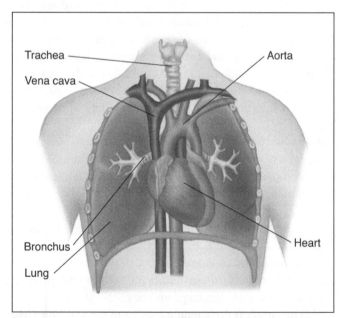

Figure 2–4. The relative size and spatial relationship of the human heart and lungs. *(Reprinted with permission from Pollack AN, ed. Emergency Care and Transportation of the Sick and Injured, 10th ed. Rosemont, IL: American Academy of Orthopaedic Surgeons, 2011.)*

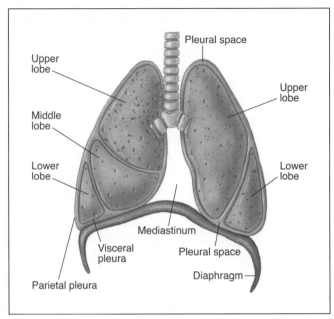

Figure 2–5. The lungs, pleura, and pleural space. *(Reprinted with permission from Pollack AN, ed.* Emergency Care and Transportation of the Sick and Injured, *10th ed. Rosemont, IL: American Academy of Orthopaedic Surgeons, 2011.)*

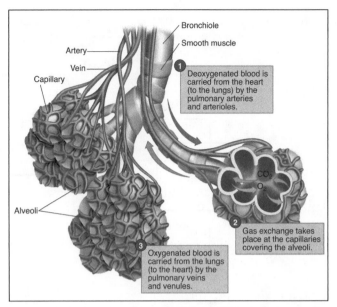

Figure 2–6. The branching characteristic of the trachea into smaller airways ending in an alveolus is shown. *(Reprinted with permission from Pollack AN, ed.* Emergency Care and Transportation of the Sick and Injured, *10th ed. Rosemont, IL: American Academy of Orthopaedic Surgeons, 2011.)*

nal bronchiole from which multiple respiratory bronchioles branch off. The respiratory bronchioles lead into several ducts; each duct ends in a cluster of air sacs, which resemble a tiny bunch of grapes called alveoli (Figure 2–6).

The walls of the alveoli are two cells thick and oxygen can pass freely across those thin membranes. It can pass freely in both directions, of course, but the blood coming to the lungs has a lower partial pressure of oxygen than inspired air, so the net exchange is from the lungs to the bloodstream.

The human respiratory tract branches successively from the trachea to 25–100 million branches. These branches terminate in some 300 million air sacs, or alveoli. The cross section of the trachea is about 0.31 sq in. (2 cm²) and the combined cross sections of the alveolar ducts, which handle about the same quantity of air, are about 8 ft² (8,000 cm²).

The respiratory surface in the lungs ranges from about 300 ft² (28 m²) at rest to about 1,000 ft² (93 m²) at deepest inspiration. The membrane separating the alveolar air space from circulating blood may be only one or two cells thick. In the course of an eight-hour day of moderate work, a human breathes about 300 ft³ (8.5 m³) of air. Contrast the forced ventilation exposure of the large delicate lung surface with the ambient air exposure of the skin, which has some 20 ft² (1.9 m²) of surface and a thickness measured in millimeters. It is evident that the lungs represent by far the most extensive and intimate contact of the body with the ambient atmosphere.

The respiratory tract, with its successive branches and tortuous passageways, is a highly efficient dust collector. Essentially all particles entering the respiratory system larger than 4 or 5 micrometers (µm) are deposited in it. About half of those of 1-µm size appear to be deposited and the other half exhaled. The sites of deposition in the system are different for various sizes. Discussion of dust deposition in the respiratory system is simplified by the concept of equivalent size of particles. The equivalent size of a particle is the diameter of a unit density sphere, which has the same terminal settling velocity in still air as does the particle.

Particles greater than 2.5 or 3 µm equivalent size are deposited, for the most part, in the upper respiratory system—that is, the nasal cavity, the trachea, the bronchial tubes, and other air passages—whereas particles 2 µm in equivalent size are deposited about equally in the upper respiratory system and in the alveolar or pulmonary air spaces. Particles about 1 µm in equivalent size are deposited more efficiently in the alveolar spaces than elsewhere; essentially no 1-µm particles are collected in the upper respiratory system. For more details, see Chapter 8, Particulates.

RESPIRATION

The process through which the body combines oxygen with food substances, and thus produces energy, is called metabolism (Figure 2–7). The term respiration refers to the process

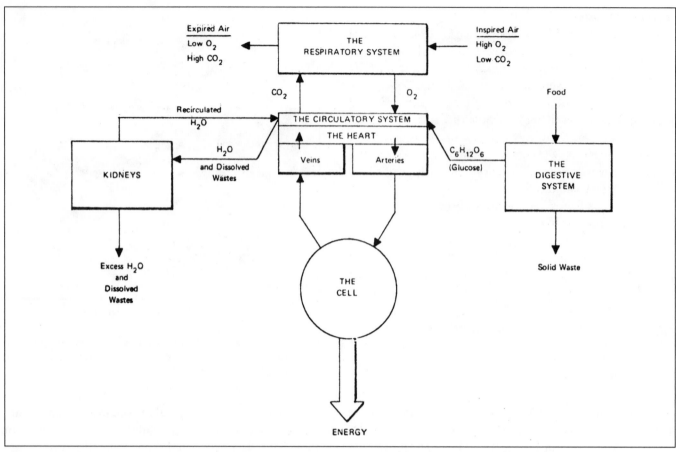

Figure 2–7. The conversion of food into energy (the metabolic process) is illustrated. *(Reprinted from* A Guide to Industrial Respiratory Protection, *NIOSH Publication No. 76-189. Atlanta: CDC, 1976.)*

by which the body exchanges gases with the ambient environment. The process involves oxygen supply and carbon dioxide removal. The following are the general subdivisions of the overall process:

- breathing—movement of chest/lung complex to ventilate the alveoli
- external respiration—exchange of gas (oxygen and carbon dioxide) between lung (alveolar) air and blood
- internal respiration—exchange of gas between blood and tissue cells
- intracellular respiration—ultimate utilization of oxygen by the cells with the coincident release of carbon dioxide.

To a biochemist, *respiration* refers to the enzymatic processes in the tissues that use oxygen and produce carbon dioxide. In the blood is an oxygen-carrying protein that contains iron, called hemoglobin. The hemoglobin binds oxygen when the blood flows through regions where oxygen is plentiful—as in the alveoli—and releases it to tissues that are consuming oxygen. Similarly, the carbon dioxide produced when the body cells burn fuel is dissolved in the bloodstream as it flows through tissues where carbon diox-

ide is plentiful, and is released in the lungs, where carbon dioxide is comparatively scarce.

Carbon dioxide is always present in the atmosphere, but the proportion of carbon dioxide in air exhaled from the lungs is 100 times greater. The proportion of water vapor in air exhaled from the lungs is about 10 times greater than that of the normal atmosphere. Everyone has no doubt noticed the moisture that accumulates on a glass window when the nose and mouth are close to it. Breath appears as a white cloud on cold days because the low temperature of the air causes the exhaled water vapor to condense.

Gas Exchange

Gases diffuse rapidly from areas of higher to lower concentrations. The concentration of oxygen is higher in alveolar air than it is in the blood coming to the lungs from the right ventricle. Therefore, oxygen diffuses into the blood from the alveolar air. On the other hand, the concentration of oxygen is low in the cells of the body tissues and in tissue fluid; therefore, oxygen diffuses from the blood in the capillaries into the tissue fluid and into cells.

Equalizing Pressures

If there is a pressure difference across a permeable membrane such as that separating the alveoli from the pulmonary capillaries, gas molecules pass from the high- to low-pressure region until the pressures are equalized (Figure 2–8).

The concentration of carbon dioxide in tissue cells and tissue fluid is higher than in the blood in capillaries. Therefore, carbon dioxide diffuses from tissue cells and tissue fluid into the blood. The concentration of carbon dioxide is higher in blood coming to the lungs from the right ventricle than it is in alveolar air; therefore, it diffuses from blood in pulmonary capillaries into the alveolar air.

On entering the bloodstream, some oxygen and carbon dioxide immediately go into simple physical solution in the plasma. However, because the plasma can hold only a small amount of gas in solution, most of the oxygen and carbon dioxide quickly enter into chemical combinations with other blood constituents.

Oxygen Tension

Only a small amount of oxygen is carried in solution in the plasma. However, it is this oxygen that exerts tension or pressure and is available for immediate diffusion when blood reaches the systemic capillaries (Figure 2–9). The remaining oxygen in the blood is combined with hemoglobin in the red blood cells to form oxyhemoglobin (HbO_2). This oxygen is given up readily by hemoglobin whenever the oxygen tension of plasma decreases, so that as oxygen diffuses from plasma in tissue capillaries, it is replenished by more from oxyhemoglobin. Hemoglobin that has given

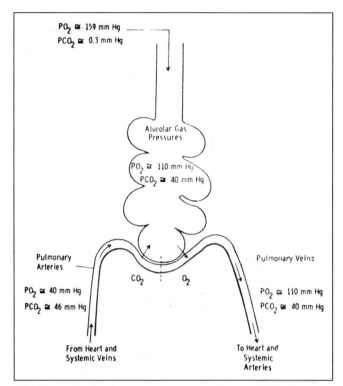

Figure 2–8. Partial pressures of various gases involved in the gas exchange in the lungs are shown. *(Reprinted from* A Guide to Industrial Respiratory Protection, *NIOSH Publication No. 76-189. Atlanta: CDC, 1976.)*

up its load of oxygen is called reduced hemoglobin (Hb) (Figure 2–10). See Chapter 6, Industrial Toxicology, for more details.

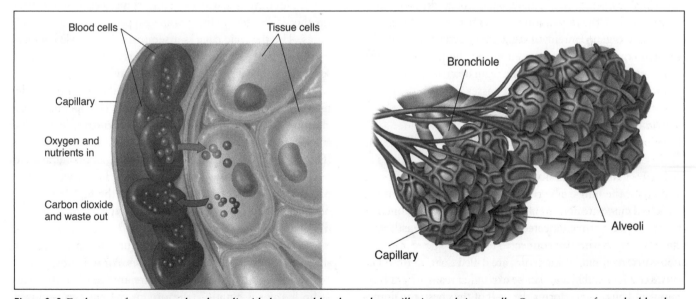

Figure 2–9. Exchange of oxygen and carbon dioxide between blood vessels, capillaries, and tissue cells. Oxygen passes from the blood to the capillaries to the tissue cells. Carbon dioxide passes from the tissue cells to the capillaries and into the blood. *(Reprinted with permission from Pollack AN, ed.* Emergency Care and Transportation of the Sick and Injured, *10th ed. Rosemont, IL: American Academy of Orthopaedic Surgeons, 2011.)*

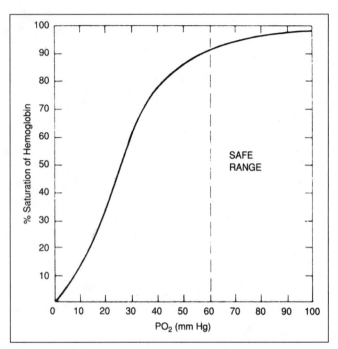

Figure 2–10. Percent saturation of hemoglobin with oxygen at various partial pressures is shown in the hemoglobin saturation curve. (*Reprinted from* A Guide to Industrial Respiratory Protection, *NIOSH Publication No. 76-189. Atlanta: CDC, 1976.*)

In most people during routine activities, the depth and rate of breathing movements are regulated for the maintenance of carbon dioxide in the arterial blood. Low oxygen tension can stimulate breathing, but only when the oxygen content of the inspired gases is reduced to nearly half that in air at sea level. Oxygen partial pressure, except in some unusual circumstances, is usually high enough that breathing is regulated by the body requirements for carbon dioxide.

The oxygen content of lung air is determined by the oxygen content of the inspired gases, the flushing of the lungs required for carbon dioxide regulation, and the rate of oxygen uptake by the blood as it passes through the lungs.

Mechanics of Breathing

Breathing is the act of taking fresh air into and expelling stale air from the lungs. Breathing is accomplished by changes in the size of the chest cavity. Twelve pairs of ribs surround and guard the lungs. The ribs are joined to the spine at the back and curve around the chest to form a cage. In front, the top seven pairs are connected to the sternum (breastbone). The next three pairs are connected to the rib above. The last two pairs, unconnected in front, are called floating ribs. The entire cage is flexible and can be expanded readily by special muscles. The rib cage forms the wall of the chest; the dome-shaped diaphragm forms the floor of the chest cavity. The diaphragm is attached to the breastbone in front, the spinal column in back, and the lower ribs on the sides.

Pressure Changes

The basic principle underlying the movement of any gas is that it travels from an area of higher pressure to an area of lower pressure, or from a point of greater concentration of molecules to a point of lower concentration. This principle applies not only to the flow of air into and out of the lungs but also to the diffusion of oxygen and carbon dioxide through alveolar and capillary membranes. The respiratory muscles and the elasticity of the lungs make the necessary changes in the pressure gradient possible, so that air first flows into the air passages and then is expelled.

Atmospheric pressure is the pressure exerted against all parts of the body by the surrounding air. It averages 760 mm of mercury (760 mmHg) at sea level. Any pressure that falls below atmospheric pressure is called a negative pressure and represents a partial vacuum.

Intrapulmonic pressure is the pressure of air within the bronchial tree and the alveoli. During each respiratory cycle this pressure fluctuates below and above atmospheric pressure as air moves into and out of the lungs. Intrapulmonic pressure is below atmospheric pressure during inspiration, equal to atmospheric pressure at the end of inspiration, above atmospheric pressure during expiration, and again equal to atmospheric pressure at the end of expiration.

This series of changes in intrapulmonic pressure is repeated with each respiratory cycle. Whenever the size of the thoracic cavity remains constant for a few seconds, or in a position of rest, the intrapulmonic pressure is equal to atmospheric pressure.

Lungs have one way of filling themselves. Movement of the thoracic cage and the diaphragm permits air to enter the lungs. The thoracic cage is a semirigid bony case enclosed by muscle and skin. The diaphragm is a muscular partition separating the chest and abdominal cavities.

The chest cage can be compared to a bellows. The ribs maintain the shape of the chest bellows. The opening of the chest bellows is through the trachea. Air moves through the trachea to and from the lungs to fill and empty the air sacs (Figure 2–11). When a bellows is opened, the volume it can hold increases, causing a slight vacuum. This lowers the air pressure inside the bellows and causes the higher pressure outside the bellows to drive air through the opening, thereby filling the bellows.

When the air pressure inside equals the pressure outside, air stops moving into the bellows. Air will move from a high-pressure area to a low-pressure area until the pressure in both areas is equal. Therefore, as the bellows is closed, the pressure inside becomes higher than outside and air is expelled (Figure 2–11).

During inspiration (inhaling), the diaphragm and rib

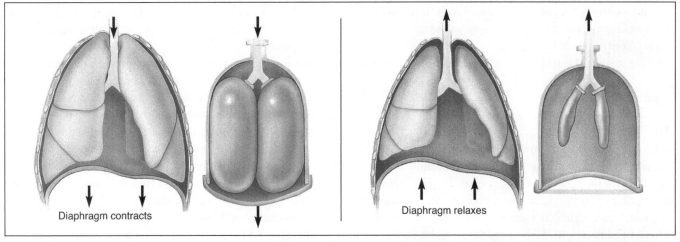

Figure 2–11. Inhalation is similar to the act of air entering a bell jar. It occurs when the diaphragm contracts and the ribs expand. Exhalation is similar to the act of air leaving a bell jar. It occurs when the diaphragm and ribs relax. *(Reprinted with permission from Pollack AN, ed. Emergency Care and Transportation of the Sick and Injured, 10th ed. Rosemont, IL: American Academy of Orthopaedic Surgeons, 2011.)*

muscles contract. When the diaphragm contracts, it moves downward and enlarges the thoracic cavity from top to bottom. When the rib muscles contract, they raise the ribs. This enlarges the chest cavity (bellows) in all dimensions. This enlargement of the thoracic cavity reduces the pressure within the chest and air rushes into the lungs. Take a deep breath to see how the chest increases in size. This is the active muscular part of breathing.

During expiration (exhaling), the diaphragm and the rib muscles relax. As these muscles relax, the chest cavity decreases in size in all dimensions. As it does so, the air in the lungs is pressed into a smaller space, the pressure increases, and air is pushed out through the trachea. Decrease in size of the chest cavity after relaxation is accomplished largely by action of elastic tissue in the lung, which stretches for inhalation and recoils after muscular relaxation.

Control of Breathing

Breathing is controlled by a series of respiratory centers in the nervous system. One center is in the medulla, the part of the brain at the top of the spinal cord (Figure 2–12).

Respiratory Center

Nerve impulses originating in the motor areas of the cerebral cortex and traveling to the respiratory center enable us to consciously alter the rate and the depth of breathing. For example, during speaking or singing, breath control is very important.

You can hold your breath voluntarily for a short period of time. However, voluntary control is limited, and the respiratory center will ignore messages from the cortex when breathing is necessary to meet the body's basic needs.

Carbon Dioxide

Breathing action can be triggered by the respiratory centers when the amount of carbon dioxide in the blood increases or when the oxygen level of the blood decreases.

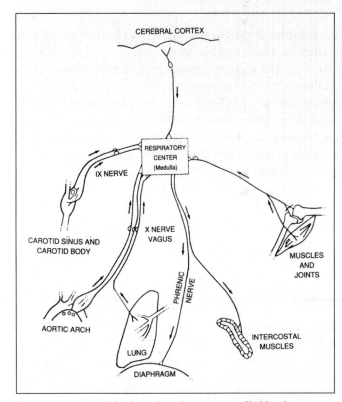

Figure 2–12. Normal rhythmic breathing is controlled by the requirement to ventilate the lungs to remove carbon dioxide as fast as it is produced by metabolic activity. The factors effective in controlling breathing are illustrated schematically. *(Reprinted from Parker JF. Bioastronautics, 2nd ed. Washington, DC: National Aeronautics and Space Administration, 1973.)*

47

If you hold your breath, carbon dioxide accumulates in the blood until, finally, it so strongly stimulates the respiratory control center of the brain that you are forced to breathe again. The length of time the breath can be held varies from 25 to 75 seconds; some people can hold their breath even longer.

Rate

Even in a relaxed state, you breathe in and out 10–14 times a minute, with each breath lasting 4–6 seconds. In a minute, 9–12 pt (4.3–5.7 L) of air are taken in. The fact is that although the body has small reserves of oxygen, all of it is consumed within less than half a minute after the start of vigorous exertion. With such exertion, the need for air increases many times over, so that the breathing rate may speed up to one breath per second and a total intake of 31 gal (120 L) of air per minute.

In a normal day, you breathe some 3,300 gal (12,491 L) of air—enough to occupy a space of about 8 ft³. In a lifetime, you will consume enough to occupy 13 million ft³ (368,120 m³) of space.

Lung Volumes and Capacities

For descriptive convenience the total capacity of the lung at full inspiration is divided into several functional subunits. These are illustrated in Figure 2–13.

The four primary lung volumes that do not overlap are as follows:

- tidal volume (TV)—the volume of gas inspired or expired during each respiratory cycle
- inspiratory reserve volume (IRV)—the maximal volume that can be forcibly inspired following a normal inspiration (from the end-inspiratory position)

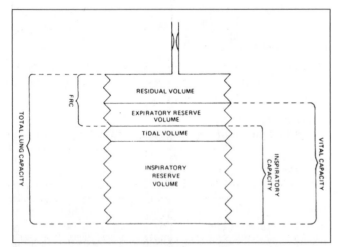

Figure 2–13. Inspiratory capacity and tidal capacity. *(Reprinted from Parker JF. Bioastronautics, 2nd ed. Washington, DC: National Aeronautics and Space Administration, 1973.)*

- expiratory reserve volume (ERV)—the maximum amount of air that can be forcibly expired following a normal expiration
- residual volume (RV)—the amount of air remaining in the lungs following a maximum expiratory effort.

Each of the four following capacities includes two or more of the primary volumes:

- total lung capacity (TLC)—the sum of all four of the primary lung volumes
- inspiratory capacity (IC)—the maximum volume by which the lung can be increased by a maximum inspiratory effort from midposition
- vital capacity (VC)—the maximum amount of air that can be exhaled from the lungs after a maximum inspiration (the sum of the inspiratory reserve volume, tidal volume, and expiratory reserve volume)
- functional residual capacity (FRC)—the normal volume at the end of passive exhalation; that is, the gas volume that normally remains in the lung after a tidal breath.

In an ordinary inhalation, the first air to enter the lungs is the air that was in the bronchi, throat, and nose—air that had left the lungs in the previous expiration but had not been pushed out as far as the outside world. Then, after an inspiration is complete, some of the fresh air that entered through the nostrils remains in the air passages; here it is useless, and is expired again before it can get to the lungs. The dead space represents the conducting airways between the nostrils and lungs in which no gas exchange occurs. Fresh air actually entering the lungs with each breath may amount to no more than 21.4 in.³ (350 cm³). This represents only ¹⁄₁₈ of the lungs' total capacity and is called the tidal volume.

The partial replacement of the air in the lungs (alveolar air) by the shallow breathing normally engaged in is sufficient for ordinary purposes. Humans are quite capable of taking a deep inhalation of air as well, forcing far more into the lungs than would ordinarily enter. After about 30.5 in.³ (500 cm³) of air have been inhaled in a normal quiet breath, an additional 153 in.³ (2,500 cm³) can be sucked in. On the other hand, 42.7 in.³ (7,000 cm³) of additional air can be forced out of the lungs after an ordinary quiet expiration is completed. By forcing all possible air out of the lungs and then drawing in the deepest possible breath, well over 1.7 ft³ (4,000 cm³) of new air can be brought into the lungs in one breath. This is the vital capacity.

Even with the utmost straining, the lungs cannot be completely emptied of air. After the last bit of breath has been forced out, about 73 in.³ (1,200 cm³) remain. This is the residual volume and is a measure of the necessary inefficiency of the lungs.

Vital capacity is measured by inhaling as deeply as possible and blowing out as much as possible into a spirometer. The quantity of expelled air varies with body size and age. A medium-sized man may have a vital capacity of 1.7–1.9 ft³ (4,000–4,500 cm³) between the ages of 20 and 40 years. However, as the elasticity of tissues decreases with age, the vital capacity diminishes and may be as much as 20 percent less at age 60 and 40 percent less at age 75.

Spirometry means measurement of air—the ventilatory capacity of the lungs. The spirometer achieves this by measuring volumes of air and relating them to time or flow.

Impaired ability to move air into and out of the lungs results in what is called either an obstructive or a restrictive ventilatory defect, or a combination of the two. In diseases associated with an obstructive ventilatory defect, such as asthma or chronic obstructive pulmonary disease (COPD), there is reduction of air flow rates during, and a prolongation of, expiration. In diseases causing a restrictive ventilatory defect, such as the pneumoconioses (e.g., asbestosis, silicosis, coal workers pneumoconiosis), there is a decreased ability to take a deep breath due to scarred, and therefore less flexible, lungs.

Forced vital capacity (FVC) is the maximal volume of air that can be exhaled forcefully after a maximal inspiration. For all practical purposes, the VC without forced effort and the FVC are identical in most people.

In the early detection of pneumoconiosis, the FVC is of variable use. In asbestosis, the FVC is regarded as a relatively sensitive indicator of early disease and may be impaired before there are radiographic abnormalities. Conversely, x-ray changes may be evident in silicosis while the FVC is still normal.

Forced expiratory volume in one second (FEV_1) is the volume of air that can be forcibly expelled during the first second of expiration. With an obstructive ventilatory defect, the FEV_1 is decreased while the FVC is relatively preserved, leading to a decreased FEV_1/FVC ratio.

Forced expiratory flow (FEF) during the middle half of the FVC ($FEF_{25-75\%}$) can be defined as the average rate of flow during the middle two quarters of the forced expiratory effort. Compared with FEV_1, it may be more sensitive in detecting early airway obstruction and tends to reflect changes in airway diameter caused by inhalation of irritants. Smoking one cigarette can lower the $FEF_{25-75\%}$ for several hours.

Peak expiratory flow (PEF) is another measure of expiratory flow. PEF is the peak of the expiratory flow-volume curve. The peak expiratory flow rate is the rate of maximal expiratory flow. The development of portable peak flow meters that directly measure flow rates has allowed workers to measure their lung function during and away from work.

HAZARDS

Let's look at some of the unhealthy conditions to which the respiratory tract is subject, the associated terminology, and some typical hazardous substances.

The membrane lining of the nasal passages can be inflamed by a number of agents, including viral infections, allergies (hayfever), and inhalation of noxious substances. The resultant condition is called *rhinitis*. Inflammation in the larynx is called *laryngitis*. Reversible narrowing of the airways (bronchoconstriction) in response to irritation, allergy, or other stimulus is called *asthma*. In the lungs, a number of conditions can develop:

- *Atelectasis* means incomplete expansion of the lungs. It is caused by occlusion of a bronchus, perhaps by a plug of heavy mucus, with subsequent absorption of the air, or by external compression, as from a tumor. The atelectatic portion of the lung will allow blood to pass through without adding oxygen or removing carbon dioxide.

- The term *emphysema* derives from Greek words meaning overinflated. The overinflated structures are the alveoli. Cigarette smoke and some occupational agents (e.g., coal dust, cadmium fumes) can cause destruction of alveolar walls that leads to emphysema. Chronic inflammation of the small and large airways (bronchiolitis, bronchitis) is also often present in patients with emphysema. The inflamed airways tend to become narrowed due to increased mucus production, swelling of the lining membrane, and enlargement (hypertrophy) of the surrounding muscle. Air flows into the alveoli easily but cannot flow out easily because of the narrowed diameter of the bronchioles. The patient can breathe in, but cannot breathe out efficiently; this leaves too much CO_2 in the lungs. As pressure builds up in the air cells, their thin walls are stretched to the point of rupture, so several air spaces communicate and the area of surfaces where gas exchange takes place is decreased.

- *Pleurisy* is caused when the outer lung lining (the visceral pleura) and the chest cavity's inner lining (the parietal pleura) lose their lubricating properties. The resultant friction causes irritation and pain. The thin, glistening layer of pleura that is inseparably bound to the lung has no pain fibers, but the opposing pleura is richly supplied. Normally the pleural layers glide over each other on a thin film of lubricating fluid. Disease may cause the pleura to become inflamed and adherent, or fluid may accumulate in the pleural space (effusion), separating the layers.

- *Pneumonitis* is any inflammation of the lung. It is essentially equivalent to the term *pneumonia*, which is usually reserved for infectious inflammation.

- Chronic *bronchitis* means that there is persistent inflammation. Smoking is the most common cause of chronic bronchitis, but occupational exposure to irritating vapors, dusts, gases, or fumes can cause this condition as well.

- *Pneumoconiosis* (dust in the lungs) is a general word for various pulmonary manifestations of dust inhalation, whether the dust is harmful or not. Two common forms of pneumoconiosis are silicosis and asbestosis. The typical pathological condition in harmful pneumoconiosis is the existence of scarring (fibrosis) in the lungs. The fibrosis, caused by some dust particles, reduces the efficiency of the lungs by making them less resilient and by reducing the effective working surface for gaseous exchange.

The fate of an inhaled air contaminant depends on its size, solubility, and chemical reactivity. As noted previously, larger particles tend to get deposited in the upper airways, trachea, and bronchi, while smaller particles (i.e., <3 μm in diameter) tend to deposit in the smaller airways and alveoli (the so-called deep lung). More soluble, reactive substances get absorbed onto the moist mucous membranes of the upper airways, trachea, and larger bronchi, leading to irritation and inflammation of these structures. Less soluble, reactive gases cause less irritation of the mucous membranes so that they cause less "warning" irritation of the mucous membranes. If any reactive substance is inhaled into the deep lung, then inflammation of the alveoli, or pneumonitis, can occur. If the chemical injury to the alveoli is severe enough, flooding of the alveoli with inflammatory material can occur, known as pulmonary edema. When there is pulmonary edema, gas exchange becomes markedly impaired.

Most of the particles that reach the deep lung (alveoli) are engulfed by cells called macrophages (literally "big eaters") that migrate proximally to the conducting airways and are either expectorated or swallowed, although some particles may enter the interstitial tissue of the lungs between the alveoli and capillaries. Once in the deep lung, however, chemical components in particles can be absorbed into the bloodstream. Of course, the lung is very efficient at absorbing gases.

Inhaled contaminants that adversely affect the lungs fall into three general categories:

- aerosols and dusts, which, when deposited in the lungs, may produce tissue reaction and/or disease
- toxic gases that may produce direct tissue injury
- toxic aerosols or gases that do not affect the lung tissue, but are passed from the lung into the bloodstream, where they are carried to other organs or have adverse effects on the oxygen-carrying capacity of the bloodstream (see Chapter 6, Industrial Toxicology).

Potential health hazards from dusts occur on three levels. The inhalation of sufficient quantities of dust, regardless of its chemical composition, can cause a person to choke or cough; it can also accumulate in the lungs. Depending on its chemical composition, dust may cause an allergic or sensitization reaction in the respiratory tract. Depending on both its size and chemical composition, dust can, by physical irritation or chemical action, damage the airway and/or lung.

Fibrosis can be produced by certain insoluble and fibrous (e.g., asbestos) and nonfibrous (e.g., silica) solid particles found in industry. It is now thought that one of the prerequisites for particle-induced bronchogenic carcinoma may be the insolubility of the particles in the fluids and tissues of the respiratory tract. More insoluble particulates can reside in the lung long enough to induce tumors. A category of aerosol hazard, *bioaerosols*, includes certain bacteria and fungi that can cause an allergic-type inflammatory disease of the lungs called hypersensitivity pneumonitis. These microorganisms are found on moldy vegetative material such as silage, compost, and sugar cane.

Some of the reactive industrial gases and vapors of high solubility that can produce immediate irritation and inflammation of the entire respiratory tract include ammonia, hydrogen fluoride, and sulfur dioxide. Less soluble gases, such as nitrogen dioxide, phosgene, and ozone primarily affect the deep lung (the bronchioles and the adjacent alveolar spaces) where they may produce pulmonary edema within a few hours.

Carbon monoxide (CO) is a toxic gas that is transferred from the lungs into the bloodstream but does not damage the lungs. Carbon monoxide passes through the alveolar walls into the blood, where it binds hemoglobin so the hemoglobin cannot accept oxygen, thus causing oxygen starvation.

Many metal oxides of submicron particle size (called fume) produce both immediate and long-term effects; the latter can occur in organs and tissues remote from the site of entry. For example, cadmium oxide fume inhaled at concentrations well above the Threshold Limit Value (TLV®) may produce immediate pulmonary edema that can be fatal; in addition, inhalation for many years of the fume at concentrations of a few multiples of the TLV can result in eventual renal injury and pulmonary emphysema.

Individual susceptibility to respiratory toxins is difficult to assess. In the occupational setting, workers exposed to the same environment for equal periods of time may develop different degrees of pulmonary disease. This can be due to the variation of the rate of clearance from the lung, the effect of cigarette smoking, coexistent pulmonary disease, and genetic factors.

NATURAL DEFENSES

The respiratory system has a rather complete set of mechanisms for shrugging off insults: the warming and humidifying effects of the nasal and throat passages (as defenses against very cold or overly dry air), the mucous lining, and physical impaction on the branching respiratory tree.

Because the mucous lining plays an important role in the cleansing of aerosols from the lungs, it deserves closer inspection. Cells in the trachea and bronchi produce mucus that is constantly being carried toward the mouth by tiny hairlike projections, called cilia, waving in synchrony. This moving blanket, sometimes called the mucociliary escalator, acts as a vehicle to carry foreign substances up and out of the system to the throat, where they can be expectorated or swallowed.

In a healthy lung, aerosols that get into a bronchiole can be carried back out of the system in a matter of hours. Given adequate recovery time (about 16 hours) after an eight-hour exposure to dust, the healthy lung can thus cleanse itself.

Other defense mechanisms include muscular contraction of the bronchial tubes upon irritation—this reaction restricts the airflow and thus minimizes intake of the irritating substance—and the cough and sneeze, which tend to rid the upper respiratory tract of irritants.

Thus far we have discussed only the defenses of the airways leading to the alveoli. In general, only very fine particles and gases reach the alveolar sacs. The larger the particle, the higher in the respiratory tract it will be deposited through impaction or gravity on the lining of the airway tubes leading to the sacs.

In the case of gases, the concentration that reaches the alveolar sacs will be nearly the same as the concentration in the air breathed. With aerosols, this is not the case. Large particles, more than 10 μm, will be deposited long before they reach the alveoli, through gravity and impaction. Only the smaller particles will reach the alveoli. In the alveoli, Brownian movement of the particles results in deposition by diffusion.

Because only the small (fine) particles are likely to reach the alveoli in great quantities, and because the alveoli are the most important area in the lungs, it is clear that fine aerosols are potentially more harmful than larger aerosols. What happens to fine particles that do reach the alveolar sacs?

Particles deposited in the alveoli will be scavenged by macrophages, which are mobile white blood cells capable of ingesting particles. Once laden with foreign matter, these cells can do the following:

- migrate to the bronchioles, where the mucociliary escalator carries them out of the system
- pass through the alveolar membrane into the lymph vessels associated with the blood capillaries
- be destroyed (if the contaminant is cytotoxic) and break up, releasing the particles back into the alveolar sac.

If the particles are not removed by these means, they can form a deposit in and around the alveoli. Such deposits may or may not affect the health of the lungs over time.

All of the defense mechanisms are subject to some deterioration and slowing down with age or ill health. Thus, an older worker's lungs will not be cleaned as quickly or efficiently as those of a younger person. Also, some contaminants may impede the defense mechanisms themselves, increasing the rate of retention of the contaminant in the lungs.

AMA GUIDES FOR EVALUATING IMPAIRMENT

This section on determining the percent impairment is adapted from the American Medical Association (AMA) *Guides to the Evaluation of Permanent Impairment* and is included to assist health and safety professionals in interpreting and understanding medical reports of workers' compensation cases.

This AMA publication assists physicians in evaluating permanent impairment of the respiratory system and the effect such impairment has on a person's ability to perform the activities of daily life. Permanent impairment of the respiratory system is not necessarily a static condition. A changing process can be present, so that it may be desirable to reevaluate the patient's impairment at appropriate intervals.

The measurable degree of dysfunction of the respiratory system does not necessarily parallel either the extent and severity of the anatomic changes of the lungs or the patient's own account of difficulties in carrying out the activities of daily life. Among the reasons for this phenomenon are the large pulmonary reserves normally present, existence of disease in other systems (particularly the cardiovascular system), wide variation in certain physiological measurements in normal individuals, and the patient's emotional response to respiratory disease or injury.

Many tests of pulmonary function have value and interest as guides to therapy and prognosis. For most patients, however, most of these are neither practical nor necessary for assignment to a particular class of impairment. Judicious interpretation of the results of ventilatory function tests and diffusion studies, combined with the clinical impression gained from weighing all the information gathered, should permit a physician to place the patient in the proper class of impairment.

Rating of Impairment

The classification of respiratory impairment is based primarily on spirometric tests of pulmonary function and diffusing capacity of the lung for carbon monoxide (DLco). For some patients, however, cardiopulmonary exercise testing may be necessary to properly classify the degree of their impairment.

Procedures useful in evaluating impairment of the respiratory system include but are not limited to complete history and physical examination with special reference to cardiopulmonary symptoms and signs; chest imaging (X-rays or computed tomographic [CT] scans; hematocrit or hemoglobin determination; electrocardiogram; FEV_1, FVC, and DLco; and other tests, such as blood gas and pulmonary exercise studies, as indicated.

Tests of Pulmonary Function—Ventilation

The tests of ventilatory function have certain limitations:

- They require maximal voluntary effort by the patient, who may be unable or reluctant to perform the tests as well as ventilatory capacity permits. For example, the performance may be affected by the patient's lack of understanding of the test; state of physical training; fear of cough, chest pain, hemoptysis, or worsening of dyspnea; motivation and cooperation; the effects of other illness, particularly heart disease; and the effects of certain temporary factors on the day of the test, such as the presence of a respiratory infection or bronchospasm.
- The results of these tests vary considerably among normal people of the same sex, age, and height.
- Infrequently, significant impairment of respiratory function can exist even though the patient can perform the tests of ventilatory function normally; that is, the bellows action of the lungs and thorax is normal, but there are abnormalities of pulmonary circulation or gas exchange that give rise to the impairment and necessitate other evaluation procedures.

Various types of spirometers are available that give a permanent record and that readily permit measurement of the FEV_1 and the FVC. These tests can be understood by patients after a short explanation and instruction period, but most patients must be encouraged to put forth their best effort. The FEV_1 and FVC should each be administered at least three times, with the best test result considered most representative of the patient's ability. The test should not be considered valid unless the best two curves agree within five percent (Table 2–A).

If the forced expiratory volume test is interpreted as showing airflow obstruction, the test might be repeated 10–15 minutes after the patient has inhaled an aerosolized bronchodilator medication. If there is at least 12–percent improvement in the performance of the test, the reversibility of the airway obstruction and, incidentally, the presumed efficiency of bronchodilator therapy are established. The best test results before or after bronchodilation should be used in determining the degree of impairment.

Results of tests of ventilatory function should be expressed both in liters or liters per minute and as a percentage of the predicted normal. The FVC as a percentage of the predicted normal is taken as a measure of restrictive impairment. The ratio of actual FEV_1 to actual FVC is a criterion for diagnosing obstructive impairment, but the value of measured FEV_1 either by itself or as a percentage of predicted FEV_1 is considered the best measure of severity. Determination of exercise capacity and arterial blood-gas determinations are useful when a patient's symptoms do not correlate well with spirometric studies. The single-breath DLco is available in most pulmonary function laboratories. It detects interference with transfer of gases across the alveolar membrane, as may occur in emphysema or interstitial fibrosis (scarring of lung tissue). Predicted values of pulmonary function tests must be adjusted for the age, height, sex and race/ethnicity of the patient. The predicted or "normal" values of FVC, FEV_1, and FEV_1/FVC recommended by the 6th edition of the AMA *Guides to the Evaluation of Permanent Impairment* are those of NHANES III because they have values for African Americans and Mexican Americans as well as North American whites. The predicted values for DLco recommended by the *Guides* are those of Crapo. As these are for North American whites, it is recommended that they be multiplied by 0.93 for African-American and Asian-American patients, who on average have smaller lungs for given age, height, and sex.

Quantitative exercise capacity measurements can be done using a treadmill or stationary bicycle. The primary exercise measurement used in respiratory impairment rating is the maximal oxygen consumption ($\dot{V}O_2$max). A patient's $\dot{V}O_2$max provides a good estimate of the maximum workload that he or she can tolerate.

Determinations of partial pressures of oxygen and carbon dioxide in arterial blood, particularly before and after exercise, can be useful in certain cases. These measurements require arterial puncture, so they are not suitable for routine evaluation.

Other measurements of pulmonary function are available in specialized laboratories, but they are not sufficiently standardized for evaluation of impairment.

The 6th edition of the AMA *Guides* classify respiratory impairment into five classes—none, 2–10 percent, 11–23 percent, 24–40 percent, and 45–65 percent—based on FVC, FEV_1, FEV_1/FVC, and DLco or $\dot{V}O_2$max. Each of these impairment classes has a corresponding range of five available ratings, A to E. For example, class 1 corresponds to a rating that ranges from 2 percent to 10 percent of whole person impairment. The examiner can choose among 2 percent (A), 4 percent (B), 6 percent (C), 8 percent (D), or 10 percent (E). Other factors such as the patient's history and

TABLE 2–A		Terminology of Certain Pulmonary Function Measurements	
Terms Used	*Symbol*	*Description*	*Remarks*
Forced vital capacity	FVC	The largest volume of air measured on complete expiration after the deepest inspiration performed with expiration as forceful and rapid as possible (in liters).	This value should be ≥ the lower 95% confidence interval of the predicted value. A lower value suggests the presence of either an obstructive or restrictive ventilatory defect. If the FEV_1/FVC is >70%, then a restrictive defect is likely present.
Forced expiratory volume in one second	FEV_1	Volume of air exhaled during the performance of a forced expiratory maneuver in the first second (in liters).	
One-second forced expiratory volume expressed as percentage of FVC	FEV_1/FVC × 100	The observed FEV_1 expressed as a percentage of the observed FVC.	This value normally should exceed 70%. A lower value suggests the presence of some degree of obstructive airway disease.
Diffusing capacity for carbon monoxide	DLco	The rate at which CO is transferred from the lungs to the blood (in mL/min/mmHg).	This value is low with emphysema, interstitial lung disease, and pulmonary vascular disease.

physical examination findings can be used to adjust the rating up or down from the default C level in the class. Special criteria independent of pulmonary function are assigned to asthma, hypersensitivity pneumonitis, pneumoconiosis, or lung cancer. The classification of impairment due to asthma involves three different parameters: post-bronchodilator FEV_1, percent change in FEV_1 post-bronchodilator or degree of methacholine responsiveness (a measure of non-specific airway hyper-responsiveness to noxious stimuli), and minimum medication needed to provide optimal control of the disease. Not all disability rating systems use the 6th edition of the AMA *Guides*. For example, the Energy Employees Occupational Illness Compensation program of the Department of Labor uses the 5th edition of the *Guides* that only has four classes of respiratory impairment and does not use other factors to adjust the rating along an A–E range.

SUMMARY

The *nose* is an external organ lined by an extensive mucous membrane that warms, moistens, and filters inhaled air. It is the organ of smell.

The *pharynx* is located at the back of the nose and mouth, and above the larynx. It is a cylindrical tube that allows passage of food and air.

The *larynx*, or voice box, is an anterior structure in the neck. Its cartilaginous walls hold it open during inspiration and expiration.

The *trachea and bronchi* are airways lined with ciliated mucous membrane and have rings of cartilage to maintain patency. At midsternal level the trachea divides into two bronchi, one going to each lung. The left bronchus is longer and more horizontal than the right to accommodate the

heart; consequently, inhaled foreign bodies find their way more easily into the right bronchus. These structures are the main sensory area for the initiation of the cough reflex. Their ciliated linings sweep mucus upward to the throat.

The *lungs* are two spongy cone-shaped organs that occupy the major portion of the thoracic cavity. The space between them is called the mediastinum and contains the heart, blood vessels, and all tubes passing to and from the abdomen. The lungs are made up of acini, or terminal lung units, that contain a terminal bronchiole to which clusters of alveoli are connected by respiratory bronchioles.

The *alveoli* are clustered at the ends of the bronchioles like bunches of grapes. They have a rich blood supply from the pulmonary arteries, allowing close contact of blood and air, thus permitting the interchange of oxygen into the blood and carbon dioxide into the air.

The bronchioles, alveoli, and blood vessels are supported by elastic connective tissue, which, with lymphatic vessels, glands, and nerves, form the substance or interstitium of the lungs.

The vital capacity of the lungs is 3–6 L of air, depending on the size of the thoracic cavity, but only half a liter is exchanged with each quiet respiration. As well as the gaseous exchange in the lungs, heat and moisture are lost from the body.

Spontaneous inspiratory nervous impulses arise from a respiratory center in the brain stem. This center is influenced by stimuli from many chemical and mechanical receptors, but the primary stimulus is the partial pressure of CO_2 in the blood. The stimulus for expiration is of a nervous origin and arises from stretching of the nerve endings in the alveolar wall. This stimulus cuts out the impulses that produced inspiration; by elastic recoil and relaxation of muscle, expiration is produced.

Human lungs are size-selective dust collectors. Only relatively small particles, generally those less than 2.5–3 μm in diameter, reach the alveolar spaces. The lungs have a very large surface, 300–1,000 ft^2 (28– 92 m^2) of very delicate tissue. This surface is exposed to contaminants in the inhaled air. The lungs have good defenses against inhaled particles; when unimpaired, these clearance mechanisms remove about 99 percent of the insoluble dust deposited in the lungs.

BIBLIOGRAPHY

American Medical Association. *Guides to the Evaluation of Permanent Impairment,* 6th ed., R. Rondinelli, ed. Chicago: American Medical Association, 2007.

American Medical Association. *The Wonderful Human Machine.* Chicago: AMA, 1971.

American Thoracic Society/European Respiratory Society. Interpretive strategies for lung function testing. *Eur Respir J* 26: 948–968, 2005.

American Thoracic Society/European Respiratory Society. Standardisation of spirometry. *Eur Respir J* 26: 319–338, 2005.

American Thoracic Society/European Respiratory Society. Standardisation of the single-breath determination of carbon monoxide uptake in the lung. *Eur Respir J* 26: 720–735, 2005.

Bateman HE, Mason RM. *Applied Anatomy and Physiology and the Speech and Hearing Mechanism.* Springfield, IL: Charles C. Thomas, 1984.

Eisen EA, Wegman DH, Kriebl D. Application of peak expiratory flow in epidemiologic studies of occupation. *Occup Med State Art Rev* 8(2):265–277, 1993.

Harber P, Schenker M, Balmes JR. *Occupational & Environmental Respiratory Diseases.* St. Louis, MO: Mosby–Yearbook, 1996.

Murray JF. *The Normal Lung,* 2nd ed. Philadelphia: WB Saunders, 1986.

Pollack AN, ed. *Emergency Care and Transportation of the Sick and Injured,* 10th ed. Rosemont, IL: American Academy of Orthopaedic Surgeons, 2011.

Rom WN, Markowitz S, eds. *Environmental and Occupational Medicine,* 4th ed. Philadelphia: Lippincott Wilkins and Williams, 2006.

CHAPTER 3

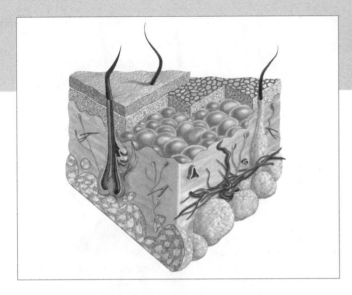

The Skin and Occupational Dermatoses

*by Josephine Gerby, MD
and Howard I. Maibach, MD*

The skin is the second largest organ. Its surface area approximates 2 m², and in most places it is no more than 2 mm thick, yet its mass exceeds that of all organs other than the lung. Skin is a tough, flexible cover and is the first body barrier to make contact with a variety of industrial hazards. The skin is subject to attack from heat, cold, moisture, radiation, bacteria, fungi, and penetrating objects.

The skin performs important functions. Among these are protecting the body from invasion by microorganisms (fungi, bacteria, etc.), injury to vital internal organs, sun, and moisture loss. The skin is also an organ of sensory perception; the sensations of pain, touch, itch, pressure, heat, cold, and warmth may be elicited in human skin.

Temperature regulation is another job performed by skin. Blood vessels dilate (widen) when the body needs to lose heat or constrict (narrow) when the body must reduce the amount of heat loss through skin. When the surrounding air is comparatively warm, the skin is cooled by evaporation of moisture excreted by the sweat glands. There are 2 to 3 million sweat glands over the body surface, excluding mucous membranes. The greatest concentration of these glands is on the palms of the hands and the soles of the feet. Their function depends on an intact nerve supply. Thermoregulatory sweating is controlled by a heat regulator in the brain. Emotions stimulate sweating primarily on the palms, soles, and axillae (armpits).

The surface of the skin may look smooth, but if it is examined under a magnifying glass, countless ridges and valleys can be seen in which the many small openings of pores, hair follicles, and sweat glands are found (Figure 3–1). There are also different patterns of skin texture; compare the palm of the hand with the back of the hand, for example. The skin generally is soft, flexible, and elastic, particularly in young people.

Numerous predisposing factors interact to determine the degree to which a person's skin responds to chemical, physical, and biological insults. These include type of skin (pigmentation, dryness, amount of hair), age, gender, season, previous skin diseases, allergies, and personal hygiene.

A worker's skin is vulnerable to occupational hazards. Surveys indicate that dermatological conditions other than injuries are the second most common cause of all occupational diseases. In 2010, 34,400 recordable skin diseases were reported by the Bureau of Labor Statistics (BLS) at a rate of 3.4 injuries per 10,000 employees, compared to 19,300 respiratory illnesses with a rate of 1.9 illnesses per 10,000 employees. Occupational skin disease is underreported and results in considerable lost time from work.

Although most occupational skin disorders are treated by primary care and occupational physicians, dermatologists are often consulted. Dermatology is the branch of medicine concerned with the diagnosis, treatment (including surgery), and prevention of diseases of the skin, hair, and nails. Some dermatologists have had special training in occupational skin disorders.

Some disorders visible in the skin do not arise primarily in the skin but in other organs. Thus, the skin is an early warning system, and its examination is important in physical diagnosis, occasionally furnishing the first clue to identification of systemic diseases.

ANATOMY

Three distinct layers of tissue comprise the skin (listed from the surface downward): epidermis, dermis, and subcutaneous layer. Thickness varies from 0.5 mm on the eyelid (the dermis is thinnest here) to 3 to 4 mm on the palms and soles (the epidermis is thickest here). Skin is relatively thin in skin folds: the axillae (armpits), under the breasts, the groin, and between the fingers and toes.

Epidermis

The top layer, composed of dead cells called the horny or keratin layer or the stratum corneum, resists chemical attack fairly well, with the notable exception of alkali. It serves as a chief rate-limiting barrier against absorption of water and aqueous solutions, but it also offers loss protection against lipid-soluble materials (such as organic solvents) or gases.

The horny layer gradually flakes off, or soaks off, when wet. It is constantly replaced by cells pushed toward the surface as new cells are formed in the deeper, germinative layer of the epidermis. This regenerative and sloughing characteristic serves to some extent as a protection against chemicals and microorganisms.

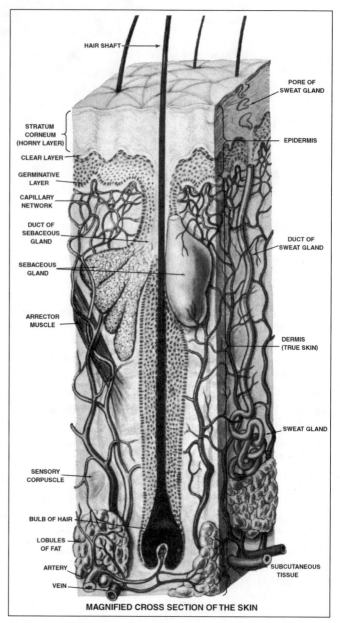

Figure 3–1. Magnified cross section of the skin. (Reprinted with permission of the AMA. *Today's Health Guide.* Chicago: AMA, 1965.)

This constant shedding of flaky material goes mostly unnoticed unless a person has dandruff or must peel off patches after a sunburn. Brisk rubbing with a towel peels off little rolls of material composed of dead outer skin cells.

Three cell types comprise the epidermis:

- Keratinocytes, which make up the bulk of the epidermis, form from below and move up to become stratum corneum.
- Melanocytes, or pigment-forming cells, synthesize melanin (pigment) granules, which are then transferred to keratinocytes. The amount of melanin in keratinocytes determines the degree of pigmentation of skin and hair.

The absolute number of melanocytes in human skin is the same for all races. Differences in coloration among races result from differences in the number, size, degree of pigment formation, distribution, and rate of degradation of pigment granules within keratinocytes. Melanin proliferates under stimulus of certain wavelengths of sunlight and becomes visible as suntan or freckles. Nevi (moles) are growths that contain melanin. Some people with little or no pigment have albinism, an inherited abnormality in which melanin (pigment) production is decreased. Vitiligo is a disorder in which loss of melanocytes also results in areas of cutaneous pigment loss. Some chemicals, such as phenolic germicides, can destroy pigment after occupational or environmental exposure.

- Langerhans' cells, located in the mid-epidermis, account for a relatively small percentage of epidermal cells and play an important role in immune processes, especially allergic contact dermatitis. Although the epidermis is an active tissue, it is not supplied with blood because vessels are absent. The blood supply to the epidermis is through the candelabra pattern of blood vessels in the upper dermal papillae (Figure 3–1).

The epidermis is thin enough that the nerve endings (Merkel cells) in the dermis are sufficiently close to the surface to supply the fine sense of touch. Some of this sensation is lost where areas of the skin are chronically subjected to friction, resulting in subsequent thickening of the epidermis that provides protection in the form of a callus. Thus, the soles are commonly callused among those who habitually walk barefoot, as are the palms of those who do heavy work.

Dermis

Beneath epidermis is dermis, which is much thicker than epidermis, in most locations. It contains connective tissue composed of collagen elastic fibers and ground substance, is strong and elastic, and is the part of animal skins that makes leather when tanned. It is laced with blood vessels, nerve fibers, and receptor organs (for sensations of touch, pain, heat, and cold) and contains muscular elements, hair follicles, and oil and sweat glands (Figure 3–1). The dermis is tough and resilient and is the main natural protection against trauma. When injured, it can form new tissue—a scar—to repair itself.

The top of the dermis is made up of a layer of tiny cone-shaped objects, called papillae. Thousands of papillae are scattered over the body. They are more numerous in the fingertips, where the skin appears to be more sensitive. Nerve fibers and special nerve endings are found in many papillae. As a result, the sense of touch is best developed in areas where papillae with nerve endings are most abundant.

The papillary layer fits snugly against the epidermis, which has ridges corresponding to those of the papillae. The ridges prevent the skin layers from slipping against one another. The ridges on the surfaces of the fingertips form the whorls, loops, and arches that make up fingerprints; dermatoglyphics is the study of the patterns of the ridges of the skin. Similar ridges appear on the soles. Because it is unlikely that two people will have the same pattern of ridges, fingertip patterns are used to identify individuals.

The larger component of the dermis (reticular dermis) extends from the base of the papillary dermis to the subcutaneous fat. Muscle fibers are commonly seen in the reticular dermis on the face and neck.

Subcutaneous Layer

Beneath the dermis is a layer of subcutaneous tissue with fatty and resilient elements that cushions and insulates the skin above it. The distinguishing feature of the subcutaneous layer is the presence of fat. Also present are the lower parts of some eccrine and apocrine sweat glands and hairs, as well as hairs, nerves, blood and lymphatic vessels and cells, and fibrous partitions composed of collagen, elastic tissue, and reticulum. This layer links the dermis with tissue covering the muscles and bones.

Loss of subcutaneous fat and softer parts of the skin removes bouncy supporting material; because the external skin does not shrink at the same rate, it tends to collapse and become enfolded in wrinkles.

Glands in the Skin

Two main types of glands are located in the dermis. One, already mentioned, is the eccrine sweat gland. Under the microscope, it appears as a tightly coiled tube deep in the dermis with a corkscrew-like tubule that rises through the epidermis to the surface of the skin.

The second type is the sebaceous or oil gland, which is usually located in or near a hair follicle. Sebaceous glands are located in all parts of the skin except on the palms and soles, and are particularly numerous on the face and scalp.

Sweat Glands

Sweat glands excrete a fluid known as sweat, or perspiration. The working or secreting parts of the glands are intricately coiled tubules in the dermis. There are two kinds of sweat glands, which produce different kinds of sweat.

Eccrine

Eccrine sweat is of great importance to our comfort and, in some cases, our lives. Numerous eccrine sweat glands are present everywhere except the lips and a few other areas. They are present in largest numbers on palms, soles, and forehead.

Eccrine sweat is largely dilute salt water whose function is to help the body to dissipate excessive internal heat by evaporation from its surface.

Apocrine

Apocrine sweat is minimally investigated but has some social significance. Apocrine sweat glands open into hair follicles and are limited to a few regions, particularly the underarms and genitals. Apocrine sweat is sterile when excreted but decomposes when contaminated by bacteria from the skin surface, resulting in a strong and characteristic odor. The purpose of the many cosmetic underarm preparations is to inhibit these bacteria or decrease gland excretion.

Sebaceous Glands

There are many sebaceous (oil-secreting) glands distributed over almost the entire body (except the palms and soles). The glands are the most common in regions of the forehead, face, neck, and chest—the areas typically involved in common acne, a condition associated with cell-clogged sebaceous glands. Their primary function remains lubrication of the hair shaft and horny surface layers of the skin. A certain amount of natural skin oil is necessary to keep skin and hair soft and pliable.

A strap of internal, plain, involuntary muscle tissue—the arrectores pilorum ("raiser of hair")—is located in the lower portion of the hair follicle below the sebaceous glands. It originates in the connective tissue of the upper dermis. Goose bumps appear on the skin when these muscles attempt to produce heat.

Blood Vessels

Skin is richly supplied with small blood vessels. This blood supply accounts for the reddening of sunburn and the coloration of the fingers beneath the nails. Engorgement of the blood vessels accounts for the reddening of the skin when we blush.

Vascular birthmarks, such as hemangiomas, strawberry marks, and port wine stains, derive their coloration from large numbers of tiny blood vessels concentrated in a small area of the skin.

Hair

Hair and nails are modified forms of skin cells containing keratin as their major structural material. Keratin is produced by the same processes that change living epidermal cells into dead, horny cells. However, hair and nails are made up largely of keratin.

With the exception of the palms and soles, hair follicles populate the entire surface—although, in many areas, they are so inconspicuous or vestigial that they are not noticed.

Hair ranges in texture from the soft, almost invisible hair on the forehead to the long hair of the scalp and the short, stiff hair of the eyelashes.

Hair follicles develop as downgrowths of the epidermis. The hair then grows outward from the bottom of the follicle. Each hair has a root, which is anchored at the bottom of the follicle, and a shaft, which extends past the top of the follicle. The hair follicle enters the epidermis and passes deep into the dermis at an angle. The follicles of long hairs can extend into the subcutaneous layer. Sebaceous glands empty into the follicle. At the root of the hair is a cone-shaped papilla similar to the peg-like papillae that underlie the ridges of the fingers, palms, and soles.

The hair shaft is covered with tiny, overlapping scales. An inner layer of cells contains pigment that gives the hair its color. Most hair tips project from the skin at a slant. Minute arrectores pilorum muscles attached to the follicle have the fascinating ability to make the hair stand on end, as in goose bumps.

Hair follicles and the eccrine sweat glands also serve as routes for percutaneous absorption. Physicians sometimes use this absorptive ability of the skin in administering certain drugs, such as nitroglycerine, scopolamine, estrogen, and nicotine. Some chemicals placed on the skin can be detected in the saliva a few minutes later. In the workplace, the skin is a potential route of entry for hazardous chemicals.

Nails

The fingernails and toenails, like hair, are specialized forms of the skin. The fully developed nail overlays a modified part of the dermis called the nail bed.

Like hair, nails contain keratin, but nails are flat, hard plates. The living part of a nail lies in the matrix in back of the half-moon, or lunula. If the dead nail plate, which constitutes most of the visible part of the nail, is destroyed, a new nail will grow if the matrix is intact. The growth rate of nails varies and depends on such factors as the person's age and health. Nails grow faster in youth and slower with serious illnesses.

PHYSIOLOGY AND FUNCTIONS

Skin performs important functions protecting the body from invasion of bacteria, injury to vital internal organs, the rays of the sun, and moisture loss.

Temperature Regulation

For a discussion of the role of the skin in heat regulation of the body, see Chapter 12, Thermal Stress.

Eccrine Sweat

Sweat is produced constantly, usually in proportion to environmental temperature. In hot environments, the body must lose heat by evaporation, which is more effective than radiation. In cool, dry weather, the amount of sweat produced is relatively small, and the skin remains dry to the touch as not aware of sweating; this is called insensible perspiration.

When heat production of the body is increased or when the ambient temperature is high, the sweat glands produce more perspiration. The rate of production outstrips that of evaporation, particularly if humidity is high, because the rate of evaporation declines with the humidity rise. Perspiration then collects on the body in visible drops, and we are conscious of sweating. However, heat is lost only when the sweat evaporates. All sweat glands are innervated by sympathetic nervous system fibers, ultimately controlled by the hypothalamus. Emotional stimulation from anxiety or fright may stimulate sweating in the palms, soles, and axillae.

One way of increasing the rate at which water is evaporated from the body is to breathe rapidly, thus moving larger quantities of air from the moist surfaces of the mouth, throat, and lungs. Humans cannot do this in comfort, but it is the chief method of cooling available to dogs; in warm weather, dogs sit with mouth open, tongue extended, and pant.

Ultraviolet Light

Skin protects not only against mechanical shocks, but also against ultraviolet (UV) light. (See Chapter 11, Nonionizing Radiation, for a discussion of the forms.) Most animals are protected from sunlight by scales, hair, and feathers, which absorb the sun's rays without harm to themselves. Humans have only the skin as protection from the sun's UV rays. Ultraviolet light energy produces chemical changes within the skin's cells; the effects vary with the time of the year, the geographic area, and the hour of the day.

Generally, after initial exposure to summer sun at midday, skin shows reddening or erythema, which may not appear for several hours. If the dose of sunlight is intense, the erythema may be followed by blistering and peeling. If the erythema is not severe, it fades in a few days, and the skin gradually acquires a tan coloration (suntan). The tan color is produced by darkening of existing pigment (immediate pigment darkening) and by an increase in pigment formation. When skin is exposed to the sun, it is believed that melanin pigment moves toward the surface of the skin and is replaced by new melanin in the lower cell layer. Along with pigmentation increase, the stratum corneum thickens to furnish additional protection against solar radiation injury. One or two weeks may be required to develop a suntan by moderate daily doses of sunlight; the tan fades if occasional exposure to sunlight is not continued. As some protection against repeated UV light exposure, human skin is equipped with the capacity to form pigment (melanin), which absorbs UV light and thus acts as a protective umbrella over the regions beneath (delayed pigment darkening).

Solar UV radiation can induce actinic (solar) degeneration and skin cancer and is a major hazard of chronic sun exposure. Chronic exposure to artificial UV light in tanning salons may induce similar changes. Additionally, sunlight and artificial UV light may induce abnormal cutaneous reactions in patients with certain hereditary or acquired diseases or in those taking certain medication. Photoaging and natural chronologic aging are different entities.

The immune system of humans is affected by UV radiation; environmental sources of radiation can have similar effects, such as contact photoallergy. One beneficial normal effect of UV radiation on skin is the photochemistry that leads to the production of vitamin D_3. In most industrial countries, sufficient vitamin D is added to food to meet normal daily requirements.

Skin Absorption

Sebum, breakdown products of keratin, and sweat—called the surface lipid film—coat the outer surface of the keratin layer, but there is no evidence that this normal coating has any barrier function.

The epidermis, especially the stratum corneum, acts as a major permeability barrier to the entry of foreign chemicals. Overall, the skin is selectively permeable— more impermeable than permeable—and shows regional variation in absorptive capacity. Absorption of materials through the skin markedly increases when the continuity of the skin is disrupted by dermatitis, lacerations, or punctures. The hair follicles and sweat ducts may play only a minor role in skin absorption. However, they act as diffusion shunts— that is, relatively easy pathways through the skin for certain substances such as polar compounds, very large molecules that move across the stratum corneum very slowly, and pharmacologically active substances, especially in very hairy areas. After this initial phase, however, most of the percutaneous absorption of all substances takes place across the stratum corneum, which has a much greater surface area than that of the hair follicles and sweat ducts.

DEFENSE MECHANISMS

Anyone who works is a candidate for occupational skin disease, yet most workers are not affected by such disorders because the skin is a primary organ of defense. The skin performs its defense functions because of its location, structure, and physiological activity.

These are the specific defenses the skin has in terms of its protection against typical industrial hazards.

- *Bacteria:* The skin is a naturally dry terrain (except in places such as axillae and the groin and during abnormal sweating) and has a normal contingent of bacteria that tends to destroy pathogenic bacteria. Free fatty acids in the surface oil also can have some antibacterial value. The immune defenses of the skin also defend against infections.
- *Sunlight:* The skin has two defenses: an increase in pigmentation and thickening of the stratum corneum.
- *Primary acute irritants:* The skin resists acids but offers much less protection against organic and inorganic alkalis. Sweat can act as a diluent to decrease the effect of water-soluble toxins. Conversely, it enhances hydration and maceration of the barrier, thereby promoting percutaneous absorption.
- *Injury:* The skin's resilience, especially of the dermis, provides a measure of resistance to forceful impact. The cutaneous nerves also provide information about the state of the external environment through sensations of touch and temperature.
- *Excessive increase or decrease in body heat:* The body's thermoregulatory mechanisms include the activity of sweat glands and blood vessels.
- *The absorption of chemicals through the skin:* This is where an important function is performed. The skin is a flexible body envelope and the epidermal barrier, especially the stratum corneum, provides a significant blockade against water loss from the body and penetration of the skin by chemical agents.

DEFINITIONS AND INCIDENCE OF OCCUPATIONAL SKIN DISORDERS

A *dermatosis* is any abnormal condition of the skin, ranging from the mildest redness, itching, or scaling to an eczematous (superficial inflammation), ulcerative (ulcer-forming), acneiform (resembling acne), pigmentary (abnormal skin color), granulomatous (tumor-like mass, nodule), or neoplastic (new, abnormal tissue growth) disorder. Occupational dermatoses include any skin abnormalities resulting directly from or aggravated by the work environment. *Dermatitis* is a more limited term referring to any inflammation of the skin, such as contact dermatitis.

Occupational skin diseases can occur in workers of all ages and in any work setting and cause much illness, personal misery, and reduced productivity. Although the frequency of occupational skin disease often parallels the level of hygiene practiced by employers, occupational skin diseases are largely preventable. Many consider this type of disease trivial and insignificant, but occupational skin disorders can result in complex impairment.

Data compiled by the U.S. Bureau of Labor Statistics (BLS) for 2010 indicate that approximately 95 percent (3,689,420) of all occupational disorders are injuries and almost 5 percent (194,180) are diseases. Of these reported diseases, 15.8 percent were skin diseases (Figure 3–2). Because large surface areas are often directly exposed, the skin is particularly vulnerable to occupational insults. Although complete data on the extent and cost of dermatological injuries are not available, the National Institute for Occupational Safety and Health (NIOSH) has estimated that workplace skin diseases account for 15 to 20 percent of all reported occupational diseases in the United States, with estimated total annual costs (including lost workdays and lost productivity) of up to $1 billion.

In the mid-1950s, skin disorders other than injuries accounted for 50 to 70 percent of all occupational diseases. This figure has been gradually decreasing and was 13 percent, or 57,900 cases, in 1997. NIOSH attributes the decline of skin diseases since 1997 to a continuing trend toward automation, enclosure of the industrial process, and educational efforts. Despite these figures, dermatitis is the second most common cause of reported occupational disease in the United States. National data indicate that as many as 20 to 25 percent of all occupational skin diseases involve lost time from work, with an average of 11 workdays lost per

TABLE 3–A	Numbers and Incidence of Occupational Skin Diseases by Major Industry, 2010	
Industry	**Number of Cases**	**Incidence***
Private Industry	24,900	2.9
Goods Producing	6800	3.8
Natural Resources and mining (includes agriculture/forestry/fishing)	800	5.1
Construction	900	1.8
Manufacturing	5,100	4.5
Service Providing	18,100	2.6
Trade/transportation/utilities	3,800	1.8
Information	600	2.2
Financial Activities	500	0.7
Professional and business services	3,500	2.7
Leisure/hospitality	2,700	3.2
Education/health services	6,600	4.6
Other services, except public administration	600	1.9
State and Local Government	9,500	6.6
State	2000	5.1
Local	7500	7.2
Total	34,400	3.4

* Per 10,000 full-time workers per year.
Source: Bureau of Labor Statistics. *Occupational Injuries and Illnesses in the United States,* 2010. U.S. Department of Labor, USDL-11-1502, October 2011.

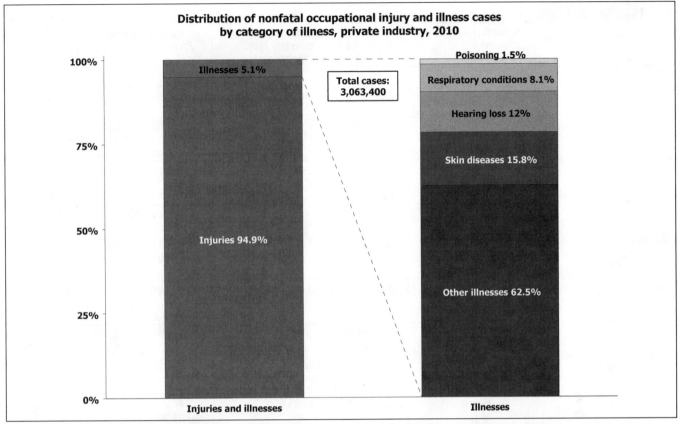

Figure 3–2. Nonfatal occupational injuries accounted for the overwhelming majority of cases reported for the SOII in 2010 (94.9 percent), with illnesses accounting for the remaining 5.1 percent of cases. Most illness cases fall into the "All other illnesses" category, which includes such things as repetitive motion cases and systemic diseases and disorders. *(Source: Bureau of Labor Statistics. Occupational Injuries and Illnesses in the United States 2010. U.S. Department of Labor, USDL-11-1502, October 2011.)*

case. California and South Carolina have reported similar data based on workers' compensation claims. The results of two studies show a serious underreporting of occupational disease of all types, which may mean that the true incidence is 10 to 50 times greater than that reported by the BLS.

NIOSH has included work-related dermatological conditions on its list of 10 leading work-related diseases and injuries in the United States. Reasons include the fact that 10 to 15 percent of requests NIOSH receives for health hazard evaluation involve skin complaints and the fact that the economic impact of dermatological conditions is substantial. The annual cost resulting from lost worker productivity, medical care, and disability payments has been estimated to range between $222 million and $1 billion.

Table 3–A gives the incidence of occupational dermatological disease by industry group for the United States in 2010.

DIRECT CAUSES OF OCCUPATIONAL SKIN DISEASE

There are unlimited substances and conditions capable of inducing a skin disorder in the workplace. Each year, new

causes are reported and most can be classified under one of five headings:

1. Chemical
2. Mechanical
3. Physical
4. Biological
5. Botanical

Chemical

Organic and inorganic chemicals are the predominant causes of dermatoses in the work environment (Table 3–B). The list of such chemicals is endless because each year additional agents capable of injuring the skin are added. Chemical agents may be divided into two groups: irritants and sensitizers.

Primary Acute Irritants

Primary acute irritants are likely to affect most people; some actually affect everyone. These agents react on contact. The reaction alters the chemistry of the skin by dissolving a portion of it by precipitating the protein of the cells or by some other chemical reaction. The result can range from tissue

TABLE 3–B			Selected Chemical Causes of Skin Disorders	
Chemical	**Primary Irritants**	**Sensitizers**	**Selected Skin Manifestations (some also have important systemic effects on other organs)**	**Selected Occupations, Trades, or Processes Where Exposure Can Occur**
ACIDS				
Acetic	X	?	Dermatitis and ulceration	Manufacturing acetate rayon, textile printing and dyeing, vinyl plastic makers
Carbolic (phenol)	X		Corrosive action on skin, local anesthetic effect	Carbolic acid makers, disinfectant manufacturing, dye makers, pharmaceutical workers, plastic manufacturing
Chromic	X	X	Ulcers ("chrome holes") on skin, inflammation and perforation of nasal septum	Platers, manufacturing organic chemicals and dyestuffs
Cresylic	X		Corrosive to skin, local anesthetic effect	Manufacturing disinfectants, coal tar pitch workers, foundry workers
Formic	X		Severe irritation with blisters and ulcerations	Rubber and laundry workers, mordanters, cellulose formate workers, airplane dope makers
Hydrochloric	X		Irritation and ulceration of skin	Bleachers, picklers (metals), refiners (metals), tinners, chemical manufacturing masons (clean cement)
Hydrofluoric	X		Severe chemical burn with blisters, erosion, or ulceration	Enamel manufacturing, etchers, hydrofluoric acid makers, flurochemical workers
Lactic	X		Ulceration (if strong solutions are used)	Adhesives, plastics, textiles
Nitric	X		Severe skin burns and ulcers	Nitric acid workers, electroplaters, old metal cleaners, acid dippers, nitrators, dye makers
Oxalic	X		Severe corrosive action on skin, cyanosis (bluish discoloration), and brittleness of nails	Tannery workers, blueprint paper makers, oxalic acid makers
Picric	X	X	Erythema, dermatitis, scaling, yellow discoloration of skin and hair	Explosives workers, picric acid makers, dyers and dye makers, tannery workers
Sulfuric	X		Corrosive action on skin, severe inflammation of mucous membranes	Nitrators, picklers (metals), dippers, chemical manufacturing
ALKALIS				
Ammonia	X		Irritation including airborne dermatitis of face from vapors	Ammonia production, fertilizers, photocopying (blueprint, diazo); gas and liquid forms
Calcium cyanamide	X		Irritation and ulceration	Fertilizer makers, agricultural workers, nitrogen compound makers
Calcium oxide	X		Dermatitis, burns, or ulceration	Lime workers, manufacturing of calcium, salts, glass, and fertilizer
Potassium hydroxide	X		Severe corrosion of skin, deep-seated persistent ulcers, loss of fingernails	Potassium hydroxide makers, electroplaters, paper, soap, and printing ink makers
Sodium hydroxide	X		Severe corrosion of skin, deep-seated persistent ulcers, loss of fingernails	Sodium hydroxide makers, bleachers, soap and dye makers, petroleum refiners, mercerizers, plastic manufacturing
Sodium or potassium cyanide	X		Blisters, ulcers	Electroplaters, case hardening, extraction of gold
Trisodium phosphate	X		Blisters, ulcers	Photographic developers, leather tanning, industrial cleaning detergents
SALTS OF ELEMENTS				
Antimony and its compounds	X	?	Irritation and lichenoid eruptions of skin	Antimony extractors, glass and rubber mixers, manufacturing of various alloys, fireworks, and aniline colors

(Continues)

TABLE 3–B			Selected Chemical Causes of Skin Disorders *(Continued)*	
Chemical	*Primary Irritants*	*Sensitizers*	*Selected Skin Manifestations (some also have important systemic effects on other organs)*	*Selected Occupations, Trades, or Processes Where Exposure Can Occur*
Arsenic and its compounds	X	X	Spotty pigmentation of skin, perforation of nasal septum, skin cancer, keratoses especially on palms and soles, dermatitis, pustules	Leather workers, manufacturing insecticides, glass industry, agriculture, pesticides, tanning, taxidermy, alloy, lubricating oils
Barium and its compounds	X		Irritation of skin	Barium carbonate, fireworks, textile dyes
Bromine and its compounds	X		Irritation, vesicles, and ulceration; acne	Bromine extractors, bromine salts makers, dye and drug makers, photographic trades
Chromium and its compounds	X	X	Pit-like ulcers (chrome holes) on skin, perforation of nasal septum, dermatitis	Chromium platers, dye industry workers, chrome manufacturing, leather tanners
Mercury and its compounds	X	X	Corrosion and irritation of skin, dermatitis	Explosives manufacturing, silver and gold extractors, manufacturing electrical appliances and scientific equipment
Nickel salts	X	X	Folliculitis, dermatitis	Nickel platers, alloy makers
Sodium and certain of its compounds	X		Burns and ulceration	Bleaching: detergent, paper, glass, tetraethyl lead manufacturing
Zinc chloride	X	?	Ulcers of skin and nasal septum	Manufacturing chemicals, dyestuffs, paper, disinfectants
SOLVENTS				
Acetone	X		Dry (defatted) skin	Spray painters, celluloid industry, artificial silk and leather workers, acetylene workers, lacquer and varnish makers, garage mechanics
Benzene and its homologues (toluene and xylene)	X		Dry (defatted) skin	Chemical and rubber manufacturing
Carbon disulfide	X	X	Dry (defatted) irritated skin	Extraction of oils, fats, and a wide range of other materials, manufacture of rayon, rubber, rubber cements, germicides, and other chemicals
Trichloroethylene	X	?	Dermatitis	Degreasers, chemical intermediates
Turpentine	X	X	Dermatitis	Painters, furniture polishers, lacquerers, artists
Alcohols (such as ethanol)	X	X	Dermatitis	Chemical manufacture; painters
SOME DYE INTERMEDIATES				
Dinitrobenzene	X		Yellow discoloration of skin, hair, and eyes	Dye manufacturing
Nitro and nitroso compounds	X	X	Dermatitis	Dye manufacturing
Phenylhydrazine	X	X	Severe chemical burns, dermatitis	Dye and pharmaceutical manufacturing
PETROLEUM AND COAL TAR DERIVATIVES				
Petroleum oils	X		Dermatitis, folliculitis	Petroleum workers, machinists, mechanics
Pitch and asphalt	X		Dermatitis, folliculitis, keratoses, skin cancer	Manufacturing pitch and asphalt, roofers
Tar (coal)	X	X	Dermatitis, folliculitis, skin cancer, eye inflammation (keratitis)	Tar manufacturing, manufacturing roofing paper and pitch, road building and repairing
DYES (such as paraphenylenediamine)	X		Contact dermatitis (erythema, blisters, edema)	Dye workers, cosmetologists
RUBBER ACCELERATORS AND ANTIOXIDANTS	X		Contact dermatitis (erythema, blisters, edema)	Rubber workers, such as compound mixers and calendar and mill operators; fabrications of rubber products
Mercaptobenzothiazole, tetramethylthiuram disulfide, diethylthiourea, and paraphenylenediamine				

(Continues)

TABLE 3–B			Selected Chemical Causes of Skin Disorders (Continued)	
Chemical	**Primary Irritants**	**Sensitizers**	**Selected Skin Manifestations (some also have important systemic effects on other organs)**	**Selected Occupations, Trades, or Processes Where Exposure Can Occur**
SOAPS AND SOAP POWDERS	X	X	Dermatitis, dry skin, paronychia (inflammation around fingernails); allergy from fragrance, germicides, or dyes	Soap manufacturing, dishwashers, soda fountain clerks, maintenance workers—all associated with wet work
INSECTICIDES				
Arsenic	X		See above under salts or elements	Manufacturing and applying insecticides
Pentachlorophenols	X	?	Dermatitis, chloracne	Pesticides and wood preservatives
Creosote	X	X	Dermatitis, folliculitis, keratoses, hyperpigmentation, skin cancer	Manufacturing wood preservatives, railroad ties, coal tar lamp black and pitch workers
Fluorides	X		Severe burns, dermatitis	Manufacturing insecticides, enamel manufacturing
Phenylmercury compounds	X	X	Dermatitis	Manufacturing and applying fungicides and disinfectants
Pyrethrum		X	Dermatitis	Manufacturing and applying insecticides
Rotenone	X		Dermatitis	Manufacturing and applying insecticides
RESINS (Natural)*				
Cashew nut oils		X	Severe poison ivy-like dermatitis	Handlers of unprocessed cashew nuts, varnish
Rosin		X	Dermatitis	Adhesive and paper mill workers, dentists, rubber industry
Shellac		X	Dermatitis	Coatings, cosmetics
Synthetic resins such as phenolformaldehyde, urea-formaldehyde, epoxy, vinyl, polyurethane, polyester, acrylate, cellulose esters	X	X	Dermatitis	Plastic workers, varnish makers, adhesives, coatings, rubber, cosmetology

*The skin reactions from this group of chemicals in some instances are due to the essential composition of the synthetic resin, but in other cases are due to the presence of added compounds such as plasticizers and other modifying agents

EXPLOSIVES				
Nitrates, mercury fulminate, tetryl, lead azide, TNT, nitroglycerin	X	X	Severe irritation, dermatitis, skin discoloration	Explosives manufacturing, shell loading
METAL WORKING FLUIDS				
Cutting oils	X		Oil acne (folliculitis), rare dermatitis	Machinists
Coolants—synthetic and semisynthetic	X	X	Dermatitis	Machinists
OXIDIZING AGENTS				
Hydrogen peroxide	X	?	Dermatitis	Chemical industry; medical disinfectant; cosmetology
Benzoyl peroxide	X	X	Dermatitis	Chemical industry; polyester manufacture
OTHER				
Isocyanates such as TDI, MDI, HDI	X	X	Dermatitis	Polyurethane makers, adhesive workers, organic chemical synthesizers
Vinyl chloride	X		Dermatitis, acro-osteolysis	Polyvinyl resin, rubber and organic chemical makers
Formaldehyde	X	X	Dermatitis	Undertakers, biologists, textile workers
Plants, weeks (such as poison oak, ivy, sumac)	X	X	Dermatitis	Outdoor workers (such as fire fighters, utility workers)

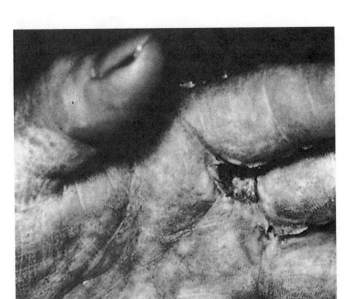

Figure 3–3. Eczematous is a form of contact dermatitis caused by contact with organic solvents. It is one of the most prevalent types of dermatitis.

destruction (chemical burn) to inflammation (dermatitis), depending on the strength of the agent and the duration of the exposure.

Primary irritants damage skin because they have an innate chemical capacity to do so. Many irritants are water-soluble and react with certain components of the skin. The water-insoluble compounds, including many solvents, react with the lipid (fatty) elements within skin. The precise mechanism of primary irritation on the skin is not known, but some useful generalizations explain the activity of groups of materials in the irritant category. Dermatitis caused by a primary irritant is referred to as irritant contact dermatitis because the skin irritation is normally confined to the area of direct contact.

Most inorganic and organic acids act as primary irritants. Certain inorganic alkalis—such as ammonium hydroxide, calcium chloride, sodium carbonate, and sodium hydroxide—are irritants. Organic alkalis, particularly amines, also are active irritants. Metallic salts—especially arsenicals, chromates, mercurials, nickel sulphate, and zinc chloride—severely irritate the skin. Organic solvents include many substances—such as chlorinated hydrocarbons, petroleum-based compounds, ketones, alcohols, and terpenes—that irritate the skin because of their solvent qualities (Figure 3–3).

Keratin solvents. All of the alkalis (organic and inorganic) injure the keratin layer with sufficient concentration and exposure time. These agents soften, dehydrate, and destroy the keratin cells, resulting in dry, cracked skin. This prepares

the way for secondary infection and, at times, for the development of allergic contact dermatitis.

Keratin stimulants. Several chemicals stimulate the skin so that it undertakes growth patterns that can lead to tumor or cancer formation. Certain petroleum products, a number of coal tar-based materials, arsenic, and some polycyclic aromatic hydrocarbons can stimulate the epidermal cells to produce these effects (Figure 3–4).

Fats and oil solvents. Just as organic solvents dissolve oily and greasy industrial soils, they remove the skin's surface lipids and disturb the keratin layer of cells so that they lose their water-holding capacity. Workers exposed each day to organic solvents develop exceedingly dry and cracked skin.

Protein precipitants. Several heavy-metal salts precipitate protein and denature it. The salts of arsenic, chromium, mercury, and zinc are best known for this action.

Reducers. In sufficient concentration, salicylic acid, oxalic acid, urea, and other substances can actually reduce the keratin layer so that it is no longer protective, and an occupational dermatosis results.

Sensitizers

Some primary skin irritants also sensitize. They can cause allergic contact dermatitis and photoallergic contact dermatitis. Certain irritants sensitize a person so that a dermatitis develops from a very low, nonirritating concentration of a compound that previously could have been handled without any problem.

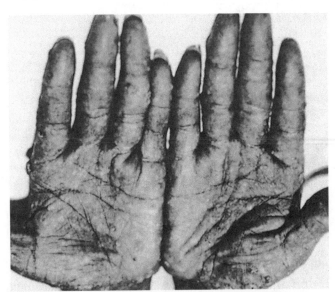

Figure 3–4. Nodules in the keratin layer of the skin may result from repeated exposure to certain tars or coal tar derivatives.

Some chemical and many plant substances and biological agents are classified as sensitizers. Initial skin contact with them may not produce dermatitis, but after repeated or extended exposure, some people develop an allergic reaction called allergic contact dermatitis. Clinically, allergic contact dermatitis is often indistinguishable from irritant contact dermatitis (see sections on contact dermatitis for further discussion of allergic contact dermatitis and patch testing).

Substances that are both irritants and allergens include turpentine, formaldehyde, chromic acid, and epoxy resin components. Common sensitizers are plant oleoresins such as poison ivy, epoxy resins, azo dyes, certain spices, certain metals such as nickel and chromium, and topical medicaments such as neomycin.

Other chemicals can sensitize the skin to light via the mechanism of photo irradiation (phototoxicity or photoallergy, photoallergic contact dermatitis). Known as photosensitizers, these chemicals include coal tar and pitch derivatives, fluorescent dyes, salicylanilides, musk ambrette, sunscreens containing p-aminobenzoic acid (PABA) and benzophenone, some plants, pesticides, and insecticides.

Mechanical

Mechanical trauma can be mild, moderate, or severe and occur as a single or repeated event. Friction results in the formation of a blister or callus, pressure in thickening and color change, sharp objects in laceration, and external force in bruising, punctures, or tears. A commonly cited example is fibrous glass, which can cause irritation, itching, and scratching. Secondary infection may complicate blisters, calluses, or breaks in the skin.

Physical

Physical agents such as heat, cold, and radiation can cause occupational dermatoses. For example, high temperatures cause perspiration and softening of the outer horny layer of the skin. This can lead to miliaria, or heat rash, common among workers exposed to hot humid weather, electric furnaces, hot metals, and other sources of heat.

High temperatures can also cause systemic symptoms and signs such as heat cramps, heat exhaustion, and even heatstroke. Burns can result from electric shock, sources of ionizing radiation, molten metals and glass, and solvents or detergents used at elevated temperatures.

Exposure to low temperatures can cause frostbite and result in permanent damage. The ears, nose, fingers, and toes are the most often frostbitten. Electric utility and telephone line workers, highway maintenance workers, agricultural workers, people working in commercial fishing, police officers, letter carriers, and other outdoor workers are most often affected.

Sunlight is the greatest source of skin-damaging radiation and is a source of danger to construction workers, fishermen, agricultural workers, foresters, and all others who work outdoors for extended periods of time. The most serious effect on the skin is skin cancer.

Increasing numbers of people come into casual or prolonged contact with artificial UV light sources such as molten metals and glass, welding operations, and plasma torches. A variety of newer lasers are being used in medicine and other scientific disciplines. Because lasers can injure the skin, eye, and other biological tissue, it is important to use appropriate protective devices.

There are three sources of ionizing radiation:
- Alpha-radiation is completely stopped by the skin and thus does not injure skin. However, alpha-radiation-emitting radioactive substances, such as plutonium, are harmful when ingested or inhaled.
- Beta-radiation can injure the skin by contact, and substances such as phosphorus-32 are dangerous when inhaled or ingested. Beta-particles are usually localized at the surface or within the outer layers of skin, with the depth of penetration depending on the energy of the beta particle.
- Gamma-radiation and x rays are well-known skin (radiodermatitis and skin cancer) and systemic (internal) hazards when sufficient exposure occurs. Radiodermatitis is characterized by dry skin, hair loss, telangiectasia, spider-like angiomas, and hyperkeratosis. Skin cancer may ultimately develop. (See Chapter 10, Ionizing Radiation, for more information.)

Biological

Bacteria, viruses, fungi, and parasites can produce cutaneous or systemic disease of occupational origin. Animal breeders, agricultural workers, bakers, culinary employees, florists, horticulturists, laboratory technicians, and tannery workers are among those at greater risk of developing infections. Examples include anthrax in hide processors; yeast infections of the nail in dishwashers, bartenders, and others engaged in wet work; and animal ringworm in agricultural workers and veterinarians. Parasitic mites are common inhabitants of grain and other foodstuffs and attack those handling such materials, such as grocers, truckers, longshoremen, and agricultural workers. Outdoor workers such as bricklayers and plumbers in southeastern states risk contracting animal hookworm via larvae deposited by infected animals in sandy soil. Health care workers, medical laboratory workers, and emergency medical technicians are exposed to a number of microorganisms, especially hepatitis B, HIV, herpes simplex (herpetic whitlow of the fingers from direct viral exposure and inoculation), fungi (Candida and superficial and deep fungi), and bacteria (staphylococci and tuberculosis), which may be acquired from patients or from biological specimens.

Botanical

Many plants and woods, of which poison ivy and poison oak are the most common, can cause contact dermatitis. Irritant contact dermatitis can also be caused by some plants, and although the chemical identity of many of the toxins is not known, the allergen or irritant occurs in the leaves, stems, flowers, bark, or other part of the plant. Other plants, such as wild parsnip and fresh or diseased celery (pink-rot) are photosensitizers. Several outbreaks of photodermatitis have been reported in grocery produce workers, especially those visiting tanning parlors. With woods, dermatitis occurs especially when they are being sandpapered, polished, and cut. Fomites can carry and transmit these allergens, which can also be dispersed by the smoke from burning.

PREDISPOSING FACTORS

In classifying and determining the severity of occupational dermatoses, numerous factors should be considered: the nature, duration, and extent of exposure to an environmental agent; the potential toxic effects of the agent; its chemical stability; and its potential for being absorbed through the skin. Other variables include preexisting skin disease or exposure to more than one agent. Indirect or predisposing factors leading to the development of occupational dermatoses are generally associated with age, gender, perspiration, season of the year, personal hygiene, and allergy.

Age and Experience

Younger, inexperienced, and inadequately trained workers have a higher prevalence of occupational dermatoses than older workers.

Sweating

Hyperhidrosis, or increased sweating, can produce maceration with softening and resultant separation of skin already irritated by rubbing in adjacent body areas, as occurs in the armpit and the groin. This predisposes the skin to secondary fungal and bacterial infection. Some materials, such as caustics, soda ash, and slaked lime, become irritants in solution. However, sweating can also serve a protective function by diluting the toxic substances.

Gender

Because the incidence of nickel allergy is much greater in women (due to ear-piercing), they are more susceptible to developing dermatitis when handling coins or when in contact with nickel salts and metal alloys. The incidence of nickel allergy in men, even those with earrings, is lower, for reasons not known.

Seasons and Humidity

Occupational dermatoses are more common in warm weather when workers wear less clothing and are more likely to come in contact with external irritants. Excessive perspiration, with resulting skin damage, is also more common in warm weather. When a work area is hot, workers may not use protective clothing. Warm weather also means that many workers have greater exposure to sunlight, poisonous plants, and insects, the effects of which may or may not be related to the job.

Winter brings chapping from exposure to cold and wind. Heated rooms are usually low in relative humidity, so skin loses moisture. Large-scale outbreaks of dermatitis in some factories have been traced to nothing more than low humidity. Clothing can keep dust particles and mechanical irritants in close contact with the skin. Infrequent bathing and changing of clothing can increase the incidence of skin irritation. (See Chapter 12, Thermal Stress, for more information.)

Atopy (Hereditary Allergy)

Atopy (the name means uncommon or out of place) is a relatively common genetic tendency toward the development of atopic dermatitis, asthma, and hay fever. Atopic people are predisposed to developing dermatitis because of their reduced skin resistance to chemical irritants, inherent dry skin, dysfunctional sweating, and a high skin colonization rate of the bacteria *Staphylococcus aureus*. In an atopic adult, the hands are the main location for dermatitis. Atopic people, especially those with eczema, are more prone to cumulative irritant dermatitis than those who are not atopic. Immunologic and contact urticaria—especially to latex—also occur in atopic workers.

Personal Hygiene

Poor personal hygiene is believed to be a significant cause of occupational skin disorders. Unwashed skin covered with unwashed and unchanged clothes may be in prolonged contact with chemicals. Responsibility for maintaining clean skin is shared by employer and employee. Thus, adequate facilities for maintaining personal cleanliness should be provided. Educating workers in the preventive aspects of personal hygiene is imperative. On the other hand, excessive skin cleansing with harsh agents can produce an irritant contact dermatitis or may aggravate preexisting dermatitis (Figure 3–5).

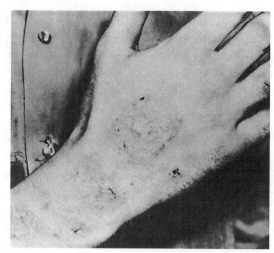

Figure 3–5. Cleaning hands with a strong petroleum solvent instead of a good industrial cleanser caused this case of dermatitis.

Preexisting Skin Disease

Other forms of skin irritation (eczema)—such as atopic eczema, nonoccupational contact dermatitis, palmar psoriasis, and lichen planus—can be aggravated by chemicals in the work environment. Ultraviolet light-sensitive disease, such as lupus erythematosus, and cold-induced disease, such as Raynaud's phenomenon, can be aggravated and precipitated by sunlight and cold exposure, respectively.

CLASSIFICATION OF OCCUPATIONAL SKIN DISEASE

Skin disorders are relatively easy to recognize because they are visible. However, accurate diagnosis and classification of disease type and its relationship to employment usually requires a high level of clinical skill and expertise. The varied nature of skin responses causing occupational skin disorders takes several forms. The appearance and pattern of the dermatosis infrequently indicate the provoking substance definitively, but can provide clues to the class of materials involved. Diagnosis depends on appearance, location, and (most importantly) on the history. Preexisting skin disorders, adverse effects of treatment, and secondary infections add to the difficulty in diagnosis. The following grouping includes most occupational dermatoses.

Contact Dermatitis

Contact dermatitis is the most frequent cause of occupational skin disease, accounting for most reported cases. Two variants are generally recognized: irritant (including photoirritant) and allergic (including photoallergic). Approximately 80 percent of all cases of occupational contact dermatitis result from irritation and 20 percent from allergy. Both are difficult to differentiate clinically because each can appear as an acute or chronic eczematous dermatitis. The acute form is erythematous (increased redness), vesicular (small blisters) to bullous (large vesicles), edematous (swollen), and oozing and is of short duration, lasting days or weeks. The chronic form is lichenified (thickened skin), scaly, and fissured and may last for weeks, months, or years. Itching is usually a major symptom.

Contact dermatitis most often occurs on the hands, wrists, and forearms, although any area can be affected. Dusts, vapors, and mists can affect the exposed areas, including forehead, eyelids, face, ears, and neck and can often collect in areas where the body bends, such as under the collar and at the tops of shoes. The palms and soles are partially protected by a thick stratum corneum. The scalp tends to be protected by the hair, but the male genitalia are commonly affected because irritants are often transferred by the hands. Contact dermatitis also localizes under rings and between fingers, toes, and other cutaneous areas that rub together.

Irritant Contact Dermatitis

A primary skin irritant is a substance that causes damage at the site of contact because of its direct chemical or physical action on the skin. Irritants are generally divided into strong (absolute) and weak (marginal) types. Strong (absolute) irritants include strong acids, alkalis, aromatic amines, phosphorus, ethylene oxide, riot-control agents, and metallic salts and produce an observable effect within minutes. In contrast, marginal irritants such as soap and water, detergents, solvents, and oils can require days before clinical changes appear. Cumulative exposure to marginal irritants causes most cases of occupational irritant dermatitis and is a major skin problem in the workplace.

Important factors to consider in irritant dermatitis are the nature of the substance such as pH, solubility, physical state, concentration, duration of contact, and host and environmental factors. Despite the prevalence of irritant dermatitis, much is unknown about the precise mechanisms of how irritants disturb the skin. Several points merit emphasis:

- Contact dermatitis can occur from contact with several marginal irritants, the effects of which are cumulative.
- Cumulative irritant contact dermatitis can lead to skin fatigue, a condition in which even mild substances can irritate the skin, or to "hardening," in which the skin eventually accommodates repeated exposure to an offending agent.
- The clinical and histological differentiation of irritant and allergic contact dermatitis is often difficult or impossible.

- Constant exposure to irritants impairs the barrier function of the skin and allows penetration of potential allergens.
- Irritant and allergic contact dermatitis often coexist in the same patient.

Allergic Contact Dermatitis

Some industrial chemicals are potential contact allergens. The incidence of allergic contact dermatitis varies depending on the nature of the materials handled, predisposing factors, and the ability of the physician to accurately use and interpret patch tests. Allergic contact dermatitis, in contrast with primary irritation, is a form of cell-mediated, antigen–antibody immune reaction. Sensitizing agents differ from primary irritants in their mechanism of action and their effect on the skin. Unless they are concomitant irritants, most sensitizers do not produce a skin reaction on first contact. Following this sensitization phase of one week or longer, further contact with the same or a cross-reacting substance on the same or other parts of the body results in an acute dermatitis (elicitation phase).

Other essential points about allergic contact dermatitis include the following:

- As a general rule, a key difference between irritation and allergic contact dermatitis is that an irritant usually affects many workers, whereas a sensitizer generally affects few. Exceptions exist with potent sensitizers, such as poison oak oleoresin or epoxy resin and components.
- Differentiation of marginal irritants from skin allergens also can be difficult. Marginal irritants may require repeated or prolonged exposure before a dermatitis appears; allergic contact dermatitis also may not develop for months or years after exposure to an agent.
- Many skin sensitizers, such as chromates, nickel salts, and epoxy resin hardeners, are also primary irritants.
- Sensitization (allergy) can be produced or maintained by allergens such as nickel, chromates, formaldehyde, and turpentine in minute amounts and in concentrations insufficient to irritate the nonallergic skin.
- Cross-sensitivity is an important phenomenon in which a worker sensitized to one chemical also reacts to one or more closely related chemicals. Numerous examples exist: rhus antigens such as poison oak, ivy, sumac, Japanese lacquer, mango, and cashew nutshell oil; aromatic amines such as p-phenylenediamine, procaine, benzocaine, and p-aminobenzoic acid (sunscreens); and perfume or flavoring agents such as balsam of Peru, benzoin, cinnamates, and vanilla.
- Systemic contact dermatitis is a widespread, eczematous contact-like dermatitis that can result from oral or parenteral (intravenous or intramuscular) administration of an allergen to which a worker is sensitized topically (such as oral administration of sulfonamides and thiazide diuretics in patients with contact allergy to p-phenylenediamine and benzocaine-containing topical anesthetics).
- Patch testing is used to differentiate allergic contact dermatitis from irritant dermatitis. Sine qua non for the diagnosis of allergic contact dermatitis is a properly performed and interpreted positive patch test.

The most common contact sensitizers in the general population have been determined from clinical experience and from published studies on the prevalence of positive patch test reactions in dermatology departments. Major sensitizers include the following:

- Rhus (poison oak, ivy, and sumac)
- p-phenylenediamine
- nickel
- rubber chemicals
- quaternium-15 (a formaldehyde-releasing preservative)
- topical medicaments containing benzocaine, antihistamines such as diphenhydramine, and antibiotics such as neomycin and bacitracin

Additional industrial allergens include the following:

- chromates
- plastics and adhesives (especially epoxy and acrylic resins)
- formaldehyde and other preservatives
- mercury
- cobalt

Contact Urticaria

Contact urticaria is characterized by the appearance of urticaria, or hives, usually within minutes at the site of contact with a variety of substances. There are three types: immunologic (ICU), nonimmunologic (NICU), and contact urticaria of uncertain mechanism. The nonimmunologic type is most common; causes include substances that release histamine or other vasoactive substances, such as plants (nettles), insects (caterpillars and moths), cobalt chloride, cinnamic aldehyde, nicotinic acid esters (trafuril), and dimethyl sulfoxide. Causes of contact urticaria of uncertain type include certain types of solar urticaria (caused by sun exposure) and aquagenic urticaria (caused by water exposure). Examples of agents that may produce immunologic contact urticaria include penicillin, nitrogen mustard, neomycin, and the insect repellant diethyl toluamide (DEET).

The paradigm for the immunologic type of contact urticaria is natural rubber latex (NRL) allergy, a significant medical and occupational health problem. Most affected patients have contact urticaria, but others have experienced generalized urticaria, angioedema, asthma, and anaphylaxis (including vascular collapse and death). Terminology established by the Latex Task Force of the Health Industry Manufacturers Association identified natural latex as the milky fluid of agriculture origin produced by the *Hevea brasiliensis* tree. NRL refers to products made directly from water-based, natural latex emulsions. Gloves, balloons, tourniquets, and condoms are examples of products produced by means of dipping porcelain forms into liquid latex. Dry rubber latex refers to products made from processed, dried, or milled sheets of latex rubber. Syringe plungers, vial stoppers, and baby-bottle nipples are examples of extruded or compression-molded dry products. Most immediate-type reactions result from exposure to NRL products that are dipped. Dry-molded rubber products contain lower residual latex protein levels or have less easily extracted proteins than do dipped products produced from NRL. This may explain the relative lack of reports of NRL allergy in the tire industry.

Latex allergy is an immunoglobulin (Ig) E-mediated hypersensitivity to one or more of a number of proteins present in raw or cured NRL. Individuals at highest risk are patients with spina bifida (30 to 65 percent prevalence), health care workers, and other workers with significant NRL exposure. Most reported series of occupational cases involve health care workers, affecting 5 to 11 percent of those studied. Studies of populations of non–health care workers are infrequent and include kitchen workers; cleaners; rubber band, surgical glove, and latex doll-manufacturing workers; and workers in miscellaneous other occupations. Predisposing risk factors are hand eczema, allergic rhinitis, allergic conjunctivitis, or asthma in individuals who frequently wear NRL gloves, mucosal exposure to NRL, and multiple surgical procedures.

The spectrum of clinical signs ranges from contact urticaria, generalized urticaria, allergic rhinitis, allergic conjunctivitis, angioedema, and asthma to anaphylaxis. The majority of cases involve reactions to NRL gloves—that is, donning NRL gloves or being examined by individuals wearing NRL gloves. Reactions from other medical and non-medical NRL devices have occurred; these include balloons, rubber bands, condoms, vibrators, dental dams, anesthesia equipment, and toys for animals and children. The route of exposure to NRL proteins is important, and it includes direct contact with intact or inflamed skin and mucosal exposure (such as inhalation of powder from NRL gloves), especially in medical facilities and in operating rooms.

NRL allergy is sometimes associated with allergic reactions to fruit, especially bananas, kiwi, chestnuts, and avocados. This results from cross-reactivity between proteins in NRL and those found in the fruits. Symptoms range from oral itching and angioedema to asthma, gastrointestinal upset, and anaphylaxis.

Diagnosis of NRL allergy is strongly suggested by obtaining a history of angioedema of the lips when inflating balloons and/or itching, burning, urticaria, or anaphylaxis when donning gloves; when undergoing surgical, medical, and dental procedures; or following exposure to condoms or other NRL devices. Diagnosis is confirmed by either a positive wear-or-use test with NRL gloves, a valid positive intracutaneous prick test to NRL, or a positive serum RAST to NRL. Severe allergic reactions have occurred from prick-and-wear tests; epinephrine and resuscitation equipment free of NRL should be available during these procedures.

Hyposensitization to NRL is not yet possible, and NRL avoidance and substitution are imperative. Because many patients with NRL allergy are atopic with hand eczema, immediate allergic symptoms, or both, the most important issues for physicians are accurate diagnosis, appropriate treatment, and counseling. Dermatologic evaluation to exclude other causes of hand eruptions and allergy or pulmonary evaluation of associated rhinitis, conjunctivitis, asthma, angioedema, or anaphylaxis is important as well.

Prevention and control of NRL allergy includes latex avoidance in health care settings for affected workers and patients. Substitute synthetic non-NRL gloves and other personal protective equipment, such as surgical masks and disposable respirators, should be available; in many cases, low-allergen NRL gloves should be worn by co-workers to accommodate those with NRL allergy in order to minimize symptoms and to decrease induction of NRL allergy. Synthetic non-NRL gloves include those made of polyvinyl chloride (vinyl), block polymers (styrene-butadiene-styrene and styrene-ethylene-butylene-styrene), chloroprene (Neoprene®), polyurethane, synthetic polyisoprene, and nitrile.

Allergen content of gloves should be requested from manufacturers and suppliers; lists of glove allergen levels have also been published. Patients with NRL allergy should obtain Medic-Alert bracelets; inform health care providers of their diagnosis; and be given lists of substitute gloves, other non-NRL devices, potentially allergenic fruits, a latex-safe anesthesia protocol, and occult sources of NRL exposure such as dog and child toys and dental prophylaxis cups. Some of this information is available in published sources and from latex allergy support groups. One group is ALAA (American Latex Allergy Association) (www.latexallergyresources.org). The National Institute for Occupational Safety and Health (NIOSH) has issued a review on preventing allergic reactions to NRL in the workplace. Other information on latex allergy is available from the Spina Bifida Association of America (www.spinabifidaassociation.org).

The Food and Drug Administration (FDA) issued a rule requiring labeling of NRL devices and outlining substitute language to replace the *hypoallergenic* label. The old hypoallergenic label was designed to prevent Type IV allergic contact dermatitis rather than Type I NRL allergy. Because these hypoallergenic gloves were still made of NRL, they caused adverse reactions in some patients with NRL allergy.

Photosensitivity

Photosensitivity is the capacity of an organ or organism or certain chemicals and plants to be stimulated to activity by light or to react to light. Two types are generally recognized: photoirritation (phototoxicity) and photoallergy. Photoirritation, like primary irritation, can affect anyone. Photoallergens, like contact allergens, involve immune mechanisms and affect fewer people.

Industrial sources of photosensitivity can be obscure, requiring careful epidemiological and clinical investigation, including photopatch testing. An example is phototoxicity from p-aminobenzoic acid used in the manufacture of ultraviolet-cured inks. Medical personnel may be occupationally exposed to photosensitizing drugs. Other workers who can have contact with topical photosensitizers include outdoor and field workers (photosensitizers in plants and chemicals); machinists (antimicrobials in metalworking fluids); pharmaceutical workers (drugs, dyes, and fragrances); and oil field, road construction, and coal tar workers (tars, pitch, and other hydrocarbons).

Photoirritants are identified by knowledge of the chemical, exposure history (typically UVA), and sometimes morphology. Photoallergy, or contact dermatitis, diagnosis is aided by photopatch testing (typically with UVA).

Occupational Acne

Occupational acne results from contact with petroleum and its derivatives, coal tar products, or certain halogenated aromatic hydrocarbons (Table 3–C). The eruption can be mild, involving localized, exposed, or covered areas of the body, or severe and generalized, with acne involving almost every follicular orifice. Chloracne, in addition to being a difficult cosmetic and therapeutic problem, is of considerable concern because it is caused by highly toxic chemicals.

Occupational acne is seen most commonly in workers exposed to cutting oils in the machine tool trades. The insoluble (straight) oils are the most common cause (Figure 3–6). Oil acne typically starts as comedones and an inflammatory folliculitis affecting the tops of the hands and extensor surfaces of the forearms. However, covered areas of the body (thighs, lower abdomen, and buttocks) can be affected by contact with oil-saturated clothing. Although the lesions are commonly called oil boils, they almost never develop from bacteria present in the oils.

Any form of occupational acne or preexisting or coexisting acne vulgaris (nonoccupational) can be aggravated by heat (acne tropicalis and aestivalis); constant friction (acne mechanica), with acne localized to the forehead (hard

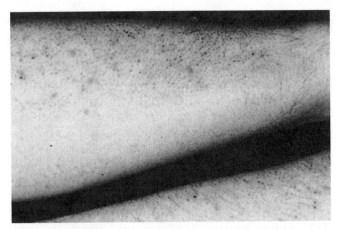

Figure 3–6. Acneiform disorder, shown on this worker's forearm, is often caused by exposure to cutting oils. Lack of splashguards and poor personal hygiene can be factors.

hat), waist (belt), or other area; excessive scrubbing with harsh soaps (acne detergicans); cosmetics (acne cosmetica); pomade and Vaseline® (pomade acne); and topical corticosteroids (steroid rosacea). Acneiform eruptions from systemic medication containing bromides, iodides, and corticosteroids and the syndrome of senile or solar comedones on the face are also to be considered in the differential diagnoses.

Coal tar oils, creosote, and pitch can produce extensive acne in coal tar facility workers, roofers, and road maintenance and construction workers. Comedones are typical of this form of acne. Phototoxic reactions involving both the skin and eye (keratoconjunctivitis) can complicate the picture and produce coal tar melanosis and exacerbations of the acne. Pitch keratoses and acanthomas (precancerous and cancerous skin lesions) can develop later.

Certain halogenated aromatic chemicals (some chloronaphthalenes, PCBs and dibenzofurans, dibenzo-p-dioxins, and chlorobenzenes) are the most potent acnegens and are among the most toxic environmental chemicals. These chemicals can produce chloracne, a type of acne that is often

TABLE 3–C	Some Causes of Occupational Acne
Petroleum and its derivatives (crude oil and fractious cutting oils)	
Coal tar products (coal tar oils, pitch, creosote)	
Halogenated aromatic compounds (chloracnegens)	
Polyhalogenated naphthalene	
Polyhalogenated biphenyls (PCBs, PBBs)	
Polyhalogenated dibenzofurans	
Contaminants of polychlorophenol compounds, especially herbicides (2,4,5-T and pentachlorophenol) and herbicide intermediates (trichlorophenols), e.g., dioxin	
Contaminants of 3,4-dichloroaniline and related herbicides (Propanil and Methazole) azo- and azoxybenzenes	

resistant to therapy, and can be accompanied by systemic toxicity. Chloracne is one of the most sensitive indicators of biological response to these chemicals and acts as a marker of the medical and environmental impact of contamination of technical-grade chemicals with potentially highly toxic intermediates.

Pigmentary Abnormalities

Pigmentary abnormalities can result from exposure to certain chemical, physical, and biological agents. They not only represent difficult cosmetic problems, but can indicate exposure to potential systemic toxins. Differentiation from various nonoccupational, genetic, metabolic, endocrine, inflammatory, and neoplastic pigmentary conditions is necessary.

Hyperpigmentation

Hyperpigmentation (skin darkening) can follow almost any dermatitis as a postinflammatory event. Chemical photosensitizers (tar, pitch, plant, and drug photosensitizers), physical agents (ultraviolet light and thermal and ionizing radiation), and trauma (chronic itching) are common causes. Exposure to certain chemicals (arsenic and acnegenic aromatic hydrocarbons) can also cause hyperpigmentation.

Hypopigmentation

Pigment loss, or hypopigmentation, can also follow inflammation (Figure 3–7). Physical or chemical damage to the skin from thermal, ultraviolet, radiation, or chemical burns may cause not only loss of pigment, but also scarring. These changes usually pose no diagnostic problem.

However, pigment loss from certain chemical exposures can be difficult to differentiate from idiopathic vitiligo (a patchy loss of pigment from otherwise healthy skin). Occupational leukoderma (white skin) of this type was first reported from exposure to monobenzyl ether of hydroquinone (agerite alba), once used as an antioxidant in industrial gloves. Several phenolic compounds have caused leukoderma among exposed workers. Sources include hospital and industrial germicidal cleaners, metalworking fluids, oils, latex glues, inks, paints, and plastic resins. Table 3–D lists some of these compounds. These chemicals interfere with melanin pigment biosynthesis, destruction, or both. Hands and forearms are usually affected, although covered parts can also be affected, possibly from ingestion or inhalation of the chemicals.

Sweat-Induced Reactions, Including Miliaria and Intertrigo

Miliaria (prickly heat or heat rash) results from obstruction of sweat ducts and is an inflammatory reaction to retained extravasated sweat. It is a common reaction of people who

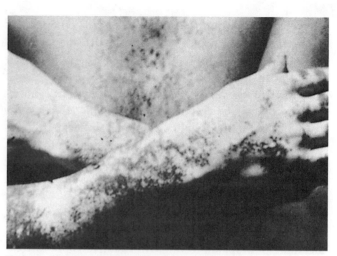

Figure 3–7. Pigment loss in the skin (hypopigmentation) was caused by exposure to a known depigmenting chemical.

sweat profusely while exposed to heat. The lesions consist of pinpoint to pinhead-sized papules and vesicles (blisters) on the chest; back; and submammary, inguinal, and axillary folds.

Intertrigo represents maceration that occurs on apposing skin surfaces and is a scaling, erythematous eruption. Superimposed yeast or superficial fungal infection can also be present. Obesity and heat exposure are aggravating factors.

Cutaneous Tumors

Neoplastic growths of the skin are classified as benign lesions, precancers, or cancers. Benign viral warts (*verrucae vulgaris*) are more common among workers in certain occupations associated with wet work (such as butchers). Keratoacanthomas can be occupationally associated with exposure to sunlight or contact with various tars, pitch, and oils (pitch warts and acanthomas). Although classed as benign lesions, keratoacanthomas can be difficult to differentiate clinically and pathologically from squamous cell carcinoma. Pitch and tar warts (keratoses) and acanthomas can be premalignant lesions.

TABLE 3–D	Some Chemicals Producing Occupational Leukoderma
Monobenzyl ether of hydroquinone	
Monomethyl ether of hydroquinone	
Hydroquinone	
P-tertiary amyl phenol	
P-tertiary butyl phenol	
P-tertiary butyl catchol	
Alkyl phenols	
Selected other phenolic compounds	

Excessive exposure to sunlight is the most common cause of precancers and cancers in human skin. Additionally, inorganic arsenic compounds, polycyclic aromatic hydrocarbon compounds associated with asphalt, paraffins, coal tars, oils (creosote, shale, hydrogenated, petroleum, insoluble cutting, and mineral), and ionizing radiation can cause cancer of the skin and other organs. Precancerous actinic keratoses (caused by rays of light that produce chemical effects) appear in sun-exposed areas, can be extensive in workers with outdoor jobs (such as utility line workers, agricultural workers, construction workers, ranchers, fishermen, and sailors), and can progress to squamous cell and basal cell carcinomas. Such workers often have other signs of sun exposure from solar degeneration of collagen, including hyperpigmentation, thin and wrinkled skin, and telangiectasia (a spider-like growth composed of blood or lymph vessels). Epidemiological studies show that sunlight can also be a factor in the increased incidence of malignant melanoma. Skin biopsy is absolutely essential for the diagnosis of all types of skin cancer.

Ulcerations

Tissue injury on a skin or mucous membrane surface can result in erythema, blisters, or pustules, which may result in necrosis and ulceration. This can be caused by trauma; thermal or chemical burns; cutaneous infection; and a number of chemicals, including certain chromium, beryllium, nickel, and platinum salts, calcium oxide, calcium arsenate, calcium nitrate, and strong acids. Cutaneous tumors can also ulcerate. Self-inflicted or unintentionally produced skin disorders commonly appear as ulcerations.

Granulomas

Granulomas represent chronic, indolent areas of inflammation and can be localized or generalized. Scar formation often results. Causes include a variety of bacterial (anthrax), mycologic (sporotrichosis), viral (herpes simplex), parasitic (protothecosis), and botanical (thorns) sources. Other causes include minerals (silica, beryllium, zirconium), bone, chitin, and grease.

Alopecia

Alopecia (absence of hair from the skin areas where it is normally present) has many causes: trauma, cutaneous and systemic disease, drugs, chemicals, and other physical factors (including ionizing radiation). Industrially caused hair loss is rare, and the differential diagnosis is long. Chemicals or medications can cause extensive hair shedding by precipitating telogen (resting hair) development, directly poisoning the anagen (growing) hair, or acting in other unknown ways. Other alopecia-producing chemicals include thallium (rodent poison) and boric acid. Medications, primarily cancer chemotherapeutic agents, can precipitate anagen hair loss (immediate loss). Drugs capable of causing telogen hair loss (delayed loss) include oral contraceptives, anticoagulants, propranolol, and thallium.

Nail Disease

Chronic inflammation of the folds of tissue surrounding the fingernail (paronychia), with associated nail dystrophy, is a common occupational disorder associated with wet work (bartenders, maintenance workers, and kitchen workers). This disorder is commonly associated with *Candida* species, *Pseudomonas* species, other bacteria, or dermatophyte fungi.

Nail discoloration can result from exposure to chemicals such as bichromates (accompanied by nail dystrophy), formaldehyde, certain amines, picric acid, nicotine, mercury, resorcinol, or iodochlorhydroxyquin (Vioform). Nail dystrophy can also accompany exposure to a number of chemicals, especially solvents; it is also caused by trauma or occupational marks in certain occupations such as weaving and the fur industry. Nail dystrophy can also be secondary to Raynaud's phenomenon, vibratory trauma, and acroosteolysis.

Systemic Intoxication

A number of chemicals with or without direct toxic effect on the skin itself can be absorbed through it and cause (or contribute to, when a substance is also inhaled) systemic intoxication; the severity depends on the amount absorbed. A partial list of substances and their systemic effects includes the following:

- Aniline (red blood cells and methemoglobinemia)
- Benzidine (carcinoma of bladder)
- Carbon disulfide (nervous system and psychological disturbances)
- Carbon tetrachloride (central nervous system, or CNS, depression; hepatotoxicity; nephrotoxicity)
- Dioxane (CNS depression)
- Ethylene glycol ethers (CNS depression; pulmonary edema; hepatotoxicity; nephrotoxicity)
- Halogenated naphthalenes, diphenyls, and dioxins (neurotoxicity and hepatotoxicity; altered metabolism)
- Methyl butyl ketone (CNS depression; peripheral neuritis)
- Organophosphate pesticides (inhibition of enzyme cholinesterase with cardiovascular, gastrointestinal, neuromuscular, and pulmonary toxicity)
- Tetrachloroethylene (CNS depression; suspected carcinogen)
- Toluene (CNS depression)

Chemicals whose absorption may contribute to the total exposure are designated with a "Skin" notation in the American Conference of Governmental Industrial Hygienists (ACGIH) book, Threshold Limit Values for Chemical Substances and Physical Agents (TLVs®) and Biological Exposure Indices (BEIs®). (Also see Appendix B.) More information can also be found in the ACGIH publication *Documentation of the Threshold Limit Values and Biological Exposure Indices,* 7th ed. Contact the ACGIH for details. Cutaneous absorption here refers to absorption by skin, mucous membranes, and eyes through either airborne or direct contact.

BURNS

Because all burns have essentially the same features, they are usually classified by degree according to depth of injury as first-, second-, or third-degree. The main types of burns are as follows:

- explosion burns, usually affecting exposed areas (hands, face)
- steam burns, often superficial on exposed areas (more serious if with eye or respiratory contact)
- hot-water burns, often leading to blistering depending on water temperature; more severe if victim is wearing heavy, permeable clothing
- molten-metal burns, often affecting lower limbs; often extremely deep with metal encrusted in skin
- hot-solid burns, normally not extensive; can be very deep
- flame burns, almost always deep and often extensive, with the type of clothing being a major factor in severity
- electricity and radiant energy burns, almost always severe, often with complications; ordinary clothing offers little protection

Nature of Chemical Burns

Burns caused by chemicals are similar to those caused by heat. In fact, some chemicals, such as sodium hydroxide, cause not only chemical burns because of their caustic action, but also thermal burns because of the heat they can generate when they react with moisture in the skin. After patients with chemical burns have been given emergency first aid, their treatment is the same as for patients with thermal burns.

Both thermal burns and chemical burns destroy body tissue. Some chemicals continue to cause damage until reaction with body tissue is complete or until the chemical is washed away by prolonged flushing with water. Strong alkalis penetrate tissue deeply, and strong acids corrode tissue with a characteristic stain.

Many concentrated chemical solutions have an affinity for water. When they come in contact with body tissue, they withdraw water from it so rapidly that the original chemical composition of the tissue (and hence the tissue itself) is destroyed. In fact, a strong caustic may dissolve even dehydrated animal tissue. The more concentrated the solution, the more rapid is the destruction.

Sulfuric, nitric, and hydrofluoric acids are the most corrosive of the inorganic acids—even more corrosive than hydrochloric acid. Some chemicals, such as phenol, are doubly hazardous. In addition to being highly corrosive, they are poisonous when absorbed through the skin. The severity of chemical burns depends on the

- corrosiveness of the chemical;
- concentration of the chemical;
- temperature of the chemical or its solution; and
- duration of the contact.

The first three factors are determined by the nature of the chemical and the requirements of the process in which it is used. The fourth factor, duration of the contact, can be controlled by the proper first-aid treatment administered without delay.

Classification of Burns

Burns are commonly classified as first, second, or third degree. Second-degree burns may be further classified as superficial or deep dermal. However, for purposes of this chapter, the common classifications of first, second, and third degree are adequate and are described here.

First-Degree Burns

First-degree burns are characterized by redness and heat accompanied by itching, burning, and considerable pain. Only the outer layer of the epidermis is involved.

Second-Degree Burns

Second-degree burns are highly painful and involve deeper portions of the epidermis and the upper layer of dermis. Generally, the skin is mottled red with a moist surface and blisters form. Such burns are easily infected.

Third-Degree Burns

Third-degree burns are severe forms of injury, involving loss of skin and deeper subcutaneous tissue. They are pearly-white or charred in appearance, and the surface is dry. They are not exceedingly painful at first because nerve endings are usually impaired or destroyed.

Special Types of Burns

Cement and hydrofluoric acid deserve special mention. There have been many reports of severe burns from kneeling in wet cement or from wet cement becoming trapped inside boots. Pressure and occlusion are important factors, as well as the need to work fast with premixed cement, which can encourage prolonged contact. Symptoms may be delayed, so workers must be alert to the danger. Adherent cement should be removed by copious and gentle irrigation with water.

Hydrofluoric acid is a strong acid widely used in industry. Hydrofluoric acid burns are characterized by intense pain (often delayed) and progressive deep tissue destruction (necrosis). Immediate treatment with topical magnesium sulfate or benzalkonium chloride and calcium gluconate gels and injections is recommended.

Complications of Burns

The dangers to life that result from extensive burns are infection (which causes most burn complications), loss of body fluid (plasma or lymph from the blood), and subsequent shock. Finally, the functional, cosmetic, and psychological sequelae may require the full attention of a rehabilitation team.

DIAGNOSIS

Anyone who works can develop a skin disorder, but not all skin disorders occurring in the workplace are occupational. Arriving at the correct diagnosis is not generally difficult, but it is more than a routine exercise. The following criteria are generally used.

Appearance of the Lesion

The dermatosis should fall into one of the accepted clinical types with respect to its morphological appearance.

Sites of Involvement

Common sites are the hands, wrists, and forearms, but other areas can be affected. Widespread dermatitis can indicate heavy exposure to dust because of inadequate protective clothing or poor hygiene habits.

History and Course of the Disease

A thorough and pertinent clinical history is the most important aspect in diagnosis of occupational dermatoses. This includes a description of the eruption, response to therapy, medical history and review of systems, a detailed work history (description of present and past jobs, moonlighting, preventive measures, cleansers, and barrier creams), and a detailed description of nonoccupational exposures. The behavior of the eruption on weekends, vacation, and sick leave can be very helpful in assessing the occupational component.

Ancillary Diagnostic Tests

When indicated, selected laboratory tests and office procedures are used for detecting skin disorders. These may include direct microscopic examination and bacterial and fungal cultures of the skin, skin biopsy for histopathological diagnosis, and patch tests and photopatch tests to detect any occupational or nonoccupational allergens and photosensitizers. Patch tests should be performed by physicians experienced with the procedure.

Treatment

Therapy of occupational skin disorders is essentially no different from that of the same nonoccupational disorder. However, two key factors are often overlooked when a worker's skin clears and he or she returns to work: identifying the cause of the disease and preventing a recurrence. Patients with skin disorders not responding to initial treatment should be referred for specialty evaluation.

WORKERS' COMPENSATION

State workers' compensation laws are no-fault statutes that hold employers responsible for the cost of occupational injury and disease claims while guaranteeing benefits to covered workers who meet the laws' requirements. All states now recognize responsibility for occupational diseases, and health professionals should become familiar with their own state workers' compensation laws and regulations. The American Medical Association's *Guides to the Evaluation of Permanent Impairment* is mandated, recommended, or often used by authorities in 40 of 53 jurisdictions (38 states and 2 territories). In general, three types of payment may be made when a claim is approved: temporary total disability payments to compensate for lost wages, payment of medical bills, and payment for permanent partial or permanent total disability.

Most claims based on occupational skin disease involve temporary total or permanent partial disability. Temporary total disability usually ceases when the patient has reached maximum medical improvement, has a valid job offer within his or her physical capabilities, or actually returns to work. Some states allow third-party liability suits arising out of workers' compensation cases.

EVALUATION OF OCCUPATIONAL DERMATOSES FOR WORKERS' COMPENSATION

In the evaluation of workers' compensation cases, the key elements are diagnosis, causation, impairment, and conclusions and recommendations.

Diagnosis

An accurate diagnosis of the claimant's condition is imperative. This often involves obtaining a detailed history of the present illness; reviewing work exposures, including Safety Data Sheets; and, whenever possible, visiting the workplace. Evaluation of the cutaneous findings should include an examination of the skin and skin biopsies, cultures, patch testing, or other ancillary tests if warranted. If diagnosis is in doubt, specialized consultation is warranted.

Causation

Determination of the cause-and-effect relationship between a skin disorder and an occupation is not always clear-cut. Questions to be considered include the following:

- Is the clinical appearance compatible with an occupational dermatosis?
- Are there workplace exposures to chemical, physical, mechanical, or biologic agents that may affect the skin?
- Is the anatomic distribution of the eruption compatible with job exposure? Many occupational dermatoses involve the hands.
- Is the temporal relationship between exposure and onset consistent with an occupational skin disease?
- Have nonoccupational exposures been excluded as causes?
- Does the dermatitis improve away from work exposure to the suspected agent(s)?
- Do patch or provocation tests identify a probable cause?

A "yes" answer to at least four of these questions is generally adequate to establish probable cause.

Impairment Evaluation

As a prelude to impairment evaluation, the physician must determine the impact of the medical condition on life activities and the stability of the condition. If the worker has a new or recent onset condition that significantly precludes working on the current job, then temporary total impairment may exist, and an appropriate amount of time away from work may be warranted under most workers' compensation laws. Unduly restrictive limitations, such as avoiding all contact with a particular substance, may jeopardize a worker's job; before writing such recommendations, the physician should generally discuss them with the worker and employer.

The AMA's *Guides to the Evaluation of Permanent Impairment* are used to evaluate *permanent* impairment of any body system(s), from both occupational and nonoccupational causes; they are not designed for use in evaluating *temporary* impairment. They are guidelines—not absolute recommendations—and are designed to bring objectivity to an area of great subjectivity. The *Guides* include clinically sound and reproducible criteria useful to physicians, attorneys, and adjudicators. They espouse the philosophy that all

physical and mental impairments affect the whole person. A 95 to 100 percent whole person impairment is considered to represent almost total impairment, a state that is approaching death. Before using the *Guides* for evaluating cutaneous impairment, the health professional should read the two introductory chapters, the glossary and then Chapter 8, The Skin. Chapter 2, Practical Applications of the *Guides*, lists a suggested outline for a medical evaluation report.

Permanent impairment of the skin is defined as "any dermatologic abnormality or loss that persists after medical treatment and rehabilitation and that is unlikely to change significantly in the next year, with or without medical treatment, and affects ADLs" (p. 159, AMA *Guides to the Evaluation of Permanent Impairment*, 6th ed., 2007). The *Guides* popularized the concept that impairment is a medical issue assessed by medical means, in contrast to disability, which is a nonmedical assessment generally determined by adjudicating authorities. *Disability* is defined as an "alteration of an individual's capacity to meet personal, social, or occupational demands or to meet statutory or regulatory requirements because of an impairment" (p. 8, AMA *Guides to the Evaluation of Permanent Impairment*, 6th ed., 2007). It is important to remember that an impaired person is not necessarily disabled. The classic example often cited is that of two people who lose the distal portion of the phalanx of the same finger. Although impairment for both people is the same, disability is likely to be greater for a concert pianist than for a bank president.

In the 2007 edition of the AMA chapter on the skin, there are still five classes of impairment, but the new edition ranges from 0 to 58 percent impairment, as compared with 0 to 95 percent impairment in previous editions of the *Guides* (Table 3-E). The reasoning for this change is that "while people with severe disease are likely to experience higher levels of impairment than this rating...it would be expected that other body systems are also involved...[T]he rater should evaluate the extent of whole person impairment related to each system" (p. 161, AMA *Guides to the Evaluation of Permanent Impairment*, 6th ed., 2007).

The impact of the disorder on the activities of daily living should be the major consideration in determining the class of impairment. The frequency and intensity of signs and symptoms and the frequency and complexity of medical treatment should guide the selection of an appropriate impairment percentage and estimate within any class.

The activities of daily living (ADLs) include self-care and personal hygiene, communication, physical activity, sensory function, hand functions (grasping, holding, pinching, percussive movements, and sensory discrimination), travel, sexual function, and sleep. Other examples of specific ADLs are listed in the glossary of the *Guides*.

TABLE 3–E	Criteria for Rating Permanent Impairment Due to Skin Disorders				
Class	*Class 0*	*Class 1*	*Class 2*	*Class 3*	*Class 4*
Whole Person Impairment Rating		*1–9%*	*11–27%*	*30–42%*	*45–58%*
History[a,c]	Skin disorders signs present in past but are currently present <1% of time[b]	Skin disorder signs and symptoms consistent with table in guide are present 1–30% of the time[b]	Skin disorder signs and symptoms consistent with table in guide are present >30–60% of the time[b]	Skin disorder signs and symptoms consistent with table in guide are present >60–90% of the time[b]	Skin disorder signs and symptoms consistent with table in guide are present >90% of the time[b]
	and	**and**	**and**	**and**	**and**
	No medication is necessary	May intermittently require treatment with topical medications[a]	Often require treatment with topical or systemic medications	Require intermittent to constant treatment with topical or systemic medication	Require treatment with topical or systemic medications on a regular basis
	and	**and**	**and**	**and**	**and**
	There is essentially no interference with activities of daily living (ADLs)	When signs and symptoms are present, there is minimal interference with ADLs	When signs and symptoms are present, there is mild interference with some ADLs	When signs and symptoms are present, there is moderate interference with ADLs	There is severe interference with most ADLs to the extent that confinement may be required. All cancers not in remission, other than basal cell carcinoma, automatically receive 58% combined with all other systemic or musculoskeletal impairments or 100% terminal

[a] Determine the patient's class using the history focusing on medically documented interference with ADLs. Objective exam findings must have been documented by a physician on at least one occasion to perform a rating.

[b] Scars are present permanently and thus the time element is not used as part of the rating.

[c] Any facial scarring should be graded according to Table 11–15 in the *Guides* and then combined with other impairments from this chapter when applicable.

Source: Guides to the Evaluation of Permanent Impairment, 6th ed. Copyright 2007. American Medical Association. All rights reserved. Reprinted with permission.

The examples within each class are important guides for the first-time user. It is critically important to remember that impairment is not determined by diagnosis alone, but also by the effect of the disease on ADLs—along with the frequency and intensity of disease and the frequency and complexity of therapy. Most cutaneous impairment falls within the first three classes ranging from 0 to 42 percent.

Unique to the *Guides'* skin chapter are the discussions of pruritus (itching), disfigurement, scars and skin grafts, and patch testing. Itching is evaluated by determining its interference with the ADLs and the extent to which the description of pruritus is supported by objective findings such as lichenification, excoriation, or hyperpigmentation. Disfigurement usually involves no loss of body function and little or no effect on the ADLs. Disfigurement may well impair self-image, cause lifestyle alteration, and result in social rejection. These changes are best evaluated in accordance with the criteria in the chapter on mental and behavioral conditions.

Evaluation of scars and skin grafts is made according to the impact on ADLs. When impairment is based on peripheral nerve dysfunction or loss of range of motion, it may be evaluated according to the criteria in the chapters on the nervous system and musculoskeletal system. When properly performed and interpreted, patch tests can make a significant contribution to the diagnosis of allergic contact dermatitis.

Conclusions and Recommendations

All diagnoses should be listed and summarized. A summary statement regarding causation is then made that states whether, within a reasonable degree of medical certainty, the disease is related to work. The diagnosis should include a description of specific clinical findings related to the impairment and how they relate to and compare with the criteria in the *Guides*. The impairment value also should be explained. Specific recommendations for therapy should be included along with a brief explanation of the treatment.

Recommendations for prevention, including work restrictions, are next; possible suggestions are environmental modification (exhaust ventilation, splash guards) and personal protective equipment. The effect of future exposures to chemical, physical, and biological agents should be addressed, along with any need for rehabilitation. In conclusion, impairment evaluation is an important and sometimes daunting task for physicians evaluating workers with putative occupational diseases.

Physical Examinations

Preplacement examinations will help identify those who may be especially susceptible to skin irritations. The physician in charge of the examination should be provided with detailed information regarding the type of work for which a person is being considered.

Routine use of preplacement patch tests to determine sensitivity to various materials is not recommended. Patch tests cannot predict whether new workers will become sensitized to certain materials and develop dermatitis, but can only tell whether people who have previously worked on similar jobs are sensitized to the chemicals with which they have worked.

The occupational physician has the primary responsibility for determining whether an applicant may be predisposed to skin irritations and for recommending suitable placement on the basis of these findings. Nevertheless, considerable responsibility may also fall to the safety and personnel departments, supervisors, industrial hygienists, and other people functionally responsible for accident prevention work and control of industrial diseases.

Care should be taken in restricting people who are not specifically sensitive to the agents involved in the job just because of a history of skin trouble unless there is active skin disease at the time of placement. In many cases, the physician is limited to simply counseling the person about risk.

PREVENTION AND CONTROL

Dermatoses caused by substances or conditions present in the work environment are largely preventable, but only through the combined effort of management and workers. This type of combined effort is best demonstrated in large industrial firms. There are two major approaches to the prevention and control of occupational diseases in general and dermatoses in particular: environmental control measures and personal hygiene methods. In both cases, the key is cleanliness—both environmental and personal.

Environment

Environmental cleanliness includes good housekeeping (discussed later in this section). Its primary function in preventing industrial dermatitis (and other industrial diseases) is to reduce the possibility of contact with the offending agent.

Planning

Proper design of equipment during construction is of great importance in the reduction of dermatitis and other industrial health problems. Ventilation must meet the industry requirements. Provisions must be made for the safe handling of irritant chemicals. Pumps, valves, pipes, fittings, and the like must be maintained to eliminate (as much as possible) the contact of workers with irritants. Empty drums or bags used to transport incoming materials of a hazardous nature should be properly disposed of to prevent accidental exposure. Containers being readied for shipment should be filled in a manner that prevents contact with workers and be left clean so that truckers, warehouse workers, and others cannot accidentally contact a harmful material on contaminated surfaces. Containers with harmful materials should be labeled with proper precautions.

Process Control

Before any new process or work procedure is introduced and before new substances are adopted in an established process, an industrial hygienist or chemist should carefully consider every aspect of the operation for possible or known dermatitis hazards, including those that can be caused by trace impurities. Analyzing work procedures and processes often requires specialized equipment and techniques. Once the potential dermatitis-causing factors have been determined, suitable engineering controls can be instituted and built into the work processes or operations.

The best way of controlling dermatitis is to prevent skin contact with offending substances; if there is no exposure, there will be no dermatitis. Unfortunately, this is more easily said than done. Operations should be planned and engineered to ensure minimal worker contact with irritants and sensitizing chemicals. When possible, chemicals of low toxicity and low irritant potential should be substituted. Enclosure guards and mechanical handling facilities may be necessary when an operation involves highly corrosive materials. Operations that give off dust, fumes, or vapors need suitable exhaust ventilation to minimize exposure. Low ambient relative humidity in the workplace may cause or contribute to some occupational skin diseases.

Selection of Materials

Much can be done to minimize hazardous conditions through careful selection of materials. Dry sodium and potassium hydroxide, for example, are now available in virtually dust-free forms; for many uses, they can be purchased in solution and handled with pumps. Other products are available as prills (beads), pellets, granules, or solutions that do an adequate job and reduce the dust hazard. Concentrated solutions are also finding favor not only for safety, but also for economy in handling.

Some compounds can be successfully used when the percentage of the irritant in the compound is reduced. In other cases, a less irritating or nonirritating material, or a less sensitizing material, can be substituted. The supplier should be asked to provide a closely related and generally satisfactory substitute for the irritating or sensitizing material. Examples include substituting one germicide for another in metalworking fluids when an allergy to the first germicide is found and using vinyl gloves in place of rubber gloves if a rubber allergy is found.

Monitoring and Control Technology

In order to correctly measure and sample skin exposure to chemicals, it is important to understand the methods of such exposure. These include contact with chemicals in a container (spill), contact with contaminated surfaces (tools or rags), exposure to aerosols (fallout of mist or soluble powder), exposure to sprays (ballistic droplets versus mist), and permeation through clothing (protective and personal). Other factors to be considered in the evaluation of skin exposure to chemicals include variable deposition rates onto the body, the effect of clothing, duration of skin contact with the chemical, and time of skin retention and permeation through the skin.

Sampling Procedures

Current sampling procedures are often difficult to apply to prevention of occupational skin disease. Some exceptions include use of wipe samples for chemical analysis, hand or skin rinses, dermal dosimeters or patches, sampling cotton socks when shoe contamination is suspected, and sampling air inside a suit when the air is contaminated. Air levels of dusts and chemicals may have some limited application. The use of fluorescent tracers, fiber-optic luminescence skin monitoring, and charcoal cloth absorptive dosimeters is currently being evaluated. Color-indicator soaps have been used to detect exposure to tetryl (used in munitions facilities) and mercury. A scientific study established methods to determine relative benefits of equipment such as gloves and clothing to protect skin against styrene in a reinforced plastics facility. Another study dealt with the biological surveillance of workers exposed to dimethylformamide and the influence of skin protection on its percutaneous absorption. Standardized techniques have improved measurement of the effectiveness of protective material such as gloves and clothing against carcinogens and polychlorinated biphenyls.

Good Housekeeping

Environmental cleanliness is nothing more than good housekeeping, and it is maintained by frequently cleaning floors, walls, ceilings, windows, and machinery. Good housekeeping work is usually performed by a special maintenance group that is given direct responsibility for maintenance cleaning. In order to be effective, cleaning should be part of a plan and should be performed on schedule. The necessary equipment and materials to do the most effective job possible in a reasonable amount of time should be assigned, and housekeeping workers should be trained so that they perform their operations efficiently and safely.

Environmental cleanliness is important to maintain good morale, reduce contact dermatitis, and set an example for workers. Floors, walls, ceilings, and light fixtures should be cleaned regularly in order to maintain the best possible conditions in the facility. (The requirements of Part 1910 of the Occupational Safety and Health Standards, Section 1910.14, Sanitation, contain details on housekeeping, waste disposal, vermin control, water supply, toilet facilities, washing facilities, change rooms, consumption of food and beverages on premises, and food handling.) As pointed out in the Occupational Safety and Health Administration (OSHA) standards, washrooms, showers, toilets, and locker rooms should be kept clean and sanitary.

Many types of cleaners are available—from simple cleaning agents to complex formulations—and come in solid, liquid, or paste forms and contain cleaners and sanitizing agents using synthetic detergents, soaps, and alkaline salts in combinations. Some mixtures include sanitizing agents to help prevent the spread of bacteria, fungi, and other biological agents. Environmental cleanliness and good housekeeping are also beneficial because they set an example for the workers and encourage personal cleanliness.

Personal Cleanliness

The importance of personal cleanliness in the prevention and control of occupational dermatoses cannot be overemphasized. When investigating contact dermatitis, one should also consider the possibility of irritants contacted at home or with a hobby.

Prevention of Contact

When facility and process design cannot eliminate all contact with irritants, personal protective equipment must be used, including gloves, gauntlets, aprons, and boots made of a material that is impervious to the particular substance. These, along with goggles, afford sufficient protection in most cases. Disposable gauntlets, aprons, boots, and gloves are available, but they are more subject to tears than heavier safety gear. Other gear may provide insulation against heat or light. All personal protective equipment required for a job should be carefully maintained and replaced when it becomes worn.

In order to minimize contact with harmful agents, workers must have access to facilities for washing hands and be furnished with other means of keeping clean. It is up to the employer to provide adequate washing facilities, good cleansing materials, and education on the need for good hygiene practices. Washbasins must be well designed, conveniently located, and kept clean; otherwise, they will be used infrequently, if at all. The farther workers must walk to clean up, the less likely they are to do so. Inconveniently located washbasins invite such undesirable practices as washing with more easily available solvents, mineral oils, or industrial detergents—none of which is intended for skin cleansing. For workers to keep their skin reasonably free of injurious agents, they must use washing facilities at least four times a day: during work (before eating, drinking, smoking, or using the restroom), before lunch, after lunch, and before leaving the facility.

Those who work with toxic chemicals and radioactive substances must receive specific safe handling instructions and should take a shower after their workshift and change their clothing. Workers should be instructed in specific procedures for cleanliness. They should be told where, how, and when to wash, and they should be given sufficient time to wash, advised that they will be rated on this part of their job performance, and informed of the possible health hazards involved.

For many exposures, frequent washing alone is a successful preventive, particularly when the dermatitis is caused by plugging of the pores, as from dust. In all cases, however, the use of large quantities of water on the skin following exposure to irritants is necessary. Safety showers and eyewash fountains should be available, and flushing should continue for at least 15 minutes.

It may be advisable in some instances to use neutralizing solutions after a thorough flushing with water. However, because some neutralizing solutions are themselves irritants, they should be used only on the advice of a physician.

The type of soap used is important. Even a generally good soap can cause irritation on certain types of skin. Harsh mineral abrasives can cause dermatitis in many people. The choice of a good soap may, in some cases, involve technical considerations, which are better left to the medical department or other qualified department than to laypeople. The basic requirements of industrial skin cleansers are as follows:

- remove industrial soil quickly and efficiently
- not harmfully dehydrate, abrade, or irritate the skin by normal application

- flow easily through dispensers
- be adequately preserved against microbial contamination
  Additional desirable qualities include the following:
- have aesthetic appeal (color and odor)
- have good foaming qualities

Many cases of industrial dermatitis are reported to be caused not by substances used in the workplace, but by cleansing materials used to remove those substances. A worker may be inclined to wash the hands with the cleaning agents that are most available and work the fastest, but these are often dermatitis-producing solvents. Overuse of waterless cleansers can irritate and dry the skin. Generally, workers should apply a good hand lotion after applying waterless cleansers.

The installation in work-area washing places of soap-dispensing units containing properly selected cleansing agents has proved to be a valuable measure. Such units should be placed in convenient locations, and enough of them should be provided to accommodate all employees who are exposed to skin irritants. Where soap-dispensing units are furnished, workers should be required to use them.

Barrier Creams

A barrier cream is the least effective way of protecting skin (Figure 3–8). However, there are instances when a protective cream may be used for preventing contact with harmful agents when the face cannot be covered by a shield or gloves cannot be worn. Several companies manufacture a variety of products, each designed for a certain type of protective purpose. Thus, there are barrier creams that protect against dry substances and those that protect against wet materials. Using a barrier cream to protect against a solvent is not as effective as using an impervious glove; however, there are compounds that offer some protection against solvents when applied with sufficient frequency.

Barrier creams and lotions should be used to supplement, but not to replace, personal protective equipment. Protective barrier agents should be applied to clean skin. When skin becomes soiled, both the barrier and any soil should be washed off and the cream reapplied. Three main types of barrier creams and lotions are available.

- *Vanishing cream* usually contains soap and emollients that coat the skin and cover the pores to make subsequent cleanup easier.
- *Water-repellent cream* leaves a thin film of water-repellent substance such as lanolin, beeswax, petrolatum, or silicone on the skin and helps to prevent ready contact with water-soluble irritants such as acids, alkalis, and certain metallic acids. Remember, however, that the protection may not be complete, especially when the barrier has been on the skin for some time. Alkaline cleaning solutions

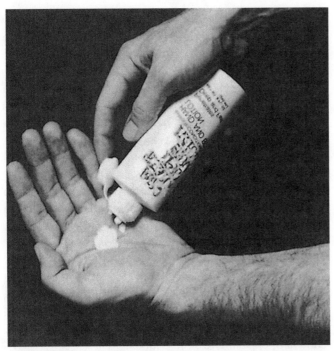

Figure 3–8. Barrier cream is applied by an employee before starting work and is washed off before lunch; it is reapplied after lunch and washed off before the worker leaves. Barrier cream is the least effective way of protecting the skin.

tend to emulsify and remove the barrier rapidly, thus leaving the skin unprotected.

• *Solvent-repellent creams* contain ingredients that repel oil and solvent. Lanolin has some oil-repellent and water-repellent properties and can be used as an ingredient. There are two types of solvent-repellent barrier preparations: one leaves ointment film and the other leaves a dry, oil-repellent film. Sodium alginates, methyl cellulose, sodium silicate, and tragacanth are commonly used. Lanolin offers some protection against oils as well as water.

In addition to these three main types, a number of specialized barriers have been developed. Creams and lotions containing ultraviolet screening and blocking agents are used to help prevent overexposure to sun or other ultraviolet sources. Others have been developed to afford protection from such diverse irritants as insects, gunfire backflash, and poison oak dermatitis.

Personal Protective Equipment
Clothing

Whenever irritating chemicals are likely to contaminate clothing, care must be taken to provide clean clothing at least daily. Because workers' families have developed contact dermatitis or chloracne from contact with clothing worn home from the job, clothing worn on the job should not be worn at home. Clothing contaminated with chem-

icals should always be thoroughly laundered before it is worn again. Clothing contaminated on the job should be changed at once.

Protective Clothing

Sometimes handling irritant, allergenic, or toxic materials cannot be avoided; in this situation, protective clothing may provide a good barrier against exposure. OSHA requirements for personal protective equipment (PPE) are described in 29 CFR Part 1910, Subpart 1, which includes general requirements on indications for use, ensuring adequacy of employee-owned equipment and safe design of PPE for the work to be performed. This section was amended in 1994 and again in 2007 and 2009. These amendments included requirements for hazard assessment and equipment selection; a ban on defective equipment; detailed training requirements; and revised sections on protection of the eyes and face (1910.133), head (1910.135), feet (1910.136), and hands (1910.138). The American National Standards Institute has also issued a new standard (ANSI/ISEA 105) for hand protection (see also "Gloves" in this chapter). The latest edition, ANSI/ISEA 105-2011, uses a numeric rating scheme for classifying hand protection against a variety of performance assessments. Perhaps the most notable update to the standard is the acceptance of different American Society for Testing and Materials (ASTM) methods for evaluating cut-resistance performance. Other protective clothing requirements appear in standards covering specific hazards (bloodborne pathogens) and specific occupations (shipyard workers). For more information, see Chapter 23, Personal Protective Equipment.

High-quality clothing should be obtained. Manufacturers provide a large selection of protective garments made of rubber, plastic film, leather, cotton, or synthetic fiber that are designed for specific purposes. For example, there is clothing that protects against acids, alkalis, and extreme exposures of heat, cold, moisture, and oils. When such garments must be worn, management should purchase them and enforce their use. Management should make sure that the clothing is mended and laundered often enough to keep it protective. If work clothes are laundered at home, the worker's other clothes may be contaminated with chemicals, glass fiber, or other dusts.

Closely woven fabrics also protect against irritating dust. Gloves and aprons of impervious materials (such as rubber or plastic) protect against liquids, vapors, and fumes. Natural rubber gloves, aprons, boots, and sleeves are impervious to water-soluble irritants but soon deteriorate if exposed to strong alkali and certain solvents.

Synthetic rubbers, such as neoprene and many of the newer plastics are more resistant to alkalis and solvents than natural rubber; however, some materials are adversely affected by chlorinated hydrocarbon solvents. The protection used should be based on the particular solvents that are used. For workers who wear rubber or plastic, the irritant will eventually penetrate and be trapped next to the skin, causing repeated exposure every time the garment is worn. So gloves should be used to protect against splashes and wet items; note, however, that gloves will not protect against immersions. Instruments or containers should be used for items that must be immersed. Reusable gloves should be washed according to the manufacturer's instructions.

Disposable paper and plastic garments can also be used for some tasks. Garments are also necessary in sterile areas to keep products from being contaminated.

Fabrics

Fabrics without coatings are generally unsuitable as protective clothing for toxic chemical exposures because they are permeable and have other weaknesses. Cotton and rayon, for instance, are degraded by acids; wool is degraded by alkalis.

Gloves

Because a high percentage of occupational contact dermatitis cases involve the hands, it is imperative for health and safety professionals to be knowledgeable about the types of glove materials available, their selection and use, and the types of adverse dermatological reactions to gloves.

Standards, guides, and rules have been published for gloves in both the United States and Europe. Categories of glove standards depend on the type of glove material used, type of work being done, and type of hazard encountered. Parameters of glove performance evaluated include physical strength, dexterity, abrasion, and heat and cold resistance. Resistance to swelling, degradation, permeation, and penetration are some of the more important chemical parameters evaluated; biological resistance to liquids and microorganisms also has been evaluated.

Another critically important factor is safety. Gloves should not be used where they may be caught in machinery, with potential for serious injury or loss of fingers or hands. Safety and health professionals should review any recommendation for glove use by health care providers who may not be familiar with a specific job.

Dermatologic reactions to gloves are classified as irritation from occlusion, friction, and maceration; allergy to glove materials and their chemical additives causing allergic contact dermatitis or allergy to certain natural rubber latex proteins causing contact urticaria; aggravation of preexisting skin diseases; and penetration of chemicals through gloves. Infrequent reactions to endotoxins and ethylene oxide and to potentially depigmenting chemical constitu-

ents of gloves have been reported. Accurate diagnosis of any suspected adverse reactions to gloves is imperative before recommending alternatives to gloves. This is especially true of workers with contact urticaria to latex (latex allergy), who may still develop a severe reaction from gloves labeled as hypoallergenic. Because so-called hypoallergenic gloves may still contain allergenic latex proteins, synthetic gloves are necessary for these workers.

Safety

It is imperative that all safety gear be worn only when safely possible. Protective clothing, especially gloves, can be caught in moving machinery, resulting in serious injury.

Responsibility for Control

Top management, the safety department, the purchasing department, the medical department or company physician, the supervisors, and the workers all have specific responsibilities for the prevention of industrial skin diseases and the control of exposure to skin irritants.

To control or eliminate dermatitis in the workplace, management should first recognize the scope of the problem and then delegate authority for action to the proper employees. When it is necessary to have more than one department work on phases of dermatitis control or elimination, the activities of those departments should be coordinated. Periodic reports on the status of the dermatitis problem within the organization should be made to management by its delegated representatives.

The industrial hygienist (or other individuals doing this type of work, such as the safety professional, safety committee members, the nurse, or the industrial hygienist) should gather information on dermatitis hazards of materials used in the plant and disseminate this information among supervisors and other operating personnel. The industrial hygienist should make periodic surveys to check for exposure to skin irritants and should suggest means to correct any hazards found.

SUMMARY

Occupational skin disorders are a significant cause of impairment and disability that, in many cases, are entirely preventable. Accurate diagnosis and a complete knowledge of the workplace are the keys to appropriate treatment and prevention. The industrial hygienist is a major player in this cooperative effort, along with the occupational physician, dermatologist, safety professional, and occupational health nurse.

Portions of this chapter in the previous editions were written by Julian B. Olishifsky, Larry L. Hipp, and James S. Taylor.

BIBLIOGRAPHY

Adams RM, ed. *Occupational Skin Diseases,* 3rd ed. Philadelphia: W.B. Saunders, 1999.

American Medical Association. *Guides to the Evaluation of Permanent Impairment,* 6th ed., R. Rondinelli, ed. Chicago: AMA, 2007.

American National Standard for Hand Protection Selection Criteria, ANSI/ISEA 105-2011. Arlington, VA: International Safety Equipment Association, 2011.

Amin S, Lahti A, Maibach HI. *Contact Urticaria Syndrome,* Boca Raton, FL: CRC Press, 1997.

Anders B, Estlander T, Wahlberg JE, et al. *Protective Gloves for Occupational Use,* 2nd ed. Boca Raton, FL: CRC Press, 2004.

Anna D, ed. *Chemical Protective Clothing,* 2nd ed. Falls Church, VA: AIHA, 2003.

Berardesca E, Lévêque J-L, Maibach HI. *Ethnic Skin and Hair.* London: Informa Healthcare, 2006.

Berardinelli S. Chemical protective gloves. *Dermatol Clin* 6:11–120, 1988.

Bronaugh RL, Maibach HI. *Percutaneous Absorption: Drugs—Cosmetics—Mechanisms—Methodology,* 3rd ed. Boca Raton, FL: CRC Press, 1999.

Bureau of Labor Statistics. *Workplace Illnesses and Injuries—2010.* Washington, DC: U.S. Department of Labor, October 2011.

Burman LG, Fryklund B. The selection and use of gloves by health care professionals. In *Protective Gloves for Occupational Use,* GA Mellstrom, JE Wahlberg, HI Maibach, eds. Boca Raton, FL: CRC Press, 1994.

Burns DA, Breathnach SM, Cox N, et al. *Rook's Textbook of Dermatology,* 8th ed. Hoboken, NJ: Wiley-Blackwell, 2010.

Centers for Disease Control. *Morbidity and Mortality Weekly Reports.* Atlanta: CDC, January 21, 1983, and September 5, 1986.

Chowdhury Mahbub MU, Maibach HI. *Latex Intolerance: Basic Science, Epidemiology, Clinical Management.* Boca Raton, FL: CRC Press, 2005.

Cohen BSM, Popendorf WA. A method for monitoring dermal exposure to volatile chemicals. *AIHA J* 50:216–223, 1989.

Fitzpatrick TB, et al. *Dermatology in General Medicine,* 8th ed. New York: McGraw-Hill, 2012.

Forsberg K, Mansdorf SZ. *Quick Selection Guide to Chemical Protective Clothing,* 5th ed. New York: John Wiley & Sons, Inc., 2007.

Frosch PJ, Menne T, Lepoitevin J-P. *Contact Dermatitis,* 4th ed. New York: Springer, 2006.

Goldsmith LA, ed. *Biochemistry and Physiology of the Skin,* 2nd ed. New York: Oxford University Press, 1991.

Hamann CP, Kick SA. Diagnosis-driven management of natural rubber latex glove sensitivity. In *Protective Gloves for Occupational Use,* GA Mellstrom, JE Wahlberg, HI Maibach, eds. Boca Raton, FL: CRC Press, 1994.

Henry N. Protective gloves for occupational use: U.S. rules, regulations, and standards. In *Protective Gloves for Occupational Use,* GA Mellstrom, JE Wahlberg, HI Maibach, eds. Boca Raton, FL: CRC Press, 1994.

Hostýnek JJ, Maibach HI. *Nickel and the Skin: Absorption, Immunology, Epidemiology, and Metallurgy.* Boca Raton, FL: CRC Press, 2002.

Hostýnek JJ, Maibach HI. *Copper and the Skin.* Boca Raton, FL: CRC Press, 2006.

Hurley HJ. Permeability of the skin. In *Dermatology,* 3rd ed., SL Moschella, HJ Hurley, eds. Philadelphia: Saunders, 1993.

Instant Gloves + CPC Data Base, Version 2.0. Blacksburg, VA: Instant Reference Sources, 1999.

International Labor Organization. *Encyclopedia of Occupational Health and Safety,* 4th ed. Geneva: ILO, 1998.

Jackson EM, Goldner R. *Irritant Contact Dermatitis.* New York: Marcel Dekker, 1990.

Jakubovic HR, Ackerman AB. Structure and Function of Skin. In *Dermatology,* 3rd ed., SL Moschella, HJ Hurley, eds. Philadelphia: Saunders, 1993.

Johansen JD, Frosch PJ, Lepoittevin J-P. *Contact Dermatitis,* 5th ed. New York: Springer, 2010.

Lachapelle J-M, Maibach HI. *Patch Testing and Prick Testing: A Practical Guide* (Official Publication of the ICDRG), 2nd ed. New York: Springer, 2009.

Leinster P. The selection and use of gloves against chemicals. In *Protective Gloves for Occupational Use,* GA Mellstrom, JE Wahlberg, HI Maibach, eds. Boca Raton, FL: CRC Press, 1994.

Loden M, Maibach HI. *Dry Skin and Moistures Chemistry and Function,* 2nd ed. In *Dermatology: Clinical & Basic Science* series. London: Informa Healthcare, 2012.

Maibach H. *Occupational and Industrial Dermatology,* 2nd ed. Chicago: Year Book Medical Publishers, 1987.

Marzulli FN, Zhai H. *Marzulli and Maibach's Dermatotoxicology,* 7th ed. Boca Raton, FL: CRC Press, 2007.

Mathias CGT, Maibach H. Perspectives in occupational dermatology. *West J Med* 137(6):486-492, December, 1982.

Mellstrom GA, Carlsson B. European standards on protective gloves. In *Protective Gloves for Occupational Use,* GA Mellstrom, JE Wahlberg, HI Maibach, eds. Boca Raton, FL: CRC Press, 1994.

Menné T, Maibach HI. *Hand Eczema,* 2nd ed. Boca Raton,

FL: CRC Press, 2000.

Mitchell JA, Rook A. *Botanical Dermatology*. Vancouver: J.A. Mitchell, 1979.

National Institute for Occupational Safety and Health. Current Intelligent Bulletin 61: *A Strategy for Assigning New NIOSH Skin Notations*. DHHS (NIOSH) Publication No. 2009–147. Cincinnati, OH: NIOSH, July 2009.

National Institute for Occupational Safety and Health. *Pocket Guide to Chemical Hazards*, pdf version. NIOSH Publication 2005-149. Cincinnati, OH: NIOSH, September 2007.

National Institute for Occupational Safety and Health. *Rubber Products Manufacturing Industry: Special NIOSH Hazard Review*. NIOSH Publication 93-106. Cincinnati, OH: NIOSH, 1993.

National Institute for Occupational Safety and Health. *What You Need to Know About Occupational Exposure to Metalworking Fluids*. NIOSH Publication 98-116. Cincinnati, OH: NIOSH, 1998.

National Safety Council. Occupational Safety and Health Data Sheet: *Poison Ivy, Poison Oak, and Poison Sumac*. Itasca, IL: NSC Press, February 2009.

Nethercott JR. The Americans with Disabilities Act. *Amer J Contact Dermatitis* 4:185–186, 1993.

Nethercott JR. Disability due to occupational contact dermatitis. *Occup Med: State of the Art Reviews* 1:199–203, 1986.

Palosuo T, Makinen-Kiljunen S, Alenius H, et al. Measurement of natural latex allergen levels in medical gloves by allergen-specific IgE ELISA inhibition, RAST inhibition, and skin prick test. *Allergy* 53:59–67, 1998.

Rietschel RL, Fowler JF. *Fisher's Contact Dermatitis*, 6th ed. Hamilton, Ont.: BC Decker, 2008.

Rustmeyer T, Elsner P, John SM, et al., eds. *Kanerva's Occupational Skin Diseases*, 2nd ed. New York: Springer, 2012.

Rycroft RJG. Low-humidity occupational dermatoses. *Dermatol Clin* 2:553–559, 1984.

Samitz MH. Assessment of cutaneous impairment and disability. In *Occupational and Industrial Dermatology*, 2nd ed., HI Maibach, ed. Chicago: Year Book Medical Publishers, 1987.

Shmunes E. Predisposing factors in occupational skin diseases. *Dermatol Clin* 6:7–14, 1988.

Taylor JS. Evaluation of impairment due to work-related skin disease. *Occup Med: State of the Art Reviews* 9:1–10, 1994.

Taylor JS. Occupational dermatoses. In *Clinical Medicine for the Occupational Physician*, MH Alderman, JJ Hanley, eds. New York: Dekker, 1982.

Taylor JS. Other reactions from gloves. In *Protective Gloves for Occupational Use*, GA Mellstrom, JE Wahlberg, HI Maibach, eds. Boca Raton, FL: CRC Press, 1994.

Taylor JS. The pilosebaceous unit. In *Occupational and Industrial Dermatology*, 2nd ed., HI Maibach, ed. Chicago: Year Book Medical Publishers, 1987.

Taylor JS, ed. Occupational dermatoses. *Dermatol Clin* 6:1–129, 1988.

Taylor JS, Parrish JA, Blank IH. Environmental reactions to chemical, physical, and biological events. *J Am Acad Dermatol* 11:1007–1021, 1984.

Taylor JS, Wattanakrai P, Charous BL, et al. Latex allergy. In *1999 Yearbook of Dermatology and Dermatologic Surgery*. BH Thiers, PG Lang, eds. St. Louis: Mosby, 1999, pp. 1–44.

Tucker SB. Prevention of occupational skin disease. *Dermatol Clin* 6:87–96, 1988.

Warner MR, Taylor JS, Leow Y-H. Agents causing contact urticaria. *Clin Dermatol* 15:623–635, 1997.

1 mm

CHAPTER 4

The Ears

*by Marjorie De Groot, MA
and Sarah A. Jewell, MD, MPH*

*T*his chapter covers the components of the external, middle, and inner ear, and how they function to produce hearing; the basic types of pathology that can affect the ears; how hearing is measured; the effects of noise on hearing and general health; and the effects of hearing loss on quality of life, and how this impairment is rated. The auditory mechanism enables us to hear sound conveyed from a source to our ears via gases, fluids, or solids. The physics of sound generation and transmission is covered in detail in Chapter 9, Industrial Noise. This chapter provides an overview of our auditory system: the anatomy, physiology, and pathology of the human ear, evaluation of hearing, types of hearing loss, effects of noise exposure on hearing, and effects of hearing loss on communication.

ANATOMY AND PHYSIOLOGY

The organ of hearing is divided into three parts—the external, the middle, and the inner ear. The entire system is shown in Figure 4–1.

External Ear
The external ear is composed of the auricle, or pinna, and the external auditory canal.

Auricle
The *auricle* (*pinna*) is the most visible part of the ear. It is a delicately folded cartilaginous structure with a few small muscles, covered by subcutaneous tissue and skin. The auricle collects sound waves from the air and funnels them into the ear canal to the tympanic membrane (eardrum).

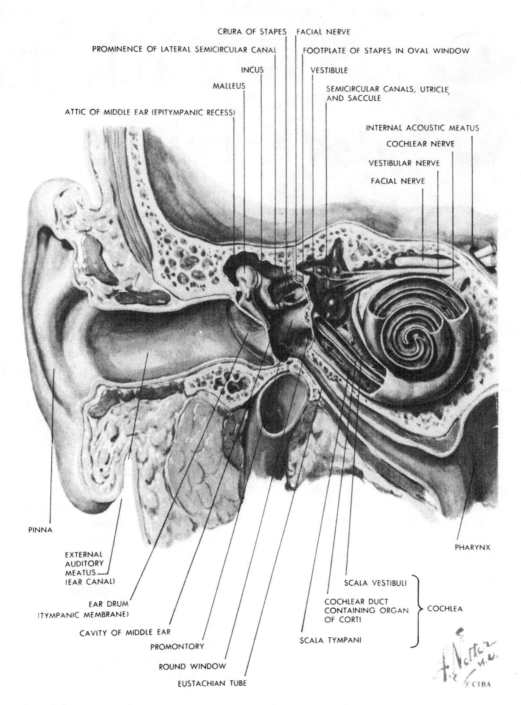

CRURA OF STAPES   FACIAL NERVE

PROMINENCE OF LATERAL SEMICIRCULAR CANAL   FOOTPLATE OF STAPES IN OVAL WINDOW

INCUS   VESTIBULE

MALLEUS   SEMICIRCULAR CANALS, UTRICLE, AND SACCULE

ATTIC OF MIDDLE EAR (EPITYMPANIC RECESS)   INTERNAL ACOUSTIC MEATUS

COCHLEAR NERVE

VESTIBULAR NERVE

FACIAL NERVE

PINNA

EXTERNAL AUDITORY MEATUS (EAR CANAL)

EAR DRUM (TYMPANIC MEMBRANE)

CAVITY OF MIDDLE EAR

PROMONTORY

ROUND WINDOW

EUSTACHIAN TUBE

SCALA VESTIBULI

COCHLEAR DUCT CONTAINING ORGAN OF CORTI   } COCHLEA

SCALA TYMPANI

PHARYNX

Figure 4–1. Illustration of the outer, middle, and inner ear. *(Reprinted with permission from Netter FH*, Clinical Symposia. *CIBA Pharmaceutical Co.)*

External Auditory Canal

The *external auditory canal* (*meatus*) is a skin-lined pouch about 1.5 in. (3.8 cm) long, supported in its outer third by the cartilage of the auricle and in its inner two-thirds by the bone of the skull. The cartilaginous meatus is curved and lies at an angle to the bony part, thus protecting the tympanic membrane and middle ear lying beyond it from direct trauma.

The small hairs, or *vibrissae*, and ceruminal glands, which secrete a waxy substance called cerumen, are located in the skin of the outer third of the ear canal. The hairs serve a protective function by filtering out particulate matter and other large pieces of debris. Cerumen, which is both sticky and bactericidal, prevents smaller particles from entering the ear canal and keeps the canal healthy and free of infection.

The function of the outer ear in the hearing process is

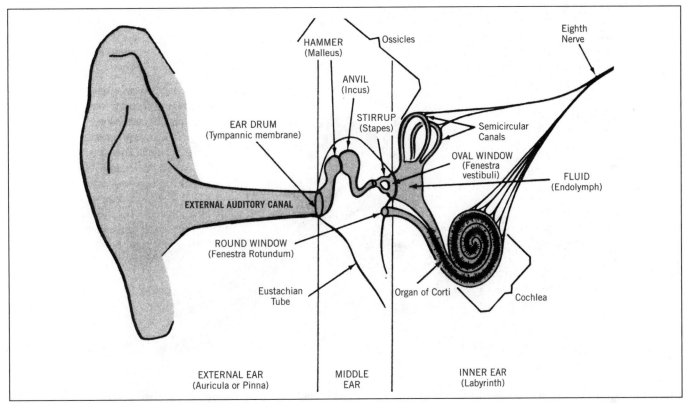

Figure 4–2. How the ear hears: Wave motions in the air set up sympathetic vibrations that are transmitted by the eardrum and the three bones in the middle ear to the fluid-filled chamber of the inner ear. In the process, the relatively large but feeble, air-induced vibrations of the eardrum are converted to much smaller but more powerful mechanical vibrations by the three ossicles, and finally into fluid vibrations. The wave motion in the fluid is sensed by the nerves in the cochlea, which transmit neural messages to the brain. *(Reprinted with permission from the American Foundry Society.)*

relatively simple: The external portion of the ear collects sound waves from the air and funnels them into the ear canal, where they are transported to the eardrum. The collected sound waves cause the eardrum to move back and forth in a vibrating mechanical motion that is transferred to the bones of the middle ear (Figure 4–2).

Middle Ear

The middle ear is the space or cavity, about 1–2 mL in volume, between the eardrum and the bony wall of the inner ear (Figure 4–3). The middle ear is lined with mucous membrane essentially the same as that lining the mouth. The ossicles, which are the smallest bones in the body, are located within the middle ear cavity. The ossicles connect the eardrum to an opening in the wall of the inner ear called the oval window.

Picture the middle ear space as a cube:
- The eardrum forms the outer wall.
- The inner wall is the bony partition separating the inner ear from the middle ear. The round and oval windows fit into this wall and are the only two movable barriers between the middle and inner ear.

- The front wall opens into the eustachian tube.
- The back wall opens into the mastoid air cells.
- The roof separates the middle ear from the temporal lobe of the brain.
- The floor separates the middle ear from the jugular vein and the internal carotid artery, which lies high in the neck.

Eustachian Tube

The *eustachian tube* serves to equalize pressure on either side of the tympanic membrane. An increase in pressure in the middle ear cavity, relative to atmospheric pressure, is usually compensated for passively by way of the eustachian tube. A decrease in pressure usually requires active ventilation by using muscles to open and close the eustachian tube (e.g., by yawning or swallowing).

Eardrum

The eardrum is a membrane that separates the external ear canal from the middle ear. It consists of an inner layer of mucous membrane, a middle layer of fibrous tissue, and an outer layer of squamous epithelium. It is shaped like a spider web, with radial and circular fibers for structural support.

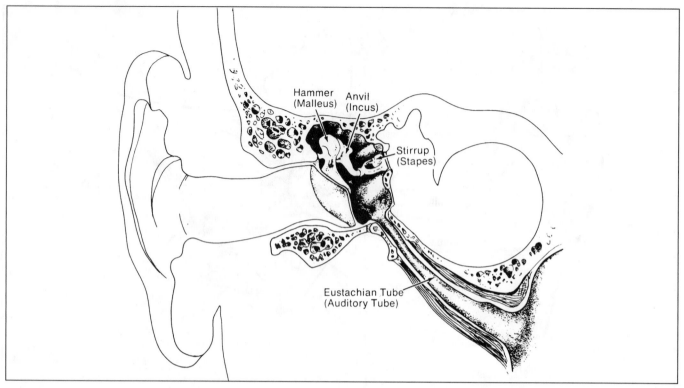

Figure 4–3. The middle ear is contained within the temporal bone and is made up of the Eustachian tube, the middle ear space, and the mastoid air cell system. (Adapted from Figure 4–1)

Ossicular Chain

The *ossicles,* which together are called the *ossicular chain,* are the *malleus, incus,* and *stapes.*

- The *malleus,* or hammer, is fastened to the eardrum by the handle. The head lies in the upper area of the middle ear cavity and is connected to the incus.
- The *incus,* also called the anvil, is the second ossicle and has a long projection that runs downward and joins the stapes.
- The *stapes,* also called the stirrup, lies almost perpendicular to the long axis of the incus. The two branches of the stapes, anterior and posterior, end in the footplate that fits into the oval window.

The primary function of the middle ear in the hearing process is to transfer sound energy from the outer to the inner ear. As the eardrum vibrates, it transfers its motion to the attached malleus. Because the bones of the ossicular chain are connected to one another, the movements of the malleus are passed on to the incus, and finally to the stapes embedded in the oval window.

As the stapes moves back and forth in a rocking motion, it passes the vibrations on to the inner ear through the oval window (Figures 4–3 and 4–4). Covering the round window is a very thin membrane that moves out as the stapedal footplate in the oval window moves in. As the action is reversed and the footplate in the oval window is pulled out, the round window membrane moves inward. Thus, the mechanical motion of the eardrum is effectively transmitted through the middle ear and into the fluid of the inner ear.

Amplification

The sound-conducting mechanism also amplifies sound by two main mechanisms. First, the large surface area of the base of the stapes (footplate) creates a hydraulic effect. The eardrum has about 25 times as much surface area as the oval window (Figure 4–5). All of the sound pressure collected on the eardrum is transmitted through the ossicular chain and is concentrated on the much smaller area of the oval window. This produces a significant increase in pressure. Second, the bones of the ossicular chain are arranged in such a way that they act as a series of amplifying levers. The long arms are nearest the eardrum and the shorter arms are near the oval window. The fulcrums are located where the individual bones meet. A small pressure on the long arm of the lever produces a much stronger pressure on the shorter arm. The magnification effect of the entire sound conducting mechanism is about 22 to 1.

Two tiny muscles attach to the ossicular chain: the stapedius to the neck of the stapes bone and the tensor tympani to the malleus. Loud sounds cause these muscles to contract, which stiffens and diminishes the movement of the ossicular

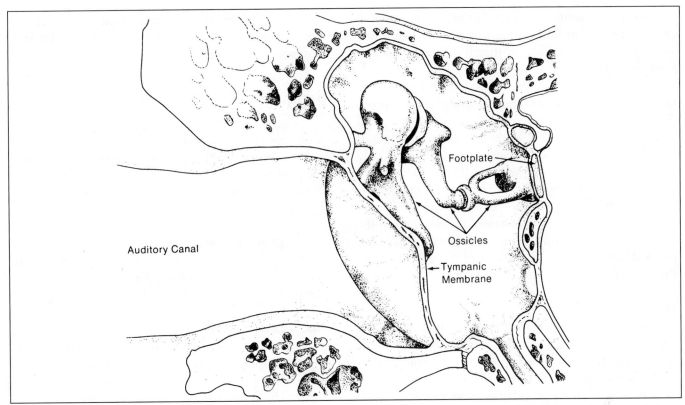

Figure 4–4. The ossicles, located in the middle ear cavity, link the eardrum to an opening in the wall of the inner ear (the oval window). (Adapted from Figure 4–1)

chain, reducing the amount of sound energy transmitted to the inner ear.

Mastoid Air Cell System
On the back wall of the middle ear space is an opening that extends into the mastoid bone. This opening resembles a honeycomb of spaces filled with air.

Inner Ear
The inner ear contains the receptors for hearing and position sense. The major components of the inner ear include the vestibular receptive system and the cochlea, housed within the compact temporal bone (Figures 4–6 and 4–7). This bony labyrinth is filled with fluid called perilymph. The inner ear components are made up of a membranous labyrinth structure, which is suspended in the perilymph. Within the membranous labyrinth are the sensory organs for hearing (the cochlea) and position (the vestibular system), bathed in endolymph fluid.

Cochlea
The *cochlea* is a tubular snail-shaped structure lined with the basilar membrane, which contains thousands of feathery *hair cells* tuned to vibrate to different sound frequen-

cies. Nerve endings are contained in a complex, slightly elevated structure over the floor of the tube forming the

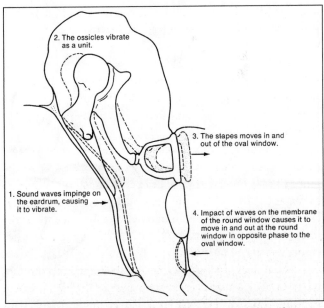

1. Sound waves impinge on the eardrum, causing it to vibrate.

2. The ossicles vibrate as a unit.

3. The stapes moves in and out of the oval window.

4. Impact of waves on the membrane of the round window causes it to move in and out at the round window in opposite phase to the oval window.

Figure 4–5. The eardrum has about 25 times as much surface area as the oval window. All of the sound energy collected on the eardrum is transmitted through the ossicular chain to the smaller area of the oval window.

cochlea. This structure, the *organ of Corti,* is the essential receptor end organ for hearing. It is a very complicated structure, consisting of a supporting framework on which the hair cells rest.

Vibrations of the stapedial footplate set into motion the fluids of the inner ear. As the basilar membrane is displaced, a shearing movement occurs on the tectorial surface that drags the hair cells attached to the nerve endings. This sets up electrical impulses that are appropriately coded and transmitted to the brain via the auditory (or cochlear) nerve (Figure 4–8). The frequency or pitch of the sound determines which part of the cochlea responds (high frequencies stimulate the wide base of the cochlea near the oval and round windows, whereas the nerve endings that respond to low frequencies are located at the small end of the cochlea).

Vestibular System

Our sense of balance is dependent not on hearing, but on organs of equilibrium. Near the cochlea are three semicircular canals lying in planes perpendicular to each other (Figure 4–9). The canals contain endolymph fluid that responds to movement of the head. Additional positional information is provided by receptors located in the vestibule. The vestibular branch of the auditory nerve (also known as the eighth cranial nerve) transmits these impulses to the cerebral cortex, and we recognize the position of our head in space as it relates to the pull of gravity.

PATHOLOGY

A number of disorders can affect the components of the auditory system. In this section, some of these conditions and their relevance to the occupational setting will be presented, along with a review of hearing assessment and the effects of noise.

Pathology of the External Ear

This section begins with a look at the pathology of the external ear—specifically the pinna and auditory canal, the eardrum, and the eustachian tube.

Pinna and Auditory Canal

Because of its prominence and its thin, tight skin, the *pinna* is especially subject to sunburn and frostbite. Thus, it must be protected from the elements. Injured cartilage is replaced by fibrous tissue and repeated injuries result in the cauliflower-shaped ear seen on many boxers. Disorders of the auricle include congenital malformations (in which the

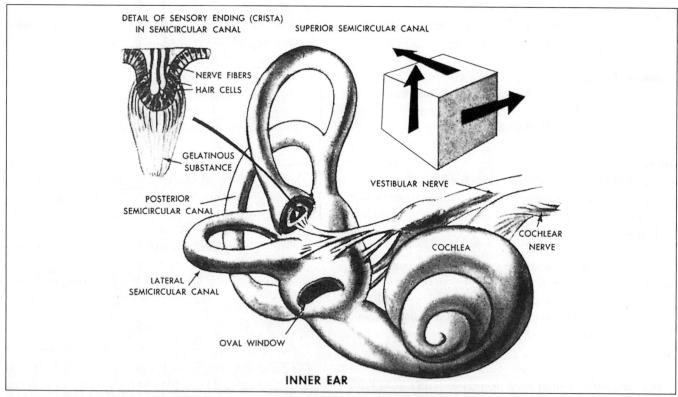

Figure 4–6. The three subdivisions of the inner ear: the cochlea, the vestibule, and the semicircular canals. *(Reprinted with permission from The Wonderful Human Machine. Copyright 1971. The American Medical Association. All rights reserved.)*

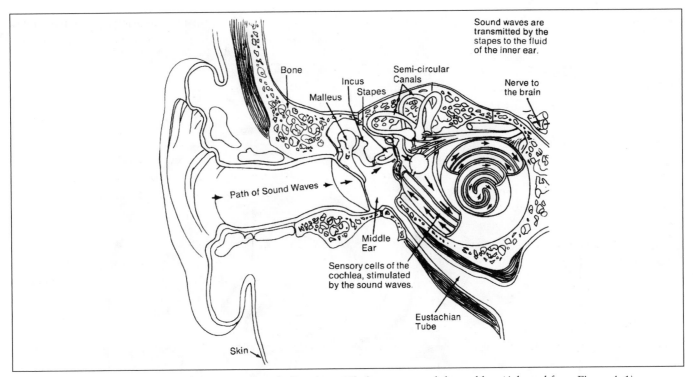

Figure 4–7. The major components of the inner ear, including the vestibular system and the cochlea. (Adapted from Figure 4–1)

cartilage is misshapen) and protruding, or lop, ears, both of which may be surgically corrected. Dermatitis and infection are common in this area, and can arise locally or spread from other body sites. Deformation or inflammation of the pinna can affect a worker's comfort in using headwear and muff-type hearing protection.

The *ear canal* is prone to infection (otitis externa) because of its high skin temperature and humidity. Bacterial or fungal infections occur more readily under circumstances of heavy perspiration or head immersion (hence the name "swimmer's ear"). Skin disorders (dermatitis) are also a common ear canal problem, and can either occur locally or spread from the scalp and other skin areas.

Foreign objects accidentally lodged in the ear canal can be dangerous and should be removed only by a physician. A live insect in the ear canal can be especially annoying or painful. If this happens, drop light mineral oil into the canal to suffocate or quiet the insect until it can be removed. Normally, the ear canals are self-cleaning but occasionally this mechanism fails, resulting in wax impaction. The use of cotton-tipped swabs for cleaning tends to pack wax into the ear canal. Also, swabbing stimulates excess production of wax.

An abnormal narrowing of the ear canal is called stenosis and may be caused by congenital malformation, bony growth (exostosis), or infection. Tumors are rare in this area. Abnormalities in ear canal anatomy, or canal infec-

tion/inflammation, can cause difficulties in using earplugs or other insert hearing protective devices. It is not common for ear canal problems to affect hearing; the canal must be almost totally occluded (blocked) before attenuation of sound occurs.

Eardrum

Infections localized to the eardrum are rare; when they do occur, they are caused by viruses such as the varicella zoster virus (shingles). However, the eardrum is often included in infections of the external auditory canal or the middle ear.

Perforation or rupture of the tympanic membrane can be caused by infection, direct injury (e.g., from a penetrating object), or sudden pressure changes (barotrauma). Examples of the latter would be a blow to the side of the head or large pressure changes associated with air flight, underwater diving, or explosions. Most perforations heal spontaneously and do not require surgical repair, the exception being those caused by hot substances such as welding splatter.

Eustachian Tube

In the presence of swelling, adhesions, or masses, the eustachian tubes can become obstructed. This is a common consequence of allergic and infectious conditions that affect the nose and throat. Failure of the eustachian tube to ventilate creates a vacuum in the middle ear space, which in turn

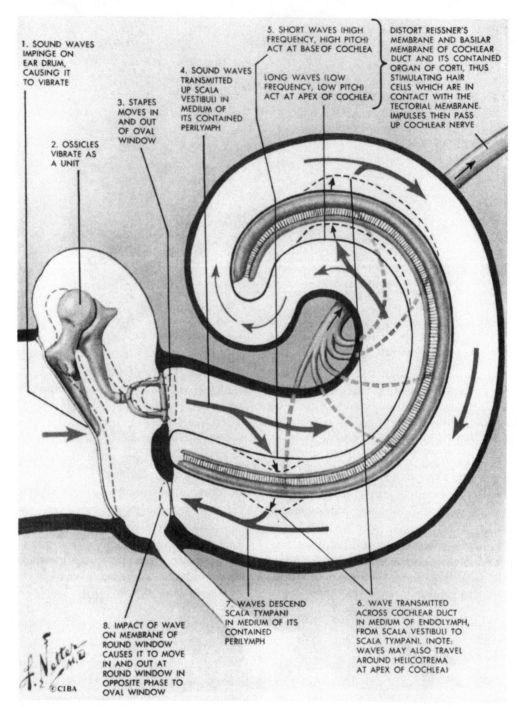

Figure 4–8. The mechanism for transmission of sound vibrations from the eardrum through the cochlea. (*Reprinted with permission from Netter FH*, Clinical Symposia. *CIBA Pharmaceutical Co.*)

causes one of two pathological events to occur: The vacuum pulls fluid into the middle ear, resulting in a condition called nonsuppurative (serous) otitis media, or it pulls the eardrum inward (retraction). Either one of these events can interfere with mobility of the tympanic membrane, causing hearing loss. Eventually, any serous fluid present can thicken and create persistent hearing problems.

The opposite condition, which is uncommon, is a pat-

ent eustachian tube in which the tube constantly remains open. This condition results in the annoying symptom of hearing one's own voice and breath sounds (autophonia) in the involved ear.

Pathology of the Middle Ear

The middle ear space is prone to infectious diseases, especially in childhood. These are predominantly bacterial in

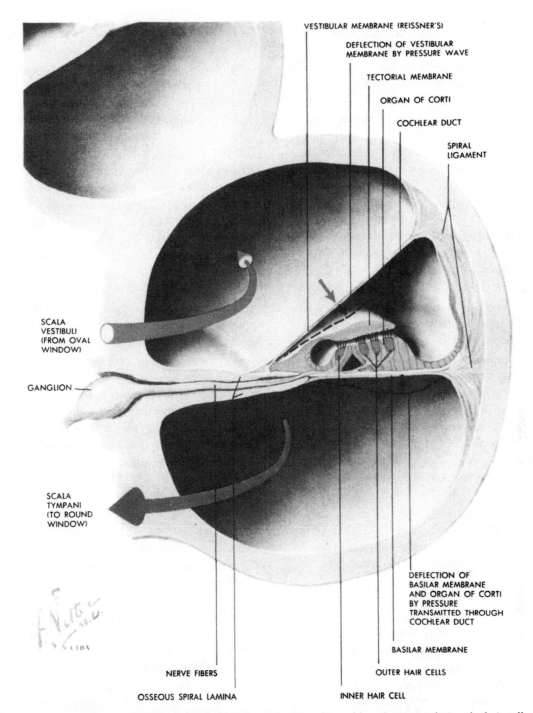

VESTIBULAR MEMBRANE (REISSNER'S)

DEFLECTION OF VESTIBULAR
MEMBRANE BY PRESSURE WAVE

TECTORIAL MEMBRANE

ORGAN OF CORTI

COCHLEAR DUCT

SPIRAL
LIGAMENT

SCALA
VESTIBULI
(FROM OVAL
WINDOW)

GANGLION

SCALA
TYMPANI
(TO ROUND
WINDOW)

DEFLECTION OF
BASILAR MEMBRANE
AND ORGAN OF CORTI
BY PRESSURE
TRANSMITTED THROUGH
COCHLEAR DUCT

BASILAR MEMBRANE

NERVE FIBERS   OUTER HAIR CELLS

OSSEOUS SPIRAL LAMINA   INNER HAIR CELL

Figure 4–9. This schematic diagram depicts the transmission of sound across the cochlear duct, stimulating the hair cells. *(Reprinted with permission from Netter FH,* Clinical Symposia. *CIBA Pharmaceutical Co.)*

origin and called suppurative otitis media. Because the middle ear space connects with the mastoid air cell system, infection can easily spread to this area (mastoiditis). Before the days of antibiotics, these were serious, often life-threatening problems because the infection could spread to the brain or major vessels surrounding the ear. Though less likely to occur today, these dangers still exist.

Disease of the middle ear ossicles can impair hearing

in two ways:
- fixation (the bony chain cannot vibrate or vibrates inefficiently)
- interruption (a gap in the chain)

Fixation can result from developmental errors, adhesions, or scars from old middle ear infections or bone diseases that affect this area. Otosclerosis is a prime example of fixation. It usually begins in early adult life. Interruptions are usually caused by middle ear infections, cholesteatomas, or head injuries.

Conductive hearing loss is hearing loss that arises from conditions affecting the outer or middle ear. This is because sound waves cannot be conducted effectively to the cochlear sensory organ via the normal pathways. Some amount of sound energy can still be transmitted to the inner ear by direct transmission through the cranial bone. Although the loudness of sounds is diminished in this case, clarity of sound is preserved because the cochlea retains its phenomenal sensitivity to a wide range of sound characteristics.

Pathology of the Inner Ear

A variety of ailments can affect the delicate cochlea, semicircular canals, and eighth cranial nerve. For example, damage to these components can result from congenital/developmental defects, systemic diseases (multiple sclerosis, diabetes), infection (mumps or chronic otitis media), exposure to noise or certain toxins (including medications such as some antibiotics or diuretics), circulatory problems (stroke), and trauma (concussion or skull fracture). In the workplace, exposure to excessive vibration, heavy metals, organic solvents and asphyxiants such as carbon monoxide may contribute significantly to the hearing loss induced by chronic ambient noise or other medical problems.

A steady loss of hearing acuity often occurs as we grow older (presbycusis). The normal young ear can hear tones within a range of 20 Hz (the lowest bass note of a piano) up to high-pitched sounds of 20,000 Hz. People in their 60s are lucky to hear normal level sounds at 12,000 Hz. This hearing loss is greater for high-frequency sounds and is considered normal because it happens to practically everybody as the years roll on.

Disorders affecting the vestibular system can cause loss of balance, vertigo, and nausea or vomiting. Examples of these disorders include *viral labyrinthitis* and *Meniere's disease*. Meniere's disease affects both parts of the inner ear (hearing and balance) and its cause is unknown. It is characterized by episodic dizziness, often severe, and is associated with nausea and vomiting, fluctuating hearing loss that is generally progressive, ringing or hissing noise (tinnitus), and a peculiar sensation of fullness in the involved ear.

Another important condition that can affect the eighth cranial nerve is acoustic neuroma. This tumor occurs most commonly in middle-aged persons. Although not malignant, it can cause disabling symptoms of both hearing loss and vestibular dysfunction. Workers with vertigo or equilibrium problems may not be medically fit for safety-sensitive tasks such as operating motor vehicles or working at heights (on ladders, etc.).

Sensorineural hearing loss is the hearing difficulty caused by inner ear damage. (*Sensori-* refers to the sense organ in the inner ear, and *-neural* refers to the nerve fibers). Sensorineural hearing loss can involve impairment of the cochlea, the auditory nerve, or both. Unlike conductive hearing loss, the hearing deficit cannot be overcome by sound transmission through the bone. Often both the perception of loudness and clarity of sound are impaired.

Tinnitus

Tinnitus is a symptom, not a disease. It is a perception of sound arising in the head. It may be heard only by the affected person (subjective tinnitus) or it may be audible to the examiner also (objective tinnitus). Objective tinnitus is usually a symptom not of a disease of the ear but of a tumor or vascular malformation. All cases should be evaluated by a qualified physician.

Subjective tinnitus is usually perceived as a ringing or hiss. Occasionally, no explanation can be found, but most cases are secondary to high-frequency hearing loss. Some cases can be caused by wax, perforation of the eardrum, or fluid in the middle ear. Drugs or stimulants such as caffeine, aspirin, or alcohol can also cause tinnitus by disturbing the inner ear.

Tinnitus can lead to psychological stress and be disabling. Maskers that match the frequency of the tinnitus, combined with a hearing aid, can be helpful. Patient education is essential to successful treatment.

A QUICK LOOK AT THE HEARING PROCESS

The external ear collects sound waves and funnels them to the tympanic membrane through the ear canal. The tympanic membrane vibrates in response to the sound waves that strike it. This vibratory movement, in turn, is transmitted to the ossicular chain in the middle ear. The vibration of the ossicles creates waves in the inner ear fluid that stimulate microscopic hair cells. The stimulation of these hair cells generates nerve impulses which pass along the auditory nerve to the brain for interpretation.

The outer and middle sections of the ear conduct sound energy to the deeper structures. Therefore, the outer and middle ear sections act together as the conductive hearing mechanism. In contrast, the deeper structures, including the inner ear and the auditory nerve, are referred to as the sensorineural mechanism. Although nature has surrounded the delicate ear mechanism with hard, protective bone, any portion of the ear can become impaired. The part of the hearing mechanism affected and the extent of damage has a direct bearing on the type of hearing loss that results. The words *conductive* and *sensorineural* describe two major types of hearing impairment.

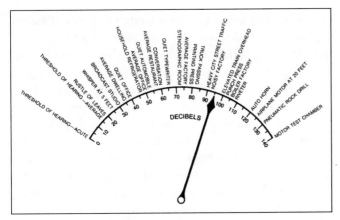

Figure 4–10. Typical sound levels associated with various activities.

As long as the hearing mechanism functions normally, the ear can detect sounds of minute intensity while tolerating sounds of great intensity. The loudest sound the normal ear can tolerate is more than 100 million (10^8) times more powerful than the faintest sound the ear can detect (Figure 4–10) (see Chapter 9). Furthermore, a young listener with normal hearing can detect sounds across a wide frequency range, from very low-pitched sounds of 20 Hz to very high-pitched sounds of 20,000 Hz.

HEARING MEASUREMENT

The basic evaluation of hearing is done using an audiometer. This is described in the next section.

Audiometer

An audiometer is a frequency-controlled audio-signal generator. It produces a pure tone signal, the frequency and intensity of which are varied for use in hearing measurement. Audiometry is used to determine hearing thresholds for both pure tone and speech, by air conduction and bone conduction.

The audiometer was developed to provide an electronic pure-tone sound similar to that of the tuning fork. With the audiometer, however, intensities can be controlled much more accurately and, therefore, the results can be more carefully quantified. The equipment is calibrated according to American National Standard Institute (ANSI) standards *Specification for Audiometers* (ANSI S3.6-1996) and *Reference Zero for the Calibration of Pure Tone Bone-Conduction Audiometers* (ANSI S3.43-1992). Standard testing is performed under controlled quiet conditions, testing each ear separately.

Air Conduction Testing

When testing hearing by air conduction, headphones are placed over the ears of the test subject. A pure tone signal

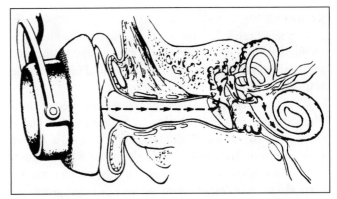

Figure 4–11. An air-conduction earphone is depicted; note that the earphone is placed directly over the external ear canal and the sound waves are conducted (by air) to the eardrum and through the middle ear to the inner ear.

from the audiometer is presented through the headphones and travels through the ear canal, the middle ear, and into the inner ear, thus allowing evaluation of the entire hearing mechanism, both conductive and sensorineural (Figure 4–11).

Bone Conduction Testing

Bone conduction audiometry evaluates only the sensorineural hearing mechanism. A bone vibrator is placed on the mastoid bone behind the outer ear. This sends vibrations directly through the skull bones to the cochlea in the inner ear, bypassing the conductive pathway of the outer and middle ear (Figure 4–12). Bone conduction testing is considered a diagnostic test and is not performed as part of routine industrial hearing assessments.

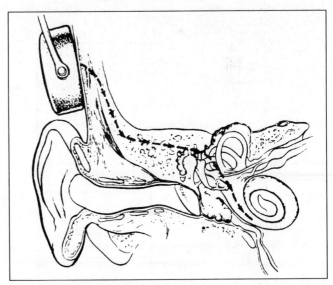

Figure 4–12. Sound can be transmitted directly to the inner ear through the bones of the skull using a bone-conduction vibrator placed on the mastoid bone behind the outer ear. The broken line (with arrows) shows the path taken by the sound waves through the bony areas of the head to the inner ear.

Audiogram

Audiometric results are recorded on a standard chart called an audiogram (Figure 4–13). It is a frequency-by-intensity graph on which a person's hearing threshold for pure tones is plotted.

The numbers across the top represent the frequency, or pitch, of the tones from the lowest frequency (125 Hz) to the highest frequency (8,000 Hz). For example, a 250-Hz tone corresponds to middle C on the piano while a 4,000-Hz tone sounds much like a piccolo hitting a high note. The vertical column of numbers on the left side of the graph represents intensity, or loudness, in decibels (dB). The smaller the number, the lower the dB level, the softer the sound (e.g., 10 dB) and conversely, the larger the number, the higher the dB level, the louder the sound (e.g., 100 dB).

Threshold of hearing is the very softest level at which a person is able to hear. When a threshold, measured in dB, is determined through audiometry at any given frequency, the result is plotted on the graph. Audiometric symbols used for recording results are specified by ANSI standards. Pure tone, air conduction thresholds are plotted with an "O" for the right ear and with an "X" for the left ear. A threshold of 0 dB indicates that there is no difference between the hearing sensitivity of a test subject compared with a normal standard.

The American Academy of Ophthalmology and Otolaryngology has recommended that audiograms be drawn to a scale like the illustration shown in Figure 4–13. For every 20-dB interval measured along one side and for one octave measured across the top (250–500 Hz, for example), there is a perfect square. The reason for a standardized scale is that the apparent hearing loss can be altered a good deal by changing the dimensions of an audiogram. If the proportions of the audiogram are different from standard dimensions, a person's hearing loss may look quite different than if it were plotted on the standard audiogram format. Customarily, audiograms are scaled in 10-dB steps. Of course, if a person has a threshold of 55 dB, it is plotted on the appropriate frequency line at the halfway point between 50 and 60 dB.

Hearing losses plotted on a standard chart produce a profile of a person's hearing. A trained person can review an audiogram to determine the type and degree of hearing loss and can estimate the difficulty in communication this loss will cause.

Otoacoustic Emissions

Otoacoustic Emissions (OAE) are inaudible acoustic signals generated by outer hair cells of the normal cochlea, either in the absence of acoustic stimulation or in response to acoustic stimulation. Outer hair cells are the first to be affected by excessive noise and are very sensitive to cochlear damage. Measurement and evaluation of OAEs allow for early detection of cochlear damage from excessive noise or ototoxicity, and provide objective confirmation of cochlear dysfunction in the patient whose audiogram may be normal.

There are three types of otoacoustic emission testing: Spontaneous, Transient (TEOAE), and Distortion Product (DPOAE). DPOAEs have greater frequency specificity and can be elicited from ears with greater hearing loss as compared to TEOAEs. To obtain DPOAEs, a probe is placed in the ear canal. This probe contains both a loud speaker, which generates clicks, and a microphone, which measures the resulting OAE reflected back from the cochlea. The data is then analysed to determine cochlear function.

When abnormalities are found on routine hearing tests, further diagnostic evaluation is usually warranted to determine the cause(s) of hearing loss. Supplemental functional testing (e.g., hearing-in-noise and sound localization testing) may also be needed to assess an individual's fitness for work duty, particularly in safety-sensitive jobs.

EFFECTS OF NOISE EXPOSURE

Exposure to noise can cause temporary or permanent damage to the auditory system. In addition, noise appears to be harmful to our general health in ways that are not yet fully appreciated.

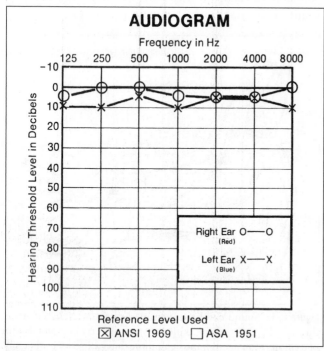

Figure 4–13. A typical manual audiogram showing hearing thresholds within the normal range.

Noise-Induced Hearing Loss

Noise (defined as unwanted sound) is a pervasive, insidious cause of hearing loss. It causes no particular pain unless it is as loud as a rifle blast. The ears have considerable comeback power from brief exposure to *intense* noise and ordinarily recover within 14 hours or so (this is called a temporary threshold shift [TTS], typically most prominent at 4,000 Hz). However, prolonged exposure to intense noise gradually damages the cochlear hair cells of the inner ear (Figure 4–14), resulting in a permanent threshold shift (PTS) across multiple frequencies (Figure 4–15).

What are the factors that determine the duration and severity of noise-induced hearing loss?

- *Sound level*—Sound levels must exceed 60–80 dB before the typical person will experience a temporary decrease in hearing sensitivity. The National Institute for Occupational Safety and Health (NIOSH) estimates that eight percent of individuals exposed at the NIOSH Recommended Exposure Limit (85 dB, A-weighted, averaged over 8 hours/day for 40 years) will develop noise-induced hearing loss.
- *Frequency distribution of sound*—Sounds having most of their energy in the speech frequencies (500 Hz–2,000 Hz) are more potent in causing a threshold shift than are lower frequency sounds.
- *Duration of sound*—For a given sound level, longer duration exposure increases the risk of hearing effects.
- *Temporal distribution of sound exposure*—The shorter and less frequent the quiet periods between periods of sound, the greater the hazard.
- *Type of sound energy* (continuous, intermittent, impulse, or impact)—The tolerance to peak sound pressure is greatly reduced by sudden changes in the sound energy level.
- *Individual differences in tolerance of sound*—Sensitivity to noise-related hearing loss varies widely among individuals. Recent research indicates that age, comorbid health conditions, and genetic factors can all contribute to individual susceptibility, but there are no reliable predictors to identify those at increased risk.
- *Concurrent exposures to ototoxic compounds*—Conversely, recent evidence also suggests that some antioxidant agents may be otoprotective.

Millions of workers in the United States are exposed to significant levels of noise on the job. For this reason, OSHA has required formal hearing conservation programs since the mid-1970s for most employees exposed above the Action Level (currently 85 dBA averaged over an eight-hour workday; see Chapter 9, Industrial Noise). Occupational health and safety professionals should also be aware that recreational (nonoccupational) noise exposure from music, firearms, and vehicles such as snowmobiles and motorcycles is fairly ubiquitous. This information should be incorporated into worker risk assessment and education programs.

Nonauditory Effects of Noise

Research on other effects of noise indicates that it may cause interference with communication, altered performance, annoyance, and physiological responses such as elevated blood pressure and sleep disturbances. Definitive studies have yet to be done on most of these issues. Certainly, levels of background noise above 80 dBA reduce the intelligibility of speech to workers with normal hearing. Furthermore, repeated shouting to overcome noise has been observed to

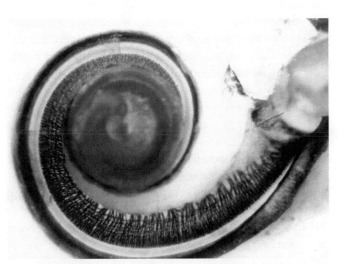
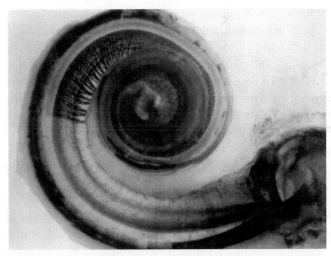

Figure 4–14. Enlarged views of human cochlear specimens. Compare the normal cochlea on the left with that of a 50-year-old patient exposed to noise during factory work and recreational hunting activities. Note the nearly complete loss of the organ of Corti and nerve fibers throughout the base of the cochlea, consistent with his irreversible high frequency hearing loss. *(Photo by Joseph Hawkins, Kresge Hearing Research Institute, University of Michigan. Used with permission.)*

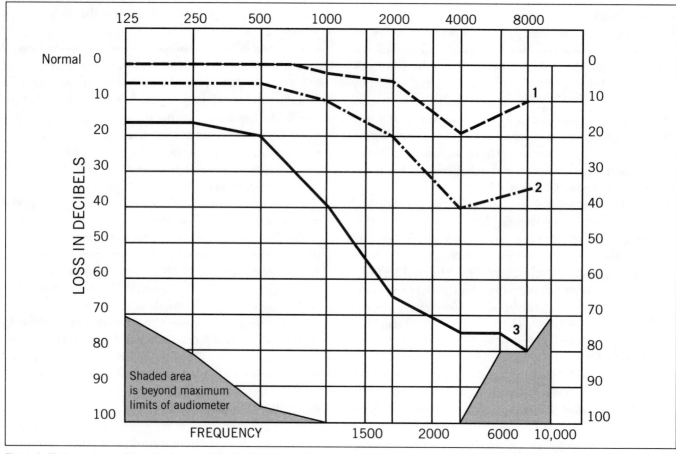

Figure 4–15. Sensorineural hearing losses of the kind produced by noise or other causes. Curve 1 = early; curve 2 = intermediate; curve 3 = advanced. (As shown, curve 3 might include some involvement of presbycusis.)

lead to chronic laryngitis and even traumatic vocal cord polyps. However, the stress effects of noise (decreased attention, accidents, hypertension, and sleep problems) are not consistently correlated with noise level.

Noise exposure does seem to have deleterious health effects during pregnancy. Women exposed to high levels of noise are at increased risk of shortened gestation and delivery of preterm or low birthweight infants. Fetal exposure to noise may result in birth defects and permanent hearing deficits, although human and animal studies have not demonstrated this conclusively.

COMMUNICATION

Quality of life can be drastically affected for individuals whose hearing has been impaired by exposure to noise. Verbal communication, our primary connection to other human beings, often becomes a source of frustration for the person with the hearing loss as well as for family and friends. Typically, this type of hearing loss produces incon-

sistent auditory behavior. That is, in certain situations there may be no problem hearing whereas in others there can be considerable difficulty.

To better understand why this occurs, we will discuss two important characteristics of hearing: loudness, the ability to hear sounds as loud as they actually are, and clarity, the ability to hear sounds clearly and distinctly.

Loudness

If Figure 4–16 is held at arm's length, the printing on the left side is obvious but almost impossible to read. A close look confirms that it is indeed a word; an even closer look reveals that the word is *Loudness*. This example is analogous to the concept of loudness as it relates to hearing and hearing loss. For some types of hearing loss, sounds only need to be made louder to hear, just as the word *Loudness* needed to be made bigger to see.

Clarity

If Figure 4–16 is held at arm's length, there is no difficulty in seeing everything on the right side. But can the word

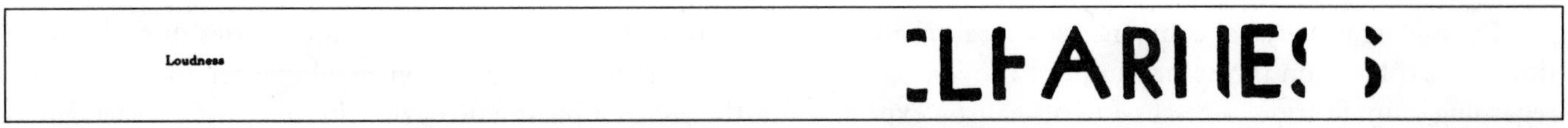

Figure 4–16. Both sides of this illustration visually represent two important dimensions of normal hearing: the ability to hear sounds as loudly as they really are and the ability to hear sounds with complete clarity. Left: it is almost impossible to read the word Loudness; this is comparable to not being able to hear faint sounds. Moving the figure closer makes it easier to read, just as increasing volume makes sound easier to hear. Right: No matter how closely the illustration is held, it is difficult to interpret. The word is not clear because some important parts of the letters are missing. This shows, by analogy, hearing difficulty caused by a loss in the ability to distinguish between various sounds (the word is CLEARNESS).

be read? If not, the reason is that too much of the word is missing, even though it is large enough. Regardless of how closely you look, it is difficult to read because some of the important parts are missing. This illustrates the problem of loss of clarity, or an inability to distinguish between the various sounds in spoken language. (The word is CLEARNESS.)

Conductive hearing loss associated with pathology in the external or middle ear generally affects a person's ability to hear at normal loudness levels. It does not usually impair the clarity with which that person hears once the sound is made loud enough to compensate for the hearing loss. The key to clarity in hearing is held by the inner ear mechanism and the nerve fibers that carry the message to the brain.

When damage occurs to the inner ear or auditory nerve, the resulting sensorineural hearing loss can affect not only the perceived loudness of incoming sounds, but also their clarity. Speech in particular can seem unclear or distorted regardless of how loud it is. The main complaint associated with this type of hearing loss is that patients can "hear" but cannot understand, especially in the presence of background noise. This occurs because the tiny hair cells that respond to specific speech sounds are so severely damaged that they cannot react when the vibrations from sound waves strike them, while hair cells for other speech sounds may be functioning normally.

Speech Sounds

Speech sounds can be classified as vowels or consonants. The vowel sounds—located in the lower frequencies—are the more powerful speech sounds. Therefore, vowels carry the energy for speech. In contrast, consonants—located in the higher frequencies—are important in distinguishing one word from another. This is the heart of the communicative problem for people with noise-induced (high-frequency) hearing loss. They are often unable to distinguish between similar words such as *stop* and *shop*. If one word in a sentence is mistaken for another, the entire meaning of the sentence may be misunderstood, leading to confusion and embarrassment.

Background Noise

People with high-frequency hearing loss often manage fairly well in quiet listening situations. However, in a noisy envi-

ronment, such as in traffic, in a restaurant, or on the job, it can become extremely difficult to communicate through hearing alone.

A listener with normal hearing can hear a speaker in the presence of typical background noise with little or no difficulty. However, if the listener developed a hearing loss for all speech sounds above 1,000 Hz, there would be a marked decrease in that person's ability to hear the speaker clearly. Most ambient (background) noise is low frequency. Since there is more energy in the low frequencies, the noise masks the weaker, high frequency speech sounds so crucial for clarity, making it even more challenging to understand what is being said.

Quality of Life

Most often, noise-induced hearing loss occurs gradually, over time. In the initial stages the person may experience little difficulty in most situations. However, as the hearing loss increases in severity and affects more frequencies, the hearing-impaired individual often begins to avoid certain situations (such as parties) and may have a tendency to withdraw socially. Everyday situations, such as listening to the grandchildren or talking to a spouse while the television is on, become sources of frustration.

Rehabilitation

There is no medical or surgical cure for sensorineural hearing loss, thus prevention measures are imperative. However, once irreversible damage has occurred, much can be accomplished with amplification (hearing aids) and counseling to minimize the effects of the hearing impairment on the quality of life.

The hearing aids of today are a vast improvement over the hearing aids of the past, although they are still unable to compensate completely for lost hearing. New technology and fitting techniques make it possible to finely tune a hearing aid by adjusting a series of parameters to compensate for the uniqueness of each person's hearing loss. This allows a hearing-impaired user to hear more naturally and with less interference from background noise. Cochlear implant technologies are now increasingly available for profound hearing loss.

Counseling is a crucial component of aural rehabilitation. An explanation of the hearing test results, options regarding amplification, a discussion of realistic expectations, and tips for easier communication are all beneficial in helping the individual to live comfortably with the hearing impairment.

Further Medical Evaluation

When should an individual be referred to a physician for further medical evaluation? The American Academy of Otolaryngology-Head and Neck Surgery recommends referral for evaluation of significant hearing loss (or other ear problems) as follows:

Hearing Loss
- Baseline audiogram
  - Average hearing level at 500, 1,000, 2,000, and 3,000 Hz is greater than 25 dB in either ear; or
  - Difference in hearing level between the ears of more than 15 dB at 500, 1,000, and 2,000 Hz or more than 30 dB at 3,000, 4,000, and 6,000 Hz
- Periodic audiogram
  - Change of average hearing (for the worse) in either ear compared to the baseline of more than 15 dB at 500, 1,000, and 2,000 Hz, or more than 20 dB at 3,000, 4,000, and 6,000 Hz

Other
- Ear pain; drainage; dizziness; severe persistent tinnitus; sudden, rapidly progressive or fluctuating hearing loss; a feeling of fullness or discomfort in the ear within the preceeding 12 months
- Excessive cerumen accumulation or foreign body in the ear canal

EVALUATING IMPAIRMENT: *THE AMA GUIDES*

Chapter 11.2 of the American Medical Association's *Guides to the Evaluation of Permanent Impairment* includes criteria for evaluating permanent impairment resulting from damage to the ear's hearing and/or vestibular functions. This determination is important in assessing employability and compensation for loss of function due to injury (e.g., workers' compensation). Because many state agencies have adopted the use of the AMA formula for determining hearing impairment, it is important that the industrial hygienist or occupational clinician understand the formula.

In these *Guides,* permanent impairment of any particular body part or system is expressed in terms of the capacity of the whole person to perform activities of daily living. The actual level of function should be determined without the aid of a prosthetic device (in this case, a hearing aid). Equilibrium and hearing are considered separately. Only general criteria are provided for disturbances of equilibrium, but the criteria for evaluating hearing impairment are relatively specific.

Hearing loss for each ear is calculated at thresholds of 500, 1,000, 2,000, and 3,000 Hz. No allowance is made for impairment of speech discrimination due to deficits at higher frequencies. The *Guides to the Evaluation of Permanent Impairment* include a formula for calculating the binaural hearing loss based on the percentage impairment of each ear, tested separately. Each ear must have an average hearing shift of more than 25 dB for the frequencies measured to be ranked as impaired. The percentage of impairment of the poorer ear is added to five times the percentage of impairment of the better ear and the total divided by six. Thus, a person with normal hearing in one ear (0 percent impairment) but totally deaf in the other (100 percent impairment) would have a binaural hearing impairment of 17 percent ([(5 × 0%) + 100 %] ÷ 6 = 17%). In our example, the 17-percent binaural impairment translates into a 6-percent whole-person impairment.

OSHA HEARING CONSERVATION PROGRAM (*29 CFR* 1910.95)

On April 7, 1983, the Hearing Conservation Amendment (HCA), included in the *Federal Register 29 CFR* 1910.95, became effective. The Occupational Health and Safety Administration (OSHA) Noise Regulation provides specifics on the content of required hearing conservation programs. The regulation covers the following:
- noise monitoring
- audiometric testing program
- definition of standard (permanent) threshold shift
- employee follow-up and referral
- hearing protection
- employee training
- recordkeeping

This amendment requires that all OSHA-covered workers be included in hearing conservation programs if they are exposed at or above an eight-hour time-weighted average (TWA) of 85 dBA or more. Chapter 9 contains a complete discussion of the requirements of the HCA. Unfortunately, a number of people develop threshold shifts on prolonged exposure to levels as low as 80 dBA. For a discussion of compensation laws as they relate to hearing, see Chapter 9, Industrial Noise.

SUMMARY

The sophisticated hearing and vestibular functions of the ear are linked to the anatomy and physiology of the external, middle, and inner ear. Damage to the external and middle ear can cause conductive hearing loss. Sensorineural hearing loss and/or equilibrium problems are consequences of dysfunction of the inner ear components. Hearing problems can be diagnosed and monitored through the use of precise, standardized audiometric testing. Occupational hazards, particularly noise, are capable of inducing temporary and permanent hearing loss. Hearing loss of any cause can have devastating effects on an individual's general well-being.

BIBLIOGRAPHY

Alberti PW, ed. *Personal Hearing Protection in Industry*. New York: Raven Press, 1982.

American Academy of Pediatrics Committee on Environmental Health. Noise: A hazard for the fetus and newborn. *Pediatrics* 100(4): 724–727, 1997.

American Medical Association. *Guides to the Evaluation of Permanent Impairment*, 6th ed., R. Rondinelli, ed. Chicago: AMA, 2007.

Berger EH, Royster LH, Royster JD, et al., eds. *The Noise Manual*, Revised 5th ed. Fairfax, VA: American Industrial Hygiene Association, 2003.

Council for Accreditation in Occupational Hearing Conservation. *Hearing Conservation Manual*, 3rd ed. Milwaukee: Council for Accreditation in Occupational Hearing Conservation, 1993.

Gray RF, Hawthorne M. *Synopsis of Otolaryngology: Part j*, 5th ed. Boston: Butterworth-Heinemann, 1992.

Hawkins JE Jr, Johnsson LG. Light microscopic observations of the inner ear in man and monkey. *Ann Otol Rhinol Laryngol* 77(4):608–628, Aug 1968.

Johnsson LG, Hawkins JE. Human inner ear pathology as seen by stereo- and phase-contrast microscopy of surface preparations. *50 Jahre Wild Heerbrugg 1921–1971*. Wild Heerbrugg AG, Heerbrugg/Switzerland, pp. 38–42, 1971.

Katz J, Burkard R, Hood L, et al. *Handbook of Clinical Audiology*, 6th ed. Baltimore: Williams & Wilkins, 2009.

Konings A, Van Laer VL, Van Kamp G. Genetic Studies on Noise-Induced Hearing Loss: A Review. *Ear and Hearing* 30: 151-159, 2009.

May JJ. Occupational hearing loss. *Am J Ind Med* 37:112–120, 2000.

National Institute for Occupational Safety and Health. *Criteria for Recommended Standard: Occupational Noise Exposure*. Atlanta: DHHS (NIOSH) Publication No. 98-126, 1998.

Sataloff RT, Sataloff J. *Hearing Loss*, 3rd ed. New York: Marcel Dekker, 1993.

Schuknecht HF. *Pathology of the Ear*, 2nd ed. Philadelphia: Lea & Febiger, 1993.

Smith A. A review of the non-auditory effects of noise on health. *Work & Stress* 5:4962, 1991.

Steyger PS. Potentiation of Chemical Ototoxicity by Noise. *Seminars in Hearing* 30(1): 38-46, 2009.

Tufts JB, Vasil KA, Briggs S. Auditory Fitness for Duty: A Review. *J Am Acad Audiol* 20:539-557, 2009.

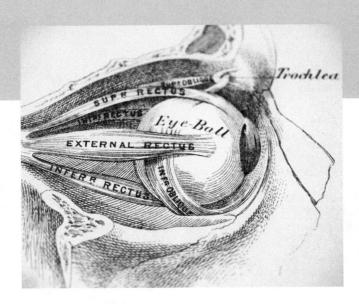

CHAPTER 5

The Eyes

by Allison S. Zaum, OD, MPH

The eye may be the organ most vulnerable to occupational injuries. Although the eye has some natural defenses, they do not compare with the healing properties of the skin, the automatic cleansing abilities of the lungs, or the recuperative powers of the ear. Consequently, the eye is at greater risk and eye and face protection is a major occupational health issue.

Potential eye hazards are found in nearly every industry. According to the U.S. Bureau of Labor Statistics, in 2008, there were 27,450 nonfatal occupational injuries or illnesses involving the eyes that resulted in days away from work, accounting for 62 percent of face injuries and 37 percent of all head injuries. These statistics represent only the OSHA-reportable injuries and illnesses.

While the majority of OSHA-reportable injuries to the eyes continue to be related to mechanical injury or contact with hazardous substances, there are other potential assaults to the eyes and visual system. "Computer Vision Syndrome" is an identified workplace condition characterized by acute and chronic eye fatigue and visual discomfort.

As with other aspects of industrial hygiene, recognition, evaluation, and control of occupational eye hazards are key to helping prevent eye injuries in all workplaces.

ANATOMY

A look at the structure of the human eye and how it can be affected by industrial hazards clarifies the need for eye protection programs. The eyeball is housed in a cone of cushioning fatty tissue that insulates it from the skull's bony eye socket. The skull has brow and cheek ridges projecting in front of the eyeball, which is composed of specialized tissue that does not react to injury like other body tissue (Figure 5–1).

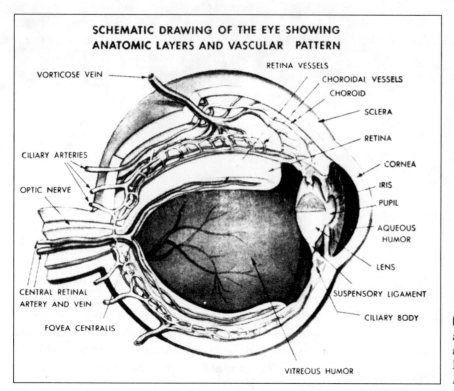

Eyeball

The eyeball consists of three coats, or layers, of tissue surrounding the transparent internal structures. There is an external fibrous layer, a middle vascular layer, and an inner layer of nerve tissue.

The outermost fibrous layer of the eyeball consists of the sclera and the cornea. The sclera, also called the white of the eye, is composed of dense fibrous tissue and is the protective and supporting outer layer of the eyeball. In front of the lens, this layer is modified from a white, opaque structure to the transparent cornea. The cornea is composed of dense fibrous connective tissue and has no blood vessels. The cornea must be transparent to let light through to the receptors in the eyeball.

The middle vascular layer of the eyeball is heavily pigmented and contains many blood vessels that help nourish other tissues.

The nerve layer, or retina, is the third and innermost layer of the eyeball. Toward the rear, the retina is continuous with the optic nerve; toward the front, it ends a short distance behind the ciliary body in a wavy border called the ora serrata. The retina is composed of two parts: the outer part is pigmented and attached to the choroid layer, and the inner part consists of nerve tissue.

The front of the eyeball is protected by a smooth, transparent layer of tissue called the conjunctiva. A similar membrane covers the inner surfaces of the eyelids. The eyelids also contain dozens of tiny tarsal glands that secrete an oil to lubricate the surfaces of the eyeball and eyelids. Still further protection is provided by the lacrimal gland, located at the outer edge of the eye socket. It secretes tears to clean the protective membrane and keep it moist (Figure 5–2).

The region between the cornea and the lens is filled with a salty, clear fluid known as the aqueous. The eyeball behind the lens is filled with a jelly-like substance called the vitreous.

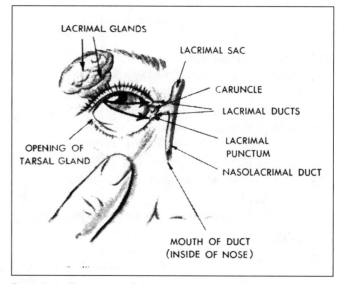

Light rays enter the transparent cornea and are refracted at the curved interface between air and the fluid bathing the cornea. After passing through the cornea and the clear liquid (the aqueous, contained in the anterior chamber), the bundle of rays is restricted by a circular variable aperture, the pupil. Its size is changed by action of the iris muscles.

The light rays are further refracted by passage through the lens, traversing the clear, jelly-like vitreous, so that, in a properly focused eye, a sharp image is formed on the retina. Scattering of light within the eye is minimized by a darkly pigmented layer of tissue underlying the retina, called the choroid. The choroid contains an extremely rich blood supply that is believed to dissipate the heat resulting from absorbed light energy. The shape of the eyeball is maintained by its enclosure in an elastic capsule, the sclera, and by the fluids within the sclera that are maintained at positive pressure.

The lens is attached by suspensory ligaments to the ciliary body, a muscular organ attached to the sclera. The ciliary body muscles alter the lens shape to fine-focus the incoming light beam. Ordinarily, these muscles are active only when looking at objects closer than 20 ft (6.1 m). Consequently, when doing prolonged work at a computer, it is helpful for the eyes to pause occasionally and look out a window into the distance. Many complaints of eye fatigue are really complaints about tired ciliary muscles. The pigmented iris, overlying the lens, is a muscular structure designed to expand or contract and thus regulate the amount of light entering the eye. The circular aperture formed by the iris is called the pupil.

The aqueous and vitreous and other eye tissues are composed primarily of water, so their absorption characteristics are similar to those of water.

Retina

The retina, a thin membrane lining the rear of the eye, contains the light-sensitive cells. These cells are of two functionally discrete types: rods and cones. They get their names from the rod and cone shapes seen when the layer is viewed under a microscope. The rods are more sensitive to light than the cones; the cones are sensitive to colors.

There are more rod cells than cones; each eye has about 120 million rods and only 6 million cones. The rods are incapable of color discrimination because they contain a single photosensitive pigment. There are fewer cone cells, and they are less sensitive to low levels of luminance. There are three types of cones in the human eye; each contains a different photopigment, with peak response to a particular part of the visible spectrum. Thus, by differential transmission of nerve impulses on stimulation, the cones encode information about the spectral content of the image so that the observer experiences the sensation of color. About 6-8 percent of males and less than 0.1 percent of females inherit a defect in one of the cone pigments, so that the wavelength of maximum absorption is somewhat shifted. People with these color defects are not color "blind," as they do see colors, but rather are color defective, in that they perceive certain colors differently from people with "normal" cone pigments.

Binocular Vision

Binocular vision refers to vision with two eyes. The advantages of binocular vision are a larger visual field and a perception of depth, or stereoscopic vision. There is a slight difference in the images on the two retinas; there is a right-eyed picture on the right retina and a left-eyed picture on the left retina. It is as if the same landscape were photographed twice, with the camera in two positions a slight distance apart. The two images blend in consciousness and give us an impression of depth or solidity. Binocular vision is not identical to depth perception but is an important clue to that visual function. Depth perception is further discussed in the section on visual performance in this chapter.

EYE PROBLEMS

Specialists in the field of vision include ophthalmologists, optometrists, and opticians. They use a variety of tests and instruments to examine a person's visual status, including the Snellen chart to test for distance acuity, ophthalmoscope, slit-lamp microscope, tonometer, perimeterbinocular indirect ophthalmoscope, pachymeter, and phoropter.

Specialists

Ophthalmologist

The American Academy of Ophthalmology defines an ophthalmologist as a doctor of medicine (MD) who specializes in the comprehensive care of the eye and visual system. Each is licensed by a state to practice medicine and surgery.

Optometrist

The American Optometric Association defines an optometrist (Doctor of Optometry, or OD) as a primary health care provider who diagnoses, manages, and treats conditions and diseases of the human eye and visual system. All states now permit optometrists to prescribe certain therapeutic pharmaceuticals and provide treatment for ocular diseases; the specifics vary with each state. Both ophthalmologists and optometrists prescribe eyeglasses and contact lenses.

Optician

The Opticians Association of America defines an optician

as an individual who manufactures, verifies, and delivers lenses, frames, and other specially fabricated optical devices.

Examining Instruments

The vision tests used in industrial preplacement examinations are screening tests. They detect possible problems in visual performance and are not by themselves diagnostic. They should not be the basis of any job restrictions without further evaluation by a qualified eye doctor (ophthalmologist or optometrist) and consideration of reasonable accommodations.

Snellen Chart

The most common industrial test for distance acuity is the Snellen wall chart in its several variations. The Snellen chart consists of block letters in diminishing sizes so that at various distances, the appropriate letter subtends a visual angle of five minutes at the nodal point of the eye. Thus, the top large letter appears to be the same size when it is 200 ft (61 m) away as the standard appears at 20 ft (6.1 m).

The distance of 20 ft (6.1 m) is considered to be infinity. This means that the rays of light coming from an illuminated object are parallel; they neither diverge nor converge. If the object is closer than 20 ft (6.1 m), the light rays diverge and must be made parallel by action of the lens within the eye or by the addition of a supplementary lens held in front of the eye; otherwise, they do not come to a sharp focus on the area of central visual acuity of the retina.

The cornea and lens of the eye bend the parallel rays to converge to a focus on the retina. Looking at an object at 20 ft (6.1 m) or more, the normal lens is relaxed into its usual biconvex shape. The parallel rays of light that are bent (refracted) by the cornea and lens cross at the nodal point of the eye (about 7 mm behind the cornea) and, continuing their straight course, fall on the retina, forming an inverted image.

It is important to check several factors. The distance from the chart to the person being tested must be 20 ft (6.1 m), or 10 ft (3 m) if a mirror and reversed chart are used. The lighting should be uniform, its source not visible to the person being tested. The chart should be clean. Finally, the tester must be trained to hold the cover correctly over the eye not being tested, to vary the order of lines and letters, and to be alert for any unusual factors, including squinting. It is important to separately test and record the vision of each eye alone and with both eyes together.

Satisfactory vision at a distance does not ensure adequate near-point vision, so it is important to recognize near-point abnormalities. Many industrial work situations involve near-point seeing even though they are not confined to near-point work.

Industrial vision testing should be done with standardized tests to detect and identify substandard visual functions. Accuracy is vital, since workers with visual defects can put themselves and others at risk. A competent examination of the eyes requires the use of a number of special examining instruments.

- An *ophthalmoscope* permits study of the interior structures of the eye, such as the retina, optic nerve, and vitreous.
- A *slit-lamp microscope* allows study of the anterior segment of the eye, and with the use of additional lenses, the posterior (interior) structures of the eye as well.
- A *tonometer* is used to measure the pressure in the eyeball (one of the tests for glaucoma).
- A *perimeter* is used to map the limits of the fields of vision.
- A *gonioscopic lens* views the angle of the anterior chamber where the outflow drainage apparatus of the eye is found.
- A *binocular indirect ophthalmoscope* allows viewing of the peripheral retina.
- A *phoropter* is used to determine refractive correction (eyeglass prescription) and binocular vision abnormalities. It consists of test lenses and prisms that are added and removed using both objective criteria and subjective responses (Figure 5–3).

Eye Defects

A 1995 study by Lighthouse International compiled statistics on visual impairments in the United States. Approximately 1.1 million Americans (0.5%) are considered legally blind,

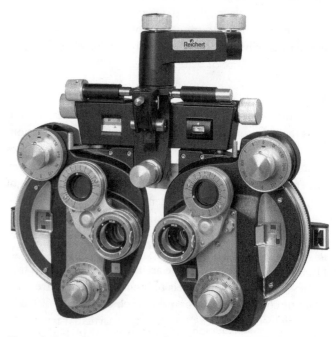

Figure 5–3. A phoropter is used with a set of test lenses to find which ones aid vision. (*Photograph reprinted with permission of Reichert Technologies.*)

as defined by clinical measurement (a visual acuity with corrective devices of 20/200 or less, or a visual field in the better eye of 20 degrees or less). In addition, more than 10 million people (about one in every 20) in the United States suffer from significant impairment of vision that cannot be improved by corrective lenses. This condition is designated as "low vision." The leading causes of existing cases of blindness are glaucoma, macular degeneration, cataracts, atrophy of the optic nerve, diabetic retinopathy, and retinitis pigmentosa. These causes account for 51 percent of all cases of blindness, according to the National Society to Prevent Blindness. The leading causes of new cases of blindness are macular degeneration, glaucoma, diabetic retinopathy, and cataract; combined, these account for 52.5 percent of all new cases. A large percentage of all cases of blindness could be prevented by taking advantage of current medical technology and proper safety measures.

It has been estimated that 40 percent of the population wear glasses, indicating that nearly one in two people have some visual defect. Three common eye defects—farsightedness, nearsightedness, and astigmatism—are the results of simple optical aberrations in the eye. Additionally, with the aging of America, *presbyopia*, the age-related decrease in near vision, will affect an increasingly larger segment of the population, as will cataracts and age-related macular degeneration.

Farsightedness

When the eyeball is too short from front to back, the light rays come to a focus behind the retina. Light rays coming from a distant object may reach their focus at the retina, so that distant vision is good, but near vision is blurred. This condition is called farsightedness or *hyperopia*. The treatment is to wear a convex lens that converges the light rays from near objects so that they are brought to a focus on the retina (Figure 5–4). When a farsighted person becomes presbyopic or starts to lose the ability to accommodate, glasses may be necessary for distance vision as well as for reading.

Nearsightedness

If the eyeball is too long from front to back, as it is in nearsightedness, or *myopia*, the image of an object 20 ft (6.1 m) or more away falls somewhere in front of the retina. The eye can focus on it sharply only by looking through a concave lens, which diverges the rays coming from the object. By bringing the object near enough to the eyes, a myopic person can get a good focus (Figure 5–5).

Astigmatism

If the curvature of the cornea is irregular so that some rays of light are bent more in one direction than in another, the resulting image is blurred because if one part of the ray is focused, the other part is not. This is something like the

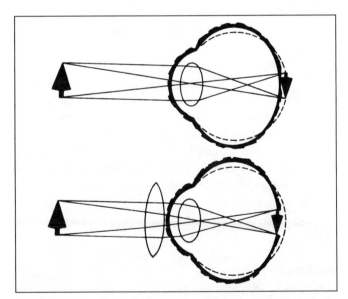

Figure 5–4. In farsightedness, or hyperopia, the eyeball is too short, so the image of an object is focused behind the retina. A convex lens brings the light rays into focus on the retina. Although hyperopic people may be able to see things sharply by thickening the lens of the eye (accommodation), this involves effort of inner muscles of the eye and may cause eye fatigue. *(Reprinted with permission from Cooley DG, ed.* Family Medical Guide. *New York: Better Homes and Gardens Books, 1973.)*

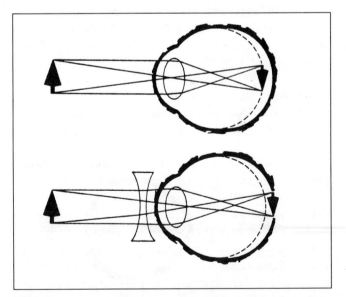

Figure 5–5. In nearsightedness, or myopia, the image of an object (unless it is held close to the eyes) falls in front of the retina instead of on it, and the object is seen indistinctly. The condition is corrected by using a concave lens of proper curvature to bring the image into focus on the retina. *(Reprinted with permission from Cooley DG, ed.* Family Medical Guide. *New York: Better Homes and Gardens Books, 1973.)*

distortion produced by the back of a spoon, and is called astigmatism. It is corrected by using a lens that bends the rays of light in only one diameter (axis). This lens is called a cylindrical lens and it can be turned in the trial frame to its proper axis to even up the focusing of the light rays in all parts (Figure 5–6).

A person can have astigmatism in addition to nearsightedness or farsightedness. Small amounts of astigmatism that do not severely affect distance vision may cause eyestrain for people who spend prolonged time working at a computer. Glasses often help provide relief for such individuals.

Presbyopia

The closer an object is brought to the eye, the more convex the human eye lens must become to focus on it. Through aging, the human lens loses its accommodative power, that is, its elasticity and its power of thickening. This condition is known as presbyopia, and usually develops after around age 40. Nearsighted individuals may find they need to remove their spectacles for reading or other close work. Farsighted people, many of whom who never needed glasses before, will start to experience near blur or eyestrain while working at the computer.

Presbyopia is corrected by wearing convex lenses, often in a bifocal or other multifocal lens. The reading prescription (or "add") gets progressively higher until around the age of 55 years, when it generally stabilizes. Contact lens wearers who experience blurry vision while reading or at the computer with their distance correction may need glasses to wear over their contacts or can try monovision or multifocal contact lenses.

Eyeglasses

The purpose of wearing eyeglasses is to help focus the rays of light on the retina. Glasses cannot change the eye or

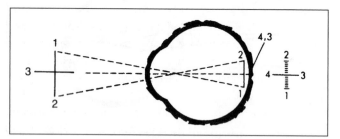

Figure 5–6. Astigmatism resulting from irregular curvature of the cornea is something like distortion produced by a wavy pane of glass. The drawing shows light rays (3,4) in sharp focus on the retina, with light rays (1,2) focused in front of the retina, resulting in a blurred image. The small diagram on the right shows horizontal image in focus, vertical image out of focus. A cylindrical lens placed in the proper axis to bring light rays to even focus corrects astigmatism.

produce any disease even if they are badly fitted. Wearing glasses does not make the eyes weaker, and not wearing glasses will not "strengthen" the eyes.

An example of a prescription for glasses is shown here:

$$+ 2.50 - 0.50 \times 180$$

The + sign indicates a convex lens suitable for a farsighted person. A – sign would indicate a concave lens for a myopic person. The 2.50 indicates the diopters, which indicate the strength or power of the lens. A diopter (D) is a unit of measurement of the refractive or light-bending power of a lens. The normal human lens in its relaxed biconvex shape has a power of about 10 D.

Thus, the prescription in the example means that the optician grinds a convex spherical lens of 2.50 diopters combined with a concave cylindrical lens of half a diopter (0.50) situated horizontally (axis 180 degrees). Bifocal or other multifocal lenses (such as progressive or "no line bifocal" lenses) also include a prescription for reading, called an addition or "add." If the person with the above hyperopic (farsighted) correction also needed 2.00 diopters additional to read, the prescription would read as follows:

$$+ 2.50 - 0.50 \times 180 \text{ with } + 2.00 \text{ add}$$

VISUAL PERFORMANCE

Normal visual performance involves a number of interdependent discriminations made in response to the visual environment and mediated by the visual system.

Visual Acuity

There are many definitions of the term visual acuity; all, however, incorporate the concept of detail resolution. Many test patterns have been used to measure acuity, from single dots to twin stars, gratings, broken rings, checkerboards, and letters. The Snellen Letter Test is probably the most familiar and is widely used. The most satisfactory expression for visual acuity is the amount of critical detail that can just be discriminated.

Some important variables affecting visual acuity are as follows:

Luminance

The level of adaptation of the eye has a profound effect on visual acuity.

Position in the field

At photopic levels, acuity is best at the fovea and drops off as the retinal periphery is approached because there are fewer cones at the periphery. Nocturnal acuity is quite poor, with essential blindness at the fovea and best resolution in the periphery, where rods are more plentiful. This can be appreciated when looking at stars, as a star can often be detected more clearly when viewed peripherally than straight on.

Duration

When the pattern is viewed for only a short time, measured acuity diminishes.

Contrast

Visual acuity decreases as the contrast between pattern and background diminishes. The strength of this correlation depends on the adapting luminance. People with visual disorders often have reduced contrast sensitivity but reasonable Snellen acuities; some states are requiring contrast sensitivity testing for driver's licenses, in addition to acuity.

Dark Adaptation

Optimal visual discrimination under conditions of very low light can be made only if the eyes are adapted to the level of the prevailing light or lower. If a fully light-adapted eye is suddenly plunged into darkness, its initial sensitivity is poor. With time, however, sensitivity increases as a result of photochemical regeneration, certain functional neural changes, and, to a much smaller degree, enlargement of the pupil. After the eye remains in total darkness for 30–60 minutes, the adaptation process is nearly complete; the sensitivity of the eye in parts of the retina where both rods and cones are present is increased by a factor of 10,000 for white light.

There are several important operational consequences of the dark adaptation process:

- Best performance on a task in low light requires that the eye be preadapted to an appropriately low level long enough to attain maximum sensitivity.
- Because the rods are more sensitive than the cones at low light levels, detection capability is highest on the parts of the retina where rods abound (10–30 degrees from the fovea) and averted vision is required for optimal performance.
- Because the rods are relatively insensitive to extreme red wavelengths, dark adaptation is facilitated if the observer wears red goggles or if the illumination provided is a very deep red, as in a spacecraft or photographic darkroom. By this means, the observer can continue to use the high-acuity capability of the central fovea at elevated luminance levels for reading instruments and such while the adaptation process goes on, although vision naturally is monochromatic in this case.
- Because the two eyes are essentially independent in adaptation, it is possible to maintain dark adaptation in one

(using an eye patch, for example) while the other is used at high light levels.

Depth Perception

Depth can be estimated by an experienced observer through use of various cues. Some of these cues are provided by the nature of the scene of interest; others are inherent in the observer.

In cases where only internal cues to distance are available—that is, when objects of interest are of unknown size and shape—the observer must depend on his or her stereoscopic acuity, accommodation, and convergence, and, where possible, movement parallax. Accommodation is the only effective cue to distances at ranges of a meter or less, and even here it is inaccurate. Convergence (bringing the eyes toward the nose) alone is a somewhat more useful cue, but only within about 20 m of the observer. Stereoscopic acuity provides a powerful clue to distance, but it should not be assumed that people with monocular vision cannot do tasks normally assumed to require stereoscopic vision; actual performance should be tested. Certain jobs (e.g., pilots), however, do require a minimum amount of depth perception.

Commercially available stereopsis tests include the Titmus "Fly" and the Randot stereo test (available from Bernell and other suppliers).

Color Vision

Color deficiencies can impose restrictions in certain occupations. These include electricians, pilots, commercial drivers, firefighters, dye workers, and many other professions. A commonly administered test is the Ishihara color plate test. These plates are extremely sensitive at identifying red-green defects, the most common inherited color defects. Another color test is the Farnsworth D-15 Panel Test. In this test, the subject arranges a series of colored caps. Some employers accept individuals with a color deficiency if they can pass certain trade tests, such as the FALANT (Farnsworth Lantern Test), used to evaluate recognition of aviation and maritime colored signal and marker lights. People with mild or borderline color deficiencies may be able to demonstrate sufficient color vision for a particular job by passing the D-15 Panel.

Even when color discrimination is not a job criterion, baseline color vision testing for all employees is useful, in that it can help distinguish between inherited color defects and those that are acquired (caused by disease). For example, certain optic nerve disorders can cause color deficiencies.

A very small percentage of the population is truly "color blind," in that they have no cones in their retinas, only rods. This condition is called rod monochromatism. These people are extremely photophobic and have markedly decreased visual acuity. They usually need to wear tinted glasses for comfort, and may require additional occupational modifications and low vision aids.

EYE DISORDERS

There are numerous eye disorders. Conjunctivitis, infections, uveitis, glaucoma, cataracts, sensitivity to excessive brightness, night blindness, eyestrain, and nystagmus are among the disorders most commonly encountered. They are briefly described.

Conjunctivitis, Infections, and Uveitis

Various types of conjunctivitis, or inflammation of the mucous membrane, can develop beneath the eyelids. The eye becomes scratchy and red and has a discharge. Most often the cause is viral, bacterial, or allergic. All causes produce varying degrees of redness, which is often referred to as "pink eye." Viral infections usually produce tearing, bacterial infections cause pus or mucous discharge, and allergic reactions cause itching and occasionally a stringy discharge. Conjunctivitis is also often related to contact lens wear.

Bacterial, viral, or fungal infections can affect the cornea. They can cause pain, decreased vision, and photophobia (light sensitivity). Contact lens wearers are particularly susceptible to bacterial infections. Employees presenting with red eyes should be immediately evaluated by an eye care practitioner, as there are bacterial strains that can penetrate an intact cornea within 24 hours.

A fairly common type of infection, especially in adults, is caused by the herpes simplex virus on the anterior surface of the eyeball. This can lead to blurred vision, scarring, and permanent damage to vision. It may affect one or both eyes and quite often recurs. Topical steroids often used for other types of conjunctivitis greatly aggravate herpes infections. Therefore, any signs suggesting inflammation near the cornea should be immediately referred to an eye care practitioner experienced in treating eye disorders.

Inflammation of the interior eye is common in adults. One of the most common areas of infection is the uveal tract, which is the middle coat of the eye. Inflammation of this type damages the retina, the lens, and the cornea. The cause of a uveal inflammation (or *uveitis*) is often idiopathic, but can also be associated with diseases of the joints, lung, or intestinal tract. A search must be made for disease elsewhere in the body that might be the cause of the eye problem. When found, the primary cause should be treated. The eye should also be treated to prevent damage to vision. Once again, an employee presenting with a red, painful,

and photophobic eye should be immediately evaluated by an eye care practitioner.

Glaucoma

Glaucoma is a leading cause of blindness in America. The most common form, *primary open-angle glaucoma* (POAG), was originally thought to develop when the fluid that normally fills the eyeball, the aqueous, fails to drain properly. Ordinarily, the fluid is continuously produced in the eye and excess drains off through a small duct near the iris. Aging, infection, injuries, congenital defects, and other causes can constrict or block the duct. Fluid pressure then builds up and the pressure, if great and of long duration, can damage the optic nerve. Recent research has hypothesized that reduced blood perfusion to the optic nerve may be a potential cause of POAG. This form of glaucoma is not painful and often can go undiagnosed for years in someone who doesn't get regular eye examinations, as early stages do not tend to cause any visual symptoms. Sometimes symptoms include the perception of colored rings and halos about bright objects, or dimming of side vision.

In another form of the disease, *acute-angle closure glaucoma*, vision dims suddenly, the eyeball becomes painful and very light-sensitive, and the patient feels quite ill. An angle closure attack should be considered an ocular emergency.

Much can be done to preserve vision in most cases when glaucoma is diagnosed early. Medication is often effective in controlling the pressure. In recalcitrant cases, laser treatment or filtering surgery may be indicated.

Cataracts

Cataracts are opacities that form on the lens and impair the vision of many elderly and some younger people. Many cases are associated with metabolic disease or aging, but there are also traumatic cases associated with industrial exposures to ionizing radiation, ultraviolet radiation, infrared radiation, foreign bodies, and certain chemicals. Cataracts can also be caused by certain medications, particularly prolonged treatment with corticosteroids. There is also evidence that cigarette smoking increases cataract development. If the vision impairment is severe, the diseased lens can be removed, and is generally replaced with a plastic implant.

Excessive Brightness

Good sunglasses can protect the eyes in bright sunlight. Glasses with scratches and irregularities should not be used. Some glasses are too lightly tinted to do much good; good glasses reduce the invisible as well as the visible light. (Injury from light will be discussed later in this chapter under irradiation burns.) In addition to helping relieve discomfort caused by glare, sunglasses provide important protection to the anterior and posterior structures of the eyes. Glasses worn outside, both clear and tinted, should provide 100% UVA and UVB protection.

Night Blindness

Inability to see well or at all in dim light can mean something is wrong not only with the eye but with the entire visual system. Night blindness, as it is called, is a threat to safety, particularly on the highway, because a driver may have 20/20 vision and not realize that his or her vision is somewhat impaired at night. The condition produces no discernible change in eye tissues, so it cannot be diagnosed unless a patient tells the physician of difficulty in reading road signs or picking out objects at night. People with small, uncorrected refractive errors (nearsightedness, farsightedness, or astigmatism) may notice decreased night vision caused by the enlargement of the pupils that occurs normally in the darkness; wearing corrective lenses will help with these symptoms. Incipient cataracts may also cause disabling glare with night driving.

Eyestrain

Eyestrain can lead to severe signs of local irritation, headaches, fatigue, vertigo, and digestive and psychological reactions. This condition can result from a need for eyeglasses or from using glasses with the wrong correction. Eye muscle strain may also result from unfavorable conditions such as improper lighting while reading or doing close work. To avoid strain when reading, do not face the light; it should come from behind and to the side. Be sure light bulbs are strong enough (75–100 watts). Hold the book or paper about 16–18 in. (0.4 m) away and slightly below eye level. Avoid glare and occasionally rest the eyes by shifting focus and looking off into the distance. ANSI/IES-RP-7 provides detailed recommendations for the design of industrial lighting.

Nystagmus

Nystagmus, involuntary movement of the eyeballs, may occur among workers who, for extended periods, subject their eyes to abnormal and unaccustomed movements. Complaints of objects dancing before the eyes, headaches, dizziness, and general fatigue are associated symptoms; all can clear up quickly if a change of work is made. The involuntary movements of the eyeball characteristic of nystagmus can sometimes be induced by occupational causes affecting the eyes through the central nervous system or by some extraneous cause. The most prevalent form of occupational nystagmus is seen in miners. However, most forms of nystagmus are congenital.

PHYSICAL HAZARDS

The eye is subject to many kinds of physical injury—blows from blunt objects, cuts from sharp objects, and damage from foreign bodies.

Blows from Objects

A blow from a blunt object can produce direct pressure on the eyeball or, if the object delivering the blow seals the rim of the bony orbit on impact, it can exert hydraulic pressure. Such blows may cause contusion of the iris, lens, retina, or even the optic nerve. Violent blows might rupture the entire globe or fracture the thin lower plate of the bony orbit, entrapping the eye muscles.

Contusions may result in serious, irreversible injury if not treated promptly and adequately. Hemorrhaging releases blood, which can be toxic to eye tissues, and physical dislocations of lens, retina, and other parts are unlikely to repair themselves. Lacerations of the cornea, lid, or conjunctiva can be caused by any sharp object, from a knife to the corner of a piece of paper.

Corneal Lacerations and Abrasions

Corneal lacerations, if full-thickness, may allow the aqueous solution behind the cornea to gush out until the iris, which has the consistency of wet tissue paper, is pulled toward the laceration and plugs the wound. The iris can be put back in place, the laceration sutured, and the eye made nearly as good as new. More common corneal injuries are scrapes or abrasions that do not penetrate to the chamber behind the cornea. Such abrasions are very painful, but heal within several days if treated properly. If they are too deep or allowed to become infected, the result can be scars that interfere with vision.

Lacerations of the lid heal, but the scar tissue can pull the lid into an unnatural position. In addition to cosmetic deformity, the lids might not close completely or lashes might turn in against the eyeball. Vertical lacerations are more serious in this respect.

Because it is composed of highly differentiated tissues, the eye is more likely than a finger to suffer permanent damage from injury. This does not mean the eye has no natural defenses. The bony ridges of the skull protect the eyeball from traumatic injury caused by massive impact. A baseball, for instance, is too big to crush the eyeball—it is stopped by the bony orbit. The cushioning layers of conjunctiva and muscle around the eyeball absorb impact. The fact that the eyeball can be displaced in its socket is also a defense against injury. In addition, the optic nerve is long enough to allow some displacement of the eyeball without rupture of the nerve.

Blink Reflex

The eye is most vulnerable to attack at the corneal surface. Here, the eye is equipped with an automatic wiper and washer combination. The washers are the lacrimal glands; the wiper is the blinking action. The teary blink washes foreign bodies from the corneal or conjunctival surfaces before they can become embedded. The triggering mechanism is irritation.

The reflex blink can also act like a door to shut out a foreign object heading for the eye if the eye can see it coming and it isn't coming too fast. Protective equipment for the eye is used in industry to improve or extend these natural defenses. These defenses might be adequate protection against light and small foreign objects and small quantities of mildly toxic liquids, but they are no match for industrial eye hazards such as small high-speed particles or caustic powders and liquids.

Foreign Bodies

Invasion by a foreign body is the most common type of physical injury to the eye. Not all foreign bodies, however, affect the eye in the same way.

Foreign bodies affecting the conjunctiva are not usually very serious. They may result in redness and discomfort, but not vision damage. Bodies on the conjunctiva, however, can be transferred to the cornea and become embedded if a person rubs the eye. Even with minor irritations of the conjunctiva, a trip to the nurse is advisable. If there is obvious irritation and no object can be found, it is advisable to see an eye doctor immediately.

Some industrial eye injuries may appear trivial, but can become serious due to complications. The most common complication is infection, which can cause delayed healing and corneal scarring. The infection can be carried into the intraocular tissues by a foreign substance and the bacteria can originate either from sources outside of the eye or from pathogenic organisms already present on the lids, conjunctiva, or in the lacrimal apparatus.

Foreign bodies in the cornea can cause the following problems:

- *Pain*. Because the cornea is heavily endowed with nerves, an object sitting on the surface of the cornea constantly stimulates the nerves.
- *Infection*. Bacteria or fungi can be carried by the foreign particle or by fingers used to rub the eye. Such infections used to be much more common, but antibiotics (and antifungals) have greatly reduced the problem.
- *Scarring*. Corneal tissue will heal, but the scars are optically imperfect and may obscure vision.

Intraocular foreign bodies can cause the following problems:

- *Infection*. Infection is much less of a problem with low-speed, low-mass particles, but in some cases, the speed of small metallic particles often creates enough heat to sterilize them. Wood particles, however, do not heat up; if they penetrate the eye, they can cause dangerous infection, which usually causes a marked reduction in vision.
- *Damage*. Depending on its angle, point of entry, and speed, an intraocular particle may cause traumatic damage to the cornea, iris, lens, or retina. Damage to the lens is especially serious because it is not supplied with blood and is slow to heal. Also, any damage to the lens can act as a catalyst for protein coagulation, resulting in opacity and loss of vision.

Pure copper particles can cause serious damage to the eye because the toxic copper molecules become deposited in the lens, cornea, and iris (chalcosis). Copper alloys do not seem to have any toxic effects.

Pain cannot be relied on to alert the worker that there is a foreign body in his or her eye. The cornea is very sensitive, but if the object has penetrated into the eyeball, there may be no acute pain.

Thermal Burns

Heat can destroy eye and eyelid tissue just as it does any other body tissue, but eye tissues do not recover as well as skin and muscle from such trauma. The lids are more likely to be involved in burns than the eye itself because involuntary closing of the eye is an automatic response to excessive heat.

Irradiation Burns

Nonionizing radiation can be an ocular hazard. Infrared, visible, and ultraviolet light and lasers can present the most significant exposures. Workplace assessments of nonionizing radiation hazards should always include the potential for damage to the eyes, and appropriate engineering controls and protective equipment specified where needed to prevent such injuries. (See Chapter 11, Nonionizing Radiation, for more details.)

Damage Mechanisms

Light in sufficient amounts may damage eye tissue, ranging from barely detectable impairment to gross lesions. The degree of damage depends on the tissue involved and the energy of the incident light photon. Far-infrared light usually effects damage through a general increase in tissue temperature, whereas far-ultraviolet light generally causes specific photochemical reactions.

Damage to lens cells may not be apparent for some time after insult because of the low level of metabolic activity. Low-degree damage is evidenced by vision clouding or cataract and usually is not reversible. When recovery does occur, it is a slow process. Lens damage may be cumulative because dead cells cannot be eliminated from the lens capsule, causing a progressive loss of visual acuity.

Retinal damage can take a number of forms. Generally, the neural components of the retina, such as the photoreceptors, may regenerate when slightly injured, but usually degenerate when extensively injured.

Ultraviolet Radiation

Harmful exposures to ultraviolet (UV) light usually occur in welding operations, particularly in electric arc welding. The effects include acute keratoconjunctivitis (welder's flash), an acute inflammation of the cornea and conjunctiva that develops within about six hours after even a momentary exposure to the arc light. The welder rarely is involved, being too close to the arc to look at it without an eyeshield, but welders' helpers and other bystanders often suffer from exposure.

Infrared Radiation

Unlike UV, infrared (IR) radiation passes easily through the cornea and its energy is absorbed by the lens and retina. With automation of metals operations, eye damage from IR radiation is not as common as it once was.

Visible Light

Various combinations of light sources, exposure duration, and experimental animals have been used to determine the threshold level of light capable of producing a visible retinal lesion. Unfortunately, the experiments recorded were not systematically designed or standardized, leaving numerous gaps and inconsistencies in the reports. Such parameters as pulse duration and irradiated spot area or diameter on the retina are notably lacking. Methods of measurement are often unstated, making comparisons and appraisals of accuracy difficult.

Many models have been proposed to explain the production of visible lesions on the retina from exposure to laser light. Most of the models consider thermal injury to be the only cause of damage. (See Chapter 11, Nonionizing Radiation, for more details.)

Chemical Hazards

The effects of accidental contamination of the eye with chemicals vary from minor irritation to complete loss of vision. In addition to accidental splashing, some mists, vapors, and gases produce eye irritation, either acute or chronic. In some instances, a chemical that does no damage to the eye can be sufficiently absorbed to cause systemic poisoning.

Exposure to irritant chemicals provokes acute inflammation of the cornea (acute keratitis), with pinpoint vacuoles (holes) of the cornea, which rapidly break down into erosions. Some industrial chemicals irritate the mucous membrane, stimulating lacrimation (excessive watering of the eyes). Other results can include discoloration of the conjunctiva, disturbances of vision, double vision from paralysis of the eye muscles, optic atrophy, and temporary or permanent blindness.

Chemical Burns

Chemical burns can be divided into three categories: alkali burns, acid burns, and irritants.

Alkali burns are the most dangerous, since they have a saponification effect on the tissues of the eye, denaturing collagen and thrombosing vessels. In general, more damage occurs from higher pH chemicals. Common alkalis include ammonia hydroxides, lye, potassium hydroxide, magnesium, fertilizers, and lime. Because alkali burns are usually much more injurious to the eyes than acids, their medical prognosis is always guarded. An eye might not look too bad on the first day after exposure to a caustic, but later it may deteriorate markedly. This is in contrast to acid burns, in which the initial appearance is a good indication of the ultimate damage.

Acid burns result from exposure to chemicals with a low pH. These are usually less severe burns, since they don't penetrate the eye as readily as the alkaline substances. The exception is hydrofluoric acid (HF), a chemical commonly used in the semiconductor industry. HF burns can have a delayed effect, whereby pain is not immediately felt; systemic fluoride poisoning can occur from exposure. Other commonly used acids include sulfuric acid, hydrochloric acid, nitric acid, acetic acid, and chromic acid. An exploding car battery (releasing sulfuric acid) is a frequent cause of acid burns to the eye.

Irritants are substances that have a neutral pH and tend to cause more discomfort to the eyes than actual damage to them. Most household detergents fall into this category, as does pepper spray.

The ultimate result of a chemical burn may be a scar on the cornea. If this is not in the central visual axis, vision may not be greatly hampered. If the scar is superficial, a corneal transplant can alleviate burn damage. Densely scarred corneal tissue cannot be repaired by transplants, but plastic implants are now available. When the chemical penetrates the anterior chamber of the eye, the condition is called iritis (irritation caused by bathing the iris with the chemical agent). Glaucoma may be a complication of chemical iritis.

Evaluating Eye Hazards

It does not take special training or engineering skills to identify most eye hazards. When people handle chemical substances, when airborne particles of dust, wood, metal, or stone are present, or when blows from blunt objects are likely, eye protection is necessary. Biohazards to hospital and other health care workers also need to be considered.

Workers directly involved with operations producing these hazards are usually included in protective equipment programs, but workers on the perimeter of eye-hazardous operations also need to be protected.

The danger from agents with delayed or cumulative effects is even less likely to be recognized. A host of new technologies carry risk of exposure to a portion of the ultraviolet spectrum: industrial photo processes, sterilization and disinfection, UV therapy and diagnosis in ambulatory medicine and dentistry, polymerization of dental and orthopedic resins, research labs, and insect traps. Nonoccupational exposures from outdoor activities or tanning parlors may enhance borderline exposures in the workplace.

First Aid

Propelled object injuries require immediate medical attention. Even for foreign bodies on the corneal surface, self-help should be discouraged; removal of such particles is a job for a trained medical staff member.

Chemical splash injuries require a different approach. Here the extent of permanent damage depends almost entirely on how the victim reacts. If the victim of a concentrated caustic splash gets quickly to an eyewash fountain, properly irrigates the eye for at least 15 minutes, and promptly receives expert medical attention, the chances are good for a clear cornea or, at most, minimal damage.

Such irrigation should be with plain water from standard eyewash fountains, emergency showers, hoses, or any other available sources. Water for eye irrigation should be clean and within certain temperature limits for comfort. Tests show that 112°F (33°C) is about the upper threshold limit for comfort, but colder water, even ice water, apparently causes no harm and is not uncomfortable enough to discourage irrigation.

ANSI Z358.1–2009

The American National Standard Institute (ANSI) standard Z358.1–2009 covers the design and function of eyewash fountains; the water should meet potable standards. It has been noted that acanthamoebae capable of infecting traumatized eyes can be present in potable water. No cases have been directly attributed to the presence of these organisms in eyewash stations, but it seems prudent to follow the ANSI recommendation of a weekly systemic flushing. At least three minutes of flushing significantly reduces the number of organisms.

Portable units are intended for brief irrigation of an injury. A full 15-minute flushing of the injured eye at a stationary station should follow. It has been suggested that water for a portable station be treated with calcium hypochlorite up to 25 ppm free chlorine to eliminate acanthamoebae.

Some industrial medical units use sterile water for irrigation. Use of water substitutes such as neutralizing solutions, boric acid solutions, and mineral oil is discouraged by nearly all industrial ophthalmologists because in many instances, such preparations can cause eye damage greater than if no irrigation were used at all.

PROTECTIVE EQUIPMENT

All eye-protection equipment is designed to enhance one or more of the eye's natural defenses. Chipper's cup goggles extend the bony ridge protecting the eye socket and provide an auxiliary, more penetration-resistant cornea. Chemical splash goggles are better than a blinking eyelid.

There is a tremendous variety of eye protection available, from throwaway visitor's eye shields to trifocal prescription safety spectacles, and from welder's helmets to clip-on, antiglare lenses. But the classic safety glasses, with or without sideshields, are probably adequate for 90 percent of general industrial work.

The requirement for proper eye protection should be vigorously enforced to ensure maximum protection for the degree of hazard involved. On certain jobs, 100 percent eye protection must be insisted on.

Protection of the eyes and face from injury by physical and chemical agents or by radiation is vital in any occupational safety program. Eye-protective devices must be considered optical instruments and should be carefully selected, fitted, and used.

Unfortunately, the very term safety glasses can be confusing. A Food and Drug Administration (FDA) ruling, effective January 1, 1972, requires that all prescription eyeglass and sunglass lenses be impact-resistant. However, such lenses are not the equivalent of industrial-quality safety lenses, and they should not be used in an industrial environment where protection is mandatory.

ANSI Z87.1–2003

Only safety eyewear that meets or exceeds the requirements of ANSI standard Z87.1–2003, Practice for Occupational and Educational Eye and Face Protection (referenced in OSHAct Regulations), is approved for full-time use by industrial workers.

The 2003 changes in the standard classified personal eye protectors as being either "basic" or "high impact" models. Basic models must pass the 1-inch drop ball test (in which the lens withstands impact from a 1-in. diameter steel ball dropped 50 in.) High impact models must comply with additional high mass and high velocity impact criteria. These requirements now apply fully to prescription safety eyewear as well as plano or nonprescription glasses.

There were also changes to the minimum thickness lens requirements. The previous Z87 standard specified that plano safety glasses must be at least 3 mm in thickness. The 2003 standard specifies that goggle lenses, faceshield windows, and welding filters must still be at least 3.0 mm thick. For high impact plano/nonprescription spectacle lenses/safety glasses that are tested as complete products, there is no minimum thickness requirements, but they must pass the high impact tests. High impact lenses that are put into prescription frames must have a minimum thickness of 2.0 mm. Basic impact spectacle lenses must be at least 3.0 mm in thickness. For more information, refer to OSHA regulations on eye protection in the general industry codes, in particular, 29 CFR 1910.133.

To differentiate basic and high impact lenses, the following lens markings must be included on nonremovable lenses: for basic impact lenses, "Z87," and for high impact, "Z87+."

Frames used for safety glasses must pass high velocity and high mass test methods. Spectacle frames intended to have prescription safety lenses must meet the same criteria.

Whether or not sideshields are required on safety glasses is a matter of professional judgment and should be decided based on the specific hazards involved in the workplace and activity.

Impact Protection

Three types of equipment are used to protect eyes from flying particles: spectacles with impact-resistant lenses, flexible or cushion-fitting goggles, and chipping goggles.

Spectacles

For safety eyewear, polycarbonate lenses are the most impact resistant, and should be considered the lens of choice for industrial environments. In addition, frames must meet the requirements for safety eyewear; an employee's personal spectacles (or "dress" frames) would not be considered appropriate eye protection by OSHA in certain occupational environments, even if the lenses were polycarbonate.

Spectacles without sideshields should be used for limited hazards requiring only frontal protection. Where side as well as frontal protection is required, the spectacles must have sideshields. Full-cup sideshields are designed to restrict side entry of flying particles. Semifold or flatfold sideshields can be used where only lateral protection is required. Snap-on and clip-on sideshield types are not acceptable unless they are secured (Figure 5–7). Whether side shields are needed should be determined by the health and safety professional who has evaluated the work environment.

Flexible-Fitting Goggles

These should have a wholly flexible frame forming the lens holder. Cushion-fitting goggles should have a rigid plastic frame with a separate, cushioned surface on the facial contact area. Both flexible and cushioned goggles usually have a single plastic lens. These goggles are designed to give the eyes frontal and side protection from flying particles. Most models fit over ordinary ophthalmic spectacles (Figure 5–8).

Chipping Goggles

These have contour-shaped rigid plastic eyecups and come in two styles: one for people who do not wear eyeglasses, and one to fit over corrective glasses. Chipping goggles should be used where maximum protection from flying particles is needed.

Figure 5–7. Full-cup sideshields are designed to restrict the entry of flying objects from the side of the wearer. *(Photo courtesy of Protective Industrial Products.)*

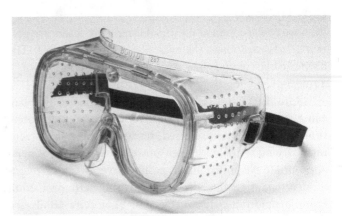

Figure 5–8. Flexible-fitting goggles should have a flexible frame forming the lens holder. *(Photo courtesy of Protective Industrial Products.)*

If lenses will be exposed to pitting from grinding wheel sparks, a transparent and durable coating can be applied to them.

Eye Protection for Welding

In addition to damage from physical and chemical agents, the eyes are subject to the effects of radiant energy. Ultraviolet (UV), visible, and infrared (IR) bands of the spectrum all produce harmful effects on the eyes, and therefore require special attention.

Welding processes emit radiation in three spectral bands. Depending on the flux used and the size and temperature of the pool of melted metal, welding processes emit UV, visible, and IR radiation; the proportion of the energy emitted in the visible range increases as the temperature rises.

All welding presents problems, mostly in the control of IR and visible radiation. Heavy gas welding and cutting operations as well as arc cutting and welding exceeding 30 amperes also emit UV radiation.

Welders can choose the shade of lenses they prefer within one or two shade numbers:

- Shades numbered 1.5–3.0 are intended to protect against glare from snow, ice, and reflecting surfaces and against stray flashes and reflected radiation from nearby cutting and welding operations. These shades also are recommended for use as goggles or spectacles with sideshields worn under helmets in arc-welding operations, particularly gas-shielded arc-welding operations.
- Shade number 4 is the same as shades 1.5–3.0, but for greater radiation intensity.

For welding, cutting, brazing, or soldering operations, the guide for the selection of proper shade numbers of filter lenses or windows is given in ANSI Z87.1–2003, Eye and Face Protection. (For more details, see Chapter 11, Nonionizing Radiation.)

Laser Protection

Because of the coherent nature of laser light, lasers are particularly hazardous to the eyes, especially the macula. The classes of lasers and their potential hazards are shown in Table 5–A.

Both direct and reflected exposures to laser light can cause serious eye damage. While containment and protection at the source is preferred, researchers and laser technicians who work with high power lasers will still need appropriate eye protection. Typically, the eyewear has maximum attenuation at a specific laser wavelength; protection falls off rapidly at other wavelengths. (For more details, see Chapter 11, Nonionizing Radiation.)

Where there is potential exposure to high power lasers

in a workplace, it may be prudent for employees to be given a baseline laser eye exam.

Sunglasses

Use of safety sunglasses is a common practice for people who work outdoors, but they are not appropriate for indoor work. Darkly tinted lenses should not be worn indoors unless specifically required because of excessive glare or eye-hazardous radiation. Some computer users feel more comfortable with a light tint on their spectacles; however, to address glare problems, the computer screen itself should be fitted with an anti-glare shield, and the computer situated properly relative to natural and artificial lighting.

Photochromic Lenses

Photochromic lenses automatically change tint from light to dark and back again, depending on their exposure to UV light. The convenience of sunglasses with variable-tint lenses is obvious, even though such lenses do not react indoors, in a car, or anywhere else that UV light cannot reach.

The ANSI Z87 standard recommends a variety of fixed-density tinted lenses for specific job situations involving radiation harmful to vision. Each tint is assigned an individual shade number, which is inscribed on the front surface

TABLE 5–A Laser Eye Hazards	
Class of Laser	*Hazards*
1	Eye safe lasers; may not produce hazardous radiation
2	Continuous intrabeam viewing can cause eye damage; momentary intrabeam exposure (<0.25 sec) is not damaging to the eye; visible radiation only
2a	Continuous intrabeam viewing can cause eye damage; the accessible radiation shall not exceed Class 1 accessible emission limit (AEL) for an exposure duration of 1000 seconds
3a	Invisible layers having an output power >5x the Class 1 AEL or visible laser having an output power of <5 mW; capable of causing damage through intrabeam viewing, with optical instruments, or through viewing a specular reflection for <0.25 sec
3b	Invisible lasers having output power <500 mW; as with 3a lasers, 3b lasers can cause injury through intrabeam viewing, viewing with optical instruments, or through viewing a specular reflection
4	Beam power >500 mW; intrabeam exposure, exposure to specular and diffuse reflections capable of causing eye and skin damage; fire hazard due to their power density

of each such lens. Such lenses may have a future for outdoor use by telephone line and brush crews and gas-line transmission workers. However, until safety eyewear manufacturers are willing—or able—to certify phototropic lenses as being fully in compliance with the Z87 standard, industry would be well-advised to follow ANSI guidelines.

Comfort and Fit

To be comfortable, eye-protective equipment must be properly fitted. Corrective spectacles should be fitted only by a qualified, licensed practitioner. However, a technician can be trained to fit, adjust, and maintain eye-protective equipment. Of course, each worker should be taught the proper care of the device being used.

To give the widest possible field of vision, goggles should be close to the eyes, but the eyelashes should not touch the lenses.

Various defogging materials are available. Before a selection is made, test to determine the most effective type for a specific application.

In areas where goggles or other types of eye protection are extensively used, goggle-cleaning stations should be conveniently located, along with defogging materials, wiping tissues, and a waste receptacle.

Computer Vision

Much concern has focused on health problems associated with the use of computers. Prolonged computer use can cause increased eye fatigue and visual discomfort. Factors that lead to visual discomfort include poor contrast between the characters and background, high contrast between the screen and other surfaces (such as the documents), and glare from and flicker on the screen. Long periods of eye fixation and refractive errors are also significant contributors.

Most desktop computer users sit about 50 cm from the screen, which is more of an intermediate working distance, as opposed to near or far focusing (laptop users may sit closer to their screens). Though many people can wear their habitual glasses or contact lens prescription at the computer, often a different prescription may be needed to improve vision or comfort. Some computer users will also be helped with a light tint on the lenses of their glasses, generally yellow or pink, along with an anti-glare treatment.

Because of the variety of visual problems and work practices of operators, proper design should allow for flexibility in the placement of the screen, keyboard, source documents, and work surfaces. Ambient lighting must be adjustable, bright backgrounds such as windows should be eliminated, and appropriate rest periods are indicated. ANSI/HSF 100–1988 gives detailed recommendations for the design of a computer workstation. (See Chapter 13, Ergonomics, for additional information.)

People who spend long hours at a time at a computer should frequently change their focus, or look off into the distance, focus on something far away, blink, and then come back to their screen. This helps the eyes relax and prevent them from getting into a spasm of accommodation at the computer working distance. Additionally, remind computer users to blink frequently; people who do interactive tasks at the computer have been noted to blink about 2/3 less than people not working at a computer. Decreased blinking dries out the tear film, causing both discomfort and blurry vision. Eye doctors may also prescribe artificial tears for such individuals.

Contact Lenses

Historically, contact lenses have been banned in industrial environments. However, there is little (to no) evidence that across-the-board prohibition of their use is warranted. In May 1998, the Contact Lens Section of the American Optometric Association issued revised "Guidelines For The Use of Contact Lenses in Industrial Environments." In these guidelines, they stated that "Contact lenses may be worn in some hazardous environments with appropriate covering safety eye-wear. Contact lenses of themselves do not provide eye protection in the industrial sense." The NIOSH Pocket Guide to Chemical Hazards, Table 6 (codes for First Aid Data, February 2004) no longer states that "contact lenses should not be worn when working with these chemicals."

Contact lenses should not be considered eye protection and are not intended as such. However, if eye protection appropriate for the job being done is worn over the contact lenses, employees should be able to safely use them. There are certain eye conditions, such as keratoconus, where an individual's vision may be significantly decreased by wearing glasses instead of contact lenses; in this situation, a greater hazard may be produced by insisting on the wearing of glasses.

OSHA has codified the ANSI Z87.1 consensus standard regarding eye protection over contact lenses, so that "the required industrial-safety eyewear for the specific hazard identified in ANSI Z87.1 must be worn over the contact lenses." Health and safety professionals must therefore specify that contact lens wearers use appropriate eye and face protective equipment to protect themselves from chemical splashes and vapors, eye irritants, optical radiation, and biological hazards.

Health and safety practitioners often have banned the use of contact lenses with respiratory protection. Lawrence Livermore National Laboratory conducted a study of contact lens wearers who used self-contained breathing apparatus, and found no adverse effects to the eyes. Some state OSHA plans may still prohibit the use of contact lenses with respiratory protection; health and safety professionals are advised to consult the applicable regulations.

Because each workplace presents its own unique hazards, the health and safety professional should assess and make the ultimate decision as to the use of contact lenses. It is recommended that each workplace where contact lenses are used do the following:

1. A written policy is in place outlining the general safety requirements and restrictions for contact lens use.
2. Eye hazard evaluations are conducted.
3. Training is provided on the employer's policies regarding contact lens use and appropriate first aid for eye injuries.
4. Appropriate personal protective equipment is provided for contact lens wearers.
5. A policy is in place for visitors wearing contact lenses.
6. Supervisors and emergency responders are notified of workers who wear contact lenses and who work in hazardous environments.

Employees must not insert or remove contact lenses in hazardous environments. In the event of a hazardous substance splash to the eyes, the person should start irrigating the eyes with water while still wearing the contacts, and remove them while irrigating (often the pressure of the water will force them out of the eyes).

VISION CONSERVATION PROGRAM

There are four steps in a vision conservation program:
1. The environmental survey
2. Vision screening program
3. Remedial program
4. Professional fitting and follow-up procedures

Environmental Survey

The environment should be surveyed by people qualified in occupational health and safety. The survey should assess the likelihood of injury and potential severity of injury from the worker's job operation, the potential for injury from adjacent operations, and the optimum visual acuity requirements for fast, safe, efficient operations.

The environmental survey includes illumination measurements and recommendations for improvements to make the workplace safer. Often, simply cleaning existing lighting can increase illumination 100 percent.

Job working distances and viewing angles should be measured so eye doctors have the necessary information to prescribe lens strengths affording optimum comfort, efficiency, safety, and ergonomic advantage.

Each workstation should be free of toxic or corrosive materials, and employees should be instructed in the correct use of eyewash facilities. Eyewash fountains should be examined to make certain they work properly and provide an even flow of water.

All environmental factors influencing an employee's visual performance and safety should be written in a visual job description, in terms understandable to the eye doctors who will care for employees with deficient vision.

Vision Screening Program

The next step, after working conditions and visual requirements are known, is to determine the visual status of the work force. Reliable vision screening instruments are available for use by nurses or trained technicians.

These instruments test the visual acuity in each eye separately, both eyes together, both at near point (usually working distance), both at far point (distant vision), and binocular coordination (the ability to make the two eyes work together). Additional specific tests—such as color vision, field of vision, glaucoma testing, and depth perception—can be added when a need is indicated.

Often, an employee actually performs many jobs. In these instances, recommendations are made after the job most frequently performed is compared with the one most visually demanding.

Remedial Program

Each employee is told the result of his or her vision screening; people showing deficiencies are referred to the eye doctor of their choice. The employee goes to the doctor with the prescription form for safety glasses and a written description of the visual aspect of the job or duties at work. The job description includes recommendations concerning the type of prescription that will make the worker more comfortable and more efficient.

Professional Fitting

The final step in a vision conservation program is professionally fitting the protective and corrective safety eyewear to the employee. Proper fitting and sizing are essential. Workers come in various sizes and shapes, as do safety glasses. Proper measurement and fitting can be the difference between a successful and an unsuccessful program. A perfect prescription is useless if the frame hurts so much that it cannot be worn.

This fitting procedure is equally important for employees required to wear nonprescription safety glasses. These employees usually are the most difficult to fit. They are not accustomed to having anything in front of their eyes or feeling weight on their nose or ears. Considerable care must be exercised in the fitting for such employees. Adjustment and alignment should be readily available.

Human vision is not static; it changes constantly. Employees, especially those over age 40, should be advised that gradual, sometimes unnoticed, changes in their vision may affect their safety and efficiency.

Guidelines

The following guidelines should be a part of every vision conservation program:

- Make it a 100-percent program; include everyone. Employees will accept it more readily and it will be easier to administer. Promote it well in advance and get union cooperation.
- Make certain that safety eyewear is properly fitted. A few jobs (welding, labs, lasers) require special types. Optical companies will assist in fitting eyewear and explaining maintenance.
- Include eye-care stations for first aid and for cleaning lenses.
- Control eye hazards at the source; install safety glass guards on machines to prevent flying chips or splashing liquids and install enclosures to control fine dusts, mists, or vapors.
- Make sure all areas have adequate lighting, are free from glare, and are painted in colors that emphasize depth perception and highlight potential hazards.
- Post signs such as ALL PERSONNEL AND VISITORS MUST WEAR PROTECTIVE EYEWEAR in all hazardous areas.
- All employees should be given preplacement eye examinations. Periodic follow-up examinations should be scheduled, especially for employees over 40 years of age.

AMA *GUIDES TO THE EVALUATION OF PERMANENT IMPAIRMENT*

This section is adapted from the AMA's *Guides to the Evaluation of Permanent Impairment*, 6th edition. It is included in this chapter to assist health and safety professionals in interpreting and understanding medical reports of workers' compensation cases. This guide provides a method for determining permanent visual impairment and its effects on a person's ability to perform the activities of daily living. The guide focuses on functional impairment of the visual system as a whole.

A permanent visual impairment is defined as a permanent loss of vision that remains after maximal improvement of the underlying conditions has been reached. Measurement of both visual acuity and visual field are obtained, and numerical assessments of these functions are used to derive an estimate of their effect on functional vision—the ability to perform generic activities of daily living.

The guide uses a Functional Vision Score (FVS), which is based on an assessment of visual acuity and visual field. Visual acuity is described as the ability of the eye to perceive details. Visual field refers to the ability to detect objects in the periphery of the visual environment.

Another important visual function is contrast sensitivity, which refers to the ability to detect larger objects of poor contrast. In addition, the guides allow for individual adjustments for other defects such as glare sensitivity, color vision, binocularity, stereopsis, suppression, and diplopia. If these deficits cause a significant loss that is not reflected in a visual acuity or visual field loss, they may be used to adjust the impairment rating.

Clinical Evaluation of Vision Loss

To accurately assess visual impairment, the clinician needs to perform a thorough visual exam, which includes the cause, severity, and prognosis of the underlying disorder and the expected or documented effects of the vision loss on the ability to perform activities of daily living. The assessment should include the following:

- medical history with an emphasis on preexisting conditions, treatments, and the major cause of the current vision loss
- current condition of the eyes and visual system, with documentation of anatomic findings
- visual acuity measurements with best correction, binocularity, and for each eye separately
- visual field measurement for each eye
- other visual functions such as contrast sensitivity or color vision
- calculation of an initial impairment rating
- other factors that may affect the individual's ability to perform activities of daily living
- discussion of factors that may cause an adjustment of the initial ability estimate.

For more complete information of assessing visual impairment consult Chapter 12 in the *AMA's Guide to the Evaluation of Permanent Impairment*, 6th ed.

Ocular Emergencies

Health and safety practitioners should be able to identify eye emergencies in order to immediately refer the individual experiencing the symptoms for outside treatment. The following symptoms or conditions constitute ocular emergencies:

- a red, painful eye, with light sensitivity, with or without discharge

- sudden loss of vision
- sudden onset of flashes of lights, floaters, or loss of peripheral vision that persists more than an hour
- any ocular trauma or penetrating injury
- chemical burns (rinse thoroughly with water or sterile saline for at least 15 minutes, pH test the eye, keep rinsing until neutral, then seek medical help).

If your company has an on-site occupational health clinic, refer the employee there immediately. If not, seek help from an eye care provider (optometrist or ophthalmologist) in your community.

SUMMARY

Ocular anatomy, visual performance, disorders, and problems were discussed. Also covered were potential hazards and how to protect and conserve vision, and ocular emergencies that health and safety professionals might encounter.

BIBLIOGRAPHY

American College of Occupational and Environmental Medicine. *Use of Contact Lenses in an Industrial Environment*. Guidance Statement, Thursday, September 18, 2008. Elk Grove Village, IL: ACOEM, 2008. http://www.acoem.org/ContactLenses_IndustrialEnvironment.aspx, accessed 5/9/2011.

American Medical Association. *Guides to the Evaluation of Permanent Impairment*, 6th ed., R. Rondinelli, ed. Chicago: AMA, 2007.

American National Standards Institute. *Practice for Industrial Lighting*. New York: ANSI/IES RP-7, 1990.

American National Standards Institute. *Practice for Occupational and Educational Eye and Face Protection*. New York: ANSI Z87.1, 2003.

American National Standards Institute. *Safe Use of Lasers*. New York: ANSI Z136.1-2007.

American National Standards Institute. Standard *for Emergency Eyewash and Shower Equipment*. New York: ANSI Z358.1, 2009.

American Optometric Association. *Guidelines for the Use of Contact Lenses in Industrial Environments*. St. Louis: AOA, 1998.

Davson H, ed. *The Eye*, 3rd ed. Orlando, FL: Academic Press, 1984.

Eskridge JB, Amos JF, Bartlett JD, et al. *Clinical Procedures in Optometry*. Philadelphia: JB Lippincott, 1991.

Fraunfelder FT, Roy FH, Hampton F, et al. *Current Ocular Therapy*. Philadelphia: W.B. Saunders, 1990.

Grant WM. *Toxicology of the Eye,* 3rd ed. Springfield, IL: Charles C. Thomas, 1986.

Hart WM, ed. *Adler's Physiology of the Eye,* 9th ed. St. Louis: Mosby Year Book, 1992.

Leonard R. *Statistics on Vision Impairment: A Resource Manual*. New York: Arlene R. Gordon Research Institute, Lighthouse International, 1999.

Rom WN, ed. *Environmental and Occupational Medicine,* 3rd ed. Philadelphia: Lipincott-Raven, 2007.

Tyndall RL, Ironside KS, Lyle MM. The presence of acanthamoebae in portable and stationary eyewash stations. *AIHA Journal* 48:933–934, 1987.

U.S. Department of Labor. Bureau of Labor Statistics 2008 data. Washington, DC: U.S. Department of Labor, 2008. http://stats.bls.gov, accessed 5/5/2011.

PART III
Recognition of Hazards

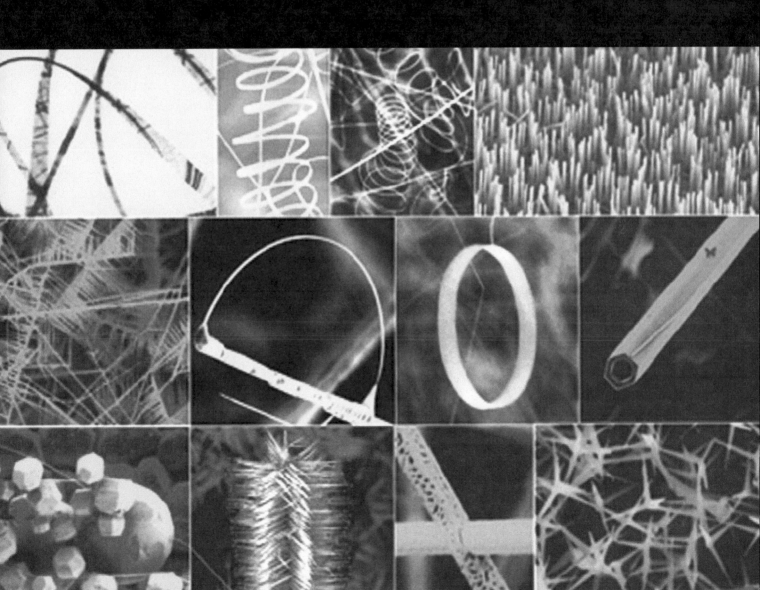

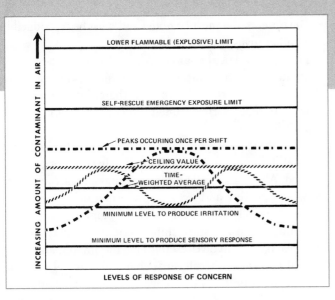

LOWER FLAMMABLE (EXPLOSIVE) LIMIT

SELF-RESCUE EMERGENCY EXPOSURE LIMIT

PEAKS OCCURING ONCE PER SHIFT

CEILING VALUE

TIME-WEIGHTED AVERAGE

MINIMUM LEVEL TO PRODUCE IRRITATION

MINIMUM LEVEL TO PRODUCE SENSORY RESPONSE

INCREASING AMOUNT OF CONTAMINANT IN AIR

LEVELS OF RESPONSE OF CONCERN

CHAPTER **6**

Industrial Toxicology

by Richard Cohen, MD, MPH

Toxicology is the science that studies the harmful, or toxic, properties of substances. We are exposed daily to a variety of substances that are not hazardous under usual circumstances. However, any substance contacting or entering the body is injurious at some excessive level of exposure and theoretically can be tolerated without harmful effect at some lower exposure.

DEFINITION

A *toxic effect* is any reversible or irreversible harmful effect on the body as a result of contact with a substance via the respiratory tract, skin, eye, mouth, or other route. Toxic effects are undesirable disturbances of physiological function caused by an overexposure to chemical or physical agents. They also arise as side effects in response to medication and vaccines. *Toxicity* is the capacity of a chemical to harm or injure a living organism. Toxicity entails the dimension of *quantity* or *dose*; the toxicity of a chemical depends on the quantity necessary to impact health.

Many chemicals essential for health in small quantities are highly toxic in larger quantities. Small amounts of zinc, manganese, copper, molybdenum, selenium, chromium, nickel, tin, potassium, and many other chemicals are essential for life. However, severe acute and chronic toxicity may result from an uptake of large amounts of these materials. For example, nickel and chromium in some of their forms are considered carcinogens.

The responsibility of the industrial toxicologist is to define how much is too much and to prescribe precautionary measures and limitations so that usual or recommended use or exposure does not result in the absorption of a harmful quantity of a particular substance. From a toxicological viewpoint, the industrial hygienist must consider all types of exposure and the subsequent effects on the living organism.

Toxicity versus Hazard

Toxicity and hazard differ. Toxicologists consider toxicity as the ability of a substance to produce an unwanted effect when the substance has reached a sufficient concentration at a certain site in the body; hazard is regarded as the probability that this concentration will occur at that site. Many factors contribute to determining the degree of hazard—route of entry, quantity of exposure, physiological state, environmental variables, and other factors. Assessing a hazard involves estimating the probability that a substance will cause harm. Toxicity, along with the chemical and physical properties of a substance, determines the level or degree of hazard. Two liquids can possess the same degree of toxicity but present different degrees of hazard. One may be odorless and not irritating to the eyes and nose whereas the other may produce a pungent or disagreeable odor at a harmless concentration. The material with the warning properties at harmless concentrations may present a lesser degree of hazard; its presence can be detected in time to avert injury.

Some chemical agents are not selective in their action on tissues or cells and can exert a harmful effect on all living matter. Other chemical agents act only on specific cells. Some agents are harmful only to certain species; other species have built-in protective mechanisms.

The term *toxicity* is commonly used in comparing one chemical agent with another, but is meaningless without data designating the biological species used and the conditions under which the harmful effects were induced.

A chemical stimulus can be considered to have produced a toxic effect when it satisfies the following criteria:

- An observable or measurable physiological deviation has been produced in any organ or organ system. The change can be anatomic in character and may accelerate or inhibit a normal physiological process, or the deviation can be a specific biochemical change.
- The observed change can be duplicated from animal to animal even though the dose-effect relationships vary.
- The stimulus has changed normal physiological processes in such a way that a protective mechanism is impaired in its defense against other adverse stimuli.
- The effect is either reversible or at least attenuated when the stimulus is removed; however, permanent anatomic and/or physiologic changes can result.
- The effect does not occur without a stimulus or occurs so infrequently that it indicates generalized or nonspecific response. When high degrees of susceptibility are noted, equally significant degrees of resistance should be apparent.

- The observation must be noted and must be reproducible by other investigators.
- The physiological change reduces the efficiency of an organ or function and impairs physiological reserve in such a way as to interfere with the ability to resist or adapt to other normal stimuli, either permanently or temporarily.

The toxic effects of many substances used in industry are well known, but the toxicity of others is not yet well defined. Although certain important analogies are apparent between structure and toxicity, important differences exist that require individual study of each compound.

In addition to establishing toxicity, evaluation of a chemical hazard involves establishing the amount and duration of exposure, the physical characteristics of the substance, the conditions under which exposure occurs, and the determination of the effects of other substances in a combined exposure. All of these may significantly influence the toxic potency of a substance.

The chemical properties of a compound are often one of the main factors in its hazard potential. Vapor pressure (an indicator of how quickly a liquid or solid evaporates) partially determines whether a substance has the potential to pose a hazard from inhalation. Many solvents are quite volatile and vaporize readily into the air to produce high concentrations of vapor. Hence, a solvent with a low boiling point would be a greater hazard than an equally toxic solvent with a high boiling point simply because it is more volatile and it evaporates faster.

Chemical injury can be local or systemic, and the toxicological reactions can be slight or severe. Local injury results from direct contact of the substance with tissue. The skin can be severely burned or the surface of the eye can be injured to the extent that vision is impaired. In the respiratory tract, the lining of the trachea and the lungs can be injured as a result of inhaling toxic amounts of vapors, fumes, dusts, or mists. Systemic toxicity usually involves passage of the agent through the blood vessels with resulting contact and injury to various internal organs (e.g., liver, kidney, nervous system).

ENTRY INTO THE BODY

In discussing toxicity, it is necessary to know how a substance enters the body and, if relevant, the bloodstream. For an adverse effect to occur, the toxic substance must first reach the organ or bodily site where it causes damage. Common "routes of entry" are inhalation, skin absorption, ingestion, and injection. Depending on the substance and its specific properties, however, entry (absorption) can occur by more than one route, such as inhaling a solvent that can also penetrate the skin.

Inhalation

For industrial exposures, a major, if not predominant, route of entry is inhalation. Any airborne substance can be inhaled.

The respiratory system is composed of two main areas: the upper respiratory tract airways (the nose, throat, trachea, and major bronchial tubes leading to the lobes of the lungs) and the lower respiratory tract, which includes smaller airways and the alveoli, where the actual transfer of gases across thin cell walls takes place. For particles, only those smaller than about 5-10 µm in diameter are likely to enter the alveolar sac (See Chapter 2, The Lungs, for more information).

The total amount of a toxic compound absorbed via the respiratory route depends on its concentration in the air, the duration of exposure, and the pulmonary ventilation volumes, which increase with higher work loads.

Gases and vapors of low water solubility but high fat solubility pass through the alveolar lining into the bloodstream and are distributed to organ sites for which they have special affinity. During inhalation exposure at a uniform level, the absorption of the compound into the blood reaches equilibrium with metabolism and elimination. Small fibers and particles (0.1-10 µm in diameter) may settle in the alveoli; small molecules and nanoparticles may pass through the alveolar wall and reach pulmonary blood vessels.

Skin Absorption

An important route of entry for many chemicals is absorption through skin. Contact of a substance with skin results in these four possible actions:

- The skin acts as an effective barrier.
- The substance reacts with the skin and causes local irritation or tissue destruction.
- The substance produces skin sensitization.
- The substance penetrates the skin to reach the blood vessels under the skin and enters the bloodstream.

For some substances (such as parathion), the skin has been the main portal of entry in many toxic occupational exposures. For other substances (such as aniline, nitrobenzene, and phenol), the amounts absorbed through the skin are roughly equivalent to the amounts absorbed through inhalation. For the majority of other organic chemicals, the contribution from skin (cutaneous) absorption to the total amount absorbed is significant. Hence, toxic effects can occur because of cutaneous penetration.

The cutaneous absorption rate of some organic chemicals rises when temperature and perspiration increase.

Therefore, absorption can be higher in warm climates or seasons. The absorption of liquid organic chemicals may follow surface contamination of the skin or clothes; for other compounds, it may directly follow the vapor phase, in which case the rate of absorption is roughly proportional to the air concentration of the vapors. The process involves a combination of deposition of the substances on the skin surface followed by absorption through the skin.

The physicochemical properties of a substance determine absorption potential through intact skin. Among the important factors are skin pH and the chemical's extent of ionization, aqueous and lipid solubility, and molecular size.

Human skin shows great differences in absorption at different anatomic regions, primarily due to differences in thickness. The skin on the palm of the hand has approximately the same penetration potential as that of the forearm for certain organic phosphates. The skin on the back of the hand and the skin of the abdomen have twice the penetration potential of the forearm, whereas follicle-rich sites such as the scalp, forehead, and scrotum show a much greater penetration potential. High temperatures generally increase skin absorption by increasing vasodilation and sweating. If the skin is damaged by abrasion dermatitis, the normal protective barrier to absorption of chemicals is lessened and penetration occurs more easily (See Chapter 3, The Skin, for more information).

Ingestion

The problem of ingesting chemicals is not widespread in industry; most workers do not deliberately swallow materials they handle. Nevertheless, workers can ingest toxic materials as a result of eating in contaminated work areas; contaminated fingers and hands can lead to accidental oral intake when a worker eats or smokes on the job. They can also ingest substances when contaminants deposited in the respiratory tract are carried out of the lung to the throat by the action of the ciliated lining of the respiratory tract and then swallowed. Approximately one quart of mucus is produced daily in an adult's lungs. This constant flow of mucus can carry contaminants out of the lungs into the throat to be swallowed with the saliva or coughed up and expectorated.

Absorption after ingestion is often less than with inhalation because of the action of stomach acid and intestinal enzymes, dilution by intestinal contents, and greater thickness of the intestinal wall.

Injection

Although infrequent in industry, a substance can be injected into some part of the body. This can be done directly into the bloodstream, peritoneal cavity, pleural cavity, skin, muscle, or any other place a needle or high-pressure orifice can reach. The effects produced vary with the location of administration. In industrial settings, injection is an infrequent route of worker chemical exposure.

There is, however, increasing attention to prevention of skin puncture and injection injuries associated with blood-borne pathogens (hepatitis B, HIV, and hepatitis C). Risk of infection is significant following accidental skin puncture by a needle or instrument contaminated with infected blood or tissue.

In the laboratory, toxic substances are injected into animals because it is far more convenient and less costly than establishing blood levels by inhalation or skin exposures. Intravenous injection sidesteps protective mechanisms in the body that prevent substances from entering the blood.

After absorption via any route into the bloodstream, the substance may enter the liver, which metabolically alters, degrades, or detoxifies many substances. This detoxification process is an important body defense mechanism. Basically, detoxification involves chemical reactions, which in some cases change the substance to a less toxic or more water-soluble compound.

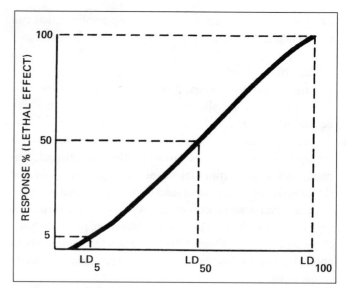

Figure 6–1. Dose-response curves for a chemical agent administered to a uniform population of test animals. (LD = lethal dose; number shown after LD indicates the percent of exposed animals that are affected. LD_{50} is the dose given at which 50 percent of exposed animals died.)

DOSE–RESPONSE RELATIONSHIP

A fundamental consideration in toxicology is the *dose-response relationship*. In animal studies, a dose is administered to test animals and increased or decreased until a range is found where at the upper end all animals show a preselected health effect (e.g., death, injury) and, at the lower end, all animals are absent the health effect. The data collected are used to prepare a dose-response curve relating health effect incidence to dose administered (Figure 6–1).

The doses given are expressed as the quantity administered per unit body weight, quantity per skin surface area, or quantity per unit volume of respired air. In addition, the length of time during which the dose was administered may be indicated.

The dose–response relationship can also be expressed as the product of a concentration (C) multiplied by the time duration (T) of exposure. This product is proportional more or less to a constant (K); or mathematically, $C \times T \approx K$. The dose involves two variables—concentration and duration of exposure. For certain chemicals, a high concentration breathed for a short time produces the same effect as a lower concentration breathed for a longer time. The CT value provides a rough approximation of other combinations of concentration of a chemical and time that would produce similar effects. Although this concept must be used very cautiously and cannot be applied at extreme conditions of concentration or time, it can be useful in predicting safe limits

for some airborne contaminants in the workplace. Regulatory exposure limits are sometimes set so that the combination of concentrations and time durations are theoretically below the levels that produce injury to exposed individuals.

To determine a dose-response relationship or curve, the dose should be delivered over a specified length of time followed by observation for another specified period of time—this may be hours or days, or even several years when testing for carcinogenesis. For example, in one study animals were exposed for a short time to nitrogen dioxide (NO_2). Initially, there was no observable response, but 36 hours after the exposure, the animals developed a chemical pneumonia and ultimately died. If the animals had been observed for only the first 24 hours after the exposure, the health effects that occurred in the second 24-hour period would have been missed.

Threshold Concept

For most chemicals there is a *threshold of effect*, a *no-effect level* or a level at which the rate of disease in the exposed population is no different than the rate in the unexposed population or "background." The most toxic chemical known, if present in small enough amounts, produces no measurable effect. It may damage one cell or several cells, but no measurable or clinically significant health effect, such as reduced lung capacity, will result. As the dose is increased, there is a point at which the first measurable effect is noted or at which the incidence of a health effect in the exposed population exceeds its incidence in unexposed populations. The (toxic) potency of a chemical is defined by the relationship between the dose (amount) of the chemical and the response produced in a biological system. A high concentration of toxic substance in the target organ causes a severe reaction and a low concentration causes a less severe or no reaction.

The word *toxic* relates to the dose or amount of a substance necessary to cause injury, illness, or significant adverse health effect. If that dose is low compared to the harmful dose for other substances, it is described as more toxic. In other words, although all substances produce harmful effects at some dose, a toxic substance causes harmful effects at low doses.

Although most exposures in industry occur by way of the respiratory tract or skin, most published dose-response data are found in studies of experimental animals. In these experiments, the test substances were usually administered by mouth (in food, in drinking water, or by intubation [tube] directly into the stomach) or injection (intravenous, intramuscular, intraperitoneal, etc.).

The harmfulness of a material depends on its chemical composition, the type and rate or level of exposure, and the fate of the material in the body. For many substances, a single large dose of a toxic substance produces a greater response than the same total dose administered in small amounts over a long period of time. Each of the small amounts can be detoxified quickly, but a large dose produces its detrimental action before appreciable detoxification occurs. If a substance is detoxified or excreted at a rate slower than the rate of intake, it may cause continuing (cumulative) effects.

Accumulation of a substance in the body is understood as a process in which the level of the substance increases with the duration of exposure and can apply to both continuous and repeated exposure. Biological tests of exposure show that an accumulation is taking place when rising levels of the substance are seen in the urine, blood, or expired air (Figure 6–2).

Exposure thresholds are most easily determined (and more available) for effects occurring soon after exposure. Other effects such as birth defects and cancer occur months or years after exposure began. Dose-related data are often imprecise in human epidemiological studies. For these and other reasons, thresholds for most carcinogens (such as asbestos) have not been identified and are considered to be zero.

Because different biological mechanisms are involved in reproductive toxicity, attempts are being made to identify exposure levels (mostly from animal studies) below which no evidence of injury or impairment can be found; these are called the *No Observable Adverse Effect Level* (NOAEL).

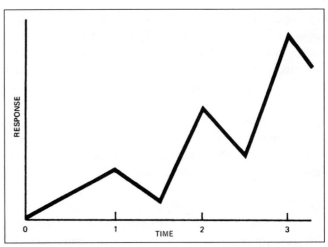

Figure 6–2. Accumulation of a substance in a body is shown in this curve; in this example the level of the substance increases with the duration of exposure.

Lethal Dose

If a number of animals are exposed to a toxic substance, when the concentration reaches a certain level, some but not all of those animals will die. Results of such studies are used to calculate the *lethal dose* (LD) of toxic substances. The LD usually pertains to acute effects and rapid death (minutes or hours); LD determinations are not typically determined for health effects due to chronic or repeated dosing such as cancer.

If the only variable being studied is the number of deaths, it is possible to use the concept of the LD. The LD_{50} is the calculated dose of a substance that is expected to kill 50 percent of a defined experimental animal population, as determined from the exposure to the substance by any route other than inhalation.

Several designations can be used, such as LD_{50}, LD_0, LD_{100}, and so on. The designation LD_0, which is rarely used, is the concentration that produces no deaths in an experimental group and is the highest concentration tolerated in animals; LD_{100} is the lowest concentration that kills 100 percent of the exposed animals. Although LD_{50} is the concentration that kills half of the exposed animals, it does not mean that the other half are in good health.

Normally, LD_{50} units are the weight of substance per kilogram of animal body weight, usually milligrams per kilogram. The LD_{50} value should be accompanied by an indication of the species of experimental animal used, the route of administration of the compound, the vehicle used to dissolve or suspend the material, if applicable, and the time period during which the animals were dosed and observed.

The slope of the dose-response curve provides useful information. It suggests an index of the margin of safety, or the magnitude of the range of doses between a noneffective dose and a lethal dose. If the dose-response curve is very steep, this margin of safety is slight. One compound could be rated as more toxic than a second compound because of the shape and slope of the dose-response curve (Figure 6–3).

Lethal Concentration

When considering inhalation exposures, the dose by inhalation is needed. *Lethal concentration* (LC) is used for airborne materials. Airborne concentrations may be expressed as mg/m³ (milligrams per cubic meter) or ppm (parts per million). An LC_{50} means that when a defined experimental animal population is exposed to a calculated concentration of a substance, that concentration (expressed in mg/m³ or ppm) is expected to kill 50 percent of the animals in a stated length of time.

The duration of exposure is very important because a half-hour exposure might produce an effect that is significantly different in severity or character from that of a 24-hour exposure. Data accompanying LCs should state the species of animal studied, the length of time the exposure was maintained, and the length of time observation was carried out after exposure.

Responses

After a substance has been administered, there are indicators the toxicologist uses to evaluate the response. For example, examining the organs removed from exposed animals reveals the site of action of the agent, mode of action, and cause of death. Important pathological changes in tissues can be observed following dose levels below those needed

to produce the death of animals. The liver and the kidney are particularly sensitive to the action of many agents.

The effect of the agent on the growth rate of the animals is another indicator of adverse response. Relatively low levels of substances that do not produce death or signs of serious illness can result in a diminished rate of growth. The food intake must also be measured to learn whether loss of appetite was a cause of diminished growth.

Changes in the ratio of organ weight to body weight can be used as an indicator of adverse response. In some instances, such alterations are specific to the chemical being tested; for example, an increase of lung weight to body weight ratio can result from pulmonary edema (accumulation of fluid) produced by irritants including ozone and oxides of nitrogen. Physiological function tests are useful in animal studies and in assessing the response of exposed workers. They can be especially useful in studies of populations with chronic conditions.

Substances can then be rated according to their relative toxicity based on animal data (and human data, if available). Unfortunately, animal experimental data are difficult to interpret and may not apply to human exposure, response, or pathophysiology. Nevertheless, because human dose-response data are not available for many substances, animal data are valuable in estimating the likely range of toxicity of a substance as well as in guiding further investigation.

TIMING: EXPOSURE AND EFFECT

The toxic action of a substance can be arbitrarily divided into acute and chronic effects. In addition to acute and chronic toxicity, we can distinguish acute and chronic exposures (Table 6–A).

Factors other than those that cause the immediate effects often determine the type and severity of a chemical's chronic adverse effects. For example, acute benzene toxicity (narcosis) has different clinical characteristics from that of chronic toxicity (bone marrow depression, leukemia).

Acute Effects and Acute Exposures

Acute exposures typically have a rapid onset, are of short duration, and are characterized by rapid absorption of the offending material. For example, inhaling high levels of carbon monoxide or swallowing a large quantity of cyanide compound produces illness very rapidly. The *health effect* of a chemical exposure is considered acute when it appears within a short time following exposure, such as within minutes or hours, and the health effect is relatively short-lived. Acute occupational exposures are often related to a brief accidental exposure.

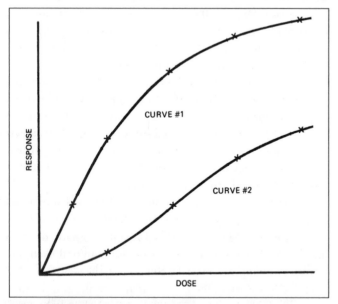

Figure 6–3. The chemical represented by curve #1 has a lower margin of safety and greater toxicity than the curve #2 chemical. In curve #1, the response increases more rapidly as dose increases.

TABLE 6–A	Brief Comparison of Acute, Prolonged, and Chronic Toxicity Tests		
	Acute	*Prolonged*	*Chronic*
Exposure lasts . . .	≤24 hours, usually single dose	Typically 2,4,or 6 weeks	≥3 months
Typically yields . . .	Single lethal dose, clinical signs of toxicity	Cumulative dose (if any), major metabolic routes, detoxification or excretion	Potential for carcinogenic effect or other delayed effects
Exemplified by . . .	Potassium cyanide rapidly depriving tissues of oxygen	Carbon tetrachloride causing destruction of liver cells after repeated exposure over several weeks	Carbon tetrachloride causing liver cancer following prolonged exposure (and observation)

Chronic Effects and Chronic Exposures

In contrast to acute health effects, *chronic effect* or illness is characterized by symptoms or disease of long duration or frequent recurrence. Chronic effects usually develop slowly, often over years or decades.

Chronic exposure refers to continued or repeated exposure over a prolonged period, usually years. For some substances, standard-setting organizations establish limits that address chronic as well as acute exposures.

Chronic exposure may cause a substance to be continuously present in the tissues. Chronic health effects, illness, or injury can be produced by exposure to a harmful substance that produces irreversible damage so that the injury, rather than the substance, accumulates or progresses. The symptoms of chronic effects are usually different from those seen in acute injury by the same agents. In chronic exposure settings, the level of exposure is often relatively low; the worker is often unaware of the exposures as they occur because the exposure levels are insufficient to cause acute effects.

EFFECTS OF EXPOSURE TO AIR CONTAMINANTS

Air contaminants can be classified on the basis of patho-physiological action into irritants, allergens, systemic toxins, or site-specific or organ-specific toxins.

Responses to toxic substances depend on the concentration and duration of exposure. For example, a vapor or gas at one concentration can exert its principal action on the body as an anesthetic, whereas at a lower concentration for a longer exposure time, the same gas or vapor can injure some internal organ or the blood system without causing central nervous system depression or anesthesia.

Irritation

Irritation is an inflammation or aggravation of the tissue the substance contacts. Contact of some substances with the face and upper respiratory system affects the eyes, the cells lining the nose, and the mouth.

There are many industrial chemicals that at fairly low concentrations irritate tissues with which they come in contact. Irritation results from direct mechanical or chemical (most frequent) reaction with constituents in the tissue having contact. Irritation or inflammation is the major health effect of corrosives.

Many irritants are liquids; for many of these, the degree of local irritation is unrelated to their systemic toxicities. Sometimes differences in viscosity are the determining factors in the type of injury. This applies especially in the lungs, where the inhalation hazard from a substance of low viscosity, such as kerosene, is quite different and more severe than the hazard from a higher viscosity substance such as mineral oil.

To a large extent, the water solubility of an irritant gas or vapor influences the part of the respiratory tract that is affected (Table 6–B).

Ammonia, which is very soluble in water, irritates the nose and throat, primarily because the moisture on the surface absorbs and reacts quickly with ammonia. Nitrogen dioxide, which is much less water soluble, acts mainly on the deeper tissues in the lungs as a result of its slower reaction with water/mucous-coated lung structures. Some irritants produce acute pulmonary edema (fluid in lungs), which usually begins as an immediate or intense inflammation that is later manifested by coughing, difficulty breathing, shortness of breath, cyanosis, or coughing up large amounts of mucus. With other chemicals, irritation can be delayed or an immediate reaction can be followed by a period of remission, typically a few hours for phosgene or 24–48 hours for nitrogen oxides.

Respiratory irritants can be inhaled in gaseous or vapor form, as a mist, or as particles with a coating of absorbed liquid. Irritants are often grouped according to their site of action (Table 6–B).

Irritants can be subdivided into *primary* and *secondary irritants*. A *primary irritant* is a material that exerts little systemic toxic action, either because the products formed on the tissues of the respiratory tract are nontoxic or because the irritant action at the contact site is far greater than any systemic toxic action.

A *secondary irritant* produces irritant action on mucous membranes, but this effect is overshadowed by systemic effects resulting from absorption. Examples of materials

TABLE 6–B	Comparison of Several Irritants Affecting the Respiratory Tract

Substance	Description	TLV (2012)*	Concentrations Exceeding TLV
A. Irritants Affecting Upper Respiratory Tract			
Formaldehyde (HCHO)	Aldehyde, colorless gas at ordinary temperatures. Soluble in water up to 55%. (Formalin is aqueous solution).	TLV = 0.3 ppm ceiling based on complaints of irritation <1 ppm, constant prickling irritation, disturbed sleep. Suspected carcinogen.	10–20 ppm causes severe difficulty in breathing, intense lacrimation, severe cough.
Acrolein (CH$_2$=CHCHO)	Aldehyde, colorless or yellowish liquid. Water soluble.	TLV = 0.1 ppm ceiling low enough to minimize, but not entirely prevent, irritation in exposed individuals.	1 ppm may be strongly irritating to eyes and nose within five minutes or less. 8–10 ppm lethal within four hours or less; 100 ppm and above may be lethal within a short time.
Ammonia (NH$_3$)	Alkali, colorless gas. Soluble in water; pungent odor detected as low as 1 ppm.	TLV = 25 ppm should protect against irritation to eyes and respiratory tract, minimize complaints of discomfort among unacclimated individuals.	Irritation of respiratory tract and conjuctiva in workers inhaling 100 ppm. Severe eye damage, lung and airway dysfunction at higher concentrations.
Sulfur dioxide (SO$_2$)	A colorless nonflammable gas with acid odor, pungent taste, one of the most common community air pollutants.	TLV SO$_2$ =0.25 ppm(STEL) expected to prevent irritation and accelerated loss of pulmonary function in most workers.	High acute exposure causes intense irritation, death may follow from suffocation due to respiratory paralysis or pulmonary edema. Industrial poisoning usually chronic—may develop as pulmonary dysfunction progressing to emphysema.
B. Irritants Affecting Both Upper Respiratory Tract and Lung Tissues			
Chlorine (Cl$_2$)	Halogen, greenish-yellow gas with suffocating odor, which may be noticeable 1–4 ppm. Soluble in water up to 0.8% by weight.	TLV = 0.5 ppm to minimize chronic lung changes, accelerated aging, teeth erosion.	30 ppm produces intense coughing.
Ozone (O$_3$)	Bluish or colorless explosive gas or blue liquid. Pleasant characteristic odor in concentrations of less than 2 ppm. Slightly water-soluble, used as disinfectant.	TLV = 0.05 ppm (heavy work), which causes no symptoms but may result in slightly reduced lung function.	Daily intermittent exposure above 5 ppm may cause incapacitating pulmonary congestion. Lung function changes are dose-dependent and reversible at lower doses.
C. Irritants Affecting Primarily Terminal Respiratory Passages and Air Sacs			
Nitrogen dioxide (NO$_2$)	Reddish-brown gas with irritating odor. Decomposes in water, nitric acid (HNO$_3$), and nitric oxide (NO).	TLV = 0.2 ppm considered sufficiently low to ensure against reduced respiratory function.	10–20 ppm may cause mucosal irritation or chronic disease. 100–500 ppm may lead to sudden death, insidious, delayed, and potentially lethal pulmonary edema (most characteristic), delayed inflammatory changes leading to death several weeks after exposure.
Phosgene (carbonyl chloride) (COCl$_2$)	Colorless, nonflammable gas. Suffocating odor when concentrated, otherwise odor suggestive of decaying fruit or moldy hay. Slightly soluble in water and hydrolyzed by it.	TLV = 0.1 ppm because of its irritating effects on the respiratory tract at levels slightly above 0.1 ppm.	3 ppm causes immediate throat irritation, 50 ppm rapidly lethal.

Source: TLVs are from the ACGIH® 2012 TLVs® and BEIs®

in this category are many of the aromatic hydrocarbons and other organic compounds. The direct contact of liquid hydrocarbons with the lung can cause chemical pneumonitis. Thus, in the case of accidental ingestion of these materials, inducing vomiting is not recommended because some of the vomited hydrocarbon could be breathed (aspirated) into the lungs.

Irritation is generally reversible after short-term exposures. If a worker goes into a cloud of ammonia, immediate irritation is experienced and unless the worker is greatly overexposed, the sensation of pain and irritation will be largely gone very shortly after removal from exposure. However, temporary damage to the respiratory epithelium can subsequently make the worker susceptible to other irritants that would otherwise be tolerated. Corrosive substances, such as strong acids and caustics, can also cause irreversible tissue damage or destruction following significant exposures.

Allergens

Allergens are agents that cause recurrent effects after the worker becomes sensitized (allergic) to the substance. The first few exposures usually cause no reaction, but after a person becomes sensitized, reactions can occur from later contact with very small quantities for very short periods of time.

Allergy to a substance almost always presents as eye, skin, or respiratory tract inflammation. Allergic skin effects appear as itching, hives, or eczema (redness, small blisters, cracking). Respiratory effects of allergy appear as nasal congestion, sneezing, discharge, or less commonly, asthma (bronchospasm) or pneumonia. Eyes can also manifest allergy as itching, redness, or swollen eyelids. Allergy due to industrial exposures does not affect the nervous system, liver, kidney, heart, or most other organ systems. Most allergic effects or symptoms begin within minutes or hours following exposure depending on the agent and type of allergy. Symptoms will recur with re-exposure.

Allergy causes only eye, skin, respiratory tract, or, rarely, vascular response after exposure to airborne levels usually far below Permissible Exposure Limits (PELs) as adopted by the Occupational Safety and Health Administration (OSHA), Threshold Limit Values (TLVs®) as determined by the American Conference of Governmental Industrial Hygienists (ACGIH®), or other occupational guidelines. Once a person develops an allergy to a substance, it will persist for years, if not for life. The occurrence of allergy to one substance, does not predict future allergy to another substance although those with allergies to one substance are more likely to develop additional allergies.

Allergy, also known medically as *hypersensitivity*, is often confused with hypersusceptibility. *Hypersusceptibility* refers to the occurrence of the usual health effects caused by a substance following exposures to air levels below that associated with effects for most individuals. With hypersusceptibility, the substance causes its typical effects but at lower doses. If exposure ends, there is no immunologic memory as there is with allergy.

Many agents can cause allergic contact dermatitis, including nickel, chromium salts, poison ivy or oak, and epoxy constituents. Known causes of allergic asthma following inhalation exposure include isocyanates, platinum salts, some wood dusts, animal dander, and organic anhydrides. Allergic pneumonia (hypersensitivity pneumonitis) is caused by some molds (farmer's lung) and sugar cane residue (bagassosis).

SYSTEMIC TOXINS

Asphyxiants are systemic toxins that interfere with oxygenation of the tissues, resulting in physiologic suffocation as the tissues become deprived of oxygen. This class is divided into *simple asphyxiants* and *chemical asphyxiants*.

Asphyxiants deprive the body of the needed oxygen that must be transported from the lungs via the bloodstream to all cells. With complete deprivation of oxygen, brain cells die in 3–5 minutes. Total asphyxiation leads to complete absence of oxygen in the blood (anoxia). Partial asphyxiation leads to low levels of oxygen in the blood (hypoxia). If allowed to continue too long, hypoxia also can result in brain damage or death.

Simple Asphyxiants

Simple asphyxiants are most often inert gases that dilute or displace atmospheric oxygen from the breathing zone or air supply. Blood levels become insufficient for normal tissue respiration. Common examples are carbon dioxide, ethane, helium, hydrogen, methane, and nitrogen. However, any substance in gaseous form can replace oxygen in the breathing zone and, in excessive quantity, cause asphyxiation.

Chemical Asphyxiants

Through their direct chemical action, chemical asphyxiants prevent the uptake of oxygen by the blood, interfere with the transportation of oxygen from the lungs to the tissues, or prevent normal oxygenation of tissues even when the blood is well oxygenated. Carbon monoxide prevents oxygen transport by preferentially combining with hemoglobin. Hydrogen cyanide inhibits enzyme systems, particularly the cytochrome oxidase system necessary for cellular oxygen use. Hydrogen sulfide paralyzes the respiratory center of the brain and the olfactory nerve. At sufficiently high levels, all three of these chemical asphyxiants can cause almost instantaneous collapse, unconsciousness, and death (Table 6–C).

The principal action of carbon monoxide is its interference with the delivery of oxygen to the tissues. The concentration of carbon monoxide required to cause death is small compared with the lethal amount for simple asphyxiants. Carbon monoxide occupies oxygen's usual binding site on hemoglobin, thus preventing the transport of oxygen through the bloodstream to all cells. Hemoglobin combines with carbon monoxide much more readily than it does with oxygen, by a ratio of approximately 300 to 1.

Another example of a chemical asphyxiant is hydrogen cyanide. It is transported by the bloodstream to the individual cells of the body, where it blocks oxygen uptake at the cellular level by combining with the enzymes that control cellular oxidation.

Organ-Specific Effects

Most substances do not damage all organs or systems,

TABLE 6–C	Comparison of Some Chemical Asphyxiants		
Substance	**Description**	**TLV 2012**	**Concentrations Exceeding TLV**
Hydrogen cyanide (HCN)	Colorless liquid or gas, flammable, inhibits cellular respiration, almond-like odor.	TLV = 4.7 ppm ceiling, which may give a seven- or eightfold margin against lethal effects.	18–36 ppm causes slight symptoms after several hours, 90 ppm fatal after 30 to 60 minutes, 270 ppm immediately fatal.
Carbon monoxide (CO)	Colorless, odorless gas, sparingly soluble in water, that combines with hemoglobin to form carboxyhemoglobin (COHb), which interferes with oxygen transport to tissues and removal of CO_2 from tissues.	TLV = 25 ppm based on an air concentration that should not generally result in COHb levels above 10%. Heavy labor, high temperatures, or altitudes 5,000–8,000 feet above sea level may require 25 ppm TLV.	Fatal in 1 minute at 1% concentration (= 10,000 ppm), which causes approximately 20% COHb. Severe poisoning from short exposure often followed by complete recovery, but neurological, cardiovascular, pulmonary, other complications may occur.
Hydrogen sulfide (H_2S)	Colorless flammable gas, burns to sulfur dioxide. Soluble in water but solutions unstable heavier than air. Characteristic odor of rotten eggs detectable at concentrations of 0.02 ppm or appreciably less. Higher toxic concentrations can rapidly deaden sense of smell. Inhibits cellular respiration.	TLV = 1 ppm based primarily on eye effects and CNS depression.	Concentrations of 300–1000 ppm cause rapid unconsciousness and death through respiratory paralysis. Associated with an unusual diversity of symptoms including chronic keratoconjunctivitis, nausea, insomnia, pulmonary edema, balance disorders, polyneuritis, and gray-green discoloration of the teeth.

but affect a few or one specific organ. For example, most organic hydrocarbons cause central nervous system (brain) depression; corrosive acids and alkalis injure skin, mucous membranes, eyes, and lungs. Some agents cause unique effects, such as cancer (e.g., benzene), reproductive effects (e.g., lead), or even liver damage (e.g., carbon tetrachloride). This section highlights a selection of organ-specific effects and their causative substances.

Central Nervous System Depressants

Central nervous system depressants (CNSDs) exert their principal action by causing simple anesthesia without serious systemic effects, unless the dose is massive. Depending on the concentration, the depth of anesthesia ranges from mild symptoms (e.g., headache, dizziness, lack of coordination, confusion) to complete loss of consciousness and death.

CNSDs include aliphatic alcohols (such as ethyl and propyl), aliphatic ketones (such as acetone and methylethylketone), aromatic hydrocarbons, ethers (such as ethyl and isopropyl), and short-chain halogenated hydrocarbons.

Cardiac Sensitization

Inhalation of certain volatile hydrocarbons can make the heart abnormally susceptible to epinephrine (adrenalin). The epinephrine then causes abnormal, dangerous cardiac rhythms, usually ventricular in origin. This has been observed with solvent misuse such as sniffing aerosols or glue, and exposure to some industrial solvents (chlorocarbons) and chlorofluorocarbon (CFC) refrigerants.

Neurotoxic Effects

Neurotoxic agents damage the nervous system. Metals such as manganese, lead, and mercury are examples. The central nervous system seems particularly sensitive to organometallic compounds such as tetraethyl lead.

A different neurotoxic effect involves acetylcholine, a neurotransmitter. In the transfer of electrical impulses (nerve conduction) from one part of the nerve to the next part, the chemical acetylcholine is essential, and the enzyme cholinesterase maintains acetylcholine at the proper levels. When acetylcholinesterase is inhibited, the acetylcholine increases and may reach a level incompatible with the orderly transfer of electrical impulses. Nerve conduction abnormalities occur that result in nervous system failure. Some cholinesterase inhibitors include organophosphate pesticides such as parathion or carbamate pesticides such as carbofuran.

Other neurotoxic effects include neurasthenia and peripheral neuropathy. Neurasthenia involves emotional irritability and loss of intellectual function; it is associated with prolonged exposure (years) to some hydrocarbon solvents (such as styrene and toluene). Peripheral neuropathy involves loss of limb strength or sensation; it is associated with exposure to agents such as lead, hexane, and acrylamide.

Pulmonary Effects

In considering health effects from inhaled dust, primary concern is given to solid material that is small enough to enter the alveoli. A certain amount of filtration by the upper respiratory system prevents large particles from getting into the lung. In the workplace, particles are dispersed in a non-uniform way and in a full spectrum of sizes; only a portion of them are small enough to get into the lung.

Inert dusts previously termed nuisance dusts are now called *Particulates* (insoluble or poorly soluble) *Not Otherwise Specified* (PNOS). The definition of inert is relative because all particulates evoke a tissue response when inhaled in sufficient amount. The TLV for PNOS has been set at 10 mg/m^3 (inhalable fraction) or 3 mg/m^3 (respirable fraction). These values pertain only to particulate matter that contains no asbestos and less than one percent crystalline silica.

Chronic exposure to some dusts (asbestos, silica, coal) is associated with various types of pneumoconiosis (lung disease caused by dust) (see Chapter 8, Particulates). Pneumoconioses associated with inert dusts are called benign pneumoconioses.

Fibrotic (formation of scar tissue) changes are produced by materials such as crystalline silica, which produces a silicotic nodule or small area of scarlike tissue. Asbestos also produces fibrotic damage to lung tissue (asbestosis) as well as various cancers. Asbestos and smoking illustrate the concept of synergy, in which the combined risk from two separate causes of health effect (lung cancer) far exceeds the sum of their individual risks.

In combination with smoking, exposure to airborne asbestos fibers leads to an excessive incidence of lung cancer. The incidence of lung cancer in nonsmokers exposed to asbestos, though lower, is still abnormally high. Asbestos exposure has also been shown to cause mesothelioma, which in non-asbestos-exposed people is a very rare cancer of the lining of the abdomen or the lung. (See Chapter 8, Particulates, for more information on asbestos-related diseases and other pneumoconioses.)

Some inhaled particles gain entrance to the body through the lung. Although they may not damage the lung tissues, they transit the lung, are absorbed into the blood, and distributed throughout the body where they may damage the nervous system, kidney, liver, or other organs.

The effects that result from heavy metals being absorbed through the respiratory tract vary appreciably from substance to substance. Often there is slow, cumulative absorption and retention of metal in the body; however, health effects may develop so slowly that the source or cause of the symptoms is often not initially recognized (e.g., lead, mercury).

Inorganic lead is a good example of a substance with unique effects in multiple organs. Excessive exposure to the inorganic form usually results from ingestion or inhalation of dust or fume, causing physiologic and tissue injury that are characterized by anemia, headache, anorexia, weakness, and weight loss. With chronic, high exposures, more serious effects include bone marrow injury, peripheral neuropathy, kidney injury, reproductive effects, and brain injury.

Organic lead, more so than inorganic lead, tends to concentrate in the brain. Some organic lead materials can easily be absorbed through the skin and add to the hazard from ingestion or inhalation. A single exposure to tetraethyl lead can cause symptoms in a few hours and absorption of a relatively small amount can be fatal.

Although mercury poisoning was described by Paracelsus among miners several centuries ago, it has recently received much more attention. Inorganic compounds of mercury are readily absorbed from the intestine and tend to concentrate primarily in the kidneys, but can also damage the brain. Organic mercury tends to be especially concentrated in blood and the brain.

Industrial manganese poisoning is primarily a chronic disease resulting from inhalation of fume or dust in the mining or refining of manganese ores. It also can be caused by cutting and welding metals containing high manganese content while in a confined space without respiratory protection. Manganese poisoning is noted for its peculiar neurological effects, especially psychomotor instability similar to Parkinson's disease.

Carcinogenesis

Although any new and abnormal tissue growth can be classed as a neoplasm, this term is most often used to describe cancerous or potentially cancerous tissue. The cells of a cancer are out of control. If neoplastic cells invade tissues or spread to new locations in the body (metastasize), the neoplasm has become cancerous or malignant. Cancer cells seldom perform a useful function or one similar to that of the cells they destroy and replace.

It is well established that exposure to some chemicals can produce cancer in laboratory animals and humans. In common usage, carcinogen refers to any agent that can produce or accelerate the development of malignant or potentially malignant tumors or malignant neoplastic proliferation of cells. Carcinogen refers specifically to agents that cause carcinoma, but the current trend is to broaden its usage to indicate an agent that possesses carcinogenic potential. The terms tumorigen and oncogen are used synonymously with carcinogen.

A number of factors have been related to the incidence of cancer—the genetic makeup of the host, viruses, ultraviolet and ionizing radiation, hormone imbalance, and exposure to certain substances. Other factors such as co-carcinogens and tumor accelerators can be involved. For some substances, a combination of factors must be present to induce cancers.

Definitions

Carcinogenesis has several possible definitions. A *carcinogen* can be defined as a substance that will induce a malignant tumor in humans following a reasonable exposure. A carcinogen has also been defined as a substance that will induce any neoplastic growth in any tissue of any animal at any dose by any method of application applied for as long as the lifetime of the animal.

Problems arise when all substances that would fulfill the second definition in the experimental laboratory are classified as carcinogens and it is assumed that they will cause malignancies in humans in accordance with the first definition. According to the National Institute for Occupational Safety and Health (NIOSH), a substance is considered a "suspected carcinogen" to humans if it produces cancers in two or more animal species.

Even if we could extrapolate from a specific strain of a laboratory animal to all species including humans, taking into consideration such factors as weight, surface area, metabolic profiles, and drug-induced changes in metabolism, carcinogenic potential is often difficult to estimate because of interactions with other agents and biological susceptibilities.

Chemicals that induce cancer do so by mechanisms that may not be completely defined. It is generally believed that the transformation of a cell from a normal to a carcinogenic state is multi-staged and influenced by both internal and external factors. For example, some materials can produce cancer in the lungs after inhalation, whereas others pass through the lung as a route of entry and produce the cancer elsewhere.

A toxicologist can look at the structure of an organic chemical and speculate that because of certain functional groups the chemical is carcinogenic, but another chemical having similar functional groups is not carcinogenic.

Carcinogens

Coal tar and various petroleum products have been identified as skin and subcutaneous carcinogens. Pitch, creosote oil, anthracene oil, soot, lamp black, lignite, asphalt, bitumen, certain cutting oils, waxes, and paraffin oils have also been implicated as potential carcinogens.

Workers can be exposed to arsenic, also recognized as a carcinogen, in the manufacture or use of roasting metallic sulfide ores as well as certain paints or enamels, dyes or tints, pesticides, and some chemicals.

Inorganic salts of metals such as chromium, beryllium, and, to a lesser extent, nickel compounds are associated with cancer of the respiratory tract, usually the lungs. Other metal compounds such as lead and cobalt are likely carcinogens, but their direct toxic effects in humans can obscure carcinogenic potential.

Leukemia is a group of diseases characterized by widespread, uncontrolled proliferation and abnormal accumulation of white blood cells and the failure of many of these cells to reach maturity. Exposures to ionizing radiation and benzene are principal occupational causes. Benzene exposure is also associated with blood dyscrasias (diseased state of the blood, generally involving abnormal or deficiently formed cellular elements), which may progress to leukemia and/or aplastic anemia.

Osteogenic sarcomas (bone tumors) have been detected in workers who applied radioactive luminous paint to instrument and watch dials. Angiosarcomas (a relatively rare malignant growth) of the liver have been found to be associated with human exposure to vinyl chloride monomer. Oat-cell carcinomas of the lung have been found in workers exposed to bis(chloromethyl)ether (BCME). BCME is carcinogenic by inhalation, skin, and subcutaneous routes in animals.

The result of exposure to chemical carcinogens is such that people who absorb a chemical carcinogen (e.g., benzidine) are at increased risk of getting bladder cancer. With many carcinogens (Table 6–D), it is clear that there is a higher incidence of cancer in certain groups of people who are exposed to carcinogenic materials. For a more complete listing and discussion of carcinogens, consult the websites of International Agency for Research on Cancer (IARC) and the National Toxicology Program.

Environmental Factors

Cancer is considered so insidious and has such severe health consequences that carcinogenic substances are isolated and looked at more carefully than all others. The statement that 80–90 percent of all cancers are environmentally caused does not mean that 80–90 percent of cancers are caused by industry. The environment includes not only the air we breathe and water we drink but our diet and all elements of our lifestyle, on and off the job. The predominant causes of environmental cancer are tobacco smoke and diet.

Mutagenesis

A *mutagen* is an agent that affects the genetic material (DNA) of the exposed organism. It may cause cancer, birth defects, or undesirable effects in later generations. People who work with a certain chemical may not be harmed, but their offspring can be.

The problem of time lag between exposure and effect is particularly difficult for mutagenic agents. Mutations will not show up until the next generation at the earliest, and may not appear for several generations. The long latency makes it difficult to discover the connection between the exposure and manifestation of genetic damage.

Mutagens are chemical or physical agents that cause inheritable changes in the chromosomes. For example, the

TABLE 6–D   Carcinogens with Possible Occupational Relevance*

Substances Known to Be Carcinogenic

4-aminobiphenyl	Bis(chloromethyl)ether and technical-grade chloromethyl methyl ether	Erionite
Arsenic and certain arsenic compounds	1-(2-chloroethyl)-3-(4-methylcyclohexyl)-1-nitrosourea (MeCCNU)	2-naphthylamine
Asbestos		Radon
Benzene	hexavalent Chromium compounds	Thorium dioxide
Benzidine	Ethylene oxide	Ultraviolet radiation
Beryllium and its compounds	Hepatitis B and C viruses	Vinyl chloride (monomer)
1, 3-Butadiene	Ionizing radiation (x, gamma, and neutrons)	Wood dust
Cadmium	Nickel and its compounds	
	Silica, Crystalline	

Substances That May Reasonably Be Assumed to Be Carcinogenic

Acetaldehyde	Diglycidyl resorcinol ether	Polychlorinated biphenyls
2-acetylaminofluorene	3,3'-dimethoxybenzidine and 3,3'-dimethoxybenzidine	Polycyclic aromatic hydrocarbons (such as benz(a)anthracene and benzo(a)pyrene)
Acrylamide	3,3- dimethylbenzidine	Nitrilotriacetic acid
Acrylonitrile	Dimethylcarbamoyl chloride	B-propiolactone
2-aminoanthraquinone	4-dimethylaminoazobenzene	Propylene oxide
O-aminoazotoluene	Dimethyl sulfate	Polybrominated biphenyls
1-amino-2-methylanthraquinone	Dimethylvinyl chloride	Sulfallate
Amitrole	1,1-dimethylhydrazine	1,3-propane sultone
O-anisidine hydrochloride	Epichlorohydrin	Tetrachloroethylene (perchloroethylene)
Benzotrichloride	Ethyl acrylate	Tetrafluoroethylene
Bromodichloromethane	1,4-dioxane	4,4-Thiodianaline
Butylated hydroxyanisole	Ethyl methanesulfonate	Thiourea
Carbon tetrachloride	Formaldehyde (gas)	Selenium sulfide
Chlorendic acid	Hexamethylphosphoramide	O-toluidine and o-toluidine hydrochloride
Chlorinated paraffins (C_{12}, 60% chlorine)	Hydranize and hydrazine sulfate	Toxaphene
Chloroform	Ethylene thiourea	2,3,7,8-tetrachlorodibenzo-p-dioxin (TCDD)
3-chloro-2-methylpropene	Kepone (chlordecone)	Toluene diisocyanate
4-chloro-o-phenylenediamine	Lead acetate and lead phosphate	2,4,6-trichlorophenol
P-cresidine	Hexachlorbenzene	Ceramic fibers
DDT	2-methylaziridine (propyleneimine)	Chlordecone
2,4-diaminotoluene	4,4'-methylendianiline and its dihydrochloride	Chloro-o-toluidine
1,2-dibromo-3-chloropropane	Methyl methanesulfonate	Chloro-o-toluidine hydrochloride
1,2-dibromoethane (EDB)	Lindane and other hexachlorocyclo-hexane isomers	Dinitropyrene
1,4-dichlorobenzene	Michler's ketone	Danthron
1,4-dichlorobenzidine and 3,3'- dichlorobenzidine dihydrochloride	4,4'-methylene bis(N,N-dimethyl)benzenamine	Glasswool
1,2-dichloroethane	2-nitropropane	Glycidol
Dichloromethane (methylene chloride)	4,4'-osydianiline	Furan
1,3-dichloropropene (technical grade)	N-methyl-n'-nitro-n-nitrosoguanidine	Hexachloroethane
Diepoxybutane	Cobalt sulfate	Nitroanisole
Di(2-ethylhexyl)phthalate	Diazoaminobenzene	Nitrochrysene
Diethyl sulfate	Diesel exhaust particulates	Nitropyrene
Vinyl bromide	Hydrazine	Tetranitromethane
Vinyl fluoride	Isoprene	Trichloropropane
	Naphthalene	Vinyl cyclohexene diepoxide
	Nitrobenzene	Nitromethane
	Trichloroethylene	Nitros amines (various)

Occupational Exposures Associated with a Technological Process That Are Known to Be Carcinogenic

Coal tars; Coal tar pitches	Mineral oils
Coke ove emissions	Strong inorganic acid mists containing sulfuric acid
Soots	

*Known carcinogens are substances for which evidence from human studies indicates that there is a causal relationship between exposure to the substance and human cancer. Substances that may reasonably be expected to be carcinogens are those for which there is limited evidence of carcinogenicity in humans or sufficient evidence of carcinogenicity in experimental animals. (Adapted from 11th Annual Report on Carcinogens, 2005 National Toxicology Program.) The list does not include medications and all occupational carcinogens listed in the 11th Annual Report.

cells of the bone marrow go on multiplying through life and shed the products of division into the blood, where they function for a time as red and white blood cells before they are removed and replaced. Mutations (changes) in the genetic material of such cells may make cell division ineffective or, alternatively, cause them to reproduce at an accelerated rate. A mutagenic effect on somatic cells can make them capable of more rapid growth and multiplication, so that they are formed far more rapidly than they can be removed from the blood, where they interfere with normal body functions. If the white cells are affected in this way, the outcome is leukemia. In this process they may also lose their physiologic functionality. Similar interference with the genetic material could theoretically start up division in cells that do not normally divide during adult life. If the products of such division displace or invade normal tissues, the result is a solid tumor or cancer. In both these instances, the mutagen responsible would have manifested activity as a carcinogen.

Reproductive Toxicity

Reproduction results from a complex series of events involving both parents. It begins with each parent's genetic contribution (chromosome) and ends with expression of the genes acquired by the offspring. Every step in the reproductive process is vulnerable to effects from external physical and chemical agents. Chromosomal replication, sexual function, ovulation, conception/fertilization, embryo implantation, placental function, fetal development, labor, delivery, and even child development are components of the reproductive process. Table 6–E lists known or suspected human reproductive toxins. Reproductive abnormalities include changes in sperm count, sperm motility, libido, menstruation and cycle length, and fertility rate; these and other changes can result in miscarriage, embryo toxicity, developmental defects, and stillbirth (Tables 6–F, 6–G).

Teratogenesis (congenital malformation) results from interference with normal embryonic development by a biological, chemical, or physical agent. Exposure of a pregnant female may, under certain conditions, produce malformations of the fetus without inducing damage to the mother or killing the fetus. Such malformations are not hereditary. In contrast, congenital malformations resulting from changes in the genetic material are mutations and are hereditary.

Teratogens

Agents currently identified as human teratogens include infections such as rubella, metals such as lead and mercury, chemicals including PCBs, and ionizing radiation.

Pregnant Women in the Workplace

A *teratogen*, by definition, is different from a mutagen in

TABLE 6-E	Selected Occupational (Nonpharmaceutical) Agents Known or Strongly Suspected to Cause Human Reproductive Toxicity and Developmental Effects*
Acrylamide	Ethylene glycol monoethyl ether acetate
Alkylating/antineoplastic agents	
Arsenic	Ethylene glycol monomethyl ether
Benzene	Ethylene glycol monomethyl ether acetate
Bromopropane (1 and 2)	
1,3-Butadiene	Ethylene oxide
Cadmium	Heat
Carbaryl	Iodine 131
Carbon disulfide	Ionizing radiation
Carbon monoxide	Lead
Chlordecone	Mercury (compounds)
Chloroform	Methyl bromide
Chromium (hexavalent compounds)	Methyl Chloride
	Polychlorinated biphenyls (PCB)
DDT	Methyl Isocyanate
1,2-dibromo-3-chloropropane (DBCP)	Methyl n-butyl ketone
1,1-Dichloro-2,2-bis (p chlorophenyl)ethylene (DDE)	N-methyl pyrrolidone
	Nickel carbonyl
Di(2-ethylhexyl)phthalate (DEHP)	Nitrobenzene
Di-n-butyl phthalate(DPP)	Nitrous Oxide
Dinitrobenzene	Sodium fluoroacetate
Dinitrotoluene	Solvent exposure
Environmental Tobacco Smoke	2,3,7,8-tetrachlorodibenzo para dioxin (TCDD)
Epichlorohydrin	Toluene
Ethyl carbamate	Tributyltin methacrylate
Ethylene dibromide	Triphenyltin hydroxice
Ethylene glycol monoethyl ether	Vinyl cyclohexene diepoxide

* Selected from list of agents known to the State of California to cause reproductive and developmental toxicity. *www.oehha.ca.gov/prop65/prop65_list/Newlist.html*

that it must affect a developing fetus. In common parlance it is thought that exposure to the teratogen usually occurs between conception and delivery. This is extremely important today because of the very considerable pressure to address the topic of pregnant women in the workplace.

The fetus is protected from some toxic chemicals because the placenta prevents them from entering the fetal bloodstream; however, many toxic chemicals, such as lead, easily cross the placenta. Damage to the fetus (embryo) is most likely to occur in early pregnancy, particularly during the first 8–10 weeks. During much of this critical period, many women are not even aware that they are pregnant.

It can be extremely difficult to establish specific cause-and-effect relationships between a teratogen and the birth defect it can produce. Animal studies must be supplemented with epidemiologic data and it may be decades before researchers know with certainty which substances pose risk for unborn infants.

The fact that there are pregnant women in the work-

TABLE 6–F	Measures of Human Reproductive Function Readily Obtainable before Fertilization

	Affected Individual		
Endpoint	**Male**	**Both**	**Female**
Sexual function	Erection Ejaculation	Libido Behavior	
Endocrine system		Luteinizing hormone Follicle-stimulating hormone Steroid hormones (androgens, estrogens, and progestins) Chromosomal integrity	Cervical mucus quality
Germ cells	Sperm number Sperm motility Sperm shape Fertilizing ability		
Fecundity (ability to conceive)	Testicular integrity Semen quality	Integrity of external genitalia	Ovarian integrity Blockage of oviduct Menstrual regularity Amenorrhea Anovulatory cycles

Source: Adapted from U.S. Congress, Office of Technology Assessment. *Reproductive Health Hazards in the Workplace*, Chapter 3, Table 3-1. Washington, DC: U.S. Government Printing Office, OTA-BA-266, Dec. 1985.

TABLE 6–G	Measures of Human Reproductive Function Readily Available after Fertilization

	Affected Individual		
Endpoint	**Female**	**Both**	**Offspring**
Endocrine system	Human chorionic gonadotropin Estrogen and progesterone		
Health during pregnancy	Hemorrhage Toxemia	Fetal death Spontaneous abortion	Morphology Chromosomal aberrations Fetal growth
Perinatal period		Premature birth Postmature birth Delivery complications	Death Chromosomal aberrations Birth defects Birth weight Apgar score
Postnatal period	Lactation		Infant death Childhood morbidity Childhood malignancies Development Behavior
Reproductive lifespan	Age at menopause Time to conception		

Source: Adapted from U.S. Congress, Office of Technology Assessment. *Reproductive Health Hazards in the Workplace*, Chapter 3, Table 3-2. Washington, DC: U.S. Government Printing Office, OTA-BA-266, Dec. 1985.

place and that they can be exposed to teratogens leads to a problem in setting occupational health standards. An embryo of a few weeks or a fetus of a few months should be given consideration and should not be exposed to a harmful environment. Although one way to solve this problem is to restrict the activities of fertile women in the workplace, this practice is no longer legally acceptable (*Auto Workers vs. Johnson Controls*). Also, the potential for adverse effects on the male reproductive system cannot be overlooked. The workplace should be safe enough that fertile men and women are able to work without likelihood of harm.

BASIS FOR WORKPLACE STANDARDS

Chemical analogy, in-vitro testing, animal experimentation, and human epidemiologic data are the bases for establishing workplace standards for substances. They are described in the following sections.

Chemical Analogy

When dealing with a new chemical, animal or human toxicity data are usually unavailable. Therefore, the nature of response to a chemical can be assumed to be analogous to that produced by contact with a substance with a similar chemical and biological structure. Chemicals that are similar have been assumed initially to produce similar biological responses. Computerized modeling uses structure-activity data, chemical analogy, and other data to derive estimates of toxicity and toxicokinetics.

In-Vitro Testing

In-vitro means "in a test tube." As a result of increasing costs and social pressures to eliminate use of animals for toxicological testing, laboratory methods are being developed to study toxicity and health effects. Depending on the effect or property being studied, different test materials or biological media may be used. For example, bacteria (e.g., *Salmonella*) are grown on a plate and exposed to a chemical to determine its mutagenicity (Ames test). Similarly, target organ cells (e.g., skin, liver) can be grown in culture and exposed to a chemical to determine the reaction at the molecular or cellular level. Other tests being developed or already in use involve human or animal tissue and cells, microbial agents (protozoa, helminths), artificial human organs, human tissue, and DNA.

Animal Experimentation

Before introducing chemical agents into the workplace, it is advisable to know their toxic effects. Then preventive measures can be designed to protect workers and emergency procedures can be put in place to minimize accidental exposure. Because there is often little or no information available about new chemicals, an important method of developing such new information quickly is animal experimentation.

Exposure Standards

The toxicological effects of vapors, gases, fumes, and dusts are initially determined in the laboratory and can be estimated by actually exposing animals to known concentrations for controlled periods of time.

Groups of animals can be exposed to controlled concentrations for eight hours a day, five days a week, for weeks, months, or years. Animals must be observed daily to ascertain physiological responses during exposure and post-exposure periods. On terminating chronic experiments, all animals are sacrificed and the internal organs are weighed and examined histopathologically. In this manner, the toxi-

cologist gains information regarding no-effect levels as well as levels that produce injury.

Screening Procedures

Toxicological screening should ideally include both acute toxicity studies, studies of repeated administration at short intervals, and long-term studies performed during the lifespan of the animal, and in some instances over several generations.

Because biological variations influence the reaction to a foreign substance in different species, it is difficult to duplicate in animal experiments the precise situation to which humans can be exposed. In the development of a specific test program, preliminary studies are necessary to select species that absorb and metabolize related classes of chemicals in ways similar to humans.

A route of administration different from that usually occurring in workers, such as parenteral (injected, i.e., intravenous, intramuscular, etc.) instead of inhalation or dermal can give results that may not be applicable to occupational exposure.

Chronic toxicity studies involve repeated administration of test substances. However, chronic effects can also be expected from a single exposure to a substance if the body stores the material so that it remains in the organism for long periods of time or if the health effect is delayed or permanent. Repeated administration of the test substance is useful in the investigation of such problems as cumulative toxicity, tolerance, and enzyme-induction phenomena.

Problem Areas

Animal testing provides only an estimate of the toxicity of a chemical for humans. It is very difficult to extrapolate an LD_{50} or an LC_{50} to an acceptable occupational exposure limit (OEL).

Because the primary concern is the prevention of harm to humans, the limitations inherent in animal-derived data should be recognized. Whether human response will resemble that of the most reactive or the least reactive species tested is often not known. Finally, whether the animal response is an exact parallel to human response cannot always be predicted.

Human Epidemiological Data

Records of human experience for exposures to many substances are available. This is particularly true for older chemicals such as carbon monoxide and lead. Epidemiological data can be descriptive, retrospective, or prospective; it pertains to health effects that are measured in groups of exposed humans.

Descriptive studies identify a change or difference in prevalence of disease in a subgroup of the population.

Retrospective studies reveal a relationship between a substance and a certain effect caused by exposure that occurred months or years before the initiation of data collection.

Prospective studies can define more precisely the temporal relationship and the magnitude of risk. Prospective studies measure present and future health effects as, or after, the exposures occur.

Epidemiological analysis may reveal the relationship between time of occurrence of an adverse effect and age at the time of the first exposure. Epidemiological study and analysis attempts to identify or clarify the influence of other variables/exposures in combination with the agent under study. Cigarette smoking is such a variable in the study of lung cancer among asbestos workers.

FEDERAL REGULATIONS

The federal regulations with implications for industrial toxicology include the Federal Occupational Safety and Health Act of 1970, the Toxic Substances Control Act of 1976, and various NIOSH, OSHA, and EPA standards.

Occupational Safety and Health Act

The Occupational Safety and Health Act (OSHAct, enacted in 1970) is administered by the Occupational Safety and Health Administration (OSHA), which has the authority to regulate occupational exposure to physical hazards (such as noise and radiation) and hazardous substances (chemicals, metals, dusts) in the work environment. OSHA monitors health and safety in the workplace, setting standards for worker exposure to specific chemicals, for permissible exposure levels (PELs), and for monitoring procedures. It also provides research, information, education, and training in occupational safety and health. By establishing the National Institute for Occupational Safety and Health (NIOSH), the act provided for studies to be conducted so that regulatory initiatives can be based on the best available information.

In 1983, OSHA enacted the Hazard Communication Standard, 29 CFR 1910.1200, which sets standards for worker notification and training for chemicals in the workplace. This also is known as the "Hazcom" or "right-to-know" regulation. For more information on hazard communication, see Chapter 30, Government Regulations, and Chapter 31, International Developments in Occupational Safety and Health.

OSHA has adopted Permissible Exposure Limits (PELs) for more than 400 substances. Although OSHA initially adopted OELs recommended by the American Conference of Governmental Industrial Hygienists (ACGIH®), it has subsequently relied on NIOSH research, evaluations, and recommendations in its standard setting process.

The ACGIH® is a private organization that began publishing OELs in 1946 that are called Threshold Limit Values (TLVs®). They were initially directed primarily at substances that caused physiological reactions such as poisoning, irritation of eyes and respiratory tract, and skin rashes. The original TLVs® were not established on the basis of carcinogenic, teratogenic, or mutagenic properties; synergistic effects of chemical mixtures were not included in tests used to determine the TLVs. Since OSHA began (1971), new standards for carcinogenic and other chemical agents have been promulgated by OSHA. ACGIH has also been updating and adding to its original list of TLVs.

The American Industrial Hygiene Association is a professional organization whose members are industrial hygienists and related specialists. It has also developed OELs that are called WEELs (Workplace Environmental Exposure Limits).

Toxic Substances Control Act

The Toxic Substances Control Act of 1976 (TSCA) is administered by the Environmental Protection Agency (EPA) and covers almost all chemicals manufactured in the United States, excluding certain compounds covered under other regulations such as the Federal Insecticide, Fungicide and Rodenticide Act (FIFRA). The act requires that chemical manufacturers and processors develop adequate data on the health and environmental effects of the chemicals they produce. The EPA is required to establish standards for the testing of chemicals.

Companies are required to notify the EPA 90 days before manufacturing any new chemical and to provide test data and other information about the safety of the product. The EPA has the authority to ban or regulate such chemicals if test information is insufficient and if the chemical is to be produced in substantial quantities with wide distribution. The EPA is required to ban or restrict the use of any chemical presenting an unreasonable risk of injury to health or the environment.

Toxic Substances List

The OSHAct requires the annual publication of a list of all known toxic substances by generic, family, or other useful grouping, and the concentrations at which such toxicity is known to occur. OSHA also requires employers to monitor employee exposure to toxic materials and to keep records of such exposure. The Registry of Toxic Effects of Chemical Substances (RTECS) is a compendium of toxicity data extracted from the scientific literature by the U.S. Department of Health and Human Services. It is intended to serve as the required toxic substances list.

The purpose of the Toxic Substances List is to identify

all known toxic substances in accordance with standardized definitions that can be used to describe toxicity. The entry of a substance on the list does not automatically mean that it is to be avoided, but that the listed substance has been found to be hazardous at the doses or exposure levels listed. The absence of a substance from the list does not necessarily indicate that a substance is not toxic but rather that the dose that causes the toxic effect is not known. There has been no attempt at an evaluation of the degree of hazard that might be expected from substances on the list; that is a goal of the hazard-evaluation studies.

Hazard Evaluation

Hazard evaluation involves a measurement of the quantity available for absorption by the user, the amount of time available for absorption, the frequency with which the exposure occurs, the physical form of the substances, toxicological properties and potency, and the presence of other substances (toxic or nontoxic), additives, or contaminants.

Ventilation, appropriate hygienic practices, housekeeping, protective clothing, and pertinent training for safe handling may eliminate or reduce hazards that might exist.

Hazard evaluation is performed by engineers, chemists, industrial hygienists, toxicologists, and physicians trained in toxicology, industrial hygiene, and occupational medicine who strive to recognize, measure, and control these hazards.

NIOSH/OSHA Standards

A complete substance-specific standard includes the regulatory exposure limit of the substance; the methods for collecting, sampling, and analyzing the substance; the engineering controls necessary for maintaining a safe environment; appropriate equipment and clothing for safe handling of the substance; emergency procedures in the event of an accident; medical surveillance procedures necessary for the detection of illness or injury from inadvertent overexposure; and the use of signs and labels to identify hazardous substances.

NIOSH Criteria Documents

Except in the case of emergency standards, the normal first step in the standard-setting process is the creation of a criteria document for the substance by NIOSH. Such documents are forwarded to OSHA for consideration as permanent OSHA standards.

NIOSH also develops recommended exposure limits (RELs) for hazardous substances in the workplace. Unless noted otherwise, RELs are time-weighted average (TWA) concentrations for up to a 10-hour workday during a 40 hour workweek. RELs are published in NIOSH criteria documents along with appropriate measures to prevent adverse health effects.

NIOSH criteria documents incorporate animal and human data, when available, on carcinogenicity, mutagenicity, teratogenicity, and effects on reproduction. When possible, attempts are made to correlate these adverse reactions with exposures and effects.

Current Intelligence Bulletins (CIBs) are issued by NIOSH for more rapid dissemination of new scientific information about occupational hazards. A CIB may draw attention to a hazard previously unrecognized or may report new data suggesting that a known hazard is either more or less dangerous than was previously thought (see Bibliography).

OSHA Standards

The U.S. Secretary of Labor is responsible for promulgating standards. In some cases, a recommended standard is referred to an advisory committee for study and review in accordance with provisions of the act. OSHA standards are adopted after extensive review including public hearings. Regardless of the status of the proposed standards in the criteria documents, these documents constitute valuable and readily available sources of information and should be consulted whenever there is interest in a substance for which a criteria document has been written.

Although the standard-setting process is extremely thorough, it is also lengthy and very costly, and has resulted in the promulgation of relatively few regulations (permanent standards).

OSHA PELs (OELs) do not necessarily represent exposure limits below which no adverse health impact will occur. The adoption of a PEL includes consideration of economic and feasibility factors. Noise and lead are examples of substances whose current PELs allow exposures that have measurable and significant adverse health impact.

ACGIH® THRESHOLD LIMIT VALUES—TLVS®

In addition to regulated PELs established and enforced by OSHA, many voluntary guides for exposure to airborne contaminants have been proposed. The most widely followed or referenced are those issued annually by the American Conference of Governmental Industrial Hygienists (ACGIH®), and are termed Threshold Limit Values (TLVs®).

The ACGIH TLVs are not recommendations of a government agency, but are the product of a committee whose members are associated with government or academia.

ACGIH TLVs, like many OSHA PELs, are not derived from cancer or reproductive risk data and, therefore, are not necessarily protective for those serious effects. For carcinogens (e.g., asbestos, benzene) and some systemic toxins (e.g., lead) whose "no effect levels" have not been determined,

PELs and other OELS (TLVs, WEELs, etc.) often represent levels of exposure that will cause such occupational effects in a small proportion of workers, such as 1 per thousand, of those exposed.

Limitations of OELs

One of the fundamental tasks confronting the industrial hygienist is assessing the possible degrees of exposure to a variety of substances in the work environment. Because the most common route of entry for a chemical in the workplace is inhalation, the practice for many years has been to sample the air being breathed by the workers and compare the result with a suitable standard. However, regulatory limits such as PELs are often the product of toxicologic and economic compromises and not exposure boundaries that protect all exposed workers; furthermore, voluntary OELs, such as TLVs, are recommended as guidelines rather than a fine line between safe and unsafe.

Although air standards and guides such as those developed by OSHA, NIOSH, and ACGIH are most widely used in industrial hygiene practice, certain shortcomings are inherent in any air standard. This limits their applicability to some situations. Some of the more common recognized problems include the following:

1. Difficulty in acquiring a truly representative breathing zone sample
2. Uncertainties about the extent of absorption of the amount inhaled
3. Nonroutine or nonrepetitive work; air samples can characterize work operations only on the day the sample is taken
4. Variations in particle size, absorption, and particle solubility
5. Accidental or deliberate contamination of sample

Formulas are available for determining OELs for the inhalable-thoracic and respirable-particulate fractions, obtained by means of a suitable particle-size–discriminating device. The asbestos OEL is unique, and is expressed in fibers per cubic centimeter of air.

Time-Weighted Average

It is implicit in all OELs that measurements are made in the breathing zone of a worker and are obtained in such a way that a TWA can be calculated. In general, for an eight-hour workday,

$$TWA = \frac{C_a T_a + C_b T_b + \ldots C_n T_n}{8}$$

where T is the time of exposure period and C is the concentration of contaminant during that period. This concept

has proven to be a useful means of estimating the long-term chronic effects of exposure to most substances in the workplace. Although the TWA does not necessarily predict the amount of a substance that will be absorbed, it does measure the amount that can be inhaled during a workday; considerations of the extent of absorption aid in the selection of a value that affords the desired degree of protection.

It is inherent in the definition of a TWA that concentrations higher than the recommended value can be permitted for some periods of time as long as these levels are offset by periods of lesser concentration. The degree of permissible excursion is related to the OEL of the substance. The relationship between threshold limit and permissible excursion is a general rule that may not apply in certain cases (Figure 6–4).

Ceiling Values

For some substances, it is not advisable to permit concentrations substantially above the recommended TWA; some PELs and TLVs are designated by the letter C, which stands for ceiling value. Most substances designated with a C tend to be irritants for which an OEL has been set slightly below the level where irritation will be noticed by most individuals. Exposures should never exceed the ceiling value.

The durations of sampling necessary to determine whether the exposures are within the limits for each group are not usually the same. A single brief sample that is applicable to a C limit is not appropriate for calculating a TWA.

The OEL list also contains another listing of values for many substances that are called short-term exposure limits

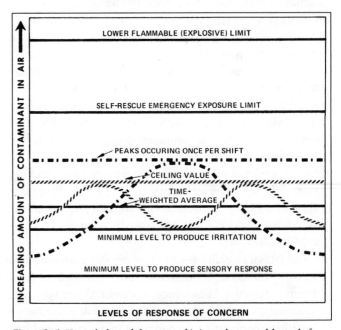

Figure 6–4. Knowledge of the type of injury that would result from exposure to various contaminant levels is important to health and safety professionals.

(STELs). These represent exposure limits that should not be exceeded during a fifteen minute period and are usually higher than the 8-hour TWA for the same substance.

Mixtures

When two or more hazardous substances that act on the same organ system are present, their combined effect, not the individual effect of either component, should be given primary consideration. In the absence of information to the contrary, the effects of the different hazards should be considered additive. Exceptions can be made when there is a good reason to believe that the chief effects of the different harmful substances are independent, as when purely local effects on different organs of the body are produced by the various components of the mixture.

The formula for additive effects is as follows:

$$\frac{C_1}{T_1} + \frac{C_2}{T_2} + \frac{C_3}{T_3} + \ldots = 1$$

where   C = the observed atmospheric concentration
         T = the corresponding TLV

If the sum of the fractions is greater than one, then the TLV has been exceeded.

Antagonistic action or potentiation may occur with some combinations of contaminants. At present, such cases must be determined individually. Potentiating or antagonistic agents may not necessarily be harmful by themselves. Potentiating effects of exposure by routes other than that of inhalation are also possible, such as the effect of ingested alcohol on an inhaled hydrocarbon (trichloroethylene).

When a given operation or process emits a number of harmful dusts, fumes, vapors, or gases, it is often feasible to attempt to evaluate the hazard by measuring a single (surrogate) substance. In such cases, the OEL used for this substance should be reduced by a suitable factor, the magnitude of which depends on the number, toxicity, and relative quantity of the other contaminants ordinarily present.

Examples of processes that are typically associated with multiple harmful atmospheric contaminants are welding, automobile repair, painting, reinforced plastic fabrication, shipbuilding, biotechnology, and chemical manufacturing.

Carcinogens

Because causal mechanisms and dose-response relationships are not well understood for many carcinogens, OSHA (and other regulatory agencies such as the EPA) has typically performed complex and comprehensive risk assessments prior to recommending exposure limits. The ACGIH has taken a different approach and rates substances according to a substance's carcinogenic potential. (See Appendix B,

for definitions of these ratings of the carcinogenicity of substances.)

Physical Factors

It is recognized that such physical factors as heat, ultraviolet and ionizing radiation, and work under high atmospheric pressure or at a high altitude cause adverse health effects following sufficient exposure. Certain physical stresses may also alter the response to a toxic substance. Although most threshold limits have built-in safety factors to guard against moderate deviations from normal environments, the safety factors of most substances are not large enough to account for gross deviations. For example, continuous work at temperatures above 32°C (90°F) or work at altitudes above 3,000 m would be considered gross deviations. In such instances, judgment must be exercised in the proper downward adjustments of the OELs.

Unlisted Substances

Many substances used or created (including by-products) in industrial processes do not appear on any OEL list. For many, there is insufficient information from which to derive an OEL. Also, some substances of considerable toxicity have not been studied, because only a limited number of workers, such as employees of a single plant, have potential exposure to possibly harmful concentrations.

Basic Data Used to Determine OELs

If possible, OEL values are based on human experience. Epidemiological studies, which include environmental data and morbidity and mortality data, are the best possible basis for an OEL. However, in most cases, such studies do not exist. In the absence of epidemiological studies, individual cases involving human exposures are considered, but usually the most useful literature available is from animal toxicological studies. The preferred studies for determining acceptable exposure limits are those based on long-term inhalation tests involving several animal species at concentrations both above and below the lowest effect level.

However, scientists often must rely on short-term inhalation data or, in many cases, toxicity studies in which the substance was introduced into the experimental animals by routes other than inhalation. The least useful toxicological data are those based on short-term oral intake, intended to measure the acute toxicity, or the ability of the substance to kill the exposed animals. It is not surprising, therefore, that the publication of new information often results in dramatic changes in some OELs.

Documentation

OELs are usually developed by a committee of specialists

that includes toxicologists, industrial hygienists, epidemiologists, occupational physicians, and other related professionals. Their recommendations are usually documented and sometimes published. In these documents, the principal data that the committee considered significant are reviewed and references are cited. The justification and documentation are presented in the some or all of the following categories:

- chemical and physical properties
- occupational exposure
- animal studies
- reproductive and developmental studies
- genotoxicity studies
- pharmacokinetic/metabolism studies
- human studies
- OEL recommendation
- other recommendations
- references

OEL SELECTION: The industrial hygienist must select the OEL to be used as the allowable limit for the exposure being measured. In all cases the OSHA PEL must be complied with, but for most substances regulated by OSHA and many others not addressed by OSHA, voluntary standards such as TLVs, WEELS, RELs and other states' PELS (e.g., Cal/OSHA) are often more current and toxicologically based; these standards should all be consulted in order to select an OEL that provides adequate worker protection.

BIOLOGICAL TESTING

A useful means of assessing occupational exposure to a harmful material is the analysis of biological samples obtained from exposed workers. Biological sampling, however, should not be considered a substitute for air sampling. Ethical considerations prohibit what some have called the use of the worker as an "integrated air-sampling device." Biological analysis may provide an indication of the body burden of the substance, the amount circulating in the blood, or the amount being excreted. Virtually every tissue and fluid in the body can be analyzed, but for practical reasons, most bioassays are confined to specimens of urine or blood. For substances such as carbon monoxide and many solvents, the analysis of exhaled breath samples indicates the level of previous exposure. Occasionally, analysis of samples of hair, nails, feces, or other tissues may be useful.

Whereas air monitoring measures the composition of the external environment surrounding the worker, biological monitoring measures the amount of chemical absorbed via any route (lungs, skin, mucosa, etc.). In addition, the effects of added stress (such as increased work load resulting

in a higher respiration rate with increased intake of the air contaminant) are reflected in the results. The total exposure (both on and off the job) to harmful materials is included.

For some chemicals, biological assays can be much more reliable indicators of health risks than measurements of air contaminants alone (Table 6–H).

Analyses that can be performed on biological samples include the following:

- analysis for the unchanged substance (such as lead, arsenic, mercury) in body fluids and tissues
- analysis for a metabolite of the substance in body fluids or tissues, such as muconic acid in urine resulting from exposure to benzene
- analysis to determine the variations in the level of a naturally occurring enzyme or other biochemical substance normally present in body fluids or tissues, such as depression of cholinesterase activity as a result of exposure to organic phosphate compounds

The rates of absorption, metabolism, and excretion for a particular substance determine when it is most appropriate to analyze samples in relation to duration and time of exposure. For rapidly excreted or exhaled substances, peak concentrations are found during or immediately after exposure. Peak excretion rates for metabolites of some organic solvents and some inorganic substances may occur minutes to hours after exposure. Biological levels of metals with cumulative properties (such as lead or mercury) may reflect the response to several days' or weeks' prior exposure. The "half-lives" of various chemicals in the body have been established and are an important consideration in biological testing for exposure.

People with virtually identical exposure histories can show a wide variation in response due to subtle differences in their rates of absorption, tissue storage, or metabolism. Greater significance should be given to the variations in an individual's level from period to period than to the variations between different individuals within a group.

Some harmful substances can be stored for long periods of time in various parts of the body. The substances are unlikely to be evenly distributed throughout the body. In many cases, the organ with the highest concentration of the material is the liver or kidney.

Many materials, including organic compounds, undergo detoxification in the body. The body converts the material to something else that may reduce its ability to cause injury and/or be more easily excreted. Occasionally, the conversion enhances the agent's toxicity. The conversion products may appear in the urine or blood as metabolites (Table 6–H).

Many organic chemicals of high molecular weight and low vapor pressure are not found in workroom air at

TABLE 6–H	Body Tissues and Fluids Suitable for Biological Analysis

Analysis of Urine Samples May Be Useful for the Following Compounds or Their Metabolites

Acetone	2-ethoxyethanol acetate (2-ethoxyacetic acid)	Pentachlorophenol
Aluminum	Ethyl benzene	Phenol
Aniline	Fluorides	2-Propanol
Antimony	Furfural (furoic acid)	Selenium
Arsenic/Arsine	N-hexane (2-5-hexanedione)	Styrene (mandelic acid)
Benzene (phenylmercapturic acid; muconic acid)	Cyanides	Tellurium
Benzidine	Isopropyl alcohol (acetone)	Tetrachloroethylene (trichloroacetic acid)
Butadiene	Lead	Tetrahydrofuran
Butoxyethanol	Manganese	Thallium
Cadmium	Mercury	Toluene (hippuric acid)
Carbon disulfide (2-thiothiazolidine-4-carboxylic acid)	Methanol (or formic acid)	1,1,1-trichloroethane (trichloroacetic acid, trichloroethanol)
Chlorobenzene (4-chlorocatecol)	Methyl ethyl ketone	Trichloroethylene
Chromium H_2O-soluble compounds	Methyl isobutyl ketone	Triethylamine (triethylamic and TEA n-oxide)
Cobalt	Methyl N-butyl ketone	Uranium
Copper	Methyl chloroform	Vanadium
Cyanide (thiocyanate)	Nickel	Xylene (methyl hippuric acid)
Cyclohexanol	N-Methyl-2-pyrrolidone	Zinc
Cyclohexanone	Nickel carbonyl (nickel)	
Dichloromethane	Nitrobenzene (p-nitrophenol)	
Dimethylacetamide (methylacetamide)	Parathion (nitrophenol)	
Dimethyl formamide (N-methylformamide)		
2-ethoxyethanol (2-ethoxyacetic acid)		

Analysis of Blood Samples May Be Useful for the Following Compounds

Acetone	Dichloromethane (carboxyhemoglobin)	Pentachlorophenol
Aniline (methemoglobin)	Ethylene oxide	Styrene
Butadiene	Lead	Tetrachloroethylene
Cadmium	Manganese	Toluene
Carbon monoxide (carboxyhemoglobin)	Mercury	1,1,1 Trichloroethane
Cholinesterase inhibitors (RBC cholinesterase)	Nitrobenzene (methemoglobin)	Trichloroethylene (or trichloroethanol)
Cobalt		Xylene
Cyanides		

Breath Analysis May Be Useful for the Following

Benzene	N-hexane	1,1,1-trichloroethane
Dichloromethane	Tetrachloroethylene	Trichloroethylene
Ethyl alcohol		

Note: Metabolites are given in parentheses where they are indicators of exposure and absorption of a compound.

elevated concentrations under normal conditions of work, but the same substances can be absorbed through the intact skin, giving rise to excessive absorption that cannot be measured by air sampling. In such cases, a suitable biological analysis can be an excellent means of detecting the failure of skin-protection measures.

For a few regulated substances, OSHA has set biological limits (e.g., blood lead). For many others, ACGIH has adopted a set of advisory biological limit values called the Biological Exposure Indices (BEIs®). These indices use urine, blood, or expired air sampled under strictly defined conditions. (See Chapter 15, Evaluation, for a more detailed discussion of Biological Exposure Indices.)

Because the collection of blood, urine, or breath samples requires the use of medical personnel, most programs of biological monitoring become a cooperative effort between the safety, industrial hygiene, and medical departments.

The analysis and interpretation of biological samples is obviously of great importance and because the quantities involved are almost always very slight, great care must be taken in performing such analyses. Ordinarily, existing plant laboratories and lab staff are not equipped or trained to perform these analyses in a satisfactory manner, and it is advisable to use a laboratory that has proven capability in this area.

PART II

Urine, Blood, and Breath Analyses

Tests for the level of metabolites of toxic agents in the urine, blood, and breath have found wide use in industrial toxicology as a means of evaluating exposure of workers. The concentration of the metabolic product is related to the exposure level of the toxic agent. Because normal values of such metabolites have been established, an increase above normal levels indicates that an overexposure has occurred. This provides a valuable screening mechanism for estimating the hazard from continued or excessive exposure. Because lead, for example, interferes with porphyrin metabolism, erythrocyte protoporphyrin can be a useful measure and the results are useful as an indicator of lead effect (and absorption).

One of the best documented examples of the effectiveness of biological sampling is that of analysis for exposure to lead and its compounds. The level of lead in the blood has been studied extensively and is well correlated to the probability of health impact resulting from lead exposure.

For many other substances, the correlation between bioassay tests and symptoms is so poor as to render a biological analysis of little value. The aim of an industrial hygienist or safety professional is to control exposure to harmful materials; both air sampling and biological monitoring contribute valuable information regarding exposure and health impact.

The industrial hygienist or safety professional is charged with maintaining a safe, healthful environment and should perform air sampling; indeed, it is required by law in many cases. Where available and indicated by exposure risk, biological testing may also be required or appropriate.

If inhaled gases and vapors are fat-soluble and are not metabolized, they are cleared from the body primarily through the respiratory system. Examples of these are the volatile halogenated hydrocarbons; the volatile aliphatic, olefinic, and aromatic hydrocarbons; some volatile aliphatic saturated ketones and ethers; esters of low molecular weight; and certain other organic solvents such as carbon disulfide.

For industrial solvents that continue clearing from the body in exhaled breath for several hours after exposure, analysis of progressive decrease in the rate of excretion in the breath can be very helpful in showing not only the nature of the substances to which the worker was exposed, but also the magnitude of the exposure and probable blood levels. By use of gas chromatography or infrared analysis of breath samples, the identification of the substance can be established, permitting comparison of the exposed workers' breath decay rate with workers' published excretion curves. There is, however, considerable individual variation and it is not easy to set standard values.

SOURCES OF TOXICOLOGAL INFOR

The health and safety professional can t
sources for information when a question a   out the
toxicity and hazard of a material.

Safety Data Sheet

The Safety Data Sheet (SDS), formerly the Material Safety Data Sheet (MSDS), is a prime source of information on the hazardous properties of chemical products. The OSHA Hazard Communication Standard (HCS) requires chemical manufacturers, distributors, or importers to provide SDSs to communicate the hazards of hazardous chemical products. As of June 1, 2015, the HCS will require new SDSs to be in a uniform format, and include the section numbers, the headings, and associated information under the headings below:

- *Section 1: Identification*—includes product identifier; manufacturer or distributor name, address, phone number; emergency phone number; recommended use; restrictions on use.
- *Section 2: Hazard(s) identification*—includes all hazards regarding the chemical; required label elements.
- *Section 3: Composition/information on ingredients*—includes information on chemical ingredients; trade secret claims.
- *Section 4: First-aid measures*—includes important symptoms/effects, acute, delayed; required treatment.
- *Section 5: Fire-fighting measures*—lists suitable extinguishing techniques, equipment; chemical hazards from fire.
- *Section 6: Accidental release measures*—lists emergency procedures; protective equipment; proper methods of containment and cleanup.
- *Section 7: Handling and storage*—lists precautions for safe handling and storage, including incompatibilities.
- *Section 8: Exposure controls/personal protection*—lists OSHA's Permissible Exposure Limits (PELs); Threshold Limit Values (TLVs); appropriate engineering controls; personal protective equipment (PPE).
- *Section 9: Physical and chemical properties*—lists the chemical's characteristics.
- *Section 10: Stability and reactivity*—lists chemical stability and possibility of hazardous reactions.
- *Section 11: Toxicological information*—includes routes of exposure; related symptoms, acute and chronic effects; numerical measures of toxicity.
- *Section 12: Ecological information*
- *Section 13: Disposal considerations*
- *Section 14: Transport information*
- *Section 15: Regulatory information*

- *Section 16: Other information*—includes the date of preparation or last revision.

    Note: Since other Agencies regulate this information, OSHA will not be enforcing Sections 12 through 15(29 CFR 1910.1200(g)(2)).

    These forms are required to be readily available to employees. Training in their use should be included in employee training required under the Hazard Communication legislation (see Chapter 30, Government Regulations).

Information Resources

The Internet now provides immediate access to current toxicology data and hazardous substance information. For all but the most common and well-studied substances (e.g., acetone, sodium hydroxide), reliable databases should be queried first for relevant data and guidelines. However, beware of data obtained from websites, the authors of which are not listed and/or are not a government agency or academic institution.

    Listed below are recommended websites—all with search capabilities.

SDS Libraries

1. Cornell University: www.med.cornell.edu/ehs/msds.htm
2. ILP, Inc.: http://www.ilpi.com/msds/#Internet

Toxicology

1. Occupational Health Guidelines to Chemical Substances (NIOSH—summaries): http://www.cdc.gov/niosh/docs/81-123/
2. TOXNET: http://toxnet.nlm.nih.gov, also a portal to very useful databases including:
   - ChemIDplus
   - Hazardous Substance Data Bank
   - Toxline
   - Chemical Carcinogenesis Research Information System (CCRIS): carcinogenicity and mutagenicity test results for over 8,000 chemicals
   - International Toxicity Estimates for Risk (ITER): risk information for over 600 chemicals
   - Integrated Risk Information System (IRIS): hazard identification and dose-response assessments for over 500 chemicals
   - Carcinogenic Potency database
   - Gene-Tox
   - Reproductive databases
3. Agency for Toxic Substances and Disease Registry (ATSDR)—detailed toxicological profiles of 275 substances: www.atsdr.cdc.gov/toxprofiles/index.asp
4. National Toxicology Program: http://ntp.niehs. nih.gov/
   a) National Toxicology Program (NTP) Report on Carcinogens: http://ntp.niehs.nih.gov/?objectid= 72016262-BDB7-CEBA-FA60E922B18C2540
5. Medicine and toxicology—PubMed: http://www.ncbi. nlm.nih.gov/sites/entrez
6. International Agency for Research on Cancer (IARC)—substance-specific data summaries and analyses: http://mongraphs.iarc.fr/index.php
7. Micromedex—proprietary toxicology database: http://www. micromedex.com
8. European Chemical Substances Information System (ESIS): http://esis.jrc.ec.europa.eu/

Public Health

1. Centers for Disease Control and Prevention (CDC): www.cdc.gov
2. World Health Organization (WHO): www.who.int/en/

Regulatory

1. Occupational Safety and Health Administration (OSHA): http://www.osha.gov
2. Environmental Protection Agency (EPA): http://www.epa.gov
3. European Union European Agency for Safety and Health at Work: http://osha.europa.eu/en/front-page
4. Cal/OSHA Permissible Exposure Limits: www.dir.ca.gov/title8/ac1.pdf
5. California Prop 65 list of carcinogens and reproductive toxins: www.oehha.ca.gov/prop65.html

Organizations

1. American Conference of Governmental Industrial Hygienists (ACGIH): http://www.acgih.org
2. American Industrial Hygiene Association (AIHA): http://www.aiha.org
3. American National Standards Institute (ANSI): http://www.ansi.org
4. American Society of Safety Engineers (ASSE): http://www.asse.org
5. National Safety Council (NSC): http://www.nsc.org
6. National Institute for Occupational Safety and Health (NIOSH): http:\\www.cdc.gov/niosh
7. World Health Organization (WHO): http://www.who.org
8. U.S. Government Printing Office (GPO): http://www.gpo.gov

SUMMARY

The word *toxicity* is used to describe the ability of a substance to have an adverse effect on the health or well-being of a human. Whether any ill effects occur depends on the properties of the chemical, the dose (the amount of the chemical acting on the body or system), the route by which the substance enters the body, and the susceptibility or resistance of the exposed individual.

There are four routes of entry, or means by which a substance may enter or act on the body: inhalation, skin absorption or contact, ingestion, and injection. Of these, inhalation and skin absorption or contact are the most important occupational exposure routes.

When a toxic chemical acts on the human body, the nature and extent of the injurious response depends on the dose received—that is, the amount of the chemical that actually enters the body or system and the time interval during which this dose is administered. Response can vary widely and might be as slight as a cough or mild respiratory irritation or as serious as cancer and death.

The practice of industrial hygiene is based on the concept that for each substance there is a level of exposure below which significant injury, illness, or discomfort rarely or never occurs. The industrial hygienist protects the health of workers by assessing potential chemical and physical agent exposures and controlling the environmental conditions so that the exposure is minimized or eliminated.

BIBLIOGRAPHY

American Conference of Governmental Industrial Hygienists. *Documentation of Threshold Limit Values,* 7th ed. Cincinnati, OH: ACGIH, 2001 with 2002-2011 supplements.

American Conference of Governmental Industrial Hygienists. *Threshold Limit Values (TLVs®) for Chemical Substances and Physical Agents & Biological Exposure Indices (BEIs®).* Cincinnati, OH: ACGIH, 2012.

Dart RC, ed. *Medical Toxicology,* 3rd ed. Philadelphia: Lippincott Williams & Wilkins, 2003.

Grant WM, Schuman JS. *Toxicology of the Eye: Effects on the Eyes and Visual System from Chemicals, Drugs, Metals and Materials, Plants, Toxins and Venoms: Also Systemic Side Effects from Eye Medications,* 4th ed. Springfield, IL: Charles C. Thomas, 1993.

Frazier LM, Hage ML. *Reproductive Hazards of the Workplace.* New York: Van Nostrand Reinhold, 1998.

Klaassen CD. *Casarett and Doull's Toxicology—The Basic Science of Poisons,* 7th ed. New York: McGraw-Hill, 2008.

LaDou J, ed. *Occupational and Environmental Medicine,* 4th ed. New York: McGraw Hill, 2006.

Lauwerys RR, Hoet P. *Industrial Chemical Exposure: Guidelines for Biological Monitoring,* 3rd ed. Boca Raton, FL: CRC Press, 2001.

Loomis TA, Hayes AW. *Loomis's Essentials of Toxicology,* 4th ed. San Diego, CA: Academic Press, 1996.

National Institute for Occupational Safety and Health, U.S. Department of Health and Human Services. *NIOSH Pocket Guide to Chemical Hazards.* Washington, DC: NIOSH, 2010. http://www.cdc.gov/niosh/npg/

Olson KR, ed. *Poisoning and Drug Overdose,* 5th ed. New York: McGraw Hill, 2006.

Rom WN, ed. *Environmental and Occupational Medicine,* 4th ed. Philadelphia: Lippincott Williams & Wilkins, 2007.

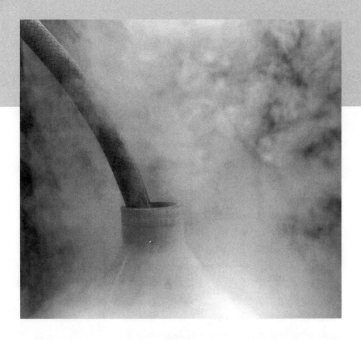

CHAPTER 7

Gases, Vapors, and Solvents

*by S. Katharine Hammond, PhD, CIH
and Sa Liu, PhD*

A potential threat to the health, productivity, and efficiency of workers in most occupations and industries is their exposure to gases and vapors from solvents, chemical products, by-products of chemical use, and chemical processes. No one fully comprehends the total effect, yet all workers are exposed and all workers are affected.

Exposures to volatile chemicals occur throughout life, from conception to death. For example, organic solvent vapors inhaled by a mother can reach the fetus. Exposures also occur in the course of daily living, ranging from the inhalation of vapors from a newspaper freshly off the press, to exposure to cleaning solvents by all routes of entry, to a worker manufacturing computer chips, to a researcher in a laboratory, to a farm worker hoeing weeds. It may occur at home or at work. Effects from the exposure may range from a simple objection to an odor to death at high concentrations. In between, there is a whole spectrum of effects.

Solvents convert substances into a form suitable for a particular use. Solvents are significant because many substances are most useful when in solution.

Organic and inorganic compounds are used in the home as cleaning agents, paint thinners, coatings, and spot removers; in the office as typewriter key cleaners, desktop cleaners, and wax removers; in commercial laundries as dry cleaning liquids; on the farm as pesticides; in laboratories as chemical reagents and drying, cleaning, and liquid extraction agents; in shops as cleaners, solvents, by-products from processes such as welding, and paints. Many consumer products packaged in cans and drums contain mixtures of organic chemicals.

Because of the nearly infinite number of combinations possible for the variables involved—hundreds of different compounds, degree of concentration, duration of exposure, *combined effects with other solvents, gases and vapors, and the health and age of an exposed person—generalizations about effects of exposure on a particular person are difficult to make.*

PROPERTIES OF GASES, VAPORS, AND SOLVENTS

Two of the three fundamental states of matter, gases and liquids, are discussed in this chapter; the solid phase is discussed in the next chapter. A gas is a formless fluid that completely fills its container and exerts an equal pressure in all directions. Gases spread rapidly throughout a room by diffusion.

Gases are materials that are in the gaseous state at normal temperature (25°C) and pressure (1 atmosphere). Chemicals that are liquids at normal temperature and pressure (NTP) will exist partially in the gaseous phase, and that portion is known as a vapor. If a liquid is spilled, or otherwise has a large surface area, some will evaporate, and, over time, equilibrium may be established between the gas and liquid phases. The vapor pressure is a measure of the concentration of the chemical in the air at equilibrium; the higher the vapor pressure, the higher the concentration of the chemical at equilibrium. Vapor pressure is very temperature dependent, so that as the temperature rises, the airborne concentration of an equilibrium mixture will rise. Although there is often insufficient time or material for equilibrium to be established, the vapor pressure remains a good measure of the tendency of a liquid to evaporate. Other factors being equal, a solvent with a higher vapor pressure will have a higher airborne concentration than a solvent with a lower vapor pressure.

Solvents are liquids in which something, called a solute, can be dissolved; solids may also be suspended in solvents. The solute may have been a solid, a gas, or another liquid before being dissolved in the solvent. Solvents are very useful both to transport solutes and to clean materials. In many cases, such as paint application, solvents work best if they evaporate relatively quickly, leaving behind an even application of the solid material; however, this very property may lead to high vapor concentrations in the air.

Although the term *solvent* is often used to describe organic solvents, water is a solvent as well. Common acids and bases are aqueous solutions. The common inorganic acids include the hydrogen halides (HF, HCl, HI, HBr), the oxygen acids (nitric [HNO_3], phosphoric [H_3PO_4], and sulfuric [H_2SO_4]), and others such as hydrogen sulfide (H_2S) and hydrogen cyanide (HCN). These are commercially available as compressed gases, liquids, aqueous solutions of various concentrations, or, in some cases, as solids. These acids may be strong (completely ionized in aqueous solu-

tion) or weak (parent acid in equilibrium with its acid anion; the parent acid predominates).

Vapor phase water is not considered hazardous, and the solutes that dissolve in water are polar or ionic, and so generally have low vapor pressures; therefore, there is less potential hazard from inhalation of vapors from aqueous solutions in general. However, the gases that dissolve in water to form acids will off-gas from solution as a result of the equilibrium between the gas phase and the solution. The more volatile acids, such as HCl, do so readily; the less volatile acids, such as H_2SO_4 and H_3PO_4, do so only at elevated temperatures. As temperatures are increased, equilibrium is driven to the gas phase; the simple acids are driven off as the gas and the oxygen acids can decompose to produce oxides such as NO/NO_2 and SO_2/SO_3. As the pH is lowered (more acidic), volatility from solution is increased; as the pH is raised (more alkaline), the acid anion is stabilized in solution and it is essentially not volatile.

Another important characteristic of solvents, in addition to their volatility, is their polarity. Some solvents are highly polar, like water, while others are nonpolar, such as hexane, and others are of intermediate polarity. A fundamental principle, "like dissolves like," states that more polar or ionic solutes will dissolve more readily in polar solvents than in nonpolar solvents. For example, more salt will dissolve in water than in hexane, that is, salt is more soluble in water than in hexane. Conversely, grease dissolves better in gasoline than in water.

Solubility is very important in understanding the hazards presented by various solvents as solubility affects absorption into the body, distribution throughout the body, storage in various tissues, and elimination of chemicals. Thus, more fat-soluble, or lipophilic, chemicals pass through the skin than those chemicals that are soluble in water only, while substances that are soluble in both water and fat are most readily absorbed. Clearly, dermal absorption will be more important for the latter compounds. Solubility is also important in evaluating the potential effect of a chemical on the central nervous system (CNS). The blood-brain barrier appears to be much more effective at excluding ionized molecules than those that are fat soluble. Water-soluble compounds tend to be excreted fairly rapidly, while fat-soluble substances are often stored in the adipose tissue.

Where a solvent system is in use, three distinct possible routes of exposure must be considered. First, if an opportunity exists for skin contact, dermal absorption may be important. If the vapor pressure is high, or the temperature is high, inhalation of vapors may be important. Finally, one must also consider the possibility of exposure to an aerosolized mist of the solution, in which case there is also exposure to the solutes. Because of the high volume of breathing and the large surface area of the lungs, which are designed for maximum interchange between blood and air in the lungs, inhalation is usually the most important route of exposure. However, in some cases the dermal route predominates, especially for less volatile solvents.

CRITICAL EXPOSURE FACTORS

The hazard presented by use of a chemical is a function not only of its inherent toxicity, but also of the potential for exposure. While one substance may be extremely toxic, and therefore very well controlled so that the exposure is negligible, a greater hazard may then exist in the same workplace as the result of an inherently less toxic chemical that is totally uncontrolled, and to which the worker is exposed at high levels.

Mode of Use and Potential for Exposure

The most important factors in exposure potential are how the material is used and what controls (e.g., engineering or personal protective equipment), if any, are in place. Processes that use gaseous reactants (as in a semiconductor chip manufacturing process) are often completely enclosed; the gases are often too reactive to coexist with air and the purity of the product demands it. In the event of a system failure, a compressed gas at pressures of several hundred pounds per square inch (psi) poses greater risk than a liquefied gas with a pressure of a few psi. Painting operations pose risk of exposure to solvents, reactive chemicals such as the isocyanates, or suspected carcinogens such as hexavalent chromium (used in primers). Spray painting poses a greater exposure risk for the worker than brush or roller application. When inhalation exposures are controlled, dermal exposure may be the major route of entry. Many organic compounds readily permeate the skin or glove materials; some, such as dimethyl sulfoxide, are of limited toxicity but may be a vehicle for transporting other toxic materials into the body.

Temperature and Volatility

The airborne concentration of a solvent vapor depends on the vapor pressure, which is a measure of the volatility of the solvent. The vapor pressure of any chemical compound is directly related to the temperature. For solvents that are liquids at room temperature, this can make a significant difference in exposure potential. For example, methyl ethyl ketone (MEK) has a vapor pressure of 100 mm Hg at 25°C and 400 mm at 60°C. Thus, for two similar processes using the same solvent, the one taking place at lower temperature poses less potential for exposure.

The boiling point and vapor pressure increase with increasing numbers of carbon atoms, provided the functional group remains the same; for example, among the three ketones, acetone, methyl ethyl ketone, and methyl isobutyl ketone (3, 4, and 6 carbon atoms, respectively), the boiling points are 56, 80, and 128°C, respectively. However, compounds with the same number of carbon atoms but different functional groups will have very different boiling points and vapor pressures; for example, the compounds with three carbon atoms have boiling points ranging from −44°F for propane (a hydrocarbon), through 133°F for acetone (a ketone), 207°F for propanol (an alcohol), to 256°F for methyl cellosolve, or 2-methoxy ethanol.

Concentration

The effect of concentration may be manifested in several ways. From the point of view of chemical kinetics, reaction rates depend on some factor of concentration; for a given concentration x, the rate is proportional to x, x^2, or some other factor depending on the reaction mechanism. Nitric oxide (NO), Threshold Limit Value (TLV®) 25 ppm, at higher concentrations reacts rapidly with oxygen to produce nitrogen dioxide (NO_2, current TLV 3 ppm, proposed TLV 0.2 ppm), but at very low concentrations the rate is very slow. The vapor pressure of a solute over a solution varies directly as the mole fraction (concentration) of the solute and the vapor pressure of the solute when it is pure, according to Raoult's law. In both cases, reducing concentration reduces the potential for exposure by limiting the amount of toxic product formed or volatilized. Some chemicals, such as sulfuric acid, are available in a variety of concentrations; the standard grade is approximately 98 percent acid. The vapor pressure is so low at room temperature that it poses minimal risk. The grade marketed as oleum, or fuming sulfuric acid, is much more reactive and off-gases sulfur dioxide; it poses significant risk to the worker. Chemical protective clothing for those working with highly reactive materials must be selected carefully; butyl rubber is satisfactory for sulfuric acid, but has significantly diminished breakthrough times for oleum.

Reactivity

Chemical reactivity can enhance or reduce health hazard potential. Other physical hazards, such as fire, become significant for pyrophoric materials such as silane (SiH_4) and yellow phosphorus. Acids or bases can react with volatile compounds to stabilize them. In a strongly alkaline solution (high pH), cyanide salts cannot form volatile hydrogen cyanide (HCN); in an acid solution (low pH), volatile amines (ammonia or organic amines) are converted to nonvolatile ammonium salts in solution. Liquid metal halides (tungsten or rhenium hexafluoride) react rapidly with moisture in the air to form gaseous hydrogen fluoride (HF).

Exposure Guidelines

Several guidelines exist to assist industrial hygienists in interpreting the hazard posed by specific concentrations of gases and vapors in the workplace. The most commonly used in the United States are Threshold Limit Values (TLVs®), Permissible Exposure Limits (PELs), and Recommended Exposure Limits (RELs). Maximum Concentrations Values in the Workplace (MAKs) are an example of European occupational exposure limits that are widely used in the industrial hygiene field.

TLVs are established by a committee of the American Conference of Governmental Industrial Hygienists (ACGIH®) and composed of professionals working voluntarily. The ACGIH has published its TLVs for over 50 years. TLVs refer to "airborne concentrations of chemical substances and represent conditions under which it is believed that nearly all workers may be repeatedly exposed, day after day, over a working lifetime, without adverse health effects" (ACGIH, 2011). For some gases and vapors, short-term exposure limits (STELs) have also been established when exposure to higher concentrations for 15 minutes may lead to serious health consequences. See Appendix B for a listing of the TLVs and STELs. The ACGIH cautions that "these values are not fine lines between safe and dangerous concentrations;" they should be used as guidelines in evaluating exposures in particular workplace. Each year some of the TLVs are revised, and often new chemicals are added to the list. Although some countries have adopted the TLVs as legal limits, they were not intended for that purpose, and do not have the weight of law in the United States.

PELs, by contrast, are legal exposure limits in the United States and are established by the Occupational Safety and Health Administration (OSHA). OSHA initially adopted the 1968 TLVs as PELs, and has since issued revised PELs for only a small number of substances. The revised PELs include much more recent data, details on health effects, and often include more details on required monitoring and protections, including biological monitoring in some cases.

The National Institute for Occupational Safety and Health (NIOSH) studies compounds of concern and issues Recommended Exposure Limits (RELs), along with reports on the scientific data upon which RELs are based, the Criteria documents. RELs may be used by OSHA in setting new PELs. In the meantime, RELs provide important guidance to the practicing industrial hygienist.

The DFG (German Research Foundation) Commission for the Investigation of Health Hazards of Chemical Compounds in the Work Area (MAK-Commission) derives Maximum Concentrations Values in the Workplace (MAKs). MAK values are health based and often derived from the *no observed adverse effect level* (NOAEL) of the most sensitive endpoint. They are legally binding and updated annually.

Each of these occupational exposure limits has its limitations. TLVs have been criticized because some feel that industry has had too much influence in their establishment, and the levels appear to be insufficiently protective given the scientific data presented; ACGIH has taken several steps to try to alleviate these concerns. The rulemaking procedure for PELs is arduous and subject to multiple hearings, comment periods, and legal appeals; this lengthy process has restricted the ability of OSHA to revise PELs as new health data have arisen in the past four decades. Thus, while TLVs have been established for more than 720 chemicals, there are only approximately 500 PELs. OSHA does state that the employer has a general duty to provide a safe workplace, and interprets this to imply that TLVs should also be considered. Therefore, the industrial hygienist is best advised to make use of all available occupational exposure limits, PELs, TLVs, RELs, and MAKs, and to understand the basis upon which such recommendations are made.

SOLVENTS

Organic Chemistry

Organic chemistry is the chemistry of the compounds of carbon. The carbon atom can form single, double, and triple covalent bonds to other carbon atoms and to atoms of other elements. A molecular chain (or skeleton) consists of a line of carbon atoms that can have branches of carbon atoms, or functional groups. These functional groups can contain oxygen (O), nitrogen (N), phosphorus (P), and sulfur (S), among others. A *functional group* in an organic molecule is a region where reactions can take place. Typical functional groups include double and triple bonds and the presence of atoms other than carbon. For example, a hydroxyl group, OH, is a functional group that defines an alcohol, and NH_2 defines an amine.

Organic compounds are named according to the number of carbon atoms in the basic skeletal chain. The location of the functional groups is designated by the number of the carbon atom to which it is attached. The common organic solvents can be classified as aliphatic, cyclic, aromatic, halogenated hydrocarbons, ketones, esters, alcohols, and ethers. Each class has a characteristic molecular structure, as shown in Table 7–A.

Compounds with only carbon and hydrogen atoms are called hydrocarbons. Hydrocarbons with all single bonds are alkanes, and are also known as saturated hydrocarbons, as they contain the maximum number of hydrogen atoms. Hydrocarbons forming chains are known as aliphatic or paraffin hydrocarbons, while those forming

TABLE 7–A   Major Classes of Organic Compounds

Aliphatic Hydrocarbons

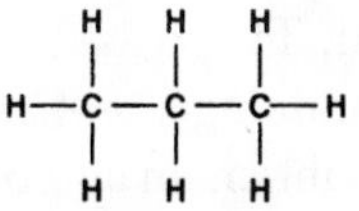

alkane, C_nH_{2n+2}
propane

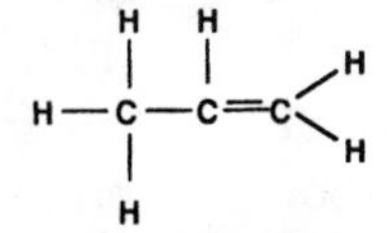

alkene, C_nH_{2n}
propene

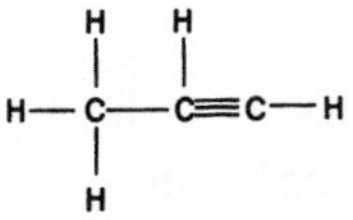

alkyne, CnH_{2n-2}
propyne (methyl acetylene)

Aromatic Hydrocarbons

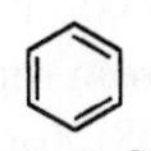

benzene, C_6H_6

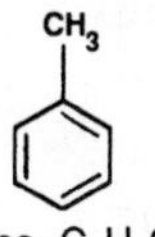

toluene, $C_6H_5CH_3$
(methyl benzene)

Cyclic Aliphatic Hydrocarbons

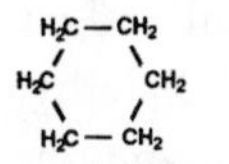

cyclohexane

Oxygen-containing Functional Groups

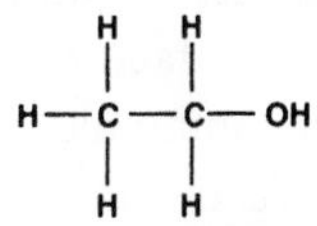

alcohol, ROH
ethanol

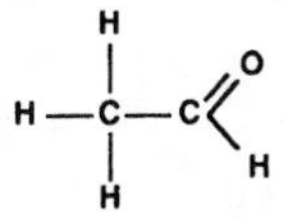

aldehyde, RCOH
ethanal (acetaldehyde)

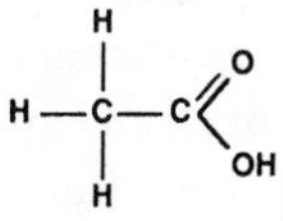

acid, RCOOH
ethanoic acid (acetic acid)

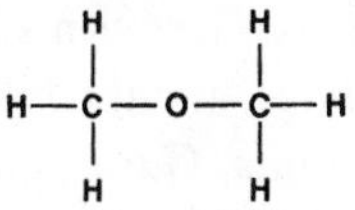

ether, ROR′
dimethy ether

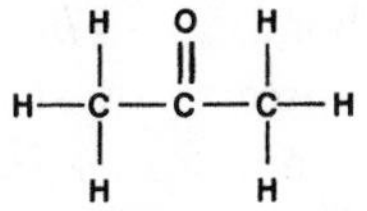

ketone, R(C = O)R′
dimethyl ketone (acetone)

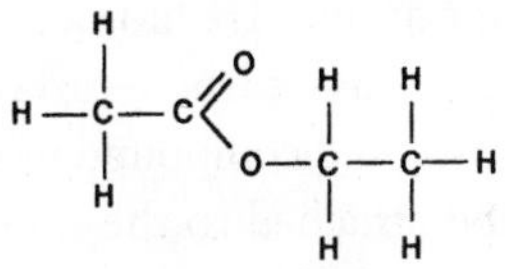

ester, RCOOR′
ethyl acetate

Nitrogen-containing Functional Groups

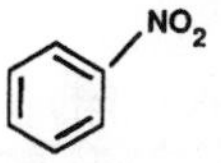

nitro-compound, RNO_2
nitrobenzene

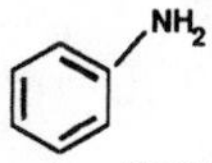

amine, RNH_2
aniline

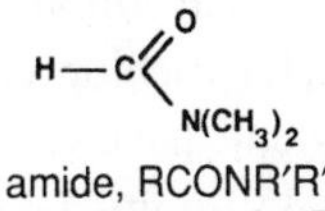

amide, RCONR′R″
dimethyl formamide (DMF)

Miscellaneous Functional Groups

$CH_3OCH_2CH_2OH$
glycol ether
2-methoxyethanol

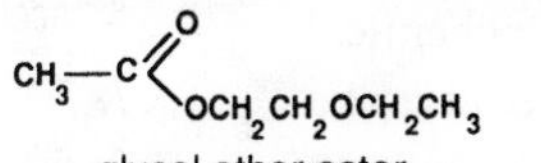

glycol ether ester
2-ethoxyethyl acetate
ethyl cellosolve

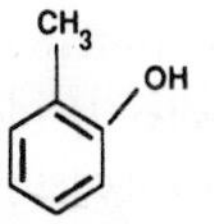

phenol, ROH
o-cresol

Halogenated Hydrocarbons

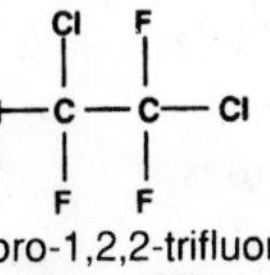

1,1,2-trichloro-1,2,2-trifluoroethane
(Freon TF)

rings may be identified with the prefix cyclic-or cyclo-. One very important cyclic hydrocarbon is benzene, which contains six carbon atoms and is very stable; compounds which contain a benzene ring are described as aromatic compounds.

Halogenated hydrocarbons have chlorine, fluoride, iodine, and/or bromine atoms attached to a hydrocarbon. Ketones, esters, alcohols, and ethers all have an oxygen atom attached to a carbon atom, and examples are given in Table 7–A.

Isomers are molecules that have the same number and kinds of atoms, but the atoms are arranged differently, and thus have different physical and chemical properties. For example, both ethanol and dimethylether have two carbon atoms, six hydrogen atoms, and one oxygen atom, but the atoms are arranged differently, and the two compounds have quite different properties (e.g., dimethylether is a gas at room temperature, while ethanol is a liquid). A good working knowledge of the nomenclature, the characteristic molecular structure, and the different toxicities is helpful in making a proper assessment of an exposure.

Nomenclature itself can often be misleading. For example, trichloroethane and trichloroethylene are chlorinated hydrocarbons differing in the types of bonds and the arrangement of chlorine atoms. Trichloroethane is saturated whereas trichloroethylene has a carbon–carbon double bond. Trichloroethane is a saturated compound in which the three chlorine atoms may be attached to the same carbon atom (1,1,1-trichloroethane), or two may be attached to one carbon and one to the other carbon atom (1,1,2-trichloroethane). Trichlorethylene has a double bond between the carbon atoms, and there is only one possible arrangement of the chlorine atoms, two on one carbon and one on the other. These three compounds, 1,1,1-trichloroethane, 1,1,2-trichloroethane, and trichlorethylene, have very different toxicities and very different TLVs, 350 ppm, 10 ppm, and 10 ppm, respectively. On the other hand, 1,1,1 trichloroethane has been identified as an ozone-destroying chemical (air pollution is discussed later in the chapter), and production was banned in the United States after January 1, 1996. This example illustrates the importance of correctly identifying the chemical being used. These chemicals are easily confused because of a slight difference in names, which might not be apparent to a worker with inadequate training.

Common names may not impart any information as to the structure of a molecule (muriatic acid as compared to hydrochloric acid) and can even be misleading (ethylene dichloride is actually the completely saturated 1,2dichloroethane); systematic names, using the International Union of Pure and Applied Chemistry rules, unambiguously describe the structure of a molecule. The

CRC *Handbook of Chemistry and Physics* describes this system in detail. Furthermore, many solvents are not single chemicals, but, rather mixtures of many compounds, often of variable composition. For example, Stoddard solvent (PEL = 500 ppm, TLV = 100 ppm) is a petroleum distillate fraction containing C_7—C_{12} hydrocarbons. It consists primarily of straight-chain and branched-chain alkanes and cycloalkanes; it may contain up to 20 percent aromatic hydrocarbons.

Even a scientifically trained user often has only a vague and sometimes completely erroneous knowledge of the chemical preparation in use. It is a good practice to verify the specific name and composition of the solvents involved with direct evidence from the label, from the manufacturer's Safety Data Sheet (SDS), formerly the Material Safety Data Sheet (MSDS), or from the laboratory. Only after verification of name and composition should one attempt to evaluate the potential effect or hazard of a solvent.

The OSHA Hazard Communication Standard (HCS) requires chemical manufacturers, distributors, or importers to provide SDSs to communicate the hazards of hazardous chemical products. As of June 1, 2015, the HCS will require new SDSs to be in a uniform format, and include the section numbers and headings listed in Table 7–B.

Hawley's *Condensed Chemical Dictionary*, Windholz's *The Merck Index*, Gleason's *Clinical Toxicology of Commercial Products*, and the NFPA *Fire Hazard Properties of Flammable Liquids, Gases, and Vapors* provide general information and descriptions of many solvents, including trade name materials. These are helpful references for classifying and understanding the composition of a solvent.

TABLE 7–B   GHS Safety Data Sheet Sections

1. Identification
2. Hazard(s) identification
3. Composition/information on ingredients
4. First-aid measures
5. Fire-fighting measures
6. Accidental release measures
7. Handling and storage
8. Exposure controls/personal protection
9. Physical and chemical properties
10. Stability and reactivity
11. Toxicological information
12. Ecological information
13. Disposal considerations
14. Transport information
15. Regulatory information
16. Other information

HAZARDS OF GASES, LIQUIDS, SOLVENTS, AND VAPORS

Compressed Gas

The use of compressed gas cylinders has inherent dangers in their handling. If the tank were to fall and the valve snap off, the cylinder can become a projectile; therefore, one should always cap the valve before transporting cylinders of compressed gas, and the cylinders should be securely stored with double chains to prevent falling. They should also be protected from heat, which may cause a liquid to volatilize or react, and so generate greater pressures inside than the cylinder was designed to withstand. Attention should be paid to the reactivity of the gases with the regulators and lines. For this reason, copper should be avoided in systems with acetylene or ammonia. Regulators should be dedicated to use with single gases, and mixed use with potentially reactive gases should be strictly avoided. Often flammable gas cylinders are reverse threaded to prevent mixing with oxygen inside the regulator.

Gases

Commercially, gases are available in compressed or liquefied form. Certain gases, such as nitrogen, helium, and some others that are available as liquefied gases, are used as a source of high-purity gas from boil-off or as a cryogenic fluid at the gas's boiling point (77°K or −196°C for liquid nitrogen). Table 7–C gives common industrial gases, cylinder pressures, and physical state. All of these readily volatilize, although some organometallic compounds typically available as liquefied gases must be heated to give an adequate working pressure.

Cryogenic Liquids

Cryogenic liquids pose several safety concerns in addition to frostbite from extreme cold. Spills of cryogenics rapidly vaporize, producing a gas that is initially significantly more dense than air, resulting in potential oxygen deficiency hazards in pits, vaults, and enclosed spaces. Given sufficient time, the gas reaches thermal equilibrium with its surroundings and disperses throughout the available space. Liquid nitrogen, the most common cryogenic fluid, boils at a lower temperature than liquid oxygen, providing a location for oxygen to condense out of the atmosphere into dewars (double-walled flasks with a vacuum between the walls) with the nitrogen. This creates a potential explosion hazard if the oxygen comes in contact with an oxidizable material. Cryogen dewars and cryogenic systems must have proper pressure relief to prevent pressure buildup and possible rupture as the liquid vaporizes. Full containment of a liquefied gas is usually not possible; helium requires about 18,000 pounds per square inch (psi) and nitrogen requires 43,000 psi. Table 7–D lists common cryogenic liquids.

Flammability, Explosions, and Reactivity

Some gases are very pyrophoric. Silane is used extensively in the semiconductor industry, but is a well-recognized fire hazard as it will ignite spontaneously when exposed to air; silane has been responsible for several serious fires causing millions of dollars of damage. Perchloric acid is a strong oxidizing agent which can cause fire and explosions. Some solvents, such as ethers, are unstable over time, and degrade into explosive compounds.

TABLE 7–C	Selected Compressed and Liquefied Gases		
Gas	**Formula**	**Form**	**Cylinder Pressure (psig)**
Ammonia	NH_3	Liquid	114
Argon	Ar	Gas	225–6,000
Arsine	AsH_3	Liquid	190–205
Carbon dioxide	Co_2	Liquid	830
Helium	He	Gas	225–6,000
Hydrogen	H_2	Gas	225–3,500
Hydrogen chloride	HCl	Liquid	613
Hydrogen fluoride	HF	Liquid	0.6
Methane	CH_4	Gas	1,500–2,300
Neon	Ne	Gas	225–1,900
Nitrogen	N_2	Gas	225–6,000
Nitrous oxide	N_2O	Liquid	745
Oxygen	O_2	Gas	225–2,200
Phosphine	PH_3	Liquid	400–590
Sailane	SiH_4	Gas	150–1,200

Source: Reprinted with permission from Matheson Gas Products, *Matheson Gases & Equipment,* 1993.

TABLE 7–D	Common Cryogenic Liquids
Cryogen	**Boiling Point (C)**
Argon	−186
Helium	−287
Hydrogen	−252
Neon	−245
Nitrogen	−196
Oxygen	−183

Source: Reprinted with permission from Lide DR, Frederickse HPR, eds. *CRC Handbook of Chemistry and Physics,* 75th ed. Boca Raton, FL: CRC Press, 1994.

Depending on their flash points, liquids may be flammable or combustible, as described by the National Fire Protection Association (see NFPA 30, Flammable and Combustible Liquids Code and NFPA 325, Fire Hazard Properties of Flammable Liquids, Gases and Volatile Solids).

Flash Points

The flash point of a liquid is the lowest temperature at which it gives off enough vapor to form an ignitable mixture with the air near the surface of the liquid or in a vessel capable of flame propagation away from the source of ignition. Some evaporation takes place below the flash point, but not in sufficient quantities to cause an ignitable mixture. Flash points can be determined by using either closed-cup or open-cup testers. Open-cup flash points are determined with the liquid in the open air and are generally 10 to 20 percent higher than closed-cup flash point figures for the same substance. When open-cup flash point figures are given, they are usually identified by the initials OC.

Flammable Liquids

A liquid with a closed-cup flash point below 100°F (37.8°C) and a vapor pressure not exceeding 40 psi absolute (psia) at 37.8°C is a Class I liquid. Class I liquids are subdivided as follows:

- Class IA liquids include those with a flash point below 73°F (22.8°C) and a boiling point below 100°F (37.8°C).
- Class IB liquids include those with a flash point below 73°F (22.8°C) and a boiling point at or above 100°F (37.8°C).
- Class IC liquids include those with a flash point at or above 73°F (22.8°C) and below 100°F (37.8°C).

Combustible Liquids

Liquids with a closed-cup flash point at or above 100°F (37.8°C) are called combustible liquids, which are subdivided as follows:

- Class II liquids include those with a flash point at or above 100°F (37.8°C) and below 140°F (60°C).
- Class IIIA liquids include those with a flash point at or above 140°F (60°C) and below 200°F (93.4°C).
- Class IIIB liquids include those with a flash point at or above 200°F (93.4°C).

Fire Point

The fire point of a liquid is the lowest temperature at which vapors evolve fast enough to support continuous combustion. The fire point temperature is usually about 5°F above the flash point temperature.

Flammable Range

A prominent factor in rating the fire hazard of a flammable liquid or gas is its flammable range, sometimes called the explosive range. For each flammable liquid or gas, there is a minimum concentration of its vapor, in air, below which propagation of flame does not occur on contact with a source of ignition because the mixture is too lean. Propagation of flame is the self-sustaining spread of flame through the body of the flammable vapor-air mixture after introduction of the source of ignition; a vapor-air mixture at or below its lower explosive limit can burn at the point of ignition without propagating. There is also a maximum concentration of vapor, in air, above which propagation of flame does not occur because the mixture is too rich. The mixtures of vapor with air that, if ignited, just propagate flame are known as the lower and upper flammable (or explosive) limits, and are usually expressed in terms of percentage by volume of vapor in air.

The flammable (or explosive) range includes all the concentrations of a vapor in air between the lower explosive limit (LEL) or lower flammable limit (LFL) and the upper explosive limit (UEL) or upper flammable limit (UFL). The lower flammable limit is important because if this percentage is small, it takes only a small amount of the liquid vaporized in air to form an ignitable mixture.

It also should be noted that if the concentration of vapor in the vapor-air mixture is above the upper flammable limit, introduction of air (by ventilation or other means) produces a mixture within the flammable range before a safe concentration of vapor below the lower flammable limit can be reached.

For a large number of common liquids or gases, the LEL is a few percent and the UEL is 6-12 percent, although there are notable exceptions. The LEL and UEL for hydrogen are 4 and 75 percent and for anhydrous hydrazine they are 4.7 and 100 percent, respectively. For specific materials, consult the SDS or NFPA 325. For hazardous vapors, if the airborne concentration is kept below the PEL or TLV, the concentration is less than the LEL (note that a concentration of 1 percent by volume is 10,000 ppm).

Requirements and Guidelines

The occupational safety requirements for the handling and use of flammable and combustible liquids and gases are given in Subpart H of 29 CFR 1910. These rules are based on the 1965–1970 editions of the NFPA guidelines current at the time the OSHA standards were first written. Best management practice suggests that current NFPA guidelines should be followed to the extent feasible. Compliance with Subpart H is a minimum.

TOXICOLOGICAL EFFECTS

Site of Action

For some toxicants, the site of action is at the point of exposure, i.e., the skin or the respiratory tract. For others, the target organ is more distant, or the effect is systemic.

Water-soluble gases are more likely to be upper respiratory tract irritants (e.g., HF, ammonia, SO_2), while the less soluble gases (nitrogen dioxide, ozone, phosgene) pass through the upper airways and penetrate to the bronchioles and alveoli where they may have a delayed reaction and cause acute pneumonitis and pulmonary edema hours later. Chemicals which might otherwise deposit in the upper respiratory tract may penetrate into the deep lung if they are adsorbed to particles.

Asphyxiation

Oxygen is essential to life, and delivery of oxygen to the cells is equally vital. Gases and vapors can interfere with the supply of oxygen in two fundamental ways: simple asphyxiants exert no direct action, but act passively by merely replacing oxygen in the air so that the concentration of oxygen falls below the 18 percent minimum required for life. Any gas or vapor, even nitrogen, can act as a simple asphyxiant if its concentration is high enough. By contrast, chemical asphyxiants react with essential cellular molecules to disrupt the transport or use of oxygen. Carbon monoxide forms a very stable complex with hemoglobin, and so blocks the readily reversible interaction of hemoglobin with oxygen that is crucial to carrying oxygen to the cells. Chemical asphyxiants may also interfere with the cell's ability to use the oxygen which is delivered. For example, cyanide and hydrogen sulfide inhibit cytochrome oxidase enzymes and so disrupt the normal reactions of the cell.

Organic and Inorganic Gases

Some gases, such as low-molecular-weight hydrocarbons (e.g., methane, ethane, and propane), nitrogen, hydrogen, the inert gases (helium, neon, and argon), and some compounds (CO_2) have no significant toxicity of their own. They are simple asphyxiants; they dilute oxygen in the atmosphere. These elements and compounds have either no or very minimal odor and thus have poor warning properties. By contrast, other gases, such as phosphine and arsine, can cause acute fatalities with short exposures to relatively low concentrations, whereas nitrogen dioxide exerts its effects several hours after exposures.

The oxides of carbon, nitrogen, and sulfur can be produced by use of oxygen acids, combustion, welding, chemical cleaning or electroplating, or a variety of other processes. Decomposition of organic material may produce toxic (hydrogen sulfide) or flammable (methane) atmospheres. Some gases, such as ammonia, boron halides, phosphine, arsine, and silane, are used as reactants in industrial and manufacturing processes. Others, such as the reactive, volatile metal halides, are used in research.

Reactivity of the gas may be important. The oxides may react with moisture in the mucous membranes to form acids; ammonia, an alkaline gas, acts as a primary irritant. Boron or volatile metal halides react spontaneously in moist air to form gaseous hydrogen halides. Phosphine and silane are spontaneously flammable in air. Arsine and phosphine are also highly toxic.

Exposure control relies primarily on engineering controls. Dilution ventilation may be sufficient for the simple asphyxiants. Local exhaust ventilation is suitable for many processes. The more reactive or highly toxic compounds require complete control (e.g., enclosure, exhaust ventilation, gas sensors, all-welded construction for gas lines, excess flow-controllers, automatic shut-down systems) to ensure protection of the workers.

Inorganic Acids and Bases

Strong acids and bases are corrosive and can burn the skin and mucous membranes. Health effects are variable and concentration-dependent, most often on the site of contact with tissue; they include irritation of mucous membranes or respiratory tract by HCl, chemical burns by the concentrated solutions, oxidation by HNO_3 (an oxidizing acid), and dehydration by H_2SO_4. The highly toxic acids H_2S and HCN act differently from other acids; they complex with metal-containing enzymes (cytochromes), preventing cellular oxygen metabolism.

Concentrated hydrogen fluoride (HF) is particularly corrosive to tissue and bone. Pain from HF solutions stronger than 50 percent is felt within a few minutes; lower concentrations may not produce pain for several hours. Serious tissue damage may result without the person being aware of it. HF burns require immediate action: Irrigate the exposed area to flush away as much HF as possible and seek medical attention immediately. Treatment is dependent on the severity of the burn; mild cases can be managed with magnesium oxide but more severe burns may require infiltration of the affected tissue with calcium gluconate.

Engineering controls and protective equipment should be used to limit exposure. Use of personal protective equipment is essential for working with concentrated acids. Chemical compatibility of the protective clothing with the acid must be considered to ensure protection of the worker.

Other Aqueous Solutions and Systems

Many of these are known for their irritant effects after prolonged exposure. Contact dermatitis from aqueous solutions is quite common, usually appearing as "dishpan hands." Excessive levels of mists in the air (resulting from heating, agitation, and spraying) can cause throat irritation and bronchitis. Many other effects and hazards are possible if chemicals react with their containers. Bretherick and Lewis each cite a number of examples. As a rule, aqueous systems, because of their low vapor pressure and ease of control, are a lesser problem, but they cannot be dismissed as potential hazards.

Solvents and Solvent Vapors

Organic solvents can have an array of toxic effects on humans; some effects are similar for all solvents, and other effects are specific to particular solvents or their metabolites. While the common effects generally occur at relatively high concentrations of solvent vapors, the specific effects tend to become manifest at lower concentrations.

Direct contact of solvents with the skin can cause irritation, defatting of the skin, and dermatitis. Some solvents, especially less polar (lipophilic) solvents, can penetrate the skin, so dermal exposure to solvents can be an additional route of exposure. Some recent experiments have demonstrated that solvent vapors can also be absorbed through the skin.

At very high concentrations (thousands of ppm), solvent vapors may cause simple asphyxiation by displacing oxygen. This is most likely to occur in confined spaces. At high concentrations (typically hundreds of ppm), solvents tend to have a rapid effect on the CNS, resulting in dizziness, disorientation, confusion, euphoria, and giddiness; prolonged exposure at high levels can lead to loss of consciousness, paralysis, convulsion, and, ultimately, death from respiratory or cardiac arrest.

In addition to these effects of solvents in general, specific solvents may have specific toxicities. Organ systems that are affected by some solvents include the liver, the kidney, the CNS, and the peripheral nervous system.

PHYSIOLOGICAL EFFECTS

Some physiologcial effects are outlined in the following paragraphs. For detailed information on specific organic solvents, consult Rose and Cohrssen's *Patty's Industrial Hygiene and Toxicology*, Gerarde's *Toxicology and Biochemistry of Aromatic Hydrocarbons*, The American Conference of Governmental Industrial Hygienists *Documentation for the Threshold Limit Values*, the American Industrial Hygiene Association (AIHA) *Hygienic Guide Series*, and the NIOSH *Registry of Toxic Effects of Chemical Substances* or the NIOSH criteria document on the subject solvent (see Bibliography).

Hydrocarbons
Aliphatic Hydrocarbons

The aliphatic compounds take their name from the Greek word aliphe, meaning fat, because fats are derivatives of this class of hydrocarbons (see Table 7–A).

Aliphatic hydrocarbons are further classified as alkanes, alkenes, cycloalkanes, cycloalkenes, alkynes (acetylenes), and arenes (where an aliphatic group is bonded to an aromatic ring). Petroleum and natural gas are the most important sources of alkanes, alkenes, and cycloalkanes. Coal tar is an important source of arenes. High-molecular-weight alkanes are broken down (cracked) catalytically to increase the yield of gasoline from petroleum. Ethylene (H_2CCH_2) is an important by-product of cracking and is used to make plastics and ethanol (CH_3CH_2OH).

The saturated aliphatic hydrocarbons, C_nH_{2n+2}, known as alkanes, are straight or branched chains with all bond positions saturated by bonding with hydrogen. Compounds in this series have the characteristic *-ane* suffix, as in isobutane, 2-methylpentane, and 2, 2-dimethylpentane. They are as inert biochemically as they are chemically. Even as air pollutants, they are among the least reactive and do not pose a significant problem. The alkanes are good solvents for natural rubber. They act primarily as CNS depressants.

A relatively high level is required for toxic effects. The TLVs generally range from 100 ppm and higher. The exception is n-hexane (or normal hexane, the straight-chained isomer), which has a TLV of 50 ppm. N-hexane is known or suspected to cause a number of adverse effects, most notably peripheral neuropathy. During the period 1989-2002, automotive parts cleaners containing n-hexane were widely used in the United States. Although measurements indicate that automotive repair workers are likely to have been exposed to n-hexane well below the TLV of 50 ppm, preliminary studies have shown that mechanics have developed peripheral neuropathy and impairment of blue-yellow color discrimination. These findings imply that the current TLV may be too high. Furthermore, animal studies suggest that n-hexane may cause testicular toxicity by a mechanism similar to the neurotoxicity, and that this reproductive effect may occur in the absence of neurologic effects. Animal studies also indicate that acetone potentiates the effects of hexane. Acetone was introduced into automotive repair products in the mid-1990s. Other isomers of hexane have not been found to have these health effects.

Similar to most of the alkanes, the unsaturated aliphatic hydrocarbons, the alkenes (C_nH_{2n}) and the alkynes (C_nH_{2n-2}), with double and triple bonds respectively, can cause CNS effects at high concentrations, but do not have the specific low-level toxic effects observed for hexane. However, they are more chemically reactive than the saturated hydrocarbons. As air pollutants, they are reactive and create a control problem. The primary health problem associated with the aliphatics is dermatitis.

Crude oil (petroleum) is mainly a very complex mixture of aliphatic compounds. It contains alkanes, alkenes, cycloalkenes, and arenes, as well as small amounts of nitrogen and sulfur compounds, which vary depending on the source.

Petroleum is separated into mixtures of hydrocarbons by fractional distillation. Gasoline is the fraction of petroleum boiling between room temperature and 200 C and is mainly made up of C_5 to C_{11} hydrocarbons, with C_8 predominating. It has been estimated that there are as many as 500 different hydrocarbons in gasoline alone. About 150 of them have been separated and identified.

Cyclic Aliphatic Hydrocarbons

The cyclic hydrocarbons act much in the same manner as the straight or branched chain aliphatics, but they are not quite as inert. A significant percentage of cyclic hydrocarbons are metabolized to compounds with a low level of toxicity.

The lower-molecular-weight cycloalkanes (cyclopropane and cyclobutane) have been used as anesthetics. The cycloalkanes typically are CNS depressants, but as molecular weight increases, the margin of safety between anesthesia and adverse health effects decreases. The unsaturated cyclic hydrocarbons generally are more irritating than the saturated forms. This may be due in part to the reactivity of the carbon–carbon double bond. For example, cyclopentane causes slight reddening and drying of the skin and cyclopentene causes moderate to severe irritation of the skin and eyes.

Aromatic Hydrocarbons

These get their names from aroma, meaning pleasant odor. The molecules are usually characterized by one or more six-carbon rings with alternating single and double bonds (benzene) or fused rings (naphthalene or larger rings). This classification once served to distinguish petroleum and coal-tar hydrocarbon solvents. Now, however, aromatics are derived from both sources.

Benzene and other aromatics do not undergo the addition reactions shown by alkenes and alkynes, but do undergo aromatic substitution reactions in which an atom, or group of atoms, replaces one of the hydrogen atoms on the ring. Aromatic substitution reactions of benzene produce a wide variety of useful products (see Table 7–A). The aromatic hydrocarbon benzene is notorious for its effect on the blood-forming tissues of the bone marrow and as a cause of aplastic anemia. Gerarde has shown that, in animals, injury may result from a single exposure. At much lower concentrations

benzene, is a leukemogenic agent. This has greatly reduced the extent of its use as a solvent. Toxic levels of benzene are easily absorbed through the skin and inhaled. Benzene should not be used for cleaning processes or for any process requiring skin contact or where the concentration in the air is not controlled by proper ventilation. The 2012 TLV for benzene is 0.5 ppm, with an ACGIH A1 (confirmed human carcinogen) and International Agency for Research on Cancer (IARC) Group 1 (carcinogenic to humans with sufficient scientific evidence) classification. However, NIOSH recommends that the PEL be reduced to 0.1 ppm, and that benzene be regulated as an occupational carcinogen.

The aromatic hydrocarbons in general are local irritants and vasodilators that cause severe pulmonary and vascular injury when absorbed in sufficient concentrations. They also are potent narcotics. The primary problems with common aromatic solvents other than benzene are dermatitis and effects on the CNS. Benzene can also be a contaminant of industrial toluene and xylene.

Halogenated Hydrocarbons

The halogens are a group of five elements: fluorine, chlorine, bromine, iodine, and astatine. The halogens are a remarkable family of elements, marked by their great chemical activity and unique properties. Stability, nonflammability, and a wide range of solvency are but a few of the characteristics imparted by their application (see Table 7–A). Halogenated hydrocarbons are organic compounds in which one or more hydrogens have been replaced by fluorine, chlorine, or bromine, or rarely, iodine. The effects of the halogenated hydrocarbons vary considerably with the number and type of halogen atoms present in the molecule. Carbon tetrachloride, for example, is highly toxic, causing acute injury to the kidneys, liver, CNS, and gastrointestinal tract. The 2012 TLV for carbon tetrachloride is 5 ppm (A2 classification—suspected human carcinogen); however, NIOSH recommends that the PEL be reduced to a short-term exposure limit (STEL) of 2 ppm averaged over a 1-hour period and that the chemical be regulated as an occupational carcinogen.

Chronic exposure to carbon tetrachloride also damages the liver and kidneys and is suspected of causing liver cancer. Carbon tetrachloride has become the classic liver toxicant for use in studies on the effects of damage to the liver. As with benzene, this solvent should not be used for open cleaning processes where there is skin contact or where the concentration in the breathing zone may exceed recommended levels. Its use should be avoided altogether.

Replacing some of the chlorine atoms with fluorine as in 1,1,2-trichloro-1,2,2-trifluoroethane (Freon TF) produces a compound with a low level of toxicity. Its present eight-hour

TLV is 1,000 ppm with 1,250 ppm as a ceiling limit. The depressant effect on the CNS and cardiac arrhythmias occur at concentrations much greater than the TLV. Because it is nonflammable and of low toxicity, it may be a suitable substitute for the more hazardous chlorinated solvents; however, environmental considerations such as ozone depletion preclude its application in many cases.

The chlorinated hydrocarbons, in general, are more toxic than the common fluorinated hydrocarbon solvents, although there are significant exceptions such as perfluoroisobutylene (TLV = 0.01 ppm, ceiling). Specific effects and toxicities vary widely, but the most common effects from the chlorinated hydrocarbons of intermediate toxicity (trichloroethylene, for example) are CNS depression, dermatitis, and injury to the liver. There is disagreement as to the carcinogenicity of 1,1,2-trichloroethane; the ACGIH TLV carcinogen classification is A3, confirmed animal carcinogen with unknown relevance to human, but other organizations, such as NIOSH, consider 1,1,2-trichloroethane to be a carcinogen.

In addition, the chlorinated hydrocarbons, especially trichloroethylene, are noted for their synergistic effects with alcohol consumption. These include flushed, red face, and personality changes. These effects must be taken into account when evaluating industrial exposure.

Methylene chloride, widely used in paint strippers and other products, is unique among these halogenated compounds as it is metabolized to carbon monoxide in the body, raising the levels of carboxyhemoglobin in the blood.

Perchloroethylene (tetrachloroethylene), commonly used in dry cleaning, textile processing, and other industrial processes, has been suggested as a potential human carcinogen. Animal lifetime exposure studies (National Toxicology Program, 1986) did show an increased tumor incidence. Earlier animal data, in some cases, are confounded by simultaneous exposure to epichlorohydrin (a known mutagen); human epidemiology is confounded by concomitant exposures to other chlorinated solvents, smoking, and other factors. In its Twelfth Annual Report on Carcinogens, 2011, the National Toxicology Program stated that perchloroethylene is reasonably anticipated to be a human carcinogen and IARC classifies it as a Group 2A (probably carcinogenic to humans) chemical.

Refrigerants (Freon, chlorofluorocarbons or CFCs, and hydrochlorofluorocarbons or HCFCs) are a subclass of the halogenated hydrocarbons. The majority of these are methane or ethane derivatives, with a few higher carbon analogues and some other inorganic and organic gaseous compounds. The materials in current use are generally of low toxicity and exposure limits and guidelines tend to be high; the TLV for trichlorofluoromethane (R-11) is a ceiling of 1,000 ppm. The TLV for chlorodifluoromethane (R-22) is 1,000 ppm. New refrigerants have come on the market as a result of the EPA incentives to produce non-ozone-depleting refrigerants. There are no exposure standards or guidelines for these compounds other than those suggested by the manufacturer. Safety of some of the new refrigerants has come under question as benign tumors have been seen in long-term animal studies. Refrigerant safety has been reviewed by Calm and engineering controls have been addressed by the American Society of Heating, Refrigeration and Air Conditioning Engineers (ASHRAE) (see Bibliography).

Nitrohydrocarbons

These vary in their toxicological effects, depending on whether the hydrocarbon is an alkane or an aromatic hydrocarbon. Nitroalkanes are known more for their irritant effects accompanied by nausea; effects on the CNS and liver become significant during acute exposures. 2-Nitropropane is listed as a confirmed animal carcinogen (TLV-A3) and possibly human carcinogen (IARC-2B, NTP-R and NIOSH-Ca), but with an assigned TLV of 10 ppm . The nitroaromatics (such as nitrobenzene with a TLV of 1ppm) are much more acutely hazardous. They cause the formation of methemoglobin and act on the CNS, the liver, and other organs.

Oxygen-Containing Functional Groups

These are found in the alcohols, aldehydes, ketones, carboxylic acids and their esters, anhydrides, and the ethers.

Alcohols

One of the most important classes of industrial solvents is characterized by the presence of a hydroxyl group (-OH). Saturated alcohols are widely used as solvents. All alcohols are formed by the replacement of one or more hydrogen atoms by one or more hydroxyl groups.

These polar compounds are classified on the basis of both the number of hydroxyl groups and the nature of the hydrocarbon chain attached to the hydroxyl groups. The monohydric alcohols, which contain one hydroxyl group, are known simply as alcohols; dihydric alcohols have two hydroxyl groups and are known as glycols; trihydric alcohols have three hydroxyl groups and are called glycerols or polyols.

The alcohols are noted for their effect on the CNS and the liver but they vary widely in their degree of toxicity. Methanol (CH_3OH) and ethanol (CH_3CH_2OH) are the two most important industrial alcohols. Methanol is made by catalytic hydrogenation of carbon monoxide and may one day replace gasoline and natural gas as a fuel because it can be made from coal. Ethanol is made by fermentation of starch (or other carbohydrates) and by hydration of ethene.

Methanol causes several types of injuries, notably impairment of vision and injury of the optic nerve. Methanol is slowly metabolized to toxic compounds (formic acid). For this reason, its chronic toxicity is greater than that of ethanol.

Ethanol is used industrially in a denatured form. It is quickly metabolized in the body and largely converted to carbon dioxide, and is the least toxic of the alcohols. Any toxicity it causes can be more related to the denaturants (such as benzene or methanol). The undesirable effects of ethanol primarily are related to its CNS effects at higher doses as a result of recreational use, which affects the drinker's physical safety and can compound the effects of other solvents or medications.

Alcohol is a depressant, not a stimulant. Medically, alcohol depresses the CNS, slowing down the activity of the brain and spinal cord. A large enough dose of alcohol can sedate the brain to a point where involuntary functions such as breathing are lost, causing death.

Propanol is metabolized to toxic by-products and is more toxic than ethanol when taken internally but less toxic than the higher homologues.

Aldehydes

The aldehydes are well-known for causing skin and mucosal irritation and CNS effects. Dermatitis from the aldehydes is common. The aldehydes also are characterized by their sensitizing properties. Allergic responses are common. Recently, formaldehyde was classified as human carcinogen (IARC Group 1) and occupational carcinogen (NIOSH-Ca and OSHA-Ca). IARC states in its 2006 monograph that epidemiological evidence for the causal relationship between formaldehyde and nasopharyngeal cancer in human is sufficient. Although IARC concludes that the evidence for leukemia is strong but not sufficient at the time, a more recent (2010) meta-analysis study, which included two large recent studies involving more than 25,000 workers in U.S. formaldehyde industries and more than 13,000 funeral directors and embalmers, found increased myeloid leukemia risk with exposure to formaldehyde.

Ketones

These have become increasingly important solvents for acetate rayon and vinyl resin coatings. Ketones are stable solvents with high dilution ratios for hydrocarbon diluents. They are freely miscible with most lacquer solvents (low molecular-weight alcohols, aromatics, and esters) and diluents, and their compatibility with lacquer ingredients gives an acceptable finish to many products. Generally, ketones are good solvents for cellulose esters and ethers and many natural and synthetic resins.

The common ketones, such as acetone or methyl ethyl ketone (MEK), generally exert a narcotic-type action. All are irritating to the eyes, nose, and throat, so high concentrations are not usually tolerated. Methyl ethyl ketone in conjunction with toluene or xylene has been reported to cause vertigo and nausea. Lower tolerable concentrations may impair judgment and thereby create secondary hazards. The lower saturated aliphatic ketones are rapidly excreted and for this reason cause only minor systemic effects. Methyl n-butyl ketone received widespread attention during the 1970s, when it was pinpointed as the etiological agent producing a high incidence of peripheral neuropathy in one working population.

Mixed solvent exposure: Potentiation of hexane by acetone. Although there has been growing concern about the effects of exposures to solvent mixture, most toxicology research and regulatory actions have targeted single chemicals without regard to other chemicals present. Exceptions include the ACGIH, which suggests that chemicals that act on the same target organ be considered in an additive manner (adding the fractional exposure of each to its own TLV), and the Food Quality Protection Act of 1996, which required the U.S. Environmental Protection Agency (EPA) to evaluate the mixture of pesticides that have a common mode of action. Over the past 15 years some toxicology research has addressed possible interactions.

The interactions of acetone with other chemicals is especially important because acetone has been exempted from regulatory control of volatile organic compounds (VOCs), and so acetone is often added to products that had not contained it prior to such regulations. For example, California required that beginning in 1997, brake-cleaning products have no more than 50 percent VOCs, with acetone exempted, so the formulation of many products quickly changed to 50 percent acetone and 50 percent other VOCs (including n-hexane). Because California is such a large market, most manufacturers changed the formulation for all their products, so the effect is national. Cory-Slechta (2005) has written that "the central nervous system may be particularly susceptible because of the interactive nature and complexity of its system. . . . Multiple insults occurring concurrently at multiple sites within the system may constrict the range and flexibility of compensatory mechanisms, thereby compromising the integrity and viability of the system. As a consequence, mixtures could have effects that are more robust, more rapid in onset, and that differ in character from effects produced by single exposures." For example, toxicology experiments on rats indicate that rather than being merely additive, acetone potentiates the effects of hexane and that the effects are more persistent than those caused by hexane alone. Clearly, the enormous number of possible combinations of multiple chemicals presents a major challenge to the scientific community.

Esters

Esters are produced by the reaction of an organic acid with an alcohol. The particular properties of the esters are, therefore, partly determined by the parent alcohol. Esters often have pleasant odors. Esters in low concentrations are used as artificial fruit essences, flavorings, or components of perfumes. The esters are good solvents for surface coatings. Esters in high concentrations are noted for their irritating effects to exposed skin surfaces and to the respiratory tract. They also are potent anesthetics. Cumulative effects of the common esters used as solvents are not significant except for conditions resulting from irritation. Esters of some mineral acids, such as dimethyl sulfate, are highly toxic.

Ethers

Ethers are made up of two hydrocarbon groups connected by an oxygen atom. They are made by combining two molecules of the corresponding alcohol. Compared with alcohols, ethers are characterized by their greater volatility, lower solubility in water, and higher solvent power for oils, fats, and greases. Because of their nonreactivity with solutes and ease of recovery, ethers are widely used for extraction. The epoxides (cyclic ethers) differ from other ethers, which are chemically inert, because their unstable three-membered rings make them highly active chemically. Because the epoxides react with the unstable hydrogen atom from water, alcohols, amines, and similar substances, they form a wide range of industrially important compounds.

The primary reactions to the saturated and unsaturated alkyl ethers, such as ethyl and divinyl ether, are anesthesia and irritation of the mucous membranes. However, the greatest safety hazard of these ethers is their tendency to form explosive peroxides. Once opened, ethers should be used within a short period of time, stored so that peroxides are destroyed as they are formed, or checked for the presence of peroxides. The ethers vary in their rate of peroxide formation; diisopropyl ether is one of the most rapid. Halogenated ethers (such as bis-chloromethyl ether) generally are highly toxic and the reader should refer to the more comprehensive references for information on these materials (see Bibliography, especially Clayton and Clayton, the AIHA *Hygienic Guide Series*, and the OSHA standards).

Glycols, Glycol Ethers, and Their Esters

The glycols, like the cellosolves and the carbitols, are colorless liquids of mild odor. They are miscible with most liquids (organic and aqueous) and owe this wide solubility to the presence of the hydroxyl, the ether, and alkyl groups in the molecule. The glycol dialkyl ethers are pure ethers with a mild and pleasant odor. They are better solvents for resins and oils than are the monoethers. As a rule, these compounds are more volatile than the monoethers with the same boiling point.

The glycol ethers exert their effects on the brain, the blood, the reproductive system, and the kidneys. Of these, 2-methoxyethanol (ethylene glycol monomethyl ether), 2-ethoxyethanol (ethylene glycol monoethyl ether), and their acetates are the most toxic. They are rapidly absorbed through the skin and elicit neurological symptoms, including changes in personality. They also affect the reproductive system in both men and women. The higher-molecular-weight glycol ethers (eg., propylene glycol and ethylene glycol monobutyl ether), on the other hand, are much less toxic. Work with 2-methoxyethanol, 2-ethoxyethanol, or their acetates should be conducted so as to preclude any skin contact. In 1993 OSHA proposed reducing the PELs for 2-methoxyethanol and its acetate from 25 ppm to 0.1 ppm and for 2-ethoxyethanol and its acetate from 200 and 100 ppm, respectively, to 0.5 ppm. Epidemiological studies in the semiconductor industry have associated spontaneous abortion and reduced fecundability among fabrication workers who used 2-methoxyethanol, 2-ethoxyethanol, or their acetates, despite the fact that airborne concentrations were under 0.1 ppm, that is, under the proposed OSHA standard.

OTHER FACTORS

Other factors must be taken into consideration. For example, handling procedures and type of clothing determine the degree of skin contact and so will affect dermal absorption. Even the degree of a user's respect for the hazard potential can be a decisive factor.

Ignition temperature, flash point, and other factors determining the potential for fire and explosion also must be considered. Although concentrations that are safe from a toxicological viewpoint are much lower than the lower flammable limits of flammable solvents, concentrations at potential points of ignition may be far higher than concentrations in the user's breathing zone.

Evaluation of hazard potential requires assessment of the consequences of exposure, the degree of exposure, and all factors contributing to the exposure.

AIR POLLUTION

In 1970 the Clean Air Act was passed by the U.S. Congress, and the U.S. EPA began regulating criteria air pollutants. Four of the six criteria pollutants are gases: carbon monoxide, sulfur dioxide, ozone, and nitrogen oxides.

For the first 20 years, the U.S. EPA regulated only six

criteria pollutants: the four gases, lead, and particulate matter. The 1990 Clean Air Act listed 189 hazardous air pollutants, most of which are vapors, and authorized the U.S. EPA to add additional hazardous air pollutants to its list; in 1999, EPA listed 33 compounds as air toxics. The concentrations of these are not regulated, but the EPA is required to develop regulations (also known as rules or standards) for all industries that emit one or more of the pollutants in significant quantities. In 2011, EPA announced it had completed the emissions standards required. U.S. EPA issued regulations to reduce emissions of toxic air pollutants from a published list of industrial sources referred to as *source categories*. As required under the Act, EPA has developed a list of source categories that must meet control technology requirements for these toxic air pollutants. EPA has issued rules covering over 80 categories of major industrial sources, such as chemical plants, oil refineries, aerospace manufacturers, and steel mills, as well as categories of smaller sources, such as dry cleaners, commercial sterilizers, secondary lead smelters, and chromium electroplating facilities. These standards are projected to reduce annual toxic air emissions by about 1.5 million tons. Furthermore, EPA and state governments (e.g., California) have reduced emissions of benzene, toluene, and other air-toxic chemicals from mobile sources by requiring the use of reformulated gasoline and placing limits on tailpipe emissions. Important new controls for fuels and vehicles are expected to reduce selected motor vehicle air-toxic chemicals from 1990 levels by more than 75 percent by 2020.

Solvents and other chemicals may become hazardous to the public in the form of air pollutants when released out doors. Hydrocarbons are a major factor in the formation of photochemical smog. In the presence of sunlight, they react with atomic oxygen and ozone to produce aldehydes, acids, oxides of nitrogen and sulfur, and a series of other irritant and noxious compounds.

The greatest portion of hydrocarbons contributing to air pollution originates from automobiles, but a significant amount also comes from the tons of solvents exhausted daily from industrial cleaning and surface-coating processes.

Nitric oxide (NO) is produced by the reaction of nitrogen with oxygen in high-temperature combustion, as in automobiles and fuel-burning power plants. Nitric oxide is photochemically oxidized to nitrogen dioxide (NO_2), a corrosive and an irritant. Nitrogen dioxide is an energy trap, reacting with sunlight to form nitric oxide and atomic oxygen:

$$NO_2 + h\upsilon \rightarrow NO + O$$

Atomic oxygen is highly reactive, forming ozone and initiating a host of secondary photochemical reactions.

The nitric oxide produced can again react to produce more nitrogen dioxide, propagating the process. The yellow-brown haze seen over many cities is made up of nitrogen dioxide and its reaction products. Ozone in the troposphere (the atmosphere less than 10 km altitude) detracts from air quality and damages the lung.

Some compounds are more reactive to sunlight and contribute heavily to the smog problem. The use of such solvents is being curtailed in more and more areas, especially large cities. Other solvents are less reactive and are exempt from stringent control. Here, as a general guide, solvents are listed in decreasing order of photochemical reactivity.

- alkenes (unsaturated open-chain hydrocarbons containing one or more double bonds)
- aromatics (except benzene)
- branched ketones, including methyl isobutyl ketone
- chlorinated ethylenes, including trichloroethylene (except perchloroethylene)
- normal ketones (for example, methyl ethyl ketone)
- alcohols and aldehydes
- branched alkanes
- cyclic alkanes
- normal alkanes
- benzene, acetone, perchloroethylene, and the saturated halogenated hydrocarbons

Opinion is divided as to the exact order of reactivity and many solvents have yet to be tested. The trend is toward the development and use of nonreactive solvent blends.

Upper Atmosphere Effects

Stratospheric ozone is constantly being created and destroyed through natural cycles. Ozone-depleting substances (ODS), however, accelerate the destruction processes, resulting in lower than normal ozone levels.

In addition to the smog-related materials discussed previously, fluorocarbons such as trichlorotrifluoroethane and related materials, as well as bromide-containing chemicals such as methyl bromide, are quite persistent and catalyze the destruction of ozone in the upper atmosphere. Ozone in the stratosphere (the atmosphere 10–50 km in altitude) absorbs solar ultraviolet radiation at the 290-nanometer (nm) wave length. The destruction of ozone by fluorocarbons and other materials results in an increase in the amount of solar ultraviolet radiation reaching Earth's surface. This can impair agricultural production and increase the incidence of skin cancer. In 1987, the industrialized nations met and signed the Montreal Protocol on Substances that Deplete the Ozone Layer. The Montreal Protocol calls for the reduction of use and elimination of the major ozone-depleting chemicals and has had a major impact. However, the persistence of ODS and the leakage of older appliances with ODS, combined with the growth of the consumer market, have blunted the expected impact of the Montreal Protocol.

Furthermore, there is an interaction between ozone depletion and climate change. ODS can allow more energy to penetrate to the earth's surface and so warm the earth further. Most ODSs are potent greenhouse gases, so the buildup of ODS abundances over the last decades contributes to global warming.

Further information can be found in the *Report of the 2010 Assessment of the Scientific Assessment Panel* of the United Nations Environment Program Ozone Secretariat.

Global Warming and Climate Change

Greenhouse gases trap heat in the atmosphere. Solar radiation penetrates the atmosphere and is absorbed by the earth; a portion is radiated back into space, and a portion is consumed in life processes and atmospheric chemical reactions, thus setting up a thermal equilibrium. Greenhouse gases absorb the shorter wavelength energy normally re-radiated into space; this energy is then manifested as heat. The effects of this heat are much more extensive than simply raising the average temperature of the earth. Some areas experience colder weather at times, some areas have increased drought while others have increased rainfall and flooding. More extreme events, such as hurricanes and tornados, become more common. The consequences of these changes are far reaching and include negative impacts on human health, forests, agriculture and food supply, the oceans, water resources, and ecosystems. Discussion of these effects is beyond the scope of this chapter and interested readers are referred to the websites of major scientific groups studying these issues, including National Oceanic and Atmospheric Administration (NOAA) and Intergovernmental Panel on Climate Change (IPCC) for more information.

Carbon dioxide, the product of combustion of wood, fossil fuels, and solid waste, is the most well-known greenhouse gas. The average annual concentration of CO_2 in the atmosphere has been measured consistently by NOAA at Mauna Loa Observatory since 1959, when the annual average was 316 ppm; that level as been increasing every year since then, and the 2010 annual average was 390 ppm. Methane, emitted during the production of coal, natural gas, and oil as well as from livestock and the decay of organic waste in solid waste landfills, is an even more potent greenhouse gas. Other major greenhouse gases of anthropogenic origin include nitrous oxide (N_2O) and fluorinated gases such as hydrofluorocarbons, perfluorocarbons, and sulfur hexafluoride.

EVALUATION OF HAZARDS

A prime question regarding any process using a volatile chemical is whether the concentration of the solvent in the air exceeds acceptable limits. Getting the answer to this is not as difficult as it may seem.

A knowledge of the chemical, its properties, and the process in which it is used should give the investigator some idea of the potential hazards.

If a chemical of high-hazard potential is being used, if the equipment and ventilation system are poorly designed, or if performance of the system is questioned, then there is a greater probability of physiological injury and immediate action should be taken to evaluate and reduce the hazard before it becomes a problem.

The evaluation procedure, where the industrial hygienist assesses the degree of risk in the workplace, is based on the following factors:
- the toxicity of the substance
- the concentration in the breathing zone
- the manner of use
- the length of time of the exposure
- the controls already in place and their effectiveness
- any special susceptibilities on the part of the employees

Samples can be collected in the field and returned to the laboratory for analysis or, and this is the trend, they may be collected and analyzed on the spot with direct-reading instrumentation (Figure 7–1).

When using direct-reading instruments that can immediately analyze samples, a much greater number of samples

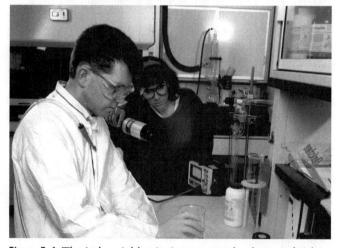

Figure 7–1. The industrial hygienist assesses the degree of risk in the workplace based on the toxicity of the substance, the concentration in the breathing zone, the manner of use, the duration of the exposure, the controls already in place and their effectiveness, and any special susceptibilities of the employees in the workplace. *(Photo courtesy Fermilab Visual Media Services.)*

and much more information can be obtained and evaluated immediately. Data loggers are used to obtain a continuous record of concentration. The data may be analyzed by programs resident in the instrument itself, or downloaded to a computer for further analysis. Standard features include plots of concentration over time and calculations of time-weighted averages over specified time periods. Peak concentrations are readily observed from these graphs; such peaks would have been obscured with integrated samples such as charcoal tubes. Peak concentrations are especially important when the vapor is an irritant or is highly odorous, or if a subjective complaint is involved. The concentration above the norm must be reduced to achieve satisfaction as quickly as possible.

Because correct operation of direct-reading field instruments often requires considerable laboratory backup for maintenance, testing, and calibration, they are not as expedient as they seem. The cost for a field evaluation may be much more than the cost of a laboratory analysis, but this may be offset because much more information is obtained.

See Chapter 15, Evaluation; Chapter 16, Air Sampling; and Chapter 17, Direct-Reading Instruments for Gases, Vapors, and Particulates for more information.

CONTROL OF HAZARDS

Responsibility of Health and Safety Personnel

Personnel concerned with health and safety should recognize that the use of toxic gases and solvents can be a major threat to health. Hazard assessment and control are necessary to prevent detrimental physiological effects.

Exposure evaluation and workplace inspection should be a routine part of any health and safety program. Exposure evaluations should be performed for new processes to ensure that controls are adequate to protect workers. Surveys or searches should also be made for evidence of disease. Dermatitis, unusual behavior, coughing, or complaints of irritation, headache, and feeling ill are all outward signs of potential disease that warrant further investigation. Positive findings justify the effort and provide convincing evidence for educating personnel to the need for corrective actions.

Note conditions and practices that contribute to excessive exposure and call them to the attention of responsible personnel. Train users to handle chemicals properly to prevent injurious exposures. Set guidelines to direct operating personnel in the selection, use, and handling of chemicals. Prohibit general use of highly toxic chemicals, highly flammable solvents, or solvents that are extremely hazardous, unless special evaluation or authorization is obtained.

Finally, provide technical assistance to help the user select the least hazardous chemicals, design and obtain proper ventilation, eliminate the risk of fire, eliminate skin contact, and evaluate situations when workers might be exposed to excessive levels.

Process Controls
Selection of Chemicals

One of the most effective means of controlling chemical exposure is to use the least hazardous material. By simply substituting a less toxic or less volatile solvent, for example, one can minimize or eliminate a hazard. The fact that a certain chemical has been specified does not mean that it is the only one or even the best one for a particular use. At times, the one specified is the most familiar one.

This fact is more apparent if one compares the TLVs and the vapor pressures or distillation ranges of different solvents in each class. Toluene and xylene are solvents that can usually be substituted for benzene, for example. If an aromatic hydrocarbon is not required, then it can be replaced with less toxic aliphatic mineral spirits. Low-molecular-weight glycol ethers are used in semiconductor manufacturing processes as a solvent for photoresists, but higher-molecular-weight analogues that have little, if any, reproductive toxicity can be suitable in some situations.

The best all-around solvent is water. It is nontoxic and nonflammable and (with the proper additives) it forms an aqueous solvent system that is a good solvent for many organic materials. For the cleanup of inorganic soils, aqueous solvent systems are still the best. The disadvantages are corrosivity of many aqueous solutions and the slow evaporation rate of water. Also, additives may leave a residue on a manufactured item, necessitating further cleaning.

Aliphatic hydrocarbons are good for dissolving nonpolar organic materials such as oils and lubricants. Products containing hexane should be avoided because of its unique toxicity and high potency. The aliphatics, however, are not effective cleaners for dissolving or removing many tenacious inorganic materials.

Aromatic hydrocarbons are especially effective on resins and polymeric materials. Between the aromatic and aliphatic hydrocarbons in solvent power are the cyclic hydrocarbons. Halogenated hydrocarbons are effective solvents for a wide range of nonpolar and semipolar compounds.

The nitrohydrocarbons have not been used to a large extent as cleaning agents. Their greatest use has been as solvents for esters, resins, waxes, paints, and the like. Because the ketones, alcohols, esters, ethers, aldehydes, and glycols are more water soluble than the other classes, they are good solvents for the more polar compounds. These solvents are often used as cleaning agents alone or combined with other solvents, especially water. They are useful as solvents for paints, varnishes, and plastics.

For nearly every process there is an effective solvent or solvent blend that has low toxicity and low flammability. For example, for cleaning hydraulic tubing, tanks, and other containers, several companies have switched to water containing an alkaline cleaner as a replacement for naphtha and other such organic solvents. Inhibited 1,1,1-trichloro-ethane has replaced carbon tetrachloride as a household spot remover. Use the following suggestions as a guide to lower toxicity and flammability.

- Use an aqueous (water) solution if possible.
- When possible, consider a different process altogether, one that does not involve chemicals.
- Solvents that are toxic are to be used only with properly engineered local exhaust systems; enclosures should be considered. Solvents such as trichloroethylene, toluene, and ethylene dichloride are in this category.
- Highly toxic or highly flammable solvents, such as benzene, carbon tetrachloride, and gasoline, should be prohibited as general cleaning solvents.

Definite dividends will result from this policy. The number of employees who might have exposures exceeding the TLV can be reduced significantly. The number of small fires resulting from the use of flammable bench solvents also can be reduced.

Engineering Controls
Enclosure and Ventilation

The major route of entry for chemicals into the body is the lungs (see Chapter 2, The Lungs). The lungs have a surface area of about 85,000–115,000 sq in. (55–75 m²); much of this area is permeated with thin-walled capillaries. Chemicals in the breathing zone are drawn into the lungs during breathing, quickly absorbed into the bloodstream, and distributed to other parts of the body. The most effective way to prevent inhalation of gases and vapors is to keep them out of the breathing zone. This is done by using closed systems and local exhaust ventilation. All open vessels should be kept covered except when in use. Systems should be designed to prevent leakage and spillage and to collect and contain the solvent in the event of a leak or spill. Proper ventilation must be installed for any process using solvents. Solvent storage cabinets should be ventilated. Even storage areas require adequate general ventilation to prevent accumulation and buildup of flammable or toxic concentrations. (See Chapters 19 through 21 on industrial and general ventilation.)

If subambient temperature storage of solvents is recommended, they should be stored only in refrigerators constructed and designated for that use (explosion-proof or explosion-safe). Such refrigerators have had their ignition sources removed. Refrigerators used for storage of food and beverages should not be used for any other purpose.

Local exhaust ventilation is necessary to capture the vapors at their point of origin and thus prevent excessive concentrations in the breathing zone. If a highly toxic solvent or gas is being used or if general ventilation is poor, a local exhaust system or completely enclosing the process, or both, is necessary to remove the vapors. All control measures should maintain concentrations of hazardous chemicals in the breathing zone well below the OSHA-specified levels. Present trends in worker's compensation insurance and federal regulations justify designs that are well on the safe side. Ventilation systems are a topic in themselves and the reader should refer to Chapters 19 through 21 and to the ACGIH *Industrial Ventilation Manual* or American National Standards Institute (ANSI) series Z9 standards on industrial ventilation (see Bibliography). Remember that the local exhaust ventilation system of removing vapors at their point of origin is usually the most satisfactory means of control.

Personal Protective Equipment
Respirators

Do not use respirators as the primary or only means of protection against hazardous chemical vapors because too many factors limit their use. They can be used as emergency or backup protection. Respiratory protective equipment, especially the air-purifying type, is limited by leakage around the mask edges, surface contamination, impaired efficiency with use, and need for adequate oxygen. Unless it is correctly used and properly cared for, a respirator may present a greater danger to an employee than no protection at all. Too often, such equipment gives a false sense of security and the wearer becomes careless and may be exposed to highly hazardous levels. Respirators should be controlled through a program that provides for proper selection, fitting, testing, education, and maintenance under the surveillance of competent personnel. Such a program is mandatory under present federal occupational safety and health standards. (See Chapter 22, Respiratory Protection.) Make sure that the level of gases or vapors in the air does not exceed the protective factor of the respirator. Air-purifying respirators should not be used for operations where the solvent is air-sprayed unless there is supplementary mechanical ventilation. OSHA has issued a respirator standard; among the new requirements is one in which the employer must develop a schedule for changing cartridges and canisters for air purifying respirators. See Chapter 22 for more details.

Protective Clothing and Gloves

Another major route of entry for hazardous chemicals is through the skin. Dermatitis is the leading industrial disease, and solvents are second only to cutting oils and lubricants in causing this disease. (See Chapter 3, The Skin and Occupational Dermatoses.) Skin contact occurs through direct immersion, splashing, spilling, contact with chemical-soaked clothing, improper gloves, and contact with solvent-wet objects. Some solvents, such as benzene, carbon tetrachloride, and methyl alcohol, can be absorbed in amounts great enough to cause physiological injury to organs other than the skin. The most effective way and often the only way to prevent harm is to keep the solvent from the skin. This can be done by using mechanical handling devices, such as tongs and baskets, and by using impermeable protective clothing, such as aprons, face shields, and gloves.

The use of gloves requires caution. A common mistake is to recommend rubber or neoprene gloves for use as hand protection against a solvent, regardless of the kind of solvent in use. Many solvents can quickly penetrate latex rubber or neoprene gloves and come in contact with the skin.

The permeability of gloves to certain solvents and chemicals is the most important characteristic to consider when selecting gloves for protection. Chemical manufacturers include permeability information with their product, often in the form of permeability tables or computer software for glove selection. They suggest appropriate glove materials for particular chemicals. The abrasion resistance of glove materials is also given in tables and this information is often more widely available. Note both permeability and abrasion resistance when considering the type of gloves to use with certain solvents.

Permeability measurements should be made on the complete glove if the effect of weak or thin spots is to be detected. A rough comparison of the permeability of gloves plus an indication of some of the other characteristics can easily be made by turning the gloves inside out, filling them three-fourths full of solvent, sealing the cuff, and measuring the loss of weight, the stretch, and other parameters. More precise methods for measuring glove permeability are available, but require the use of an analytical laboratory. A standard method has been published by the American Society for Testing and Materials.

The time required for a chemical to penetrate a glove is affected by the glove's thickness and its composition. In some cases, the time to break through can be as brief as five minutes. For example, it has been shown that benzene breaks through a 0.03-mm polyethylene glove in five minutes. Conversely, the same glove material had a two-hour breakthrough time when tested against butyl acetate.

Note that gloves made of the same material and nominal thickness, but from different manufacturers, may have significantly different breakthrough times. This difference may result from differences in formulation of glove materials or manufacturing procedures used.

Neoprene is good for protection against most common oils, aliphatic hydrocarbons, and certain other solvents, but is not satisfactory for use against the aromatic hydrocarbons, halogenated hydrocarbons, ketones, and many other solvents. Natural rubber is not effective against these solvents.

Polyvinyl alcohol (PVA) gloves provide adequate protection against the aromatic and chlorinated hydrocarbons, but they must be kept away from water, acetone, and other solvents miscible in water to prevent deterioration. Butyl rubber gloves can be a suitable compromise when polyvinyl alcohol cannot be used.

Regular periodic cleaning and drying of gloves is as important as using the proper type. Keep an extra pair of gloves available for use while the cleaned pair is being aired and dried. When the gloves become soiled with hard-to-remove hazardous materials such as insecticides and epoxy resins, it is often better to discard the glove than to try to clean it. In some situations, gloves must be replaced after only a few minutes' work. If the outside of any glove becomes thoroughly wetted, remove it promptly.

Disposable gloves are useful for light laboratory or assembly work, but are too easily torn or punctured for heavier work. Latex medical gloves provide good manual dexterity, but they tear easily and are permeable to virtually all solvents; their use is not recommended in an industrial setting except to protect the hands from grease and dirt. There is no set recommendation for the use of gloves; what works well for one group of workers may not work for another. In many cases, a certain amount of trial and error is required. Gloves are subject to small tears that may go unnoticed, but drastically reduce their efficiency. Gloves may also increase the absorption of solvents if they do penetrate the glove, and the solvent is then trapped in close contact with the skin and cannot evaporate. (See Chapter 23, Personal Protective Equipment, for more details on proper PPE).

Barrier creams are the least effective way of protecting skin. Barrier creams are not a substitute for gloves, except when there is only occasional and minor contact with a solvent, or around rotating machinery when gloves cannot be worn because of the catching hazard. Barrier creams are not as effective as an impervious glove. (See Chapter 3 for more information on barrier creams.)

Good personal hygiene is important whenever chemicals are used. Remove spills and splashes from skin immediately with soap and water. This includes showering and replacing solvent-soaked or splattered clothing with clean clothing immediately and as often as necessary.

Protective Eyewear

Workers at risk for a splash of chemicals in the eyes must wear appropriate protective eyewear. It must be noted that protective eyewear should not be used as the sole protection, but in conjunction with engineering controls, guards, and good manufacturing practice. OSHA, in 29 CFR 1910.133, requires eye and face protection when injury can be prevented by its use. The standard practice is given by ANSI Z87.1, *Practice for Occupational and Educational Eye and Face Protection.*

For chemical splash or irritating mists, eye protection should be selected from unvented chemical goggles, indirect-vented chemical goggles, or indirect-vented eyecup goggles. Direct vented goggles and spectacle-type eye protection do not provide protection against liquid exposures and should not be used. For severe exposures, a face shield should be used in conjunction with goggles; a face shield by itself does not provide adequate protection against liquid splashes. Where both an inhalation and splash hazard exists, full-face respiratory protection is preferable over a half-mask and goggles.

Traditionally, the recommendation has been that contact lenses should not be worn in eye hazard areas. However, the new ANSI standard removed the prohibition on contact lenses. (See Chapter 5, The Eyes, for more information.)

SUMMARY

Critical exposure factors include how the material is used and what controls (engineering or personal protective equipment) are in place, temperature and volatility, concentration, and reactivity. Guidelines for exposure are discussed. In this chapter, solvents are classified as aqueous or organic systems. Gases as cryogenic liquid and simple and chemical asphyxiants and their characteristics are discussed. Flammable and combustible liquids, flash points, flammable range, and requirements and guidelines are given. The physiological effects of aqueous systems, organic compounds, aliphatic hydrocarbons, cyclic hydrocarbons, aromatic hydrocarbons, halogenated hydrocarbons, nitrohydrocarbons, oxygen-containing functional groups, inorganic acids, and organic and inorganic gases as well as hazard potential, evaluation, and control are covered.

BIBLIOGRAPHY

American Conference of Governmental Industrial Hygienists. *Industrial Ventilation – A Manual of Recommended Practice,* 27th ed. Cincinnati, OH: ACGIH, 2010.

American Conference of Governmental Industrial Hygienists. *Threshold Limit Values (TLVs)® and Biological Exposure Indices (BEIs)® for 2012.* Cincinnati, OH: ACGIH, 2012.

American Conference of Governmental Industrial Hygienists. *Documentation of Threshold Limit Values Including Biological Exposure Indices (BEIs®) and Issue of Supplements,* 7th ed. Cincinnati, OH: ACGHI, 2011.

American Industrial Hygiene Association. Hygienic Guide Series on specific materials. Fairfax, VA: AIHA.

American Industrial Hygiene Association. *Laboratory Ventilation Guidebook.* Fairfax, VA; AIHA, 1999.

American Industrial Hygiene Association. *Respiratory Protection: A Manual and Guideline,* 3rd ed. Fairfax, VA: AIHA, 2001.

American National Standards Institute. *Practice for Occupational and Educational Eye and Face Protection.* New York: ANSI Z87.1, 2003.

American National Standards Institute/American Industrial Hygiene Association. *Fundamentals Governing the Design and Operation of Local Exhaust Ventilation Systems.* New York: ANSI, current edition: Z9.2.

American Society of Heating, Refrigerating and Air Conditioning Engineers, Inc. *Handbook of Fundamentals.* Atlanta: ASHRAE, 2009.

American Society for Testing and Materials. *Annual Book of ASTM Standards.* Philadelphia: ASTM, 2012.

American Society for Testing and Materials. *Standard Test Methods for Flash Point by Small Scale Closed Tester* (ASTM D3828-09). Philadelphia: ASTM, 2009.

American Society for Testing and Materials. *Standard Test Method for Flash Point by Tag Closed Tester* (ASTM D56-05 (2010)). Philadelphia: ASTM, 2010.

American Society for Testing and Materials. *Standard Test Method for Resistance of Protective Clothing Materials to Permeation by Liquids or Gases Under Conditions of Continuous Contact* (ASTM F739-07). Philadelphia: ASTM, 2007.

American Society for Testing and Materials. *Standard Test Method for Flash and Fire Points by Cleveland Open Cup* (ASTM D92-05a(2010)). Philadelphia: ASTM, 2010.

American Society for Testing and Materials. *Standard Test Method for Flash Point by Pensky–Martens Closed Tester* (ASTM D93-11). Philadelphia: ASTM, 2011.

American Society for Testing and Materials. *Standard Test Method for Flash Point of Liquids by Small Scale Closed-Cup Apparatus* (ASTM D327-96(2011)). Philadelphia: ASTM, 2011.

American Society for Testing and Materials. *Standard Test Method for Flash Point and Fire Point of Liquids by Tag Open-Cup Apparatus* (ASTM D1310-01(2007)). Philadelphia: ASTM, 2007.

Boekelheide K. 2,5-Hexanedione alters microtubule assembly. I. Testicular atrophy, not nervous system toxicity, correlates with enhanced tubulin polymerization. *Toxicol Appl Pharmacol* 88:370-82, 1987.

Bretherick L. *Handbook of Reactive Chemical Hazards,* 6th ed. London: Butterworths, 1999.

Calm JM. Refrigerant safety: The alternative refrigerants are as safe or safer than those they replace, but more care is needed with all refrigerants. *ASHRAE J,* July, p. 17-26, 1994. Reprint: TECH-R-135.

Chapin RE, Morgan KT, Bus JS. The morphogenesis of testicular degeneration induced in rats by orally administered 2,5-hexanedione. *Exp Mol Pathol* 38:149-69, 1983.

Clayton GD, Clayton FE, eds. *Patty's Industrial Hygiene and Toxicology,* 4th ed. Vols 2A-2F. New York: Wiley, 1993, 1995.

Correa A, Gray RH, Cohen R, et al. Ethyleneglycol ethers and the risks of spontaneous abortion and subfertility. *Am J Epidemiology* 143(7):707–717, 1996.

Cory-Slechta DA. Studying toxicants as single chemicals: Does this strategy adequately identify neurotoxic risk? *Neurotoxicol* 26:491-510, 2005.

Cralley LV, Cralley LJ, eds. *Industrial Hygiene Aspects of Plant Operations,* vol. 3. New York: Macmillan, 1986.

Dean JA. *Lange's Handbook of Chemistry,* 15th ed. New York: McGraw-Hill, 1998.

Eskenazi B, Gold EB, Samuels S, et al. Prospective assessment of fecundability of female semiconductor workers. *Am J Ind Med* 28:817–831, 1995.

Forsberg K, Mansdorf SZ. *Quick Selection Guide to Chemical Protective Clothing,* 5th ed., Hoboken, NJ: John Wiley and Sons, 2007.

Gerarde HW. *Toxicology and Biochemistry of Aromatic Hydrocarbons.* New York: Elsevier, 1960.

Gerarde HW. Toxicological studies on hydrocarbons: 111. The biochemorphology of phenylalkanes and phenylalkenes. *Arch Ind Health* 19:403, 1959.

Gleason MN, Gosslin RE, Hodge HC. *Clinical Toxicology of Commercial Products,* 5th ed. Baltimore: Williams & Wilkins, 1981.

Hamming WJ. *Photochemical Reactivity of Solvents.* Paper No. 670809 presented at the October 2–6, 1969, Aeronautic and Space Engineering and Manufacturing meeting sponsored by the Society of Automotive Engineers.

Hammond SK, Hines CJ, Hallock MF, et al. Glycol ether exposures in the semiconductor industry. *Occup Hyg* 2:355–366, 1996.

Harrison R, Israel L, Larabee P, et al. n-Hexane Related Peripheral Neuropathy among Automotive Mechanics – California. *Morbidity and Mortality Weekly Report.* 50(45):1011-1013, 2001.

International Committee of Contamination Control Societies. *Proceedings of the 4th International Symposium on Contamination Control,* September 1978, Washington, DC. Mt. Prospect, IL: Institute of Environmental Sciences (formerly American Association for Contamination Control).

Ladefoged O, Hass U, Simonsen L. Neurophysiological and behavioural effects of combined exposure to 2,5-hexanedione and acetone or ethanol in rats. *Pharmacol Toxicol* 65(5): 372-375, 1989.

Ladefoged O, Perbellini L. Acetone-induced changes in the toxicokinetics of 2,5-hexanedione in rabbits. *Scand J Work Environ Health* 12(6): 627-629, 1986.

Ladefoged O, Roswall K, Larsen JJ. Acetone potentiation and influence on the reversibility of 2,5-hexanedione-induced neurotoxicity studied with behavioural and morphometric methods in rats. *Pharmacol Toxicol* 74(4-5): 294-299, 1994.

Lam H R, Larsen JJ, Ladefoged O, et al. Effects of 2,5-hexanedione alone and in combination with acetone on radial arm maze behavior, the "brain-swelling" reaction and synaptosomal functions. *Neurotoxicol Teratol* 13(4):407-412, 1991.

Lewis RJ. *Hawley's Condensed Chemical Dictionary,* 15th ed. New York: Van Nostrand Reinhold, 2007.

Lide DR, Frederikse HPR, eds. *CRC Handbook of Chemistry and Physics,* 85th ed. Boca Raton, FL: CRC Press, 2004.

Lunche RG, et al. L.A.'s rule 66 nips air pollution due to solvents. *SAE J* 76:25, 1968.

McFee D, Garrison RP. Process characteristics—Open systems. In *Industrial Hygiene Aspects of Plant Operations,* vol. 3, Cralley LV, Cralley LJ, eds. New York: Macmillan, 1986.

McFee DR. How well do gloves protect hands against solvents? *J Am Soc Safety Eng,* May 1964.

National Draeger, Inc. *Dräger Detector Tube Handbook,* 8th ed. Pittsburgh: National Draeger, 1992.

National Fire Protection Association. *Fire Protection Handbook.* Quincy, MA: NFPA, latest edition.

National Fire Protection Association. *Fire Hazard Properties of Flammable Liquids, Gases, and Volatile Solids* (NFPA no. 325). Quincy, MA: NFPA.

National Fire Protection Association. *National Electrical Code* (NFPA no. 70). Quincy, MA: NFPA.

National Fire Protection Association. *Flammable and Combustible Liquids Code* (NFPA no. 30). Quincy, MA: NFPA.

National Institute for Occupational Safety and Health. *Certified Equipment List.* Cincinnati, OH: DHHS/

NIOSH, latest edition.

National Institute for Occupational Safety and Health. Criteria Documents. http://www.cdc.gov/niosh/pubs/criteria_date_desc_nopubnumbers.html

National Institute for Occupational Safety and Health. *NIOSH Pocket Guide to Chemical Hazards, 2010.* Cincinnati, OH: NIOSH, 2010. http://www.cdc.gov/niosh/npg/

National Institute for Occupational Safety and Health. *Registry of Toxic Effects of Chemical Substances,* 1985–86 ed. Cincinnati, OH: DHHS/NIOSH Pub. no. 87–114.

National Research Council. *Rethinking the Ozone Problem in Urban and Regional Air Pollution.* Washington, DC: National Academy Press, 1991.

National Toxicology Program. *Twelfth Annual Report on Carcinogens.* Research Triangle Park, NC: NTP, 2011.

National Toxicology Program. *Toxicology and Carcinogenesis of Tetrachloroethylene (Perchloroethylene) in F344/N Rats and B6C3F1 Mice (Inhalation Studies).* NTP TR 3111 DHHS (NIH) Pub no. 86–2567. Research Triangle Park, NC: NTP, 1986.

Nelson D, Cox M. *Lehninger Principles of Biochemistry,* 4th ed. New York: WH Freeman, 2004.

Nelson GO, Lum BY, Carlson GJ, et al. Glove permeation by organic solvents. *AIHA Journal* 42:217–225, 1981.

Noraberg J, Arlien-Soborg P. Neurotoxic Interactions of Industrially Used Ketones. *NeuroToxicology* June 21:409–418, 2000.

Pastore C, Marhuenda D, Marti J, et al. Early diagnosis of *n*-hexane–caused neuropathy. *Muscle & Nerve* 17(9):981–986, 1994.

Rose VE, Cohrssen B, eds. *Patty's Industrial Hygiene and Toxicology,* 6th ed. New York: Wiley, 2010.

Sansone EB, Tewari YB. Differences in the extent of solvent penetration through natural rubber and nitrile gloves from various manufacturers. *AIHA Journal* 41:527, 1980.

Sansone EB, Tewari YB. The permeability of laboratory gloves to selected solvents. *AIHA Journal* 39:169–174, 1978.

Sax NI. *Dangerous Properties of Industrial Chemicals,* 11th ed. New York: Van Nostrand Reinhold, 2004.

Schwilk E, Zhang L, Smith MT, et al. Formaldehyde and leukemia: An updated meta-analysis and evaluation of bias. *J Occup Environ Med* 52(9):878-886, 2010.

Schwope AD, Costas PP, Jackson JO, et al. *Guidelines for Selection of Chemical Protective Clothing,* 3rd ed. Cincinnati, OH: ACGIH, 1987.

Spencer PS, Kim M-S, Sabri MI. Aromatic as well as aliphatic hydrocarbon solvent axonopathy. *Int J Hyg Environ Health* 205:131–136, 2002.

Swan SH, Beaumont J, Hammond SK, et al. Historical cohort study of spontaneous abortion among fabrication workers in the semiconductor health study: Agent-specific analysis. *Am J Ind Med* 28:751–769, 1995.

Strange P, Moller A, Ladefoged O, et al. Total number and mean cell volume of neocortical neurons in rats exposed to 2,5-hexanedione with and without acetone. *Neurotoxicol Teratol* 13(4): 401–406, 1991.

Urone P. The primary air pollutants—Gaseous: Their occurrence, sources, and effects. In *Air Pollution,* Vol. 1, 3rd ed., A. Stern, ed. New York: Academic Press, 1976.

U.S. Environmental Protection Agency. *Pollutants & Sources,* on the EPA Air Toxics Website: http://www.epa.gov/ttn/atw/pollsour.html

Van Dolah RW, Zabetakis MG, Burgess DS, et al. Flame propagation, extinguishment and environmental effects on combustion. *Fire Technol* 1(2):138–145, 1965.

Wang J-D, Chang Y-C, Kao K-P, et al. An outbreak of n-hexane induced polyneuropathy among press proofing workers in Taipei. *Am J Ind Med* 10(2):111-118, 1986.

Williams JR. Permeation of glove materials by physiologically harmful chemicals. *AIHA Journal* 40:877–882, 1979.

Wilson M, Hammond SK, Hubbard A, et al. Worker exposure to volatile organic compounds in the vehicle repair industry. *J Occ and Env Hyg* May (4):301-310, 2007.

Windholz M, ed. *The Merck Index,* 12th ed. Rahway, NJ: Merck & Co., 1996.

Yaws C. *Matheson Gas Data Book,* 7th ed. Parsippany, NJ: McGraw Hill, 2001.

Zabetakis MG. *Safety with Cryogenic Fluids.* New York: Plenum, 1967.

CHAPTER 8

Particulate Matter

by Richard J. Kelly, MS, CIH

P*articulate matter is probably the type of environmental chemical hazard most on the minds of the public. Lead in paint, environmental ultrafines, engineered nanoparticles, and radioactive fallout are all current issues in the popular press. Industrial hygienists see many other emerging particulate matter issues, including exposures to beryllium, cadmium, endotoxins, and toxic fungal spores.*

The objective of this chapter is to familiarize the reader with the basic approach for anticipating, recognizing, and evaluating occupational particulate matter exposures. Basic concepts of aerosols, aerosol behavior, sampling, analysis, filtration, lung deposition, and biological responses are introduced, with many specific examples discussed in detail and within a historical context. Regulatory and consensus guidelines are reviewed whenever appropriate. Air, surface, bulk, dermal, and biological sampling are described, and the relative roles of each are discussed. New to this edition, there is an extensive discussion of the potential occupational and environmental risk of exposure to engineered nanoscale particulate matter.

BACKGROUND

In the field of industrial hygiene, particulate matter (PM) is traditionally defined as small discrete pieces of solid materials or liquid droplets. Occupational exposure to particulate matter most frequently occurs when the PM is suspended in air, forming an aerosol, which can be inhaled. Particles larger than about 100 μm simply fall to the ground quickly, obviating their potential for inhalation. Particles smaller than about 0.001 μm (1 nm) start to act like gases, rather than like particles. Thus the range of PM sizes under consideration is five orders of magnitude, from 0.001 μm (1 nm) to 100 μm.

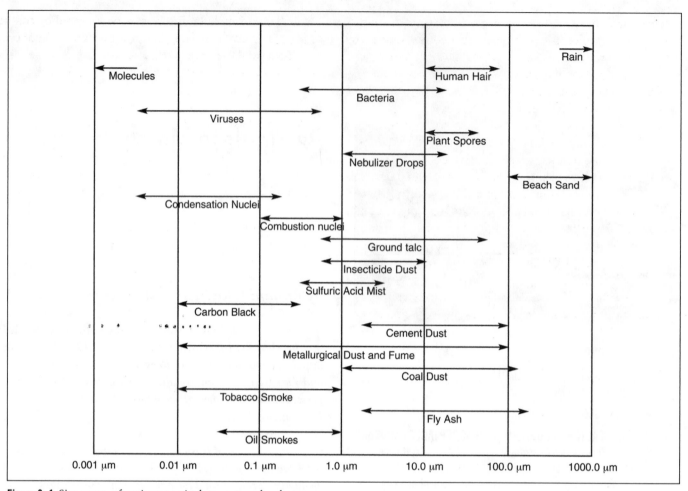

Figure 8–1. Size range of various particulate matter clouds.

The adjective *particulate* is often used as a noun in the industrial hygiene field in lieu of the full term *particulate matter* (PM). While this is incorrect English, it is common enough that it is generally accepted jargon in the field. Recently, some organizations such as the American Conference of Governmental Industrial Hygienists have systematically purged the term *particulate* in favor of the correct form.

The most important route of exposure for most particulate matter is inhalation, with toxicity occurring subsequent to removal of the particulate matter from the air by deposition in the respiratory tract. Substantial exposure to PM can induce a wide variety of biological responses ranging from acute to chronic, local to systemic, mild to life threatening. Figure 8–1 represents the size range of different types of occupationally significant particles.

The hazards associated with chronic occupational inhalation of aerosols have long been recognized. Pliny the Elder (AD 23–79) wrote of lead inhalation hazards during scraping of lead-containing paint. Agricola (1491–1555) and Ramazzini described the hazards of aerosols in mining, and PM was a major topic of work by Alice Hamilton as the

industrial revolution flourished and the field of industrial hygiene evolved in the very early 20th century.

The concern with inhalation of PM is not limited to the occupational environment. Compelling evidence has accumulated to indicate that exposure to environmental particles, particularly the ultrafine combustion derived nanoparticle fraction, can trigger effects ranging from asthma attacks to heart attacks. In air pollution crises, it is thought that ultrafine PM is responsible for the bulk of the excess morbidity and mortality that is measured.

PM deposited in the respiratory tract may be handled and distributed in several different ways. Soluble PM (and mists) often dissolve into the fluids that line the respiratory tract and thus may directly damage the lung or be absorbed into the body where they may cause systemic toxic effects.

Insoluble PM either will be cleared from the respiratory tract by the various defenses of the lungs or may remain in the lungs for an extended period of time. PM that is cleared from the respiratory tract is often swallowed, giving the material another shot at absorption into the body via the digestive tract. Particles may also enter the lymphatic system, where they can dissolve or remain. Recently, another route of clearance has been demonstrated for some metal oxide nanoparticles. At least in rodents, some nanoparticles are transported directly from the nasal mucosa into the central nervous system along olfactory neurons, where they have been shown to cause inflammation.

PM that persists in lung tissue for weeks or months may cause chronic lung disease including lung cancer, or may indirectly cause systemic toxicity by triggering inflammation in the lungs. Classic chronic lung toxins include silica, coal dust, and asbestos. Some insoluble carbonaceous nanoparticles including combustion-derived nanoparticles and carbon nanotubes may pose a risk of lung damage as well as cardiovascular system disease secondary to lung inflammation.

Some types of PM may be hazardous by ingestion or skin contact. Skin contact with dusts alone may result in burns (sodium hydroxide), sensitization (coal tar dust), systemic toxicity (diaminobenzene), or cancer (carbon soot). Sir Percival Pott identified cancer caused by skin contact with soot among chimney sweeps as early as 1775. Lead particles that have settled out of the air onto eating surfaces can be absorbed through the gastrointestinal tract to cause systemic poisoning. Recently it has been suggested that chronic beryllium disease may be triggered by contact of insoluble beryllium-containing dust with the skin or eyes.

Some of the least toxic airborne particles have been traditionally classified as *nuisance dusts*, a term that has fallen out of favor because of its imprecise definition. Now the American Conference of Governmental Industrial Hygienists (ACGIH®) has defined "Particles (insoluble or poorly soluble) Not Otherwise Classified (PNOC)." By definition, PNOC do not have a substance-specific Threshold Limit Value (TLV®), are insoluble or poorly soluble in lung fluid and typically have no well-documented, agent-specific health impact. At high lung doses, PNOCs cause nonspecific types of toxic effects (e.g., lung overload), leaving no important long-term lung damage or impairment. PNOC are not radioactive, sensitizing, cytotoxic, or genotoxic. Any particle that does not meet these criteria cannot be classified as a PNOC. The recommended limit, which is not officially called a TLV, is 3 mg/m^3 of respirable dust and 10 mg/m^3 inhalable dust.

OSHA uses the somewhat parallel older term Particulates Not Otherwise Regulated (PNOR) but includes organic dusts that may be soluble in lung fluids.

Particulate matter typically encountered in the occupational environment can be divided into a number of dif-

TABLE 8–A		General Types of Particulate Matter	
Type of PM*	**Sub-Type**	**Defining Characteristic**	**Examples/Sources**
Dusts	General	Produced by mechanical action on larger pieces of the material (e.g., grinding, cutting, tearing).	• Lead dust while scraping paint • Quartz dust when jack hammering
	Fibers	Dust classified because of its shape as long thin tendrils.	• Asbestos • Ceramic fibers • Fiberglass
	Biological (not micro-organisms)	Typically organic dusts created by disturbance of plant or animal materials.	• Wood dust • Cotton dust • Animal dander
	Radioactive	Radiotoxicity is often more significant than chemical toxicity.	• Radon progeny • Radioactive waste • Uranium
Mists	General	Droplets of liquid. Always defined in the context of an aerosol. Created by mechanical action breaking liquid into small particles.	• Droplets from bubbling dip tanks • Paint overspray
	Fog	Droplets of liquid caused by recondensation of vapor.	• Boiling acids in chemical digestion
Fume	All	Formed by the evaporation and rapid condensation of metal vapor into very small particles.	• Welding • Arc or torch cutting • Foundry work
Biological agents	All	These include living and nonliving agents that may be allergenic, toxigenic, or infectious.	• Bacteria (and related organisms) • Viruses • Fungal spores • Prions
Smokes	All	Smokes are the products of incomplete combustion of organic materials. Created by vaporization of organic material with subsequent condensation. Sometimes used interchangeably with "fumes."	• Diesel exhaust • Coke- or coal-powered furnaces • Human tissue during laser surgery • Secondhand cigarette smoke

*PM – particulate matter

TABLE 8–B	Selected Hazardous Particulate Matter	
Agent	*Typical Industries/Occupations for Exposure*	*Summary of Health Effects*
Arsenic and inorganic Compounds	Agriculture; wood treatment; semiconductor wafer fabrication (gallium arsenide); alloy production; pesticide manufacture; lead smelting	Inhalation of inorganic arsenic compounds can cause chronic poisoning with weakness, nausea, respiratory tract symptoms, and damage to the peripheral nervous system; cancer.
Asbestos	Asbestos abatement; demolition; building maintenance; custodial work; brake repair and replacement	Inhalation increases the risk of lung cancer, mesothelioma (a cancer of the lining of the lungs and peritoneum), asbestosis.
Bacteria	Office work; hospitals; sewer repair and maintenance; biological research; social service industries; grade school teaching	Exposure to airborne bacteria may cause indoor air quality problems, humidifier fever, alveolar inflammation or infection.
Beryllium and compounds	Aerospace; nuclear industries; electronics; mining and processing; tool manufacturers; refractory ceramic industries; chemical research; sporting goods manufacturing; machining	Chronic exposure to beryllium metal, the oxides, and other insoluble compounds may cause chronic beryllium disease and cancer. Very high exposure to soluble compounds may cause acute beryllium disease.
Cadmium and compounds	Metal brazing; alloy making; welders; metal coating; construction	Acute exposure may cause potentially fatal pulmonary edema. Chronic exposure may cause systemic illness or cancer.
Chromium and compounds	Metal plating; chemical research; welding; stainless steel production and use; machining	Chromium in the +VI oxidation state is the most toxic. Exposure may be to dust in some operations and mist in electroplating. Exposure to chromium +VI compounds may cause a range of irritation effects, allergic sensitization, and lung cancer.
Cotton (primary)	Cotton and flax workers	Byssinosis, which results in progressive difficulty in breathing, probably caused by an allergic or pharmacological agent in the bract associated with fresh cotton.
Cobalt and compounds	Alloy making; pigment manufacture; machine tool sharpening; electroplating; aerospace; blue glass manufacturing	Inhalation may cause asthma-like illness, which may progress to fibrosis. A specific form of pneumoconiosis associated with cobalt and some other metals, especially metal carbides, is called hard metal disease.
Diesel exhaust	Operation of diesel-powered industrial trucks; toll takers; construction	Potential increase in asthma and lung cancer.
Isocyanates (e.g. TDI, MDI, HDI)	Paint sprayers; polyurethane manufacturing; organic chemical synthesis; construction	Effects range from transient irritation of the respiratory tract to chronic sensitization and reduction in lung function. Exposure may occur as a mist or as a vapor.
Lead and compounds	Painting; demolition; lead abatement; battery manufacture and maintenance; welding and cutting; brazing; building maintenance; radiation users; machining	One of the most common industrial illnesses is chronic lead poisoning, which damages the peripheral and central nervous systems, sometimes irreversibly.
Manganese and compounds	Steel manufacturing; alloy making; paint manufacture; chemical research	Inhalation may cause severe damage to the central nervous system, sometimes mimicking Parkinson's disease.
Mold (fungal) spores	Office work; farming; biological research; mining; earth-moving trades (geographically specific); grain milling; migrant farm work; cotton mill workers; silo operators; sawmill operations; mushroom farming; cork production; sugarcane harvesting	Exposure to mold spores may cause allergy (hypersensitivity reaction), poisoning (if the spores contain mycotoxins), or infection. Some spores infect healthy hosts; others infect mostly compromised hosts. A combination of these responses is possible.
Nickel	Nickel refining; stainless steel manufacture; alloy production; welding and cutting; chemical research; electroplating; battery manufacture; machining	Nickel and some compounds are probable human respiratory tract carcinogens. Other systemic toxicity has been reported.
Pesticides	Pesticide manufacture; pesticide application; farming; gardening; fumigation	There are a wide variety of pesticides with varying toxicity. Many former pesticides have been banned because of either toxicity or biopersistence. One common class, the organophosphates, can cause damage to the peripheral and central nervous system as well as a host of other body systems.
Radon progeny	Mining; work in underground vaults; work at homes with cellars or concrete office buildings	Radon is a radioactive gas, but when it decays, it forms single ions of other radioactive species that bind electrostatically with other dust to form radioactive particles.

TABLE 8–B	Selected Hazardous Particulate Matter, Continued	
Agent	**Typical Industries/Occupations for Exposure**	**Summary of Health Effects**
Silica-quartz, cristobalite, and tridymite	Sand blasters; concrete demolition; building demolition; hard rock mining; building maintenance; cement manufacture	Exposure to these specific crystalline forms of silicon dioxide typically produces a chronic lung nodular fibrosis called silicosis which impairs lung function. This effect can occur in a matter of months at very high exposure levels.
Sodium hydroxide	Electroplating; chemical metal cleaning; metal etching; plastic production; soap manufacture; chemical laboratory work	Sodium hydroxide is not volatile, so all exposure occurs to the dust or mist. These are extremely alkaline and may cause local tissue irritation or destruction.
Thallium and compounds	Pesticide manufacture; pesticide application; chemical laboratory work; optics fabrication; alloy making	Thallium is very toxic and the effect is cumulative. Early symptoms of exposure include fatigue and myalgia, with later symptoms including those associated with nervous system damage.
Thorium and compounds	Gas mantle fabrication; alloy making; welding rod production; welding; chemical laboratory work; ceramic production	The main hazard posed by this material is due to the accumulation of the radioactive thorium. Although not a high-activity material, it still must be controlled due to its radioactivity.
Uranium and compounds	Uranium mining; nuclear industries; uranium refining; uranium fuel reprocessing; uranium enrichment; low levels may also be present in other rare earth compounds	Naturally occurring uranium is a mixture of three isotopes. The isotopic ratio does not effect the chemical toxicity but influences the radiotoxicity. Soluble uranium compounds pose the highest toxic hazard and generally the lowest radiohazard. The target of the chemical toxicity is the kidney. Radiotoxicity increases the risk of cancer.
Wood dust	Saw-milling; lumbermen; furniture makers; carpenters	Depending on the wood, inhalation of dust may cause toxic, irritant, or allergic effects. Severe sensitization can occur in some cases, notably with mahogany and western red cedar. Inhalation of some hardwood dusts may contribute to nasal cancer.
Zinc oxide fume	Welding; torch or arc cutting—all where zinc is present	Most common metal fume associated with metal fume fever, a transient flu-like illness occurring 2-24 hours after exposure and lasting hours to several days.

ferent types, based on how the PM was created, its shape, its size, and its composition. Table 8–A lists the broader classifications and some subclassifications of PM. There are thousands of types of inorganic and organic particulate matter that may be found in the occupational environment. Table 8–B lists some of the more ubiquitous PMs, as well as certain types of PMs that are of special interest in industrial hygiene and air pollution.

The recent revolution in nanotechnology has added a new class of potential PM hazards, the *engineered nanoparticle*. At the nanoscale, the chemical and physical properties of a material may be strikingly different from the behavior of the chemically identical material of larger particle size. It is not a stretch to imagine that the toxicity of novel nanoparticles may also vary qualitatively or quantitatively from particles of similar materials at the micro or macro scale. To date, limited evidence suggests that some materials are uncharacteristically toxic at the nanoscale. Some, such as carbon nanotubes, may be much more dangerous than would be expected based on their chemistry.

Many of the classic chronic respiratory tract diseases that have been attributed to inhalation of insoluble PM result in a type of illness that is broadly called *pneumoconiosis*. Derived from Greek, this simply translates as *dust in the lungs*. This term has been rather widely used to describe a number of lung diseases, many of which do not share mechanisms, symptoms, or prognoses. Some diseases classified as pneumoconiosis are not known to result in any clinical symptoms, whereas others are potentially fatal as a result of the formation of fibrotic scarring. Some are reversible upon cessation of exposure, some often remain stable if exposure is stopped, and a few may progress even without further exposure. A few are associated with lung cancer.

While attempts to define pneumoconiosis were made as early as 1916, there was no universally accepted definition until 1950. A more recent definition of pneumoconiosis is *the accumulation of insoluble dust in the lungs and the tissue reaction to its presence*. This assumes that the dust is solid and relatively insoluble when deposited in the alveolar region of the lungs. It is applied almost exclusively to diseases caused by exposure to mineral and metallic dust (byssinosis, from primary cotton work, is an exception).

TABLE 8-C	Agents Associated with Pneumoconiosis	
Asbestos (Asbestosis)	Aluminum w/silica (Shaver's disease)	Beryllium (Chronic Beryllium Disease)
Barium	Bentonite	Cement
Cerium	Coal (Black lung)	Diatomite
Fuller's Earth	Hematite	Iron (Siderosis)
Kaolin	Mica	Mixed Dust
Silica (Silicosis)	Tin (Stannosis)	Titanium

Classically, the severe forms of pneumoconiosis are associated with lung fibrotic changes (scarring). Different exposures result in distinct patterns of fibrosis on chest x-ray images. Clinically, there are several defined subforms of fibrosis associated with pneumoconiosis, including hyaline-nodular fibrosis pneumoconiosis, coal miners pneumoconiosis, mixed dust pneumoconiosis, and diffuse interstitial fibrotic pneumoconiosis. Interpretation of chest x-ray films for signs of pneumoconiosis is a complex specialty, and such trained physicians are referred to as B readers.

Table 8-C lists many of the agents that have been associated with a type of pneumoconiosis.

BASIC CONCEPTS AND EXAMPLES

Particle Deposition Mechanisms

The removal of a particle from an aerosol is called "particle deposition." Particle deposition happens in the respiratory tract, on industrial hygiene air sampling filters, and inside bag houses in factories. Deposition is driven by the same physical mechanisms in all cases. Overall deposition is the sum of five primary mechanisms of particle deposition. The deposition mechanisms are shown diagrammatically in single-filter fiber models (Figure 8–2).

1. *Inertial impaction*—As a particle moves within an aerosol, it gains momentum. When an aerosol is forced to change direction abruptly, the gas phase does so easily. However, a suspended particle with significant mass and inertia follows Newton's Law that states "a mass in uniform motion tends to remain in motion unless acted upon by an outside force." Thus the particle tends to resist this change in direction and deviates from the airstream. This may cause the particle to impact on the surface (of lung, filter, etc.) and stick there—this is impaction. Impaction is directly proportional to the density of the particle and the speed of movement and to the square of its diameter. Impaction is most effective for large and dense particles in high-velocity air.

2. *Interception*—Particles not deposited by inertial impaction may be deposited by interception. In this case, the particle follows the airstream fairly well but still contacts the surface of the filter or lung. It sticks, and has

effectively been removed from the aerosol. Interception is most effective for midsized particles. A special case of interception, sieving, is an important deposition mechanism for very large airborne particles.

3. *Sedimentation (Settling)*—All particles are acted upon by gravity and tend to move toward the center of the earth. If the particle settles onto a surface it will be removed from the aerosol. In a vacuum, the particle would accelerate continuously until it reached the surface, independent of its mass or shape. In air, particle movement is resisted by aerodynamic drag and convection upward within the gaseous phase. In a still environment, where drag is the primary force resisting sedimentation, the terminal rate of settling (Vt) for most particles can be estimated by Equation 1, which combines Newton's Second Law of gravitational acceleration with Stokes' Law pertaining to drag forces of particles moving in a viscous medium. When the increasing particle velocity creates a drag equal and opposite to the force imposed by gravity, the particle attains its terminal settling velocity.

The effectiveness of sedimentation in a still aerosol is proportional to the particle's mass, and large particles settle out much faster than small particles.

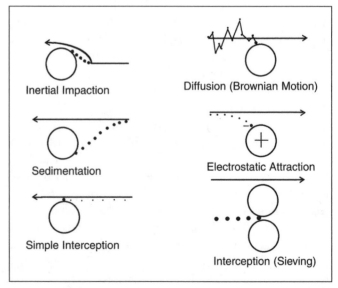

Figure 8–2. Particle deposition mechanisms.

$$Vt = \frac{\text{(particle density)(gravity)(Cunningham correction)(diameter}^2)}{18 \text{ (air viscosity)(dynamic shape factor)}}$$

(1)

The terminal settling velocity *(Vt)* in centimeters per second is found when

- particle density is in grams per cubic centimeter;
- an average value of the gravitational constant is in CMS units of 980 cm/second^2;
- particle diameter is in centimeters;
- standard air viscosity can be assumed to be 1.8×10^{-4} g/ (cm • s);
- Cunningham correction factor is looked up (unitless); and
- the dynamic shape factor is looked up or approximated from Table 8–D (unitless).

4. *Electrostatic attraction*—Charged collection surfaces will attract and hold oppositely charged particles. Most airborne particles carry some net charge. While air filters are not known as a major mechanism of deposition in the respiratory tract, some are designed to hold sustained electrostatic charges, and this can greatly increase the efficiency at which the filters remove particles from aerosols. Also, some industrial hygiene sampling methods still use electrostatic attraction to collect particles, and unintended electrostatic effects hamper other sampling methods.

5. *Diffusion (Brownian movement)*—Very small particles do not experience the gas in which they are suspended

TABLE 8–D Dynamic Shape Factors

Shape/Type	Typical Dynamic Shape Factors
Sphere	1.0
Cubic	1.08
Clustered spheres (e.g. aged fume)	1.15
Quartz particles	1.36
Talc particles	2.04
Fibers	<<1.0

as a continuum. Instead, they react to individual atoms of the gas or uneven impact by groups of air molecules over time. As a result the particles wander around in a seemingly random path, an effect termed Brownian motion. Many people have seen small bacteria quiver in liquid suspension through a microscope; this is the same effect. As the particles flow with the air, they tend to wander from the airflow lines, and may bump into a collection surface and be removed from the aerosol. The effectiveness of diffusion as a deposition mechanism is inversely related to the square of the particle diameter and to the velocity of the aerosol. Thus, slow movement of small particles favors deposition by diffusion.

The net deposition of particles on an air-cleaning filter, on a sampling device, or in the lungs is usually the result of the action of two or more of these deposition mechanisms. Figure 8–3 shows the relative contribution of many of these

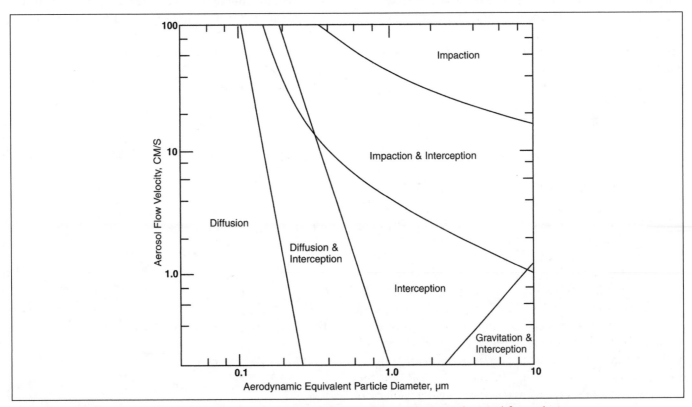

Figure 8–3. Relative contribution of deposition mechanisms as a function of particle size and aerosol flow velocity.

mechanisms to collection of particles on a mechanical filter, as a function of both effective aerodynamic diameter and aerosol flow velocity. It is evident that impaction becomess increasingly important as both particle size and airflow rate go up. Gravitational settling predominates for larger particles at low flow rates, and diffusion is the only active mechanism for particles less than 0.1 µm, regardless of the flow rate.

As might be expected, there is a particle size range that is least efficiently collected because none of the deposition mechanisms are highly effective at that size. The exact nadir point in the collection efficiency of a filter varies somewhat with the flow velocity and filter type, but for mechanical filters it generally lies between about 0.1 and 0.4 µm in aerodynamic equivalent diameter.

This low point or nadir in mechanical filtration occurs because the effectiveness of impaction and interception tails off rapidly below a diameter of about 0.5 µm, and diffusional mechanisms do not become effective until about 0.1 µm. Thus, particles between 0.1 and 0.4 µm are collected inefficiently by all mechanisms. This effect for a certain type of air-cleaning filter is shown in Figure 8–4.

Historically, high-efficiency particulate air (HEPA) filters, developed to support nuclear material production facilities and used extensively in respirators, have been tested and certified at a presumed efficiency nadir point of 0.3 µm using a narrowly dispersed mass of dioctylphthalate oil (or other oil) droplets. Better understanding of filtration principles and improvements in technology allow some filters, such as ultrahigh-efficiency air (ULPA) filters, to be tested using a nearly monodisperse aerosol with an aerodynamic equivalent diameter of about 0.12 µm. At usual flow rates, this is a slightly more challenging test than the 0.3 µm HEPA test.

In 1991, it was proposed that nanoparticles smaller than about 10 nm might not be effectively captured by mechanical air filters because of a *thermal rebound* effect. The authors calculated that at some size the nanoparticles would rebound from the filter matrix as a result of their propensity to diffuse and thus not be captured, much in the way that individual vapor or gas molecules pass unchecked through a filter. In 2004, a study was published that purported to demonstrate this effect for very small nanoparticles. Other authors reported similar findings.

Overwhelming data are now available from numerous investigators showing that mechanical filters work as expected for particles as small as 2 nm. The earlier negative reports suffered from methodological problems that resulted in erroneous conclusions. Of course, at some size, filtration efficiency must drop off, as air and vapor molecules are not captured in a particulate filter. Data suggests that thermal rebound does appear below about 2 nm, just above the diameter of a buckyball, or Buckminsterfullerene particle.

Filters designed to work electrostatically, the so-called electret filters, do behave slightly differently. Many filtering facepieces are made with electret media. In these cases, the filters maximum leakage in terms of number of particles occurs at about 0.04–0.05 µm (40-50 nm) rather than

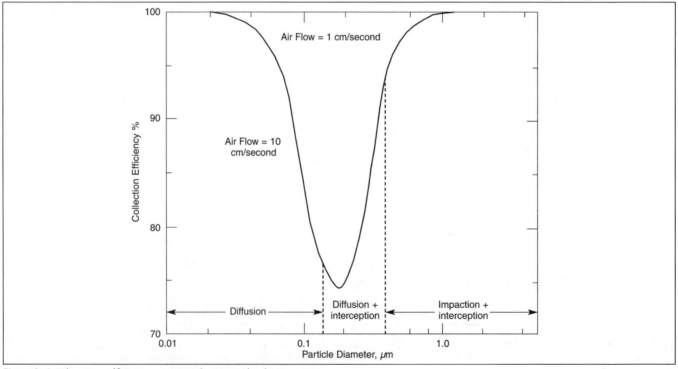

Figure 8–4. Filtration efficiency vs. particle size and velocity.

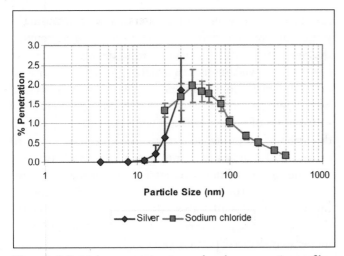

Figure 8–5. Particle penetration curve for electret respirator filter showing maximum penetration at ~40 nm. *(From proceedings of the 5th International Nanomaterial Occupational Safety and Health [NanOSH] conference, Boston, 2011.)*

between 0.1 and 0.3 µm, as shown in Figure 8–5. Particles smaller than 0.05 µm are efficiently captured, until thermal rebound starts to show up below 0.002 µm (2 nm).

PARTICLE SIZE DISTRIBUTIONS

Employees are not exposed to single particles, but rather to large masses of particles suspended in air, commonly called a particle cloud. Particle clouds have a variety of characteristics that often must be understood to fully evaluate and control the hazard they may present.

Particle clouds may be fairly monodisperse, consisting mostly of particles that fall within a very narrow size range, or polydisperse, containing a wide range of particle sizes. Fresh welding fume or fog from condensed boiling acid are examples of fairly monodisperse particle clouds. Both of these types of PM result from vaporization and recondensation, which has a tendency to form uniformly sized particles. Fresh welding fume is typically very small, on the order of 0.01 µm in diameter. The mist caused by boiling acid tends to be formed of larger particles, several micrometers in diameter.

The majority of occupational aerosol-generating activities make polydisperse particle clouds. Sand blasting usually leaves some of the large incident particles (>100 µm) unbroken, yet also forms very small fine particles. The size distribution of particles is very broad. The same is true for many demolition and construction activities, such as concrete breaking. For a given agent, the distribution of particle sizes can range over several orders of magnitude.

Another characteristic of particle clouds is that they may be unimodal or multimodal, that is, they can have

either a single peak when size is plotted against count, or they can have multiple peaks. This may occur with a single agent in a number of ways, or may result from the mixing of several different forms of aerosol clouds. For example, fresh welding fume tends to be composed of very small, spherical particles, but as the fume ages it has a strong predilection to agglomerate or flocculate into irregularly shaped, extended, and enlarged groups of small spheres. A person working near the process may be exposed to both the larger agglomerates and fine primary fume, a distribution with two peaks.

Alternatively, bimodal or trimodal distributions of particle sizes may occur when several operations are occurring in the same area of a workplace. In a foundry, a pouring location that generates very fine fumes may be located close to a polishing operation that creates midsized metal particles and also to a needle gunning operation that forms very large particles. Thus the chemical composition may be the same, but when evaluated with a size-selective instrument, three distinct modes or peaks are detected. More commonly, chemically heterogeneous multimodal particle clouds are found, such as in a machine shop, where large particles of cutting fluid are mixed with midsized particles of metal from grinding operations, and with very small particles of organic smoke from an electronic discharge machining operation. Idealized examples of particle cloud distributions are shown in Figure 8–6.

It is unusual to find a normally distributed particle cloud. When you plot the number of particles on the y-axis and the diameter of the particles on the x-axis, it rarely results in a normal, bell-shaped distribution. This is unfortunate, as basic descriptive statistical techniques are easily applied to normally distributed variables. In normal distributions, the mean (which is the same as the mode and

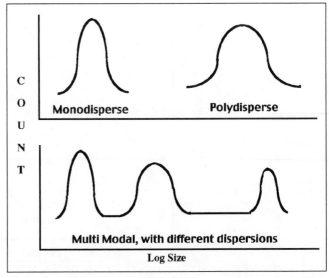

Figure 8–6. Ideal monodisperse, polydisperse, unimodal, and multimodal particulate matter clouds (log-normal plots).

median) is the measure of central tendency, and the standard deviation is the measure of the dispersion. A large mean implies that the average particles are large, and a small standard deviation indicates a fairly monodisperse distribution of particle sizes.

If you measure and plot particle number versus size in a polydisperse distribution, the most common picture that emerges is a highly skewed curve, with the largest number of particles forming a peak, followed by an elongated, asymptotic slope to the right (larger particle sizes). This may occur for a variety of reasons, including the selective loss by sedimentation or impaction of the larger particles.

Fortunately, it is often possible to convert the skewed plot of particle count versus size into a fairly normal-shaped curve by plotting the log of the particle sizes against the count. The resulting distribution, called a log-normal distribution, is often bell-shaped in appearance and can be described in terms analogous to those applicable to a normal distribution.

The mean of a log-normal distribution is called the geometric mean and corresponds to the mean in a normal-normal distribution—the size below and above which lie 50% of the particles. The geometric standard deviation can be calculated, which is analogous to the standard deviation

calculated to define set intervals in normal distributions. The biggest difference is that instead of adding and subtracting the geometric standard deviation from the geometric mean to define known subsets of the data (as is done in normal-normal distributions), the mean is multiplied or divided by the geometric standard deviation. Thus, a lognormal distribution of a particle cloud with a geometric standard deviation of 10 μm in diameter and a geometric standard deviation of 2 indicates that 67 percent (1 geometric standard deviation) of the particles fall within the size range of 10 × 2 and 10/2, or 5–20 μm. Ninety-five percent of the particles fall within about +/– two geometric standard deviations of the geometric mean, 2.5 to 40 μm. This is a moderately disperse particle cloud.

The geometric mean of a log-normal distribution can be calculated directly, by log transforming the data (calculating the $\log_{10}$ of the diameter of each particle) and dividing by the number of particles. It can also be picked directly off a special type of plot, a cumulative log-probability plot. Using this unusual type of graph format, log-normal distributions plot as straight lines. The geometric mean and geometric standard deviations can be measured directly from this plot, as shown in Figure 8–7.

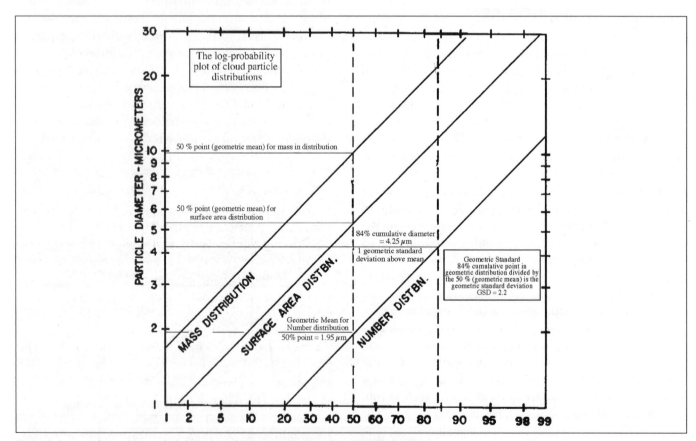

Figure 8–7. Cumulative log-probability plot of log-normally distributed particle cloud.

Sometimes particle clouds are described in terms of the geometric mass equivalent diameter instead of the geometric count diameter as described above. This is particularly true when the mass of the particles deposited, rather than the number, determines toxicity. For example, soluble lead or arsenic compounds are toxic, no matter where they deposit in the respiratory tract.

To calculate this, one multiplies the volume of each particle by its mass before plotting or manipulating the data. The geometric mass equivalent distribution has the same geometric standard deviation as the geometric count distribution, but the mean particle size is always much larger than the mean particle diameter of the count distribution. This occurs simply because mass is a third-power function of diameter, and most of the mass in a polydisperse cloud of PM will reside in the larger particles. The extremely fine particles, which appear prominently in the count distribution, are almost irrelevant in the mass distribution.

In contrast, the mass of inhaled asbestos is not a very useful metric. It is the count, the number of fibers inhaled, that best correlates with the probability of developing disease. Thus, the count distribution would be appropriate for the characterization of a cloud of asbestos fibers. Figure 8–7 shows the number and mass distributions of a particle cloud plotted on a cumulative log-probability chart. Also shown is the surface area distribution, which is not often relevant to the toxicology of the PM, but significant for some types of direct-reading particle enumerators (e.g., forward light scattering photometers).

Some types of intrinsically low-toxicity, low-solubility nanoparticles (e.g., TiO_2, $BaSO_4$) demonstrate an increased toxicity when compared to chemically identical larger particles *for the same mass*. However, when you compare the toxicity for these same particles *per unit surface area*, instead of per unit mass, it turns out that they exhibit roughly the same level of effect. Thus for this class of nanoparticle, the excess toxicity can likely be accounted for by the difference in surface area. This is discussed in detail later in this chapter.

Figure 8–8 graphically illustrates, for the same mass, the relationships between surface area and particle number as particles are made smaller and smaller. Every time the particle size is cut in half, the particle number doubles and the particle surface area increases by a factor of $2^2 = 4$. Thus, for a given mass, nanoparticles have much greater surface area than larger particles. It appears that the tremendous surface area of these otherwise low-toxicity materials catalyzes the formation of reactive oxygen species, resulting in cell damage and toxicity.

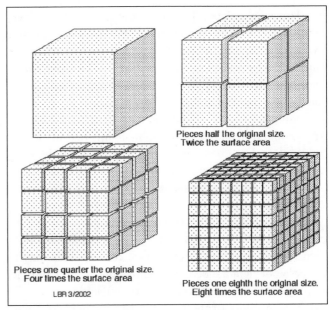

Pieces half the original size. Twice the surface area

Pieces one quarter the original size. Four times the surface area

LBR 3/2002

Pieces one eighth the original size. Eight times the surface area

Figure 8–8. Demonstration of increasing particle number and surface area as a large particle is subdivided.

CRITICAL FACTORS IN DETERMINING ACCEPTABLE EXPOSURE

The nature of the health problems caused by inhalation of PM is influenced by a number of factors, including

- chemical and biological composition of the particles and stability of their nuclei (radioactivity);
- crystalline, structural, isotopic, and allotropic forms of the particles;
- the shape of the particles;
- the size of the particles;
- dose: concentration of particles in the work environment and exposure duration;
- preexisting health or genetic status of the workers; and
- concurrent exposure to other toxic agents.

This has been demonstrated again with the advent of nanotechnology where it quickly became apparent that many variables actually impacted the toxic potential of a nanoparticle.

Chemical Composition

The elemental composition is sometimes the primary driver for the toxicity of a material. For example, as reflected in their respective Threshold Limit Values (TLVs) and OSHA Permissible Exposure Limits (PELs), beryllium metal is considered more hazardous than metallic lead, which is in turn more toxic than metallic iron. This reflects the intrinsic toxic nature of the metal in the particle.

The same is true of organic compounds, where very minor structural differences can change a compound from low to very high toxicity. Among smokes and soots, molecules with identical chemical compositions may have widely varying toxicity depending on the exact chemical arrangement of the atoms that make up the molecule. For example, the polynuclear aromatic compound benzo-a-pyrene is a known mutagen and carcinogen. By slightly rearranging the atoms that shape benzo-a-pyrene and breaking the polynuclear structure, the material loses its mutagenic and carcinogenic potency, without significantly changing its elemental composition.

Even less dramatic structural alterations can vastly change the toxicity of an organic compound. For example, some pharmaceuticals have a chiral center, which may be either left or right handed. Frequently only one stereoisomer of pharmaceuticals is effective (or toxic), left or right. The other enantiomer of the molecule can be ineffective with different toxicity. This variation in structure is extremely subtle, but has a big impact on the drug effectiveness and potential for occupational illness.

The type of molecule to which a radioactive atom is bound also affects its radiotoxicity. Soluble uranium compounds are much less carcinogenic than are insoluble or minimally soluble forms. The former, once deposited in the alveolar portion of the lungs, is rapidly removed by dissolution and often excreted promptly. Insoluble compounds of uranium, in contrast, can remain on the alveolar surface for a much longer period of time, all the while depositing ionizing energy into cells in the vicinity of the particle.

Isotopic Composition

Inhaled radiological materials vary in toxicity for a number of reasons, but in most cases, a primary factor is the specific activity of the radioactive atom. Species with high specific activities emit a lot of ionizing radiation per unit of time and mass, and thus more rapidly affect tissue, causing genetic and somatic cell damage. Also important is the type and energy of the radioactive particle (or photon) emitted when the atom decays.

Plutonium, which has a high specific activity and releases very densely ionizing alpha particles, is considered to be one of the most radiotoxic atoms in existence. Natural uranium has a much lower specific activity and is correspondingly much less radiotoxic. A tritium compound, because of the very low energy beta particle it emits when it decays and its fast clearance from the body, is considered a minor hazard when inhaled in moderate amounts.

Some unstable, radioactive elements have two or more distinct radioactive isotopes, varying structurally only in the number of neutrons in the nucleus of the atom. For example, naturally occurring uranium consists of three isotopes, U-238 (99.28%), U-234 (0.0006%), and U-235 (0.714%). The U235 is the fissile isotope, capable of powering nuclear reactors and nuclear bombs. Because of its high specific activity, it is also the most radiotoxic isotope, with an additional contribution by U-234. Remove U-235, as is done to produce fuel for reactors, and the remaining material, almost exclusively U-238, is primarily a kidney toxin, not a radiotoxic hazard. In contrast, U-235 enriched uranium is predominantly a radioactive hazard.

Crystalline and Structural

The chemical composition of various particles may be virtually identical, but other qualities of the molecular structure may render them more or less toxic. Silicon is interesting in this regard, as its toxicity depends not on the intrinsic toxicity of the element silicon, but on the types of compounds silicon makes with other elements and their crystalline structure.

Pure silicon is a metalloid of low toxicity when inhaled. Silicates (SiO_2-containing) minerals make up the bulk of the earth's crust and vary in toxicity from very toxic (e.g., asbestos) to relatively inert. SiO_2 also commonly occurs in the free state, generically called silica. Silica may be found or made in both a noncrystalline form (pumice, obsidian, glass) or a crystalline form (quartz).

Quartz is very toxic to lung tissue. Chronic inhalation of very fine, respirable particles of quartz may lead to *silicosis*, a nodular, potentially progressive, and often severe form of pneumoconiosis. It also causes lung cancer. Other toxic forms of free, crystalline silica, tridymite and cristobalite, may be formed upon heating quartz. The eight-hour TLV-TWA for quartz and cristobalite is 0.025 mg/m^3 as respirable dust; there is currently no TLV for tridymite or tripoli (yet another form of free crystalline silica).

In contrast, amorphous, noncrystalline silica is much less toxic. Amorphous silica arises naturally in the formation of rocks such as pumice and obsidian, the latter displaying the appearance associated with manmade glass. Other examples of free silica that are not crystalline include diatomaceous earth, fumed silica, fused silica, and silica gel. Once there were TLV limits for these materials, but they were withdrawn in 2006 for lack of sufficient data supporting them. Although chemically identical to quartz and the other free crystalline silicas, amorphous silica lacks a fully formed repetitive crystalline structure. As a result of this difference, glass, natural or manmade, is of low toxicity and is generally managed as a PNOC. In between these two extremes are other forms of silicon dioxide that have different levels of crystalline organization, and thus intermediate toxicity and Threshold Limit Values.

Crystalline structure is also a major determinant of the toxicity of carbon, with the carbon nanotube allotrope apparently much more toxic than the graphite allotrope.

Shape of the Particles

Shape is often the defining characteristic that makes a particle toxic.

By commercial convention, there are six varieties of asbestos: chrysotile (a serpentine mineral), Amosite, crocidolite, and fibrous tremolite, anthophyllite, and actinolite. While these minerals vary in chemical composition, all of them share a general shape—they are fibrous. More specifically, they are *asbestiform*, a type of fibrous habit that is much more specific than the general term *fibrous*. When shredded apart from their bulk rock form, they exist in bundles of long, skinny fibers that are much longer than they are wide. As you further tear the bundles apart, you just get smaller and smaller bundles with the same general morphology. Ultimately, when all of the adhering particles are separated, the unit piece of an asbestos fiber, the fibril, retains the same general shape, long and narrow. This fibril, especially in the case of chrysotile asbestos, is a naturally occurring nanoparticle

Asbestos fibers are said to have a high aspect ratio, length divided by width. In mineralogical terms, asbestos always has an aspect ratio of at least 10:1; that is, it is 10 times as long as it is wide. Current OSHA air sample analysis regulations define asbestos as having an aspect ratio of >3:1; the EPA defines it as >5:1. These regulatory aspect ratios are arbitrary and may introduce errors by being too low, especially the 3:1 OSHA/NIOSH ratio.

Each fibrous asbestos mineral is matched by a chemically identical nonasbestiform mineral. These nonfibrous analogues to asbestos do not present the same hazards of lung cancer, asbestosis, and mesothelioma as the asbestiform varieties. Thus it is the shape of the asbestos fibers that is determined by the crystalline structure, which to a large extent defines their toxicity.

Because asbestos fibers can travel through the lung lengthwise, like an arrow, they can penetrate much deeper into the lung than a nonfibrous particle with a diameter equal to the length of the fiber. As a result, asbestos fibers tens of micrometers long can make it to the alveolar region of the lungs, which would almost never happen with more regularly shaped particles of this size. Once deposited in this region of the lungs, it is believed that the fibers trigger an ineffective immune response by resident macrophages, which not only fails to remove the relatively insoluble fiber, but kills the macrophages in the process. This sets off a chain of immunological events, which results in scarring of the lungs and lung cancer. Other similar mechanisms result in mesotheliomas of the pleural or other linings. See Figure 8–9

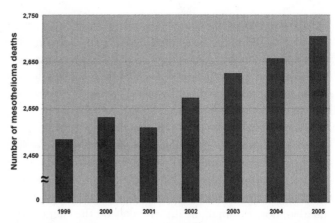

Figure 8–9. Ongoing cases of mesothelioma in the United States (NIOSH).

for the number of mesothelioma cases in the United States.

Note that the name *asbestos* is a term of commerce, not science. There are other fibrous minerals, such as erionite and fibrous attapulgite, that pose similar respiratory hazards to asbestos. And it is likely that some manmade vitreous fibers may as well.

In the 1970s M.F. Stanton proposed that fibers' dimensional characteristics (<0.25 μm diameter, length >8 μm) and solubility (low) were the strongest predictive factors for the induction of mesothelioma. Chemistry, he argued, was secondary. While Stanton's hypothesis has been criticized and clearly doesn't account for all the variability in toxicity among fibrous particles, overall it has held up pretty well over the years. By extension of this hypothesis, other High Aspect Ratio Nanoparticles (HARN) like carbon nanotubes may pose a risk of causing mesothelioma. In very preliminary animal studies, this does seem to be the case.

Carbon nanotubes are a group of new crystalline forms (allotropes) of carbon discovered in the 1950s and brought to international attention by Sumio Iijima of NEC in 1991. Composed entirely of carbon atoms arranged in nanoscale hollow needles of various sizes, they are related to Buckminsterfullerene, a pure carbon molecule/particle composed of 60 carbon atoms arranged in a geodesic sphere, also known as a buckyball. These novel nanoscale carbon allotropes are chemically identical to the historically known forms of carbon, graphite, and diamond. But the toxicity varies greatly based on the crystalline form.

Pure graphite dust is regarded as moderate in toxicity, with a TLV-TWA of 2.0 mg/m³ as respirable dust. In contrast, inhalation of the various forms of carbon nanotubes reliably causes fibrotic lung changes and lung scarring, at least in animal studies, at lower exposure levels. NIOSH has recommended an exposure limit of 0.007 mg/m³ (7 μg/m³) for carbon nanotubes, 286 times lower than the TLV for graphite. However, as of mid-2011 some manufacturers of carbon nanotubes still quote the synthetic graphite PEL (15 mg/m³ total dust or 5 mg/m³ respirable dust) or TLV in their material safety data sheets (MSDSs). No cases of occupational disease from carbon nanotube exposure have yet been reported.

Size of the Particles

The toxicity of some agents depends very directly on the size of the individual particles to which people are exposed. To be of inhalation concern, a particle must not be too big, as it would not stay suspended in the air long enough to be inhaled, nor too small, as it then takes on the characteristics of a gas rather than a particle. Asbestos fibers are of particular concern if they are very long and skinny. Quartz particles are of concern only if they are of respirable size, <10 μm. Low-solubility, low-intrinsic toxicity metal oxide nanoparticles appear to be unusually toxic because of the very high surface area that goes with their small size.

This chapter has often referred to "particle sizes." It is important to understand that, with the exception of the high-aspect-ratio particles like asbestos, the reference is not to the actual physical size of airborne particles. For example, when it states that the nadir in collection efficiency of a HEPA filter occurs at a particle size of 0.3 μm, or that respirable dust includes particles smaller than 10 μm, it is not referring to the actual physical size of the particle.

Instead, these values are in terms of the *equivalent aerodynamic diameter (EAD)* of a particle, also called the *aerodynamic equivalent diameter (AED)*. This value predicts how a particle will behave when inhaled or passing through a respirator or sampling filter much more reliably than the actual size of the particle. The aerodynamic equivalent diameter removes all of the aerodynamic variability induced by the shape and density of the particle and relates it to a standardized, theoretical spherical particle of unit density. One way to look at the AED is that it is the spherical particle of unit density that achieves the same terminal settling velocity as the actual particle, as shown in Figure 8–10. Almost all of the exposure standards that require measurement of a limited size fraction of a dust actually require the measurement of the aerodynamic equivalent size of the dust, not its physical size.

For moderately sized spherical particles (1–10 μm physical diameter), the aerodynamic equivalent diameter (AED) can be pretty well estimated by the simple equation provided below.

$$AED = \frac{particle}{diameter} \times \sqrt{particle\ density} \qquad (2)$$

This is accurate as long as the density measurements are made in the specified units of g/cc.

Thus, the AED is related to the actual particle diameter by multiplication with the square root of the particle density in relationship to the density of water, or the specific gravity, which amounts to the same thing.

In the example provided in Equation 2, it was assumed that the particles were spherical. With the exception of mists, some mold spores and very fresh fume and smoke, most PM is not spherical, and a correction must be made for the differential resistance to airflow induced by other shapes. This has been called the dynamic shape factor, which is the ratio of the actual terminal settling velocity of a nonspherical particle to its predicted settling rate. The net AED for a nonspherical particle in the middle size range (1–10 μm) can be estimated in many cases by adding the dynamic shape factor to Equation 2.

$$AED = \frac{diameter\ of}{the\ particle} \times \left[\frac{Particle\ density}{(standard\ particle\ density \times dynamic\ shape\ factor)} \right]^{0.5}$$

- If using g/cc, the "standard density" is 1, thus nothing changes when you divide by it and it can be left out. If another unit, it will not be 1 and thus has to appear as a variable.
- actual particle diameter
- specific gravity or particle density
- dynamic shape factor estimated from Table 8–D (unitless)

Thus, a talc particle, which tends to be in the shape of a flake, has a high dynamic shape factor, resulting in increased drag as it moves through air, making it appear aerodynamically smaller than it is physically. A fiber, which travels lengthwise as it moves in an aerosol and thus resembles an arrow, has a low dynamic shape factor, and moves in a manner more of a function of its diameter rather than its

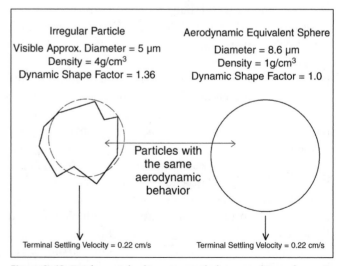

Figure 8–10. Real particle diameter and shape and aerodynamic equivalent diameter.

length. Typical dynamic shape factors for differently shaped particles are provided in Table 8–D.

The usefulness of these simple methods for determining AED starts to degrade progressively with very small and relatively large particles. Large particles tend to flow through the air with the creation of a lot of turbulence rather than laminarly, in effect making the particles', AED smaller than would be calculated. Very small particles enter another flow regime, where they start to see the air as individual molecules rather than a continuum, and are subject to slippage between the molecules with reduced drag. Thus, they have an AED that is larger than these simple calculations would suggest. More sophisticated calculations, with consideration of Cunningham slip correction factors and Reynolds' numbers, can be made to partially correct for these effects, but such calculations are beyond the scope of this chapter.

In practice, aerodynamic equivalent diameter is usually determined empirically. When it is important to know the full size distribution of the dust, it can be sampled through a multistage separator, each stage collecting a certain aerodynamic cut, or fraction, of dust. Devices such as multistage cascade impactors can be used very effectively to show the distribution of a particle cloud. In one research project, the particle size distribution created by laser machining of a carbon composite was compared to the particles created by mechanical machining by use of a cascade impactor. Simply by looking at the filters on the six stages in each impactor, it was obvious that mechanical machining produced a cloud dominated by large particles, whereas laser machining, which works mostly by a vaporization-condensation

mechanism, produced only very fine particles.

The aerodynamic equivalent diameter of the particle is important because it determines where in the respiratory tract the particle is most likely to be deposited. As described in Chapter 2, the lung has different clearance mechanisms and particle residence times in different sections. In the nose, nasal turbinates, and throat (collectively the head airways region or nasopharyngeal region) inhaled air moves rapidly through small diameter passageways with several sharp changes in direction. The larger particles, especially those with AEDs greater than 20 μm, are subject to removal by impaction in this area and are either ejected through blowing the nose or passed into the GI tract, completely avoiding the lungs. In the thoracic region of the lungs, also known as the tracheobronchial region (which includes the bronchi and larger bronchioles), the air slows down because of the greater cross section of flow, and impaction and inertial settling remove smaller particles, between 1 and 20 μm AED. Particles deposited in this region are usually reliably removed from the lung in a matter of hours by the mucociliary escalator or dissolve, and thus have a limited residence time in the lung.

Finally, very small particles, those with AEDs significantly less than 10 μm, have an increasingly good chance of penetrating all the way to the terminal bronchioles and the alveolar sacs in the air exchange region of the lungs. In this region, they may be deposited by diffusion (Brownian motion). Nanoscale particles below about 20 nm have the unique fate of being deposited efficiently both in the alveolar regions of the lungs and in the nasal turbinates (Figure 8–11).

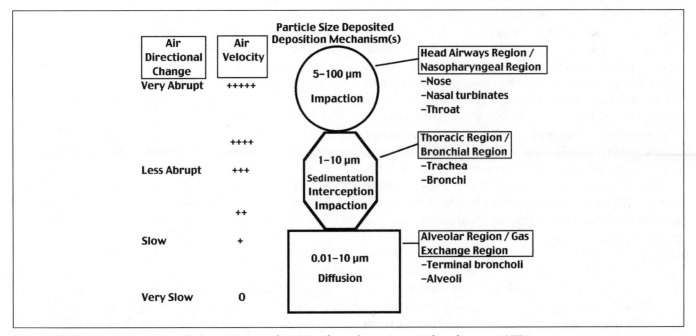

Figure 8–11. Respiratory tract particle deposition as a function of aerodynamic equivalent diameter (AED).

Particles that dissolve are transported directly into the bloodstream by diffusion across the very thin capillaries that line the alveolar sacs. Lung macrophages attempt to transport insoluble particles to a nearby lymph node. Particles that are effectively moved from the alveoli by macrophages without dissolution pass into the lymphatic drainage where they may accumulate to cause illness or gain access to the systemic circulation. Particles that do not dissolve and are harmful to macrophages are often the serious pneumoconiosis-inducing particles, and they simply accumulate in the alveoli or in lung tissue.

Real health consequences may arise when the deposited particle is toxic and the macrophages are ineffective at removing it. One example of such a case has already been presented—asbestosis. The macrophages do not destroy the asbestos particle, and in the process of trying, actually die and degrade, apparently triggering a cascade of biological responses that may be responsible for much of the fiber's toxicity. Quartz is another highly insoluble compound, the toxicity of which is completely dependent on its penetration to the alveolar portion of the lungs. Quartz deposited in the nose, throat, bronchi, or larger bronchiole is completely nontoxic. Only when it is small enough to come to rest in the alveoli does it trigger the start of silicosis and cancer, probably by killing macrophages somewhat like asbestos. Many, but not all of the nonbenign-pneumoconiosis-producing dusts act like this.

Dose: Concentration of PM in the Work Environment and Exposure Duration

"All substances are poisons; there is none which is not a poison. The right dose differentiates a poison and a remedy." This statement, written by Paracelsus (1493–1541), is an important starting point in understanding the concept of dose and dose-response relationships. At some dose, everything, including water, becomes toxic. Common table salt will kill half the people who consume four grams per kilogram of body weight in a short period of time. On the other extreme, botulism toxin will kill half of the people who consume 10 nanograms per kilogram of body weight, a toxicity range of 400 million.

The development of the pneumoconioses typically requires many years of exposure. The same is true of carcinogenic PM, such as polynuclear aromatic hydrocarbons and cadmium fume. Some metals, such as arsenic and lead, typically result in poisoning that occurs after exposure of at least several months. A few hours of heavy overexposure to some metal fumes from welding or cutting, such as zinc, can result in a transient illness known as metal fume fever.

Of course, all of these timeframes are affected by the concentration of the contaminant in the air. High exposure to cadmium fume can cause acute pulmonary edema, which

can be fatal in days. At very high levels, lead toxicity may manifest itself in less than a week.

Silicosis can occur quickly when the exposure level is very high. This happened en masse in 1935 during the drilling of a tunnel to Gauley Bridge, West Virginia. Approximately 1500 people became sick, some in weeks, as a result of massive exposures to quartz. Many ultimately died from this exposure. During a congressional inquiry, it came out that company officials and engineers wore respirators to enter the tunnel diggings, but respirators were not offered to the workers.

Exposure Limits

What is a safe level for exposure to a potentially toxic PM in the workplace? There are a number of possible references an industrial hygienist can use to find an appropriate occupational exposure limit (OEL).

Frequently, the industrial hygienist can rely on published exposure limits from the federal or state governments, for example, federal and state OSHA programs. In 1971 OSHA came into being as a result of the Williams-Steiger OSH act of 1970, and promptly adopted the 1968 Threshold Limit Values (TLVs) from the American Conference of Governmental Industrial Hygienists (ACGIH). This is how the Permissible Exposure Limits (PELs) were initially established.

Unfortunately, for political reasons, federal OSHA rarely updates its PELs, which continue to be based mostly on the 1968 TLVs. Some states, like California, have a much better program for updating exposure standards, and their exposure limits are often fairly current with the toxicological literature. In some circumstances, the EPA or other federal or state agencies like the FCC also establish exposure limits. For example, the EPA has an exposure limit for asbestos for part of the population not regulated by the OSHA standard. Other governmental agencies (e.g., Defense, Energy) may adopt their own internal exposure limits that differ from the OSHA limits.

Many employers also consider the guidelines established by the aforementioned American Conference of Governmental Industrial Hygienists via the TLVs. The ACGIH is a private, not-for-profit, nongovernmental professional organization composed of industrial hygienists, physicians, and allied health professionals. Legally, the TLVs are not considered consensus standards, but they are used similarly and in many cases are the most thoroughly considered exposure recommendations available.

The National Institute of Occupational Safety and Health (NIOSH) is a center among the Centers for Disease Control that periodically proposes Recommended Exposure Limits (RELs), which are intended primarily to guide OSHA in future rulemaking. However, as federal OSHA rarely completes any new rulemaking for chemicals, the REL may become a default exposure guideline or limit adopted by employers. NIOSH recently established an REL for carbon nanotubes at 0.007 mg/m³ averaged over an eight-hour work day. With little else to go by, some employers are implementing this standard.

The American Industrial Hygiene Association publishes voluntary guidelines called WEELs, "Workplace Exposure Evaluation Levels." It is also possible to look to the exposure standards established by other nations, particularly Germany and England, but be aware that certain countries establish very low exposure standards that are not based on good data or are politically motivated and really cannot be relied upon. Also, the emphasis on exposure standards is waning in the European Union (EU) in favor of alternative approaches, so over time they may not be updated regularly.

Lacking a PEL, REL, WEEL, or TLV, some manufacturers or employers will develop their own recommended exposure limits, based on toxicity testing or their working experience. One company, for example, set an exposure limit for carbon nanotubes of 0.05 mg/m³ well before NIOSH presented its REL. Another company for a while had a lower exposure limit for beryllium than either the PEL or TLV.

OELs for particulate matter (and other stressors) are defined against several different time bases. Most TLVs and PELs are defined as eight-hour time-weighted average (TWA) exposures. Actual airborne dust levels may be higher or lower during the workday, but must, on average, be below the eight-hour (TWA) exposure limit. Many NIOSH RELs are based on a 10-hour averaging period. Some TLVs and PELs also sometimes include short-term exposure limits (STELs), which are 15-minute average of exposure. A relatively small number of particulate matters have STEL limits. Another form of limit is the *ceiling* limit, abbreviated simply as "C," which is a concentration of the chemical agent that is usually intended as an absolute limit, a value never to be exceeded even for a short time.

OSHA retains the legacy concept of *Peak Above Ceiling*, which is a limit that allows short periods of exposure above a ceiling value. The time basis for the Peak Above Ceiling varies from agent to agent. Among PM, only beryllium and its compounds, chromic acid and chromates, and fluoride-containing dust list a peak above ceiling limit. Most of these are grossly out of step with the current toxicology literature. Finally, the OSHA standard for asbestos provides an *excursion* limit, which is a 30-minute average exposure.

For radioactive particles, the airborne limits are termed *Derived Air Concentrations* or DACs, which are published by the International Conference on Radiation Protection (ICRP). These figures are airborne limits that are back-calculated from the preestablished limit for radiation dose to the lungs and other tissues. Unlike chemical exposure limits, which are usually expressed as eight-hour average exposure limits, the DACs are year-long averages. Exposure slightly above a DAC on one or several days is not important if exposure is well below the DAC on the majority of workdays.

It is important to be aware that the exposure limits for materials that are carcinogenic or genotoxic may not be fully protective. Assuming a nonthreshold dose-response relationship, any exposure carries some risk of adverse effect. For example, according to OSHA, exposure to asbestos at the current limit of 0.1 fibers per cubic centimeter of air averaged over an eight-hour day for a working lifetime will increase an individual's risk of developing asbestos-related cancer by about 0.3–0.4 percent. Against the total likelihood of developing cancer over an individual's life of 22 percent, this residual risk is considered acceptable in an occupational setting.

Many occupational exposure limits carry poorly defined residual risks, and in the case of the TLVs, the ACGIH states that the limits "refer to airborne concentrations ... under which it is believed that nearly all workers may be repeatedly exposed day after day without adverse effects. Because of individual susceptibility ... (some people) may be affected more seriously ... by development of an occupational illness."

The environmental limits for exposure of the general population to PM are generally much lower than the occupational limits. For example, the limit for beryllium in the environment is 0.01 μg/m³, 20 times less than the modern California OSHA occupational exposure limit and 200 times less than the seriously outdated federal OSHA standard. This arises from a variety of considerations, including the potential of exposure to the sick, young, and elderly in the general population, 24-hour-a-day exposure, and a general attitude that residual risk rates for the public should be much lower than residual risk rates acceptable in an occupational setting.

Preexisting Health or Genetic Status of the Worker

Occupational exposure limits for particulate matter (or other classes of stressors) are generally set for "healthy workers." They do not, in most cases, take into account the variable susceptibility of individual employees because of prior exposures, preexisting health problems, or genetic endowment. No screening for these conditions is required. The *Expanded OSHA Standards* (found in 29CFR1910.1001–1052) are an exception to this rule. The expanded OSHA standards for PM do generally require some medical evaluation of workers before significant exposure to a specific PM (e.g., asbestos, lead, cadmium, and arsenic). Additional medical monitoring requirements may apply in states with their own OSHA programs.

Some people will have genetic variants that predispose them to certain occupational diseases. For example, chronic beryllium disease is mediated by an immune system hypersensitivity reaction, essentially an allergy. Only about 33% of the population possesses the HLA-DPB Glu69 allele and thus are strongly susceptible to developing this hypersensitivity reaction. Other individuals without this gene variant are relatively resistant to beryllium dust. However, this is not accounted for in the exposure limit, and genetic testing is not yet widely used to screen potential beryllium workers.

Immune system hypersensitivity also drives the toxicity of many types of wood dust, including redwood, walnut, and western red cedar. Typical of allergy-mediated toxicity, it is not readily possible to predict who will be resistant to the development of sensitization and who will rapidly become very sensitive to the dust.

Recently there was the case of a university researcher. He was working with a weakened strain of *Yersinia pestis*, also known as the plague. He was infected by these bacteria, which do not normally infect people with healthy immune systems. Unfortunately the researcher had a genetic abnormality that lead to a condition called *hemochromatosis*, the presence of very high iron levels in his body. This allowed the otherwise nonvirulent strain to infect and kill him. The relationship between hemochromatosis and susceptibility to this type of attenuated virus was not known prior to the researcher's death.

Pregnancy is a temporary medical condition that may predispose either the pregnant woman or her fetus to occupational disease. The ACGIH and the Centers for Disease Control and Prevention recommend blood lead levels much lower for pregnant or potentially pregnant women than for other women, not to protect them against lead health effects, but to protect the fetus from the teratogenic and fetotoxic effects of the mother's elevated blood lead level. In a comprehensive industrial hygiene program, all women who become pregnant or are trying to become pregnant should have their workplace evaluated for potential exposure to teratogenic or fetotoxic exposures, including radiation exposure when applicable. However, a court decision has made it clear that a woman cannot be forcibly discharged or even shifted from one job to another to protect her fetus, as long as her exposure and biological monitoring results fall below the minimum OSHA standards.

For the vast majority of PM hazards, there is no requirement to perform preexposure medical assessment of workers to determine if they have conditions that might make it imprudent to be exposed to the PM in question. No generally applicable regulation requires prescreening for individuals who are to be exposed to beryllium, chromium, cobalt, barium, diesel exhaust, nickel, pentachlorophenol, thallium, or dozens of other occupational particles.

In recent years, there has been discussion of the role of preplacement medical exams and ongoing medical monitoring for people exposed to novel engineered nanoscale PM. As of mid-2011, NIOSH does not recommend any specific preplacement or medical monitoring based specifically on the small size of a PM. NIOSH does suggest a general medical surveillance program to identify early emerging disease from novel nanoparticle exposures.

Some have proposed using the OSHA asbestos medical monitoring program for workers exposed to carbon nanotubes, but this has largely been rejected because of the low sensitivity and questionable usefulness of this protocol. Better medical monitoring tools are on the horizon.

Concurrent Exposure to Other Toxic Agents

Often, exposure to particulate matter or other types of airborne hazardous materials does not occur in isolation. Rather, exposure occurs to more than one type of PM, or PM plus gases, vapors, or infectious agents. While in many cases these multiple exposures do not interact, in some cases they may interact additively or synergistically.

An example of a noninteractive concurrent exposure would be lead and asbestos. While they are both primarily occupational hazards as aerosols, their target organs, health effects, and pharmacokinetics are very different. Lead is primarily toxic to the central nervous system and bone marrow, even though it typically gains access to the body through the lungs. Asbestos is toxic mostly in the lungs, and causes lung diseases such as cancer and asbestosis. Lead is somewhat cumulatively toxic, but it has a threshold below which there is no risk of developing lead poisoning. Asbestos is usually assumed to be cumulatively toxic (especially the less soluble forms amosite and crocidolite) with no threshold below which exposure is completely safe. When both exposures are measured simultaneously, the results are treated independently, and if both exposures are below the appropriate limits, then the operation is in compliance.

Other exposures are known or assumed to be additive. For example, it is prudent to assume that coexposure to any of the pneumoconiosis-producing dusts listed in Table 8–C would be additive, as they produce variably related conditions. Thallium and lead have very similar toxicological profiles, so again it would be appropriate to consider these concurrent exposures as additive. The more closely the particulate-matter-related health effects are, the more appropriate it is to judge them to be additive. When both exposures are measured simultaneously, the TWA fractions of the respective exposure limits found for each agent are added together, and if the value exceeds 1.0, then an overexposure situation is assumed to exist.

$$\frac{\text{Measured exposure agent 1 (TWA)}}{\text{TLV–TWA for agent 1}} + \frac{\text{Measured exposure agent 2 (TWA)}}{\text{TLV–TWA for agent 2}}$$

$$(4)$$

Note: PEL, REL, or WEEL may be used instead of TLV, as is most appropriate.

An example of application of additive calculation for measured concurrent exposures to lead and a soluble thallium compound is provided below:

Lead	Thallium

$$\frac{\text{Measured exposure is 0.03 mg/m}^3 \text{ (TWA)}}{\text{+ PEL-TWA = 0.05 mg/m}^3} + \frac{\text{Measured exposure is 0.05 mg/m}^3 \text{ (TWA)}}{\text{PEL-TWA = 0.10 mg/m}^3}$$

$$(5)$$

The sum of these is 1.1. As this exceeds 1.0, the measured worker is assumed to be overexposed to the additive metals (lead and thallium in this case). If taken separately, each metal would be below its corresponding PEL, and an overexposure would not exist. Note that this type of additive analysis can be conducted for three, four, or even more agents sampled at the same time. It may even include a mixture of PM, vapors, and even physical agents. This is a determination that must be made on a case-by-case basis by an industrial hygienist.

Some PM exposures are synergistic. For reasons not totally clear, the health consequences of concurrent inhalation of cigarette smoke and asbestos exposure are much greater than the sum of the parts. Both attack the lung and both cause cancer, but when exposure occurs at the same time, there is a very large synergistic increase in the risk of developing lung cancer, on the order of 50 to 100 times. There is no routine mathematical way to account for synergistic effects in most cases.

Lung infection and exposure to pneumoconiosis-producing dusts often seem to act synergistically. Silicosis predisposes workers to the development of active tuberculosis that progresses along with the pneumoconiosis and makes the pneumoconiosis much worse. While some cases of silicotuberculosis may result from activation of latent disease, it appears that other cases arise as a result of concurrent exposure to silica and mycobacterium tuberculosis.

BIOLOGICAL REACTIONS

There is a wide range of biological responses to inhaled particulate material. Some of these are described below.

- Acute sensory irritation of the upper and middle air passageways, including a burning sensation in the upper airways and coughing from laryngeal stimulation. Continued exposure may result in bronchioconstriction.
- Pulmonary irritants stimulate sensory receptors in the lungs and induce rapid shallow breathing, dyspnea, and breathlessness. If the exposure is high enough or prolonged, more severe responses, including airway constriction and pulmonary edema, may occur. Secondary infection may complicate severe cases.
- Lung edema occurring without sensory irritation. For example, cadmium oxide can be fatal by this mechanism in high doses.
- Some irritants can cause acute or chronic bronchitis, which is the overproduction of mucus, and lead to cough and dyspnea (e.g., vanadium compounds, endotoxin).
- Allergic sensitization resulting in extrinsic allergic alveolitis or asthma arises from many exposures, including isocyanates, certain wood dusts, complex biomolecules, mite feces, pollen, cotton bract (byssinosis), mold spores (mushroom picker's lung, maple bark stripper's lung, cheese washer's lung), thermophilic actinomycetes (farmer's lung), and dried sugarcane (bagassosis). Chronic beryllium disease appears to be another form of hypersensitivity-related lung disease.
- Fibrosis, which is a type of scarring of the lung tissue, results in loss of flexibility, difficulty breathing, and in severe cases, damage to the right side of the heart as it tries to compensate for reduced blood oxygenation. Many of the pneumoconioses result in fibrosis. There are many different types of fibrosis, some localized and some very diffuse, as discussed previously. They may present a restrictive or obstructive pulmonary function profile, or a mixture of the two.
- Emphysema, resulting in obstructive lung function. Particulate matter examples include cadmium oxide and cigarette smoke. Many gas exposures result in emphysema as well.
- Systemic toxicity resulting from dissolution of inhaled particles in the lung or in the digestive tract after being removed from the upper and middle airways. Examples include lead, arsenic, thallium, pentachlorophenol, fluoride salts, manganese, soluble radioactive compounds, and toxic fungal spores.
- Systemic toxicity that arises from insoluble PM remaining in the lungs. For example, in animal studies it appears that lung exposure to carbon nanotubes results in changes in the cardiovascular system that may be detrimental. This may arise secondary to inflammation and fibrosis in the lungs.
- Lymphatic toxicity from particles physically moved to the lymphatic system from the alveoli by macrophages. Insoluble radioactive particles may cause this type of damage.

- Oncogenesis, which is the initiation or promotion of cancer. Examples are many, and include arsenic, asbestos, beryllium, chromium +VI compounds, coke oven emissions, nickel, free crystalline silica, cigarette smoke, and certain hard wood dusts.
- Infection (e.g., *Coccidioides immitis*, *Mycobacterium tuberculosis*, *Legionella* species, *Hanta virus*).
- Metal fume fever, which typically resembles flu, and results from overexposure to fresh metal particles, especially fume of zinc, magnesium, and copper or a number of other metals or their corresponding oxides. It tends to occur in employees who have not been recently exposed to these fumes. Symptoms start 4 to 12 hours after inhalation and are self-limiting in almost all cases.

Of course, other routes of exposure must be considered as well. Many PMs are also toxic if ingested and many will cause local damage or systemic toxicity based on skin contact alone.

ENGINEERED NANOPARTICLES

Nanotechnology is most generally defined as the intentional manipulation of matter to form novel structures with one or more dimensions or features less than 100 nm. In the broadest sense, nanotechnology includes work at the nanoscale in the fields of inorganic and organic chemistry, biochemistry, engineering, electronics, and materials science. One class of product from nanotechnology is the *engineered nanoparticles* (ENPs).

ENPs are particles that are intentionally made to be very small, well under a micrometer in diameter. While no perfect definition of engineered nanoparticle has arisen, ENP materials typically include four specific characteristics:

1. They are very small, generally less than 100 nm in at least two dimensions.
2. They are either free independent particles with no strong bonds to a larger substrate, or, if they are attached to a substrate, they are readily displaced.
3. They are novel, that is, only recently used or studied.
4. They are made intentionally as a product.

Some references will include particles up to 1000 nm (1 μm) as nanoscale or include particles that are under 100 μm in only *one* dimension. Some definitions include a requirement that the nanoparticles have a unique physical or chemical property or they delete the novelty requirement. However, this discussion assumes that all four characteristics must be present to classify a particle as an ENP.

Incidentally produced nanoparticles, such as diesel smoke or welding fume, are not considered ENPs. Intentionally produced but longstanding nanoparticles such as carbon black are likewise excluded, even though they meet the other three criteria. ENPs are distinct from naturally occurring environmental ultrafine particles, although some engineered structures are also found in air pollution.

Common examples include carbon nanotubes, metal or metal oxide nanoparticles, nanoclays, and quantum dots. Table 8-E shows the range of chemistries used by just one specific research lab. Figure 8–12 shows the range of particle shapes based on just one chemistry, zinc oxide.

The first generation of passive nanoscale materials is now appearing in industrial and consumer products. This includes carbon nanotubes in composite materials used to make sporting equipment, nanoclays in cements and plastics, fluoropolymers in stain-repellant clothing, and metals oxides in batteries, paints, and sunscreens. Second-generation active nanomaterials are being developed in laboratories around the world, and a few are on the verge of commercialization. Medicine, in particular, is predicted to benefit tremendously from these more advanced materials. Third- and fourth-generation materials, which include the holy grail of nanotechnology, molecular manufacturing, are still largely beyond the horizon at this time.

ENP chemical and physical behavior is often strikingly different from the behavior of the chemically identical or similar larger particle. These new properties form the basis

TABLE 8–E	Range of Chemistries Used for Nanoparticles in Just One Research Lab	
Elements used in engineered nanoparticles		
Aluminum	Antimony	Barium
Bismuth	Boron	Cadmium
Calcium	Carbon	Cerium
Chromium	Cobalt	Copper
Dysprosium	Erbium	Europium
Gadolinium	Gallium	Germanium
Gold	Hafnium	Holmium
Indium	Iridium	Iron
Lanthanum	Lead	Lithium
Lutetium	Magnesium	Manganese
Molybdenum	Neodymium	Niobium
Nitrogen	Nickel	Osmium
Oxygen	Palladium	Platinum
Potassium	Praseodymium	Promethium
Rhodium	Rhenium	Ruthenium
Samarium	Scandium	Silicon
Silver	Sodium	Strontium
Sulfur	Tantalum	Technetium
Terbium	Thulium	Tin
Titanium	Tungsten	Ytterbium
Yttrium	Vanadium	Zinc
Zirconium		

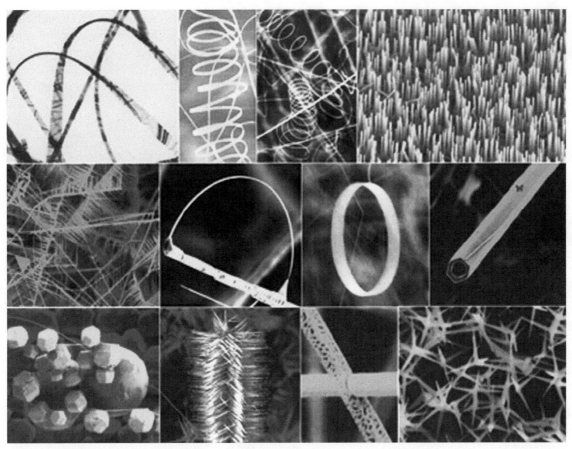

Figure 8–12. Wide variety of forms of nano zinc oxide.

for the optimistic claims of nanotechnology pundits. The toxicity of new ENP may also vary qualitatively or quantitatively from that of identical or similar materials at the micro or macro scale. To date, limited evidence suggests that some materials are uncharacteristically toxic at the nanoscale. Employees involved in the development, production, distribution, and use of these nanoparticles are already potentially being exposed to materials of uncertain toxicity.

The challenge to occupational health professionals is to prevent the development of disease in employees handling these novel nanomaterials despite the lack of toxicological information, consensus exposure standards, air sampling methodologies, and medical monitoring protocols. This is particularly difficult in research and development laboratories, where completely novel materials are developed and processes change frequently.

In any nanoparticle, a surprisingly large fraction of the atoms are on the surface of the particle, available for interaction with biological molecules. In the case of a zinc sulfide quantum nanodot, 4 µm in diameter, roughly half of all the molecules in the particle are on the surface. For a single-walled carbon nanotube or buckyball, every single atom in

the particle is on the surface. This makes the particle surface much more available for interaction with biological tissues than in larger particles with the same mass.

In numerous studies, poorly soluble, low-toxicity nanoscale particles (PSLT) have been shown to be more toxic than microscale materials of the same composition and mass (Figure 8–13). There is significant evidence that in the nanoscale, these materials are uncharacteristically toxic due in part to catalytically driven generation of free radicals, hydrogen peroxide, and hydroxyl atoms. This is driven by the materials' extremely high surface area. While there are several proposed pathways leading to these reactive oxygen species, in the end they all ultimately result in damaged DNA, proteins, lipids, and other biomolecules, inflammation, and even cell death.

In fact, for PSLT particles, the better metric of exposure is surface area rather than mass. If you take the same data as shown in Figure 8–13 and plot it as surface area vs. toxicity, the dose-response data all falls along the same line rather than different lines (Figure 8–14). SiO_2 is also plotted on this graph for comparison to the less hazardous PSLT particles TiO_2 and $BaSO_4$.

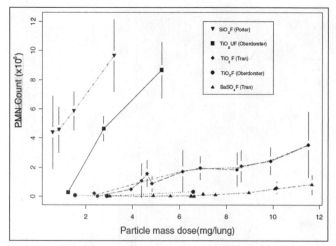

Figure 8–13. Pulmonary inflammation (PMN count) of high-toxicity dust (crystalline silica) particles compared to low-toxicity dust (TiO_2 and $BaSO_4$) of both fine and ultrafine size, based on particle mass dose in rat lungs; particle size: F (fine), UF (ultrafine). *(Source: Dankovic D, Kuempel E, Geraci C, et al. NIOSH Current Intelligence Bulletin 63: Occupational Exposure to Titanium Dioxide, Pub. no. 2011-160. Cincinnati, OH: NIOSH, 2011.)*

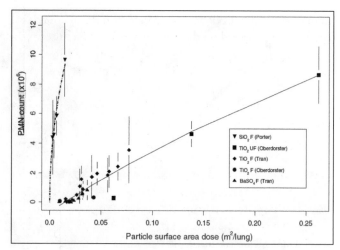

Figure 8–14. Pulmonary inflammation (PMN count) of high-toxicity dust (crystalline silica) particles compared to low-toxicity dust (TiO_2 and $BaSO_4$) of both fine and ultrafine size, based on particle surface area dose in rat lungs; particle size: F (fine), UF (ultrafine). *(Source: Dankovic D, Kuempel E, Geraci C, et al. NIOSH Current Intelligence Bulletin 63: Occupational Exposure to Titanium Dioxide, Pub. no. 2011-160. Cincinnati, OH: NIOSH, 2011.)*

This suggestion that very small particles may exhibit unique toxicity is not without precedent. There is mounting evidence that exposure to environmental ultrafine particles, particularly combustion-derived nanoparticles (CDNP), contributes to community respiratory and cardiovascular morbidity and mortality. Epidemiological and experimental studies have consistently indicated that exposure to these incidental nanoparticles predisposes compromised people to illness from one to a few days postexposure. Originally attributed to larger particles, it is now likely that much of this observed health impact is due to ultrafine CDNP in air pollution. It is likely that the toxic potential of some engineered nanoparticles will parallel this effect of CDNP. For example, it appears that pulmonary deposition of carbon nanotubes has some of the same adverse remote cardiovascular effects as CDNP.

Distribution Across Anatomical Barriers and Systemic Toxicity

Exposure to nanoscale particles can occur via any of the usual routes of exposure, that is, inhalation, ingestion, and skin contact. As with other chemical occupational stressors, each of these routes of exposure must be evaluated to determine the extent of deposition, absorption, distribution, excretion and ultimately, toxicity. Insoluble nanoparticles may be more mobile across anatomical barriers than microscale or larger insoluble particles of the same chemistry. Surprisingly, insoluble nanoparticles may exert systemic toxicity away from their point of retention in the body.

Digestive Tract

It has been known for many years that some intact nanoparticles cross the digestive tract and respiratory tracts and appear elsewhere in the body. Although subject to ongoing controversy related to methodological limitations, inhaled nanoparticles have some ability to cross through or around the cells in the lungs, enter the interstitial space, and be distributed systemically. This clearly happens, but the extent of this process and significance remains in question. Early studies that suggested very rapid translocation of nanoparticles out of the lungs were likely flawed. More recent work has suggested a slow migration of a small percentage of nanoparticles out of the lung that is exacerbated by lung inflammation

Skin

Many sunscreens contain microscale or nanoscale zinc or titanium oxide particles. In general, studies suggest that intact skin is a good barrier to these particles. Under some circumstances, submicrometer particles can penetrate the skin, at least as far as the living tissue underlying the stratum corneum. It is not clear that these particles travel as far as the systemic circulation or if they are toxicologically significant. This route of exposure is likely to be of greater importance for damaged skin or concomitant exposure to solvents and nanoparticles.

Brain

Although not completely unprecedented, it was certainly striking when it was demonstrated that carbon ENP and manganese oxide ENP deposited in the olfactory mucosa in rodents translocated up the olfactory neuron axons into the brain and in some studies triggered inflammation in neural tissue. This is intriguing in light of the lung deposition model proposed by the International Council on Radiation Protection that shows that nanoparticles less than ~10 nm in aerodynamic diameter will deposit in the head airways region as well as the alveolar space. There is also limited evidence that some nanoparticles can penetrate the blood–brain barrier and gain access to the brain via the bloodstream.

The importance of these brain translocation mechanisms in humans is unknown. Humans have far less olfactory mucosa than rodents. For perspective, welders have been inhaling adventitious metal oxide nanoparticles for decades with relatively little apparent adverse neurological effect for metals other than manganese.

Placenta

Several studies have been published that purport to show that nanoparticles that make it as far as the bloodstream, regardless of route of exposure, do cross the placental barrier and may have an effect on the fetus. However, there are conflicting reports, so it is not possible to say with certainty that this observed effect is real or of concern.

Nanoparticle Case Studies

Case Study: Carbon Nanotubes

The special case of carbon nanotubes is illustrative of many of the difficulties in assessing the toxicity of novel nanostructures. Carbon nanotubes come in two primary forms—single-walled nanotubes (SWCNT) and nested multiwalled nanotubes (MWCNT) (Figure 8–15). They are now being produced by the ton and incorporated into many commer-

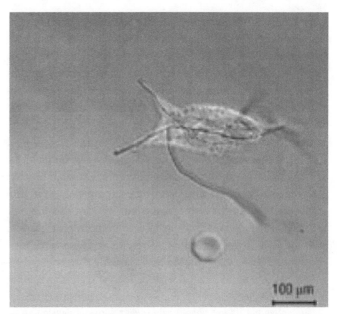

Figure 8–16. Lung cell struggling with a carbon nanotube. *(From proceedings of the 5th International Nanomaterial Occupational Safety and Health [NanOSH] conference, Boston, 2011.)*

cial products including baseball bats, bicycles, and other sporting equipment. Carbon nanotubes range in diameter from about one nanometer (SWCNT) to dozens of nanometers (MWCNT) and can have lengths into the micrometer range. Together they are referred to as CNTs.

A large number of in vitro toxicity studies have been reported for carbon nanotubes, with most demonstrating unusual cytotoxicity to a range of target cells. In some of these in vitro studies, nanotubes appeared to be more toxic than quartz or asbestos, both of which induce lung inflammation, fibrosis, and ultimately cancer. If carbon nanotubes are instilled or aspirated into the lungs of rodents, they induce signs of oxidative stress, much like the metal oxide nanoparticles discussed previously, and in most cases cause fibrosis and granuloma formation (Figure 8–16). More recent inhalation studies have consistently demonstrated that inhaled carbon nanotubes cause granuloma formation and diffuse fibrosis at levels far below what is safe for graphite.

CNTs may also cause lung cancer and mesothelioma, based on their morphology and biodurability. CNTs can be viewed as rolled-up layers of graphite that form a single tube about a nanometer in diameter (SWCNT) or a series of concentric nanotubes that can be a few or dozens of nanometers in diameter (MWCNTs). Carbon nanotubes can be thousands of nanometers in length; they have high tensile strength and relatively low solubility in biological systems. They tend to cling together to make larger structures called nanoropes that are many nanometers or even micrometers in diameter. These characteristics are all remarkably similar to a naturally occur-

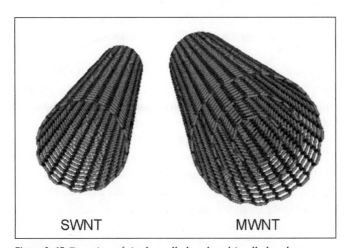

SWNT   MWNT

Figure 8–15. Drawing of single-walled and multiwalled carbon nanotubes. *(From proceedings of the 5th International Nanomaterial Occupational Safety and Health [NanOSH] conference, Boston, 2011.)*

ring magnesium silicate nanotube, chrysotile asbestos.

A number of preliminary studies have involved carbon nanotubes injected into the peritoneal cavity or other sensitive parts of the body. In one of these studies, carbon nanotubes were found to be the most potent cause of mesothelioma ever measured, exceeding even crocidolite asbestos. Further, the long, straight tubes were the most toxic, consistent with the previously discussed Stanton Hypothesis. These studies used methods that were not physiological, so it is possible that the results may be epiphenomenal. Further studies are required, but prudence dictates that carbon nanotubes should be treated as carcinogens at this time.

NIOSH has put forth a REL of 7 µg/m³ for carbon nanotubes as respirable mass averaged over an 8-hour day. However, NIOSH also makes the following observation:

> NIOSH recognizes that the REL may not be completely health protective but its use should help lower the risk of developing work-related lung disease and assist employers in establishing an occupational health surveillance program that includes elements of hazard and medical surveillance.

NIOSH recommends that airborne exposures to CNTs be reduced as low as possible below the REL.

Case Study: Quantum Nanodots

Quantum nanodots are single-digit-sized crystals made up of semiconductor metals and other elements that demonstrate the amazing feature of changing fluorescence wavelength based on their size. Quantum nanodots present an interesting case in that many of these are intrinsically cytotoxic as a result of their metal content. Uncoated nanodots are quite cytotoxic, and it is possible that their toxicity exceeds the sum of the toxicity of the constituent metals.

For example, one study showed that cytotoxicity of a variety of coated nanodots in a breast cancer cell line did not fully correlate with the generation of Cd_2+ ions. Instead, the quantum nanodots were consistently more toxic than predicted by their release of Cd_2+ ion. In this study, quantum dot net toxicity appears to be a result of both intrinsic metal ion toxicity and induction of oxidative stress by the surface of the intact nanoparticle, the latter effect the same as seen for TiO_2, carbon nanotubes, and other nanoparticles.

Case Study: Nanoscale TiO₂

From the health perspective, nanoscale titania (TiO_2, Figure 8–17) is one of the most studied ENPs because of its ubiquity in industry. While large particles of titania are of very low toxicity and treated as "nuisance dust" or "particulate matter not otherwise regulated/classified," exposure to nanoscale titania causes lung inflammation and may cause cancer.

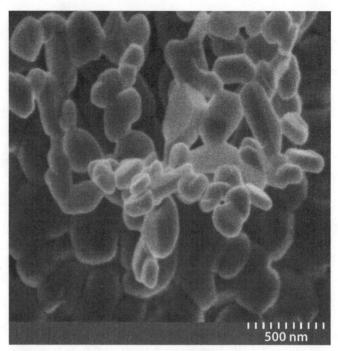

Figure 8–17. Nanoscale titanium dioxide. *(Source: Dankovic D, Kuempel E, Geraci C, et al. NIOSH Current Intelligence Bulletin 63: Occupational Exposure to Titanium Dioxide, Pub. no. 2011-160. Cincinnati, OH: NIOSH, 2011.)*

Much of the guidance on titania comes from NIOSH. In their *Current Intelligence Bulletin #63*, "Occupational Exposure to Titanium Dioxide" published in 2011, NIOSH states:

> Titanium dioxide (TiO_2), an insoluble white powder, is used extensively in many commercial products, including paint, cosmetics, plastics, paper, and food, as an anticaking or whitening agent. It is produced and used in the workplace in varying particle-size fractions, including fine and ultrafine sizes. The number of U.S. workers currently exposed to TiO_2 dust is unknown.

Nanoscale TiO_2 appeared to be much more inflammatory in lung than microscale TiO_2 particles when compared on the basis of mass of material introduced into the lung. However, when the data were plotted on the basis of surface area rather than mass, the inflammatory response was identical for both nano- and microscale particles. See Figure 8–13. The carcinogenic potential of nanotitania likewise seems to be driven by surface area rather than mass.

NIOSH further states:

> TiO_2 and other poorly soluble, low-toxicity (PSLT) particles of fine and ultrafine sizes show a consistent dose-response relationship for adverse pulmonary responses in rats, including persistent pulmonary inflammation and lung tumors, when dose is expressed as

particle surface area. The higher mass-based potency of ultrafine TiO_2 compared to fine TiO_2 is associated with the greater surface area of ultrafine particles for a given mass. The NIOSH RELs for fine and ultrafine TiO_2 reflect this mass-based difference in potency.

NIOSH has concluded that TiO_2 is not a direct-acting carcinogen, but acts through a secondary genotoxicity mechanism that is not specific to TiO_2 but primarily related to particle size and surface area.

Based on data such as these, it is the surface area, not the mass, that is the relevant health metric for PSLT. Data demonstrate that there is a threshold dose of nanotitania below which neither lung inflammation nor cancer are likely to be observed, as shown in Figure 8–18. Unfortunately, there are few options to measure surface area of particles in the air at this time. The tools that do exist are in the realm of research, not routine application.

The Occupational Safety and Health Administration (OSHA) permissible exposure limit for TiO_2 is 15 mg/m³, based on total TiO_2 dust. In 2005 NIOSH proposed an REL for nanoscale titania of 0.1 mg/m³, and 1.5 mg/m³ for fine (respirable) particles. As of 2011, NIOSH has finalized and changed their recommendation:

NIOSH recommends exposure limits of 2.4 mg/m³ for fine TiO_2 and 0.3 mg/m³ for ultrafine (including engineered nanoscale) TiO_2, as time-weighted average (TWA) concentrations for up to 10 hours per day during a 40-hour workweek. NIOSH has determined that ultrafine TiO_2 is a potential occupational carcinogen but that there are insufficient data at this time to classify fine TiO_2 as a potential occupational carcinogen.

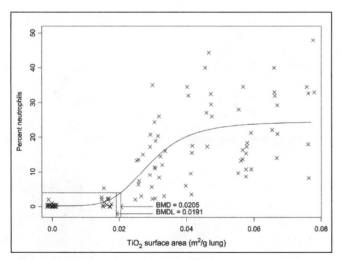

Figure 8–18. Rat data on pulmonary inflammation (percent neutrophils) and particle surface area dose of TiO_2. *(Source: Dankovic D, Kuempel E, Geraci C, et al. NIOSH Current Intelligence Bulletin 63: Occupational Exposure to Titanium Dioxide, Pub. no. 2011-160. Cincinnati, OH: NIOSH, 2011.)*

These recommendations represent levels that over a working lifetime are estimated to reduce risks of lung cancer to below 1 in 1,000.

In this REL, NIOSH does not distinguish between the two common crystalline forms of TiO_2. The relevant cancer is adenocarcinoma. Note that the 1 in 1000 residual cancer risk is something of a default U.S. national policy standard for occupational exposure to carcinogens, arising out of a court decision involving an emergency temporary standard for benzene exposure in the early 1980s.

NIOSH recommends treating agglomerated nanoparticles as if they were independent nanoparticles, because the agglomerates have been shown to disassociate in biological fluids.

Finally, many people may be exposed to nanotitania that has some sort of coating applied. It was hypothesized that this would make the titania particles less toxic, but this is not the case per NIOSH:

NIOSH also evaluated the potential for coatings to modify the toxicity of TiO_2, as many industrial processes apply coatings to TiO_2 particles. TiO_2 toxicity has been shown to increase after coating with various substances. However, the toxicity of TiO_2 has not been shown to be attenuated by application of coatings.

NIOSH concluded that the TiO_2 risk assessment could be used as a reasonable floor for potential toxicity, with the notion that toxicity may be substantially increased by particle treatment and process modification.

SAMPLING AND ANALYSIS OF PARTICULATE MATTER

Most samples taken to assess exposure to PM are air samples. Most often, the particles are removed from the aerosol by filtration, impaction, electrostatic attraction, or wetting, with subsequent analysis of the collected particles in a laboratory by chemical or microscopic direct-reading. Real-time instruments are also used to measure airborne PM, typically by detecting their scattering of light.

Other modes of particle sampling are also common in industrial hygiene. Surface sampling in areas where hazardous aerosols are present is a fairly common tool, recognized by OSHA as industrial hygiene sampling data, with the same rules about record retention that apply to air samples. Occasionally, PM from clothing or skin surfaces will be collected as an indication of dermal exposure. This method is commonly used in research on particles that pose substantial transcutaneous hazards, such as some pesticides.

Bioassays exist for many particulates that provide an

indication of actual absorbed dose or biological changes resulting from absorbed dose. This may be done by analysis of urine or blood. The American Conference of Governmental Industrial Hygienists has established a number of recommended bioassays for PM, mostly for metals. OSHA requires bioassays for some materials such as lead and arsenic.

It is rather common to use two or three of these sampling methods to monitor or evaluate the exposure of a particular individual or group. Personal air samples serve as an indicator of PM exposure on that workshift, biological monitoring may provide a measure of exposure across many shifts, and surface sampling provides information on the effectiveness of engineering and administrative controls over the longer term.

Sampling for Particulate Matter

Air sampling for particulate matter is a fundamental industrial hygiene activity. The vast majority of occupational exposure limits are tied to air sampling. Air sampling can be integrated over various periods of time, ranging from samples that last days or weeks for environmental measurements or point-source release of radioactive particulate matters, to direct-reading real-time sampling intended to measure ceiling or peak exposures. For occupational exposure purposes, the eight-hour time-weighted average is the most commonly measured value.

Personal integrated industrial hygiene air samples are most typically collected onto filters placed in the breathing zone of the worker (within ~9 inches of the nose and mouth), with air drawn through the filter at a rate of 0.5 to 4 liters per minute. Personal sampling assures that the filter goes where the worker goes, and collects particles representative of the airborne concentration of PM wherever that employee works (Figure 8–19). Although common in the past, a liquid impinger is only occasionally used to collect particles in modern industrial hygiene practice. Before the 1960s, asbestos and coal dust were usually collected in impingers, but now they are collected on filters. There are dozens of types of filters that are used by industrial hygienists to collect PM as shown in Table 8–F.

Less common now, although a standard in the past, is the *general area* sample, typically taken with a plug-in pump. One version of this type of instrument is operated by a 1/5–1/3 horsepower vacuum pump, and draws air through a 25 to 47 millimeter diameter filter at rates varying from a fraction of a cubic foot per minute (CFM) to a couple of CFM. This is sometimes casually referred to as a high volume (or simply hi-vol) sampler.

Another version of an area sampler, a true high-volume sampler, uses a vacuum cleaner motor to draw air through a filter as large as 8 × 10 inches at a rate of 20 to hundreds of CFM. Sampling devices that collect specific size fractions of PM are used extensively in the environmental or community setting. Samplers such as the PM 10 collect particles at 50 percent efficiency with AEDs of 10 μm, and the PM 2.5 and PM 1.0 act similarly for those smaller particles.

General area sampling is used extensively in specific settings, asbestos abatement in particular. Typically, samplers are set up around the perimeter of an isolated asbestos dust containment area as a means of verifying the adequacy of the controls. With phase contrast microscopy (the primary OSHA analytical method for counting asbestos fibers) the samples, which may be collected in as little as one to two hours and analyzed on site in a matter of 30 minutes, provide rapid feedback on the effectiveness of the dust containment.

Following an asbestos abatement action in a full containment, it is typical to take one or more *clearance samples* as a means of verifying the complete decontamination of the air and surfaces in the contained area. These area samples, collected on 25 or 37 mm filters at 10 to 16 liters per minute (depending on the analytical procedure), are usually taken using aggressive techniques, traditionally using a leaf blower and fans to stir up any settled or residual dust and make it accessible to the air filter. Thus the result(s), whether analyzed by phase contrast or by transmission electron microscopy, are a hybrid sample, partially reflecting what was actually in the air, and partially counting what was on the surface but capable of being made airborne.

Size-Selective Particle Sampling and Analysis

There is growing emphasis in industrial hygiene to use particle-size-selective sampling rather than total dust sampling

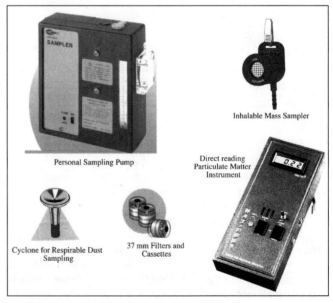

Figure 8–19. Tools of industrial hygiene.

TABLE 8–F	Filter Particulate Matter Collection Media Used in Industrial Hygiene	
Plain Filters	*Diameters/Pore sizes*	*Uses*
Cellulose	37 mm/undefined	Radioactive particles
Mixed cellulose ester	25–47 mm/0.45–1.2 µm	Welding fume, asbestos, lead, cadmium, beryllium, sodium hydroxide mist
Pvc	25–47 mm/0.8–5.0 µm	Gravimetric dust, chromium paint overspray, silica, aluminum oxide, cotton dust
Glass fiber	13–47 mm/1.0 µm	PCB mist, carbaril, chloramphenicol
Polycarbonate	25–47 mm/0.4–0.8 µm	Asbestos for TEM
Silver membrane	25–37 mm/0.45–0.8 µm	Coke oven emissions
Teflon	13–47 mm/0.45–5.0 µm	Assorted polynuclear aromatic hydrocarbons (as in soot, diesel exhaust, petroleum asphalt fumes, cigarette smoke)
Nylon	25–37 mm, 1.0 µm pore size	
Quartz	37–47 mm/undefined	Diesel particles
Coated Filters	*Characteristics*	*Examples*
Glass fiber/sulfuric acid	Stabilized MOCA on filter	4-amino biphenyl 4,4-methylene dianiline MOCA
Mixed cellulose ester/sodium carbonate		Arsenic trioxide
Glass fiber/1-(2-pyridyl) piperazine	Chemical reaction with isocyanates to stabilize them on filter	Toluene, diisocyanates, methylene, diphenylisocyanate, 1 and 2 napthylamine
Unusual Filters	*Characteristics*	*Examples*
Osha versatile sampler	Combination vapor/particle collectors. Filter portion may be glass or quartz fibers	Pesticides, organotin compounds, TNT, DNT, phthalate esters, glycols
Polyurethane foam (puf) tubes	Very thick plugs of foam are used to collect mist phase of mixed vapor/mist	Pesticides, PCBs, dioxins, polynuclear aromatic hydrocarbons (area samplers)

to better characterize the level of exposure and better relate to risk.

This can be done in a couple of ways. The oldest size-selective analysis, which is still used in a few cases, observes each particle microscopically and counts only those that meet the preestablished size criterion. Starting in the 1920s, mineral dust was collected by hand-operated pumps into 1-liter water-filled impingers. Under the microscope, only particles with an approximate physical diameter of less than 10 µm were counted, in an effort to limit the measurement to the size fraction that was thought to be toxicologically significant.

Asbestos remains one of the few PMs that is routinely analyzed by size-selective microscopic counting. Optical (or electron) microscopy visualizes the collected fibers. The counting rules specify which size particles are counted and which are discounted. Under OSHA and the "A" NIOSH optical counting rules, the fibers must be >5 µm long and have an aspect ratio of at least 3:1 to be counted. Under the more recent EPA electron microscope counting rules, the fibers must be >0.5 µm long and meet a 5:1 aspect ratio.

If the fibers do not meet these size and shape criteria, they are not counted.

Most of the optical asbestos (and other fiber) methods used historically and around the world specify 5 µm in length as the minimum length fiber to be counted. When the U.S. Public Health Service formally adopted the membrane filter collection method in 1969, the optical microscopy size-selective counting rules were designed to limit the time burden on the microscopist. Counting all of the short fibers would be highly time consuming. This is how the 5 µm limit was born, despite other published accounts suggesting a prescient knowledge of toxicology drove this decision. Recent toxicological evidence does suggest that fibers shorter than ~5 µm do have reduced toxicity. Just lucky in this case.

Fibrous glass or other manmade vitreous fibers (MMVF) have a mass per volume standard under OSHA—they are treated as a nuisance dust and evaluated gravimetrically. However, more recently, the ACGIH has established a TLV for fibrous glass in units of fibers per cubic meter of air, like asbestos (they still retain their gravimetric standard, however).

The usual analytical procedure for MMVF is the NIOSH 7400 method, using the "A" counting rules, as for asbestos. However, this makes it necessary to count OSHA fibers no matter how large in diameter. Many fibrous glass products tend to be composed mainly of fibers that are quite large in diameter, and thus will be nonrespirable. Thus, many nonrespirable and presumably nonharmful fibers are counted. This can result in what is probably an unreasonable overcount. Use of the "B" counting rules under the NIOSH 7400 method or the AIA RTM 1 method allows the discounting of fibers larger than 3 µm in diameter, thus avoiding overcounting associated with very large-diameter and likely fairly harmless particles.

Other size-selective sampling and analytical methods use some sort of mechanical separator in front of the collection medium to limit the size of the collected particles to a specified equivalent aerodynamic diameter. Typically, large particles are rejected and only small particles, of a specified size fraction, are collected for analysis. Over the years, several types of size-selective separators have been used. After collection of the appropriate size fraction, analysis can then proceed by chemical, gravimetric, or other means.

In 1952, the British Medical Research Council first defined the *respirable mass fraction*, intended for use with pneumoconiosis-producing dusts, which are toxic only when they land in the alveolar portions of the lungs. This method was an area sampling method and used a horizontal elutriator to remove the nonrespirable fraction. The U.S. Atomic Energy Commission (AEC) in 1961 followed this with a modified curve for use in nuclear facilities.

The respirable mass fraction is intended to reflect the relative probability of differently sized particles being deposited in the alveolar regions of the lung. Large particles, bigger than 10 µm in equivalent aerodynamic diameter, are completely discounted as they get deposited higher up in the respiratory tract. Extremely small particles, less than 1 micrometer, are all counted. In between, there is a sliding scale where increasingly large particles are increasingly discounted. The result is the respirable dust curve in Table 8–G.

By 1968, the ACGIH developed its own respirable dust curve, very similar to the one used by the AEC, and specified its use for free crystalline silica-containing dust. Size selectivity was to be provided by a cyclone, specifically a 10-mm nylon Dorr-Oliver cyclone for personal samples, and a 2-in. cyclone for high-volume area samples. As it turned out, the Occupational Safety and Health Act was passed in the United States in 1970, and when OSHA was created a year later, it adopted verbatim the ACGIH TLVs, including the respirable dust curve, as it applied to free crystalline silica-containing dust.

In 1991 and 1992, the ISO (International Organization

TABLE 8–G	The ACGIH/ISO/CEN/NIOSH Respirable Particulate Mass (RPM) Criteria
AED	*% RPM**
0	100
1	97
2	91
3	74
4	50
5	30
6	17
7	9
8	5
10	1

*This table indicates the percentage of particles of a given aerodynamic equivalent diameter (AED) in a polydisperse particle cloud that should pass through the size-selective sampler and be collected on the sample medium. Larger particles are not collected for analysis.

for Standardization) and CEN (the European Standardization Committee) had settled on a slightly modified respirable dust curve, which in 1993 was adopted by the ACGIH. NIOSH joined in the consensus at the same time. At this time, the ACGIH/ISO/CEN/NIOSH respirable dust curves are the same; only the OSHA curve differs, but the difference is usually negligible. Both OSHA and the ACGIH accept the continued use of the 10-mm Dorr-Oliver cyclone operated at 1.7 liters per minute, as established many years before in 1969, even though it slightly underestimates the mass of respirable dust.

Figure 8–20 is a picture of a Dorr-Oliver 10-mm cyclone in line with a special crystal filter that is commonly used for measurement of diesel soot. The cyclone removes larger particles according to the respirable dust curve, and the crystalline filter removes everything that gets past the cyclone that is >1 µm in diameter. This is typically clipped to the worker's clothing in their breathing zone and runs off of a personal sampling pump.

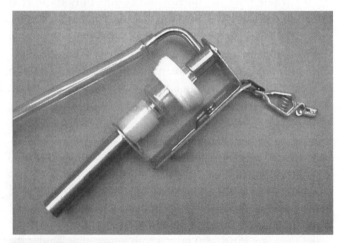

Figure 8–20. Dorr-Oliver 10 mm cyclone in line with 1.0-micrometer crystalline particle filter commonly used for sampling diesel particles (MSHA).

Other respirable dust cyclonic separators are available as well. One company has long sold an aluminum cyclone that was originally designed to meet the old BMRC curve at 1.9 liters of air per minute. However, when operated at 2.5 liters of air per minute, it produces a respirable cut fraction that very closely follows the current ACGIH/ISO/CEN/NIOSH curve. A slightly different flow rate is recommended to better match the OSHA curve. Because it is composed of conductive metal, it is not subject to the disruptive effect of localized charge accumulation seen in nonconductive nylon cyclones like the Dorr-Oliver. Also available are conductive plastic respirable mass separators, which are advertised to reduce some of the other sources of bias inherent in the traditional Dorr-Oliver cyclone. These cyclones operate at 2.75 liters a minute to match the respirable dust curve. Still other variations are likely available.

Table 8–H lists a number of types of particulate matter for which the ACGIH has established respirable particulate mass standards. Some of the same chemicals with respirable TLVs also have nonrespirable particulate mass standards.

The ACGIH has also established a PM subfraction called *thoracic particulate mass* (TPM). TPM includes particles smaller than about 25 μm in AED, and represents those particles that make it past the head airways region and are available for deposition in either the tracheobronchial or alveolar regions (Table 8–I). At this time (2011), raw, untreated cotton dust is the only TLVs assigned to the TPM fraction.

The ACGIH has also established an inhalable particle mass (IPM) criterion for particles that are hazardous no matter where they deposit in the respiratory tract, such as lead. This is an improved version of total dust sampling. Formally recognizing the general belief that particles larger than 100 μm are not inhalable, the acceptance function is undefined above 100 μm AED (Table 8–J). Evidence suggests that IPM sampling methods typically collect more PM than total dust methods, so IPM sampling should be conservative most of the time. OSHA, however, continues to define their standards in terms of total-dust air sampling without using a size-selective device in front of the filter.

Special sampling devices are sold to implement the IPM sampling procedures, just as cyclones are sold to implement the respirable particle mass criteria. A few of the chemicals already assigned to inspirable particulate matter TLVs include:

- asphalt fume
- benomyl
- inorganic borate
- beryllium
- calcium sulfate
- captan

TABLE 8–H	Some TLVs with Respirable Particulate Mass (RPM) Standards	
Particulate Matter	**TLV RPM (mg/m³)**	**Comments**
Cadmium	0.002	RPM TLV, but not part of OSHA standard
Coal dust (Anthracite) (Bituminous)	0.4 0.9	Under OSHA, limit is: $\dfrac{2.4 \text{ mg/m}^3}{\% \text{ SiO}_2 + 2}$ where quartz is <5%, otherwise use OSHA quartz formula
Diquat dibromide	0.1	An herbicide, also has nonrespirable TLV
Graphite	2.0	All forms except fibers
Kaolin	2.0	Under OSHA, standard still only exists in mppcf units.
Mica	3.0	Under OSHA, standard still only exists in mppcf units
Paraquat	0.1	A pesticide, also nonrespirable TLV
Particulates not otherwise classified	3.0	Under OSHA, 5 mg/m³
Silica: Free crystalline (quartz, tridymite, cristobalite) Tripoli Fumed Fused Diatomaceous earth	0.05 0.1 2.0 0.1 3.0	In Federal OSHA, the quartz standard is given by: $\dfrac{10 \text{ mg/m}^3 \text{ (total respirable dust)}}{\% \text{ SiO}_2 + 2}$ which is equal to essentially 0.1 mg/m³ for pure quartz. Tridymite and cristobalite limits are given as ½ the quartz standard. Limits for amorphous forms are given by: $\dfrac{80 \text{ mg/m}^3 \text{ (total respirable dust)}}{\% \text{ SiO}_2}$
Soapstone	3.0	Also nonrespirable TLV
Talc	2.0	Not containing asbestos. Under OSHA, standard still only exists in mppcf units.

- diquat
- PNOCs
- nickel, all forms of PM
- thallium

Inhalable mass samplers are often handled differently from typical total dust sample cassettes. In one common protocol developed by the Institute of Occupational Medicine in Scotland, a 25-mm filter is used inside a special holder. It is operated at 2.0 L/min to simulate the inhalable mass criteria. The cassette and filter are weighed pre- and postsampling as a unit, reducing any loss of particles on the interior walls of the cassette, sometimes a severe problem when sampling for total dust with nonconductive polycarbonate cassettes. Also, this prevents the loss of any larger particles that might fall off the filter when it is removed for analysis using more traditional techniques.

TABLE 8–I	Thoracic Particulate Mass*
AED (µm)	**% TPM***
0	100
2	94
4	89
6	80.5
8	67
10	50
12	35
14	23
16	15
18	9.5
20	6
25	2

*This table indicates the percentage of particles of an aerodynamic equivalent diameter in a polydisperse particle cloud that should be passed through the thoracic particle mass sampler and collected on the sample medium. Larger particles are not collected for analysis.

TABLE 8–J	Inhalable Particulate Mass (IPM)*
AED (µm)	**% IPM**
0	100
1	97
2	94
5	87
10	77
20	65
30	58
40	54.5
50	52.5
100	50

* Table 8–J indicates the percentage of particles of a given aerodynamic equivalent diameter (AED) in a polydisperse particle cloud that should pass through the inhalable particulate mass selective sampler and be collected on the sample medium. Larger particles are not collected for analysis.

There is one other significant size-selective separator still used in industrial hygiene. It is unique to the measurement of lint-free dust from primary cotton operations. Dust is collected on a filter for gravimetric analysis, but first the air must be passed through a vertical elutriator designed to provide a 50-percent cut size of 15 µm AED. This device is an area sampler only and cannot be used for personal samples.

For environmental PM sampling, particle size selectors with 50 percent cut points of 10, 2.5, and 1 µm AED are used. These devices are not normally used in the occupational environment, although personal separators for PM 2.5 and 10 are commercially available, mostly for use in community air pollution work.

Dual-Phase Monitoring

On occasion it is necessary to sample for both the PM and vapor phases of a material to get a full understanding of their exposures. The ACGIH identifies many materials like this, such as many pesticides, tetraethyl pyrophosphate, iodine, diesel fuel, and butylated hydroxy toluene.

Polychlorinated biphenyls (PCBs) are an agent that can expose employees to either a mist (if agitated or condensed) or vapor (if heated). NIOSH has a method that specifically addresses this by using a 13-mm glass fiber filter for mist, inline with an appropriate vapor sorbent tube.

Oil mist is usually collected on a filter, as in the NIOSH 5026 method. Depending on the vapor pressure of the oil, mass can be lost after collection by evaporation. A method that allows the evaporating oil to be adsorbed onto a collection tube after the filter would be desirable for high-vapor-pressure oils.

Microbiological Sampling

General area samples are still commonly used for sampling airborne bacteria and fungal spores. Traditionally, samples were collected by impingement in a liquid with a device called the "all glass impinger-30," with subsequent dilution and plating out and culturing of the suspension or direct optical counting of the collected bioparticles. While this method is still in use, especially for bacteria, in the 1970s and 1980s it became more common to collect viable bacteria and fungal spores on a petri plate filled with a growth medium loaded into a modified single-stage Anderson impactor. Buoyed by the publication of an ACGIH guideline for using this method in 1986, the collection of viable microorganisms by drawing air through a 400-hole sixth stage of a multistage cascade impactor became the norm. When air from each hole hits the growth medium, a viable bacterial or fungal spore can impact and eventually grow.

Originally, these samplers were built by cannibalizing multistage cascade impactors. In time, appropriate single-stage impactors became available commercially. Eventually, NIOSH developed written sampling methods for these impactors (NIOSH 0800 and 0801). Standard collection agars came to be tryptic soy and tryptic soy with five percent sheep blood for bacteria (sometimes with mold-inhibiting additives), and malt extract, rose bengal, potato dextrose, dichloran glycerol, Czepak Cellulose, and corn meal for molds. Almost all of the single-stage, 400-hole agar impactors are designed to operate at 1 CFM (28.3 LPM). Smaller personal versions of single-stage impactors are commercially available.

Other viable spore collection devices that acted similarly, such as the RCS sampler, were marketed successfully, although the RCS unit was inefficient for smaller bacteria and spores in its original version. Once cultured under specified conditions, the number of colonies was counted and the total airborne loading of viable bacteria or fungal spores was determined in units of total colony-forming units per cubic meter (CFU/m³).

In time, it became apparent that live culture/total colony count method had several limitations, including its relative difficulty of use and the inability to detect the presence of potentially large numbers of airborne nonviable microorganisms or spores that would not grow once collected, but retained their potential allergenic or toxigenic properties. While the viable sampling methods are still in common use with some modification, methods of collecting all cells and spores whether viable or not, were developed. These include the Burkhart Spore Trap, and most recently, the Air-O-Cell cassette. The cassette, usable with any pump capable of providing the required 15 liters of air per minute flow rate, impacts particles onto a sticky surface. The particles are then analyzed optically by a trained microbiologist to determine not only the number of spores or organisms, but also their genus and in some cases species.

It is unusual for an industrial hygienist to be asked to sample for *infectious* airborne bacteria, fungal spores, or viruses, primarily because it is difficult to culture some organisms, and the sensitivity of the methods is too low to detect meaningful levels of infectious agents. For example, soil-borne spores of *Coccidioides immitis* when inhaled can lead to coccidiomycosis, a potentially severe lung infection, but air sampling is almost impossible, leading to false negative results. *Legionella*, the bacteria responsible for the outbreak of lung disease among the Legionnaires in 1978 as well as Pontiac fever, is often sampled in bulk water sources such as cooling tower water, but almost never in the air. Tuberculosis is clearly transmissible person to person. A standard sampling and analysis protocol requires that the collected and cultured organisms then be inoculated into sensitive animals like guinea pigs to demonstrate infectivity. Anthrax and Q fever are common bacterial diseases transmitted by the air from animals to people (potentially over miles in the case of anthrax), and while there have been instances where these have been sampled by cascade impactor or impinger, it is rather unusual. Q fever has been sampled in animal rendering plants for occupational purposes. Some viruses, including measles, have been sampled as part of larger mists or dusts in hospitals and other health care settings, but industrial hygienists do not routinely do this. To the extent that this is done, infection control specialists usually do it.

In some industries and many indoor air quality evaluations, it is common to sample for *endotoxin*, which is a family of lipopolysaccharides in the outer membrane of gram-negative bacteria. Inhalation of endotoxin can induce flu-like or asthma-like symptoms or more serious lung illnesses. Endotoxin can occur in bacteria growing in humidifier water in buildings, and in cotton dust, agricultural dusts, and machining oils. It is often collected on polycarbonate capillary pore filters or in impingers.

Radon and Radon Progeny

Radon is one of the *noble gases*, which generally refuse to react with other compounds and therefore are almost always found as gases. Radon is a naturally occurring gas that is usually formed by the radioactive decay of uranium. Even though the gas is radioactive, it is not usually an occupational hazard, as it is not significantly absorbed as a gas when in contact with surface of the lungs.

However, as radon radioactively decays by the release of an alpha particle (nucleus of a helium atom), it turns first into radioactive polonium, then through several other radioactive isotopes including two forms of radioactive lead, and finally into Lead 206, which is not radioactive and makes no pretense of nobility. These intermediate radioactive materials are charged particulate matter and rapidly attach themselves to oppositely charged particles in the air. Very quickly, a radioactive particle is formed, and when inhaled, is subject to lung deposition with subsequent radioactive decay through a series of other radioactive forms. These particulate matter decay products have traditionally been called *radon daughters*, or more recently, *radon progeny*.

Deposition of radioactive particles in the lungs presents the risk of inducing respiratory tract cancer. Airborne radon tends to accumulate where uranium is stored or inside poorly ventilated basements in certain geographical locations. Indeed, radon accumulation from naturally occurring uranium in the soil is common inside houses and some workplaces where the soil uranium concentration and soil gas permeability is high. Many thousands of homes across the United States have radon levels above the guidance level set by the EPA of four picocuries per liter.

However, the classic workforce subject to radon daughter exposure is miners. This is an obvious hazard in uranium mining (and processing and handling), but also occurs with some regularity in other types of mining where uranium is present in fairly high concentrations. Elevated incidences of lung cancer has been demonstrated in miners working where radon daughters are present at elevated levels, although oddly enough, to date increased cancer rates have not been firmly associated with living in houses with high levels of radon daughters. It is likely that some additive or synergistic effect is occurring among miners.

Most radon or radon daughter sampling is done using area methods. While radon daughters are sometimes measured directly by collection on a filter and counted under a gas proportional or thin-window solid-state scintillation counter, in many settings the radon itself is collected by diffusion onto treated, activated charcoal-containing sorption media. The charcoal is then analyzed by a method such as liquid scintillation counting to directly determine the radon content. While the radon concentration itself is of no importance, in many settings the radon is in equilibrium with the many radon daughters, and the hazard posed by the radon daughters can be inferred from the radon levels. Control the radon level, and effectively the radon daughters are controlled.

Diesel Particulate Matter

Diesel particulate matter (DPM) is a specific form of smoke from the diesel cycle internal combustion of diesel fuels. It has been shown to be carcinogenic and can cause a range of respiratory tract and cardiovascular problems. Traditionally, the carcinogenicity has been ascribed to its high content of polynuclear hydrocarbons, which are known carcinogens. However, diesel smoke can also contain other carcinogenic PM such as arsenic and cadmium, as well as carcinogenic vapors adsorbed to the surface of the PM. Diesel particles are very small and thus respirable. Indeed, like other smokes, much of freshly formed DPM is composed of nanoparticles.

Exposure to DPM is a known occupational hazard to truckers, railroad workers, and miners using diesel-powered equipment in underground mines (Figure 8–21). It is also a significant contributor to community cardiovascular morbidity and mortality in communities subject to high DPM. As many workplaces that make intensive use of diesel engines are located in economically disadvantaged neighborhoods, DPM is also an issue for the environmental justice movement.

Sampling and analysis for DPM poses a range of difficulties. There are a number of gravimetric analytical methods that can be used to analyze air filters for DPM. Unfortunately, many other dusts can be collected as well, resulting in positive interference. Sampling can be corrected for some of these interferences by burning off the combustible organic carbon while leaving behind the inorganic carbon.

Figure 8–21. Truck belching diesel exhaust (EPA).

NIOSH has developed an analytical method, 5040, meant to sample for total elemental carbon as a simple surrogate for DPM. This is difficult to use in environments where coal dust or organic dust is also present (such as mining) as these substances lead to positive interference and overestimation of the DPM. Typically, industrial hygienists use a cyclonic separator and a crystalline filter to remove all particles >1.0 μm before they reach the final sampling filter so that only submicron diesel smoke is collected. An example of this sampling system is shown in Figure 8–19. NIOSH also uses a continuously reading diesel particle-measuring tool, and versions of this are available commercially.

The history of the development of exposure limits for DPM has also been convoluted. Federal OSHA has no specific PEL for DPM, although it does recommend sampling for a number of gases and vapors that are found in diesel exhaust. Similarly, ACGIH proposed a standard in 1996 that it was forced to withdraw in 2004. NOISH has not issued a REL. The EPA has issued a "reference concentration" of 5 μg/m³, but this is not applicable to occupational settings. The California EPA has recommended that occupational exposure be kept below 20 μg/m³, the same as the withdrawn ACGIH TLV. The Mine Safety and Health Administration proposed a standard in 2001, but was forced to withdraw it. Since 2008, MSHA enforces a standard of 160 μg/m³ of total carbon averaged over a shift. Total carbon is a surrogate for diesel smoke. (Note that total carbon is different from elemental carbon as assessed by the NIOSH method 5040). Germany established a standard of 100 µg/m³ for nonmining operations and 300 µg/m³ for mines.

Engineered Nanoparticles

NIOSH has championed a general approach to identifying employees potentially exposed to ENP (Table 8–K.) They use portable direct-reading particle counters to screen for PM exposure. A CNC/laser scattering photometer is used that is sensitive to particles from 10 nm to >1000 nm, alongside an instrument that detects only particles >300 nm. The concentration measured with the nanoparticle-sensitive

meter is corrected by subtracting the particle count provided by the larger particle photometer, presumably yielding a nanoparticle-only concentration. It is also possible to use only the nanoparticle-sensitive meter and just assume that all particles detected are in the nano range. This is a conservative and relatively inexpensive and easy approach that is widely used in Department of Energy labs.

More sophisticated direct-reading instruments called "differential mobility particle sizers" are available that automatically bin measured particles into different size ranges, even subdividing the nanoparticle range into 2 or several subranges (Table 8–L). However, as of 2011 this equipment is very expensive and challenging to use and is largely in the

TABLE 8–K	Summary of Some Early Findings from NIOSH Field Surveys in Facilities Using or Manufacturing ENP (NIOSH)		
Type of Facility	**Type of Particle, Morphology**	**Size of Particle**	**Range of "Potential" Exposure Concentrations**
University research lab	Carbon nanofibers	Approx. 100 nm diameter, 1–10 microns long	60–90 µg/m³
Metal oxide manufacturer	TiO₂, lithium titanate, powder	100–200 nm	<100 nm: 1.4 µg/m³ (TiO₂) Total dust: 4–149 µg/m³ (TiO₂) <100 nm: ND (Li) Total dust: ND -3 µg/m³ (Li)
Manufacturer	Carbon nanofibers	Approx. 100 nm diameter, 1–10 microns long	15–1800 µg/m³
Research and development lab	Quantum dots, spheres	2–8 nm	ND
Metal oxide manufacturer	Manganese, silver, nickel, cobalt, iron oxides, spheres	8–50 nm	67–3619 µg/m³
Research and development lab (pilot-scale)	Aluminum, spheres	50–100 nm	40–276 µg/m³
Research and development lab	Elemental metals – silver, copper, TiO₂	15–40 nm	ND
Filter media manufacturer	Nylon 6 nanofiber	70–300 nm diameter, continuous length	ND

TABLE 8–L	Summary of Techniques That Can Be Applied to the Measurement of Nanoparticle Mass (NIOSH)	
Metric	**Instrument or Method**	**Remarks**
Mass—Direct (total and/or elemental)	Size-Selective Static Sampler	The only instruments offering a cut point around 100 nm are cascade impactors (Berner-type low-pressure impactors, or micro-orifice impactors). Allows gravimetric and chemical analysis of samples on stages below 100 nm.
	TEOM® (Tapered Element Oscillating Microbalance) Filter Collection and Elemental Analysis	Sensitive real-time monitors such as the TEOM may be usable to measure nanoaerosol mass concentration on-line with a suitable size selective inlet. Filters may be collected with size-selective presamplers or open face. Elemental analysis (e.g., carbon, metals) for mass determination.
Mass—Indirect (calculation)	ELPI™ (Electrical Low-Pressure Impactor)	Real-time size-selective (aerodynamic diameter) detection of active surface area concentration giving aerosol size distribution. Mass concentration of aerosols can be calculated when particle charge and density are known or assumed.
	MOUDI (Micro-Orifice Uniform Deposit Impactor) DMAS (Differential Mobility Analyzing System)	Real-time size-selective (aerodynamic diameter) by cascade impaction. Real-time size-selective (mobility diameter) detection of number concentration, giving aerosol size distribution. Mass concentration of aerosols can be calculated when particle shape and density are known or assumed.

TABLE 8–M	Summary of Methods That Can Be Used to Determine Nanoparticle Count or Surface Area (NIOSH)	
Metric	**Instrument or Method**	**Remarks**
Number—Direct	CPC (Condensation Particle Counter)	CPCs provide real-time number concentration measurements between their particle diameter detection limits. Without a nanoparticle preseparator they are not specific to the nanometer size range. Some models have a diffusion screen to limit top size to 1 μm.
	OPC (Optical Particle Counter)	OPCs provide real-time number concentration measurements between their particle diameter detection limits. Particle size diameters begin at 300 nm and may go up to 10,000 nm.
	DMAS and SMPS (Scanning Mobility Particle Sizer)	Real-time size-selective (mobility diameter) detection of number concentration giving number-based size distribution.
	Electron Microscopy	Off-line analysis of electron microscope samples can provide information on size-specific aerosol number concentration.
Number—Indirect	ELPI™ and MOUDI	Real-time size-selective (aerodynamic diameter) detection of active surface-area concentration giving aerosol size distribution. Data may be interpreted in terms of number concentration. Size-selective samples may be further analyzed off-line.
Surface Area—Direct	Diffusion Charger	Real-time measurement of aerosol active surface area. Active surface area does not scale directly with geometric surface area above 100 nm. Note that not all commercially available diffusion chargers have a response that scales with particle active surface area below 100 nm. Diffusion chargers are specific to nanoparticles only if used with appropriate inlet preseparator.
	ELPI™ and MOUDI	Real-time size-selective (aerodynamic diameter) detection of active surface-area concentration. Active surface area does not scale directly with geometric surface-area above 100 nm.
Mass—Direct (total and/or elemental)	Size-Selective Static Sampler	The only instruments offering a cut point around 100 nm are cascade impactors (Berner-type low-pressure impactors, or micro-orifice impactors). Allows gravimetric and chemical analysis of samples on stages below 100 nm.
	TEOM® (Tapered Element Oscillating Microbalance)	Sensitive real-time monitors such as the TEOM may be usable to measure nanoaerosol mass concentration on-line with a suitable size-selective inlet.
	Filter Collection and Elemental Analysis	Filters may be collected with size-selective presamplers or open face. Elemental analysis (e.g., carbon, metals) for mass determination.
Mass—Indirect (calculation)	ELPI™ (Electrical Low-Pressure Impactor)	Real-time size-selective (aerodynamic diameter) detection of active surface-area concentration giving aerosol size distribution. Mass concentration of aerosols can be calculated when particle charge and density are known or assumed.
	MOUDI (Micro-Orifice Uniform Deposit Impactor)	Real-time size-selective (aerodynamic diameter) by cascade impaction.
	DMAS (Differential Mobility Analyzing System)	Real-time size-selective (mobility diameter) detection of number concentration, giving aerosol size distribution. Mass concentration of aerosols can be calculated when particle shape and density are known or assumed.

realm of research. This may change in the future as there are increasing demands for better nanoparticle measuring tools.

Direct-reading instruments are useful as a screening tool to identify exposed employees and to find nanoparticle leakage paths from processing equipment and ventilation systems. For several reasons, they are not very useful for measuring integrated average exposures. Nanoparticle meters readily detect environmental ultrafines and condensation nuclei, typically reading thousands or tens of thousands of particles per cubic centimeter in outdoor or indoor air, with constant varia-

tion of 15 to 25 percent (Table 8–M). Occupational exposures have to rise to a large fraction of background to be observed against this background variability; thus lesser exposures will not be detected. The Lawrence Berkeley National Laboratory has used HEPA-filtered low background enclosures to eliminate the contribution of environmental ultrafines to the measured exposure, resulting in an increase of sensitivity of several hundredfold. This approach is not viable in most factory settings, but was used effectively by NIOSH in an early study of carbon nanotube exposure in a small factory (Figure 8–22).

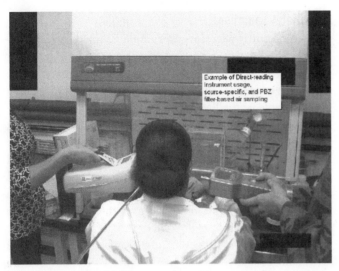

Figure 8–22. NIOSH field survey for carbon nanotubes using two direct-reading instruments with different particle size range sensitivities and integrated air sampling filters for electron microscope analysis. *(Source: Methner M, Hodson L, Geraci C. Nanoparticle Emission Assessment Technique (NEAT) for the identification and measurement of potential inhalation exposure to engineered nanoparticles: Part A.* J Occup Env Hygiene 7(3):127–132, 2010.)

Carbon Nanotubes

Integrated exposure to airborne carbon nanotubes (CNTs) can be measured in several ways. If the material is the only likely air contaminant and the concentration of residual metal catalyst on the nanotubes is known, it is possible to measure the metal contaminant(s) using standard metal detection methods and back-calculate the concentration of CNTs. NIOSH pioneered this method in 2001 and used a cyclone in front of the filter. This is very easy and inexpensive.

Alternatively, the CNTs can be collected on a filter and measured gravimetrically, again assuming that they are pure and are the only significant airborne PM in the workplace. A cyclone should be used before the filter to limit the collection to respirable particles, although this has not been fully validated. It should also be possible to measure CNTs using the NIOSH elemental carbon method 5040, although this has not been widely used for this purpose.

Finally, at great expense, CNTs (or other nanoparticles) can be collected on air sampling filters with or without a cyclone preseparator and evaluated under scanning or transmission electron microscopes (TEM). While TEM is the closest thing to a definitive analytical procedure available, the method has not been fully standardized or validated and there are only a few labs that can do it, at a 2011 cost of about $1000 per sample. Also, the analysis provides results in terms of fibers or structures per unit volume of air, which cannot be compared to the NIOSH REL for CNTs of 0.007 mg/m^3. Some professionals compare the results of TEM analysis to the OSHA asbestos exposure limits, which seems like a reasonable approach if the fibers are discrete in the sample. More typically, CNTs are seen in clusters as shown in Figure 8–23.

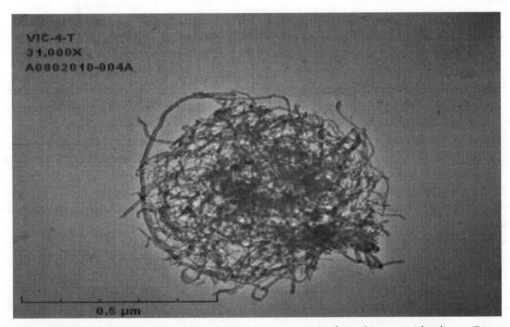

Figure 8–23. Cluster of CNTs under TEM. From an operation involving sonication of a carbon nanotube slurry. *(From proceedings of the 5th International Nanomaterial Occupational Safety and Health [NanOSH] conference, Boston, 2011.)*

Nanoscale Titanium Dioxide

Nanoscale titanium dioxide is now common in industry. NIOSH has provided guidance on measuring exposure to nanoscale titanium dioxide that should be equally applicable to other similar metal and metal oxide nanoparticles. In the 2011 *Current Intelligence Bulletin #63*, "Occupational Exposure to Titanium Dioxide," NIOSH says:

> Based on the observed relationship between particle surface area dose and toxicity, the measurement of aerosol surface area would be the preferred method for evaluating workplace exposures to TiO_2....however, personal sampling devices that can be routinely used in the workplace for measuring particle surface area are not currently available.
>
> An initial exposure assessment should include the simultaneous collection of respirable dust samples with one sample using a hydrophobic filter (as described in NIOSH Method 0600) and the other sample using a mixed cellulose ester filter (MCEF). If the respirable exposure concentration for TiO_2 (as determined by Method 0600) is less than 0.3 mg/m³, then no further action is required. If the exposure concentration exceeds 0.3 mg/m³, then additional characterization of the sample is needed to determine the particle size and percentage of TiO_2 and other extraneous material on the sample. To assist in this assessment, the duplicate respirable sample collected on a MCEF should be evaluated using transmission electron microscopy (TEM) to size particles and determine the percentage of fine (> 0.1 µm) and ultrafine (< 0.1 µm) TiO_2. NIOSH Method 7300 can be used to assist in differentiating TiO_2 from other aerosols collected on the filter while electron microscopy, equipped with X-ray energy dispersive spectroscopy (EDS), may be needed to measure and identify particles.

For metals-containing nanoparticles, rather than using a gravimetric analysis, it is possible to analyze the filter by atomic absorption or ICPES. This destroys the filter, so if TEM analysis is contemplated, it is appropriate to run a second breathing zone filter. Also, for particles that are not pure metal (e.g., metal oxides), remember to back-calculate the concentration of the actual metal compound, not just the metal component.

For most engineered nanoparticles, there are no substantiated or recommended exposure limits and no well-established sampling or analytical procedures. In this situation, an employer may choose to treat the nanoparticles as toxic until further data can be developed and limit exposure to "as low as reasonably practicable," as recommended by ASTM standard E 2535-07. A *control banding* approach, now popular in the European Union and used in the United States for biosafety and pharmaceutical safety, may be useful.

Isokinetic Sampling

Sometimes, it is necessary to sample PM in a moving airstream, such as after a HEPA filter bank or in an exhaust stack. This introduces new aerodynamic problems into the sampling procedure that must be accounted for to obtain a valid sample of the PM in the airstream.

When sampling in a moving airstream, the sampling head or filter cassette must draw air at the same flow rate as the air is moving in the duct. If the air is drawn into the head or filter too slowly, large particles that have high inertia will be oversampled and the result will be higher than it should be. On the other hand, if air is drawn through the head or cassette faster than it is flowing in the duct, large particles will not be sampled properly and the measured result will be low. One must also account mathematically for temperature differences between the duct air and the air where the air pump is located.

The effect of nonisokinetic sampling in a duct or stack can be quite severe. These effects occur primarily with the larger particles as a result of inertial forces, as shown diagrammatically in Figure 8–24. Errors start to show up at particle AEDs of 3 µm and become increasingly severe above 6 µm in equivalent aerodynamic diameter.

If the temperature or airflow rate in the duct or stack is subject to change during sampling, it will be very difficult to maintain isokinetic conditions without constant attention. In a nicely flowing system, in contrast, once the system is set, it should operate reliably on its own.

Sampling in ducts and stacks can be difficult if the particle concentration is not uniform and the air flow laminar. It is necessary to either do a duct traverse or install a multipoint sampling head in the stack. Both approaches are used routinely.

Surface Sampling for Particulate Matter

Surface sampling in some workplaces is useful as an adjunct to air sampling. This may include sampling from an employee's skin or clothing.

Typically, surface sampling is conducted for several reasons. First, surface sampling is conducted to determine adequacy of housekeeping and effectiveness of engineered controls in minimizing the spread of highly toxic PM. The OSHA *Industrial Hygiene Field Manual* says: "In instances where surface contamination is suspected and the employer has not required the use of effective Personal Protective Equipment (PPE) for employees, wipe sampling may be an effective means of documenting that a skin hazard exists."

Surface sampling is not needed where the contaminant is of low toxicity, as a visual observation will usually suffice. However, for materials with high toxicity and correspondingly

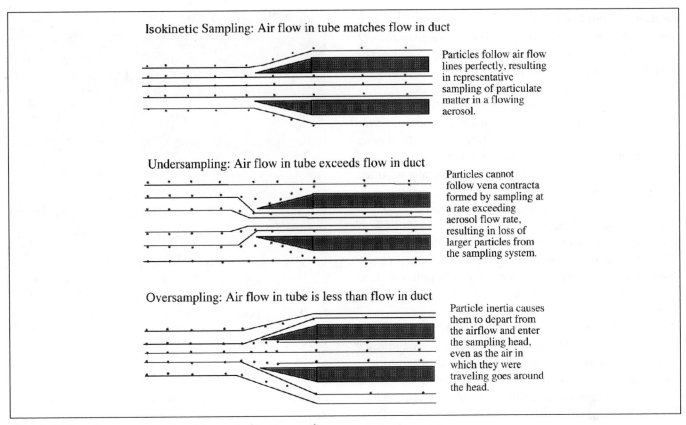

Isokinetic Sampling: Air flow in tube matches flow in duct

Particles follow air flow lines perfectly, resulting in representative sampling of particulate matter in a flowing aerosol.

Undersampling: Air flow in tube exceeds flow in duct

Particles cannot follow vena contracta formed by sampling at a rate exceeding aerosol flow rate, resulting in loss of larger particles from the sampling system.

Oversampling: Air flow in tube is less than flow in duct

Particle inertia causes them to depart from the airflow and enter the sampling head, even as the air in which they were traveling goes around the head.

Figure 8–24. Sampling error introduced by nonisokinetic sampling.

low occupational exposure limits, surface sampling should be considered. In the facilities owned or operated by the Department of Energy, surface sampling of beryllium work areas is required. In U.S. Housing and Urban Development (HUD) housing, surface sampling for lead dust is required (also used more broadly in other settings). A seldom-utilized but potentially very useful type of swipe is the Ames test swipe for mutagenic stressors. Subjecting the surface dust to a revertant mutation assay (e.g., Ames test) provides some semi-quantitative data about the potential spread of that material.

Federal OSHA has no specific requirements for surface sampling for particulate matters, but does require that if such sampling is conducted in the workplace, it be treated the same as air sampling data with respect to records retention.

Other settings where surface sampling for PM is useful include the following:

- When working on laboratory fume hoods, surface sampling can verify that no potentially explosive perchlorate residue is present in the hood, plenum, duct, or fan.
- Prior to releasing excess equipment for reuse, utilization, sale, or donation. For example, it would be inappropriate to donate a machine tool contaminated with beryllium or other highly toxic metal to a local high school.

- When it is necessary to determine what metals are/were used in an area in the past, surface samples can be analyzed for many metals by inductive coupled plasma emission spectroscopy or similar tool.
- Where the contaminant has a high percutaneous toxicity, as in the case of some organophosphate pesticides.
- Where the surface dust is a major component of the source term for airborne exposure.
- Following certain types of hazard abatement actions (lead in particular), surface sampling can verify the adequacy of the decontamination and contamination control procedures.
- Whenever working with radioactive PM.

A variety of surface sampling techniques are available to the industrial hygienist. The traditional method is a dry swipe sample, where the surface is rubbed in a known area with a cellulose filter or a special swipe tab often called a smear tab. These are quick and easy, and it is common to combine samples from several related areas onto one swipe, but this is also the least reliable, most technique-sensitive surface sampling technique.

A move up from the dry swipe is the wet swipe, where the Whatman filter or swipe tab is prewetted with water or another liquid prior to application to the surface to be tested. This procedure is a little more precise than the dry swiping methods, but still subject to a lot of variability. The OSHA field-sampling manual leaves the decision to wet the swipe tab or filter to the industrial hygienist.

The Housing and Urban Development (HUD) procedure for lead dust sampling introduced many industrial hygienists to the process of wet wiping, using a large, wet wiping medium and a specified wiping technique. While still very much semiquantitative, this procedure is generally regarded as an advancement over prior wipe sampling methods.

The American Society for Testing Materials (ASTM) has issued standards D7659, E1792, D7296, D5438, E1728, E1792, and D6966 related to swipe sampling techniques. The Department of Energy requires swipe testing of equipment that is potentially contaminated with beryllium before the equipment is sold, given away, or scrapped, but does not specify a method.

If dust is visible on the surface, the industrial hygienist can collect surface samples for analysis. A common variation on this is the surface microvacuum technique. Microvacuuming is usually performed by using a standard 25-mm or 37-mm mixed cellulose ester filter attached by hose to a relatively high-flow-rate pump. A short extension tube, cut off at a 45-degree angle on the front end, is attached to the front nipple on the cassette. A known area of surface is carefully vacuumed onto the filter, and the entire cassette is submitted to the laboratory for analysis. Sometimes the desired result is mass of contaminant per mass of total dust (i.e., percent or ppm) or mass of contaminant per given surface area (e.g., micrograms per square foot). The ASTM has developed specific standards for microvacuuming: D7144, D5755, and D5756. Figure 8–25 shows how the microvacuuming technique is used.

Tape lift is another possible method to evaluate surface contamination. ASTM method E1216-99, *Standard Practice for Sampling for Surface Particulate Contamination by Tape Lift*, provides a procedure for sampling surfaces with pressure-sensitive tape to determine the presence of particulate contamination, 5 μm and larger. This is used periodically when testing for mold spores on a surface associated with indoor mold problems. Table 8–N lists several available surface sampling methods.

Direct-reading surface sampling tools also exist. Lead on surfaces can be detected by the use of sodium rhodizinate-based swipes meeting the specifications of the NIOSH 7700 method. Although lacking the sensitivity and specificity of the more traditional field collection/lab analysis method, the advantage of instantaneous results, at least for screening purposes, is substantial in some settings. Similar single-use surface sampling tubes are available for mercury

Figure 8–25. Microvacuuming a specified area of a contaminated surface. *(From proceedings of the 5th International Nanomaterial Occupational Safety and Health [NanOSH] conference, Boston, 2011.)*

droplets, nickel dust, cadmium dust, and chromate dust. For metals, it is possible to use a direct-reading x-ray fluorescence meter, as is often done when testing potentially lead-containing paint.

All surface samples of PM should be regarded as qualitative or at best semiquantitative, and used as an adjunct to air sampling and other aspects of a comprehensive industrial hygiene program. See Chapter 17 for more information on direct-reading instruments.

Dermal Monitoring

A related type of PM surface monitoring is dermal monitoring, typically for particles that present significant skin absorption hazards, such as pesticides. NIOSH 9201 is a method that was developed to measure chlorinated and organonitrogen pesticides from patches of fabric attached in aluminum holders to the clothing of workers. One product available to implement this method is the Dermal PUF (polyurethane foam) patch. It is a section of polyurethane foam fabric that is clipped to the worker's clothing or taped directly to the skin. After sampling, the patches are removed and sent to a laboratory for analysis of the pesticide.

Analysis of hand washing rinsate is another technique sometimes used to evaluate dermal exposure. For example, NIOSH 9202 is a method for the detection of captan and tihophanate-methyl in hand washings. Increasingly common, at least in research, they will mix ultraviolet fluorescent powders with powdered pesticides so they can visualize surface contaminants using an ultraviolet light and camera.

TABLE 8–N	Surface Sampling Methods That Are Available	
Method	**Media/Device**	**Surfaces**
OSHA ID-125G & ID-206	Wet or dry filter swipe	Smooth/hard; dermal
NIOSH 9100, 9102	Wet swipe	Smooth; dermal
ASTM D6966	Wet swipe	Smooth/hard
ASTM E1216	Adhesive tape lift	Smooth
OSHA and NIOSH (Several)	Patch or skin rinse sampling	Dermal samples
ASTM D5438	Vacuum cleaner	Carpets
ASTM D7144	Microvacuuming	Rough or fragile
ASTM D 7296	Dry swipe	Oily or fragile

This is an old trick used in the training of radioactive material handlers: have the trainees handle fluorescent powder instead of radioactive powder and at the end of the exercise, demonstrate with a long wave ultraviolet light the spread of contamination and problems in their practices.

ANALYSIS OF AIR SAMPLES

Once the particles are removed from the airstream and collected onto a filter or in liquid, they then must be analyzed. Historically, the most common methods of analysis were optical microscopy, gravimetric (weighing), and sometimes wet-chemical analysis. While these methods are still fairly common, more sophisticated analytical procedures have been developed for all metals, free crystalline silica, many organic materials, isocyanates, and certain other materials.

Metals (Spectroscopic Analysis)

Wet-chemical analysis of most metals ended with the advent of the flame emission photometer, a device that siphons dissolved metal ions into a flame and measures the characteristic optical emission lines of the metal. The intensity of the lines is proportional to the concentration of the metal.

The flame photometer was improved by the introduction of the flame atomic absorption photometer. Here, the flame-excited metal ion is exposed to a collimated beam of light created by a source that produces the emission lines characteristic of that metal. The ions in the flame absorb the intense light in proportion to their concentration. This method has the advantage of being more stable and sensitive than flame photometry, but is also more expensive and limited, as it requires separate light sources for each element to be analyzed. A further improvement, still in broad use, is the graphite furnace atomic absorption spectrophotometer, where the flame is replaced by a graphite furnace.

The next major improvement in metal analysis, which is the workhorse instrument in most sophisticated labs that perform many different types of metal analyses, is the inductively coupled plasma atomic emission spectrometer (ICPAES). Here, the flame is replaced with very high temperature gas plasma, created by induction from the fields created by a radiofrequency generator.

Other than changing the excitation source and computerizing the operation of the device, an ICPAES operates largely like an old flame photometer. The liquid containing the digested metal ions is siphoned into the plasma, and as it is turned into plasma it produces characteristic emission lines. A monochrometer allows selection of a particular line, and the intensity of that line is proportional to the concentration of metal analyte. Typically, it is possible to automatically scan the different lines to determine many metals at the same time, and to compare the intensity of several lines produced by a metal to assure that no positive or negative interference is occurring. A further improvement of this device eliminates the monochrometer and photometer, and replaces them with a spectrometer consisting of a light dispersion element (e.g., reflective diffraction grating) and a charge-coupled device that allows simultaneous measurement of all lines of all elements.

The most recent big step in analytical instruments for metals is the inductively coupled plasma-mass spectrometer (ICP/MS). In this device the metal ion is first run through radiofrequency induced plasma, and then directed into a mass spectrometer, which weighs the atom to determine its exact atomic weight and concentration. Like the ICPAES, this instrument can analyze many metals all at the same time. For many metals, this is the most sophisticated and sensitive routinely used analytical instrument.

It should be noted that in many cases, such sophistication and sensitivity are unnecessary and needlessly expensive. For routine analysis of a single analyte like lead, a simple atomic absorption spectrophotometer is perfectly adequate and much less expensive than an ICP/MS. The ICPAES and ICP/MS are very helpful when you need low detection limits, do not know the exact metal composition of the PM you are sampling, or require the analysis of several metals on the same filter.

Free Crystalline Silica

Free crystalline silica (e.g., quartz, cristobalite, and tridymite) can be analyzed by a couple of methods. One involves infrared spectrophotometry, as in the NIOSH 7602, 7603, and MSHA P-7 methods. However, the most common and reliable analytical method is powder x-ray diffraction, as in NIOSH 7500 and OSHA ID 142. This approach is more sensitive and precise and can measure all three free crystalline silica species at the same time. It can be used for personal air samples, settled dust samples, bulk samples, or high-volume air samples. In the past, it was considered necessary to submit either high-volume samples or at least settled-dust samples along with the air samples, in order to allow proper calibration of the instrument. In recent years, many laboratories no longer require the cosubmission of high-volume or settled-dust samples, although if the concentration of silica in the source material is not known, it is a prudent practice to submit a settled-dust sample or bulk sample to ascertain this value.

Unfortunately, all of the analytical methods available for free crystalline silica are quite imprecise by industrial hygiene standards. The variability among labs or even within a lab is quite high, with a relative interlaboratory standard deviation (SD) up to about 40 percent for the infrared method. The variability is much improved, albeit still poor (SD in the range of 20 percent) for the x-ray diffraction method. Among common analytes, only the analysis of asbestos approaches the level of analytical imprecision characteristic of silica analysis.

Asbestos

Asbestos is still measured mostly by optical techniques. From about 1925 until 1969, asbestos-containing dust in the United States was usually collected in a water-filled impinger. An aliquot of the shaken impinger fluid was placed in a special well slide and fibers were counted through an optical microscope. Results were expressed in terms of millions of particles per cubic foot of sampled air (mppcf). (Note: There are a few OSHA standards that still exist only in terms of mppcf, namely soapstone, talc, cement, and mica.)

Following the lead of the British, in 1968 the United States adopted a filter sampling method that still required optical analysis. A wedge of the filter, with fibers embedded, was cut from the whole and placed on a slide, and the filter wedge was rendered transparent by the application of a drop of solvent. The fibers were then counted through the eyepiece of a phase-contrast microscope using a Porton-type reticule. Fields were semirandomly selected, and if the particle was at least 5 μm long, had an aspect ratio of 3:1 or greater, and fell within the bounds of the engraved reticule, it was counted. The results were now expressed in units of fibers per cubic centimeter of air (f/cc, occasionally f/mL), very difficult to accurately relate to the older mppcf units.

The National Institute of Occupational Safety and Health and OSHA adopted essentially the same method. Originally called Physical and Chemical Analytical Method 239 (P&CAM 239), over time several changes to the method have been made (changing to a Walton and Beckett reticle, replacement of the liquid clearing solution with a vapor phase clearing chemical, adjustment of acceptable flow rates, resolution testing of the microscope). The method was renumbered NIOSH 7400 in 1984. It has been through several revisions since, but retains the designation NIOSH 7400. OSHA adopted the new NIOSH 7400 in lieu of the P&CAM 239 method almost verbatim when it revised the asbestos exposure standard in 1986. In this case, they called it the OSHA Reference Method, which is similar, but not identical, to NIOSH 7400.

In Figure 8–26, fibers 1–6 would be counted as one fiber, fiber 8 would not be counted (too short), structure 9 would be counted as 2 fibers, fiber 10 would not be counted (outside of reticule area), and fiber 11 would not be counted as it crosses the edge of the reticule twice. There are 2 #7 fibers in this drawing; the one inside the circle would be counted as 1 fiber, and the one crossing the edge of the circle once would be counted as a half fiber.

Other less commonly used optical analytical methods for asbestos also exist, including the OSHA 160 method

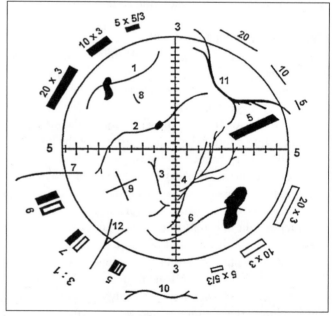

Figure 8–26. Walton and Beckett reticle with example fibers. *(Source: National Institute of Occupational Safety and Health. Asbestos and other fibers, by PCM: Method 7400. In NIOSH Manual of Analytical Methods, 4th ed. Washington, DC: U.S. Department of Health, Education, and Welfare (NIOSH), 1994.)*

and the Asbestos International Association Membrane Filter Reference Method RTM 1.

The analysis of asbestos by optical methods is usually quite imprecise and often inaccurate. Especially at low fiber loading on the filter, the imprecision of the NIOSH 7400 method is severe, as shown in Figure 8–27. Assuming proper procedures are used, the equipment is adequate and well set up, and the analysts well experienced, the variability seen at the low end of the fiber loading curve is largely intrinsic to the method and random in nature. The inevitable error is the tendency of less skilled analysts to over count fibers at very low loading relative to higher loadings.

At excessive fiber loading not shown in Figure 8–28, systematic undercounting of fibers starts to occur, eventually reaching the point where the filter is not analyzable. The method is best used by controlling fiber loading to levels between 100 and 1,300 fibers/mm^2 of filter surface area, which can be back-calculated from the expected airborne asbestos concentration, given that the usable surface area of the 25-mm filter used for asbestos collection is 385 mm^2. For example, if the expected fiber concentration is 1.0 f/cc, to get the desired loading on the filter, the sample volume should be between 38 and 490 liters.

In addition, the limited resolution of optical microscopes (about 0.25 μm for most phase-contrast microscopes) means that the narrowest and potentially most toxicologically significant fibers are systematically undercounted. While a significant percentage of the fibers of amosite (20–60%) will usually be visible under the optical microscope, only a tiny fraction of chrysotile and crocidolite asbestos fibers will be visible. This fraction, depending on the analytical methods used, may be as low as 1–5 percent (95–99% not counted).

The inaccuracy of optical methods of asbestos analysis arises from the fact that the analyst counts all fibers that meet the method specifications, not just asbestos fibers. If they are present, fibrous glass, cellulose, nonasbestiform mineral cleavage fragments, and mineral wool fibers get counted as asbestos fibers. Within the rules for NIOSH 7400 and for the OSHA Reference Method, there are no provisions for discriminating among different types of fibers, even though a skilled microscopist can readily tell a glass fiber from an asbestos fiber. The method authors are well aware of this limitation, and the NIOSH 7400 method is actually termed the analysis of "fibers," not asbestos.

The counting of particles with an aspect ratio as low as 3:1 results in the enumeration of pseudofibers. While true asbestos minerals have aspect ratios of 10:1 or more, many minerals, including many nonasbestiform polymorphs of asbestos and other minerals like talc, form cleavage fragments or scrolls, which are somewhat fibrous but clearly not asbestiform, but must be counted under the NIOSH/OSHA methods. In 1990, NIOSH explicitly recommended including both asbestiform particles and fibrous particles of the nonasbestiform mineral when they occur together in an air sampling filter. This has been an ongoing area of contention since that time.

The NIOSH "A" counting rules and the OSHA method require counting all fibers meeting the length and aspect ratio rule, regardless of their diameter. The Asbestos International Association method RTM 1 discounts fibers wider than 3 μm. The rarely used "B" counting rules offered in NIOSH 7400 make the same concession. Research has

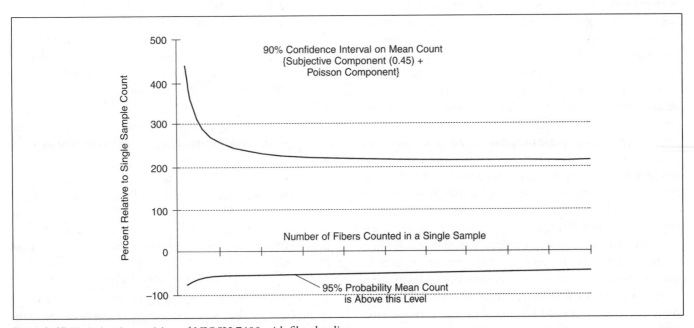

Figure 8–27. Variation in precision of NIOSH 7400 with fiber loading.

suggested that fibers, regardless of length, tend to demonstrate AEDs that are about three times their physical width. Three times 3 µm is 9 µm, and when multiplied by the density of asbestos, which exceeds 1, makes such wide particles essentially nonrespirable and toxicologically of lower significance.

These nonspecific analytical methods were developed primarily with work settings such as asbestos mines, mills, and asbestos manufacturing facilities as the target. In these settings, most of the airborne fibers are asbestos. In modern times, at least in the United States, these are not major industries. Asbestos exposure and therefore asbestos monitoring are now mostly associated with building maintenance and renovation and asbestos abatement. In these settings, asbestos exposure usually occurs along with other fibrous or pseudofibrous materials, often making the measured "asbestos" exposure a severe overestimate. Perhaps the worst example of this occurs during controlled removal of Sheetrock® with asbestos-containing surface coating or joint spackling. Fiber exposures when measured by phase-contrast microscopy (PCM) in accordance with the NIOSH or OSHA methods can be very high, but if subjected to analyses that allows discrimination between asbestos and nonasbestos fibers, few of the fibers counted by optical microscopy may turn out to be asbestos.

Several methods are used to get around the inherent nonspecificity of phase contrast optical fiber counting. In some cases, experienced optical microscopists can simply discount morphologically obvious nonasbestos fibers and count only those fibers that are likely to be asbestos. This method, however, is subject to the experience of the microscopist, and is more of an art than science. Alternatively, procedures have been developed (OSHA ID 160) that allow phase contrast counting microscopy to be used in tandem with polarized light mineralogical analysis (PLM), morphological observations, scanning electron microscopy (SEM), and transmission electron microscopy (TEM). This procedure is designed to be used by OSHA compliance officers when they sample for asbestos in a multifiber aerosol environment.

The Asbestos International Association has developed a scanning electron microscope procedure, RTM 2, as has the International Agency for Research on Cancer, but these are rarely used. The most common method for differential fiber counting is transmission electron microscopy. It is routine to consider fiber morphology in determining if they are asbestos under the electron microscope. Also, individual fibers beamed with electrons emit soft x-rays characteristic of their elemental composition. If the asbestos under analysis is chrysotile, a magnesium silicate, very large peaks should represent magnesium and silicon only. If the fiber also contains a large peak for iron, it could be crocidolite, amosite,

or actinolite. Many other interfering fibers would lack one or more of these major components. This qualitative analytical tool is called energy dispersive x-ray fluorescence.

A more definitive differential counting technique used with the electron microscope is electron diffraction testing. Selected area electron diffraction (SAED) patterns are quite specific for chrysotile and fairly specific to the amphibole series. Combined with morphological observations and qualitative elemental analysis, TEM can provide nearly definitive asbestos differentiation.

One of the earliest TEM methods specifically designed for asbestos analysis was the EPA method of 1978, named after its principal author, A. Samurai. This early method expressed asbestos concentrations in gravimetric terms, monograms per cubic meter (ng/m^3). This archaic unit was replaced in the early 1980s.

A long-useful electron microscope method published in by the EPA in 1984 is usually called the Yamate method, after its principal author, George Yamate. Here, and in subsequent TEM methods, the unit of measure is *asbestos structures per cubic centimeter of sampled air (s/cc)*. *Structures* includes asbestos fibers, bunches of asbestos fibers, clustered fibers, sets of fibers sticking out of other materials, etc.

When the Asbestos Hazard Emergency Response Act (AHERA) was signed into law, the EPA developed a new TEM method, usually just called the AHERA method (40 CFR Part 763), which differs in some ways from the Yamate method. It is more than just an analytical method, as it is tied in with sampling protocols required of schools in other parts of the AHERA-driven regulations. Still, it can be teased away from these additional school requirements and used in various ways in nonschool settings. NIOSH also has a TEM method numbered 7402. The AHERA and NIOSH 7402 methods are the most commonly used TEM analytical procedures for asbestos.

TEM analysis also solves the problem of undercounting narrow, toxicologically important fibers in optical microscopy. TEM can visualize all asbestos fibers, even the narrowest, with no difficulty. Thus, TEM analysis of asbestos can be both highly specific and highly sensitive.

Historically, the biggest drawback of TEM analysis has been high cost and slow turnaround. As the asbestos abatement and handling industries have evolved from a novelty job to a commodity, the time and money costs of TEM analysis have plummeted. It is still more expensive than PCM analysis, but unless the PCM lab is on-site, the turnaround time for TEM almost matches that of PCM.

Another major problem with fiber type-selective analysis protocols is that they are generally not addressed in the OSHA regulations. However, since even the OSHA laboratory in Salt Lake City makes use of fiber-type selective counting, it is clear that there is some leeway here if the methods are sound and carefully applied.

Radioactive Particles

Radioactive particles are collected on filters, with the exception of activated charcoal sampling of radon as described in the sampling section of this chapter. Filters can be submitted for analysis by several means, almost all of them taking advantage of the readily detectable alpha, beta, or gamma emissions.

In many jobs, people handling radioactive materials are handling only one element at a time. Thus, simple counting of total emissions gives a picture of the total amount of that radioactive material on the filter. Knowing the radioelement, the amount of radioactive material in the air can be compared to the derived air concentration, which is a year-long weighted exposure limit. This is often termed gross alpha, beta, gamma analysis. Only if the radioisotope analyzed is in question or completely unknown (as might occur in a multielement contaminated legacy facility or waste disposal site) is more sophisticated analysis necessary to differentiate radioactive materials based on the energy and type of their emission (radiospectroscopy).

Analysis of filters is often performed nondestructively by counting with a gas-proportional counter or, more often, a solid-state scintillation detector. Solid-state scintillators emit a burst of photons when hit by a radioactive emission within their range of sensitivity, and a sensitive photomultiplier tube typically detects this. Because only one surface of the filter is exposed to the detector crystal, compensation must be made for the geometry, and the results are typically increased by a factor of two or more to determine the complete emission rate. The exact correction value is determined empirically with a standard source.

In place of the solid-state scintillator is often a Geiger-Mueller (GM) tube, which is useful for gamma and higher energy beta emissions. Geiger-Mueller tubes do not typically perform well for alpha particle emitters, so when measuring alpha emission, the solid-state detector would be more appropriate.

An alternative type of analysis, which does destroy the filter, is liquid scintillation counting. In this equipment, the filter or particles removed from the filter are placed in small vials, to which is added a fluor. The fluor will act like a solid-state scintillation crystal and will give off a burst of light when stimulated by a radioactive decay. This light is detected by a photomultiplier tube and eventually counted as radioactive decay, but first must pass through a coincidence gate to compensate for thermal noise and cosmic radiation, and allow compensation for internal "quenching." One of the big advantages of this method is it can detect very low-energy emissions, such as the weak beta particles released by tritium-containing particles (an isotope of hydrogen with three neutrons in the nucleus of the atom). However, it has fallen out of favor due to the unavoidable generation of large quantities of hazardous waste and is not frequently used.

Many of these types of instruments come in simple versions, some of which are field-portable, and more sophisticated laboratory versions, sometimes with radiospectroscopic capability.

Under some circumstances, it is advantageous to analyze radioactive particles by chemical means rather than by radiodetection means. ICP/MS can be much faster or much more sensitive than decay counting when the contaminant level is low.

Gravimetric Analysis

A shrinking list of particles are still analyzed gravimetrically, that is, by simply weighing the PM collected. With the advent of more sophisticated and specific analytical tools, gravimetric analysis is used most often when sampling for nuisance dust or PNOC. Some materials still analyzed gravimetrically are shown in Table 8–O. More recently, gravimetric analysis has been applied to the measurement of carbon nanotubes and titanium dioxide nanoparticles.

Note that many agents that can be analyzed gravimetrically could also be measured by much more specific means. Fibrous dust can be analyzed microscopically, oil mist chemically, the metals by ICPAES. In a mixed-dust environment, it is often much better to use the specific analysis rather than gravimetric analysis.

Several compensations must be made to be able to properly weigh dust collected on a filter. These must deal with the unknown weight of the filter as it arrives from the manufacturer, and the potential for water absorption by the filter or collected dust during the sampling or analysis procedure.

TABLE 8–O	Materials Still Commonly Analyzed Gravimetrically	
Cement	Coal dust (<5% silica)	Cotton
Emery	Fibrous glass*	Glycerin
Graphite	Gypsum	Grain dust
Kaolin	Limestone	Magnesite
Marble	Metal working fluids	Mineral wool (occasionally)
Oil mist	Palladium	Paper fibers
Plaster of Paris	Soapstone	Starch
Sucrose	Talc (<1% asbestos)	Titanium dioxide
Wood dust	Zinc oxide	

*Recent TLV analyzes fibrous glass microscopically as well as gravimetrically.

Without knowing something about the *tare* (original) weight of the filter, it is impossible to weigh it and know how much of the mass is filter and how much is collected PM. If the original weight of the filter is known prior to sampling, it may change if it or the collected PM is hydroscopic and gains weight from atmospheric water vapor, again making analysis difficult or impossible.

In the traditional procedures, the collection filter is desiccated by vacuum, and then immediately tared (weighed) to obtain a base weight. It is assembled into a sampling cassette, with the tare weight (base weight) written in a log corresponding to a numbered cassette, or written directly on the cassette, or both. The filter is then used to sample for dust in the field and returned to the laboratory. The filter is vacuum-desiccated a second time. The dry filter is then immediately weighed on a highly sensitive Mettler-type balance or a Cahn-type electrobalance. The difference in the final weight and the tare weight is the total dry dust collected. When divided by the sample volume, the airborne concentration of dust is determined.

Commercially preweighed filters tared to 10 ng are also available, but these are not run through the desiccation process on either end of the analysis. The use of hydrophobic PVC filters minimizes the effect of atmospheric water on the filter, but does not compensate for atmospheric water absorbed into the particulate matter on the filter.

A more convenient, although probably less precise, method of measuring PM gravimetrically is the use of stacked matched-weight filters. Starting with low-water-absorbing filters (PVC typically), the manufacturer or laboratory weighs out many of the same filters, pairing sets that happen to weigh about the same. These *matched-weight* filter sets are stacked and loaded into a single filter cassette. The cassette with stacked filters is used and submitted to the laboratory. In the lab, both the collection filter and the control filter are weighed without any special pretreatment. The difference in weight is the total dust collected. An assumption is made that any weight gain of the filter caused by water absorption affects both filters equally and the blank value can be used to adjust the sample filter result.

Matched-weight filters are much more easily analyzed than the more traditional desiccation/tareing procedure. But because of a lack of compensation for water absorption by the collected particles, and small variation in weight between the matched sets of filters, this method is generally considered less accurate. When sampling and analyzing for an agent like nuisance dust or PNOCs, which have comparatively high occupational exposure limits or no limits at all, these effects become unimportant, and matched-weight filter sampling is common and accepted. If sampling for an agent with a lower exposure limit, with the intention of

gravimetric analysis, the desiccation/tared filter method is preferred.

Microorganisms

Microorganisms most often of interest to the typical industrial hygienist are bacteria, fungi (and their spores), and viruses. These materials may cause allergic reactions in sensitive persons, infections, or toxic effects. Everyone is probably aware that ubiquitous environmental mold spores contribute to community allergy.

Analysis of some microorganisms has improved dramatically in recent years. The analysis of fungal spores is a good example. Traditional sampling methods pick up only viable spores by collection via inertial impaction onto a growth medium or into a special type of impinger. The spores are grown on the collection or plating medium (in the best case, a couple of different media) in a controlled environment until the individual spores establish colonies. The plates are allowed to grow as long as possible, but curtailed before the colonies start to merge or overlap. Then, the plates are placed on a gridded, illuminated stage called a *plate counter* and the total number of *colony-forming units (CFUs)* is counted with either the naked eye or a low-power magnifying glass.

In 1986 the ACGIH established an occupational exposure standard, using the direct impaction of viable particles onto growth agar with analysis of total viable CFUs/m^3. One could also take samples inside a workplace and outside to determine if there were more viable spores in the building than in the ambient air (an occurrence referred to as *amplification*). Inherent in this standard is the assumption that a colony is a colony, and thus a spore is a spore, and the genera and species do not matter. In fact, this early attempt at establishing a standard considered fungal spores primarily as an allergenic bioaerosol, in particular as contributors to indoor air quality problems. While this standard was useful in many circumstances, and the ACGIH should be applauded for leading the effort to establish standards for fungal spore occupational exposure limits in office environments, it soon became apparent that the standard is too simple for many settings.

The first problem surrounds the issue of viability. Many airborne spores are dead, including up to 90 percent of the spores of *Stachybotrys chartarum* (formerly *Stachybotrys atra*), a still-controversial but almost certainly toxic spore. These dead spores will never grow on any growth media, and thus their number will be greatly underestimated by viable sampling, yet the spores remain toxic.

Furthermore, different genera and even different species require different growth media to prosper. The standard microbiological media suggested in the 1986 standard are good at supporting growth of many common fungi, but not all of them, and not some of the more problematic. Once again, *S. chartarum* serves as a good example. The media commonly used are poor substrates for the proliferation of this toxigenic fungus. When sampled in a mixed-spore environment, it is almost certain that *S. chartarum* will be under detected, even if living spores are collected. Other spore types will grow much more vigorously, and the culturing period will have to be suspended long before any growth of *S. chartarum*. It is necessary to use a high-cellulose growth medium for *S. chartarum*, traditionally Czepak 10 percent cellulose agar, or more recently, corn meal agar.

Another way to avoid the viability problem is nonviable sampling, which can be done with a Burkhart spore trap or other similar instruments or by using an Air-O-Cell cassette. The collected spores are then counted under a microscope, usually with determination down to the genus level, and their viability or ability to grow on available media is irrelevant. However, the analysis typically requires a much more sophisticated analyst than is needed for simple colony enumeration without genus identification.

The second major problem with earlier fungi sampling procedures is the lack of specificity. Generally, industrial hygienists just counted all of the colonies appearing on the petri dish, and compared the net count per cubic meter to the ACGIH standard. On some occasions, when the expertise was available, the genus of the colonies might be determined, although separate standards were not available for genera and not much was known of their specific pathogenic properties.

The lack of specificity resulted in two problems. When comparing outside to inside samples using gross colony counts, the colony count might be the same, but the genera on the two samples might differ radically. When this occurs, it is usually true that the outside spores, usually phyloplane fungi, are being removed from the incoming air by filtration in the air supply units, and the different set of organisms seen in the building are caused by internal growth sources, often with much more hazardous fungi. A problem with amplification of spores inside the building might go unnoticed.

Gross colony counting also ignored the obvious problem, that different fungal spores have different health consequences. While it is possible to become allergic to almost any type of fungus, some genera and species are more likely to cause problems than others. Even more important, fungal spores vary radically in terms of acute and chronic toxicity, even within the same genus. There are at least 160 identified species of penicillium mold, some of which are not known to produce any *exomycotoxins*, but others produce potent toxins. Inhalation of spores of toxic species can cause signif-

icant toxic responses, whereas non-toxin-producing species only cause allergy and other types of irritation. The same problem exists with other large genera, such as *Aspergillus* and *Fusarium*.

While determination of genus by optical microscopic examination (including the analysis of genus by observation of spores captured in a spore trap or an Air-O-Cell cassette) is relatively straightforward for a microbiologist, determination of the exact species in large genera is much more complicated. Often it requires growth on multiple media, extensive microscopy, and a highly skilled analyst. This kind of analysis takes time and is expensive. Recently, several U.S. laboratories have started to offer speciation based on matching the DNA of cultured spores to banked DNA segments. The results are reported as the species. This procedure is almost certain to largely replace standard optical microbiological speciation, at least for highly diverse genera.

Still, the practicing industrial hygienist is left without hard guidelines or occupational exposure limits on a species-by-species basis. Other countries have adopted guidelines, at least for certain settings (e.g., schools). Canada has a zero-tolerance policy for known exotoxigenic species in schools and some other public buildings. Some European countries also have occupational exposure limits. In the United States, the rules remain rather vague: if amplification of a mold is found inside a building, work to track down the source and remediate it. If amplification of a potentially toxigenic species is found, consider more aggressive action, such as hiring experts in the area of detecting these organisms and specialized remediation firms. In extreme cases, many buildings, public and private, all across the United States have been evacuated until serious mold problems could be mitigated.

Actually, with toxin-forming species of fungi, even speciation by DNA matching leaves a certain level of uncertainty in assessing hazards. Any given species, indeed any given colony of potentially toxigenic mold, may or may not produce and release toxins under the conditions of growth. Most toxins are released into the environment when the mold sporulates, which it does when conditions for vegetative growth start to deteriorate. Depending on factors that are not well understood, these spores might contain high levels of toxins or very low levels of toxins. Thus, the ultimate air sampling procedure to determine the hazard posed by airborne mold might be to subject the collected spores to chemical analysis for mycotoxins known to be associated with the species. Unfortunately, this is still primarily a research tool or a semiquantitative agricultural tool, not widely available in a sensitive form to the industrial hygiene community. Another untapped analytical resource is cytotoxicity testing, where the mold extract is added to a growing colony of animal cells, and any adverse effect of the mold extract on cell growth or survival provides a general indicator of the mold's toxicity. This procedure has the advantage that, unlike chemical toxin analysis, you do not have to know or guess at the toxins present to effectively use the method.

A major component of noninfectious airborne bacteria that may contribute to their ability to cause allergic extrinsic alveolitis or other less serious lung effects is endotoxin, a portion of the cell wall of gram-negative bacteria. As described previously, endotoxins are collected on filters or in impingers. Subsequently, the endotoxin can then be analyzed chemically or biologically.

For the most part, bioassays are used, the most common being the *Limulus amebocyte lysate (LAL)* test. This procedure is simple, sensitive, and quick. The LAL determines the approximate bioactivity of the endotoxin present in the sample rather than the physical amount of endotoxin. The bioactivity is the most important characteristic. The analytical method has some constraints depending on the source of the sampled bacteria or fragments, contaminants, and specifics of the analytical process. One highly touted specific method is the *Kinetic Limulus Assay with Resistant-Parallel-Line Estimation (KLARE)*. The results are reported in terms of *endotoxin units (EUs)*, which is useful for comparison to control samples. There is no widely accepted guidance standard to which to compare the results.

Organic Particles

A wide range of analytical tools, including gas chromatography and high-performance liquid chromatography, are used to analyze organic particles collected on filters. Table 8–P lists organic PM commonly analyzed by these other types of chemical analyses.

Gas chromatography-mass spectrometry is sometimes used where very high sensitivity is needed or the composition of the dust is diverse or unknown. Tandem GC mass-mass spectroscopy is used for extreme sensitivity against a high background of similar organic molecules (e.g., mycotoxins in is spores).

Direct-Reading Particle Detectors

Direct-reading particulate matter samplers are available and commonly used. Direct-reading instruments are the sample collection device and the sample analysis device, all in a field-portable format. The results are provided immediately, as there is no delay for laboratory analysis.

A few grab-sampling *detector tubes* can be used for particles, such as oil mist, nickel, chromic acid, ethylene glycol, and sulfuric acid mist. More commonly, electro-optical particle enumeration devices are used. The earliest generation of these devices were forward-light-scattering photometric dust monitors. The aerosol is passed continuously through the device, illuminated by a light, and the amount of forward-scattered light is detected and used as an index of particle concentration.

More recent devices use lasers rather than noncoherent light sources, but the principle is generally the same. Scattering of light at a 90-degree angle by particles in the aerosol is used to enumerate the particles. Assuming fairly regular shape and refractive index of the particles, a pulse height analyzer can estimate the size of each particle as it passes through the light. Thus, a curve of the particle size against number can be generated with the more sophisticated versions of this type of instrument.

The range of particles detectable by laser instruments exceeds the range of noncoherent, polychromatic light-scattering photometers. Some more sophisticated devices display specific size fractions (respirable, thoracic, inhalable dust, PM 10, PM 2.5, PM 1.0), detect only fibers, and interface with computers to perform data logging and time-weighted average calculations. Some devices may be alarmed.

To see really small particles, some instruments include a condensation system that draws the particles through a saturated water or alcohol vapor chamber before counting. As the vapor condenses on the particles, their size increases and they become detectable by light scattering. A so-called *condensation nucleus counter* is therefore able to detect PM down to perhaps 10 nm in diameter. Selected CNC/laser counters are recommended by NIOSH for screening of engineered nanoparticle exposure.

In general, these instruments should not be considered as a substitute for traditional sampling, but are especially useful when sampling well-characterized dust or when monitoring for time-varying levels of dusts to detect peaks or point sources. They can be particularly useful in detecting leaks from lead or asbestos abatement or concrete demolition work containments. Used properly, they greatly enhance the industrial hygienist's ability to monitor particle exposure. Personal sampling versions are available as well.

A few gravimetric, real-time particle detectors are available. One is a modified multistage cascade impactor, with each stage, starting from the top, collecting a smaller and smaller average AED particle size. Each stage is equipped with a piezoelectric balance, and the change in weight on each stage is recorded and displayed constantly.

Historically, other direct-reading devices have used the attenuation of beta particles through an impaction membrane to provide an indication of dust accumulation. As more dust accumulated, the ability of beta particles to pass through the membrane and dust cake declined in direct proportion to the deposited dust. Konimeters were used to deposit dust on the surface of a sticky slide, which was then examined in the field through a built-in microscope.

TABLE 8–P	Examples of Organic Particulate Matter Analysis by Various Chemical Means	
Agent	**Analytical Tool**	**Method Number**
Polynuclear aromatic hydrocarbons	High-performance liquid chromatography (HPLC), gas chromatography (GC)	NIOSH 5506, 5515
2-Acetylaminofluorine	HPLC	OSHA Chemical Sampling Information
Acridine	HPLC	OSHA 58
Alkaline dusts	Acid titration	NIOSH 7401
Ammonium sulfamate	Ion chromatography	OSHA ID 188
b-benzene hexachloride	GC	EPA IP 8A
t-butyl chromate	Differential pulse polarography (DPP)	OSHA 1D 103
Carbaryl	Visible absorption spectrophotometry	NIOSH 5006
Chromium, hexavalent	Ion chromatography-electrolytic conductivity detector	NIOSH 7604
Crag herbicide	Colorimetric photometry	OSHA Chemical Sampling Information
Cyanide ion	Ion-specific electrode	NIOSH 7904, OSHA ID 120
Dimethyl arsenic acid	Ion chromatography-atomic absorption	NIOSH 5502
Elemental carbon (surrogate for diesel exhaust)	Evolved gas analysis with thermal analysis sensor	NIOSH 5040
Bacterial endotoxins	Limulus method	LAL method
Mycotoxins	Cell cytotoxicity	Experimental
N-nitrosodiethanolamine	GC-thermal energy analyzer	OSHA 31
Oil mist	Fluorescence	OSHA ID 128
Oil mist	Infrared spectrophotometry	OSHA ID 178, NIOSH 5026

BIOLOGICAL MONITORING FOR INDIVIDUALS EXPOSED TO PARTICULATE MATTER

Another tool in the industrial hygiene arsenal to assess occupational exposures to PM is biological monitoring. Biological monitoring gives an index of absorbed dose, whether by inhalation, percutaneous absorption, or ingestion. The *determinant* in biological monitoring can be the chemical itself or one of its metabolites (in urine, blood, or expired air), or a reversible biochemical change in the body indicative of a biological response to the exposure. Depending on the determinant, specimen, and time of sampling, biological monitoring may be representative of the intensity of recent exposure, an average daily exposure, or chronic cumulative exposure.

Tests that can detect permanent physiological impairment or disease are not usually classified under the category of biological monitoring, but rather fall under the broader heading of *medical surveillance*.

OSHA has promulgated a number of expanded standards for PM that include requirements for biological monitoring, including lead, arsenic, and cadmium. The lead biological monitoring procedure is particularly interesting, as it evaluates both the level of lead in the blood as a primary determinant, and the body's response to the lead in the blood in terms of the formation of zinc protoporphyrin. The latter is a better indicator of long-term chronic exposure.

ACGIH has published a list of Biological Exposure Indices (BEIs®), which are widely used as guidelines in assessing employees' exposure and response to occupational stressors. There are a number of BEIs® for PM. Some of these are shown in Table 8–Q.

A very unusual blood test for beryllium is being used more frequently. This test, called the Beryllium Lymphocyte Proliferation Test (BLPT), helps to identify workers who have become sensitized to beryllium. Sensitization is a necessary first step in the development of chronic beryllium disease (CBD). Not all sensitized employees will go on to develop CBD, but many will eventually develop granulomas in the lungs detectable by bronchoscopy or sensitive ergospirometry. A subset of these employees will develop clinically detectable chronic beryllium disease over time—shortness of breath upon exertion, chest tightness, and chest pain that may progress to debilitating or even fatal illness. Beryllium exposure also increases the risk of developing lung cancer.

Unlike many other lung diseases classically termed *pneumoconioses*, the macrophage probably plays a different role in CBD, that of presenting the beryllium, bound as a hapten to some other biological molecule, to a T lympho-

TABLE 8–Q	Biological Monitoring for Personnel Exposed to Selected Particulate Matter	
Agent	**Determinant**	**Sampling Time**
Arsenic and inorganic compounds	Inorganic arsenic and methylated metabolites in urine	End of workweek
Cadmium and inorganic compounds	Cadmium in urine Cadmium in blood	Not critical Not critical
Chromium IV, water-soluble fume	Total Cr in urine	Before and after shift End of workweek
Cobalt	Cobalt in urine or Cobalt in blood	End of workweek
Fluorides	Fluorides in urine	Before and after shift
Lead	Lead in blood	Not critical
Organophosphorous which may inhibit cholinesterase	Cholinesterase activity in red blood cells	Discretionary
Parathion	Total p-nitrophenol in urine Cholinesterase in red blood cells	End of shift Discretionary
Pentachlorophenol	Total PCP in urine Free PCP in plasma	Prior to last shift in week End of a shift
Vanadium pentoxide	Vanadium in urine	End of workweek

cyte of the T4 subtype. The T4 memory lymphocytes appear to sustain the immunological process that leads to CBD.

The BLPT test, like many medical tests, is imperfect and can lead to false-positive and false-negative results. However, it is the best tool available for biological monitoring of adverse biological changes caused by exposure to beryllium. In the event of two consecutive positive responses on the BLPT test, the employee is usually offered a bronchoscopy with lung tissue biopsy to look for subclinical CBD. This is a major procedure with real risks. Given that there are generally no medical interventions that are appropriate for subclinical cases of CBD, many employees forgo this test. Ceasing further exposure to beryllium is the only useful intervention in these cases. While there is not a clear dose-response relationship between exposure and sensitization, there almost certainly is a relationship between exposure and the likelihood of disease.

NIOSH has recommended many other biological monitoring and medical surveillance protocols for individuals exposed to PM, such as platinum in urine or blood, pentachlorophenol metabolites in blood, and reduced immunological competence after exposure to 4-aminodiphenyl.

SUMMARY

Particulate matter is usually an occupational hazard when suspended in air to form an aerosol. However, there are exceptions to this, and skin exposure or ingestion can be significant routes of exposure in some occupational settings. Exposure to particulate matter is assessed primarily by air sampling, although often with special reference to equivalent aerodynamic subfractions of the particle cloud.

Adjuncts to air sampling include surface sampling, skin or clothing sampling, biological sampling, and medical surveillance. While many aspects of an aerosol control program are stipulated in OSHA regulations, many other features are provided only in guidance form by the ACGIH, NIOSH, or consensus organizations.

The hazard posed by a cloud of particulate matter depends on a variety of factors, including its chemical composition, crystalline structure, isotope, solubility, shape, concurrent exposures, and particle size. It is often necessary to consider two or more of these factors when sampling for a particular agent.

Many industrial hygiene sampling and analytical methods are burdened with imprecision, inaccuracy, biases, and other technical problems that the industrial hygienist must understand to place the results in proper perspective.

BIBLIOGRAPHY

General References
Abba TI. Allergic diseases. In *Basic and Clinical Immunology,* 7th ed., edited by DP Stites, AI Terr. Norwalk, CT: Appleton & Lange, 1991, pp. 367–422.
Amdur MO, Klaassen CD, Doull J. *Casarett and Doull's*

Toxicology: The Basic Science of Poisons, 4th ed. New York: McGraw-Hill, 1991.

American Conference of Governmental Industrial Hygienists. *Air Sampling Instruments for Evaluation of Atmospheric Contaminants,* 5th ed. Cincinnati, OH: ACGIH, 1978.

American Conference of Governmental Industrial Hygienists. *Documentation of Threshold Limit Values, Including Biological Exposure Indices.* Cincinnati, OH: ACGIH, 2001.

American Industrial Hygiene Association. *Field Guide for the Determination of Biological Contaminants in Environmental Samples.* Fairfax, VA: AIHA, 1996.

Burge HA. *Bioaerosols.* Ann Arbor, MI: Lewis Publishers, 1995.

Centers for Disease Control/National Institutes of Health. *Biosafety in Microbiological and Biomedical Laboratories,* 4th ed. Washington, DC: GPO, 1999.

Cohen BS, Hering SV, eds. *Air Sampling Instruments for Evaluation of Atmospheric Contaminants,* 8th ed. Cincinnati, OH: ACGIH, 1995.

DiNardoi SR, ed. *The Occupational Environment—Its Evaluation and Control,* 4th ed. Fairfax, VA: AIHA, 1999.

Hathaway GJ, Proctor NH, Hughes JP. *Chemical Hazards of the Workplace,* 4th ed. New York: Van Nostrand and Reinhold, 1996.

Hinds WC. *Aerosol Technology.* New York: John Wiley and Sons, 1992.

Hogan TJ. Particulates. In *Fundamentals of Industrial Hygiene,* 4th ed., B Plog, ed. Chicago: National Safety Council, 1996, pp. 175–196.

Levine RJ, ed. *Asbestos: An Information Resource.* Washington, DC: Department of Health, Education and Welfare, National Cancer Institute, DHEW Document # 79-1681, 1978.

Nagda NL, Rector HE, Koontz MD. *Guidelines for Monitoring Indoor Air Quality.* Washington, DC: Hemisphere Publishing Corp, 1987.

Shapiro J. *Radiation Protection,* 2nd ed. Cambridge, MA: Harvard University Press, 1981.

U.S. Department of Health, Education and Welfare, Public Health Service, Centers for Disease Control, National Institute for Occupational Safety and Health. *The Industrial Environment, Its Evaluation and Control,* 3rd ed. Washington, DC: GPO, 1973.

U.S. Department of the Interior, U.S. Bureau of Mines. *Crystalline Silica Primer.* Washington, DC: U.S. Department of the Interior, 1992.

Wald PH, Stave GM. *Physical and Biological Hazards of the Workplace.* New York: Van Nostrand and Reinhold, 1994.

Sampling and Analytical References

Alwis U, Mandryk J, Hocking AD, et al. Dust exposure in the wood processing industry. *AIHA Journal* 60:641–646, 1999.

American Conference of Governmental Industrial Hygienists. Particle size selective sampling procedures in the workplace: Report of the Air Sampling Procedures Committee. *Ann Am Conf Hyg* 11:23–102, 1984.

American National Standards Institute and American Welding Society. *Method for Sampling Airborne Particulate Generated by Welding and Allied Processes,* F1 1-1978. New York: ANSI, 1978.

American Society for Testing and Materials. *Standard Practice for Field Collection of Settled Dust Samples Using Wipe Sampling Methods for Lead Determination By Atomic Spectroscopy Techniques,* E-1728-95. West Conshohocken, PA: ASTM, 1995.

Archibald BA, Solomon KR, Stephenson GR. Estimation of pesticide exposure to greenhouse applicators using video imaging and other assessment techniques. *AIHA Journal* 56:226–235, 1995.

Asbestos Fibre Measurements in Building Atmospheres: Proceedings of a Three Day Workshop. Ontario, Canada: Ontario Research Foundation, 1985.

Asbestos International Association. *Recommended Technical Method 1. Reference Method for the Determination of Airborne Asbestos Fibre Concentrations at Workplaces by Light Microscopy (Membrane Filter Method).* London: AIA, 1982.

Asbestos International Association. *Recommended Technical Method 2 (RTM 2). Method for the Determination of Airborne Asbestos Fibers and Other Inorganic Fibres by Scanning Electron Microscopy.* London: AIA, 1984.

Birch ME, Cary RA. Elemental carbon based method for monitoring occupational exposures to particulate diesel exhaust. *Aerosol SciTechnol* 25(3):221–241, October 1996.

Breysse PN, Lees PS, Rooney BC. Comparison of NIOSH 7400 A and B counting rules for assessing synthetic vitreous fiber exposure. *AIHA Journal* 60:526–532, 1999.

Carter CM, Axten CW, Byers CD, et al. Indoor airborne fiber levels of MMVF in residential buildings and commercial buildings. *AIHA Journal* 60:794–800, 1999.

Chen CC, Huang SH. Shift of aerosol penetration in respirable cyclone samples. *AIHA Journal* 60:720–729, 1999.

Chen CC, Lai CY, Shih TS, et al. Laboratory performance comparison of respirable samplers. *AIHA Journal* 60:601–611, 1999.

Christensen VR, Eastes W, Hamilton RD, et al. Fiber diameter distributions in typical MMVF wool insulation products. *AIHA Journal* 54:323–328, 1993.

Clifton RA. *What Is Talc? In Definitions for Asbestos and Other Health Related Silicates, American Society for Testing and Materials* (ASTM) STP 834, B. Levadie, ed. Philadelphia: ASTM, 1984, pp. 158–174.

Cossette M. Defining Asbestos Particulates for Monitoring Purposes. In *Definitions for Asbestos and Other Health Related Silicates,* American Society for Testing and Materials STP 834, B. Levadie, ed. Philadelphia: ASTM, 1984, pp. 5–50.

Eller P, Feng HA, Song RS, et al. Proficiency Analytical Testing (PAT) silica variability 1990–1998. *AIHA Journal* 60:533–539, 1999.

European Standardization Committee. *Size Fraction Definitions for Measurement of Airborne Particles in the Workplace,* EN 481. Brussels: CEN, 1992.

Feng AH, Schlect P. Proficiency Analytical Testing (PAT) program: May 1999. *AIHA Journal* 60:690–691, 1999.

Fenske RA. Validation of dermal exposure monitoring by biological monitoring: The fluorescent tracer technique and the patch technique. In *Biological Monitoring for Pesticide Exposure: Measurement, Estimation and Risk Reduction,* RG Wand, CA Franklin, RC Honeycutt, et al., eds. Washington, DC: American Chemical Society, 1989.

Friedrich NJ, Bauer NM, Shultz BD, et al. The use of composite dust wipe samples as a means of assessing lead exposure. *AIHA Journal* 60:326–333, 1999.

Gibbs GW. Techniques for asbestos analysis: Understanding the problem. In *Asbestos Rip Out: Dealing with Asbestos in the Industrial Environment.* Washington, DC: Organizational Resources Counselors, Inc, 1984, pp. 87–108.

Hinds WC. Basis for particle size selective sampling for wood dust. *Appl Ind Hyg* 3:67–72, 1988.

International Organization for Standardization. *ISO 7708 Air Quality Particle Size Fraction Definitions for Health-Related Sampling.* Geneva: ISO, 1993.

Jensen PA, Todd WF, Davis GN. Evaluation of eight bioaerosol samplers challenged with aerosols of free bacteria. *AIHA Journal* 53:660–667, 1992.

Karoly WJ. Stability studies of diphenylamine diisocyanate (MDI) on glass fiber filters. *AIHA Journal* 59:645–647, 1998.

Kim SY, Que Hee S, Froines J. Optimized portable cordless vacuum methods for sampling dry, hard surfaces for dust. *Appl Occup Environ Hyg* 15(6): 503–511, 2000.

Li SN, Lundgren DA. Weighing accuracy of samples collected by IOM and CIS inhalable samplers. *AIHA Journal* 60:235–236, 1999.

Liden G, Gudmundsson A. Optimization of a cyclone to the 1993 international sampling convention for respirable dust. *Appl Occup Environ Hyg,* 1996.

Liden G, Kenny LC. The performance of respirable dust samplers: Sampler bias, precision and inaccuracy. *Ann Occup Hyg* 36:1–22, 1992.

Lippmann M, Yeates DB, Albert RE. Deposition, retention and clearance of inhaled particles. *Br J Ind Med* 37: 337–362, 1980.

Liu D, Wong H, Quinlan P, et al. Welding helmet airborne fume concentrations compared to personal breathing zone sampling. *AIHA Journal* 56:280–283, 1995.

Lynch JR, Ayer HE. Measurement of asbestos exposure. *J Occup Med* 10(1):21–24, 1968.

Middendorf PJ, Lehocky AH, Williams PL. Evaluation and field calibration of the miniram PDM-3 Aerosol Monitor for measuring respirable and total coal dust. *AIHA Journal* 60:502–511, 1999.

Miles WJ. Issues and controversy: The measurement of crystalline silica; Review papers on analytical methods. *AIHA Journal* 60:396–402, 1999.

Milton DK. Endotoxin. In *Bioaerosols,* HA Burge, ed. Ann Arbor, MI: Lewis Publishers, 1995.

Morawska L, Barron W, Hitchins J. Experimental deposition of environmental tobacco smoke submicrometer particulate matter in the human respiratory tract. *AIHA Journal* (60):334–339, 1999.

National Research Council. *Environmental Tobacco Smoke: Measuring Exposures and Assessing Health Effects.* Washington, DC: NRC, 1986.

Qiong JQ. A portable vapor/particle sampler. *AIHA Journal* 59(9):614–621, 1998.

Rudzinski WE, Aahlquist B, Svejda SA, et al. Sampling and analysis of isocyanates in spray painting operations. *AIHA Journal* 56:284–289, 1995.

Saltzman BE. Generalized performance characteristics of miniature cyclones for atmospheric particulate sampling. *AIHA Journal* 45:671–680, 1984.

Samudra A, Harwood CF, Stockham JD. *Electron microscope measurement of airborne asbestos concentrations: A provisional methodology manual.* Washington, DC: U.S. EPA, 1978.

Sattelmeier J. Monitoring methods for asbestos. In *Asbestos Rip Out: Dealing with Asbestos in the Industrial Environment.* Washington, DC: Organizational Resources Counselors Inc., 1984, pp. 133–140.

Seixas NS, Hewett P. Robbins TG, et al. Variability of particle size-specific fractions of personal coal mine dust exposures. *AIHA Journal* 56:243–250, 1995.

SKC Incorporated. *Environmental Catalogue and Sampling Guide.* Eighty Four, PA: SKC Incorporated, 2000.

SKC Incorporated. *Occupational Catalogue and Air Sampling*

Guide. Eighty Four, PA: SKC Incorporated, 2000.

Soderholm SC, Perez C. Some chemicals requiring special consideration when deciding whether to sample the particle, vapor or both phases of an atmosphere. *Appl Occup Environ Hyg* (59)9: 859–864, 1991.

Spanne M, Grzybowski P, Bohgard M. Collection efficiency for sub-micron particles of a commonly used impinger. *AIHA Journal* 60:540–544, 1999.

Thorne PS, Reynolds SJ, Milton DK, et al. Field evaluation of endotoxin air sampling assay methods. *AIHA Journal* 58:792–799, 1997.

Thorpe MJ. *A method for evaluating surface contamination using the BGI-SMAIR.* Poster Session, American Industrial Hygiene Conference, Detroit: 1984.

Tsai CJ, Shis TS, Lin DJ. Laboratory testing of three direct reading dust monitors. *AIHA Journal* 57:557–563, 1996.

U.S. Department of Health and Human Services, National Institute of Occupational Safety and Health. *NIOSH Manual of Analytical Methods*, 4th ed. (and updates). Eller PM, ed. Cincinnati, OH: NIOSH, 1994.

U.S. Department of Health, Education and Welfare, Centers for Disease Control, National Institute for Occupational Safety and Health. P&CAM 239, Asbestos fibers in air. In *NIOSH Manual of Analytical Methods,* 2nd ed., vol. 1. Washington, DC: NIOSH, 1977.

U.S. Department of Labor, Occupational Safety and Health Administration. 29 CFR Part 1910 Subpart Z, Part 1000, *Toxic Air Contaminants.* Washington, DC: OSHA, 1999.

U.S. Department of Labor, Occupational Safety and Health Administration. 29 CFR Part 1910 Subpart Z, Section 1001 Asbestos, Appendices A and B, *OSHA Reference Method.* Washington, DC: OSHA, 1999.

U.S. Department of Labor, Occupational Safety and Health Administration. 29 CFR Part 1926 Subpart Z, Section 1101, Appendices A and B, *OSHA Reference Method.* Washington, DC: OSHA, 1999.

U.S. Department of Labor, Occupational Safety and Health Administration. Sampling for surface contamination. In *OSHA Technical Manual.* Washington, DC: U.S. DOL, 1999. http://www.osha-slc.gov/dts/osta/otm/ otm_ii/ otm_ii_2.html

U.S. Environmental Protection Agency. 40 CFR Part 763, *Asbestos.* Washington, DC: EPA, 1999.

U.S. Environmental Protection Agency. *Measuring Airborne Asbestos Following an Abatement Action.* EPA Document 600/4-85-049. Washington, DC: EPA, 1985.

U.S. Environmental Protection Agency. Test Methods for Evaluating Solid Waste, Volume 1A: *Laboratory Manual, Physical/Chemical Methods,* SW-846, Methods 3050A, 6010A, 7000A and 7402, 3rd ed. Washington, DC: EPA, 1986.

Vaughn NP, Chalmers CP, Botham RA. A field comparison for personal samplers for inhalable dust. *Ann Occup Hyg* 34:553–573, 1990.

Volckens J, Boundy M, Leith D, et al. Oil mist concentration: A comparison of sampling methods. *AIHA Journal* 60:684–689, 1999.

World Health Organization, International Association for Research on Cancer. *Measurement of Inorganic Fibrous Particulates in Ambient Air and Indoors with the Scanning Electron Microscope,* IARC Scientific Publication no. 90:361–366. Lyons, France: WHO, 1989.

Yamate G, Agarwal SC, Gibbons RD. *Methodology for the Measurement of Airborne Asbestos by Electron Microscopy.* Research Triangle Park, NC: EPA, 1984.

Health Effects References

Auger PL, Gourdeau P, Miller D. Clinical experience with patients suffering from a chronic fatigue-like syndrome and repeated upper airways infections in relation to airborne molds. *Am J Ind Med* 25:41–42, 1994.

Croft W, Jarvis BB, Yatawara CS. Airborne outbreak of trichothecene toxicosis. *Atmos Environ* 20:549–552, 1986.

Eisenbud M. The standard for control of chronic beryllium disease. *Appl Occup Environ Hyg* 13(1):25–31, 1998.

Enarson DA, Chan-Yeung M. Characterization of health effects of wood dust exposure. *Am J Ind Med* 17:33–38, 1990.

Gross P. Consideration of the aerodynamic equivalent diameter of respirable mineral fibers. *AIHA Journal* 42:449–542, 1981.

Johanning E, Biagini R, Hull D, et al. Health and immunology study following exposure to toxigenic fungi (*Stachybotrys chartarum*) in a water damaged office building. *Occup Environ Health* 68:207–218, 1996.

Milne J, Gandevia B. Occupational asthma and rhinitis due to western red cedar *(Thuja plicata),* with special reference to bronchial reactivity. *Br J Ind Med* 27:235–244, 1970.

National Institute for Occupational Safety and Health. *Current Intelligence Bulletin No. 50. Carcinogenic Effects of Exposure to Diesel Exhaust.* Cincinnati, OH: NIOSH, 1988, pp. 88–116.

National Research Council. *Environmental Tobacco Smoke: Measuring Exposures and Assessing Health Effects.* Washington, DC: NRC, 1986.

U.S. Department of Health and Human Services, Agency for Toxic Substances and Disease Registry. *Toxicological*

Profile of Thallium. TP-91/26, Washington, DC: GPO 1992.

World Health Organization. *Diesel and Gasoline Engine Exhausts and some Nitroarenes. IARC Monograph on the Evaluation of Carcinogenic Risks to Humans,* Vol. 46. Lyons, France: WHO, 1989.

World Health Organization. *Diesel Fuel and Exhaust Emissions (International Program on Chemical Safety Monographs of Environmental Health Criteria,* no. 171). Lyons, France: WHO, 1996.

World Health Organization. *Wood Dust and Formaldehyde. IARC Monographs on the Evaluation of Carcinogenic Risks to Humans,* vol. 62. Lyons, France: WHO, 1995.

World Health Organization, International Agency for Research on Cancer (IARC). *IARC Monograph on the Evaluation of Carcinogenic Risk to Humans: Man Made Mineral Fibers and Radon,* vol. 43. Lyons, France: WHO, 1988.

World Health Organization, International Agency for Research on Cancer. *IARC Monograph on the Evaluation of the Carcinogenic Risk of Chemicals to Humans, Silica and Some Silicates.* Vol 42. Zurich: WHO, 1987.

CHAPTER 9

Industrial Noise

by John J. Standard, MS, MPH, CIH, CSP

The sounds of industry, growing in volume over the years, have heralded not only technical and economic progress, but also an ever-increasing incidence of hearing loss and other noise-related hazards in exposed employees. Noise is not a new hazard. Indeed, noise-induced hearing loss was observed centuries ago. In 1700, Ramazzini in "De Morbis Artificium Diatriba" described how workers who hammer copper "have their ears so injured by that perpetual din . . . that workers of this class become hard of hearing, and if they grow old at this work, completely deaf." Before the Industrial Revolution, however, comparatively few people were exposed to high levels of noise in the workplace. The advent of steam power during the Industrial Revolution first brought general attention to noise as an occupational hazard. Workers who fabricated steam boilers were found to develop hearing loss in such numbers that the malady was dubbed boilermakers' disease. The increasing mechanization that has occurred in all industries and in most trades has since aggravated the noise problem. Noise levels in the workplace, particularly those levels maintained in mechanized industries, are likely to be more intense and sustained than any noise levels experienced outside the workplace.

The recognition, evaluation, and control of industrial noise hazards are introduced in this chapter. Basically, this involves assessing the extent of the noise problem, setting objectives for a noise abatement program, controlling exposure to excessive noise, and monitoring the hearing of exposed employees.

COMPENSATION ASPECTS

The trend toward covering hearing losses under state workers' compensation laws has stimulated interest on the part of employers in controlling industrial noise exposures.

Compensation laws that cover loss of hearing due to noise exposure have been enacted in many states; compensation is being awarded in other states even though hearing loss is not specifically defined in many compensation laws.

Occupational hearing loss can be defined as a hearing impairment of one or both ears, partial or complete, that results from one's employment. It includes acoustic trauma as well as noise-induced hearing loss.

Acoustic trauma denotes injury to the sensorineural elements of the inner ear. Acoustic trauma is produced by one or a few exposures to sudden intense acoustic forms of energy resulting from blasts and explosions or by direct trauma to the head or ear. The worker should be able to relate the onset of hearing loss to one single incident. For details on ear anatomy, see Chapter 4, The Ears.

Noise-induced hearing loss, on the other hand, describes the cumulative permanent loss of hearing—always of the sensorineural type—that develops over months or years of hazardous noise exposure.

Noise-induced hearing loss usually affects both ears equally in the extent and degree of loss. It should also be kept in mind that the onset of hearing loss, its progression, its permanency, and the characteristics of the audiograms obtained, vary depending on whether the injury is a noise-induced hearing loss or acoustic trauma.

To establish a diagnosis of noise-induced hearing loss and a causal relationship to employment, the physician considers the following factors:

• the employee's history of hearing loss—onset and progress
• the employee's occupational history, type of work, and years of employment
• the results of the employee's otological examination
• the results of audiological and hearing studies performed (preplacement, periodic, and termination)
• the ruling out of nonindustrial causes of hearing loss

It has been estimated that 1.7 million workers in the United States between 50 and 59 years of age have compensable noise-induced hearing loss. Assuming that only 10 percent of these workers file for compensation and that the average claim amounts to $3,000, the potential cost to industry could exceed $500 million.

Estimates show that 16.9 percent of the working population are employed in jobs where the noise level equals or exceeds 85 dBA (Table 9–A).

At present, no test can predict which individuals will incur a hearing loss. If enough people are placed in an environment where the predominant noise level exceeds 85 dBA for a sufficient period of time, some individuals incur a hearing impairment greater than that caused by presbycusis (loss of hearing as a result of aging). The number of workers subjected to noise hazards exceeds that of those exposed to any other significant occupational hazard.

The audiometer provides an easily reproducible means of measuring the status of an individual's hearing with appreciable accuracy. Partial hearing losses are easily measurable by commercially available audiometers.

PROPERTIES OF SOUND

Sound can be defined as any pressure variation (in air, water, or some other medium) that the human ear can detect.

Sound produces a sensory response in the brain. The perception of sound resulting in the sensation called hearing is the principal sensory response; however, under certain conditions, additional subjective sensations ranging from pressure in the chest cavity to actual pain in the ears can be produced (see Chapter 4, "The Ears"). There are certain effects produced by sounds that appear to be universally undesirable for all people. These effects include

• the masking of wanted sounds, particularly speech;
• auditory fatigue;
• damage to hearing; and
• annoyance.

Noise

What we call noise is usually sound that bears no information and whose intensity usually varies randomly in time. The word *noise* is often used to mean unpleasant sound that the listener does not want to hear. Noise interferes with the perception of wanted sound and is likely to be physiologically harmful.

Noise does not always have particular physical characteristics that distinguish it from wanted sound. No instrument can distinguish between a sound and a noise—only human reaction can.

A variety of methods have been devised to relate objective physical measurements of sound to subjective human perception. The purpose of this section is to outline both the objective physical properties of sound and its important subjective aspects.

The term *sound* usually refers to the form of energy that produces a sensation perceived by the sense of hearing in humans, whereas *vibration* usually refers to nonaudible acoustic phenomena that are recognized by the tactile experience of touch, or feeling. However, there is no essential physical difference between the sonic and vibratory forms of sound energy.

The generation and propagation of sound are easily visualized by means of a simple model. Consider a plate suspended in midair (Figure 9–1). When struck, the plate vibrates rapidly back and forth. As the plate travels in either

TABLE 9–A   Estimated Number of Workers Exposed to Noise at or Above 85 dBA, by Economic Sector (two-digit SIC)*

Economic Sector	SIC	Total No. Production Workers	No.	As % of Total Production Workers
Agriculture, forestry, and fishing:				
Agriculture services	07	89,189	17,618	19.8
Mining:				
Oil and gas extraction	13	330,841	76,525	23.1
Construction:				
General building contractors	15	664,833	105,299	15.8
Heavy construction, except building	16	517,969	124,610	24.0
Special trade contractors	17	1,228,744	191,087	15.6
Manufacturing:				
Food and kindred products	20	1,188,267	343,030	28.9
Tobacco products	21	106,399	57,764	54.3
Textile mill products	22	615,322	262,108	42.6
Apparel and other finished products	23	1,082,236	150,824	13.9
Lumber and wood products	24	475,730	196,489	41.3
Furniture and fixtures	25	428,539	121,271	28.3
Paper and allied products	26	488,101	164,808	33.8
Printing and publishing	27	724,707	154,862	21.4
Chemicals and allied products	28	592,059	102,671	17.3
Petroleum and coal products	29	160,516	31,998	19.9
Rubber and misc. plastics products	30	595,525	135,611	22.8
Leather and leather products	31	144,200	9,346	6.5
Stone, clay, and glass products	32	457,983	98,215	21.5
Primary metal industries	33	824,725	269,270	32.7
Fabricated metal products	34	1,151,777	336,919	29.3
Industrial machinery and equipment	35	1,544,883	229,509	14.9
Electronic and other electric equipment	36	1,287,842	104,553	8.1
Transportation equipment	37	1,311,750	238,609	18.2
Instruments and related products	38	555,108	48,014	8.7
Miscellaneous mfg. Industries	39	418,805	39,307	9.4
Transportation and public utilities:				
Local and inter-urban passenger transit	41	171,428	14,832	8.7
Trucking and warehousing	42	561,058	39,150	7.0
Transportation by air	45	312,931	94,656	30.3
Communications	48	387,505	23,124	6.0
Electric, gas, and sanitary services	49	588,041	89,730	15.3
Wholesale trade:				
Wholesale trade – durable goods	50	528,659	110,283	20.9
Wholesale trade – nondurable goods	51	99,410	5,287	5.3
Retail trade:				
Automotive, dealers and service stations	55	334,063	4,543	1.4
Services:				
Personal services	72	366,545	33,462	9.1
Business services	73	766,108	11,246	1.5
Auto repair, services, and parking	75	320,459	33,997	10.6
Misc. repair services	76	143,302	12,682	8.9
Health services	80	2,679,610	15,677	0.6
Total		**24,245,169**	**4,098,986**	**16.9**

*SIC= Standard industrial classification. Source: OBM (1987).

Source: Reprinted from NIOSH Criteria Document, *Occupational Noise Exposure- Revised Criteria,* 1998. Cincinnati: NIOSH, 1998.

Note: Based on data collected by NOES (NIOSH 1988a,b, 1990). Not all two-digit SIC sectors and not all four-digit SIC industries within each two-digit SIC sector were surveyed. The NOES covered 39 of 83 two-digit SIC sectors, and the NOES estimates were representative of only the four-digit SIC industries actually surveyed. For example, within agricultural services (SIC 07), the estimates are for crop preparation services (SIC 0723), veterinary services for animal specialties (SIC 0742), lawn and garden services (SIC 0782), and ornamental shrub and tree services (SIC 0783) only, because no surveys were done for soil preparation services (SIC 0724), crop planting and protecting (SIC 0721), crop harvesting (SIC 0722), cotton ginning (SIC 0724), veterinary services for livestock (SIC 0741), livestock services (SIC 0751), animal specialty services (SIC 0752), farm labor contractors (SIC 0761), farm management services (SIC 0762), and landscape counseling and planning (SIC 0781).

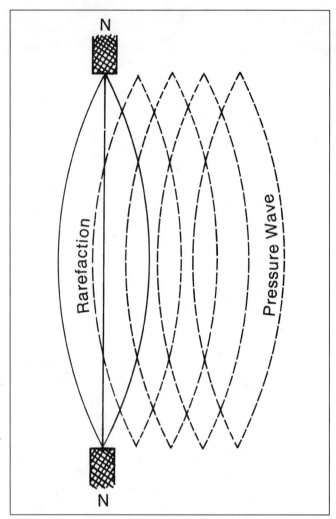

Figure 9–1. As the vibrating plate moves back and forth, it compresses the air in the direction of its motions. When it reverses direction, it produces a partial vacuum, or rarefaction, imparting energy to the air, which radiates away from the plate as sound.

direction, it compresses the air, causing a slight increase in its pressure. When the plate reverses direction, it leaves a partial vacuum, or rarefaction, of the air. These alternate compressions and rarefactions cause small but repeated fluctuations in the atmospheric pressure that extend outward from the plate. When these pressure variations strike an eardrum, they cause it to vibrate in response to the slight changes in atmospheric pressure. The disturbance of the eardrum is translated into a neural sensation in the inner ear and is carried to the brain, where it is interpreted as sound (Figure 9–2).

Sound is invariably produced by vibratory motion of some sort. The sounding body must act on some medium to produce vibrations that are characteristic of sound. Any type of vibration can be a source of sound, but by definition, only longitudinal vibration of the conducting medium is a sound wave.

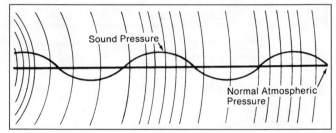

Figure 9–2. Air is an elastic medium and behaves as if it were a succession of adjoining particles. The resulting motion of the medium is known as wave motion, and the instantaneous form of the disturbance is called a sound wave.

Sound Waves

Sound waves are a particular form of a general class of waves known as elastic waves. Sound waves can occur in any elastic medium such as air, water, or steel. One sound wave may have three times the frequency and one-third the intensity (amplitude) of another sound wave. However, if both the waves cross their respective zero positions in the same direction at the same time, they are said to be in phase (Figure 9–3).

Frequency

Using sound propagating through air as an example, *frequency* is the number of times per second that an air molecule at the sound source is displaced from its position of equilibrium, rebounds through the equilibrium position to a maximum displacement opposite in direction from the initial

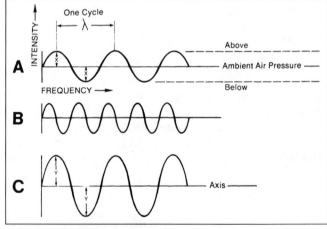

Figure 9–3. The curves shown are pictorial representations of sound waves. Pitch is related to frequency, and loudness is related to the intensity of a sound. Curve B represents a sound that has a higher frequency—a higher perceived pitch—than the sound represented by curve A because the variations in air pressure, as represented by a point on the curve, cross the axis more often. The intensity of a sound can be shown by the height of the curve. Curve C represents a sound that has a greater intensity—a greater perceived loudness—than the sound represented by curve A (distance Y is greater than distance X).

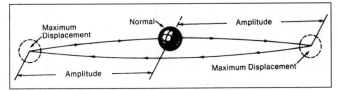

Figure 9–4. Relative positions of an air molecule during one complete cycle of motion.

displacement, and then returns to its equilibrium position. In other words, frequency is the number of times per second a vibrating body traces one complete cycle of motion (Figure 9–4). The time required for each cycle is known as the period of the wave and is simply the reciprocal of the frequency. The phrase formerly used to describe frequency, cycles per second, has now been replaced by *Hertz*, abbreviated *Hz*.

Frequency is perceived as pitch. The audible range of frequencies for humans with good hearing is between 20 Hz and 20,000 Hz. Most everyday sounds contain a mixture of frequencies generated by a variety of sources. A sound's frequency composition is called its spectrum. The frequency spectrum can be a determining factor in the level of annoyance caused by noise; high-frequency noise generally is more annoying than low-frequency noise. Also, narrow frequency bands or pure tones (single frequencies) can be somewhat more harmful to hearing than broadband noise.

Wavelength

Wavelength is the distance measured between two analogous points on two successive parts of a wave. In other words, wavelength is the distance that a sound wave travels in one cycle. The Greek letter lambda (λ) is used to express wavelength, and it is measured in feet or meters (Figure 9–3).

Wavelength is an important property of sound. For example, sound waves that have a wavelength that is much larger than an obstacle are little affected by the presence of that obstacle; the sound waves bend around it. This bending of the sound around obstacles is called *diffraction*.

If the wavelength of the sound is small in comparison with the size of an obstacle (small wavelengths are characteristic of high-frequency sounds), the sound is reflected or scattered in many directions, and the obstacle casts a "shadow." Actually, some sound is diffracted into the shadow, and there is significant reflection of the sound. As a consequence of diffraction, a wall is of little use as a shield against low-frequency sound (long wavelength), but it can be an effective barrier against high-frequency sound (short wavelength) (Figure 9–5).

Velocity

The velocity at which the analogous pressure points on successive parts of a sound wave pass a given point is called the speed of sound. The speed of sound is always equal to the product of the wavelength and the frequency:

$$c = f\lambda \qquad (1)$$

where c = speed of sound (feet or meters per second)
  f = frequency of sound (Hz)
  λ = wavelength (feet or meters)

The speed with which the sound disturbance spreads depends on the mass and elastic properties of the medium. In air at 72°F, the speed of sound is about 1,130 ft/sec (344 m/sec). Its effects are commonly observed in echoes and in the apparent delay between a flash of lightning and the accompanying thunder.

In a homogeneous medium, the speed of sound is independent of frequency; that is, in such a medium, sounds of all frequencies travel at the same speed. However, the speed of sound varies with the density and compressibility of the medium through which it is traveling. Speed increases as medium density increases and medium compressibility decreases. For example, the speed of sound is approximately 1,433 m/sec in water, 3,962 m/sec in wood, and 5,029 m/sec in steel. Sound, therefore, can be transmitted through many media before it is eventually transmitted through air to the ear of the receiver.

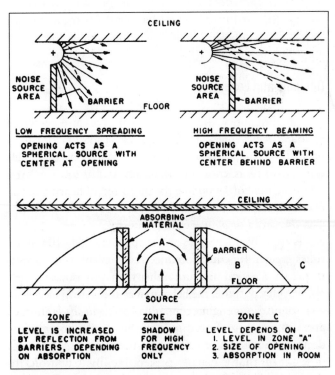

Figure 9–5. The effects of a barrier as a shield to contain noise or low or high frequency.

Sound Pressure

Sound is a slight, rapid variation in atmospheric pressure, caused by some disturbance or agitation of the air. The sounds of normal conversation amount to sound pressure of only a few millionths of a pound per square inch, yet they can be easily heard because of the remarkable sensitivity of the human ear. The sounds that can damage our hearing have sound pressures of only a few thousandths of a pound per square inch.

Most common sounds consist of a rapid, irregular series of positive pressure disturbances (compressions) and negative pressure disturbances (rarefactions) measured against the equilibrium pressure value. If we were to measure the mean value of a sound pressure disturbance, we would find it to be zero because there are as many positive compressions as negative rarefactions. Thus, the mean value of sound pressure is not a useful measurement. We must look for a measurement that permits the effects of rarefactions to be added to (rather than subtracted from) the effects of compressions.

The *root-mean-square (rms) sound pressure* is one such measurement. The rms sound pressure is obtained by squaring the value of the sound pressure disturbance at each instant of time. The squared values are then added and averaged over the given time. The rms sound pressure is the square root of this time average. Because the squaring operation converts all the negative sound pressures to positive squared values, the rms sound pressure is a useful, nonzero measurement of the magnitude of the sound wave. The units used to measure sound pressure are micropascals (μPa), newtons per square meter (N/m^2), microbars (μbar), and dynes per square centimeter (d/cm^2). Relations among these units are as follows: 1 Pa = 1 N/m^2 = 10 μbar = 10 d/cm^2.

Decibels and Levels

Even though the weakest sound pressure perceived as sound is a small quantity, the *range* of sound pressure perceived as sound is extremely large. The weakest sound that can be heard by a person with very good hearing in an extremely quiet location is known as the *threshold of hearing*. At a reference tone of 1,000 Hz, the threshold of hearing for an average person is taken to be a sound pressure of 20 μPa. The *threshold of pain,* or the greatest sound pressure that can be perceived without pain, is approximately 10 million times greater. It is therefore more convenient to use a *relative scale* of sound pressure rather than an absolute scale.

For this purpose, the bel, a unit of measure in electrical-communications engineering, is used. The *decibel*, abbreviated dB, is the preferred unit for measuring sound. One decibel is one-tenth of a bel and is the minimum difference in loudness that is usually perceptible. By definition, the decibel is a dimensionless unit used to express the logarithm of the ratio of a measured quantity to a reference quantity.

In acoustics, the decibel is used to describe the level of quantities that are proportional to sound power.

Sound power (W) is the amount of energy per unit time that radiates from a source in the form of an acoustic wave. *Sound power level* (L_W), which is expressed in decibels relative to the reference power of 10^{-12} watts (W_0), expresses the total amount of sound power radiated by a sound source, regardless of the space into which the source is placed. The relationship is shown below.

$$L_W = 10 \log \frac{W}{W_0} \qquad (2)$$

where W = sound power (watts)
W_0 = reference power (10^{-12} watts)
log = a logarithm to the base 10

Consider for example, a large chipping hammer having a sound power of 1 watt. Expressing this sound power in decibels,

$$L_W = 10 \log \frac{W}{W_0} \;=\; 10 \log \frac{1}{10^{-12}} \qquad (3)$$
$$= 10 \log 10^{12} = 120 \text{ dB}$$

As sound power is radiated from a point source in free space, the power is distributed over a spherical surface, so that at any given point there exists a certain sound power per unit area. This is designated as *intensity* and is measured in units of watts per square meter. Although intensity diminishes as distance from the source increases, the power that is radiated, being the product of the intensity and the area over which it is spread, remains constant.

Sound power cannot be measured directly. It is possible to measure intensity, but the instruments are expensive and must be used carefully. Under most conditions of sound radiation, sound intensity is proportional to the square of sound pressure. Sound pressure can be measured more easily, so sound level meters are built to measure *sound pressure level* (L_p) in decibels.

The sound level meter directly indicates sound pressure level referenced to a sound pressure of 20 μPa, the approximate threshold of hearing. The equation for sound pressure level is:

$$L_p = 10 \log \frac{p^2}{p_0^2} = 20 \log \frac{p}{p_0} \qquad (4)$$

where p = measured root-mean-square (rms) sound pressure
p_0 = reference rms sound pressure (20 μPa)

Note that the multiplier is 20 and not 10 as in the case of the sound power level equation. This is because sound power is proportional to the *square* of sound pressure and because $10 \log p^2 = 20 \log p$.

Table 9–B shows the relationship between sound pressure in micropascals and sound pressure level in decibels for some common sounds. The table also illustrates the advantage of using decibel notation rather than the wide range of pressure (or power). Note that a change of sound pressure by a factor of 10 corresponds to a change in sound pressure level of 20 dB. Also note that any range over which the sound pressure is doubled is equivalent to 6 dB whether at low or high levels. For example, sound pressures of 20 µPa and 40 µPa are equivalent to the following sound pressure levels:

$p = 20$ µPa:
$$L_p = 20 \log \frac{p}{p_0} = 20 \log \frac{20}{20} = 20 \log 1 = 0 \text{dB} \quad (5)$$

$p = 40$ µPa:
$$L_p = 20 \log \frac{p}{p_0} = 20 \log \frac{40}{20} = 20 \log 2 = 6 \text{dB} \quad (6)$$

Although a doubling of sound pressure represents an increase of 6 dB in the sound pressure level, doubling the *sound power* results in an increase of 3 dB in the sound power level:

$$W = 1 \text{ watt: } L_W = 10 \log \frac{1}{10^{-12}} = 120 \text{ dB} \quad (7)$$

$$W = 2 \text{ watt: } L_W = 10 \log \frac{2}{10^{-12}} = 123 \text{ dB} \quad (8)$$

Again, as seen in the above examples, doubling the sound power increases the sound power level 3 dB, whereas doubling the sound pressure increases the sound pressure level 6 dB. These results are not contradictory because doubling the sound power is equivalent to doubling the *square* of the sound pressure. Remember, sound power is proportional to the *square* of sound pressure.

There is a common tendency to confuse sound power with sound pressure. Sound power and sound pressure can be illustrated simply with an analogy between light and sound.

Light bulbs are rated in terms of their power consumption (60-W bulbs, 25-W bulbs, etc.). From experience, we know that, in a given location, the intensity or illumination of a 60-W bulb is greater than that of a 25-W bulb at a given distance. Analogously, a sound source of 60 W produces a greater sound pressure level than a 25-W source at a given distance.

Sound power is somewhat analogous to the power rating of the light bulb. A "weak" sound source would produce low sound levels, whereas a "stronger" sound source would produce higher sound levels. Sound power level is independent of the environmental surroundings. Sound pressure, on the other hand, is related to intensity and is analogous to the illumination produced by the light bulb. The magnitude of the sound pressure from a given sound source depends on the distance from the source. As discussed earlier, sound pressure is readily measured by a sound level meter, but sound power cannot be measured directly.

It is important to note that the decibel scale of measurement is not used only in the description of sound pressure level and sound power level. By definition, the decibel is a

TABLE 9–B	Sound Pressure and Sound Pressure Level Values for Some Typical Sounds	
Sound Pressure (µPa)	**Overall Sound Pressure Level (dB, re: 20 µPa)**	**Example**
20	0	Threshold of Hearing
63	10	
200	20	Studio for sound pictures
630	30	Soft whisper (5 feet)
2,000	40	Quiet office; Audiometric testing booth
6,300	50	Average residence; Large office
20,000	60	Conversational speech (3 ft)
63,000	70	Freight train (100 ft)
200,000	80	Very noisy restaurant
630,000	90	Subway; Printing press plant
2,000,000	100	Looms in textile mill; electric furnace area
6,300,000	110	Woodworking; casting shakeout area
20,000,000	120	Hydraulic press; 50-hp siren (100 ft)
200,000,000	140	Threshold of pain; jet plane
20,000,000,000	180	Rocket-launching pad

*A change of sound pressure by a factor of 10 corresponds to a change in sound pressure level of 20 dB.

dimensionless unit related to the logarithm of the ratio of a measured quantity to a reference quantity. The decibel has no meaning unless a reference quantity is specified. Because of the mathematical properties of the logarithmic function, the decibel scale can compress data involving entities of large and small magnitude into a relative scale involving a small range of numbers. The decibel is commonly used to describe levels of such things as acoustic intensity, hearing thresholds, electrical voltage, electrical current, and electrical power, as well as sound pressure and sound power.

Because decibels are logarithmic values, it is not proper to add them by normal algebraic addition. For example, 60 dB plus 60 dB *does not* equal 120 dB but only 63 dB. To show how to combine decibel levels of sound sources, we present some examples.

Example 1

Two sources are radiating noise in a free field. One source has a sound power level of 123 dB and the other source has a sound power level of 117 dB (re: 10^{-12} W). What is the combined sound power level of these two sources?

Solution:

$$L_W = 10 \log \frac{W}{W_0} \tag{9}$$

or

$$\frac{W}{W_0} = 10^{L_W/10} \tag{10}$$

$$\frac{W_1}{W_0} = 10^{L_{W_1}/10} = 10^{123/10} = 10^{12.3} = 1.995 \times 10^{12} \tag{11}$$

$$\frac{W_2}{W_0} = 10^{L_{W_2}/10} = 10^{117/10} = 10^{11.7} = 5.012 \times 10^{11} \tag{12}$$

$$\frac{W_1}{W_0} + \frac{W_2}{W_0} = 2.496 \times 10^{12} \tag{13}$$

The combined sound power level of the two sources, L_W (total), can then be calculated as

$$L_W \text{ (total)} = 10 \log \left(\frac{W_1}{W_0} + \frac{W_2}{W_0} \right)$$

$$= 10 \log (2.496 \times 10^{12}) \tag{14}$$

$$= 10 \log (12.40)$$

$$L_W \text{ (total)} = 124 \text{ dB}$$

The same process can be used for sound pressure levels.

Example 2

Suppose the sound pressure level of each of three individual noise sources is measured at a point such that with only the first source running, the L_p = 86 dB; with only the second source running it is 84 dB; and with only the third source running it is 89 dB (re: 20 μPa). What will the sound pressure level at the point be with all three sources running concurrently?

$$L_p = 10 \log \left(\frac{p}{p_0} \right)^2 \tag{15}$$

or

$$\left(\frac{p}{p_0} \right)^2 = 10^{L_p/10} \tag{16}$$

$$\left(\frac{p_{total}}{p_0} \right)^2 = 10^{L_{P_1}/10} + 10^{L_{P_2}/10} + 10^{L_{P_3}/10}$$

$$= 10^{8.6} + 10^{8.4} + 10^{8.9} \tag{17}$$

$$= (3.982 + 2.512 + 7.944) \, 10^8$$

$$\left(\frac{p_{total}}{p_0} \right)^2 = 14.438 \times 10^8$$

The sound pressure level at the point with all three sources running is then equal to

$$L_p \text{ (total)} = 10 \log \left(\frac{p_{total}}{p_0} \right)^2$$

$$= 10 \log (14.438 \times 10^8) \tag{18}$$

$$= 10 \, (9.16)$$

$$L_p \text{ (total)} = 91.6 \text{ dB}$$

In general then, the procedure for adding decibels can be summarized as follows:

$$L_{total} = 10 \log \left(\sum_{i=1}^{N} 10^{L_i/10} \right) \tag{19}$$

where L can be sound power level or sound pressure level.

It is often adequate to use the simplified schedule shown below for adding decibels.

Difference in Decibel Values	Add to Higher Value
0 or 1 dB	3 dB
2 or 3 dB	2 dB
4 to 9 dB	1 dB
10 dB or more	0 dB

Examples: 83 dB + 82 dB = 86 dB
83 dB + 80 dB = 85 dB
83 dB + 78 dB = 84 dB
83 dB + 73 dB = 83 dB

More than two levels can be combined using the above simplified schedule by taking the combinations in pairs.

Example 3

When measured at the same location, four noise sources have sound pressure levels of 89, 87, 78, and 81 dB, respectively. What would the sound pressure level at this location be if all four sources were running concurrently? Using the simplified method,

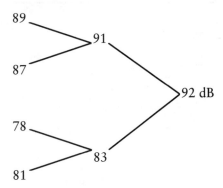

Using the calculated method,

$$L_p = 10 \log (10^{8.9} + 10^{8.7} + 10^{7.8} + 10^{8.1}) = 91.7 \text{ dB} \qquad (20)$$

Although the simplified method is less accurate than the calculated method, the difference may not be significant. Even so, when accurate results are required, the calculated method should be used.

Loudness

Although loudness depends primarily on sound pressure, it is also affected by frequency. (Pitch is closely related to frequency.) The reason for this is that the human ear is more sensitive to high-frequency sounds than it is to low-frequency sounds.

The upper limit of frequency at which airborne sounds can be heard depends primarily on the condition of a person's hearing and on the intensity of the sound. For young adults, this upper limit is usually somewhere between 16,000 and 20,000 Hz. For most practical purposes, the actual figure is not important. It is important, however, to realize that most people lose sensitivity for the higher-frequency sounds as they grow older (presbycusis).

The complete hearing process seems to consist of a number of separate processes that, in themselves, are fairly complicated. No simple relationship exists between the physical measurement of a sound pressure level and the human perception of the sound. One pure tone may sound louder than another pure tone, even though the measured sound pressure level is the same in both cases.

Sound pressure levels, therefore, are only a part of the story and can be deceiving. The fundamental problem is that the quantities to be measured must include a person's reaction to the sound—a reaction that can be determined by such varied factors as the state of the person's health, characteristics of the sound, and the person's attitude toward the device or the person that generates the sound. In the course of time, various loudness level–rating methods have been suggested, and a number of different criteria for tolerable noise levels have been proposed.

A complete physical description of sound must include its frequency spectrum, its overall sound pressure level, and the variation of both of these quantities over time. *Loudness* is the subjective human response to sound pressure and intensity. At any given frequency, loudness varies directly as sound pressure and intensity vary, but not in a simple, straight-line manner.

The physical characteristics of a sound as measured by an instrument and the "noisiness" of a sound as a subjective characteristic may bear little relationship to one another. A sound level meter cannot distinguish between a pleasant sound and an unpleasant one. A human reaction is required to differentiate between a pleasant sound and a noise. Loudness is not merely a question of sound pressure level. A sound that has a constant sound pressure can be made to appear quieter or louder by changing its frequency.

Equal-Loudness Contours

Results of experiments designed to determine the response of the human ear to sound were reported by Fletcher and Munson in 1933. A reference tone and a test tone were presented alternately to the test subjects (young men), who were asked to adjust the level of the test tone until it sounded as loud to them as the reference tone (1,000 Hz). The results of these experiments yielded the familiar Fletcher–Munson, or equal-loudness, contours (Figure 9–6). The contours represent the sound pressure level necessary at each frequency to produce the same loudness response in the average listener. The nonlinearity of the ear's response is represented by the changing contour shapes as the sound pressure level is increased, a phenomenon that is particularly noticeable at low frequencies. The lower, dashed, curve indicates the threshold of hearing, which represents the sound pressure level necessary to trigger the sensation of hearing in the average listener. The actual threshold varies as much as ±10 dB among healthy individuals.

Sound Pressure Weighting

Electronic circuits with sensitivity that varies with frequency similar to human hearing have been developed. There are three different internationally standardized characteristics called weighting networks A, B, and C. The A-network

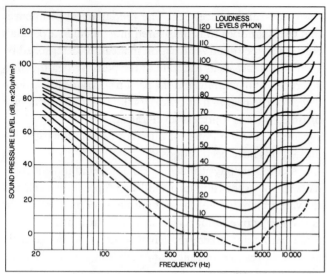

Figure 9–6. Free-field equal-loudness contours of pure tones. Because the human ear is more sensitive to the higher frequencies of sound, changing the frequency of a sound changes its relative loudness. These are also called Fletcher–Munson contours. *(Adapted from the* Handbook of Noise Measurement, *9th ed. GenRad, Inc., 1980.)*

	Octave-Band Correction Factors of the A-Weighted Network
TABLE 9–C	

Octave-Band Center Frequency (Hz)	A-Network Correction Factor (dB)
31.5	-39.4
63	-26.2
125	-16.1
250	-8.6
500	-3.2
1,000	0
2,000	+1.2
4,000	+1.0
8,000	-1.1
16,000	-6.6

Source: Adapted from ANSI, 1983.

was designed to approximate the equal-loudness curves at low sound pressure levels, the B-network was designed for medium sound pressure levels, and the C-network was designed for high levels. In current applications, the B-network is rarely used.

The weighting networks are the sound level meter's means of responding to some frequencies more than to others. The very low frequencies are discriminated against (attenuated) quite severely by the A-network, moderately attenuated by the B-network, and hardly attenuated at all by the C-network (Figure 9–7). Therefore, if the measured sound level of a noise is much higher on C-weighting than on A-weighting, much of the noise energy is probably of low frequency.

By definition, a weighted-frequency scale is simply a series of correction factors that are applied to sound pressure levels on an energy basis as a function of frequency. Shown in Table 9–C are the corrections for the A-weighting network at each of the octave-band center frequencies commonly used in noise measurements.

The A-weighted sound level measurement has become popular in the assessment of overall noise hazard because it is thought to provide a rating of industrial broadband noises that indicates the injurious effects such noise has on human hearing.

As a result of its simplicity in rating the hazard to hearing, the A-weighted sound level has been adopted as the measurement for assessing noise exposure by the American Conference of Governmental Industrial Hygienists (ACGIH®). The A-weighted sound level as the preferred unit of measurement was also adopted by the U.S. Department of Labor as part of its Occupational Safety and Health Standards. The A-weighted sound level has also been shown to provide reasonably good assessments of speech interference and community disturbance conditions and has been adopted by the U.S. Environmental Protection Agency (EPA) for these purposes (Figure 9–8).

OCCUPATIONAL DAMAGE-RISK CRITERIA

The purpose of damage-risk criteria is to define maximum permissible noise levels during given periods that, if not exceeded, would result in acceptable small changes in the hearing levels of exposed employees over a working lifetime. The acceptability of a particular noise level is a function of many variables.

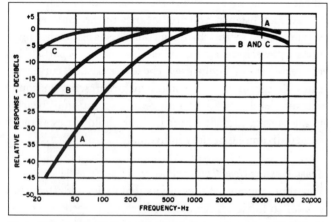

Figure 9–7. Frequency-response attenuation characteristics for the A-, B-, and C- weighting networks.

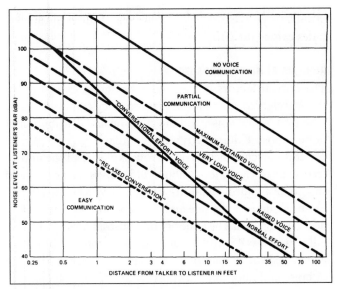

Figure 9–8. Distance at which ordinary speech can be understood (as a function of the A-weighted sound levels of the masking noise in an outdoor environment). *(Reprinted from* Public Health and Welfare Criteria of Noise, *July 27, 1973, U. S. Environmental Protection Agency.)*

Increasing attention is being given by regulatory agencies, and industrial and labor groups, to the effects of noise exposures on employees; therefore, equitable, reliable, and practical damage-risk noise criteria are needed.

A criterion is a standard, rule, or test by which a judgment can be formed. A criterion for establishing levels for damage-risk noise requires one or more standards for judgment. Damage-risk criteria can be developed once standards are selected by which the effects of occupational noise exposure on employees can be judged.

Hearing Ability

Tests for evaluating the ability to hear speech have been developed. These tests generally fall into two classes: those that measure the hearing threshold or the ability to hear very faint speech sounds and those that measure discrimination, or the ability to *understand* speech (see Chapter 4, "The Ears").

Ideally, hearing impairment should be evaluated in terms of an individual's ability (or inability) to hear normal speech under everyday conditions. The ability of an individual to hear sentences and to repeat them correctly in a quiet environment is considered to be satisfactory evidence of adequate hearing ability. Hearing tests using pure tones are extensively employed to monitor the status of a person's hearing and the possible progression of a hearing loss. A person's ability to hear pure tones is related to the hearing of speech.

People who work in noisy environments should have their hearing checked periodically to determine whether the noise exposure is producing a detrimental effect on hearing. The noise-induced hearing losses that can be measured by pure-tone audiometry are the threshold shifts that constitute a departure from a specified baseline. This baseline, or normal hearing level, can be defined as the average hearing threshold of a group of young people who have no history of previous exposure to intense noise and no otological malfunction.

AMA Guides

Chapter 11.2 of the American Medical Association's (AMA) *Guides to the Evaluation of Permanent Impairment,* 6th edition (American Medical Association © 2008) includes criteria for evaluating permanent impairment resulting from the principal dysfunctions of the ear. Permanent impairment is expressed in terms of impairment of the whole person.

Monaural hearing impairment is evaluated by determining hearing threshold levels for each ear at test frequencies of 500, 1,000, 2,000, and 3,000 Hz. If the average of these hearing levels is 25 dB or less, no impairment is considered to exist in the ability to hear everyday sounds under everyday listening conditions.

The AMA describes the method to convert monaural hearing impairments to a binaural hearing impairment. The binaural hearing impairment is then used to determine impairment of the whole person (see Chapter 4, The Ears).

Risk Factors

If the ear is subjected to high levels of noise for a sufficient period of time, some loss of hearing will occur. There are many factors that affect the degree and extent of hearing loss, including the following:

- the intensity of the noise (sound pressure level)
- the type of noise (frequency spectrum)
- the period of exposure each day (worker's schedule per day)
- the total work duration (years of employment)
- individual susceptibility
- the age of the worker
- coexisting hearing loss and ear disease
- the character of the surroundings in which the noise is produced
- the distance from the source
- the position of the ear with respect to sound waves

The first four factors are the most important, and they are called *noise exposure factors.* Thus, it is necessary to know not only the intensity of the noise, but also what type of noise it is and its duration.

Because of the complex relationship of noise and exposure time to threshold shift (reduction in hearing level) and its many possible contributory causes, the criteria designed to protect workers from hearing loss took many years to develop and establish.

The Intersociety Committee on Guidelines for Noise Exposure Control published the results of their study to establish a basis for reliable noise criteria. A significant part of their report is shown graphically in Figure 9–9. The curves in the figure relate the incidence of significant hearing loss to age and the magnitude of noise exposure over a working lifetime.

Without attempting to explain the full significance of the graph, it can be stated that 20 percent of the general population between the ages of 50 and 59 experience hearing losses without having had any exposure to industrial noise, but groups of workers exposed to steady-state industrial noise over a working lifetime show a greater increase in the incidence of hearing loss. For example, exposure to steady-state noise at 90 dB on the A-scale of the sound level meter (90 dBA) results in significant hearing losses in 27 percent of the exposed group. If the working lifetime exposure is 95 dBA, 36 percent of the group shows significant hearing loss.

Essentially, the graph in Figure 9–9 supplies industry and other interested groups with information from which the risk of developing compensable hearing loss among

groups of workers exposed to noises of different magnitudes can be predicted.

Analysis of Noise Exposure

The critical factors in the analysis of noise exposure are the A-weighted sound level; the frequency composition, or spectrum, of the noise; and the duration and distribution of noise exposure during a typical workday.

It is currently believed that any exposure of the unprotected ear to sound levels above 115 dBA is hazardous and should be avoided. Exposure to sound levels below 70 dBA can be assumed to be safe and does not produce any permanent hearing loss. The majority of industrial noise exposures fall within this 45-dBA range; thus, additional information is required for evaluation of damage risk, such as the type of noise and duration of exposure.

It would be very helpful to know the predominant frequencies present and the contributions from each of the frequency bands that make up the overall level. It is currently believed that noise energy with predominant frequencies above 500 Hz has a greater potential for causing hearing loss than noise energy concentrated in the low-frequency regions. It is also believed that noises that have a sharp peak in a narrow-frequency band (such as a pure tone) present a greater hazard to hearing than noises of equal energy levels that have a continuous distribution of energy across a broad frequency range.

The incidence of noise-induced hearing loss is directly related to total exposure time. In addition, it is believed that intermittent exposures are far less damaging to the ear than are continuous exposures, even if the sound pressure levels for the intermittent exposures are considerably higher than those during continuous exposures. The rest periods between noise exposures allow the ear to recuperate.

At present, the deleterious effects of noise exposure and the energy content of the noise cannot be directly equated. For example, doubling the energy content does not produce twice the hearing loss. In general, though, the greater the total energy content of the noise, the shorter the time of exposure required to produce the same amount of hearing loss. However, the exact relation between time and energy is not known.

Another factor that should be considered in the analysis of noise exposures is the type of noise. For instance, impact noise is generated by drop hammers and punch presses, whereas steady-state noise is generated by turbines and fans. Impact noise is a sharp burst of sound; therefore, sophisticated instrumentation is necessary to determine the peak levels for this type of noise. Additional research must be done to fully define the effects of impact noise on the ear.

The total noise exposure during a person's normal

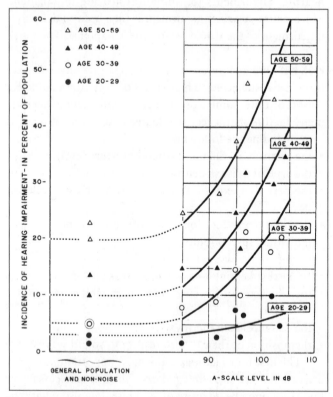

Figure 9–9. The incidence of hearing impairment in the general population and in selected populations by age group and by occupational noise exposure. *(Reprinted with permission from the American Industrial Hygiene Association Journal, 1967.)*

working lifetime must be known in order to arrive at a valid judgment of how noise will affect that person's hearing. Instruments such as noise dosimeters can be used to determine the exposure pattern of a particular individual. Instruments such as sound level meters can be used to determine the noise exposure at a given instant in time (that is, during the time the test is being taken). An exposure pattern can be established using a series of such tests and the work history of the individual.

SOUND MEASURING INSTRUMENTS

A wide assortment of equipment is available for noise measurements, including sound survey meters, sound level meters, octave-band analyzers, narrowband analyzers, noise dosimeters, tape and graphic level recorders, impact sound level meters, and equipment for calibrating these instruments.

For most noise problems encountered in industry, the sound level meter and octave-band analyzer provide ample information (Figure 9–10).

Sound Level Meters

The basic instrument used to measure sound pressure variations in air is the sound level meter. This instrument contains a microphone, an amplifier with a calibrated attenuator, a set of frequency-response networks (weighting networks), and an indicating meter (Figure 9–11). The sound level meter is a sensitive electronic voltmeter that measures the electrical signal emitted from a microphone, which is ordinarily attached to the instrument. The alternating electrical signal emitted from the microphone is amplified sufficiently so that, after conversion to direct current by means of a rectifier, the signal can be displayed. An attenuator controls the overall amplification of the instrument. The response-

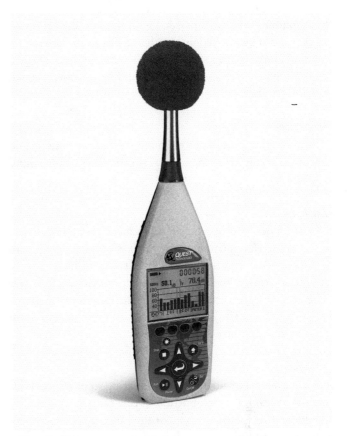

Figure 9–10. The multipurpose instrument shown here can be used as a sound level meter and octave-band analyzer. *(Courtesy 3M Company© 2011.)*

versus-frequency characteristics of the amplified signal are controlled by the weighting networks.

Some sound level meters have a measurement range of about 40–140 dB (re: 20 µPa) without the aid of special accessory equipment. Special microphones permit measurement of lower or of considerably higher sound levels. An amplifier that can register the electrical output signal of the

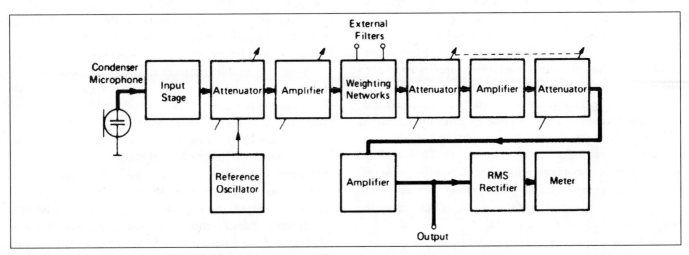

Figure 9–11. Schematic diagram of a sound level meter with auxiliary output.

microphone is usually provided with the sound level meter so that it can be hooked up to other instruments for recording and analysis. The sound level meter is designed to be a device for field use and as such should be reliable, rugged, reasonably stable under battery operation, and lightweight.

Microphone

The microphone responds to sound pressure variations and produces an electrical signal that is processed by the sound level meter.

Amplifier

The amplifier in a sound level meter must have a high available gain so that it can measure the low-voltage signal from a microphone in a quiet location. It should have a wide frequency range, usually on the order of 20–20,000 Hz. The range of greatest interest in most noise measurements is 50–6,000 Hz. The inherent electronic noise floor and hum level of the amplifier must be low.

Attenuators

Sound level meters are used for measuring sounds that differ greatly in level. A small portion of this range is covered by the indicating meter. The rest of the range is covered by an adjustable attenuator, which is an electrical resistance network inserted into the amplifier to produce known ranges of signal level.

Weighting Networks

The sound level meter response at various frequencies can be controlled by electrical weighting networks. The response curves for these particular networks have been established in the American National Standards Institute's publication ANSI S1.4-1983 (R2006). C-weighting approximates a uniform response over the frequency range from 25–8,000 Hz. Changes in the electronic circuit are sometimes made to compensate for the response of particular microphones, so that the net response is uniform (flat) within the tolerance allowed by the standards. The C-weighting network is generally used when the sound level meter supplies a signal to an auxiliary instrument for a more detailed analysis.

The A-weighting network is used to determine compliance with Occupational Safety and Health Administration (OSHA) noise standards. (The weighting networks are shown in Figure 9–7.)

Measurements taken with the C-weighting network differ little from those taken with no frequency weighting unless the sound being measured has strong frequency content below 25 Hz or above 10,000 Hz. The use of no frequency weighting is referred to as a *flat-frequency response*. Octave band and one-third octave band analyzers (discussed

later) typically employ flat-response weighting networks.

Metering System

After the electrical signal from the microphone is amplified and sent through the attenuators and weighting networks, the signal is used to drive a metering circuit. This metering circuit displays a value that is proportional to the electrical signal applied to it. The ANSI S1.4–1983 (R2006) standard for sound level meters specifies that the rms value of the signal should be indicated. This requirement corresponds to adding up the different components of the sound wave on an energy basis. When measuring sound, the rms value is a useful indication of the general energy content.

A running average of the rectified output of the metering circuit is displayed. The average time (or response speed) is determined by the meter ballistics and the response circuit chosen.

Two modes of operation—fast and slow—are provided on every sound level meter. In the fast mode, the meter responds relatively quickly to rapidly changing noise levels, whereas in the slow mode, the meter responds rather slowly. The use of each mode is best illustrated by example. If one were to measure the noise level of a passing vehicle, the fast mode would be used to obtain the maximum level. In a factory, where an average noise level is often more useful, the slow mode would be selected to reduce rapid, hard-to-read excursions. OSHA requires the use of slow response for measurements to check for compliance with its noise standards.

Octave-Band Analyzers

For many industrial noise problems, it is necessary to use some type of analyzer to determine where the noise energy lies in the frequency spectrum. This is especially true if engineering control of noise problems is planned, because industrial noise is made up of various sound intensities at various frequencies (Figure 9–12).

In order to properly represent the total noise of a noise source, it is usually necessary to break the total noise down into its various frequency components—low frequency, high frequency, or middle frequency. This is necessary for two reasons: people react differently to low-frequency and high-frequency noises (for the same sound pressure level, high frequency noise is much more disturbing and is more capable of producing hearing loss than is low-frequency noise); and the engineering solutions for reducing or controlling noise are different for low-frequency and high-frequency noise (low-frequency noise is more difficult to control, in general).

It is conventional practice in acoustics to determine the frequency distribution of a noise by passing that noise through several different filters that separate the noise into eight or nine octaves on a frequency scale. Just as with an

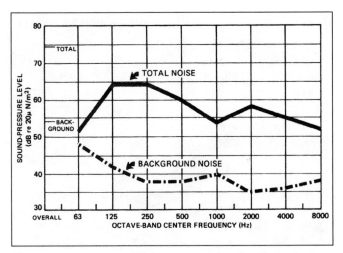

Figure 9–12. Data obtained from an octave-band analysis of a noise source, showing the total noise and the background noise levels when the noise source is not in operation.

octave on a piano keyboard, an octave in sound analysis represents the frequency interval between a given frequency (such as 250 Hz) and twice that frequency (500 Hz).

A young, healthy ear is sensitive to sound frequency in the range from about 20 to 20,000 Hz. Most octave-band analyzing filters now cover the audio range from about 22 Hz to about 11,300 Hz in nine-octave frequency bands. These filters are identified by their geometric mean frequencies, as shown in Table 9–D.

Notice that these filters are *constant-percentage* filters. The width of the band being utilized (bandwidth) is a fixed percentage of the frequency at which the instrument is operating. Octave-band filters have bandwidths that are 70.7 percent of the mean frequency (this is easily seen in the 1-kHz band).

For a more detailed analysis of the distribution of sound energy as a function of frequency, still narrower bands are

used. The next commonly used division is a split of the octave into three parts.

Some of the mean frequencies for such a series would be, for example, 100, 125, 160, 200, 250, 315, 400, 500, 630, and 800 Hz. One-third-octave filters have bandwidths that are 23.2 percent of the mean frequency.

Still narrower band filters are available, such as one-tenth-octave band filter. The narrower the band for analysis, the more sharply defined the data.

The identification of pure tone components, when present, is an extremely useful diagnostic tool for locating and quieting the noise source.

Some noise sources have a well-defined frequency content. For example, the hum generated by a fan or blower is usually centered at the *blade-passage frequency*, which is the product of the number of blades of the fan multiplied by the speed (revolutions per second) of the fan.

The fundamental blade-passage frequency (f_B, in Hertz) of fans is given by the following equation:

$$f_B = \frac{(\text{rpm})\ (N)}{60} \qquad (21)$$

where   rpm = shaft rotational speed (revolutions per minute)

N = number of blades

60 = a constant to convert rpm to revolutions per second

Higher harmonics are usually present with diminished sound pressure amplitude at integral multiples of the fundamental (that is, $2f_B$, $3f_B$, . . .).

The above relation can also be used to predict the fundamental tones from blowers, gears, and so on by letting N represent the number of impeller lobes or gear teeth. For example, consider the following.

Example 4

What is the frequency of the predominant tone that would be emitted from an axial fan with four blades rotating at 6,000 rpm?

$$f_B = \frac{(\text{rpm})\ (N)}{60} = \frac{(6000)\ (4)}{60} = 400\,\text{Hz} \qquad (22)$$

The fundamental blade-passage frequency is then 400 Hz. One would also expect additional tones at integral multiples of the predominant tone at

$$f_2 = (2)(400) = 800\,\text{Hz}$$
$$f_3 = (3)(400) = 1{,}200\,\text{Hz}$$
$$\vdots$$
$$f_N = (N)(400)\,\text{Hz}$$

	Octave-Band Mean Frequencies and Corresponding Band Limits ANSI S1.11-2004 (R2009)	
TABLE 9–D		
Lower Band Limit (Hz)	*Geometric Mean Frequency of Band (Hz)*	*Upper Band Limit (Hz)*
22	31.5	44
44	63	88
88	125	177
177	250	354
354	500	707
707	1,000	1,414
1,414	2,000	2,828
2,828	4,000	5,656
5,656	8,000	11,312

The higher-frequency tones would have progressively diminished sound pressure amplitude.

Electrical transformers usually hum in frequencies that are multiples of 60 Hz. Positive-displacement pumps have a sound pressure distribution that is directly related to the pressure pulses on either the inlet or the outlet of the pump.

Noise resulting from the discharge of steam- or air-pressure relief valves has a frequency peak that is related to the pressure in the system and the diameter of the restriction preceding the discharge to the atmosphere. A peak energy content in any single-octave band would provide information as to the predominant frequency of a particular noise source.

Sound level meters have evolved from relatively simple devices capable of measuring weighted sound levels and performing octave-band frequency analysis to highly sophisticated instruments that serve as the front end of a data acquisition system.

The instrument shown in Figure 9–13, for example, not only functions as a sound level meter and octave-band or one-third-octave-band analyzer, but is also capable of measuring all the relevant parameters defined by OSHA and ANSI standards for industrial and environmental noise. The output of this instrument can be recorded, printed, or transferred to a personal computer for additional analysis or graphical presentation.

Noise Dosimeters

In many work environments, it may not be adequate to measure noise exposure at a fixed location for the duration of a workshift. Some workers move about to several locations in the course of their duties or perform a variety of operations during the day and are therefore subjected to different noise levels. The practical way to measure the noise exposure in these circumstances is with a noise-exposure monitor, or dosimeter, that can be worn by the worker and that moves with the worker during the day. The noise dosimeter records the noise energy to which the worker is exposed during the workshift.

A dosimeter (Figure 9–14) includes a microphone, placed in the person's hearing zone, and the remainder of the instrument. The dosimeter automatically computes the desired noise measures—most commonly the daily noise dose. This measure is used to check for compliance with the OSHA noise standard.

Dosimeters have evolved from simple devices that compute single-number exposure measures to highly sophisticated monitors that compute and store comprehensive data on the sound field encountered by the subject. The instrument shown in Figure 9–15, for example, not only functions as two independent noise dosimeters, but also as a multipurpose data-logging sound level meter. It is also capable of producing several types of printed reports, including sta-

Figure 9–13. Precision integrating sound level meter. *(Courtesy Bruel & Kjaer Instruments, Inc.)*

Figure 9–14. Dosimeter being worn to monitor noise exposure. *(Courtesy Quest Technologies.)*

tistical analyses of data and graphical time history reports.

It is important to recognize the fact that dosimeters were derived directly from sound level meters. Dosimeters were developed to simplify measurement and computational procedures. To obtain comparable results, dosimeters must correctly duplicate the dynamic characteristics of sound level meters. Specific requirements prescribing these characteristics are set forth in the American National Standards Institute (ANSI) Standard S1.25–1991 (R2007), *Specification for Personal Noise Dosimeters.*

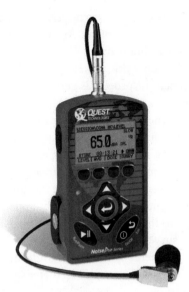

Figure 9–15. Noise dosimeter/multipurpose data-logging sound level meter. *(Courtesy 3M Company© 2011.)*

SOUND SURVEYS

Sound measurement falls into two broad categories: source measurement and ambient-noise measurement. Source measurements involve the collection of acoustic data for the purpose of determining the characteristics of noise radiated by a source.

The source might be a single piece of equipment or a combination of equipment or systems. For example, a single electrical motor or an entire facility can be considered a noise source.

Ambient-noise measurements can be used to study a single sound level or to make a detailed analysis showing hundreds of components of a complex vibration. The number of measurements taken and the type of instruments needed depend on the information that is required. If compliance with a certain noise specification must be checked, the particular measurement required is reasonably clear. Only some guidance as to the selection of instruments and their use is needed. But if the goal is to reduce the noise produced by industrial operations in general, the situation is more complex, and careful attention to the acoustic environment is essential.

Measurement of the noise field may require using different types of sound level–measuring instruments. These measurements must be repeated as changes in noise-producing equipment or operating procedures occur.

The use of the dBA scale for preliminary noise measurement greatly simplifies the collection of sound level survey data. Detailed sound level survey and octave-band analysis data are necessary to provide sufficient information so that

the proper remedial measures for noise-control procedures can be determined. Calibration checks of the instruments should be made before, during, and after the sound level survey.

Source Measurements

Source measurements frequently are made in the presence of noise created by other sources that form the background- or ambient-noise level. Although it is not always possible to make a clear distinction between source- and ambient-noise measurement, it is important to understand that source measurements describe the characteristics of a particular sound source, while ambient-noise measurements describe the characteristics of a sound field of largely unspecified or unknown sources.

A uniform, standard reporting procedure should be established to ensure that sufficient data are collected in a form suitable for subsequent analysis. To be effective, this standard reporting procedure should include detailed descriptions of the techniques of measurement position, operating conditions, instrument calibration, exposure time, amplitude patterns, and other important variables.

Several forms have been devised to record data obtained during a screening survey. Use of these forms facilitates the recording of pertinent information that will be extremely useful if more detailed studies are conducted later. An employee noise exposure survey is conducted by measuring noise levels at each workstation that an employee occupies throughout the day or by acquiring a sufficient sampling of data at each workstation so that the exposure of an employee while at that workstation can be evaluated. Workstations that pose particular noise-exposure hazards can be readily identified by using measured sound level contours if these are obtained in adequate detail.

In many industrial situations, however, it is extremely difficult to accurately evaluate the noise exposure to which a particular worker is subjected. This is due in part to the fact that the noise level to which the stationary worker is exposed throughout the workday fluctuates, making it difficult to evaluate compliance or noncompliance with the OSHA standards. Another problem arises when a worker's job requires that he or she spend time in areas where the noise levels vary from very low to very high.

Because of the fluctuating nature of many industrial noise levels, it would not be accurate or meaningful to use a single sound level meter reading to estimate the daily time-weighted average (TWA) noise level.

Preliminary Noise Survey

A hearing conservation program should start with a preliminary facility-wide noise level survey using appropriate sound-level-measuring equipment to locate operations or areas where workers may be exposed to hazardous noise levels.

Those conducting the survey have to decide whether to purchase sound-level-measuring equipment and train personnel to use it or to contract the work to an outside firm. The extent of the noise problem, the size of the facility, and the nature of the work affect this decision. In most facilities, noise surveys are conducted by a qualified engineer, an audiologist, an industrial hygienist, or a safety and health professional.

A noise survey should be carried out at work areas where it is difficult to communicate in normal tones. A common rule of thumb is that if you have to shout to communicate at a distance of three feet, noise levels may be excessive. A noise survey should also be performed if, after being exposed to high noise levels during their work shift, workers notice that speech and other sounds are muffled for several hours or they develop ringing in the ears.

As a general guideline for conducting a noise survey, the information recorded should be sufficient to allow another individual to take the report, use the same equipment, find the various measurement locations, and, finally, reproduce the measured and/or recorded data.

The preliminary noise survey normally does not define the noise environment in depth and therefore should not be used to determine employee exposure time and other details. The preliminary noise survey simply supplies sufficient data to determine whether a potential noise problem exists and, if so, to indicate how serious it is.

Detailed Noise Survey

From the preliminary noise survey, it is relatively easy to determine specific locations that require more detailed study and attention. A detailed noise study should then be made at each of these locations to determine employees' TWA exposures.

The purposes of a detailed noise survey are

- to obtain specific information on the noise levels existing at each employee's work station;
- to develop guidelines for establishing engineering and/or administrative controls;
- to define areas where hearing protection will be required; and
- to identify those work areas where audiometric testing of employees is desirable and/or required.

In addition, detailed noise survey data can be used to develop engineering control policies and procedures and to determine whether specific company, state, or federal requirements have been complied with.

An effective hearing conservation program always starts with the question, "Does a noise problem exist?" The answer must not be based simply on the subjective feeling that the problem exists but on the results of a careful technical definition of the problem. Answers to the following questions must be obtained:

- How noisy is each work area?
- What equipment or process is generating the noise?
- Which employees are exposed to the noise?
- How long are they exposed?

Line supervisors can provide basic job function information concerning the duration of operation, the types of noise-producing equipment in work areas, and the percentage of time a worker spends in each of the areas. Production records can be examined, and on-site evaluation can provide information as to the extent of the noise problems.

The noise survey should be made using a general-purpose sound level meter that meets standards set by ANSI S1.4 1983 (R2006). The sound level meter should be set for A-scale slow response.

Sound level measurements should be taken as close as practical to the worker's hearing zone (Figure 9–16). No worker should be exposed to steady-state or interrupted steady-state sound levels that exceed the maximum listed in the current noise standard. Other information should include the name of the individual making the noise survey as well as the date, location of measurement, and time the measurement was made. The serial numbers of the sound level meters and the date of calibration are also essential for compliance records.

The noise survey procedure is a three-step process.

Step 1: Area Measurements

Using a sound level meter set for A-scale slow response, the regularly occurring maximum noise level and the regularly occurring minimum noise level are recorded at the center of each work area. (For measurement purposes, the size of

Figure 9–16. Take sound level measurements as close as practical to the worker's hearing zone. *(Courtesy Coffey Environments.)*

the work area should be limited to 1,000 sq ft [93 sq m] or smaller.) If the maximum sound level in a work area does not exceed 80 dBA, it can be assumed that all employees in that area are working in an environment with an acceptable noise level. If the noise levels measured at the center of the work area fall between 80 and 92 dBA, then more information is needed.

Sound level contours (Figure 9–17) can be used during this screening survey to identify workstations that may pose particular noise-exposure hazards. Sound level contours provide a visual depiction of the degree of the noise hazard in a work area, at a particular time.

To construct a sound level contour, the work area is divided into a grid whose lines are evenly spaced at an approximate distance of 10 ft (3.05 m). A-weighted sound level measurements are recorded at each measurement position. When the observed sound levels vary significantly, then the grid spacing should be decreased. It is usually necessary to decrease the grid spacing in the proximity of dominant noise sources due to rapidly changing sound levels. The contour lines drawn in Figure 9–17 are based on 2-dBA changes in the measured sound level.

Step 2: Workstation Measurements

To evaluate the noise exposure for people working in locations where measurements at the center of the work area range from 80–92 dBA, measurements should be made at each employee's normal workstation. If the level varies on a regular basis, both the maximum and minimum levels should be recorded. If the noise level never goes below 90 dBA, an unsatisfactory noise exposure is indicated. If the measured level is never greater than 85 dBA, the noise expo-

sure to which the employee is subjected can be regarded as satisfactory.

Step 3: Exposure Duration

At workstations where the regularly occurring noise varies above and below the 85-dBA level, further analysis is needed.

If an employee has varying work patterns in different work areas, it is necessary to ascertain the sound level and duration of noise exposure within each work area. A breakdown of hours worked in each area can be obtained by consulting the employee or the employee's supervisor, or by visual monitoring. A briefing/debriefing approach for a particular day's activities can also be used. This approach consists of requesting each employee to keep a general work area/time log of his or her daily activities. The employee is then debriefed at the end of the work period to ensure that sufficient information was logged. In many cases, it may be desirable for an employee to wear a noise dosimeter that records daily exposure in terms of the current OSHA requirements.

The procedure for determining an employee's daily noise-exposure rating is discussed in the section that follows.

General Classes of Noise Exposure

There are three general classes into which occupational noise exposures can be grouped: continuous noise, intermittent noise, and impact-type noise.

Continuous Noise

Continuous noise is normally defined as broadband noise of approximately constant level and spectrum to which an

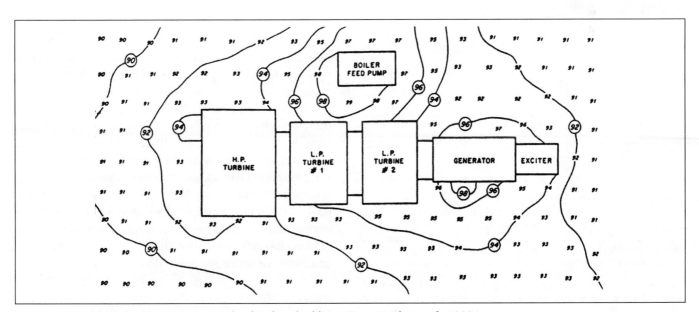

Figure 9–17. Sound level contours: operating level turbine building. *(From DiBlasi et al., 1983.)*

employee is exposed for a period of 8 hours per day, 40 hours per week. A large number of industrial operations fit into this class of noise exposure. Most damage-risk criteria are written for this type of noise exposure because it is the easiest to define in terms of amplitude, frequency content, and duration.

The OSHA Noise Standard, 29 CFR 1910.95(a) and (b) http://www.osha.gov/pls/oshaweb/owadisp.show_document?p_table=STANDARDS&p_id=9735, establishes permissible employee noise exposures in terms of duration in hours per day at various sound levels. The standard requires that the employer reduce employee exposures to the allowable level by use of feasible engineering or administrative controls. The standard defines the permissible exposure level (PEL) as that noise dose that would result from a continuous 8-hour exposure to a sound level of 90 dBA. This is a dose of 100 percent. Doses for other exposures that are either continuous or fluctuating in level are computed relative to the PEL based on a 5-dBA trading relationship between noise level and exposure time (Table 9–E).

Every 5-dBA increase in noise level cuts the allowable exposure time in half. This is known as a *5-dB exchange rate*.

When employees are exposed to different noise levels during the day, the mixed exposure, E_m, must be calculated by using the following formula:

$$E_m = \frac{C_1}{T_1} + \frac{C_2}{T_2} + \frac{C_3}{T_3} + \cdots + \frac{C_n}{T_n} \quad (23)$$

TABLE 9–E   OSHA Permissible Noise Exposures

Duration Per Day (Hours)	Sound Level, Slow Response (dBA)
8	90
6	92
4	95
3	97
2	100
1 ½	102
1	105
½	110
¼ or less	115

Note: When the daily noise exposure is composed of two or more periods of noise exposure of different levels, their combined effect should be considered, rather than the individual effect of each. If the sum of the fractions $C_1/T_1 + C_2/T_2 + ... + C_n/T_n$ exceeds unity, the mixed exposure should be considered to exceed the limit value. C_n indicates the total time of exposure at a specified noise level, and T_n indicates the total time of exposure permitted at that level.

where C_n = the amount of time an employee was exposed to noise at a specific level

T_n = the amount of time the employee can be permitted to be exposed to that level

If the sum of the fractions exceeds 1, the mixed exposure is considered to exceed the allowable limit value, according to the OSHA standard. Daily noise dose (D) is an expression of E_m in percentage terms. For example, E_m = 1 is equivalent to a noise dose of 100 percent. (Note: OSHA does not consider noise levels below 90 dBA in determining the need for engineering controls.)

Example 5
An employee is exposed to the following noise levels during the workday:
- 85 dBA for 3.75 hr
- 90 dBA for 2 hr
- 95 dBA for 2 hr
- 110 dBA for 0.25 hr

Thus, the daily noise dose is as follows:

$$D = 100 \left(\frac{3.75}{\text{no limit}} \quad \text{or} \quad 0 + \frac{2}{8} + \frac{2}{4} + \frac{0.25}{0.50} \right) = 125\% \quad (24)$$

Because the dose exceeds 100 percent, the employee received an excessive exposure during the workday.

The permissible exposures given in Table 9–E are based on the presence of continuous noise rather than intermittent or impact-type noise. By OSHA definition, "if the variations in noise level involve maxima at intervals of one second or less, it is considered to be continuous."

Example 6
A drill runs for 15 seconds and is off 0.5 second between operations. This noise is rated at its "on" level for an entire eight-hour day. The noise generated by the drill would be "safe" only if the level were 90 dBA or less.

As discussed earlier, daily noise dose can be measured using a noise dosimeter. For OSHA use, the dosimeter must have a 5-dB exchange rate, 90-dBA criterion level, slow response, and either an 80-dBA or 90-dBA threshold gate for the appropriate standard to be evaluated. OSHA prescribes a 90-dBA threshold level for compliance with 29 CFR 1910.95 (a) and (b), which require implementation of engineering or administrative controls. An 80-dBA threshold level is prescribed in 29 CFR 1910.95 (d) for monitoring situations for hearing conservation.

Intermittent Noise
Exposure to intermittent noise can be defined as exposure to

a given broadband sound-pressure level several times during a normal working day. The inspector or facility supervisor who periodically makes trips from a relatively quiet office into noisy production areas may be subject to this type of noise.

With steady noises, it is sufficient to record the A-weighted sound level attained by the noise. With noises that are not steady, such as impulsive noises, impact noises, and the like, the temporal character of the noise requires additional specification. Both the short-term and long-term variations of the noise must be described. Intermittent noise-exposure measurements are most easily made using dosimeters.

Impact-Type Noise

Impact-type noise is a sharp burst of sound, and sophisticated instrumentation is necessary to determine the peak levels for this type of noise. Noise types other than steady ones are commonly encountered. In general, sounds repeated more than once per second can be considered as steady. Impulsive or impact noise, such as that made by hammer blows or explosions, is generally less than one-half second in duration and does not repeat more often than once per second. Employees should not be exposed to impulsive or impact noise that exceeds a peak sound pressure level of 140 dB.

NOISE-CONTROL PROGRAMS

The degree of noise reduction required is determined by comparing the measured levels with acceptable noise levels. The next step is to consider various noise-control measures such as making alterations in engineering design, limiting the time of exposure, or using personal protective devices to achieve the desired level of reduction.

Every noise problem can be broken down into three parts: a source that radiates sound energy, a path along which the sound energy travels, and a receiver such as the human ear (Figure 9–18). The "system" approach to noise-problem analysis and control assists in understanding both the problem and the changes that are necessary for noise reduction. If each part of the system—source, path, and receiver—is examined in detail, the overall problem is greatly simplified. To help translate these principles into practical terms, specific examples of controlling industrial noise exposure are outlined in this section.

Source

The most desirable method of controlling a noise problem is to minimize the noise at the source. This generally means modifying existing equipment and structures, or possibly introducing noise-reduction measures at the design stage of new machinery and equipment.

Noise Path

Because the desired amount of noise reduction cannot always be achieved by control at the source, modification along the noise path and at the receiver must also be considered.

Noise reduction along the path can be accomplished in many ways: by shielding or enclosing the source, by increasing the distance between the source and the receiver, or by placing a shield between the source and the receiver. Noise can be reduced along the path by means of baffles and enclosures placed over noise-producing equipment to minimize the transmission of noise to areas occupied by employees. Use of acoustical material on walls, ceilings, and floors to absorb sound waves and to reduce reverberations can result in significant noise reduction.

Noise produced by a source travels outward in all directions. If all of the walls, the floor, and the ceiling are hard, reflecting surfaces, all the sound is reflected again and again. The sound level measured at any point in the room is the sum of the sound radiated directly by the source plus all the reflected sounds. Almost all industrial machine installations are located in such environments. These locations are known as semireverberant. Noise measured around a machine in a semireverberant location is the sum of two components: the noise radiated directly by the machine and the noise reflected from the walls, floor, and ceiling.

Close to the machine, most of the noise is radiated directly by the machine. Close to the walls, the reflected component may be predominant. Sound-absorption materials applied to the walls and ceiling can reduce the reflected noise but have no effect on the noise directly radiated by the source.

Enclosures

In many cases, the purpose of an acoustic enclosure is to prevent noise from getting inside. Soundproof booths for machine operators and audiometric testing booths for testing the hearing of employees are examples of such enclosures. More often, however, an enclosure is placed around a noise source to prevent noise from getting outside. Enclosures are normally lined with sound-absorption material to decrease internal sound pressure buildup.

Noise can best be prevented from entering or leaving an enclosure by sealing all outlets. In extreme cases, double structures can be used. Special treatment, including the use of steel and lead panels, is available to prevent noise leakage in certain cases. Gaskets around doors can also reduce noise transmission from one space to another.

Control Measures

Noise control can often be designed into equipment so that little or no compromise in the design goals is required. Noise

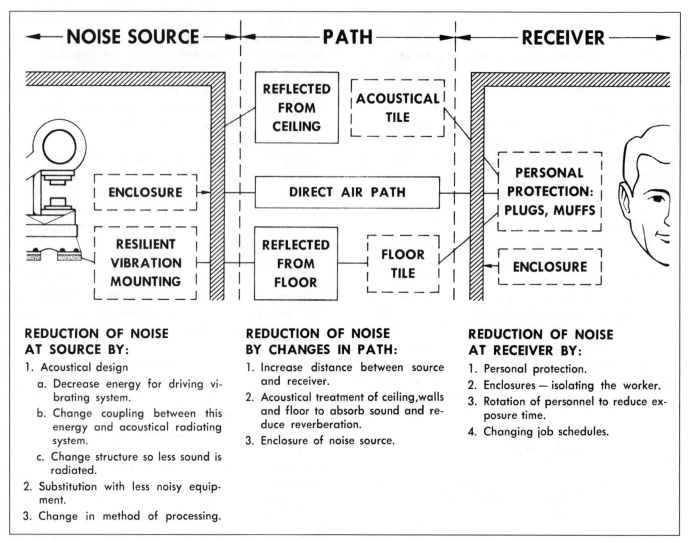

Figure 9–18. Every noise problem can be broken down into three component parts: a source that radiates sound energy, a path along which the sound energy travels, and a receiver such as the human ear.

control measures undertaken on existing equipment are usually more difficult. Engineering control of industrial noise problems requires the skill of individuals who are highly proficient in this field.

Noise-control strategies require careful objective analysis on both a practical and economic basis. Complete redesign requires that product and equipment designers consider noise level a primary product or equipment specification in the design of all new products and equipment. Full replacement of all products or equipment would eventually take place, the schedule depending on the service life of each. Many designers feel this approach minimizes the cost increases associated with noise-control measures. Existing products or equipment modifications would require manufacturers to modify or replace existing products and equipment to lower the noise levels of noisy equipment.

The existing equipment within any facility was probably

selected because it was economical and efficient. However, careful acoustic design can result in quieter equipment that would even be more economical to operate than noisier equipment. Examples of noise-control measures applied at the source include the substitution of quieter machines, the use of vibration-isolation mountings, and the maximum possible reduction of the external surface areas of vibrating parts. Machines mounted directly on floors and walls can cause them to vibrate, resulting in sound radiation. Proper machine mounting can isolate the machines and reduce the transmission of vibrations to the floors and walls.

Although substitution of less noisy machines may have limited application, there are certain areas in which substitution has a potentially wider application. Examples include using "squeeze"-type equipment instead of drop hammers, welding instead of riveting, and instituting chemical cleaning of metal rather than high-speed polishing and grinding.

Engineering

When starting a noise-reduction program, it is most desirable to apply engineering principles that are designed to reduce noise levels. The application of known noise-control principles can usually reduce any noise to any desired degree. However, economic considerations or operational necessities can make some applications impractical.

Engineering controls are procedures other than administrative or personal protection procedures that reduce the sound level either at the source or within the hearing zone of workers. Table 9–F lists examples of engineering principles that can be applied to reduce noise levels.

Some of the noise-control measures described in Table 9–F can be executed quite inexpensively by facility personnel. Other controls require considerable expense and highly specialized technical knowledge to obtain the required results. The services of competent acoustical engineers should be contracted when planning and carrying out engineering noise-control programs.

The possibility that excessive facility noise levels exist should be considered at the planning stage. Vendors supplying machinery and equipment should be advised that specified low noise levels will be considered in the selection process. Suppliers should be asked to provide information on the noise levels of currently available equipment. The inclusion of noise specifications in purchase orders has been used successfully to obtain quiet equipment. If purchasers of industrial equipment demand quieter machines, designers will give more consideration to the problem of noise control. It is not enough to specify that the sound pressure level of a single machine shall be 90 dBA or less at the operator's station; if another identical machine is placed nearby, the sound level produced by the two machines could be 93 dBA at the operator's station. (As mentioned earlier in this chapter, an increase of 3 dB represents a doubling of sound energy.)

To estimate the effect of a given machine on the total work environment, it is necessary to know the sound power that the machine produces. If there is no operator's work station in the machine's immediate vicinity, the sound power specifications may be sufficient; if, however, there is an operator in the near sound field, more information is generally needed.

Objectionable noise levels that are by-products of manufacturing operations are found in almost every industry. Practical noise-control measures are not easy to develop, and few ready-made solutions are available. Unfortunately, a standard technique or procedure that can be applied to all or even most situations cannot be presented here. The same machine, process, or noise source in two different locations can present two entirely different problems that must be solved in two entirely different ways.

Noise-control techniques are now being incorporated into products during the design stage. Machine tool buyers are one group who currently specify maximum noise levels in their purchase orders. Equipment can be designed with lower noise levels, but performance tradeoffs involving weight, size, power consumption, and perhaps increased maintenance costs may be necessary. These new, quieter products will probably weigh more, be bigger and bulkier, cost more, and be more difficult and expensive to service and maintain.

To attain quieter products, the engineer must be prepared to trade off, to some degree, many of the design goals that have been achieved in response to market demands. However, lightweight, low-cost, portable machines that are easily operated and simply maintained should not be cast aside lightly, even though price increases may be inevitable. The cost/benefit relationship should be examined in each case. In addition to paying higher prices for original equipment, the user (both as a consumer and as a taxpayer) pays for increased indirect costs.

The success of a noise-reduction project usually depends on the ingenuity with which basic noise-control measures can be applied without decreasing the maximum use and accessibility of the machine or other noise source that is being quieted.

Administrative Controls

There are many operations in which the exposure of employees to noise can be controlled administratively; for instance, production schedules can simply be changed or jobs rotated so that individual workers' exposure times are reduced. Employees can be transferred from job locations with high noise levels to job locations with lower ones if this procedure would make their daily noise exposure acceptable.

Administrative controls also include scheduling machine operating times so as to reduce the number of workers exposed to noise. For example, if an operation is performed during only one eight-hour day per week, and the operator is overexposed on that one day, it might be possible to perform the operation in two half-days of four hours each. The employee might then not be overexposed.

Employees who are particularly susceptible to noise can be transferred and allowed to work in a less noisy area. The benefits from transferring employees can be limited, however, because personnel problems can be caused by loss of seniority and prestige and lower productivity and pay.

Administrative controls include any administrative decision that results in lower noise exposure, such as complying with purchase agreements that specify maximum noise levels at the operator's position.

The sound level specification that is made part of a pur-

TABLE 9–F	Applying Engineering Principles to Reduce Noise Levels
I. Maintenance	Replacement or adjustment of worn, loose, or unbalanced parts of machines Lubrication of machine parts and use of cutting oils Use of properly shaped and sharpened cutting tools
II. Substitution of Machines	Larger, slower machines for smaller, faster ones Step dies for single-operation dies Presses for hammers Rotating shears for square shears Hydraulic presses for mechanical presses Belt drives for gears
III. Substitution of Processes	Compression riveting for impact riveting Welding for riveting Hot working for cold working Pressing for rolling or forging
IV. Reduction of the Driving Force of Vibrating Surfaces	Reduction of the forces Minimization of rotational speed Isolation
V. Reduction of the Response of Vibrating Surfaces	Damping Additional support Increased stiffness of the material Increased mass of vibrating members Change in the size to change resonance frequency
VI. Reduction of the Sound Radiation from Vibrating Surfaces	Reduction of the radiating area Reduction of the overall size Perforation of the surfaces
VII. Reduction of the Sound Transmission Through Solids	Use of flexible mountings Use of flexible sections in pipe runs Use of flexible-shaft couplings Use of fabric sections in ducts Use of resilient flooring
VIII. Reduction of the Sound Produced by Gas Flow	Use of intake and exhaust mufflers Use of fan blades designed to reduce turbulence Use of large, low-speed fans instead of smaller, high-speed fans Reduction of the velocity of fluid flow (air) Increase in the cross section of streams Reduction of the pressure Reduction of air turbulence
IX. Reduction of Noise by Reducing Its Transmission Through Air	Use of sound-absorptive material on walls and ceiling in work areas Use of sound barriers and sound absorption along the transmission path Complete enclosure of individual machines Use of baffles Confinement of high-noise machines to insulated rooms
X. Isolation of the Operator by Means of a Relatively Soundproof Booth	

chasing agreement must be more than just a general compliance statement such as "Must meet the requirements of the OSHA." It is important to realize that OSHA sets allowable noise limits relative to the exposure of the people involved. OSHA does not set specific standards for noise-generating equipment. The OSHA noise standard is not intended to be used as an equipment design specification and thus cannot be used as such.

Personal Hearing Protection

Pending the application of engineering control measures, employee exposure to noise can be reduced by the mandatory use of hearing-protective devices. OSHA's noise standard requires that whenever employees are exposed to excessive noise levels, feasible administrative or engineering controls should be used to reduce those levels. When these control measures cannot be completely accomplished, or while such controls are being initiated, personnel should be protected from the effects of excessive noise levels. Such protection can, in most cases, be provided by wearing suitable hearing-protection devices. Once management has decided that hearing protectors should be worn, the success of such a program depends largely on the method of initiation used and on the proper indoctrination of supervisory personnel and workers. Supervisors should set an example by wearing their hearing protectors when they go into noisy areas.

Some companies have found it very helpful to meet with employees or their representatives to thoroughly review the contemplated protection program and reach an understanding of the various problems involved. This process includes reviewing work areas where hearing protection will be provided or required and complying with state and federal regulations that require the use of hearing-protective devices.

Hearing-protective devices. Hearing-protective devices such as earplugs and earmuffs have one serious drawback—they do nothing to reduce or eliminate the hazard. Their failure means immediate exposure to the hazard. The fact that a hearing protector can become ineffective without the knowledge of the wearer is particularly serious. Training on the purpose, benefits, proper fitting, use, and care of hearing protectors is essential to the success of the program and is required by OSHA. Distributing a flyer (Figure 9–19) highlighting the care and use of the hearing protectors is also helpful.

Personal hearing-protective devices are acoustic barriers that reduce the amount of sound energy transmitted through the ear canal to receptors in the inner ear.

The sound attenuation (reduction) capability of a hearing-protective device (in decibels) is the difference in the measured hearing threshold of an observer wearing hearing protectors (test threshold) and the measured hearing threshold when the observer's ears are unprotected (reference threshold).

Inserts or muffs are hearing-protective devices that are in common use today. The insert-type protector attenuates noise by plugging the external ear canal, whereas the muff-type protector encloses the auricle of the ear to provide an acoustic seal. The effectiveness of hearing-protective devices depends on several factors that are related to the manner in which the sound energy is transmitted through or around the device. Figure 9–20 shows four pathways by which sound can reach the inner ear when hearing-protective devices are worn: seal leaks, material leaks, hearing-protective device vibration, and conduction through bone and tissue.

Seal leaks. For maximum protection, the device must form a virtually airtight seal against the ear canal or the side of the head. Inserts must accurately fit the contours of the ear canal, and muffs must accurately fit the area surrounding the external ear. Small air leaks in the seal between the hearing protector and the skin can significantly reduce the low-frequency sound attenuation or permit a greater proportion of the low-frequency sounds to pass through. As the air leak becomes larger, attenuation lessens at all frequencies.

Material leaks. Another possible transmission pathway for sound is directly through the material of the hearing-protective device. Although the hearing-protective device can attenuate or prevent the passage of most of the sound energy, some sound is still allowed to pass through.

Vibration of the hearing-protective device. Sound can also be transmitted to the inner ear when the hearing-protective device itself is set into vibration in response to exposure to external sound energy.

Because of the flexibility of the flesh in the ear canal, earplugs can vibrate in a piston-like manner within the ear canal. This limits their low-frequency attenuation. Likewise, an earmuff cannot be attached to the head in a totally rigid manner. Its cup vibrates against the head like a mass/spring system. The muff's effectiveness is governed by the flexibility of the muff cushion and the flesh surrounding the ear, as well as by the air volume entrapped under the cup.

Bone conduction. If the ear canal were completely closed so that no sound entered the ear by that path, some sound energy could still reach the inner ear by means of bone conduction. However, the sound reaching the inner ear by such means would be about 50 dB below the level of air-conducted sound received through the open ear canal. It is therefore obvious that no matter how the ear canal is blocked, the hearing-protective device will be bypassed by the bone-conduction pathway through the skull. A perfect hearing-protective device cannot provide more than about 50 dB of effective sound attenuation.

When a hearing-protective device is properly sized and carefully fitted and adjusted for optimum performance on a laboratory subject, air leaks are minimized, and material leaks, hearing-protective device vibration, and bone conduction are the primary sound transmission paths. In the workplace, however, this is usually not the case; sound transmission through air leaks is often the primary pathway.

All hearing protectors must be properly fitted when they

LET'S REVIEW THE FACTS

1. It is necessary for employees in certain noisy areas to wear ear protectors.
2. Prolonged exposure to excessive noise can harm the delicate hearing mechanism.
3. Ear protectors such as ear plugs or ear muffs will reduce the noise before it reaches the ear drum.
4. Your job assignment will determine whether you should wear ear plugs (inserts) or muffs (covers).
5. Speech and warning signals can be fully heard with ear protectors in noisy shop areas.

WEAR YOUR EAR PROTECTORS

1. The nurse will fit them and instruct you how to wear them.
2. Wear them for short periods to start and gradually increase the wearing time. After a few days you will be able to wear them all day with minimum discomfort.

SUGGESTED WEARING TIME SCHEDULE

		A.M.	P.M.
1st day	=	30 minutes	1 hour
2nd day	=	1 hour	1 hour
3rd day	=	2 hours	2 hours
4th day	=	3 hours	3 hours
5th day	=	all day	all day thereafter

3. If after five days the ear protectors feel uncomfortable, come in and see the nurse in the Company hospital.
4. Ear protectors should be replaced when they become worn, stiff, or lose their shape.
5. If ear protectors are misplaced, a new pair should be obtained without delay.
6. Never put soiled ear plugs into your ears. Wash the ear plugs at least once a day with soap and water.
7. With proper care, ear plugs should last for several months and ear muffs should last for several years.

OTHER POINTS TO REMEMBER

1. The best ear protector is the one that is properly fitted and worn.
2. Good protection depends on a snug fit. A small leak can destroy the effectiveness of the protection.
3. Ear plugs tend to work loose as a result of talking or chewing, and they must be re-seated from time to time during the working day.
4. If ear plugs are kept clean, skin irritations and other reactions should not occur.

YOUR HEARING IS PRICELESS

PROTECT IT

Figure 9–19. An example of a flyer distributed to all company employees who are required to wear some form of hearing protection. The flyer highlights care and use of the protectors.

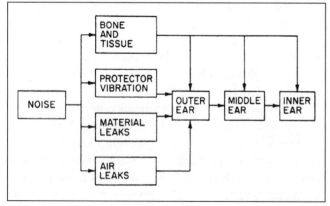

Figure 9–20. When a person is wearing a hearing protector, sound reaches the inner ear by different pathways.

are initially dispensed. Comfort, motivation, and training are also very important factors to consider if hearing protectors are to be successfully used.

Classes of Hearing Protection

Personal hearing-protective equipment can be divided into four classifications:

- enclosures (entire head)
- aural inserts, or earplugs
- superaural protectors, or canal caps
- circumaural protectors, or earmuffs

Enclosures. The enclosure-type hearing-protective device entirely envelops the head. A typical example is the helmet worn by an astronaut. In this case, attenuation at the ear is achieved through the acoustic properties of the helmet.

The maximum amount that a hearing protector can reduce the sound reaching the ear is from about 35 dB at 250 Hz to about 50 dB at the higher frequencies. By wearing hearing protectors and then adding a helmet that encloses the head, an additional 10-dB reduction of sound transmitted to the ears can be achieved.

Helmets can be used to support earmuffs or earphones and cover the bony portion of the head in an attempt to reduce bone-conducted sound. Helmets are particularly well-suited for use in extremely high-noise-level areas and where workers need to protect their heads from bumps or missiles. With good design and careful fitting of the seal between the edges of the helmet and the skin of the face and neck, 5–10 dB of sound attenuation can be obtained beyond that already provided by the earmuffs or earphones worn inside the helmet. This approach to protection against excessive noise is practical only in very special applications. Cost, as well as bulk, normally precludes the use of helmet-type hearing protectors in a general industrial hearing conservation program.

Aural insert protectors. Aural insert hearing-protective devices are normally called inserts or earplugs. This type of protector is generally inexpensive, but the service life is limited, ranging from single-time use to several months. Insert-type protectors or plugs are supplied in many different configurations and are made from such materials as rubber, plastics, fine glass down, foam, and wax-impregnated cotton. The pliable materials used in these aural inserts are quite soft, and there is little danger of injury resulting from accidentally forcing the plug against the tender lining of the ear canal.

It is desirable to have the employee's ears examined by qualified medical personnel before earplugs are fitted. Occasionally, the physical shape of the ear canal precludes the use of insert-type protectors. There is also the possibil-

ity that the ear canal is filled with hardened wax. If wax (cerumen) is a problem, it should be removed by qualified personnel. In some cases, the skin of the ear may be sensitive to a particular earplug material, and earplugs that do not cause an allergic response should be recommended.

Earplugs fall into three broad categories of general classification: formable, custom-molded, and premolded.

Formable earplugs (Figure 9–21) can provide good attenuation and fit any ear. Many of the formable types are designed for one-time use only, after which they are thrown away. The most common material currently used for formable earplugs is foam. Formable foam earplugs are generally rolled into a conical shape before being inserted in the ear. Employees must be trained in the proper use and care of their hearing protectors.

Custom-molded earplugs are, as the name implies, custom fit for the individual user. Generally, two or more materials (packaged separately) are mixed together to form a compound that resembles soft rubber when set. For use as a hearing-protective device, the mixture is carefully placed into the outer ear with some portion of it in the ear canal, in the manner prescribed by the manufacturer. As the material sets, it molds itself to the shape of the individual ear and external ear canal. In some cases, the materials are premixed and come in a tube from which they can be injected into the ear.

The custom-molded earplugs shown in Figure 9–22 offer very good hearing protection while enabling users to communicate better with each other. They also have a service life of several years.

Premolded earplugs are often referred to as prefabricated, because they are usually made in large quantities in a multiple-cavity mold. The materials of construction range from soft silicone or rubber to other plastics.

There are two versions of premolded insert protector. One is known as the universal-fit type. In this type, the plug is designed to fit a wide variety of ear canal shapes and sizes. The other type of premolded protector is sup-

Figure 9–21. Formable earplugs. *(Courtesy Cabot Safety Corp.)*

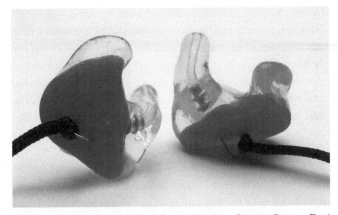

Figure 9-22. Custom-molded earplugs. *(Courtesy Custom Protect Ear.)*

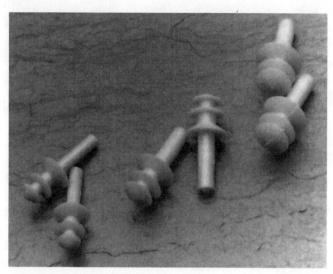

Figure 9–23. Premolded triple-flange earplugs. *(Courtesy The Bilsom Group.)*

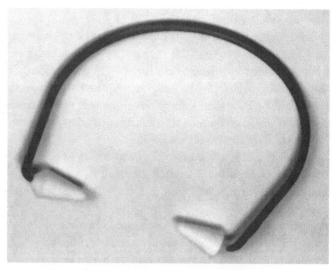

Figure 9–24. Canal caps. *(Courtesy Cabot Safety Corp.)*

plied in several different sizes to ensure a good fit (Figure 9–23). The design of the plug is important. For example, the smooth bullet-shaped plug is very comfortable and provides adequate attenuation in straight ear canals; however, its performance falls off sharply in many irregularly shaped canals.

The use of premolded earplugs requires proper fitting by trained personnel. In many individuals, the right and left ear canals are not the same size. For this reason, properly trained personnel must prescribe the correct protector size for each ear canal. Sizing devices are available to aid in proper fitting.

The premolded type of earplug has a number of disadvantages that limit its practical acceptability. To be effective, it has to fit snugly and, for some users, this is uncomfortable. Because the plug must fit tightly and because many people have irregularly shaped ear canals, an incorrect size of plug can be selected, or the plug may not be inserted far enough, and a good fit is not obtained.

Some premolded earplugs can shrink and become hard. This is caused primarily by ear wax (present in all ear canals). The wax extracts the plasticizer from some plug materials, causing hardening and possible shrinkage of the plug. The degree of hardening and shrinkage varies from one individual user to another, depending on such factors as temperature, duration of use, and the personal hygiene of the user. Regular cleaning of the protectors with mild soap and water prolongs their useful life. To keep the plugs clean and free from contamination, most manufacturers provide a carrying case for storing the plugs when they are not in use.

Superaural protectors. Hearing-protective devices in this category (commonly known as canal caps) seal the external opening of the ear canal to achieve sound attenuation (Figure 9–24). A soft, rubberlike material is held in place

by a lightweight headband. The tension of the band holds the superaural device against the external opening of the ear canal. Canal caps do not offer the protection provided by earplugs or earmuffs. They can be effective in intermittent noise exposures, such as a walk through the plant.

Circumaural protectors. Circumaural hearing-protective devices, or earmuffs, consist essentially of two cup- or dome-shaped devices that fit over the entire external ear, including the lobe, and a cushion or pad that seals against the side of the head. The ear cups are generally made of a molded rigid plastic and are lined with a cell-type foam material. The size and shape of the ear cup vary from one manufacturer to another (Figure 9–25). The cups are usually held in place by a spring-loaded suspension assembly or headband. The force applied against the head is directly related to the degree of attenuation desired. The width, circumference, and material of the earmuff cushion must be considered to maintain a proper balance of performance and comfort. To provide a good acoustic seal, the required width of the contact surface depends to a large degree on the material used in the cushion. The cup with the smallest possible circumference that can accommodate the largest ear lobes should be chosen. A slight pressure on the lobe can become painful in time, so it is very important to select a muff dome that is large enough.

The earmuffs currently on the market come with replaceable ear seals or cushions that are filled with either foam, liquid, or air—the foam-filled type is the most common. The outer covering of these seals is vinyl or a similar thermoplastic material. Human perspiration tends to extract the plasticizer from the seal material, which results in an eventual stiffening of the seals. For this reason, the seals

Figure 9–25. Earmuffs. *(Courtesy Howard Leight/Sperian Hearing Protection, LLC.)*

require periodic replacement; the frequency of replacement depends on the conditions of exposure.

Selection of Protector

The attenuation characteristics of a particular hearing protector must be considered before it is used for a specific application. As part of a well-planned hearing conservation program, characteristics of the noise levels in various areas should be known. From these data and from the attenuation information available from manufacturers, it can be determined whether a given device is suitable for the intended application. One must also consider the work area where the individual will use the hearing-protective device. For example, a large-volume earmuff would not be practical for an individual who must work in confined areas where there is very little head clearance. In such instances, a very small or flat ear cup or insert-type protector would be more practical.

When using muff-type protectors in special hazard areas (such as power-generating stations where there are electrical hazards), it may be desirable to use nonconductive suspension systems with muff-type protectors. Also, if other personal protective equipment such as safety hats or safety spectacles must be worn, the degree of hearing protection required must not be compromised. The efficiency of muff type protectors is reduced when they are worn over the frames of eye-protective devices. When eye-protective devices are required, it is recommended that ones with cable-type temples be used, because they create the smallest possible opening between the seal and the head.

When selecting a hearing-protective device, one should also consider how often a worker is exposed to excessive noise. If the noise exposure is intermittent, the muff-type protector is probably more desirable, because earplugs are somewhat more difficult to remove and reinsert.

If communication with other workers is an important consideration, the use of uniform, or flat, attenuation hearing protectors should be considered. Conventional hearing protectors offer unbalanced attenuation—greater attenuation at high frequencies than at low frequencies, making voices sound muffled and unclear. If the user already has some high-frequency hearing loss (common in noise-exposed workers), hearing protection that muffles high frequencies further reduces the ability to communicate if noise levels are high. Uniform attenuation hearing protectors (Figures 9–22 and 9–25) allow speech frequencies to be heard with less distortion by providing more equal reduction in sound at these frequencies.

Better hearing perception and adequate protection should be achievable with properly fitted uniform attenuation hearing protectors. However, when selecting hearing protectors, the characteristics of the workplace noise levels must be compared with attenuation information available from manufacturers.

When determining the suitability of a hearing-protective device for a given application, the manufacturer's reported test data must be examined carefully. It is necessary to correlate that information with the specific noise exposure the device is intended to control. The manufacturer should provide attenuation characteristics of the individual hearing-protective devices over a range of frequencies.

The most convenient method by which to gauge the adequacy of a hearing protector's attenuation capacity is to check its Noise Reduction Rating (NRR), a rating that was developed by the EPA. According to the EPA regulation, the NRR must be printed on the hearing protector's package. The NRR can be correlated with an individual worker's noise environment to assess the adequacy of the attenuation characteristics of the particular hearing-protective device. Appendix B of 29 CFR 1910.95 describes methods of using the NRR to determine whether a particular hearing-protective device (HPD) provides adequate protection within a given exposure environment. It must be noted, however, that NRRs are based on data obtained under laboratory conditions using trained listeners who are fitted by professionals. Their ratings differ significantly from what is achieved in the real world. In 1998, the National Institute of Safety and Health (NIOSH) published *Occupational Noise Exposure, Revised Criteria*. Based on studies conducted by numerous researchers of real world NRRs achieved by 84 percent of wearers in 20 independent studies, they recommend lowering the manufacturer's NRRs significantly. NIOSH recommended using subject fit data based on ANSI S12.6-1997 to estimate HPD attenuation. If this is not available, they recommend that the labeled NRRs be de-rated as follows:

- Earmuffs—subtract 25 percent from the manufacturer's labeled NRR
- Formable earplugs—subtract 50 percent from the manufacturer's NRR
- All other plugs—subtract 70 percent from the manufacturer's NRR (NIOSH, 1998)

INDUSTRIAL AUDIOMETRY

Audiometry, or the measurement of hearing, is central to industrial hearing conservation programs because all follow-up activities and program evaluations are based on such test results. Briefly, the objectives in industrial audiometry are as follows:

- Obtain a baseline audiogram that indicates an individual's hearing ability at the time of the preplacement examination.
- Provide a record of an employee's hearing acuity.
- Check the effectiveness of noise-control measures by measuring the hearing thresholds of exposed employees.
- Record significant hearing threshold shifts in exposed employees during the course of their employment.
- Comply with government regulations.

An audiometer is required to help assess an individual's hearing ability. An audiometer is an electronic instrument that converts electrical energy into sound energy in precisely variable amounts. It should meet the standards set forth in ANSI/ASA S3.6-2010, *Specifications for Audiometers*.

An audiometer consists of an oscillator, which produces pure tones at predetermined frequencies; an attenuator, which controls the intensity of the sound or tone produced; a presenter switch; and earphones, through which the person whose hearing is being tested hears the tone.

Threshold Audiometry

Threshold audiometry is used to determine an employee's auditory threshold for a given stimulus. Measurements of hearing are made to determine hearing acuity and to detect abnormal function in the ear. Before hearing can be described as abnormal, a reference point, or normal value, must be designated.

The quantity that is of interest, however, is not the sound pressure level of the normal hearing threshold, but rather the magnitude of departure from a standard reference threshold. Levels that depart from the norm can be easily detected by their divergence from the reference threshold.

Hearing threshold levels are those intensities at specific frequencies at which a sound or a tone can just barely be heard. The term *air conduction* refers to the air path by which the test sounds generated at the earphones are conducted through air to stimulate the eardrum.

The record of measured hearing thresholds is called a *threshold audiogram*. Audiometric tests can also be recorded in the form of audiograms, on which are plotted both sound intensity (in dB) and frequency (in Hz). A sample audiogram is shown in Figure 9–26. This audiogram shows a noise-induced sensorineural hearing loss. This is the type of hearing loss associated with chronic exposure to loud noise. On an audiogram, it is characterized by the decided notch at the 4000 Hz test frequency. For details on noise-induced hearing loss, see Chapter 4, The Ears.

Who Should Be Examined

Preplacement hearing-threshold tests should be taken by all job applicants, not just those who are to work in noisy areas. This establishes a baseline hearing threshold for each employee for future comparison. Preplacement hearing tests are essential if a company is to protect itself from liability for preexisting hearing loss incurred elsewhere. If an employee is hired with hearing damage and he or she is subsequently exposed to high noise levels, the company may be liable for all the employee's hearing loss—unless it can be proved that the employee had a preexisting hearing loss when hired.

Periodic follow-up hearing tests should be administered per the requirements in the OSHA noise standard, 29 CFR 1910.95.

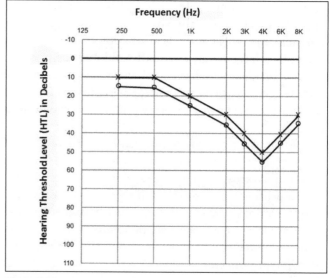

Figure 9–26. This audiogram shows the initial effects of exposure to excessive noise. Note the decided notch at the 4,000-Hz frequency.

Effective Programs

An effective industrial audiometric program should include consideration of the following components:

- medical surveillance
- qualified personnel
- suitable test environment
- calibrated equipment
- adequate record keeping

Medical Surveillance

Medical surveillance is essential in a hearing-testing program so that the program can fulfill its dual purpose of detecting hearing loss and providing valid records for compensation claims. Although many smaller companies do not have a medical department, they can satisfy the general medical surveillance requirement by using part-time medical consultants.

During the preplacement examination, the applicant should provide a detailed history covering his or her prior occupational experience and a personal record of illnesses and injuries. For applicants who will work in noisy environments, the history should include noise exposures in previous jobs, including any in the military services. The medical phase of the history should detail frequency of earache, ear discharge, ear injury, surgery (ear or mastoid), head injury with unconsciousness, ringing in the ears, hearing loss in the immediate family, the use of drugs, and history of allergy and toxic exposures. A standard form can be created for this purpose.

Qualified Personnel

Audiometric tests should be administered by a qualified individual such as a specially trained nurse, an audiologist, or an occupational hearing conservationist. An occupational hearing conservationist (OHC) is an individual who has satisfactorily completed a course of training that meets, as a minimum, the guidelines established by the Council for Accreditation in Occupational Hearing Conservation.

The duties of the OHC are to perform baseline and periodic pure-tone air-conduction threshold tests. Systematic supervision and encouragement of the OHC by the physician, audiologist, or other qualified person in charge of the audiometric program is recommended to maintain the high motivation required for proper audiometric testing. The supervision should include periodic review of the testing procedures used by the audiometric technician to make sure that they conform to established procedures.

Suitable Test Environment

Hearing measurements must be made in a test room or booth that conforms to the requirements in the OSHA noise standard, 29 CFR 1910.95. It must be sufficiently quiet within the enclosure so that external noises do not interfere with the employee's perception of the test sounds. This usually requires a special sound-treated enclosure (Figure 9–27).

Hearing-testing rooms should be located away from outside walls, elevators, and locations with heating and plumbing noises. If the background noise levels in the test area do not exceed the sound levels allowed by the standard, the background noise does not affect the hearing test results. The hearing test booth or room can be either a prefabricated unit or one that is built on the premises. Doors, gaskets, and other parts of the room or booth that can deteriorate, warp, or crack should be carefully inspected periodically.

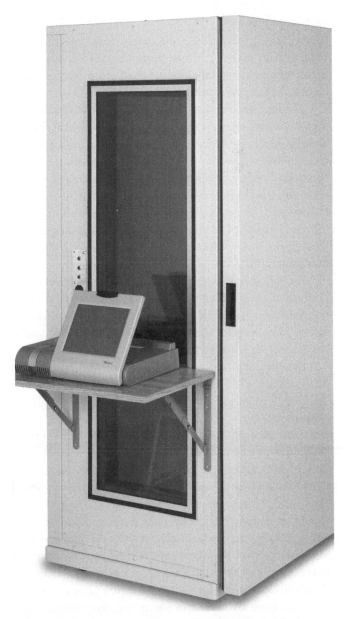

Figure 9–27. Audiometric test room. *(Courtesy Tremetrics.)*

In addition to proper acoustical standards, the booth or room should allow for ease of access and egress and be provided with good, comfortable ventilation and lighting. The audiometric technician should be able to sit outside the room or booth but be able to see the interior of the room through a window.

To select the proper room, it is necessary to conduct a noise survey at the proposed test location. Sound pressure levels at each test frequency should be measured and recorded using an octave-band analyzer. The audiometric booth selected must have sufficient noise attenuation so that the background noise levels present at each test frequency are reduced and do not exceed the maximum permissible background levels listed in the OSHA noise standard.

Calibrated Equipment

Limited-range, pure-tone audiometers must conform to the requirements in the OSHA noise standard. Two basic types of audiometers are available: automatic recording audiometers and manually operated audiometers.

The audiometer must be subjected to a biological check each day before the instrument is used. The biological check is done by testing the hearing of a person whose hearing threshold is known and stable. The check should include the movement and bending of cords and wires, knob turning, switch actuating, and button pushing to make sure that no sounds are produced in the earphones other than the test tones.

Audiometer calibration must be checked acoustically at least annually in accordance with Appendix E of the OSHA noise standard.

An exhaustive calibration of the audiometer must be performed at least every two years by a repair and calibration facility that has the specialized equipment and skilled technical personnel necessary for this work. A certificate of calibration should be kept with the audiometer at all times.

Detailed requirements for audiometer calibration can be found in the OSHA noise standard, 29 CFR 1910.95.

Adequate Records

The medical form used in audiometric testing programs should include all basic data related to the hearing evaluation. Hearing threshold values, noise-exposure history, and pertinent medical history should be accurately recorded each time an employee's hearing is tested. The employee should be identified by name, social security number, gender, and age. Additional information such as the date and time of the test (day of the week, time of day), conditions under which the test was performed, and the name of the examiner should also be included.

Audiometric test records for an employee must be kept for at least the duration of employment per the OSHA noise standard. Also, the records could become the basis for a settlement of a hearing loss claim.

Periodic audiograms are a profile of the employee's hearing acuity. Any change from the results of previous audiograms should be investigated. One possible reason for a hearing loss is that the employee's hearing protectors are inadequate or improperly worn.

The audiometric testing program should be both practical and feasible. In small companies, where the total number of employees to be tested is small, it would be impractical to purchase a booth and audiometer. It would be more economical to consider a mobile audiometer testing service or to refer the employees to a local, properly equipped and staffed hearing center or to a qualified physician or audiologist for an audiometric examination.

Audiometric testing is an integral part of a comprehensive hearing conservation program. The OSHA Hearing Conservation Standard discussed in the following section details specific requirements for audiometric testing and other required components of an effective hearing conservation program.

NOISE-EXPOSURE REGULATIONS

Background

The federal regulation of occupational noise exposure started with the rules issued by the Bureau of Labor Standards under the authority of the Walsh–Healey Public Contracts Act. These rules required that occupational noise exposure be reasonably controlled to minimize fatigue and the probability of accidents. The federal occupational noise-exposure standards were originally written to apply only to contractors under the Walsh–Healey Public Contracts Act and the McNamara–O'Hara Service Contracts Act. Under the Williams–Steiger Occupational Safety and Health Act of 1970, the Bureau of Labor Standards was replaced by the Occupational Safety and Health Administration (OSHA).

The National Institute for Occupational Safety and Health (NIOSH) was established within the Department of Health and Human Services (formerly the Department of Health, Education and Welfare) by the Occupational Safety and Health Act of 1970 to conduct research and to recommend new occupational safety and health standards. The recommendations are transmitted to the Department of Labor (DOL), which is responsible for the final setting, promulgation, and enforcement of the standards.

In 1972, NIOSH provided the DOL with a document called *Criteria for a Recommended Standard: Occupational Exposure to Noise*. Subsequently, the assistant secretary of labor determined that a standard advisory committee on noise should be formed. The purpose of this OSHA Advisory Committee was to obtain and evaluate additional recommendations from labor, management, government, and independent experts. The committee considered written and oral comments directed to it by interested parties. The committee then transmitted its recommendations for a revised standard to OSHA on December 20, 1973.

In 1974, OSHA published a proposed standard in the *Federal Register* that limited an employee's exposure level to 90 dBA, calculated as an 8-hour, time-weighted average (TWA). NIOSH commented on OSHA's proposed standard, stating that there was a need for reducing the 8-hour exposure level to 85 dBA. However, NIOSH was unable to recommend a specific future date after which the 85-dBA noise level should become mandatory for all industries. Sufficient data were not available to demonstrate the technological feasibility of this level.

The EPA reviewed the OSHA proposal and recommended that the limit not exceed 85 dBA. They also recommended that additional studies be undertaken to explore the efficacy of reducing the permissible level still further at some future date. The proposed revisions to the OSHA rules for occupational noise exposure were published in the *Federal Register* on October 24, 1974.

After years of collecting oral and written public testimony, which resulted in an unwieldy public record of almost 40,000 pages, OSHA promulgated revisions for the noise standard (46 *FR* 4078) in January 1981. These revisions were followed by deferrals, stays (46 *FR* 42622), further revisions, further public hearings, and a multiplicity of lawsuits, all of which culminated in the promulgation of a hearing conservation amendment (48 *FR* 9738) on March 8, 1983, with an effective date of April 7, 1983.

It was estimated by OSHA (46 *FR* 4078) that there were 2.9 million workers in American production industries who experience 8-hour noise exposures exceeding 90 dBA. An additional 2.3 million workers experience exposure levels in excess of 85 dBA. The Hearing Conservation Amendment (HCA) applies to all those employees whose noise exposures equal or exceed an 8-hour TWA of 85 dBA, except for those in oil and gas well drilling and servicing industries, which are specifically exempted. Additionally, the Amendment does not apply to those engaged in construction or agriculture, although a Construction Industry Noise Standard exists (29 CFR 1926.52 and 1926.101). This standard is essentially identical to paragraphs (a) and (b) of the General Industry Noise Standard, 29 CFR 1910.95.

The OSHA Noise Standard

Prior to promulgation of the HCA, the existing Noise Standard (29 CFR 1910.95[a] and [b]) established a permissible noise-exposure level of 90 dBA for 8 hours and required the employer to reduce exposure to that level by use of feasible engineering and administrative controls. In all cases in which sound levels exceeded the permissible exposure, regardless of the use of hearing-protective devices, "a continuing, effective hearing conservation program" was required. However, the details of such a program were never mandated. Paragraphs (c) through (p) of the HCA replaced paragraph (b)(3) of 29 CFR 1910.95 and supplemented OSHA's definition of an "effective hearing conservation program."

Hearing Conservation Programs

An effective hearing conservation program prevents hearing impairment as a result of noise exposure on the job. In terms of existing workers' compensation laws, an effective hearing conservation program is one that limits the amount of compensable hearing loss in the frequency range over which normal hearing is necessary for communication. It should be noted that "compensable" loss at present does not include frequencies over 4,000 Hz, although such loss impairs enjoyment of sound and may interfere with speech discrimination. In compliance with the OSHA requirements, an effective hearing conservation program must be instituted if any employee's noise exposure exceeds current limits as defined in the OSHA Noise Exposure Standard 29 CFR 1910.95.

All employees whose noise exposures equal or exceed an 8-hour TWA of 85 dBA must be included in a hearing conservation program comprised of five basic components: exposure monitoring, audiometric testing, hearing protection, employee training, and record keeping. Note that although the 8-hour TWA permissible exposure limit remains 90 dBA, a hearing conservation program becomes mandatory at an 8-hour TWA exposure of 85 dBA (also referred to as the action level).

The following summary briefly discusses the required components of the hearing conservation program.

Monitoring. The HCA requires employers to monitor employee noise-exposure levels in a manner that can accurately identify employees who are exposed at or above an 8-hour TWA exposure of 85 dBA. The exposure measurement must include all noise within an 80- to 130-dBA range. The requirement is performance oriented and allows employers to choose the monitoring method that best suits each situation.

Employees are entitled to observe monitoring procedures, and, in addition, they must be notified of the results of exposure monitoring. However, the method used to notify employees is left to the discretion of the employer.

Employers must remonitor workers' exposures whenever changes in exposures are sufficient to require new hearing protectors or whenever employees not previously included, because they were not exposed to an 8-hour TWA of 85 dBA, are included in the program.

Instruments used for monitoring employee exposures must be calibrated to ensure that the measurements are accurate. Because calibration procedures are unique to each instrument, employers should follow the manufacturer's instructions to determine when and how extensively to calibrate.

Audiometric Testing

Audiometric testing not only monitors employee hearing acuity over time but also provides an opportunity for employers to educate employees about their hearing and the need to protect it. The audiometric testing program includes obtaining baseline and annual audiograms and initiating training and follow-up procedures. The audiometric testing program should indicate whether hearing loss is being prevented by the employer's hearing conservation program. Audiometric testing must be made available to all employees who have 8-hour TWA exposure of 85 dBA.

A professional (audiologist, otolaryngologist, or physician) must be responsible for the program, but need not be present when a qualified occupational hearing conservationist is actually conducting the testing. Professional responsibilities include overseeing the program and the work of the OHCs, reviewing problem audiograms, and determining whether referral is necessary. Either a professional or an OHC can conduct audiometric testing. In addition to administering audiometric tests, the tester (or the supervising professional) is also responsible for ensuring that the tests are conducted in an appropriate test environment, for seeing that the audiometer works properly, for reviewing audiograms for standard threshold shifts (as defined in the HCA), and for identifying audiograms that require further evaluation.

Audiograms. There are two types of audiograms required in the hearing conservation program: baseline and annual audiograms. The baseline audiogram is the reference audiogram against which subsequent audiograms are compared. Baseline audiograms must be provided within 6 months of an employee's first exposure at or above an 8-hour TWA of 85 dBA. However, when employers use mobile test vans to do audiograms, they have up to 1 year after an employee's first exposure to workplace noise at or above an 8-hour TWA of 85 dBA to obtain the baseline audiogram. Additionally, when mobile test vans are used and employers are allowed to delay baseline testing for up to a year, those employees exposed to 8-hour time-weighted average levels of 85 dBA or more must be issued and fitted with hearing protectors 6 months after their first exposure. The hearing protectors are to be worn until the baseline audiogram is obtained. Baseline audiograms taken before the effective date of the amendment are acceptable as baselines in the program if the professional supervisor determines that the audiogram is valid. The annual audiogram must be conducted within 1 year of the baseline. It is important to test hearing on an annual basis to identify changes in hearing acuity so that protective follow-up measures can be initiated before hearing loss progresses.

Audiogram evaluation. Annual audiograms must be routinely compared to baseline audiograms to determine whether the audiogram is accurate and whether the employee has lost hearing ability; that is, to determine whether a standard threshold shift, or STS, has occurred. An effective program depends on a uniform definition of an STS. An STS is defined in the amendment as an average shift (or loss) in either ear of 10 dB or more at the 2,000-, 3,000-, and 4,000-Hz frequencies. A method of determining an STS by computing an average was chosen because it diminishes the number of persons identified as having an STS who are later shown not to have had a significant change in hearing ability.

Example 7

An example of computing the STS is shown in Table 9–G. Considering the values for 2,000, 3,000, and 4,000 Hz, there are changes in hearing threshold of 10, 15, and 25 dB, respectively. Thus,

$$STS = \frac{(10 + 15 + 25)}{3} = \frac{50}{3} = 16.7 \qquad (25)$$

Conclusion— Example 7

The STS is +16.7 dB. Therefore, hearing has deteriorated, the employee must be notified in writing within 21 days, and, depending on professional discretion, the employer can elect to revise the baseline.

If an STS is identified, the employee must be fitted or refitted with adequate hearing protectors, shown how to use them, and required to wear them. In addition, employees must be notified within 21 days from the time the determination is made that their audiometric test results indicate an STS. Some employees with an STS should be referred for further testing if the professional determines that their test results are questionable or if they have an ear problem of a medical nature caused or aggravated by wearing hearing protectors. If the suspected medical problem is not thought to be related to wearing protectors, employees must merely

TABLE 9–G Computing the Standard Threshold Shift (STS)			
Frequency (Hz)	**Baseline Audiogram Threshold (dB)**	**Annual Audiogram Threshold (dB)**	**Change**
500	5	5	0
1,000	5	5	0
2,000	0	10	+10
3,000	5	20	+15
4,000	10	35	+25
6,000	10	15	+5

be informed that they should see a physician. If subsequent audiometric tests show that the STS identified on a previous audiogram is not persistent, employees exposed to an 8-hour TWA of less than 90 dBA can discontinue wearing hearing protectors.

A subsequent audiogram can be substituted for the original baseline audiogram if the professional supervising the program determines that the employee has experienced a persistent STS. The substituted audiogram becomes known as the revised baseline audiogram. This substitution ensures that the same shift is not repeatedly identified. The professional may also decide to revise the baseline audiogram after an improvement in hearing has occurred, which ensures that the baseline reflects actual thresholds as much as is possible. When a baseline audiogram is revised, the employer must, of course, also retain the original audiogram. To obtain valid audiograms, audiometers must be used, maintained, and calibrated according to specifications detailed in appendices C and E of the standard.

Hearing Protectors

Hearing protectors must be made available to all workers exposed at or above an 8-hour TWA of 85 dBA. This requirement ensures that employees have access to protectors before they experience a loss in hearing. When baseline audiograms are delayed because it is inconvenient for mobile test vans to visit the workplace more than once a year, protectors must be worn by employees for any period exceeding 6 months from the time they are first exposed to 8-hour TWA noise levels of 85 dBA and above until their baseline audiograms are obtained. The use of hearing protectors is also mandatory for employees who have experienced an STS, because these workers are particularly susceptible to noise.

With the help of a person who is trained in fitting hearing protectors, employees should decide which size and type protector is most suitable for their working envi-

ronment. The protector selected should be comfortable to wear and offer sufficient attenuation to prevent hearing loss. Employees must be shown how to use and care for their protectors, and they must be supervised on the job to ensure that they continue to wear them correctly.

Hearing protectors must provide adequate attenuation in each employee's work environment. The employer must reevaluate the suitability of an employee's present protector whenever there is a change in working conditions that might render the hearing protector inadequate. If workplace noise levels increase, employees must be given more effective protectors. The protector must reduce the level of exposure to at least as low as 90 dBA, or to 85 dBA or below when an STS has occurred.

Training

Employee training is important because when workers understand the hearing conservation program's requirements and why it is necessary to protect their hearing, they are better motivated to actively participate in the program. They are more willing to cooperate by wearing their protectors and by undergoing audiometric tests. Employees exposed to 8-hour TWAs of 85 dBA and above must be trained at least annually in the following: the effects of noise; the purpose, advantages, disadvantages, and attenuation characteristics of various types of hearing protectors; the selection, fitting, and care of protectors; and the purpose and procedures of audiometric testing. Training does not have to be accomplished in one session. The program can be structured in any format, and different individuals can conduct different parts as long as the required topics are covered. For example, audiometric procedures could be discussed immediately before audiometric testing. The training requirements are such that employees must be reminded on a yearly basis that noise is hazardous to hearing, and that they can prevent damage by wearing a hearing protector, where appropriate, and by participating in audiometric testing.

Record Keeping

Records of noise-exposure measurement must be kept for 2 years. It may be prudent, however, to keep these records for a longer time in accordance with other medical records requirements under OSHA. Records of audiometric test results must be maintained for the duration of the affected employee's employment. Audiometric test records must include the name and job classification of the employee, the date the test was performed, the examiner's name, the date of acoustic or exhaustive calibration, measurements of the background sound pressure levels in audiometric test rooms, and the employee's most recent noise-exposure measurement.

NIOSH and ACGIH Noise Exposure Guidelines

As stated above, both NIOSH and the EPA recommended to OSHA that the 8-hour TWA for noise be reduced to 85 dBA. In 1998, NIOSH issued *Occupational Noise Exposure, Revised Criteria*. In this document, NIOSH revised its 1972 recommendation, going beyond attempts to conserve hearing by focusing on prevention of noise induced hearing loss. They continued to recommend an 8-hour TWA of 85 dBA. However, they recommended switching from a 5-dB exchange rate to a 3-dB exchange rate, as they believed that current scientific evidence supported this change. This 3-dB doubling rate is used by ACGIH in their threshold limit value (TLV) (see Appendix B).

NIOSH also recommended a new criterion for the definition of standard threshold shifts (STS). Instead of OSHA's definition of an STS as a 10-dB loss in either ear averaged over the frequencies of 2,000, 3,000, and 4,000Hz, NIOSH recommended defining an STS as a 15-dB loss in either ear at any of these frequencies—500, 1,000, 2,000, 3,000, 4,000, or 6,000 Hz. This loss is determined by two consecutive tests.

The use of Age Correction Factors, which are in the OSHA standard, Appendix F, have been dropped by NIOSH in the 1998 revised criteria. Finally, as mentioned in the previous section on NRRs, NIOSH recommended significant reductions in the NRRs of hearing protectors.

Both NIOSH and ACGIH recommend an 8-hour TWA of 85 dBA, with a 3-dB exchange rate, while OSHA's 8-hour TWA is 90 dBA with a 5-dB exchange rate. Table 9–H compares the NIOSH REL and ACGIH TLV for noise exposure with OSHA's noise standard. As the noise level increases, there are significant differences in allowable exposure between the current OSHA standard and the NIOSH/ACGIH recommendations.

| TABLE 9–H | Comparison of OSHA's PEL for Noise with NIOSH/ACGIH Recommendations |

Sound Level (dBA)	Duration per Day (hours) OSHA	Duration per Day (hours) NIOSH/ACGIH
85	16	8
88	10.6	4
90	8	2.5
91	7	2
94	4.6	1
95	4	47 min
97	3	30 min
100	2	15 min

Source: Occupational Noise Exposure, Revised Criteria, NIOSH, 1998.

SUMMARY

Because industrial noise problems are extremely complex, there is no one "standard" program that is applicable to all situations. To protect the hearing of employees and to avoid compensation costs, it behooves industry to consider and evaluate its noise problems and to take steps toward the establishment of effective hearing conservation procedures. The OSHA standards require the control of noise exposures, employee protection against the effects of noise exposures, and the initiation of comprehensive and effective hearing conservation programs.

As outlined in this chapter, an effective hearing conservation program consists of the following:
- noise measurement and analysis
- engineering control of noise exceeding permissible levels
- hearing protection for those employees working in areas where noise cannot be feasibly controlled
- audiometric examinations for all employees
- employee training
- record keeping

The effectiveness of a hearing conservation program depends on the cooperation of employers, supervisors, employees, and other concerned parties. Management's responsibility in this type of program includes taking noise measurements, initiating noise-control measures, undertaking the audiometric testing of employees, providing hearing-protective equipment where it is required, enforcing the use of such protective equipment with sound policies and by example, and informing employees of the benefits to be derived from a hearing conservation program.

It is the employee's responsibility to make proper use of the protective equipment provided by management. It is also the employee's responsibility to observe any rules or regulations in the use of equipment designed to minimize noise exposure.

Detailed references to noise and its management, effects, and control can be found in a great many books and periodicals. For those companies needing assistance in establishing hearing conservation programs, consultation services are available in a number of professional areas through private consultation, insurance, and governmental groups.

BIBLIOGRAPHY

Alberti PW, ed. *Personal Hearing Protection in Industry.* New York: Raven Press, 1982.

American Conference of Government Industrial Hygienists. *2011 TLVs® and BEIs®.* Cincinnati, OH: ACGIH, 2011.

American Industrial Hygiene Association. *The Noise*

Manual, Revised, 5th ed. Fairfax, VA: AIHA, 2003.

American Medical Association. *Evaluation of Permanent Impairment,* 6th ed., R. Rondinelli, ed. Chicago: AMA, 2007.

American National Standards Institute. *Specification for Audiometers,* ANSI/ASA S3.6-2010. New York: ANSI, 2010.

American National Standards Institute. *Maximum Permissible Ambient Noise Levels for Audiometric Test Rooms,* ANSI/ASA S3.1-1999 (R2008). New York: ANSI, 2008.

American National Standards Institute. *Methods for Measuring the Real-Ear Attenuation of Hearing Protectors,* ANSI/ASA S12.6-2008. New York: ANSI, 2008.

American National Standards Institute. *Specification for Personal Noise Dosimeters,* ANSI S1.25-1991 (R2007). New York: ANSI, 2007.

American National Standards Institute. *Specification for Sound Level Meters,* ANSI S1.4-1983 (R2006)/ANSI S1.4A-1985 (R2006). New York: ANSI, 2006.

American National Standards Institute. *Octave-Band and Fractional-Octave-Band Analog and Digital Filters,* ANSI/ASA S1.11-2004 (R2009). New York: ANSI, 2009

Bell LH. *Industrial Noise Control.* New York: Marcel Dekker, 1982.

DiBlasi FT, Suuronen DE, Horst IJ, et al. *Statistics Audio Dosimeter Guide for Use in Electric Power Plants.* New York: Empire State Electric Energy Research Corp., 1983.

Harris CM, ed. *Handbook of Acoustical Measurements and Noise Control,* 3rd ed. New York: McGraw-Hill, 1991.

Jones RS. *Noise and Vibration Control in Buildings.* New York: McGraw-Hill, 1984.

Kryter KD. *The Effects of Noise on Man,* 2nd ed. New York: Academic Press, 1985.

National Institute for Occupational Safety and Health. *Criteria for a Recommended Standard—Occupational Noise Exposure—Revised Criteria,* 1998. Washington, DC: GPO, DHHS Pub No. 98-126, 1998.

Newby HA, Popelka GR. *Audiology,* 5th ed. Englewood Cliffs, NJ: Prentice-Hall, 1985.

Occupational Safety and Health Administration. *Occupational Noise Exposure and Hearing Conservation Amendment.*
Federal Register 46(11) (1981):4,078–4,181.
Federal Register 46(162) (1981):42,622–42,639.
Federal Register 48(46) (1983):9,738–9,783.

Petersen APG. *Handbook of Noise Measurement,* 9th ed. Concord, MA: GenRad, 1980.

Sataloff J, Michael P. *Hearing Conservation.* Springfield, IL: Charles C. Thomas, 1973.

U.S. Department of Health and Human Services, CDC, National Institute for Occupational Safety and Health. *NIOSH Hearing Protector Device Compendium.* Atlanta: CDC. http://www.cdc.gov/niosh/topics/noise/hpcomp.html

Ward WD, Fricke FE, eds. *Noise as a Public Hazard.* Washington, DC: American Speech and Hearing Association, 1969.

Ionizing Radiation

by Elsa Nimmo, CHP

W**hile only a small subset of all safety professionals is involved in ionizing radiation safety, radiation safety is made up of many subspecialties, each with its own set of hazards and controls and sometimes with unique vocabulary, quantities, and units. This chapter presents an overview of basic radiation safety concepts that are widely applicable regardless of the setting and sources of radiation. The reader in need of specialized information will find a number of excellent references listed at the end of this chapter.**

IONIZING RADIATION

Ionizing radiation is a general term used to mean particles (charged or uncharged) that are energetic enough to knock electrons out of the material that the radiation is passing through. As ionizing radiation makes its way through air, water, wood, human tissue, lead, or any other substance, it uses up its energy by detaching electrons from atoms, and generating ions in the substance.

Electron Volts

Throughout this chapter, the energy of radiation will be expressed in *electron volts* (eV), or multiples of this unit, such as keV (1×10^3 eV) or MeV (1×10^6 eV). An electron volt is the kinetic energy gained by an electron by falling through a potential difference of 1 volt. In terms of other energy units, 1 eV is equivalent to 1.6×10^{-12} ergs or 1.6×10^{-19} joule. To detach the negatively charged electron from the positively charged nucleus in a hydrogen atom (creating an ion pair) requires 13.6 eV of energy.

Dose

When used in the radiation safety context, *dose* (more correctly called *absorbed dose*) is simply a measure of the amount of energy that ionizing radiation deposits (in the process of ejecting electrons) in a mass of material. Dose has units of energy per mass (e.g., ergs/gram). There will be a further discussion of radiation dose units later in this chapter. For a person exposed to a significant amount of ionizing radiation, the health risk is generally proportional to the amount of energy that the radiation has lost in the mass of tissue the radiation has traversed. That is, the health risk is proportional to the dose.

IONIZING RADIATION SOURCES

This chapter deals with ionizing radiation only. Radiation with insufficient energy to produce ions in other materials (e.g., lasers) may also require controls and precautions (see Chapter 11, Nonionizing Radiation). Different kinds of ionizing radiation will be discussed later in the chapter. Producers of ionizing radiation are commonly referred to as *sources*. Ionizing radiation is generated by a wide variety of sources, some of which are natural and some of which are man-made. The production of ionizing radiation is something that the sun, radioactive materials, certain types of machines, nuclear reactors, and the cosmos all have in common.

The Cosmos

The cosmos is a continual producer of ionizing radiation, and much of the universe has ionizing radiation levels that would be damaging or lethal to humans if they were exposed on a continuous basis.

From Deep and Not-So-Deep Space

Besides objects in deep space, our sun is also a source of ionizing radiation, emitting particularly intense bursts during solar flares. However, only a fraction of this cosmic radiation (either from the sun or from deep space) reaches the surface of the Earth. Because much of this radiation is in the form of energetic charged particles, the Earth's magnetic field acts to divert much of the radiation. Some of the diverted radiation misses the Earth, some ends up trapped in bands above the Earth's surface (the Van Allen Belts), and some is directed towards the largely uninhabited polar regions of Earth. The ionizing radiation that continues on a path towards Earth must pass through the Earth's thick atmosphere. Much of the radiation loses enough energy that it is no longer energetic enough to be ionizing by the time it finally reaches the Earth's surface.

Still, all life on Earth is constantly exposed to cosmic ionizing radiation. That amount is higher near the Earth's poles and at high elevations.

Radioactive Materials

Radioactive materials are unstable forms of the elements that make up the periodic table. These forms of the elements (which may be referred to as either *radioisotopes* or *radionuclides*) decay to stable elements, emitting ionizing radiation in the process. From long before humans walked the Earth, radioactive materials have made up part of the Earth's crust and its atmosphere. Humans have always been exposed to the ionizing radiation these substances emit. In addition, all living species contain small amounts of radioactive materials within their bodies, since these materials are naturally present in the soil, water, and air. Humans are constantly exposed to ionizing radiation from the naturally occurring radioactive materials that are both inside and outside their bodies.

Additionally, many human activities like mining, living in houses, burning coal, etc., cause people to receive slightly higher radiation doses from naturally occurring radioactive materials than they otherwise would.

Some radioisotopes do not decay directly to a stable isotope, but instead decay to a different radioisotope. Naturally occurring uranium, for example, slowly undergoes a sequence of decays on its way to eventually becoming a stable isotope of lead.

Under certain circumstances, radioactive materials can also be created out of nonradioactive materials. In fact, this is an ongoing natural process as cosmic radiation interacts with the Earth's atmosphere and is a major source of the radioactive material that is naturally present in the atmosphere and on Earth. This topic will be addressed in a later section of this chapter.

Regardless of whether radioactive materials are naturally occurring in their original concentrations and locations, have been extracted and concentrated by humans, or are artificially produced by human activity, they are sources of ionizing radiation.

Radioactivity is a general term for the defining characteristic of radioactive material; that it decays by emitting radiation.

Radiation-Producing Machines

Radiation-producing machines (RPMs) produce ionizing radiation by electronic means, for example by accelerating a beam of electrons inside a vacuum tube such that x rays are emitted when the energetic electrons slam into a high density target. Some radiation-producing machines can produce very intense beams of ionizing radiation that have the potential of resulting in extremely large radiation doses.

Radiation-producing machines are radiation sources that must be considered when reviewing worker safety. However, unlike the other sources of ionizing radiation discussed in this section, the ionizing radiation that is produced by machines can be turned on and off; when the power source is removed, there is no radiation remaining. (An exception to this rule is discussed later in the chapter.)

RPMs include machines that are designed to produce radiation as well as machines where the ionizing radiation is unwanted, but is an unavoidable consequence of the machine's function. Some examples of machines that produce radiation by design are: x-ray machines used in airport security; a wide variety of medical, dental, veterinary, and industrial x-ray units; linear accelerators and cyclotrons; x-ray diffraction units; electron microscopes; and many gauges and imaging devices used in nondestructive testing.

While flat screen televisions and computer screens do not produce ionizing radiation, older televisions and computer monitors that used cathode ray tubes are examples of devices that produce small amounts of unwanted ionizing radiation. Many countries, including the United States, have required manufacturers to certify that their devices stay within established radiation emission standards.

Nuclear Reactors

Whether used for generation of power or for research, current nuclear reactors' production of power is based on the splitting of atoms. This atom-splitting is referred to as *fission*. When bombarded with neutrons, some large atoms, such as uranium or thorium, can be induced to fission. When fission occurs, it releases two or more smaller atoms, several energetic neutrons, and a significant amount of energy in the form of heat. Under the right circumstances, the neutrons released in the fission reaction can then go on to induce further fission events in the uranium (or other) reactor fuel. At some point, a balance can be achieved where there are enough neutrons produced to continue inducing more fissions and the fission reactions become self-sustaining. At this point, it is said that the reactor has gone *critical*.

To slow or interrupt the fission reactions, reactors use special materials that absorb neutrons without undergoing fission, a sort of neutron sponge. Reactor control rods contain this type of material. Control rods are inserted between the rods that contain the reactor fuel when the fission reaction rate is to be slowed down or halted.

While producing ionizing radiation is not the point of nuclear reactors, reactors necessarily generate radiation. The radiation is from several different sources:

- *Fuel rods*. Even before the fuel rods have ever been used in a reactor, the rods are radiation sources because the materials they contain (uranium, thorium, etc.) are themselves radioactive.
- *Neutron production*. Neutrons are a type of ionizing radiation and when the reactor is running, energetic neutrons are produced in abundance.
- *Activation*. While some of the neutrons emitted in the fission process are reabsorbed by the fuel that is undergoing fission, others are absorbed by nonradioactive materials elsewhere in the reactor. In some case, the neutron-irradiated materials become radioactive and emit ionizing radiation.
- *Fission fragments*. Assume the discussion is about a reactor where the fuel is uranium. As the reactor runs and the uranium inside the fuel rods fissions into smaller atoms, the amount of uranium decreases, or "burns up." But the smaller atoms created when uranium splits (the fission products) are often themselves unstable isotopes. So even though the amount of uranium in the fuel rods slowly decreases as a reactor is run, the uranium is replaced by fission products, many of which are themselves radioactive.

Nuclear Weapons and Weapons Testing

Above-ground nuclear weapon testing was conducted by many countries, especially before the Limited Test Ban Treaty was adopted in 1963. While a large fraction of the radioactive materials produced in those tests had a very short life span and is no longer present, some of the long-lived radioactive materials that were created were distributed throughout the Earth's atmosphere. These have added a small, artificially created increment to the radioactive substances that are naturally present in the atmosphere and on Earth.

The various sources of radiation described in this section (the cosmos, natural and artificially produced materials, some machines, etc.) can result in radiation doses to humans, as shown in Figure 10–1.

RADIATION vs RADIOACTIVITY

The terms radiation and radioactivity are often used as if they were synonyms. However, despite how they are commonly used, the two words are not synonyms and it is important, especially for safety professionals, to be clear on the difference in their meanings.

Radioactivity is the term for the defining characteristic of radioactive materials—that their nuclei are unstable and decay, emitting ionizing radiation in the process. As discussed above, *radiation*—energetic particles—can come from any one (or a combination) of different sources. The presence of radioactive materials always implies the pres-

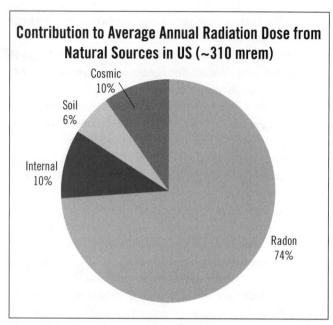

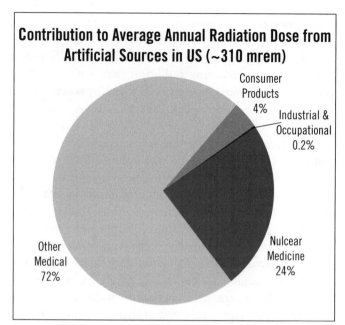

Figure 10–1. These diagrams show the relative contributions to the annual radiation dose of the average U.S. inhabitant. Notice that on average, the dose is split half and half between dose from natural sources and man-made (mostly medical) radiation sources.

ence of radiation. But the presence of radiation does not require the presence of radioactivity. Radioactivity and radiation can be compared to fire and heat. A fire guarantees that there will be heat, but heat can come from many different sources and is not necessarily from fire. Similarly, radioactivity guarantees that there will be radiation present, while radiation can be produced in many different ways and is not necessarily from something that is radioactive.

PRODUCTION OF RADIOACTIVE MATERIAL

As described below, there are several different processes by which nonradioactive elements or items may become radioactive.

Activation

When used in the radiation safety context, *activation* means the process of producing radioactive material by bombarding something that is not radioactive with high energy radiation. Activation of stable elements is a natural and continual process in the Earth's upper atmosphere as it is bombarded with high energy radiation from the cosmos.

Artificial activation of stable materials also takes place. However, activation can only take place in limited circumstances involving the right materials and very large exposures to radiation of the right type and energy. People receiving a diagnostic x ray do not become activated, nor do medical items that are deliberately irradiated for sterilization, or food that is irradiated to reduce spoilage. However,

artificial activation can be an issue at nuclear reactors and for high energy research or medical accelerators.

Artificially Making Stable Substances Radioactive

Rather than being an undesirable side effect, there are situations where changing stable elements into radioisotopes is precisely what is intended. For example, many hospitals have particle accelerators and create some of the radioactive materials they use in nuclear medicine by bombarding the appropriate nonradioactive target with an intense beam of particles accelerated to the required energy.

Fission and Spallation

Another physical process that can create radioactive materials from nonradioactive elements is *fission*, also called *spallation*. Both terms refer to the breaking up of heavier atoms into lighter atoms as the result of bombardment by extremely energetic radiation. And in both cases, the lighter atoms that are produced may be either stable or radioactive. The term fission is usually used to refer to the breaking up of atoms that occurs in a research or power reactor while spallation is generally reserved for nonreactor situations (e.g., the breaking up of atoms that occurs as Earth's upper atmosphere is bombarded by extremely energetic cosmic radiation).

Contamination

Contamination is a more familiar concept. Many human activities result in the contamination of our air, water, and soil with chemical and biological substances that may be detrimental to our health or to the environment. In cases where radioactive materials are in a dispersible form (liquid, gas, powdered, etc.) and not sealed inside a leak-proof container, contamination may result if the radioactive chemical is spilled or released. In this case the item with the contamination is not intrinsically radioactive, any more than a shirt with mud on it is intrinsically dirty. If the radioactive contamination can be removed (e.g., by washing or some chemical process), then the item will no longer be radioactive.

Alternate Definition of Radioactive Contamination

Some define the phrase radioactive contamination as "radioactive material where it is not wanted," a definition that extends beyond radioactivity that is present due to a spill or other unintentional release of radioactive material. Under that broader definition, equipment or materials that have become activated or soil containing unwanted, naturally occurring radioactive material could also be called contaminated.

DIFFERENT TYPES OF RADIATION

Earlier in this chapter, it was stated that "Ionizing radiation is a general term used to mean particles (charged or uncharged) that are energetic enough to knock electrons out of the material that the radiation is passing through." The particles that are classified as ionizing radiation are summarized in Table 10-A and further described below.

Alphas

Alphas consist of two protons and two neutrons (basically, helium nuclei). With a mass of four atomic mass units and a double positive charge, they interact very quickly with whatever substance they are passing through, creating a dense trail of ions and depositing all their energy within in a very short distance. The amount of energy ionizing radiation deposits per unit distance is called the linear energy transfer (LET). Alphas are a type of radiation characterized by high LET.

Given the quick transfer of energy, alpha radiation is easily stopped by minimal shielding, a few centimeters of air, a sheet of paper, the outer dead layer of skin. This means an alpha-emitting source does not present any hazard to a person when it is external to the body. But while the quick energy loss and high density of ionization prevent alpha emitters from being an external hazard, those characteristics also mean that an alpha emitter can deliver a radiation dose that is particularly damaging to cells if it is inhaled, ingested, or otherwise taken into the body.

TABLE 10–A							Types of Radiation
Radiation Type (alternate names)	**Mass**	**Charge**	**Directly Ionizing?**	**LET**	**Range?**	**External Hazard?**	**Typical Source(s) / Comments**
Alpha	4 amu	+2	Yes	High	Few cm in air*	No*	Decay of naturally occurring or artificially produced radionuclides; cosmic radiation * Range/external hazard information applies only to alphas from radioactive decay.
Electrons (betas), positrons	~1/1836 amu	-1 (electrons/ betas) +1 (positrons)	Yes	Low	Varies depending on energy, absorber	Potentially	Decay of naturally occurring or artificially produced radionuclides; accelerators; cosmic radiation
Protons	1 amu	+1	Yes	Low/High (see text)	Varies depending on energy, absorber	Potentially	Accelerators; cosmic radiation
Neutrons	1 amu	None	No	High	N/A	Potentially	Fission (induced or spontaneous) or decay of naturally occurring or artificially produced radionuclides; radionuclide or machine neutron generators, secondary radiation from high energy accelerators
Ionizing EM radiation (photons, gammas, x rays, Bremsstrahlung)	N/A	None	No	Low	N/A	Potentially	Decay of naturally occurring or artificially produced radionuclides (either as primary or significant secondary radiation); radiation-producing machines

In the previous paragraph it was noted that alpha radiation is easily stopped by just a few centimeters in air. Alternatively, it could be said that alpha particles typically have a range of just a few centimeters in air. The range is the distance that energetic charged particles of a particular energy can travel from their source until essentially all the primary particles have lost their kinetic energy and are no longer capable of ionization. The range depends on the mass and charge of the particles in question, their energy, and the material the radiation is traveling through. On the other hand, the range is completely independent of how many charged particles strike the material. At a thickness greater than the range, all the primary particles will have been absorbed, whether the initial intensity was tens of particles per square centimeter per second or billions (Figure 10–2).

Note however that the range of a radiation in a material applies only to the particles that make up the primary radiation. In some cases, there is a significant production of secondary radiation which must be considered in any design of radiation shielding. This topic will be discussed later in the chapter.

For alphas of a specific energy, their range in air is larger than their range in denser materials, like wood, water, or iron.

Alphas are also a directly ionizing form of radiation. Alphas cause the ionization of atoms in the materials they pass through due to the interaction of their charge with the electrons in those materials. Some other types of ionizing radiation are not charged and do not interact with the electrons in the absorbing material in the same way. Those types of radiation are called indirectly ionizing radiation.

Note that if a type of radiation is directly ionizing, this does not automatically mean that the radiation's biological effect will be by direct action. Direct action in the radiobiological sense is a separate concept.

Alphas are emitted by a number of natural and artificial radioisotopes. Alpha radiation is the radiation of concern from the inhalation of naturally occurring radon in our environment. Thus alphas are responsible for most of the natural background radiation dose received by the average person living in the United States (more than ⅔ of the U.S. annual average) (Figure 10–1). Units of radiation dose will be discussed later in this chapter.

Electrons and Positrons

Electrons and positrons have a mass that is about 1/2000th that of a proton or neutron and a charge (negative for electrons, positive for positrons) of one. Electrons emitted by radioactive materials are called beta particles, or betas.

Electrons may also be accelerated to ionizing energies in various types of medical and research accelerators.

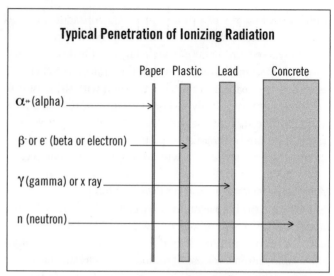

Figure 10–2. Because alpha particles lose their energy so quickly, they are easy to shield. But losing energy quickly also means alphas can be more hazardous than other types of radiation if an alpha-emitting substance is inside the body. The typical penetration of other radiation types are also shown.

With their smaller mass and charge, electrons and positrons do not interact as much as alpha particles, and they lose less energy per unit distance traveled in a material. This means that electrons and positrons are considered low LET radiation. Energetic electrons and positrons moving through a material interact with the electrons in that material. In doing so, several things occur:

- The energetic electrons and positrons gradually lose their energy.
- Ionization takes place in the material the electrons and positrons pass through (like alphas, electrons and positrons are directly ionizing).
- Secondary radiation in the form of x rays is released. These secondary x rays are known as *Bremsstrahlung*.

The degree to which electrons and positrons present a radiation hazard when their source is external to the body depends on the electron energy. Some sources emit electrons and positrons that are energetic enough (that is, they have a long enough range in human tissue) to be potentially damaging to the lens of the eye or even deeper lying internal organs even when the electron or positron source is external to the body. In other cases, an external source would emit electrons potentially capable of damaging skin, but not energetic enough to reach the lens of the eye. (At energies of about 70 keV and above, electrons can penetrate to the live layer of skin; at energies of about 800 keV and above, electrons can penetrate to the depth of the lens of the eye.)

There are many natural and artificially produced radioactive materials that emit betas sufficiently energetic to be ionizing radiation. Beta-emitting radionuclides are commonly used in a wide variety of medical, research, and industrial applications.

Positrons are the less-common antimatter twin of electrons. Positron-emitting radioactive materials have relatively short life spans, so although they are constantly created as cosmic radiation interacts with the atmosphere, positron-emitters are not found as a component of naturally occurring radioactive material. However use of positron-emitting radioactive materials has grown rapidly, along with an understanding of the value of positron emission tomography (PET) to medicine. It is increasingly common for hospitals and clinics to operate on-site cyclotrons for the purpose of producing positron emitters.

The usefulness of PET relies on the fact that when a positron has moved through a substance and lost nearly all of its energy, it interacts with an electron and is annihilated. At the location of the annihilation, two photons are released. Each photon has an energy of 511 keV and is ionizing radiation. The photons are emitted in opposite directions; that is there is an angle of 180° between their initial paths.

Other than the emission of annihilation radiation, which only occurs with positrons, electrons and positrons are otherwise very similar in how they interact with the material they are passing through. But shielding positron emitters requires more material than shielding an energetically and numerically equivalent electron emitter, as a result of the annihilation photons.

Protons

Protons are somewhat less commonly encountered, at least as a form of ionizing radiation, by most people who specialize in radiation safety. However, protons are an issue for those concerned with the protection of astronauts and others who may be exposed to cosmic radiation at levels much greater than what is found on the Earth's surface. Protons are also particles that may be accelerated to high energy in research accelerators and, increasingly, in accelerators used for radiation therapy.

With a mass of 1 amu and a +1 charge, an energetic proton loses its energy relatively slowly as it moves through a material (low LET). However, near the end of a proton's path through a material, it deposits a relatively large amount of energy in a short distance (high LET). When graphically displaying the LET for protons of a specific energy in a particular material, this spike in LET is known as the Bragg Peak (Figure 10–3).

Varying LET

The fact that the LET of protons varies with depth in the absorbing material is both troublesome and useful. It is troublesome in that protons are a major component of cos-

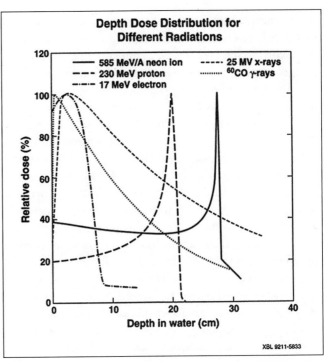

Figure 10–3. Many types of external radiation beams deliver their highest radiation dose at a depth near the surface of water (or near the surface of the skin in radiation therapy). Compare this to depth of the maximum dose from an external beam of charged particles like protons or neon ions. Note the characteristic Bragg Peak. *(Diagram courtesy of Dr. Inder Daftari, Senior Physicist, Department of Radiation Oncology, University of California- San Francisco, San Francisco, CA.)*

mic radiation and their variable LET nature makes very energetic protons both more difficult to shield and more hazardous. This presents challenges for astronaut safety, especially given the constraints of spacecraft design.

The positive aspect of protons' variable LET is that it reduces one of the inherent problems in external beam radiation therapy (e.g., for cancer treatment). In most cases, the treatment site (e.g., the tumor) is an internal one, and the goal is to deliver cell-killing amounts of radiation to that site, while minimizing the radiation damage to the surrounding tissues. Protons appear intrinsically suited for this purpose. By tuning the energies of the protons in the treatment beam, it is possible to produce a composite Bragg Peak that is broad and flat and that will deliver a uniform and large radiation dose over the volume of a tumor, while delivering relatively little radiation to the surrounding healthy tissue.

Neutrons

Neutrons are also a type of ionizing radiation that is encountered only under limited circumstances. So while some radiation safety professionals, such as those working at reactors or high energy accelerators, deal with neutrons at all times, others may work their entire careers without ever needing to consider neutrons.

Neutrons have a mass of 1 amu and no charge. Unlike charged particles, neutrons are indirectly ionizing radiation.

Another way in which neutrons differ from charged particle radiation is that for a given neutron energy and absorbing material, it is not possible to specify the range of the neutrons. As neutrons emitted by a neutron source pass through the appropriate type of shielding material, the number of neutrons gradually decreases. However, there is no set thickness of the shield that can be selected for neutrons of a particular energy that will stop 100% of the neutrons, regardless of how many are initially present.

Finally, neutrons are unlike all of the other types of radiation considered in this chapter in that the types of materials that are particularly effective as radiation shielding (e.g., dense substances like lead or tungsten) are not effective when it comes to shielding neutrons. What does work well as neutron shielding are materials with high hydrogen content, such as water, polyethylene, paraffin, and concrete. This is because energetic neutrons are unaffected by the presence of electrons but interact by colliding with the atomic nuclei of the material they encounter. If the nucleus is similar in mass to the neutron's mass, the neutron will transfer more of its kinetic energy to the nucleus.

Billiard Balls, Bowling Balls, and Neutron Shielding

To understand how neutrons lose energy, it may help to think of what happens if a moving billiard ball strikes a stationary billiard ball. Following the collision, it is often the case that both balls will be moving because the kinetic energy of the first ball has been shared with the originally stationary ball. By contrast, if a moving billiard ball runs into a much more massive stationary ball (say a bowling ball), the billiard ball will simply bounce off the massive ball, retaining most its original kinetic energy.

The first case is a representation of what can happen when an energetic neutron strikes a hydrogen nucleus in a radiation shield. The second represents what happens when an energetic neutron strikes the nucleus of a heavier atom, like iron or lead. So since the purpose of the shielding is to cause the neutron to lose kinetic energy until it can travel no further, materials with high hydrogen content are especially effective.

Depending on their energy and the composition of the material they encounter, neutrons may also cause some of the nuclei to break up and be emitted as energetic, positively charged ions (spallation) or the nuclei may undergo other types of nuclear reactions, accompanied by the emission of alphas, protons, more neutrons, and the production of other stable or radioactive materials. Because energetic neutrons generate energetic and relatively heavy charged particles

that are themselves high-LET forms of radiation, neutron radiation is high LET.

Ionizing Electromagnetic Radiation

Electromagnetic radiation is a form of radiation that we all encounter day in and day out. It includes visible light (from the sun or artificially produced), radio waves, microwaves, and infrared and ultraviolet light. All these radiations travel at the speed of light, but they are characterized by different wavelengths—the more energetic the radiation, the shorter its wavelength and the higher its frequency.

Visible light has wavelengths ranging from about 700 nm (red) to about 400 nm (violet). At wavelengths less than 300 nm (and energies above 4 eV), electromagnetic radiation begins to be capable of producing ionization (the amount of energy required for ionization depends on the material the radiation passes through) (Figure 10–4).

Historically, scientists performing experiments with electromagnetic radiation learned that radiation acted as if it had two separate personalities, depending on the type of experiment they performed. In some cases, electromagnetic radiation acts strictly as if it is a wave that transmits energy. In other situations, electromagnetic radiation behaves as if it is made up of particles—photons—that have kinetic energy. As a result, there are discussions that focus on electromagnetic radiation's wave-like nature and others that focus on its particle-like nature in the literature about this type of radiation. (Electrons also have a wave nature, so these comments could apply to them as well.)

Three additional terms are commonly used for types of ionizing electromagnetic radiation: gamma rays, x rays, and Bremsstrahlung. The additional information each term conveys is simply the origin of the electromagnetic radiation under discussion.

- *Gamma rays* are energetic photons produced by transitions within atomic nuclei, for example, as a result of radioactive decay.
- *X rays* are electromagnetic radiation that arises from interactions of electrons (including photons emitted when electrons drop from one atomic orbital to another that is at a lower energy state).
- *Bremsstrahlung* refers to x rays that are emitted whenever an energetic charged particle is slowed down as it encounters electrons in the material the charged particle is moving through. (Bremsstrahlung is a compound noun from the German verb "bremsen" which means "to brake" and the noun "Strahlung" which means "radiation.") By definition, Bremsstrahlung is secondary radiation—it cannot exist without primary radiation in the form of energetic charged particles.

All Bremsstrahlung is made up of x rays. But not all

x rays are Bremsstrahlung, since x rays can also be primary radiation (e.g., x rays emitted when electrons change orbitals in a radioactive material).

Excluding cosmic radiation or secondary radiation due to neutrons from reactors or high energy accelerators, most gamma rays are emitted by radioactive materials, while x rays are produced either by machines that accelerate electrons to high energies or in radioactive decays that involve electron energy transitions.

Although electromagnetic radiation sometimes behaves as if it was made up of particles, photons have no mass and no charge. This means that energetic photons can travel through a material unaffected by the charge of the electrons in that material. As a result, electromagnetic radiation is low LET—it loses relatively little energy per unit distance along its path.

Like neutrons, electromagnetic radiation is indirectly ionizing radiation. And like neutrons, for a given photon energy and material, it is not possible to specify the range of the photons. If an energetic photon beam is passing through material, the number of photons gradually decreases (the processes that make this happen will be described below), but the decrease is an exponential drop off; there is no absorber thickness that will eliminate all the primary photons. This means that the amount of shielding required when photons are involved depends not only on the shielding material and the energy of the photons, but how much radiation is present.

While photons are not slowed by electronic attraction or repulsion, other interactions do take place. The three most important processes are:

- *Photoelectric Effect.* This process is the most important one for relatively low energy photons and materials with high atomic numbers. When it occurs, the photon transfers its energy (less the electron binding energy) to a tightly bound electron that is ejected from its orbital. The ejected electron proceeds to lose its energy by interacting as described in the earlier section on electrons.
- *Compton Scattering.* This process is the most common one at intermediate photon energies and in materials with low atomic numbers. When Compton scattering takes place, the photon shares its energy with a loosely bound orbital electron. The orbital electron is ejected while the photon appears to continue on its way, but at a lower energy and moving in a different direction than how it started.
- *Pair Production.* This process requires relatively high photon energies. It does not take place below 1.02 MeV and becomes increasingly important at high energies. In pair production, the photon's energy is converted to mass, creating a positron and electron pair. These particles carry off any of the photon energy in excess of the 1.02 MeV that was used in their creation. The positron and electron lose their energy in the absorbing material as previously described.

RADIOACTIVITY

Earlier in this chapter, a number of different sources of ionizing radiation were mentioned, with the list including the cosmos, radioactive materials, radiation-producing

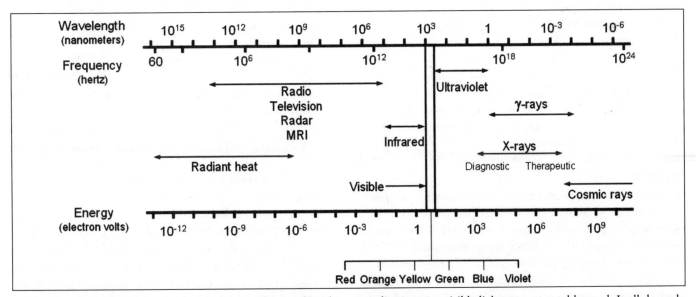

Figure 10–4. The electromagnetic spectrum ranges from radiant heat to radio waves to visible light to x rays and beyond. It all depends on the wavelength. *(Reprinted by permission of the Society of Nuclear Medicine from: Seibert JA. X-Ray Imaging Physics for Nuclear Medicine Technologists. Part 1: Basic Principles of X-Ray Production. J Nucl Med Technol. 2004; 32(3): 139-147, Figure 2.)*

machines, and nuclear reactors. Each of the different types of radiation listed in the previous section can originate from more than one of these radiation sources.

Radioactive materials are not the only source of ionizing radiation or even the only source of any particular type of radiation. But radioactive materials do have some characteristics that present special safety challenges. Some of these characteristics are as follows:

- Radioactive materials cannot be switched on or off; they go on emitting ionizing radiation until all the unstable nuclei in the material have decayed to stable nuclei. In some cases, the original radioactive material decays through a long series of different radioisotopes before reaching a stable form.
- Each radioisotope decays at its own rate and there is nothing that can be done to slow down, stop, or accelerate that decay rate.
- Radioactive materials naturally make up part of our world and they are everywhere. Unlike radiation-producing machines, which are localizable, countable radiation sources, naturally occurring radioactive materials are distributed radiation sources that exist both inside and outside of human bodies.
- When artificially created (or artificially concentrated) radioactive materials are in a dispersible form (e.g., an uncontained gas, liquid, or powder), they can become distributed radiation sources if they contaminate soil, structures, or items or if they are inhaled or ingested. (If radioactive materials are released in a spill or leak, their movement, and dilution or concentration take place in exactly the same ways as would be the case with non-radioactive forms of the same materials. There are no unique mechanisms that transport radioactive materials from one location to another.)
- While all life on earth is constantly exposed to naturally occurring radioactive materials and constantly takes in some of that material, human activities can involve exposure to much larger amounts and/or concentrations. Or they can involve types of radioactive materials that would not naturally be present.

Half-Life

Different radioactive materials decay (emitting radiation in the process) at widely different rates. For example, assume you start out with one mole (6.022×10^{23} atoms) each of two different unstable forms of carbon, C^{14} and C^{11}. After 5730 years, about 3.011×10^{23} (half) of the C^{14} atoms will still be C^{14} while the other 3.011×10^{23} atoms will have decayed to N^{14}, which is stable. By comparison, after 20.4 minutes, half the C^{11} will have decayed to B^{11}, also stable. The time it takes for half of the unstable nuclei

TABLE 10–B Half-Lives of Various Radioisotopes

Radio nuclide	Half-life	Notes
H^3	12.35 y	
Be^7	53.44 d	
C^{11}	20.38 m	
C^{14}	5730 y	
F^{18}	109.74 m	
P^{32}	14.29 d	
S^{35}	87.44 d	
K^{40}	1.277×10^8 y	
Cr^{51}	27.704 d	
Co^{60}	5.271 y	
Ni^{63}	96 y	
Sr^{90}	29.12 y	Decays to Y^{90}
Y^{90}	64 h	
Mo^{90}	66 h	Decays to Tc^{99m}
Tc^{99m}	6.02 h	Decays to Tc^{99}
Tc^{99}	2.13×10^5 y	
I^{125}	60.14 d	
I^{131}	8.04 d	
Cs^{137}	30.0 y	Decays to Ba^{137m}
Ba^{137m}	2.552 m	
Po^{210}	138.38 d	
Ra^{226}	1600 y	Decays to Rn^{222}
Rn^{222}	3.8235 d	Decays to Po^{218}
Po^{218}	3.05 m	Decays to Pb^{214}
Pb^{214}	26.8 m	Decays to Bi^{214}
Bi^{214}	19.9 m	Decays to Po^{214}
Po^{214}	164.3 μs	Decays to Pb^{210} (decay chain ends with stable Pb^{208})
U^{235}	703.8×10^6 y	Decays to Th^{231}
U^{238}	4.468×10^9 y	Decays to Th^{234}
Am^{241}	432.2 y	Decays to Np^{237}
Cf^{252}	2.638 y	Decays to Cm^{248}

Note: y = year, m = month, d = day, m = minute, s = second
(Table based on information from Shleien, 1992)

of a radioisotope to decay to a different isotope is called the *half-life*.

Over the years since the discovery of radioactivity, many different radioisotopes have been studied and their half-lives tabulated; Table 10–B shows a small subset. Note that some of these half-lives are microseconds long, while others are billions of years.

It is fairly common for people to be more concerned about radioactive substances that have very long half-lives than those that have a shorter half-life. However, a long half-life goes along with a substance that is not very intensely radioactive per unit mass. In fact, it may be difficult to tell the difference between a radioactive substance with a long half-life and a substance that is stable; a material that is stable can be thought of as having an infinitely long half-life. In any case, having a long half-life does not automatically make a radioactive material more of a hazard than one with a short half-life. In terms of hazard, what matters is the radiation dose that a person can receive from the material.

Activity and Decay Constant

Another important quantity applicable to radioactive sources is activity. The *activity* of a particular radioactive source is the number of radioactive decays that source undergoes per unit time. Note that the activity tells how many decays happen per second, but activity says nothing about the energy or type of radiation emitted. In cases where there is a quantity of a radioactive material, but nothing is known about it other than its activity, there is too little information to determine the hazard (or lack of hazard) that radioactive material presents.

At any point in time, the activity of a source (call it A_1) is directly proportional to how many atoms of the radioactive material are present at that time (N_1) and inversely proportional to the half-life of the material ($t_{1/2}$):

$$A_1 = \left[\frac{0.693}{t_{1/2}} \right] N_1 \qquad (1)$$

The factor in brackets, the natural log of 2 divided by the half-life, is known as the decay constant, normally represented as λ. So an alternate representation of this equation is:

$$A_1 = \lambda N_1 \qquad (1a)$$

$$\text{where } \lambda = \frac{0.693}{t_{1/2}}$$

Because radioactive sources decay, their activity is constantly decreasing at a rate that depends on the half-life ($t_{1/2}$) of the particular radionuclide. If the initial activity is measured to be A_1, then after a time Δt we can calculate the new activity A_2 using the formula:

$$A_2 = A_1 \, e^{\left(\frac{-0.693 \times \Delta t}{t_{1/2}} \right)} \qquad (2)$$

or

$$A_2 = A_1 \, e^{(-\lambda \, \Delta t)} \qquad (2a)$$

Table 10–C indicates the units used for activity and half-life.

Activity calculations using Equation 1a:
What is the activity of 1 milligram of pure C^{11}?
The weight of one mole (6.022×10^{23}) of C^{11} atoms is 11 g.

So the number of C^{11} atoms in a milligram is:

$$N_1 = \left(\frac{1 \times 10^{-3} \text{ g}}{11 \text{ g/mole}} \right) \times 6.022 \times 10^{23} \text{ atoms/mole}$$

$$N_1 = 5.47 \times 10^{19} \text{ atoms}$$

From Table 10–B, $t_{1/2} = 20.4$ m for C^{11}. Using these values in Equation 1:

$$A_1 = \frac{0.693 \times 5.47 \times 10^{19} \text{ atoms}}{(20.4 \text{ m}) \times (60 \text{ s/m})}$$

$$A_1 = 3.1 \times 10^{16} \text{ s}^{-1}$$

So the activity of 1 mg of pure C^{11} is about 3.1×10^{16} decays/s, which is 3.1×10^{16} Bq (or about 8.4×10^5 Ci).

Repeat the calculation for C^{11}'s longer-lived sibling, C^{14}.

$$N_1 = \left(\frac{1 \times 10^{-3} \text{ g}}{14 \text{ g/mole}} \right) \times 6.022 \times 10^{23} \text{ atoms/mole}$$

$$N_1 = 4.30 \times 10^{19} \text{ atoms}$$

In this case, $t_{1/2} = 5730$ years. So the calculation is:

$$A_1 = \frac{0.693 \times 4.30 \times 10^{19} \text{ atoms}}{(5730 \text{ y}) \times (365 \text{ d/y}) \times (24 \text{ h/d}) \times (60 \text{ m/h}) \times (60 \text{ s/m})}$$

$$A_1 = 1.65 \times 10^8 \text{ s}^{-1}$$

The activity of 1 milligram of C^{14} is about 1.65×10^8 decays/s or 1.65×10^8 Bq (about 4.5 mCi), just a tiny fraction of the activity of the same weight of C^{11}.

C^{14} decays by beta emission (100%); C^{11} decays by positron emission (100%). Notice that for equal masses, the radionuclide with the short half-life (C^{11}) emits about 188 million times more positrons per second than the number of betas per second emitted by its longer-lived counterpart (C^{14}). If you compared the dose rate at the surface of two ampules, one containing 1 milligram of C^{11} and the other with 1 milligram of C^{14}, the contrast would be even more extreme, due to the high energy of the C^{11} positrons and the annihilation photons they create.

Activity calculations using Equation 2:
Using equation 1, it is possible to calculate the activity (A_1) of a radioactive source at a particular moment in time. But that activity is constantly changing, since the number of atoms of the radioactive material (N_1 at time t_1) decreases as a result of decay. If the initial activity and the half-life of the

	TABLE 10-C	Review of Units		

Quantity	Old Unit Name (abbreviation)	SI Unit Name (abbreviation)	Relationship between Units
Activity	Curie (Ci)	Becquerel (Bq)	$1\ Ci = 3.7 \times 10^{10}$ decays/second
			$1\ Bq = 1$ decay/second
			$1\ Ci = 3.7 \times 10^{10}\ Bq$
Half-life	Seconds (s), minutes (m), hours (h), days (d), years (y)	Seconds (s)	

source are known, Equation 2 allows the source's activity to be calculated at any time.

Above, an activity of 3.1×10^{16} Bq was calculated for 1 milligram of pure C^{11}. In terms of activity, how much of that C^{11} would be left after a decay time (t_2-t_1) of 24 hours? Substituting the values for the initial activity, the decay time, and half-life into Equation 2, the result is:

$$A_2 = (3.1 \times 10^{16}\ Bq) \times e^{\left(\frac{-0.693 \times (24\ h \times 60\ m/h)}{20.4\ m}\right)}$$

$$A_2 \sim 0.00002\ Bq$$

Since 1 Bq is 1 decay per second, after 24 hours (which is about 71 half-lives in the case of C^{11}) there is really no radioactivity left.

Repeating this calculation for the milligram of pure C^{14}, we can see the effect of its much longer half-life:

$$A_2 = (1.65 \times 10^{8}\ Bq) \times e^{\left(\frac{-0.693 \times (1\ d)}{5730\ y \times 365\ d/y}\right)}$$

$$A_2 = 1.65 \times 10^{8}\ Bq$$

The value of the exponential term in Equation 2 (or 2a) is the fraction of the activity that is left at the end of the decay time. Notice that this term equals 0.5 if a decay time equal to the half-life is used.

For a 24 hour decay time and C^{14}, the fraction of the remaining activity is 0.9999997, or essentially 1. The activity of the C^{14} is essentially the same after 24 hours as it was at the start of the period. But then 24 hours is just a tiny fraction of the C^{14} half-life.

THE EFFECTS OF RADIATION ON HUMANS

Radioactive Materials in the Body

As noted earlier in this chapter, the universe naturally produces a lot of ionizing radiation, some of which creates radioactive materials in the atmosphere and everywhere on earth. As a result, all humans contain radioactive substances in their bodies. For example, a small fraction of all potassium, including the potassium in human bodies, is naturally occurring K^{40}. K^{40} mainly decays by emission of an energetic beta particle and so contributes to the natural background radiation dose humans receive year in and year out.

The Banana Dose

People sometimes talk about the radiation dose received each time someone eats a banana, since bananas are a particularly good source of potassium. But unless a person is potassium deficient or has a health condition that interferes with potassium elimination, the human body regulates the amount of potassium around a set point. Eating a banana really is not going to make any difference in the amount of K^{40} contained in the body or the dose received from that K^{40}. Similarly, human bodies contain C^{14}, since a fraction of all carbon consists of this naturally occurring radionuclide. For a 70 kg person about 7000 of the radioactive atoms (K^{40} and C^{14}) within the body decay each second. The annual radiation dose that results from the internal K^{40} and C^{14} is shown on the pie chart in an earlier section of this chapter (Figure 10–1).

From the air and from food, different tissues in the human body accumulate a variety of materials. Healthy thyroids tend to concentrate iodine, while bones and teeth contain about 99% of the calcium present in the human body. The fact that a substance is radioactive does not affect how it is transported or used inside any plant or animal. Within the body, radioactive K^{40} is used exactly the same as its stable and more abundant potassium counterpart, K^{39}. As a person breathes, drinks, or eats a substance that has a radioactive component, or is injected with a radioactive compound (e.g., in a nuclear medicine procedure), the radioactive substance may be:

- promptly exhaled or excreted;
- trapped in the lungs (depending on whether it is attached to a particle of a certain size);

- distributed fairly uniformly throughout body fluids; or
- concentrated in one or several particular organs in the body.

Biological Half-Life

The previous section described the half-life of a radioactive material, based on the fact that each radioisotope decays at a known rate. But there is another type of half-life that is important to radiation safety, especially in cases where a person has an intake of radioactive material. Such an intake could occur in a medical procedure or in an occupational or other setting that involves radioactive material. The *biological half-life* is the time it takes for half of any substance to be eliminated from the body as a result of natural biological processes.

Effective Half-Life

In the case of a radioactive compound, both the decay (or physical) half-life of the radioisotope and the biological half-life cause the amount of the radioisotope in the body to decrease. The overall half-life of the substance in the body is called the *effective half-life*. The effective half-life [$t_{1/2}(\text{eff})$] is shorter than either the physical half-life [$t_{1/2}(\text{phy})$] or the biological half-life [$t_{1/2}(\text{bio})$] and can be calculated using the following equation:

$$t_{1/2}(\text{eff}) = \frac{t_{1/2}(\text{phy}) \times t_{1/2}(\text{bio})}{t_{1/2}(\text{phy}) + t_{1/2}(\text{bio})} \qquad (3)$$

An alternate, simpler equation calculates the effective clearance rate constant from the sum of the physical decay constant and the biological clearance rate constant. From the effective clearance rate constant, it is easy to calculate the effective half-life:

$$\lambda(\text{eff}) = \lambda(\text{phy}) + \lambda(\text{bio}) \qquad (4)$$

$$t_{1/2}(\text{eff}) = \frac{0.693}{\lambda(\text{eff})} \qquad (5)$$

Effective half-life calculation using Equation 3:

H³ (tritium: a radioactive isotope of hydrogen) is commonly used in biomedical research. Its physical half-life is just over 12 y (4500 d), as shown in Table 10–B. If tritium is taken into the body, it has a biological half-life that is the same as that of water, about 10 d. So the effective half-life of H³ will be:

$$t_{1/2}(\text{eff}) = \frac{4500 \text{ d} \times 10 \text{ d}}{4500 \text{ d} + 10 \text{ d}}$$

$$t_{1/2}(\text{eff}) \sim 10 \text{ d}$$

Alternatively, using the knowledge that $\lambda = 0.693 / t_{1/2}$ and then applying Equations 4 and 5 with the same half-life values:

$$\lambda(\text{phy}) = 1.54 \times 10^{-4} \text{ d}^{-1} \quad \text{and} \quad \lambda(\text{bio}) = 6.93 \times 10^{-2} \text{ d}^{-1}$$

Using Equation 4, $\lambda(\text{eff}) = 6.95 \times 10^{-2} \text{ d}^{-1}$ and (using Equation 5), $t_{1/2}(\text{eff}) \sim 10$ d, the same result as with Equation 3.

In this particular example, the shorter biological half-life dominates, and the effective half-life is nearly identical to its value. If the calculation is repeated for a radioactive substance where the physical half-life is 10 days and the biological half-life is also 10 days, the effective half-life is found to be 5 days.

Health Effects of Radiation on the Human Body

Of factors that can affect human health, ionizing radiation (beyond what is naturally present) may be the most thoroughly studied and understood of all health hazards.

Remarkably soon after Roentgen's 1898 discovery that he could use some mysterious rays from a vacuum tube (which he dubbed "x" rays to indicate their unknown nature) and photographic film to create an image of the bones in another person's hand, medical practitioners began making use of similar equipment in their treatment of soldiers. The mysterious x rays were the Bremsstrahlung produced when electrons were accelerated into a dense target inside the vacuum tube. Having a way to "see" embedded bullets or shrapnel was an amazing medical breakthrough.

X-ray images are blurred by motion just as with a photograph (digital or otherwise). The early x-ray tubes did not produce anywhere near the x-ray intensity of current x-ray tubes. To minimize blurring, these early adopters of the technology often held their patient's arm or leg (whatever was to be imaged) to minimize motion during the relatively long exposure time required to get an image. Also, since no one had reason to associate ionizing radiation with any negative health effect, the x-ray tubes were not always well collimated. Some emitted a broader beam of x rays than what was needed for imaging. After x raying many patients over months and years, quite a few medical personnel accumulated significant radiation doses. Medical personnel administering these early x rays received radiation doses that would be unthinkable today, especially to their hands but also to the rest of their bodies.

Many of these early medical users of x rays damaged their hands and in the longer term, a larger percentage of them developed cancers than would normally be the case.

From a vantage point well over a century later, it is known that these early x-ray users developed two different types of health effects that can result from large ionizing radiation exposures, *deterministic* and *stochastic*.

Deterministic Effects

Radiation dermatitis was noticed early on. It is a deterministic effect of a large radiation dose to the skin. Deterministic effects are health effects that all individuals will experience, if the exposure to (or dose of) the potentially damaging agent is large enough. For example, if 1000 people grasp a sufficiently hot piece of metal for a minute, 1000 people will develop burns. It is not a matter of an increased risk; the burn is a certainty.

For deterministic effects, once the threshold for the effect has been exceeded, the severity depends on the magnitude of the agent (e.g., how much heat, or how much radiation). There is some variation between individuals when it comes to the threshold, but the effect can be avoided by staying below the threshold for the most sensitive individual. Also, in the case of deterministic effects, the damage is to the tissues that are exposed to the agent. For example, a large radiation dose to the skin of a person's right hand may cause radiation dermatitis to that hand, but not to the left hand or to other unirradiated areas of the body.

Examples of deterministic health effects associated with large radiation doses are listed in Table 10–D, along with information on the dose threshold, etc. Table 10–D includes absorbed dose units (Gy, rad), where absorbed dose is the amount of energy absorbed from the ionizing radiation per unit mass of irradiated tissue. More information on these units can be found later in the chapter.

In the case of a very large radiation dose to the whole body (again where the dose is delivered at once, not spread over weeks), a dose of ~ 4 Gy (400 rad) would cause death within 60 days for about half of those exposed. This value is sometimes expressed as $LD_{50/60}$, which means the lethal dose for 50% of an exposed population within 60 days. Note

that in the table, the minimum absorbed dose to the eye for cataracts (at 1% incidence) is the same order of magnitude as the $LD_{50/60}$. A very large radiation dose that is limited to the eye, say 4 Gy, (as could occur in a radiation beam alignment accident) would not be life threatening, while a whole body dose would be.

Stochastic Effects

In the decades following the first widespread diagnostic use of x rays, health effects of the second type, stochastic effects, gradually became evident. Stochastic effects are health effects where the risk of developing a particular condition or disease increases with the increase in exposure to a particular agent, but where only a fraction of those exposed develops the health effect. They are all-or-nothing effects; while the risk of coming down with the disease or injury increases with exposure to the agent, the severity of the condition (for those affected) is the same, regardless of the exposure.

Lung cancer is a stochastic effect of smoking, and while the risk of developing lung cancer increases the more an individual smokes, lung cancer is by no means a certain outcome. And for those who do develop lung cancer, the severity of the cancer is unrelated to how often or how many years they smoked.

Increased rates of a variety of cancers were eventually noted for early x-ray users. In the years since then, data on human health effects due to radiation have been collected from several different groups of people. Among those who received large radiation doses are the populations of Hiroshima and Nagasaki (where the United States used fission bombs at the end of World War II), people receiving significant radiation doses in medical treatments, and people who received radiation doses in accidents.

Stochastic health effects (or possible health effects) associated with radiation dose are

• cancer and
• possible heritable (genetic) effects.

TABLE 10–D	Deterministic Health Effects Associated with Large Radiation Doses		
Effect	*Irradiated Organ/Tissue*	*Minimum Absorbed Dose (Photon) for Effect*[1,2]	*Delay Time Before Effect Manifest*
Skin burns/dermatitis/hair loss	Skin (large areas)	~4 Gy (400 rad)	2-3 weeks
Cataracts	Eye	2 Gy (200 rad)	Several years
Sterility	Testes	~6 Gy (600 rad)	3 weeks
Sterility	Ovaries	~3 Gy (300 rad)	< 1 week
Microcephaly/growth retardation	Embryo/fetus (*in utero*)	0.1 Gy (10 rad)	
Mental retardation	Embryo/fetus (*in utero*)	0.3 Gy (30 rad)	

1. Assumes single dose, rather than a dose delivered over weeks, months, years.
2. For most effects in table, the "Minimum Absorbed Dose" (i.e. threshold for most sensitive individual) is set at the dose where a 1% incidence of the effect is observed.
Source: Table based on information from Hall, Giaccia, 2006 and Valentin, 2007.

About genetic effects. When it comes to radiation, genetic effects should not be confused with birth defects resulting from exposure of a pregnant woman. Radiation-induced birth defects are deterministic effects from a radiation dose to the unborn. Genetic effects are stochastic effects due to radiation doses to individuals (men or women or both) who later conceive children. Although there have been some relatively large groups of people who received significant ionizing radiation doses in the past century, no direct evidence of heritable effects has been found in the children who later were conceived by these men and women. However, given the results of studies involving animals, the various scientific organizations continue to make their recommendations assuming that heritable effects also occur in humans.

About cancer risk. Based on the observed cancer risk from relatively high radiation doses, the International Commission on Radiological Protection (ICRP) puts the lifetime risk of developing a fatal cancer due to radiation exposure at approximately 0.05/person-Sv. A Sievert (Sv) is the basic unit for dose equivalent. Further information on this unit and quantity will be provided later in this chapter. Before applying the ICRP's risk value, it is important to note that the ICRP and the Health Physics Society both explicitly caution against using small individual doses (especially small doses accumulated over an extended period) in risk projections.

There is a basis for that caution. Worldwide average annual dose due to natural background radiation is reportedly about 2.4 mSv (240 mrem), ranging from 1 mSv (100 mrem) to 10 mSv (1000 mrem). Studies of populations who live in areas with much higher than average natural background radiation do not find elevated cancer rates (or other health issues). This does not prove anything because there are many factors that potentially affect cancer incidence, but it supports the idea that one should be wary of using cancer risk values to predict the impact of small radiation doses.

The normal U.S. lifetime fatal cancer incidence rate is about 1 in 5 for women and 1 in 4 for men (National Cancer Institute, SEER Cancer Statistics Review 1975-2007). In a population of 100,000 people living in the United States, 21,150 are expected to eventually develop a fatal cancer. Assume another group of 100,000 United States inhabitants each received a whole body radiation dose of 10 mSv (1000 mrem). While understanding that cancer risk estimates are likely not valid at such a low dose, if the risk of developing a fatal cancer due to radiation was 0.05/person-Sv, then the 10 mSv dose would theoretically result in 50 additional cancer fatalities. One would predict 21,200 of the 100,000 people would eventually develop a fatal cancer instead of the 21,150 expected in the absence of the 10 mSv dose.

RADIATION BIOLOGY

Following is a brief review of a few concepts from radiation biology. For more information, the interested reader will find an excellent reference (Hall, 2006) in the list of publications at the end of this chapter.

Relative Biological Effectiveness

Relative Biological Effectiveness (RBE) is a unitless measure of how effective a particular type of radiation is at producing a specific biological outcome relative to a standard type of radiation (often 250 kVp x rays, where the unit kVp indicates the peak voltage used in producing the x rays). For example, if the goal is the sterilization of syringes or other medical supplies using radiation, it might make sense to compare the doses required to kill 100% of a certain form of bacteria using two different types of radiation:

RBE (100% bacteria lethality) =
$$\frac{\text{dose required using 250 kVp x rays}}{\text{dose required using 1 MeV electrons}}$$

The higher the value of the RBE for a particular type of radiation and a particular biological outcome, the more effective the radiation is at causing that specific outcome. If the radiation of interest is less effective than the radiation used as the standard, then the RBE for that outcome will have a value less than one.

The LET (e.g., in keV/μm) of a particular type of radiation affects its RBE for a particular biological effect. Types of radiation that lose about 100 keV/μm generally have the highest RBE. At lower LET, cellular repair decreases the effect of the irradiation. At higher LET, "overkill" occurs, with an overabundance of energy dissipated within too short a distance.

Quality Factor

A factor related to RBE, the *quality factor*, is used in radiation protection standards and regulations. This is a type of weighting factor that allows us to have a single set of ionizing radiation limits, regardless of the type of ionizing radiation. The quality factor indicates the effectiveness of various types of radiation, relative to photons or electrons, in increasing the risk of stochastic effects. Current U.S. regulations (10 CFR 20.1004; June 2011, based on ICRP 26) specify the quality factors found in Table 10–E.

For neutrons of known energy, U.S. regulations include quality factors that are a function of the neutron energy. The values of Q range from 2 (for thermal to 1 keV neutrons) up to 11 (for 500-1000 keV neutrons). At neutrons energies above 1000 keV, the value of Q gradually drops to 3.5.

TABLE 10–E	Quality Factors
Type of Radiation	**Quality Factor (Q)**
photons (x rays, gamma rays)	1
electrons	1
alpha particles	20
fission fragments and heavy particles of unknown charge	10
neutrons of unknown energy	10
high energy protons	10

The section that follows on quantifying radiation will address how the quality factor is used.

Tissue Dose Weighting Factor

There is another weighting factor that is often used in radiation safety. The organ (or tissue) dose weighting factor takes into account that the risk of developing a stochastic effect depends on whether all of the body receives a uniform dose, or whether only certain organs are irradiated. Current U.S. regulations (10 CFR 20.1003; June 2011, based on ICRP 26) specify the organ weighting factors found in Table 10–F. Use of these factors will be addressed in the following section.

QUANTIFYING RADIATION

External Radiation Dose

For professionals involved in occupational radiation safety who are concerned about people possibly exposed to radiation from radiation sources outside the body (external radiation sources), the most useful quantity is usually the dose equivalent (DE) or a closely related quantity. Recall that earlier in this chapter we said that radiation dose is the amount of energy that ionizing radiation deposits per unit mass of tissue. But in the previous section, we also saw that identical doses of two different types of radiation may cause different health impacts. This is where the radiation weighting factor comes into use in scaling the radiation dose for the health impact:

Dose Equivalent =
   Dose (energy deposited/mass) ×
   Q (radiation quality or weighting factor)   (6)

If the radiation dose is from a number of different types of radiation, then the dose equivalent will be the sum of the products of the various dose and quality factors:

   Dose Equivalent (DE) = Σ Dose × Q (7)

Dose equivalent calculation using Equation 7:

TABLE 10–F	Organ-Weighting Factors
Organ or Tissue	**Organ/Tissue Dose Weighting Factor (W_t)**
Gonads	0.25
Breast	0.15
Red bone marrow	0.12
Lung	0.12
Thyroid	0.03
Bone surfaces	0.03
Remainder	0.30
Whole body	$\Sigma = 1$

Assume a person receives a 0.04 Gy (4 rad) absorbed dose from a 6 MeV photon beam and a 0.01 Gy (1 rad) absorbed dose from a 190 MeV proton beam. Using the quality factors from the table above, the dose equivalent would be calculated as:

$$DE = (0.04 \text{ Gy}) \times (1) + (0.01 \text{ Gy}) \times (10)$$

$$DE = 0.14 \text{ Sv (14 rem)}$$

When the body is not uniformly irradiated, an additional scaling factor is applied so that the resulting quantity, the effective dose equivalent (EDE), is an appropriate measure of the overall health risk. The scaling factor, the tissue weighting factor (W_t), accounts for both the reduced health risk from a partial-body irradiation AND the fact that the overall risk to health varies, depending on which tissues are irradiated.

Effective Dose Equivalent =
   Σ Dose Equivalent × W_t (tissue weighting factor)   (8)

As of June 2011, the scaling factors prescribed by U.S. regulations were not identical to those used in most other countries. It is expected that the U.S. regulations will soon be revised to require the use of scaling factors consistent with those used elsewhere.

U.S. regulations also include some additional dose quantities. Since not all ionizing radiation is penetrating enough to affect internal tissues, it is sometimes useful to consider the deep dose equivalent (DDE). The deep dose equivalent is the dose equivalent at a tissue depth of 1 cm when the whole body has been exposed to an external radiation source. Similarly, the lens dose equivalent is the dose equivalent at a tissue depth of 0.3 cm when the eye has been exposed to an external radiation source. And the shallow dose equivalent is defined as the dose equivalent at a tissue depth of 0.007 cm when the skin of the whole body or the skin of an extremity has been exposed to an external radiation source.

Table 10–G summarizes the quantities and their associated units.

TABLE 10-G	Ionizing Radiation Dose Quantities			
Quantity	**Old Unit Name**	**SI Unit Name**	**Relationship between Units**	**Applicability**
Dose (Absorbed Dose)	Rad	Gray (Gy)	1 rad = 100 erg/g 1 Gy = 100 rad	For internal or external radiation. Must know details of radiation type to assess health impact.
Dose Equivalent	Rem	Sievert (Sv)	1 Sv = 100 rem	For internal or external radiation. Should not be used for a very large acute dose; use Absorbed Dose with information on radiation type.
Effective Dose Equivalent	Rem	Sievert (Sv)	1 Sv = 100 rem	
Deep Dose Equivalent	Rem	Sievert (Sv)	1 Sv = 100 rem	For tissue depth of 1 cm, whole body exposure to external radiation source.
Lens Dose Equivalent	Rem	Sievert (Sv)	1 Sv = 100 rem	For tissue depth of 0.3 cm, eye exposure to external radiation source.
Shallow Dose Equivalent	Rem	Sievert (Sv)	1 Sv = 100 rem	For tissue depth of 0.007 cm, skin (whole body or extremity) exposure to external radiation source.

INTERNAL AND EXTERNAL RADIATION SOURCES

The quantities and units described in the previous section apply to radiation doses that result from external radiation sources. Regardless of whether the radiation source is a radiation-producing machine, cosmic radiation, or natural or artificial radioactive materials, these quantities and units are appropriately applied to the radiation received from sources outside the body. However, in cases where a person has radioactive materials inside their body (materials that would not be there naturally), some additional quantities and units are needed. These will be briefly described below.

As mentioned earlier, when there is an uptake of radioactive materials, the body treats the material exactly as it would the same element or chemical compound in a nonradioactive form. This fact is extremely useful in medicine; physicians, by selection of the appropriate radioactively labeled compound, can target an organ or cell type that they wish to image or treat. Once the labeled compound has reached its destination, the imaging or treatment of the target tissue can proceed, using radiation emitted by the radioactive substance.

The fact that the body treats radioactive and nonradioactive forms of the same chemical compounds identically is also very important in radiation safety. For example, thyroids need iodine for proper function. If a researcher works with a volatile form of radioactive iodine, the researcher's thyroid is the organ of concern if some of the material could be inhaled.

When looking at the impact from radiation emitted by radioactive materials inside the body, we also have to take into account that the radiation will be emitted over a period of time. If the effective half-life of the radioactive material is short, maybe all of the radiation dose will be received within hours of when the radioactive material intake occurred. But if the effective half-life is long, the radiation dose may be delivered over a period of many years, at a rate that slowly decreases.

Committed Dose Equivalent and Committed Effective Dose Equivalent

To deal with quantifying the impact of radioactive materials inside the body in occupational or public health, the committed dose equivalent (CDE) and the committed effective dose equivalent (CEDE) are used.

For a given organ or tissue that contains radioactive materials, the *committed dose equivalent* (units: Sv or rem) is the total dose equivalent delivered to that organ or tissue in the 50 years following the intake of the radioactive material.

The committed effective dose equivalent (units: Sv or rem) takes into account which body tissue or tissues receive the radiation during a 50-year period. Each tissue's committed dose equivalent is scaled by the applicable tissue weighting factor, and those values are summed to determine the *committed effective dose equivalent*.

Total Effective Dose Equivalent

In cases where a person receives a radiation dose from both external and internal radiation sources, the *total effective dose equivalent* (TEDE) is the sum of the deep dose equivalent resulting from the external radiation sources and the committed effective dose equivalent from internal sources. U.S. regulations require organizations using radiation sources to operate so that they limit the TEDE that anyone may receive in a year (or other specified period). The limits vary, depending on whether the person is a member of the public, an occupationally exposed adult, an occupationally exposed minor, or a pregnant woman. The values of the U.S. dose limits are summarized later in this chapter.

Notice that the annual limit on the TEDE treats the radiation dose from external radiation and internal radiation differently. The DDE is the total penetrating radiation dose from external sources that was received during the year. However the CEDE includes the total dose from a radioactive materials uptake that occurs within the 50 years following the uptake. So the U.S. regulatory limit on the TEDE treats the CEDE as if the total dose from the radioactive materials uptake was received within the year that the uptake took place.

DETECTION AND MEASUREMENT OF RADIATION

This section will briefly address some of the common devices and instruments used to detect and, in some cases, measure radiation. The list of references at the end of this chapter include a text with a useful overview of radiation instruments and detectors (Stabin, 2008) as well as an excellent book devoted entirely to the topic of radiation detection (Knoll, 2010).

Dosimeters

Dosimeters are used for personnel and area monitoring of radiation from external sources. Historically, these devices have primarily been passive monitoring; that is, devices used for a set period of time after which they are checked or processed to determine the total dose accumulated during the period. Examples of passive dosimeters include film badges, thermo-luminescent dosimeter (TLD) badges, optically stimulated luminescent dosimeter (OSLD) badges, and pen dosimeters. While film badges were once widely used for personnel monitoring, their use is now much more limited. Film is quite sensitive to environmental conditions and may lose dose information if exposed to heat or humidity.

Many passive dosimeters contain multiple individual detectors sensitive to different types of radiation. For example, they may contain an element (or otherwise be designed) to detect radiation that is not penetrating enough to result in a deep dose, but that could result in a dose to the skin. Or they may contain an element to detect certain types of neutrons. Many passive dosimeters are also designed to determine the radiation type and energy as needed to correctly assess the dose equivalent.

Workers may be assigned multiple passive dosimeters that are worn simultaneously on different locations of the body. Extremity monitoring is especially common, with workers using ring dosimeters on one or both hands.

Electronic dosimeters capable of measuring radiation doses and dose rates in real time are also seeing increasing use. Since many passive dosimeters are worn a set period

(typically 1 to 3 months) before they are read, instant read-out dosimeters are often used in addition to a passive dosimeter to allow personnel to monitor the dose they receive during a particular operation. Instant-read dosimeters are also used by emergency responders.

Presently, most electronic dosimeters do not provide all the information available from passive dosimeters, nor are they available for as wide a range of radiation types. Perhaps in the future, new types of instant-read dosimeters will largely replace passive dosimeters for personnel monitoring.

Portable Instruments for Radiation Detection and Measurement

Geiger Mueller (GM) counters are useful in detecting the presence of certain types of ionizing radiation (photons, electrons). GM probes consist of a gas-filled volume inside a metal container with a thin window on one side. Radiation is detected when the gas inside the GM probe is ionized and the ions attracted to an anode and cathode. In terms of measuring the dose rate, standard GMs are typically calibrated for a single radiation type (often the photon emitted in Cs^{137}/Ba^{137m} decay. For other photons and electrons, standard GMs provide qualitative rather than quantitative information.

GMs are often used to detect the presence of radioactive contamination. However, GMs generally are not useful for the detection of H^3 since its beta's range is not sufficient to penetrate the window of the GM probe.

Under the right circumstances, ion chamber instruments are appropriate for use in measuring the photon dose rate (or total dose, when switched to "integrate" mode) over a fairly wide range of energies. As with all radiation detection instrumentation, users of ion chambers should study the user manual carefully to understand the instrument's use and limitations.

In attempting to make dose or dose rate measurements, users should also be aware of two issues that may not be highlighted in instrument manuals and that can cause the dose (or dose rate) reading to be less than it should be.

In the case of rapidly pulsed, high-intensity radiation (e.g., from an accelerator or a pulsed x-ray generator), the instrument may not have had enough time to fully respond between pulses. If so, the instrument may record a dose (or dose rate) that is lower than the true dose (or dose rate). A more common problem is partial irradiation of the ion chamber. Ion chamber instruments are normally calibrated using radiation that uniformly irradiates the volume of the gas-filled ion chamber. If such an instrument is used in a situation where its ion chamber is only partially irradiated (e.g., checking for radiation escaping through narrow cracks between shielding panels), the dose rate it will record will be lower than the true dose rate.

While GMs and ion chambers are probably the most common hand-held instruments for radiation detection and measurement, scintillation detectors and proportional counters are also used, especially to detect specific types of radiation for which other detectors are not suited (e.g., betas from H^3, alphas, very low energy photons). The instruments most commonly used to measure the dose rate from neutrons have a rather striking appearance and heft; these instruments typically include a bulky spherical or cylindrical shield. The shield is made of a hydrogen-rich material and is needed to decrease the energy of the incident neutrons to the point where they will interact with the detection elements located inside shielding. Neutron meters with spherical shields are sometimes called Rem Balls.

Instruments for Radioactivity Detection, Measurement, and Identification

Safety professionals also rely on a variety of specialized instruments to detect radioactive contamination, to measure radioactive material uptakes, and to help identify which radionuclides are present. A few of the more common instruments are briefly described below.

In situations where there is a possibility of radioactive contamination (e.g., in biomedical labs using radioactively labeled compounds in liquid form), workers are required to periodically confirm that there has been no unexpected spread of the radioactive material. Checks for removable contamination are also required promptly upon the receipt of packages containing radioactive materials. When checking for removable radioactive contamination, a common technique is to use filter paper (or a cotton-tipped swab, or some alternate material) to wipe an area of a specific size and then to check the wipe for the presence of radioactive materials.

Often the material used in the wipe will be counted using a liquid scintillation counter (LSC). When using an LSC, the material to be counted is inserted in a vial filled with a scintillation fluid (sometimes called scintillation cocktail). Liquid scintillation counting is especially useful for detecting contamination from radionuclides that are otherwise difficult to detect, such as H^3 and alpha emitters.

To assess the possibility that a person has inhaled or otherwise ingested radioactive material, a bioassay may be done. Bioassays can involve direct measurements of radioactive materials in the body or may involve analysis of urine, feces, nasal swabs, etc. For example, a liquid scintillation counter might be used in the routine checking for the presence of H^3 in the urine of a worker using large amounts of H^3. Or a worker handling significant amounts of volatile radioiodine might be enrolled in a thyroid bioassay program. Thyroid bioassays are typically performed by posi-tioning a specially calibrated scintillation probe next to the neck of a person and taking a count for a set period of time.

In recent years, hand-held instruments for use in radionuclide identification have become increasingly available and affordable. Units commonly available today rely on gamma spectroscopy, a technique that examines the energies of the detected photons and uses that information as a fingerprint to identify the radionuclide(s) that may be present. As with all radiation detection and measurement instrumentation, it is critical that the user understand the instrument model and its limitations. Gamma spectroscopy instruments are not useful in identifying radionuclides unless the radionuclides (or daughter radionuclides) emit photons in the process of decay.

RADIATION REGULATIONS AND STANDARDS

Regulatory Agencies

Regulatory agencies worldwide base their dose limits on the work of scientific and advisory groups such as the International Commission on Radiological Protection (ICRP) and the United Nations Scientific Committee on the Effects of Atomic Radiation (UNSCEAR). Other groups that influence U.S. radiation safety regulations include the National Council on Radiation Protection and Measurements (NCRP), and the National Academy of Sciences (NAS). Scientific and advisory groups worldwide continue to be active in studying radiation effects on human health and in revising their recommendations for dose determination methods, appropriate weighting factors, and dose limits as new research findings become available.

The ICRP and other groups recommend specific dose limits that will prevent deterministic health effects (e.g., cataracts, radiation dermatitis) and minimize the risk of stochastic effects (e.g., cancer).

U.S. Regulatory Agencies

The United States has a rather complicated regulatory framework for occupational radiation safety. Depending on a worker's location, the facility type, and the kinds of radiation sources present, the worker will likely be subject to different regulations. The Nuclear Regulatory Commission (NRC) has ultimate authority over most of the civilian uses of radioactive materials in the United States, but radioactive materials are just one source of ionizing radiation. In addition, NRC has granted over half the states permission to regulate radiation safety for radioactive materials uses. States with this sort of NRC permission are called Agreement States. States where the NRC continues to regulate most radioactive materials use are called NRC States (or non-Agreement States). Up-to-date lists of Agreement States are easily found on the internet.

Table 10–H attempts to summarize the current regulatory situation applicable to occupational radiation safety in the United States. Note that even this is a simplification; the Environmental Protection Agency (EPA), Occupational Safety and Health Administration (OSHA), Department of Transportation (DOT), and other agencies also have a role in U.S. radiation safety regulation and enforcement.

U.S. Occupational Dose Limits

Despite the large number of different agencies involved in occupational radiation safety regulation in the United States, there is consistency about the values of the occupational (and public) radiation dose limits within the country. (Note that different United States agencies may prescribe the use of different radiation and tissue weighting factors.) The occupational dose limits in the United States, as of June 2011, are shown in Table 10–I.

U.S. radiation safety regulations address many topics beyond dose limits. They include requirements for registration or licensing of radiation sources, radiation monitoring, testing of safety features on devices that contain radiation sources, incident reporting, shipment and disposal of radioactive material, training, security, labeling, and recordkeeping.

PROTECTIVE MEASURES IN RADIATION SAFETY

As noted in the previous section, U.S. radiation safety regulations contain detailed requirements for the protection of workers and the public. Safety professionals involved in radiation safety will find it necessary to carefully consider the sections of the regulations that apply to their radiation source uses and to develop a program that addresses those requirements.

ALARA

Beyond just maintaining the radiation dose to workers and the public within the regulatory limits, U.S. regulations and radiation safety professionals stress the goal of keeping radiation doses as low as reasonably achievable (ALARA). Several measures used to reduce radiation doses so that they are ALARA are reviewed below.

For most radiation workers, minimizing the dose from external radiation sources is important. (The exception would be workers who use only radioactive materials – like H^3 – that emit nonpenetrating radiation and that are generally only a concern if the material is taken into the body.) Three factors are critical to reducing dose levels from external sources: time, distance, and shielding.

Time

This factor is intuitive. For a person in a particular loca-

TABLE 10–H   Occupational Radiation Safety Regulations

Worker Location	Facility Type	Radiation Sources	Applicable Regulations for Occupational Radiation Safety	Agency Responsible for Regulations
any U.S. location	Department of Energy (DOE)	Radioactive materials or radiation-producing machines	10 CFR 835	DOE
New York City	Any except DOE, federal, or reactor	Radioactive materials or radiation-producing machines	Rules of the City of New York, Title 24, Article 175	New York City Department of Health & Mental Hygiene
any U.S. location	Any except DOE	Radiation-producing machines; most naturally occurring radioactive materials	State-regulated; refer to state code [example: Title 17 California Code of Regulations]	Varies by state
any U.S. location	Federal	Most radioactive materials	10 CFR 19 & 20	Nuclear Regulatory Commission (NRC)
any U.S. location	Nuclear power plants	Reactor/radioactive materials	10 CFR 19 & 20	NRC
NRC (or non-Agreement) States	Any except DOE	Most radioactive materials (generally not naturally occurring)	10 CFR 19 & 20	NRC
Agreement States (except in New York City)	Any except DOE or federal or reactor sites	Radioactive materials	State-regulated; refer to state code	Varies by state

TABLE 10–1	U.S. Occupational Radiation Dose Limits (June 2011)	
Applies to	**Dose Limit**	**Time Period**
Adult workers	The more limiting of: • TEDE[1] of 5 rem (0.05 Sv) • Dose to any organ or tissue of 50 rem (0.5 Sv) where "dose" is sum of the deep-dose equivalent and the CDE to the organ/tissue	Annual
Adult workers: lens of eye	Dose equivalent to lens of 15 rem (0.15 Sv)	Annual
Adult workers: skin of whole body, skin of any extremity[2]	Shallow-dose equivalent of 50 rem (0.5 Sv)	Annual
Minors[3]	10% of the limits for adult workers	Annual
Declared pregnant workers	Dose equivalent to embryo/fetus of 0.5 rem (0.005 Sv)	During pregnancy

1. Recall that TEDE includes dose from any radioactive material uptakes in the body as well as the deep-dose from external radiation sources. In the summation, the deep-dose equivalent used must generally be the one that corresponds to the part of the body receiving the highest dose.
2. *Extremity* means hand, elbow, arm below the elbow, foot, knee, or leg below the knee.
3. *Minor* means an individual less than 18 years of age.

tion, whether they are exposed to radiation emitted by a machine or by radioactive materials, halving the exposure time halves the amount of radiation (assuming all other factors remain the same). Workers planning operations involving manipulation of radiation sources sometimes carry out practice runs to test their techniques and to make them as efficient as possible.

Distance

Increasing the distance between a person and a radiation source can dramatically decrease the radiation dose rate. In the case of a physically small (point) source of energetic photons (say a Cs-137 source), the dose rate decreases with increased distance according to the Inverse Square Law:

$$DR_2 = DR_1 \times \frac{r_1^2}{r_2^2} \qquad (9)$$

Where:

DR_1 is the dose rate at a distance r_1 from the point source

DR_2 is the dose rate at a distance r_2 from the point source

Dose rate calculation using Equation 9:

If the dose rate at 10 cm from a small-sized Cs-137 source is 1 Sv/h (100 rem/h), the dose rate can be calculated at 20 cm:

$$DR_2 = (1 \text{ Sv/h}) \times \frac{(10 \text{ cm})^2}{(20 \text{ cm})^2}$$

$$DR_2 = 0.25 \text{ Sv/h}$$

So if multiple Cs-137 sources needed to be transferred between storage containers using either 10 cm-long tongs or 20 cm-long tongs, the longer tongs would be generally be the better choice, as long as the length does not interfere in some other way. (It may make sense to practice the operation with a nonradioactive "dummy" source first to be sure the operation can be done without dropping sources.)

The Inverse Square Law can also be used to estimate the photon dose rate closer to a photon source, if the dose rate at a larger distance is known. For example, if the dose rate at 100 cm from the Cs-137 source is known to be 0.01 Sv/h, the dose rate DR_2 at 10 cm is calculated to be:

$$DR_2 = (0.01 \text{ Sv/h}) \times \frac{(100 \text{ cm})^2}{(10 \text{ cm})^2}$$

$$DR_2 = 1 \text{ Sv/h}$$

The Inverse Square Law is very useful, but it is important to recognize its limitations:

• *Ignores shielding by air.* The Inverse Square Law assumes that there is no shielding in the space between the two distances r_1 and r_2. In reality, some of the radiation will interact with the air molecules between the two locations. This will usually be a small effect for energetic photons.

• *Not for charged particles.* While the dose rate from a source of charged particles does decrease as distance from the source increases, the Inverse Square Law does not describe how the dose rate changes. This is a consequence of the fact that it does not account for the shielding provided by air, as just discussed. In any case, the Inverse Square Law should not be used to predict the dose rate from charged particles; doing so risks estimating a dose rate that is very significantly higher or lower than the true dose rate.

• *Point source.* The Inverse Square Law is also not useful unless the distances from the source, r_1 and r_2, are significantly larger (at least three times larger) than the largest dimension of the radiation source. For example, avoid applying the Inverse Square Law to the photon dose rate of a cylindrical Cs-137 source 0.5 cm in diameter and 2 cm in length unless the distances used in the calculation are both at least 6 cm.

Shielding

The section on the different types of ionizing radiation discussed the ways in which alphas, electrons, protons, neutrons, and photons interact with the material in the radiation's path. The interactions that take place are what make certain materials and amounts of material effective as radiation shields. This section will briefly describe considerations in shielding the two most common types of external radiation sources; radioactive materials or machines that emit energetic negatively charged electrons or photons.

Electrons

The fact that electrons of a particular energy have a specific range in material makes their shielding somewhat simpler than is the case for photons.

Table 10–J provides information on the range of electrons at several different energies in select materials. This is relevant to shielding electrons but it also makes a difference in what parts of the body could possibly be affected by an external source of electrons, depending on the energy.

Electrons emitted by radioactive materials (betas) have a distribution of energies up to a maximum energy that is specific to the radionuclide. For example, betas emitted by P^{32} have an average energy of about 0.7 MeV and a maximum energy of about 1.7 MeV. Among the betas emitted by P^{32} (or any other radionuclide that emits betas), there are more at the lower end of the energy distribution than close to the maximum beta energy. These lower energy betas have shorter ranges and are more easily shielded. While it makes sense to select beta shielding thick enough to stop the most energetic betas, lesser amounts of shielding such as typical personal protective equipment (gloves, lab coats, glasses) are highly effective in dose reduction.

Energetic electrons produce more secondary photon radiation (Bremsstrahlung) when shielded by dense, high atomic number materials (e.g., lead) than when shielded by a plastic. For this reason, it is common to prefer a plastic, typically an acrylic glass, as shielding for electrons. (Note: acrylic glass is sold under trade names such as Lucite®, Plexiglas®, and Perspex®.)

The best material for shielding electrons should be evaluated on a case-by-case basis. Considerations include the following:

- Where there is limited room for shielding, lead (or another high atomic number, high density material) may be the most effective choice. Per unit shielding thickness, it will range out the electrons much more effectively than a plastic. While it will result in more Bremsstrahlung, it will also be much more effective at attenuating that secondary radiation than a plastic would be.

- Where there is no critical limit on shielding thickness and where transparency is important, a plastic will likely be the ideal choice.

- In some situations, composite shields, such as a layer of acrylic glass backed by a layer of lead, will be the best of both worlds for shielding electrons.

Composite shield orientation. Note that if a composite shield is used, it must be oriented so that the low-atomic number material is nearest the electron source. An appropriately chosen thickness of plastic will slow or stop most of the electrons without generating too much Bremsstrahlung, while the lead will be quite effective in attenuating any Bremsstrahlung that is produced. If the shield is reversed, the high atomic number/dense layer will reduce the number of electrons. But it will produce more Bremsstrahlung than the plastic would and that Bremsstrahlung will be minimally attenuated when it strikes the plastic layer.

TABLE 10–J	**Range of Electrons at Various Energies**		
Electron Energy (MeV)	**Approx. Range in Air (cm)**	**Approx. Range in Water/Plastic/Tissue (cm)**	**Approx. Range in Lead (cm)**
0.1	15	0.02[1]	0.002
0.5	130	0.2[1]	0.01
1	330	0.4[2]	0.04
1.5	560	0.7[2]	0.06
2	760	1[3]	0.09
2.5	1000	1.3[3]	0.1

1. Notice that electrons of this energy are capable of delivering a dose to the live layer of skin at a depth of 0.007 cm beneath the skin's surface (Shallow Dose Equivalent), but cannot contribute to the Lens Dose Equivalent (the lens is at depth of 0.3 cm) or the Deep Dose Equivalent (at a depth of 1 cm).
2. Electrons of this energy can contribute to Shallow Dose Equivalent and Lens Dose Equivalent, but not to Deep Dose Equivalent.
3. Electrons of this energy can contribute to Shallow Dose Equivalent, Lens Dose Equivalent, and Deep Dose Equivalent.
Source: Based on information from Schleien, Terpilak, 1984.

Photons

As already noted, unlike charged particles, energetic photons do not have a set range in a particular type of material. However, for a particular photon energy and a specific material, it is possible to determine the thickness of the material that will stop half (or one tenth) of the radiation. These thicknesses are known as the half value layers (or tenth value layers), abbreviated as HVL (or TVL). Some half value layers are shown in Table 10–K. The photon dose rate through a shield (DR_s) can be calculated as follows:

$$DR_s = DR_u e^{\left(\frac{-0.693\,\Delta x}{HVL}\right)} \qquad (10)$$

Where:

> DR_u is the unshielded dose rate at a particular location.
> DR_s is the dose rate at the same location, but with a shield of a thickness Δx.
> HVL is the half value layer that applies for the photon energy and shielding material.

Alternatively, Equation 10 can be expressed as:

$$DR_s = DR_u e^{[-\mu\,\Delta x]} \qquad (10a)$$

Where: μ is the linear attenuation coefficient for the material and photon energy. The linear attenuation coefficient is equal to the natural log of 2 divided by the HVL.

Do Equations 10 and 10a look familiar? The decay of radioactive material is exponential and the amount of radioactive material left depends on the material's half-life and how much time has passed (Equation 2). The decay constant is the natural log of two divided by the half-life. The attenuation of photons by shielding is exponential and the amount of radiation that passes through shielding depends on the shielding material's half value layer and the shielding thickness. The linear attenuation coefficient is the natural log of 2 divided by the half value layer.

Dose rate calculation using Equation 10:

Assume there is an unshielded dose rate (DR_u) of 0.01 Sv/h (1 rem/h) at a particular location as a result of 0.5 MeV photons. If a 1 cm-thick (Δx) lead shield is to be placed between the photon source and the location, one can calculate the shielded dose rate (DR_s) at that location using the appropriate HVL from Table 10–K and Equation 10:

$$DR_s = 0.01 \text{ Sv/h } e^{\left(\frac{-0.693 \times 1 \text{ cm}}{0.36 \text{ cm}}\right)}$$

$$DR_s = 1.46 \text{ mSv/h (146 mrem/h)}$$

One caution: depending on how the HVL used in Equation 10 (or the attenuation coefficient) was determined, the HVL (or attenuation coefficient) may fail to account for the fact that some of the photons will scatter in a forwards direction and continue to contribute to the dose rate that makes it through the shield. If the HVL or attenuation coefficient is for narrow beam geometry (meaning it considers only photons that have not been scattered), then using it in Equation 10 or 10a without a correction will likely underestimate the shielded dose rate. The underestimate could be significant, especially in cases of shields that are thick relative to the half value layer. It is becoming increasingly common for shielding designers to use specialized software that takes photon scattering into account.

Unsealed radioactive materials. For most workers using unsealed radioactive materials, time, distance, and shielding considerations remain important in minimizing radiation dose. However, additional precautions are necessary to minimize the possible uptake of the radioactive material. The measures used to prevent radioactive materials uptake are the same ones that are used to prevent uptakes of other hazardous materials: use of proper personal protective equipment (gloves, glasses, lab coats); the use of fume hoods for volatile substances; and measures to prevent, contain, and promptly clean up any spills, etc.

TABLE 10–K	Half Value Layers		
Photon Energy (MeV)	*Approx. HVL in Air (cm)*	*Approx. HVL in Water /Plastic/Tissue (cm)*	*Approx. HVL in Lead (cm)*
0.5	6243	7.5	0.4
1	8451	9.8	0.82
1.5	10,343	12.2	1.2
2	12,375	13.9	1.36
2.5	13,860	15.8	1.44

Source: Based on information from Schleien, 1992.

SUMMARY

Humans have always been exposed to ionizing radiation from space and from naturally occurring radioactive materials. But some human activities result in additional radiation doses to Earth's inhabitants. Those who take airline flights, or are astronauts, or undergo certain diagnostic or therapeutic medical procedures, or live in certain areas receive a larger radiation dose than they otherwise would. And we all receive very small radiation doses as a result of ongoing energy production (including dose contributions from the fossil fuel cycle); spending time inside brick, stone, or concrete buildings; and past atmospheric testing of nuclear weapons. While health impacts have only been detected in studies of people who have received relatively large doses of radiation (far greater than the doses received from background radiation), international scientific groups recommend protective measures and regulatory requirements based on the assumption that any radiation dose above the normal background carries risk and is to be avoided whenever feasible to do so.

In the United States, the concept of dose minimization is described by the phrase "as low as reasonably achievable" (ALARA). People who are occupationally exposed to radiation can maintain their radiation doses ALARA by minimizing the time they spend near radiation sources and maximizing both their distance from radiation sources, and the shielding between them and radiation sources. When the radiation source is a dispersible radioactive material, additional measures should be considered to prevent radioactive materials from being taken into the body.

BIBLIOGRAPHY

Hall EJ, Giaccia AJ. *Radiobiology for the Radiologist.* Philadelphia: Lippincott Williams & Wilkins, 2006.

Hall EJ. *Radiation and Life.* Oxford: Pergamon Press Ltd., 1984.

Health Physics Society. *Radiation Risk in Perspective,* 2010. Mclean, VA: Health Physics Society, 2010. http://hps.org/documents/risk_ps010-2.pdf, accessed June 2011

Howlader N, Noone AM, Krapcho M, et al., eds. *SEER Cancer Statistics Review, 1975-2007*, Lifetime Risk (Percent) of Dying from Cancer (Table 1.17). Bethesda, MD: National Cancer Institute, 2011. http://seer.cancer.gov/csr/1975_2007/results_merged/topic_lifetime_risk_death.pdf, accessed June 2011

Knoll GF. *Radiation Detection and Measurement.* New York: John Wiley & Sons, 2010.

Shleien B, ed. *The Health Physics and Radiological Health Handbook.* Silver Spring, MD: Scinta, Inc., 1992.

Shleien B, Terpilak MS, eds. *The Health Physics and Radiological Health Handbook.* Olney, MD: NucLeon Lectern Associates, Inc., 1984.

Stabin MG. *Radiation Protection and Dosimetry.* New York: Springer, 2008.

United Nations Scientific Committee on the Effects of Atomic Radiation. UNSCEAR 2000 Report Vol. I. *Sources and Effects of Ionizing Radiation.* Vienna: UNSCEAR, 2000. http://www.unscear.org/unscear/en/publications/2000_1.html, accessed June 2011

U.S. Nuclear Regulatory Commission. Title 10, Part 20 of the Code of Federal Regulations (10 CFR 20), *Standards for Protection Against Radiation.* Rockville, MD: NRC. http://www.nrc.gov/reading-rm/doc-collections/cfr/part020/, accessed June 2011

Valentin J, ed. *The 2007 Recommendations of the International Commission on Radiological Protection,* Publication 103. Stockholm: Elsevier, 2007.

CHAPTER **11**

Nonionizing Radiation

by Michael Yost, MS, PhD

Radar was one of the scientific wonders to emerge from World War II, but there is controversy over whether it is safe. Microwaves are finding more and more uses as portable communications change from luxury to necessity. There is a radar in a box in most kitchens, and no food products supplier can ignore the need to package food so it is microwavable. Lasers were a scientific wonder of the 1960s, but now laser CDs have displaced phonograph disks, and most offices have at least one laser printer. One hallmark of technological change is the increasing use of the electromagnetic spectrum, and it is certain that new uses of electromagnetic energy will be found after this edition is published. Perhaps the scientific controversy regarding the safety of power line fields will be at least partially resolved before this chapter is revised for the next edition. This chapter presents the basic principles of electromagnetic fields and radiation and how to protect people from the hazards associated with this energy.

ELECTRIC AND MAGNETIC FIELDS

Electric Fields

All matter is made of atoms, which are divided into a central part, the nucleus containing protons and neutrons, and electrons that orbit around the nucleus. The *protons* in the atomic nucleus carry a unit of positive charge, and the electrons orbiting about the nucleus carry a unit of negative charge. Usually, objects are electrically neutral because the amount of positive and negative charge in the matter is equally balanced so the net charge is zero. However, objects can become charged when this balance is altered. When an object has an excess of electrons, it will have a negative charge; objects with a deficit of electrons will likewise have a positive charge. Negative charges attract positive charges and repel other negative charges; positive charges attract negative charges and repel other positive charges. Electric charges exert a force on other charges that are nearby; that is, electric charges create a force field in space. This field is called an electric field, often visualized as lines of force that originate on a positively charged object and end at a negatively charged object, as shown in Figure 11–1. The charge state (positive or negative) is called the polarity. The electric force exerted by a charged object on another charged object at some distance depends on the amount of charge on both the objects, the polarity of the charges on the objects, and the distance between them. Force on the charged objects is directly proportional to the amount of charge and decreases with distance according to an inverse square relationship described by Couloumb's law. The force between two point charges this can be stated as:

$$F_e = k_e \frac{q_1 q_2}{r^2}$$

where F_e is the electric force between the objects, q_1 and q_2 are the net charges on the two objects, r is the distance between the objects, and k_e is a constant that depends on the system of units. For SI units, k_e is ~$9{\times}10^9$ Nm²/C. The inverse square relationship causes the force to fall off rapidly with increasing distance. If some level of electric force exists at a given distance, the force is one-quarter as great at twice the distance, one-ninth as much at three times the distance, and so on. Any charged object creates an electric field whether it is stationary or in motion.

The electric force is very powerful. Opposite charges attract and meet to cancel each other out. For example, the protons in the nuclei of atoms attract an identical number of electrons so the atom is neutral. Electrical imbalances are rare, so a much weaker force created by all matter—gravity—dominates. An atom or molecule carrying an electric charge

is called an ion. Larger objects that have a charge imbalance are said to be electrostatically charged.

Magnetic Fields

The electric force just described exists regardless of whether the charges are stationary or not. However, a moving electric charge creates yet another type of field that exerts a force on other moving charges. This field is called the magnetic field. Imagine electric charges are moving in some direction, such as electrons flowing as a current through a wire. The amount of charge flowing past a given point in a defined period of time is called the electric current. Magnetic fields exist in a direction perpendicular to the direction of the current flow. The orientation of the field is such that the north-seeking end of a compass needle points as shown in Figure 11–2 *(left)*. The magnetic field lines can be visualized by pointing the thumb of the right hand in the direction of the conventional current flow in the wire and then curling the fingers around the wire. The magnetic field lines will follow the curl of the fingers, forming a series of closed loops surrounding the wire. Magnetic field polarities are given as north and south, and magnetic fields are usually visualized as lines of force that start at the north pole of a magnet and come back around, land on the south pole of the magnet, and complete a loop by going through the body of the magnet until they reemerge at the north pole. Thus, magnetic fields don't radiate out into space as electric field lines do; they return to the other pole, as shown in Figure 11–2 *(right)*. The north pole of a magnet points to the north pole of the Earth.

A magnetic field exerts a force on moving electrically charged particles in a direction perpendicular to both the field

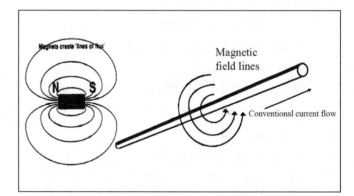

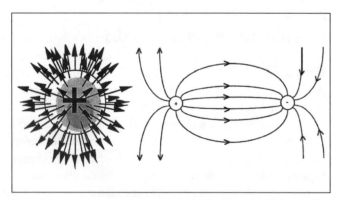

Figure 11–1. Depictions of an electric field. Electric field lines originating at a positively charged object and extending out equally in all directions *(left)*. Electric field lines leaving a positively charged object and landing on a negatively charged object *(right)*. If the objects had the same charge, the field lines would push away from each other.

Figure 11–2. Depictions of a magnetic field. Magnetic field created by current flow *(left)*. In this figure, current flows from negative to positive, as shown by the arrow pointing right at the upper end of the wire. The north-pointing needle of a compass will point in the direction of the smaller arrows around the wire. Fields around a common bar magnet *(right)*. Fields from loops that are assumed to start at the north pole, come around to land at the south pole, and move through the magnet. The current flow that creates the field of a permanent magnet is the movement of electrons around atoms.

and the direction of motion. The force is proportional to the amount of moving charge (the current flow) and the distance between the system carrying that current and a charged object.

When a magnetic field changes in time, it causes nonmoving charges to move, and induces a current flow in objects that conduct electricity, including the human body. The human body is mostly made of salt water and behaves as a good conductor filled with ions. Thus, a person in a changing magnetic field experiences current flows in loops inside the body, oriented perpendicular to the direction of the magnetic field, as shown in Figure 11–3.

People usually are unaware of this internal current flow, but it is always happening because they are immersed in magnetic fields that change with time (time-varying fields) arising from the transmission and use of alternating current (AC) electricity. In AC electricity, the polarity (direction) and strength of the current flow keeps alternating between positive and negative, so it is called alternating current. In the United States and Canada, polarity changes occur 60 times a second (50 times a second in Europe and elsewhere).

The history of AC power is worth describing because it underlies concerns about power line fields and introduces a basic law of electrical engineering: Ohm's law. Resistance describes the proportionality between the current flow in

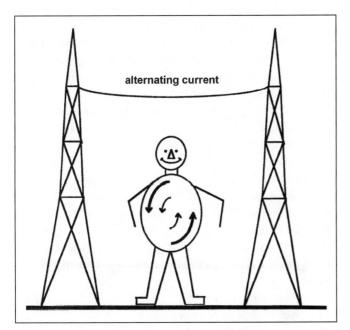

Figure 11–3. Interaction of an AC magnet field with a person. The field will induce a flow of current at a right angle to the direction of the field. The field radiates out from the line overhead, but changes direction as the line current changes polarity. The current induced in the body also changes direction. The magnitude of the current is proportional to the radius of the loop it is traveling in, so magnetic fields would be of greatest concern in big organs that are electrically active, such as the brain and heart. *(Adapted from Nair, Morgan, and Florig, 1989.)*

a conductor and the potential difference (voltage) across the conductor. According to Ohm's law, the source voltage equals the current flow in a circuit times the resistance ($V = I \times R$). In a circuit, electric current flows in a closed loop from one pole of a source through the circuit and back to the other pole, through the source, and back out again for further rounds in the pathway or circuit. The current is measured in units of amperes (A, amps), which is equivalent to the flow of charge per time (Couloumb/s). A useful mechanical analogy is that of the closed-circuit water pump in an aquarium. The pump requires a source of energy to give the water pressure to keep it moving because there is resistance to flow in the system. Electrical circuits also have resistance to current flow. The unit of electrical resistance (R) is the ohm (Ω), and the unit of potential energy (analogous to water pressure) that keeps the current flowing is the volt (V). The volt is a measure of the energy (joules) available per unit charge, so a Volt = Joule/Couloumb. The power (P) used in the circuit is the product of the voltage times the current, expressed in units of watts; $P = I \times V$. Applying the units described here shows that the power in watts also equivalent to the energy dissipated in Joule/s. From these relationships, it follows that the power dissipated in an electrical circuit due to resistance is proportional to the square of the current. This relationship is described by Joules' law, where $P = I^2 \times R$.

Electrical engineers in the early 20th century faced a problem figuring out how to transmit electric power to distant points; the power losses became prohibitive when large direct currents were transmitted over long wires. The solution to this problem was to transmit electric power over the wires using a high voltage and a small current so that the power losses were smaller. However, to meet electrical safety and insulation needs, this approach required that the high voltage be converted back down to a lower voltage (and corresponding higher current) at the place where the electric power was being used. The answer to this problem is to keep changing the polarity of the voltage and current and use the resulting changes in magnetic fields to induce another current to flow in a secondary distribution circuit connected to the user facilities. This allows electric power to be distributed in the system, while allowing the voltage and current to be varied in different points as needed. The device that does this is the transformer, which swaps current for voltage and vice versa while maintaining an approximate constant power flow across the device. A transformer couples two circuits, a primary circuit that feeds in power, and a secondary circuit where a load consumes the power. Say that a utility generates 20 megawatts (MW) of power at a power plant consisting of a current of 1,000 A at a voltage of, say, 20,000 V. The power is sent to a transformer, which steps up the voltage to 400,000 V and creates a much smaller current (50 A) that is

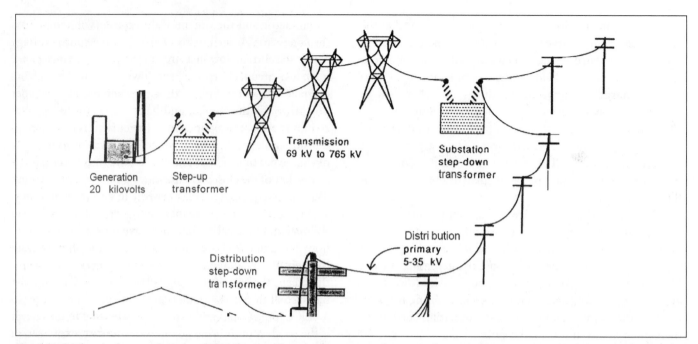

Figure 11–4. Electrical transmission and distribution. Transformers are used at several points, first to step up the voltage and reduce the current so the electricity can be transmitted over large distances with minimal resistance losses, then to step down to lower voltages at higher current levels before final distribution. Transmission lines are designed to operate with little variation in current, but distribution systems are designed to take broad ranges of current flows. The voltages are fixed at each step and currents vary. *(From Nair, Morgan, and Florig, 1989.)*

transmitted over large distances with lower resistance losses. The transmitted current then passes through a sequence of other transformers at the distribution point that steps down the voltage in exchange for higher currents and is finally distributed to many users at a modest 115-V potential, as shown in Figure 11–4. Thus, electric power is transmitted as a high voltage at a low current, and distributed to customers at a relatively low voltage but larger total current. Transmission line voltages range from 69,000 up to 765,000 V, and the intermediate distribution voltages created by the step-down transformers range from 4,000 to 35,000 V. AC current makes long-distance electrical power systems practical; otherwise, resistance losses would become intolerable.

ELECTROMAGNETIC RADIATION

So far, we have discussed electric and magnetic fields as single entities. There is a common phenomenon where the two exist together: electromagnetic radiation.

As described earlier, a time-varying magnetic field is able to induce an electric potential in a conductive object. This effect is described by Faraday's law, which defines how a time-varying magnetic field creates or induces an electric field. This aspect of electromagnetic induction is the operating principle behind many electric generators.

Electric and magnetic fields change polarities as the fields pass by any given location in space, as shown in Figure 11–5. The number of times the fields change polarity and return to the beginning polarity in a given unit of time is called the frequency. The frequency (ν) is usually specified in full cycles of polarity reversals and returns that occur in one second: cycles per second. If the electric field is zero at a given moment and starts climbing to a peak positive value, it will peak, fall back through zero, reach a maximum negative value, and climb back to zero. This is a full cycle. If this happened once in a second, then the frequency would be one cycle per second. If it happens one thousand times a second, then the frequency is one thousand cycles per second. One cycle per second is also called 1 hertz (Hz), after Heinrich Hertz, who discovered radio waves. One cycle per second equals 1 Hz, 1,000 cycles per second equals 1,000 Hz or, using proper metric prefixes, 1 kilohertz (kHz). See Table 11–A for a list of metric prefixes.

Not only do the electric and magnetic fields change polarity and strength with time in a propagating electromagnetic wave, but they are mutually coupled together. If the electric field is pointing in some direction, then the magnetic field also must exist in a direction perpendicular to the electric field, and the wave must travel in yet another direction perpendicular to the other two, as shown in Figure 11–5. Note how the shape of the fields is similar to that of waves

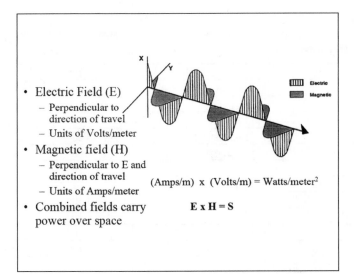

- Electric Field (E)
  - Perpendicular to direction of travel
  - Units of Volts/meter
- Magnetic field (H)
  - Perpendicular to E and direction of travel
  - Units of Amps/meter
- Combined fields carry power over space

(Amps/m) x (Volts/m) = Watts/meter²

E x H = S

Figure 11–5. The components of electromagnetic radiation. Note that the electric field (*E*) is oriented in one direction (shown by line-filled curves), whereas the magnetic field (*H*) (shown by dot-filled curves) is perpendicular to the electric field and the direction of travel is perpendicular to the other two. The number of times that the fields change from a given strength and polarity to the opposite polarity and back to the starting strength and polarity in a second is the frequency. Polarization (not to be confused with polarity or change state) is the direction of the electric field in relation to the surface of the earth. If the earth were below this page, then this wave would be horizontally polarized. If the electric field were turned 90 degrees (vibrating perpendicularly to the earth's surface), then it would be vertically polarized. The electric field can be caused to change direction constantly; it is circularly polarized if it points in all directions equally or elliptically polarized if it points more in one direction than another.

on the ocean. They can be drawn by plotting the trigonometric sine or cosine functions and are often called sine waves.

In air and a vacuum, the speed of electromagnetic radiation is 299,792,458 m/s, or about 186,000 mi/s. The speed of light is often rounded off to 300,000,000 m/s. An important way of expressing the distance the wave travels through one cycle is the wavelength (*l*). The amount of time elapsed during one cycle is called the period, which is just the inverse of the frequency, in Hz. The frequency times the wavelength must equal the speed of light, so as frequency increases, wavelength *decreases*. Wavelength can be calculated by dividing the speed of light—300,000,000 m/s—by the frequency. Thus, radiation with a frequency of 300 MHz has a wavelength of 1 m; 60 Hz radiation, if encountered, would have a wavelength of 5,000,000 m (about 3,100 mi).

Electromagnetic Spectrum

Electromagnetic radiation spans an immense range of frequencies, and when we arrange the electromagnetic waves into an increasing order of frequencies (or decreasing wavelength), we find that similar types of radiation cluster together. This arrangement is known as the electromagnetic spectrum, which is summarized in Table 11–B. A gamma-ray might have a frequency of about 3,000,000,000,000,000,000,000 Hz (300 EHz, wavelength about 0.1 pm), a helium-neon laser pointer has a frequency of about 474,400,000,000,000 Hz (about 474 THz, wavelength 0.632 µm), a microwave oven has a frequency of 2,450,000,000 Hz (2.45 GHz, wavelength 12.2 cm), a well-known New York AM radio station broad-

TABLE 11–A				Metric Prefixes
Prefix	**Abbreviation**	**Definition**	**Scientific Notation**	**Common Uses in Nonionizing Radiation**
Atto	a	pentillionth	10^{-18}	—
Femto	f	quadrillionth	10^{-15}	—
Pico	p	trillionth	10^{-12}	Picometer (ionizing radiation wavelengths)
Nano	n	billionth	10^{-9}	Nanometer (UV, visible, and IR-A wavelengths)
Micro	µ	millionth	10^{-6}	Micrometer (IR-B, IR-C wavelengths), microjoule (energy level), microwatt (power level)
Milli	m	thousandth	10^{-3}	Millimeter (microwave or IR-C wavelength), milliwatt (power level)
Centi	c	hundredth	10^{-2}	Centimeter (microwave wavelength)
Kilo	k	thousand	10^{3}	Kilohertz (radiofrequencies), kilometers (wavelengths of radiofrequency and extremely low-frequency radiation), kilowatt (power level)
Mega	M	million	10^{6}	Megahertz (higher microwave frequencies), megawatt (power level), megajoule (energy level)
Giga	G	billion	10^{9}	Gigahertz (higher microwave frequencies), gigawatt (power level)
Tera	T	trillion	10^{12}	Terahertz (IR and visible frequencies)
Peta	P	quadrillion	10^{15}	Petahertz (UV frequencies)
Exa	E	pentillion	10^{18}	Exahertz (ionizing radiation frequency)

TABLE 11–B   Two Views of the Electromagnetic Spectrum

Frequency (Hz)	Name		Wavelength (m)	1 (other units)	Photon Energy (eV)
3×10^{21}	Gamma rays		10^{-13}		10^7
3×10^{20}	x rays	"Hard" x rays	10^{-12}		10^6
3×10^{19}			10^{-11}		10^5
3×10^{18}			10^{-10}	1 Ångstrom	10^4
3×10^{17}			10^{-9}	1 nanometer	1,000
3×10^{16}		"Soft" x rays	10^{-8}		100
3×10^{15}	Optical	Ultraviolet	10^{-7}		10
3×10^{14}		Visible (400–760 nm)*	10^{-6}	1 µm	1
3×10^{13}		Infrared	10^{-5}		10^{-1}
3×10^{12}			10^{-4}		10^{-2}
3×10^{11}	Radiofrequency	Millimetric microwaves	10^{-3}	1 mm	10^{-3}
3×10^{10}			10^{-2}		10^{-4}
3×10^{9}		Microwaves	10^{-1}		10^{-5}
3×10^{8}			1	1 m	10^{-6}
3×10^{7}			10		10^{-7}
3×10^{6}			10^2		10^{-8}
3×10^{5}			10^3		10^{-9}
3×10^{4}			10^4		10^{-10}
3,000	Subradiofrequency ELF		10^5		10^{-11}
300			10^6		10^{-12}
30			10^7		10^{-13}
0	DC				0

*LIA/ANSI Z136.1-1993 lists the range of visible radiation as 400–700 nm. The eye can perceive longer-wave radiation, but the visual response to it is poor.

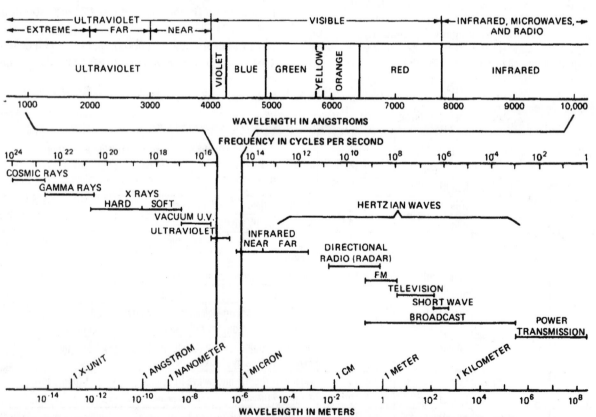

The electromagnetic spectrum, encompassing the ionizing radiations and the nonionizing radiations (expanded portion and right). Top portion expands spectrum between 10^{-7} and 10^{-8} m. Note: cycles per second (cps) = hertz (Hz).

casts at 710,000 Hz (710 kHz, wavelength 422 m), and the U.S. Navy's submarine communications system operates at 76 Hz (wavelength about 3,945 km). This is an immense span of frequencies. Frequency is extremely important because the energy of a discrete parcel of electromagnetic radiation, or photon, is directly proportional to its frequency. The electromagnetic spectrum is divided into four parts in this chapter: subradiofrequency ranges from 0 to 3 kHz, radiofrequency/microwave (RF/MW) ranges from 3 kHz to 300 GHz, optical radiation ranges from 300 GHz to 3×10^{15} Hz, and ionizing radiation that exists at higher frequencies. This chapter covers all of the electromagnetic spectrum except ionizing radiation, which is covered in Chapter 10.

The strength of the electric and magnetic fields in a free, propagating electromagnetic wave are related to one another. The ratio of the two is a constant that represents the resistance of the medium in which the radiation is traveling. In air and a vacuum, the resistance is 377 Ω.

The two fields together transmit power away from the source through an area of space that can be expressed in watts of power passing through an area of space or striking a given surface area. It is customary to adjust the units to milliwatts of power per square centimeter of area. Radiofrequency and microwave specialist call this power density; laser and optical specialist call it irradiance. These different terms have the same unit and the same meaning.

Because power losses are proportional to current, today we use AC electricity. This results from the second basic relationship of electrical engineering: power (P), in watts, equals current (I), in amps, times resistance, (R), in ohms. Recall Ohm's law, which states that volts equal amps times ohms. Combining these two relationships gives the relationship watts equal amps times amps times ohms, or $P = I^2 \times R$. Given that the resistance of air and space is 377 Ω, the relationships given in Table 11–C are widely used by people who do field surveys of radiofrequency and microwave radiation.

TABLE 11–C	Relationships Among Electric Field Strength, Magnetic Field Strength, and Power Density (Irradiance) for Electromagnetic Radiation

$$Sm = E2/3,770$$
$$S_m = 37.7\ H^2$$
$$E^2 = 3,770\ S_m$$
$$E = (3,770\ S_m)^{1/2}$$
$$H^2 = S_m/37.7$$
$$H = (S_m/37.7)^{1/2}$$

S_m = Power density in units of mW/cm
E^2 = Electric field strength^2 (V^2/m^2)
E = Electric field strength (V/m)
H^2 = Magnetic field strength^2 (A^2/m^2)
H = Magnetic field strength (A/m)

WHEN ARE FIELDS IMPORTANT AND WHEN IS RADIATION IMPORTANT?

This question is important in the radiofrequency and microwave portion of the spectrum for two reasons:

- The strengths of the fields in radiation are rigidly related to each other so only one field must be measured (usually the electric field). Both the electric and magnetic field must be measured where radiation does not exist.
- Radiation obeys the inverse square law unless the source happens to be a laser, so a field strength measurement at one location can be used to calculate the field strengths at other distances in the same direction from the source.

Separate electric and magnetic fields are commonly found at lower frequencies (longer wavelengths) or when measurements are taken "close to the source." Radiation is commonly found at higher frequencies (shorter wavelengths). As a rule, we interpret "close to the source" in terms of the wavelength so that separate fields are found within one to a few wavelengths of a source. Light has wavelengths ranging between 400 and 760 nm, so light is always found as radiation. A 60-Hz wave has a wavelength of 3,100 miles (mi), so it follows that fields, rather than radiation, are found around power lines. Electrical engineers refer to separate fields as *near fields* (because they are found close to sources) and to places where radiation is found as *far fields*. Near fields are divided into reactive near fields, which are electric fields created by the voltages and magnetic fields created by current flows in the source, and radiating near fields, where electric and magnetic fields combine to form radiation that travels away from the source. The relationship between electric and magnetic field strengths in near fields is not rigid, so both fields must be measured separately. Electrical engineers have formulas and rules for calculating the distance from specific antennas where far fields exist. It is customarily assumed that separate fields exist when the wavelength is more than about 1 m (frequency of 300 MHz) and that radiation exists at shorter wavelengths or higher frequencies. As a result, separate electric and magnetic field surveys are usually needed for frequencies of 300 MHz and less.

Parts of an Electromagnetic Device

Any electromagnetic device—whether it is a microwave antenna, junkyard electromagnet, or laser—can be visualized as having three parts: a source, a transmission path, and a receiver. A laser scanner in a CD player has a laser embedded in the device, optics to transmit the energy to the disk, and a sensor to receive the reflected energy. A 27.12-MHz plasma etcher has an energy source, a cable to transfer the energy, and a chamber where the energy is deposited to do work; these are often all located in one cabinet. A surveyor always needs to be aware of these parts and their locations. Particular attention should be paid to the transmission path, which could pass through open air, or be contained in an enclosed passage such as a microwave waveguide that could leak at joints or connections, or be a fiber-optic cable that could be cut or broken.

SUBRADIOFREQUENCY FIELDS: 0 TO 3,000 Hz

Because the distance where radiation is dominant is longer than about one wavelength, fields (rather than radiation) are considered in this section. The wavelength of the highest frequency in this section, 3 kHz, is 100,000 m, or about 61 mi. Static fields do not produce radiation. As shown in Table 11–D, the subradiofrequency portion of the spectrum includes the extremely low frequency (ELF) band, which includes AC fields and radiation up to 300 Hz, and the voice frequency band, which includes frequencies from 300 to 3,000 Hz. Power lines use 50 or 60 Hz currents, which create fields at these frequencies; these frequencies are often called power frequencies.

Field Strengths

Electric fields can be measured by inserting a displacement sensor—a pair of flat conductive plates—into the field and measuring the electric potential between the plates. The electric field lines land on one plate and induce a voltage that drives a current through the meter to the other plate, where the field lines continue as shown in Figure 11–6. The electric field can be calculated by dividing the voltage between the two plates by the distance between the plates. If a 1-kV

TABLE 11–D			Uses of Radiofrequency and Subradiofrequency Fields			
Frequency, n	Wavelength, l	Name	Uses	ISM Bands Center Frequency and ± Range	Radar Band and Frequencies	WWII Radar Bands and Frequencies
>300 GHz	<1mm		Infrared			
300 GHz	1mm	EHF	Satellite communications, radio relay, navigation aids	None	M 60-100 GHz L 40-60 GHz	H 44-56 GHz Q 36-46 GHz
30 GHz	1 cm	SHF	Satellite communications, radar, fire, police speed guns (24.15 GHz)	22.125 GHz ±0.125 GHZ 5.86 GHz ±0.075	K 20-40 GHz J 10-20 GHz I 8-10 GHz H 6-8 GHz G 4-6 GHz	Ka 22-36 GHz X 5.2-10.9 GHz C 5.9-6.2 GHz
3 GHz	10 cm	UHF	TV 14-82, CB, taxi dispatch, radar, ovens, celluar phones	2.45 GHz ±0.05 915 MHz ±0.025	F 3-4 GHz E 2-3 GHz D 1-2 GHz	S 1.55-5.2 GHz L 0.36-1.55 GHz
>300 MHz	<1m		Microwaves			
300 MHz	1 m	VHF	TV 2-13, FM radio, fire, police	40.68 MHz ±0.02	B 250-500 MHz A 0-250 MHz	P 220-390 MHz
30 MHz	10 m	HF	CB radio, diathermy (VDT flyback fields)	27.12 MHz ± 0.16 13.56 MHz ±0.00678 (both used for plasma etch)	A	None
3 MHz	100 m	MF	AM radio, amateur radio, navigation aids	None	A	None
300 kHz	1 km	LF	Navigation aids, marine and long-range communications	None	A	None
30 kHz	10 km	VLF	Communications, long-range navigation, induction heating (flyback rate of VDTs)	None	A	None
<3 kHz	>100 km		Subradiofrequency			
3 kHz	100 km	Voice	Modulation, induction heating	None	A	None
300 Hz	1,000 km	ELF	Submarine communications, induction heating (electric power, refresh fields of VDTs)	None	A	None
0 Hz	DC					

potential were found to exist and the plates were 1 m apart, then the electric field strength would be 1 kV/m; if the plates were 0.5 m apart and the potential were 1 kV, then the electric field strength would be 2 kV/m. Instruments like this are widely used for measuring electric fields at frequencies ranging up to 100 kHz.

Magnetic fields are often measured with loops of conducting wire, as shown in Figure 11–7. The lines of magnetic flux passing through the loop induce current flow. The field can be calculated by measuring the amperes of induced current and dividing that by the circumference of the loop. The common unit of magnetic field strength in the United States was the gauss (G), but it is commonly replaced by an SI unit, the tesla (T): 1 T = 10,000 G, 1 mT = 10 G, and 1 μT = 10 mG; 1 G ≅ 80 A of induced current per meter of circumference of conducting loop (A/m).

How Fields Interact with the Body

The body is a good conductor of electricity, but it does not have well-known magnetic structures. (Research suggests that microscopic magnetic structures exist in the human brain.) We have seen that electric charge imbalances are balanced as quickly as possible. Imagine you were below a high-voltage electric transmission line, as shown in Figure 11–8, and the line's polarity was positive. Your body would develop a corresponding negative charge: because you are a conductor, the positive charge above would attract movable negative charges toward it. These charges would come from your body and from the infinite pool of charges you

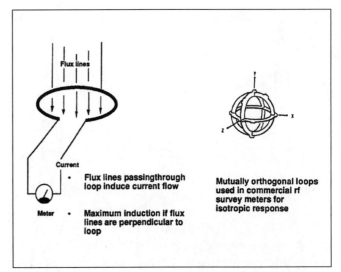

Figure 11–7. Most AC magnetic field survey instruments use looped conductors. The changing magnetic field induces a flow of current in the loop. The unit of field measurement is the amperes of current induced to flow through a specified distance of loop (A/m). The induced current is proportional to the sine of the angle between the loop and the field. If the loop is parallel to the field, the sine of 0 degrees is 0 and no current is induced to flow. If the loop is perpendicular to the field, as shown, the sine of 90 degrees is 1, so the loop will give a maximum response. Thus, measurements made with one loop are highly directional. Rotating a loop like this in a magnetic field produces a sinusoidally changing current.

were standing on—that is, the ground. The electric field lines would originate at the power line and land on your body. If the electric field were time varying, as the polarity reversed, the charge in your body would also subside and reverse; the rush of negative charges into your body would be replaced by an exodus of negative charges and a rush of positive charges, so you would take on a positive charge as the line overhead became negatively charged. The time-varying electric field would induce a time-varying electric current from the earth into your body, at the same frequency as the alternating voltage in the overhead power line. The electric field lines are perpendicular to the conducting surface they end at or leave. The result of this perpendicularity phenomenon is that a person in an electric field created by a source above the person, such as a power line, distorts field lines in the nearby space so they land perpendicular to the head. As a result, the electric field around the head becomes highly concentrated and intense. At other regions of space, the electric field lines are spread further apart, lowering the field intensity. If this person was holding an electric field meter at waist height, the surveyor's body would largely shield it, and the reading would be falsely low. The reading also could be falsely increased if the surveyor was the tallest object in the area and the field source was above the surveyor.

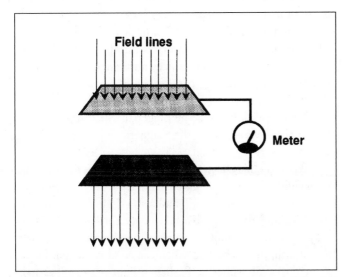

Figure 11–6. Displacement (split-plate) electric sensor used for AC field instruments in extremely low-frequency through medium-frequency regions (>0 Hz to 3 MHz). Note that field lines impinge on the upper plate, drive a current through the meter, and reemerge at the other plate. The field strength is the voltage difference between the two plates divided by the distance (V/m).

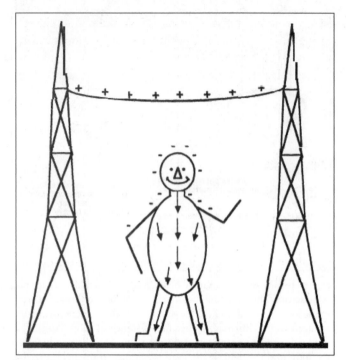

Figure 11–8. Induction of current by an external electric field. The overhead transmission line has a positive voltage corresponding to the positive ½ cycle of the AC waveform. The electric field from the positive charge in the line induces negative charges to accumulate in the person's body. The negative charges enter the body as a flow of electrical current from the ground. This happens 60 times a second. During the negative ½ cycle, the line's charge will be negative, inducing a positive charge in the body causing a flow of electrical current into the ground. Radiofrequency fields can create similar current flows, but at higher frequencies. *(Source: U.S. Congress, Office of Technology Assessment.* Biological Effects of Power Frequency Electric & Magnetic Fields: Background Paper, OTA-BP-E-53. *Washington, DC: U.S. GPO, May 1989.)*

Magnetic fields are easier to measure because the human body does not perturb the magnetic field as it perturbs the electric field. We are filled with conductive brine, so a magnetic field that changes with time induces loop-shaped current flows in a direction perpendicular to the orientation of the time-varying magnetic field, as shown in Figure 11–3. The strength of the induced current is proportional to the strength of the magnetic field and the radius of the loop in which the current is flowing. The current at the center of the loop is zero and reaches a maximum level at the rim of the loop.

BIOLOGICAL EFFECTS AND STANDARDS FOR STEADY ELECTRIC FIELDS

Steady (DC) fields are created with charges and currents that do not change polarity or strength with time. Steady electric fields are not a significant area of concern today; in fact,

no instrument is marketed that is intended for use in safety surveys for DC fields (although there are instruments that can be adapted for exposure surveys). The adverse effects identified by the International Commission for Non-Ionizing Radiation Protection (ICNIRP) are as follows:

- Irritating sparks could occur at electric field strengths of 5 kV/m or more.
- Painful sparks could occur at electric field strengths of 15 kV/m.

The 2012 Threshold Limit Value (TLV®) for DC electric fields from 0 Hz to 220 Hz is 25 kV/m as a ceiling limit (a limit that should not be exceeded for any length of time). Between 220 Hz and 3kHz, the ceiling value $E_{tlv} = 5.525 \times 10^6/f$, where f is the frequency; from 3 kHz to 30kHz, the ceiling value is 1.842 kV/m. The field strengths in the TLV are the field levels present in air away from the surfaces of conductors (where spark discharges and contact currents pose significant hazards). It applies to both partial-body and whole-body exposures.

BIOLOGICAL EFFECTS AND EXPOSURE STANDARDS FOR STATIC MAGNETIC FIELDS

Magnetic effects are caused by charges in motion or changes in magnetic fields. The static fields from permanent magnets or superconducting magnets do not change with time, so any interaction would need to occur where charges are in motion. Blood is briny material, so magnetic field effects can be expected in the circulatory system where charges are in motion. The effect can be seen on an electrocardiogram (ECG) made while an animal is in a static magnetic field. The entire output of the heart is pumped into the aorta at high speed. This flow induces a magnetohydrodynamic (MHD) voltage that appears on the ECG at the same time as the T-wave of the heart. The added MHD voltage makes the T-wave look bigger. The bigger the magnetic field, the bigger the T-wave; when the magnetic field is shut off, the T-wave reverts to normal.

Based on this effect, the current TLV is 2 Tesla (T), which is an eight hour time-weighted average (TWA) criterion. The peak exposure is set at 8 T and a maximum value of 20 T for exposure to the limbs. Humans exposed to 4-T fields may experience symptoms such as nausea, metallic taste in the mouth, dizziness, and when the head is moved, known as magnetic phosphenes (flashes of light in the eyes caused when induced currents stimulate the retina). Therefore, workers who are exposed above the 2-T criterion should receive special training to limit rapid movements in high field areas.

Another effect is worth noting. Rotating the earth's magnetic field, which is usually about 0.5 G, disrupts the circadian rhythms of test animals and fluctuations in body function that are associated with time of day, such as hormone levels and body temperature. This is related to our sense of time, which is perceived as jet lag. This effect occurs if the animal is unaware of the day–night cycles around it due to a lack of light exposure to the eye, but even 9-T fields did not break the sense of time of animals are aware of light–dark cycles. People who work in strong magnetic fields should avoid unusual shift work that causes them to lose track of day–night cycles.

Other Safety Concerns of Static Magnetic Fields

Before leaving static magnetic fields, it is necessary to consider two related issues: the effects on medical electronic devices and classic safety concerns. Artificial cardiac pacemakers work by amplifying the electrical activity of the natural pacemaker tissues of the heart. The electrical output of the pacemaker changes as the electrical activity of the heart's pacemaker tissue changes. Artificial cardiac pacemakers can be fooled by ambient electric and magnetic fields, including very strong AC fields. When this happens, they could amplify the AC fields instead of boosting the activity of the natural pacemaker, and the heart, now trying to work at 60 Hz, would not circulate blood. Pacemakers have built-in protective circuits that sense malfunctions and cause the pacemaker to send impulses to the heart at a fixed rate. The wearer tests these circuits in a cardiologist's office (or at home while in telephone/telemetry contact with a cardiologist) by changing the setting of a switch in the artificial pacemaker so it fires at the fixed rate. A permanent magnet held over the pacemaker is used to reset the switch. Thus, strong static fields could cause this switch setting to inadvertently change in places where no medical supervision is available. Magnetic fields stronger than 0.31 mT (3.1 G) could reset some very susceptible pacemakers, so a pacemaker safety criterion of 0.5 mT (5 G) has been set.

Magnetic fields exert forces on objects that can be magnetized. The degree to which material can be magnetized depends on its permeability. Aluminum, stainless steel, plastics, and organisms are not permeable. Soft iron, steel, and various transition metal alloys (such as those of nickel and cobalt) are permeable. Tools and some medical implants are made of permeable alloys so they can move in a strong magnetic field. The force of such a field is proportional to the strength of and gradient of the field (the rate at which that field changes intensity through some part of space). A steel wrench in a perfectly uniform, super-strong magnetic field would not move because there is no gradient, but it would move as it was taken from the strong field through a weak field. The force is also proportional to the object's permeability and volume. A nonpermeable stainless steel

wrench would not move even in a strong and rapidly changing field. Thus, limits are needed to prevent unintended motion of tools, and other objects like compressed gas cylinder controls or metal prosthetic implants in workers. The simplest test devised to locate hazardous locations is to tie a washer or other small permeable object to a string and tie off the other end to a belt loop and watch for places where the washer is pulled out by magnetic fields. Stainless steel, widely used in prosthetic implants, is normally nonpermeable but can be made permeable where it is machined. The ICNIRP advises that mechanical hazards due to flying tools and movement of metallic medical implants become a potential hazard when fields are as low as 3 mT (30 G). The ICNIRP also advises that magnetic media—such as the magnetic stripes on the backs of credit cards and diskettes—can be erased by fields above 1 mT (10 G).

BIOLOGICAL EFFECTS AND EXPOSURE STANDARDS FOR TIME-VARYING SUBRADIOFREQUENCY FIELDS

Time-varying subradiofrequency fields, particularly ELF fields from power lines, have emerged as an area of concern because of widespread fear that they may lead to cancer. The initial concern arose as a result of epidemiological studies. These studies are not discussed further here because they have been reviewed widely by other organizations. A large body of research results from in vivo and in vitro experiments has accumulated about the possible biological effects of such fields, but much of it is contradictory. The National Institute of Environmental Health Sciences (NIEHS) conducted a comprehensive review of the literature on health effects and found limited evidence of any concern. However, it did classify ELF magnetic fields as a possible human carcinogen. The International Agency for Research on Cancer (IARC) completed a comprehensive review of the literature and also classified ELF magnetic fields as a possible human carcinogen; both findings were largely based on an elevated the risk of childhood leukemia associated with electric power lines.

It is now generally, but not universally, accepted that power line fields can influence cell membranes. This effect is observable as an increase in the rate at which calcium ions are moved from the inside of a cell through the cell membrane to the outside. The possible effects of these interactions are potentially far-reaching and include promotion of tumor growth, but adverse effects have not been demonstrated in replicated experiments at the time this chapter was written. It is also generally accepted that power line fields affect circadian rhythms much as static fields do. Circadian rhythm is controlled by the pineal gland, located in the center of the brain. The pineal receives electrical impulses from the eyes via the optic nerve. The pineal secretes the hormone melatonin at night. Altered pineal function could reduce the ability of the immune system to eliminate infections or suppress tumors, and this finding is supported by animal studies.

Health regulations fall into two broad categories: exposure criteria, which specify the amount of exposure for an individual, and emission criteria, which describe how much can be released into or be present in the environment near a source. Both types of regulations exist for nonionizing radiation. Before setting science-based exposure standards, it is necessary to establish a mechanism for effects on living tissue. The one well-established mechanism of interaction is based on induced current flows through tissue, which can cause electrical stimulation of nerves and muscles, and tissue heating. Many possible alternative mechanisms have been proposed, but none have been proven. This uncer-

tainty about mechanisms is important because some of the proposed mechanisms do not involve either of the classic monotonic dose-response models. If a nonlinear dose response model is found, it is possible that a range of moderate field intensities could be hazardous, whereas stronger or weaker fields would not be hazardous. Regulations generally have assumed that less is safer, so the possibility of "windowed" effects with respect to field strength is not considered.

The standards that do exist based on the known effects of currents induced in the body follow an increasing dose-response curve for effects and are function of frequency. According to the International Commission on Non-Ionizing Radiation Protection, guidelines for electric and magnetic fields and exposure limits can be created that are intended to place a basic restriction on induced currents in the body. The ICNIRP has issued general public and occupational exposure criteria (1Hz to 100 kHz) based on induced current flow considerations, as shown in Table 11–E.

TABLE 11–E	ICNERP Exposure Criteria for DC and Subradiofrequency Fields				
Frequency	**Exposure Group**	**Exposure Duration**	**Exposed Part of Body**	**Electric (kV/m)**	**Magnetic (mT)**
Static	Occupational	Ceiling	Trunk		2,000*
Static	Occupational	Ceiling	Limbs		8,000
Static	Public	Ceiling	Whole		400
1 Hz–8 Hz	Public	24-Hr day	Whole	5	$40/f^2$
8 Hz–25 Hz	Public	24-Hr day	Whole	5	$5/f$
25 Hz–50 Hz	Public	24-Hr day	Whole	5	0.2
50 Hz–400 Hz	Public	24-Hr day	Whole	$250/f$	0.2
400 Hz–3kHz	Public	24-Hr day	Whole	$250/f$	$80/f$
1 Hz–8 Hz	Occupational	Full Shift	Whole	20	$200/f^2$
8 Hz–25 Hz	Occupational	Full Shift	Whole	20	$25/f$
25 Hz–300 Hz	Occupational	Full Shift	Whole	$500/f$	1
300 Hz–3kHz	Occupational	Full Shift	Whole	$500/f$	$300/f$

* Spatial peak magnetic flux density; up to 8T allowed in highly controlled settings where motion induced currents are limited

TLV Exposure Criteria for DC and Subradiofrequency Fields

Frequency [†]	**Exposure Group**	**Exposure Duration**	**Exposed Part of Body**	**Electric (kV/m)**	**Magnetic (mT)** [††]
Static	Occupational	Ceiling	Whole	25	2,000*
Static	Occupational	Ceiling	Limbs	25	20,000
1 Hz–300 Hz	Occupational	Ceiling	Whole	18.4**	$60/f$
300 Hz–3 kHz	Occupational	Ceiling	Whole & partial	$5530/f$	0.2
3kHz–30 kHz	Occupational	Ceiling	Whole & partial	1.8	0.2

* Spatial peak magnetic flux density; up to 8T allowed in highly controlled settings; medical device wearers limited to 0.5 mT
** Peak up to 25kV/m allowed for f<220 Hz
[†] ACGIH considers frequencies <30 kHz to be Sub-Radiofrequencies
[††] 1 mT = 10 G ~= 800 A/m.
Note: ACGIH advises that pacemakers can malfunction at field strengths of 0.1 mT (1G), but only at 50 and 60 Hz.
Note: ACGIH advises that pacemakers can malfunction at field strengths of 1 kV/m, but only at 50 and 60 Hz.

Induced Current Density (mA/m2)	Effect
<1	None established
1–10	Minor biological effects
1–10	Magnetophosphenes, possible nervous system effects, enhancement of bone fracture healing
1–10	Changes in CNS excitability, stimulation thresholds, possible health hazards
>1,000	Extra systoles, possible ventricular fibrillation, definite health hazards

The American Conference of Governmental Industrial Hygienists (ACGIH®) also issued TLV exposure criteria for workers, based on avoiding induced currents that are stronger than those that already exist in the body due to the normal functioning of nerves and muscles. A number of states have established emission criteria for power transmission lines by specifying maximum fields that can exist along the edges of the right of way occupied by a power transmission line. These limits tend to restrict field strengths to around 20 µT (200 mG) for magnetic fields and 1 kV/m for electric fields.

The clamor for action has prompted researchers and regulators to develop a number of ideas. Two are worth noting. The first, termed *prudent avoidance*, relies on reducing magnetic or electric fields when possible by means that do not involve great expense, similar to the *as low as reasonably achievable* (ALARA) concept applied to reducing ionizing radiation exposures. The second, called the *precautionary principle,* states that in the absence of established safety information or uncertainty about health effects, uncontrolled exposures should be limited to the extent this is practical in situations where new sources are being introduced. When applying either approach, one may not define the field strengths that might actually cause harmful effects; such levels could be much higher. Thus, applying these approaches in the absence of definitive scientific data may result in overly restrictive exposure limits.

Before leaving the topic of biological effects, it is necessary to return to the subject of pacemakers. The ICNIRP advises that power frequency AC fields could interfere with normal pacemaker function at field strengths of 2 kV/m and 1 G. This is because such fields might create potentials inside the body that the pacemaker could confuse with the heart's natural electrical activity, which has a similar ELF frequency. The ACGIH advises that pacemakers could be influenced by 1-kV/m electric fields and 1-G magnetic fields. There is no generally accepted guidance about how to address this potential hazard.

MEASURING SUBRADIOFREQUENCY FIELDS

Electric fields are measured using variations of the displacement sensor described earlier. The surveyor must stand away from the detector when measuring electric fields because the surveyor's body (or any other large nearby conductive object) will shield the detector and create a falsely low measurement. Thus, these instruments come with long nonconductive handles so they can be held as far from the operator's body as possible. One vendor supplies a long pole, another supplies a long handle and instructs the surveyor to hold the detector as far away as possible or to use a fiber-optic readout, and a third uses an electrician's hot stick. The sensors of these instruments resemble paddles or clamshells, with a nonconducting seam separating the shell halves. These instruments are directional; that is, they do not respond equally to fields coming from all directions. These instruments must be held so that the electric field is perpendicular to the paddle or to the seam between the clamshells. The reading reaches a peak level when the sensor is aligned properly.

Magnetic fields are measured with loops. The induced current in the loop, and detector sensitivity, can be boosted by increasing the number of wire turns in the loop or by putting a core of permeable material in the loop. Loops are highly directional. The current induced in a loop reaches a peak value when the plane of the loop coil is perpendicular to the flux lines of a magnetic field; the coil does not respond when the opening is parallel to the lines of flux. The response is proportional to the sine of the angle between the loop opening and the flux lines. The sine of 0 degrees is 0, the sine of 90 degrees is 1, and sine values cannot be higher than 1.

When using a single-loop detector, it is necessary either to know how the field is oriented (from a knowledgeable person or other reliable source) or to measure the field with the detector pointed in one direction, then in another perpendicular direction, and finally in a third direction perpendicular to the other two. The center of the detector must be the same for these three measurements. The magnitude of the field vector is estimated by taking the squares of each measurement, adding the squares, and then taking the square root of the sum of the squares. This calculation is easily done using a spreadsheet. A word of caution about loops: an instrument using a loop or coil sensor will display the average magnetic field across the area surrounded by the loop; magnetic fields at specific points in the loop may be different.

Another method of magnetic field measurement relies on the Hall effect. An object with a current flowing through it in a magnetic field will develop a voltage that can be measured across it in a direction perpendicular to the magnetic field. Hall effect sensors are less sensitive than loops but are used for DC field surveys where concern begins at a few gauss, whereas AC field concerns begin at 1 mG or less. Hall effect instruments also can be used to read very strong strength fields of a Tesla or more. Hall effect probes also are directional and come in axial response and transverse response types. Transverse response probes are handled just like the single-axis loops just mentioned; peak response occurs when the field is perpendicular to the flat side of the tip of the sensor blade. Axial probes are aligned to give peak response when the field is parallel to the long axis of the probe, so the measurement protocols mentioned earlier must be modified to account for the fact that the peak response occurs when the field is parallel with, rather than perpendicular to, the probe. Personal dosimeters are now available that have three mutually orthogonal coils or Hall effect sensors for isotropic response to magnetic fields. Loops are often ganged together in mutually orthogonal arrays of three loops so that the detector does not operate in a directional manner; such an instrument is shown in Figure 11–9.

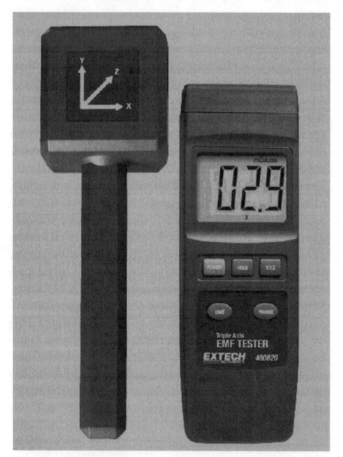

Figure 11–9. Loops are often ganged together in mutually orthogonal arrays of three loops. *(Courtesy www.extech.com.)*

Magnetic field survey instruments using orthogonal triple-loop detector arrays are now available for all frequencies of interest. Orthogonal loops (or Hall effect sensors) confer isotropic response; that is, the response is about equal for all probe orientations in the field, and the sensor is largely nondirectional.

Field loggers, often called dosimeters, are available for ELF magnetic field measurements. The EMDEX loggers for ELF fields were developed for the Electric Power Research Institute and closely resemble modern audio dosimeters in the kind of data they provide. They use mutually orthogonal loop sensors (for time-varying fields). The EMDEX loggers read out through a computer to provide a minute-by-minute summary of exposures in all three axes plus the overall field. Several vendors offer wheeled harnesses for EMDEX loggers, which can be used to precisely map locations when the logger is used to log field strengths at various points in a measurement area.

CONTROLS AND SHIELDING

Blocking or reducing electric fields is relatively easy using a grounded conductor. Imagine that a person is standing below a power transmission line. If a sheet of conductive material was placed between the person and the overhead source and that conductor were grounded, induced charges would flow between the conductor and the earth. As a result, the field lines would begin at the source above the person, induce current flow in the sheet through the ground, and not reach down to the person. The material can be solid, but in practice a mesh will do, as long as the opening of the mesh is much smaller than about one-quarter of a wavelength. This means that screen or chicken wire can block a 60-Hz electric field. Operational shields must be grounded in accordance with electrical safety codes. A practical result of the ease of blocking electric fields for surveyors is that the electric fields in most structures are created by appliances inside the structure, even if a high-voltage transmission line passes overhead.

Magnetic fields are much more difficult to shield. Shields used to block magnetic fields are different from other forms of shielding, which work by stopping an agent with a barrier. Magnetic fields are controlled using permeable alloy that confines the magnetic flux lines into the material and diverts them around the shielded area. Recall that magnetic fields exist as circuits; they do not reach out into space like electric field lines. Magnetic shielding can be made using high nickel alloys called *mu metal* or soft iron. Forming mu metal into complex shapes is expensive, and mu metal is easily damaged. Magnetic field shielding alloys are less permeable at low field strengths than at high field strengths, so they work best at high field strengths. Such shielding is best applied near the field source, whenever practical. Materials that work at lower magnetic field strengths could become commercially available in the future. Another approach is to use nonpermeable metals such as copper or aluminum to produce eddy currents that cancel out the original magnetic field. Active shielding, or field cancellation using an electrical coil system and feedback controls to oppose an unwanted field, is also possible and has been used in studies to produce highly controlled environments.

Exposures of people to magnetic fields is routinely but unintentionally reduced by canceling fields, as in appliance cords with two closely spaced conductors. If a current flows in one direction through a wire—say, from the power outlet in a wall to an appliance—and then the return current flows back in the opposite direction through the neighboring conductor next to the first one, each conductor creates a magnetic field, but the orientations of the fields are opposite and the fields nearly cancel each other out. The closer the two conductors are, the more cancellation occurs. Overhead power lines use widely spaced conductors to avoid arcing, so relatively little cancellation occurs compared with

underground power lines, where the insulated conductors are close together. This is why magnetic fields around underground lines are lower than those of overhead lines. Soil has no shielding value for magnetic fields, although, as a conductor, it does block electric fields.

Field cancellation technology is being increasingly used for AC fields. Some low-field video display terminals (VDTs) use it in the form of additional field coils next to the coils that steer the electron beam to create a canceling field. Utilities can rewire transmission lines to obtain more cancellation. One utility company has developed a technique for creating canceling fields around transmission lines. Field cancellation may also prove useful in households where poorly wired appliances are leaking currents to the ground. The current leaving a house through the ground often does not enter where the current entered the house, so it cannot cancel the magnetic fields created by the incoming current. A house with leaking appliances can have two magnetic hot spots: one where the service enters the house and the other by the ground carrying the leakage current, as shown in Figure 11–10. Any changes made to household wiring to reduce magnetic field exposure must comply with electrical safety codes.

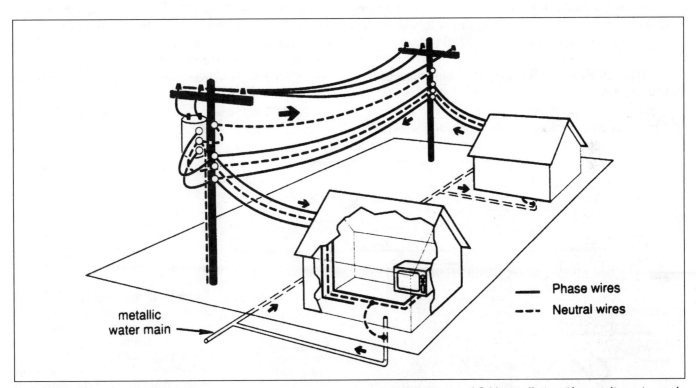

Figure 11–10. Current can leave a house next to where it came in, in which case there is a good field cancellation. If an appliance is poorly grounded, however, some current leaves through the ground and returns to the utility by flowing through the earth. The current flow into the house is not balanced and canceled by the return current, so the magnetic fields are higher at the unbalanced supply wires and where the current flows into the ground. The phase wires bring the current in and the neutral wires return it. *(Reprinted from Electric Power Research Institute, Electric and Magnetic Field Fundamentals—An EMF Effects Resource Paper.)*

RADIOFREQUENCY/MICROWAVE RADIATION AND FIELDS

This portion of the electromagnetic spectrum covers a huge range of frequencies, from 3 kHz to 300 GHz or wavelengths ranging from 100 km to just 1 mm. Recall the earlier section about when fields are important and when radiation is important. Some radiofrequency/microwave (RF/MW) scenarios involve fields and others involve radiation. It is generally agreed that radiation is likely to be found at frequencies above about 300 MHz (wavelength = 1 m), whereas fields are likely to be found at lower frequencies, particularly near antennas. The practical consequence of this is that two surveys (one for electric fields and the other for magnetic fields) are required at lower frequencies, but only one survey is needed at higher frequencies.

Table 11–D provides a summary of divisions and uses of the RF/MW portion of the spectrum, which includes very low frequency or VLF (3–30 kHz), low frequency or LF (30–300 kHz), medium frequency or MF (300 kHz–3 MHz), high frequency or HF (3–30 MHz), very high frequency or VHF (30–300 MHz), ultrahigh frequency or UHF (300 MHz–3 GHz), super high frequency or SHF (3–30 GHz), and extremely high frequency or EHF (30–300 GHz). Microwaves are the portion of the radiofrequency spectrum ranging from 300 MHz to 300 GHz; strictly speaking, the radiofrequencies extend from 3 kHz to 300 GHz.

Industrial, Scientific, and Medical Bands and Frequency Nomenclature

A band is a part of the entire electromagnetic spectrum. Safety and health specialists often find equipment working in the industrial, scientific, and medical (ISM) bands, which anyone can freely use because no licensing is required. The most popular ISM band is the 2.45-GHz band used by microwave ovens. Electrical engineers often use the traditional band designations originally used for radars and military electronics in World War II. Thus, you may hear or read about a Ka band police radar speed gun that works at 24.15 or 35 GHz. These designations were not user-friendly; the modern designation system uses letters of the alphabet, in ascending order, to describe increasing frequencies. For example, the MiG-25 radar operates in the J band, which is somewhere between 10 and 20 GHz. Table 11–D also lists the ISM bands and the traditional and new band designations.

Interactions of Radiation and Matter

The interactions of radiation and matter can be described in terms of how much energy in the radiation is lost to the matter it strikes, as shown in Figure 11–11. If all of the energy in the radiation is lost to the matter, it is absorbed. If some energy, but not all, passes from a chunk of matter, then the radiation is scattered because the remaining, less energetic radiation often leaves in a different direction. If none of the energy is lost, then the radiation was transmitted. Electrical engineers call objects such as radio broadcast towers and radar sets emitters rather than transmitters. Finally, radiation does not pass from one medium to another when the electrical properties are too dissimilar. When this occurs, the radiation is reflected back into the medium it came from. Reflection is the basis of radar; controlling reflections from mirrors and other shiny objects is a major concern in laser safety.

RF/MW that is absorbed or scattered can impart energy to living matter by induction of current flow, which in turn

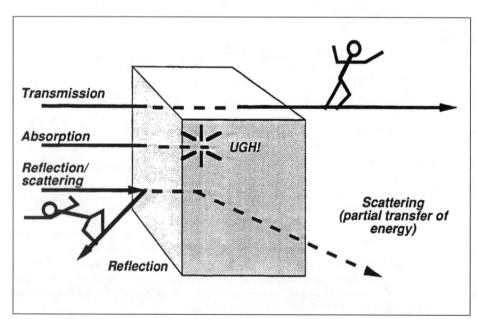

Figure 11–11. Electromagnetic energy can be completely absorbed by matter (absorption), pass through without any interaction (transmission), lose some of its energy (scattering), or not enter at all (reflection). Reflection occurs when the electrical properties of the material the radiation comes from and those of the material it strikes are too different. Radar works when electromagnetic radiation in air, a fair insulator, strikes metal, a superb conductor.

encounters resistive parts of tissues such as cell membranes, or by interactions between the electric field and charged portions of water or organic molecules such as proteins. Electrically charged portions of molecules can be caused to vibrate and ions of metals dissolved in water can be caused to move in response to the electric fields. In both cases, the energy finally appears as heat.

BIOLOGICAL EFFECTS AND EXPOSURE STANDARDS FOR RADIOFREQUENCY FIELDS

The status of biophysics research in the radiofrequencies is somewhat more certain than it is for the subradiofrequencies. More research is needed to answer concerns about the safety of consumer radiofrequency devices such as cellular phones, wireless Internet technology, and police radars (which have used 10, 24.15, and now 35 GHz). The research to date has been sufficient to develop generally accepted safety standards. Radiofrequency and microwave energy causes a wide variety of biological effects (summarized in Table 11–F), especially if exposures are intense enough to cause significant heating. The health significance of doses that are not sufficient to cause measurable heating (athermal effects) is uncertain.

Dosimetry

It is not enough in radiofrequency biophysics research to state that rats were exposed to 10 mW/cm² of 2.45-GHz continuous wave radiation and certain effects were observed. Researchers must address physics problems that determine how much of the power density in the rats' ambient environment is absorbed into power deposited in the rats' tissues. The issues to be addressed are the size of the organism compared with the wavelength of the radiation, the polarization of the radiation (how the electric field is aligned relative to the earth's surface) as compared with the orientation of the exposed organism, and the interaction of exposed tissues with the radiation or fields. The response of tissue to radiation and fields is determined by the electrical properties of the tissue. The discipline that addresses this concern is RF/MW *dosimetry*.

The dose rate, the rate at which energy is transferred to tissue, is called the specific absorption rate (SAR), expressed in watts of power deposited per kilogram of tissue (W/kg). The term for the quantity of energy transferred to tissue is *specific absorption* (SA), expressed in joules of energy per kilogram (J/kg) of tissue. Note that energy is equal to power times time. Power is expressed in watts and 1 W times 1 second equals 1 J of energy. One kilowatt-hour of energy use equals 3,600 s × 1,000 W, or 3.6 million J. Joules are used in exposure standards for pulsed laser energy.

An organism acts as an antenna. An object absorbs the most radiation energy if it is about 40 percent of the wavelength and not well-grounded or when it is about 20 percent of the wavelength and well-grounded. Thus, the resonant frequency for a rat is much higher than for a human. Present

TABLE 11–F	Biological Effects Reported for Radiofrequency and Microwave Radiation	
Target Organ/Overall Effect	**Effect**	**Exposure**
Eyes (animals and humans)	Cataracts	Hours at 120 mW/cm²
	Keratitis	40 mW/cm²
Behavioral (animals only)	Various test changes	≥1.1 W/kg
	Behavioral thermoregulation	≥1.1 W/kg
Endocrine (animals only)	Corticosteroid and thyroid increases	>8.3 W/kg
Immune (animals only)	B and T cell activity changes	≥1.4 W/kg
Neurological (animals only)	Tests of blood/brain barrier contradictory	
Mutations	Not found in replicated studies to date	
Cancer	Not found in humans or animals to date	
Reproduction	Temporary male sterility	5.6 W/kg
	Testicular changes	≥15 W/kg
	Leutenizing hormone changes	>2 W/kg
Teratology (animals only)	Malformed offspring	≥31 W/kg
Thermoacoustic/inner ear (pulsed only)	Observed in radar operators in WWII as perceived clicking sound while in beam	
	Possible cause of neurological effects observed in test animals	0.6 W/kg

regulations assume that peak absorption, or resonance for humans, occurs at frequencies of 30 to 300 MHz. At frequencies below 30 MHz, absorption diminishes in proportion to the square of the frequency, so the person absorbs about 25 percent as much radiation at half the frequency and 1 percent as much radiation at one-tenth of the frequency. At higher frequencies (>300 MHz), absorption also falls off for a while and then flattens out at about 8 percent of that at the resonant peak. This is illustrated in Figure 11–12.

Another significant factor is *polarization*. Radiofrequency radiation is absorbed most when the electric field is parallel to the long axis of the organism and is absorbed least when the magnetic field is parallel to the long axis of the organism, as shown in Figure 11–13. Rats typically best absorb horizontally polarized radiation, whereas upright humans best absorb vertically polarized radiation. Some absorption occurs within "H" (magnetic field).

Dosimetry can be done by measurement or mathematically. Measurement dosimetry was hampered by using common thermocouples, which include a pair of conducting wires trailing from the object being tested. The wires

interact with the electric fields, so only one temperature measurement could be made even in a human-sized object. Fiber-optic devices are now available so that several concurrent temperature measurements can be made in one animal. Another way of making dosimetric measurements is to sacrifice animals and cut the remains in two longitudinal halves. The halves are joined, irradiated at intense levels, and separated; the temperature change is then measured using an infrared device. The irradiation takes place in the same place as the irradiation of live animals, but at higher levels to produce more easily measured heating.

Mathematical dosimetry is also progressing. Newer mathematical models make more efficient use of computer memory and offer adequate capacity to do complex, tedious calculations. The original models used to develop the relationships just described between wavelength and polarization and the size and orientation of the organism simply estimated the average, whole-body SAR. Newer models are based on MRI images of human internal organs and structures and can estimate the SAR for specific organs and small parts of the body. The University of Utah pioneered the development of mathematical dosimetry, with funding from the U.S. Air Force School of Aerospace Medicine, and published a series of dosimetry handbooks.

The most common dosimetric standard in the United States today is 0.4 W/kg as a whole-body average. This objective is based on heat avoidance behavior of animals at an SAR of 4 W/kg, divided by a safety factor of 10. Higher local SARs are permitted (10 W/kg averaged over a cubic volume of 10 g of tissue for specific parts of the trunk and nonextremity parts of the body, and up to 20 W/kg at the extremities).

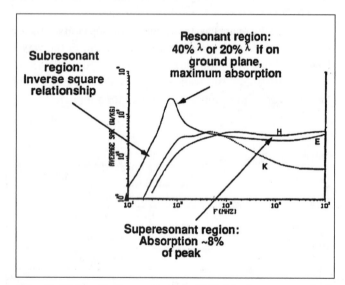

Figure 11–12. Specific absorption rates (SARs) for humans as a function of frequency. The letters *E, H,* and *K* show that the radiation is aligned so the electric field axis points along the long axis of the organism (vertically polarized), the magnetic field points along the long axis of the organism, and the radiation travels through the long axis of the organism. E = electric field; H = magnetic field; K = direction of travel. Note that there are three major regions. In the *subresonant region*, the body does not function well as an antenna. Absorption drops in an inverse square relationship to wavelength. In the *resonant region*, the body is a good antenna that maximizes absorption. In the *superresonant region* (6 to 300 GHz), the body no longer acts as a good antenna and absorption levels off at about 10 percent of peak absorption. Quasi-optical focusing occurs from 6 to 15 GHz, and skin absorption dominates at >15 HGz (penetration <1 cm).

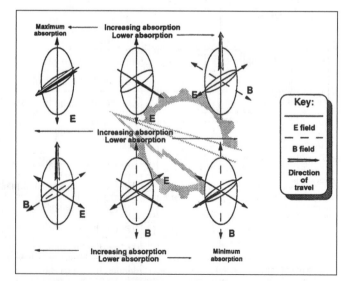

Figure 11–13. An elongated object (prolate spheroid) absorbs the most energy when the electric field is parallel to its long axis and the least energy when the magnetic field is parallel to its long axis.

Target Organs

A variety of effects are known to occur at SARs above 4 W/kg, but the target organs are the eyes and testes, based on limits of circulation and heat dissipation at these two organ systems. It is assumed that the thermal equilibrium time for these target organs could be as brief as six minutes, so the standards specify exposure limits that apply for six minute time intervals (until the frequency rises above 3 GHz, where the time interval gradually drops to 10 seconds). The only proven adverse effects for humans, regardless of SAR, are eye cataracts, facial burns, and electric shocks and burns. Cataracts occur in animals at power densities above 120 mW/cm² if the exposures last for hours, but only minutes of exposure are needed at 350 mW/cm². Electric shocks and strong current flows through the ankles have occurred in humans and are important at frequencies below 100 MHz. Other effects have been demonstrated in animals, such as teratogenic effects in animals subjected to intense SARs and neurochemical and eye effects in animals exposed to pulsed radiofrequency and microwave radiation, but these effects have not been duplicated in humans.

Standard-Setting Rationale

We now see that the radiofrequency portion of the electromagnetic spectrum can be divided into three major parts, as shown in Figure 11–14. At lower frequencies, current flow considerations dominate. The goal of the standard is to prevent burns caused by radiofrequency electric current (at frequencies of a few megahertz and below) and excessive ankle heating caused by the surge of electricity to and from the ground through the feet (from a few megahertz through the resonant frequencies). There was no convenient way to measure contact current until about 1991. Regulators approached the problem by limiting the ambient field strengths allowed to strengths that were equivalent to 100 mW/cm² if the fields existed as electromagnetic radiation. The risk of electrical burns caused by touching an object energized by radiofrequency fields and the risk of significant ankle heating are covered by current flow criteria.

At the resonant frequencies, where our bodies act as good antennas, controlling SAR becomes the main concern and remains a serious concern at higher frequencies until skin absorption becomes dominant. For regulatory purposes, the resonant portion of the spectrum ranges from 3 MHz (for electric fields) or 100 kHz (for magnetic fields) to 3 GHz and is most restrictive at frequencies ranging from 30 to 300 MHz, wavelengths where an adult or child functions as a good antenna.

At higher frequencies (above 3 GHz) skin absorption predominates, and mathematical modeling reveals that

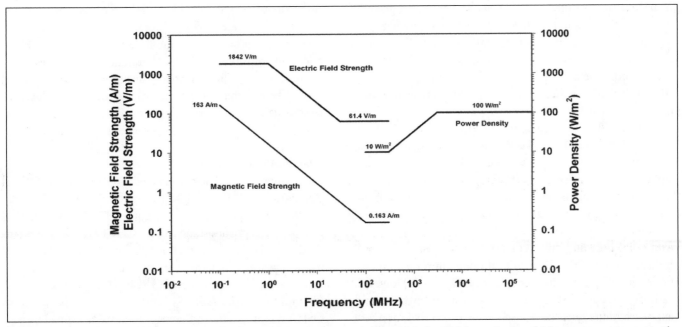

Figure 11–14. The inverse of the absorption curves shown in Figure 11–12. These are the C95.1 standards, which are most stringent in the frequencies where absorption is at its peak and levels off at higher frequencies. The leveling off at lower frequencies reflects the risk of RF electric burns caused by contact with conductors immersed in strong fields. The *subresonant region* (<3 MHz) is the region in which current flow considerations are most important. In the *resonant region* (3 MHz to 6 GHz), current flow and SAR are both important considerations where current is ≤ 100 MHz. Absorption falls off in proportion to the square of the frequency between 3 MHz and 30 MHz. Standards are most stringent between 30 MHz and 300 MHz. Between 300 MHz and 3 GHz, absorption falls off linearly as frequency increases. The *superresonant region* ranges from 3 GHz to 300 GHz. *(From IEEE Std C95.1-2005.)*

absorption is about 8 percent of absorption at the resonant peak. Above about 6 GHz, most of the radiation is absorbed in the skin and outer tissue layers; at frequencies above 15 GHz, most radiation is absorbed in the first centimeter of tissue. The properties of microwaves become similar to those of infrared (IR) radiation, and thermal damage to the skin becomes a major concern.

The regulatory community also examined the question of how magnetic fields should be regulated in near-field scenarios. Magnetic fields passing through conductors induce current loops, as discussed in the ELF section of this chapter. Based on this and calculations of the current density induced by magnetic fields, it was agreed that magnetic fields would be subject to relatively lenient regulations.

Most occupational exposure standards used in the United States are based on the Institute of Electrical and Electronic Engineers' C95.1 standard, *IEEE Standard for Safety Levels with Respect to Human Exposure to Radio Frequency Electromagnetic Fields, 3 kHz to 300 GHz.* This standard provides separate recommendations for the general public and for occupational exposures. The basic restriction (BR) for exposures, which is the limiting biophysical quantity used for calculating maximum permissible exposure (MPE) limits, is 0.4W/kg for whole-body exposures in occupational settings in the frequency range from 100 kHz to 3 GHz. The occupational setting assumes that workers operate in a controlled environment and are appropriately trained, warned, and informed of the RF exposure hazards. The nonoccupational recommendations generally are five times more restrictive than occupational standards and are considered to be an action level that also applies to uncontrolled or public settings where the person may be unaware of the RF hazard.

The MPE for the current (2005) C95.1 standard are presented in Tables 11–G, 11–H, and 11–I. These are whole-body average exposures that are calculated based on measurements made at 20-cm vertical intervals beginning at the floor and reaching to the head at distances of 20 cm or more from radiating or energized objects.

Averaging Time and Pulsed Fields

Industrial hygienists are used to thinking in terms of eight hour averaging times for exposures to chemicals. However, radiofrequency heating occurs much more rapidly, and exposure limits must be devised to be protective for acute damage to the target organs. In the case of whole body exposure thermal equilibrium of the target organs (eyes and testes), occurs rapidly and is assumed to be about six minutes for limbs, organs, and partial body structures. Thus, time-averaging calculations can be made much as they are for chemicals, but the exposures must not exceed the C95.1

limit over a six minute averaging interval rather than an eight hour shift. Put another way, a person can be exposed to twice the limit for three minutes if no other radiation exposures occur for the other three minutes. For other hazards, such as direct electro-stimulation of nerves or other tissue by electric fields or currents, a much shorter averaging time of 0.2 s applies. The averaging interval for uncontrolled exposure situations is 30 minutes for frequencies ranging between 3 MHz and 3 GHz. Above 3 GHz, exposures in human tissue become quasi-optical, and the depth of penetration is about 1 cm or less. As a result, the thermal time constant decreases and shorter averaging times apply. For example, for a 30-GHz exposure the MPE limit for occupational settings would call for a 30-s (0.5-min) averaging time rather than six minutes. As shown in Table 11–G, averaging time varies as a function of frequency across the 3- to 300-GHz region.

The idea of limiting above-average exposures so the six minute time-weighted average is below the standard has limitations in the case of exposures to very short term but intense pulses of energy. Pulsed fields are common in some radar and laboratory settings, and recent military devices that simulate the electromagnetic pulses from nuclear weapons stimulated public concern about pulsed electromagnetic fields. As with chemical exposures, a simple TWA allows for extremely intense exposures if they are brief enough. Thus, an exposure to a 360-ns pulse could be a billion times more than the C95.1 limit if there were no other exposures for six minutes. The resolution has been to limit electric fields to 100 kV/m and, and additionally, to stipulate that for pulses less than 100 ms, the total incident energy during any 100-ms interval should be less than 20 percent of the total energy permitted during the entire averaging time. For pulses greater than 100-ms duration, normal time averaging calculations apply.

Regulatory Considerations

The standard paperback volume of Title 29 Code of Federal Regulations (CFR), Part 1910, the OSHA general industry regulations, includes the original 1970 radiofrequency/microwave exposure standard, 29 CFR 1910.97. This standard, based on ANSI C95.1-1966, is obsolete. The original regulation was struck down by the Occupational Safety and Health Review Commission in 1981, but the *UAW, Brock v. General Dynamics Land Systems Division* decision allows OSHA to apply state-of-the-art standards developed by others when OSHA has no standard of its own. IEEE adopted a revision of C95.1 in 2005 as IEEE C95.1-2005 and the American National Standards Institute (ANSI) adopted the revision. Hence, OSHA can enforce ANSI/IEEE C95.1-2005, so the reader should become acquainted with this standard (Figure 11–15).

TABLE 11–G IEEE C95.1-2005 MPE for Radiofrequency and Microwave Radiation for People in Controlled Environments When an RF Safety Program is Available

Frequency range (MHz)	RMS electric field strength (E)[a] (V/m)	RMS magnetic field strength (H)[a] (A/m)	RMS power density (S) E-field, H-field (W/m²)	Averaging time $\|E\|^2$, $\|H\|^2$ or S (min)
0.1–1.0	1842	$16.3/f_M$	$(9000, 100\,000/f_M^2)$[b]	6
1.0–30	$1842/f_M$	$16.3/f_M$	$(9000/f_M^2, 100\,000/f_M^2)$	6
30–100	61.4	$16.3/f_M$	$(10, 100\,000/f_M^2)$	6
100–300	61.4	0.163	10	6
300–3000	–	–	$f_M/30$	6
3000–30 000	–	–	100	$19.63/f_G^{1.079}$
30 000–300 000	–	–	100	$2.524/f_G^{0.476}$

TABLE 11–H IEEE C95.1-2005: Action Level MPE for Radiofrequency and Microwave Radiation for the General Public When an RF Safety Program is Unavailable

Frequency range (MHz)	RMS electric field strength (E)[a] (V/m)	RMS magnetic field strength (H)[a] (A/m)	RMS power density (S) E-field, H-field (W/m²)	Averaging time[b] $\|E\|^2$, $\|H\|^2$ or S (min)	
0.1–1.34	614	$16.3/f_M$	$(1000, 100\,000/f_M^2)$[c]	6	6
1.34–3	$823.8/f_M$	$16.3/f_M$	$(1800/f_M^2, 100\,000/f_M^2)$	$f_M^2/0.3$	6
3–30	$823.8/f_M$	$16.3/f_M$	$(1800/f_M^2, 100\,000/f_M^2)$	30	6
30–100	27.5	$158.3/f_M^{1.668}$	$(2, 9\,400\,000/f_M^{3.336})$	30	$0.0636\,f_M^{1.337}$
100–400	27.5	0.0729	2	30	30
400–2000	–	–	$f_M/200$	30	
2000–5000	–	–	10	30	
5000–30 000	–	–	10	$150/f_G$	
30 000–100 000	–	–	10	$25.24/f_G^{0.476}$	
100 000–300 000	–	–	$(90f_G-7000)/200$	$5048/[(9f_G-700)f_G^{0.476}]$	

Footnotes for Tables 11–G and 11–H

Note: f_M is the frequency in MHz, f_G is the frequency in GHz.

[a] For exposures that are uniform over the dimensions of the body, such as certain far-field plane-wave exposures, the exposure field strengths and power densities are compared with the MPEs in the Table. For non-uniform exposures, the mean values of the exposure fields, as obtained by spatially averaging the squares of the field strengths or averaging the power densities over an area equivalent to the vertical cross section of the human body (projected area) or a smaller area depending on the frequency are compared with the MPEs in the Table.

For frequencies between 100 kHz and 3 GHz, the MPE for fields are derived on the basis of limiting the whole body averaged (WBA) SAR, which is proportional to the spatial average of the incident plane wave equivalent power density (or squares of electric and magnetic field strengths), averaged over the projected area of the body. In practice, a measurement over the length of the body is sufficient for assessing exposures for comparison with the MPE in this frequency range. At Frequencies greater than 3 GHz the MPE is expressed in terms of the incident power density. To provide a transition in the frequency range 3 GHz to 6 GHz, compliance with this standard may be demonstrated by evaluation of either incident power density or local SAR. From 3 GHz to 30 GHz. The power density is spatially averaged over any contiguous area corresponding to 100 λ², where λ is the free space wavelength of the RF field in centimeters. For frequencies exceeding 30 GHz, the power density is spatially averaged over any contiguous area of 0.01 m² (100 cm²), not to exceed a maximum power density of 1000 W/m² in any one square centimeter as determined by a calculation or a conventional field measurement. (See IEEE C95.1 2005 for further details.)

[b] The left column is the averaging time for $\|E\|^2$, the right column is the averaging time for $\|H\|^2$. For frequencies greater than 400 MHz, the averaging time is for power density S

[c] These plane-wave equivalent power density values are commonly used as a convenient comparison with MPEs at higher frequencies and are displayed on some instruments in use.

TABLE 11–I   Relaxations for Partial Body Exposures for Table 7 and 8* of the ANSI/IEEE Standard

	Frequency (GHz)	Peak Value of Mean Squared Field	Equivalent Power Density (mW/cm²)
Controlled Access Exposures	$0.001 \leq f_g < 0.3$	$<20\ E^2$ or $20\ H^{2**}$	
	$0.3 < f_g \leq 6$		<20
	$6 < f_g \leq 96$		$<20\ (f_g/6)^{1/4\dagger\dagger}$
	$96 < f_g \leq 300$		40
Uncontrolled Access Exposures	$0.0001 \leq f_g \leq 0.3$	$<20\ E^2$ or $20\ H^{2\dagger}$	
	$0.3 < f_g \leq 6$		4
	$6 < f_g \leq 30$		$f_g/1.5^{\dagger\dagger}$
	$30 < f_g \leq 300$		20

* These relaxations do not apply to the eyes and testes
** E and H are spatially averaged values from Table 2 of the standard
† E and H are spatially averaged values from Table 3 of the standard
†† f_g in GHz
Source: ANSI/EEE C95. 1-2005, 2005

MEASURING RADIOFREQUENCY RADIATION AND FIELDS

Recall that fields rather than radiation are presumed to exist at frequencies below 300 MHz, so two surveys (one for electric fields and the other for magnetic fields) are needed. Only one survey is needed for frequencies above 300 MHz.

Electric fields at frequencies above 100 kHz are measured using small dipole antennas. The electric field induces a current in the dipole, which is connected to a diode. A diode is the electrical equivalent of a one-way valve, so the induced current is allowed to leave the detector and go to an amplifier. The amplified current drives a display. Alternatively, the electric field induces current flow and heating in an array of thermocouples, and the change of resistance caused by heating is measured to drive the display. Dipoles and diodes can be used at lower frequencies (below about 100 kHz), but displacement sensors are also used.

Most dipole/diode field survey instruments gang three sensors together so they are mutually orthogonal (perpendicular to each other) to provide an isotropic response (a response that is about equal regardless of how the sensor is aligned in the field), as shown in Figure 11–16. Microwave oven survey instruments have two dipole/diode sensors that are perpendicular to each other. The lack of the third sensor makes them directional, and they must be held so the probe handle is perpendicular to the surface being measured. When measuring electric fields using a single detector, it is often apparent where the field source is located, so alignment of the detector is simple. A displacement sensor is oriented so that its flat surface faces the source; such an instrument is shown in Figure 11–17. Most instruments used for radiofrequency measurements below 300 MHz have displays marked to read in volts per meter (V/m). Instruments operating in the microwave region can be marked to read out in square volts per square meter (V²/m²) or milliwatts per square centimeter (mW/cm²); microwave power density meters usually measure the electric field intensity and convert it to power density at the display.

Magnetic fields below 300 MHz are measured with single loops or triple mutually orthogonal loops. Single

Figure 11–15. The internationally recognized radiofrequency hazard icon, "the radiator." OSHA has not updated its published radiofrequency standard but has informed IEEE that it will not cite an organization using this symbol instead of the obsolete symbol found in the OSHA regulations.

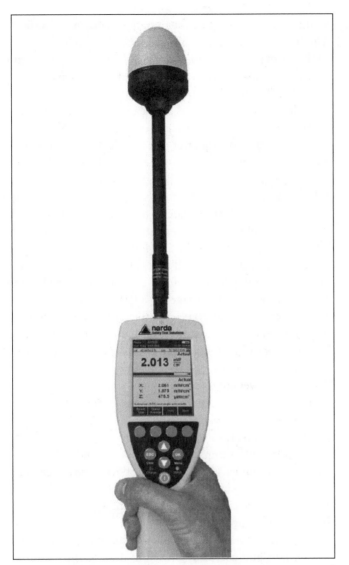

Figure 11–16. Isotropic (nondirectional) antenna arrays are used for RF survey meters. Mutually orthogonal dipoles respond to electric fields, and mutually perpendicular magnetic field loops. *(Narda NBM-550 Broadband Field Meter with electric field probe is shown.)*

Figure 11–17. A displacement sensor is oriented so that its flat surface faces the source. *(HI-3603 VLF survey meter courtesy of ETS-Lindgren, Inc.)*

loops are highly directional, so the surveyor must follow the protocol outlined earlier in the section on measuring subradiofrequency fields. Triple orthogonal loops are isotropic, so probe orientation is not critical.

Radiofrequency field and radiation measurements should be made where the worker would normally be, but without the person present, so reflections and induced fields do not create falsely high results. (This is similar to noise measurements, which are best done where the ears would normally be, but while the operator is away.) Either the sensor is held just above floor level and raised up through the body position at 8-in. (20-cm) vertical intervals and

the result recorded for each point, or the probe is steadily moved through the body positions using an instrument with an add-on module that averages the readings. The sensor must be kept 20 cm or one sensor dimension (whichever is greater) away from energized objects. At this time, measurements must be made at the locations of the eyes and testes. Exposures above the standard and their locations must also be recorded. Excursions up to 20 times the standard are allowed at the extremities (hands and feet), and excursions up to eight times the standards are allowed elsewhere (except at the locations of the eyes and testes).

Contact- and induced-current meters are now available. The contact-current meter has electrodes that are pressed against an object that may be electrically charged due to ambient RF fields, as well as a cable and built-in ammeter. Induced-current meters look like bathroom scales and are meant for people to stand on. The induced current flows through the instrument and drives an AC ammeter before going to ground. One manufacturer sells a cylindrical antenna that electrically simulates an upright human and can be placed on an induced-current meter.

MICROWAVE OVENS

Microwave ovens use the 2.45-GHz ISM band. Power is supplied by a magnetron tube and routed to the cooking chamber via a waveguide. The radiation leaving the waveguide passes over a rotor (or rotating waveguide) set in motion by moving air. The rotor is shaped to reflect the radiation around the cooking chamber to obtain a somewhat even distribution of energy. This caused concern when microwave ovens first appeared because the radiation leaking from an oven was amplitude-modulated by the rotor and could be picked up by cardiac pacemakers of that era. The pacemakers could amplify the leaking radiation rather than the heart's own electrical activity, with serious consequences for the user. Since that time, pacemaker manufacturers have added capacitors and protective circuits to block out extraneous fields, and most pacemakers are now tested against electric fields equivalent to 10 mW/cm², the ANSI C95.1 exposure standard (1966) in effect when microwave ovens first appeared. The present emission standard for microwave ovens, 21 CFR 1930.10, from the Food and Drug Administration, allows new ovens to leak no more than 1 mW/cm² when measured at 5 cm and old ovens to leak no more than 5 mW/cm² when measured at 5 cm (microwave oven survey meters have Styrofoam spacer cones to guarantee this 5-cm separation). Excessive leakage from a microwave oven could occur if the oven was mechanically damaged, so oven users should check the condition of the door, door jamb, vision screen, and interlock when they use an oven and have damaged ovens repaired or replaced. Annual surveys are not warranted.

RF/MW CONTROLS

RF/MW shielding is relatively simple and can be installed using relatively inexpensive materials. Lead is not needed. The most effective form of shielding is applied at the source as an enclosure. Absorbing foams (porous polyurethane foam filled with carbon in a manner that causes the arriving radiation to pass through, gradually lowering impedance) can be used. Electromagnetic radiation does not pass from one medium to another if the difference in electrical conductivities is large; it is simply reflected from the object. Air is a fairly good insulator, whereas metals are good conductors, so devices such as radar work by causing radiation arriving from air to strike and be reflected by metal. The foam manufacturer makes the impedance change gradually so the radiation is not reflected from the absorber. This can be done by forming the foam into pyramid shapes so the arriving radiation passes the tips and travels toward the bases of the pyramids. The impedance gradually drops as the radiation encounters less air and more carbon. The arriving radiation eases into the foam and induces a flow of electric current in the foam. Graphite is a poor conductor,

so the current induced by the radiation is dissipated as heat. The foam manufacturer can also make the carbon content of the foam increase from nothing at the outside of the foam to a maximum level at the base of the foam. Then the foam can be sold as flat sheet because pyramids are not needed.

Metal screens or sheets also can be used for shielding or enclosures. The key concept is that the mesh openings be no more than one-quarter of a wavelength in dimension. Metal screens and sheets must be electrically bonded to each other where they join and the whole assembly grounded; otherwise, fields can pass through the gaps. A Faraday cage is a grounded enclosure made of continuously bonded conductors. An object inside is protected from electric fields and radiation on the outside. The doors and door jambs of Faraday cages are lined with resilient alloy strips that make contact when the door is shut so the door is bonded to the jamb and the rest of the cage.

Waveguides and coaxial cables are used to transfer power and act as enclosures. Waveguides are open metallic conduits with flanged ends. The flanged ends allow waveguides to be fastened to other waveguides, sources, or receivers. Waveguides must be snugly attached or leakage will occur. Similarly, coaxial cables can be bent and fail. Leakage can occur where they fail.

Copper tape is most commonly used in electrical engineering. It is used to patch leak points in enclosures or in runs of waveguide. Very high power devices have been successfully enclosed in wooden boxes lined on the inside with well-joined copper sheets and absorbing foam and finished outside with copper tape at the seams.

Distance is very effective in far fields, due to the inverse square law, and can also be used in near fields. Examples of using distance as a control include enclosing a source in a barricade to keep people away from the source or using long-handled tools to manipulate objects immersed in strong radiation fields.

Time limitations are possible, based on a six minute averaging time, but often are not practical. Another control, the sign found in the OSHA nonionizing radiation standard, became obsolete in 1992; the symbol shown in Figure 11–15 should be used instead of the aluminum, black, and red diamond found in the old OSHA standard. The magenta and yellow trefoil associated with ionizing radiation should never be used!

OPTICAL RADIATION AND LASERS

CIE Bands

Optical radiation includes infrared/visible and ultraviolet radiation. Optical radiation is manipulated with nonconductive optics (with the exception of mirrors, which use metal to reflect the radiation). It is customary to describe optical radiation by wavelength rather than frequency. Nomenclature has been developed by the Commission Internationale d'Eclairage (CIE), or International Lighting Commission. The band designations for infrared and ultraviolet radiation begin at the border of each band starting with visible radiation (wavelength of 400 to 750 nm) and extend each way from the visible band:

CIE Band	Wavelength	Non-CIE Nomenclature
Microwaves	>1 mm	
IR-C	3 μm–1 mm	Far IR: 25 μm–1 mm
IR-B	1.4 μm–3 μm	Intermediate IR: 2500 nm–25 μm
IR-A	760–1400 nm	Near IR: 760–2500 nm
Visible		400–760 nm
UV-A	315–400 nm	Near UV, black light
UV-B	280–315 nm	Middle UV, actinic UV
UV-C	100–280 nm	Far UV, actinic UV, Vacuum UV: <200 nm
x rays	<4 nm	

BIOLOGICAL EFFECTS AND EXPOSURE STANDARDS FOR OPTICAL RADIATION

Biological effects of optical radiation result from thermal and photochemical mechanisms. The scientific controversy and uncertainty that plague efforts to protect people from microwave, RF, and ELF do not apply to optical radiation. Thermal effects are dominant in the IR portion of the spectrum, photochemical effects dominate in the UV, thermal effects are more important at the red end of the visible spectrum, and photochemical effects are dominant at the blue end of the visible spectrum. The target organs are the eyes and skin. Visible and IR-A radiation, 400 to 1,400 nm, is particularly hazardous to the eye because it is transmitted through the cornea, is focused by the lens, and strikes the retina. The potential for retinal damage is great because the radiation can be highly concentrated by focusing.

The Eye

The exterior of the eye is protected by a transparent layer that contains living tissue, the cornea. The cornea is wetted by continual blinking of the eyelids when they are open. The vitreous humor, a sac of watery material, lies inside the cornea. The cornea and vitreous humor form the anterior portion of the eye, which is divided from the posterior region by the iris, which is opaque and pigmented. The iris can absorb energy and be heated by radiation. The iris contains muscles that adjust the size of the central opening, the

pupil, to control the amount of light passing into the rest of the eye. Behind the iris lies the lens, a flexible mass that is made thicker or thinner by the ciliary muscles to provide the sharpest possible image on the retina. It transmits visible and IR-A radiation, but other bands of IR and UV are absorbed here or at the cornea. Light passes through the aqueous humor and strikes the retina, where photosensitive cells convert the energy of light to electrical signals that are fed to the vision centers of the brain and the pineal. There are two types of photoreceptor cells in the retina: rods, which work in a broad range of lighting conditions but cannot differentiate between wavelengths (see colors), and cones, which perceive colors in brightly lit conditions. Rods cover the entire retina, but cones cover only the macula, a small area in the back of the retina. The fovea, a small region that is rich in cones and essentially rod-free, is located in the center of the macula directly opposite the center of the iris, which makes color vision particularly vulnerable to overexposures to visible and IR-A radiation. When the lens is removed surgically, creating an aphakic condition, then UV-A that normally is blocked by the lens also passes through and evokes a retinal response. The rods lie on a bed of highly pigmented tissue, the retinal pigmented epithelium (RPE); although the rods are essentially transparent and do not absorb light, the underlying RPE can absorb light, become hot, and damage the rods. (See Chapter 5, The Eyes, for anatomical illustrations of the human eye.)

The target portions of the eye are summarized below:

CIE Band	Wavelengths	Primary Visual Hazard	Other Visual Hazards
IR-C	1 mm–3.0 μm	Corneal burns	
IR-B	3 μm–1.4 μm	Corneal burns	
IR-A	760–1400 nm	Retinal burns	Cataracts of lens (glassblowers' cataracts)
Visible	400–760 nm	Retinal burns	Night and color vision impairment (chronic exposures to intense sunlight)
UV-A	315–400 nm	Cataracts of lens	
UV-B	280–315 nm	Corneal injuries (welder's flash)	Cataracts of lens (at longer wavelengths of UV-B band)
UV-C	100–280 nm	Corneal injuries (welder's flash)	

See Figure 11–18 for a summary of the CIE bands and target organs of optical radiation.

The blood circulating through the choroid below the retina is an important defense mechanism. The capillaries in the choroid have larger diameters than typical capillar-

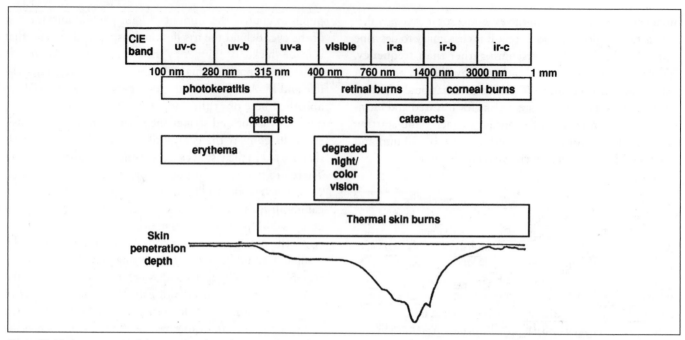

Figure 11–18. A summary of the CIE bands and target organs for the various types of radiation. *(From Sliney & Wolbarsht, 1985.)*

ies elsewhere, but the oxygen demand of the living retinal and other eye tissues is modest; this capillary net is a vast liquid cooling system that extracts heat from the retina. This defense can be overwhelmed by an extremely brief but intense pulse of light into the retina, providing energy above the rate at which the heat can be extracted by blood flow. Pulsed lasers are particularly hazardous; they can deposit energy so rapidly that the water in the retinal tissue flashes to a boil and "explodes," causing local tissue damage. If the same amount of energy is deposited in a shorter time period in briefer pulses, more damage is created by the shorter pulses because less heat dissipation can occur. This thermo-acoustic mechanism of damage was unknown until the laser was invented. Alternatively, large quantities of light can be hazardous when deposited over larger areas of the retina; this is why it is unsafe to look at the sun through a telescope. The choroid circulation can remove the heat of glimpsing at the sun for a brief period because the image of the sun on the retina is so small that only a small part of the retina is strongly illuminated. A telescope makes the retinal image much larger, and the brightness that was limited to just a small retinal area now strikes a much larger area. This can overwhelm the heat-removing capacity of choroid circula-tion. Visible radiation can cause retinal injuries or burns because it is transmitted and focused. If the resulting lesion, or scotoma, damages some portion of most of the retina, very little visual impairment will result, but if the scotoma occurs in the macula, serious visual impairment results.

Another defense is afforded by aversion reflex actions such as blinking or looking away from bright light. Excessively bright light prompts these responses, which end exposure in about 0.25 s; this is enough to provide protec-tion from injuries caused by sunlight and most artificial light sources other than lasers. One reason lasers are hazardous is because they can deposit damaging amounts of energy into the eye well before the aversion reflex ends the exposure.

The Skin

See Chapter 3, The Skin and Occupational Dermatoses, for anatomical illustrations of the skin. The outermost layer of skin, the epidermis, contains a single sheet of cells at its base, consisting of keratinocytes (cells that divide and move outward) and melanocytes (cells that form dark granules of melanin pigment that are transferred to the keratinocytes). The keratinocytes divide and are pushed outward by newer cells being created by the basal cells. As they move outward they flatten, develop pigment granules, and finally die. Thus, the dividing and moving keratinocytes carry pigment with them. This pigment absorbs UV and prevents the genera-tion of excessive levels of vitamin D and UV injuries to the dermal and subcutaneous tissues below. The inner layer of living cells is called the stratum malpighii; the outermost layer of dead cells the stratum corneum.

IR and visible light skin injuries are confined to thermal burns. About 0.67 mW/cm^2 irradiance produces a feeling of warmth. UV also causes skin effects through photochemical mechanisms. Sunbathers now use sunscreen lotions to allow UV-A to reach the skin and stimulate melanin production by the melanocytes, but absorb UV-B before it can reach the skin. UV-B and UV-C produce two undesirable effects: the skin toughening evident among desert dwellers and skin cancer. (Outdoor exposures do not include UV-C because it is absorbed by oxygen in the atmosphere to produce ozone.) Research now shows that UV-A can also cause skin cancer. Thermal and photochemical damage mechanisms again dominate. The most common skin effect is erythema, or reddening, which is commonly called sunburn. UV penetrates to the living cells of the dermis and causes damage, which is repaired. Blood supply to the skin is increased as part of the repair process, causing the reddening. Repeated exposure to UV, particularly UV-B, causes the skin to thicken and harden. This is why people who live in sunny areas can develop leathery skin.

The exposure standards that address UV and far IR exposure to the skin are about the same as the standards addressing eye exposures, but the standards for visible and near IR skin exposure are much more lenient than those for eye exposure because of the possibility of retinal damage caused by focusing.

Standards

Optical radiation and laser safety standards use radians rather than degrees as a measure of angle. The length of an arc (segment of a circle) created (subtended) by a given angle is equal to the radius of the circle times the size of the angle in radians. Therefore, the size of a source that is emitting radiation, or a surface that is reflecting radiation, is equal to the distance between the source and the viewer times the angle in radians. The customary symbol for the angle is alpha (α). The use of radian units is shown in Figure 11–19. For comparison purposes, half a circle, 180 degrees, is π (about 3.1416) radians and a full circle, 360 degrees, contains 2π (about 6.2832) radians. Another angular measure is also used to describe portions of the surface of a sphere: the steradian. Radians and degrees cover familiar two-dimensional circles and arcs, but the steradian unit applies to three-dimensional situations such as areas that are reflecting or generating radiation. The area of the surface of a sphere is equal to the solid angle subtended by that area times the radius of the sphere. A sphere subtends a solid angle of 4π steradians. Therefore, the size of an illuminated or radiating area is equal to the square of the distance between the area and the observer times the solid angle, in steradians.

The principal standards for nonlaser optical radiation are found in the back of the TLV booklets issued annually by the ACGIH. ACGIH groups visible radiation with IR radiation and addresses UV separately. These TLVs are fundamentally identical in concept to the more familiar noise standard in that they use spectral effectiveness factors to account for the difference in damage caused by energy of

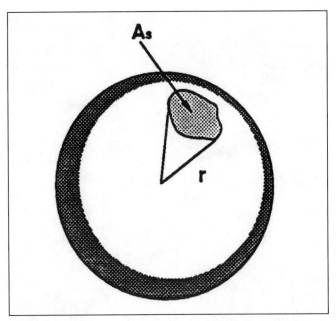

Figure 11–19. An angle in radians can be calculated by dividing its arc by the radius. A solid angle can be calculated in steradians by dividing the area subtended by the solid angle by the radius squared. In optical safety applications, the arc is the long dimension of an illuminated or luminous area. The area for a solid angle calculation is the illuminated or luminous area. In both cases, the radius is the distance between the illuminated or luminous area and an observer.

different wavelengths (much as the A-weighting curve does for noise exposures), and they trade exposure intensity off against permissible exposure time. Instruments are now on the market that have wavelength response characteristics that approximate the spectral effectiveness curves of the TLVs; such an instrument is shown in Figure 11–20.

The TLV for visible/IR radiation has two basic elements: one for situations where visible radiation is present and a much simpler standard that applies when only IR is present. The visible standards must account for both photochemical injuries at the blue end and thermal injuries at the red end and IR. The thermal injury standard covers wavelengths from 400 to 1,400 nm and balances ambient irradiances multiplied by the appropriate spectral effectiveness factors (listed in a table that shows that the maximum thermal hazard exists almost at the UV end, wavelength = 435 and 440 nm) against the angle being viewed and the exposure time. Thus, stronger exposures to more hazardous wavelengths from bigger sources warrant shorter permissible exposures. The TLV also specifies making a second comparison to account for blue light photochemical hazards of visible radiation (wavelengths from 400 to 700 nm). A table of spectral effectiveness factors is given for red light and blue light injury. Stronger exposures of more hazardous wave-

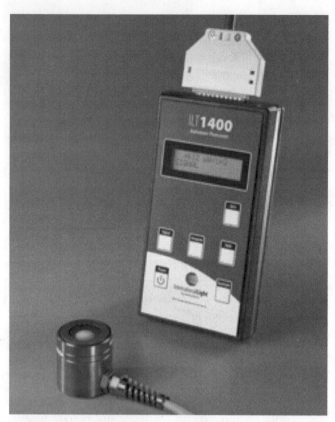

Figure 11–20. Instruments are now on the market that have wavelength response characteristics that approximate the spectral effectiveness curves of the TLVs. *(Courtesy International Light, Inc.)*

lengths from bigger sources (sources covering larger solid angles) are balanced against permissible exposure duration. Special spectral effectiveness factors are required for those who have had their lenses removed (aphakes); these require assessments down to 305 nm (through all of UV-A and just into the high wavelength end of UV-B).

The TLV does not extend to wavelengths >1.4 μm; one must consult LIA/ANSI laser safety standard Z136.1 for guidance about wavelengths between 1.4 μm and 1 mm. The Z136 standard can be applied to nonlaser sources at wavelengths above 1.4 μm because the concern about retinal focusing does not exist above 1.4 μm, so eye and skin hazards are the same for laser and nonlaser sources.

Two formulas are given for situations such as heat lamps where IR is not accompanied by visible radiation. One formula addresses corneal hazards from 770 nm to 3 μm by limiting exposure times if irradiances exceed those allowed for viewing intervals greater than 1,000 seconds (10 mW/cm²). The other addresses retinal hazards from 770 to 1,400 nm.

The TLV for UV uses similar logic and relies on a combined eye and skin hazard weighting curve so only one set of measurements is needed. The combined curve shows maximum potency at 270 nm. Neither the skin nor the eye

hazards curve peaks at 270 nm, but the combined curve does. Instruments have been developed in which the sensor response approximates the combined UV spectral effectiveness curve.

Controls for Nonlaser Sources

It is necessary to discuss optical density before proceeding to controls. Optical density (OD) is the base-10 logarithm of the ratio of the intensity of the radiation leaving the filter divided by the intensity of the radiation entering the filter (the attenuation provided by the filter). If a filter absorbs all but 1 percent, or $1/100$, of the radiation entering it, then the OD is the logarithm of 100, or 2. If a (1-kW) laser beam strikes a filter and only 1 mW is transmitted through the filter, then the filter reduced the beam intensity by a factor of 1,000,000 and its OD is 6.

A variation of optical density, shade number, has been used in ANSI Z49.1 to describe welders' eye protection for several decades. The shade number is 1 plus the product of $7/3$ multiplied by the optical density of the filter.

Baffles and sight barriers are common engineering controls for optical radiation, particularly for welding areas. A number of vendors sell absorbing plastic panels that allow observers to see welders without being exposed to hazards from arcs.

A wide variety of personal protective equipment is now available for nonlaser optical radiation hazards. Some points of interest follow:

- The shade numbers for welding eyewear are summarized in Table 11–J. They are excerpted from ANSI Z49.1-2005. OSHA is still using the ANSI Z.49.1-1988 in its 1994 revisions of 29 CFR Subpart I, personal protective equipment standards.

- Common glass does not offer complete protection against UV-A, although it is very effective against UV-B and UV-C. Tinted eyewear is often effective against UV-A. Eyewear vendors will send transmission curves for their products that can be used to select UV-A protective eyewear for applications that do not involve intense exposures to UV-A.

- The use of photochemically darkened lenses should be avoided because the lenses can darken fairly rapidly in response to sunlight, but become paler slowly. One can enter a building or drive into a tunnel and experience impairment of vision by such glasses, particularly immediately after entry, until the tinting adjusts to the reduced light levels.

- Special lenses are available for nonlaser light and IR sources such as glass blowing and steel making.

- OSHA standard 29 CFR 1910.133 requires eye and face protectors to be distinctly marked to facilitate identification of the manufacturer and to meet ANSI Z87.1 impact criteria. OSHA standard 29 CFR 1910.133 also requires that protective eyewear for users with prescriptions either have the prescription built in or be worn over prescription lenses without disturbing the prescription lenses. Several eyewear vendors now offer clip-on adapters so prescription lenses can be worn behind eyewear that filters optical radiation.

LASER

Laser is an acronym for *light amplification by stimulated emission of radiation*. Its original derivation has been obscured by years of common use. The original lasers followed microwave devices called masers (the *m* stands for microwave) and were called optical masers. Masers and

TABLE 11–J		Guide for Shade Numbers		
Process	*Electrode Size in. (mm)*	*Arc Current (Amperes)*	*Minimum Protective Shade*	*Suggested* Shade No. (Comfort)*
Shielded Metal Arc Welding (SMAW)	Less than 3/32 (2.4)	Less than 60	7	—
	3/32–5/32 (2.4–4.0)	60–160	8	10
	5/32–1/4 (4.0–6.4)	160–250	10	12
	More than 1/4 (6.4)	250–550	11	14
Gas Metal Arc Welding (GMAW) and Flux Cored Arc Welding (FCAW)		Less than 60	7	—
		60–160	10	11
		160–250	10	12
		250–500	10	14
Gas Tungsten Arc Welding (GTAW)		Less than 50	8	10
		50–150	8	12
		150–500	10	14
Air Carbon Arc Cutting (CAC-A)	(Light)	Less than 500	10	12
	(Heavy)	500–1000	11	14
Plasma Arc Welding (PAW)		Less than 20	6	6 to 8
		20–100	8	10
		100–400	10	12
		400–800	11	14
Plasma Arc Cutting (PAC)		Less than 20	4	4
		20–40	5	5
		40–60	6	6
		60–80	8	8
		80–300	8	9
		300–400	9	12
		400–800	10	14
Torch Brazing (TB)		—	—	3 or 4
Torch Soldering (TS)		—	—	2
Carbon Arc Welding (CAW)		—	—	14

	Plate Thickness			*Suggested* Shade No. (Comfort)*
	in.	*mm*		
Oxyfuel Gas Welding (OFW)				
Light	Under 1/8	Under 3		4 or 5
Medium	1/8 to 1/2	3 to 13		5 or 6
Heavy	Over 1/2	Over 13		6 or 8
Oxygen Cutting (OC)				
Light	Under 1	Under 25		3 or 4
Medium	1 to 6	25 to 150		4 or 5
Heavy	Over 6	Over 150		5 or 6

Note: Shade numbers are given as a guide only and may be varied to suit individual needs.
*As a rule of thumb, start with a shade that is too dark to see the weld zone. Then go to a lighter shade which gives sufficient view of the weld zone without going below the minimum. In oxyfuel gas welding, cutting, or brazing where the torch and/or the flux produces a high yellow light, it is desirable to use a filter lens that absorbs the yellow or sodium line of the visible light spectrum.
Source: AWS F2.2, *Lens Shade Selector*

lasers work by pumping the electrons in a suitable material, the lasing medium, with strong energy and directing some of that energy out in the form of a beam of radiation. To do this, most lasers include the parts shown in Figure 11–21: a source of pumping energy such as a flash lamp or electrodes embedded in a gas-filled tube, a lasing medium that emits radiation when pumped, and a resonant cavity that is a multiple of the product radiation's wavelength and is formed by placing a mirror at each end of the lasing material. The pumping energy strikes electrons of atoms in the lasing medium, which quickly lose the pumping energy as radiation. Some of the radiation produced hits electrons in other pumped atoms in the lasing medium and makes them yield their stored energy as more radiation. The radiation reaches one end of the cavity and is reflected off a mirror back into the lasing medium, where it strikes more electrons in other pumped atoms and causes them to yield their energy until it strikes a mirror at the opposite end of the cavity, where the process begins again. The radiation surges back and forth along the cavity, gaining strength until it emerges from one end (with a partially reflective mirror) as a beam with parallel sides.

Laser radiation has unique properties. It is monochromatic, which means that it has only one color of light and is made of one or a few wavelengths of radiation, determined by the lasing material. It is coherent, which means the waves are in phase and have maximum intensity. It is also bright. It can have very high irradiance and be focused to deposit

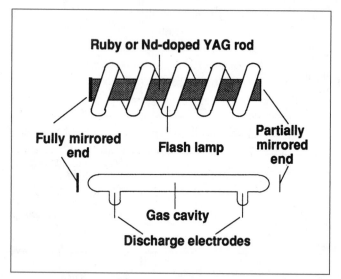

Figure 11–21. Parts of two types of lasers: solid state and gas. The top drawing is a solid-state laser, the bottom, a gas laser. Both lasers fit in protective housings that include cooling equipment for high-power lasers and a beam-blocking device for Class 4 lasers. Power supplies and control panels are usually located elsewhere; the power supply and cooling cables leading to the laser enclosure give a rough indication of the laser's power.

intense energy on small surfaces. Coherent radiation can be very sharply focused, whereas common, noncoherent radiation cannot. The parallel-sided and coherent nature of the product radiation means that the beam does not spread as rapidly as radiation from other sources. Thus, a laser beam keeps its strength over long distances. Visible and IR-A laser beams can be focused to create extremely intense exposures on the retina that deliver up to 300,000 times as much power or energy per unit area on the retina as on the outside of the eye. This is why laser safety standards are much stricter in this band than at other bands and why laser standards are stricter than standards for noncoherent sources in this band.

Lasers can be operated in two major modes, much like other radiation sources: pulsed and continuous wave (CW). Exposure standards and laser outputs for pulsed and relatively brief exposures are expressed in joules per square centimeter (J/cm^2) of illuminated area; exposure standards and outputs for continuous wave lasers are expressed in watts per square centimeter (W/cm^2) of illuminated area.

Lasers can be made from gases, liquids, and solids. The first lasers used ruby rods; the pumping energy came from high-intensity flash lamps. Yttrium aluminum garnets doped with neodymium (Nd:YAG) followed for IR-A lasers. Helium-neon (He-Ne) lasers (essentially, neon lamps filled with helium-neon mixtures surrounded by mirrors to create an appropriate resonant cavity) are very common. Similar lamps filled with krypton, argon, or carbon dioxide gas are also in common use. Carbon dioxide lasers produce 10.6-μm IR beams; the other lasing media just mentioned produce mostly visible wavelengths, as shown in Tables 11–K and 11–L. Organic dyes are sometimes used because the output wavelengths can be precisely adjusted at the discretion of the user, unlike other media, which have fixed product wavelengths. Solid-state diodes made from selectively blended compounds of gallium arsenide can be used to produce radiation in the IR-A band, and diode lasers are now used in consumer settings like supermarket bar code scanners and lecture hall pointers. Diode lasers producing dangerous outputs can be smaller than a fingertip. Excimer lasers use ionized halogen atoms in inert gases to emit UV radiation.

Energy sources are needed to pump the atoms in the lasing medium into an excited state; this can come from fire flash lamps or energize electrodes in a gas cavity, but other forms of pumping energy can be used. The energy released by the combustion of deuterium and fluorine is harnessed in gas dynamic lasers (rocket engine–like devices that exhaust in one direction and produce an IR beam in a perpendicular direction). Dye lasers use light from a flash lamp or from another laser for pumping.

TABLE 11–Ka		Classification Table for Continuous Wave (CW) Small-Source Lasers by Accessible Emission	
Class FDA	**Class IEC**	**Laser Product Hazard**	**Product Examples**
I	1, 1M	Considered non-hazardous. Hazard increases if viewed with optical aids, including magnifiers, binoculars, or telescopes.	• laser printers • CD players • DVD players
IIa, II	2, 2M	Hazard increases when viewed directly for long periods of time. Hazard increases if viewed with optical aids.	• bar code scanners
IIIa	3R	Depending on power and beam area, can be momentarily hazardous when directly viewed or when staring directly at the beam with an unaided eye. Risk of injury increases when viewed with optical aids.	• laser pointers
IIIb	3B	Immediate skin hazard from direct beam and immediate eye hazard when viewed directly.	• laser light show projectors • industrial lasers • research lasers
IV	4	Immediate skin hazard and eye hazard from exposure to either the direct or reflected beam; may also present a fire hazard.	• laser light show projectors • industrial lasers • research lasers • lasers used to perform LASIK eye surgery

Source: CRDH and ANSI Z136.1 – 2007

Biological Damage Mechanisms of Lasers

Laser beams produce biological damage by the two mechanisms mentioned earlier (thermal burns and photochemical injuries), and visible and IR-A lasers produce retinal damage by a third mechanism unique to lasers. The highly focused beam generates a steam bubble near the retina that pops, sending shock waves into the retinal tissue that produce thermoacoustic tissue damage. Briefer pulses are more hazardous than longer pulses of equal energy content because the heat does not dissipate as much during a shorter pulse. Q-switching is a method of reducing the pulse duration of a laser and releasing all the energy in a short burst. Q-switched lasers can produce a light pulse less than 10 ns, whereas the original unswitched beams may last milliseconds. Thus, joule for joule, Q-switched pulses are more hazardous than non-Q-switched pulses. Mode-locked lasers can produce even shorter duration pulses, in some cases lasting only a few pico- or femto-seconds. These short pulses can reach very high peak power levels of 100 MW or more. The bursting bubble produced in the eye when exposed to such pulses can damage blood vessels and blood is toxic to nerve tissue, so the degree of lasting impairment caused by thermoacoustic injury is a matter of luck determined by what part of the retina was struck and whether blood reached nerve tissue.

It is important to note that both coherent visible light and IR-A radiation with wavelengths of 400 to 1,400 nm can be focused into an ultra-small (diffraction-limited) spot at the back of the retina. The brightness of the radiation striking the retina can be as much as 300,000 times stronger than that entering the eye. Thus, visible and IR-A lasers are particularly hazardous to the eye. This explains why laser exposure standards are so strict.

Standards

The dominant standard for laser safety in the United States is the Laser Institute of America's LIA/ANSI Z136.1 (2007) standard, *American National Standard for Safe Use of Lasers*, last revised in 2007. A companion secondary standard, ANSI Z136.4 (2010), *Recommended Practice for Laser Safety Measurements for Hazard Evaluation*, was issued in 2010 that provides guidance for measurements associated with laser safety requirements. This revision of the Z134.1 (2005) standard harmonizes laser measurements with the most recent ANSI Z136.1 (2007) safety standard series. Regulations for commercial laser products in the United States are promulgated by the Center for Devices and Radiological Health (CDRH) of the Food and Drug Administration, 21 CFR Part 1040. These FDA regulations are important for commercial laser devices and place requirements on the labeling, use, and classification of laser devices in the United States.

The ANSI standard addresses facility and program elements as well as laser safety features. The 21 CFR 1040 standard addresses product safety features. Both standards were early uses of the hazard control class type of regulation. Control class regulations require assigning a classification that reflects the severity of the hazard. For lasers, the

TABLE–Kb	Classification Table for Continuous Wave (CW) Small-Source Lasers by Accessible Emission (cont.)					
Wavelength (μm)	**Laser type**	**Wavelength (μm)**	**Class 1* (W)**	**Class 2* (W)**	**Class 3** (W)**	**Class 4* (W)**
Ultraviolet 0.180 to 0.280	Nd:YAG (Quadrupled)	0.266	$\leq 9.6 \times 10^{-9}$ for 8 hours	None	>Class 1 but ≤ 0.5	>0.5
	Argon	0.275				
Ultraviolet 0.315 to 0.400	He-Cd	0.325	$\leq 3.2 \times 10^{-6}$	None	>Class 1 but ≤ 0.5	>0.5
	Argon	0.351, 0.363				
	Krypton	0.3507, 0.3564				
Visible 0.400 to 0.700	He-Cd	0.4416 only	$\leq 4 \times 10^{-5}$	> Class 1 but $\leq 1 \times 10^{-3}$	> Class 2 but ≤ 0.5	>0.5
	Argon (visible)	0.457	$\leq 5 \times 10^{-5}$			
		0.476	$\leq 1 \times 10^{-4}$			
		0.488	$\leq 2 \times 10^{-4}$			
		0.514	$\leq 4 \times 10^{-4}$			
	Krypton	0.530				
	Nd:YAG (doubled)	0.532				
	He-Ne	0.543				
	Dye	0.400 – 0.500	$\leq 0.4 C_B \times 10^{-4}$			
	He-Se	0.460 – 0.500				
	Dye	0.550 – 0.700	$\leq 4 \times 10^{-4}$			
	He-Ne	0.632				
	InGaAlP	0.670				
	Ti:Sapphire					
	Krypton	0.6471, 0.6764				
Near Infrared 0.700 to 1.400	GaAlAs	0.780	$\leq 5.6 \times 10^{-4}$	None	> Class 1 but ≤ 0.5	>0.5
	GaAlAs	0.850	$\leq 7.7 \times 10^{-4}$			
	GaAs	0.905	$\leq 9.9 \times 10^{-4}$			
	Nd:YAG	1.064	$\leq 1.9 \times 10^{-3}$			
	He-Ne	1.080	$\leq 1.9 \times 10^{-3}$			
		1.152	$\leq 2.1 \times 10^{-3}$			
	InGaAsP	1.310	$\leq 1.5 \times 10^{-2}$			
Far Infrared 1.400 to 1000	InGaAsP	1.550	$\leq 9.6 \times 10^{-3}$	None	> Class 1 but ≤ 0.5	>0.5
	Holmium	2.100				
	Erbium	2.940				
	Hydrogen Fluoride	2.600 – 3.00				
	He-Ne	3.390 only				
	Carbon Monoxide	5.000 – 5.500				
	Carbon Dioxide	10.6				
	Water Vapor	118	$\leq 9.5 \times 10^{-2}$			
	Hydrogen Cyanide	337				

* Assumes no mechanical or electrical design incorporated into laser system to prevent exposures from lasting to T_{max} = 8 hours (one workday); otherwise the Class AEL could be larger than tabulated.

** Class 3a lasers and laser systems include lasers and laser systems which have an accessible output between 1 and 5 times the Class 1 AEL for wavelengths shorter than 0.4um or longer than 0.7 um, or less than 5 times the Class 2 AEL for wavelengths between 0.4 and 0.7 um.

TABLE 11–L	Classification Table for Single-Pulse, Small-Source Lasers by Accessible Emission					
Wavelength (µm)	**Laser type**	**Wavelength (µm)**	**Pulse Duration (s)**	**Class 1 (J)**	**Class 3b (J)**	**Class 4 (J)**
Ultraviolet 0.180 to 0.400	Excimer (ArF)	0.193	20×10^{-9}	$\leq 2.4 \times 10^{-5}$	> Class 1 but ≤ 0.125	> 0.125
	Excimer (KrF)	0.248	20×10^{-9}	$\leq 2.4 \times 10^{-5}$		
	Nd:YAG Q-switched (quadrupled)	0.266	20×10^{-9}	$\leq 2.4 \times 10^{-5}$		
	Excimer (XeCl)	0.308	20×10^{-9}	$\leq 5.3 \times 10^{-5}$		
	Nitrogen	0.337	20×10^{-9}	$\leq 5.3 \times 10^{-5}$		
	Excimer (XeF)	0.351	20×10^{-9}	$\leq 5.3 \times 10^{-5}$		
Visible 0.400 to 0.700	Rhodamine 6G (Dye laser)	0.450 – 0.650	1×10^{-6}	$\leq 1.9 \times 10^{-7}$	> Class 1 but ≤ 0.03	> 0.03
	Copper vapor	0.510, 0.578	2.5×10^{-9}			
	Nd:YAG (doubled) (Q-switched)	0.532	20×10^{-9}			
	Ruby (Q-switched)	0.6943	20×10^{-9}			
	Ruby (Long pulse)	0.6943	1×10^{-3}	$\leq 3.9 \times 10^{-6}$		
Near Infrared 0.700 to 1.400	Ti:Sapphire	0.700 – 1.000	6×10^{-6}	$\leq 1.9 \times 10^{-7}$		
	Alexandrite	0.720 – 0.800	1×10^{-4}	$\leq 7.6 \times 10^{-7}$	> Class 1 but ≤ 0.033	> 0.033**
	Nd:YAG (Q-switched)	1.064	20×10^{-9}	$\leq 1.9 \times 10^{-6}$	> Class 1 but ≤ 0.125	>0.125
Far Infrared 1.400 to 1000	Erbium:Glass	1.54	10×10^{-9}	$\leq 7.9 \times 10^{-3}$	> Class 1 but ≤ 0.125	> 0.125
	Co:Mg-Fl	1.8 – 2.5	80×10^{-6}	$\leq 7.9 \times 10^{-4}$		
	Holmium	2.1	250×10^{-6}	$\leq 7.9 \times 10^{-4}$		
	Hydrogen Fluoride	2.600 – 3.000	0.4×10^{-6}	$\leq 1.1 \times 10^{-4}$		
	Erbium:Glass	2.94	250×10^{-6}	$\leq 5.6 \times 10^{-4}$		
	Carbon Dioxide	10.6	100×10^{-9}	$\leq 7.9 \times 10^{-5}$		
	Carbon Dioxide	10.6	1×10^{-3}	$\leq 7.9 \times 10^{-4}$		

* Assuming that both eye and skin may be exposed, i.e., 1.0 mm beam (area of limiting aperture = 7.9×10^{-3} cm²)
** Class 3b AEL varies from 0.033 to 0.480 J corresponding to wavelengths that carry between 0.720 and 0.800 um.
Source: ANSI Z136.1 – 2000

principal parameters that describe the anticipated hazard severity are wavelength and output power or energy.

Other measures of anticipated severity are pulse duration and the size of extended sources such as groups of diode lasers or the reflection of a spread laser beam from a surface. The LIA/ANSI and CDRH standards have slightly different classifications, but both specify precautions based on the anticipated hazard of the accessible beam by setting accessible emission limits (AELs) for the amount of laser energy people could encounter from each class of laser. Precautions can be relaxed when the beam is thoroughly enclosed or reduced in power before it can enter a place where people could be exposed to it; this gives laser equipment suppliers a strong incentive to apply effective engineering controls. Precautions become more stringent in a series of defined steps (classes) as the output of the laser increases from Class 1 (so low powered as to be intrinsically safe) through Class 4 (very dangerous). The related classifications for lasers for the ANSI and CDRH are given in Table 11–K. CRDH designations will be used here because they are of regulatory importance. Extremely weak beams are deemed nonhazardous (Class 1) and no precautions are needed. Low-power visible beams that could be hazardous if viewed for prolonged periods (Class 2 and 2a) warrant limited precautions. Class 2a visible lasers are those that could cause excessive exposures if the beam was viewed at 1,000 s or more; Class 2 lasers are visible light lasers that could produce excessive exposures if viewed for more than the 0.25-s response time of the aversion reflexes. Class 3 moderate power lasers warrant more precautions and include moderately high-powered visible lasers and moderately powered invisible UV and IR lasers. Class 3 lasers are subdivided into Class 3a and 3b; Class 3a includes lasers that could be hazardous only if stared at or viewed through an optical device such as a telescope. All other Class 3 lasers are Class 3b and are presumed to have beams powerful enough to harm the eye during incidental exposure without an optical instrument. Class 4 high-power lasers warrant rigorous precautions because the beam can harm the skin and eyes and even diffuse reflections could be harmful. Table 11–L gives some examples of pulsed lasers that commonly are used in industrial applications. The precautions specified by CRDH for each class are summarized in Table 11–M.

TABLE 11–M   Summary of Principal Laser Hazard Control Measures

Engineering Control	CLASS I/IM	CLASS 2/2M	CLASS 3R	CLASS 3B	CLASS 4
Protective Housing	REQUIRED	REQUIRED	REQUIRED	REQUIRED	REQUIRED
Interlocks; Removable Protective Housing	Required if enclosed 3B/4	Required if enclosed 3B/4	Required if enclosed 3B/4	REQUIRED	REQUIRED
Service Access Panel	Required if enclosed 3B/4	Required if enclosed 3B/4	Required if enclosed 3B/4	REQUIRED	REQUIRED
Key Control				Recommended	REQUIRED
Fully Open Beam Path				REQUIRED	REQUIRED
Limited Open Beam Path				REQUIRED	REQUIRED
Remote Interlock Connector				Recommended	REQUIRED
Beam Stop or Attenuator				Recommended	REQUIRED
Activation Warning Systems				Recommended	REQUIRED
Indoor Laser Controlled Area	Recommended M	Recommended M		REQUIRED	REQUIRED
Temporary Laser Controlled Area	Required if enclosed 3B/4	Required if enclosed 3B/4	Required if enclosed 3B/4		
Controlled Operation					Recommended
Equipment Labels	REQUIRED	REQUIRED	REQUIRED	REQUIRED	REQUIRED
Area Warning Sign and Activation Warning			Recommended	REQUIRED	REQUIRED

Administrative Control	CLASS I/IM	CLASS 2/2M	CLASS 3R	CLASS 3B	CLASS 4
Standard Operating Procedures				Recommended	REQUIRED
Education and Training		Recommended	Recommended	REQUIRED	REQUIRED
Authorized Personnel				REQUIRED	REQUIRED
Alignment Procedures	Required if enclosed 3B/4	Required if enclosed 3B/4	Required if enclosed 3B/4	REQUIRED	REQUIRED
Protective Equipment				Recommended	REQUIRED
Spectator Control				Recommended	REQUIRED
Specified Service Personnel	Required if enclosed 3B/4	Required if enclosed 3B/4	Required if enclosed 3B/4	REQUIRED	REQUIRED
Protective Eyewear				REQUIRED	REQUIRED
Window Protection				REQUIRED	REQUIRED
Protective Barriers and Curtains				Recommended	Recommended
Skin Protection				REQUIRED for UV excimers	REQUIRED for UV excimers
Warning Signs and Labels		Recommended	Recommended	REQUIRED	REQUIRED
Eye Examination				Recommended	Recommended

Source: ANSI Z136.1 – 2007

The use of hazard control classes reduces the need for measurements to determine personnel exposures and puts reliance on being able to estimate exposures by calculations.

The CRDH also sets maximum permissible exposures (MPEs) for lasers, as listed in Tables 11–N, 11–O, and 11–P. The MPEs are directly equivalent to OSHA PELs for chemicals or the MPEs for radiofrequency/microwave radiation set by ANSI/IEEE C95.1. Adjustment factors are applied to calculate MPEs for extended sources, based on the size of the angle subtended by that source in radian units. The AELs used to define laser classes are equal to the MPEs for the maximum allowable viewing time listed in the standard for visible and IR-A lasers, multiplied by the limiting aperture (typically, the size of the pupil opening, which can range from 1 to 7 mm, as defined in the standard [see Table 11–P]). The MPEs for wavelengths above 1,400 nm are the only available guidance for nonlaser IR sources emitted at frequencies above 1,400 nm. Limiting aperture dimensions depend on wavelength and the expected duration of an exposure.

LIA/ANSI Z136.1-2007 uses different averaging times depending on the wavelength of the radiation involved. The averaging time for UV exposures is the duration of the exposure throughout a shift, similar to the averaging time for chemicals. The standard is actually based on accumulating a dose of UV energy rather than measuring or calculating the average exposure. The averaging time for visible exposures is 0.25 s based on a blink avoidance response; the averaging time for IR exposure is 10 s based on thermal damage.

This standard also gives protocols for evaluating repetitively pulsed exposures that are used when the pulse repetition rate exceeds one pulse per second. Pulses that occur less frequently than once per second are addressed by the standards shown in Table 11–Q. Computer applications are available to do routine laser safety calculations, but the user should know how to do the calculations on paper before beginning to routinely use the application and should verify that the application works for the pulsing and wavelength scenarios of interest by comparing computer results to the results of paper calculations.

Pulsed laser exposure criteria are more complicated and harder to apply. LIA/ANSI Z136.1-2007 specifies that the exposure interval for visible lasers is 0.25 seconds (it defines visible as ranging between 400 and 700 nm, rather than 760 nm), whereas the exposure interval for IR lasers is 10 seconds. These exposure durations are applied concurrently in two procedures for determining MPEs and AELs for pulsed lasers. Table 11–L shows a classification table for single-pulse lasers and describes some typical laser sources and associated limiting accessible emission levels. People working with pulsed lasers need to understand this part of the standard completely, but a full discussion is beyond the scope of this chapter.

Controls

Engineering and administrative controls and personal protective equipment are used for lasers and optical radiation. The main engineering control for lasers is enclosure, often in the form of interlocked rooms and protective housings. Interlocked laser beam enclosures can range from plastic panels on a framework for research setups to sturdy metal boxes with person- or vehicle-sized access doors for IR laser cutting tools. Laser beams can be routed over or below walkways using mirrors and, possibly, elevated enclosures or tunnels. LIA/ANSI Z136.1 calls for fail-safe interlocks (such as double interlocks connected in series) on access panels of enclosures of Class 3b or 4 laser beams. The interlocks either shut off the electrical power to the laser or drop a shutter into the beam at or within the housing of the laser itself. An important extension of interlocks is the remote interlock connection, which allows additional interlocks, including those located remotely, to trigger a shutdown of electric power to a laser or drop a shutter or filter into the beam. Remote interlocks can make up safety chains for laser systems covering large areas and include emergency panic button shutoffs.

Viewing portals, viewing screens, and optical instruments must be connected to interlocks or reduce beam intensity to acceptable levels for Class 4 lasers. LIA/ANSI Z136.1 recognizes the use of fasteners requiring special tools as providing equivalent safety to interlocks for access panels. It is convenient to add room status lights (green for safe to enter, yellow for possibly unsafe to enter, and red for unsafe to enter) to the laser interlock system and to install a loudspeaker and buzzer near the room status lights so visitors can talk to the room occupants during laser operations. These boxes were developed and are used extensively at Lawrence Livermore National Laboratory; they are also commercially available.

A simple control, especially useful for lasers located in places where unauthorized people could find them, is a key-in-lock control, which makes it very unlikely that the laser could be inadvertently operated by unauthorized people. Of course, the operator must remove the key and take it when the laser is turned off.

Engineering controls are effective when a laser system is set up, but not while it is being set up or during maintenance. Thus, special caution, including heavy reliance on administrative controls and special warning signs, is needed during setup and maintenance. A recent review of laser accidents shows that 37.2 percent of laser accidents occurred during alignment. Techniques for reducing hazards during

TABLE 11–N — Maximum Permissible Exposures for Ocular Exposure (Intrabeam Viewing)

Wavelength (μm)	Exposure Duration, t (s)	MPE (J cm⁻²)	MPE (W cm⁻²)
Ultraviolet			
0.180 to 0.302	10^{-9} to 3×10^4	3×10^{-3}	
0.303	10^{-9} to 3×10^4	4×10^{-3}	
0.304	10^{-9} to 3×10^4	6×10^{-3}	
0.305	10^{-9} to 3×10^4	1.0×10^{-2}	
0.306	10^{-9} to 3×10^4	1.6×10^{-2}	
0.307	10^{-9} to 3×10^4	2.5×10^{-2}	
0.308	10^{-9} to 3×10^4	4.0×10^{-2}	
0.309	10^{-9} to 3×10^4	6.3×10^{-2}	
0.310	10^{-9} to 3×10^4	0.1	
0.311	10^{-9} to 3×10^4	0.16	
0.312	10^{-9} to 3×10^4	0.25	
0.313	10^{-9} to 3×10^4	0.4	
0.314	10^{-9} to 3×10^4	0.63	
0.315 to 0.400	10^{-9} to 10	$0.56\, t^{0.25}$	
0.315 to 0.400	10 to 3×10^4	1	

Note: To calculate MPE, use the J/cm² value shown or $0.56\, t^{0.25}$, whichever is lower

Wavelength (μm)	Exposure Duration, t (s)	MPE (J cm⁻²)	MPE (W cm⁻²)
Visible and Near Infrared			
0.400 to 0.700	10^{-9} to 18×10^{-6}	0.5×10^{-6}	
0.400 to 0.700	18×10^{-6} to 10	$1.8\, t^{0.75} \times 10^{-3}$	
0.400 to 0.450	10 to 100	1.0×10^{-2}	
0.450 to 0.500	10 to T1		1×10^{-3}
0.450 to 0.500	T1 to 100	$C_B \times 10^{-2}$	
0.400 to 0.500	100 to 3×10^4		$C_B \times 10^{-4}$
0.500 to 0.700	10 to 3×10^4		1×10^{-3}
0.700 to 1.050	10^{-9} to 18×10^{-6}	$5.0\, C_A \times 10^{-7}$	
0.700 to 1.050	18×10^{-6} to 10	$1.8\, C_A\, t^{0.75} \times 10^{-3}$	
0.700 to 1.050	10 to 3×10^4		$C_A \times 10^{-3}$
1.050 to 1.400	10^{-9} to 50×10^{-6}	$5.0\, C_C \times 10^{-6}$	
1.050 to 1.400	50×10^{-6} to 10	$9.0\, C_C\, t^{0.75} \times 10^{-3}$	
1.050 to 1.400	10 to 3×10^4		$5\, C_C \times 10^{-3}$

Wavelength (μm)	Exposure Duration, t (s)	MPE (J cm⁻²)	MPE (W cm⁻²)
Far Infrared			
1.400 to 1.500	10^{-9} to 10^{-3}	10^{-1}	
1.400 to 1.500	10^{-3} to 10	$0.56\, t^{0.25}$	
1.400 to 1.500	10 to 3×10^4		0.1
1.500 to 1.800	10^{-9} to 10	1.0	
1.500 to 1.800	10 to 3×10^4		0.1
1.800 to 2.600	10^{-9} to 10^{-3}	0.1	
1.800 to 2.600	10^{-3} to 10	$0.56\, t^{0.25}$	
1.800 to 2.600	10 to 3×10^4		0.1
2.600 to 10^3	10^{-9} to 10^{-7}	1×10^{-2}	
2.600 to 10^3	10^{-7} to 10	$0.56\, t^{0.25}$	
2.600 to 10^3	10 to 3×10^4		0.1

1. For multiple pulses, apply correction factor C_P given in Table 11–P.
2. For information on correction factors T_1, C_B, CA, CP and CE, see Table 11–P.
3. The MPE for diffuse reflections at wavelengths between 0.400 and 1.400μm is obtained by multiplying the corresponding MPEs above by CE (see Table 11–P for correction factors and T_1).
4. The MPE for diffuse reflections at wavelengths between 0.400 and 1.400μm is obtained by multiplying the corresponding MPEs above by CE (see Table 11–P for correction factors and T_1).
5. For repeated (pulsed) exposures see ANSI Z136.1-2000, section 8.2.3

Source: ANSI Z136.1-2000

TABLE 11–0 Maximum Permissible Exposures for Laser Radiation Skin Exposures

Ultraviolet

Wavelength (μm)	Exposure Duration, t (s)	MPE (J cm⁻²)	MPE (W cm⁻²)
		$(J\ cm^{-2})$	$(W\ cm^{-2})$
0.180 to 0.302	10^{-9} to 3×10^4	3×10^{-3}	
0.303	10^{-9} to 3×10^4	4×10^{-3}	
0.304	10^{-9} to 3×10^4	6×10^{-3}	
0.305	10^{-9} to 3×10^4	1.0×10^{-2}	
0.306	10^{-9} to 3×10^4	1.6×10^{-2}	
0.307	10^{-9} to 3×10^4	2.5×10^{-2}	
0.308	10^{-9} to 3×10^4	4.0×10^{-2}	
0.309	10^{-9} to 3×10^4	6.3×10^{-2}	
0.310	10^{-9} to 3×10^4	1.0×10^{-1}	
0.311	10^{-9} to 3×10^4	1.6×10^{-1}	
0.312	10^{-9} to 3×10^4	2.5×10^{-1}	
0.313	10^{-9} to 3×10^4	4.0×10^{-1}	
0.314	10^{-9} to 3×10^4	6.3×10^{-1}	
0.315 to 0.400	10^{-9} to 10	$0.56\ t^{0.25}$	
0.315 to 0.400	10×10^3	1	
0.315 to 0.400	10^3 to 3×10^4		1×10^{-3}

Note: To calculate MPE, use the J/cm² value shown or $0.56\ t^{0.25}$, whichever is lower

Visible and Near Infrared

Wavelength (μm)	Exposure Duration, t (s)	MPE (J cm⁻²)	MPE (W cm⁻²)
		$(J\ cm^{-2})$	$(W\ cm^{-2})$
	10^{-9} to 10^{-7}	$2\ CA \times 10^{-2}$	
0.400 to 1.400	10^{-7} to 10	$1.1 CA\ t^{0.25}$	
	10 to 3×10^4		0.2 CA

Far Infrared

Wavelength (μm)	Exposure Duration, t (s)	MPE (J cm⁻²)	MPE (W cm⁻²)
		$(J\ cm^{-2})$	$(W\ cm^{-2})$
1.400 to 1.500	10^{-9} to 10^{-3}	10^{-1}	
1.400 to 1.500	10^{-3} to 10	$0.56\ t^{0.25}$	
1.400 to 1.500	10 to 3×10^4		0.1
1.500 to 1.800	10^{-9} to 10	1.0	
1.500 to 1.800	10 to 3×10^4		0.1
1.800 to 2.600	10^{-9} to 10^{-3}	0.1	
1.800 to 2.600	10^{-3} to 10	$0.56\ t^{0.25}$	
1.800 to 2.600	10 to 3×10^4		0.1
2.600 to 10^3	10^{-9} to 10^{-7}	1×10^{-2}	
2.600 to 10^3	10^{-7} to 10	$0.56\ t^{0.25}$	
2.600 to 10^3	10 to 3×10^4		0.1

1. For multiple pulses, apply correction factor CP given in Table 11–P.
2. For information on correction factors T1, CB, CA, CP and CE, see Table 11–P.
Note: The MPE for diffuse reflections at wavelengths between 0.400 and 1.400μm is obtained by multiplying the corresponding MPEs above by CE (see Table 11–P for correction factors and T1). For repeated (pulsed) exposures see ANSI Z136.1-2000, section 8.2.3.
Source: ANSI Z136.1-2000

TABLE 11–P	Correction Factors for Intrabeam Viewing MPEs of Tables 11–N and 11–O	
Parameters/Correction Factors		**Wavelength (μm)**
$T1 = 10 \times 10^{20(\lambda-0.450)}$ *		0.450 to 0.500
$T2 = 10 \times 10^{(\alpha-1.5)/98.5}$ **		0.400 to 1.400
$CB = 1.0$		0.400 to 0.450
$CB = 10^{20(\lambda-0.450)}$		0.450 to 0.600
$CA = 1.0$		0.400 to 0.700
$CA = 10^{2(\lambda-0.700)}$		0.700 to 1.050
$CA = 5.0$		1.050 to 1.400
$CP = n^{-0.25}$ ***		0.180 to 1000
$CE = 1.0$	$\alpha < \alpha min$	0.400 to 1.400
$CE = \alpha/\alpha min$	$\alpha min \le \alpha \le \alpha max$	0.400 to 1.400
$CE = \alpha^2/(\alpha max \alpha min)$	$\alpha > \alpha max$	0.400 to 1.400
$CC = 1.0$		1.050 to 1.150
$CC = 10^{18(\lambda-1.150)}$		1.150 to 1.200
$CC = 8$		1.200 to 1.400

* T1 = 10 s for λ = 0.450 μm, and T1 = 100 s for λ = 0.500 μm.
** T2 = 10 s for α < 1.5 mrad, and T2 = 100 s for α > 100 mrad.
*** See ANSI Z136.1-2000 Section 8.2.3 for discussion of CP and Section 8.2.3.2 for discussion of pulse repetition frequencies below 55 kHz (0.4 to 1.05 μm) and below 20 kHz (1.05 to 1.4 μm)
Note: For wavelengths between 0.400 and 1.400 μm: αmin = 1.5 mrad and αmax = 100 mrad. Wavelengths must be expressed in micrometers and angles in milliradians for calculations. The wavelength region λ1 to λ2 means λ1 < λ < λ2, e.g., 0.550 to 0.700 μm means 0.550 < λ < 0.700 μm.

alignment include using low-powered alignment lasers. The alignment laser beam is brought into the path of the main laser beam, and system adjustments are made using the less dangerous alignment beam; the accessible main laser beam power can also be reduced for setup or alignment, if practical. Alternatively, special laser alignment eyewear that blocks most of the light can be used during alignment after steps have been taken to ensure that the main beam cannot enter the eyes. ANSI Z136.1 specifies special warning signs to be used during setup. A variety of aids are available to make alignment easier even with protective eyewear:

- An IR disc that is mounted in an optical-component holder.
- IR or UV cards that glow with visible light when struck by an IR or UV laser beam.
- IR cameras or viewers that make the beam visible on a remote display screen.
- Strong white paper or colored paper that fluoresces in different wavelengths (colors) when struck by a visible laser beam. The fluorescent radiation can pass through the lenses of laser safety eyewear intended for the laser wavelength. Some experimentation is needed to find which papers work.

Specular (mirror-like) reflections are more hazardous than diffuse reflections because virtually all of the beam's power is retained, as shown in Figure 11–22, and safety precautions always include eliminating all unnecessary specular reflectors. Most optical instrument manufacturers mount their products on shiny posts, but the posts are cylindrical, so a reflected beam will still be spread out. LIA/ANSI Z136.1 includes formulas for calculating reflections from rounded mirrors. Painted walls and stipple-finished tools can easily be specular reflectors for CO_2 laser beams because the surface roughness that causes the diffuse reflections we see is smaller than 10.6 μm, so the surface acts as if it is slick and causes specular reflections at 10.6 μm.

Administrative controls are used during setup and maintenance. Z136.1 calls for calculating the nominal hazard zone (NHZ), where people could be exposed to laser beam levels above the MPEs, and excluding people from the NHZ by barriers, signs, flashing beacons, and the diligence of personnel authorized to be inside the NHZ. Warning signs should follow international conventions, applied in the United States through the ANSI Z535 series of standards; these specify colors, warning words, standard symbols, and warning sign layout. The laser warning symbol is the familiar sunburst. The word CAUTION is used on signs and labels for Class 2, 2M, and 3R (2, 2a, and 3a) lasers and laser systems that do not exceed the appropriate MPE. The word DANGER must

TABLE 11–Q	Limiting Apertures Used to Develop Accessible Emission Limits (AELs)		
		Eye Aperture	**Skin Aperture**
Spectral Region (μm)	**Duration (s)**	**Diameter (mm) Area (cm²)***	**Diameter (mm) Area (cm²)***
>0.180 to <0.400	10^{-9} to 0.25	1 0 (.0078)	3.5 (0.0962)
	0.25 to 3 310⁴	3.5 (0.0962)	3.5 (0.0962)
>0.400 to <1.400	10^{-4} to 3 3 10⁴	7 0 (.3848)	3.5 (0.0962)
>1.400 to <100	10^{-5} to 0.25	1 0 (.0078)	3.5 (0.0962)
	0.25 to 3 × 10⁴	3.5 (0.0962)	3.5 (0.0962)
>100 to <1 mm	10^{-9} to 3 × 10⁴	11.0 (0.9503)	11.0 (0.9503)

* Area in cm² is used to calculate AELs.
Source: Adapted from ACGIH TLV-2011; derived from ANSI Z136.1-2007

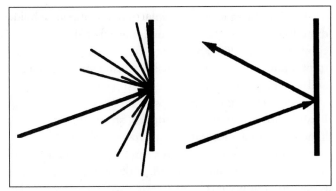

Figure 11–22. Diffuse reflections *(left)* dissipate the energy of incident radiation, so the reflection is not as bright as the incident radiation because it is scattered in many directions. Specular reflections *(right)* are much more dangerous because the beam bounces in only one direction, retaining most of its original intensity and hazard.

Medical surveillance and training programs are required by CRDH for users of Class 3b and 4 lasers. The laser safety program must include the following:

- a laser safety officer and, if the number and diversity of laser operations warrants, a laser safety committee
- education of authorized personnel
- application of the controls specified in the standard
- accident reporting and investigation and action plans to prevent recurrence of incidents
- medical surveillance as specified in the standard

Laser protective goggles must show the manufacturer, wavelengths they work against, and optical density and must meet the provisions of the latest edition of ANSI Z87.1 for safety eyewear. As with all personal protective equipment, it is necessary to select laser eyewear of appropriate optical density for the type (wavelengths) of radiation encountered and the severity of exposure. Color-coding is recommended for multilaser environments, and eyewear manufacturers offer color-coded frames. Laser-protective eyewear usually includes glass or plastic lenses. In general, glass lenses are heavier, but offer more resistance to direct strikes by laser beams and often let through more light. As a rule, glass is often used when the average power of a laser exceeds about 100 mW.

be used for other Class 3B and 4 lasers. Existing laser-safety signs and labels are grandfathered in by Z136.1. The signs must specify essential precautions above the tail of the sunburst (shown in Figure 11–23) and describe the properties of the laser and the laser class below the center of the tail and the lower-right-hand corner of the sign, respectively.

Class 2	*Class 2M*	*Class 3R*	*Class 3B*	*Class 4*
Class 2 lasers are safe because the aversion response limits exposure to no more than 0.25 seconds. Class-2 lasers are limited only to visible-light (400-700 nm) at 1 mW continuous wave. Higher limits may apply if the emission time is less than 0.25s or if the light is not spatially coherent. Intentional suppression of the aversion response could lead to eye injury. Many laser pointers are class 2.	Class 2M lasers are safe because of the aversion response if not viewed through optical instruments. As with class 1M, this applies to laser beams with a large diameter or large divergence, for which the amount of light passing through the pupil cannot exceed the limits for class 2.	Class 3R lasers are safe if handled appropriately, with restricted beam viewing. The MPE of a 3R laser can be exceeded, but with a low risk of injury. Visible continuous lasers in Class 3R are limited to 5 mW. Other limits apply at other wavelengths or for pulsed lasers.	Class 3B lasers are hazardous for direct eye exposure; diffuse reflections are not likely to cause harm. CW lasers from 315 nm to infrared are limited to 0.5W; pulsed lasers from 400 and 700 nm, are limited to 30 mJ. Protective eyewear and a key safety interlock typically are required if direct viewing may occur.	Class 4 lasers are all lasers with beam power greater than class 3B. Class-4 lasers will cause permanent eye damage from direct or diffuse beam vierwing; they can burn the skin, and ignite combustible materials. A key safety interlock and protective eyewear are required.
⚠️**CAUTION** LASER RADIATION DO NOT STARE INTO BEAM — Class 2 LASER	⚠️**CAUTION** LASER RADIATION DO NOT STARE INTO BEAM OR VIEW DIRECTLY WITH OPTICAL INSTRUMENTS — Class 2M LASER	⚠️**DANGER** LASER RADIATION DO NOT STARE INTO BEAM OR VIEWED DIRECTLY WITH OPTICAL INSTRUMENTS — CLASS 3R LASER	⚠️**DANGER** LASER RADIATION AVOID DIRECT EXPOSURE TO BEAM — CLASS 3B LASER	**DANGER** LASER RADIATION - AVOID EYE OR SKIN EXPOSURE TO DIRECT OR SCATTERED RADIATION (LASER TYPE, WAVELENGTH, PULSE DURATION, MAXIMUM OUTPUT) CLASS 4 LASER PRODUCT

Figure 11–23. The internationally recognized sunburst laser warning icon. ANSI Z535 standards eliminate the tradition of using special colors for specific warnings, but ANSI Z136.1 makes limited use of a red symbol for DANGER signs. Symbols and narrative text now appear in black and colors are used to indicate degree of hazard (yellow and black for CAUTION; orange and black for WARNING; and red, black, and white for DANGER). The long tail symbolizes how laser beams retain their power over long distances. The same symbol, but without the tail, was proposed for intense nonlaser sources of optical radiation, but it is not widely used.

Laser Pointers

Laser pointers are now available at retail office supply stores. The first laser pointers were helium-neon (He-Ne) lasers emitting at 632 nm (red). But they were delicate because of the glass envelope of the He-Ne laser. Diode lasers rapidly replaced He-Ne lasers because they are more rugged and allow for compact, pen-sized pointers. Unfortunately, the early diodes emitted at 670 nm, where the visual response of the eye is much poorer than it is at 632 nm. This difficulty was overcome by raising the laser output from somewhere below 1 mW to a few mW. Although the visual response of the eye is exquisitely wavelength sensitive, the vulnerability of the eye to thermal injury is not. The old He-Ne pointers were Class 2 lasers; the original diode pointers were Class 3a. The original He-Ne pointers bore a caution label; the diode laser pointers bear danger labels. Stories of cavalier use of laser pointers at lectures are common, and these lasers are accessible to children. Fortunately, diode pointers emitting at 635 nm are now on the market, and even shorter wavelength pointers can be expected as solid-state laser technology advances. The new Class 2 laser diode pointers are both more brilliant and safer.

Safety officers should

- warn employees about the hazard of misusing diode laser pointers—they could cause injury if someone stares into the beam for a prolonged period; and
- replace Class 3a 670-nm pointers with Class 2 635-nm pointers.

Safety officers working for retailers should advise management to market only Class 2 laser pointers. The possibility that a child could misuse a Class 3a pointer cannot be overlooked.

Nonbeam Hazards of Lasers

The two greatest hazards of lasers, other than laser weapons, are electricity and fire. Electrocution from high-voltage power supplies and capacitor banks is a real hazard and can kill, while most laser beam exposures cause some loss of vision at worst. The National Fire Protection Association (NFPA) standard for laser fire protection advises that a continuous wave laser radiation creating an irradiance above beam irradiances <2 W/cm^2 is an ignition hazard. The beam could ignite flammable substances such as paper and solvents, so flammable materials must be kept out of Class 4 and some focused Class 3 laser areas. One partial exception is plastic walls of enclosures that glow where they are struck by visible or strong invisible laser beams while the area is occupied; fire-resistant plastics should be used for these applications. Objects that could be struck by laser beams must be selected to avoid toxic pyrolysis products; for example, some polyurethanes and epoxies produce hydrogen cyanide when they burn. Dye lasers are particular

fire hazards because most use solutions of dye in an alcohol, dimethyl sulfoxide (DMSO) or some other flammable or combustible solvent. The dye solution may be located close to pumping energy sources such as flash lamps, which can add the energy needed to ignite the solvent.

Some lasers use flash lamps to supply pumping energy. Flash lamps can explode if dropped, struck, or improperly handled, posing a laceration hazard.

Laser beams can pyrolyze organic materials, and investigators who have looked at the pyrolysis products report finding polycyclic aromatic hydrocarbons (PAHs), the carcinogenic substances found in chimney soot. Thus, pyrolysis products must be controlled both in the air and as deposits on surfaces. For example, Kwan (1990) found that epoxy-reinforced graphite composite materials emit a variety of PAHs when cut by CO_2 lasers. It is also now known that viable organisms can be found in the plumes created when lasers are used to cut tissue.

Many laser dyes were brought to the market with essentially no toxicology screening and often come from chemical families that include mutagens or highly toxic materials. Mosovsky and Miller (1986), working with Avila, Felton, and Lewis, found that a number of laser dyes are mutagenic; the chemistries of these dyes are such that a positive mutagenicity finding is cause for concern that the material may be a carcinogen. The original dye recipes used DMSO solvent, which carries other materials through the skin. However, most butyl and some neoprene and nitrile gloves are effective for blocking DMSO. DMSO can increase absorption through the skin of the dye, which may be toxic or mutagenic; it also contains sulfur, which makes disposal by incineration difficult. Dioxane, a potential carcinogen that also forms explosive peroxides if left in contact with air for prolonged time periods, should be avoided as a solvent. Chlorinated solvents are costlier to dispose of than glycols or alcohols because it is difficult to send chlorinated solvents to incinerators. Precautions for laser dyes developed at Lawrence Livermore National Laboratory are summarized in Tables 11–R and 11–S. A variation on this theme is found in the recipe for Q-switching dyes. Dye-filled cells can be used for Q-switching. Some Q-switching dyes use ethylene dichloride, a potential carcinogen, as the solvent.

Excimer lasers use halogen mixtures such as 5 percent or less of fluorine or hydrogen chloride in inert gas. These mixtures are toxic, but fortunately the corrosiveness of the halogens is moderated by dilution in inert gases. Care is still needed in selecting corrosion-resistant materials, and consideration must be given to venting these gases during cavity refilling and emergencies. Passivation procedures—which use small quantities of the reactive gas to lay down a nonreactive deposit on surfaces that will later be exposed to larger flows

TABLE 11–R	Summary of Laser Dye Handling Precautions Developed at Lawrence Livermore National Laboratory		

| | Dye hazard class | | |
Action	L	M	S
Work Practices			
Avoid eating, drinking, smoking, or storing food, drinks, materials, or cosmetics in dye work areas	X	X	X
Post signs to this effect	—	—	X
Keep dye areas clean; clean up after work	X	X	X
Cap off dye lines not in use	X	X	X
Minimize quantities of dyes and solutions >1% in use or storage	—	—	X
Limit access to dye and work areas with signs	—	—	X
Avoid having janitors do dye cleanup	—	X	X
Store dyes and solutions >1% in double, labeled containers	—	—	X
Use toxic-dust vacuum to clean up dye spills	—	—	X
Personal Protective Equipment			
Use safety eyewear	X	X	X
Use lab coat	—	X	X
Use nitrile or neoprene gloves to handle solutions, impervious gloves to handle powders	X	X	X
Fire Safety			
Keep heat, flames, ignition sources away	X	X	X
Keep solvents and dye solutions in colored, labeled containers	X	X	X
Keep alcohol wastes in labeled safety cans	X	X	X
Avoid oxidizers	X	X	X
Equipment			
Pressure test systems	X	X	X
Install drip pans under systems, enclose systems if possible	X	X	X
Provide safety shower/eyewash	—	X	X
Mix dyes in hood or glove box	—	X	X
Mix dyes in glove box	—	—	X
Avoid cracks, crevices, matte-textured surfaces, and dark colors	—	—	X
Avoid false floors, if possible	—	—	X
Provide a designated dye-storage area	—	—	X
Provide separate storage for dye-soiled equipment	—	—	X
Use mechanical pipetting aids	—	—	X
Spills			
Clean up spills	X	X	X
Call for help if more than 100 ml of solution is spilled, or if exposure to dye powder is possible	X	X	X
Notify safety and health department of all spills	—	—	X

X = listed precaution
— = not a listed precaution
L = limited precaution class (good chemical lab practice, assigned to dyes known to be neither highly toxic nor mutagenic/carcinogenic)
M = moderate precaution (dyes known to be highly toxic or to have unknown toxic, mutagenic, or carcinogenic properties)
S = strict precaution (mutagenic materials, treated with same precautions as carcinogens)

of that gas—must be used to prepare piping for halogen gas service and avoid serious piping failures. Gas-handling equipment that is corrosion-resistant, highly automated, and designed to maximize safety and convenience is now very common in the semiconductor industry. Excimer laser users can obtain information about this technology from gas suppliers affiliated with gas-handling equipment manufacturers.

Other forms of radiation, such as flash lamp radiation, electromagnetic fields from power supplies, and x rays from high-voltage devices, can also be hazardous. It may be necessary to provide additional shielding or implement additional controls for these fields and other forms of radiation. Radiation from flash lamps, which can contain 100 to 1,000 times the energy of the laser beam, could be a hazard during setup and maintenance.

Hazardous materials can be found in optical components (such as heavy metals in detectors), components of lasers (such as beryllia heat sinks of electronic parts), or miscellaneous applications (such as coolants). Thus, an industrial hygiene review of laser maintenance procedures is warranted.

Other Regulatory Concerns with Lasers

OSHA has promulgated construction safety standard 29 CFR 1926.54 for the use of lasers in tasks such as alignment, although general industry uses of lasers are covered by ANSI Z136.1 through the *UAW, Brock v. General Dynamics Land Systems Division* decision because OSHA general industry standards do not address lasers. The use of laser protective eyewear is covered by the eye and face protection standard, 29 CFR 1910.132. The OSHA construction standard specifies that those who could be exposed to direct or reflected light above 5 mW must be provided with laser eye protection and that only mechanical or electronic devices may be used to guide the alignment of a laser. The standard also sets exposure criteria summarized below:

Direct staring limit	$1 \ \mu W/cm^2$
Incidental observing limit	$1 \ mW/cm^2$
Diffused reflected light	$2.5 \ W/cm^2$

The LIA/ANSI Z136 committee has also issued standards Z136.2 and Z136.3 for use of lasers in fiber-optic communications systems and medical applications, respectively. The Z136.3 standard addresses the same concerns as the Z136.1 standard but allows for greater flexibility and use of administrative controls.

The Center for Devices and Radiological Health (CDRH) of the Food and Drug Administration sets standards for commercial laser products that specify the types of safety devices that must be installed for commercial equipment using lasers. The CDRH also uses control classes based on AELs that are defined in their standard for laser devices (21 CFR 1040). CDRH specifies using interlocks,

TABLE 11–S		Laser Dye and Solvent Control Classes in Use at Lawrence Livermore National Laboratory
Materials/Synonyms	**Control Class**	**Comments**
BBQ	M	Nonmutagenic, unknown toxicity
Benzyl alcohol	L	Moderate toxicity, low vapor pressure
Carbazine 720	M	Nonmutagenic, unknown toxicity
Coumarin 1/460	M	Nonmutagenic, moderately toxic
Coumarin 2/45	M	Nonmutagenic, unknown toxicity
Coumarin 30/515	S	Mutagenic, unknown toxicity
Coumarin 102/480	S	Strong mutagen, unknown toxicity
Coumarin 120/440	M	Nonmutagenic, unknown toxicity
Coumarin 314/504	M	Nonmutagenic, unknown toxicity
Coumarin 420	M	Nonmutagenic, unknown toxicity
Coumarin 481	M	Nonmutagenic, unknown toxicity
Coumarin 498	M	Unknown mutagenicity, unknown toxicity
Coumarin 500	S	Mutagenic, unknown toxicity
Coumarin 535	S	Mutagenic, unknown toxicity
Coumarin 540A	M	Nonmutagenic, unknown toxicity
Cresyl violet 670	S	Very strong mutagen, unknown toxicity
1,3,5,7-Cyclooctatetrene (COT)	M	Unknown mutagenicity, unknown toxicity
DCM	S	Very strong mutagen, unknown toxicity
p,p_-diaminoquaterphenyl	M	Nonmutagenic, unknown toxicity
p,p_-diaminoterphenyl	S	Mutagenic, unknown toxicity
Dioxane	M	Moderate toxicity
DMSO	M	Moderate toxicity
DODCI	M	Unknown mutagenicity, unknown toxicity
DQOCI	M	Unknown mutagenicity, unknown toxicity
DPS	M	Doubtful bacterial mutagen, unknown toxicity
Ethylene dichloride (1,2 dichloroethane)	M	Suspected carcinogen; avoid inhalation of vapors
Ethyl alcohol	L	Low toxicity
Ethylene glycol	M	Moderate toxicity, low vapor pressure
Fluorescein 548	M	Unknown mutagenicity, unknown toxicity
IR-26	M	Unknown mutagenicity, unknown toxicity
IR-125	M	Unknown mutagenicity, unknown toxicity
IR-132	M	Unknown mutagenicity, unknown toxicity
IR-140	M	Unknown mutagenicity, unknown toxicity
IR-144	M	Unknown mutagenicity, unknown toxicity
Kiton Red 620	L	Nonmutagenic, practically nontoxic
Kodak Q-Switch #2	M	Unknown mutagenicity, unknown toxicity
Kodak Q-Switch #5	M	Unknown mutagenicity, unknown toxicity
LD-390	M	Unknown mutagenicity, unknown toxicity
LD-490	S	Mutagenic, unknown toxicity
LD-688	S	Mutagenic, unknown toxicity
LD-700	M	Nonmutagenic, unknown toxicity
LDS-698	S	Mutagenic, unknown toxicity
LDS-722	S	Strong mutagen, unknown toxicity
LDS-750	M	Unknown mutagenicity, unknown toxicity
LDS-751	M	Unknown mutagenicity, unknown toxicity

TABLE 11–S	Laser Dye and Solvent Control Classes in Use at Lawrence Livermore National Laboratory, continued	
Materials/Synonyms	*Control Class*	*Comments*
LDS-820	M	Unknown mutagenicity, unknown toxicity
LDS-867	M	Unknown mutagenicity, unknown toxicity
9-Methylanthracene	S	Mutagenic, unknown toxicity
Methyl alcohol	L	Moderate toxicity
Bis-MSB	M	Nonmutagenic, unknown toxicity
Nile Blue 690	S	Commercial grade is strongly mutagenic: purified dye is not Unknown toxicity
Oxazine 720	M	Nonmutagenic, unknown toxicity
Rhodamine 6G/590	M	Moderately toxic. National Toxicology Program tests did not demonstrate strong carcinogenicity. Commercial-grade dye has been found to induce injection-site tumors
Rhodamine 110/560	S	Weak mutagen, unknown toxicity
Rhodamine 610/B	M	Nonmutagenic, moderately toxic
Rhodamine 640	M	Nonmutagenic, unknown toxicity
Sulforhodamine	M	Unknown mutagenicity, unknown toxicity
Stilbene 420/3	L	Nonmutagenic, practically nontoxic
N,N,N',N'-tetraethyldiaminoquaterphenyl	M	Nonmutagenic, unknown toxicity
N,N,N',N'-tetraethyldiaminoterphenyl	S	Strong mutagen, unknown toxicity

beam stops/shutters, and key-in-lock controls. CDRH also has very explicit requirements for audible and visible alarms to announce when a laser is functioning and, for Class 4, when a laser is about to function. The CDRH regulations also include an incident reporting procedure.

MEASURING OPTICAL RADIATION

Two types of detectors are widely used: thermal and quantum. Thermal detectors are fundamentally no different from globe thermometers used in heat stress studies. They consist of a sensor embedded in an object that is dark-colored to absorb IR radiation, warm up, and produce a measurable response in the detector. Relatively small, lightweight objects are desirable for thermal sensors because they change temperature rapidly, leading to faster response times (but still not fast enough to measure pulsed lasers). A variant of the thermal detector is the pyroelectric detector, which measures the rate of temperature change in crystals. This is much faster than a conventional thermal detector; with some caution, these can be used for repetitively pulsed lasers. Thermal detectors are best for IR measurements. The heat-absorbing coatings vary in how well they absorb IR, so one should obtain information about the absorption properties of the coating before buying a thermal sensor. Another note of caution is that these detectors respond to temperature changes, so changing the room thermostat can produce a response in the instrument.

Quantum detectors emit electrons in response to being struck by radiation and are best suited for use in the UV, visible, and IR-A bands (up to 1,100 nm). These can be very fast. The detectors are often made of alloys such as cesium telluride, lead telluride, or lead selenide, and the responses of the detectors to radiation of differing wavelengths are different. A buyer should check with the instrument vendor about the suitability of a detector for the radiation of interest. Note that no procedure exists for field verification of the ODs of laser eyewear.

LIGHTING

Insufficient light causes accidents and reduces work performance. One needs adequate lighting to see hazards in the workplace and to read information such as text and dials. Most lighting concerns are quantitative, but some qualitative concerns may also arise such as contrast, reflections, and color.

The Illumination Engineering Society (IES) advises that 20 footcandles of illuminance are needed for tasks requiring sustained seeing. This is also one aspect of nonionizing radiation covered by various OSHA regulations, as summarized in Table 11–T. IES/ANSI RP-7-1991 specifies the following illuminance levels for safety in normal conditions (where light will not ruin a process or pose a safety hazard):

TABLE 11–T	Summary of OSHA Regulations Concerning General Lighting	
Regulation	**Summary**	
1910.179(c)(4): Cranes	Cab lighting shall be adequate.	
1910.303(g)(1)(v): Electrical work areas	Illumination shall be provided.	
1910.303(h)(3)(ii): Lighting maintenance	Adequate illumination shall be provided.	
1910.333(c)(4): Electrical work practices	Spaces containing energized parts shall be illuminated; work shall not be performed in and people shall not reach into unlit spaces.	
1910.38(q): Exits	Exit signs shall be lit by a reliable light source >5 footcandles.	
1910.120: Hazardous waste site operations	Quantitative specifications: Area	Illumination (footcandles)
	General work areas	5
	Excavation and waste areas, loading platforms, refueling, and field maintenance areas.	3
	Indoors: warehouses, corridors, hallways, and exit ways.	5
	Tunnels, shafts, and general underground work areas. (Exception: _10 footcandles is required at tunnel and shaft heading during drilling, mucking, and scaling. MSHA- approved cap lights acceptable for use in the tunnel heading).	5
	General shops (mechanical and electrical equipment rooms, active storerooms, barracks or living quarters, locker or dressing rooms, dining areas, indoor toilets, and workrooms).	10
	First-aid stations, infirmaries, and offices.	30
1910.142(g): Labor camps	Each habitable room shall have at least one ceiling light fixture and a floor or wall outlet. Laundry rooms, toilets, and rooms where people congregate shall contain a ceiling or wall fixture. Toilets and storage rooms shall be lit at _20 footcandles 30 in. above the floor. Other rooms, including kitchens and living quarters, shall be lit _30 footcandles 30 in. above the floor.	
1910.219(c)(5)(iii): Power transmission equipment in basements	Lighting shall conform to ANSI A11.1-1970.	
1910.68(b)(6)(iii): Manlifts	Lighting _5 footcandles shall be provided at each landing when lift is operating.	
1910.68(b)(14): Manlifts	Lighting _1 footcandles shall be provided in runs when lift is operating.	
1910.178(h): Industrial trucks	Supplemental lighting shall be provided where lighting is _2 lumens/ft².	
1910.261(b)(7): Pulp and paper mills	Emergency lighting shall be provided where operators must stay during emergencies, in passageways, stairways, and aisles used for emergency exit, and at first-aid and medical facilities.	
1910.261(c)(10): Pulp and paper mills	Loading/unloading areas shall be lit in accordance with ANSI A11.1-1970.	
1910.266(e)(15): Pulpwood logging	Lighting shall be provided for night work if needed.	
1910.265(c)(5)(iii): Sawmills	Stairway shall be adequately illuminated.	
1910.265(c)(9): Sawmills	Work areas shall be provided with adequate illumination.	
1910.265(c)(23)(iii): Sawmills	Fuel houses and bins shall have adequate exits and lighting.	
1910.268: Telecommunications	Adequate lighting shall be provided.	
1926.56: Construction	Areas not covered by the following table shall be illuminated in accordance with ANSI A11.1-1970.	Illumination (footcandles)
	Quantitative specifications: Area	5
	General construction area lighting	3
	General construction areas, concrete placement, excavation and waste areas, access ways, active storage areas, loading platforms, refueling, and field maintenance areas.	
	Indoors: warehouses, corridors, hallways, and exit ways.	5
	Tunnels, shafts, and general underground work areas. (Exception: _10 footcandles is required at tunnel and shaft heading during drilling, mucking, and scaling. MSHA-approved cap lights acceptable for use in the tunnel heading).	5
	General construction plant and shops (batch plants, screening plants, mechanical and electrical equipment rooms, carpenter shops, rigging lofts and active storerooms, barracks or living quarters, locker or dressing rooms, dining areas, and indoor toilets and workrooms).	10
	First-aid stations, infirmaries, and offices.	30

Degree of Hazard	Illuminance Level (footcandles)	
	Low Activity Level	High Activity Level
Slight Hazard	0.5	2
High Hazard (obstacle in path)	1	5

Illuminance is similar to irradiance and power density, but the levels of light of various wavelengths are weighted in terms of their impact on the functioning of the cone cells of the retina, which are involved in color and detailed vision. The units of illuminance are the lux and the footcandle; 1 lux = 10 footcandles. The dominant quantitative standards for industrial lighting in the United States are IES/ANSI RP-1-1982 and RP-7-1991 (or RP-7-2001), which address office and industrial lighting, respectively. These standards replace the historical telephone-directory-style list of tasks and listed lighting levels with a procedure in which workplaces, work force, and tasks are analyzed for type of task, age, reflectance of room surfaces, and (in some cases) whether the seeing task is unimportant, important, or critical. Important aspects of any seeing task are object size (the bigger it is, the easier it is to see), contrast, time available to do the seeing job, and luminance. RP-7 notes that luminance is often the only factor that can be controlled. Illuminances are specified in ranges for nine categories (A through I); ranges of three levels of illuminance are specified for each category. The analyst reviews the other factors to determine whether to select from the low, middle, or high end of the illuminance range for each category. The catego-

ries and specified illuminances are listed in Table 11–U; the work force and environmental/task factors are summarized in Table 11–V.

Common qualitative concerns include glare (particularly off computer screens), contrast, and color. Glare, either reflected or direct, is still a major concern. Reflected glare is usually a specular reflection of a sunlit window or lamp off a screen or other shiny surface that partially obscures or veils the scene at the reflection. Direct glare is a relatively bright object, such as an unshaded window, in an otherwise dark area. Reflected glare can be controlled by locating the screen or other surface of interest so it does not reflect the images of windows or lamps.

A screen can be angled so it does not reflect the images of lamps or windows into the user's eyes. In some cases, visors or partitions can be used to block light from lamps or windows. Another option is to place a textured surface above the object that breaks up specular reflections while allowing the light from the object below it to pass through. Dimpled plastic is often used.

RP-7 devotes an entire annex to the subject of glare. RP-7 also gives guidance for lighting contrast, listed in Table 11–W. A gradation of contrasts is sought between the task and its immediate and more remote visual surroundings. In essence, strong lighting can exist in an area of moderate lighting, which can be surrounded by a dimly lit or unlit expanse, but darkness should not immediately surround brightness. An example of harsh contrast is a lit desk in a poorly lit warehouse. The lamp at the desk should be

TABLE 11–U Illuminance Categories of ANSI/IESNA RP-7-01

Type of Activity	Examples	Illuminance Category	Illuminance (footcandles)	Reference Workplane
Public spaces with dark surroundings	Aircraft ramp area	A	3	
Simple orientation for short visits	Active storage area of a farm, VDT screens	B	5	General lighting throughout spaces
Working spaces where visual tasks are only occasionally performed	Active traffic area of a garage, elevators/escalators	C	10	
Performance of visual tasks of high contrast or large size	Simple assembly or inspection	D	30	
Performance of visual tasks of medium contrast or small size	Hand decorating in a bakery, mail sorting	E	50	Illuminance on task
Performance of visual tasks of low contrast or very small size	Finished lumber grading, model making	F	100	
Performance of visual tasks of low contrast and very small size over a prolonged period	Sewing clothes	G	300–1000	Illuminance on task obtained by a combination of general and local (supplementary) lighting
Performance of very prolonged and exacting visual tasks	Exacting inspection	H	500–750–1,000	Specific examples found in Annex A2
Performance of very special visual tasks of extremely low contrast and small size	Cloth inspection and examining (perching) of sewn products	I	1,000–1,500–2,000	

TABLE 11–V	Factors Influencing Assigning Illumination Levels Within Illuminance Categories of ANSI/IESNA RP-1

For Illuminance Categories A Through C in Industrial and Office Settings

Room and Occupant Characteristics	Weighting		
	Low End of Range	Mid-Range	High End of Range
Occupant ages	<40	4055	>55
Room surface reflectances	>70%	3070%	<30%

For Illuminance Categories D Through I in Industrial and Office Settings

Task and Worker Characteristics	Weighting		
	Low End of Range	Mid-Range	High End of Range
Occupant ages	<40	4055	>55
Speed or accuracy of seeing	Not important	Important	Critical
Reflectance of task background	>70%	3070%	<30%

supplemented by area lighting to avoid contrast problems. People look away from their visual tasks from time to time, so the person at this desk would probably not wish to stay there because the visual contrast between the desk and its visual surroundings is too great for comfort.

Nonlaser lighting adheres to the *inverse square law*. This means that lights must be placed close to areas being lit if the lighting is needed to perform a task. Sometimes, this cannot be done by area lighting alone. A warehouse may need area lights placed above the heights of shelves and forklift trucks, so supplemental lighting, provided by floor or desk lamps, may be needed at desks located in the warehouse. The limits of supplemental lighting include harsh

TABLE 11–W	ANSI/IESNA RP-7-01 Recommended Maximum Luminance Ratios

Situation	Environmental Group		
	A	B	C
Between tasks and adjacent darker surroundings	3 to 1	3 to 1	5 to 1
Between tasks and adjacent lighter surroundings	1 to 3	1 to 3	1 to 5
Between tasks and adjacent more remote darker surfaces	10 to 1	20 to 1	Control not practical
Between tasks and adjacent more remote darker surfaces	1 to 10	1 to 20	Control not practical
Between luminaires (or windows, skylights, etc.) and surfaces adjacent to them	20 to 1	Control not practical	Control not practical
Anywhere within normal field of view	40 to 1	Control not practical	Control not practical

Environmental groups: A-interior areas where reflectances of entire space can be controlled in line with recommendations for optimum seeing conditions; B-areas where reflectances of immediate work area can be controlled, but control of remote surroundings is limited; C-areas (indoor or outdoor) where it is impractical to control reflectances and difficult to alter environmental conditions.

contrast, already mentioned, and also the possibility that the supplemental lighting could cause direct glare for people in the surrounding area. Energy conservation and safety needs can be reconciled by using motion detectors to activate area lighting when a person enters an area. Cleaning and painting of the building and it lighting can make a tremendous difference in lighting by causing more of the light emitted from lamps to be reflected to places where people are working. Light, matte-textured surfaces are preferred. Matte textures avoid specular reflections are reflected glare. RP-1 and RP-7 give guidance about how reflective surfaces should be.

Color can be a problem if unusual fluorescent tubes or colored incandescent bulbs are installed. White light contains radiation associated with every color we can see; colored lights radiate selected wavelengths more intensely. Colored lighting is useful for some jobs, such as blue-enhanced fluorescent tubes for greenhouse lighting or yellow-orange low-pressure sodium lamps for abundant yet cheap safety lighting at night. Colored lighting without some benefit can create difficulties. Colors may be harder to perceive when nonwhite lighting is used. Yellow and white objects could, for example, both appear the same in yellow or red lighting, so yellow signs and warning devices could become unreliable and blue surfaces would appear to be black.

Concern has been expressed about the safety of fluorescent tubes. Fluorescent tubes contain a minute amount of mercury that conducts electric current and glows in the ultraviolet portion of the spectrum. The UV is absorbed by phosphors that line the tubes and is reradiated as visible light. ICNIRP issued a position statement that advises that UV emissions from fluorescent tubes are not a problem. Mercury vapor lamps are also used for lighting, and they generate UV that is absorbed by an outer glass sheath. Mercury vapor lamps are safe unless the outer sheath is broken. A mercury vapor lamp with a broken sheath should be turned off and replaced immediately. It should be noted that disposing of fluorescent tubes is associated with other industrial hygiene concerns. Tube-breaking equipment can be noisy and heavily contaminated with toxic mercury metal, which can accumulate in tube breaking equipment. Fluorescent tubes contained highly toxic beryllium salts in the 1940s. Cadmium compounds were used, but their use was discontinued in the late 1980s, so cadmium exposure remains a potential hazard for tube breakers.

Lighting measurements are usually made 30 in. above the floor to measure the illumination striking surfaces that are to be seen. Special measurements can be made on surfaces of interest, such as desktops and working surfaces. The instruments used are typically inexpensive photoelectric devices. It is noted that IES developed guidance for lighting workplaces with computer displays, RP-24-1989, which is listed in the Bibliography.

SUMMARY

- Nonionizing "radiation" is often not radiation, but rather discrete electric and magnetic fields that exist independently of one another, whereas the fields in radiation are rigidly interrelated. The frequency below which it is assumed one is dealing with fields rather than radiation is about 300 MHz.
- Electric fields are caused by nonmoving or moving electric charges, and the electric field increases as the quantity of charge increases. Magnetic fields are caused by the flow of electric charges, known as electric currents, and increase as more current flows. In other words, electric charges create electric fields and moving them creates magnetic fields.
- The frequency of electromagnetic radiation times its wavelength equals its speed of travel, very close to 300 million m/s in air or a vacuum. The frequency of electromagnetic radiation is the number of times the fields go through a complete cycle of polarity and strength change. Frequencies are expressed in hertz (Hz), the number of polarity and strength changes that occur in a second. The wavelength is the distance traveled as the radiation goes through one cycle of polarity and strength change. Higher frequencies mean shorter wavelengths, and lower frequencies mean longer wavelengths.
- The various frequencies of the electric and magnetic field are divided into the electromagnetic spectrum. This is divided into subradiofrequency fields, which have frequencies below 3000 Hz, radiofrequencies from 3000 to 300 GHz including microwaves, which span 300 MHz to 300 GHz, and optical radiation with higher frequencies and energies.

- Electromagnetic devices can be thought of as containing a source of energy, a transmission path, and a receiver of the energy.
- The exposure guideline for static magnetic fields was set by ICNIRP at 200 mT (2,000 G). The exposure guideline for static electric fields was set by ACGIH at 25 kV/m.
- ACGIH and ICNIRP issued ELF exposure criteria for workers based on avoiding induced currents that are stronger than those already created in the body by the normal functioning of nerves and muscles.
- Radiofrequency exposure standards are based on avoiding hazardous electric current flows at frequencies below a few megahertz and on avoiding excessive rates of energy deposition at higher frequencies. Energy deposition is most significant at frequencies where a person's height is 20 to 40 percent of the wavelength of the radiation in air (30 to 300 MHz). At frequencies above a few gigahertz, energy deposition occurs mainly in the skin. The frequency of 300 GHz has a wavelength of 1 mm, and higher frequencies are classified as IR radiation.
- Optical radiation is described by its wavelength and is divided into IR (760 nm to 1 mm), visible (400 to 700 nm), and UV (variously 4 or 100 nm to 400 nm). There are TLVs for all nonlaser optical radiation from 180 to 1,400 nm, and LIA/ANSI Z136.1 addresses wavelengths from 180 nm to 1 mm. Shorter wavelengths are absorbed by oxygen to make ozone.
- Laser radiation is monochromatic (literally one color) or has just a few wavelengths, is coherent (well-organized), and is bright. Coherent radiation is very directional, so lasers can project intense or hazardous energies over longer distances than nonlaser sources of optical radiation.
- Laser radiation with wavelengths between 400 and 1,400 nm—the ocular hazard region—can be intensely focused on the retina. This makes lasers operating in this wavelength range particularly hazardous.
- Lasers are controlled by dividing them into hazard classes ranging from 1 (essentially harmless) to 4 (very hazardous). Precautions become more stringent as the hazard class increases.
- OSHA has limited standards for nonionizing radiation but can enforce consensus standards according to the *UAW, Brock v. General Dynamics Land Systems Division* decision. These standards come from the ACGIH, the ICNIRP, the IEEE, and the LIA and are referenced in the Bibliography. European international organizations, particularly Swedish and Finnish organizations, are also active in this area.
- Industrial lighting standards relate to safety and productivity. They are promulgated by the IES.

Nonionizing radiation is becoming more and more a

part of our lives on and off the job. Dealing with it will be one of the larger challenges facing the industrial hygiene profession in the future.

BIBLIOGRAPHY

American Conference of Governmental Industrial Hygienists. *2012 Threshold Limit Values® for Chemical Substances and Physical Agents and Biological Exposure Indices®.* Cincinnati, OH: ACGIH, 2012.

American Conference of Governmental Industrial Hygienists. *Documentation of the Threshold Limit Values and Biological Exposure Indices,* 7th ed., vol. III, PA-45–PA-70. Cincinnati, OH: ACGIH, 2001, with 2002–2011 supplements.

Anderson LE. ELF: Exposure levels, bioeffects, and epidemiology. *Health Phys* 61:41–46, 1991.

Anderson LE. Biological effects of extremely low-frequency electromagnetic fields: In vivo studies. *AIHAJ* 54:186–196, 1993.

Bates MN. Extremely low frequency electromagnetic fields and cancer: The epidemiologic evidence. *Environ Health Perspect* 95:147–156, 1991.

Bonneville Power Administration. *Electrical and Biological Effects of Transmission Lines—A Review,* DOE/BP-945. Portland, OR: BPA, 1993.

Bracken TD. Exposure assessment for power frequency electric and magnetic fields. *AIHAJ* 54:165–177, 1993.

Breysse PN, Gray R. Video display terminal exposure assessment. *Appl Occup Environ Hyg* 9:671–677, 1994.

David A, Savitz DA. Overview of epidemiologic research on electric and magnetic fields and cancer. *AIHAJ* 54:197–204, 1993.

Department of Energy and Public Policy. *Part 1: Measuring Power Frequency Magnetic Fields.* Pittsburgh, PA: Carnegie Mellon University, 1993.

Department of Energy and Public Policy. *Part 2: What Can We Conclude from Measurements of Power Frequency Magnetic Fields?* Pittsburgh, PA: Carnegie Mellon University, 1993.

Environmental Protection Agency. *Laboratory Testing of Commercially Available Power Frequency Magnetic Field Meters,* Final Report, 400R-92-010. Washington, DC: EPA, 1991.

Feero WE. Electric and magnetic field management. *AIHAJ* 54:205–210, 1993.

Floderus B, Persson T, Stenlund C, et al. *Occupational Exposures to Electromagnetic Fields in Relation to Leukemia and Brain Tumors: A Case Control Study.* Solna, Sweden: Department of Neuromedicine, National Institute of Occupational Health, 1992.

Gandhi OP, ed. *Biological Effects and Medical Applications of Electromagnetic Energy.* Englewood Cliffs, NJ: Prentice Hall, 1990.

Hitchcock RT. *Nonionizing Guide for Radio-Frequency and Microwave Radiation.* Fairfax, VA: AIHA, 1994.

Hitchcock RT, McMahan S, Miller GC. *Nonionizing Radiation Guide for Extremely Low Frequency (ELF) Electric and Magnetic Fields.* Fairfax, VA: AIHA, 1995.

Illumination Engineering Society. *American National Standard Practice for Industrial Lighting,* RP-7. New York: IES, 1991

Illumination Engineering Society. *VDT Lighting— IES Recommended Practices for Lighting Offices Containing Computer Visual Display Terminals,* IES RP-24. New York: IES, 1989.

Illumination Engineering Society. *Office Lighting— American National Standard Practice,* ANSI/IES RP-1-1982. New York: IES, 1982.

Institute of Electrical and Electronic Engineers. *American National Standard Safety Levels with Respect to Human Exposure to Radio Frequency Electromagnetic Fields, 3 kHz to 300 GHz,* C95.1-2005. Piscataway, NJ: IEEE, 2005.

International Commission on Non-Ionizing Radiation Protection. Guidelines for limiting exposure to time varying electric and magnetic fields. *Health Phys* 99 (6):818–836, 2010.

International Commission on Non-Ionizing Radiation Protection. Guidelines on limits of exposure to static magnetic fields. *Health Phys* 96(4):504-514, 2009.

Juutilainen J. Effects of low-frequency magnetic fields on embryonic development and pregnancy. *Scand J Work Environ Health* 17:149–158, 1991.

Laser Institute of America. *American National Standard for Safe Use of Lasers,* Z136.1(2007) Orlando, FL: LIA, 2007.

Laser Institute of America. *Safe Use of Optical Fiber Communication Systems Using Laser Diode and LED Sources,* Z136.2-1988. Orlando, FL: LIA, 1988.

Laser Institute of America. *Safe Use of Lasers in Health Care Facilities,* Z136.3-2005 Orlando, FL: LIA, 2005.

Lindbohm M-L, Hietanen M, Kyyronen P, et al. Magnetic fields of video display terminals and spontaneous abortions. *Am J Epidemiol* 136:1041–1051, 1992.

Luben RA. Effects of low-energy electromagnetic fields (pulsed and DC) on membrane signal transduction processes in biological systems. *Health Phys* 61:15–28, 1991.

Michaelson SM. Biological effects of radiofrequency radiation: Concepts and criteria. *Health Phys* 61:3–14, 1991.

Miller GC. Exposure guidelines for magnetic fields. *AIHAJ* 48:957–968, 1987.

Miller GC. Precautions for handling laser dyes. In *Hazards Control Annual Technology Review 1986,* UCRL-50007-86. Livermore, CA: Lawrence Livermore National Laboratory, 1987.

Mosovsky JA. *Laser Dye Toxicity, Hazards and Recommended Controls,* UCRL-89148. Livermore, CA: Lawrence Livermore National Laboratory, 1983.

Nair I, Morgan MG, Florig HK. *Biological Effects of Power Frequency Electric and Magnetic Fields.* Background paper prepared for U.S. Congress Office of Technology Assessment. Technical Information Service accession no. PB89209985. Springfield, VA: National Technical Information Service, 1989.

National Council for Radiological Protection and Measurements. *A Practical Guide to the Determination of Human Exposure to Radiofrequency Fields,* NCRP Report No. 119. Washington, DC: NCRPM, 1993.

Occupational Safety and Health Administration, 21 CFR Subchapter J, "Radiological Health."

Olsen JH, Nielsen A, Schulgen G. Residence near high voltage facilities and risk of cancer in children. *Br Med J* 307:891–895, 1993.

Petersen RC. Radiofrequency/microwave protection guides. *Health Phys* 61:59–67, 1991.

Pool R. Is there an EMF-cancer connection? *Science* 249:1096–1098, 1990.

Pool R. Electromagnetic fields: The biological evidence. *Science* 249:1378–1381, 1990.

Pool R. Flying blind: The making of EMF policy. *Science* 250:23–25, 1990.

Rockwell RJ. Laser accidents: Reviewing 30 years of incidents. What are the concerns old and new. *Laser Appl* 6:203–211, 1994.

Savitz DA. Health effects of low-frequency electric and magnetic fields. *Environ Sci Technol* 27:52–54, 1993.

Savitz DA, Wachtel H, Barnes FA, et al. Case-control study of childhood cancer and exposure to 60 Hz magnetic fields. *Am J Epidemiol* 128:21–38, 1988.

Savitz DA, Pearce NA, Poole C. Methodological issues in the epidemiology of electromagnetic fields and cancer. *Epidemiol Rev* 11:59–78, 1989.

Schnorr TM, Grajewski BA, Hornung RW, et al. Video display terminals and the risk of spontaneous abortions. *N Engl J Med* 324:727–733, 1991.

Sliney D, Wolbarsht M. *Safety with Lasers and Other Optical Sources—A Comprehensive Handbook.* New York: Plenum, 1985.

Steneck NH, Cook HJ, Vander AJ, et al. The origins of U.S. safety standards for microwave radiation. *Science* 208:1230–1237, 1980.

Suess MJ, ed. *Nonionizing Radiation Protection.* WHO Regional Publications European Series No. 10. Copenhagen, Denmark: WHO Regional Office for Europe, 1982.

Swedish Board for Technical Accreditation. *Test Methods for Visual Display Units,* MPR 1990:8 1990-12-01. Northridge, CA: Standards Sales Group, 1990.

Tenforde TS. Health effects of low-frequency electric and magnetic fields. *Environ Sci Technol* 27:56–58, 1993.

Varanelli AG. Electrical hazards associated with lasers. *Laser Appl* 7:62–64, 1995.

Verkasalao PK, Pukkala E, Hongisto MY, et al. Risk of cancer in Finnish children living close to power lines. *Br Med J* 307:895–899, 1993.

Wiley MJ, Corey P, Kavet R, et al. The effects of continuous exposure to 20-kHz sawtooth magnetic fields on the litters of CD-1 mice. *Teratology* 46:391–398, 1992.

World Health Organization. *Environmental Health Criteria 69—Magnetic Fields.* Albany, NY: WHO Publications Centre, 1987.

World Health Organization. *Environmental Health Criteria 35—Extremely Low Frequency (ELF) Fields.* Albany, NY: WHO Publications Centre, 1984.

Yost M, Lee GM, Duane D, et al. California protocol for measuring 60 Hz magnetic fields in residences. *Appl Occup Environ Hyg* 7:772–777, 1992.

Periodicals

Biological Effects of Nonionizing Electromagnetic Radiation (BENER Digest Update—A Digest of Current Literature). Information Ventures, 1500 Locust St., Suite 3216, Philadelphia, PA 19102; phone (215) 732-9083, fax (215) 732-3754. Quarterly listing of literature abstracts worldwide.

EMF Health & Safety Digest (formerly *Transmission/ Distribution Health & Safety Report*). EMF Information Project, 2701 University Avenue Southeast, Minneapolis, MN 55414- 0501; phone (612) 623-4600, fax (612) 623-3645. Project's support includes utility organizations worldwide. Reviews of conferences, literature developments, and lists of papers are very useful.

Journal of the Bioelectromagnetics Society and the Society for Physical Regulation in Biology and Medicine. Bioelectromagnetics Subscription Department, John Wiley and Sons, 9th Floor, 605 Third Avenue, New York, NY 10158-0012; phone (212) 850-6543. The Bioelectromagnetics Society administrative office is managed by W/L Associates, Ltd., at 7519 Ridge Road, Frederick, MD 21702-3519; phone (301) 663-4252.

Journal of Laser Applications. Laser Institute of America, 12424 Research Parkway, Suite 125, Orlando, FL 32826; phone (407) 380-1553, fax (407) 380-5588. Official journal of the Laser Institute of America.

Laser Focus World. 10 Tara Boulevard, Fifth Floor, Nashua, NH 03062; phone (603) 891-0123, fax (603) 891-0574. Free to those who make or influence procurement decisions.

Microwave News. P. O. Box 1799, Grand Central Station, New York, NY 10163; phone (212) 517-2800, fax (516) 734-0316. Editorial viewpoint contrasts with that of *EMF Health & Safety Digest.*

Photonics Spectra. Berkshire Common, P. O. Box 4949, Pittsfield, MA 01202; phone (413) 499-0514, fax (413) 442-3180. Free to those who make or influence procurement decisions.

VDT News. P. O. Box 1799, Grand Central Station, New York, NY 10163; phone (212) 517-2800, fax (516) 734-0316. This is published by the Microwave News organization and also covers ergonomic issues.

CHAPTER 12

Thermal Stress

by Thomas E. Bernard, PhD, CIH

Thermal stress is a significant physical agent in many working environments. Just considering routine work out-of-doors, air temperatures between −20°F to 110°F are expected over different regions of the United States. Other countries may reasonably expect temperatures beyond that range. Human-made environments from freezers to ovens extend the range of thermal environments in which work is expected. Because tasks must be performed under adverse thermal conditions, this chapter provides guidance for recognition, evaluation, and control of work in thermal extremes.

DEGREES OF THERMAL STRESS

Conceptually, work can occur in one of five zones along the continuum of thermal stress. In the middle is the comfort zone. Here, most people would report thermal sensations as being acceptable (neither hot nor cold). In the comfort zone, the demands for physiological adaptation are modest and productivity should be the greatest. The comfort zone is described at the end of this chapter to provide information to health and safety professionals who may be asked to evaluate the thermal conditions with comfort as a goal.

On either side of the comfort zone are the discomfort zones for heat and cold stress. Under these conditions, most people should be able to safely work without experiencing a disorder related to the stress (i.e., heat-related or cold-related disorders). They will report sensations of cold or heat, productivity and quality of work may decrease, and the risk of accidents may increase.

The health risk zone for heat and cold stress are the outer zones of the thermal stress continuum. The physiological adaptations have reached their limits and work capacity is severely limited. In the health risk zone, the likelihood of heat and cold stress-related disorders increases markedly. The goal of most evaluation schemes for occupational heat and cold stress is to limit exposures at the transition to the health risk zone. Health and safety professionals should closely manage and limit or reduce exposures in the health risk zone.

Of course, there are no firm boundaries to these zones because the boundaries depend on the environment, individuals, and season as well as many unknown variables. But we should try to control the thermal stress factors for the less tolerant workers to minimize the risk of injuries and illness to the lowest reasonable level. The major emphasis on evaluation and control is placed on the transition from the discomfort zone to the health risk zone for both heat and cold stress.

THERMAL BALANCE

Model of Thermal Balance

Three factors influence the degree of thermal stress. The most obvious factor is the climatic conditions of the environment. The other two factors are work demands and clothing. The tradition for more than 40 years is to describe thermal balance by an equation with major avenues of heat exchange between the body and the environment represented by a term in the equation. (There is no uniformly accepted version but the reader will not have problems reconciling different versions as they are found.)

$$S = (M - W) + R + C + K + (C_{resp} - E_{resp}) - E \qquad (1)$$

Where S = heat storage rate (gain [+] or loss [–])
M = metabolic rate (internal heat generation)
W = external work rate (energy delivered to environment)
R = radiant heat exchange rate (gain [+] or loss [–] to environment)
C = convective heat exchange rate (gain [+] or loss [–] to environment)
K = conductive heat exchange rate (gain [+] or loss [–] to environment)
C_{resp} = rate of convective heat exchange by respiration (gain [+] or loss [–] to environment)
E_{resp} = rate of evaporative heat loss by respiration
E = rate of evaporative heat loss

Most versions of the heat balance equation use ± instead of +, especially in front of R and C. The purpose is to emphasize that the heat exchange represented by R, C, K, and C_{resp} can be in either direction. A positive value for any of these terms (as opposed to the sign in front of the term) means that the heat is gained by the body and a negative value means that heat is lost from the body. The values for M and $(M - W)$ are only positive and represent a heat gain. The values for W, E_{resp}, and E are positive and always represent a loss; thus they are preceded by a minus sign. Each term has the unit of energy per unit of time; that is, the terms represent rates of energy transfer. The international units (SI units) are watts, and other units that are reported include kcal/h, kcal/min and Btu/h. Sometimes the rates are reported as normalized values to body surface area.

S—Heat Storage Rate

If the value for S is zero, the body is in thermal equilibrium, and heat gain is balanced by loss from the body. If S is positive, the body is gaining heat at the rate indicated by the value of S. If the value of S is negative, the body is losing heat, and body temperature is decreasing.

M—Metabolic Rate

Chemical reactions occur continuously inside the body. These serve to sustain life (basal metabolism) and meet the demands of work (muscle metabolism). As muscle metabolism increases to meet work demands, the rate of energy conversion from chemical energy to kinetic energy increases. Because the energy conversion from chemical energy to kinetic energy is inefficient, increased metabolism results in increased rates of heat gain to the person. The metabolic rate depends directly on the rate and type of external work demanded by the job.

W—External Work Rate

W is the amount of energy that is successfully converted from internal chemical energy to mechanical work on external objects. This route of energy transfer is called external work and it does not contribute to body heat. The rate of external work depends directly on forces applied against external resistance and distance moved. W is usually about 10 percent of M.

R—Radiant Heat Exchange Rate (Radiation)

Solid bodies of different temperatures have a net heat flow from the hotter surface to the cooler surface by electromagnetic radiation (primarily infrared radiation). The rate of heat transfer by radiation depends on the average temperature of the surrounding solid surfaces, skin temperature, and clothing.

C—Convective Heat Exchange Rate (Convection)

The exchange of heat between the skin and the surrounding air is referred to as convection. The direction of heat flow depends on the temperature difference between the skin and air. If air temperature is greater than skin temperature, C is positive and heat flows from the air to the skin. If the air is cooler than the skin, C is negative and heat flows from the body. The rate of convective heat exchange depends on the magnitude of the temperature difference, the amount of air motion, and clothing.

K—Conductive Heat Exchange Rate (Conduction)

When two solid bodies are in contact, heat will flow from the warmer body to the cooler body. The rate of heat transfer depends on the difference in temperatures between the skin and the solid surface, the thermal conductivity of the solid body that the person contacts and clothing that may separate the person from the solid surface.

C_RESP—Rate of Convective Heat Exchange by Respiration

The fact that air is moved in and out of the lungs, which have a large surface area, means there is an opportunity to gain or lose heat. The rate of heat exchange depends on the air temperature and volume of air inhaled.

E_RESP—Rate of Evaporative Heat Loss by Respiration

The large surface area of the lungs provides an opportunity to lose heat by evaporation. The rate of heat exchange depends on the air humidity and volume of air inhaled.

E—Rate of Evaporative Heat Loss

Sweat on the skin surface will absorb heat from the skin when evaporating into the air. The process of evaporation cools the skin and, in turn, the body. The rate of evaporative heat loss depends on the amount of sweating, air movement, ambient humidity, and clothing.

Because W, K, C_{resp}, and E_{resp} are small relative to the other routes of heat exchange in industrial applications, they are usually ignored. When calculating heat storage, Equation 1 becomes Equation 2 as a general statement of heat balance.

$$S = M + R + C - E \qquad (2)$$

Excessive heating or cooling of a small portion of the skin can occur when it comes in contact with a hot or cold surface. The contact can be either intentional or incidental. Injury occurs when there is sufficient heat gain to cause a burn, or sufficient heat loss to cause the tissue to freeze (or at least become very cold for a period of time). In these cases, the local storage rate (S_{local}) becomes important.

$$S_{local} = K + D \qquad (3)$$

where K is conductive heat transfer between the skin and an object, and D is the rate of heat transfer to or from the local area by conduction through the local tissue and by the heat supplied or removed via local blood flow.

Factors Affecting Thermal Balance

As mentioned at the beginning of the discussion on thermal balance, three factors play an important role. They are the climatic conditions, work demands, and clothing. Climatic conditions are widely used to describe the degree of stress, as seen in casual descriptions by air temperature, relative humidity, and wind chill. They are not the only determinant of thermal stress.

The role of metabolic rate in heat balance is very important because it is a substantial contributor to heat gain. In heat stress, metabolic rate can add 10 to 100 times more heat to the body than radiation and convection combined. In cold stress, metabolic rate affects heat balance on the same order as radiation and convection losses.

Clothing is also a major contributor to thermal balance. Clothing has three characteristics: insulation, permeability, and ventilation.

Insulation is a measure of the resistance to heat flow by radiation, convection, and conduction. The greater the amount of insulation there is, the less the rate of heat flow from the warmer temperature to the cooler temperature. During heat stress exposures, it reduces heat flow by radiation and convection. It also reduces heat flow by conduction if a person has a substantial portion of the body in contact with a warm surface. Insulation plays a very important role in preventing burns by contact with a hot surface. In cold stress, it is used to reduce heat losses by convection and radiation as well as conduction, and it prevents cold injury to local tissues in contact with cold surfaces.

Permeability is a measure of the resistance to water vapor movement through the clothing by diffusion. It is a factor in thermal stress because it influences the amount of evaporative cooling that can be achieved. Permeability is related to both insulation characteristics and the clothing fabrics. Generally, as insulation increases, permeability decreases. In addition, some clothing fabrics designed as a contamination barrier can reduce the magnitude of permeability. This means that there may actually be a trade-off between the risks of heat stress and the risks from skin contact with harmful chemicals. There are clothing fabrics that provide protection against some chemical hazards while permitting water vapor transmission. These new fabrics provide a greater range of opportunity to find a balance between prevention of chemical exposure and prevention of heat stress.

Clothing ventilation is the third factor. Depending on the nature of the fabric, garment construction, and work demands, ambient air can move through the fabric or around the garment openings. Clothing ensembles that support the movement of air can enhance evaporative and convective cooling; while those that are designed and worn to limit such movement, limit evaporative and convective cooling. A good example of using ventilation characteristics to regulate heat balance is arctic parkas with drawstrings around the waist, cuffs, and hood. As metabolism heats a person, cooling can be achieved by loosening some of the closures to increase the amount of air flow (ventilation) under the clothing.

HEAT STRESS

Remembering that thermal stress is a combination of environmental, work, and clothing factors, heat stress is a combination that tends to increase body temperature, heart rate, and sweating. These physiological adaptations are collectively known as heat strain. Figure 12–1 is a schematic representation of the physiological responses to heat stress.

Looking first at metabolic rate, the heat generated by muscular work heats the deep body tissues, which means that there is a tendency for core temperature to increase. Blood circulating through the core picks up heat energy, and the warmer blood is directed to the skin where the blood is cooled. The cooler blood returns to the core to pick up more heat energy. The skin is the site of heat exchange with the environment. Convection and radiation depend on temperature differences between the skin and the environment. The net heat exchange by $R + C$ can be either positive (heat gain) or negative (heat loss). In addition, the skin secretes sweat onto the surface. As the water evaporates, it removes more heat energy from the skin, cooling the skin surface. Under ideal conditions, the body balances heat gains with losses so that the storage rate, S, is zero. This is accomplished by increasing the sweating rate until evaporative cooling is sufficient to remove the heat generated by metabolism plus any heat gained from (or lost to) the environment through $R + C$. The required evaporative cooling is denoted as E_{req}. Then Equation 2 becomes

$$E_{req} = M + R + C \qquad (4)$$

Thus, E_{req} marks the degree of physiological adjustment required to establish a thermal equilibrium between the body and the environment so that the body does not store heat. In many heat stress exposures, M is the dominant term, and E_{req} increases to meet additional cooling requirements of the work demands.

Heart rate is another important physiological parameter in assessing heat strain because it reflects the demands on the cardiovascular system to move blood (and heat) from the core to the skin. The total blood flow through the heart

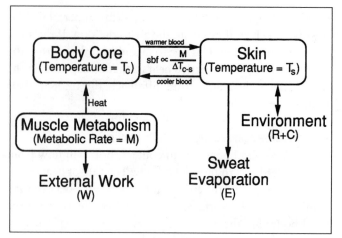

Figure 12–1. Heat flow through the body, beginning with heating the body core by metabolism, the transfer of heat by blood flow to the skin, heat gain or loss to the skin from the environment by radiation and convection, heat loss by sweat evaporation, and cooler blood returning to the core. Skin blood flow (sbf) to promote heat transfer is proportional to metabolic rate (M) divided by the difference between core and skin temperature (ΔTc-s). *(Adapted from Bernard TE, et al.* Heat Stress Management Program for Power Plants. *Electric Research Institute, NP4453L, 1991.)*

is proportional to the metabolic rate and inversely proportional to the temperature difference between the core and the skin. As work demands and metabolic rate increase, cardiac output increases, as seen in the heart rate. Sometimes skin temperature increases because evaporative cooling is limited or the net heat gain from $R + C$ is high. As the skin temperature increases toward core temperature, more blood must be delivered to the skin to achieve the same rate of cooling.

Finally, sweat rate (and total sweat volume) is another important measure of physiological strain. The greater the level of heat stress, the greater is the sweat loss. The body has a natural ability to increase the tolerance to heat stress exposures through a process called acclimation (also called acclimatization). As people become acclimated, they are able to sweat more and therefore increase their cooling capability. With increased cooling, heart rate and core temperature are lower for the same work conditions.

The following material on heat stress describes recognition, evaluation, and control of heat stress as it may affect the whole body. At the end, there is information on special topics including contact with hot surfaces and breathing of hot air.

Recognition of Heat Stress

Heat stress in the workplace can be recognized in terms of workplace risk factors and in terms of the effects it has on workers. The workplace risk factors, broadly stated, are hot or humid environments, high work demands, and protective clothing requirements. These factors are the traditional considerations in the evaluation of heat stress, and the details are in the section on evaluation of heat stress. In essence, if the workplace is generally considered as being hot through subjective judgment of workers and supervisors, then heat stress may be present. If the demands for external work are high (e.g., high metabolic rate), heat stress may be a factor in environments that are considered comfortable by casual observers (those not exerting themselves in the environment). Clothing is the third factor. While light-weight, loose-fitting, woven clothing is the ensemble of choice during exposures to heat stress, many workplaces require protective clothing that decreases permeability and ventilation and increases insulation. The added weight of personal protection may increase the metabolic heat load and therefore the level of heat stress.

The responses of workers are a good tool for the recognition of heat stress in the workplace. At the extreme end are a pattern of heat-related disorders. Intermediate markers are physiological adjustments (e.g., notable sweating) and worker behaviors.

Heat-Related Disorders

Heat-related disorders are manifestations of over-exposures to heat stress. Table 12–A is a list of common or important heat-related disorders. The table includes the signs a trained observer may see, the symptoms the person may report, likely causes of the disorder, first aid, and steps for

TABLE 12–A	Heat-Related Disorders Including the Symptoms, Signs, Causes, and Steps for First Aid and Prevention				
Disorder	**Symptoms**	**Signs**	**Cause**	**First Aid**	**Prevention**
Heat stroke	• Chills • Restlessness • Irritability	• Euphoria • Red face • Disorientation • Hot, dry skin (usually, but not always) • Erratic behavior • Collapse • Shivering • Unconsciousness • Convulsions • Body temperature ≥104°F (40°C)	• Excessive exposure • Subnormal tolerance (genetic or acquired) • Drug/alcohol abuse	• Immediate, aggressive, effective cooling • Transport to hospital • Take body temperature	• Self-determination of heat stress exposure • Maintain a healthy lifestyle • Acclimation
Heat exhaustion	• Fatigue • Weakness • Blurred vision • Dizziness, headache	• High pulse rate • Profuse sweating • Low blood pressure • Insecure gait • Pale face • Collapse • Body temperature: Normal to slightly increased	• Dehydration (caused by sweating, diarrhea, vomiting) • Distribution of blood to the periphery • Low level of acclimation • Low level of fitness	• Lie down flat on back in cool environment • Drink water • Loosen clothing	• Drink water or other fluids frequently • Add salt to food • Acclimation
Dehydration	• No early symptoms • Fatigue/weakness • Dry mouth	• Loss of work capacity • Increased response time	• Excessive fluid loss caused by sweating (vomiting or diarrhea), alcohol consumption	• Fluid and salt replacement	• Drink water or other fluids frequently • Add salt to food
Heat syncope	• Blurred vision (gray-out) • Fainting (brief black-out) • Normal temperature	• Brief fainting or near-fainting behavior	• Pooling of blood in the legs and skin from prolonged static posture and heat exposure	• Lie on back in cool environment • Drink water	• Flex leg muscles several times before moving • Stand or sit up slowly
Heat cramps	• Painful muscle cramps, especially in abdominal or fatigued muscles	• Incapacitating pain in muscles	• Electrolyte imbalance caused by prolonged sweating without adequate fluid and salt intake	• Rest in cool environment • Drink salted water (0.5% salt solution) • Massage muscles	• If hard physical work is part of the job, workers should add extra salt to their food
Heat rash (prickly heat)	• Itching skin • Reduced sweating	• Skin eruptions	• Prolonged, uninterrupted sweating • Inadequate hygiene practices	• Keep skin clean and dry • Reduce heat exposure	• Keep skin clean and periodically allow the skin to dry

Note: Salting foods is encouraged as both treatment and prevention of some heat-related disorders. Workers on salt-restricted diets must consult their personal physicians.

prevention. Figure 12–2 is a simple illustration of normal responses to heat stress and how these responses may lead to a heat-related disorder.

Heat stroke is the most serious heat-related disorder. While it may be relatively rare, it must be immediately recognized and treated to minimize permanent damage. The risk of death is high in heat stroke. It is important to have an emergency response plan for heat stroke. Heat exhaustion is the most commonly seen disorder when treatment is sought. Dehydration is a precursor to heat exhaustion, but it is usually not noticed or reported by workers.

As part of the recognition process, the health and safety professional examines reports to a medical or first aid facility. Because no specific heat-related disorders are listed does not mean heat stress is not present. It is worthwhile to examine the records for reports of faintness, weakness, nausea, cramps, headaches, and skin rashes. If temperatures are taken, some may be elevated. If urine samples are taken, some may have high specific gravity due to dehydration. There may also be an increase in the number of accidental injuries that are related to heat stress conditions.

Physiological Markers

Physiological responses to heat exposures can be used as a recognition tool. The most readily accessible are oral temperature, heart rate, and water loss. By noting one or more physiological responses of members of the work force, the health and safety professional can begin to see if a more detailed evaluation is necessary. When selecting workers to sample, it is important not to be biased toward those that appear to be the most tolerant. The sampling process should be random or favoring those who appear to be having more problems (see behaviors below).

While rectal, esophageal, and tympanic temperatures are the preferred measures of core temperature, oral temperature has long been used as an indicator of core temperature in industrial environments. Oral temperature can be measured by an electronic thermometer or disposable strips. (A caution using oral temperatures is that the person should not eat or drink for 15 minutes prior to taking the temperature and the person must keep the mouth closed.) Core temperature is estimated by adding 0.5°C or 1°F to the measured value of oral temperature. If core temperature

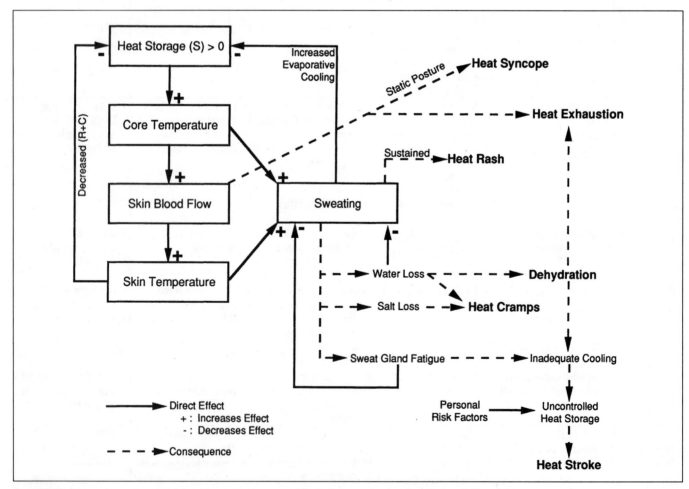

Figure 12–2. Normal responses to heat stress exposures and how they can lead to heat-related disorders.

is above 38°C (100.4°F), then heat stress is high enough to warrant evaluation. Core temperature can also be assessed using an ingested sensor. This technology is readily available but somewhat expensive for routine use.

There are devices that can measure heart rate using electronic means. Among heart rate methods, recovery heart rate is most useful as a tool for recognition. Recovery heart rate methods require that the person stop in at the end of a work cycle, sit down, and determine the pulse rate at a given point in recovery. One method of recovery heart rate proposes that the heart rate at 1 min after sitting down be at or below 110 beats per minute (bpm). Another method recommends that the heart rate at three minutes be below 90 bpm. If either of these circumstances does not exist then the work including the heat stress may be excessive and an evaluation is appropriate.

Because there are devices for measuring and logging heart rate readily available, finding the average heart rate over an eight-hour day is reasonable. If the average heart rate over a day is greater than 110 bpm, the work and heat stress may be excessive. Examination of the log for peak heart rates is also informative. If heart rates are above a nominal threshold of 160 bpm, then the demands of the work should be evaluated. (For individually set thresholds, see physiological methods for evaluation below.)

Monitoring dehydration is a third means of recognizing potential heat stress conditions. This is accomplished by noting the change in body weight from the beginning to the end of a shift. If there is more than 1.5-percent loss of body weight, then excessive dehydration is likely and an evaluation is appropriate.

Worker Behaviors

Heat stress not only induces physiological changes but also affects behavior. Likely behaviors associated with heat stress are actions that reduce exposures such as adjusting the clothing to increase evaporative losses, slowing the work rate or taking small breaks to lower the metabolic rate, and taking short cuts in work methods. Attitudes are reflected in irritability, low morale, and absenteeism. There are also an increased number of errors and machine breakdowns, and the frequency of unsafe behaviors increases.

Summary of Recognition

Basically, there are four questions you may ask to determine whether the work conditions should be evaluated for heat stress.

1. Is the environment recognized as being hot, are the work demands high, or is protective clothing required?
2. Are worker behaviors indicative of attempts to reduce heat stress, is morale low or absenteeism high, or are people making mistakes or getting hurt?
3. Do the medical records show a pattern of fatigue, weakness, headache, rashes, or high body temperature?
4. Are body temperatures, heart rates, or sweat losses high on a sample of workers?

When the answer to any of these questions is "yes", an evaluation is probably in order.

Evaluation of Heat Stress

In 1969, the World Health Organization (WHO) set the tone for worker protection against heat stress. One recommendation centers around body core temperature, which may be estimated from oral temperature as described in the discussion above on physiological markers. Core temperature should not exceed 38°C (100.4°F) during prolonged daily exposures to heat stress. The panel did recognize that 39°C (102.2°F) is acceptable as an upper limit for short periods followed by an adequate recovery. The average heart rate over a day should not exceed 110 bpm. It is the prolonged daily exposure goal that is the foundation of evaluation schemes proposed by the National Institute for Occupational Safety and Health (NIOSH) in a 1986 criteria document, and the basis for heat stress assessment as described by the American Conference of Governmental Industrial Hygienists (ACGIH®) in earlier TLVs®.

Prolonged daily exposures to heat stress are evaluated assuming that the work conditions are prevalent for a full eight hours with nominal breaks. Often, the heat stress exposure may be more episodic. In this case, heat stress is evaluated in terms of safe exposures times for a given level of heat stress. The safe exposure times are prescribed through work-rest cycles based on prolonged daily exposure criteria or through heat-balance analyses. The methods to evaluate heat stress require at least an assessment of metabolic rate and some measures of the thermal environment. Some methods assume one kind of clothing and others have provisions for different ensembles.

Evaluation of workplace heat stress can also be accomplished by demonstrating that there is not an excessive physiological strain in the work force. That is, the exposure is less important in the evaluation than the dose or the outcome. First, an overview of the current ACGIH TLV for heat stress and strain is provided to set the stage for the evaluation of occupational exposures to heat stress. This is followed by a discussion of methods to assess metabolic rate and environmental conditions. Methods to evaluate chronic and time-limited exposures to heat stress and methods to evaluate physiological strain are described in this section.

Overview of ACGIH® TLV® for Heat Stress and Strain

The current ACGIH TLV for Heat Stress and Strain (2011) recognizes the differences between eight-hour and short-duration exposures, and the value of physiological monitoring in the evaluation and control of heat stress. A flowchart in the TLV guides the thought process for the evaluation of heat stress and strain (Figure 12–3). The flow chart is entered at the top when heat stress is suspected in the workplace.

The first decision centers on the availability of a WBGT (wet bulb globe temperature)-based clothing adjustment factor (CAF) for clothing that may be worn. Values for CAF may be found in the TLV (Table 12–B), published in the literature, available in open sources, or estimated based on similar clothing properties. If a CAF is not available, then the usual means to evaluate heat stress do not apply and heat strain monitoring is the most feasible approach for evaluation.

The second decision is a simple screening test. Using available information on WBGT in the environments, the CAF, and the work demands, a table of $WBGT_{effective}$ limits for broad categories of work and work/rest proportions is provided in the TLV and in Table 12–C ($WBGT_{effective}$ = WBGT + CAF). If the action limit is not exceeded, then heat stress is low. On the other hand, exceeding the TLV screening criteria does not mean that the exposures are excessive. It means that a more detailed analysis is called for.

If the data are not available for a detailed analysis, then physiological monitoring is necessary. The detailed analysis requires a task analysis. From that information, time-weighted averages of $WBGT_{effective}$ and metabolic rate can be compared to the TLV criteria (Figure 12–4). In addition, a time-limited analysis using WBGT-based methods like the Navy PHEL (Figure 12–5) or a rational model of heat stress, like the International Organization for Standardization (ISO) Predicted Heat Strain (PHS). If the exposures do not exceed the detailed analysis limits, then general controls should be implemented. If the exposures do exceed the time-limited criteria, then physiological monitoring is the next step.

No matter which route is taken to physiological monitoring, at least general controls are necessary. If these alone are associated with acceptable heat strain, then the analysis is complete. If there is excessive physiological strain, then job specific controls must also be implemented. Success is demonstrated when both general controls and job specific controls result in acceptable physiological strain.

Assessment of Metabolic Rate

Metabolic rate is the rate of internal heat generation, which must be dissipated from the body to maintain thermal equilibrium. (In cold stress, metabolic rate is important to maintain deep body temperature.) First, there is a base level of metabolism that is necessary to support life. Beyond basal metabolism, there is a work-driven metabolism that is

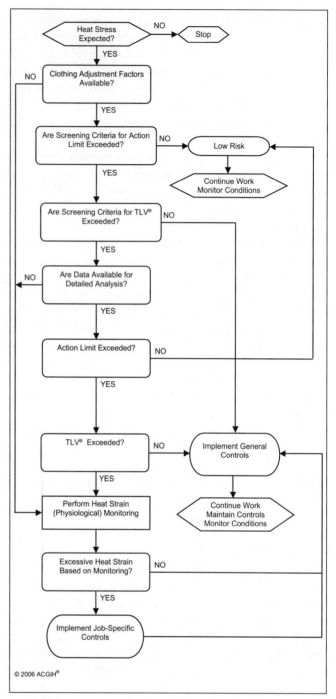

Figure 12–3. Flow chart for the ACGIH TLV for heat stress and strain.

largely the result of muscular effort. The greatest metabolic rate resulting from muscular effort occurs when the muscles exert a force with motion (dynamic work), and much less metabolic demand is required to exert a force with no motion (isometric contraction or static work). Therefore, the greatest metabolic rates occur when the body must be moved over a distance, especially upwards, and when objects are moved in space. Lesser metabolic rates are seen

TABLE 12–B			WBGT Clothing Adjustment Factors (CAFs) for Different Clothing Ensembles in Degrees C-WBGT*
Ensemble	**CAF from USF [°C-WBGT]**	**CAF from ACGIH [°C-WBGT]**	**Comments**
Work Clothes	0	0	Work clothes made from a woven fabric is the reference ensemble
Cloth Coveralls	0	0	Woven fabric that includes FR® treated cotton and Nomex®
SMS Nonwoven Coveralls as a single layer	-1	0.5	SMS is a nonproprietary process to make nonwoven fabrics from polypropylene
Tyvek® 1422A Coveralls as a single layer	2	1	Tyvek® is a proprietary fabric made from polyethylene. Tyvek® 1422A has a somewhat higher CAF than 1424 and 1427, which were used for the TLV.
Vapor-barrier apron with long sleeves and long length over cloth coveralls	4		The apron configuration was designed to protect the front of the body against spills from chemical agents
Double layer of woven clothing		3	
NexGen® coveralls as a single layer	2.5	–	NexGen® is a proprietary microporous fabric that is water-barrier, vapor-permeable. There is great variability in these types of fabrics and one CAF will not apply for another fabric.
Microporous coveralls (generic)	6		The CAFs of microporous barriers vary widely and the generic value represents a higher observed value in the range
Vapor-barrier coveralls as a single layer	10		No hood. The real effect depends on the level of humidity and in many cases the effect is less.
Vapor-barrier coveralls with hood as a single layer	11	11	It was assumed that a hood would be worn with vapor-barrier coveralls.
Vapor-barrier over cloth coveralls w/o hood and w/ NP respirator	12		
Hood†	+1		Wearing a hood of any fabric with any clothing ensemble
Full-face negative pressure respirator†	+0.3		Military style respirator and should be a worst-case condition. The difference is not statistically or substantially different from 0 but added for those who insist that a factor should be used.

*The clothing adjustment factors are added to the measured WBGT to obtain WBGT$_{effective}$.
**University of South Florida
†This value is added to the CAF of the ensemble without hood or respirator.

TABLE 12–C		Screening Criteria for Heat Stress*		
%Work	**Light**	**Moderate**	**Heavy**	**Very Heavy**
Action Limit Screening [°C-WBGT]				
75 to 100	28.1	25.0	–	–
50 to 75	28.7	26.0	24.2	–
25 to 50	29.3	27.2	25.7	24.6
0 to 25	30.0	28.8	27.8	27.0
TLV® Screening [°C-WBGT]				
75 to 100	30.8	28.2	–	–
50 to 75	31.2	29.0	27.6	–
25 to 50	31.8	30.1	28.8	27.9
0 to 25	32.3	31.3	30.5	29.8

Note: In the TLV Booklet, these values are rounded to the nearest 0.5°C-WBGT.
*These screening criteria should not be used to prescribe work/recovery cycles.

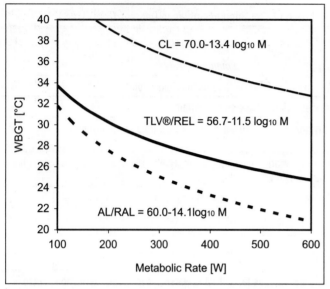

M	TLV	Action Limit	Ceiling
100	33.7	31.8	43.2
125	32.6	30.4	41.9
150	31.7	29.3	40.8
175	30.9	28.4	39.9
200	30.2	27.6	39.2
225	29.6	26.8	38.5
250	29.1	26.2	37.9
275	28.6	25.6	37.3
300	28.2	25.1	36.8
325	27.8	24.6	36.3
350	27.4	24.1	35.9
375	27.1	23.7	35.5
400	26.8	23.3	35.1
425	26.5	22.9	34.8
450	26.2	22.6	34.4
475	25.9	22.3	34.1
500	25.7	21.9	33.8
525	25.4	21.6	33.5
550	25.2	21.4	33.3
575	25.0	21.1	33.0
600	24.8	20.8	32.8

Figure 12–4. Heat stress limits proposed by NIOSH (Ceiling Limit/CL, Recommended Exposure Limit/REL, and Recommended Alert Limit/RAL) and ACGIH (TLV and Action Limit/AL).

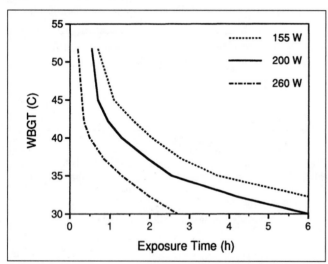

Figure 12–5. Example of U.S. Navy Permissible Heat Exposure Limit (PHEL) chart. Clothing is work clothes of long sleeve shirt and long pants.

for sedentary activities or simply holding objects without any motion.

One very simple method to assess metabolic rate is to assign the work demands into one of three to five categories of metabolic rate (e.g., light, moderate, and heavy). Another simple method is to look for similar activities in published tables of metabolic rates for specific activities (or assume the demands are equivalent by subjective matching). Either of these methods is expedient, but not very accurate (and perhaps prone to over-estimation).

Some discipline is required in the assessment of metabolic rate. The first step is to divide the job into discrete,

homogeneous tasks, and then determine their duration. Then a metabolic rate can be assigned to each task. Finally, the time-weighted average for metabolic rate can be determined (TWA-M). Using categories or tables to assign values of metabolic rate to a task reduces some of the error, but the ISO method is recommended and outlined in the following paragraph. In addition there are other published methods that provide good results.

Following the ISO method for a given task, the metabolic rate can be estimated by summing together five components. The components are basal metabolism (B), posture (P), activity based on degree of body involvement (A), the horizontal travel (H), and vertical travel (V). That is,

$$M_{task} = B + P + A + H + V \qquad (5)$$

Table 12–D describes values of metabolic rate associated with each of the components. The SI units for metabolic rate are watts, and conversion factors to change from watts to units reported in other sources (i.e., kcal/min, kcal/h, Btu/h, L/min of oxygen consumption) are provided at the bottom.

Assessment of the Environmental Conditions

The environmental factors that are central to the assessment of heat stress are air temperature, humidity, air speed, and average temperature of the solid surroundings. How these factors are incorporated into the evaluation of heat stress depend on the evaluation tool. The SI unit for temperature is degrees Centigrade.

Dry bulb temperature (T_{db}) is the direct measure of air

TABLE 12–D	Values for the Four Components of Equation 5 to Estimate the Metabolic Rate for a Task (in watts)		
		Average (watts)	Range (watts
Basal metabolism (B)		70	
Posture metabolism (P)			
Sitting		20	
Standing		40	
Walking		170	140–210
Activity (A)			
Hand	Light	30	15–85
	Heavy	65	
One arm	Light	70	50–175
	Heavy	120	
Both arms	Light	105	70–245
	Heavy	175	
Whole body	Light	245	175–1,050
	Moderate	350	
	Heavy	490	
	Very heavy	630	

Walking (H)
H_{hor} = rate of horizontal travel (meters/min)
$H = 3.3\,H_{hor}$
Climbing (V)
V_{vert} = rate of vertical ascent (meters/min)
$V = 56\,V_{vert}$

Unit Conversions for Metabolic Rate

From Watts to Other Units	From Other Units to Watts
kcal/min = 0.014 × W	W = 70 × kcal/min
kcal/h = 0.86 × W	W = 1.2 × kcal/h
Btu/h = 3.4 × W	W = 0.29 × Btu/h
l O_2/min = 0.0029 × W	W = 350 l × O_2/min

temperature. The temperature sensor is surrounded by air, which is allowed to freely flow around the sensor. The sensor, however, may be influenced by radiant heat sources and therefore should be shielded from them.

Psychrometric wet bulb temperature (T_{pwb}) is based on the degree of evaporative cooling that can occur. In practice, a wetted wick is placed around a temperature sensor and enough air is forced over the wick to maximize the rate of evaporative cooling (> 3 m/s). The amount of temperature reduction that can be achieved depends directly on the amount of water vapor in the air. When humidity is high (high water-vapor pressure), the reduction in temperature is low. When the humidity is lower, the reduction is higher.

Ambient water vapor pressure (P_v) is commonly known as humidity. There are two ways humidity is expressed—relative and absolute. At any given temperature, the partial pressure of water vapor that can be in the air has a maximum value, the saturation pressure. At low temperatures, the saturation pressure is low, and it increases exponentially with temperature. Relative humidity is the ratio of the water

vapor pressure in the air to the saturation pressure at that temperature. So 50 percent relative humidity means that the water vapor pressure is 50 percent of the saturation pressure. Unfortunately, relative humidity is not very useful as a tool to assess heat stress because the water vapor pressure represented by a value of relative humidity can be substantially different depending on the air temperature. Absolute humidity is expressed as the amount of water vapor in the air in terms of partial pressure or weight per unit volume of air. The usual practice for heat stress evaluation is to use the partial pressure and the SI unit is kPa (kiloPascals). (To convert from kPa to mmHg, the value in kPa is multiplied by 7.5.) Usually a psychrometric chart is used to determine humidity from T_{db} and T_{pwb}.

Natural wet bulb temperature (T_{nwb}) is similar to the psychrometric wet bulb except that air is allowed to flow over the sensor naturally rather than being forced. When air flow is less than 3 m/s, the temperature reduction is less than psychrometric wet bulb temperature for the same absolute humidity. That is, natural wet bulb temperature is sensitive to both humidity and air movement.

Air speed (V_{air}) is measured using an appropriate anemometer. The anemometer should not be unidirectional. Because the speed will vary in space and time, an average value is used.

Globe temperature (T_g) responds to radiant heat from the solid surroundings and convective heat from the ambient air. The globe temperature is classically measured using a six-inch, thin-walled, copper sphere, painted matte black on the outside. The temperature sensor is placed at the center of the globe. When all the surrounding surfaces are the same temperature as the air, the globe temperature is equal to air temperature. If one or more of the surfaces are different, then the globe temperature will increase or decrease depending on the average temperature of the solid surroundings. Finally, for a given level of radiant heat exchange with the globe, the globe temperature will differ the most from air temperature with little air movement, and will differ the least with a significant air motion because it is also sensitive to convective heat exchange with the air. Globe temperature is used to estimate the average wall temperature of the surroundings.

Effective Temperature (ET) and Corrected Effective Temperature (CET) are indices of the thermal environment that were first developed to equate thermal sensation, and later used to describe thermal stress. ET is determined from a nomogram that requires knowledge of T_{db}, T_{pwb}, and V_{air}. For a sedentary person dressed in light clothing, equal values of ET would indicate similar sensations of warmth. Because of its history, it was used in the early studies of heat stress as an index of the environment. Because ET did not account for radiant heat, CET was proposed. It uses T_g instead of T_{db} when entering the nomogram. Neither ET nor CET is used to evaluate heat stress today. Instead a new index was required that could be more easily determined and was indicative of thermal stress from the environment. The wet bulb globe temperature (WBGT) was the evolutionary step from ET and CET.

Wet bulb globe temperature (WBGT) is an index of environmental heat that is widely used to evaluate industrial heat stress. In environments that are indoors, in the shade, or on a cloudy day, it is computed as

$$WBGT_{in} = 0.7T_{nwb} + 0.3T_g \qquad (6)$$

Under conditions of direct sunlight (outdoors and no cloud cover), it is computed as

$$WBGT_{out} = 0.7T_{nwb} + 0.2T_g + 0.1T_{db} \qquad (7)$$

Instrumentation to assess WBGT was originally a large copper globe and mercury-in-glass thermometers. There are several manufacturers of electronic instrumentation and they often use smaller globes. In addition to computing the WBGT directly, some can perform data logging functions as well as real-time analysis of the environment (e.g., safe work times). The electronic instrumentation has virtually replaced the conventional WBGT "Christmas tree apparatus" (Figure 12–6).

Evaluation of Prolonged Exposures to Heat Stress

With a goal of limiting the heat stress dose (core temperature not to exceed 38°C or 100.4°F), the problem becomes one of relating exposure (combinations of environment, metabolic rate, and clothing) to dose. Lind proposed the concept of the upper limit of the prescriptive zone (Bernard et. al., 1994). In a set of classic experiments, he demonstrated several important relationships between work, environment, and core temperature. In essence, Lind found that for a given metabolic rate, core temperature would remain relatively constant for increasing levels of environmental heat until a critical level. Then the core temperature would steeply rise with increasing levels of environmental heat, creating an increased risk for heat disorders. This critical level of heat stress was the upper limit of the prescriptive zone, and the person could work eight hours at or below this level without significant risk of a heat disorder. The upper limit is at lower levels of environmental heat for higher metabolic rates, and vice versa.

By exploring the upper limit of the prescriptive zone for different worker populations, Dukes-Dobos developed protective limits for the 95th percentile of the general worker population. At these protective limits, core temperature should not exceed 38°C (100.4°F) and first-minute recovery heart rates should not exceed 110 bpm. The upper limit of the prescriptive zone was first adapted by NIOSH in 1972 and revised in 1986. It was adopted by the ACGIH in 1973 (and revised in 1990) for the TLV for Heat Stress. The International Organization for Standardization (ISO) also adapted the NIOSH thresholds in 1983. The limits are expressed in hourly time-weighted averages for both the WBGT and metabolic rate. The thresholds are illustrated in Figure 12–4 using both the NIOSH and ACGIH nomenclature.

The middle curve is called the recommended exposure limit (REL) by NIOSH. For workers wearing ordinary cloth summer-weight work clothes and who are acclimated to heat, there should be practically no risk of heat-related disorders when working for eight hours with nominal breaks every two hours. Notice that as the metabolic rate increases, the threshold for WBGT decreases. This means that maintaining core temperature below 38°C (100.4°F) requires a "cooler" environment for higher internal heat generation.

Figure 12–6. An example of an electronic device used to measure WBGT. *(QUESTempºTM 36 Heat Stress Monitor a product of Quest Technologies, a 3M company. Photo used with permission.)*

The ACGIH calls this threshold the TLV. The lower curve is called the recommended alert limit by NIOSH and the action limit by the ACGIH. This curve is proposed in recognition that unacclimated workers are less able to tolerate heat-stress exposures and this lower tolerance can be accommodated by a lower level of environmental heat at the same work demands. The upper curve is the ceiling limit proposed by NIOSH, but not included in the TLV. Special care should be taken for exposures above the ceiling limit for more than 15 minutes.

Because clothing is also a factor in determining the level of heat stress, the ACGIH has provided a table of adjustment factors that can be added to the measured values of WBGT in the environments of interest. These are given in Table 12–B. Also included in the table are adjustment factors for other kinds of clothing that may be found in the workplace. An important note about using the adjustment factors is that they represent the current best guess about the effects of clothing other than ordinary work clothes, and some caution is necessary in using them. Using physiological strain indicators (i.e., personal monitoring) to confirm the evaluation may be appropriate.

To evaluate a job for heat stress, a one- to two-hour interval for time-weighted averaging (TWA) must be selected. If the work is repeated in an hourly pattern, a one-hour TWA can be used. If the work is intermittent, up to a two-hour TWA may be more representative of the demands. TWA-M and TWA-WBGT must be calculated for the selected interval. Adjust the WBGT for each location by adding the clothing adjustment factor to the measured value as appropriate. With these TWA values, the work can be located in the graph of Figure 12–4. If it is below the RAL/Action Limit, there is no practical risk for heat-related disorders to develop even for the least heat-tolerant but otherwise healthy workers. If it is between the RAL/Action Limit and REL/TLV, then a program of heat-stress management should be in place. The program should include at least the general controls described in the section on controls. If it is above the REL/TLV, then heat stress is a hazard in the work environment and control actions should be taken.

Evaluation of Time-Limited Exposures to Heat Stress

For heat-stress exposures above the REL/TLV, the question may become, how long can someone safely work? This question can be answered either by WBGT-based methods or by heat balance analysis (rational method).

WBGT techniques. WBGT techniques fall into two methods. One method uses TWAs and the TLV. Then the question is asked in terms of how much time in an hour can someone work above the TLV compared to the time work or recovery is below the TLV? This first question is a general case of work-rest cycles. A way to use the WBGT/TLV method is to iterate on a solution by testing various combinations of exposure time and recovery time that equal one hour so that the combination of TWA-M and TWA-WBGT lands on the TLV line. (A spreadsheet solution can be developed by using the equation for the TLV line provided in the Figure 12–4.)

The U.S. Navy and the Electric Power Research Institute have proposed WBGT methods to determine safe exposure times from charts. An example of the Navy Permissible Heat Exposure Limit (PHEL) chart is illustrated in Figure 12–5 (clothing is ordinary work clothes). Clothing adjustment factors can be used for other clothing ensembles. A full recovery should be allowed before repeating the exposure. A rule of thumb is one hour in a cool location with low metabolic demands.

Heat-balance analysis. Heat balance analysis uses a rational model of heat exchange between a hypothetical person and the environment. While the WBGT methods mentioned previously are empirical methods of heat-stress evaluation, the method of heat-balance analysis is considered a rational method because it considers the biophysics of heat exchange. If thermal equilibrium can be established, then there is no risk of an excessive level of heat stress. If thermal equilibrium cannot be established, then the amount of time to reach an upper limit of heat storage (nominally to a core temperature of 38.5°C or 101.3°F) can be determined. That desktop evaluations of potential countermeasures can be performed is another advantage of heat balance analysis.

A classic, but dated, method is called the Heat Stress Index (HSI) (proposed by Belding and Hatch in the 1950s). It is described in some detail here to appreciate the overall approach a rational method takes. It starts from the premise that Equation 2 describes heat balance and Equation 4 describes the evaporative cooling requirements. Equation 4 is repeated here.

$$E_{req} = M + R + C \tag{4}$$

The HSI is based on simple relationships for computing R and C, which have been updated over the years. The equations that follow are for workers wearing ordinary woven cloth work clothes and the units are watts, degrees Celsius, meters per second (m/s) for air speed (V_{air}), and kiloPascals (kPa) for water-vapor pressure.

Basically, R is equal to a clothing-related constant multiplied by the difference between the mean temperature of the surroundings (T_r) and a mean skin temperature of 35°C (95°F). Obviously, if the average surrounding temperature is greater than skin temperature, there is a gain of heat by radiation.

$$R = 7.7(T_r - 35) \tag{8}$$

Where

$$T_r = T_g + 1.8V_{air}^{0.5}(T_g - T_{db}) \tag{9}$$

C is equal to a clothing-related constant multiplied by a power function of air speed multiplied by the difference between air and skin temperature, as follows

$$C = 8.1V_{air}^{0.6}(T_{db} - 35) \tag{10}$$

If the air temperature is greater than skin temperature, there is a heat gain by convection; if air temperature is less than skin temperature, there is a heat loss.

The method also provides for the determination of the maximum rate of evaporative cooling (E_{max}), which has either an environmental or physiological limit. The environmental limit on E_{max} is determined as a clothing-related constant multiplied by a power function of air speed multiplied by the difference between skin and air water-vapor pressure (P_v).

$$E_{max} = 122V_{air}^{0.6}(5.6 - P_v) \tag{11}$$

Because P_v is less than 5.6, E_{max} will have a positive value representing the evaporative heat loss. The physiological limit is based on a limiting sweat rate of 1 L/h, which is equivalent to a heat flow of 675 W. Therefore E_{max} is the greater value of that computed from Equation 6 or 675. Then

$$\text{HSI} = 100\frac{E_{req}}{E_{max}} \tag{12}$$

If the HSI is less than 40, then heat stress is low and no further actions are required. If the HSI is between 40 and 70, heat stress is a significant workplace hazard. If HSI is between 70 and 100, heat stress is high and workers are at risk for heat-related disorders. If HSI is greater than 100, there is significant heat storage and the exposure is time-limited.

A number of variations to HSI, as well as alternatives, have been proposed. The International Organization for Standardization (ISO) has published the most recent and comprehensive rational method for heat balance analysis. It is called the Predicted Heat Strain (PHS) (ISO7933, 2004). The principle of the ISO method is to determine (1) the amount of evaporative cooling that is required for thermal equilibrium (E_{req}), (2) whether the required cooling can be achieved by sweating and evaporation with consideration of the time it takes for these mechanisms to take effect, and (3) what time limits may apply if sweating or evaporation is insufficient. The limits are based on inadequate cooling and potential dehydration. The standard applies to a variety of clothing ensembles when the insulation and evaporative resistance is known or can be estimated. If the heat-balance analysis indicates that thermal equilibrium can be achieved, then heat stress does not play a limiting role in the work. If the time limits are less than six hours, then serious consideration must be given to heat-stress controls.

The accuracy of PHS analysis is limited because certain variables are not easily measured, but fair assumptions can be made. The important advantage of heat-balance analysis is the ability to compare the relative advantages of proposed changes in the environment, work demands, and clothing requirements. There are Excel®-based workbooks to compute PHS. Care should be taken in using it to evaluate or prescribe short-term exposures. Based on unpublished data, if PHS is used to estimate a short-term exposure time limit for evaluation or control, it is protective with a time limit of less than 60 min. For PHS times between 60 and 120 min, it is best to multiply the incremental PHS limit above 60 min by 0.2 and then add that to 60 min to be sufficiently protective. For example, if PHS provides a limit of 90 min, the protective limit would be 60 plus 0.2(90-60) or 66 min.

Evaluation of Physiological Strain

As mentioned earlier, physiological strain resulting from heat-stress exposures is seen as elevations in core temperature, heart rate, and sweating. They are therefore candidates as evaluation tools for heat stress exposures. Physiological evaluation is a valid approach because it uses direct assessment of the effects of heat stress (dose) rather than an index of exposure, which is then related to dose through empirical evidence and models. The TLV for Heat Stress and Strain reflects the value placed on physiological monitoring. If no excessive physiological strain is demonstrated in the working population at a workplace, then heat stress is controlled by the work practices in place.

Physiological evaluation as an alternative or confirming evaluation of heat stress may be worthwhile when protective clothing is required. It might also be used to demonstrate compliance with the spirit of the NIOSH and ACGIH thresholds when some work occurs just above the thresholds. In selecting workers to sample for the physiological evaluations, the choice should be random and sufficient to ensure statistical reliability.

Core temperature is a physiological construct used to

describe internal body temperature. There are several laboratory methods used to assess core temperature that are not acceptable in a workplace. Acceptable surrogate methods are available. The surrogate with the longest history is oral temperature. To take an accurate oral temperature, the individual must not eat or drink for 15 minutes prior to the sample and the mouth must remain closed. Core temperature is approximately equal to oral temperature plus 0.5°C or 1°F. Other alternatives are available. One is a commercial personal monitor with data-logging capabilities that monitors ear canal temperature with a thermistor held in place by a disposable ear plug. There are swallowable "pills" that can transmit a value for temperature to a receiver outside of the body.

As a criterion for core temperature, 38°C (100.4°F) is the limit if the temperature is sustained over the course of the workday. If the work is intermittent, then transient increases to 39°C (102.2°F) should be acceptable as long as there is sufficient recovery to allow core temperature to return toward 37 to 37.5°C (98.6 to 99.5°F). That is, the time-weighted average should not exceed 38°C (100.4°F). As a matter of practice, core temperature should not exceed 38.5°C (101.3°F) for industrial exposures to heat stress to allow for measurement errors and for an overshoot before recovery occurs.

Heart rate is another indicator of heat strain. Four methods proposed for assessing heart rate are in use. Three methods mentioned previously are recovery heart rate, peak heart rate, and average heart rate over an eight-hour duration. Another method evaluates a set of averaged heart rates over a typical exposure period.

Recovery heart rate was mentioned previously as a tool for recognition. It has also been used to evaluate workplaces. To demonstrate effective control of heat stress, the recovery heart rate at one minute (HRR_1) should be less than 110 bpm. Alternatively, the heart rate at three minutes (HRR_3) should be less than 90 bpm or the value of $HRR_1 - HRR_3$ should be at least 10 bpm.

If the daily average heart rate exceeds 110 bpm, then heat stress and/or very strenuous work may be the cause. This limiting average has been recommended by the WHO experts and confirmed in laboratory and field studies.

Setting a threshold for heart rate is a third approach. A recording of heart rate during a heat stress exposure is shown in Figure 12–7. As a rule of thumb, peak heart rates should not exceed 90 percent of a person's maximal heart rate (HR_{max}). Sometimes this value is known from a stress test and other times it must be estimated from age (e.g., $HR_{max} = 195 - 0.67[age-25 years]$). Brief periods above this threshold are not significant, but sustained for several minutes may be excessive. The ACGIH has recommended limiting sustained heart rates of several minutes to 180 – age.

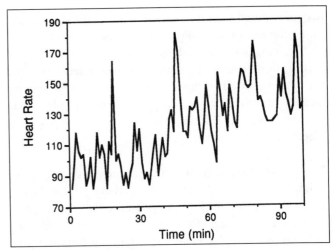

Figure 12–7. Example of a heart rate response to a heat stress exposure.

When looking over a history of heart rate for the day, an obvious trend toward higher heart rates also indicates heat stress above the thresholds because the body is having trouble maintaining thermal equilibrium. The momentary peaks in Figure 12–7 are not significant, but the trend in the second half is a classic representation of the response to moderately high heat stress and eventually excessive cardiovascular strain.

Sweat rate and volume are theoretically measures of physiological strain, but less practical than core temperature and heart rate. Sweat volume over a given period of time is equal to an initial body weight plus the weight of food and drink consumed minus the weight of anything excreted minus a final body weight. The overall weight change in kilograms is equal to the sweat volume in liters. If there is more than a five-liter sweat volume, heat stress is sufficient to cause dehydration and therefore significant. Over a two- to four-hour interval, the sweat rate should be less than one liter per hour.

Control of Heat Stress

The control of heat stress and heat strain centers around the causes of heat stress and the resulting physiological strain. It takes the form of general controls that are applicable to all heat-related jobs, and specific controls that must be evaluated and selected based on the constraints of the working conditions. The controls are divided into general and specific controls.

General Controls

General controls are those actions that are universally applicable to heat stress work. The general controls are training, heat-stress hygiene practices, medical surveillance, heat-alert program, and emergency plan. Any time a group of workers may be exposed to heat stress that is above the RAL/Action Limit, the general controls should be implemented.

Training is an essential feature of managing heat stress. It is for those employees working on heat-related jobs and their supervisors. The information gained from the training enables them to recognize heat stress and to control the risks associated with it. Training is divided into two types—preplacement and periodic.

Preplacement training. Preplacement training is directed to an employee who is reporting to a heat-related job for the first time. The preplacement training can be given during other job training including safety or skill training. It is not necessary to repeat preplacement training for an employee who has had it once. The formal content of the preplacement training is the same as that for annual or periodic training (see the next paragraph). A complement to the preplacement training is any counseling medical personnel may give an individual employee relating to that employee's physical condition.

Periodic training. Annual heat-stress training should be given to employees working on heat-related jobs to refresh their knowledge of heat stress and controls. The following topics should be covered during training:

- Description of heat stress
  - environment, work demands, and clothing
  - physiological responses including acclimation
- Recognition of, and first aid for, heat-related disorders
  - description of heat-related disorders including symptoms and causes
  - description of first aid measures for each disorder
- Heat stress hygiene practices (see following for details)
  - description of heat stress hygiene practices
  - emphasis on individual responsibility
- Overview of heat stress policy and guidelines
  - company policy
  - management responsibilities
  - employee responsibilities

The format of the training can be similar to other health and safety training. Using commercially available videotape and written materials is effective and efficient. However, it is important to point out those issues that may be particular to the work site.

Heat stress hygiene practices. Heat-stress hygiene practices are the actions taken by an individual to reduce the risks of a heat disorder. The individual is responsible for practicing good heat stress hygiene. Site management informs the workers of good practices and helps the workers practice them. Some practices are listed.

Fluid replacement—A great deal of water is lost from the body as sweat for evaporative cooling. Losses may be up to six liters or quarts of water in one day, equivalent to about 13 pounds. This water should be replaced by drinking cool water or flavored drinks (e.g., dilute iced tea, artificially sweetened lemonade, or commercial fluid-replacement drinks). Because thirst is not a sufficient driver for water replacement, workers should drink small quantities as frequently as possible. This helps instill drinking as a habit and the volumes do not cause discomfort. If work is to be performed in a drinking-restricted area, drinking about one pint per hour of work before the work begins will help meet the demands for water during the work.

Self-determination—One aspect of self-determination is limiting an exposure to heat stress. It is a responsibility of the worker and supervisor. In self-determination, the person terminates an exposure to heat stress at the first symptom of a heat-related disorder or extreme discomfort. Serious injury can occur if the onset of symptoms is ignored.

Another aspect of self-determination is reducing the effects of heat stress by lowering peak work demands and making the work demands lighter. For instance, when a fixed amount of work is assigned to a portion of the shift, peak demands can be reduced by leveling out the work effort over the allocated time or taking more frequent breaks. For those working in crews, the pace should be set for the least heat-tolerant worker.

Diet—A well-balanced diet is important to maintain the good health needed to work under heat stress. Large meals should not be eaten during work breaks because they increase circulatory load and metabolic rate. Diets designed to lose weight should be directed by a physician who understands that the patient is working under conditions of potential heat stress. Weight control for overweight workers is recommended because obesity increases the risk of heat-related disorders.

Salt intake as part of a normal diet is usually sufficient to meet the salt demands during heat-stress work. Added salt may be desirable when repeated heat stress exposures are first experienced (i.e., during acclimation). If salt is restricted by a physician's order, the physician should be consulted.

Lifestyle—A healthy lifestyle is important to lowering the risk of a heat-related disorder. A worker should have adequate sleep, a good diet, and regular exercise also helps. A healthy lifestyle also means no abuse of alcohol or drugs, which have been implicated in heat strokes. In addition, exposures to heat stress immediately before work may increase the risk of a heat disorder at work.

Health Status—All workers should recognize that chronic illnesses, such as heart, lung, kidney, or liver disease, indicate a potential for lower heat tolerance and therefore an increased risk of experiencing a heat-related disorder during heat-stress exposures. As a matter of principle, workers suffering from any chronic disorder should inform the physician of occupational exposures to heat stress and seek advice about the potential effects of the disorder or drugs used to treat it.

If a worker is experiencing the symptoms of any acute illness and still reports to work, that worker should inform the immediate supervisor. The ability to tolerate heat is likely to be diminished, not to mention the risk of infecting others.

Acclimation—Acclimation is the adaptation of the body to prolonged daily heat stress exposures. The ability to work increases and the risk of heat disorders decreases with acclimation. Acclimation is lost when there are no heat exposures. The loss is accelerated when an illness occurs. The process should be recognized and expectations adjusted. Workers will be able to work better after several days of heat exposures, and they should expect less of themselves in the early days.

Table 12–E provides a framework for how acclimation can be induced and reinduced after an absence from heat exposures. Recommendations for new worker acclimation usually start at lower levels to further account for the lack of familiarity with the job and therefore greater risk of accidents. This is reflected in the five-day schedule that begins at 20 percent of daily exposure. For experienced workers, three days of increasing exposures followed by full exposures should be sufficient. Recognizing that full acclimation is normally lost over three weeks, the reacclimation schedule in Table 12–E is recommended by the author.

Medical surveillance—This surveillance encompasses the evaluation of individual risk for adverse effects to heat-stress exposures, provides treatment for heat-related disorders, and helps assess the information collected from heat-related disorder incidents. Medical surveillance should be under the direction of a licensed physician.

Evaluation of risk—The medical surveillance activity includes identifying those workers who may be at extraordinary risk for heat-related disorders. Preplacement and routine physicals under the direction of the physician are used to identify these people. The physician should consult the 1986 NIOSH Criteria Document for more information, but ultimately the physician must set the criteria.

Before an employee is placed on a heat-related job, the employee should receive a preplacement physical examination that covers the following items:

- comprehensive work and medical history with an emphasis on past intolerance to heat stress and relevant information on the cardiovascular, respiratory, and nervous systems; skin; liver; and kidneys
- comprehensive physical examination that gives special attention to the cardiovascular, respiratory, and nervous systems; skin; liver; kidneys; and obesity
- assessment of the use of prescription and over-the-counter drugs as well as the abuse of alcohol or other drugs that may increase the risk of heat intolerance
- assessment of ability to wear and use personal protection that may be required
- assessment of other factors that may affect heat tolerance as deemed important by the physician-in-charge

TABLE 12–E Basic Acclimation Schedule and a Schedule for Reacclimation after Periods Away from Heat Stress Exposures Due to Routine Absence of Illness

Basic Acclimation Schedule		
Day	Activity (% of full work assignment)	
	Experienced	New
Day 1	50	20
Day 2	60	40
Day 3	80	60
Day 4	100	80
Day 5		100

Reacclimation Schedule					
Days Away from Heat-Related Schedule		Exposure Sequence (% of full work assignment)			
Routine Absence	Illness	Day 1	Day 2	Day 3	Day 4
<4	—	100			
4-5	1-3	R/E*	100		
6-12	4-5	80	100		
12-20	6-8	60	80	100	
>20	>8	50	60	80	100

*Reduce expectations, some diminished capacity

The physician should provide a written opinion of the results, which is placed in the employee's medical file. A copy should be provided to the employee. The written opinion should contain the following:

- results of the examination and tests
- physician's opinion on potential risk to the employee
- physician's opinion on the employee's capability to work on heat-related jobs
- any recommended limitations or restrictions
- statement that the employee has been informed of the results

Because an employee's health status can change over time, periodic re-evaluations are appropriate. These periodic physicals should be scheduled approximately yearly. There may be times when the physician or management believes that the ability of an individual to tolerate heat stress has diminished. In this case, the physician may perform a timely physical outside the schedule for a periodic physical examination.

Response to heat-related disorders—The organization's medical department is responsible for providing response to reported heat-related disorders directly through medical department facilities, by medical department personnel at the job site, or by providing first aid training to selected department foremen or safety personnel.

In addition to providing for response, the physician or designee (e.g., safety department personnel) should periodically review heat-stress incidents to update the program.

Heat-alert programs are a collection of activities taken in anticipation of heat-stress conditions or an unusually high level of heat stress. These conditions may be the approaching of summer, of a maintenance outage, of special operating conditions, or of a heat wave. The first step in a heat-alert program is to appoint a committee whose members are responsible for the annual review of heat stress management activities and to make adjustments as necessary. This committee should be comprised of management representatives from such departments as operations, maintenance, engineering, medical, industrial hygiene, safety, and human resources as well as representatives of labor from different departments that may be affected. It should meet well before the anticipated presence of heat stress in the workplace. At a minimum, the committee should complete the following activities:

- review training materials and set training schedule for the current year
- oversee the preparation of the facility for heat stress conditions (e.g., reverse winterization) and check the operability of heat stress controls (e.g., fans, air conditioners, drinking stations, personal protection)
- oversee the preparations for changes in staffing and work practices if appropriate

- review policies and procedures regarding heat-related disorders
- prepare for extraordinary heat stress conditions by
  - setting criteria for a Heat-Alert State (such as a sudden increase in ambient temperatures from a heat wave) and how it will be announced;
  - preparing special administrative controls (see below) such as rescheduling work, increasing the number of workers, further restricting overtime, personal monitoring for excessive heat strain, etc.; and
  - closely monitoring workers for heat-related disorders.

Emergency plan—An emergency plan for heat stroke should be part of the overall emergency plan for the site. The plan should include the ability to recognize early symptoms of heat stroke by first line supervisors and workers, a method for immediate emergency cooling of the victim (ice bath immersion or other aggressive method), and arrangements for transport to the hospital. It is crucial to start cooling immediately and not to wait for an emergency service to arrive.

Specific Controls

The two major factors in heat stress are work demands and environmental conditions (i.e., air temperature, humidity, air movement, and hot surfaces). Clothing requirements are a third factor when multiple layers, nonwoven clothing, or vapor-barrier fabrics are worn. For specific jobs, the control of heat stress and the resulting physiological strain on workers is accomplished through engineering controls, administrative controls, and personal protection.

Table 12–F is a checklist of controls suggested by NIOSH in the revised criteria document. The table is one way to begin to understand what might be done to manage the level of heat stress. While each job must be examined in light of the work to be accomplished and the constraints of the workplace, the following discussion highlights the principles of the control measures and can be used to focus discussion of controls.

To select controls for specific jobs, the first step is to discuss the job among production, engineering, and health and safety functions using the following discussion of control measures. A long list of ideas that emphasizes engineering controls, followed by administrative controls, and finally personal protection should be generated. Imagination is essential during the development of candidate controls for the long list, and no candidate control should be rejected out-of-hand. Controls should then be judged on their merits as they relate to being effective and technically and economically reasonable. The result is a short list of controls that can be prioritized and implemented over a reasonable timeframe. It is reasonable to have short-term solutions while long-term solutions are planned and executed.

Engineering controls. These are the kind of controls that reduce or contain the hazard. For heat stress, engineering controls are directed toward reducing physical work demands, adjusting clothing requirements, reducing external heat gain from the air and hot surfaces, and enhancing external heat loss by increasing sweat evaporation and decreasing air temperature.

Reduce physical work demand. The metabolic cost of doing work is the greatest contributor to heat gain by a worker. Reducing the physical work demand can greatly reduce the level of heat stress. Ways that the physical work demands can be reduced usually include powered tools or new processes to reduce manual effort.

Reduce air temperature. When air temperature is above 40°C (104°F), workers gain a significant amount of heat from the air. If the air temperature is below 32°C (90°F), there is a significant loss of body heat. Lowering air temperature serves to either reduce heat gain or enhance the loss of heat. It is a significant factor in the control of heat stress. Air temperature can be reduced by dilution ventilation and active cooling. Dilution ventilation brings in a supply of cooler air from another area and reduces the temperature in the work area by diluting the hot air with cooler air. This can be accomplished using general area ventilation or local (spot) ventilation. Active cooling means that mechanical refrigeration, evaporative cooling, or a water chiller is employed to reduce the temperature of supplied air for dilution ventilation. Cool rooms are an example of providing a local area of cooling near work areas. By spending some time of the work cycle in the cooler area, the effective exposure to heat stress is reduced.

Reduce air humidity. The rate of evaporative cooling of sweat is affected by the air humidity. Many times the rate of cooling is sufficiently restricted that excessive heat strain occurs. The rate of evaporative cooling can be enhanced by lowering the water content of the air. Water is best removed from air by cooling the air using water chillers or mechanical refrigeration. Thus heat stress is reduced by both removing water vapor and lowering air temperature. Again, the use of cool rooms reduces heat stress by lowering air temperatures and humidity (and increasing the rate of evaporative cooling).

Change clothing. Clothing is an important contributor to heat stress if it is not a light-weight cloth work uniform. Frequently, when clothing is chosen for good barrier properties against contaminants, not enough thought is given to the effects on heat stress. For instance, when the WBGT is 32°C (90°F) (T_{db} = 38°C or 100°F) at a moderate rate of work (about 260 W), a person in work clothes can work

TABLE 12–F	Overview of Specific Controls for Heat Stress Provided by NIOSH in the Criteria Document for Heat Stress
Item	**Actions for Consideration**
Controls	
M, Body heat production of task	Reduce physical demands of the work, powered assistance for heavy tasks.
R, Radiative load	Interpose line-of-sight barrier, furnace wall insulation, metallic reflecting screen, heat reflective clothing, cover exposed parts of body.
C, Convective load	If air temperature is above 35°C (95°F), reduce air temperature, reduce air speed across skin, wear clothing.
	If air temperature is below 35°C (95°F), increase air speed across skin and reduce clothing.
E_{max}, Maximum evaporative Increase by sweating	Increase by: decreasing humidity, increasing air speed
	Decrease clothing
Work practices	Shorten duration of each exposure; more frequent short exposures are better than fewer long exposures.
Exposure limit	Schedule very hot jobs in cooler part of day when possible.
Recovery	Self-limiting, based on formal indoctrination of workers and supervisors on signs and symptoms of overstrain.
	Air-conditioned space nearby
Personal protection R, C, and E_{max}	Cooled air, cooled fluid, or ice cooled conditioned clothing.
	Reflective clothing or aprons
Other considerations	Determine by medical evaluation, primarily of cardiovascular status
	Careful break-in of unacclimatized workers
	Water intake at frequent intervals to prevent hypohydration
	Fatigue or mild illness not related to the job may temporarily contraindicate exposure (e.g., low-grade infection, diarrhea, sleepless night, alcohol ingestion)
Heat wave	Introduce heat alert program

Source: NIOSH Criteria for a Recommended Standard, Occupational Exposure to Hot Environments—Revised Criteria 1986. Washington, DC: U.S. Government Printing Office, 1986.

for about two hours while a person in vapor-barrier clothing can work about 30 min. Changing the vapor-barrier to water-barrier (vapor-transmitting) clothing can increase the tolerance time to 70 min.

Reduce radiant heat. When the globe temperature is greater than 43°C (109°F), radiant heat is a significant source of heat stress. Radiant heat can come from well-defined or diffuse sources with high surface temperatures. If a source of radiant heat is well defined and localized, it can be effectively controlled by shielding. Diffuse sources of radiant heat are more difficult to control. For diffuse sources, control can come from shielding, but two other means are also available. One is insulating surfaces to reduce surface temperature and the other is to decrease emissivity of the surface. Increasing the insulation may also reduce air temperature and decrease energy costs.

Increase air movement. The advantage of increasing air movement is to enhance evaporative cooling and convective cooling if the air temperature is less than 35°C (95°F). Between 35° and 40°C (95° and 104°F), heat gain by convection may increase with increases in air movement, but it will be more than off-set by increases in evaporative cooling. Above 40°C (104°F), increases in air movement actually increase the overall heat stress. The greatest reduction in heat stress occurs when air motion is increased from less than one meter per second (m/s) to 2 m/s. There is no further improvement in evaporative cooling for air speeds greater than 3 m/s. When clothing is fairly heavy, higher air speeds can better penetrate the clothing and move the air near the skin (clothing ventilation is increased). The chief mechanism for increasing air movement around a worker is to use a fan in the workspace. Another means of increasing air motion is local ventilation. Increasing air movement, however, frequently increases the level of airborne particles.

Administrative controls. These are controls that change the way work is performed in order to limit exposures or risks. For heat stress, administrative controls are directed toward limiting exposures so that increases in heart rate and core temperature do not exceed accepted limits.

Acclimation. Acclimation is the process that allows a worker to become accustomed to the heat stress; the worker is better able to work in the heat. Acclimation is a powerful adaptation that comes naturally to more than 95 percent of the workforce. Acclimation is usually set according to a schedule of increasing exposures. A schedule for acclimation and reacclimation is provided in Table 12–E.

Pacing of the work. Because work metabolism is an important contributor to heat stress, methods to reduce the metabolic rate can go a long way toward reducing heat stress. The rate is reduced when the same amount of work is performed over a longer period of time. Any idle time inherent in the work should be spent in cooler areas to realize the full benefit. For instance, many jobs have a fixed amount of work to be accomplished, and the workers are given an allotted time. The tendency in cool conditions is to work very fast and have

the remaining time idle. The same pace in hot environments can cause excessive heat strain. So when the environment is hot, the work should be leveled out to reduce the rate of metabolism and the potential for excessive heat stress.

Sharing the work. Another way to reduce metabolic rate is to share or distribute the work among other workers. This may require some work to be delayed to another time. In scheduling the work, thought should be given on how to use the staff most efficiently and effectively. For instance, it may be possible that a worker can move between two crews during the same work period and still have an effect on reducing heat stress. Further, workers might straddle a work shift so that they work the second half of the day shift and the first half of the afternoon shift, when heat stress is most likely to be a problem.

Scheduling of work. An administrative control to reduce the contribution of environmental heat to heat stress is to schedule nonessential work at cooler times of day or during cooler periods.

Work times, self-determination, and personal monitoring. Preplanned work times, self-determination, and personal monitoring are ways to control a high heat-stress exposure. Predetermined work times are assigned to a worker or crew before a job begins. They may extend the work time with the knowledge that heat stress will eventually affect their ability to work and there is a risk of heat-related disorder. The extension should be under the controls of self-determination aided by personal monitoring.

The purpose of self-determination with personal monitoring is to allow more heat-tolerant workers to work longer than less-tolerant ones by letting the worker stop an exposure. These kinds of administrative controls apply better to self-paced and nonroutine work, and may be more difficult to manage during externally paced work. Self-determination is best instituted as a periodic query to the individual workers about their subjective judgment of heat strain and their ability to continue. Because subjective decisions are unreliable, objective data on heat strain should be obtained from personal monitoring of body temperature and/or heart rate. There are electronic personal monitors. One device examines body temperature through a measure of ear canal temperature. There is a type that measures deep body temperature through an ingested "pill." There are also heart-rate monitors and oral temperature devices suitable for occupational applications.

Personal protection. Personal protection is a control that provides protection for an individual worker. For heat stress, personal protection is primarily some form of personal cooling, but can include reflective clothing for high radiant heat conditions. Personal cooling systems, if chosen to match the job situation, can significantly increase the safe exposure time. When personal protection is used, conventional evaluation methods do not apply and work practices must be developed for the successful use of personal protection for heat stress.

Circulating air systems. Circulating air as a personal cooling method is achieved by circulating air under the clothing and around the torso. It requires the delivery of air to the individual either (1) through a high-pressure airline and a pressure reducer or (2) through a portable (self-contained) blower. Circulating air under the clothing effectively increases the amount of convective and evaporative cooling of the body. (Note: The circulating air must be breathing-grade air.) While airline systems can be used continuously for work that is relatively stationary, the technique can be used effectively by workers as temporary relief during pauses in the work. If there is a sufficient supply of compressed air, vortex devices can be used to significantly reduce the air temperature (on the order of a 10°C [18°F] reduction) going into the clothing. Portable blower systems are just receiving attention. Because they use air in the work locale, they may not provide as much cooling capacity as airline systems delivering the same volume flow rate.

Circulating water systems. A second type of personal cooling is a system that circulates cool water through tubes and channels around the body. There are a variety of systems available. First, systems range from those that can cover virtually the whole body to those that cover only portions of the back and chest. There are also portable versions as well as versions with a heat sink that is connected to the person through a tether. The degree of cooling that can be achieved depends on surface area covered, rate of water circulation, and the capacity of the heat sink. The selection of circulating water systems should be done in consultation with the vendors and someone very familiar with personal cooling to obtain a good match.

Ice garments. Several frozen-water (ice) garments, frequently called ice vests, are commercially available. They control heat strain by removing body heat via conduction from the skin to packets of ice. The typical vest weighs about 5 kg. The vests provide good mobility with some bulk around the torso. The ability to cool and service time depend on the rate of work, the amount of ice, and design of the garment. For a given amount of work, the time is limited by the ice.

Reflective clothing. While personal cooling is designed to take up body heat, reflective clothing is designed to reduce the amount of heat reaching the individual. Reflective clothing is best suited for sources of high radiant heat. There is a trade-off with reflective clothing in that it reduces sweat evaporation. That means that the level of heat stress may actually increase if the reflective clothing is not selected to best match the source of radiant heat and the job.

Hot Surfaces, Hot Air, and Respirators

Work in hot environments usually means that there are hot surfaces with the accompanying potential to cause a burn. The potential for a burn (or to elicit pain at a somewhat lower level of heat transfer) depends on the thermal conductivity of the solid, the temperature of the solid, and the contact time with skin. Table 12–G provides approximate surface temperatures for common surfaces that may elicit pain or a burn with brief (1 s) contact time and burns with longer contact times. For prolonged contact, surface temperature is the dominant characteristic. To avoid tissue injury, the surface temperature should be less than 48°C (118°F) for up to 10 min of contact time and 43°C (109°F) for prolonged contact. There will be reports of extreme discomfort with surface temperatures greater than 38°C (100°F).

Sometimes there is a concern about the temperature of the air that is being breathed. If the wet bulb temperature of the air is less than 45°C (113°F), breathing the air is not likely to cause extreme discomfort or ill effects. There are laboratory observations of sustained breathing at wet bulb temperatures of 50°C (122°F) without complaint. Above these temperatures, the probability of individual discomfort will increase.

There is a frequently expressed concern about the effects of tight-fitting, full-face respirator facepieces on heat stress—usually that negative-pressure respirators increase the level of heat stress and that air-supplied respirators may give a false sense of cooling. There are small changes in the level of physiological response, but not enough that the heat-stress guidelines for evaluation described previously should be adjusted to account for respirator use. There is also no doubt that subjectively measured discomfort increases while wearing a respirator facepiece in hot environments, and this may affect performance.

COLD STRESS

Cold stress is fundamentally a different kind of problem than heat stress. While adaptive mechanisms (i.e., sweating and acclimation) are crucial during heat-stress exposures, the physiological adaptations to cold stress have less dramatic effects. The first physiological response to cold stress is to conserve body heat by reducing blood circulation

TABLE 12–G	Limits on Surface Temperature (in degrees Centigrade) to avoid Pain and Burns with Different Contact Periods Against Skin				
	Pain	**Burn**	**Burn**	**Burn**	**Burn**
Material	(1 s)	(1 s)	(4 s)	(10 min)	(prolonged)
Metals	45	65	60		
Glass	55	85	75		
Wood	75	115–140	95–120		
	(depends on dryness of wood)				
Any material				48	43

Source: Adapted from Eastman Kodak, 1983; Siekmann, 1990.

through the skin. This effectively makes the skin an insulating layer. A second physiological response is shivering, which increases the metabolic rate. However, it is relatively weak as a protective mechanism. Shivering is a good sign that the cold stress is significant and that hypothermia may be present. Behavior is the primary human response to preventing excessive exposure to cold stress. Behaviors include increasing clothing insulation, increasing activity, and seeking warm locations.

Insulation is a critical characteristic of clothing worn during cold-stress exposures. Clothing materials used for their insulating characteristics include cotton, wool, silk, nylon, down, and polyester insulation. Generally, the insulating value of clothing ensembles comes from layering clothes rather than having one garment. The further advantage of layers is that the person can add or remove layers to adjust for differing insulation needs during the work period.

The insulating value of clothing is greatly diminished by moisture. Sources of water are the work environment and sweat. Water-vapor permeability is also important. If sweat is allowed to evaporate through the clothing, it will not accumulate in the clothing. Once clothing becomes wet, it is important to replace it immediately.

Like layering, clothing ventilation is a valuable means to adjust the heat-transfer properties of the ensemble. During low levels of work, insulation demands are high; as the work rate increases, insulation must decrease to maintain thermal equilibrium. Besides removing layers, the effective insulation of the ensemble can be reduced by increasing the clothing ventilation and therefore increasing the air movement under the clothing.

Hazards associated with cold stress are manifested in two distinct fashions: systemic (hypothermia) and local (localized tissue damage). There is also a concern for manual dexterity. The disorders related to cold stress exposures are described in Table 12–H.

As hypothermia progresses, depression of the central nervous system becomes more severe. This accounts for the progression of signs and symptoms from sluggishness through slurred speech and unsafe behaviors to disorien-

tation and unconsciousness. The ability to sustain metabolic rate and reduced skin blood flow is diminished by fatigue. Thus fatigue increases the risk of severe hypothermia through decreasing metabolic heat and increased heat loss from the skin. Because blood flow through the skin is reduced to conserve heat, the skin and underlying tissues are more susceptible to local cold injury.

Model of Thermal Balance

Systemic cold stress can be examined in terms of heat exchange.

$$S = M + (R + C) + K - E \tag{13}$$

M is metabolic rate and represents a source of internal heat gain. $(R + C)$ is the combination of heat loss due to cooler air and surroundings. K is conduction to a solid surface in contact with the body. E is evaporative cooling by sweat evaporation. Thermal equilibrium is established when $S = 0$.

M can be increased as a behavioral response to cold stress, and significant contributions to thermal balance are reductions in $(R + C)$ and K with behavioral adaptations like clothing and avoidance of cold environments. For a given level of clothing, the greater the work demands (greater metabolic rate), the greater the level of cold stress that can be tolerated.

The goal of systemic cold stress control is to avoid hypothermia by limiting the reduction in core temperature to 36°C (96.8°F) for prolonged exposures and to 35°C (95°F) for occasional exposures of short duration.

Measurement of Cold Stress

Two climatic factors in the environment influence the rate of heat exchange between a person and the environment. These factors are air temperature and air speed. As the difference between skin and ambient temperatures increases and/or the air speed increases, the rate of heat loss from exposed skin increases. The *Equivalent Chill Temperature (ECT)* was developed by the U.S. Army to account for both air temperature and air speed based on empirical observations of the time for water to freeze. It has been used and

TABLE 12–H   Cold-Related Disorders Including the Symptoms, Signs, Causes, and Steps for First Aid

Disorder	Symptoms	Signs	Causes	First Aid

Hypothermia	Chills
	Pain in extremities
	Fatigue or drowsiness
		Euphoria
		Slow, weak pulse
		Slurred speech
		Collapse
		Shivering
		Unconsciousness
		Body temperature
		  <95°F (35°C)
			Excessive exposure
			Exhaustion or dehydration
			Subnormal tolerance (genetic
			  or acquired)
			Drug/alcohol abuse
				Move to warm area and
				  remove wet clothing
				Modest external warming
				  (external heat packs,
				  blankets, etc.)
				Drink warm, sweet fluids if
				  conscious
				Transport to hospital

Frostbite	Burning sensation at first
	Coldness, numbness, tingling
		Skin color white or grayish
		  yellow to reddish violet to
		  black
		Blisters
		Response to touch depends
		  on depth of freezing
			Exposure to cold
			Vascular disease
				Move to warm area and
				  remove wet clothing
				External warming (e.g., warm
				  water)
				Drink warm, sweet fluids if
				  conscious
				Treat as a burn, do not rub
				  affected area
				Transport to hospital

Frostnip	Possible itching or pain	Skin turns white	Exposure to cold (above freezing)	Similar to frostbite

Trench Foot	Severe pain
	Tingling, itching
		Edema
		Blisters
		Response to touch depends
		  on depth of freezing
			Exposure to cold (above
			  freezing) and dampness
				Similar to frostbite

Chilblain	Recurrent, localized itching Painful inflammation	Swelling Severe spasms	Inadequate clothing Exposure to cold and dampness Vascular disease	Remove to warm area Consult physician

Raynaud's phenomenon	Fingers tingle
	Intermittent blanching and
	  reddening
		Fingers blanch with cold
		  exposure
			Exposure to cold and
			  vibration
			Vascular disease
				Remove to warm area
				Consult physician

Note: Hypothermia is related to systemic cold stress, and the other disorders are related to local tissue cooling.

updated by the National Weather Service as the *Wind Chill Index (WCI)*. The recently published Wind Chill Index chart is shown in Table 12–I as it relates air temperature and speed. The equation with air temperature (T_{air}) in degrees centigrade and air speed (v_{air}) in km/h follows.

$$T_{wind\text{-}chill}\,[C]$$
$$= 13.12 + 0.6215 \times T_{air} - 11.37(V_{air}^{0.16})$$
$$+ 0.3965 \times T_{air}(V_{air}^{0.16}) \qquad (14)$$

Recognition

Subjective responses of workers are a good tool for recognition of cold stress in the workplace. If the workplace is generally described as cold, then cold stress may be present. Worker behavior response to cold stress exposure will generally be seeking warm locations, adding layers of clothing, or increasing the work rate. Other behaviors are loss of manual dexterity, shivering, accidents, and unsafe behaviors.

Using the first-aid logs and other records, is there a pattern of signs and symptoms that might be attributed to hypothermia? A physiological marker is reduced core temperature to below 36°C (96.8°F).

If there is a noticeable drop in manual dexterity reported by workers or supervision, local cold stress is possible. In addition, if there is a pattern of cold-related disorders reported in the first-aid logs, injury and illness logs, and workers compensation records, the work conditions should be evaluated. There is also good evidence that cold stress increases unsafe behaviors and acute injuries.

Evaluation

Workplace Monitoring

When temperatures fall below 16°C (61°F), workplace monitoring should be instituted. Below –1°C (30°F), the dry bulb

| TABLE 12–1 | National Weather Service Wind Chill Index in Degrees F for Different Combinations of Air Temperature and Air Speed |

Air Speed (mph)	Temperature (F)																		Air Speed m/s
Calm	40	35	30	25	20	15	10	5	0	-5	-10	-15	-20	-25	-30	-35	-40	-45	Calm
5	36	31	25	19	13	7	1	-5	-11	-16	-22	-28	-34	-40	-46	-52	-57	-63	2
10	34	27	21	15	9	3	-4	-10	-16	-22	-28	-35	-41	-47	-53	-59	-66	-72	4
15	32	25	19	13	6	0	-7	-13	-19	-26	-32	-39	-45	-51	-58	-64	-71	-77	7
20	30	24	17	11	4	-2	-9	-15	-22	-29	-35	-42	-48	-55	-61	-68	-74	-81	9
25	29	33	16	9	3	-4	-11	-17	-24	-31	-37	-44	-51	-58	-64	-71	-78	-84	11
30	28	22	15	8	1	-5	-12	-19	-26	-33	-39	-46	-53	-60	-67	-73	-80	-87	13
35	28	21	14	7	0	-7	-14	-21	-27	-34	-41	-48	-55	-62	-69	-76	-82	-89	16
40	27	20	13	6	-1	-8	-15	-22	-29	-36	-43	-50	-57	-64	-71	-78	-84	-91	18
45	26	19	12	5	-2	-9	-16	-23	-30	-37	-44	-51	-58	-65	-72	-79	-86	-93	20
50	26	19	12	4	-3	-10	-17	-24	-31	-38	-45	-52	-60	-67	-74	-81	-88	-95	22
55	25	18	11	4	-3	-11	-18	-25	-32	-39	-46	-54	-61	-68	-75	-82	-89	-97	25
60	25	17	10	3	-4	-11	-19	-26	-33	-40	-48	-55	-62	-69	-76	-84	-91	-98	27
Time to Frostbite							30 min		10 min					5 min					Time to Frostbite
Calm	4	2	-1	-4	-7	-9	-12	-15	-18	-21	-23	-26	-29	-32	-34	-37	-40	-43	Calm
	Temperature (C)																		

Note: Cross-reference to metric units for air speed and temperature are provided.

temperature and air speed should be measured and recorded at least every four hours. When air speed is greater than 2 m/s (5 miles per hour), the WCI should be determined from Table 12–I. When the WCI falls below –7°C (19°F), it should be noted.

Systemic Cold Stress

Hypothermia can occur with air temperatures up to 10°C (50°F). The ACGIH recommends that the employer become involved with protective measures when air temperature is less than 5°C (41°F). Equation 15 can be used to approximate the amount of clothing insulation (I_{clo} in clo units, where 1 clo = 0.155 m² C/W) required for a specific task in a given air temperature (T_{db} in C) and metabolic rate (M in watts). Figure 12–8 illustrates the relationship among temperature, work rate, and clothing to maintain thermal equilibrium based on Equation 15.

$$I_{clo} = 11.5 (33 - T_{db}) / M \qquad (15)$$

Remember that the clothing must be kept dry and that I_{clo} will change with different tasks and environments.

ISO 11079 (2007), *Ergonomics of the Thermal Environment – Determination and Interpretation of Cold Stress When Using Required Clothing Insulation (Ireq) And Local Cooling Effects*, describes a rational model to determine the required clothing insulation. An implementation of this model is available at a website (http://fhvmetodik.se/dokument/PPE/IREQ2009ver4_2.html) that also provides the WCI. It provides the Ireq for a neutral sensation (upper limit) and a cold sensation (lower limit). If there is a net heat loss, it will also provide a range of time limits.

Local Cold Stress

Skin cannot freeze until the air temperature is less than –1°C (30°F) and there is little risk of local cold injury associated with WCIs greater than –24°C (–11°F). The limiting surface temperature to protect exposed skin making incidental contact with the surfaces is –7°C (19°F). If the contact is prolonged (e.g., for tools), the limit is –1°C (30°F).

Manual dexterity of hands drops when there is uninterrupted work for 10–20 min at temperatures below 16°C (61°F).

General Controls

As with heat stress, general controls are actions that should be taken when workers may be exposed to cold stress. The general controls include training, hygiene practices, and medical surveillance.

Training

When the air temperature may be below 5°C (41°F), the workers should be informed that cold stress may be a hazard, what is proper clothing, and that self-determination

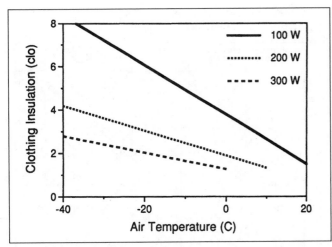

Figure 12–8. Estimation of clothing insulation (clo) required as a function of air temperature for different levels of work.

and cold stress hygiene should be practiced.

When work is performed at or below –12°C (10°F) WCI, additional training topics should include safe work practices and the recognition and first aid treatment of hypothermia and other cold-related disorders.

Hygiene Practices
Cold stress hygiene practices center around fluid replacement with warm, sweet, noncaffeinated drinks and self-determination. Warm drinks are palatable in cold stress and the fluid replacement is important because significant dehydration can occur. Sweetened drinks provide a readily usable energy source to reduce the risk of fatigue. In addition, employees should be encouraged to eat a normal, balanced diet. If a worker experiences extreme discomfort or any of the symptoms of hypothermia (or any other cold-related disorder), the person should stop work and seek a place to rewarm.

Safe work practices include at least the following. In air temperatures below 2°C (36°F), replace clothing immediately if it becomes wet, and treat the workers as if they are experiencing hypothermia. When handling liquids with boiling points below 4°C (39°F), special precautions should be taken that clothes do not become soaked in the liquid.

Medical Surveillance
Medical certification is suggested for those who are routinely exposed below –24°C (–11°F) WCI. The certification should be based on a physical that considers fitness, weight, cardiovascular health, and other conditions that may affect cold-stress tolerance. Further, the personal-care physician should be consulted by any employee who is under care for chronic disease.

If there is reason to suspect that a person cannot properly thermoregulate, a medical restriction is appropriate in air temperatures below –1°C (30°F).

Specific Controls
Engineering Controls
Engineering controls attempt to reduce heat loss from the person as a whole or from exposed skin. Control includes increasing air temperature and decreasing air speed in the work zone, and providing rewarming areas. Specifically, engineering controls include

* general or spot heating including hand warming;
* hand warming for fine hand work below 16°C (61°F);
* minimize air movement (e.g., shielding, adjusting ventilation);
* reduce conductive heat transfer (e.g., no metal chairs or uninsulated tools);
* redesign equipment, process, etc. to control systemic and local cold stress; and
* provide warming shelters if exposures below –7°C (19°F).

Administrative Controls
Administrative controls attempt to reduce the exposure time, allow individual control over the work, and provide for mutual observation. Recommended administrative controls include

* work/rest cycle;
* schedule work to warmest times;
* move work to warmer areas;
* assign additional workers;
* encouraging self-pacing and extra breaks if required;
* buddy system, emphasizing mutual observation;
* avoid long periods of sedentary effort;
* allow for productivity reductions and extra effort from protective clothing;
* provide an adjustment or conditioning period for new employees; and
* monitor weight changes for dehydration.

Personal Protection
Because clothing is so important, personal protection is fundamental to managing cold stress. Clothing should be carefully selected in consultation with knowledgeable vendors and participation with the workers. The workers must be educated about the role of clothing items and what may compromise effectiveness. Some of these factors include

* properly selected insulated clothing;
* wind-barriers;
* special attention to feet, fingers, ears, nose, and face;
* gloves when air temperature is less than 1°C (61°F) for light work, 4°C (39°F) for moderate work, and –7°C

(19°F) for heavy work;

- mittens when air temperature is less than –17°C (1°F);
- water-barriers to external liquids;
- appropriate active warming systems (e.g., circulating air or liquids, electric); and
- appropriate eye-protection for snow or ice-covered terrain.

Thermal Comfort

Thermal comfort is "that condition of mind in which satisfaction is expressed with the thermal environment." Factors that affect thermal comfort include air temperature, humidity, air motion, surface temperatures, metabolic rate, and clothing. Age, gender, season, cultural background, and intraindividual variation play minor roles once the previously mentioned factors are accounted for. For instance, gender and seasonal changes in a comfortable environment can be explained by differences in clothing. Factors that can disrupt a theoretically comfortable environment are asymmetric thermal radiation, drafts, vertical temperature gradients, and floor temperatures.

The ASHRAE Standard 55-2010 describes comfort zones based on operative temperature and humidity. These are illustrated in Figure 12–9. One zone is for the winter season and another, overlapping zone is for the summer season. The seasonal zones are specified to account for changes in clothing habits in the winter and summer. The operative temperature is approximately the globe temperature, and with little radiant heat it is the air (dry bulb) temperature. See Chapter 21, General Ventilation of Nonindustrial Occupancies, for a more detailed discussion of Standard 55-2010.

Under ideal conditions, no less than 95 percent of the working occupants will be dissatisfied with the thermal environment. As the climatic conditions deviate from the ideal, more people will be dissatisfied with the conditions. For those who wish to gain a better understanding of how a group of people will respond to an environment, the ISO has published a standard on thermal comfort. The standard considers such factors as climate, clothing, and metabolic rate.

SUMMARY

This chapter was divided into three sections: heat stress, cold stress, and comfort. The heat stress and cold stress sections described methods to recognize that the stress may be present and significant in the workplace. Recognition is through types of work that are usually associated with the stress and the manifestations of disorders and worker behaviors due to the stress. Methods to evaluate the stress are then described with an emphasis on those recommended by the ACGIH in the documentation of the Threshold Limit Values (TLVs) for Heat Stress and Strain and the ISO. Controls for heat and

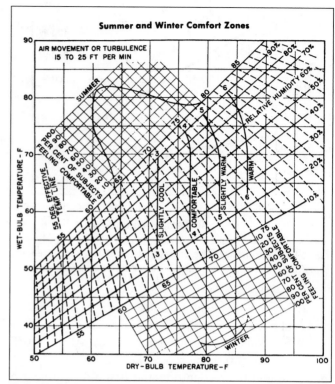

Figure 12–9. ASHRAE chart for comfort zones for sedentary activities. *(Reprinted with permission from ASHRAE.)*

cold stress are then described in terms of general controls and specific controls.

General controls are broadly applicable when there is a potential for an excessive exposure. General controls include training, hygiene practices, and medical surveillance. With regard to training, annual sessions within the format for other health and safety training is encouraged. The content should include the nature of the hazard, when and how it may occur, the physiological responses, recognition of disorders related to the stress, hygiene practices, and proper use of personal protection and other controls.

Specific controls are those controls that are appropriate to a specific job and are selected based on the job and site constraints. They include the traditional hierarchy of controls: engineering controls, administrative controls, and personal protection.

Finally, means to evaluate thermal comfort were described. The parameters in the evaluation can be manipulated to improve the degree of comfort in the work environment.

BIBLIOGRAPHY

While direct reference is not made, many ideas in this chapter have been adopted from sources in the bibliography.

American Conference of Governmental Industrial Hygienists. *Threshold Limit Values® and Biological Exposure Indices® for 2011*. Cincinnati, OH: ACGIH, 2011 (updated annually).

American Society of Heating, Refrigerating and Air Conditioning Engineers. ASHRAE Standard 55-2010: *Thermal Environmental Conditions for Human Occupancy*. Atlanta: ASHRAE, 2010.

Ashley CD, Bernard TE. Effects of hoods and flame retardant fabrics on WBGT clothing adjustment factors. *J Occup Environ Hyg* 5:59-62, 2008.

Bernard TE, Dukes-Dobos FN, Ramsey JD. Evaluation and control of hot working environments. Part II—The scientific bases (knowledge base) for the guide. *Int J Ind Ergonom* 14:119–138, 1994.

Bernard TE, Luecke CL, Schwartz SW, et al. WBGT clothing adjustments for four clothing ensembles under three relative humidity levels. *J Occup Environ Hyg* 2:251-256, 2005.

Holmér I. Cold stress. Part I—Guidelines for the practitioner; Part II—The scientific basis (knowledge base) for the guide. *Int J Ind Ergonom* 14:139–159, 1994.

International Organization for Standardization. ISO 7933:2004 *Ergonomics of the thermal environment—Analytical determination and interpretation of heat stress using calculation of the predicted heat strain*. Geneva: ISO, 2004.

International Organization for Standardization. ISO 11079:2007 *Ergonomics of the thermal environment—Determination and interpretation of cold stress when using required clothing insulation (IREQ) and local cooling effects*. Geneva: ISO, 2007.

International Organization for Standardization. ISO 7730:2005 *Ergonomics of the thermal environment—Analytical determination and interpretation of thermal comfort using calculation of the PMV and PPD indices and local thermal comfort criteria*. Geneva: ISO, 2005.

National Institute for Occupational Safety and Health. *Criteria for a recommended standard: Occupational exposure to hot environments (Revised criteria 1986)*. Washington, DC: USDHHS (NIOSH) 86–113, 1986.

Ramsey JD, Dukes-Dobos FN, Bernard TE. Evaluation and control of hot working environments. Part I—Guidelines for the practitioner. *Int J Ind Ergonom* 14:119–138, 1994.

Tri-Services Document. Prevention, Treatment and Control of Heat Injury. *Army TB Med 507*, 2003.

World Health Organization. Health factors involved in working under conditions of heat stress. *Technical Report Series 142*. Geneva: WHO, 1969.

Note: Some forms and spreadsheet-based analyses can be obtained as downloads from Stone Wheels on http://personal.health.usf.edu/tbernard/tebstonewheels.html.

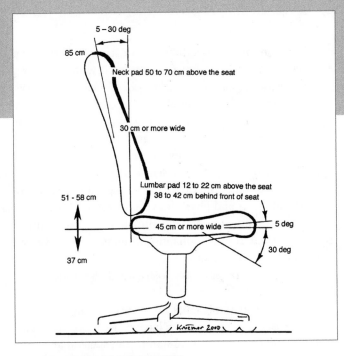

CHAPTER 13

Ergonomics

*by David L. Lee, PhD, OTR/L
and David Rempel, MD, MPH, CPE*

The terms ergonomics *and* human factors *(including human engineering and human-factors engineering) are in essence synonymous. They all indicate the application of scientific principles, methods, and data to the development of engineering systems in which people play a significant role.*

The word ergonomics *was coined in 1950 in the United Kingdom by a group of physical, biological, and psychological scientists and engineers to describe their interdisciplinary efforts to design equipment and work tasks so that they fit the operator. The term is derived from the Greek-language word roots* ergon, *(human) work and strength, and* nomos, *indicating law or rule. In 1957, U.S. behavioral scientists, anthropometrists, and engineers working in this emerging discipline decided to call their new professional association the Human Factors Society. The words* and Ergonomics *were inserted in 1992.*

DEFINITION OF ERGONOMICS

Ergonomics is the study of human characteristics for the appropriate design of the living and work environment. Ergonomic researchers study human characteristics (capabilities, limitations, motivations, and desires) so that this knowledge can be applied to the design of human-made environments to promote productivity and health. Human capabilities, and limitations of human capabilities, can affect complex technical systems or work tasks, equipment, and workstations, or the tools and utensils used at work, at home, or during leisure times. Hence, ergonomics is human-centered, transdisciplinary, and application-oriented.

The goals of ergonomics range from the basic aim of making work safe through increasing human efficiency to the purpose of optimizing human well-being. According to the definition of ergonomics or human-factors engineering by the International Ergonomics Association, the profession applies theory, scientific principles, data, and methods to the understanding and design of interactions among humans and systems. The theory and data are drawn from a variety of disciplines and applied to the development of engineering systems in which people play a significant role. We measure successful application by improved productivity, efficiency, safety, and acceptance of the resultant system design. The disciplines that can be applied are broad and include psychology, biomechanics, human physiology and anatomy, and industrial and systems engineering. The systems range from the use of a simple tool by a consumer to multiperson-sociotechnical systems. They typically include both technological and human components.

The National Research Council said: "Human-factors specialists are united by a singular perspective on the system design process: that design begins with an understanding of the user's role in overall system performance and that systems exist to serve their users, whether they are consumers, system operators, production workers, or maintenance crews. This user-oriented design philosophy acknowledges human variability as a design parameter."

Broadly speaking, the discipline extends from physical to cognitive to organizational ergonomics.

- Physical ergonomics is concerned with human anatomical, physiologic, and biomechanical capabilities as they relate to physical activity. Topics include working postures, material handling, repetitive movements, work-related musculoskeletal disorders, workplace layout, safety, and health.
- Cognitive ergonomics is concerned with mental processes, such as perception, memory, and reasoning as related to working in a system. Topics include mental workload, decision making, skilled performance, human-computer interaction, human reliability, work stress, and training.
- Organizational ergonomics is concerned with optimizing the structures, policies, and processes of sociotechnical systems. Topics include communication, crew resource management, work design, teamwork, participatory design, telework, quality management, and cooperative work.

Figure 13–1 shows how ergonomics interacts with related applied disciplines and sciences. Among the primary foundations of ergonomics are the biological sciences, particularly anatomy and physiology. Leonardo da Vinci in the 16th century, Giovanni Alfonso Borelli in the 17th century, Lavoisier, Amar, Rubner, Johannson, and many others in the 19th and early 20th centuries contributed ideas, concepts, theories, and practical data to forward the understanding of the role of the human body in a work environment. Among the social and behavioral sciences, anthropologists, psychologists, and sociologists have contributed to modeling and understanding the human role in societal and technological systems, including management theories. Among the engineering disciplines, industrial engineers (using, for example, the groundwork laid by Frederick Taylor and the Gilbreths), mechanical and computer engineers and designers are the major users of ergonomic knowledge. A typical application is in computer-aided design (CAD), which incorporates the systematic consideration of human attributes, especially anthropometric and biomechanical information. Ergonomists have developed their own theories, methods, techniques, and tools to perform scientific research. Formal college undergraduate and graduate degree curricula are offered by many universities, usually in departments of industrial engineering, psychology, or public health. Productivity, health, and safety at work, the quality of work life, and participatory management are some well-known programmatic aspects of ergonomics.

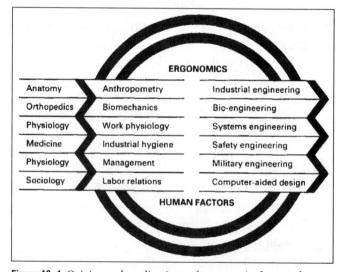

Figure 13–1. Origins and applications of ergonomics/human factors.

MATCHING PERSON AND TASK

People perform widely differing tasks in daily work situations. These tasks must be matched with human capabilities to avoid underloading, in which human capabilities are not sufficiently used, as well as overloading, which may cause the employee to break down and suffer reduced performance capability or even permanent damage. Engineering psychologists, work physiologists, and occupational biomechanists evaluate the capacities and limitations of the worker to perform work; they also determine human tolerance to stresses produced by the environment.

THE HUMAN AS INFORMATION PROCESSOR

In the traditional system concept of engineering psychology, the human is considered a receptor and processor of information or energy, who then outputs information or energy. Input, processing, and output follow each other in sequence. The output can be used to run a machine, which may be a simple hand tool or a space craft. This basic model is depicted in Figure 13–2.

The actual performance of this human-technology system (in the past often called a man-machine system) is monitored and compared with the desired performance. Hence, feedback loops connect the output side with the input side. The difference between output and input is registered in a comparator, and corrective actions are taken to minimize any output/input difference. In this system, the human controls, compares, makes decisions, and corrects.

Affordance is the property of an environment that has certain values to the human. An example is a stairway that affords passage for a person who can walk but not for a person who uses a wheelchair. Thus, passage is a property of the stairway, but its affordance value is specific to the user. Accordingly, ergonomics or human engineering provides affordances.

Traditional engineering psychologists describe our activities as a linear sequence of stages from perception to decision to response. Research is done separately on each of these stages, on their substages, and on their connections. Such independent, stage-related information is then combined into a linear model.

Ecological psychologists believe that this linear model is invalid; they consider human perception and action to be based on simultaneous rather than sequential information. This concept requires fundamentally new models of information, cognition, and performance assessment. Yet, current behavioral knowledge is still almost completely based on the traditional sequential-system concept.

HUMAN REACTION TIME

The time passing from the appearance of a proximal stimulus (for example, a light) to the beginning of an effector action (such as moving a foot) is called reaction time. The additional time to perform an appropriate movement (for instance, stepping on a brake pedal) is called motion or movement time. Motion time added to reaction time results in the response time. (Note that in everyday use, these terms are often not clearly distinguished.)

Experimental analysis of reaction time goes back to the very roots of experimental psychology: many of the basic results were obtained in the 1930s, with additional experimental work done in the 1950s and 1960s. Innumerable experiments have been performed, and many tables of such

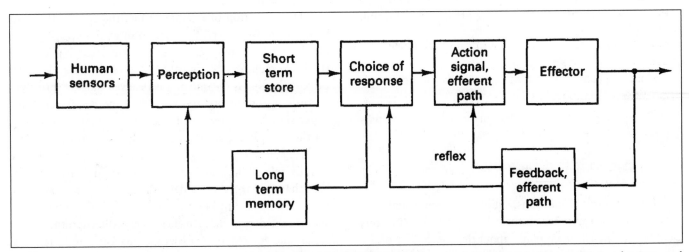

Figure 13–2. The human as energy or information processor. (*Adapted from Kroemer et al*. Ergonomics: How to Design for Ease and Efficiency. *Upper Saddle River, NJ: Prentice Hall, 2001. Reprinted with permission by the publisher. All rights reserved.*)

times have been published. In engineering handbooks, some of these apparently have been consolidated from various sources. However, the origin of the data, the experimental conditions (for example, the intensity of the stimulus) under which they were measured, the measuring accuracy, and the subjects participating are no longer known.

The following table is typical of generally used but fairly dubious reaction time information, often applied without much consideration or confidence:

Electric shock	130 ms
Touch, sound	140 ms
Sight, temperature	180 ms
Smell	300 ms
Taste	500 ms
Pain	700 ms

While accepting the fact that, in real-life situations, the times may be considerably longer, there appears to be little difference in reaction time to electrical, tactile, and sound stimuli. The slightly longer times for sight and temperature sensations may be well within the measuring accuracy, or within the variability among persons. However, the time following a smell stimulus is distinctly longer, and the time for taste again longer, while it takes by far the longest to react to the infliction of pain.

If a person knows that a particular stimulus will occur, is prepared for it, and knows how to react to it, the resulting reaction time (RT) is called simple reaction time. Its duration depends on the stimulus modality and the intensity of the stimulus. If one of several possible stimuli occurs, or if the person has to choose between several possible reactions, one speaks of *choice reaction time*. Choice reaction time is a logarithmic function of the number of alternative stimuli and responses:

$$RT = a + b \log_2 N \qquad (1)$$

with a and b empiric constants and N the number of choices. N may be replaced by the probability $p = 1/N$ of any particular alternative:

$$RT = a + b \log_2 p - 1 \text{ (the Hick-Hyman equation)} \quad (2)$$

Under optimal conditions, simple auditory, visual, and tactile reaction times are about 0.2 seconds. If conditions deteriorate, such as uncertainty about the appearance of the signal, reaction slows. For example, simple reaction time to tones near the lower auditory threshold may increase to

0.4 seconds. Similarly, visual reaction time is dependent on intensity, size, and flash duration of the stimulus. Reactions to visual signals in the periphery of the visual field (e.g., 45 degrees from the fovea) are about 15 to 30 ms slower than to centrally located stimuli.

Reaction times of different body parts to tactual stimuli vary only slightly, within about 10 percent, for finger, forearm, and upper arm. Reaction time slows if it is difficult to distinguish between several stimuli that are quite similar, but only one should trigger the response. Also, reaction time increases if one has to choose between several possible responses to one signal—as described by the Hick-Hyman formula. Simple reaction time changes little with age from about 15 to 60 years, but is substantially slower at younger ages and slows moderately as one grows old.

Motion time follows reaction time. Movements may be simple, such as lifting a finger in response to a stimulus, or complex, such as swinging a tennis racket. Swinging the racket contains not only more complex movement elements, but also larger body and object masses that must be moved, which takes time. Movement time also depends on the distance covered and on the precision required. Related data are contained in many systems of time and motion analyses, often used in industrial engineering.

These relations have been expressed in a Motion Time (MT) equation called Fitts' Law:

$$MT = a + b \log_2 (2D/W) \qquad (3)$$

D is the distance covered by the movement, and W is the width of the target. The expression $\log_2 (2D/W)$ is often called Index of Difficulty. The constants a and b depend on the situation, such as body parts involved, masses moved, tools or equipment used, the number of repetitive movements, and training.

The reduction of response time, the sum of the reaction and motion lags, is a common engineering goal. It can be achieved by optimizing the stimulus and selecting the body member that is best suited to the task. The best proximal signal is the one that is received quickly (primarily according to modality and intensity) and is different from other signals. Afferent and efferent transmission depend on the composition, diameter, and length of nerve fibers and on synaptic connections; practically, the ergonomist usually selects the shortest transmission distance. Yet the best chances for reducing delays are in the processing time needed in the central nervous system for perceptual tasks such as the detection, identification, and recognition of the signal and for cognitive tasks like deciding and planning. Thus, a clear signal leading to an unambiguous choice of action is the most efficient approach to reducing delays.

Choosing the most suitable body member for the fastest response includes making sure that the minimal segment mass must be moved. Thus, moving an eye is faster than moving a finger, which is faster than moving a leg.

HUMAN CAPACITY FOR WORK

Individuals differ from each other in their capacities to perform tasks. Thus, the workload imposed by a given task differs from person to person; also, the workload may depend on the temporal state of an individual—for example on training, fatigue, and motivation. Workload is often defined as the portion of the maximal performance capacity that is expended in performing a given task. One should obviously avoid any condition in which more is demanded from the operator than he or she can give. Otherwise, an overload condition results: the performance of the task will not be optimal and the operator is likely to suffer, physically or psychologically, from the overload. However, a task demand that is below the operator's capacity leaves a residual capacity. Its measurement provides an assessment of the actual workload. (Note that using too little of a person's capacity creates an underload with negative effects of its own, such as boredom.)

Human Capacity for Mental Work

Common sense and general understanding make the distinction between physical (physiological) and mental (psychological) workload obvious and, in that juxtaposition, explain the meaning of both. Yet, as Tsang and Wilson state, there is no distinct, universally accepted definition of mental workload. In fact, its meaning has shifted and changed. During World War II, attention was of predominant interest, which was followed by concern about information processing and cognitive issues as human-operated systems became increasingly complex. With more internal automation, the system demands on the operator shifted to supervisory control responsibility, situation awareness, and strategic task management. However, these concepts do not completely replace, nor totally encompass, each other. Criteria that have been developed for classic workload metrics also apply to measurement of situation awareness in complex environments, even though the two load concepts are not interchangeable.

Measuring Mental Workload

We can use four different approaches to empirically assess mental workload. Three rely on objective measures: of primary-task performance, of secondary-task performance, and of physiological events. The other measurement uses subjective assessments. Measures of task performance, as well as of subjective assessment, presume that both zero and full capacities are known since they assess the portion of capacity loading.

The fourth empirical approach to measure workload relies on the measurement of the primary-task performance by observing how noncritical components of the primary task are performed. The hypothesis is that, as the workload increases, performance changes measurably. Candidates for such unobtrusive measures are the status of a person's speech, the depletion of stock, disorder, or clutter at the workplace, and the length of a line of customers. Such embedded measures of workload would not add to the task at hand. The following are examples of secondary tasks employed in measuring workload:

- *simple reaction time*—draws on perceptual and response execution resources
- *choice reaction time*—same as for simple reaction time, but with greater demands
- *tracking*—requires central processing and motor resources, depending on the order of control dynamics
- *monitoring of the occurrence of stimuli*—draws heavily on perceptual resources
- *short-term memory tasks*—heavy demand on central-processing resources
- *mathematics*—draws most heavily on central-processing resources
- *shadowing*—subject repeats verbal or numerical material as presented: heaviest demands on perceptual resources
- *time estimations*—(a) subject estimates time passed: draws upon perceptual and central processing resources; (b) subject indicates sequence of regular time intervals by motor activity: makes large demands on motor output resources

Physiological measures, especially heart rate, eye movements, pupil diameter, and muscle tension can often be measured without intruding on the primary task. However, these measures may be insensitive to the task requirements or may be difficult to interpret.

Subjective assessments are a common means to assess mental workload. Humans are able to internally integrate the demands of the task, and to make statements about the perceived demand, often in terms of ratings and rankings. However, the subjective assessment of the perceived workload may be unreliable, invalid, or inconsistent with other performance measures. If subjective measures are taken after the task has been completed, they are not real-time evaluations; on the other hand, if performed during the task, they may intrude on the task.

Several pragmatic measures of the workload have been widely used, even though they have been criticized on both theoretical and technical grounds. Prominent among them are the modified Cooper-Harper scale, the overall workload (OW) scale, the NASA task load index (TLX), and the subjective workload assessment technique (SWAT). The first two are unidimensional rating scales; the last two are subjective techniques using multidimensional scales. While there are good theoretical and statistical reasons for using the TLX, SWAT, and OW, they are more complex to administer than the Cooper-Harper scale, which is fairly self-explanatory.

Human Capacity for Physical Work

An individual's capacity for physical work is usually determined by the limits of his or her respiratory and cardiovascular systems to deliver oxygen to the working muscles, and by the limits of the metabolic system to use chemically stored energy to do muscular work. Maximal oxygen uptake often is used to describe the upper limit of the aggregate capacity. Tolerance times for maximal efforts are measured in hours and minutes, even in seconds for a sprint runner. In a modern industrial setting, maximal effort may be required for brief periods, such as when an employee must heave heavy loads onto a hand truck; but during an eight-hour shift, the average energy required usually falls well below human peak capacity.

The biochemical steps to transform foodstuffs into energy available for work are quite complex; some are anaerobic, but, altogether, the process is aerobic. Consequently, measurement of the volume of oxygen consumed provides an overall index of energy consumption and hence of the energy demands of work. Use of one liter (L) of oxygen yields approximately five kilocalories (kcal or Cal; equivalent to about 21 kiloJoules, kJ). To put oxygen consumption and energy demands into proper perspective, consider that a trained athlete may reach a maximal oxygen uptake of 6 L/min. Aside from a person's physique and training, age and gender influence the oxygen intake capacity substantially. Men in their 20s have an average maximal capacity of 3–3.5 L/min; women of the same age have an average capacity of 2.3–2.8 L/min. At age 60, the capacities commonly diminish to about 2.2–2.5 L/min for men and 1.8–2.0 L/min for women. As with most physiological characteristics, there is considerable individual variability.

Energy Cost of Work

Industrial jobs seldom demand continuous energy expenditure close to the maximum over the course of a workday. Rest pauses, fetching tools, mopping the brow, and receiving instruction reduce the average energy expenditure considerably. Table 13–A lists several typical activities and their average metabolic costs; resting values are included for

reference. The given values must be adjusted according to one's body weight; the table applies to a man of 70 kg (155 lb). Other tables published in the physiological literature may be in different units (Calories, Joules, Btu; per hour or minute), and may or may not include basal rates—be careful to use these tables correctly.

Many jobs consist of intermittent tasks of different energy requirements. The total metabolic expenditure for the job may be calculated using the following formula:

$$M = M_1 t_1 + M_2 t_2 + \ldots M_n t_n \qquad (4)$$

In this formula, M is the total metabolic energy cost, $M_1 \ldots M_n$ are the metabolic costs of individual tasks; $t_1 \ldots t_n$ indicate the durations of each individual task. Using the values listed in Table 13–A, an example of estimating energy expenditures during the day is shown in Table 13–B.

There is close interaction between the human circulatory and metabolic systems. Nutrients and oxygen must be brought to the working muscles and metabolic by-products removed from them to ensure proper functioning. Therefore, heart rate (which is an important indicator of circulatory functions) and oxygen consumption (representing the metabolic processes taking place in the body) have a linear and reliable relationship in the range between light and heavy work. (However, when very light work or extremely heavy work is done, that relationship may not be stable. It is also

TABLE 13–A	Metabolic Energy Costs of Several Typical Activities	
Activity	**kcal/h**	**Btu/h**
Resting, prone	80–90	320–360
Resting, seated	95–100	375–397
Standing, at ease	100–110	397–440
Drafting	105	415
Light assembly (bench work)	105	415
Medium assembly	160	635
Driving automobile	170	675
Walking, casual	175–225	695–900
Sheet metal work	180	715
Machining	185	730
Rock drilling	225–550	900–2,170
Mixing cement	275	1070
Walking on job	290–400	1,150–1,570
Pushing wheelbarrow	300–400	1,170–1,570
Shoveling	235–525	930–2,070
Chopping with axe	400–1,400	1,570–5,550
Climbing stairs	450–775	1,770–3,070
Slag removal	630–750	2,500–2,970

Values are for a male worker of 70 kg (154 lb). *(Reprinted with permission from: Ergonomics guide to assessment to metabolic and cardiac costs of physical work. American Industrial Hygiene Association Journal 32: 560–564, 1971.)*

TABLE 13–B	Example of Energy Expenditure During Leisure and at Work		
Activity	**Duration (h)**	**Energy Cost**	
		kcal/h	**kcal/Duration**
Sleeping	8	85	680
Sitting, resting	4.5	100	450
Walking	1.5	170	255
Driving automobile	1	200	200
Subtotal for leisure	15		1,585
Work, light assembly	7	105	735
Work, walking	1	200	200
Work breaks, sitting	1	100	100
Subtotal for work	9		1,035
Total per day	**24**		**2,620**

TABLE 13–C	Classification of Light to Heavy Work According to Energy Expenditure and Heart Rate	
Classification	**Total Energy Expenditure (kcal/min)**	**Heart Rate (beats/min)**
Light work	2.5	90 or less
Medium work	5	100
Heavy work	7.5	120
Very heavy work	10	140
Extremely heavy work	15	160 or more

not reliable under severe environmental conditions or when workers are under mental stress.) Assuming such a linear relationship, one can often simply substitute heart-rate recording for measurement of oxygen consumption. This is a very attractive shortcut since heart rate can be recorded rather easily. Heart rate reacts faster to work demands and therefore more easily indicates quick changes in body functions caused by changes in work requirements.

The simplest technique for heart-rate assessment is to palpate an artery, often in the wrist. The measurer counts the number of heartbeats over a given period of time—such as 15 seconds—and then calculates the average heart rate per minute. More refined methods use various plethysmographic techniques, which rely on the deformation of tissue that results when imbedded blood vessels fill with blood with each pulse. More expensive techniques rely on electric signals that are associated with the contractions of the heart. When using this technique, electrodes are usually placed on the person's chest.

Instead of measuring a person's reactions to actual job loads, it is often desired to determine the individual's capabilities using standardized loadings in the laboratory. Bicycle ergometers, treadmills, or steps are commonly used to simulate stressful job demands. The reactions of the individual in terms of oxygen consumption, heart rate, and blood pressure are used to assess that person's ability to meet or exceed such demands. However, the examining physician needs to know what the actual work demands are. The industrial hygienist may be called upon to help in the assessment of the existing work demands.

Classification of Work

The work demands listed in Table 13–C are rated from light to extremely heavy in terms of energy expenditure per minute, and the relative heart rate in beats per minute is also given. Light work is associated with rather small

energy expenditures and is accompanied by a heart rate of approximately 90 beats/min. At this level of work, the energy needs of the working muscles are supplied by oxygen available in the blood and by glycogen in the muscle. There is no buildup of lactic acid or other metabolic by-products that would limit a person's ability to continue such work.

At medium work, which is associated with about 100 beats/min, the oxygen required by the working muscles is still covered, and lactic acid developed initially at the beginning of the work period is resynthesized to glycogen during the activity.

In heavy work, during which the heart rate is about 120 beats/min, the oxygen required is still supplied if the person is physically capable to do such work and specifically trained in this job. However, the lactic acid concentration produced during the initial phase of the work is not reduced but remains high until the end of the work period. The concentration returns to normal levels after cessation of the work.

In the course of light, medium, and, if the person is capable and trained, even heavy work, the metabolic and other physiological functions can attain a steady-state condition during the work period. This indicates that all physiological functions can meet the demands and will remain essentially constant throughout the duration of the effort.

However, no steady state exists in the course of very heavy work during which the heart rate level attains or exceeds 140 beats/min. In this case, the original oxygen deficit incurred during the early phase of the work increases throughout the duration of the effort and metabolic by-products accumulate. This accumulation makes intermittent rest periods necessary, sometimes even forcing the person to stop this effort completely. At even higher energy expenditures, which are associated with heart rates of 160 beats/min or more, the lactic acid concentration in the blood and the oxygen deficit achieve such magnitudes that frequent rest periods are needed. Even highly trained and capable persons are usually unable to perform such a demanding job throughout a full working day.

Hence, energy requirements or heart rate allow one to judge whether a job is energetically easy or hard. Of course, such labels as light, medium, or heavy reflect judgments of physiological events (and of their underlying job demands) that rely very much on the current socioeconomic concept of what is comfortable, acceptable, permissible, difficult, or excessive.

Rating the perceived effort is another way to classify work demands. We are all able to perceive the strain generated in our body by a given work task and we can make absolute and relative judgments about this perceived effort. Around the middle of the 19th century, Weber and Fechner described models of the relationship between physical stimulus and the perceptual sensation of that stimulus, in other words, the psychophysical correlate. Weber suggested that the "just noticeable difference" that can be perceived increases with the absolute magnitude of the physical stimulus I:

$$\Delta I = \alpha \bullet I \qquad (5)$$

with α a constant.

In the 1950s, Stevens at Harvard and Ekman in Sweden introduced ratio scales, which assume a zero point and equidistant scale values. These scales have since been used to describe the relationships between the perceived intensity and the physically measured intensity of a stimulus in a variety of sensory modalities (e.g., related to sound, lighting, and climate) as follows:

$$P = \beta . I^n \qquad (6)$$

where β is a constant, and n ranges from 0.5 to 4.

Since the 1960s, Borg and his coworkers have modified these relationships to take deviations from previous assumptions (such as zero point and equidistance) into account and to describe the perception of different kinds of physical efforts. Borg's "general function" is as follows:

$$P = a + c (I + b)^n \qquad (7)$$

In the formula, the constant a represents "the basic conceptual noise" (normally less than 10% of I), and the constant b indicates the starting point of the curve; c is a conversion factor that depends on the type of effort.

Ratio scales indicate proportions between percentages but do not indicate absolute intensity levels; they allow neither intermodal comparisons nor comparisons between intensities perceived by different individuals. Borg has tried to overcome this problem by assuming that the subjective range and intensity level are about the same for each subject at the level of maximum intensity. In 1960, this led to the development of a category scale for rating the perceived exertion (RPE). The scale ranges from 6 to 20 and matches heart rates from 60 to 200 beats/min. A new category begins at every second number. Borg claims that his General Scale is a category scale with ratio properties that could yield ratios, levels, and allow comparisons, but still retain the same high correlation with heart rate as the 1960 scale. Table 13–D shows Borg's General scale.

The instructions for the use of the scale are as follows (modified from Borg's publications): While the subject looks at the rating scale, the experimenter says, "I will not ask you to specify the feeling, but do select a number that most accurately corresponds to your perception of [specific symptoms]. If you don't feel anything, for example, if there is no [symptom], you answer zero—nothing at all. If you start feeling something, just about noticeable, you answer 0.5—extremely weak, just noticeable. If you have an extremely strong feeling of [symptom], you answer 10—extremely strong, almost maximal. This would be the absolute strongest you have ever experienced. The more you feel—the stronger the feeling—the higher the number that you choose. Keep in mind that there are no wrong numbers; be honest, and do not overestimate or underestimate your ratings. Do not think of any other sensation than the one I ask you about. Do you have any questions?"

Let the subject get well acquainted with the rating scale before the test. During the test, let the subject do the ratings toward the end of every work period, about 30 seconds before stopping or changing the workload. If the test must be stopped before the scheduled end of the work period, let the subject rate the feeling at the moment of stoppage.

TABLE 13–D	Borg's "General" RPE Scale (Ratings of Perceived Exertion CR-10)

The Borg General Scale (1980)
0—nothing at all
0.5—extremely weak (just noticeable)
1—very weak
2—weak (light)
3—moderate
4—somewhat strong
5—strong (heavy)
6
7—very strong
8
9
10—extremely strong (almost maximal)
11 or higher–the individual's maximum

The terms *weak* and *strong* may be replaced by *light* and *hard*, respectively.

Work/Rest Cycles

If a task demands more of the worker than can be sustained, rest pauses must be taken. A general principle governing the schedule of work/rest cycles is to break up excessively heavy work into bouts of work that are as short as is practical for the task at hand. Frequent short rest periods reduce cumulative fatigue better than a few long breaks. The worst procedure is to let the worker go home early, exhausted.

A formula has been used to estimate the percentage of time that should be allotted to rest:

$$T_{rest} (\%) = \frac{M_{max} - M}{M_{rest} - M} 100 \qquad (8)$$

In the formula, T_{rest} is the percentage of rest time; M_{max} is the upper limit of the metabolic cost for sustained work; M is the metabolic cost of the task; and M_{rest} represents the resting (sitting) metabolism.

For example, suppose that M_{max} equals 350 kcal/h; and that an average value for M_{rest} is 100 kcal/h. Then assume that the task requires 525 kcal/h, which is obviously too high. Apply these values to the formula as follows:

$$T_{rest} (\%) = \frac{350 - 525}{100 - 525} 100 = \frac{-175}{-425} 100 = 41\% \qquad (9)$$

Thus, for this kind of work, rest pauses should be scheduled to last a total of 41 percent (24 minutes) of the hour.

As an alternative to the idle-rest pause, one may consider intermingling a light task with the heavy task. To calculate the proportion of time that should be allocated to the two tasks, consider a heavy task that requires 500 kcal/h, interrupted by a light task that requires 250 kcal/h. Again, assume that M_{max} equals 350 kcal/h.

$$T_{light} \text{ task } (\%) = \frac{350 - 500}{250 - 500} 100 = \frac{-150}{-250} 100 = 60\% \quad (10)$$

Accordingly, the hard work could consume 40 percent of the time, the light task 60 percent. The light, secondary work task thus actually constitutes rest time from the heavy, primary task. Sharpening tools or walking to get material or cleaning the work place can provide productive respites from heavy work.

Rohmert proposed another model on work/rest cycles, specifically on rest allowance. Sometimes referred to as Rohmert's curves, this model determines the required rest allowance in terms of a percentage of work time. The curves are based on the level of work and the duration of the continued work period. The level of work is on a scale corresponding to the level of energy expenditure in kcal/min: light (1–2.5 kcal/min), moderate (2.6–3.75 kcal/min), heavy (3.8–6.0 kcal/min), very heavy (6.1–10 kcal/min), and extremely heavy (>10 kcal/min). As an example, a worker completing a light task for 120 minutes would require a rest allowance of 12 minutes (10% of 120 minutes), which is equivalent to a heavy task for 30 minutes (40% of 30 minutes).

Fatigue

If the energetic work demands exceed about half the person's maximal oxygen uptake, anaerobic energy-yielding metabolic processes play increasing roles. Anaerobic metabolism results in accumulations of potassium and lactic acid that force the muscle to stop working. Accumulations of potassium and lactic acid are believed to be the primary reason for muscle fatigue. The length of time during which a person endures anaerobic work depends on the person's motivation and will to overcome the feeling of fatigue. The sense of fatigue usually coincides with the depletion of glycogen deposits in the working muscles, a drop in blood glucose, and an increase in blood lactate. However, the processes involved are not fully understood, and highly motivated subjects may maintain work that requires very high oxygen uptake for many minutes, while others feel that they must stop after just a brief effort.

Fatigue is operationally defined as a reduced muscular ability to continue an existing effort. The phenomenon of fatigue is best researched in regard to maintained static (isometric) muscle contraction. If the effort exceeds about 15 percent of a maximal voluntary contraction (MVC), blood flow through the muscle is reduced—even cut off in a maximal effort—in spite of a reflex increase in systolic blood pressure. Insufficient blood flow brings about an accumulation of potassium ions and depletion of extracellular sodium in the extracellular fluid. Combined with an intracellular accumulation of phosphate (from the degradation of ATP), these biochemical events perturb the coupling between nervous excitation and muscle-fiber contraction. This uncoupling of central nervous system (CNS) control and muscle action signals the onset of fatigue. The depletion of ATP or creatine phosphate as energy carriers, or the accumulation of lactate, once believed the reasons for fatigue, also occur but are not the primary reasons. The increase in the number of positive hydrogen ions resulting from anaerobic metabolism causes a drop in intramuscular pH, which then inhibits enzymatic reactions, notably those in the breakdown of ATP.

When severe exercise brings about a continuously growing oxygen deficit and an increase in lactate content in the blood because of anaerobic metabolic processes, a balance between demand and supply cannot be achieved; no steady state exists, and the work requirements exceed capacity levels. The resulting fatigue can be counteracted by the insertion of rest periods. Given the same ratio of *total resting time* to *total working time*, many short rest periods have more recovery value than a few long rest periods. Avoiding fatigue

- allows short bursts of dynamic work and avoids long periods of static effort;
- keeps energetic work and muscle demands low; and
- encourages taking many short rest pauses, which is better than taking a few long breaks.

The subjective sensation of fatigue is feeling tired. When tired, a person has reduced capability and desire for either physical or mental work, and feels heavy and sluggish. The sensation of fatigue has a protective function similar to hunger and thirst. Feeling fatigued forces one to avoid further stress and allows recovery to take place.

Subjective feelings of lowered motivation and deteriorated mental and physical activities may result from fatigue. Fatigue may occur together with monotony, a sensation associated with the lack of stimuli. Fatigue-induced low performance can be completely restored to its full level by rest.

The most important factors that produce fatigue are physical work intensity (static and dynamic work); illness, pain, lack of rest (sleep), poor eating habits; and psychological factors—worry, conflict, and possibly monotony. Hence, many different sources can be responsible for the sensation and the state of fatigue, which may be the result of an accumulation of effects stemming from various sources.

ENGINEERING ANTHROPOMETRY

Anthropometry literally means *measuring the human*, traditionally in metric units, of heights, breadths, depths, and distances—all straight-line, point-to-point measurements between landmarks on the body. Typically, functional dimensions are recorded, such as sitting eye height and hand reach. However, body segment shape (e.g., face or torso) and joint range of motion may be measured. For biomechanical modeling, body segment lengths, joint centers of rotation, body segment mass, and centers of gravity may be useful.

Engineering anthropometry involves the use of this data to design workplaces, workstations, equipment, and tools. Not considering anthropometry may lead to reduced productivity, injuries, or inability to do work. For example, excessive bending or reaching to retrieve parts may result in extra time to complete a task or back pain.

For typical measurements, the body is placed in a standing or sitting position. In the standing posture, the subject stands erect; heels together, buttocks, shoulder blades, and

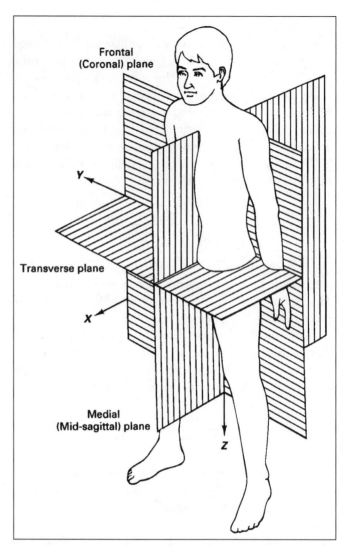

Figure 13–3. Measuring planes and terms used in anthropometry. (*Adapted from Kroemer et al.* Ergonomics: How to Design for Ease and Efficiency. *Upper Saddle River, NJ: Prentice Hall, 2001. Reprinted with permission by the publisher. All rights reserved.*)

back of head touching the wall; arms hanging straight down (or extended straight forward), palms forward, and fingers straight. This is similar to the so-called anatomical position. In the sitting posture, the subject is seated on a horizontal surface adjusted so that the thighs are horizontal, the lower legs are vertical, and the feet are flat on the ground. The subject is nearly nude and without shoes. Figure 13–3 shows reference planes and descriptive terms often used in anthropometry. Figures 13–4 and 13–5 show important anatomical landmarks of the human body. The NASA-Webb Anthropometric Sourcebook contains much information on measurement techniques in general and on military anthropometric data in particular. Most anthropometric data has been gathered while the subjects assume the standardized postures just described. Since these postures are quite different from the body posi-

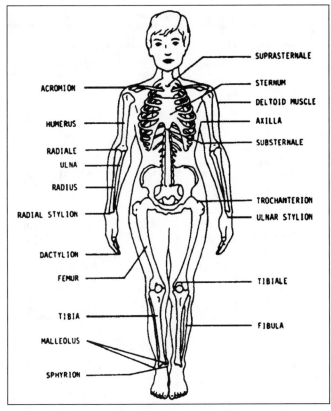

Figure 13–4. Landmarks on the human body in the frontal view.

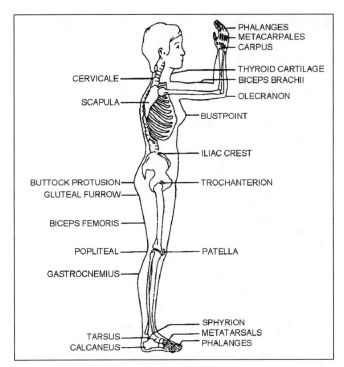

Figure 13–5. Landmarks on the human body in the lateral view.

Population Changes

Since World War I, increases in certain body dimensions have been observed. Many children grow to be taller than their parents. This increase in stature has been in the range of about 1 cm per decade, but now seems to be leveling off.

While the U.S. population height has changed little in the past decade, the population girth has been increasing dramatically. From 1998 to 2008 the prevalence of obesity (BMI > 30) has increased from 26 percent to 40 percent. These changes need to be considered in the design of seating, workstations, clothing and safety equipment.

The working population in North America has been changing in gender, abilities, occupation, age, and ethnicity. Today, the general work force has many more women in occupations that were dominated by men just a few decades ago. Occupations have changed drastically; computers and service industries are pulling people from traditional blue-collar work.

Design for special population subgroups does require the consideration of other-than-normal ranges of body sizes. These groups of people include pregnant women and the elderly. Average life expectancy has increased in the United States since 1900 by 27 years to nearly 80 years, and approximately one in five North Americans is 65 years and older. Thus, the number of elderly workers in the U.S. work force is gradually increasing. Their strengths and joint range of motions are less than a young working population.

More U.S. employees use a wheelchair at work.

tions assumed while working, particularly when the worker is moving around, the ergonomic designer must interpret the data for practical applications.

Civilian Body Dimensions

The anthropometric literature abounds with data on military personnel. The height and weight of the U.S. civilian population are measured regularly, for example, by the National Health and Nutrition Examination Survey (NHANES), www.cdc.gov/nchs/nhanes.htm. However, no large and reliable surveys of more complete anthropometry data from the U.S. civilian population have been measured during recent decades. Hence, anthropometric data applied describing the body sizes of the civilian population are taken from those of soldiers who are generally young and healthy. Head, hand, and foot dimensions are the same for soldiers and civilians; and the other body dimensions measured in the 1988 (latest) survey of the U.S. Army compare well with the few data available on the working population. Yet body weight is distinctly different between soldiers and civilians; civilians have more extreme values. An up-to-date compilation of estimated civilian body dimensions is presented in Table 13–E. This table shows the 5th, 50th, and 95th percentile dimensions as well as the standard deviations. Assuming a normal distribution of the data, the 50th percentile coincides with the mean (average) value.

TABLE 13–E   Anthropometric Measured Data in mm of U.S. Adults, 19 to 60 Years of Age

Dimension	Men				Women			
	5th Percentile	Mean	95th Percentile	SD	5th Percentile	Mean	95th Percentile	SD
Heights, Standing								
1. Stature [99]	1647	1756	1867	67	1528	1629	1737	64
2. Eye height, standing [D19]	1528	1634	1743	66	1415	1516	1621	63
3. Shoulder height (acromion), standing [2]	1342	1443	1546	62	1241	1334	1432	58
4. Elbow height, standing [D16]	995	1073	1153	48	926	998	1074	45
5. Hip height (trochanter) [107]	853	928	1009	48	789	862	938	45
6. Knuckle height, standing	na	na	na	na	na	na	na	na
7. Fingertip height, standing [D13]	591	653	716	40	551	610	670	36
Heights, Sitting								
8. Sitting height [93]	855	914	972	36	795	852	910	35
9. Sitting eye height [49]	735	792	848	34	685	739	794	33
10. Sitting shoulder height (acromion) [3]	549	598	646	30	509	556	604	29
11. Sitting elbow height [48]	184	231	274	27	176	221	264	27
12. Sitting thigh height (clearance) [104]	149	168	190	13	140	160	180	12
13. Sitting knee height [73]	514	559	606	28	474	515	560	26
14. Sitting popliteal height [86]	395	434	476	25	351	389	429	24
Lengths, Reaches								
15. Shoulder-elbow length [91]	340	369	399	18	308	336	365	17
16. Elbow-fingertip length [54]	448	484	524	23	406	443	483	23
17. Overhead grip reach, sitting [D45]	1221	1310	1401	55	1127	1212	1296	51
18. Overhead grip reach, standing [D42]	1958	2107	2260	92	1808	1947	2094	87
19. Forward grip reach [D21]	693	751	813	37	632	686	744	34
20. Arm length, vertical [D3]	729	790	856	39	662	724	788	38
21. Downward grip reach [D43]	612	666	722	33	557	700	664	33
Depths								
22. Chest depth [36]	210	243	280	22	209	239	279	21
23. Abdominal depth, sitting [1]	199	236	291	28	185	219	271	26
24. Buttock-knee depth, sitting [26]	569	616	667	30	542	589	640	30
25. Buttock-popliteal depth, sitting [27]	458	500	546	27	440	482	528	27
Breadths								
26. Shoulder breadth (bicrominal) [10]	367	397	426	18	333	363	391	17
27. Shoulder breadth (bideltoid) [12]	450	492	535	26	397	433	472	23
28. Hip breadth, sitting [66]	329	367	412	25	343	385	432	27
29. Span [98]	1693	1823	1960	82	1542	1672	1809	81
Head, Hand, and Foot Dimensions								
30. Head length [62]	185	197	209	7	176	187	198	6
31. Head breadth [60]	143	152	161	5	137	144	153	5
32. Hand length [59]	179	194	211	10	165	181	197	10
33. Hand breadth [57]	84	90	98	4	73	79	86	4
34. Foot length [51]	249	270	292	13	224	244	265	12
35. Foot breadth [50]	92	101	110	5	82	90	98	5
36. *Weight* (kg), estimated by Kroemer	58	78	99	13	39	62	85	14

These are measured, not estimated, data that may be slightly different from values calculated from Mean plus or minus 1.65 Standard Deviation—see Table 13–F.

Excerpted from Gordon, Churchill, Clauser, et al. (1989) and Greiner (1991), who used the numbers in brackets.

Wheelchair anthropometry research provides guidelines for accessibility standards and workstation design.

Another population subgroup is a result of immigration, for example, Central and South Americans, who may be relatively short in stature. This can have a conspicuous effect on the anthropometry of the working population in certain regions. Hence, the anthropometric data that describe local workers on the shop floor, in the office, or users and operators of equipment can be quite different from national statistics.

Anthropometric Statistics

Anthropometric data are dispersed in a reasonably normal (Gaussian) distribution (with the occasional exception, especially of muscle strength data). Hence, regular parametric statistics apply in most cases. The data cluster in the center of the set at the 50th percentile, coincides with the mean m (the average). The peakedness or flatness of the data cluster is measured by the standard deviation. Commonly used formulas to calculate the most often needed statistical descriptors of normal distributions follow.

A normally distributed set of n data is described by two simple statistics:

The 50th percentile is by definition the same as the mean m (also commonly called average):

$$m = \sum x/n \tag{11}$$

where $\sum x$ is the sum of the individual measurements.

The standard deviation (SD) describes the distribution of the data:

$$SD = [\sum (x-m)^2/n-1]^{1/2} \tag{12}$$

It is often useful to describe the variability of a sample by dividing the standard deviation by the mean m. The resulting coefficient of variation (CV) (in percent) is:

$$CV = 100 \, SD/m \tag{13}$$

A percentile value p of a normal distribution is calculated by multiplying the standard deviation by a factor k, selected from Table 13–F. Then subtract the product from the mean m if p is below the mean:

$$p = m - k \, SD \tag{14}$$

If p is above the average, add the product to the mean m:

$$p = m + k \, SD \tag{15}$$

A new mean from the sum of two distributions is simply the sum z of the means of the x and y:

$$m_z = m_x + m_y \tag{16}$$

The standard deviation of the summed distribution z is

$$SD_z = [SD_x^2 + SD_y^2 + 2 \, r \, SD_x \, SD_y]^{1/2} \tag{17}$$

The mean of the difference between two distributions is

$$m_z = m_x - m_y \tag{18}$$

The standard deviation of the new distribution is

$$SD_z = [SD_x^2 + SD_y^2 - 2 \, r \, SD_x \, SD_y]^{1/2} \tag{19}$$

Equations 16 and 18 contain (Pearson's) correlation coefficient r. It describes the relationship between two sets of data. The value of r ranges from +1 (a perfect positive correlation; as x increases, y increases as well) over 0 (no correlation at all between x and y) to –1 (also perfect, but negatively so: as x increases, y decreases).

Determining Percentiles

Anthropometric data often are best presented in percentiles. They provide a convenient means of describing the range of body dimensions to be accommodated, making it easy to locate the percentile equivalent of a measured body dimension. Also, the use of percentiles avoids the misuse of the average in design (as is discussed later). There are two ways to determine given percentile values p.

TABLE 13–F		Calculation of Percentiles	
Percentile p		**Central Percentage**	
$x_i = x - kS$ (below mean)	$x_j = x + kS$ (above mean)	included in the range xp_i to xp_j	k
0.5	99.5	99	2.576
1	99	98	2.326
2	98	96	2.06
2.5	97.5	95	1.96
3	97	94	1.88
5	95	90	1.65
10	90	80	1.28
15	85	70	1.04
16.5	83.5	67	1.00
20	80	60	0.84
25	75	50	0.67
37.5	62.5	25	0.32
50	50	0	0

One is to calculate values of *p*, as described above. The other is to simply graph the data distribution and find the critical percentile values from the curve by measuring, counting, or estimating. This technique works well whether the distribution is normal, skewed, binomial, or in any other form.

The following examples for calculating *p*-values are selected and adapted from those used by Kroemer, Kroemer, and Kroemer-Elbert.

Arm Length

The Task: Calculate the 95th percentile (95p) shoulder-to-fingertip length.

The Solution: The mean lower arm (LA) link length (with the hand) is 442.9 mm with a standard deviation of 23.4 mm. The mean upper arm (UA) link length is 335.8 mm, and its standard deviation is 17.4 mm.

The multiplication factor of $k = 1.65$ (from Table 13–F) leads to the 95th percentile. But simply adding the two 95p lengths would be a mistake because that would disregard their correlation; instead, establish the sum of the mean values first, using Equation 15:

$$m_A = m_{LA} + m_{UA} = 442.9 + 335.8 = 778.7 \text{ mm}$$

Then compute the standard deviation for m_A from Equation 16 with an assumed correlation coefficient of 0.4:

$$SD_A = [23.4^2 + 17.4^2 + 2\,(0.4)\,(23.4)\,(17.4)]^{1/2} \text{ mm} = 34.3 \text{ mm}$$

Finally, the 95th percentile total arm length can be calculated via Equation 14:

$$A_{95} = 778.7 \text{ mm} + 1.65\,(34.3 \text{ mm}) = 835.3 \text{ mm}$$

Keyboard Height Above the Seat

The Task: Establish the surface height of a keyboard so that the sitting operator has the forearms and wrists horizontal.

The Solution: Assume that having the tops of the keys at elbow height will allow the operator to keep the wrists straight and the forearms horizontal while the upper arms hang vertically from the shoulder joints. It appears appropriate to adjust the key height in a range where lowest is proper for the 10th percentile female elbow clearance and the highest fits the 90th percentile male clearance.

The elbow height above the seat pan is listed for Americans in Table 13–E: females have a mean of 220.5 mm with a SD of 26.8 mm; the corresponding numbers for males are 230.6 mm and 27.2 mm.

To use Equation 14 above, take $k = 1.28$ from Table 13–F as the multiplication factor for determining the 10th

and 90th percentile. The calculations show 10th percentile values of 186 mm for females and 196 mm for males; the 90th percentile values are 265 mm for males and 255 mm for females.

Consequently, under the assumptions made, the height of the key tops should be adjustable from about 19 to 27 cm above the seat pan level.

Percentiles serve the designer in several ways. First, they establish the portion of a user population that will be included in (or excluded from) a specific design solution. For example: a certain product may need to fit everybody who is taller than the 25th percentile or smaller than the 95th percentile in a specified dimension, such as grip size or arm reach. Thus, the 25 percent having values smaller than the 25th percentile and the 5 percent having values larger than the 95th percentile will not be fitted while 70 percent of all users will be accommodated.

Second, percentiles are easily used to select subjects for fit tests. For example: if a product needs to be tested, persons with 25th or 95th percentile values in the critical dimensions can be recruited for use tests.

Third, any body dimension, design value, or score of a subject can be located exactly. For instance: a certain foot length can be described as a given percentile value of that dimension, a certain seat height can be described as fitting a certain percentile value of popliteal height (a measure of lower leg length), or a test score can be described as being a certain percentile value.

Fourth, the use of percentiles helps in the selection of persons who can use a given product. For example: if the cockpit of an airplane is designed to fit the 5th to 95th percentiles, one can select cockpit crews whose body measures are between those percentiles in the critical design dimensions.

Principles for Applying Anthropometric Data

There are three basic choices when applying anthropometric data in the design of a workplace, workstation, or tools:

1. Design for the average
2. Design for extremes
3. Provide for adjustability

Depending on the circumstances, each of these principles has its applications. The following examples will provide an illustration of their use.

Design for the Average

Designing for average body dimensions is common but may lead to problems or discomforts among the smallest and largest persons in the workforce. For example, if the reach to a brake pedal is designed for the average person, then the smaller 50 percent of the workforce may not be able to fully depress the brake. Another example: a conveyor line set to the height of the average person may require the smaller individual to reach up causing shoulder fatigue while the larger operators may bend down causing neck and back fatigue.

Design for Extremes

A better approach may be to consider the anthropometry of the largest or smallest individuals who may be expected to do a task. Dimensions for the largest individual, the 95th percentile, are used to determine clearance dimensions such as the minimum height for overhead conveyors or the height of a doorway. This dimension will permit almost all of the working population (i.e., 95%) to walk beneath without hitting their heads. The dimensions of the large individual should also determine the necessary width for aisles, the size of access openings to repair machines and the necessary leg clearance between a chair seat and the bottom of a table or workbench.

Dimensions for the smallest person, for example, the 5th percentile, are used to determine reach dimensions, such as the maximum height and depth of shelves or controls, the location of parts bins in the workplace or the height of a nonadjustable chair seat that will permit the small person's feet to touch the floor.

Provide for Adjustability

The previous two design criteria assume that the workplace components (conveyors, work benches, shelves, parts bins, etc.) are fixed and cannot be adjusted. The alternative to these approaches is to provide adjustability in the workplace. The advantage of this approach is that a large proportion of the workforce can be optimally accommodated. The disadvantages include higher design and manufacturing costs, time for adjustment, need for additional training, and higher likelihood of the adjustable component breaking.

Where adjustment is a practical approach, the proportion of the population to be accommodated must be determined. Typically the range of adjustment will include the middle 80 or 90 percent of the population. For example, a standing workplace for medium assembly work should be at approximately elbow height. Accommodating the 5th percentile female through the 95th percentile male (90% of the population) requires the following range of adjustment (Table 13–E):

Female 5th percentile elbow height (dimension 4)
    = 926 mm (+ shoe height)
Male 95th percentile elbow height (dimension 4)
    = 1153 mm (+ shoe height)
Range of adjustment: 1153 – 926 = 227 mm

Alternatives to Adjustment

In workplaces with a large number of similar workstations, accommodating workers in fixed-height workstations may also be accomplished by providing workstations with several different heights and matching the worker height to the workstation.

Using Anthropometry Data for Design

When using anthropometric data to determine workplace dimensions, the following four steps can be useful:

1. Determine relevant body dimensions. Which body dimensions are important in the design? For example, display locations should be based on eye height while reach distances should be based on arm length.

2. Determine the percentage of the population to be accommodated and the appropriate design principle (e.g., average, smallest, largest, or adjustable) for each dimension.

3. Obtain the appropriate dimensions from the proper anthropometry table.

4. Add allowances for clothing and equipment where necessary. All anthropometric data reflect dimensions of lightly clad individuals. Clothing, shoes, gloves and personal protective equipment all add bulk which must be considered in the final design. Shoe height adds 25 mm for males and 15 mm for females. Clothing increases torso breadths by 8 mm.

BIOMECHANICS

Biomechanics explains characteristics of the human body in mechanical terms. More than 300 years ago, Giovanni Alfonso Borelli described a model of the human body that consisted of links (bones) joined in their articulations and powered by muscles bridging the joints. This stick person, refined and embellished with mass properties and material characteristics, still underlies most current biomechanical models of the human body. More than 100 years ago, Harless determined the masses of body segments; Braune and Fischer investigated the interactions between mass distribution, body posture, and external forces applied to the body; and von Meyer discussed the body's statics and mechanics. Biomechanical research has investigated responses of the body to vibrations and impacts, functions and strain properties of the spinal column, and human motion and strength characteristics.

When treating the human body as a mechanical system, many gross simplifications are necessary, and many functions, such as mental processes, may be disregarded. However, within its limitations and simplifications, a large body of useful biomechanical information is already available, and this scientific and engineering field is developing rapidly.

Body Strength

Assessment of human muscle strength is a biomechanical procedure. This assessment uses Newton's Second and Third Laws, which state that force is proportional to mass times acceleration, and that each action is opposed by an equivalent reaction. Since human muscle strength currently is not measurable at the muscle in vivo and in situ, human strength is described by the amount of force or torque applied to an external measuring instrument—which is the kind of data that the engineer needs to design tools and equipment.

Inside the body, muscular force vectors develop *torque* (also called moment) around the body joint bridged by the muscle. Torque is the product of force and its lever arm to the body joint, with the direction of the force perpendicular to its lever arm. In kinesiology, the lever arm is often called the mechanical advantage.

Figure 13–6 uses the example of elbow flexion to illustrate these relationships. The primary flexing muscle (biceps brachii) exerts a force (M) at the forearm at its lever arm (m) about the elbow joint. This generates a torque: $T = mM$. Since, by torque definition, a right angle must exist between lever arm and force vector, the useful lever arm is smaller when the elbow angle is wide open, or acute, than when the elbow angle is a right angle.

The correct unit to express force is the newton (N) while torque (moment) is measured in newton-meters (Nm). A 1-lb force is approximately 4.45 N, and a 1-kg force (kgf) equals 9.81 N. The pound, ounce, and gram are not force

but mass units. According to Newton's Second Law, force equals mass times acceleration; hence, weight (of a mass) generates a force proportional to gravitational acceleration. Force (as well as torque) has vector qualities, which means that it must be described not only in terms of magnitude, but also by direction, by the line of force application, and by the point of its application.

Figure 13–7 shows a more realistic model of the muscle forces that flex or extend the forearm about the elbow joint. It indicates an external force, E, and hand/forearm weight, W, at their respective lever arms, e and w. It also shows the force vectors of the two major flexor muscles, the biceps, B, and the radiobrachialis, R, acting at their specific lever arms, b and r, about the elbow. Also shown is the force vector of the triceps, T, with its lever arm, t. With a change in elbow angle, α, all force vectors change their angles of application, τ, ρ, β, and ε.

For static equilibrium, all forces and all torques must sum to zero. This provides three equilbrium equations, one each for the horizontal forces, the vertical forces, and the moments about the elbow joint. Including the joint reactions, indicated by H for horizontal and V for vertical force, and M for moment, these equations are as follows:

$$\text{(Horizontal Forces)} = 0$$
$$= T \sin\tau + R \sin\rho + B \sin\beta - E \sin\varepsilon - H \quad (20)$$

$$\text{(Vertical Forces)} = 0$$
$$= T \cos\tau + R \cos\rho + B \cos\beta - E \cos\varepsilon - W - V \quad (21)$$

$$\text{(Moments About Joint)} = 0$$
$$= tT \cos\tau - rR \cos\rho - bB \cos\beta + eE \cos\varepsilon + wW - M \quad (22)$$

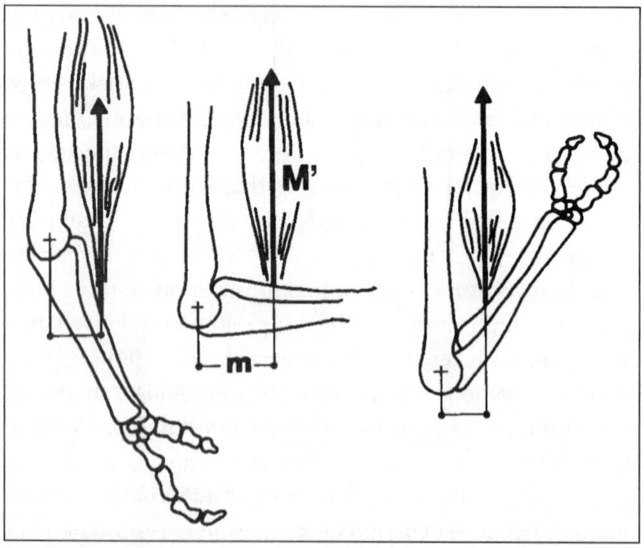

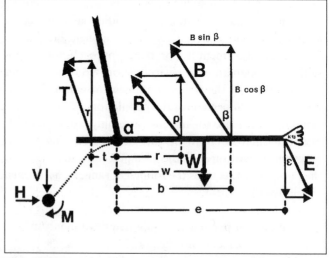

Figure 13–6. Changing lever arm (m) of the muscles force (M) with varying elbow angle.

Figure 13–7. A more sophisticated biomechanical model of elbow flexion with indications of force vectors, vector directions, and lever arms.

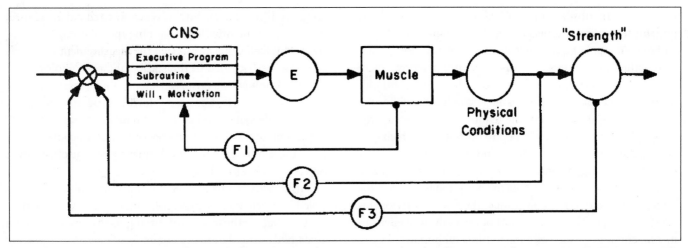

Figure 13–8. Model of generation and control of muscle strength exertion. *(Reprinted with permission from Kroemer KHE, Kroemer HB, and Kroemer-Elbert KE.* Ergonomics: Designing for Ease and Efficiency, *2nd ed. Englewood Cliffs, NJ: Prentice Hall, 2001.)*

These equations can be solved only if there are no more unknowns than equations. One can determine the length of the lever arms from anatomy. The angles are measured or taken from anatomy and geometry. The weight of the forearm can be calculated from geometry or taken from biometric tables. The external force can be measured. Still, this leaves the muscular force vectors (T, R, B) unknown, as well as the joint reaction forces (H and V) and the joint reaction moment (M). Various possibilities exist to reduce that number of unknowns to three, which is the same as the number of equations. These approaches include assumption of no coactivation, or of certain coactivation ratios (e.g., according the cross-sections of the muscles) or according to electromyographic (EMG) signals. Other techniques rely on statistical optimization procedures.

When movement occurs, the biomechanical conditions become more complex than those just described for the static case. In dynamics, additional forces must be considered as body segments rotate about their proximal joints. This introduces tangential, centrifugal, and Coriolis forces, which may also generate new torques, as does the inertia of the segment and possibly of an external load.

The principles of vector algebra can be applied to a chain of body segments; for example, pushing or lifting with the hands transmits torques (forces) from the wrist to the elbow joint, to the shoulder, down the spinal column, and across hip, knee, and ankle joints to the ground where the torques (forces) are generated that counteract the hand effort. Such kinematic chain models are used to assess the weakest links of the human body. These are often in the spinal column where low-back injuries, in particular, are frequent.

Measuring Body Strength

Voluntary muscle strength moves the segments of the body and generates energy exerted on outside objects when one performs work. There are more than 200 skeletal muscles in the body. They consist of bundles of muscle fibers: each is wrapped—as is the total muscle—in connective tissue in which nerves and blood vessels are embedded. At the ends of the muscle, the tissues combine to form tendons that connect the muscle to bones.

The only active action a muscle can take is to contract; elongation is brought about by force external to the muscle. Contraction actually occurs in fine structures of the muscle, called filaments, that slide along each other. The nervous control for muscular contraction is provided by the neuromuscular system, which carries signals from the brain forward to the muscle and also provides feedback. Electrical events associated with contraction of motor units of the muscle are observable in an electromyogram.

Model of Strength Generation

Figure 13–8 shows a simple model of the generation of muscular strength. Activation signals E travel from the central nervous system (CNS) along the efferent pathways to the muscle. Here, they generate contraction, which, modified by the existing physical conditions, generates the strength that is applied to a measuring instrument (or a work piece or hand tool). Three feedback loops are shown—the first one indicates reflexes; the second, transmitted sensations of touch, pressure, and kinesthetic signals; and the third, sound and vision events related to the strength exerted.

Consider the feed-forward section of the model. Currently there is no suitable means to measure the executive program or the subroutines in the CNS, or the effects of will or motivation, on the motor signals generated. The efferent excitation impulses travel along the efferent nerves to the muscles where they generate contraction signals. These signals can be observed in an EMG, which, however, is difficult to interpret, especially under dynamic conditions. Although it would be very useful to directly measure the tension within muscles in situ, at the time of this writing there are no instruments available that can do so. It is difficult to record and control the mechanical conditions within the body (i.e., the lever arms of the tendon attachments or the pull angles of muscles with respect to the bones to which they are attached), but the mechanical conditions outside the body can be observed and controlled. This concerns the kind and location of the coupling between the body and the device; the direction of exerted force or torque; the time history of this exertion; the position and support of the body; and environmental conditions, such as temperature and humidity.

Hence, with current means, only the output of this complex system, called muscle strength, can be defined and measured. Since strength has vector qualities and is time-dependent, it must be recorded not only in magnitude, but also in direction, point of application, and time history.

Measuring Techniques

According to Newton's Second Law (force equals mass times acceleration, or torque equals moment of inertia times rotational acceleration), the measurer first has to decide whether or not acceleration shall be present.

If there is no acceleration, there will be no change in speed. If speed is set to zero, then adjacent body seg-

ments will not move with respect to each other. Hence, the length of the muscle(s) spanning the joint remains constant. Physically, this means that the measurement of muscle strength is performed in the static condition. Biologically, this condition is called isometric, meaning constant muscle length. Thus, in this case, the terms static and isometric are factually synonymous. Measurement of static strength is straightforward and involves only simple instrumentation; and almost all current information on muscle strength reflects data on isometric exertions.

If velocity is not zero but is constant, the condition is called isokinematic, meaning constant motion. Measurement devices that establish a constant angular velocity around a given body articulation are commercially available. During their constant-speed phase (but neither at the beginning nor at the end of the motion), these devices provide a defined condition for which the exerted strength can be recorded. Only the angular velocity is controlled, while the amount of strength actually exerted at any moment remains under control of the subject. (Hence, the devices are not isokinetic even if falsely labeled so.)

During acceleration (the velocity is not constant but variable), strength is exerted under dynamic conditions that need to be defined and controlled depending on the circumstances selected. Such experimental control is possible in the laboratory, but likely to be very difficult and often impractical. Extreme cases of dynamic conditions are feats

---

TABLE 13–G   Dependent and Independent Variables in the Measurement of Muscle Strength

Variables	Isometric (Static) Indep.	Dep.	Isovelocity (Dynamic) Indep.	Dep.	Isoacceleration (Dynamic) Indep.	Dep.	Isojerk (Dynamic) Indep.	Dep.	Isoforce (Static or Dynamic) Indep.	Dep.	Isoinertia (Static or Dynamic) Indep.	Dep.	Free Dynamic Indep.	Dep.
Displacement, linear/angular	constant* (zero)		C or X		C or X		C or X		C or X		C or X			X
Velocity, Linear/angular	0		constant		C or X		C or X		C or X		C or X			X
Acceleration, Linear/angular	0		0		constant		C or X		C or X		C or X			X
Jerk, Linear/angular	0		0		0		constant		C or X		C or X			X
Force, torque	C or X		C or X		C or X		C or X		constant		C or X			X
Mass, moment of inertia	C		C		C		C		C		constant		C or X	
Repetition	C or X		C or X		C or X		C or X		C or X		C or X		C or X	

Indep = independent
Dep = dependent
C = variable can be controlled
* = set to zero
0 = variable is not present (zero)
X = can be dependent variable
The boxed constant variable provides the descriptive name.

Source: Adapted from Kroemer, Marras, McGlothlin, et al., 1990.

380

of strength at sports events, which can neither be easily measured nor controlled since they are highly specific to the situation and the person. Table 13–G presents an overview of classifications of strength exertions and their experimental control and measurement.

One technique commonly used to control dynamic conditions is to have the subject work isoinertially, that is, move constant masses (weights). To assess lifting capability, the weight is usually increased from test to test until one can determine the largest mass that the subject can lift (see the section on material handling later in this chapter).

The Strength Test Protocol

After choosing the type of strength test to be done and the appropriate measurement technique, an experimental protocol must be devised. This includes the protection of the subjects and of the information obtained from them; the control of the experimental conditions; the use, calibration, and maintenance of the measurement devices; and (usually) the avoidance of training and fatigue effects.

When selecting subjects, take care to ensure that they are a representative sample of the population about which data are to be gathered. Representative demographic variables considered include age, gender, handedness, race/ethnicity, etc. When managing experimental conditions, control of motivational aspects is particularly difficult. It is widely accepted (outside sports and medical function testing) that the experimenter should not give exhortations and encouragements to the subject. The so-called *Caldwell regimen* pertains to isometric strength but can be adapted for a dynamic test. The following is an edited excerpt of this regimen.

Definition: "Static body strength is the capacity to produce torque or force by a maximal voluntary isometric muscular exertion. Strength has vector qualities and therefore should be described by magnitude and direction."

1. *Measure static strength according to the following conditions: (a) Static strength is assessed during a steady exertion sustained for four seconds. (b) The transient periods of about one second each, before and after the steady exertion, are disregarded. (c) The strength datum is the mean score recorded during the first three seconds of the steady exertion.*

2. *Treat the subject as follows: (a) The person should be informed about the purpose of the test and the involved procedures. (b) Instructions should be kept factual and not include emotional appeals. (c) The subject should be told to "increase to maximal exertion (without jerk) in about one second and then maintain this effort during a four-second count." (You may want to use a different procedure and time for special conditions, e.g., for the*

measurement of finger strength.) (d) During the test, the subject should be informed about his/her general performance in qualitative, noncomparative, positive terms. Do not give instantaneous feedback during the exertion. (e) Rewards, goal setting, competition, spectators, fear, noise, etc., can affect the subject's motivation and performance and therefore should be avoided.

3. *Provide a minimal rest period of two minutes between related efforts; more if symptoms of fatigue are apparent.*

4. *Describe the conditions existing during the strength testing: (a) Body parts and muscles chiefly used. (b) Body position (or movement). (c) Body support or reaction force available. (d) Coupling of the subject to the measuring device. (e) Strength measuring and recording device.*

5. *Describe the subjects: (a) Population and sample selection including sample size. (b) Current health: a medical examination and a questionnaire are recommended. (c) Gender. (d) Age. (e) Anthropometry (at least height and weight). (f) Training related to the strength testing.*

6. *Report the experimental results: (a) Number of data collected. (b) Minimum and maximum values. (c) Median and mode. (d) Mean and standard deviation for normally distributed data points; for a nonnormal distribution, lower and upper percentile values such as 1st, 5th, 10th, 25th, 75th, 90th, 95th, or 99th percentiles.*

Designing for Body Strength

The engineer or designer who wants to consider human strength has to make a number of decisions, including the following:

- Is strength use mostly static or dynamic? If it is static, information about isometric strength capabilities can be used. If it is dynamic, other additional considerations apply, concerning, for example, physical endurance (circulatory, respiratory, metabolic) capabilities of the operator, prevailing environmental conditions, etc. Physiology and ergonomic texts provide such information.

- Is the exertion by hand, by foot, or with the whole body? For each of these situations, specific design information is available. If a choice is still possible, it must be based on physiological and ergonomic considerations to achieve the safest, least strenuous and most efficient performance. In comparison to hand movements over the same distance, foot motions consume more energy and are less accurate and slower, but they are stronger.

- Is a maximal or a minimal strength exertion the critical design factor? Maximal user output usually determines the structural strength of the object, so that the strongest operator may not break a handle or a pedal. The design value is set, with a safety margin, above the highest perceivable strength application.

- Minimal user output is that exertion expected from the weakest operator, which still yields the desired result, so that a door handle or brake pedal can be successfully operated or a heavy object moved.
- The range of expected strength exertions is, obviously, that between the specified minimum and maximum. Average user strength is usually of no design value.
- Most body-segment strength data are available for static (isometric) exertions. They provide reasonable guidance also for slow motions, although they are probably a bit too high for concentric motions and too low for eccentric motions. As a general rule, strength exerted in motion is less than that measured in static positions located on the path of motion.
- Measured strength data are often treated statistically as if they were normally distributed and reported in terms of averages (means) and standard deviations. This dubious procedure is not of great practical concern, however, because usually the data points of special interest are the extremes. Often the 5th and 95th percentile values are selected. These can be determined easily, if not by calculation, then by estimation.

HANDLING LOADS: LIFTING, LOWERING, PUSHING, PULLING, CARRYING

We all handle material daily. We lift, hold, carry, push, pull, and lower while moving, packing, and storing objects. The objects may be soft or solid, bulky or small, smooth or with corners and edges; the objects may be bags, boxes, or containers that come with or without handles. We may handle material occasionally or repeatedly. We may handle material during leisure activities or as part of paid work. Manual handling involves lifting light or heavy objects. Heavy loads pose additional strain on the body because of their weight or bulk or lack of handles. But even lightweight and small objects can strain us because we have to stretch, move, bend, or straighten out body parts using fingers, arms, trunk, and legs.

Material handling is among the most frequent and the most severe causes of injury in U.S. facilities and all over the world. The most common injuries are strains in the low back. The direct and indirect costs are enormous, and the human suffering associated with material-handling injuries is severe.

Seven Keys of Load Handling

Kroemer identified seven keys as the major ergonomic tools for safe and efficient material handling:

Key 1. Facility Layout—Initial layout or improvement of facilities contributes essentially toward safe and efficient material transfer. The selection of either product or process layout and accordingly how the flow of material is organized and designed in detail determines how people are involved and how they must handle material.

Key 2. Job Design—Job design determines the stress imposed on the worker by the work. Initially, the engineer must decide whether to assign certain tasks to a person or a machine. Furthermore, the layout of the task, the kind of material-handling motions to be performed, the organization of work and rest periods, and many other engineering and managerial techniques determine whether a job is well-designed, safe, efficient, and agreeable for the operator.

Key 3. Equipment—Selection, use, and improvement of equipment, machines, and tools strongly affect material handling requirements. Ergonomic principles must be considered, for example, when determining operator space requirements, control design, visibility, and color and sign coding.

Key 4. People—This key concerns people as material handlers, particularly with regard to body size, strength, and energy capabilities. People are the kingpins in manual material activities because they supervise, control, operate, drive, and actually handle material. If people are not needed in the system, then it should be automated. If they are needed, the system must be designed for them.

Key 5. Training Material Handlers—For decades, training in safe lifting procedures has been advocated and conducted. Training is expected to reduce severity and frequency of injuries, develop specific material handling skills, further awareness and responsibility for one's own safety, and improve specific physical fitness characteristics. Participants have been selected at random, or chosen according to risk (previous injuries, age, etc.); they were volunteers or they included all employees. Many studies on training outcomes are scientifically deficient because they do not follow an experimental design that allows the assessment of reliability and validity of the results of the experimental treatment. Granted, it is difficult (because of work interference, time needed, and expenses) to conduct a field experiment in which one varies only the independent variable and excludes confounding variables and uncontrollable interferences. Still, including a control group in the experimental design is often feasible, and it allows the evaluation of the claimed effect of the experimental training treatment.

Key 6. Screening Material Handlers—While training is one approach to "fit the person to the job," another is to select suitable persons, that is, screening individuals to place on strenuous jobs only those who can do them safely. This screening may be done either before employment, before placement on a new job, or during routine examinations during employment. A basic premise of personnel selection by physical characteristics is that the risk of overexertion injury from manual material handling decreases as the handler's capability to perform such activity increases. This means that a test should be designed to allow judgment about the match between a person's capabilities for load handling, and the actual load-handling demands of the job. Hence, this matching process requires that one quantitatively knows both the job requirements and the related capabilities of the individual. Of course, if the job requirements are excessive, they should be lowered before any matching is attempted.

Key 7. Ergonomic Design of Workplace and Work Task— The most effective and efficient way to reduce material handling injuries is to design equipment ergonomically, so that job demands are matched to human capabilities. Designing to fit the human can take several approaches. The most radical solution is to design out manual material movement by assigning it to machines: no people involved, no people at risk. If people must be involved, load weight and size shall be kept small, best accompanied by ergonomic design of the work task, that is, by selecting the proper type of material handling movements (e.g., horizontal push instead of vertical lift) and their frequency of occurrence. The location of the object with respect to the body is very important: best between hip and shoulder height, directly in front of the body so as to avoid twisting or bending the trunk. The object itself is important, of course, regarding its bulk, its pliability (e.g., firm box versus pliable bag), and whether it can be grasped securely (shape, handles). Naturally, the workplace itself must be well designed and maintained. Important aspects are proper working height; material provided in containers from which it can be removed easily; and nonslip floor and a clean, orderly environment that is free of avoidable noise and climate stressors.

Training

Training in Proper Lifting Techniques

Instructions on how to lift are meant to improve lifting technique and behavior and thus to reduce the likelihood of an overexertion strain or injury. In the laboratory, it has been shown that training regimens can increase the ability for lifting. Sharp and Legg reported that after four weeks of training, initially inexperienced lifters increased their work output significantly while maintaining their energy expenditures. The improvement was attributed to better skill through improved neuromuscular coordination and to possible increases of muscular endurance. Genaidy et al. used six weeks of training and also found that muscular endurance, muscular strength, and cardiovascular endurance were improved. Yet, to date, there have been no reports of tightly controlled studies with large numbers of industrial material handlers, and the validity of laboratory findings for industrial environments has not been established.

What to Train?

From the 1940s on, the advocated lift method was the straight-back/bent-knees lift (squat lift), in which workers lowered themselves to the load by bending the knees and then lifted by using the leg muscles. Yet, results of biomechanical and physiological research have shown that the leg muscles used in this lift method do not always have the needed strength. Also, awkward and stressful postures may be assumed if one tries to enforce this technique under unsuitable circumstances, such as when the object is bulky. Hence, the straight-back/bent-knees action evolved into the so-called kinetic lift, in which the back is kept mostly straight while the knees are unbent; but feet, chin, arm, hand, and torso positions are prescribed. Another variant was the free-style lift that appeared to be better for some workers than the straight-back/bent-knees technique. In some situations, the stoop lift (with a strong bend at the waist and straight knees) may be superior to the squat (bent knees, flat back) posture, which is usually advocated. Sedgwick and Gormly discussed the suitability of leg and stoop lifts and believed that an intermediate "semi-squat" lift was most versatile. The contradictory findings confirm Jones's 1972 statement that no single lifting method is best for all situations. Therefore, training of proper lifting technique is an area of confusion: What method should be taught?

Unsuccessful Training

Reviews by Brown, Snook, and Yu et al. detected no significant reductions in back injury as a result of training during a four-decade period. Several studies on nurses did not find effects on the incidence of low-back injury after receiving repeated instruction on lifting procedures; the principles taught were seldom used. Although neither the quality nor the content of the programs was investigated, the general conclusion was that training was not an effective preventive program for low-back injuries. Scholey and Hair reported that 212 physical therapists involved in back care education had the same incidence, prevalence, and recurrence of back pain as a carefully matched control group.

Successful Training

In 1981, Hayne suggested that the three essential components of a training program are "knowledge, instruction, and practice," but did not provide sufficient information on the contents of such a program nor indicate how to make reliable evaluations of its effectiveness. Davies reported decreases in back-injury incidence after three carefully designed and properly carried-out training programs. Miller reported success in decreasing the frequency of back injuries by using a five-minute slide/cassette program, a film, and posters to emphasize the theme "when you lift, bend your knees." A cohort was not observed.

Typical industrial case studies of training involve use of a training program, new safety rules and job redesign, and a publicity effort using posters, booklets, and paycheck stuffers. Reported results frequently indicate large reductions in compensation costs and fewer lost workdays per injury. However, these studies do not usually include a control group. One exception is a study of 3,424 employees of the Boeing Company, results of which showed no significant differences in the occurrence of back pain or in the number of lost work days between (healthy) employees who attended back school and a control group that did not.

Content of Training

A basic question, "What to teach?" has not yet been answered. The content of a training course depends on its aims. Previous efforts usually were in three areas:

1. Training specific lifting techniques, i.e., skill improvement
2. Teaching biomechanics, awareness of and self-responsibility for back injuries, thereby changing attitudes
3. Making the body physically fit so that it is less susceptible to injury

Although the goal of injury prevention is the same in each case, the methods of how to achieve that goal are quite different. The traditional approach of training a specific lifting technique alone does not appear effective, primarily because there is no one technique appropriate for all lifts. Most courses are therefore considered unrealistic and centered too much on protecting the back, as Sedgwick and Gormly reported from consensus meetings with more than 900 Australian health professionals. Yet, they proposed to teach semi-squat lifting throughout their course.

Preventing injury by increasing knowledge of the body and promoting attitude changes so that workers feel responsible for their bodies has a basic, almost simplistic, appeal and should be quite applicable. However, exactly what should be taught, and how, is still undetermined. How much knowledge is needed of kinesiology, biomechanics, and physiology?

What method is most effective? Barker and Atha reported that written guidelines, such as those commonly handed to untrained industry personnel, worsened lifting performance.

Another key to awareness and attitude change may be the attention paid to material handling problems by management, supervisors, or training instructors. Making employees aware of management's concern is an underlying theme in the training received from back schools.

Who to Train

Most industrial back injuries are not associated with objective pathological findings, and only about half of back pain episodes can be linked to a specific incident. Yet, many actions and events at work are associated with low-back injuries. In the mining industry, overexertion, slips/trips/falls, and jolts in vehicles are the most frequently mentioned events. Back injuries have been directly associated with lifting (37%–49% of the cases), pulling (9%–16%), pushing (6%–9%), carrying (5%–8%), lowering (4%–7%), bending (12%–14%), and twisting (9%–18%). The percentages vary considerably among industries and occupations. Construction and mining industries have reported the largest incidence ratios for compensation claims for back injuries. Other occupations with high ratios were garbage collectors, tire makers, truck drivers, nurses, and, as expected, material handlers.

Load-handling specifics differ much among industries and jobs (tire-making, mining, nursing) as well as within one industry or profession. They depend on the specific task, on available handling aids and equipment, and on many other conditions. Therefore, it is a question of how training recommendations are applied across settings. Even the group characteristics of material handlers in different industries might be important in designing a training program. For example, hospital workers might have higher educational skills than heavy-industry workers. Female employees may predominate in a given industry or occupation, which might influence the type of training, because usually women are about two-thirds as strong as men. It is not known how personal or task-specific characteristics should influence training.

In the United States, only about 2 of every 100 employees report a back injury per year. This poses another problem regarding the effectiveness and cost of back-care instructions. Of the injuries actually reported, about every tenth is serious, yet these few serious injuries cause the largest portion of the total cost. Hence, to specifically prevent these serious injuries, 2 of every 1,000 employees would be the target sample, while all 1,000 must be in the educational program. Even to address all persons who may suffer from any kind of back problem, about 20 out of 1,000, this is still a rather expensive approach, which may not appear cost-effective to the administrator.

Most training targets the individual worker or groups of workers. But one can also educate supervisors, health and safety professionals, and management personnel in

- awareness of load-handling problems;
- ergonomic job design principles; and
- how to respond to low-back pain and injury once it has occurred.

Such supervisor and manager training is probably important for an effective injury prevention program—but there are no actual data to support that.

Review of Training

Immediately after training, there can be an increase in the incidences of reported pain. This can be attributed to a change in management attitude and a willingness on the part of employees to report back problems early—positive steps toward avoiding more serious injury.

With currently available information, hardly any specific (or general) training guidelines are well supported by controlled research. This leaves much room for speculation, guesswork, and charlatanism regarding the best way to train people for the prevention of back injuries related to load handling. This condition is deplorable and needs to be remedied since common sense indicates that training should be successful.

The issue of training to prevent back injuries in material handling still is confused, at best. Some, possibly most, training approaches are not effective in injury prevention, or their effects may be so uncertain and inconsistent that money and effort paid for training programs might be better spent on ergonomic job design. Per Hadler, "In spite of more than 50 years of concerted effort to diminish task demand, the incidence of compensable back injuries has not wavered. Rather than pursuing the 'right way to lift,' the more reasonable and humane quest might be for workplaces that are comfortable when we are well and accommodating when we are ill."

The legal responsibility of employers to provide training cannot be ignored; thus, the idea to abandon material handling training appears unrealistic. The National Institute for Occupational Safety and Health stated that ". . . so long as it is a legal duty [in the United States] for employers to provide such training or for as long as the employer is liable to a claim of negligence for failing to train workers in safe methods of [modern materials handling], the practice is likely to continue despite the lack of evidence to support it."

If the job requirements are stressful, "doctoring the symptoms," such as behavior modification, will not eliminate the inherent risk. Designing a safe job is fundamentally better than training people to behave safely. Yet it appears plausible to expect that at least certain training approaches should show positive results. Among these, training for the following appeal to common sense and appear theoretically sound even though none of these has yet proven successful according to the literature:

- *lifting skills*—body and load positioning and movement
- *awareness and attitude*—physics and biomechanics associated with lifting, self-control
- *fitness, strength, and endurance*

It appears plausible that back pain may be related to job satisfaction and attitude. This finding generates important questions regarding psychosociological aspects on and off the job which, so far, have found few answers.

DESIGN OF WORK TASK AND WORKPLACE

The first design decision is to allocate load-handling tasks to either machines or humans. If people must handle material, then the specific job requirements must be analyzed.

Human versus Machine Load Handling

For the initial design decision, the unit size principle is of particular interest. According to this principle, one can increase the quantity (size, weight) of the unit load so that equipment use becomes feasible and appropriate for the movement of material—this is the big unit outcome. The other option is to reduce the size and weight of the load so that one operator can safely handle the material—this is the small unit outcome.

If all opportunities to automate or mechanize the movement of material have been exhausted, some material handling may have to be assigned to people. In this case, establish job requirements that will not overload the person or pose possible hazards. One must organize the task, establish job procedures, and determine details to enable the operator to perform the work safely and efficiently. Here are some guidelines:

- If people must move material, make sure the movement is predominantly in the horizontal plane. Push and pull, rather than lift or lower, and avoid severe bending of the body.
- If people must lift or lower material, let them do so between knuckle height and shoulder height. Lifting and lowering below knuckle height or above shoulder height are most likely to result in overexertion injuries.
- If lifting and lowering must be done by people, make sure these activities occur close to and in front of the body. If the worker must bend forward or, worse, twist the body sideways, overexertion injuries are most likely.
- If people must move material, make sure the material is light, compact, and safe to grasp. A light object will

strain the spinal column and body tissues less than heavy objects. Compact material can be held more closely to the body than a bulky object. A solid object with good handles is more safely held and more easily moved than pliable material.

- If people must handle material, make sure it does not have sharp edges, corners, or pinch points.
- If material is delivered in bins or containers, make sure it can be easily removed from them, specifically make sure that the operator does not have to "dive" into the container to reach the material.
- People tend to revert to previous habits and customs if practices to replace previous ones are not reinforced and refreshed periodically.
- Emergency situations, the unusual case, the sudden quick movement, increased body weight, or impaired physical well-being may overly strain the body since training usually does not include these conditions.
- If the job requirements are stressful, "doctoring the system" through behavioral modification will not eliminate the inherent risk. Designing a safe job is basically better than training people to behave safely in an unsafe job.

Rules for Lifting

There are no comprehensive and sure-fire rules for safe lifting. Manual load handling is a very complex combination of moving body segments, changing joint angles, tightening muscles, and loading the spinal column. The following DOs and DO NOTs appear helpful, however:

- DO design manual lifting and lowering out of the task and workplace. If a worker nevertheless must do it, perform it between knuckle and shoulder height.
- DO be in good physical shape. If a worker is not used to lifting and vigorous exercise, they should not attempt to do difficult lifting or lowering tasks.
- DO think before acting. Place material conveniently within reach. Have handling aids available. Make sure sufficient space is cleared.
- DO get a good grip on the load. Test the weight before trying to move it. If it is too bulky or heavy, get a mechanical lifting aid or somebody else to help, or both.
- DO get the load close to the body. Place the feet close to the load. Stand in a stable position with the feet pointing in the direction of movement. Lift mostly by straightening the legs.
- DO NOT twist the back or bend sideways.
- DO NOT lift or lower awkwardly.
- DO NOT hesitate to get mechanical help or help from another person.
- DO NOT lift or lower with the arms extended.
- DO NOT continue heaving when the load is too heavy.

Permissible Load Handling

Tables of lift weights for men, women, and children were used in the United States until the National Institute of Occupational Safety and Health (NIOSH) Work Practices Guide for Manual Lifting appeared in 1981. Since then, new knowledge about human material-handling capabilities has been gained, based on epidemiological, medical, physiological, biomechanical, and psychological approaches. However, even new guidelines are still based on assumptions and approaches that need refinement and further evaluation.

Limits for Lifting and Lowering

In 1981, a panel of experts prepared a *Work Practices Guide for Manual Lifting* for the U.S. NIOSH. For the first time, this document contained distinct recommendations for acceptable masses to be lifted. This differed from the previous assumptions that one could establish just one given weight each for men, women, or children that would be safe to lift. This 1981 NIOSH guide established two different threshold curves. The lower, called Action Limit (AL) was thought to be safe for 99 percent of working men and 75 percent of women in the United States. The AL values depended on the starting height of the load, the length of its upward path, its distance in front of the body, and the frequency of lifting. If the existing weight was above the AL value, engineering or managerial controls had to be applied to bring the load value down to the acceptable limit. However, under no circumstances was lifting allowed if the load was three times larger than the action limit values. This threshold was called the Maximum Permissible Load (MPL).

A decade later, NIOSH revised the technique for assessing overexertion hazards of manual activity. The new NIOSH guideline no longer contains two separate weight limits, but has only one Recommended Weight Limit (RWL). It represents the maximal weight of a load that may be lifted or lowered by about 90 percent of American industrial workers, male or female, physically fit and accustomed to physical labor.

The 1991 equation used to calculate the RWL resembles the 1981 formula for AL, but includes new multipliers to reflect asymmetry and the quality of hand-load coupling. Yet, the 1991 equation allows as maximum a load constant (LC), permissible only under the most favorable circumstances, with a value of 23 kg (51 lb). This is quite a reduction from the maximal 40 kg in the 1981 NIOSH guidelines.

The following assumptions and limitations apply:

The equation does NOT include safety factors for such conditions as unexpectedly heavy loads, slips, or falls, or for temperatures outside the range of 19°C (66°F) to 26°C (79°F) and for humidity not within 35 to 65 percent.

- The equation does NOT apply to one-handed tasks while

seated or kneeling, or to tasks in a constrained work space.

- The equation assumes that other manual handling activities and body motions requiring high energy expenditure such as in pushing, pulling, carrying, walking, climbing, or static efforts as in holding, are less than 20 percent of the total work activity for the work shift.
- The equation assumes that the worker/floor surface coupling provides a coefficient of static friction of at least 0.4 between the shoe sole and the standing surface.
- The equation may be applied under the following circumstances:
  - Lifting or lowering tasks, i.e., the acts of manually grasping and moving an object of definable size without mechanical aids to a different height level.
  - The time duration of such an act is normally between two and four seconds. The load is grasped with both hands.
  - The motion is smooth and continuous.
  - The posture is unrestricted (see above).
  - The foot traction is adequate (see above).
  - The temperature and humidity are moderate (see above).
  - The horizontal distance between the two hands is no more than 65 cm (25 in.).

For these conditions, NIOSH provides an equation for calculating the Recommended Weight Limit (RWL):

$$RWL = LC \cdot HM \cdot VM \cdot DM \cdot AM \cdot FM \cdot CM \qquad (23)$$

LC is the Load Constant of 23 kg (51 lb).

Each multiplier can assume values between zero and one:

- *HM* represents the horizontal multiplier where *H* is the horizontal location (distance) of the hands from the midpoint between the ankles at the start and at the end points of the lift.
- *VM* is the vertical multiplier where *V* is the vertical location (height) of the hands above the floor at the start and end points of the lift.
- *DM* is the distance multiplier where *D* is the vertical travel distance from the start to the end points of the lift.
- *AM* is the asymmetry multiplier where *A* is the angle of asymmetry, i.e., the angular displacement of the load from the medial (midsagittal plane), which forces the operator to twist the body. It is measured at the start and end points of the lift, projected onto the floor.
- *FM* is the frequency multiplier where *F* is the frequency rate of lifting, expressed in lifts per minutes. It depends on the duration of the lifting task.
- *CM* is the coupling multiplier where *C* indicates the quality of coupling between hand and load.

The following values are entered in the equation for RWL:

	Metric	*U.S. Customary*
LC = Load constant =	23 kg	51 lb
HM = Horizontal multiplier =	25/H	10/H
VM = Vertical multiplier =	$1 - (0.003|V{-}75|)$	$1 - (0.0075|V{-}30|)$
DM = Distance multiplier =	0.82 + (4.5/D)	0.82 + (1.8/D)
AM = Asymmetry multiplier =	1 − (0.0032A)	1 − (0.0032A)
FM = Frequency multiplier (see listing below)		
CM = Coupling multiplier (see listing below)		

These variables can have the following values:

H is between 25 cm (10 in.) and 63 cm (25 in.). Although objects can be carried or held closer than 25 cm in front of the ankles, most objects that are closer cannot be lifted or lowered without encountering interference from the abdomen. Objects farther away than 63 cm (25 in.) cannot be reached and cannot be lifted or lowered without loss of body balance, particularly when the lift is asymmetrical and the operator is small.

V is between zero and (175 − V) cm [(70 − V) in.] because few people can lift higher. For a lifting task, $D = V_{end} - V_{start}$; for a lowering task, $D = V_{start} - V_{end}$.

A is between 0° and 135°.

F is between one lift or lower every five minutes (over a working time of eight hours) to 15 lifts or lowers every minute (over a time of one hour, or less), depending on the vertical location *V* of the object. Table 13–H lists the frequency multipliers (FM).

C is between 1.00 (good) and 0.90 (poor). The effectiveness of the coupling may vary as the object is being lifted or lowered: a good coupling can quickly become poor. Three categories are defined in detail in the NIOSH publication and result in the following listing of values for the coupling multiplier (CM):

Couplings	*V < 75 cm (30 in.)*	*V = 75 cm (30 in.)*	
Good	1.00	1.00	
Fair		0.95	1.00
Poor	0.90	0.90	

To help apply the 1991 NIOSH recommended weight limit, a lifting index (LI) is calculated: LI = L/RWL, with *L* the actual load. If LI is at or below one, no action must be taken. If LI exceeds one, the job must be ergonomically redesigned. More information on the NIOSH Lifting Equation, including the applications manual, can be found on the NIOSH website (http://www.cdc.gov/niosh/).

TABLE 13–H Frequency Multipliers for the 1991 NIOSH Equation

Frequency, lifts/min	Work Duration (Continuous)					
	≤ 8 h		≤ 2 h		≤ 1 h	
	V < 75*	V ≥ 75	V < 75	V ≥ 75	V < 75	V ≥ 75
0.2	0.85	0.85	0.95	0.95	1.00	1.00
0.5	0.81	0.81	0.92	0.92	0.97	0.97
1	0.75	0.75	0.88	0.88	0.94	0.94
2	0.65	0.65	0.84	0.84	0.91	0.91
3	0.55	0.55	0.79	0.79	0.88	0.88
4	0.45	0.45	0.72	0.72	0.84	0.84
5	0.35	0.35	0.60	0.60	0.80	0.80
6	0.27	0.27	0.50	0.50	0.75	0.75
7	0.22	0.22	0.42	0.42	0.70	0.70
8	0.18	0.18	0.35	0.35	0.60	0.60
9	0	0.15	0.30	0.30	0.52	0.52
10	0	0.13	0.26	0.26	0.45	0.45
11	0	0	0	0.23	0.41	0.41
12	0	0	0	0.21	0.37	0.37
13	0	0	0	0	0	0.34
14	0	0	0	0	0	0.31
15	0	0	0	0	0	0.28
>15	0	0	0	0	0	0

* V is expressed in centimeters.

Source: From Putz-Andersson & Waters, 1991.

Limits for Lifting, Lowering, Pushing, Pulling, and Carrying

In 1978, Snook published extensive tables of loads and forces found acceptable by male and female workers for continuous manual material handling jobs. These data were first updated in 1983 by Ciriello and Snook, then revised in 1991 by Snook and Ciriello and in 1993 by Ciriello, Snook, and Hughes (Tables 13–I to 13–M). The following prerequisites apply for the application of their data:

- two-handed symmetrical material handling in the medial (midsagittal) plane, that is, directly in front of the body; yet, a light body twist may occur during lifting or lowering
- moderate width of the load such as 75 cm or less
- good couplings of hands with handles and shoes with floor
- favorable physical environment, such as about 21°C at a relative humidity of 45 percent
- only minimal other physical work activities
- material handlers who are physically fit and accustomed to labor

The format of the recommendations of Ciriello, Snook, and Hughes differs from the layout of the NIOSH guidelines. The NIOSH values are unisex, while the Ciriello et al. data are separated for female and males. The Ciriello et al. data are also grouped by the percentages of the worker population to whom the values are acceptable. The data do not indicate individual capacity limits; rather, they represent the opinions of more than 100 experienced material handlers as to what they would do willingly and without overexertion.

Tables 13–I through 13–M show, in much abbreviated form, the recommendations of Ciriello et al. for suitable loads and forces in lifting, lowering, pushing, pulling, and carrying. The tables are shown here only as examples; the original tables as updated in 1993 by Ciriello et al. must be consulted for complete information.

Note that, similar to NIOSH recommendations, the data in the Snook and Ciriello studies also indicate that lack of handles reduces the loads that people are willing to lift and lower by an average of about 15 percent. If the objects become so wide or so deep as to be difficult to grasp, the lifting and lowering values are again considerably reduced. If several material handling activities occur together, the most strenuous task establishes the handling limit.

If actual loads or forces exceed table values, engineering or administrative controls should be applied. Snook believes that industrial back injuries could be reduced by about one third if the loads that lie above the values acceptable to 75 percent of the material handlers could be eliminated.

Comparing NIOSH with the Ciriello et al. Recommendations

The guidelines by NIOSH are based mostly on biomechanical considerations particularly referring to a threshold compression of force in the lower spine of 3,400 N, with some consideration of physiological strains. The calculation of the RWL of the lifting or lowering is done twice, once for the beginning point and again for the ending point.

TABLE 13–I   Maximal Acceptable Lift Weights (kg)

| | | | Floor Level to Knuckle Height One Lift Every | | | | | | | | Knuckle Height to Shoulder Height One Lift Every | | | | | | | | Shoulder Height to Overhead Reach One Lift Every | | | | | | | |
| | | | s | | | min | | | | h | s | | | min | | | | h | s | | | min | | | | h |
Width*	Distance**	Percent†	5	9	14	1	2	5	30	8	5	9	14	1	2	5	30	8	5	9	14	1	2	5	30	8
	Males	90	9	10	12	16	18	20	20	24	9	12	14	17	17	18	20	22	8	11	13	16	16	17	18	20
34	51	75	12	58	18	23	26	28	29	34	12	16	18	22	23	23	26	29	11	14	17	21	21	22	24	26
		50	17	20	24	31	35	38	39	46	15	20	23	28	29	30	33	36	14	18	21	26	27	28	31	34
	Females	90	7	9	9	11	12	12	13	18	8	8	9	10	11	11	12	14	7	7	8	9	10	10	11	12
34	51	75	9	11	12	14	15	15	16	22	9	10	11	12	13	13	14	17	8	8	9	11	11	11	12	14
		50	11	13	14	16	18	18	20	27	10	11	13	14	15	15	17	19	9	10	11	12	13	13	14	17

*Handles in front of the operator (cm).
**Vertical distance of lifting (cm).
†Acceptable to 50, 75, or 90 percent of industrial workers.

Source: Adapted from Snook & Ciriello, 1991.

TABLE 13–J   Maximal Acceptable Lower Weights (kg)

| | | | Knuckle Height to Floor Level One Lower Every | | | | | | | | Shoulder Height to Knuckle Height One Lower Every | | | | | | | | Overhead Reach to Shoulder Height One Lower Every | | | | | | | |
| | | | s | | | min | | | | h | s | | | min | | | | h | s | | | min | | | | h |
Width*	Distance**	Percent†	5	9	14	1	2	5	30	8	5	9	14	1	2	5	30	8	5	9	14	1	2	5	30	8
	Males	90	10	13	14	17	20	22	22	29	11	13	15	17	20	20	20	24	9	10	12	14	16	16	16	20
34	51	75	14	18	20	25	28	30	32	40	15	18	21	23	27	27	27	33	12	14	17	19	22	22	22	27
		50	19	24	26	33	37	40	42	53	20	23	27	30	35	35	35	43	16	19	22	24	28	28	28	35
	Females	90	7	9	9	11	12	13	14	18	8	9	9	10	11	12	12	15	7	8	8	8	10	11	11	13
34	51	75	9	11	11	13	15	16	17	22	9	11	11	12	14	15	15	19	8	9	10	10	12	13	13	16
		50	10	13	14	16	18	19	20	27	11	13	13	14	16	18	18	22	10	11	11	12	14	15	15	19

*Handles in front of the operator (cm).
**Vertical distance of lowering (cm).
†Acceptable to 50, 75, or 90 percent of industrial workers.

Source: Adapted from Snook & Ciriello, 1991.

TABLE 13–K   Maximal Acceptable Push Forces (N)

| | | | One 2.1-m Push Every | | | | | | | | | | One 30.5-m Push Every | | | | |
| | | | 6 | 12 | 1 | 2 | 5 | 30 | 8 | Height | Percent | 1 | 2 | 5 | 30 | 8 |
	Height (a)	Percent (b)	s		min				h	(a)	(b)	min				h
							Initial Forces									
Males	95	90	206	235	255	255	275	275	334	95	90	167	186	216	216	265
		75	275	304	334	324	353	353	432		75	206	235	275	275	343
		50	334	373	422	422	442	442	530		50	265	294	343	343	432
Females	89	90	137	147	167	177	196	306	216	89	90	118	137	147	157	177
		75	167	177	296	216	235	245	265		75	147	157	177	186	206
		50	196	216	245	255	285	294	314		50	177	196	206	226	255
							Sustained Forces									
Males	95	90	98	128	159	167	186	186	226	95	90	79	98	118	128	157
		75	137	177	216	216	245	255	304		75	108	128	157	177	206
		50	177	266	225	285	324	335	392		50	147	167	196	226	265
Females	89	90	59	69	88	88	98	108	128	89	90	49	59	59	69	88
		75	79	106	128	128	147	157	186		75	79	88	88	98	128
		50	168	147	177	177	196	206	255		50	98	118	118	128	167

(a) Vertical distance from floor to hands (cm).
(b) Acceptable to 50, 75, or 90 percent of industrial workers.
Conversion: 1 kg$_f$ = 2.2 lb$_f$ = 9.81 N. 1 cm = 0.4 in.
Note that this is only an excerpt. Please see the complete table from Ciriello et al., *Hum Factors* 35: 175–186, 1983.

Source: Adapted from Ciriello, Snook, and Hughes, 1983.

TABLE 13–L   Maximal Acceptable Pull Forces (N)

	Height (a)	Percent (b)	One 2.1-m Pull Every						
			6	12	1	2	5	30	8
			s		min				h
Initial Pull									
Males	95	90	186	216	245	245	265	265	314
		75	226	265	304	304	314	324	383
		50	275	314	353	353	383	383	461
Females	89	90	137	157	177	186	206	216	226
		75	157	186	206	216	245	255	265
		50	186	226	245	255	285	294	314
Sustained Pull									
Males	95	90	98	128	157	167	186	196	235
		75	128	167	206	216	245	255	294
		50	157	206	255	265	304	314	363
Females	89	90	59	88	98	98	108	118	137
		75	79	118	128	128	147	157	196
		50	98	147	157	167	186	196	245

(a) Vertical distance from floor to hands (cm).
(b) Acceptable to 50, 75, or 90 percent of industrial workers.
Conversion: 1 kg$_f$ = 2.2 lb$_f$ = 9.81 N. 1 cm = 0.4 in.
Note that this is only an excerpt. Please see the complete table from Ciriello et al., *Hum Factors* 35: 175–186, 1983.

Source: Adapted from Ciriello, Snook, and Hughes, 1983.

TABLE 13–M   Maximal Acceptable Carrying Weights (kg)

	Height* (a)	Percent** (b)	One 2.1-m Carry Every						
			6	12	1	2	5	30	8
			s		min				h
Males	79	90	13	17	21	21	23	26	31
		75	18	23	28	29	32	36	42
		50	23	30	37	37	41	46	54
Females	72	90	13	14	16	16	16	16	22
		75	15	17	18	18	19	19	25
		50	17	19	21	21	22	22	29

(a) Vertical distance from floor to hands (cm).
(b) Acceptable to 50, 75, or 90 percent of industrial workers.
Conversion: 1 kg$_f$ = 2.2 lb$_f$ = 9.81 N. 1 cm = 0.4 in.
Note that this is only an excerpt. Please see the complete table from Snook et al., *Ergonomics* 34: 1197–1213, 1991.

Source: Adapted from Snook et al., 1991.

The guidelines by Ciriello et al., in contrast, rely on the psychophysical assessments of experienced industrial material handlers performing controlled material handling activities in the laboratory. These activities go beyond lifting and lowering; they also include pushing/pulling, carrying, and holding. Thus, the Ciriello et al. tables have wider applicability than what can be calculated from the NIOSH formula.

Direct comparisons are possible only between the lifting and lowering recommendations. In general, the results are quite similar, but with some larger deviations in the extremes of frequencies. To be prudent, one should take the lower values of either set of recommendations.

In general, one should prefer pushing and pulling to carrying and lifting and lowering. Figure 13–9 schematically shows engineering interventions applied to solve the prob-

lems associated with material handling. The main intent is to eliminate, or at least to reduce, overexertion injury risks to material handlers. Kroemer et al. provide detailed recommendations for activities other than industrial material handling, including outdoor load transport and moving of patients in hospitals and nursing homes. They also discuss ergonomic selection of material transport and handling equipment, and the design and use of trays and containers.

Use of Back Belts

When preparing to lift or lower a load, we instinctively develop intra-abdominal pressure within the trunk cavity. This pressure is believed to help support the curvature of the spine during the lifting or lowering effort. An external wrapping around the abdominal region might help to

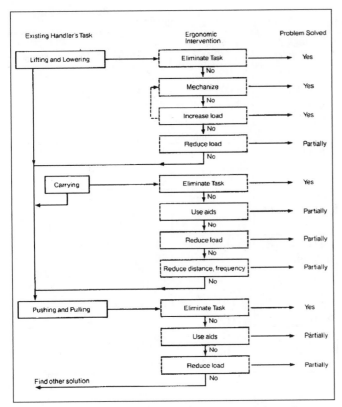

Figure 13–9. Reducing overexertion risks in material handling.

maintain this internal pressure because it makes the walls of the pressure column stiffer. Porters and workers in Nepal traditionally wear a cloth wound around the waist, called a patuka, while weight lifters commonly use fairly stiff, wide, and contoured belts. It has been advocated that people who do heavy manual material handling should also wear such abdominal belts (called, variously, back belts, lift belts, back braces, or back supports). A large number of studies have been performed, summarized, and reviewed. Their conclusions neither summarily support nor condemn the wearing of support belts in industrial jobs.

- Certain material handlers, especially persons who have suffered a back injury, may benefit from a suitable belt.
- Candidates for belt wearing should be screened for cardiovascular risk, which may be increased by belt pressure.
- Belt wearers should receive training similar to that given in back school because the presence of the belt may provide a false sense of security.
- Belts should not be considered for long-term use.
- Belts are not a substitute for ergonomic design of work task, workplace, and work equipment.

Altogether, the use of lifting belts for professional material handling does not seem to be an effective way of preventing overexertion injuries; even competitive weight lifters suffer back injuries.

HAND TOOLS

Hand tools are used in every industry to accomplish tasks and communicate with machines. They are used in construction (drills, pliers), manufacturing (in-line driver), health care (surgical tools), agriculture (hoe, shears, chain saw), mining (jack leg drill), and service/finance (keyboards, mice, smart phones). Too often, hand tool designs are focused on the working end of the tool rather than how it interfaces with the hand. A well-designed hand tool can lead to large improvements in productivity. However, hand tools can also cause serious injuries to the hand, arm, or shoulder.

Injuries occur for a number of reasons: the hand tool requires high forces to use, it imparts high forces to the arm, it applies a high contact pressure to a sensitive part of the hand, it is used for many hours in awkward hand or shoulder postures, it transmits high levels of vibration to the hand, or the action end of the tool comes in contact with another part of the body.

Because tools are so specialized for tasks, it is difficult to generalize design concepts. However, some guidelines can be provided.

Hand Force

Table 13–N lists forces that can be applied by the fingers in different hand postures. Hand tools should not be designed so that they require the user's full strength to use. Use in this way increases the likelihood of a ligament, tendon, or muscle strain or sprain. Occasional and brief application of 30 to 50 percent of strength may be allowable. However, if the tool is used repeatedly, the applied force should be less than 15 percent of the person's strength to avoid fatigue and injury. Applied pinch forces of less than 10 N (1 kg-force) appear to be safe if performed repeatedly.

Some tools can kick back when used and exceed the strength of the worker. For example, hand drills can suddenly apply greater torque when in use. If a bit seizes while drilling, the drill can suddenly twist in the hand and cause an injury to the wrist, elbow, or shoulder. To prevent this, use a drill with a clutch or automatic cutoff. Another solution used in manufacturing is to attach an anti-torque bar to an in-line driver or drill. The bar then transmits the high drill torque to an adjacent structure and not through the worker's wrists.

Use sharp tool blades. To improve productivity and decrease the force applied to the hand tool, the cutting edges of the tool should be sharp. Dental hygienists typically sharpen their scaling tools several times a day so that they can apply less pinch force when cleaning teeth. Drill bits should be sharpened or replaced when dull.

TABLE 13–N	Grip and Grasp Forces* Exerted by 21 Male Students and 12 Machinists					
Couplings	**Digit 1 (Thumb)**	**Digit 2 (Index)**	**Digit 3 (Middle)**	**Digit 4 (Ring)**	**Digit 5 (Little)**	**All Digits Combined**
Push with digit tip in direction of the extended digit ("poke")	91 (39)** 138 (41)	52 (16)** 84 (35)	51 (12)** 86 (28)	35 (12)** 66 (22)	30 (10)** 52 (14)**	
Digit touch (Coupling #1) perpendicular to extended digit	84 (33)** 131 (42)	43 (14)** 70 (17)	36 (13)** 76 (20)	30 (13)** 57 (17)	25 (10)** 55 (16)	—
Same, but all fingers press on one bar	—	Digits, 2, 3, 4, 5, combined: 162 (33)				
Tip force (as in typing; angle between distal and proximal phalanges about 135 degrees)	— 65 (12)	30 (12)** 69 (22)	29 (11)** 50 (11)	23 (9)** 46 (14)	19 (7)**	—
Palm touch (Coupling #2) perpendicular to palm (arm, hand, digits extended and horizontal)	—	—	—	—	—	233 (65)
Hook force exerted with digit tip pad (Coupling #3, "scratch") All digits combined:	61 (21) 118 (24)	49 (17) 89 (29)	48 (19) 104 (26)	38 (13) 77 (21)	34 (10) 66 (17)	108 (39)** 252 (63)
Thumb-fingertip grip (Coupling #4, "tip pinch")	—	1 on 2 50 (14)** 59 (15)	1 on 3 53 (14)** 63 (16)	1 on 4 38 (7)** 44 (12)	1 on 5 28 (7)** 30 (6)	—
Thumb-finger palmar grip (Coupling #5, 1 on "pad pinch")	2 and 3 85 (16)** 95 (19)	1 on 2 63 (12)** 34 (7)	1 on 3 61 (16)** 70 (15)	1 on 4 41 (12)** 54 (15)	1 on 5 31 (9)** 34 (7)	—
Thumb-forefinger side grip (Coupling #6, "side pinch")	—	1 on 2 98 (13)** 112 (16)	—	—	—	—
Power grasp (Coupling #10, "grip strength")	—	—	—	—	—	318 (61)** 366 (53)

*Means and standard deviations in N.
** Students' results; all others are machinists' results.
Source: Adapted from Kroemer et al. *Ergonomics: How to Design for Ease and Efficiency.* Upper Saddle River, NJ: Prentice Hall, 2001. Reprinted with permission by the publisher. All rights reserved.

Select fasteners that reduce hand forces. For example, Torx, square, and hex head screws resist cam-out better than Phillips or slot head screws and, therefore, reduce the force applied by the hand and prevent overtightening. In manufacturing, the driver torque should match the fastener torque specifications.

Handle Shape

The tool designer's task is to make sure that the handle can be held securely (without fatiguing muscle unnecessarily, and avoiding pressure points) while one exerts linear force or rotating torque to the tool. In most tools, force must be applied by the hand in two directions: one perpendicular to the handle surface (e.g., by the palm closing the handles of pliers), the other perpendicular to that direction (in pulling an object with the pliers). Hence, both the cross-sectional and longitudinal shape of the tool must be considered. Furthermore, the presence of oil or dirt between the hand and handle or the wearing of gloves can reduce the coupling of the hand to the tool.

If a task is performed repeatedly, select a tool with a handle so that the wrist is straight when used. That is, neither rotated (pronated or supinated) nor bent (flexed, extended, or laterally deviated). For example, if drilling straight ahead at elbow height, a pistol grip drill allows the wrist to be straight. But if drilling down on a workbench, use of the pistol grip drill requires wrist flexion and ulnar deviation. Instead, use a straight, in-line driver.

The handle should be of such cross-sectional size that the hand nearly encircles the handle, with no more space than about 1.3 cm (0.5 in.) between the fingertips and the thumb. This means that the diameter, if circular, should be between 2.5 and 6.5 cm (1.0–2.5 in.). The shape of the handle, in cross section, depends on the task to be performed; that is, on the motions involved in opening and closing the handle and on the magnitude of force or torque (moment) to be developed for use of the tool. In many cases, elliptical shapes (or rectangular ones with well-rounded edges) are advantageous if twisting (torqueing or turning such as with screwdrivers) must be performed. However, more circular cross sections are preferred if the tool must be grasped in many different manners.

For fine work, such as dental hygiene or jewelry work, a larger tool diameter (10 mm) will lead to less applied pinch force that a narrower (7 mm) tool diameter.

The handle should easily accommodate the length of the hand in contact with it. For example, a knife handle should be at least as long as the hand enclosing it. The contour of the handle can follow the contour of the inside of the hand enfolding the handle. Gloves, especially poorly fitting gloves, can interfere with finger sensation and may lead to workers applying more force to the hand tools than necessary. Make sure that gloves actually help the activity and do not hinder motion.

Generally, tool handles should not have sharp edges or be sculpted. A form-fitting handle shape might prevent people with different hand sizes or people who grasp the handle in a different way from using the tool comfortably. Pressure points should be avoided. These are often present if the form of the handle has pronounced shape components, such as deep indentations for the fingers or sharp edges or contours.

Rough surfaces of the handle might be uncomfortable for sensitive hands, but can counteract the effects of grease that make the handle slippery. Flanges at the end of the handle can guide the hand to the correct position and prevent the hand from sliding off the handle.

Hand Tool Vibration

Hand tools with high levels of vibration require special attention. Tools, such as grinders, chippers, rock hammers, chain saws, etc. can cause vibration injuries to the small nerves and blood vessels of the fingers. This type of injury typically occurs over years of use and is associated with blanching of the fingertips and finger pain. The condition is called vibration white finger disease or hand-arm-vibration-syndrome (HAVS). Once it occurs is cannot be treated, so it needs to be prevented. Prevention involves

- selecting vibrating hand tools with low levels of vibration amplitude;
- using vibrating hand tools for a limited number of hours per day;
- keeping the hands warm; and
- training employees so that they recognize the symptoms when they first appear.

Tool selection and use should follow ISO and ACGIH standards. There is no evidence that anti-vibration gloves are effective in preventing HAVS.

Tool Guards

The action end of a hand tool may easily injure a worker. Blade guards should be maintained so they work well. If the blade guard interferes with work, it will be disabled by the worker. Meat packing workers, who work with sharp knives, can protect their nondominant hand from cuts with an armored glove.

WORKSTATION DESIGN

The goal in designing a workstation is to promote ease and efficiency for the working person. Productivity will suffer in quantity and quality if the operator is uncomfortable, or if the layout of the workstation or the job procedures are awkward. Conversely, productivity will be enhanced if the operator is comfortable physiologically and psychologically, and if the layout of the workstation is conducive to performing the task well. Keeping this in mind, try to establish an ideal workstation, task, and work environment first and to make concessions to practical limitations only if absolutely necessary.

General Principles

Five general rules govern the design of workplaces:

1. Plan the ideal, then the practical.
2. Plan the whole, then the detail.
3. Plan the work process and the equipment to fit the human.
4. Plan the workplace layout around the process and the equipment.
5. Use mockups to evaluate alternative solutions and to check the final design.

In this design process, the following aspects are of primary importance:

- *Space:* clearance for the operator's body entrance and egress (including emergency exit); suitable body movements and postures at work; operation of controls and equipment (without bumping elbows, knees, or head)
- *Manipulation:* operation of tools, controls, and work pieces by hand (or foot) including seat adjustment; avoidance of excessive forces or inadvertent operation of controls; use of emergency items (stop button, flashlight, survival equipment)
- *Seeing:* visual field and information both inside (displays and control settings) and outside (road, machine being controlled); visual contact with co-workers; lighting (illumination, luminance, shadows; avoid glare)
- *Hearing:* auditory information, such as oral communication with other workers; signals (including warning signals); and sounds from equipment (engine underload, cutting tool)

More detailed design guidelines depend on the special workstation, on the specific work task, and on the environment. Military Standards 759 and 1472 also provide a wealth of human engineering information.

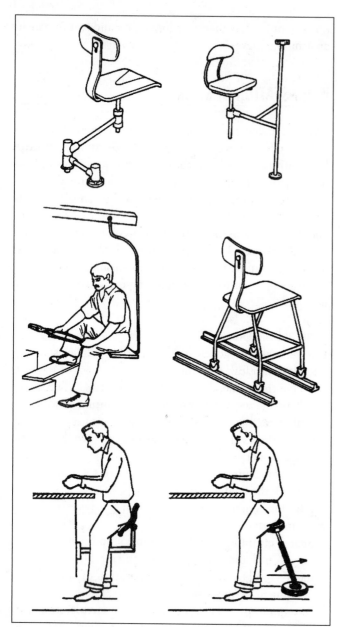

Figure 13–10. Examples of stand-seats. *(Adapted from Kroemer et al.* Ergonomics: How to Design for Ease and Efficiency. *Upper Saddle River, NJ: Prentice Hall, 2001. Reprinted with permission by the publisher. All rights reserved.)*

Standing or Sitting

Whether the operator should stand or sit at the workstation depends on several factors: the mobility required, the forces needed, the size of the work piece, and the required precision. The advantages of standing over sitting include more mobility, more body strength available, less front-to-rear room required, no seat needed, and greater latitude in workstation design. The advantages of sitting are that pedals can be operated with the foot more effectively (more strongly, and with more precision), it is less fatiguing to

maintain the sitting posture (if a good seat is available), and manipulation and vision may be more precise. Unless the specific work task or the environment or conditions strictly demand either sitting or standing, provisions should be made to allow the operator to sit or stand at will. Figure 13–10 shows *stand-seats*, which can offer a useful compromise. (More information on seat design is contained in the section on computer workstations in this chapter.)

WORKPLACE DESIGN

The most basic requirement for a workplace is that it must accommodate the person working in it. Specifically, this means that the work space for the hands should be between hip and chest height in front of the body. Within this region, the lower locations are preferred for heavy manual work, and the higher locations are suitable for tasks that require close visual observation. Contours of reach envelopes indicate the maximum distances at which objectives can be manipulated or placed. Figure 13–11 shows an example of such reach capabilities.

Work objects should be located close to the front edge of the work surface so that the worker does not have to bend over and lean across the surface to grasp items. To allow the person to be close to the front edge of the work surface, sufficient room must be provided so that thighs, knees, and toes can be placed somewhat under the work

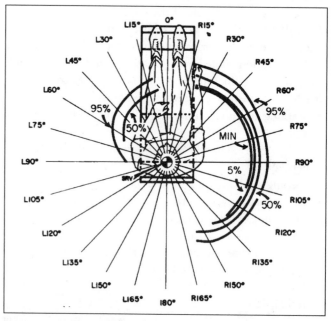

Figure 13–11. Grasping reach contours of the right hand in a horizontal plane 25 centimeters above the seat reference point. *(Reprinted with permission from Damon, Stoudt, and McFarland:* Human Body in Equipment Design, *1966.)*

surface if the work is performed while standing. For sitting operators, deeper and wider leg room must be provided under the bench, table, or desk. If foot controls are used, additional room for foot and leg motions may be needed. Pedals that must be operated continuously or frequently normally require a seated operator because if a person operated them while standing, the body weight would have to be supported on one foot.

Visual displays including instruments, counters, dials, and signal lights are preferably placed in front of the body and below eye level so that the line of sight (which runs from the eyes to the visual target) is declined 10 degrees to 40 degrees below the horizontal level. Table 13–O lists general principles for workstation design; specifics for computer workstations follow later in this chapter.

Work-Space Dimensions

Work-space dimensions can be grouped into three basic categories: minimal, maximal, and adjustable dimensions. Minimal work-space dimensions provide clearance for the worker. Many minimal clearance dimensions, such as the open leg space under a work table, can be determined using large percentile values from anthropometric tables (see Table 13–E). For example, if a 95th-percentile knee height were used to determine the height of the legroom, nearly everybody's legs would fit under the table. Even larger val-

ues need to be considered for other clearances: if the opening of a doorframe were at the 95th-percentile value, at least five percent of all users would bump their heads. Maximal dimensions are selected to permit smaller workers to use the equipment; for example, in terms of the distance at which one can reach. A related case is setting force requirements so low that even a weak person can operate the equipment. Often, the fifth percentile value of the relevant body attribute is used for determining minimal design measurements.

Adjustability permits the operator to modify the work environment and equipment so that it conforms to that individual's particular set of physical (anthropometric, biomechanical) characteristics as well as to subjective preferences. A six-way adjustable seat in a truck is an example of the proper adjustability that accommodates individual operators. Adjustable dimensions are particularly important when optimal performance with minimum effort is necessary to accomplish the work task.

The requirements for an industrial work seat are essentially the same as those for an office chair (see the following section in this chapter on computer workstations). However, the industrial work seat is probably somewhat more rugged and has soil-resistant upholstery. As shown in Figure 13–12, the industrial work seat should be adjustable in seat pan height between about 38 and 51 cm (15–20 in.). Its front edge should be well rounded to avoid pressure to the

---

TABLE 13–O	Ergonomic Guidelines for Workplace Design

1. In the design of the facility, ensure a proper match between the facility and the operator to avoid static efforts, such as holding a work piece or hand tool. Static (isometric) muscle tension is inefficient and leads to rapid fatigue.

2. The design of the task and the design of the workplace are interrelated. The work system should be designed to prevent overloading the muscular system. Forces necessary for dynamic activities should be kept to less than 30% of the maximal forces the muscles are capable of generating. Occasionally, forces of up to 50% are acceptable when maintained for only short durations (approximately 5 minutes or less). If static effort is unavoidable, the muscular load should be kept quite low—less than 15% of the maximal muscle force.

3. Aim for the best mechanical advantage in the design of the task. Use postures for the limbs and body that provide the best lever arms for the muscles used. This avoids muscle overload.

4. Foot controls can be used by the seated operator. They are not recommended for continuous use by a standing operator because of the imbalanced posture imposed on the operator. If a pedal must be used by the standing operator, it should be operable with either foot. Avoid hard floors for the standing operator; a soft floor mat is recommended, if feasible.

5. Maintain a proper sitting height, which is usually achieved when the thighs are about horizontal, the lower legs vertical, and the feet flat

on the floor. Use adjustable chairs and, if needed, footrests. When adjusting the chair, make sure that:
   a. elbows are at proper height in relation to work surface height;
   b. the footrest is adjusted to prevent pressure at undersides of the thighs;
   c. the backrest is large enough to be leaned against, at least for a break, and
   d. special seating devices are used if the task warrants them.

6. Permit change of posture—static posture causes problems in tissue compression, nerve irritation, and circulation. The operator should be able to change his or her posture frequently to avoid fatigue. Ideally, the operator should be able to alternate between sitting and standing; therefore, a workplace that can be used by either a sitting or standing operator is recommended.

7. In designing the facility, accommodate the large operator first and give that operator enough space. Then provide adjustments and support so that the smaller operator fits into the work space. For standing work, the work surface should be designed to accommodate the taller operator; use platforms to elevate shorter operators. (But watch out for stumbles and falls!) For reach, design to accommodate the shorter operator.

8. Instruct and train the operator to use good working postures whether sitting or standing, working with machines and tools, lifting or loading, or pushing or pulling loads.

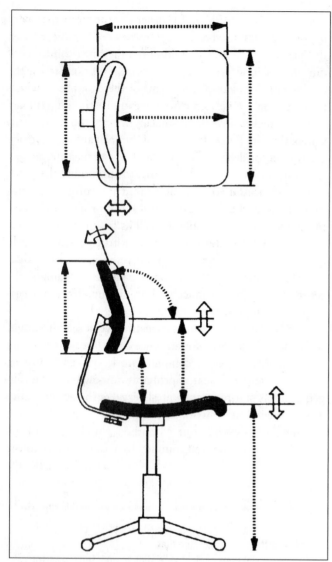

Figure 13–12. Main design features of an industrial work seat. *(Reprinted with permission from the American Industrial Hygiene Association.)*

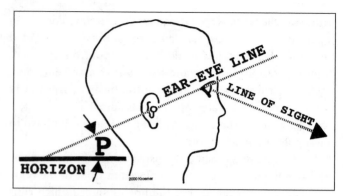

Figure 13–13. Ear-eye line and the line of sight.

should be placed in the center of the preferred viewing area. To determine this preferred visual field, one first establishes a reference line, the Ear-Eye line, which runs—seen on the side of the head—through the ear and the juncture of the eyelids, as shown in Figure 13–13. (The Ear-Eye line is much more easily established than the Frankfurt line, often used in older texts; for more information, see Kroemer et al., 2001.) When the angle between the horizon and the Ear-Eye line (P in Figure 13–13) is about 15 degrees, the head is held erect on an upright neck and trunk. Looking at an object in the distance, the preferred line of sight is approximately horizontal, that is, about 15 degrees below the Ear-Eye line. But for focusing at close targets, such as when reading a text either printed or displayed on a computer screen, most people prefer to look down steeply, as much as 60 degrees below the Ear-Eye line.

OFFICE (COMPUTER) WORKSTATIONS

Complaints related to posture (musculoskeletal pain and discomfort) and vision (eye strain and fatigue) are, by far, the most frequent health problems voiced by computer operators in North America and Europe. Apparently, some of these complaints are related. Difficulties in viewing (focusing distance, angle of the line of sight, glare), together with straining curvatures of the spinal column, particularly in the neck and lumbar regions, if joined by fatiguing postures of shoulders and arms, result in a stress-strain combination in which causes and effects intermix, alternate, and build on each other, especially if socio-psychological conditions are faulty.

Improperly designed workstations, ill-selected furniture, and poorly arranged equipment are the principal causes of postural problems. The questionable design idol of sitting upright at the old office desk has been carried over to the computer workplaces. Even the 1988 ANSI 100 standard on visual display terminal workstations used an "upright, or

underside of the thighs. A backrest should be provided, if the work activities allow it. The backrest should be adjustable in height and in distance from the front edge of the seat pan. To allow free mobility of the arms and shoulder blades, the backrest probably should not extend up to the neck (as the office chair may); however, a large backrest allows relaxing during a break from the work activities. The backrest should have a protrusion or pad at lumbar height, just like an office chair.

Objects that must be seen and observed (displays, signal lights, controls, dials, keyboards, written documents) should be placed well within the worker's visual field. This is the area, described in degrees, in which form and color of objects can be seen by both fixated eyes. The more important visual targets, especially those that must be read exactly,

near straight" posture for deriving furniture dimensions. In reality, many other working postures exist that are suitable for the work, and subjectively comfortable. Current design strategies recognize and build upon the great variety of individually preferred body movements and work postures in the computerized office.

Successful ergonomic design of the office workstation depends on proper consideration of several interrelated aspects, sketched in Figure 13–14. The postures that a person assumes and the ways to perform activities are strongly influenced by workstation conditions including furniture, equipment, and environment. All must fit the person and the task.

Body Positioning in Relation to the Computer

The use of computers has profoundly changed many tasks in the office, in the company building, and at home. Working with a computer establishes special demands on the operator's visual and motor capabilities. The eyes have three important tasks:

1. To search for specific keys (the exorbitant number of keys on most computer keyboards requires visual search and identification; "blind" touch typing is seldom possible)
2. To read a source document (for input into the computer)
3. To scan the display of the monitor (either to obtain new information or to receive feedback about the material already transmitted to the computer system)

The fingers input information to the system via keyboard, mouse, trackball, and other controls, such as light pen and trackpad for gestural input. Voice communication with the computer, both as input and output, is being refined and more commonly used both in the work and home environments.

The operator interfaces with the computer mostly through eyes and fingertips. The ears are input channels to the operator, and the mouth is a natural output device. However, sound and speech are not often used to communicate with computers even though these signals can travel through the air or can be transmitted through speaker phones attached to the head. Use of acoustic signals would not restrict the operator's head position and hence, the posture of the whole body. However, with current technology, the operator receives primary input through the eyes, as they focus their sight on the monitor, on the source document, and on the keys. Thus, the position of the operator's eyes is rather immovable with respect to the visual target. This eye fixation has the consequence that head, neck, and hence, trunk cannot be moved much but must remain in place, making for a rigid body posture at work.

Instead of voice, the digits of the hands are the user's major output links to the computer, just as they are with the old-fashioned typewriter. As keyboard keys, mouse pad, trackball, or trackpad (for gestural input) are fixed within the workstation, the operator has no choice but to keep the hands on them. This often determines, in fact, fixates, the person's body posture, even more so if foot controls are in use.

Healthy Work Postures?

In the 1880s, it was generally believed that an upright trunk, as when standing still and erect, was part of a healthy posture. For about 100 years, this idea had been used—usually with presuming right angles at hips, knees, and ankles—to design office chairs and other furniture. However, contrary to what we have been taught, today there are no compelling physiological or orthopedic reasons to make people stand or sit up straight. Nothing is wrong with this posture when it is freely chosen, but, if left alone, few people choose and maintain this posture over extended periods of time.

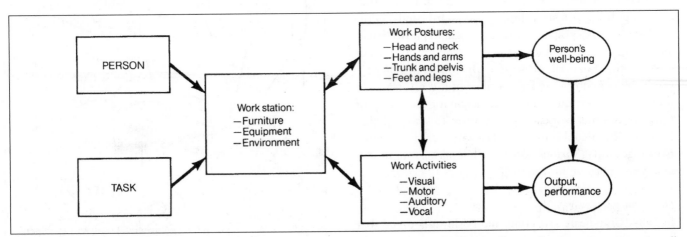

Figure 13–14. Interactions among workstation design, work postures, and work activities and their effect on the computer operator's well-being and performance.

An upright trunk has a straight spinal column on the frontal or posterior view but, in the lateral view, the spine forms one forward bend (lordosis) each in the neck and in the low-back region, and a slight rearward bulge (kyphosis) in the chest region. Sitting (or standing) upright does not mean that the spinal column is ramrod straight.

For nearly a century, physicians, orthopedists, physical therapists, parents, teachers, and military officers advocated the 19th-century "normal" posture of erect standing, as recommended by Staffel and his contemporaries. Even today, that upright standing posture is commonly considered good and proper. But it is certainly impractical for working because people do move about—and should do so—instead of standing (or sitting) stiff and still. Maintaining any one body position becomes unpleasant after a while; even while resting in bed, or relaxing in a comfortable easy chair, humans must move their bodies and reposition themselves after some time.

In recent years, the term *neutral posture* has become popular. It suggests a healthy, desirable, or central position of body members. What does *neutral* mean? Is that the middle of the total motion range in a joint? This would make some sense for the wrist, indicating the hand is straight, that is, in line with the forearm. But there is no obvious significance to the middle joint position in elbow or knee, shoulder or hip, or the spinal column. Does the term *neutral* suggest that all tissue tensions about a joint are balanced, so that the position is stable? Does the term infer a minimal sum of tissue tensions (torques) around a body joint? Or does this apply to tensions about several joints, or all body joints? Does *neutral* imply minimal joint discomfort? Does it infer a relaxed posture? Or a posture instinctively assumed for a task, to generate high body strength, or to avoid fatigue?

The simplistic concept that sitting upright, with thighs horizontal and lower legs vertical, is "sitting healthily" endured for a surprisingly long time. Even today, that upright posture with slight lordoses (forward bends) in the lumbar and cervical spine areas and a light kyphosis (backward bend) in the thoracic spine is stereotypically considered healthy, balanced, or neutral. Obviously, this posture can be quite appropriate for a while, but it is erroneous to use it as the overriding guiding principle for the design of the chair or other workstation furniture. To simply design for this postural idol completely disregards that it is healthy to change among various postures while sitting, not to stay in any one position for too long.

Free-Flowing Motion

In 1984, Grandjean, Huenting, and Nishiyama found that persons sitting in offices did not sit upright but leaned backward even if their chairs apparently were not designed for such a posture. Bendix et al. reported in 1996 that persons, while reading, often assumed a kyphotic lumbar curve even when sitting on a chair with a lumbar pad that should have produced a lordosis. These findings support the everyday observation that people sit any way they want, regardless of how experts think they should sit.

Allowing persons to freely select their posture has led in two instances to surprisingly similar results. In 1962, Lehmann showed the contours of five persons resting under water, where the water fully supports the body. Sixteen years later, NASA astronauts were observed when they relaxed in space. The similarity between the postures under water and in space is remarkable. One might assume that, in both cases, the sum of all tissue torques around body joints has been nulled. Apparently not incidentally, the shape of so-called easy chairs is quite similar to the contours of the relaxed body.

Dynamics is a label than can be applied to the current design of office chairs, as opposed to the statics of maintained posture. People do move about as they please. Design should encourage and support free-flowing motions, as sketched in Figure 13–15, with halts for temporary postures at personal whim.

The free-flowing motion design idea has these basic tenets:

- The user is allowed to freely move in and with the chair and to halt at will in a variety of sitting postures, each of

Figure 13–15. Moving, not sitting still, at work.

which is supported by the chair; and to get up and move about.

- It easy for the user to adjust the chair and other furniture, especially keyboard and display, to the changing motions and postures.
- The design allows for a variety of user sizes and user preferences.
- The design has taken into acount that new technologies develop quickly and should be usable at the workstation. For example, radically new keyboards and input devices, including voice recognition, may be available soon; display technologies and display placement are undergoing rapid changes; laptop and heldheld computers with small key sets and attached screens are widely used.

Designing for Vision, Manipulation, and Body Support

It is helpful for the layout of a work task and workstation to think of three main links between a person and the task.

- The first link is the visual interface. One must look at the keyboard, the computer screen or the printed output, and source documents.
- The second link is manipulation. The hands operate keys, a mouse, trackpad, or other input devices, and manipulate pen, paper, and telephone. Occasionally, the feet operate controls, for example, starting and stopping a dictation machine. The intensities of the visual and motor requirements depend on the specific job.
- The third link is body support. The seat pan supports the body at the undersides of the thighs and buttocks, and the backrest supports the back. Armrests or a wrist rest may be other support links.

Designing for Vision

The location of the visual targets greatly affects the body position of the computer operator. Many studies have shown what is intuitively apparent: objects upon which we focus our eyesight should be located directly in front, at a convenient distance and height from the eyes. If one is forced to turn the head to the side or tilt it up to view the computer screen or the document, he or she will often experience eyestrain. Eyestrain is often accompanied by pain in the neck, shoulders, and back. Yet, two basic mistakes are often made in many workstations: the monitor is set up much too far and too high and source documents are often laid flat to the side. In either case, the operator must crane his or her neck.

Monitor support. It is advantageous to use a separate support for a separate computer monitor so that the display can be adjusted in height independently from the keyboard, work surface, and table or desk. Adjustment is facilitated if the surface can be easily moved up or down, such as by a hand crank or an electric motor.

The common practice of putting the monitor on the CPU box, and possibly also on a stem for angle adjustment, lifts the screen much too high for most users, who consequently tilt their heads back and then may suffer from neck and back problems. Instead, the monitor should be located low behind the keyboard so that one looks down at it.

As a rule, the screen or source document should be about half a meter from the eyes, at the proper viewing distance for the operator's eyes. This is the distance for which corrective eye lenses are usually ground.

Document holder. If one reads from a source document often, one should use a document holder that holds the document close and parallel to the monitor screen, about perpendicular to the line of sight. A document placed far to one side causes a twisted body posture and lateral eye, head, and neck movements.

Proper lighting. The computer office should be illuminated at about 200 to 500 lx with today's self-lit displays. Paper documents may be difficult to read at this fairly low level, so one might want to shine a special task light on them—making sure that this does not create glare. For offices without computers, the proper illumination range is from 500 to 1,000 lx, even more if there are many dark (light-absorbing) surfaces present.

Designing for Manipulation

In addition to the eyes, our hands are usually very busy doing various office tasks: grasping and moving papers, taking notes, dialing phone numbers, and using various computer input devices. If our hands do many different activities, the varied manipulation is likely to keep our arms and the upper body moving around in our work space. Motion is desirable—in contrast to maintaining a fixed posture, such as when tapping the keyboard over an extended time.

Keyboard and input device placement. The keyboard should be placed directly in front and centered with the midline of the body at about elbow height when the shoulders are relaxed and the upper arms hanging by the sides of the upper body. A keyboard that is set up too high forces one to lift the arms and shoulders, requiring unnecessary muscle tension in the shoulders and neck region. Other peripheral input devices (e.g., mouse, trackpad for gestural input, trackball, joystick) should be placed as close to the center of the body as possible, reducing reach distance and shoulder abduction and muscle tension in the back, neck, and shoulders. Placing the keyboard and mouse at different levels, to the side, or too far away may cause muscle tension in the back, neck, and arms of the user. Prolonged durations in these awkward postures may lead to irritation and pain, and occasionally to overuse disorders such as bursitis, tendinitis, or cervico-brachial syndrome. These and other overuse disorders are discussed later in this chapter.

Resting one's wrist or arm on a hard surface or, worse, on a hard edge often occurs when a working surface is pushed up too high, above the operator's elbow height. This leads to sharp local pressure at the point of contact that can cause painful reactions. Examples are cubital tunnel syndrome, when the cubital nerve is compressed by placing the elbow on a hard surface, or carpal tunnel syndrome, when a sharp edge (e.g., a keyboard housing) presses into the wrist and palm area of the hand. These conditions can be avoided by placing the manipulation area low, by soft-ening surfaces that support the arm and hand (rounding edges, padding surfaces, giving wrist supports), and by proper working habits.

Designing for Motion

The human body is built to move about, not to hold still. It is uncomfortable and tiresome to maintain a body position without change over extended periods. While driving a car, a driver must hold his or her head in a mostly static position in order to see the road and instruments, and keep the hands and foot fixed on the steering wheel and gas pedal. After a while, it becomes very difficult to stay in the same seated position and posture, even though the nearly immobile pos-ture is supported by a relatively comfortable seat. A similar situation arises often at computer workstations—where the chair is often much less suitable than the car seat. But unlike driving, in the office one can get up and move around at will, which is a good habit.

At work, the body needs to move, not keep a static posture. Therefore, the primary aim of ergonomic worksta-tion design is to facilitate body movement, not to support maintenance of certain body positions. A convenient way to do so is for the designer to consider the extreme body postures expected to occur and to lay out the work space for motion between these. In the computerized office, this means to design for walking (standing) and for sitting. The seat should be designed for relaxed and upright sitting, for leaning backward and forward, and for getting in and out.

Designing the Sit-Down Workstation

One of the first steps in designing the office workstation for seated persons is to establish the main clearance and exter-nal dimensions. The size of the furniture derives essentially from the body dimensions and work tasks of the people who will be using the workstation. Main vertical anthropometric

inputs to determine the height requirements are lower leg (popliteal and knee) heights, thigh thickness, and the heights of elbow, shoulder, and eye—all listed in Table 13–E for North Americans.

The common design procedure is to start from the floor: upon it one stacks the height of the chair, then the height of supports for input devices (such as the keyboard, mouse pad, etc.), and finally the height of table and desk surfaces. To truly fit all the sizes and preferences of everyone in the office, all the furniture heights should be widely and easily adjustable.

Another furniture design strategy starts with the prem-ise of a fixed height of the major work surface (the desk or table in traditional offices), with adjustable heights of the seat and of the computer support. This regularly requires narrower height adjustment ranges for seat and equipment, but smaller persons need footrests. Another design approach relies on the same seat height for all, which results in the smallest adjustment needs for desks, tables, and supports, yet all but the most long-legged individual need footrests. The depths and widths of the furniture must fit the horizon-tal body dimensions (especially popliteal and knee depths, hip breadth and reach capabilities) as well as work task and equipment space needs.

The furniture at the computer workstation consists pri-marily of the seat, the support for the data-entry device, the support for the display, and a working surface (table or desk). It is best, and most expensive, to have all of these independently adjustable. These ranges should make the office furniture fit practically everybody in Europe or North America, tall or short. Of course, if the workplace is used by just one person, such as in the case of a personal home office, then only that one user must be fitted and little or no subsequent adjustments may be necessary.

The Office Chair

As discussed earlier, proper sitting at work was long believed to mean an upright trunk, with the thighs (and forearms) in essence horizontal and the lower legs (and upper arms) vertical. This model, with all major body joints at zero, 90, or 180 degrees makes for a convenient but misguiding design template: the 0-90-180 posture is neither commonly employed nor subjectively preferred, and it is not even espe-cially healthy.

To suit the seated person, the designer of office fur-niture, especially of chairs, has to consider a full range of motions and postures, as discussed by Kroemer and Kroemer.

Principles of seated chair design include:
- preserve/promote lumbar lordosis
- minimize disc pressure

- minimize static loading of back muscles
- reduce postural fixity
- provide easy adjustability

Many types of office chairs are available commercially today. Which is the most ergonomic? The following areas should be taken into consideration when evaluating the ergonomic design of a chair:

- *Chair Adjustments.* This includes usability and range of seat, back height, backrest recline, seat pan depth, and arm support adjustment while sitting. Chair seat, back, and arms should adjust independently to allow for comfortable sitting.
- *Body Support.* The chair should provide mid/upper back support with various recline positions (no forward push or fall back), lumbar (low back) support, seat pan support, and an appropriate armrest height support range (below thigh level to above seated elbow height). A chair with a five-pedestal base improves stability and prevents excessive tilting when the worker is in a reclined position.
- *Seating Comfort.* This includes seat pan/cushion comfort evaluated after 30–60 minutes of sitting, seat edge contour comfort (no pressure points under buttocks, thighs, or knees (at least one inch distance between the back of knees and front seat edge)), backrest cushion comfort evaluated at various recline positions, and armrest comfort evaluated when sitting back and resting arms.
- *Ease of Use.* This includes ease of chair seat height, seat pan depth, armrest height, and backrest recline adjustment while sitting. The ease of cleaning chair parts and materials should also be taken into consideration.
- *Overall Chair Experience.* The chair should provide an overall ease of use of the chair and controls. Ideally the number of movements necessary for adjustment, as well as the adjustment time, should be minimal. Appropriate training should be provided to the worker if necessary. The overall appearance, aesthetics, and comfort of the chair should be taken into consideration.

When selecting an appropriate office chair for the worker, the following steps should be taken when choosing an ergonomic chair:

- *Initial Evaluation.* The worker should be evaluated at their workstation. Factors such as body size, posture, demands of work, pain/discomfort, and cost should be evaluated and measured. Other factors, such as the need for a footrest and worker preference of the chair covering (e.g., fabric) should also be taken into consideration.
- *Recommendation.* Based on the initial evaluation, make a recommendation and have the worker try out an ergonomic chair.
- *Follow-up Evaluation.* After 1–2 weeks, reassess the worker's comfort and satisfaction levels with the chair.

If the worker is not satisfied, reevaluate and try another chair. This process may need to be repeated until a chair that meets the needs of the worker is found. Questions during the follow-up evaluation should include: Do the chair backrest (upper and low back), seat pan, and armrests feel comfortable? Does the chair provide a good fit, support, and ease of adjustability for you? Even after sitting on it for 30–60 minutes? Does the chair backrest recline and support your back in different positions?

Seat pan. When one sits down on a hard flat surface, not using a backrest, the ischial tuberosities (the inferior protuberances of the pelvic bones) act as fulcra around which the pelvic girdle rotates under the weight of the upper body. Since the bones of the pelvic girdle are linked by connective tissue to the lower spine, rotation of the pelvis affects the posture of the lower spinal column, particularly in the lumbar region. If the pelvis rotation is rearward, the normal lordosis of the lumbar spine is flattened.

Leg muscles (hamstrings, quadriceps, rectus femoris, sartorius, tensor fasciae latae, psoas major) run from the pelvis area across the hip and the knee joints to the lower legs. Therefore, the angles at hip and knee affect the location of the pelvis and hence the curvature of the lumbar spine. With a wide-open hip angle, a forward rotation of the pelvis on the ischial tuberosities is likely, accompanied by lumbar lordosis. (These actions on the lumbar spine take place if associated muscles are relaxed; muscle activities or changes in trunk tilt can counter the effects.)

Accordingly, in 1884 Staffel proposed a forward-declining seat surface to open up the hip angle and bring about lordosis in the lumbar area. In the 1960s, a seat-pan design with an elevated rear edge became popular in Europe. Since then, Mandal and Congleton et al. again promoted that the whole seat surface slope fore-downward. To prevent the buttocks from sliding down on the forward-declined seat, the seat surface may be shaped to fit the human underside, or one may counteract the downward-forward thrust either by bearing down on the feet or by propping the upper shins on special pads. A seat surface that can be tilted throughout the full range (from declined forward, kept flat, to inclined backward) naturally allows one to assume various curvatures of the lower spinal column, from kyphosis (forward bend) to lordosis (backward bend).

The surface of the seat pan must support the weight of the upper body comfortably and securely. Hard surfaces generate pressure points that can be avoided by suitable upholstery, cushions, or other surface materials that elastically or plastically adjust to body contours.

The only inherent limitation to the size of the seat pan is that it should be short enough that the front edge does not press into the sensitive tissues near the knee. Usually, the seat pan is between 38 and 42 cm deep and at least 45 cm wide. A well-rounded front edge is mandatory. The side and rear borders of the seat pan may be slightly higher than its central part.

The height of the seat pan must be widely adjustable, preferably down to about 37 cm and up to 51 or even 58 cm, to accommodate persons with short and long lower legs. It is very important that all adjustments, especially in height and tilt angle, can be easily done while one sits on the chair.

Figure 13–16 illustrates major dimensions of the seat pan.

Backrests. Two opposing ideas have been promoted. One advocates not having a backrest at all, so that trunk muscles must remain continually active to keep the upper body in balance. However, this concept (called active sitting) has not become very popular, for obvious reasons.

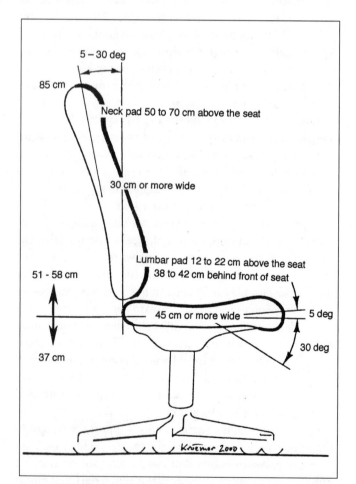

Figure 13–16. Essential dimensions of seat pan and backrest. *(Adapted from Kroemer et al.* Ergonomics: How to Design for Ease and Efficiency. *Upper Saddle River, NJ: Prentice Hall, 2001. Reprinted with permission by the publisher. All rights reserved.)*

Most people think that a backrest is desirable for several reasons. One is that the back support carries some of the weight of the upper body and hence reduces the load that otherwise the spinal column must transmit to the seat pan. A second reason is that a lumbar pad, protruding slightly in the lumbar area, helps to maintain lumbar lordosis, believed to be beneficial. A third, related reason is that leaning against a suitably formed backrest is relaxing.

Studies have shown the importance of supporting the back by leaning it on a rearward-declined backrest. Andersson et al. summarized the available findings in 1987 and concluded, "In a well-designed chair the disc pressure is lower than when standing" (p. 1113). Relaxed leaning against a declined backrest is the least stressful sitting posture. This is often freely chosen by persons working in the office if there is a suitable backrest available: "... an impression which many observers have already perceived when visiting offices or workshops with VDT workstations: Most of the operators do not maintain an upright trunk posture.... In fact, the great majority of the operators lean backwards even if the chairs are not suitable for such a posture" (Grandjean et al., 1984, pp. 100–101).

Of course, the backrest should be shaped to support the back fittingly. Apparently independently from each other, Ridder (1959) in the United States and Grandjean and his co-workers (1963) in Switzerland found in experiments that their subjects preferred similar backrest shapes. In essence, these shapes follow the curvature of the rear side of the human body. At the bottom, the backrest is concave to provide room for the buttocks; above is slightly convex to fill in the lumbar lordosis. Above the lumbar pad, the backrest surface is nearly straight but tilted backward to support the thoracic area. At the top, the backrest is again convex to follow the neck lordosis.

Combined with a suitably formed and upholstered seat pan, this shape has been used successfully for seats in automobiles, aircraft, passenger trains, and for easy chairs. In the traditional office, the boss enjoyed these first-class shapes while the rest of the employees had to use simpler designs. The so-called secretarial chairs had a small, often hard-surfaced seat pan and a slightly curved back support for the low back. The more recently designed task chair is an improved version.

The backrest should be as large as can be accommodated at the workplace: this means up to 85 cm high and at least 30 cm wide. To provide support from the head and neck on down to the lumbar region, it is usually shaped to follow the back contours, specifically in the lumbar and the neck regions. Many users appreciate an adjustable pad or an inflatable cushion for supporting the lumbar lordosis. The lumbar pad should be adjustable from 12 to 22 cm, the cervical pad from 50 to 70 cm above the seat surface.

The angle of the backrest must be easily adjustable while the person using it is seated. It should range from slightly behind upright (95 degrees from horizontal) to about 30 degrees behind vertical (120 degrees), with further declination for rest and relaxation desirable. Whether the seatback angle should be mechanically linked to the seat pan angle is apparently a matter of personal preference.

Figure 13–16 illustrates major dimensions of the backrest.

Armrests. Armrests can provide support for the weight of hands, arms, and even portions of the upper trunk. Thus, armrests can be of help, when they have a suitable load-bearing surface and are padded, even if only for short periods of use. Adjustability in height, width, and possibly direction is desirable. However, armrests can also hinder moving the arm, pulling the seat toward the workstation, or getting in and out of the seat. In these cases, having short armrests, or none, is appropriate.

Footrests. Hassocks, ottomans, and footstools have long been popular to put up one's feet, but footrests in the office usually indicate deficient workplace design, especially that a seat pan cannot be sufficiently lowered for the seated person. If a footrest is used, it should not be so high that the sitting person's thighs are nearly horizontal. A footrest should not consist of a single bar or other small surface because this restricts the ability to change the posture of the legs. Instead, the footrest should provide a support surface that is about as large as the total legroom available in the normal work position.

Work Surface, Keyboard Support

The height of the workstation depends largely on the activities to be performed with the hands, and how well and exactly the work must be viewed. Thus, the main reference point for ergonomic workstations is the elbow height of the person, and the location of the eyes. Both depend on how one sits or stands, upright or slumped, and how one alternates among postures.

The table or other work surface should be adjustable in height between about 60 and 70 cm, even a bit higher for very tall persons, to permit proper hand/arm and eye locations. Often, a keyboard or other input device is placed on the work surface, or connected to it by a tray. A keyboard tray can be useful, especially if the table is a bit high for a person, but it also may reduce the clearance height for the knees. The tray should be large enough for keyboard and trackball or mouse pad unless these are built into the keyboard.

Sitting and Back Pain

The posture and movements of the spinal column have been of great concern to physiologists and orthopedists. This is due to the fact that so many persons suffer from annoyance, pain, and disorders in the spinal column, particularly in the low back and neck areas. Explanations have been sought in the human body's not being built for long sitting or standing, or not being fit because of lack of exercise, or having undergone degeneration, particularly of the intervertebral discs. Physical activities and special exercises can improve fitness. Caution must be applied, however, when selecting exercises; some are appropriate, others are of questionable value, but several are outright dangerous or injurious, as Lee and co-authors pointed out in 1992.

The most easily applied remedy is to alternate often between walking, standing, and sitting. When long-time sitting is required, then the design of the seat and other furniture and equipment is critical; e.g., a tall and well-shaped backrest that reclines helps to support the back and head during work and allows one to take relaxing breaks. While sitting, one should change position often. This can be done purposefully by the person, perhaps with the help of automatic devices that make cushions on the seat or backrest pulsate on and off, or that effect small changes in the angles of seat pan and backrest.

Designing the Stand-Up Workstation

Standing up while doing computer work seems like a return to the habits of office clerks common around 1900. Yet, moving about and standing on one's feet, at least for a period of time, can be a welcome change from sitting, provided that the person does it at his or her own choosing. One may opt to stand for reading or writing or telephoning. Stand-up workstations can use a second computer to which work activities can be switched from the sit-down workstation for a while, or one can use a laptop computer there. Some people prefer standing and walking altogether to sitting in the office.

Stand-up workstations should be adjustable to have the working area used for writing or computer inputs at approximately elbow height when standing, between 0.9 and 1.2 meters above the floor. As in the sit-down workstation, the display should be located close to the other visual targets and directly behind the keyboard. If the work surface is used for reading or writing, it may slope down slightly toward the person. A footrest at about two-thirds knee height (approximately 0.3 m) allows the person to prop one foot up on it temporarily. This brings about welcome changes in pelvis rotation and spine curvature.

Nonresilient floors, such as made of concrete, can be hard on people's feet, legs, and backs. Carpets, elastic floor mats, and soft shoe soles can reduce strain. Appropriate friction between soles and the walkway surface helps to avoid slips and falls.

Designing the Home Office

Everything said previously applies to the home office. If you work only for short periods of time in your office at home, then the old dining table and the odd kitchen chair probably will not harm you. But as soon as you get serious about using your home office, working in it for hours, you should become very conscious about the working conditions there. Equip your office with carefully selected furniture, where the chair and other components of the workstation fit each other well—and, most importantly, fit you well.

Get a quality computer with an up-to-date display and with input-suitable devices. Select a keyboard that feels convenient to you, but consider voice input that might serve you well. If you travel much with your hand-held or laptop computer, consider a docking station. Do you want to use a laptop computer in your office as well? Select a room with good lighting that is separate and quiet and well heated and cooled. You will probably spend more time in your home office than you expected, and your well-being is worth the effort and money that you spend.

Fitting It All Together

A bad or mediocre office is not instantly converted into a good one by changing to a different computer or by simply putting up a better chair. All the components, equipment, furniture, lighting, and climate, must fit each other (Figure 13–17) and the person in the office must be willing and able to take advantage of all the offered possibilities. Equipment change must go with change in mental attitude. This applies not only to the working person, but also to the attitude of management. The expectation that all furniture and the postures of all the office workers must look alike is not reasonable; the micromanaging style of the 1980s is insufferable; the 1990s' "lean and mean" behavior of the almighty boss who calls all the shots is counterproductive.

Healthy, productive organizations use ergonomics on all levels. In 1999, Liberty Mutual Insurance Company completed an investigation of the impact of flexible office work spaces and ergonomic training on employee health and performance. Twenty office workers moved into new, adjustable work spaces while another twenty occupied new but corporate-specific workplaces. All 40 people received training in ergonomics. The expectation was that by giving employees more control over their environment and a better understanding of ergonomic principles, performance would improve and health problems diminish. The results

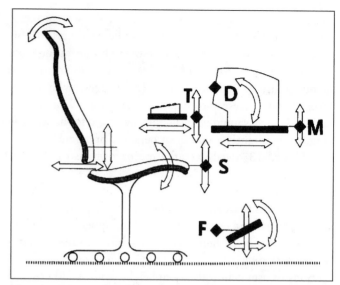

Figure 13–17. Adjustment features of a computer workstation. Key S = seat height; T = table height; F = footrest height; D = monitor height; M = support height. *(Reprinted with permission from Kroemer et al.* Ergonomics: How to Design for Ease and Efficiency. *Upper Saddle River, NJ: Prentice Hall, 2001. All rights reserved.)*

of the 18-month study confirmed the expected: Combined with ergonomic training, the flexible work space increased individual performance and group collaboration. This was accompanied by a nearly one-third reduction in back pain and a two-thirds reduction in upper limb pains among the employees who had more control over their environment.

CONTROLS AND DISPLAYS

Much research has been performed on controls and displays; in fact, in human factors engineering, the period after World War II is often called the "knobs and dials era." The following recommendations are brief excerpts from Chapter 10 of the Kroemers' 2001 book.

Light Signals

A red signal light shall be used to alert an operator that the system or any portion of the system is inoperative or that a successful mission is not possible until appropriate corrective or override action is taken. Examples of indicators that should be coded in red light are those that display such information as *no-go, error, failure,* or *malfunction.*

A flashing red signal light shall be used only to denote emergency conditions that require immediate operator action or to avert impending personnel injury, equipment damage, or both.

A steady red signal alerts the operator that the system or a portion thereof is inoperative and that a successful operation is not possible until appropriate correcting or overriding action has been taken.

A yellow signal light shall be used to advise an operator that a marginal condition exists. Yellow shall also be used to alert the operator to situations for which caution, rechecking, or unexpected delay is necessary.

A green signal light shall be used to indicate that the monitored equipment is in satisfactory condition and that it is all right to proceed; therefore, green signifies *go ahead, in tolerance, ready, function activated, power on,* and the like.

A white signal light shall be used to indicate system conditions that do not have right or wrong implications, such as alternative functions (e.g., *rear steering on*) or transitory conditions (e.g., *fan on*), provided such indication does not imply the success or failure of the operation.

A blue signal light may be used as an advisory, but common use of blue should be avoided.

Labels

Controls, displays, and any other items of equipment that must be located, identified, manipulated, or read shall be appropriately and clearly labeled to permit rapid and accurate performance. No label will be required on equipment or controls whose use is obvious to the user.

Labeling characteristics are determined by such factors as

- the accuracy of identification required;
- the time available for recognition or other responses;
- the distance at which the labels must be read;
- the illumination level and color characteristics of the illuminant;
- the critical nature of the function labeled; and
- the consistency of label design within and between systems.

Orientation. Labels and the information printed thereon should be oriented horizontally so that the labels may be read quickly and easily from left to right.

Location. Labels shall be placed on or very near the items they identify so as to eliminate confusion with other items and labels.

Standardization. Placement of labels shall be consistent throughout the equipment and system.

Equipment functions. Labels should primarily describe the functions of equipment items. Secondarily, the engineering characteristics or nomenclature may be described.

Abbreviations. Standard abbreviations shall be selected. If a new abbreviation is required, its meaning shall be obvious to the intended reader. Capital letters shall be used. Periods shall be omitted except when needed to preclude misinterpretation. The same abbreviation shall be used for all tenses and for both singular and plural forms of a word.

Brevity. Labels shall be as concise as possible without distorting the intended meaning or information and shall be unambiguous. Redundancy shall be minimized. If the general function is obvious, only the specific function shall be identified (e.g., frequency as opposed to frequency factor).

Familiarity. Words shall be chosen on the basis of operator familiarity whenever possible, provided the words express exactly what is intended. Brevity shall not be stressed if the results will be unfamiliar to operating personnel. Common, meaningful symbols (e.g., %, and +) may be used as necessary.

Visibility and legibility. Labels and placards shall be designed to be read easily and accurately at the anticipated operational reading distances, within the anticipated vibration/motion environment, and at minimally expected illumination levels. The following factors must be taken into consideration: contrast between the lettering and its immediate background; the height, width, stroke width, spacing, and style of letters; and the specular reflection of the background, cover, or other components.

PREVENTING UPPER EXTREMITY MUSCULOSKELETAL DISORDERS

Musculoskeletal disorders of the upper extremity, such as ligament sprains, tendon or muscle strains, tendinopathies, and nerve entrapments, are becoming the most common type of occupational injury in the workplace, even replacing work-related low back injuries. The sprains and strains may be due to a single acute event while tendinopathies and nerve entrapments appear to be due to repeated, forceful hand activities that are present over weeks or months. Common locations for tendinopathies are at the wrist (de Quervains disease, wrist tendinitis), elbow (medial or lateral epicondylitis) and shoulder (biceps tendinitis, supraspinatus tendonitis, rotator cuff tear). Common locations for nerve entrapments are at the wrist (carpal tunnel syndrome), elbow (ulnar neuropathy), shoulder (thoracic outlet syndrome), or neck (cervical radiculopathy). The entrapment neuropathies usually present with symptoms of numbness or tingling while the tendon, ligament, and muscle injuries present with pain. Weakness can be a symptom in all.

Not a New Problem

Nearly 300 years ago, Bernadino Ramazzini described health problems (that today we would call musculoskeletal disorders [MSDs]) appearing in workers who do violent and irregular motions and assume unnatural postures. Yet, Ramazzini also reported MSDs to occur among office clerks, believing that these events were caused by repetitive movements of the hands, by constrained body postures, and by excessive mental stress. Such activity-related disorders have been known for a long time, for example, washer woman's sprain, game keeper's thumb, telegraphist's cramp, writer's cramp, trigger finger, and tennis or golfer's elbow.

Causes of MSDs

It is usually not hard to relate an acute sprain or strain to a single high-force event, such as a fall, the twist of a drill, or the application of high force with a wrench. However, due to the gradual progression of the tendinopathies and entrapment neuropathies, it may not be easy to associate them to a single cause. However, epidemiologic studies have investigated their relationship to personal and work-related factors. Both tendinopathies and entrapment neuropathies are related to repeated forceful exertions with the hand or sustained awkward joint postures. Entrapment neuropathies may also be related to personal factors such as obesity, age, thyroid disorders, diabetes, and pregnancy.

Work-Related Physical Factors

Work-related musculoskeletal disorders (WRMSDs) have a complex interaction and multifactorial etiology that includes both physical and psychosocial factors. Physical risk factors include high forces, awkward postures, extended duration of exposure, repetition, velocity/acceleration, cold, and vibration. Both quantitative and qualitative measures can be used to measure these physical factors. Quantitative methods are preferred (barring cost and time consideration barriers) given its objective value and use with post-experimentation statistical analyses. Quantitative measurement methods for force include load cells, force sensors, and dynamometers for grip force. Manual goniometers, electrogoniometers, and videocameras are often used to measure posture and joint angles. Accelerometers are used to quantitatively measure vibration in the x, y, and z axes. Managing and controlling work-related physical factors include reducing the magnitude, intensity, and duration of these physical risk factors.

Work-Related Psychosocial Factors

There is increasing evidence that psychosocial factors also play a role in the development of work-related musculoskeletal disorders. However, separating these psychosocial factors from the physical factors in the job and work environment prove to be a difficult task due to the limited quantitative measurement methodologies. Furthermore, the underlying etiologic mechanisms are still unclear. However, there is evidence from previous studies to suggest that work-related risk factors include low job control and clarity, monotonous work, poor social support, and perceptions of intensified workload. Managing and controlling work-related psychosocial factors include job rotation and enhancement. The goal of these strategies is to reduce stress, increase job control, reduce repetitiveness and boredom on the job, and provide prospects for workers to develop and increase their skills. Work-related psychosocial factors need to be considered in the practice of occupational ergonomics, in addition to the physical factors.

Tools for Job Analysis

There are a variety of workplace assessment tools that can be used to quantify and assess the workplace risk factors, from custom-designed checklists to more objective instrumentation methods, such as electromyography (used to measure peripheral muscle activity load/amplitude and muscle fatigue). Each assessment tool has its intended purpose and limitations, which should be taken into consideration when applying (and generalizing) the results for management and control purposes. Below are current assessment tools in the literature that have been developed to assess the risk of work-related musculoskeletal disorders. These tools can also be used in the workplace as a method for prioritizing job modifications and interventions.

- Rapid Upper Limb Assessment (RULA)

   The purpose of RULA is to assess the individual worker's risk factors associated with work-related musculoskeletal disorders for tasks involving repeated and/or sustained motions or actions in the upper limbs and/or trunk and lower limbs. This observational assessment tool provides an assessment of the force, posture, and duration of the neck, trunk, and upper limbs along with muscle function and the external loads experienced by the body. The rater produces a final score, based on a coding system, which then can be used to represent the required intervention level in reducing the physical risks of the worker. Three general steps are taken:

   1. *Arm and Wrist Analysis:* The rater assesses and adds up the scores for each of the following items: upper arm position, lower arm position, wrist position, wrist twist, muscle use, and force/load. A final wrist and arm score is determined.
   2. *Neck, Trunk, and Leg Analysis:* The rater assesses and adds up the scores for each of the following items: neck position, trunk position, legs, muscle use, and force/load. A final neck, trunk, and leg score is determined.

3. *Determine final score and assess if action should be taken:* The rater determines the final score (1–7+) on a table based upon the final wrist and arm score and the final neck, trunk, and leg score.
   - A score of 1 or 2 indicates the task is acceptable. The worker is in a posture with little or no risk of injury.
   - A score of 3 or 4 indicates further investigation is recommended. The worker is in a posture that could present some risk of injury. This score may be the result of one body part being in an awkward position. Therefore, this should be investigated and corrected.
   - A score of 5 or 6 indicates further investigation and changes should be made soon. The worker is in a poor posture with a risk of injury. A change in the near future may need to be made to prevent an injury.
   - A score of 7+ indicates further investigation and changes be made immediately. The worker is in a poor posture with an immediate risk of injury. A change may need to be made immediately to prevent an injury.

- The American Conference of Governmental Industrial Hygienists (ACGIH®) Threshold Limit Value (TLV®) for Hand Activity (ACGIH TLV HAL)

  The ACGIH HAL evaluates job risk factors associated with musculoskeletal disorders of the hand and wrist. The tool assesses hand activity and level of effort for a typical posture while performing a short cycle mono-task job that lasts for more than 4 hours a day. A mono-task job is defined as a job requiring the same set of motions and/or repeated exertions. There are three steps:

  1. *Determine hand activity level:* The rater first identifies the level of hand activity on a scale from 0 to 10. On this scale, 0 represents virtually no activity (hands idle most of the time; no regular exertions), and 10 represents the highest imaginable hand activity (rapid steady motion/difficulty keeping up or continuous exertion). Hand activity includes effort from repetition and duration.

  2. *Determine normalized peak force (NPF):* The rater characterizes the level of effort associated with typical high force within the work cycle. The NPF is the relative level of effort on a scale of 0 to 10 that a person of average strength would exert in the same posture required by the task. Methods for assessing hand force include worker and observer ratings using a subjective scale from 0 to 10 of perceived exertion (0–nothing at all; 10–extremely strong), biomechanical analyses, force gauges, or electromyography, in terms of percent of maximum voluntary contraction (%MVC).

  3. *Determine ergonomic risk of the task by matching both the hand activity and NPF values on a TLV chart:* After determining the hand activity level and the NPF, draw a vertical line from the hand activity value and a horizontal line from the NPF value on the TLV chart. The intersection of these two lines, with respect to the TLV and action limit (AL) lines, determines the ergonomic risk of the task. If the intersection point falls below the AL, the mono-task job is likely safe. If the intersection point falls above the AL and below the TLV line, then the job likely has a greater risk of injury. If the intersection point falls above the TLV line, then the job should be modified. As an example, if the task has a hand activity rating of 5 and a NPF of 7, then the intersection point falls above both the AL and TLV lines. The ACGIH HAL TLV would recommend that the mono-task job be modified. See the ACGIH website for further details: www.acgih.org.

SUMMARY

The industrial hygienist is largely responsible for the health and well-being of people employed in industry, commerce, service, and administration. Of course, this concern must be seen in the light of the goal to be productive, both in quantity and in quality. Fortunately, ergonomic/human factors recommendations usually bring about, directly or indirectly, improved job performance together with increased safety, health, and wellness. In recent years, both management and employee representatives, including unions, have cooperated in using ergonomics to increase the ease and efficiency at work.

BIBLIOGRAPHY

American Conference of Governmental Industrial Hygienists. *Threshold Limit Values for Chemical Substances and Physical Agents & Biological Exposure Indices.* Cincinnati, OH: ACGIH, 2011.

Barker KL, Atha J. Reducing the biomechanical stress of lifting by training. *Appl Ergonomics* 25:373–378, 1994.

Bendix T, Poulsen V, Klausen K, et al. What does a backrest actually do to the lumbar spine? *Ergonomics* 39:533–542, 1996.

Bernhard TE, Joseph BS. Estimation of metabolic rate using qualitative job descriptors. *AIHA Journal* 55:1021–1029, 1994.

Bobick TG, Gutman SH. Reducing musculoskeletal injuries by using mechanical handling equipment. In *Manual Material Handling: Understanding and Preventing Back Trauma*, edited by K.H.E. Kroemer, J.D. McGlothlin, and T.G. Bobick. Akron, OH: AIHA, 1989, pp. 87–96.

Boff KR, Lincoln JE, eds. *Engineering Data Compendium: Human Perception and Performance.* Wright-Patterson AFB, OH: Armstrong Aerospace Medical Research Laboratory, 1988.

Borg GAV. Psychophysical bases of perceived exertion. *Medicine and Science in Sports and Exercise* 14:377–381, 1982.

Borg G. Psychophysical scaling with applications in physical work and the perception of exertion. *Scandinavian Journal of Work, Environment and Health* 16 (Suppl1):55–58, 1990.

Brain W, Wright A, Wilkinson M. Spontaneous compression of both median nerves in the carpal tunnel: Six cases treated surgically. *Lancet* 1:277–282, 1947.

Caldwell LS, Chaffin DB, Dukes-Dobos FN, et al. A proposed standard procedure for static muscle strength testing. *AIHA Journal* 35, 201–206, 1974.

Carayon P, Smith MJ, Haims MC. Work organisation, job stress, and work-related musculoskeletal disorders. *Hum Factors* 41:644–663, 1999.

Chaffin DB, Andersson GBJ, Martin BJ. *Occupational Biomechanics,* 4th ed. New York: Wiley, 2006.

Chengalur SN, Rodgers SH, Bernard TE. *Kodak's Ergonomic Design for People at Work,* 2nd ed. Hoboken, NJ: John Wiley & Sons, 2004.

Christensen WC, Manuele FA, eds. *Safety Through Design.* Itasca, IL: NSC Press, 1999.

Ciriello VM, Snook SH, Hughes GJ. Further studies of psychophysically determined maximum acceptable weights and forces. *Hum Factors* 35:175–186, 1993.

Cochran DJ, Riley MW. The effects of handle shape and size on exerted forces. *Hum Factors* 28:253–265, 1986.

Colle HA, Reid GB. Context effects in subjective mental workload ratings. *Hum Factors* 40:591–600, 1998.

Cushman WH, Rosenberg DJ. *Human Factors in Product Design.* Amsterdam, The Netherlands: Elsevier, 1991.

Driessen MT, Proper KI, Anema JR, et al. The effectiveness of participatory ergonomics to prevent low-back and neck pain: Results of a cluster randomized controlled trial. *Scan J Work Environ Health* 37(5):383-93, 2011.

Gordon CC, Churchill T, Clauser CE, et al. *1988 Anthropometric Survey of U.S. Army Personnel: Summary Statistics Interim Report* (Technical Report NATICK/TR-89-027). Natick, MA: U.S. Army Natick Research, Development and Engineering Center, 1989.

Grandjean E, Huenting W, Nishiyama K. Preferred VDT workstation settings, body posture and physical impairment. *Appl Ergonomics* 15:99–104, 1984.

Greiner TM. *Hand Anthropometry of U.S. Army Personnel* (Technical Report TR-92/011). Natick, MA: U.S. Army Natick Research, Development and Engineering Center, 1991.

Harris C, Eisen E, Goldberg R, et al. Workplace and individual factors in wrist tendinosis among blue-collar workers: The San Francisco study. *Scan J Work Environ Health* 37(2):86–98, 2011.

Hart SG, Staveland IE. Development of NASA-TLX (Task Load Index): Results of Experimental and Theoretical Research. In *Human Mental Workload,* edited by P.A. Hancock and N. Meshkati. Amsterdam, The Netherlands: Elsevier, 1988, pp. 185–218.

Helander MG, Zhang L. Field studies of comfort and discomfort in sitting. *Ergonomics* 40I:895–915, 1997.

HFES 300 Committee. *Guidelines for Using Anthropometry Data in Product Design.* Santa Monica, CA: Human Factors and Ergonomics Society, 2004.

Karwowski W, ed. *International Encyclopedia of Ergonomics and Human Factors.* London: Taylor & Francis, 2001.

Konz S, Johnson S. *Work Design: Industrial Ergonomics,* 5th ed. Scottsdale, AZ: Holcomb Hathaway, 2000.

Kroemer KHE. *Ergonomic Design of Material Handling Systems.* Boca Raton, FL: CRC, 1997.

Kroemer KHE, Kroemer AD. *Office Ergonomics.* London: Taylor & Francis, 2001.

Kroemer KHE, Kroemer HB, Kroemer-Elbert KE. *Ergonomics: Designing for Ease and Efficiency,* 2nd ed. Englewood Cliffs, NJ: Prentice Hall, 2001.

Kroemer KHE, Kroemer HJ, Kroemer-Elbert KE. *Engineering Physiology: Bases of Human Factors/Ergonomics,* 3rd ed. New York: Wiley, 1997.

Kuorinka I, Forcier L, eds. *Work Related Musculoskeletal Disorders: A Reference Book for Prevention.* London: Taylor & Francis, 1995.

Kuorinka I, Jonsson B, Kilbom A. Standardized Nordic questionnaires for the analysis of musculoskeletal symptoms. *Appl Ergonomics* 18:233–237, 1987.

Lee K, Swanson N, Sauter S, et al. Review of physical exercises for VDT operators. *Appl Ergonomics* 23:387–408, 1992.

Lohman TG, Roche AF, Martorel R, ed. *Anthropometric Standardization Reference Manual.* Champaign, IL: Human Kinetics, 1988.

Marras W, Karwowski W, eds., *The Occupational Ergonomics Handbook,* 2nd ed., CRC Press, 2006.

McAtamney L, Nigel Corlett E. RULA: A survey method for the investigation of work-related upper limb disorders.

Appl Ergonomics 24(2):91-99, 1993.

McGill SM. Update on the use of back belts in industry: More data—same conclusion. In *The Occupational Ergonomics Handbook,* edited by W. Karwowski and W.S. Marras. Boca Raton, FL: CRC Press, 1999, pp. 1,353–1,358.

MIL-STD-1472F. *Department of Defense Design Criteria Standard.* AMSAM-RD-SE-TD-ST. Redstone Arsenal, AL: U.S. Army Aviation and Missile Command.

Moon SD, Sauter SL, eds. *Beyond Biomechanics: Psychosocial Aspects of Musculoskeletal Disorders in Office Work.* London: Taylor & Francis, 1996.

Moore JS, Garg A. The Strain Index: A proposed method to analyze jobs for risk of distal upper extremity disorders. *Am Ind Hyg Assoc J* 56(5):443-58, 1995.

NASA/Webb, eds. *Anthropometric Sourcebook* (3 volumes). Houston, TX: LBJ Space Center, NASA Reference Publication 1024, 1978.

National Institute for Occupational Safety and Health. *Musculoskeletal Disorders and Workplace Factors: A Critical Review of Epidemiologic Evidence for Work-Related Musculoskeletal Disorders of the Neck, Upper Extremity, and Low Back,* DHHS (NIOSH) Publication No. 97B141. Washington, DC: U.S. GPO, 1997.

National Research Council. *Work-Related Musculoskeletal Disorders and the Workplace.* Washington, DC: National Academy Press, 2001.

Nordin M, Andersson GBJ, Pope MH. *Musculoskeletal Disorders in the Workplace: Principles and Practices.* St. Louis, MO: Mosby, 1997.

Rohmert W. Problems in determining rest allowances: Part 1: Use of modern methods to evaluate stress and strain in static work. *Appl Ergonomics* 4(2), 91-95, 1973a.

Rohmert W. Problems in determining rest allowances: Part 2: Determining rest allowances in different human tasks. *Appl Ergonomics* 4(2), 158-162, 1973b.

Shields M, Carroll MD, Ogden CL. Adult obesity prevalence in Canada and the United States. *NCHS Data Brief* March 2011; 56:1-8.

Phalen GG. The carpal-tunnel syndrome syndrome. Clinical evaluation of 598 hands. *Clinical Orthopaedics and Related Research* 83: 29–40, April-March 1972.

Pheasant S, Haslegrave CM. *Bodyspace:Anthropometry, Ergonomics and the Design of Work,* 3rd ed. London: Taylor & Francis, 2005.

Radwin RG. Hand tools: Design and evaluation. In *The Occupational Ergonomics Handbook,* edited by W. Karwowski and W.S. Marras. Boca Raton, FL: CRC, 1999, pp. 851–863.

Ramazzini B. *De Morbis Articum (Diseases of Workers).* Translated from the 1713 edition by WC Wright. Thunder Bay, ON: OH&S Press, 1993.

Rempel DM, Harrison RJ, Barnhart S. Work-related cumulative trauma disorders of the upper extremity. *JAMA* 267(6):838–842, 1992.

Rempel D, Tittiranonda P, Burastero S. Effect of keyboard keyswitch design on hand pain. *J Occup Environ Med* 41:111–119, 1999.

Rempel D, Evanoff B. Overall approach to managing musculoskeletal disorders. In *Textbook of Occupational and Environmental Medicine,* edited by L. Rosenstock, M. Cullen, D. Brodkin, et al. Edinburgh, UK: Elsivier, 2004.

Roquelaure Y, Ha C, Fouquet N, et al. Attributable risk of carpal tunnel syndrome in the general population: Implications for intervention programs in the workplace. *Scan J Work Environ Health* 35(5):342-8, 2009.

Roebuck JA. *Anthropometric Methods: Designing to Fit the Human Body.* Santa Monica, CA: Human Factors and Ergonomics Society, 1995.

Snook SH, Ciriello VM. The design of manual handling tasks: Revised tables of maximum acceptable weights and forces. *Ergonomics* 34:1197–1213, 1991.

Steinfeld E, Maisel J, Feathers D, et al. Anthropometry and standards for wheeled mobility: An international comparison. *Assist Technology* 22(1):51-67, 2010.

Waters TR, Putz-Andersson B, Garg A, et al. Revised NIOSH equation for the design and evaluation of manual lifting tasks. *Ergonomics* 36:749–776, 1993.

Waters TR, Putz-Anderson V. Revised NIOSH lifting equation. In *The Occupational Ergonomics Handbook,* edited by W. Karwowski and W.S. Marras. Boca Raton, FL: CRC, 1999, pp. 1037-1061.

Woodson WE, Tillman B, Tillman P. *Human Factors Design Handbook,* 3rd ed. New York: McGraw/Hill, 1991.

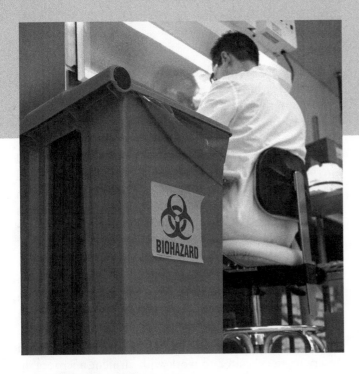

CHAPTER 14

Biological Hazards

by Jennifer Gaudioso, PhD
Susan A. Caskey, BS
Robert J. Hashimoto, MS, CBSP
Sean Barry, MS, RBP
and Janet M. Macher, ScD, MPH

*T*his chapter provides basic information on those hazards that are considered biological in nature. The authors are indebted to A. Lynn Harding, Diane O. Fleming, and Janet M. Macher for writing earlier editions of this chapter. We have kept much of their original content and focused on updating the sections that have been most impacted by the continued evolution of the field of biosafety in the intervening years.

While the chapter focuses on work-related exposures to infectious microbiological agents, exposures to other biohazardous materials not associated with infectious agents are reviewed. Background on the development of the field of biological safety and considerations on the role of industrial hygienists and environmental health and safety professionals in the field are discussed. The AMP principles of Assessment (including hazard identification, assessment, and classification), Mitigation (control), and Performance are examined; these general concepts are broadly applicable across the diverse environments associated with biological hazards. Current topics in biological safety, including bloodborne pathogens, tuberculosis, bioterrorism, legionellosis, building-related bioaerosol problems, organic dust toxic syndrome, mycotoxins, endotoxins, and Pfiesteria, are covered. Information on assessing compliance, current regulations and guidelines including the latest biorisk management standards, standard-setting groups, and relevant professional associations is reviewed. This chapter cannot begin to adequately cover biological hazards, so the reader is encouraged to use the provided references and resources to further gain insight into the field of biological safety.

Exposure to biological hazards in the workplace results in a significant amount of occupationally associated disease. Work-related illnesses caused by biological agents such as infectious microorganisms, biological allergens, and toxins have been widely reported. However, in many workplaces their presence and resultant illnesses are not recognized. It has been estimated that the population at risk from occupational biohazards may be several hundred million workers worldwide.

Dutkiewicz et al., in a review of occupational biohazards, noted that some 193 biological agents are known to produce infectious, allergenic, toxic, and carcinogenic reactions in workers. Most of the identified biohazardous agents (listed with their effects on humans) belong to the following groups:

- microorganisms and their toxins (viruses, bacteria, fungi, and their products): infection, inflammatory disease, or allergic reaction
- arthropods (crustaceans, arachnids, and insects): bites or stings resulting in skin inflammation, systemic intoxication, transmission of infectious agents, or allergic reaction
- allergens and toxins from higher plants: dermatitis from skin contact or allergic rhinitis or asthma as a result of inhalation
- protein allergens from vertebrate animals (urine, feces, hair, saliva, and dander): hypersensitivity and inflammatory disease
- other groups that pose a potential biohazard include lower plants other than fungi (lichens, liverworts, and ferns) and invertebrate animals other than arthropods (parasites such as protozoa, flatworms such as Schistosoma, and roundworms such as Ascaris)

Workers engaging in agricultural, medical, and laboratory activities have been identified as being most at risk to occupational biohazards, but many varied workplaces have the potential for such exposure. A number of potentially hazardous workplaces are described in this chapter. Although biological hazards encompass a wide variety of biological agents, in large part this chapter concentrates on exposures to microorganisms and the substances associated with them. Although the chapter deals extensively with laboratory and medical environments, the concepts, principles, and exposure controls discussed here can be extrapolated to suit most occupations.

BIOLOGICAL SAFETY

Laboratories that handle dangerous pathogens need to manage their safety and security risks in a responsible manner. This need was highlighted in the December 2008 *World at Risk* report, which specifically called for bioscience laboratories that handle dangerous pathogens to implement a unified laboratory biorisk management framework to enhance their safety and security. In recent years, the discipline of biological safety (biosafety) has evolved into the discipline of laboratory biorisk management. Biorisk management

is the combination of biosafety and biosecurity, and has received growing public scrutiny.

Biosafety had its beginnings in the U.S. offensive biological warfare program at Fort Detrick in Frederick, MD. The Chemical Warfare Service (for chemical and biological warfare) was established by the U.S. Army in 1941, and in 1942 the National Academy of Sciences (NAS) formed a biological warfare committee. Microbiologists from the American Society for Microbiology (ASM) served as advisors for biological warfare activities instituted by the Chemical Warfare Service.

From 1955 to 1968, the ASM maintained an advisory committee for the Fort Detrick Biological Defense Research Program (BDRP) to provide scientific advice on research programs, peer review for publications, and assistance with staff recruitment. Members of the safety staff at Fort Detrick were well-trained microbiologists capable of advising on safety matters related to work with virulent microorganisms. Because of the considerable concern for worker safety, as well as the need to protect the surrounding community, great care was taken to prevent accidental exposure and release of infectious agents. The containment principles developed at Fort Detrick by Dr. Arnold G. Wedum and his colleagues form the framework for the discipline of biosafety today. It is noteworthy to observe that this profession, which was formed as the result of concerns about biological warfare, is once again forced to address that same threat.

Following the discovery of recombinant DNA technology in the 1970s, the new era of biotechnology began. The ability to insert into host cells specific pieces of foreign DNA that replicate to produce a desired product has revolutionized the field of biology. Recombinant DNA technology, hybridoma technology, and protein and enzyme engineering are all components of the new biotechnology. The impact of biotechnology on research in health care, diagnostics, and agriculture, as well as many other industries such as food, chemical, mining, and petroleum, has been significant. Whether real, potential, or imaginary, genetic manipulation of microorganisms and cells has brought with it a renewed concern for biological hazards. This includes not only the genetic manipulation of existing microorganisms but the ability to create viable, virulent microorganisms through *de novo* synthesis. Examples of recent synthetic advances include the synthesis of live infectious polio virus in 2002, followed by Phi174 phage which was produced in just 2 weeks by the Venter Institute in 2003. The synthesis of the 1918 influenza and Marburg virus were reported in 2005 and 2006 by Tumpey and Enterlein, respectively. In 2008, scientists produced both SARS virus and the bacteria *M. genitalium*. While polio virus is a relatively simple and small virus with only 7,751 base pairs (bp), SARS virus contains approximately 30,000 bp and *M. genitalium* 582,970 bp. The latest milestone, involving the creation of a bacterium controlled by a synthesized genome, demonstrates that not only are the technical barriers being pushed in terms of length of the genome and overall size, but also the complexity of the synthesized organisms is increasing and the technology is becoming easier to handle. Employers and regulatory agencies have taken note of these concerns and there is a renewed focus on implementing or strengthening workplace biorisk management programs in settings as diverse as in the research laboratory and a patient's bedside.

The appearance of a virus capable of destroying the human immune system (human immunodeficiency virus, or HIV) in the 1980s, coupled with the high incidence of occupationally acquired hepatitis B virus infection among health care workers, prompted the Occupational Safety and Health Administration (OSHA) to establish a standard that mandates protection of workers from occupational exposure to bloodborne pathogens. This standard has heightened awareness and improved biosafety controls in the workplace considerably.

The biosafety professional uses similar practices to define and control hazards in the workplace as those used by industrial hygienists. Both are responsible for helping to anticipate, recognize, evaluate, and control hazards in the workplace and then assess the performance of those controls to ensure they are functioning as intended. The biosafety professional typically has a microbiology background and the primary focus of their work is biological hazards (microorganisms), while the industrial hygienist is trained to deal with multiple hazards in the workplace—biohazards usually represent only a small portion of their workload. Biosafety professionals include microbiologists, biologists, molecular biologists, environmental health scientists, industrial hygienists, clinical health care professionals, veterinarians, chemists, and engineers. Regardless of their background and education, they must develop knowledge of the principles of epidemiology, disease transmission patterns, risk-assessment management, disinfection and sterilization, disease prevention, aerobiology, and environmental control. The global biosafety community is currently working to define core competencies and paths to obtain those competencies (CEN WS 53) to aid the growing biosafety community.

BIOLOGICAL HAZARD IDENTIFICATION

Microorganisms are a diverse group of microscopic organisms that include bacteria, fungi, algae, protozoa, viruses, and prions. Although pathogenic or disease-producing microorganisms represent only a small portion of the total microbial population, attention is often focused on them because of their negative impact on humans, plants, and animals. In addition to their ability to produce infectious diseases, microorganisms such as fungi produce spores capable of causing allergic and inflammatory reactions among workers. Toxins such as endotoxin, a component in the cell walls of gram-negative bacteria, and mycotoxins, natural products produced by fungi, have also been identified as occupational biohazards. Other biological agents such as pollen, mites, urine proteins, animal dander, and snake venoms, to list only a few, also fit within the broad scope of biological hazards.

Microorganisms

Microorganisms are divided into two categories: prokaryotes (organisms in which DNA is not physically separated from the cytoplasm) and eukaryotes (organisms containing a membrane-bound nucleus). Prokaryotes and eukaryotes are organisms because they contain all of the enzymes required for their own replication, as well as the biological equipment necessary to produce metabolic energy. This distinguishes them from viruses, which depend on host cells for replication.

Prokaryotes, characterized by their relatively small size (around 1 µm in diameter) and the absence of a nuclear membrane, are divided into two major groups: eubacteria and archaebacteria (also known as archae). The more commonly known bacteria fall into the eubacteria category and they are further divided into three groups: gram-negative eubacteria with cell walls, gram-positive eubacteria with cell walls, and eubacteria with no cell walls (*Mycoplasma*). The fourth group, archaebacteria, differ from eubacteria in that they live in extreme environments (high temperatures, high salt, or low pH) and carry out unusual metabolic reactions. The majority of microorganisms of medical interest are gram-negative or -positive cell walled organisms that are either aerobic, microaerophilic, or anaerobic rods, cocci, or spirals. These characteristics are used as the framework for an identification scheme in *Bergey's Manual of Determinative Bacteriology*, by Holt et al.

In contrast to prokaryotes, eukaryotes are larger and contain a membrane-bound nucleus and organelles such as mitochondria. The microbial eukaryotes, or protists, fall into four major groups: algae, protozoa, fungi, and slime molds, with protozoa such as species of *Giardia*, *Trypanosoma*, *Toxoplasma*, and *Plasmodium* and species of fungi such as *Histoplasma*, *Aspergillus*, *Cryptococcus*, and *Coccidioides* being infectious agents of medical importance.

Viruses, whose unique properties distinguish them from other microorganisms, are totally dependent on their hosts for replication. They are inert outside a host cell, and host-virus interactions are highly specific. Viruses, the smallest infectious agents, are 20–300 nm in diameter. Viral particles consist of nucleic acid molecules, either DNA or RNA, enclosed in a protein coat, or *capsid*. The capsid protects the nucleic acid and facilitates attachment to and penetration into the host cell by the virus. Once inside a cell, viral nucleic acid uses the host's enzymatic machinery for functions associated with viral replication. The host range of a given virus may be broad or extremely narrow, and viruses can infect unicellular organisms such as mycoplasmas, bacteria, algae, and all higher plants and animals. Classification of viruses is based on a number of properties such as nucleic acid type, size and morphology, susceptibility to physical and chemical agents, and presence of enzymes.

Viroids—small, single-stranded, covalently closed circular RNA molecules that cause diseases in plants. Because of their characteristics, it is thought that they have evolved from transposable elements or retroviruses by deletion of internal sequences. To date, viroids have not been detected in animals or humans.

Prions—agents smaller by an order of magnitude than viruses that have been reported to have properties similar to viruses and cause degenerative disease in humans and animals. Scrapie, a disease of the nervous system of sheep, is caused by such an agent. Because of the novel properties of this agent, the term *prion* has been designated to denote these small proteinaceous infectious particles, which are resistant to inactivation by most procedures that modify nucleic acids. The tropical disease kuru and Creutzfeldt-Jakob (a form of human dementia) are caused by similar agents.

Cell lines and primary cells—although not microorganisms, these must be mentioned because of their potential to be contaminated with infectious agents. When assessing the potential hazard associated with cells in culture, consider the source of the cells (human, rodent, etc.), the potential for the cells to harbor viruses or mycoplasma, whether they are tumor cells or have been transformed with virus, or whether they are established lines or only recently isolated from a host (primary cells).

Although the amount of information provided here is necessarily limited, a wealth of accessible material is readily available. Readers are encouraged to consult microbiology references such as *Medical Microbiology* (Brooks et al., 1998), *ASM Manual of Environmental Microbiology* (ASM, 1997), *Microbial Ecology* (Atlas & Bartha, 1998), *Manual of Clinical Microbiology* (Murray et al., 1999), *Bioaerosols Handbook* (Cox & Wathes, 1995), and *Bioaerosols* (Burge, 1995). See the Bibliography for more information.

Infection

Infection is a general term applied to the entry and development or multiplication of an infectious agent such as bacteria, protozoa, and the larval forms of multicellular organisms such as the helminths (intestinal parasites including roundworms and tapeworms) in the bodies of people, animals, or plants. It is further defined as an invasion of the body by pathogenic microorganisms and the reaction of the tissues to their presence and to the toxins generated by them.

Although human beings have microorganisms on every surface and in every external orifice of their bodies, only a small proportion of those agents are capable of producing an infection that could lead to disease in that person or, if communicable, in others. If the disease-causing agent arises from the microbial flora normally present in or on the body of a person (indigenous flora), its resulting infection is called endogenous. For example, most urinary tract infections are caused by agents such as *Escherichia coli* or *Pseudomonas* spp., which are normally found in the feces of the patient. This example demonstrates the disease-causing potential of normal flora when they are able to reach a different site in the body. Normal flora can also take advantage of a lowering of host immunity to produce an infectious disease. Such infections occur in those who are immunocompromised by underlying disease processes or certain medications such as steroids and chemotherapy. Further information on normal flora can be found in Isenberg and D'Amato, 1991.

Individuals harboring communicable infectious agents without exhibiting signs of disease are called carriers. They can be a source of infection in coworkers, especially if the agent is transmitted by the aerosol route, as with measles or tuberculosis. Certain of these "wild-type" agents—strains found in nature, and therefore in the community—can sometimes also contaminate a sterile product in a laboratory environment. A vaccine strain being grown in cell culture can be contaminated by a worker who carries a different, potentially more virulent strain obtained in the community. The restriction of visitors and the use of approved vaccines are thus recommended when appropriate to protect the work being done.

Infections from microorganisms not normally found in or on the human body, but which gain entrance from the environment, are called exogenous infections. These agents gain entry into the host by inhalation, indirect or direct contact, penetration, or ingestion. These routes are important factors in understanding the likelihood of exposure (discussed in more detail in the later risk assessment section). Some agents routinely cause disease in healthy adult humans, whereas others, known as opportunists, require special circumstances of lowered host defense or overwhelming dose of exposure. Thus, infectious disease is not always the end result of the exposure to and colonization by an infectious agent. The end result depends on the virulence of the agent, the route of infection, and the relative immunity and health of the host.

Workers are expected to be healthy human adults, but should be medically assessed during a preplacement examination to determine fitness for specific work. Because exposures can occur to those involved with the work and, potentially, to those who merely enter the work area, all such individuals should be identified and assessed to prevent exposure and subsequent infection. The spread of infectious agents used in research or production to the outside environment, including the neighboring community, is rare.

Epidemiology of Work-Associated Infections

An unfortunate consequence of working with infectious microorganisms or materials contaminated with them is the potential for acquiring a work-associated infection. The literature includes numerous descriptions of occupational exposures indicating that persons who handle infectious materials are clearly at higher risk for infection than the general population.

It is generally accepted that work-associated infections are underreported in the scientific literature. This may be the result of employees' unwillingness to report such incidents for fear of loss of employment, issues of liability, or an employer's refusal to publish such material. Literature on work-associated infections, reported as case studies, usually focuses on diagnosis and treatment of the patient and frequently fails to assess the circumstances related to the occupational exposure.

In the absence of a comprehensive database on work-associated infections, epidemiological methods provide the tools to evaluate the extent and nature of worker exposure. Defining the event or illness/infection, determining the population at risk, establishing the factors affecting exposure, and developing intervention controls are all part of the process to prevent occurrence or recurrence of infections. Several times during the past 79 years these tools have been applied to the study of laboratory-associated infections. A review of this information is instructive.

A comprehensive survey of laboratory-associated infections gathered by Sulkin and Pike focuses specifically on laboratory-acquired infections. Data compiled between 1930 and 1978 revealed 4,079 cases of clinically apparent infection classified by agent, source of infection (when known), and type of work involved. Of the total, 168 cases resulted in the worker's death. These numbers are considered low because the reporting of work-related infections is not required, and data on seroconversion (the production of antibodies in response to an infectious agent) or asymptomatic response to occupationally acquired microorganisms are rarely reported. The 10 most frequently reported

agents or diseases associated with laboratory-acquired infections described by Pike were brucellosis, Q fever, hepatitis, typhoid fever, tularemia, tuberculosis, dermatomycosis, Venezuelan equine encephalitis, psittacosis, and coccidiodomycosis.

The Sulkin and Pike surveys revealed the most common routes of exposure to be percutaneous inoculation (needles/syringes, cuts or abrasions from contaminated items, and animal bites), inhalation of aerosols generated by accidents or by work practices and procedures, contact between mucous membranes and contaminated material (hands and surfaces), and ingestion. Eighteen percent of the infections were attributable to known accidents caused by either carelessness or other human error. Twenty-five percent of these acknowledged accidents involved needles or syringes. Most of the remaining accidents involved spills and sprays, injury with broken glass or other sharp objects, accidental aspiration using a pipet, and animal bites, scratches, or contact with ectoparasites. Unfortunately, the sources of exposure for the remaining 82 percent of infections were not easily identifiable. Although some could be attributed to aerosols and to handling infectious animals, clinical specimens, and discarded glassware, all that was known about most exposures was that the person had worked with or was in the vicinity of work with the agent.

From these laboratory data, it is apparent that people engaged in research activities acquired the greatest number of infections. Trained investigators, technical assistants, animal caretakers, and graduate students experienced over three-quarters of the research-associated illnesses. The remainder occurred among clerical staff, dishwashers, janitors, and maintenance personnel. With rare exceptions, laboratory-acquired infections were not spread to the outside community.

In an attempt to extend the Sulkin and Pike data, Harding and Byers reviewed 206 U.S. and worldwide publications from between 1979 and 1999 to determine the microorganisms associated with laboratory infections, the types of facilities in which the infection occurred, and the type of work activity associated with the event. During this 20-year period, 1,267 symptomatic laboratory-associated infections were reported with 22 deaths. Aborted fetuses accounted for five of the deaths with four of these associated with *Brucella melitensis* and one with Parvovirus B19. The 10 most frequently reported infections were associated with *Mycobacterium tuberculosis*; *Coxiella burnetii*; hantavirus; arboviruses; hepatitis B virus; *Brucella* spp.; *Salmonella* spp.; *Shigella* spp.; non-A, non-B hepatitis virus; and *Cryptosporidium* spp. Clinical (diagnostic) and research laboratories accounted for 96 percent (45 percent and 51 percent respectively) of the symptomatic infections in this recent survey, whereas 76 percent of the infections occurred in clinical and research laboratories (17 percent and 59 percent, respectively) in the earlier Pike and Sulkin data. While it would appear that clinical laboratory infection may be increasing, these increases may be due more to active employee health programs, an absence of containment equipment in some laboratories, or the fact that during the early stages of culture identification, personnel are working with unknowns and not using adequate containment procedures. Similar findings to those observed by Pike and Sulkin were seen in this recent survey with respect to the number of laboratory infections associated with accidents.

More recently, workplace infections have been associated with new or emerging viruses such as human immunodeficiency virus (HIV), the etiologic agent associated with acquired immune deficiency syndrome (AIDS), and the hantavirus that causes Korean hemorrhagic fever. Herpes B virus continues to infect workers who handle certain nonhuman primates and their tissues, and an Ebola-related filovirus was associated with workplace asymptomatic seroconversions following an exposure to nonhuman primates in 1989 in Virginia. While the number of hepatitis B infections has decreased as the result of widespread immunization, improved work practices, and the use of engineering controls, hepatitis C virus (formerly non-A, non-B) has become a significant concern for workers because of the number of infected persons who develop chronic (long-term) infections.

Attempts to determine incidence rates of occupationally acquired infections among laboratory personnel must be interpreted cautiously, because estimates of the number of infections and the population at risk are imprecise. Sulkin and Pike indicated that the risk of infection for researchers was six to seven times higher than for hospital and public health workers. They estimated that the annual attack rate for researchers was 4.1 per 1,000 employees (the attack rate being the number of cases divided by the population at risk). A 1971 survey of laboratory-acquired cases of tuberculosis, shigellosis, brucellosis, and hepatitis in England and Wales reported an annual incidence of 4.3 infections per 1,000 medical laboratory workers. A 1988 survey of laboratory-associated infections and injuries among public health and hospital clinical laboratory employees estimated the annual incidence rate for full time equivalent (FTE) employees to be 1.4 infections per thousand for public health and 3.5 infections per thousand for hospital laboratories, whereas rates for those working directly with infectious agents were 2.7 and 4.0 per thousand for public health and hospital laboratories, respectively. Another study showed an estimated annual incidence rate for clinical laboratories of 3.0 infections per 1,000 employed and 9.4 infections per 1,000 when only microbiologists were considered. A Japanese survey of clinical laboratory workers revealed an annual incidence rate of 2.0 infections per 1,000 workers.

Despite the admitted flaws in the existing data and the fact that much of the information on work-associated infections focuses specifically on laboratory-associated infections, it seems reasonable to accept the fact that some workers handling infectious materials will become infected. Epidemiological data provide the information necessary to make decisions regarding prevention or minimization of work-related infections. Accurate estimates of and surveillance for occupationally associated infections are lacking because reports of infections usually do not include occupational data. A report of proportionate mortality from pulmonary tuberculosis as associated with occupation reflects a new effort to identify the potential for exposure. Ideally, though, infections rather than death should have been used to identify the risk of exposure in certain workplaces. For additional information on laboratory-associated infections, see Sewell, 1995 and Collins & Kennedy, 1999.

Potentially Hazardous Workplaces

Although most pathogenic microorganisms have the potential to cause occupationally acquired infections, knowledge of the hazard, containment practices, and preventive therapeutic measures such as use of vaccines greatly reduce their incidence. In workplaces where awareness of the hazard is high and the potential risk is understood, compliance with control practices minimizes exposure. However, there are some workplaces where controls are difficult to implement or are not readily available and where hazard recognition of the potential for work-associated infections is low, for example, agricultural environments and processing facilities. Workers in these environments may be exposed to potentially infectious microorganisms that are intrinsically associated with some of the animals or plants. Controls and barriers become challenging to implement in these environments.

Because workplaces are varied and microbial habitats diverse, it can be difficult to find concise, detailed information on microbial agents. The American Public Health Association publication *Control of Communicable Diseases Manual* is an excellent resource for information on a disease, the infectious agent, its occurrence, reservoir, mode of transmission, incubation period, and methods of control.

The prevention of emerging infectious diseases presents an increasing problem as societal, technological, and environmental factors continue to have a dramatic effect on infectious diseases worldwide. Modern demographic and ecologic conditions that favor the spread of infectious diseases include rapid population growth; increasing poverty and urban migration; more frequent movement across international boundaries by tourists, workers, immigrants, and refugees; alterations in habitats of animals and arthropods that transmit disease; increasing numbers of persons with impaired host defenses; and changes in the way food is processed and distributed. As research, clinical, and public health laboratories respond to the disease problems of the 21st century, workers will handle microorganisms that are increasingly resistant to antimicrobials (such as *Staphylococcus aureus*, *M. tuberculosis*, *Enterococcus* spp.). Food and waterborne diseases (hepatitis A virus, *E. coli* 0157:H7, *Cryptosporidium* spp.) and vector-borne and zoonotic diseases, including disease not previously known to infect humans (Asian flu virus–Hong Kong, a new variant of Creutzfeldt-Jakob disease—bovine spongiform encephalopathy [BSE], hemorrhagic fevers), will continue to infect developing as well as developed countries.

Case Study

SARS Corona Virus: A case study in the spread of disease

An outbreak of a coronavirus, Severe Acute Respiratory Syndrome Corona Virus (SARS-CoV), occurred in late 2002. The initial cases originated in rural southeast China and then spread to Hong Kong and other countries, including Canada, due to infected patients traveling out of the country. This outbreak illustrated the dangers of emerging illnesses in the era of jet travel; the spread of disease can be almost instantaneous. Because of the nature of this disease, it is spread efficiently between patient and health care worker and can be a serious nosocomial infection. SARS-CoV also illustrated the concept of *super spreaders*. These patients appear to have infected more than 10 health care workers, family and social contacts, or visitors to the health care facilities where the patients were hospitalized. To combat the effects of the super spreaders, isolation of infected patients and mandatory use of personal protective equipment requirements, such as gloves, gowns, goggles, and N95 or equivalent respirators are necessary. Positive air purifying respirators (PAPR) are required for high-risk or aerosol-generating procedures and eventually helped reduce the number of cases.

Microbiology, Public Health, Clinical, and Molecular Biology Laboratories

The potential threat of occupational infection has long been recognized by microbiologists. However, new potential for exposure exists with the increasing number of nonmicrobiologists who work in the field of molecular biology. The previous review of laboratory-related infections summarizes experiences to date. Exposures tend to be directly related to the hazard classification of the organisms being manipulated, the potential for release of the organism during required manipulations, and the level of competency of personnel.

Staff in research laboratories, the type of workplace where the majority of laboratory-acquired infections have occurred, tend to work with more hazardous agents, including those of emerging diseases. They often handle concentrated preparations of infectious microorganisms, and some test procedures require complex manipulations. Because of inherent containment difficulties, the use of infected laboratory animals, including those taken from the wild, also increases the potential for worker exposure to infectious agents. More information on animals is covered later in this section.

Increased rates of occupational infections have also been noted among public health and clinical laboratory workers as compared to the general population. A recent review of laboratory-associated infections noted an increased number of clinical lab infections being reported.

Hospitals and Health Care Establishments

In addition to infectious agents, health care facilities (which include physicians' and dentists' offices, blood banks, and outpatient clinics) may expose their personnel to multiple hazards including cytotoxic drugs, anesthetic gases, ethylene oxide, radiation sources, steam, injuries from lifting heavy objects, and electrical shock. Infections in hospitals can be categorized as community acquired (transmitted to either patients or workers); occupationally acquired (resulting from worker exposure); and nosocomial (hospital-acquired infections of patients).

The Joint Commission on Accreditation of Healthcare Organizations (JCAHO), the CDC guidelines for hospital infection control, the OSHA bloodborne pathogens standard, and the Biosafety in Microbiological and Biomedical Laboratories all provide guidance concerning the control of nosocomial infections in patients and the protection of health care personnel. Because of the nature of hospital activities, nosocomial infections have become a complication of hospitalization. To prevent or reduce the incidence of such complications, infection control programs were developed and implemented in U.S. hospitals during the 1950s and 1960s. The CDC coordinates surveillance of hospital infections and recommends infection control practices and procedures.

In most instances, a hospital epidemiologist (usually a physician who specializes in infectious diseases) and an infection control practitioner (often a nurse or, occasionally, a microbiologist) manage and oversee infection control activities. The prevalence of hospital infections has created a need for infection control procedures (barriers), rigorous disinfection and sterilization techniques, meticulous cleaning and waste-handling procedures, and, in some cases, special design criteria. The role of the industrial hygienist or environmental health and safety professional in hospital infection control may include assisting in the selection and testing of personal protective equipment, environmental testing in outbreak situations such as nosocomial fungal infections in oncology patients, and the design of engineering controls such as ventilation and containment systems.

Because it is not within the scope of this chapter to provide detailed material on the many topics covered here, the reader is referred to the Hospital Infection Program at the CDC in Atlanta and the JCAHO in Oakbrook Terrace, IL, for guidelines and standards covering infection control programs and practices in the United States. For more information, two U.S. journals provide current information on hospital infection control: the *American Journal of Infection Control* from the Association of Professionals in Infection Control (APIC) in Washington, DC, and *Infection Control and Hospital Epidemiology*, the journal of the Society for Healthcare Epidemiology of America (SHEA), published by Slack, Inc., in Thorofare, NJ.

Biotechnology Facilities

With the discovery of recombinant DNA technology and the resulting advances in the field of molecular biology, many opportunities for the development of products in medicine, industry, agriculture, and environmental management are now possible. Industrial microbiology, long associated with the chemical and pharmaceutical industries, has attained a position of prominence with the advent of "the age of biotechnology."

From the early stages of discovery to the ultimate marketing of a pharmaceutical, large volumes of material, whether it be a metabolite or an organism, are required. Depending on the hazard level (pathogenicity or biological activity), an increase in the production or concentration of a material brings with it the need for adequate barriers to protect personnel, the product, and the community.

With some exceptions, the microorganisms most often used in manufacturing operations are those requiring minimum containment, such as genetically engineered bacteria (*E. coli* K12), fungi, and plant and animal cells. Production operations usually involve the use of closed systems (either a primary container or a combination of primary and secondary containers) and validated inactivation of waste materials and contaminated by-products.

In addition to the possibility of experiencing the direct effects of the biological activity of an agent, workers may develop allergies to proteins (that is, biological products that are derived from raw materials, fermentation products, or enzymes), other chemicals, or animal dander, aerosolized urine, or other matter from animals. Allergic responses following exposure to proteins in the work environment can produce significant health effects, but they are not addressed here. For additional information on allergic response and safety issues in biotechnology, consult Nellis and Van Houten, 1995; Ducatman and Liberman, 1991; Cottam, 1994; AIHA, 1995; and Ladics and Selgrade, 2008.

Animal Facilities and Veterinary Practices

Although generally only work activities in research, medical, and industrial facilities involve handling laboratory animals, there are a wide range of occupations in which workers are exposed to animal-related allergens and to infectious agents or their toxins. Agricultural workers, veterinarians, workers in zoos and museums, taxidermists, and workers in animal product-processing facilities are all at risk for occupational exposure to animal-related biological hazards. A number of these workers may be exposed to wild (captured) or exotic animal populations. Factors to be considered when handling animals include the nature of the animal (its aggressiveness and tendency to bite or scratch), the normal flora and natural ecto- and endoparasites of the animal, the zoonotic diseases to which it is susceptible, and the possible dissemination of allergens.

The development of laboratory animal allergy (LAA) is a significant and common problem for laboratory personnel, veterinarians, and others who work with animals. The manifestations of LAA include cough, wheezing (asthma), watery and itchy eyes, itchy skin, sneezing, and skin rash. Following contact with animals, symptoms can develop in less than one year, but may take up to several years to develop. Often, workers react to the proteins in shed animal dander and hair or to those in animal urine, serum, saliva, or tissues. Aerosolized mold spores and proteins from animal food and bedding can also act as allergens. The prevalence in Europe and the United States of LAA among lab workers and animal handlers has been reported to range between 11 and 44 percent. Specific equipment is available to reduce exposures to animal fur and dander, such as electric shavers with built-in vacuum attachments.

During the past 50 years, diseases that affect both humans and animals (zoonotic diseases) have been among the most commonly reported occupational illnesses of laboratory workers. Most of these have been caused by viral and bacterial (including rickettsial) agents.

Infection is most often the result of one of the following types of exposure:
- animal bites or scratches
- contaminated needles, scalpels, or other inanimate objects
- infectious aerosols resulting from animal respiration or excretion, or dust from infectious materials such as bedding
- contact with infected tissue and cells during histological

procedures, homogenization, or manipulation of cells in culture

Zoonotic infections among veterinarians are common. Several excellent references listing zoonotic diseases of laboratory animals and zoonotic pathogens causing diseases in man have been published, including Fox & Lipman (1991), National Research Council (1989,), Constantine (1998), Merchant et al. (1994,), and Merianos (2007). See the Bibliography for more information.

Animal-related infections can be expected at certain kinds of worksites. The infections frequently observed among personnel involve microorganisms with a low infectious dose (ID) where exposure results from aerosolized infectious materials. Numerous accounts of *C. burnetii*, the rickettsial agent that causes Q fever, have been reported. *C. burnetii* has an estimated ID_{25-50} of 10 organisms by inhalation. This means that 25 to 50 percent of a population becomes infected after inhaling only 10 *C. burnetii* bacteria. Many hospital and laboratory personnel have been exposed to *C. burnetii* as the result of research involving naturally infected asymptomatic sheep. In addition to being extremely infectious, the organism is very resistant to drying and remains viable for long periods of time. Q fever control measures for research facilities using sheep were published in 1982.

Hantavirus, the etiologic agent of Korean hemorrhagic fever, produces an asymptomatic infection in wild rodents. In the past twenty years, at least 169 work-related hantavirus infections, apparently resulting from inhalation of aerosols produced by chronically infected laboratory animals, were reported in the scientific literature. In the 1990s a unique hantavirus, the sin nombre virus (SNV), was detected in the southwestern United States. Reports of a pulmonary illness (HPS) caused by SNV underscore the infectious potential of this zoonotic agent. Cases continue to be reported from throughout the United States and abroad now that the virus has been identified. Refer also to Weigler (1995) for a review of zoonotic hantaviruses in the United States.

Work-acquired infections contracted while handling nonhuman primates have been a concern for many years. Serious health consequences, including hemorrhagic disease and death, have resulted from Marburg virus (a human filovirus) infections in Europe.

Ebola-related filovirus seroconversion was documented among several animal handlers in U.S. primate facilities. No evidence of clinical disease was detected, but these events warrant close scrutiny of nonhuman primate colonies. Guidelines for handling nonhuman primates during transit and quarantine have been published.

At least 50 cases of *Herpesvirus simiae* (*Cercopithecine herpesvirus* or B virus) infections have been documented, most with lethal or serious outcomes. In all instances exposure was related to activities involving macaques. Fifteen infections occurred between 1979 and 1999 and in 1987 the CDC published guidelines for prevention of *Herpesvirus simiae* (B virus) infection in monkey handlers.

Significant similarities between the simian immunodeficiency virus (SIV) and HIV have led to the development of guidelines to prevent simian immunodeficiency virus infection in laboratory workers and animal handlers. While no illnesses have been noted in workers to date, seroconversions (one of them persistent) have been reported.

Certainly not all agents associated with zoonotic disease carry the same potential for occupational exposure as some of those described above. Nevertheless, it is critical to evaluate the risk and to determine the control measures necessary to contain the hazard before initiating work with potentially infectious or experimentally infected animals.

West Nile virus (WNV) is often spread by mosquitoes that bite infected birds and then other mammals, including humans. Birds are the natural reservoir for West Nile virus. The spread of this disease depends on the life cycle of the Culex (sp) mosquito, mainly the availability of clean water. Horses, humans, and birds are the most vulnerable hosts. Even though most of the occupational exposures are through agriculture, there is documentation of laboratory-acquired West Nile virus illnesses. During 1999–2008, a total of 28,961 confirmed and probable cases of WNV disease, including 11,822 (41%) WNV neuroinvasive disease cases, were reported to CDC from 47 states and the District of Columbia. WNV disease symptoms vary in the population with older adults (55 and over) being among the most vulnerable. This disease is difficult to diagnose because the early symptoms are often cold and flu like and may not prompt medical attention.

There are three types of influenza viruses—A, B, and C—but only two are associated with human disease. In influenza A virus, the ability to cause disease is based on the surface glycoprotein antigens, hemagglutin (HA) and neuraminidase (NA). It is possible to have new variations of the virus emerge as a result of the random mixing of the surface antigens. This is called antigenic drift and the resulting change affects the human body's ability to fight the disease. Sometimes a totally different influenza strain emerges, one that is totally new to the human immune system. Because the human immune system does not recognize the newly emerging strain, there is no innate immunity and the new emerging virus can cause a pandemic in vulnerable populations, similar to the 1918 influenza pandemic, where the entire world was at risk to potential infection. Influenza is also a risk zoonotically because horses, pigs, and birds are also reservoirs. In the event of a coinfection with an influenza A virus that has infected a human and a different strain that might simultaneously infect a pig, the resulting virus that has reproduced in the host may now infect both humans and pigs, due to new reassortment of HA and NA surface proteins. This resulting strain's HA and NA surface proteins may not be recognizable by the human immune system and therefore this new emerging virus may now be capable of a pandemic outbreak within the population.

Agriculture

Agriculture, mining, and construction were considered to be among the most hazardous occupations of the 20th century. Agricultural workers and those who process agricultural products are exposed to numerous safety and physical hazards as well as chemical and biological agents. Workers are readily exposed to infectious microorganisms as well as their spores and toxins through inhalation, ingestion resulting from contact with contaminated materials, direct exposure of nonintact skin and mucous membranes, and inoculation resulting from traumatic injury. Factors such as host susceptibility, virulence of the agent, dose, and exposure route all influence the potential for disease development.

Biological agents associated with fungal diseases (such as coccidioidomycosis, histoplasmosis, and blastomycosis) are found on plants and animals and in soils. These agents cause endemic disease and, as occupational hazards, affect primarily farmers and horticultural workers. Food and grain handlers, farmers, and laborers are exposed to parasitic diseases such as echinococcosis and toxoplasmosis. Processors who handle animal products may acquire bacterial skin diseases such as anthrax from working with contaminated hides, tularemia from skinning and dressing infected animals, and erysipelas from skin abrasions infected during contact with contaminated fish, shellfish, meat, or poultry. Infected turkeys, geese, squab, and ducks or the aerosolized feces from these birds expose poultry processing workers and farmers to psittacosis, a bacterial infection caused by *Chlamydia psittaci*.

At least 24 out of the 150 zoonotic diseases known worldwide are considered to be a hazard for agricultural workers in North America. These diseases can be contracted directly from animals, but more often they are acquired in the work environment. Risk of infection varies with the type and species of animal and geographic location. Controls include awareness of specific hazards, use of personal protective equipment (PPE), preventive veterinary care, worker education, and medical monitoring or prophylactic therapy, where appropriate.

There is extensive literature on occupational exposure of agricultural workers. For additional information, the reader is referred to Macher & Rosenberg, 1999; Popendorf & Donham, 1991; AIHA, 1995; and the 1986 Agricultural Respiratory Hazards Education Series published by the American Lung Association.

Miscellaneous Worksites

The potential for exposure to occupational biohazards exists in most work environments. The following list, though incomplete, cites many of the diverse workplaces where the potential for exposure to biohazardous agents exists, along with the diseases or agents to which workers may be exposed. For additional references of infectious diseases by occupations see Macher & Rosenberg (1999), Dutkiewicz et al. (1988), and Cohen (1997).

- workers maintaining water systems: *Legionella pneumophila* and *Naegleria* spp.
- workers associated with birds (such as parrots, parakeets, and pigeons) in pet shops, aviaries, or zoos with avian exhibits, or on construction and public works jobs near perching or nesting sites: *C. psittaci*, *Histoplasma capsulatum*
- workers in wood-processing facilities: wood dust, endotoxins, allergenic fungi growing on timber, and fungi that cause deep mycoses
- miners: zoonotic bacteria, mycobacteria, dermatophytic fungi, fungi causing deep mycoses, mycotoxin-producing fungi (miners may be immunocompromised because of exposure to coal dust, which results in black lung disease)
- sewage and compost workers: enteric bacteria and other infectious bacteria, endotoxin, hepatitis A virus, parasitic protozoa such as *Giardia* spp., allergenic fungi
- renovators of items such as books, buildings, and paintings; librarians: endotoxin, allergenic microorganisms and toxigenic fungi growing on surfaces
- workers in textile manufacturing who process plant fibers (such as cotton, flax, hemp): organic dust, endotoxin
- workers in the fishing industry: zoonotic bacteria (such as *Leptospira interrogans*, *Erysipelothrix rhusiopathiae*, and *Mycobacterium marinum*) and parasitic flukes (such as *Schistosoma* spp.)
- forestry workers: zoonotic diseases or agents (such as rabies virus, Russian spring summer fever virus, Rocky Mountain spotted fever, Lyme disease, and tularemia), viruses and bacteria transmitted by ixodid ticks, and fungi that cause deep mycoses
- workers who handle animal hair and rough leather: zoonotic diseases (such as Q fever, anthrax, and tularemia) and dermatophytic fungi
- workers who handle products of plant origin: endotoxin, allergenic actinomycetes, allergenic or mycotoxin-producing storage fungi, allergenic or toxic substances of plant origin, and allergenic storage mites
- child care workers: bacterial enteric diseases (Campy-

lobacter, shigellosis), viruses (hepatitis A, chickenpox, measles), dermatophycoses, and protozoal diseases (cryptosporidiosis and Giardiasis)
- Public safety workers: bloodborne pathogens (hepatitis B and C viruses), viral respiratory diseases including influenza

RISK ASSESSMENT

In the late 19th century, as scientists became aware of the presence of microorganisms and their potential to cause illness, many microbiologists suffered significant health consequences as a result of their work. Diseases such as cholera, typhus, yellow fever, Rocky Mountain spotted fever, and tuberculosis claimed the lives of those dedicated to studying or eradicating these diseases. Health care and agricultural workers suffered ongoing exposure to biological hazards before advances in medical science and animal husbandry could reduce the consequences of infectious diseases.

As has been previously stated, it is possible to work with infectious agents (or people, animals, or substances infected or contaminated by them) and still avoid exposure and subsequent infection or illness. Infections do not necessarily occur simply because the exposed person works with a disease-producing agent or substance. A series of circumstances are necessary for an exposure to lead to infection or illness. An understanding of the potential for the hazardous agent to cause human disease, known as its *pathogenicity*, and through what routes of infection the agent is efficiently delivered to a worker permits one to make informed decisions about biological agents since they are not all equally dangerous to workers.

By performing a risk assessment on an operation or event, it is possible to make a systematic evaluation of the exposure and infection potential and the possible consequences, and then to make decisions as to how the risk can best be avoided, reduced, or otherwise managed. The leading guidelines on laboratory biosafety and biosecurity, such as the WHO Laboratory Biosafety Manual and the U.S. Biosafety in Microbiological and Biomedical Laboratories, all emphasize that risk assessment is the fundamental planning step for managing these risks. They outline risk assessment principles, but do not provide detailed guidance or suggested methodologies for conducting such assessments.

Biological risk assessment appears generally as a two-step technical approach, based on (1) the hazard identification involving the characterization of the biological agents or materials (often on the basis of official lists and procedures) and the evaluation of their potential impact, and (2) a risk analysis of the activities. The result of the risk assessment informs the selection of the biological containment level, together with possible additional measures aiming at protecting the personnel, the external community, and the environment. Although most regulations leave room for possible adaptations and other alternative measures provided they are justified by risk assessment, decisions with respect to facility design or biosafety practices are often made on the basis of rather prescriptive standards and a box ticking approach, resulting in facilities and practices that may, in some circumstances, not be fully adapted to the needs of the organization and the actual level of risk. Technical elements that are not mentioned explicitly in the regulations are sometimes neglected and other issues, such as biosecurity, are sometimes omitted. Moreover, wider considerations like the influence of public perception, the impact of operating costs, or the risk acceptance level are generally not really taken into account.

A biosafety risk assessment has historically been a subjective and qualitative process that relies heavily on expert opinion and unique personal experiences. Individuals who conduct biosafety risk assessments generally depend on predetermined biological safety risk groups as the basis of their evaluations. Biological agents have been classified into biological safety risk groups based upon their properties to cause infectious disease or other harm to the personnel, the community, livestock, or the environment. Such classification does not take into account the likelihood of accidental release or exposure in a particular laboratory during a particular experiment, which should be evaluated during the risk assessment of the laboratory activities. Different national and international organizations and experts have developed their own scheme for defining agent risk groups, leaving more or less freedom to the risk assessor to define the risk group according to possible specific characteristics (e.g. strain, modifications, and attenuation). Moreover, the risk also depends on how that agent will be used in the laboratory.

There is general consensus on the high-level risk assessment process; as defined by Kaplan and Garrick, risk analysis consists of answering three specific questions:
1. What can happen?
2. What is the chance that it will happen?
3. If it happens, what are the consequences?

For biosafety, this can be broken down into three steps: identification of the biological agent or hazard and its unique biochemical properties; assessment of the probability of the hazard to cause an undesired event (exposure, disease, etc.) and the potential consequences; and management of the risk through established control measures and reassessment if necessary. Hazard identification was discussed in the preceding section; this section gives an overview of factors to be considered in an assessment of the probability and consequences; subsequent sections will review control measures and management approaches.

Whoever assesses the biosafety risks should start by looking at their specific setting and asking what can happen. For biological laboratories, the scenarios of what can happen can be grouped into the risks to individuals in the laboratory, risks to individuals outside the laboratory (the community), risks to environment (e.g. plants, animals) outside the laboratory, and risks from secondary exposure to people and the environment outside the laboratory.

For biological hazards, the chance of the undesired event (disease) occurring depends on both the likelihood of exposure and the likelihood of infection. The likelihood of exposure depends on the laboratory procedures and the in-place mitigation measures. The likelihood of infection depends upon the biochemical properties of the biological agent, including its specific potential routes of infection.

The following section will cover factors that can affect the likelihood of exposure, the likelihood of infection, and potential consequences. Some factors impact more than one aspect of the risk; for example, some agents cause different diseases (consequences) depending on the route of exposure. However, for simplicity, factors are captured only once in the discussion below.

Factors Affecting Likelihood of Exposure

A major factor in the likelihood of exposure is the route of exposure. The principal routes of exposure in a laboratory setting include inhalation exposure, percutaneous exposure, contact exposure (typically with broken skin or mucosal membranes), and through the gastrointestinal tract. Other routes of exposure may be more prominent outside a laboratory, such as from vectors or other exposure to infected individuals.

Inhalation Route of Exposure

The inhalation of airborne infectious particles into the respiratory system constitutes airborne transmission. This mode is important in the transmission of certain pathogens such as *M. tuberculosis*. The contaminated air in a room may escape to the outside and act as a conduit for contamination of the environment. In the workplace, many technical procedures (such as pressurizing liquids, sonicating, and grinding or sawing infectious materials), equipment, and spills release microbes into the air where workers can inhale them.

As noted earlier, Pike's survey of laboratory-associated infections indicated that only 18 percent of the documented infections had resulted from known accidents. For the remaining 82 percent, a connection between the infected person and the causative agent was difficult to determine. In many instances, all that is known is that the person worked with or was in the vicinity of work being done with the causative agent. The fact that no specific event could be associated with so many infections led earlier reviewers to implicate many routine laboratory procedures as the source of airborne contamination. Workers are exposed to airborne microorganisms through direct contact with or inhalation of minute airborne particles or by contact following the deposition of droplets, through splashing or spilling, onto surfaces, equipment, and personnel. Contamination as the result of splashing and spilling can also occur through transmission routes other than inhalation.

Liquid, when under pressure and passed through a small opening or when dropped onto a solid surface, is aerosolized into a cloud of very small droplets. The droplets vary in size; the larger ones settle quickly onto surfaces, inanimate objects, clothing, and skin, whereas the water in smaller particles evaporates rapidly. Bacteria and other material in the droplets remain in a dried state as droplet nuclei. These particles, or droplet nuclei, can remain suspended in air for some time and be moved to remote areas by air currents or ventilation systems.

Laboratory procedures involving the manipulation of infectious materials generate infectious particles of various sizes. For example, particles released by opening or dropping lyophilized cultures are ~10 μm in diameter, and particles generated by mixing, sonicating, or blending cultures range from 2 to 5 μm, depending on the operation. It has been shown that particles <5 μm in diameter are most effective in producing respiratory infection in animals. (See Chapter 2, The Lungs, and Chapter 8, Particulates, for additional aerosol information.)

Infectious airborne particles can be generated not only from aerosolized liquids but also from lyophilized cultures, dried bacterial colonies, dried material on stoppers and caps of culture tubes and bottles, dried exudates, fungal and actinomycete spores released when cultures are opened or contaminated material is disturbed, and dusts from animals. Diseases documented to have been associated with airborne infection in the laboratory and other workplaces, as well as in the community, include tuberculosis, psittacosis, Q fever, pulmonary mycoses, influenza, measles, legionnaires' disease, Pontiac fever, HPS, and, in special circumstances, brucellosis, rabies, and plague.

The use of epidemiological tools to study workplace infections confirms the observation that people whose work brings them into contact with pathogenic microorganisms are at greater risk of infection than the general population. However, the mere presence of an agent does not necessarily lead to occupational exposure and infection. Certain conditions—the multiple interrelated factors of route of entry, dose, viability, virulence, mode of transmission, and host susceptibility—must be present before an infection occurs. For an infection to occur, the agent must be pathogenic and viable, present in sufficient numbers to produce infection, and transmitted successfully and delivered to a susceptible host at a suitable entry site. It may be possible to reduce or eliminate susceptible hosts through immunization.

Percutaneous Route of Exposure

Infectious agents can be introduced into the body when contaminated objects (such as hypodermic needles, broken glassware, scalpels, and other tools) or animals puncture, cut, or scratch the skin (percutaneous exposure).

Contact Route of Exposure

Contact exposure occurs through mucosal membranes or skin surfaces that are not intact, that is, when open wounds, cuts, hangnails, dermatitis, or eczema are present. Spills or splashes of infectious materials (gross contamination) onto a receptive site such as an open wound, cut, eczematous skin, or mucous membranes are an effective means of transmitting microorganisms. The mucous membranes of the eyes, nose, and mouth are readily exposed to agents when rubbed with contaminated fingers or gloved hands and when splashes or sprays of infectious material occur. There have been reports of HIV and *Trypanosoma cruzi* infections related to splashes of the eyes and mucous membranes.

Unbroken skin is a barrier to infectious agents. Exceptions occur only in instances where skin penetration is the normal route of entry for an agent, such as with the infective cercariae stage of the parasitic agent *Schistosoma* spp.

Gastrointestinal Route of Exposure

Ingestion of infectious materials can occur when workers mouth-pipet or suction infectious materials or by hand-to-mouth contamination as the result of eating, drinking, smoking, or applying cosmetics in contaminated work areas. Hand-washing minimizes the opportunity for oral and ocular exposure.

Other Routes of Exposure

Direct contact of an infected person with another person is rare in the laboratory environment, but such transmission occurs commonly in the community and in medical settings where patients are treated. Animal-to-human (zoonotic) transmission through bites and scratches can occur when animals are associated with work activities. Indirect transmission occurs when common environmental surfaces (such as equipment, work benches, or laboratory accessories) become contaminated, and the infectious material is transferred to a host.

Vector-borne infection results when a causative agent is transmitted to a host mechanically or biologically by a living vector (such as a mosquito or tick) through a bite, directly through the skin in rare cases, or by mechanical means. Biological transmission involves propagation, multiplication, cyclic development, or a combination of these in the host before the arthropod can transmit the infective form of the agent. Infected ticks and mosquitoes have transmitted Rocky Mountain spotted fever, malaria, and yellow fever to investigators in the laboratory and in the field and are a potential hazard for other outdoor workers.

Factors Affecting Likelihood of Infection

The infectious, or infective, dose is the number of microorganisms required to initiate an infection. Although there are data available from animal studies on ID_{50} (the number of organisms needed to infect 50 percent of a test population), only a modest amount of information exists for humans. Data accumulated by the NIH on route of entry and infectious dose are shown in Tables 14–A and 14–B.

The viability and virulence of an agent are also important in determining whether a person becomes infected. If a microorganism is not viable and able to replicate, the opportunity for infection does not exist. The external environment is critical in the replication of microorganisms. Factors such as temperature, humidity, and the presence or absence of growth factors or other chemicals all play an important role in viability. For example, some bacterial agents, such as *Bacillus anthracis*, are capable of producing spores that survive under adverse conditions, and agents such as *M. tuberculosis* or *S. aureus* are unaffected by drying and remain viable on environmental surfaces, whereas other agents such as the herpes virus are very susceptible to drying.

The virulence, or relative pathogenicity, of microorganisms varies greatly among types and strains. Some microbes are highly pathogenic, even in healthy adults, whereas others are opportunistic pathogens, able to infect only hosts with lowered immunity or sites other than their normal habitat. Some microbial strains are attenuated, or weakened, after reproducing through numerous generations in the laboratory. Certain vaccine strains, selected because they are immunogenic and do not produce significant disease, are also examples of attenuated organisms. Even though the vaccine strain of an organism may be attenuated, it is best to limit exposure to planned circumstances such as vaccination rather than by an accidental, work-related exposure.

The stability of the biological agent outside the host also impacts the likelihood of infection. Biological agents have varying ability to survive different environmental stressors before becoming inactivated.

TABLE 14–A	Infectious Dose for 25 to 50 Percent of Volunteers	
Disease or Agent	**Inoculation Route**	**Dose***
Scrub typhus	Intradermal	3
Q fever	Inhalation	10
Tularemia	Inhalation	10
Malaria	Intravenous	10
Syphilis	Intradermal	57
Shigella flexneri	Ingestion	180
Anthrax	Inhalation	≥ 1,300
Typhoid fever	Ingestion	10^5
Cholera	Ingestion	10^8
Escherichia coli	Ingestion	10^8
Shigellosis	Ingestion	10^9

*Dose given in number or organisms.
Source: Adapted from Wedum et al., 1972, p. 1558.

TABLE 14–B	Minimal Human Infective Dose in Volunteers	
Viral Agent	**Inoculation Route**	**Dose***
Measles virus	Intranasal spray	0.2**
Rhinovirus	Nasal drops	≤ 1
Venezuelan encephalitis virus	Subcutaneous	1†
West Nile virus	Intramuscular	1††
Parinfluenza 1 virus	Nasal drops	≤ 1.5
Poliovirus 1	Ingestion	2**§
Rubella virus	Pharyngeal spray	≤ 10**
Coxsackie A21 virus	Inhalation	≤ 18
Rubella virus	Subcutaneous	30**
Adenovirus 27	Conjunctival swab	≤ 32
Rubella virus	Nasal drops	60**
Adenovirus 7	Nasal drops	≤ 150
Respiratory syncytial virus	Intranasal spray	≤ 160–640
Influenza A2 virus	Nasopharyngeal	≤ 790
SV-40 virus	Nasopharyngeal	10,000

Note: There was illness after all inoculations except poliovirus, rubella virus (nasal drops), adenovirus (nasal drops), and SV-40 virus; in these four there were serologic conversions.
* Median infectious tissue culture dose
** Children
† Guinea pig infective unit
†† Mouse infective unit
§ Plaque-forming unit
Source: Adapted from Wedum et al., 1972, p. 1558.

Factors Affecting Potential Consequences

The potential consequences of infection are impacted by many factors (SAND 2010-6487), such as:

- Does this agent or one of its by-products cause a carcinogenic or mutagenic reaction in a host?
- Does this agent produce a toxin or enzyme that has a negative impact in a healthy host?
- Does this agent suppress a host's immune system (e.g. cause dramatic suppression that renders the host susceptible to other infections)?
- Does this agent have the ability to mutate once in a host or in the natural environment to become infectious through a new route or new hosts, or to cause increased consequences?
- What is the duration of illness (the average length of time of clinical signs of infection) in a normally healthy host?
- What is the severity of illness (the average severity of illness, ranging from no signs of illness to hospitalized in critical condition) in a normal healthy host?
- What is the duration of infection (the length of time the host is infected with the organism) in a normal healthy host?
- Does this disease cause any long-term conditions (sequelae) in a normal healthy host?
- What is the frequency of death caused by this disease in a defined population during a specified interval of time (mortality rate)?
- What level of national or international reporting is required for outbreaks of this disease?
- Do effective diagnostic tests exist?
- Do post-exposure treatments (including immuno-globulin, vaccines, and antimicrobials) exist?
- Do preventive measures (vaccines) exist?

- What is the host range of the biological agent and the extent of its ability to spread in the environment?
- Is it endemic or exotic to the area?

Host susceptibility is often underestimated because the majority of laboratory persons working with potentially infectious material are healthy. The CDC and NIH recommendations presume a population of immunocompetent workers. Employees working with infectious agents can be put at increased risk of infection because of a variety of medical conditions such as diseases, allergies, inability to receive particular vaccines, and pregnancy or by taking drugs that alter host defenses.

Conditions that alter host defenses at body surfaces or impair the functioning of the immune system may put a worker at risk for certain infections. Skin disorders such as chronic dermatitis, eczema, and psoriasis leave a worker without an intact skin barrier against infection. The gastrointestinal mucosa, colonized by a resident population of normal bacterial flora, offers protection against infection by pathogenic microorganisms. However, this protection is usually disrupted when antibiotic therapy is administered. The body's immune system, consisting mainly of antibody-mediated B-cells, cell-mediated T-cells, and phagocytic cells, offers a significant line of defense against invading microorganisms.

Women who are pregnant or intend to become pregnant are at risk of exposure to certain infectious agents, as well as other potentially hazardous materials in their work environment. Foremost among the infectious hazards is the potential for congenital infection of the fetus, caused by exposure to cytomegalovirus (CMV), rubella, hepatitis B virus (HBV), herpes simplex virus, varicella virus, syphilis, or toxoplasmosis.

The development of allergies to proteins (such as biological products from raw plant and animal materials, fermentation products or enzymes, chemicals, animal dander, or aerosolized animal urine proteins) also presents a risk to employees. If an employee cannot be immunized because of an allergy to a constituent of a vaccine, the safety of that person may be compromised. A higher level of work practices and personal protective equipment may provide the required level of protection for such a worker. All of these factors must be recognized and evaluated in relation to an employee's potential exposure. Decisions should be made on a case-by-case basis, with input from the employee, the employee's physician, institutional management, and an occupational health service professional. All activities or actions associated with worker health or medical surveillance must be performed in such a manner so that their confidentiality is not compromised. The results of medical testing or evaluation may be released only with the worker's permission.

In summary, the importance of assessing the work activity (including the facility, contamination potential, volume of material, and the agent concentration) in relation to the host and agent cannot be overemphasized.

MITIGATION (HAZARD CONTROL)

The process of developing controls to minimize occupational exposure to infectious agents or other biological agents becomes straightforward once the actual risk of work with the organism or agent is known and the major risks identified. Reducing the risk of exposure to potentially infectious agents can be achieved by source control, minimization of accidental release, and protection of the worker. Physical barriers, used along with the other components of a comprehensive biosafety program, provide the means to work with biological agents without unacceptable adverse effect. Protection of workers and the immediate work environment is achieved through the use of good work practices and appropriate safety equipment. Effective vaccines also decrease worker risk. Protection of personnel in the immediate area outside the laboratory and the community (environment external to the workplace) is attained by using adequately designed, constructed, and maintained facilities and operational practices.

Unless the risk is eliminated, there will always be some level of risk. Risk elimination may be possible through substitution of a nonhazardous biological agent for the hazardous one, if the scientific objectives can still be met through substitution. If substitution is not feasible, then part of the risk management decision is determining if the risk is acceptable, controllable, or unacceptable. There are several factors that can influence risk acceptance. These factors include such considerations as the level of available resources to mitigate or control the risks, the regulatory requirements for the risk, the value of work to the community or to the researcher, and the public's general perception regarding the risk.

Containment

Containment is the mechanism for ensuring that workers, the immediate work environment, and the community, including those outside the immediate workplace, are protected or shielded from exposure during workplace activities involving infectious or biological agents. As stated in the 5th edition of *Biosafety in Microbiological and Biomedical Laboratories* (BMBL, 2009), "the term 'containment' is used in describing safe methods, facilities and equipment for managing infectious materials in the laboratory environment where they are being handled or maintained." Varying configurations of these components are used depending on the hazard category of the work.

The CDC and NIH have designated four default configurations of work practices, safety equipment, and facility design as biosafety levels (BSLs) for work involving infectious agents or activities in which experimentally or naturally infected vertebrate animals are manipulated. The combination must be specifically appropriate for the operations performed, the documented or suspected routes of transmission of the agent, and the laboratory function or activity. The use of increasingly stringent procedures and more complex laboratory facilities permits higher risk activities to be carried out safely. Specific mitigation measures should be selected based on the identified risks. As a simple example, minimizing sharps would be a good practice for handling an agent that causes disease through percutaneous exposure. Depending on the sophistication of the mitigation measures, containment can be expensive to operate and maintain and/or procedurally burdensome, so optimizing the control measures for the identified risks ideally provides the best return on investment to improve safety.

Tables 14–C and 14–D summarize the recommended biosafety levels for handling different categories of infectious agents and experimentally or naturally infected animals. These levels are not meant to replace the risk assessment as the basis for selecting the appropriate mitigation measures. Rather, they should be viewed as starting points.

TABLE 14–C   Summary of Recommended Biosafety Levels for Infectious Agents

BSL	Agents	Practices	Primary Barriers and Safety Equipment	Facilities (Secondary Barriers)
1	Not known to consistently cause diseases in healthy adults	Standard microbiological practices	• No primary barriers required • PPE: laboratory coats and gloves; eye, face protection, as needed	Laboratory bench and sink required
2	• Agents associated with human disease • Routes of transmission include percutaneous injury, ingestion, mucous membrane exposure	BSL-1 practice plus: • Limited access • Biohazard warning signs • Sharps precautions • Biosafety manual defining any needed waste decontamination or medical surveillance policies	Primary barriers: • BSCs or other physical containment devices used for all manipulations of agents that cause splashes or aerosols of infectious materials • PPE: Laboratory coats, gloves, face and eye protection, as needed	BSL-1 plus: • Autoclave available
3	Indigenous or exotic agents that may cause serious or potentially lethal disease through the inhalation route of exposure	BSL-2 practice plus: • Controlled access • Decontamination of all waste • Decontamination of laboratory clothing before laundering	Primary barriers: • BSCs or other physical containment devices used for all open manipulations of agents • PPE: Protective laboratory clothing, gloves, face, eye and respiratory protection, as needed	BSL-2 plus: • Physical separation from access corridors • Self-closing, double-door access • Exhausted air not recirculated • Negative airflow into laboratory • Entry through airlock or anteroom • Hand-washing sink near laboratory exit
4	• Dangerous/exotic agents which post high individual risk of aerosol-transmitted laboratory infections that are frequently fatal, for which there are no vaccines or treatments • Agents with a close or identical antigenic relationship to an agent requiring BSL-4 until data are available to redesignate the level • Related agents with unknown risk of transmission	BSL-3 practices plus: • Clothing change before entering • Shower on exit • All material decontaminated on exit from facility	Primary barriers: • All procedures conducted in Class III BSCs or Class I or II BSCs in combination with full-body, air-supplied, positive-pressure suit	BSL-3 plus: • Separate building or isolated zone • Dedicated supply and exhaust, vacuum, and decontamination systems • Other requirements outlined in the text

Source: Reprinted from *Biosafety in Microbiology and Biomedical Laboratories,* 5th ed. CDC, 2009, p. 319.

Biosafety Levels

The following section covers BSLs, guidelines, and the interpretation of the guidelines. BSLs are default combinations of risk mitigation measures that biosafety professionals often use as a starting point in determining the most appropriate risk mitigations for the biological agent and work procedures. The same biological agent may be handled in different containment levels depending on the nature of the work, e.g. in the United States, *Bacillus anthracis* is handled both in BSL-2 and BSL-3. And, the most efficient use of resources to mitigate the risks could be a mix of mitigation measures resulting in a control system that does not align clearly with any of the traditional BSL categorizations.

Background. In the 1970s, the CDC classified etiologic agents on the basis of hazard. The list compiled for that purpose still exists in slightly modified form in some government documents, including a document describing interstate shipment of etiologic agents. For appropriate identification

TABLE 14–D Summary of Recommended Biosafety Levels for Activities in Which Experimentally or Naturally Infected Vertebrate Animals Are Used

BSL	Agents	Practices	Primary Barriers and Safety Equipment	Facilities (Secondary Barriers)
1	Not known to consistently cause diseases in healthy adults	Standard animal care and management practices, including appropriate medical surveillance programs	As required for normal care of each species: • PPE: Laboratory coats and gloves; eye, face protection, as needed	Standard animal facility: • No recirculation of exhaust air • Directional airflow recommended • Hand-washing sink available
2	• Agents associated with human disease • Hazard: percutaneous injury, ingestion, mucous membrane exposure	ABSL-1 practice plus: • Limited access • Biohazard warning signs • Sharps precautions • Biosafety manual • Decontamination of all infectious wastes and animal cages prior to washing	ABSL-1 equipment plus primary barriers: • Containment equipment appropriate for animal species • PPE: Laboratory coats, gloves, face, eye and respiratory protection, as needed	ABSL-1 plus: • Autoclave available • Hand-washing sink available • Mechanical cage washer recommended • Negative airflow into animal and procedure rooms recommended
3	Indigenous or exotic agents that may cause serious or potentially lethal disease through the inhalation route of exposure	ABSL-2 practice plus: • Controlled access • Decontamination of clothing before laundering • Cages decontaminated before bedding is removed • Disinfectant foot bath as needed	ABSL-2 equipment plus: • Containment equipment for housing animals and cage dumping activities • Class I, II, or III BSCs available for manipulative procedures (inoculation, necropsy) that may create infectious aerosols • PPE: Appropriate respiratory protection	ABSL-2 facility plus: • Physical separation from access corridors • Self-closing, double-door access • Sealed penetrations • Sealed windows • Autoclave available in facility • Entry through anteroom or airlock • Negative airflow into animal and procedure rooms • Hand-washing sink near exit of animal or procedure room
4	• Dangerous/exotic agents which post high risk of aerosol-transmitted laboratory infections that are frequently fatal, for which there are no vaccines or treatments • Agents with a close or identical antigenic relationship to an agent requiring BSL-4 until data are available to redesignate the level • Related agents with unknown risk of transmission	ABSL-3 practices plus: • Entrance through change room where personal clothing is removed and laboratory clothing is put on; shower on exiting • All wastes are decontaminated before removal from the facility	ABSL-3 equipment plus: • Maximum containment equipment (i.e., Class III BSC or partial containment equipment in combination with full-body, air-supplied positive-pressure suit) used for all procedures and activities	ABSL-3 facility plus: • Separate building or isolated zone • Dedicated supply and exhaust, vacuum, and decontamination systems • Other requirements outlined in the text

Source: Reprinted from Biosafety in Microbiology and Biomedical Laboratories, 5th ed. CDC, 2009, p. 103.

of the categories to be used in packaging, labeling, and shipping etiologic agents, lists were provided by the CDC in 1974 and 42 *CFR* Part 72 in 1980. The 1974 list came to be used as a classification scheme in which an organism, genus, or group of microorganisms can be categorized into a specific hazard group by users and other federal agencies. The 1980 list identified organisms that were required to

be sent by registered mail. At the present time, etiologic agents and other infectious materials are considered hazardous materials under the U.S. Department of Transportation (U.S. DOT) 49 *CFR* Parts 171–180, although they are not included as hazardous agents under the OSHA hazard communication standard. The U.S. DOT inclusion and the OSHA hazard communication Safety Data Sheet (SDS), formerly the Material Safety Data Sheet (MSDS), exemptions cause some confusion. Obviously, information similar to that found in certain sections of an SDS is needed to allow appropriate spill cleanup and to alleviate inappropriate public perception of risk for any shipment of microorganisms. On the other hand, if the organism being shipped is not pathogenic, there should be a mechanism for declaring an exemption from the U.S. DOT list so as not to restrict packaging to the small size limitations required for infectious substances.

Lists currently in use should be reviewed at least annually and updated accordingly because of numerous taxonomic changes and the recognition that any species of organism may have avirulent and virulent strains. Information on the more commonly recognized human pathogens can be found in peer-reviewed scientific literature and in numerous microbiology textbooks. Unfortunately, it is rare to find an assessment of the level of risk or any directives regarding the containment to be used in working with pathogens in such references. However, if the agent is listed in one of the guidelines, the first estimation of its biosafety containment level can be ascertained.

If allergens or chemical agents are used, appropriate precautions to prevent sensitization should be based on exposure control limits that have been established by a reputable association, as was done by the working party of the European Federation of Biotechnology. Biosafety levels were developed for use in protection against living microorganisms that have the potential to cause infectious disease in healthy human adults; they are not usually appropriate for the control of other hazards.

Published Guidelines of Containment Levels

The biosafety guidelines most commonly used in the United States for containment of biohazardous agents in the workplace are those recommended by the CDC, the NIH, and the National Research Council (NRC). Other guidelines found in the literature are based on interpretations of the recommendations of these agencies.

The CDC/NIH Guidelines for Biosafety in Microbiological and Biomedical Laboratories.

The BMBL recommends that laboratory directors establish work practices involving containment equipment and facilities in the workplace. In doing this, they must take into account interactions of the virulence of the agent, immune status of potential hosts, and the hazards of the procedure. In addition, laboratory directors are responsible for making appropriate risk assessments of agents. The director must be familiar with the subject of risk assessment regarding biological agents or seek the advice of someone who has such expertise.

Risk management is achieved through use of practices, facilities, and equipment to create appropriate containment. Biosafety practices are an important part of a program to manage the risk of exposure to potentially infectious agents. The general agent descriptions and applicable work environments described by the CDC and NIH in each of the biosafety levels for both small and large scale are listed below as compiled directly from the guidelines. An addendum at the end of this chapter outlines large-scale guidelines applicable to nonrecombinant organisms.

Biosafety level 1 (BSL-1) is used for work involving defined and well-characterized strains of viable microorganisms of no known or of minimal potential hazard to laboratory personnel or the environment. This level is appropriate for high school and undergraduate college teaching and training laboratories. No special competence is required, although training in the specific procedures should be provided, and there should be supervision by a scientist with general training in microbiology or a related science. The laboratory is not separated from general building traffic, and work is conducted on the open bench. Examples of organisms typically used under these conditions are *Bacillus subtilis*, *Naegleria gruberi*, and canine hepatitis virus. Much of the recombinant DNA work with *E. coli* K12 and *Saccharomyces cerevisiae* has been approved at BSL-1.

BSL-1LS is for large-scale work (greater than 10 liters of production volumes). BSL-1LS is used for the agents that can be handled at BSL-1 on a small scale. Microbial agents that have been safely used for large-scale industrial production for many years may qualify for good large-scale practices (GLSP) status. Examples include *Lactobacillus casei*, *Penicillium camembertii*, *Saccharomyces cerevisiae*, *Cephalosporium acremonium*, *Bacillus thuringiensis*, and *Rhizobium mellioti*. The criteria for GLSP were originally developed for the European Economic Community (now known as the European Union) by the Organization for Economic Cooperation and Development (OECD) as "good industrial large scale practices" (GILSP) and were slightly revised by the NIH for acceptance and use in the United States.

Biosafety level 2 (BSL-2) is used for work with many moderate-risk agents present in the community (indigenous) and associated with human disease of varying degrees of severity. Agents are usually of moderate potential hazard to personnel and the environment. This level is appropriate for clinical, diagnostic, teaching, and other research facilities in which work is done by individuals with a level of competency equal to or greater than one would expect in a college department of microbiology. Workers must be trained in good microbiological techniques in order for the handling of these agents on the open bench to be allowed when the potential for aerosol production is low. Laboratory personnel must have specific training in handling pathogenic agents and must be directed by competent scientists. Workers must be trained in proper use of biological safety cabinets or other appropriate primary containment equipment when the risk of aerosol production is high, as in such tasks as centrifuging, grinding, homogenizing, blending, vigorously shaking or mixing, performing sonic disruption, opening containers with increased internal pressure, inoculating animals intranasally, harvesting infected tissues from animals or eggs, and harvesting human cells from tissues using a cell separator. Access to the laboratory should be limited when work is in progress. Primary hazards to workers include accidental inoculation, exposure of nonintact skin or mucous membranes, and ingestion. Examples of organisms used under BSL-2 conditions are hepatitis B virus, *Salmonella* spp., and *Toxoplasma* spp.

BSL-2LS is for large-scale, in vitro work with agents that require BSL-2 containment when work is at small scale. A detailed description of the containment requirements for BSL-2LS can be found in Appendix K-IV of the NIH's recombinant DNA guidelines.

Biosafety level 3 (BSL-3) is used for work with indigenous or exotic agents where the potential for infection by aerosols is real and the disease may have serious or lethal consequences. Indigenous and exotic agents vary by country, and within regions of some countries, so there must be some flexibility for assignment of containment levels. Biosafety level 3 is appropriate for clinical diagnostic microbiology work when tuberculosis or brucellosis is suspected and also for special teaching and research situations that require the handling of such agents. Partial containment equipment such as Class I or Class II biological safety cabinets is used for all manipulations of infectious material at BSL-3. There are special engineering design criteria and work practices associated with BSL-3 containment. Worker competency must equal or exceed that of college-level microbiologists, and workers must have special training in handling these potentially lethal human pathogens and infectious materials. Supervisors must be competent scientists who are experienced in working with these agents.

Primary routes of exposure of workers to BSL-3 hazards include inhalation, with relatively few infections reported as a result of accidental auto-inoculation or ingestion. The extra personal protective clothing probably serves as a reminder of the hazard level and promotes an awareness that reduces such incidents. Examples of organisms used under BSL-3 conditions are *M. tuberculosis*, *Brucella* spp., St. Louis encephalitis virus, *Borna* virus (an exotic agent when used in the United States), and *C. burnetii*.

BSL-3LS: The detailed requirements for BSL-3LS are to be found in Appendix K-V of the NIH recombinant DNA guidelines.

Biosafety level 4 (BSL-4) is used for work with dangerous and exotic agents that pose a high individual risk of life-threatening disease. Such an agent has a low infectious dose and poses a danger for the community from person-to-person spread. BSL-4 containment is appropriate for all manipulations of potentially infectious diagnostic materials, isolates, and naturally or experimentally infected animals. Maximum containment equipment, such as a Class III biological safety cabinet, or partial containment equipment in combination with a full-body, air-supplied, positive-pressure personnel suit is used for all procedures and activities. Because of the stringent requirements associated with BSL-4 containment, only a few facilities that meet this standard have been built and are operational.

The main hazard to laboratory or animal care personnel working with agents requiring such extreme caution and containment is respiratory exposure to infectious aerosols. Mucous membrane exposure to infectious droplets and accidental parenteral inoculation also play a role in transmission of infections. Worker competency must equal or exceed that of college-level microbiologists, and workers must receive specific, thorough training in handling extremely hazardous infectious agents. They must understand the function of the primary and secondary containment equipment and the facility design. Supervisors must be competent scientists trained and experienced in such work.

Laboratory access is strictly controlled. The facility is either separated from other buildings or completely isolated from other areas of the building. A separate facility operations manual is required. The maximum containment facility has special design and engineering features that prevent dissemination of microbes to the environment. Some examples of organisms used under these conditions are the agents of viral hemorrhagic fevers, filoviruses, and certain arboviruses.

The requirements for large-scale BSL-4 are described in BMBL. Appendix K of the NIH recombinant guidelines (Physical containment for large scale uses of organisms) does not include a description of requirements for BSL-4LS because the requirements should be determined on a case-by-case basis if they are requested.

Animal biosafety levels: Other special biosafety precautions described in these guidelines apply to the use of naturally or experimentally infected animals. Animals are restricted from the laboratory unless they are part of the experiment at BSL-2 and higher, and decorative plants are restricted from use at BSL-3 and higher. Animals and plants harbor their own microbial flora, which could infect the worker or contaminate the work, so it is prudent to prohibit their use or presence in microbiology laboratories.

There are intrinsic hazards associated with the use of certain animals (for example, from herpes B virus in macaques), which must be taken into account in assessing the risk to the worker. There are also extrinsic hazards when infectious agents are purposely used to infect animals and vector-host interactions are being studied (*in vivo*) as opposed to the "controlled work" in culture media (*in vitro*). These hazards must be addressed.

NIH guidelines for research involving recombinant DNA molecules. The CDC's *Classification of Etiologic Agents on the Basis of Hazard* (1974) was slightly modified and incorporated into Appendix B of the NIH guidelines. The original CDC classification system provided "points to consider" in estimating the degree of hazard, noting that it depended on the etiologic agent and its nature and use. These notes were not included in the NIH document, implying to the user that all members of the groups, species, and strains on that list were pathogenic. Because the NIH guidelines could not take into account all existing and anticipated information on special procedures, users were encouraged to recommend changes to the guidelines. For example, Appendix B has been revised and updated as can be seen in the current guidelines.

The NIH guidelines provide the same message as the BMBL guidelines, that the agent/product rather than the process of recombinant DNA work should be evaluated for worker safety. The basic biosafety requirements for work with all microorganisms are the same. However, nonpathogenic, genetically modified organisms are currently registered and regulated at most institutions because of the public's perception of risk, whereas work with true pathogens is often done without internal oversight and review because the public has not been made aware of the risk. For large-scale guidelines, see Appendix K.

National Research Council guidelines. In *Biosafety in the Laboratory: Prudent Practices for the Handling and Disposal of Infectious Materials*, published in 1989, the NRC's Committee on Hazardous Biological Substances in the Laboratory recommended seven basic prudent biosafety practices to avoid exposure to infectious agents, which are listed later in the chapter. These prudent practices provide barriers against the known routes of exposure for most diseases and are the basic recommendations for working with biohazardous agents. The recommendations are supplemented with additional practices, equipment, and facility design as the severity of the hazard increases. The practices recommended by the NRC, when accompanied by recommendations for facility design and containment equipment, are compatible with the CDC and NIH biosafety levels.

Introduction of recombinant DNA-engineered organisms into the environment: Key issues. The NRC has concluded that there is no evidence of any unique hazards posed by recombinant DNA techniques. The risks associated with recombinant DNA are the same in kind as those associated with unmodified organisms or organisms modified by other means. The NRC recommended that risk assessments be based on the nature of the organism and the environment into which it is introduced, and not on the method by which it was produced. This recommendation was also accepted by the Office of Science and Technology Policy. Given this conclusion, two sets of guidelines, one for recombinant work and another for work with human pathogens, are redundant. Guidelines for a single code of practice for protection of workers from exposure to biohazardous agents are appropriate and have already been accepted in Europe.

Interpretation of guidelines. Using the BMBL guidelines previously described, decisions on containment levels for work at BSL-1 through BSL-3 at small and large scale can be made at the institutional level. BSL-4, because it is limited to so few facilities, is not considered here. The expertise of an institution's biosafety committee or biosafety officer is needed for risk assessment of pathogenic agents, infectious materials, and work activities. A professional biosafety consultant may be needed for facilities that do not have such in-house expertise. The American Biological Safety Association, www.absa.org, can be contacted for a list of certified biosafety professionals.

Risk assessment for agents to be used at large scale, especially for industrial production, should begin early as an integral part of the research and development process. The level of pathogenicity should be determined before production of the organism is scaled up, because special large-scale containment facilities are too costly to be built and maintained if they are not needed.

The Coordinated Framework for Biotechnology has added the U.S. Environmental Protection Agency (EPA), the U.S. Department of Agriculture, the Food and Drug Administration, and OSHA to the list of federal agencies such as the CDC and NIH who can provide oversight and information on risk assessment. Work with certain agents associated with terrorist activities or biological warfare may require oversight from federal defense agencies as well. The Department of Commerce also restricts the export of such agents/materials because of their potential use for biological warfare.

Facility Design

The laboratory facility provides the shell, or barrier, necessary to protect the community and those outside the immediate work area from exposure to hazardous materials. When agents of increasing hazard are manipulated, facility design plays a more important role in reducing the potential for dissemination of the agent, particularly when an accidental release within the laboratory occurs.

BSL-1 and BSL-2 laboratories have no special design features beyond an ordinary laboratory, except that a handwashing sink is required, doors should be present for access control, and windows opening to the exterior must have fly screens. BSL-2 laboratories may require lockable doors for certain restricted agents and in new facilities, directional air flow into the laboratory is encouraged.

In 1993, the WHO characterized agents handled in BSL-1 and BSL-2 laboratories as those having no or very low individual or community risk (BSL-1) or moderate individual risk and low community risk (BSL-2). Therefore, the need for special design features to protect the community does not arise in these labs.

The biosafety level 3 laboratory includes design features of BSL-1 and BSL-2 laboratories, plus it must be separated from areas of unrestricted traffic flow within the building. In addition, these facilities have controlled access (double-door entry), a specialized ventilation system that creates a directional one-pass airflow into the laboratory from surrounding "clean" areas, special hand-washing controls (elbow, foot, or knee operated), and a means to decontaminate biological waste, preferably within the BSL-3 area.

BSL-3 facility requirements impose additional expense for containment features. In some circumstances where existing facilities do not meet BSL-3 requirements or cannot be made to do so, some accommodation may be made. Work involving routine or repetitive operations (such as diagnostic procedures involving propagation of agents for identification, typing, and susceptibility testing) can be carried out in a BSL-2 facility as long as the work practices and safety equipment associated with BSL-3 containment are used. Exhaust air from the laboratory is also discharged to the outdoors and ventilation to the laboratory is balanced to provide directional airflow into the lab. The decision to alter containment conditions should be made only by the laboratory director. The publication *BMBL* contains agent summary statements for most microorganisms handled at BSL-3 and identifies those agents where modification of containment conditions may be appropriate.

The BSL-4 facility, though rare, draws a great deal of attention, perhaps because it conjures visions of an "Andromeda strain." Agents handled in such a facility have no available vaccines and pose a high risk to both workers and the community, so design criteria must prevent both worker and community exposure. In addition to having the design components of level 3 facilities, a BSL-4 facility is housed in a separate building or in isolated zones that have dedicated ventilation, stringent access requirements, and decontamination systems. For more detailed information, see CDC/NIH (2009).

Safety Equipment

Because most experimental procedures are recognized as having the potential to generate aerosols, safety equipment designed to reduce the likelihood of worker and environmental exposure has become standard in biological laboratories during the last decade.

Biological safety cabinets. The most frequently used and effective example of laboratory containment equipment is the biological safety cabinet (BSC), which provides a primary barrier to prevent escape of infectious aerosols into the work environment. When used and maintained properly these cabinets provide a combination of worker, product, and environmental protection that varies according to the class and type of cabinet selected.

All three classes of biological safety cabinets (Class I, II, and III) have high-efficiency particulate air (HEPA) filters for exhaust air. Of these, the Class II cabinet is most widely used. Selection of the class and type of cabinet must be based on the hazard level of the microorganism to be manipulated, the nature of the work activity (the potential of a technique to produce aerosols), and the need to protect the worker or the work environment from airborne contamination (Table 14–E). Class I and II cabinets, when used in conjunction with good microbiological practices, provide an effective means to safely manipulate moderate- and high-risk microorganisms.

Class I ventilated cabinets provide personnel and environmental protection (not product protection) by means of an unrecirculated inward airflow away from the operator. The minimum face velocity at the work opening is at least 75 linear feet per minute (lfpm). The cabinet exhaust air is HEPA filtered to protect the environment before it is discharged either to the laboratory or through duct work to the outside atmosphere. In practice this cabinet functions in a manner similar to a chemical fume hood, except for the additional HEPA filtration of exhaust air. The use of Class I cabinets is relatively rare, although they are increasingly used to provide containment for aerosol-producing equipment (or procedures) such as centrifuges, pressurized apparatus, and necropsy of infected animals. Figure 14–1 shows the design and airflow patterns of this cabinet.

Because Class II biosafety cabinets provide protection to workers, experimental materials, and the environment and are easily accessed through a front work opening, they are often used in biological laboratories for manipulation of microorganisms and tissue cultures. Class II cabinets have a face velocity of 75–100 lfpm and are divided into types A and B (Figures 14–2a through 2d). Class II, type A2 cabinets may be used for microbiological activities when volatile or toxic substances and radionuclides are not used. The exhaust air

TABLE 14–E   Comparison of Biological Safety Cabinets

| BSC Class | Face Velocity | Airflow Pattern | Applications | |
			Nonvolatile Toxic Chemicals and Radionuclides	Volatile Toxic Chemicals and Radionuclides
I	75	In at front through HEPA to the outside or into the room through HEPA (Figure 14–1)	Yes	When exhausted outdoors[1,2]
II, A1	75	70% recirculated to the cabinet work area through HEPA; 30% balance can be exhausted through HEPA back into the room or to outside through a canopy unit (Figure 14–2a)	Yes (minute amounts)	No
II, B1	100	30% recirculated, 70% exhausted. Exhaust cabinet air must pass through a dedicated duct to the outside through a HEPA filter (Figure 14–2b)	Yes	Yes (minute amounts)[1,2]
I, B2	100	No recirculation; total exhaust to the outside through a HEPA filter (Figure 14–2c)	Yes	Yes (small amounts)[1,2]
II, A2	100	Similar to II, A1, but has 100 lfpm intake air velocity and plenums are under negative pressure to room; exhaust air can be ducted to the outside through a canopy unit (Figure 14–2d)	Yes	When exhausted outdoors (FORMALLY "B3") (minute amounts)[1,2]
III	N/A	Supply air is HEPA filtered. Exhaust air passes through two HEPA filters in series and is exhausted to the outside via a hard connection (Figure 14–3).	Yes	Yes (small amounts)[1,2]

[1] Installation requires a special duct to the outside, an in-line charcoal filter, and a spark-proof (explosion proof) motor and other electrical components in the cabinet. Discharge of a Class I or Class II, Type A2 cabinet into a room should not occur if volatile chemicals are used.

[2] In no instance should the chemical concentration approach the lower explosion limits of the compounds.

Source: Reprinted from *Biosafety in Microbiology and Biomedical Laboratories,* 5th ed. CDC, 2009, pp. 311-312.

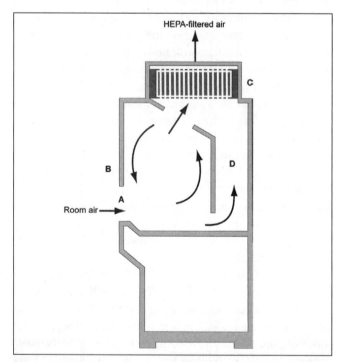

Figure 14–1. Class I biological safety cabinet. A. front opening, B. sash, C. exhaust HEPA filter, D. exhaust plenum. *(Reprinted from* Biosafety in Microbiology and Biomedical Laboratories, *5th ed. CDC, 2009, p. 315.)*

from this cabinet is usually discharged to the work environment, although it may be connected to exhaust ductwork by a thimble connection. The design criteria for this cabinet permit contaminated ducts and plenums under positive pressure.

All Class II, type B cabinets are hard-ducted to the outside atmosphere and have 100 lfpm face velocity, and when contaminated plenums exist, they are under negative pressure or are surrounded by negative-pressure ducts or plenums, depending on the cabinet type. Work associated with minute or small amounts of volatile and toxic chemicals and radionuclides associated with microbiological activities may be handled in a type B cabinet. The B2 cabinet is a "total exhaust" cabinet with no air recirculation; it can be used for cell work involving small amounts of hazardous or toxic chemicals, such as carcinogens and radionuclides.

The Class III cabinet is a totally enclosed, ventilated, negative-pressure cabinet of gas-tight construction that is used for work requiring the highest level of containment (Figure 14–3). It offers maximum protection for personnel, the environment, and work materials. Personnel protection equivalent to that provided by the Class III cabinet can also be attained by using a positive-pressure ventilated suit in a maximum containment facility in conjunction with a Class I or II cabinet.

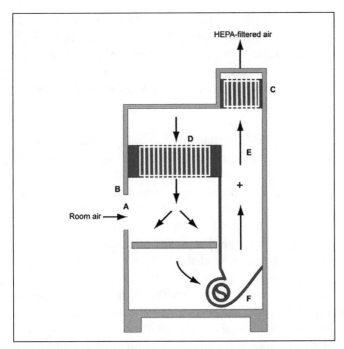

Figure 14–2a. Class II, type A biological safety cabinet. A. front opening, B. sash, C. exhaust HEPA filter, D. Rear plenum, E. supply HEPA filter, F. blower. *(Reprinted from* Biosafety in Microbiology and Biomedical Laboratories, *5th ed. CDC, 2009, p. 315.)*

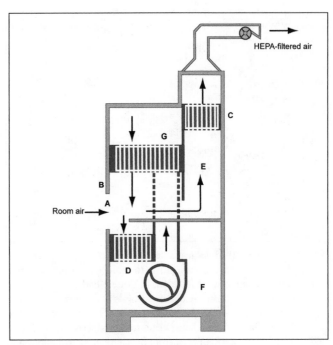

Figure 14–2b. Class II, type B biological safety cabinet. A. front opening, B. sash, C. exhaust HEPA filter, D. supply HEPA filter, E. negative-pressure exhaust plenum, F. blower, G. additional HEPA filter for supply air. Note: The cabinet exhaust needs to be connected to the building exhaust systems. *(Reprinted from* Biosafety in Microbiology and Biomedical Laboratories, *5th ed. CDC, 2009, p. 316.)*

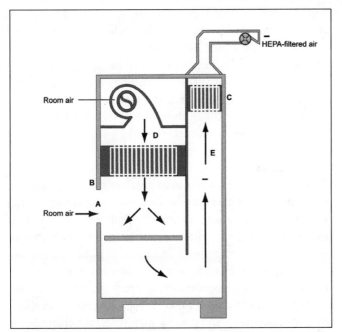

Figure 14–2c. Class II, type B2 biological safety cabinet. A. front opening, B. sash, C. exhaust HEPA filter, D. supply HEPA filter, E. negative-pressure exhaust plenum. Note: The cabinet exhaust needs to be connected to the building exhaust systems. *(Reprinted from* Biosafety in Microbiology and Biomedical Laboratories, *5th ed. CDC, 2009, p. 318.)*

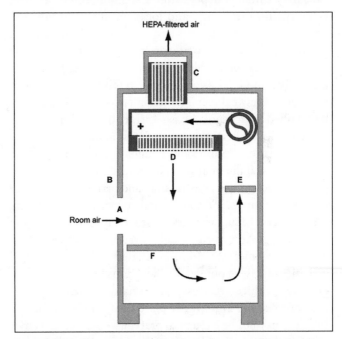

Figure 14–2d. Class II, type A2 biological safety cabinet (tabletop model). A. front opening, B. sash, C. exhaust HEPA filter, D. supply HEPA filter, E. positive-pressure exhaust plenum, F. negative-pressure plenum. The A2 BSC should be canopy connected to the exhaust system. *Note:* The Class II Type A2 BSC is not equivalent to what was formerly called a Class II, B-3, unless it is connected to the laboratory exhaust system. *(Reprinted from* Biosafety in Microbiology and Biomedical Laboratories, *5th ed. CDC, 2009, p. 318.)*

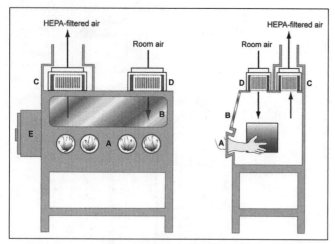

Figure 14–3. Class III biological safety cabinet. A. glove ports, with O-ring for attaching arm-length gloves to cabinet. B. sash, C. exhaust HEPA filter, D. supply HEPA filter, E. double-ended autoclave or pass-through box. Note: A chemical tank may be installed that would be located beneath the work surface of the BSC with access from above. The cabinet exhaust needs to be connected to the building exhaust systems. *(Reprinted from* Biosafety in Microbiology and Biomedical Laboratories, *5th ed. CDC, 2009, p. 319.)*

Certification of biosafety cabinets. The effectiveness of biological safety cabinets depends on a combination of airflow velocity, filter integrity, and location in the laboratory, because ventilation currents and even workers' movements can disrupt cabinet air patterns. It should not be assumed that equipment (or a facility) is providing worker protection merely because it is designed to do so. To be assured that a biological safety cabinet is functioning as designed, it must be certified on a regular basis (prior to initial use, when moved, after a filter change, or at least annually).

The National Sanitation Foundation (NSF) Standard #49 for Class II (laminar-flow) biohazard cabinetry specifies materials, design and construction, and performance criteria for manufacturers. It also outlines recommended field tests for certifiers. Manufacturers must submit new models for NSF testing. Approved models carry the NSF seal. Only approved cabinets should be purchased and used for work activities involving potentially hazardous biological agents.

Even with correct design, materials, and construction; rigorous testing; and proper placement, biological safety cabinets may not be enough to prevent workplace and environmental exposures. These features along with well-trained, knowledgeable, and conscientious workers are required for optimal safety conditions. Poor work practices can easily cancel the containment features designed into the cabinet, permitting the release of infectious particles into the environment. It is for this reason that worker training is so critical.

Horizontal- or vertical-flow clean benches, which force air out of the front opening into the room, should not be confused with biosafety cabinets. They do not protect workers from exposure; they protect the work product. Therefore, clean benches must not be used for work with materials that are potentially infectious, toxic, allergenic, or irritating.

Centrifugation. Centrifugation can present two serious hazards: mechanical failure and dispersion of aerosols. A mechanical failure such as a broken drive shaft, a faulty bearing, or a damaged rotor can produce not only aerosols but also fast-moving fragments. Even when functioning correctly, a centrifuge is capable of producing hazardous aerosols if improperly operated or when poor laboratory practices are used. Mechanical failure can be minimized by routine maintenance and meticulous observance of the manufacturer's instructions. Generation of aerosols is avoided by using good work practices such as balancing containers and not overfilling them, checking containers for cracks and signs of stress, and checking and greasing O-rings where applicable. Aerosolization is minimized by placing primary containers into centrifuge safety cups and opening rotors and centrifuge containers in a biosafety cabinet.

Laboratory procedures where force or energy acts on cell walls or tissue to disrupt them result in the dispersion of aerosols and splatter. Particular attention should be paid to containment when procedures such as homogenization and sonication are planned. Some manufacturers of homogenizers design models that prevent the release of infectious material and specially gasketed blenders are also available. The use of properly designed and maintained containment equipment is essential in minimizing release of infectious aerosols to the environment.

Work Practices

Work practices—how one actually does the work—are the most important component in preventing occupational exposure. Understanding the concepts of transmission, infectious dose, and route of entry, as well as the potential for various procedures to release infectious material, is critical to the implementation of appropriate containment practices. It becomes straightforward to identify the potential hazard and implement the safeguards necessary to protect workers, when a risk assessment is performed on work activities in advance.

The safeguards known as the seven basic rules of biosafety are summarized here:
- Do not mouth pipette.
- Manipulate infectious fluids carefully to avoid spills and the production of aerosols and droplets.
- Restrict the use of needles and syringes to procedures for

which there are no alternatives; use needles, syringes, and other sharps carefully to avoid self-inoculation; and dispose of sharps in leak- and puncture-resistant containers.

- Use protective laboratory coats and gloves.
- Wash hands after all laboratory activities, after removing gloves, and immediately following contact with infectious materials.
- Decontaminate work surfaces before and after use, and immediately after spills.
- Do not eat, drink, store food, apply cosmetics, or smoke in the laboratory.

Although not a complete listing, these rules represent baseline or minimum practices to be followed. They can be amplified with additional protective clothing such as goggles, full-face shields, or masks when face protection from splatter is needed, and with different types of clothing such as back-fastening gowns, jumpsuits, impervious aprons, sleeve covers, and head and foot covers as suitable. Personal habits such as nail biting and eye and nose rubbing must be avoided because they offer an excellent means for ingesting pathogens and contaminating mucous membranes. The use of good microbiological practices is critical for a worker's own protection and the protection of adjacent colleagues.

Decontamination

The protection of personnel and the environment from exposure to infectious agents and the prevention of contamination of experimental materials by a variable, persistent, and unwanted background of microorganisms is an integral part of good microbiological procedure. Decontamination, the use of physical or chemical means to render materials safe for further handling by reducing the number of organisms present, must be differentiated from disinfection, a process that kills infectious agents outside the body. Neither of these terms should be confused with sterilization, which implies complete elimination or destruction of all forms of microbial life. In the laboratory setting, the application of heat, either moist or dry, is the most effective method of sterilization. Steam at 250°F (121°C) under pressure in an autoclave is the most widely used and convenient method of rapidly achieving sterilization. However, many variables such as time, temperature, configuration and size of load, and permeability and dimensions of containers must be taken into account to successfully sterilize materials.

Chemical disinfectants inactivate microorganisms by one or more of a number of chemical reactions, primarily coagulation and denaturation of protein, lysis, or inactivation of an essential enzyme by either oxidation, binding, or destruction of the enzyme substrate. The level of effectiveness of chemical disinfectants is altered by changes in the concentration of active ingredients, contact duration, temperature, humidity, the concentration of organic matter, and the pH of the material being disinfected. Chemical disinfectants, classified by their active ingredients, include halogens, acids and alkalis, alcohols, heavy-metal salts, quaternary ammonium compounds, phenolics, aldehydes, ketones, and amines.

Specific terminology and classification schemes for chemical disinfectants used by the medical community and licensed by the U.S. EPA can be found in several excellent references and texts (Rutala, 1996; Garner & Favero, 1986; Block, 1991; Favero & Bond, 1991; Klein & Deforest, 1963; NAIN website).

The most frequently used disinfectants in the workplace include sodium hypochlorite (household bleach), isopropyl or ethyl alcohol, iodophors (Wescodyne), and phenolics (Lysol and amphyl). It is essential when choosing a disinfectant to review the manufacturer's literature to determine the disinfectant's efficacy (what microorganisms the disinfectant inactivates) and the recommended application (as an inanimate surface disinfectant, topical disinfectant, surgical scrub, liquid sterilant, or sanitizer). Table 14–F highlights various chemical disinfectants and their uses.

By definition, chemical disinfectants are toxic to viable cells, so it is important that users be familiar with the hazard potential of compounds they use and take necessary precautions to prevent workplace exposure. Compounds such as ethylene oxide, formaldehyde, glutaraldehydes, and concentrated acids and bases require special handling procedures. Consult federal and local OSHA regulations on specific chemical hazards.

Infectious Waste

During the past two decades the management of infectious waste has come under scrutiny from regulatory agencies. Public fear of exposure to AIDS and hepatitis viruses has prompted demands for implementation of rigorous controls for infectious hospital and medical wastes. Most states have promulgated what can only be described as a patchwork of infectious waste regulations. Historically, such wastes were treated by autoclaving before disposal into a sanitary landfill, by incineration, or, in the case of some liquid wastes, by chemical disinfection. Today, these technologies coupled with newer ones (grinding infectious lab wastes in the presence of chemical disinfectants or alkaline hydrolysis at elevated temperature and pressure for disposal of animal carcasses [suitable for large animals]) provide alternative options for waste generators. Local regulations should be consulted for individual state requirements. Federal regulations such as the U.S. DOT Hazardous Materials Regulations, 49 *CFR* 170 series, establish some packaging and volume limitations for the shipment of regulated medical wastes.

TABLE 14–F   Summary of Practical Disinfectants

	Ethylene Oxide	Paraformaldehyde (gas)	Vaporized Hydrogen Peroxide	Quaternary Ammonium Compounds	Phenolic Compounds	Chlorine Compounds	Iodophor Compounds	Alcohol (ethyl or isopropyl)	Formaldehyde (liquid)	Glutaraldehyde	Hydrogen Peroxide (liquid)
Use Parameters											
Concentrations of active ingredients	400–800 mg/L	0.3 g/ft³	2.4 mg/L	0.1–2%	0.2–3%	0.01–5%	0.47%	70–85%	4–8%	2%	6%
Temperature, °C	35–60	>23	4–50								
Relative humidity, %	30–60	>60	<30								
Contact time, min.	105–240	60–180	8–60	10–30	10–30	10–30	10–30	10–30	10–30	10–600	10–600
Effective against*											
Vegetative bacteria	+	+	+	+	+	+	+	+	+	+	+
Bacterial spores	+	+	+			±			±	+	+
Lipoviruses	+	+	+	+	+	+	+	+	+	+	+
Hydrophilic viruses	+	+	+		±	+	±	±	+	+	+
Tubercle bacilli	+	+	+		+	+	+	+	+	+	
HIV	+	+		+	+	+	+	+	+	+	
HBV	+	+			±	+	±	±	+	+	
Applications*											
Contaminated liquid discard						+			±		
Contaminated glassware	±			+	+	+		+	±	+	+
Contaminated instruments	±								±	+	+
Equipment total decontamination	±	+	+								

*A + denotes very positive response; ±, a less positive response; and a blank, a negative response or not applicable.
Source: Adapted from: National Research Council. *Biosafety in the Laboratory: Prudent Practices for the Handling and Disposal of Infectious Materials.* 1989, p. 40; and Vesley D, Lauer JL. *In Laboratory Safety: Principles and Practices*, 1995, pp. 226–227.

Because of the many misconceptions regarding hospital waste, the CDC published the following statement:

There is no epidemiologic evidence that most hospital waste is any more infective than residential waste. Moreover, there is no epidemiological evidence that hospital waste has caused disease in the community as the result of improper disposal. Therefore, identifying wastes for which special precautions are indicated is largely a matter of judgment about the relative risk of disease transmission. The most practical approach to the management of infectious waste is to identify those wastes with a reasonable potential to cause infection during handling and disposal, and for which some special precautions appear prudent. Hospital wastes for which special precautions appear prudent include microbiology laboratory waste, pathology waste, and blood specimens and blood products. Although any item that has had contact with blood, exudates, or secretions may be potentially infective, it is not usually considered practical or necessary to treat all such wastes as infective. (CDC, 1987b)

Spill management. The management of spills in the laboratory usually consists of flooding the contaminated area with liquid disinfectant, being careful not to generate aerosols, allowing adequate contact time with disinfectant, cleaning up the spill, reapplying fresh disinfectant, and final cleanup. Protective clothing is always worn. When spills involve large volumes of infectious agents, personnel should leave the area until aerosols have settled before cleanup is begun. Variations of this procedure are used for hospital spills, where emphasis is placed on first absorbing and cleaning the spill and then disinfecting the area. The reason for the difference is the concentration of the microorganisms present in the spill and the likelihood that the general public may be exposed and inadvertently spread contamination elsewhere.

Summary

Containment of microorganisms in laboratories (or other workplaces) is critical to the health of workers and to the community. Engineering controls such as safety equipment and facility design are important because, except for monitoring and appropriate maintenance, they do not require worker input to be effective. Despite this, experience indicates that the use of worker-initiated workplace controls in the form of good work practices and carefully executed techniques is critically important in minimizing biohazardous exposures in the workplace.

Biorisk Program Management

Laboratory biorisk management ideally involves a multitude of stakeholders, including regulatory authorities, the public, and the scientific community and should help establish trust and a safe and secure workplace while enabling the continued progress of science. The level of regulation by authorities should be proportional to the risks. To achieve the appropriate level of regulation, there needs to be a good understanding across sectors and communities to give a meaningful level of control but also mesh well with daily operations.

Managing laboratory biorisks is a complex, multivariate problem, involving many interrelated processes. Management systems are designed to address such risk management problems across many fields, such as the chemical, aerospace, and mining industries. Common management systems include ISO 9000, a quality management system to help organizations continually improve the quality of their product, customer service, and productivity; ISO 14000, an environmental management system to help organizations conduct their work in a way that minimizes impact on the environment and continually improves their environmental performance; and OHSAS 18000, an occupational health and safety management system to help organizations continually improve health and safety within their activities. Recognizing the uniqueness of laboratory biorisks, the biosafety community came together to develop the CWA Laboratory Biorisk Management Standard. This standard is a management system approach to enable an organization to identify, monitor, and control the laboratory biosafety and biosecurity aspects of its activities effectively. As laboratories begin to implement this a new standard, useful lessons can be learned from the implementation of other management systems to help determine how such a system can be implemented effectively in a biological research environment. An effective management system approach is built on the concept of continual improvement through a cycle of planning, implementing, reviewing, and improving processes that an organization takes to meet goals. To review and improve processes, performance indicators must be defined for the organization's system. This is one of the major challenges to effective implementation of any biorisk management system.

In most settings, incidents and accidents involving biological agents or materials are very rare (but they could have major consequences), so incident rates, a classical performance indicator in general safety, typically lack statistical robustness when applied to biorisk. In many places, the reporting of small incidents that had no negative consequences, such as minor spills and small injuries without direct exposure (near misses), is not required, not informative, or not effective. The best performance indicators should not only be quantifiable and usable as monitoring tools on a dashboard, but should also provide a way to evaluate the management program qualitatively to identify needed improvements.

Understanding all of the elements relevant to a biorisk management system is the first step in developing a sustainable program. These include but are not limited to policy and general management, assessment and planning, administrative controls, operational controls, reporting, monitoring, response, review, and revision. Beyond the specific risk mitigation measures implemented, some specific typical components include a biosafety officer or specialist, an institutional biosafety committee (IBC), written policies and procedures, an occupational health program for potentially vulnerable employees, training, and emergency response plans. Biorisk management programs vary markedly depending on the size of the institution and its activities, such as education, industrial research and development, manufacturing, medical patient care, or food service.

Without strong administrative and financial support, even the best biorisk management program has little chance of succeeding. For example, in the absence of support from upper management it is impossible to implement committee decisions and biosafety policies that affect the entire institution. Inadequate financial support of biosafety activities is equally problematic. Program financing usually comes from either "fee for service" or institutional overhead. Each has its advantages and its drawbacks, but it is important to prevent a situation where health services and safety consulting services are not accessed because of their cost.

Biosafety Officer

As institutional activities vary, so do the responsibilities and duties of the biosafety officer (also known as biosafety specialist or biorisk management advisor). This person must interact successfully with the scientific and technical community thus a strong scientific background is essential. Technical knowledge in general microbiology, molecular biology, infectious diseases, public health, sanitation, industrial hygiene, environmental microbiology, and epidemiology is extremely useful. A thorough understanding of workplace procedures and equipment becomes invaluable when performing a risk assessment on a work activity or designing workable containment for experiments. Without such experience and an appropriate academic background, a health and safety professional will find it difficult to interact with scientific and technical staff and provide needed biosafety assistance.

Because it is often necessary to receive input not only from the scientific staff but also from the institutional biosafety committee, the administration, and numerous other stakeholders, the biosafety professional must be able to lead diverse groups to a consensus. Biosafety officers work with architects, contractors, facility engineers, commissioning agents, medical staff, animal facility personnel, and mainte-

nance and custodial services, to mention only a few groups. The ability to communicate at reasonably high levels with individuals who represent each of these groups as well as with scientists and technical staff probably outweighs in importance every other qualification that characterizes an effective biosafety officer.

Institutional Biosafety Committee

The original requirement to empanel the Institutional Biosafety Committee (IBC) is found in the first publication of the "NIH Guidelines for Research Involving Recombinant DNA Molecules" in 1976. NIH mandated that institutions receiving NIH funding conduct recombinant DNA research in compliance with these guidelines. Every such institution was required to appoint an IBC as the local body to enforce the guidelines. Committees were charged to review and approve research activities involving recombinant technology for compliance with the guidelines and to oversee the safe conduct of work. Initially, many institutions chose to have their IBCs oversee only work activities involving the use of recombinant technology; consequently, work with infectious agents was not scrutinized. Perhaps surprisingly, IBC or similar committee review of research involving infectious agents without a recombinant DNA component is still not a legal or agency requirement. Nevertheless, today most biosafety committees are charged by their institutions with review and approval of all biohazardous research and other activities, and setting policy and procedures for all activities involving infectious agents, materials, and animals, in addition to review and approval of experiments using recombinant technology.

As defined by the NIH, IBCs that oversee activities involving recombinant DNA must have no fewer than five members selected for their experience and expertise in the technology and their capability to assess the safety of the work and any potential risk to public health and the environment. At least two members must be chosen from outside the institution to represent the interests of the community. As institutions diversify, committee responsibilities broaden—NIH requires the IBC to include membership expertise to evaluate every type of research involving recombinant DNA that is conducted at the institution. Thus, in addition to a strong core of microbiologists and molecular biologists, experts in other disciplines, such as animal resources, plant pathology, and human gene therapy, may be needed. IBCs at large, diverse institutions may include more than 25 members.

IBCs must interact with other review bodies within the institution. The research use of experimentally infected animals and biohazardous species, such as nonhuman primates, alters the safety considerations to be addressed and adds more questions, so institutional animal care and use committees (IACUCs) must work closely with the IBC and the biosafety officer. When research activities involve the development of treatments for human diseases or the use of other types of hazardous materials, the IBC must interact with institutional (human subject) review boards (IRBs), radiation safety committees (RSCs) and radiation safety officers, and chemical safety committees (CSCs) and chemical hygiene officers in order to evaluate research proposals. In the interest of facilitating the timely review of work, it is imperative that the committees work together effectively.

Biosafety Manual

One of the more challenging tasks of a health and safety professional is getting information about health and safety policy, regulations, safety, and security practices into the workplace. A biosafety manual is one accepted method, although not the only acceptable method, of handling the communication of information and policy.

The CDC Third National Symposium on Biosafety in 1994 included a workshop covering biosafety manuals and their use and maintenance. Most of the health and safety professionals attending the workshop agreed that it is useful to have some type of biosafety manual. On the other hand, many participants indicated that their institution had manuals but that these manuals were not used, and for a variety of reasons. Some reasons noted were that the manuals were difficult to use or out of date, employees did not know of their existence, or policies outlined in the manual lacked administrative and supervisory support. To help avoid some of these problems, including devoting excessive time to writing a manual that is destined to be underused, some preparation and planning is helpful. Answers to the following questions will help define the type of document appropriate for an institution:

• Why have a biosafety manual?
• What is the manual supposed to accomplish? (What should its scope be?)
• What support is needed for acceptance?
• Who should write it?
• What should be included?
• Should the manual be printed or available electronically?
• How should the manual be distributed to users?
• How can the document be kept current?

The answer to the last question will probably determine the long-term success or failure of the institutional biosafety manual. No single type of biosafety document is suitable for all work settings; at least five manual formats were identified at the CDC workshop. They included a formal, lengthy, administrative manual that covers all safety topics; a user manual or handbook that has safety information specific to a worksite such as a laboratory; a complete reference docu-

ment on one subject, such as a bloodborne pathogen exposure control plan; a worksite procedure-specific manual for a defined group of people (waste handlers, glass washers); and a booklet or binder of work practices with all standard operating procedures. Manuals need to be updated frequently and now are usually included on the institution's computer network. However, availability online does not make periodic updates very much easier, and the institution should perhaps be prepared to explore alternative methods if frequent review and updating of the biosafety manual prove too cumbersome. Further, biosafety manuals must also never be used as a substitute for a formal training program.

Occupational Health Surveillance Program

When developing an occupational health surveillance program for workers potentially exposed to infectious agents or other hazardous materials, decisions must be made regarding the focus of the program and whether it will include acute exposure-related problems and disease-prevention and wellness programs. Most occupational health surveillance programs have four objectives:

1. To provide a mechanism to detect job-related illnesses
2. To determine the adequacy of protective equipment and procedures and verify that hazardous agents are not being released into the general environment
3. To establish baseline preexposure status
4. To identify preexisting conditions that would put an employee at increased risk

Health surveillance programs vary greatly, depending on the microorganisms being handled, the nature of the technical activities being conducted, the volume or concentration of material, and available medical facilities. Exposures to toxic chemicals, radionuclides, physiologically active biological and pharmaceutical products, animal allergens, and physical stresses also require consideration.

Some possible occupational health surveillance program activities include taking medical and occupational histories, conducting physical examinations, laboratory testing, immunization, and serum storage, where indicated. If possible, it is desirable to include the in-house or on-call medical services of occupational medicine and infectious disease specialists, or to integrate the health surveillance program with the institutional Occupational Health Services clinic, if applicable.

Work with infectious agents requires the evaluation of specific immunizations. Although there is no question that persons working with human blood and related products should receive hepatitis B immunization, there may be reasons to waive immunization with some less effective vaccines. An infectious disease specialist physician should be consulted on such matters. Recommendations for the use of vaccines are included in the agent summary statements in Section VII of the BMBL, and a comprehensive listing of immunoprophylaxis for personnel at risk is found in the NRC resource *Biosafety in the Laboratory*. See the Bibliography for more information.

Serum banking, another component of a medical surveillance program, has less support now than in the past. Although such a resource can provide potentially useful information regarding work-related exposures, this benefit must be weighed against such basic considerations as whether adequate facilities and technical support for long-term storage exist. Decisions regarding serum storage and testing should be based on agents handled, availability of reliable tests, likelihood that infection will produce a serological change that would not be detected without comparison to a baseline sample in exposed persons, and the ability to maintain a secure storage facility. Results of employee medical evaluations must remain confidential, with information being released only with the employee's consent.

Considerations involving host susceptibility must be taken into account, and some of these have been mentioned earlier in the risk assessment section. The employee, the employer, and the physician should work together in the decision-making process regarding employee health issues.

Training

Training and raising awareness are the keys to making a biorisk management program sustainable—all stakeholders need some level of training. Management and leadership must understand regulatory obligations, program objectives, and necessary resources. Individuals working with biohazards must have the appropriate lab level skills. Biosafety officers must understand the details of the biorisk management program, in addition to topics appropriate for management and for laboratory workers. All persons whose work involves the handling of infectious organisms or materials must receive adequate information and education to enable them to work safely, securely, and responsibly. Biorisk management programs should include a mechanism to provide relevant information to employees at all stages of their employment (new, altered work tasks, and long term) and must include periodic updates (annual refreshers).

Where regulations mandate training, such as the OSHA bloodborne pathogen standard or the Select Agent Regulations, training content may be specified and written plans required. Many regulations address frequency of training, record-keeping requirements, and qualifications of trainers.

Training materials developed for work with infectious materials must include a description of the biology of the agent(s), including

- symptoms of the disease;
- a review of the operations and procedures, with emphasis on potential sources of exposures and means of control;
- the correct use of containment equipment when applicable;
- a review of acceptable work practices;
- decontamination methods and waste disposal; and
- emergency procedures.

Equally important, personnel must be made aware of the human factors (such as fatigue, inattentiveness, and haste) that predispose workers to accidents. Employees should understand that although the employer must provide appropriate facilities and equipment to conduct work safely, securely, and responsibly, the employees are responsible for following the practices and procedures in order to protect themselves, their colleagues, and the community.

One challenge of biorisk training is to provide appropriate and factual information that is geared to the language and educational level of the employees. Information is more readily received when it is presented in an interesting or creative format and when it is periodically updated. Although trainers now have access to an excellent collection of tools such as professionally produced videotapes and interactive computer educational programs, it is critical that training not be a solitary or senescent event.

Ideal Biorisk Management Programs

The ideal biorisk management program has strong administrative support from upper management and is funded adequately so that worker safety is not compromised. If the volume of microbiological activity and the hazard associated with the microorganisms handled warrant it, an institutional biosafety professional should handle health and safety considerations. If the volume of work is low and the organisms handled are of minimal or low risk, it may be more cost effective to retain a biosafety professional consultant to work with the health and safety staff. When clinical activities are involved, infection control practitioners are an excellent resource for safety departments. In hospital settings, infection control practitioners may oversee clinical laboratory biosafety matters using policies approved by an infection control committee.

Institutional biosafety committee policies and decisions must have institutional support at the highest level. IBC members must be knowledgeable, make informed and realistic decisions, and have credibility among their peers so that committee decisions will be accepted and implemented. IBC business and, ultimately, research activity are facilitated by timely attention to pertinent matters and, where needed, interaction with other institutional bodies such as animal resources, IACUCs, RSCs, CSCs, and IRBs.

No single biosafety manual or training program is appropriate for all work settings. Rather, institutions must strive to prepare material and training that provide their employees with pertinent material in a format that will be understood and utilized. It is the challenge of every safety professional to develop these educational components so that they are not only relevant but interesting.

For the occupational health program to be effective and used, providers must offer services as required by law, be familiar with workplace activities, be responsive to the needs of employees, and interact with the IBC and biosafety officer. Employees who are indifferent to occupational health programs, such as immunization and serum storage, are more likely to use them if, where possible and practical, services are performed at the worksite.

ASSESSING PERFORMANCE

Although there is often urgency to develop and implement programs and controls, the need to assess their efficacy following implementation is sometimes overlooked. Such a review is imperative to be assured that the safety practices have been incorporated into work activities and that they are performing as designed to reduce the risks to an acceptable level. Many recent articles in the safety literature advocate the use of proactive measures (e.g., safety climate, hazard identification, and observed percent safe behavior) that focus on current safety activities to ascertain system success rather than system failure. In combination, both approaches can help organizations to ascertain the effects of their safety programs. Ideally, at least two independent measures are used to assess performance or to gauge program effectiveness.

Use of Audits to Identify Problem Areas
Self-audits of required safety practices provide a measure of compliance achievement. In work environments where hazardous aerosols are generated, such as agricultural processing facilities, one would begin by monitoring for compliance with personal protective equipment and clothing requirements. In laboratory settings the criteria for the designated biosafety level(s) can be used for the critical elements of the audit. Routine operating procedures should include a safety check, for example, to determine that equipment (such as a biosafety cabinet or hematocrit centrifuge) is functioning properly or that work surface disinfectants and spill kits are on hand. When agents requiring higher containment are handled, ventilation system function must be checked and actual work practices and techniques reviewed to ensure containment.

Regular safety audits should be carried out at least annually (quarterly or semiannually is preferred) by designated safety specialists accompanied by the laboratory supervisor. Deficiencies can be pointed out and abated during the inspection. A written report, suggesting corrective actions, can be sent to the laboratory supervisor, who should report progress on remediation within a designated period of time. Notification of biohazards in use and a list of associated personnel should be obtained from the laboratory supervisor. The inspection program can be used to review information on the facility, work, and workers and serve as a reminder to update the biohazard database.

Annual Biorisk Review
Requiring each responsible supervisor to undergo an annual renewal of their registration to do their specific biohazard work is one tool to help remind them to review the work in progress and keep the information updated. Pathogen or biohazard registration programs used by many institutions provide supervisors with a form to expedite such an update.

Incident/Accident Statistics
Although small statistical changes in incident/accident figures do not usually indicate real deficiencies in a biosafety program, some institutions judge the status of their safety program only by a statistical review of changes in OSHA-recordable incidents.

The positive changes brought about through education and training in preventive methods can be measured with specific outcome audits. For example, in determining the effect of training and safety equipment on the number of needlestick incidents, trends in reports on such injuries show the cost-benefit of the changes. Observations of increases in such injuries, or the reporting of sentinel events (events whose single occurrence is of sufficient concern to trigger systematic response) highlight the need for intervention efforts. Such events can be used as tools for continuous quality improvement if action limits (the criteria for intervention) are defined. Work practices must be assessed for efficacy so that protective practices can be reinforced and unsafe practices altered.

CURRENT TOPICS IN BIOSAFETY

Bloodborne Pathogens
Hepatitis B virus has been the most significant occupational infector of health care and laboratory personnel during the past 50 years. This fact, coupled with the identification of the human immunodeficiency virus (HIV), the causative agent of acquired immune deficiency syndrome (AIDS),

prompted the development and implementation of measures that would promote worker protection. In 1991, OSHA pioneered the regulation of work environments associated with potentially infectious microorganisms with its publication of a standard regulating occupational exposure to bloodborne pathogens. In addition to the standard, OSHA continues to publish new compliance assistance instructions for their enforcement officers that provide useful information for those covered by the regulation.

The standard applies not only to the health care community, but to all occupations (such as emergency responders, law enforcement officers, and morticians) in which there is a potential for exposure to human blood. Bloodborne pathogens are defined as microorganisms that may be present in human blood and body fluids and are capable of causing disease in human beings. While HIV and hepatitis B and hepatitis C viruses are the bloodborne pathogens most frequently associated with occupational infections, other bloodborne microorganisms associated with diseases, such as syphilis and malaria, have also been responsible for work-related infections.

Hepatitis B Virus
Epidemiology. Hepatitis B virus (HBV) now infects less than 50,000 persons in the general U.S. population annually, with an estimated 1,012 of these infections attributed to high-risk health care workers, who have frequent occupational contact with blood. Among these 1,012 infected health care workers there will be an estimated 250 cases of clinical hepatitis, 50 HBV carriers, 13 cases of chronic hepatitis, and 22 deaths. Prior to licensure of the hepatitis B vaccine in 1981, an estimated 17,000 health care workers were infected annually with HBV. The estimated incidence of HBV among health care workers in 1983 was threefold higher (386/100,000) than the incidence in the general population (122/100,000). By 1995 the incidence of HBV infections among health care workers decreased by more than 95 percent (9.1/100,000) and was fivefold lower than the incidence of HBV infection in the general population (50/100,000), which had decreased by 60 percent. The periods of greatest decline in infections occurred between 1986 and 1987, when the recombinant DNA vaccines were licensed, and from 1992 to 1993 when the OSHA bloodborne pathogen standard was implemented.

Disease. Hepatitis B virus, a DNA virus and member of the *Hepadnaviridae* family, infects liver cells and has the potential to cause serious liver disease. The incubation period (the time between exposure to the virus and onset of illness) ranges from two to six months, and at least 50 percent of the cases of acute infection are asymptomatic. For the remainder, disease varies from mild to severe or even fatal.

Symptoms of clinical illness may include loss of appetite, rash, fever, abdominal discomfort, nausea and vomiting, jaundice, extreme fatigue, anorexia, fever, and joint pain. The majority of infections in adults are self-limited with symptoms lasting several weeks. Most infected persons clear their virus and have lifelong immunity to reinfection; however, 5 to 10 percent of persons with acute HBV infection develop chronic infection and generally remain infected for their lifetime. Some with chronic infection may be asymptomatic carriers, while others develop liver inflammation, cirrhosis, or hepatocellular carcinoma. Persons with chronic HBV infection have an estimated 20 percent lifetime risk of dying of cirrhosis and a 6 percent risk of dying of hepatocellular carcinoma. A safe effective recombinant vaccine is available and immunization of high-risk health care workers is strongly recommended. The CDC also makes recommendations for postexposure prophylaxis for percutaneous and permucosal exposure to HBV.

Transmission. In occupational settings, hepatitis B virus is transmitted by parenteral inoculation and mucous membrane and nonintact skin exposure to human blood, blood products, bloody body fluids, semen, vaginal secretions, and saliva. Airborne transmission has been postulated, but true airborne transmission of HBV probably does not occur; rather transmission occurs as the result of direct contact with droplet-contaminated surfaces. Sexual and perinatal transmission occurs in the general population. Persons exposed to HBV-contaminated needlesticks have a 6 to 30 percent risk of HBV infection.

Hepatitis C Virus
Epidemiology. Hepatitis C virus (HCV), an RNA virus in the *Flaviviridae* family, is the primary etiologic agent of parenterally transmitted non-A, non-B hepatitis. HCV is the most common chronic bloodborne infection in the United States. There are an estimated 3.9 million infected persons nationwide with 8,000–10,000 associated deaths each year. There were 16,000 cases of HCV among health care workers worldwide in 2000, including orthopedic, general, and oral surgeons, which is significantly lower than that of HBV infection.

Disease. Persons with acute HCV infection have either asymptomatic or mild clinical disease: 60–70 percent have no apparent symptoms, 20–30 percent may have jaundice, and 10–20 percent may have nonspecific symptoms such as anorexia, malaise, or abdominal pain. The average incubation period is six to seven weeks.

Following acute infection, 15 to 25 percent of persons appear to resolve their infection. However, chronic HCV infection with persistent viremia develops in most persons (75–85%). The course of chronic liver disease is usually insidious, progressing slowly without symptoms or physical signs in the majority of patients during the first two or more decades after infection. Frequently this status goes unrecognized until the person is identified as HCV-positive during blood-donor screening. Studies indicate that cirrhosis develops in 10 to 20 percent of persons with chronic disease older than 20–30 years, and hepatocellular carcinoma in 1–5 percent. An HCV vaccine is currently not available and antiviral therapy is recommended for patients with chronic HCV who are at greatest risk for progression to cirrhosis.

Transmission. HCV is transmitted primarily through large and repeated direct percutaneous exposure to blood. Work-related infections have resulted from HCV-contaminated needlesticks or cuts with sharp objects and blood splashed to mucous membranes. The average incidence of anti-HCV seroconversion following needlesticks or sharps exposures from an HCV-positive source is 1.8 percent (range 0–7%). Risk factors associated with transmission include blood transfusion, injection-drug use, employment in patient care or clinical laboratory work, exposure to a sex partner or household member who has a history of hepatitis, exposure to multiple sex partners, and low socioeconomic level. With the advent of blood screening technologies, transfusion-related infections are now rare. Injection-drug use currently accounts for most of the HCV transmission in the United States.

Human Immunodeficiency Virus

Epidemiology. Through the end of 1998, the CDC had received reports of 188 cases of documented or possible occupationally acquired human immunodeficiency virus (HIV) infection among health care workers. A documented means of occupational exposure has been identified in 54 of the cases and 25 of these individuals have developed AIDS (acquired immunodeficiency syndrome). The remaining 134 workers were classified as possible occupational HIV exposures because neither the date of infection nor its source could be documented. Forty-six of the documented cases resulted from percutaneous exposures, five from mucocutaneous (mucous membrane and/or skin injury) exposures, two from dual percutaneous and mucocutaneous exposure, and one from an unknown source. Forty-nine of the 54 documented seroconversions resulted from exposure to blood from HIV patients, three to concentrated virus, one to visibly bloody fluid, and one to an unspecified fluid. By occupation, 19 laboratory workers and 22 nurses sustained the greatest number of documented seroconversions. The last confirmed case of occupationally acquired HIV was reported in 1999.

Disease. HIV is an RNA virus in the family *Retroviridae*, subfamily *Lentivirinea*. Lentiviruses encompass agents able to cause chronic infections with slowly progressive neurological impairment. Persons infected with HIV may remain healthy for years before the virus, which infects the cells of the immune system, ultimately destroys that system. AIDS represents the later clinical stage of HIV infection. Following infection with HIV, persons may be asymptomatic or within several weeks to several months develop an acute self-limited flu-like illness that lasts for one to two weeks. Because symptoms disappear and individuals often remain healthy for a number of years, many infected individuals are unaware of their HIV status. Presently there is no vaccine to prevent infection with HIV nor is there a cure for AIDS. A number of anti-retroviral therapies are currently available to help keep HIV replication under control. Guidelines for treatment of exposed health care personnel have been published by the CDC.

Transmission. HIV is transmitted through exposure to human blood and certain body fluids. In the work setting, infection can result from parenteral, nonintact skin, or mucous membrane (eyes, nose, and mouth) exposure to contaminated materials. Data from needlestick studies indicate that persons exposed to HIV-contaminated needles have a 0.3 percent chance of seroconversion to HIV and a 0.09 percent seroconversion rate as the result of mucous membrane exposures.

Epidemiological data on the consequence of parenteral exposure to HIV, HBV, and HCV indicate that one of the most critical workplace controls is the reduction of sharps-related incidents.

OSHA Bloodborne Pathogens Standard

The intent of the OSHA Bloodborne Pathogens Standard is to prevent or minimize parenteral, nonintact skin, and mucous membrane exposure to human blood and body fluids in the workplace. To achieve this goal, the standard requires employers whose employees are potentially exposed as the result of their work activities to implement an administrative mechanism for compliance and a series of workplace controls to prevent or minimize exposure. Employers must develop an exposure determination plan (a systematic means of determining which of their employees is at risk from occupational exposure to bloodborne pathogens) and an exposure control plan that outlines how their institution will meet the standard requirements. Compliance methods specific to an institution or facility are included in the exposure control plan.

The infection control concept of universal precaution—that all human blood and certain human body fluids are to be treated as if known to be infectious for HIV, HBV, HCV, and other bloodborne pathogens—is a key component in prevention of work-related exposure. The OSHA standard outlines potentially infectious materials (including HIV-, HBV-, and HCV-infected cells, tissues, and animals) and specifies control measures that will prevent or minimize work-related infections.

The standard mandates

- engineering controls (needle-disposal containers and equipment for reducing aerosols and splatter);
- work practice controls with special emphasis on personal protective clothing and equipment (such as gloves and face and eye protection) and hand-washing;
- sharps management procedures (needle-handling procedures such as not resheathing needles by hand and the use of rigid sharps-disposal containers);
- culture and specimen labeling and transport requirements;
- housekeeping (including disinfection, disposal of infectious waste, and spill management);
- handling of contaminated laundry;
- communication of hazard to employees (training); and
- general workplace practices and procedures.

Biosafety level 2 (BSL-2) practices are required for laboratory activities involving clinical materials. Work may be performed on the open bench as long as procedures do not generate significant aerosols. Aerosol-generating procedures must be performed in a BSC or otherwise contained. The BMBL provides guidance (agent summary statements) for handling hepatitis viruses and HIV (retroviruses).

Immunization is a critical component of the bloodborne pathogen hazard control. There is currently no means of immunizing people against HIV or HCV, but an effective vaccine for HBV is available. Employers must offer hepatitis B vaccination to employees whose work activities bring them into contact with bloodborne pathogens, as well as document their refusal to be immunized. Some latitude on up-front HBV immunization is given to employers whose employees render first aid only as a collateral duty, not as part of their job description. Employers must also provide for the immediate and follow-up medical and counseling needs of employees who sustain an occupational exposure.

Because there is widespread agreement among the medical community and other regulated workplaces that indeed workers are at risk from bloodborne pathogens, significant progress has been made toward reducing the hazard of bloodborne pathogens in the workplace.

Tuberculosis

Tuberculosis (TB) is a bacterial disease, caused by *M. tuberculosis* complex (*M. tb*), that is responsible for morbidity and mortality worldwide. This complex consists of *M. tuberculosis* and *M. africanum*, for which man is the primary source of infection, and *M. bovis*, primarily from cattle; it occurs only rarely in primates, badgers, and other animals.

Epidemiology

Tuberculosis, common outside the United States, is estimated to affect one-third of the world's population. There are 8.8 million new cases of TB each year. If prevention and control methods are not improved, during this decade approximately 90 million new cases of TB can be expected worldwide. Transmission of most infections occurs prior to the initiation of antituberculosis therapy. The emergence of drug-resistant TB is also being reported worldwide and is a serious problem in the United States. In the United States, only 10 percent of *M. tb* strains were resistant to one or more drugs in the years prior to 1984. Since 1988, there have been numerous outbreaks caused by multiple drug-resistant strains of TB (MDR-TB). The mortality rate is approximately the same (40–60%) in those with MDR-TB, despite treatment, as in TB cases that go untreated.

The number of TB cases had declined by 74 percent between 1953 and 1984, but decline slowed in 1985, and new cases of TB in the United States began to increase significantly. There was an increase in the cases reported in every racial or ethnic group except non-Hispanic whites and American Indians/Alaskan natives from 1985 to 1992. The CDC has estimated that there are between 10 and 15 million asymptomatic, infected people in the United States. These facts indicate that the routine processing of sputum in high-risk urban areas is a potential source of laboratory-acquired infection.

Risk assessment and epidemiological studies show that the prevalence of TB is not distributed evenly throughout a population. Some groups are at higher risk of TB because of increased risk of exposure; others have a higher risk of progressing to active TB following infection. Those with increased risk of exposure include the foreign-born from areas with high prevalence of TB (Asia, Africa, the Caribbean, and Latin America); the medically underserved, such as African Americans, Hispanics, Asians and Pacific Islanders, American Indians, and Alaskan Natives; homeless persons; current or former correctional-facility inmates; alcoholics; intravenous drug users; and the elderly. Those who are at higher risk of progressing to active TB from latent infection include those recently infected (within the previous two years); young children (less than 4 years old); persons with fibrotic lesions that show up on chest radiographs; and persons with certain underlying medical conditions such as HIV infection, silicosis, gastrectomy or jejunoileal bypass, being 10 percent below ideal body weight, chronic renal failure with renal dialysis, diabetes mellitus, immuno-suppression from receipt of high-dose corticosteroid or other immunosuppressive therapy, and some malignancies.

Much of the current increase in cases of tuberculosis has been attributed to HIV-infected people, particularly in Africa and Southeast Asia. Among persons coinfected with HIV and *M. tuberculosis*, the risk for developing active TB is increased because of the concurrent immunosuppression induced by HIV. The annual risk of progression into active TB among individuals infected with both HIV and TB is 5–15 percent, depending on the degree of immunosuppression. In 1989, the CDC Advisory Committee on the Elimination of Tuberculosis recommended that HIV-infected individuals be screened for active TB as well as latent TB and be offered appropriate curative or preventive therapy. Current studies indicate that HIV-positive TB carriers are no more likely than their HIV-negative counterparts to spread TB to close contacts.

Transmission

Tuberculosis is usually transmitted by the inhalation of infectious droplet nuclei suspended in the air, from coughing, sneezing, singing, or talking, by an individual who has a pulmonary or laryngeal TB infection. Prolonged close contact with an infectious person may expose individuals such as family members or coworkers and lead to their infection. Although direct exposure to mucous membranes or invasion through breaks in the skin can result in infection, it is extremely rare. With the exception of laryngeal infections, extrapulmonary TB infection, even with a draining sinus, is usually not communicable. Bovine tuberculosis, caused by *M. bovis*, results from drinking unpasteurized milk or dairy products from infected cattle, although there have also been cases in which farmers or animal handlers have been exposed to infectious aerosols.

Disease Symptoms and Progress

Symptoms of TB include fatigue, fever, and weight loss early in the disease. Hoarseness, cough, and hemoptysis (blood-tinged sputum) appear later as the disease is localized in the respiratory tract.

It can take from one to four months from the time of infection to a demonstrable pulmonary lesion or a positive tuberculin reaction. Thus it is understandable that the transmission of most infections occurs prior to the initiation of antituberculosis therapy.

The initial infection with the tubercle bacillus is usually asymptomatic, but in a few weeks sensitivity to tuberculin (a purified protein derivative of *M. tuberculosis* used for skin testing) usually develops, as manifested in a positive skin test. Progression to active disease is most likely in the first two years after infection, but can occur any time throughout life. Those who are actively shedding viable tubercle bacilli in sputum, including those who are inadequately treated, are a risk to others, but children with primary TB do not usually infect others. When effective treatment is given, communicability can be eliminated in several days or a few weeks, when tubercle bacilli are no longer visible in an acid-fast smear of patient sputum.

The internal lesions that develop in the respiratory tract usually heal with minor or no change, except for occasional calcifications in pulmonary or tracheobronchial lymph nodes. There is a lifelong risk of reactivation in 95 percent of those infected who enter this latent stage. In about five percent of those infected, the initial infection progresses to pulmonary TB or bacteremia with dissemination to other organs. Infants, adolescents, and young adults have a more serious outcome from the initial infection in tuberculosis. Tuberculosis is not very infectious in terms of unit of time exposed to the bacillus; that is, brief exposure rarely results in infection. However, long terms of exposure to chronic, asymptomatic cases, as with household contacts, lead to an overall 30-percent risk of infection and a one- to five-percent risk of active disease within a year. Reinfection or reactivation of the latent disease leads to progressive pulmonary tuberculosis, which can lead to death within two years if untreated. The lifetime risk of developing active disease for those infected as infants is estimated at 10 percent.

Risk of Occupational Exposure

The key element in protecting workers from the risk of occupational exposure is risk assessment. The current CDC guidelines for protection of workers from tuberculosis address the health care industry. Risk assessment procedures can identify settings (bronchoscopy performed on suspected TB patients, autopsies on deceased patients who had active TB) in which a higher level of protection is needed, and if so, the situation should be documented and the protection implemented. A risk assessment can be done at any worksite, after which the appropriate administrative and engineering controls and personal respiratory protection can be implemented.

In the workplace, health care workers, including nursing home and emergency personnel, who provide patient care are at risk of aerosol-borne infectious droplet nuclei from patients. Those who work in clinical, research, or production facilities with *M. tuberculosis*, *M. africanum*, or *M. bovis* are at risk from contact and percutaneous routes as well as from inhalation of droplet nuclei in aerosols produced during common work procedures. Others who provide service to high-risk individuals such as those in shelters and prisons are also at increased risk.

In 1995, CDC published a report on the risk for occupational exposure to TB. Although there are certain recognized limitations to this study, it is encouraging to find published data on the relationship between occupational exposure and illness. Of the 2,206 deaths from TB from 1979 to 1990, 1,024 (46.4%) were in workers in 21 groups that met the criteria for occupational risk. These groups were further categorized into four risk groups: high potential for exposure to TB, potential for exposure to silica, low socioeconomic status (SES), occupation without other recognized risk factors, and unknown risk factors. It should be noted that the high-risk groups include funeral directors and health care service workers, such as nursing aides, orderlies, and attendants. A list of the occupations in the four risk groups and the proportionate TB mortality rates is included in the CDC (1995) reference.

Mycobacteria have shown to be very adaptable to drug regimens and consequently, several multi-drug resistant strains have evolved to make treatment that much more difficult. In 2009, the CDC released a plan published in the *Morbidity and Mortality Weekly Report* (MMWR) designed to combat tuberculosis. Unlike the emphasis before, they initiated a global effort since TB care and the lack of established regimens overseas may have contributed to the evolution of exotic drug resistant strains. This has led to virtually untreatable strains of *M. tuberculosis* such as extensively drug-resistant (XDR) TB. XDR-TB is defined as MDR-TB that also is resistant to the most effective second-line therapeutic drugs used commonly to treat MDR-TB: fluoroquinolones and at least one of three injectable second-line drugs used to treat TB (amikacin, kanamycin, or capreomycin). XDR-TB has been identified in all regions of the world, including the United States.

Employee Protection from Exposure

The 5th edition of BMBL provides few instructions on the use of respirators with microbial pathogens. Guidance for respirator selection is not included. Respirators are just one of the primary barriers to be considered when working outside a biological safety cabinet at biosafety level 3 (BSL-3). Respiratory protection is specifically recommended when the worker is in a room containing an infected animal. Even at vertebrate animal biosafety level 2 (ABSL-2), respirators should be considered whenever procedures with a high potential for creating aerosols are done, i.e., vigorous shaking or mixing, necropsy, intranasal inoculation, and harvesting infected tissues. When working at ABSL-3, respiratory protection is to be worn by all personnel entering animal rooms and for all work that is not done within a BSC or other primary barrier. Personnel working at BSL-4 or ABSL-4 may use a one-piece positive-pressure suit, ventilated

by a life support system with HEPA filtration. Those using these suits should be in a respiratory protection program.

The Center for Infectious Disease, Infection Control Branch of the CDC issued *Guidelines for Preventing the Transmission of* Mycobacterium tuberculosis *in Health Care Facilities*. The CDC recommended the use of respirators by health care workers when entering the room of a patient in isolation for TB or suspected TB, when present during cough-inducing or aerosol-generating procedures on such patients, and in other settings where administrative and engineering controls cannot be ensured. These would include emergency transport, urgent surgical care, or urgent dental care of such patients. These guidelines outline minimum criteria for acceptable respiratory protection. According to the CDC Guidelines published in 2005, facilities that do not have isolation rooms and do not perform cough-inducing procedures on patients who might have TB may not need to have a respiratory protection program for TB. Such facilities should have written protocols for the early identification of patients with signs and symptoms of TB and procedures for referring such patients to a facility for proper evaluation and management. In 2005, the FDA approved the QuantiFERON®-TB Gold Test. This test detects the release of interferon-gamma (IFN-g) when it is incubated with mixtures of synthetic peptides representing two proteins present in *M. tuberculosis*. These antigens impart greater specificity than is possible with tests using purified protein derivative as the TB antigen. In direct comparisons, the sensitivity of QFT-G was statistically similar to that of the tuberculin skin test (TST) for detecting infection in persons with untreated culture-confirmed TB.

Enforcement of OSHA regulations. In February 1996, OSHA published enforcement procedures for occupational exposure to tuberculosis. This document indicated that inspections would be conducted in response to employee complaints, fatalities, and catastrophes; or in workplaces where the incidence of tuberculosis infection is greater than in the general public, such as health care facilities, correctional institutions, long-term care facilities for the elderly, homeless shelters, and drug treatment centers. A written program must be implemented for respiratory protection and meet the performance criteria for respiratory protection outlined in the 1994 CDC guidelines as well as those for compliance with OSHA 1910.134.

In 2006, the CDC released guidelines designed to address the TB problem in correctional facilities. Effective TB-prevention and control measures in correctional facilities include

- early identification of persons with TB disease through entry and periodic follow-up screening;

- successful treatment of TB disease and latent TB infection;
- appropriate use of airborne precautions (e.g., airborne infection isolation, environmental controls, and respiratory protection);
- comprehensive discharge planning; and
- thorough and efficient contact investigation.

These measures should be instituted in close collaboration with local or state health department TB-control programs and other key partners.

Respiratory protection equipment standards. In 1997, OSHA published a proposed rule on occupational exposure to tuberculosis. This rule was withdrawn in 2003 and the users of respiratory protective devices for protection against tuberculosis now follow the General Industry OSHA respiratory protection standard, 29 *CFR* 1910.134.

According to the CDC, the standards to be met by respiratory protective equipment used in health care settings to protect against TB include the following:

- the ability to filter particles as small as 1 µm in size in the unloaded state with a filter of 95 percent (filter leak of less than 5 percent), given flow rates of up to 50 L/min
- the ability to quantitatively or qualitatively test fit in a reliable way to obtain a face-seal leakage of no more than 10 percent
- the ability to fit different facial sizes and characteristics of health care workers, that is, to be available in at least three sizes
- the ability to be checked for facepiece fit, according to OSHA and good industrial hygiene practices, by the health care worker each time the respirator is put on

Although certain regional OSHA requirements may still include mandatory positive-pressure air-purifying particulate respirators (PAPRs) or full-face, HEPA-filtered respirators, the most recent recommendations from the CDC (in 2005) outline the performance-based criteria listed above for the selection of respiratory protection. These recommendations are based upon the premise that aerosolized microorganisms are particles that can be removed by a filter; that is, a particulate filter will remove the organism with at least the efficiency it is certified for (95 percent for a N95 filter).

All particulate respirators approved under 42 *CFR* Part 84 NIOSH certification procedures and all atmosphere-supplying respirators meet the OSHA criteria. However, if the procedures require sterility, respirators with exhalation valves and respirators that may be under positive pressure cannot be used. Circumstances in which the risk may justify a level of respiratory protection exceeding the minimum criteria include, but are not limited to, bronchoscopy performed on patients with suspected or known TB and autopsy performed on persons who were suspected of or known to have TB.

Workplace Containment
Specific recommendations for protection from TB are made in regulatory as well as advisory documents; it is recommended that the current literature be reviewed regularly for revised standards and guidelines.

Patient care. Infection control guidelines for the care of patients with TB have been provided and updated periodically since the mid-1970s by the CDC's Hospital Infections Branch. Concern for employee health in the hospital environment was the subject of a separate set of CDC guidelines. The CDC has published draft guidelines for preventing the transmission of TB in health care facilities, extending them to include protection of both patients and personnel. The CDC made it clear that the purpose of the guidelines was to make recommendations to reduce the risk of transmitting TB to health care workers, patients, volunteers, visitors, and other persons in health care settings. The recommendations were written to apply to inpatient facilities where health care is provided, such as hospitals, prison medical wards, nursing homes, and hospices.

In patient care settings, it is important to control TB at the source by identifying TB patients or those at high risk for TB. Take the time to train such patients to control the formation and release of infectious droplets, for example, by using tissues to cover sneezes and coughs.

Ambulatory care facilities. Ambulatory care facilities are of special importance because of the increase in patient users and the front-line health care worker status in the United States. Health care employers in outpatient settings should be aware of the risk of TB among their patient population, especially those who have both HIV and TB infections. Infection control policies should be developed accordingly.

Those who are HIV-positive or are otherwise at risk for contracting TB should receive a tuberculin skin test, and the results should be noted in the patient's medical record. Tuberculosis diagnostic procedures should be initiated if signs and symptoms of TB develop.

Ambulatory patients who have pulmonary symptoms of uncertain etiology should be instructed to cover their mouths and noses when coughing or sneezing; they should spend a minimum time in common waiting areas. Personnel who are the first point of contact in facilities serving patients at risk for TB should be trained to recognize, and bring to the attention of the appropriate person, any patients with symptoms suggestive of TB, such as a productive cough of greater than three weeks' duration, especially when accompanied by other tuberculosis symptoms such as weight loss, fever, fatigue, or anorexia.

Ventilation systems in clinics serving patients who are

at high risk for TB should be designed and maintained to reduce TB transmission. This is particularly important if immunosuppressed patients are treated in the same, or a nearby, area. In some settings, enhanced ventilation or air disinfection techniques (HEPA filters or indirect or contained ultraviolet germicidal irradiation [UVGI]) may be appropriate for common areas such as waiting rooms. Air from clinics serving patients at high risk for tuberculosis should not be recirculated unless it is first passed through an effective decontamination system such as a HEPA filtration system.

In outpatient settings where cough-inducing procedures are carried out, infection control precautions for TB (respiratory precautions) should be implemented. A special concern is the drug treatment facility. TB patients who have substance abuse problems are likely to be noncompliant with TB therapy, and may develop drug-resistant disease as a result.

Emergency medical services. Emergency medical services (EMS) personnel should be included in a respiratory program and in a comprehensive tuberculin skin-testing program with a baseline test and follow-up testing according to risk assessment.

EMS personnel and others who provide patient services should ensure that a surgical mask is placed over the patient's mouth and nose (if possible) when a patient who has confirmed or suspected TB is being transported. Because of the lack of engineering controls in the transport vehicle, and because administrative controls cannot be ensured under such circumstances, EMS personnel are advised to wear respiratory protection as well.

Laboratory. Exposure to laboratory-generated aerosols is the most insidious hazard. Sputa and other clinical specimens from suspected or known cases should be handled with appropriate precautions to preclude the release of infectious droplets and spatter. Organisms can survive in heat-fixed smears and can be aerosolized during the preparation of frozen sections and the manipulation of liquid cultures. In a practical approach to control aerosol hazards in laboratories, Gilchrist et al. provided guidance on the personal protective equipment and the safe procedures necessary for handling liquid-amplified cultures, as opposed to those needed for the less hazardous work of planting primary clinical specimens on solid media.

In 1997 the CDC published proposed guidelines for working with *M. tuberculosis* in laboratories. The goal of this document was to present health and safety information, to be used in conjunction with the BMBL, for those persons working with *M. tuberculosis* in laboratories. This docu-

ment was a proposal; public comment was collected but a revised final draft has not been published. With regard to respiratory protection, the CDC proposed the worker wear an air-purifying respirator with either N100 or HEPA filters during collection of sputum specimens in an open laboratory. The guidelines also recommended that all personnel working with *M. tuberculosis* in BSL-3 laboratories wear an air-purifying respirator with N95 filters.

In 2005, the CDC prepared the current health care guidelines in consultation with experts in TB, infection control, environmental control, respiratory protection, and occupational health. The new guidelines have been expanded to address a broader concept; current health care settings go beyond the previously defined facilities. The term *health care setting* includes many types of settings, such as inpatient settings, outpatient settings, TB clinics, settings in correctional facilities in which health care is delivered, settings in which home-based health care and emergency medical services are provided, and laboratories handling clinical specimens that might contain *M. tuberculosis*.

Aerosolized Infectious Diseases

In 2009, the State of California released a standard designed to prevent airborne transmissible disease (ATD), and TB was cited as one of the primary reasons for the standards development (along with SARS-CoV and avian influenza, H5N1). There are two standards; one is a zoonotic standard, for agriculture and other occupations with animals, and the other standard addresses health care and laboratory occupations.

§5199 of Title 8 of the California Code of Regulations (CCR) requires hospitals and other health care facilities, services, or operations to do the following:

1. Develop a written ATD exposure control plan that addresses infection control measures for ATDs and identifies the individuals responsible for plan implementation and annual review [§5199(d)].
2. Implement source control procedures (e.g., respiratory hygiene or cough etiquette) for persons entering the facility, such as provision of masks, tissues, and hand hygiene materials [§5199(e)(1)(B)].
3. Reduce exposures by implementation of engineering controls and work practices and provision of personal protective equipment (PPE) [§5199(e)(1)].
4. Establish procedures for the early identification and appropriate placement of patients requiring AII isolation (e.g., cases or suspected cases of TB, measles, SARS, monkeypox, smallpox, varicella, and novel or unknown ATDs, such as pandemic influenza strains that are not fully characterized) [§5199(e)(5)].
5. Establish communications procedures within the facil-

ity and with facilities, services, and operations that refer ATD patients including §5199(d)(2)(L) and (M) and §5199(h)(6):

   a. notification of the unit to which a patient is sent of the suspected disease status of the patient and recommended isolation precautions

   b. reporting to the local health officer of cases and suspected cases of reportable ATDs, i.e., diseases reportable under Title 17 of the CCR §2500(j)(1) and §2647–2643

   c. notification of employees and other employers of persons who were exposed to reportable cases

6. Ensure that AII rooms function correctly and that negative pressure is verified daily when the room is in use for isolation [§5199(e)(5)(D)].

7. Perform high hazard procedures in isolation rooms or isolation areas such as booths [§5199(e)(5)(C)].

8. Provide appropriate respiratory protection for employees while they perform work that places them at increased risk of exposure to pathogens requiring AII, such as entering AII rooms, performing high hazard procedures, or maintaining ventilation systems from AII rooms [§5199(g)]. Higher levels of respiratory protection are required for high hazard procedures unless it would interfere with the employee's task.

9. Implement procedures for decontamination or disposal of equipment, work areas, and PPE [§5199(e)(2)].

10. Provide medical services for employees who have occupational exposure including [§5199(h)]:

   a. annual TB test and follow up for TB conversion

   b. vaccination of susceptible health care workers for mumps, measles, and rubella (MMR); varicella-zoster; and tetanus, diphtheria, and acellular pertussis (TDAP) and provision to all employees of vaccination for seasonal influenza vaccine (Employees may decline vaccinations.)

11. Follow up of exposure incidents (e.g., events in which a worker was exposed to a case of a reportable ATD), including continuation of pay for a period during which an employee is not sick but a physician or other licensed health care professional (PLHCP) recommends removal from the workplace because the employee may be contagious (unless alternate work is available) [§5199(h)(6) through (h)(9)].

12. Ensure that a biosafety program is in place for laboratory operations [§5199(f)].

13. Provide initial and annual training on the ATD exposure control plan and on infection control procedures [§5199(i)].

14. Keep records, including medical records, records of testing of ventilation systems and other engineering controls, training records, and records of exposure incidents [§5199(j)].

The impact of this standard on research laboratories is as follows:

1. The biological safety officer shall perform a risk assessment in accordance with the methodology included in Section II of the 5th edition of the BMBL for each agent and procedure involving the handling of the list of Airborne Transmissible Pathogens-Laboratory (ATPs-L) found in Appendix D of the Standard. The Biological Safety Officer shall record the safe practices required for each evaluated agent/procedure in the Biosafety Plan.

2. Based on this risk assessment, the institution shall implement feasible engineering and work practice controls, in accordance with the risk assessment performed by the Biological Safety Officer to minimize employee exposures to ATPs-L. Where exposure still remains after the implementation of engineering and work practice controls, the institution shall provide, and ensure that employees use, personal protective equipment and, where necessary to control exposure, respiratory protection. Control measures will be consistent with the recommendations in the 5th edition of the BMBL.

3. The institution shall establish, implement, and maintain an effective written Biosafety Plan to minimize employee exposures to ATPs-L that may be transmitted by laboratory aerosols, similar to what is required for bloodborne pathogen potential exposure, the Exposure Control Plan. The Biosafety Plan may be incorporated into an existing Exposure Control Plan for bloodborne pathogens or as an Airborne Transmissible Disease Exposure Control Plan.

Bioterrorism

Biological terrorism, or *bioterrorism,* has been defined as the deliberate use of a biological agent to harm civilian populations, in contrast to biological warfare, which is the deliberate induction of disease in humans, animals, or plants as a hostile act in a context of war. The inclusion of biological agents with chemicals, nuclear materials, and high explosives as weapons of mass destruction emphasizes the potential catastrophic effects of biological attacks. These potential effects became very real to U.S. citizens just a few weeks after the September 11, 2001, terrorist attacks in New York and Washington, DC, when postal letters that contained "weaponized" spores of the infectious agent *Bacillus anthracis,* the causative agent of the disease anthrax, began to arrive at various media and political offices in the eastern United States. Opening, or even simply handling, these letters exposed many individuals to the spores, which resulted in at least 22 inhalation and cutaneous anthrax infections and 5 inhalation anthrax-related deaths. These extremely callous attacks prompted a myriad of government responses including congressional hearings, increased funding for research on infectious disease agents, CDC bulletins, and new laws regarding possession, use, and transfer of select infectious agents including, *Bacillus anthracis* and many other disease agents.

Based on the historical record, large-scale bioterrorism events are unlikely to occur and are probably even less likely to succeed. However, complacency is dangerous; the Report of the Commission on the Prevention of Weapons of Mass Destruction Proliferation and Terrorism (World at Risk: 2008), concluded that:

- " . . . terrorists are more likely to be able to obtain and use a biological weapon than a nuclear"
- we " . . . should be less concerned that terrorists will become biologists and far more concerned that biologists will become terrorists"
- we need to " . . . promote a culture of security awareness in the life sciences community"

Furthermore, the second Presidential Policy Directive (PPD-2) issued by the Obama administration articulated a national strategy for countering biological threats:

1. Promote global health security
2. Reinforce norms of safe and responsible conduct
3. Obtain timely and accurate insight on current and emerging risks
4. Take reasonable steps to reduce the potential for exploitation
5. Expand capabilities to prevent, attribute, and apprehend
6. Communicate effectively with all stakeholders
7. Transform the international dialogue on biological threats

Clearly U.S. policy makers believe that the threat of bioterrorism is real and worthy of continued attention.

Biological Agents and Federal Biosecurity Laws

Before the 2001 anthrax attacks the only significant federal regulation involving possession or transfer of etiological agents was 42 *CFR* 72, Interstate Transfer of Etiological Agents (1996). The regulations required that all such transfers be documented and that entities engaging in them develop robust programs for transfer and storage of these agents. The regulation covered by name virtually every etiologic agent known to cause disease of any severity in humans.

In 2000 and 2001, the Centers for Disease Control and Prevention (CDC) defined three categories of biological agents with the potential to be used as weapons, based on ease of dissemination or transmission, potential for

major public health impact (e.g., high mortality), potential for disrupting health care delivery, potential for causing public panic and social disruption, and requirements for public health preparedness (Table 14–G). Category A included agents that could easily be transmitted among people and cause serious disease with high mortality rates. Examples include the causative agents of anthrax, botulism (*Clostridium botulinum* and its toxins), and smallpox (Variola major virus). Category B includes agents that are moderately easy to transmit and result in high morbidity but low mortality rates. Examples include the causative agents of brucellosis (*Brucella* species), glanders (*Burkholderia mallei*), and certain viral encephalitis agents. Category C is limited to emerging disease agents, such as hantavirus, some of which may represent unusually serious threats and also may be easy to adapt to weapons use.

The U.S. Congress reacted to the 2001 anthrax attacks by including provisions in the PATRIOT Act that specified legitimate uses of etiologic agents, and by enacting the

TABLE 14 – G   CDC List of Bioterrorism Agents by Category
Disease/Agent
Category A
Anthrax (*Bacillus anthracis*)*
Botulism (*Clostridium botulinum* toxin)*
Plague (*Yersinia pestis*)*
Smallpox (*Variola major*)*
Tularemia (*Francisella tularensis*)*
Viral hemorrhagic fevers (filoviruses [e.g., Ebola, Marburg] and arenaviruses [e.g., Lassa, Machupo])*
Category B
Brucellosis (*Brucella* species)*
Epsilon toxin of *Clostridium perfringens**
Food safety threats (e.g., *Salmonella* species, *Escherichia coli* O157:H7, Shigella)
Glanders (*Burkholderia mallei*)*
Melioidosis (*Burkholderia pseudomallei*)*
Psittacosis (*Chlamydia psittaci*)
Q fever (*Coxiella burnetii*)*
Ricin toxin from *Ricinus communis* (castor beans)*
Staphylococcal enterotoxin B
Typhus fever (*Rickettsia prowazekii*)*
Viral encephalitis (alphaviruses [e.g., Venezuelan equine encephalitis,* eastern equine encephalitis,* western equine encephalitis])
Water safety threats (e.g., *Vibrio cholerae*, *Cryptosporidium parvum*)
Category C
Emerging infectious diseases such as Nipah virus* and hantavirus

*HHS or HHS/USDA overlap select agent
Source: Centers for Disease Control and Prevention. *Emergency Preparedness and Response, Bioterrorism Agents and Diseases.* http://www.bt.cdc.gov/agent/agentlist-category.asp

Public Health Security and Bioterrorism Preparedness and Response Act of 2002, also known as the "Select Agent Law." The Select Agent Law built on the limited scope of 42 *CFR* 72 and empowered the Department of Health and Human Services (through the CDC) to regulate the possession, use, and transfer of select agents and toxins. CDC adopted new regulations (42 *CFR* 73) that named the biohazardous select agents covered under the regulations (Table 14–H) and established requirements for registration, security, and biological safety for work with these agents. Entities and researchers who work with select agents must now register with the Secretary of Health and Human Services, obtain special Department of Justice basic background checks for all individuals who need to have access to select agents, and are required to follow rules for security, inventory control, and biological safety. Similar regulations covering agricultural select agent possession, use, and transfer were adopted at the same time and specified approximately 30 additional select agents subject to USDA oversight (9 *CFR* 121, 7 *CFR* 331).

Until September 2001, no successful biological attack with an aerosolized agent had occurred in the United States, although other "biocrimes" and hoaxes had occurred. The intentional release of weaponized *B. anthracis* and subsequent inhalation and cutaneous infections as well as many subsequent false alarms have tested the ability of local agencies to handle a bioterrorism event. Early recognition of a bioterrorism event would allow a rapid response that could save lives, increase the probability of interdicting or apprehending the perpetrators, and deny terrorists their goal of creating panic and crisis. Preparations for a bioterrorist attack also improve the ability of public health agencies to address all kinds of infectious disease outbreaks, food safety concerns, and environmental hazards. These preparations also overlap ongoing research and other activities to meet the threats posed by new and re-emerging infectious diseases. Industrial hygienists and environmental health professionals can contribute to efforts to anticipate biological hazards and can advise on appropriate protection for emergency personnel and medical staff who would respond to a biological attack.

Release of Biological Agents

Biological agents of potential use in bioterrorism include certain bacteria, viruses, and toxins of microbial, plant, or animal origin. Common characteristics of most such agents are that they can be used directly as weapons or readily adapted (*weaponized*) to forms that are easy to disseminate, such as into crowded buildings via the supply air system, or in the mail or other common carrier. Effective biological weapons are also easy to conceal and the diseases that

TABLE 14–H	HHS and HHS/USDA Overlap Select Agents and Toxins

HHS Select Agents

Abrin
Botulinum neurotoxins
Botulinum neurotoxin producing species of *Clostridium*
Cercopithecine herpesvirus 1 (Herpes B virus)
Clostridium perfringens epsilon toxin
Coccidioides posadasii/Coccidioides immitis
Conotoxins
Coxiella burnetii
Crimean-Congo haemorrhagic fever virus
Diacetoxyscirpenol
Eastern Equine Encephalitis virus
Ebola virus
Francisella tularensis
Lassa fever virus
Marburg virus
Monkeypox virus
Reconstructed replication competent forms of the 1918 pandemic
    influenza virus containing any portion of the coding regions of all
    eight gene segments (Reconstructed1918 Influenza virus)
Ricin
Rickettsia prowazekii
Rickettsia rickettsii
Saxitoxin
Shiga-like ribosome inactivating proteins
Shigatoxin
South American Haemorrhagic Fever viruses
    Flexal
    Guanarito
    Junin
    Machupo
    Sabia
Staphylococcal enterotoxins
T-2 toxin
Tetrodotoxin
Tick-borne encephalitis complex (flavi) viruses
    Central European Tick-borne encephalitis
    Far Eastern Tick-borne encephalitis
    Kyasanur Forest disease
    Omsk Hemorrhagic Fever
    Russian Spring and Summer encephalitis
Variola minor virus (Alastrim)
Yersinia pestis

HHS/USDA Overlap Select Agents

Bacillus anthracis
Brucella abortus
Brucella melitensis
Brucella suis
Burkholderia mallei (formerly *Pseudomonas mallei*)
Burkholderia pseudomallei (formerly *Pseudomonas pseudomallei*)
Hendra virus
Nipah virus
Rift Valley fever virus
Venezuelan Equine Encephalitis virus

Note: List is current as of July 2011 and does not include USDA Agricultural Select Agents.

they cause have rapid onset and severe morbidity. Biological agents differ in the dose required, the time from exposure to symptom onset, and the type of disease they cause, but all can be dispersed in 1- to 5-μm diameter aerosolized particles. Particles of this size may remain suspended for long periods and penetrate to the distal bronchioles and terminal alveoli. However, not all biological agents can cause disease by the inhalation route. In the context of the strategic use of biological agents as weapons, agents requiring noninhalation exposure routes such as oral or percutaneous are believed to be less efficient than the respiratory route. On the other hand, in 1984 terrorists successfully contaminated at least 10 restaurant salad bars in Oregon with *Salmonella typhimurium*, a CDC category B fecal/oral contaminant that causes severe gastroenteritis. This attack resulted in at least 751 diagnosed human illnesses of varying severity, but caused no mortality. Municipal water supplies are not thought to be attractive bioterrorism conduits because of the large quantity of agent required and because the water purification procedures used in most U.S. cities might neutralize and destroy many such agents.

Recognition of a Biohazardous Agent Release

Infectious diseases occur as spontaneous outbreaks or epidemics of known, endemic diseases or of new or re-emerging diseases. Outbreaks could also follow an intentional release of an infectious agent. Clues that suggest an intentional release resulting in a disease outbreak include:

- a large epidemic with greater case loads and more rapid onset than expected;
- more severe disease than expected from the identified infectious agent;
- an unusual exposure route;
- a disease that is unusual for a given geographic area, found outside the normal transmission season, or in the absence of a normal vector;
- multiple simultaneous epidemics of different diseases;
- animal as well as human cases;
- unusual genetic strains or variants of an organism or strains with uncommon antimicrobial resistance patterns;
- different attack rates in certain areas (for example, higher rates inside a building if the agent was released indoors and lower rates in a sealed building if the agent was released outdoors); and
- claims of responsibility or other evidence of agent release.

The CDC maintains routine infectious disease surveillance systems, provides reference laboratory diagnosis and epidemiological support, disseminates public health information, issues quarantine measures, and provides expert advice on worker health and safety. CDC can assist public health officials with decision making if a threat occurs

alleging the use of a biological agent and can deploy public health response teams to assist with agent identification and consult on medical management and disease control.

Unlike some chemical agents, aerosolized biological agents generally do not have warning properties to alert persons who were exposed in an unannounced or unrecognized attack. While chemical agents typically lead to acute symptoms in persons near the site of exposure, diseases resulting from infectious biological agents have incubation periods of days, sometimes weeks. During the interval between exposure and disease onset, affected persons may have dispersed widely, further diluting the evidence that a deliberate release has occurred. Warning systems technologically based on detection of minute quantities of agent-specific characteristics are being developed for deployment in population centers. Pending that breakthrough, early detection of a covert attack with a biological agent remains problematic and relies on existing public health systems to notice a suspicious disease outbreak in time to initiate effective treatment. Therefore, a physician or laboratory technician may be the first to encounter evidence of a biological attack.

Infectious Disease Treatment

Rapid identification of the agents used in a biological attack is critical to prescribing appropriate therapy for exposed persons. Active immunization or antibiotic prophylaxis may prevent illness if exposure to an infectious agent is expected and the treatment is administered before a person is exposed. After confirmed or suspected exposure, but before symptoms arise, post-exposure prophylaxis (PEP) (such as active or passive immunization or antibiotic treatment) may ameliorate the symptoms of an infectious disease. However, once an infection is established, health care providers can only diagnose the disease and provide supportive care and treatment specific to the infection.

Response to a Biohazardous Agent Release

The components of an epidemiological investigation of any disease outbreak (natural or artificial) are
- documentation of who is affected;
- identification of possible sources and routes of exposure;
- recording of signs and symptoms of disease; and
- rapid identification of the causative agent.

The 2001 anthrax attack incidents confirmed that public health nurses, disease investigators, environmental health specialists, and other state and local health department employees will handle many of the tasks of responding to a bioterrorism attack. Key elements of an effective response plan include prompt recognition of the incident, staff and facility protection, decontamination and triage of potentially exposed persons, medical therapy, and coordination with external emergency response and public health agencies.

In 1999, CDC published interim guidelines on the management of bioterrorism threats (based on experience with pre-2001 ineffective anthrax episodes) and a strategic plan for terrorism preparedness and response. CDC and the Association for Professionals in Infection Control and Epidemiology (APIC) have written a plan specifically for health care facilities. The guidelines direct that the proper authorities be notified immediately if release of a biological agent is threatened, suspected, or known to have occurred. In most cases, the local emergency response system is activated by someone dialing 911 or by contacting local law enforcement authorities. Local and state public health authorities and the local field office of the Federal Bureau of Investigation (FBI) also should be notified. The FBI has lead responsibility for crisis management for all cases of domestic terrorism and coordinates the collection of evidence. Crisis management involves resolution of hostile situations and the investigation and preparation of a criminal case for prosecution under federal law. The Federal Emergency Management Agency (FEMA) is the lead agency for the coordination of federal assistance to state and local governments, including emergency relief to affected individuals and businesses, decontamination of the affected area, and measures to protect public health and safety and to restore essential government services. Even for a domestic incident, it is unlikely that the response would be left entirely to local law enforcement and health officials, the FBI, FEMA, and the U.S. Public Health Service. The military has also used its resources, capabilities, and expertise to assist civilian agencies.

Some civilian-based protocols have been established by the U.S. Public Health Service and the Working Group on Civilian Biodefense. Consultation also is available through the National Response Center. Some consultant groups offer risk analysis and training in emergency response and some programs market equipment packages, but none of these services and programs has been validated by experience or by agency analysis. The Institute of Medicine (IOM) has published its assessment of existing research, development, and technology information on the detection of potential chemical and biological agents and the protection and treatment of the targets of attack and health care providers. They also recommend specific research and development priorities.

Decontamination. Decontamination of persons exposed to biological agents to lessen the effects of primary exposure and prevent secondary exposure may be necessary but is considered less important than with chemical agents. Exposure to toxins may call for decontamination procedures similar to those used for chemical agents, but significant reaerosolization of infectious particles is considered unlikely. Thus, decontamination following exposure to an infectious agent could be as simple as showering and changing clothes. In the past, biocide use to neutralize biological agents has been recommended (for example, a 0.5 percent solution of sodium hypochlorite, i.e., 10 percent bleach). However, the lack of clear data on the safety and efficacy of bleach decontamination under those circumstances suggests that it should be avoided, especially if soap and water are immediately available. Biological agents may pose only a temporary risk to the environment or to persons not directly exposed because of the usually rapid degradation of the organisms in the environment and difficult reaerosolization.

Personal protective equipment. Health care professionals and laboratory personnel may need physical protection when dealing with the victims of a biological attack, and autopsy and interment of remains could present unusual hazards. Persons who are caring for potentially contaminated individuals should be outfitted properly in personal protective equipment (PPE). Level D protection (standard work clothes) plus latex or nitrile gloves, eye splash protection, and properly fit-tested N-95 respirators (used in many places for protection against *M. tuberculosis*) is considered to be adequate. A high-efficiency particulate air (HEPA) half- or full-face respirator should be substituted for the N-95 respirator if aerosols may be generated. If the agent class for a sudden release cannot be identified, Level C PPE is recommended, that is, a nonencapsulated, chemical-resistant suit, gloves, and boots and a full-face respirator with an organic vapor/HEPA filter cartridge. Hand-washing after potential exposure to disease agents or after contact with patients or patient clothing is critically important.

When collecting or handling clinical specimens following a suspected bioterrorism related attack, laboratory personnel should

- use biological safety level 2 (BSL-2) or level 3 (BSL-3) facilities and practices as appropriate to the suspected agent when working with clinical samples considered potentially infectious (if a BSL-3 facility is not available, most clinical samples can be handled safely in a Class II biological safety cabinet in a BSL-2 laboratory, but all waste should be bagged in the biological safety cabinet and autoclaved before it leaves the facility or building);
- handle all specimens and perform all manipulations in a certified Class II biological safety cabinet;
- use protective eyewear (e.g., safety glasses or face shields) and a closed-front laboratory coat or preferably a wraparound gown with full sleeves;
- stretch two pairs of latex or nitrile gloves over the sleeves;

- remove the outer pair of gloves when withdrawing the hands from the biological safety cabinet—these gloves should be disposed in a biohazardous waste receptacle within the biological safety cabinet;
- don a new outer pair of gloves before extending the hands back into the biological safety cabinet;
- avoid any activity that might cause exposure to infectious agents, especially activities that might create aerosols or droplet dispersal outside the biological safety cabinet;
- decontaminate laboratory benches after each use and dispose of contaminated supplies and equipment in properly labeled biohazardous waste receptacles;
- avoid touching skin or mucosal surfaces with the hands (gloved or ungloved); and
- never eat, drink, smoke, apply cosmetics, or insert or remove contact lenses in the laboratory.

Before leaving the laboratory, personnel should remove and reverse the inner pair of gloves and dispose of them in a labeled biohazardous waste container, wash hands, and remove laboratory coats. Do not touch surfaces in the laboratory with unprotected hands—if it is not possible to exit without touching a doorknob, use a paper towel to operate the knob and wash hands again immediately after exiting the laboratory.

Role of health and safety professionals. The CDC strategic plan includes collaboration with professional societies and the manufacturers of safety and medical equipment. The skills and training that industrial hygienists and environmental health, infection control, and biosafety professionals use to handle work-related and environmental diseases may help responders to detect, investigate, identify, and manage a civilian bioterrorist threat. Industrial hygienists and environmental health professionals are familiar with the use of PPE, dilution and exhaust ventilation, decontamination procedures, environmental sampling, and physical safety and security. Effective risk communication following a threat or event is of critical importance in order to disseminate accurate information and minimize or neutralize rumors. Employers and building operators should assess their vulnerability to attack and their ability to respond effectively. Prior identification of the appropriate offices or agencies to contact is essential preparation for the threat or suspicion of a release of a biological agent. Finally, do not overlook the importance of training and drills in any efforts to prepare for a bioterrorism attack.

Legionellosis
Background
The legionellae may be the most important water-borne disease agents in the United States, causing serious morbid-

ity and mortality. Legionellosis is an acute bacterial disease with two clinically and epidemiologically distinct manifestations. Legionnaires' disease (Legionnaires' pneumonia) is a rapid and potentially fatal pulmonary infection, whereas Pontiac fever (nonpneumonic legionellosis) is a mild, febrile illness. Respectively, symptoms appear two to ten days and 24 to 48 hours following exposure. Both diseases can begin with anorexia, malaise, myalgia, headache, and fever followed by a chills and cough with abdominal pain and diarrhea also common. With Legionnaires' disease, a chest film often shows patchy or focal areas of consolidation that may progress to respiratory failure. Pontiac fever is a self-limited influenza-like illness that may represent a reaction to inhaled antigens or endotoxin rather than bacterial invasion.

Cases of legionellosis have been reported from North and South America, Asia, Australia, Africa, and Europe. The number of reported cases has increased substantially in recent years, particularly in the eastern United States but also internationally with no clear explanation. Legionnaires' disease also has been associated with travel (20%–50% of all cases). Several occupations have been associated with increased risk of exposure, for example, cooling tower workers and dental office staff, but the relative importance of the workplace as a setting for transmission of non-outbreak-related legionellosis is unknown.

Subclinical *Legionella* infections likely are frequent given the worldwide occurrence of antibodies in the absence of recognized episodes of pneumonia. The prevalence of antibodies has ranged from 5 to 30 percent, although some positive findings may be due to cross reactions with other microorganisms. The majority of Legionnaires' disease cases are sporadic, with less than 5 percent related to outbreaks. A legionellosis outbreak has been defined as the occurrence of two or more confirmed cases in a limited time period (weeks to months) and geographic region (a building, a limited area within a building, or up to several kilometers around a potential source).

Both brief explosive and prolonged outbreaks of Legionnaires' disease have been documented. The former occur most often in association with a point source, such as a contaminated cooling tower or evaporative condenser or a hot tub, natural spa pool, or thermal spring. Prolonged outbreaks in hospitals and hotels have been attributed to contaminated potable water, humidifiers, respiratory equipment, and potting soil. Pontiac fever is recognized solely in its epidemic form, that is, associated with outbreaks; single, sporadic cases probably would be misclassified as influenza or other viral syndrome.

Conditions such as pre-existing illness may predispose exposed persons to infection but not to Pontiac fever. The male-female ratio for Legionnaires' disease is approximately

2.5:1, and recognized risk factors include age greater than 50 years, cigarette smoking, diabetes mellitus, chronic lung or cardiovascular disease, renal disease, malignancy, and immune suppression caused by underlying disease or therapy. Attack rates in Legionnaires' disease outbreaks are low (<5% for the general population; <14% in hospital outbreaks), but the case-fatality rate for persons who require hospitalization exceed 40 percent. In contrast, Pontiac fever affects a wider range of persons and attack rates typically are much higher (~95%), but patients recover spontaneously in two to five days. In North America and Europe, Legionnaires' disease has been identified in two to eight percent of community-acquired pneumonia cases that lead to hospitalization. In the United States, an estimated 8000 to 18,000 cases of Legionnaires' disease occur each year, of which more than three-quarters are undiagnosed or unreported.

The Agent

Legionellae are poorly staining, gram-negative, rod-shaped bacteria. They are aerobic, somewhat fastidious in their growth requirements, and relatively slow growing in culture. The bacteria do not survive desiccation and do not form spores. The motile cells measure 0.3–0.9 × 1–20 μm. As of 2009, 52 species and 71 serogroups had been recognized, approximately half of which were implicated in human disease. It is likely that most legionellae can cause human disease under appropriate conditions, but infections by some of them are rarely reported because of a lack of diagnostic reagents. *L. pneumophila* causes over 90 percent of Legionnaires' disease cases, and serogroup 1 accounts for more than 70–80 percent of these. Serogroups 4 and 6 also are commonly associated with infection. *Legionella long-beachae* and *Legionella micdadei* account for the majority of nonpneumophila legionellosis, with most other *Legionella* species associated with only a few reported cases. Pontiac fever also is most frequently caused by *L. pneumophila* serogroup 1 as well as by *Legionella anisa*, *Legionella feeleii*, and *L. micdadei*. Possible explanations for the manifestation of two disease syndromes caused by the same bacteria include differences in host susceptibility and the inability of some legionellae to multiply in human tissue (for a variety of reasons, including bacterial virulence, host range, or viability).

Legionellae survive in the environment with their primary hosts, single-cell free-living protozoa, and in humans the bacteria persist within alveolar macrophages. In addition to recognized *Legionella* species, a number of *Legionella*-related bacteria (designated *Legionella*-like amoebal [amebal] pathogens, LLAPs) have been described, many of which have been associated with Legionnaires' disease. Most LLAPs cannot be grown by routine culture methods, making them difficult to detect and suggesting that they may be responsible for some pneumonias of unknown etiology. Protozoa help protect legionellae from the effects of biocides and thermal disinfection and may be the mechanism by which they survive adverse environmental conditions and within aerosols.

Sources

Legionellae are indigenous microorganisms associated almost exclusively with surface and potable waters and other moist environments, such as soil. However, natural freshwater environments are rarely associated with legionellosis outbreaks, and descriptions of legionella prevalence and distribution depend on the method used to detect the bacteria. Surveys have found legionellae in large percentages of tested hospitals, large buildings, and residences, often in hot-water supplies and cooling waters for heat-transfer systems. However, even when the bacteria are detected at high concentrations, their presence may not be related to health risk. Hot-water systems, water-cooled heat-transfer systems, humidifiers, whirlpool spas, respiratory therapy devices, and decorative fountains have been implicated epidemiologically in legionellosis outbreaks. These sources are of two general types:

- contaminated potable water sources, such as showers, faucets, and respiratory therapy equipment
- contaminated nonpotable water sources, such as cooling towers, evaporative condensers, whirlpool spas, decorative fountains, ultrasonic mist machines, humidifiers, and water-based cutting fluids

Factors known to enhance legionella colonization of man-made water environments include warm temperature (25–45°C), suitable pH (2.5–9.5), water stagnation followed by agitation, and the presence of other organisms, sediment, and scale.

Transmission

There is no evidence that Legionnaires' disease or Pontiac fever is transmitted other than by inhalation of aerosolized bacteria of a respirable size (1–5 μm) from an environmental source or by aspiration or direct inoculation of contaminated water into the lower respiratory tract. There is no established dose–response relationship for legionella infections, and the concentration necessary to cause an outbreak is unknown. Studies have indicated that aerosols from contaminated cooling towers, aeration ponds, and other sources may carry bacteria hundreds of meters and perhaps further. Human-to-human transmission has not been observed. At least one case of laboratory-associated legionellosis has been reported caused by presumed aerosol or droplet exposure to *L. pneumophila* during animal challenge studies. Respectively, BSL-2 and ABSL-2 practices, containment equipment, and facilities are recommended for all activities involving the use or manipulation of potentially infectious materials (including environmental water samples) and experimentally infected animals. BSL-2 with BSL-3 practices is recommended for activities likely to produce aerosols and for manipulation of large quantities of bacteria. Legionella infections that do not fit the clinical syndromes of Legionnaires' disease or Pontiac fever also have been reported in immunosuppressed persons and include endocarditis, peritonitis, and skin and soft tissue infections. These extrapulmonary infections occur via metastatic spread of bacteria and direct contact with contaminated waters.

Environmental Sampling

Sampling of suspected sources for the presence of legionellae has proven useful to investigate outbreaks, study the ecology of these bacteria, and evaluate the efficacy of various prevention measures. However, the value of routine water sampling (unrelated to outbreak investigations) has not been demonstrated and is not recommended except for health care settings and even there the value has not been clearly established. Thus, CDC recommends aggressive maintenance and disinfection protocols for devices known to transmit legionellae but does not recommend regularly scheduled microbiological testing in the absence of legionellosis or as a substitute for proper maintenance. Testing programs have been developed for high-risk facilities, such as hospitals. These plans include suggestions for environmental parameters to monitor, record keeping, where to collect samples and how many samples to collect, and the frequency for conducting various tests.

Collection of at least 1 L of water allows concentration of the sample, if necessary, and the application of various treatments that enhance legionella isolation. See the recommendations for personal protective equipment (PPE) in the section on the prevention of legionellosis. Water samples should be collected into clean, sealable containers. Samples should include sediment and swabbings or scrapings of the walls of water containers and fixtures (for example, hot-water tanks and shower heads). Legionellae are more readily detected from swab samples of biofilms than from flowing water. Chlorinated water should be treated with sodium thiosulfate (0.5 mL of 0.1 $Na_2S_2O_3$ per liter). Environmental samples should be transported to the laboratory in insulated containers that protect the materials from extreme heat or cold as well as light. Samples that cannot be processed within 72 hours of collection should be refrigerated.

Legionellae are detected by isolation in bacterial culture, direct fluorescent antibody staining, and polymerase chain reaction (PCR) or other method to identify specific nucleic acid sequences. The latter two detection methods are more sensitive than culture and have high negative predictive value, but they do not distinguish between viable and nonviable bacteria. Culture isolation often is preferred because it identifies all *Legionella* species and environmental culture isolates can be typed for comparison with clinical isolates. Culture and enumeration of legionellae from environmental sources involve several steps including concentration, resuspension, pretreatment, and use of complex media. CDC created the Environmental Legionella Isolation Techniques Evaluation (ELITE) program as a way for laboratories to test their isolation techniques against standardized samples.

To date, no direct relationship has been established between the risk of infection and the number of legionellae in a water system. A close match between an environmental isolate and one from a clinical specimen may identify the source of a person's exposure and the water system in need of attention. Criteria for the interpretation of culture results and health-based target concentrations have been proposed. The criteria include recommendations for remedial actions and time frames for follow-up testing and remediation.

Air sampling is relatively insensitive at identifying viable legionellae, but assays not based on culture may detect even nonviable bacteria if present in sufficient numbers. Viable legionellae have been collected onto agar-based culture medium or into liquid for transfer to growth media or molecular analysis, but air samples can be negative even when water samples are positive. Therefore, examination of source samples is considered more efficient than air sampling to identify potential exposure to legionellae.

Prevention of Legionellosis

The factors that contribute to legionellosis are not completely understood, but certain events are considered to be prerequisites. These include the presence of the bacterium in a water environment, multiplication of the bacterium to an infectious dose (currently unknown), and transmission of the agent via an aerosol to a susceptible human host.

Primary prevention involves control of legionellae in water systems before disease occurs while secondary prevention focuses on eradiation of the bacterium after case recognition. The WHO has guidelines for drinking water, recreational waters, and ships. The American Society of Heating, Refrigerating and Air-Conditioning Engineers (ASHRAE) issued guidelines for legionella control in buildings and currently is updating them (Standard Project Committee 188 [SPC 188], *Prevention of Legionellosis Associated with Building Water Systems*). Fields and Moore reviewed 13 reference documents from professional associations and federal, state, and local governments and provide convenient tables comparing the recommendations for legionella control in potable water systems, cooling towers and evaporative condensers, and heated spas and hot tubs.

Given the impossibility of eliminating legionellae from most water systems, disease prevention generally focuses on limiting bacterial multiplication and aerosolization. A water safety or risk management plan is the preferred approach to managing specific health risks of exposure to legionellae from water systems. Animal models with legionella vaccines have shown promise, but no immunization of humans against legionellosis has been attempted.

The risk of legionellosis can be reduced through proper design and operation of ventilation, humidification, and water-cooled heat-transfer equipment. Practices to control the multiplication of legionellae in potable water systems can be divided into routine maintenance and emergency decontamination. Appropriate maintenance includes regular use, cleaning, and biocide treatment, where appropriate (for example, chlorination to achieve 1–2 mg/L of free residual chlorine at the tap). Monochloramine disinfection of water supplies is associated with a decreased risk of Legionnaires' disease, and conversion of municipal water supplies from free chlorine to monochloramine has been associated with decreases in the percentages of buildings colonized with legionellae.

Molmeret et al. emphasized that interventions should be directed at both protozoa and legionellae. The control of biofilm-associated legionellae may be the most effective approach to preventing legionellosis. Precautions specific to the prevention of legionella multiplication in water systems include the following:

- Keep hot water above 60°C and cold water below 20°C; deliver water to taps at >50°C and <20°C, respectively.
- Separate or insulate water lines to prevent heat transfer.
- Avoid tepid water systems (for example, deliver hot and cold water in separate lines and mix them at the point of use rather than in a warm-water holding tank).
- Flush faucets and showers briefly before use; flush infrequently used water supply lines on a regular basis (for example, weekly or monthly).
- Remove *deadlegs* in water systems (for example, disconnect and drain unused plumbing and equipment).

Additional recommendations for reducing the risks of legionellosis that also help prevent other problems associated with biological contamination include the following:

- Choose HVAC and water systems and other equipment of the best design and capacity for a facility's needs.
- Label equipment for easy identification.
- Keep up-to-date blueprints or schematic drawings that identify control equipment and access points.
- Operate and maintain (inspect, clean, and repair) equipment according to the manufacturer's recommendations.
- Outline responsibilities in writing and see that staff understand and are trained for their assignments.
- Deal with identified problems promptly.

- Outline emergency responses in writing and have important names and phone numbers readily available.
- Keep good records and see that reports are dated and signed.
- Seek expert advice when needed.

ASHRAE, OSHA, the Cooling Technology Institute, and WHO have procedures for disinfection and cleaning of cooling towers and related equipment that may be contaminated with legionellae. Most guidelines recommend the use of drift eliminators and location of cooling towers and evaporative condensers away from building outdoor air intakes. However, the information is neither detailed nor specific. The principal methods for disinfecting potable water systems are

- heat shock at temperatures above 70°C for 2 to 24 hours;
- hyperchlorination (>10 mg/L of free residual chlorine); and
- physical cleaning of hot water tanks.

PPE has been suggested for workers examining equipment or collecting environmental samples. These include disposable garments, slip-proof footwear, and eye protection in areas that are wet, potentially contaminated, or recently treated with biocides, disinfectants, detergents, or other chemicals. An N95 or HEPA respirator is recommended for work near potentially contaminated equipment that might generate aerosols. A combination respirator may be needed for protection from aerosols and gases or vapors (e.g., chlorine).

Building-Related Bioaerosol Problems

Recognition is increasing of the potential adverse health effects of inhaling particles, gases, and vapors from plants, animals, and microorganisms. Airborne particles and volatile compounds from living, decomposing, and dead biological matter are abundant outdoors and enter buildings via natural and mechanical ventilation. Indoor bioaerosol sources include humans, their activities, and the materials they bring into buildings in addition to the indoor growth of microorganisms and pests. Weather and climate change are expected to affect indoor and outdoor air quality and, therefore, human health, with more frequent and serious water damage among the concerns. The biological agents found in office and commercial buildings overlap those common in agricultural and manufacturing environments. However, concentrations typically are orders of magnitude lower in buildings than in agriculture or industry, with the exception of infectious agents that are transmitted from person to person. In addition, the indoor workforce is more diverse in terms of age range, general health status, and the mental and physical requirements of their jobs. Table 14–I lists terms used in the study of bioaerosol-related problems.

TABLE 14–1   ACGIH Definitions of Biohazard Terms
Bioaerosol: airborne particles composed of or derived from living organisms; microorganisms and fragments, toxins, and particulate waste products from all varieties of living things.
Biologically derived airborne contaminant: a term used when the presence of bioaerosols or volatile compounds causes adverse health effects, disturbs occupant comfort, reduces worker productivity, or damages materials.
Biological contamination: the presence of (a) biologically derived aerosols, gases, or vapors of a kind and concentration likely to cause disease or predispose humans to disease; (b) inappropriate concentrations of outdoor bioaerosols, especially in buildings designed to prevent their entry; or (c) indoor microbial growth and remnants of biological growth that may become aerosolized and to which people may be exposed.
Biological agent: a substance of biological origin that is capable of producing an adverse effect, for example, an infection or a hypersensitivity, irritant, inflammatory, or other response.

Source: ACGIH, 2011.

Building-Related Illnesses and Symptoms

Human reactions to the indoor environment fall into one of three main categories, the first and most common being subjective indoor environmental quality complaints. Some examples of these complaints are thermal discomfort; perception of stuffy, stale, or dry air; or malodors. Second are specific building-related illnesses (BRIs), which are diagnosable conditions whose causes can be attributed to indoor exposure to a chemical, physical, or biological agent. BRIs have known etiologies and frequently are accompanied by documentable physical signs and laboratory findings. Examples of chemical and physical agents responsible for BRIs are carbon monoxide, formaldehyde, and glass fibers. The following BRIs are known to be caused by biological agents: (a) infections, such as acute viral infections, Legionnaires' disease, and tuberculosis; (b) immunologically mediated diseases, such as hypersensitivity pneumonitis and allergic rhinitis, sinusitis, and asthma; and (c) inhalation fevers, such as humidifier fever, Pontiac fever, organic dust toxic syndrome, and other febrile, flu-like illnesses.

Infectious diseases that have been associated with exposures in office and commercial buildings include acute respiratory infections, varicella (chicken pox), measles, tuberculosis, and Legionnaires' disease. For all but the last disease, the infectious agents are transmitted from person to person. Tuberculosis and legionellosis are described in more detail in other sections of this chapter. Residential dampness and mold have been found to be associated with substantial and statistically significant increases in respiratory infections and bronchitis. If these associations were confirmed

as causal and applicable to other indoor environments, effective control of dampness and mold in buildings could prevent a substantial proportion of respiratory infections.

The terms *sick-building syndrome* and *tight-building syndrome* have been used when building occupants experience mucous membrane irritation, nasal symptoms, skin irritation, headache, fatigue, or breathing problems in a building. This third category of complaints will be referred to as nonspecific building-related symptoms (BRSs) because they are linked with time spent in a building but cannot be associated with a well-defined agent. The EPA has found that more than 40 percent of workers experience frequent, work-related symptoms consistent with BRSs. Because BRSs have many potential causes (physical, chemical, and psychosocial, as well as biological), investigators must consider the contributions to worker performance and comfort of factors related to the individual and job demands. Various bacterial and fungal agents have been proposed to explain some BRSs, for example, endotoxin, peptidoglycans, mycotoxins, and microbial volatile organic compounds. Some proportion of BRSs likely are early stages of specific, unrecognized illnesses, and if left unchecked could progress to BRIs.

Building ventilation rates are determined, in part, to dilute human bioeffluents to concentrations that the majority of occupants find acceptable. Providing more outdoor air ventilation has been shown to improve work performance and reduce BRS prevalence. Indoor carbon dioxide (CO_2) concentrations exceed outdoor levels in proportion to human occupancy and ventilation rate, but indoor CO_2 concentration has not been found to predict the likelihood of BRSs. Studies of sick leave among office workers suggests that outdoor air ventilation may play a role in worker absences for common, communicable, respiratory infections. A review panel also concluded that there is strong and sufficient evidence to demonstrate an association between ventilation, air movement in buildings, and the transmission of infectious diseases such as measles, tuberculosis, chickenpox, influenza, and SARS. However, the data were insufficient to specify the minimum ventilation requirements for hospitals, schools, offices, homes, or isolation rooms to prevent the spread of infectious agents via the airborne route.

Persons allergic to pollen from outdoor plants generally find some relief when indoors. Common allergens for which exposures typically are higher indoors include arthropods (for example, dust mites and cockroaches), birds, and mammals (for example, cats, dogs, and rodents). People's responses to airborne allergens depend on genetic factors, prior exposures, and the duration and intensity of subsequent exposures. Immune reactions to indoor aeroallergens may involve the upper or lower airways and include familiar responses, such as allergic asthma, rhinitis, sinusitis, and atopic dermatitis, as well as less common allergic mycosis (most often allergic aspergillosis) and hypersensitivity pneumonitis.

Inhalation fevers, other inflammatory responses to bioaerosols, and responses to inhaled biological toxins are discussed in the following sections on organic dust, mycotoxins, endotoxin, and *Pfiesteria*. Investigations of specific BRIs may be fairly straightforward because a clear diagnosis has been made, the causative agent (or class of agents) is known, and sources of the agent can be anticipated and examined. By their nature, it is more difficult to identify the cause of a BRS, and the assistance of an industrial hygienist may be required to identify appropriate measures to reduce exposures.

Investigation of Building-Related Symptoms

Typical indoor sources of biological agents are

- people, who shed bacteria and viruses from their persons and allergenic particles from their clothing (for example, pet owners);
- building materials, furnishings, and ventilation system components that provide a suitable environment for survival, growth, and distribution of microorganisms;
- accumulations of biological materials on indoor surfaces; and
- animals that shed allergens.

Many investigations of problem buildings are based on the development and testing of hypotheses (i.e., carefully formulated, logical answers or explanations). Investigators combine available environmental, epidemiological, medical, and toxicological evidence to develop hypotheses, and then devise ways to check these theories to determine which are consistent with available information. The EPA has checklists and protocols to guide building evaluations and manage indoor air quality as well as a mold remediation checklist for schools and commercial buildings. Section III, Chapter 2 of the OSHA *Technical Manual* describes how to conduct an indoor air quality investigation. NIOSH has developed a one-page *Mold and Dampness Assessment Sheet* to help identify mold or moisture in classrooms and school buildings.

Mendell et al. identified associations between BRSs and several indicators of moisture or contamination in office buildings. They found almost a tripling of weekly, building-related, lower respiratory symptoms in association with lack of cleaning of drip pans under air-conditioner cooling coils. In addition, increased mucous membrane symptoms were associated with lack of cleaning of either drip pans or cooling coils and with past water damage in mechanical rooms. More recently, Fisk et al. and Mendell et al. evaluated peer-reviewed epidemiological studies or quantitative meta-analyses on dampness, mold, or other microbiological agents and respiratory or allergic effects. Evident dampness or mold had consistent positive associations with multiple allergic and respiratory effects. However, microbiological agents in air samples had no associations with health outcomes and agents in dust samples had only limited, suggestive, including both positive and negative associations for endotoxin, (1-3)-β-D-glucan, and house dust mite antigen. The evidence indicated multiple biological mechanisms, including both allergic and nonallergic reactions. These findings suggest that still unrecognized dampness-related agents are responsible for the adverse health effects associated with dampness and mold. These agents could be components or products of bacteria, fungi, or other microorganisms; dampness-produced chemicals; or various combinations of them. The conclusion was that, while prevention and remediation of indoor dampness and mold are likely to reduce health risks, current evidence does not support the measurement of specific indoor microbiological factors to guide health-protective actions.

Environmental Sampling

The presence of biologically derived contaminants may be determined from air or source samples. Particles of biological origin are collected from the air by three primary methods: inertial impaction onto an adhesive surface, inertial impaction in a liquid impinger or wetted cyclone, and filtration. Water, building materials and furnishings, settled dust, and surfaces are sources that may be tested to identify contaminated materials and to evaluate the effectiveness of mitigation and remediation efforts. AIHA publications describe in detail procedures for the collection and analysis of environmental samples.

Typical bulk samples are settled dust collected with a vacuum device and sections of wallboard, pieces of duct lining, or segments of carpet cut from representative areas. Samples from intact surfaces (e.g., tape lifts or vacuum samples from wood, plaster, metal, or vinyl surfaces) and porous materials (e.g., vacuum samples from carpets, drapes, or upholstered furniture) can identify whether materials are contaminated beyond background levels. Bioaerosols may be released from contaminated surfaces via natural spore discharge and through disturbances that reaerosolize particles. Building occupants and clean-up workers also may be exposed to biological agents through skin contact with contaminated surfaces and while handling contaminated porous materials.

Sampling Strategy

Investigators collect environmental samples to characterize exposure to biological agents by measuring

- background or baseline air or surface concentrations for comparison with samples from other locations;

- concentrations representative of worst-case or highest exposures; and
- concentrations representative of average or typical exposures.

The first type of sample is collected outdoors or in an area of a building where there is no history of water damage, visible microbial growth, or other problem and in which the occupants have not been diagnosed with BRIs and do not complain of BRSs. Samples collected under conditions that simulate occupant activity and ventilation system operation (semiaggressive sampling) may reflect the highest bioaerosol exposures that persons in a contaminated building may experience. Sampling without additional disturbances is used to represent exposures that occur at other times.

Sample Analysis

Environmental samples are used qualitatively and quantitatively

- to identify biological agents and understand the environmental conditions that lead to their indoor presence;
- to demonstrate possible pathways by which bioaerosols and gases and vapors of biological origin may travel from environmental sources to workers; and
- to measure worker exposure to biological agents and learn about exposure–response relationships.

Culture-based methods and direct microscopic examination traditionally were the analytical procedures most commonly used to assess the extent of indoor microbial growth. Consequently, the largest databases on indoor fungi and bacteria are those reporting measurements of culturable and countable microorganisms. Investigators may test for an indicator of a specific agent, such as *E. coli* for contamination with raw sewage following a plumbing leak, glucan or ergosterol for fungal biomass, or guanine for dust mites. The term *indicator* also is used when referring to a microorganism or chemical marker whose detection may reflect the simultaneous occurrence or presence of the actual biological agent responsible for an adverse health effect. For example, the detection of a particular fungus may be used to indicate that a particular allergen is present, and detection of high concentrations of peptidoglycans may be used to indicate the likely presence of elevated concentrations of bacteria. Nucleic acid probes, chemical assays, bioassays, and other analytical methods are used when specific organisms or biological agents are under investigation, such as legionella, animal allergens, endotoxin, or fungal toxins.

Interpretation of Data

The lack of exposure criteria for most biological agents precludes identifying excessive exposures solely by measurement as is done for many chemical and physical agents.

Therefore, assessments for bioaerosol exposures rely on visual inspections of buildings, tabulation of occupant symptoms, evaluations of building performance, application of professional judgment, and in special circumstances sampling of potential environmental sources. Hung et al. and Macher et al. discuss the limitations of different analytical procedures to measure biological agents in indoor samples, and Horner and Prezant et al. provide guidance on the interpretation of indoor mold reports. Several groups have attempted to develop numerical guidelines for bioaerosol measurements. However, occupant health has not always been the primary criterion considered. Furthermore, the validity of broadly applying concentration guidelines to all types of buildings, climate zones, and worker populations is uncertain. Numeric guidelines may be misinterpreted as recommended limits or goals that identify safe or healthy work environments. Confusing the issue, there are potential protective effects of microbial exposures on atopy, and atopic diseases and some bioaerosol exposures are beneficial.

Guidelines on the interpretation of environmental exposures to fungi have received special attention. Occupational exposure limits (i.e., lowest observed effect levels) have been proposed for diverse and specific fungi and for specific risk groups of workers. Other reviews of available data concluded that visible or otherwise evident dampness or mold have consistent positive associations with multiple allergic and respiratory effects but that environmental measurements of microbiological agents do not. Therefore, prevention and remediation of water damage, indoor dampness, and microbial growth likely will reduce health risks, but there is less evidence that results of air, dust, surface, or other samples can appropriately be used to guide health-protective actions.

Summary. Evaluating indoor environmental quality can be a challenging endeavor. There is little formal regulation in this area and enforcement often is difficult. Nevertheless, some groups have recommended exposure limits for certain biological agents even though there is little or no scientific evidence that exposures at or below these concentrations prevent BRIs or BRSs. Because assessment of exposures through the measurement of specific biological or other agents is not especially useful, investigators are encouraged to exhaust other approaches to the identification of the causes of BRSs (such as medical evaluation of affected individuals and identification of their illnesses) and to implement interventions that have been demonstrated in homes to affect health outcomes such as asthma, respiratory allergies, and infections. These interventions include integrated pest management and elimination of moisture intrusion and leaks as well as removal or cleaning of moldy materials. The elimination of moisture sources may require analysis and correction of deficiencies in building design, maintenance, or operation and should be completed before considering environmental sampling for biological agents. Because salaries are a major cost in the nonindustrial sector, improvement of indoor environmental quality that results in increased worker productivity and well being can be cost effective.

Biological Hazards Associated with Noninfectious Agents

Various biological hazards are discussed in the following section.

Organic Dust Toxic Syndrome

Dusts of vegetable, animal, or microbial origin often are referred to as organic dusts. Workers are exposed to organic dust in a variety of environments including agricultural operations, industrial and manufacturing processes, and office and commercial settings. High organic dust exposures are common in occupations involving work with confined animals and the handling of grains or wood products. The composition of organic dust varies with the source material, but may contain fractured vegetable matter, textile fibers, paper dust, bacteria, fungi, arthropods, and other animal dander and proteins. Organic dust exposure increases the risk of a variety of pulmonary diseases such as airway inflammation, toxic pneumonitis, hypersensitivity pneumonitis, and asthma.

Organic dust toxic syndrome (ODTS, synonymous with grain, mill, or humidifier fever; silo unloaders' syndrome; inhalation fever; toxic pneumonitis; and pulmonary mycotoxicosis) appears to result from inhaling microbiological particles and toxins. Bacterial contamination of organic dust is common. Therefore, endotoxin is a component of many organic dusts and may be involved in ODTS. However, exposures in agricultural and other settings may be highly complex, and agents other than endotoxin may be important contributors to the acute and chronic health effects associated with organic dust exposure. For example, tannins, fungal glucans, and mycotoxins may contribute to inflammation resulting from grain dust exposure. Persons cleaning building materials extensively contaminated with fungi or bacteria also may be at risk of developing ODTS, but the role of fungal toxins (mycotoxins) or glucans in ODTS is unclear. Eduard & Halstensen identify methods to collect and analyze the various components that may be present in organic dust but point out that occupational exposure limits have been proposed for only some agents, for example, endotoxin and fungal spores.

ODTS is a poorly characterized condition similar to humidifier fever and other acute inflammatory responses to heavy exposures to organic material. It is a nonallergic, acute illness, characterized by fever, muscle pain, chest tightness, cough, headache, and dyspnea. The symptoms resemble those of influenza but usually disappear in one day provided the affected person is removed from exposure. Cormier & Schuyler describe and contrast clinical features of hypersensitivity pneumonitis and ODTS. The diagnosis of ODTS is based on a clinical presentation of fever, chills, cough, minimal dyspnea, chest tightness, myalgias, malaise, nausea, and headache four to twelve hours after exposure and lack of radiological, functional, immunological, or microbiological evidence of infectious disease or hypersensitivity pneumonitis.

Unlike hypersensitivity pneumonitis, ODTS is not an immune-mediated disease and does not require repeated exposures. The hypothesis that ODTS is toxic is supported by
- a delay between exposure and symptom onset too short for an infectious process;
- lack of necessity for prior exposure or sensitization;
- absence of serum antibodies to the suspected etiological agent;
- susceptibility of all similarly exposed persons; and
- spontaneous recovery within approximately 24 hours after withdrawal from exposure.

Formerly, ODTS was not associated with permanent lung damage, but studies now suggest an increased risk of chronic bronchitis in farmers. No specific therapy is needed for ODTS. Repeated episodes can occur after re-exposure to organic dusts, although workers may develop tolerance to the febrile effects. ODTS is not widely recognized because only serious cases or clusters of cases attract medical attention and many physicians may fail to recognize this reaction.

ODTS can be prevented through engineering and administrative controls and use of respiratory protection. Engineering controls can minimize the generation of dust and reduce air concentrations in many occupational settings. For agricultural workers handling organic dusts, CDC recommends using the most practical respirator with the highest assigned protection factor. Workers should be informed of the adverse health effects of breathing organic dusts and the symptoms associated with ODTS. Workers experiencing such symptoms should inform their physicians about recent dust exposure to avoid inappropriate treatment.

Mycotoxins

Bennet (1987) described mycotoxins as "... natural products produced by fungi that evoke a toxic response when introduced in low concentrations to higher vertebrates by a natural route." According to Samson, between 300 and 400 fungal metabolites (excluding mushroom poisons) are toxic, most of which are small molecules between 200 and

500 mass units (Daltons). These compounds constitute a toxigenically and chemically heterogeneous category. Among the most studied mycotoxins are aflatoxins, produced by certain strains of *Aspergillus flavus* and *Aspergillus parasiticus*; ochratoxins, produced by some species of *Penicillium* and *Aspergillus*; and thrichothecenes, produced by *Fusarium, Myrotecium, Trichoderma, Cephalosporium, Verticimonosporium,* and *Stachybotrys* species, primarily because of their importance in agriculture.

Not all strains of potentially toxigenic fungi produce mycotoxins in nature or under laboratory conditions. The kinds and amounts of toxin a fungus produces depend on complex and poorly understood interactions of factors that include

1. fungal species and strain;
2. colony maturity;
3. available water and food sources;
4. gases, temperature, and light in the environment;
5. presence of competitors; and
6. other, as yet unknown factors.

More than one fungal genus or species may produce the same mycotoxin. For example, *Aspergillus versicolor* and *Chaetomium* species can make sterigmatocystin. Conversely, a single fungal species may produce more than one mycotoxin. For example, *Stachybotrys chartarum* produces many toxic substances including satratoxin F, G, and H; roridin E; and verrucarin J and B.

Humans may be exposed via ingestion of contaminated food or by skin contact or inhalation. Exposure route affects toxic effect because poisons entering the lung pass directly into the circulation, unlike those ingested, which can be detoxified in the mouth or liver before entering general circulation. For instance, Creasia et al. performed acute inhalation experiments on rodents using pure T-2 toxin (a simple trichothecene toxin produced by various *Fusarium* species). They found in rats that inhalation was at least 20 times more toxic than intraperitoneal injection.

Mycotoxins have been detected in building materials and dust from moldy buildings even when the toxin-producing fungi were not found. When using spore counts to estimate exposure, Dean et al. advised investigators to consider the fungal species that are present because they found that the amount of mycotoxin in a spore was directly related to spore size (i.e., surface area). Spores have been considered the most common vehicle for inhalation exposure, but fungal allergens, ergosterol, glucan, and mycotoxins also have been detected in spore fragments, other small particles of fungal origin, and dust. These findings suggest that calculations based on spore counts could underestimate actual exposures. Mycotoxins associated with small particles are potentially more potent than equal masses of larger particles

because of the greater aggregate surface area of the smaller particles. Smaller particles also penetrate more deeply into the lung and are not cleared as readily, allowing for greater accumulation and longer contact at the point of deposition.

Health effects. In contrast to fungal infections (mycoses), mycotoxicoses are poisonings by natural and typically accidental means. The effects of a mycotoxin depends on the route of exposure (oral, dermal, or inhalation), the dose received, and the exposure pattern (acute or chronic). Mycotoxins have a broad range of known and suspected health effects, including immune system, inflammatory, carcinogenic, teratogenic, cardiovascular, pulmonary, and neurologic effects. Mycotoxins can be grouped by the organ they affect (e.g., hepatotoxin, nephrotoxin, neurotoxin, or immunotoxin), health effect (e.g., teratogen, mutagen, carcinogen, or allergen), chemical structure (e.g., lactone or coumarin), or biosynthetic origin (e.g., polyketide or amino acid-derived).

Interest in mycotoxins arises from the potent health effects that have been elicited in laboratory animals, clear associations between respiratory disease and fungal exposure in agricultural settings, concern about military use (as inhalant weapons) or terrorist use (primarily in food or water), and conclusions from case studies in residential and office buildings. Recent mouse model work showed that a β-D-glucan and a number of mycotoxins in moldy buildings activated gene clusters that produce markers for asthma-like symptoms in mice. Homology between mouse model and human genes is high; therefore, these results have implications for both atopic and nonatopic asthma in humans.

Attention to the potentially fatal effects of mycotoxins on infants began with a 1994 investigation in Cleveland, Ohio. A reanalysis of the data without age-matching of exposed and control infants reduced the odds ratio between exposure to *S. chartarum* and pulmonary hemorrhage from 9.8 to 1.5. The reanalysis identified valid criticisms about sampling methodology and misclassification linked to the difficulty of diagnosing idiopathic pulmonary hemosiderosis. *S. chartarum* may be a contributing factor to BRIs as evidenced by animal models that indicate that airway exposure can evoke allergic sensitization, inflammation, and cytotoxicity in the upper and lower respiratory tracts. Trichocethene toxicity appears to be the underlying cause of many of the adverse effects, along with allergenic proteins, atranones, proteinases, hemolysins, and glucans. However, the large variation in experimental design and difficulty of obtaining well-characterized exposure preparations have made it difficult to compare studies. Long-term, low-dose experiments that mimic conditions found in indoor environments, including coexposures with other environmental agents and factors, will be needed to clarify the role of *S. chartarum* in human health effects.

Fungi and their secondary metabolites also have been hypothesized to be contributors to BRSs (e.g., headaches, eye and throat irritation, sleep disturbances, nausea, dizziness, nose bleeds, and physical and mental fatigue). Others disagree, pointing out that at a toxic dose, specific mycotoxins elicit specific illness patterns rather than a panoply of nonspecific symptoms. However, this assertion ignores the complexity of exposure as outlined by Pestka et al.

Biological markers of mycotoxin exposure (e.g., the presence of an antigen or metabolite in blood, urine, or sputum) have been sought, and some serological markers have been proposed as evidence of exposure. Unfortunately, the reliability and significance of associations between potential indicators of inhalation exposure and various clinical signs and symptoms have not been established. Edmondson et al. found no significant differences between patients with mold-related health complaints and controls for T-cell proliferation, macrocyclic trichothecenes, mold-specific IgG, or mold-specific IgA levels. However, 70 percent of the patients had positive skin test reactions for molds, indicating that IgE-mediated or other nonimmune mechanisms could be the cause of their symptoms. Because people can be exposed to mycotoxins in food as well as through inhalation, estimates of exposure indoors also must consider possible ingestion exposure.

Environmental sampling. Exposure to mycotoxin can be measured through collection of air and source samples. For example, Broom et al. detected at least one of seven mycotoxins in 66 percent of samples of mold-contaminated building materials but not in air, dust, or material samples from indoor environments without water damage. Environmental samples are analyzed using chemical assays for specific mycotoxins or bioassays that demonstrate toxicity on selected cell lines or in whole animals. However, few laboratories have experience in these analyses for applications other than the testing of foods.

Data interpretation. No measurements of any airborne biological agents have shown consistent associations with occupant-reported symptoms, and measurements from dust samples have shown only limited, suggestive associations. While a few risk assessments have been performed for mycotoxins in food or animal feed, no credible risk assessments have been published for indoor inhalation or contact exposures. Kelman et al. modeled a hypothetical, maximum possible dose that an occupant could inhale over 24 hours of continuous exposure to a high concentration of fungal spores containing the maximum reported concentrations of nine mycotoxins. This group concluded (based on acute, i.e., short-term, rodent studies) that human mycotoxicoses are implausible for inhalation exposures to mycotoxins in mold-contaminated home, school, or office environments. Hardin et al. also concluded that air concentrations encountered in agricultural environments have the potential to produce mycotoxin concentrations greater than the concentration of no toxicologic concern that they calculated, but that common mycotoxin exposures in daily life, including in the built indoor environment, do not. However, the Kelman et al. risk assessment did not follow EPA protocols. Rather, they used animal studies not designed to find the most sensitive or critical end-point, the Lowest Observed Adverse Effect Level (LOAEL) or No Observed Adverse Effect Level (NOAEL), and labeled these as risk assessment terms. They then used a standard risk assessment model to derive exposure concentrations of no concern to humans of all ages.

Other researchers have pointed out that exposure estimates have not considered local toxic effects that may occur at the site of deposition of fungal particles where toxins can reach millimolar concentrations. In addition, there are no widely accepted guidelines on safe concentrations of fungal spores or mycotoxins in indoor air, and the additive or multiplicative effects of exposure to more than one toxin, to toxins with different target organs, and to combinations of biological agent are poorly understood. New tools, such as genomics and proteomics, may give insight that can be used in future risk assessments.

Endotoxins

The term *endotoxin* designates a class of lipopolysaccharide- or lipooligosaccharide-protein complexes that are integral parts of the outer membranes of gram-negative bacteria (e.g., species of *Aeromonas*, *Citrobacter*, *Enterobacter*, *Escherichia*, *Helicobacter*, *Klebsiella*, *Serratia*, and *Pseudomonas*). Gram-negative bacteria and endotoxins are found widely in soil and water, ambient air, dust, and on animals and plants. Endotoxins are present in whole bacterial cells and fragments of cell membranes. Endotoxin exposure has been studied in occupational settings, in particular, agricultural environments (where workers may be exposed to grains, silage, hay, straw, and animal bedding), waste processing facilities, textile industries, and machining operations, where workers may be exposed to contaminated metal-working fluids (MWFs). Other sources of occupational exposure are composted wood chips, stored timber, tobacco, and cotton dust. Workers in nonmanufacturing workplaces, such as office buildings and libraries, may be exposed to endotoxin if spray humidification systems contain gram-negative bacteria or other contaminated materials become aerosolized.

Health effects. The health effects of endotoxin exposure are mixed. Occupational studies have shown that exposure increases the likelihood of ODTS, chronic bronchitis, and asthma-like symptoms, but endotoxin exposure also can protect workers from respiratory allergies and allergen sensitization. Furthermore, endotoxin exposure can reduce the risk of allergic (atopic) asthma but increase the risk of non-allergic asthma. Responses may depend on an individual's immunological status, interaction between the dose and timing of exposure (with early life exposure protective, but exposure later in life a risk factor), environmental factors, and genetic predisposition.

Subjects exposed to endotoxin in inhalation experiments have experienced clinical effects such as fever, shivering, arthralgia, influenza-like symptoms (malaise), blood leukocytosis, neutrophilic airway inflammation, asthma symptoms (such as dry cough, dyspnea, and chest tightness), and bronchial obstruction, as well as dose-dependent lung function impairment and decreased lung diffusion capacity. Animal and human toxicity tests have shown that inhaled endotoxin causes inflammation with the release of proinflammatory cytokines and increased production of oxygen metabolites. Alveolar macrophages and bronchial epithelial cells are the primary targets and endothelial cell damage also has been observed. The concentrations of cytokines peak a few hours after inhalation. Using an established animal model, *Mycobacterium immunogenum* in MWFs has been shown to induce hypersensitivity pneumonitis, and coexposure with endotoxin can augment the severity of this response. Poole et al. studied the relative contribution of the microbial components muramic acid, endotoxin, 3-hydroxy fatty acids, and ergosterol to determine if single or a synergy of multiple microbial components mediated the inflammatory responses of human monocytes and bronchial epithelial cells to agricultural dusts. They concluded that in addition to endotoxin testing, muramic acid and possibly ergosterol testing is warranted when sampling in an agricultural environment in order to develop health hazard control measures and to determine effective interventions.

Sample collection and analysis. Endotoxin exposure is measured primarily by collection of filter air samples, settled dusts, or dust fall samples. Analysis is by the Limulus amebocyte lysate (LAL) assay (relative reactivity), fatty acid analysis by gas chromatography–mass spectrometry (GC–MS, total endotoxin), the recombinant Factor C (rFC) bioassay (free bioactive endotoxin), or whole blood assay (pyrogenic activity). Accurate characterization of endotoxin exposures requires agreement on and standardization of methods for sample collection and analysis. Consensus recommendations have been published for the measurement of endotoxin concentration in MWFs and workplace atmospheres. Sampling medium,

transport and storage conditions, and extraction methods have been studied to determine what differences they have on measured endotoxin. Spaan et al. proposed a protocol that prescribes glass-fiber filters, transport with desiccation, frozen sample storage, extraction in pyrogen-free water with 0.05 percent polysorbate 20 with rocking/shaking, frozen storage of extracts, and analysis in pyrogen-free water. In The Netherlands, the Dutch Expert Committee on Occupational Standards (DECOS) has recommended a health-based, eight-hour, exposure limit of 50 EU m^{-3}.

Spaan et al. found greater variability in exposure to airborne endotoxin between workers than day-to-day exposures, in contrast to what has been observed for exposures to chemical agents. They also observed that the total variance in endotoxin exposures was higher than for chemical exposures, with fewer and less-homogeneous exposure groups. They concluded that large measurement variability is an inherent part of endotoxin exposure, caused by many factors that influence bacterial growth and aerosolization, which investigators should take into account when sampling for endotoxin. Tager et al. found greater variability in ambient endotoxin concentrations than in measurements of other air contaminants. Therefore, researchers need to evaluate the spatial and temporal variability of endotoxin concentrations rather than rely on a few measurements from a single location.

Pfiesteria piscicida Organism

In the last decade a number of massive fish-kills have been observed in the mid-Atlantic estuarine waters. These events have been attributed to a presumptive toxin produced by *Pfiesteria piscicida*, a single-celled microorganism found in brackish waters. Under most conditions this protozoan-like dinoflagellate exists in a benign state. The organism generally lives on bacteria, algae, microfauna, and sloughed organic materials from fish prey. Twenty-four life stages have been identified, which include flagellate, amoeboid, and cyst stages. Most of these stages are nontoxic. Based upon observations, the optimum conditions for *Pfiesteria* toxin production that result in fish-kill include calm, shallow water with poor flushing; brackish conditions; warm temperatures; and abundant prey (fish) that produce the appropriate signal for toxin production.

Disease. Adverse health effects in humans have been described in connection with fish-kills and research associated with field and laboratory activities. These effects range from respiratory and eye irritation, skin rashes, and gastroenteritis (stomach cramps, nausea, vomiting) to cognitive and personality changes. Persons at risk for *Pfiesteria* toxin exposure include commercial and recreational fishermen, divers, biologists working with *Pfiesteria*, and other persons whose activities involve contact with contaminated water during fish-kills.

Unlike human exposures to several other dinoflagellate-produced toxins (e.g., paralytic shellfish poisoning [saxitoxin] or ciguatera fish poisoning), where exposures are associated with eating fish or shellfish with high levels of accumulated toxin, *Pfiesteria* toxin exposure is not known to be associated with eating affected fish. Rather, illness is thought to be related to exposure to toxin-laden water either by direct skin contact or by inhalation of aerosolized contaminated water.

Prevention. The need to implement suitable containment conditions becomes important with the knowledge that aerosol exposure and skin contact with *Pfiesteria* toxin-contaminated water has caused instances of human illness. The difficult question is what guidelines to use, biological or chemical. *P. piscicida* is not a human pathogen; it is the toxin that produces adverse health effects. The CDC/NIH BMBL guidelines specify four biosafety levels that are relevant for work with infectious microorganisms. Since the traditional biosafety levels do not apply in this situation, Appendix 1 in BMBL does give guidance for work with toxins of biological origin. Recently guidelines have been published that address handling chemicals in microbiology and biomedical laboratories. Four chemical safety levels (CSLs) are described that take into consideration the chemical hazard and the nature of the work with the chemical. Hill suggests that *Pfiesteria* toxin might be handled at CSL3 (substantial risk) rather than at BSL-2 or BSL-3. In addition to laboratory containment, field containment must also be addressed. State guidelines have been prepared for state employees in Maryland and North Carolina, both states that have had toxic *Pfiesteria* fish-kills. These varied guidelines provide good insight into *Pfiesteria* toxin containment based upon the work activity, the level of contamination, and the work environment.

Much remains to be learned about *P. piscicida*, its presumed toxin(s), the environmental conditions that promote toxin production, and the mechanisms by which the toxins produce adverse health effects in human beings. Long-term, multistate, cohort studies funded by the CDC are underway to collect baseline neurocognitive data and regular follow-up data on cohort members, and to study the linkage of neurocognitive findings with data on exposure to estuary water and the presence of *Pfiesteria* in these environments.

REGULATIONS AND GUIDELINES

There are few specific regulations that target work environments where employees might be exposed to infectious microorganisms or other biological agents, except those for which Threshold Limit Values® have been established (e.g., cellulose; some wood, cotton, and grain dusts; nicotine; pyrethrum; starch; subtilisins [proteolytic enzymes]; sucrose; and vegetable oil mist). The OSHA General Duty Clause (employers shall provide a workplace free of recognized hazards that cause or are likely to cause death or serious physical harm) is an example of an early, nonspecific regulation. Various government agencies (such as NIH, the National Cancer Institute, and the CDC) published guidelines in the 1970s that addressed issues relevant to microbiological safety. Although guidelines do not have the same impact as regulations, they are considered the accepted standard of practice at the time of their publication. Activities conducted in a manner contrary to published guidelines are generally considered unacceptable. Unlike guidelines, regulations define detailed requirements for specific activities, with penalties for noncompliance.

The following lists highlight relevant agencies, regulations, guidelines, and standards applicable to manipulation, transport, and disposal of infectious microorganisms or materials and professional organizations where biosafety and infection control assistance can be obtained. See also Appendix A, Additional Resources, in this text.

Regulations That Affect Laboratory Biosafety Practices
- OSHA: 29 *CFR* 1910.1030: Occupational Exposure to Bloodborne Pathogens.
- OSHA: Occupational Health and Safety Act; General Duty Clause, Section 5(a)(1).
- OSHA: 29 *CFR* 1910.132–133: Personal Protective Equipment Including Eye and Face Protection.
- OSHA: 29 *CFR* 1910.134: Respiratory Protection.
- U.S. EPA: Genetically engineered organisms in industry and registration of disinfectants (TSCA). Infectious wastes are not regulated by U.S. EPA. For information on EPA-registered disinfectants, see National Antimicrobial Information Network in Bibliography.
- U.S. DOT: 49 *CFR* Parts 106–107 and 171–180: Packaging and Transport of Hazardous Substances, Including Infectious Substances. (For further information contact the Office of Hazardous Materials at 202-366-4488.)
- U.S. PHS: 42 *CFR* Part 72: Interstate Shipment of Etiologic Agents, July 1980; Update: CDC Notice of proposed rulemaking, Oct. 28, 1999.
- U.S. PHS: 42 *CFR* Part 71.54: Foreign Quarantine, Etiologic Agents, Hosts, and Vectors. (An application and information on importation permits may be obtained by calling 1-888-CDC-FAXX and when prompted entering document # 101000.)
- U.S. PHS 42 *CFR* Part 72.6: Transfer of Select Biological Agents of Human Disease.
- U.S. Department of Commerce: Export of Infectious

Agents of Humans, Animals, Plants and Related Materials. (For information contact DOC Bureau of Export Administration at 202-482-4811.)

- U.S. Postal Service: 39 *CFR* Part 111: Mailability of Etiologic Agents. Codified in the Domestic Mail Manual 124.38: Etiologic Agent Preparations. A copy can be obtained from the GPO.
- U.S. Department of Agriculture: For importation of infectious agents of livestock, poultry, and other animal diseases, contact 301-734-3277. For importation of plant pests, contact 301-734-3277. Importation of both types of materials requires a permit.
- Public Law 107-188: the "Public Health Security and Bioterrorism Preparedness Response Act of 2002."
- 7 *CFR* Part 331 and 9 *CFR* Part 121: Agricultural Bioterrorism Protection Act of 2002; Possession, Use, and Transfer of Biological Agents and Toxins; Final Rule (published March 18, 2005).
- 42 *CFR* Parts 72 and 73 Office of Inspector General 42 *CFR* Part 1003: Possession, Use, and Transfer of Select Agents and Toxins; Final Rule (published March 18, 2005).
- Clinical Laboratory Improvement Act (CLIA) PL 100578, 1988. CDC published "Regulations for implementing the clinical laboratory improvement amendments of 1988: A summary," in *MMWR* 41:#RR2, pp. 1–17, 1992.
- Other: The FDA regulates antiseptics and disinfectants.

Guidelines for the Safe Use of Pathogenic or Oncogenic Microorganisms

- NIH: Guidelines for Research Involving Recombinant DNA Molecules. (Guidelines available on the NIH Office of Biotechnology Activities website. http://oba.od.nih.gov/oba/index.html)
- CDC/NIH: Biosafety in Microbiological and Biomedical Laboratories; U.S. safety guidance for work involving infectious agents.
- NRC/NAS, National Research Council of the National Academy of Sciences: *Biosafety in the Laboratory—Prudent Practices for Handling and Disposal of Infectious Materials.*
- CDC: *Infection Control Guidelines.* (Hospital Infections Branch.)
- WHO *Laboratory Biosafety Manual,* 3rd edition, 2004.
- WHO *Biorisk Management: Laboratory Biosecurity Guidance,* 2006.
- CWA15793: Laboratory Biorisk Management Standard.

Standard-Setting or Credentialing Groups

- JCAHO, Joint Commission on Accreditation of Healthcare Organizations, Oakbrook Terrace, IL. (Certification of laboratories in health care organizations.)
- NSF, National Sanitation Foundation Ann Arbor, MI. (Standard #49—Class II laminar flow biohazard cabinetry.)
- NCCLS, National Committee for Clinical Laboratory Standards, Villanova, PA. (Guidelines for: the protection of laboratory workers from instrument biohazards and infectious disease transmitted by blood, body fluids and tissue; and the handling and transport of clinical specimens.)
- ASTM, American Society for Testing and Materials, Philadelphia, PA.

Professional Associations

- American Biological Safety Association, Mundelein, IL
- American Society for Microbiology, Public and Scientific Affairs Board, Laboratory Practices Committee, Laboratory Safety Subcommittee, ASM, Washington, DC
- American Industrial Hygiene Association, Biosafety Committee, Fairfax, VA
- American Conference of Governmental Industrial Hygienists, Committees on Agricultural Health and Safety, Air Sampling Instruments, Bioaerosols, Construction, and Infectious Agents, Cincinnati, OH
- Association of Professionals in Infection Control, Washington, DC
- American Society of Heating, Refrigerating and Air Conditioning Engineers, Atlanta, GA
- Campus Safety Association (associated with the National Safety Council)
- National Safety Council, Itasca, IL
- Society for Healthcare Epidemiologists of America, Woodbury, NJ

ROLE OF INDUSTRIAL HYGIENISTS IN BIOSAFETY

Industrial hygienists are trained to anticipate and identify workplace and environmental hazards, evaluate their significance, and recommend programs and control measures to eliminate or minimize exposures (see Chapter 24, The Industrial Hygienist). Some of these roles are similar to those of a biosafety professional who develops and participates in programs to promote safe microbiological practices, procedures, and proper use of containment equipment and facilities; stimulates responsible activities among workers; and provides advice on laboratory design. Although industrial hygienists may focus on chemical, physical, or ergonomic hazards, they often also evaluate work-related illnesses caused by biological agents. Examples of such illnesses are infectious, hypersensitivity, or inflammatory diseases in agriculture, mining, textile manufacturing, and water treatment facilities. Industrial hygienists have also helped the medical community resolve PPE-related questions.

Biology is among the core scientific disciplines (along with physics, chemistry, and engineering) that address the nature of the work environment and that provide industrial hygienists with the necessary expertise to identify solutions. A few industrial hygienists may cover the broad range of biohazards described in this chapter. However, because the majority of them lack training in medical microbiology, infection control, or epidemiology, they deal only with environmental agents such as *Legionella* spp. and those that affect indoor air quality, such as microbial, plant, or animal allergens. An example of successful cooperation between the industrial hygiene and biosafety communities was the development of the Cal/OSHA ATD standards discussed previously.

Given their knowledge of engineering controls, ergonomics, and protective equipment selection and use, industrial hygienists can play an important role in the development and implementation of a biosafety program or an ATD exposure control plan. By training and experience, industrial hygienists generally can understand and monitor low-risk activities and situations (BSL-1 or -2). However, industrial hygienists who are not experienced microbiologists should seek the assistance of a biosafety professional when the work involves aerosol transmissible pathogens or agents requiring BSL-3 containment, such as *M. tuberculosis*. The pool of certified or registered biosafety specialists is relatively small but growing. The American Biological Safety Association (ABSA) is a good resource for locating qualified advisors. Since 2002, ABSA has had an alliance with the OSHA, and ABSA identifies rules, regulations, and guidelines from OSHA, the National Institute for Occupational Safety and Health, and other authorities at its website (www.absa.org). Fortunately, industrial hygienists and biosafety professionals have a history of successfully drawing upon each other's unique and overlapping expertise to resolve biological hazards in the workplace and can be expected to continue to do so as, together, they face current and future challenges.

SUMMARY

Agricultural, medical, and laboratory workers are most at risk for occupational biohazards, but many workplaces have the potential for such exposure, including microbiology, public health, and molecular biology laboratories; hospitals and other health care institutions; biotechnology facilities; veterinary practices; farms; wood-processing facilities; mines; textile manufacturers; and fishing and forestry industries. Therefore, containment of microorganisms and other biological hazards in all workplaces is critical to the health of workers and to the community. Engineering controls—safety equipment and facility design—and worker-initiated workplace controls—good work practices and carefully executed techniques—can minimize occupational biohazardous exposures.

BIBLIOGRAPHY

Acha PN, Sayfres B. *Zoonoses and Communicable Diseases Common to Man and Animals.* Scientific Publication #354. Washington, DC: Pan American Health Organization, 1980.

Addiss DG, Davis JP, LaVenture M, et al. Community-acquired Legionnaires' disease associated with a cooling tower: Evidence for longer-distance transport of *Legionella pneumophila. Am J Epidemiol* 130:557–568, 1989.

Adhikari A, Jung J, Reponen T, et al. Aerosolization of fungi, (1→3)-β-D glucan, and endotoxin from flood-affected materials collected in New Orleans homes. *Environ Res* 109:215–224, 2009.

Advisory Committee on Dangerous Pathogens (ACDP). *Categorisation of biological agents according to hazards and categories of containment,* 4th ed. London: Her Majesty's Stationery Office, 1995.

Advisory Committee on Dangerous Pathogens (ACDP). *The large scale contained use of biological agents.* London: Her Majesty's Stationery Office, 1998.

Allegheny County Health Department. *Approaches to Prevention and Control of Legionella Infection in Allegheny County Health Care Facilities.* Pittsburgh: Allegheny County Health Department, 1997.

Alter MJ. The epidemiology of acute and chronic hepatitis C. *Clinics in Liver Disease* 1:559–568, 1997.

American Conference of Governmental Industrial Hygienists. Introduction. In Macher JM, Ammann HM, Burge HA, et al., eds. *Bioaerosols: Assessment and Control.* Cincinnati, OH: ACGIH, 1999a, pp. 1-1–1-5.

American Conference of Governmental Industrial Hygienists. Health effects of bioaerosols. In Macher JM, Ammann HM, Burge HA, et al., eds., *Bioaerosols: Assessment and Control.* Cincinnati, OH: ACGIH, 1999b, pp. 3-1–3-12.

American Conference of Governmental Industrial Hygienists. Developing an investigation strategy. In Macher JM, Ammann HM, Burge HA, et al., eds., *Bioaerosols: Assessment and Control.* Cincinnati, OH: ACGIH, 1999c, pp. 2-1–2-10.

American Conference of Governmental Industrial Hygienists. The building walkthrough. In Macher JM, Ammann HM, Burge HA, et al., eds. *Bioaerosols: Assessment and Control.* Cincinnati, OH: ACGIH, 1999d, pp. 4-1–4-9.

American Conference of Governmental Industrial Hygienists. Developing a sampling plan. In Macher JM, Ammann HM, Burge HA, et al., eds. *Bioaerosols: Assessment and Control.* Cincinnati, OH: ACGIH, 1999e, pp. 5-1–5-13.

American Conference of Governmental Industrial Hygienists. Introduction to the biologically derived airborne contaminants. In *2011 TLVs® and BEIs®.* Cincinnati, OH: ACGIH, pp. 225–228, 2011.

American Industrial Hygiene Association. *Biosafety Reference Manual.* Fairfax, VA: AIHA, 1995.

American Industrial Hygiene Association. *Legionella* bacteria in air and water samples. In Dillon HK, Heinsohn PA, Miller JD, eds. *Field Guide for the Determination of Biological Contaminants in Environmental Samples.* Fairfax, VA: AIHA, 1996a, pp. 97–117.

American Industrial Hygiene Association. Viable air sampling instruments: Description and operating procedures. In Dillon HK, Heinsohn PA, Miller JD, eds. Field Guide to the Determination of Biological Contaminants in Environmental Samples. Fairfax, VA: AIHA, 1996b, pp. 75–95.

American Industrial Hygiene Association. Viable fungi and bacteria in air, bulk, and surface samples. In Dillon HK, Heinsohn PA, Miller JD, eds. *Field Guide to the Determination of Biological Contaminants in Environmental Samples.* Fairfax, VA: AIHA, 1996c, pp. 37–74.

American Industrial Hygiene Association. Substances derived from bacteria in air, water, and bulk samples. In Dillon HK, Heinsohn PA, Miller JD, eds. *Field Guide for the Determination of Biological Contaminants in Environmental Samples.* Fairfax, VA: AIHA, 1996d, pp. 131–148.

American Industrial Hygiene Association. Total (viable and nonviable) fungi and substances derived from fungi in air, bulk, and surface samples. In Dillon HK, Heinsohn PA, Miller JD, eds. *Field Guide for the Determination of Biological Contaminants in Environmental Samples.* Fairfax, VA: AIHA, 1996e, pp. 119–130.

American Lung Association. *Agricultural Respiratory Hazards Education Series (9 parts).* Ames, Iowa: American Lung Association of Iowa, 1986.

American Public Health Association. American Water Works Association. Water Environment Federation. 9213. Recreational Waters. 9260. Detection of Pathogenic Bacteria. In Clesceri LS, Greenberg AE, Eaton AD, eds. *Standard Methods for the Examination of Water and Wastewater,* 20th ed. Washington, DC: APHA, 1998, pp. 9-28–9-31, 9-91–9-110.

American Society for Testing and Materials. *Standard Guide for Inspecting Water Systems for Legionellae and Investigating Possible Outbreaks of Legionellosis (Legionnaires' disease or Pontiac fever),* D 5952–08. West Conshohocken, PA: ASTM, 2008.

American Society for Testing and Materials. *Standard Practice for Personal Sampling and Analysis of Endotoxin in Metalworking Fluid Aerosols in Workplace Atmospheres, Practice* E2144-07. West Conshohocken, PA: ASTM, 2007.

American Society of Heating, Refrigerating and Air-Conditioning Engineers Standard Project Committee 12-2000. *Minimizing the Risk of Legionellosis Associated with Building Water Systems.* Atlanta: ASHRAE, Inc., 2000.

Ammann AJ. Immunodeficiency diseases. In Stites DP, Stobo JD, Wells JU, eds. *Basic and Clinical Immunology.* Norwalk, CT: Appleton & Lange, 1987, pp. 317–355.

Ammann HM. Mycotoxins in indoor environments. *Mycotoxin Res* 21:157–163, 2005.

Ammann HM, Hodgson M, Nevalainen A, et al. Indoor mold: Basis for health concerns. In Prezant B, Weeks B, and Miller JD, Eds. *Recognition, Evaluation, and Control of Indoor Mold.* Fairfax, VA: AIHA, 2008, pp. 3–19.

Ammann HM. Microbial volatile organic compounds. In Macher JM, Ammann HM, Burge HA, et al., eds. *Bioaerosols: Assessment and Control.* Cincinnati, OH: ACGIH, 1999, pp. 26-1–26-17.

Ammann HM. IAQ and human toxicosis: Empirical evidence and theory. In Johanning E, ed. *Bioaerosols, Fungi and Mycotoxins: Health Effects, Assessment, Prevention and Control.* Albany, NY, and New York: Eastern New York Occupational and Environmental Health Center (Albany) and Mount Sinai School of Medicine (New York), 2000, pp. 84–93.

Andrews JH, Hirano SS, eds. *Microbial Ecology of Leaves.* New York: Springer-Verlag, 1992.

Arey IB, Burrows W, Greenhill JP, et al., eds. *Dorland's Illustrated Medical Dictionary,* 28th ed. Philadelphia: WB Saunders, 1994.

Arlian LG. House dust mites. In Macher JM, Ammann HM, Burge HA, et al., eds. *Bioaerosols: Assessment and Control.* Cincinnati, OH: ACGIH, 1999, pp. 22-1–22-9.

Association for Professionals in Infection Control and Epidemiology Bioterrorism Task Force and Centers for Disease Control and Prevention Bioterrorism Working

Group. *Bioterrorism Readiness Plan: A Template for Healthcare Facilities.* April 13, 1999. Available at www.apic.org/educ/readinow.html and www.cdc.gov/ncidod/hip/13apr99APICCDCBioterrorism.PDF

Atlas RM, Bartha R. *Microbial Ecology: Fundamentals and Applications*, 4th ed. San Francisco: Benjamin-Cummings Publishing Co., 1998.

Baek SH, You K, Katano T, et al. Effects of temperature, salinity, and prey organisms on the growth of three *Pfiesteria*-like heterotrophic dinoflagellates. *Plankton Benthos Res* 5:31–38, 2010.

Baron RC, McCormick JB, Zubeir OA. Ebola virus disease in southern Sudan: Hospital dissemination and intrafamilial spread. *Bull World Health Organ* 61:997–1003, 1983.

Bartram J, Bentham R, Briand E, et al. Approaches to risk management. In Bartram J, Chartier Y, Lee JV, et al., eds. *Legionella and the Prevention of Legionellosis.* Geneva: World Health Organization, 2007, pp. 39–50.

Beasley RP, Hwang L-Y. Epidemiology of hepatocellular carcinoma. In Vyas GN, Dienstag JL, Hoofnagle JH, eds. *Viral Hepatitis and Liver Disease.* Orlando, FL: Grune & Stratton, p. 209, 1984.

Becker MM, Graham RL, Donaldson EF, et al. Synthetic recombinant bat SARS-like coronavirus is infectious in cultured cells and in mice. *Proc Natl Acad Sci USA* 105:19944–19949, 2008.

Bennett JW. Mycotoxins, mycotoxicoes, mycotoxicology and mycopathologia. *Mycopathologia* 100:3–5, 1987.

Bennett JW, Klich M. Mycotoxins. *Clin Microbiol Rev* 16:497–516, 2003.

Bentham R, Surman-Lee S, Lee JV, et al. Potable water and in-building distribution systems. In Bartram J, Chartier Y, Lee JV, et al., eds. *Legionella and the Prevention of Legionellosis.* Geneva: World Health Organization, 2007, pp. 57–68.

Bernard KW, Parham GL, Winkler WG, et al. Q fever control measures: Recommendations for research facilities using sheep. *Infect Control* 3:461–465, 1982.

Biagini RE. From fungal exposure to disease: A biological monitoring conundrum. In Johanning E, ed. *Bioaerosols, Fungi and Mycotoxins: Health Effects, Assessment, Prevention and Control.* Albany, NY, and New York: Eastern New York Occupational and Environmental Health Center (Albany) and Mount Sinai School of Medicine (New York), 2000, pp. 320–329.

Binding N, Jaschinski S, Werlich S, et al. Quantification of bacterial lipopolysaccharides (endotoxin) by GC–MS determination of 3-hydroxy fatty acids. *J Environ Monit* 6:65–70, 2004.

Birenzvige A. *Inhalation Hazard from Reaerosolized Biological Agents: A Review.* Aberdeen, MD: U.S. Army Chemical Research, Development and Engineering Center, Report TR–413, 1992.

Birnbaum D. Statistics for hospital epidemiology: CQI tools, sentinel events, warning and action limits. *Infect Control Hosp Epidemiol* 14:537–539, 1993.

Block SS. *Disinfection, Sterilization and Preservation,* 4th ed. Philadelphia: Lea & Febiger, 1991.

Blatny JM, Reif BAP, Skogan G, et al.. Tracking airborne *Legionella* and *Legionella pneumophila* at a biological treatment plant. *Environ Sci Technol* 42:7360–7367, 2008.

Bloom E., Bal K, Nyman E, et al. Mass spectrometry-based strategy for direct detection and quantification of some mycotoxins produced by *Stachybotrys* and *Aspergillus* spp. in indoor environments. *Appl Environ Microbiol* 73:4211–4217, 2007.

Bloom E., Nyman E, Must A., et al. Molds and mycotoxins in indoor environments: A survey in water-damaged buildings. *J Occup Environ Hyg* 6:671–678, 2009.

Blyth CC, Adams DN,Chen SCA. Diagnostic and typing methods for investigating *Legionella* infection. *NSW Pub Health Bull* 20:157–161, 2009.

Boehlecke B, Jacobs R. Endotoxins. In Wald PH, Stave GM, eds. *Physical and Biological Hazards of the Workplace.* New York: Van Nostrand Reinhold, 1994, pp. 483–487.

Brandt M, Brown C, Burkhart J, et al. Mold prevention strategies and possible health effects in the aftermath of hurricanes and major floods. *MMWR* 55:1–27, 2006.

Brasel TL, Douglas DR, Wilson SC, et al. Detection of airborne *Stachybotrys chartarum* macrocyclic trichothecene mycotoxins on particulates smaller than conidia. *Appl Environ Microbiol* 71:114–122, 2005a.

Brasel TL, Martin JM, Carriker CG, et al. Detection of airborne *Stachybotrys chartarum* macrocyclic trichothecene mycotoxins in the indoor environment. *Appl Environ Microbiol* 71:7376–7388, 2005b.

Breiman RF, Cozen W, Fields BS, et al. Role of air sampling in investigation of an outbreak of Legionnaires' disease associated with exposure to aerosols from an evaporative condenser. *J Infect Dis* 161:1257–1261, 1990.

Breiman RF. Modes of transmission in epidemic and nonepidemic *Legionella* infection: Directions for future study. In Barbaree JM, Breiman RF, Dufour AP, eds. *Legionella: Current Status and Emerging Perspectives.* Washington, DC: ASM Press, 1993, pp. 30–35.

Breiman RF, Butler JC. Legionellosis. In Wallace RB, ed. *Public Health & Preventive Medicine,* 14th ed. Stamford, CT: Appleton & Lange, 1998, pp. 246–248.

Brooks GF, Butel JS, Morse SA, eds. *Jawetz, Melnick, & Adelberg's Medical Microbiology,* 21st ed. Norwalk, CT: Appleton & Lange, 1998.

Brosseau LM, McCullough NV, Vesley D. Mycobacterial aerosol collection efficiency by respirator and surgical mask filters under varying conditions of flow and humidity. *App Occ Environ Hyg* 12(6):435–445, 1997.

Bryan JL, Fields HF. An ounce of prevention is worth a pound of cure: Shoring up the public health infrastructure to respond to bioterrorist attacks. *Am J Infect Control* 27:465–467, 1999.

Burch JB, Svendsen E, Siegel PD, et al. Endotoxin exposure and inflammation markers among agricultural workers in Colorado and Nebraska. *J Toxicol Environ Health A* 73:5–22, 2010.

Burge HA. *Bioaerosols*. Boca Raton, FL: CRC/Lewis Publishers, 1995.

Burge HA. Fungal toxins and "α-(1,3)-D-glucans." In Macher JM, Ammann HM, Burge HA, et al., eds. *Bioaerosols: Assessment and Control*. Cincinnati, OH: ACGIH, 1999, pp. 24-1–24-13.

Burge HA, Otten JA. Fungi. In Macher JM, Ammann HM, Burge HA, et al., eds. *Bioaerosols: Assessment and Control*. Cincinnati, OH: ACGIH, 1999, pp. 19-1–19-13.

Burkholder JM, Glasgow HB. Interactions of a toxic estuarine dinoflagellate with microbial predators and prey. *Arch Protistenkd* 145:177–188, 1995.

Burkholder JM, Gordon AS, Moeller PD, et al. Demonstration of toxicity to fish and to mammalian cells by Pfiesteria species: Comparison of assay methods and strains. *P Natl Acad Sci* 102:3471–3476, 2005.

Burkholder JM. The lurking perils of pfiesteria. *Sci Amer* August 1999, pp. 42–49.

Bush RK, Portnoy JM, Saxon A, et al. The medical effects of mold exposure. *J Allergy Clin Immunol* 117:326–333, 2006.

California Department of Public Health. Reportable Diseases and Conditions. http://www.cdph.ca.gov/HealthInfo/Pages/ReportableDiseases.aspx

California Department of Public Health, Division of Environmental and Occupational Disease Control, Environmental Health Laboratory Branch. *Statement on Building Dampness, Mold, and Health*. Richmond, CA: California Dept. of Public Health, 2011.

California Occupational Safety and Health Administration. *Aerosol Transmissible Disease Standard* and *Aerosol Transmissible Disease Standard—Zoonotic*. Title 8, California Code of Regulations, Sections 5199 and 5199.1. www.dir.ca.gov/title8/5199.html

Caskey S, Gaudioso J, Salerno R, et al., *Biosafety Risk Assessment Methodology, Sandia Report, SAND 2010-6487*. Albuquerque, NM: Sandia National Labs, October 2010.

Castranova V, Robinson VA, Frazer DG. Pulmonary reactions to organic dust exposures: Development of an animal model. *Environ Health Perspec* 104(suppl 1):41–53, 1996.

Cello J, Paul AV, Wimmer E. Chemical synthesis of poliovirus cDNA: Generation of infectious virus in the absence of natural template. *Science* 297:1016–1018, 2002.

CEN, European Committee for Standardization. *Workplace Atmospheres—Determination of Airborne Endotoxin*, CEN/TC 137 Work Programme, Project Reference EN 14031. Brussels: CEN, 2003.

Centers for Disease Control. *Classification of Etiologic Agents on the Basis of Hazard*, 4th ed. Washington, DC: U.S. Dept. of Health, Education and Welfare, Public Health Service, Office of Biosafety, 1974.

Centers for Disease Control. Unpublished data. Center for Infectious Diseases. HEW, Public Health Service, 1976.

Centers for Disease Control. Interstate shipment of etiologic agents (42 *CFR* Part 72). Part 72.2: Transportation of diagnostic specimens, biological products and other material; Part 72.3: Transportation of materials containing certain etiologic agents: Minimum packaging requirements. *Fed Reg* 45(141), July 21, 1980.

Centers for Disease Control. Guidelines for prevention of *Herpesvirus simiae* (B virus) infection in monkey handlers. *MMWR* 36:680–689, 1987a.

Centers for Disease Control. Recommendations for prevention of HIV transmission in health care settings. *MMWR* 36:2 Supplement, 1987b.

Centers for Disease Control. Guidelines to prevent simian immunodeficiency virus infection in laboratory workers and animal handlers. *MMWR* 37:693–694, 699–704, 1988.

Centers for Disease Control. Ebola virus infection in imported primates—Virginia, 1989. *MMWR* 38:831–832, 837–838, 1989.

Centers for Disease Control. Update: Ebola-related filovirus infection in nonhuman primates and interim guidelines for handling nonhuman primates during transit and quarantine. *MMWR* 39:22–30, 1990a.

Centers for Disease Control. Update: Filovirus infection in animal handlers. *MMWR* 39:221, 1990b.

Centers for Disease Control. Update on adult immunization: Recommendations of the immunization practices advisory committee (ACIP). *MMWR* 40:RR–12, 1991a.

Centers for Disease Control. Nosocomial transmission of multi-drug-resistant tuberculosis among HIV-infected persons: Florida and New York, 1988–1991. *MMWR* 40:585–591, 1991b.

Centers for Disease Control. Seroconversion to simian immunodeficiency virus in two laboratory workers.

MMWR 41:678–681, 1992.

Centers for Disease Control and Prevention. Recommendations of the advisory committee on immunization practices (ACIP): Use of vaccines and immune globulins in persons with altered immunocompetence. *MMWR* 42:RR–4, 1993b.

Centers for Disease Control and Prevention. Tuberculosis morbidity: United States, 1992. *MMWR* 42:696–704, 1993c.

Centers for Disease Control and Prevention. Update: Hantavirus pulmonary syndrome: U.S. *MMWR* 42:816–820, 1993d.

Centers for Disease Control and Prevention. *Procedures for the Recovery of* Legionella *from the Environment.* Atlanta: Centers for Disease Control and Prevention, 1994a.

Centers for Disease Control and Prevention. Guidelines for preventing the transmission of *Mycobacterium tuberculosis* in health-care facilities. *MMWR* 43:RR–13, 1994b.

Centers for Disease Control and Prevention. Request for Assistance in Preventing Organic Dust Toxic Syndrome. (DHHS NIOSH publication no. 94-102.) Cincinnati, OH: U.S. Department of Health and Human Services, CDC, 1994c.

Centers for Disease Control and Prevention. Proportionate mortality from pulmonary tuberculosis associated with occupations: 28 states, 1979–1990. *MMWR* 44:14–19, 1995.

Centers for Disease Control and Prevention. *Final Recommendations to Minimize Transmission of Legionnaires' Disease from Whirlpool Spas on Cruise Ships.* Atlanta: CDC, 1996.

Centers for Disease Control and Prevention. Immunization of Health-Care Workers. *MMWR* 46:22–23, 1997a.

Centers for Disease Control and Prevention. Legionnaires disease. Prevention and control of legionnaires disease. Appendix B. Maintenance procedures used to decrease survival and multiplication of *Legionella* sp. in potable-water distribution systems. Appendix C. Culturing environmental specimens for *Legionella* sp. Appendix D. Procedure for cleaning cooling towers and related equipment. In Guidelines for Prevention of Nosocomial Pneumonia, *MMWR* 46:RR–1, 1997b.

Centers for Disease Control and Prevention. Public Health guidelines for the management of health-care worker exposures to HIV and recommendations for postexposure prophylaxis. *MMWR* 47:RR–7, 1998a.

Centers for Disease Control and Prevention. Preventing emerging infectious diseases: A strategy for the 21st century. *MMWR* 47:RR–15, 1998b.

Centers for Disease Control and Prevention. Recommendations for prevention and control of hepatitis C virus (HCV) infection and HCV-related chronic disease. *MMWR* 47:RR–19, 1998c.

Centers for Disease Control and Prevention. Packaging and handling of infectious substances and select agents: Notice of proposed rulemaking. 42 *CFR* Part 72. *Fed Reg* 64(208):58022–58031, 1999a.

Centers for Disease Control and Prevention. Bioterrorism alleging use of anthrax and interim guidelines for management: United States, 1998. *MMWR* 48:69–74, 1999b.

Centers for Disease Control and Prevention. Biological and chemical terrorism: Strategic plan for preparedness and response. *MMWR* 49(RR–4):1–14, 2000a.

Centers for Disease Control and Prevention. Guidelines for surveillance, prevention, and control of West Nile virus infection—United States. *MMWR* 49(2):25–28, 2000b.

Centers for Disease Control and Prevention. Update: Investigation of anthrax associated with intentional exposure and interim public health guidelines, October 2001. *MMWR* 50:889-893, 2001a.

Centers for Disease Control and Prevention. Recognition of illness associated with the intentional release of a biologic agent. *MMWR* 50:893–897, 2001b.

Centers for Disease Control and Prevention. Guidelines for environmental infection control in health-care facilities: Recommendations of CDC and the Healthcare Infection Control Practices Advisory Committee (HICPAC). *MMWR* 52:RR-10, 2003.

Centers for Disease Control and Prevention. Update: Pulmonary hemorrhage/hemosiderosis among infants: Cleveland, Ohio, 1993–1996. *MMWR* 49:180–184, 2000c.

Centers for Disease Control and Prevention. Legionnaires disease: Prevention and control of Legionnaires disease. In *Guidelines for Prevention of Health-Care-Associated Pneumonia. MMWR* 53:RR-3, 2004.

Centers for Disease Control and Prevention. Guidelines for preventing the transmission of *Mycobacterium tuberculosis* in health-care settings. *MMWR* 54:RR-17, 2005.

Centers for Disease Control and Prevention. *Procedures for the Recovery of Legionella from the Environment.* Atlanta: CDC, 2005.

Centers for Disease Control and Prevention. Viral Hepatitis Statistics and Surveillance (website). Atlanta: CDC, 2009. http://www.cdc.gov/hepatitis/Statistics/index.htm

Centers for Disease Control and Prevention. Occupational HIV Transmission and Prevention among Health Care Workers. Atlanta: CDC, August 2011. http://www.cdc.gov/hiv/resources/factsheets/hcwprev.htm#1

Centers for Disease Control and Prevention. The ELITE Program: Environmental Legionella Isolation Techniques Evaluation (ELITE). Atlanta: CDC, 2011. http://www.cdc.gov/legionella/elite-intro.htm

Centers for Disease Control and Prevention and National Institutes of Health. Primary Containment of Biohazards: Selection, Installation, and Use of Biological Safety Cabinets. Washington, DC: U.S. Government Printing Office, 1995.

Centers for Disease Control and Prevention and National Institutes of Health. *Proposed guidelines for goals for working safely with* M. tuberculosis *in clinical, public health, and research laboratories*. Atlanta: U.S. Department of Health and Human Services, Public Health Service, 1997.

Centers for Disease Control and Prevention and National Institutes of Health. *Biosafety in Microbiological and Biomedical Laboratories,* 5th ed. Washington, DC: Department of Health and Human Services: Public Health Service, U.S. Government Printing Office, stock number 017-040-00561-0, 2009.

Chan-Yeung M, Enarson DA, Kennedy SM. The impact of grain dust on respiratory health. *Am Rev Respir Dis* 145:476–487, 1992.

Chun DTW, Chew V, Bartlett K, et al. Preliminary report on the results of the second phase of a round-robin endotoxin assay study using cotton dust. *Appl Occup Environ Hyg* 15:152–157, 2000.

Clark PK. OSHA Memorandum: Changes to OSHA Instruction CPL 2–2.44C Regarding First Responders, July 1, 1992.

Clark RA. OSHA directorate of compliance programs, OSHA enforcement policy and procedures for occupational exposure to tuberculosis. *Infect Control Hosp Epidemiol* 14:694–699, 1993.

Cohen R. Occupational Infections. In LaDou J, ed. *Occupational and Environmental Medicine,* 2nd ed. Stamford, CT: Appleton and Lange, 1997, pp. 221–234.

Cole LA. Risks of publicity about bioterrorism: Anthrax hoaxes and hype. *Am J Infect Control* 27:470–473, 1999.

Collins CH, Aw TC, Grange JM. *Microbial Diseases of Occupations, Sports & Recreations.* Oxford: Butterworth-Heinemann, 1997, pp. 29–30, 70, 107–108, 117.

Collins CH, Kennedy DA, eds. *Laboratory-Acquired Infections: History, Incidences, Causes, and Preventions,* 4th ed. Oxford, UK: Butterworth-Heinemann, 1999.

Constable PJ, Harrington JM. Risks of zoonoses in a veterinary service. *Br Med J* 284:246–248, 1982.

Constantine DG. Diseases transmitted primarily from animals to humans (zoonoses). In Wallace RB, ed. *Public Health and Preventive Medicine,* 14th ed. Stamford, CT: Appleton & Lange, 1998, pp. 349–371.

Cooling Tower Institute. *Legionellosis Guideline: Best Practices for Control of Legionella.* Houston, TX: Cooling Tower Institute, 2006.

Cooper M, Phillips R. Exploratory analysis of the safety climate and safety behavior relationship. *Journal of Safety Research* 35:497-512, 2004.

Cormier Y, Schuyler M. Hypersensitivity pneumonitis and organic dust toxic syndromes. In Bernstein DI, Chan-Yeung M., Malo J-L, eds. *Asthma in the Workplace, and Related Conditions.* 3rd ed. New York: Taylor and Francis, 2006, pp. 713–736.

Cottam AN, Biotechnology. In Raffle PAB, Adams PH, Baxter PJ, et al., eds. *Hunter's Diseases of Occupations.* Boston: Edward Arnold, 1994, pp. 577–589.

Cox CS, Wathes CM. *Bioaerosols Handbook.* Boca Raton, FL: CRC/Lewis Publishers, 1995.

Cox-Ganser JM, Park J-H, Kreiss K. Office workers and teachers. In Tarlo S, Cullinan P, and Nemery B., eds., *Occupational and Environmental Lung Diseases: Diseases from Work, Home, Outdoor and Other Exposures.* Hoboken, NJ: Wiley-Blackwell, 2010, pp. 313–335.

Crandall MS, Sieber WK. The National Institute for Occupational Safety and Health indoor environmental evaluation experience. Part one: Building environmental evaluations. *Appl Occup Environ Hyg* 11:533–539, 1996.

Creasia DA, Thurman JD, Wannemacher RW. Acute inhalation toxicity of T-2 mycotoxin in the rat and guinea pig. *Fund Appl Toxicol.* 14:54–59, 1990.

Danzig R, Berkowsky PB. Why should we be concerned about biological warfare? *JAMA* 278:431–432, 1997.

Dean TR, Black JA, Foarde K, et al. Analysis of fungal spore mycotoxin and the relationship between spore surface area and mycotoxin content utilizing a protein translation inhibition assay. *Open Mycol J.* 2:55–60, 2008.

Decker MD. OSHA enforcement policy for occupational exposure to tuberculosis. *Infect Control Hosp Epidemiol* 14:689–693, 1993.

Dennis PJ, Brenner DJ, Thacker WL, et al. Five new *Legionella* species isolated from water. *Int J Syst Bacteriol* 43:329–337, 1993.

Desmyter J, Johnson KM, Deckers C, et al. Laboratory rat associated outbreak of haemorrhagic fever with renal syndrome due to hantaan-like virus in Belgium. *Lancet* ii:1445–1448, 1983.

Dietrich R, Johanning E, Gareis M, et al. Immunochemical detection of mycotoxins associated with stachybotryotoxicosis. In Johanning E, ed., *Bioaerosols,*

Fungi and Mycotoxins: Health Effects, Assessment, Prevention and Control. Albany, NY, and New York: Eastern New York Occupational and Environmental Health Center (Albany), Mount Sinai School of Medicine (New York), 2000, pp. 482–491.

Dillon HK, Miller JD, Sorenson WG, et al. Review of methods applicable to the assessment of mold exposure to children. *Environ Health Perspect* 107(suppl 3):473–480, 1999.

do Pico GA. Grain dust. In Rylander R, Jacobs RR, eds., *Organic Dusts: Exposure, Effects, and Prevention.* Boca Raton, FL: Lewis Publishers, 1994, pp. 193–218.

Donham KJ. Zoonotic diseases of occupational significance in agriculture: A review. *Int J Zoonoses* 12:163–191, 1985.

Donham KJ. Swine confinement buildings. In Rylander R, Jacobs RR, eds. *Organic Dusts: Exposure, Effects, and Prevention.* Boca Raton, FL: Lewis Publishers, 1994, pp. 219–232.

Douwes J, Pearce N, Heederik D. Does environmental endotoxin exposure prevent asthma? *Thorax* 57:86–90, 2002.

Douwes J, Thorne P, Pearce N, et al. Bioaerosol health effects and exposure assessment: progress and prospects. *Ann Occup Hyg* 47:187–200, 2003.

Douwes J, Brooks CPN. The protective effects of farming on allergies and asthma: Have we learnt anything since 1873? *Exp Rev Clin Immunol* 5:213–219, 2009.

Ducatman AM, Liberman DF. The biotechnology industry. *Occup Med* 6(2), 1991.

Dungan RS, Leytem AB. The effect of extraction, storage, and analysis techniques on the measurement of airborne endotoxin from a large dairy. *Aerobiologia.* 25:265–273, 2009.

Dutch Expert Committee on Occupational Standards. *Health Based Recommended Occupational Exposure Limit for Endotoxins,* publication 1998/03WGD. Rijswijk, The Netherlands: Dutch Expert Committee on Occupational Standards (DECOS), Health Council for the Netherlands, 1998.

Dutkiewicz J, Jablonski L, Olenchock SA. Occupational biohazards: A review. *Am J Indust Med* 14:605–623, 1988.

Dworzack DL. Freshwater: From lakes to hot tubs. In Schlossberg D, ed., *Infections of Leisure,* 2nd ed. Washington, DC: ASM Press, 1999, pp. 93–124.

Edelstein PH. Legionella. In Murray, PR, ed., *Manual of Clinical Microbiology,* 9th edition. Washington, DC: ASM Press, 2007, pp. 835–849.

Edmondson DA, Barrios CS, Brasel TL, et al. Immune response among patients exposed to molds. *Int J Mol Sci* 10:5471–5484, 2009.

Eduard W. Fungal spores: A critical review of the toxicological and epidemiological evidence as a basis for occupational exposure limit setting. *Crit Rev Toxicol* 39:799–864, 2009.

Eduard W, Halstensen AS. Quantitative exposure assessment of organic dust. *SJWEH Suppl* 7:30–35, 2009.

Eitzen E, Pavlin J, Cieslak T, et al., eds. *Medical Management of Biological Casualties Handbook,* 3rd ed. Fort Detrick, MD: U.S. Army Medical Research Institute of Infectious Disease, appendix B, 1998.

English JF. Overview of bioterrorism readiness plan: a template for health care facilities. *Am J Infect Control* 27:468–469, 1999.

Enterlein S, Volchkov V, Weik M, et al. Rescue of recombinant Marburg virus from cDNA is dependent on nucleocapsid protein VP30. *J Virol* 80:1038–1043, 2006.

Erdogan H, Erdogan A, Lakamdayali H, et al. Travel-associated Legionnaires disease: Clinical features of 17 cases and a review of the literature. *Diagn Microbiol Infect Dis* 68:297–303, 2010.

Espinal et al. Infectiousness of *Mycobacterium tuberculosis* in HIV-1 infected patients with tuberculosis: A prospective study. *Lancet* 355:275–280, Jan 22, 2000.

European Committee on Standardization. Laboratory biorisk management standard (CWA 15793:2008). Brussels: European Committee on Standardization (CEN), 2008. ftp://ftp.cenorm.be/PUBLIC/CWAs/workshop31/CWA15793.pdf

European Economic Community. Document No 4645/1/91 EN Draft proposal for a council directive amending directive 90/679/EEC on the protection of workers from risks related to exposure to biological agents at work. Brussels: EEC, 1991.

Fattovich G, Guistina G, Degos F, et al. Morbidity and mortality in compensated cirrhosis type C: A retrospective follow-up study of 384 patients. *Gastroenterology* 112:463–472, 1997.

Favero MS. Dialysis-associated diseases and their control. In Bennet JV, Brachman PS, eds. *Hospital Infections.* Boston: Little, Brown & Co, 1985, pp. 267–284.

Favero MS, Bond WW. Sterilization, disinfection and antisepsis in the hospital. In Balows A, ed. *Manual of Clinical Microbiology.* Washington, DC: American Society for Microbiology, 1991, pp. 183–200.

Fields BS. Legionellae and Legionnaires' disease. In Hurst CJ, ed., *Manual of Environmental Microbiology.* Washington, DC: ASM Press, 2007a, pp. 1005–1015.

Fields BS. *Legionella* in the environment. In Hoffman PS, Klein TW, and Friedman H, eds. Legionella pneumophila *Pathogenesis and Immunity,* New York: Springer Publishing Corp., 2007b, pp. 85–94.

Fields BS, Benson RF, Besser RE. *Legionella* and Legionnaires' disease: 25 years of investigation. *Clin Microbiol Rev* 15:506–526, 2002.

Fields B, Haupt T, Davis JP, et al. Pontiac fever due to *Legionella micdadei* from a whirlpool spa: Possible role of bacterial endotoxin. *J Infect Dis* 184:1289–1292, 2001.

Fields BS, Moore MR. Control of legionellae in the environment: A guide to the U.S. guidelines. *ASHRAE Tran* 112:691–699, 2006.

Fields B, Geary DF, McCoy W, et al. Cooling towers and evaporative condensers. In Bartram J, Chartier Y, Lee JV, et al., eds. Legionella *and the Prevention of Legionellosis*. Geneva: World Health Organization, 2007, pp. 69–88.

Fischman ML. Building-associated illnesses. In LaDou J, ed. *Occupational and Environmental Medicine*. Stamford, CT: Appleton & Lange, 1997, pp. 723–732.

Fisher R, Saunders WB, Murray SJ, et al. Prevention of laboratory animal allergy. *J Occup Environ Med* 7:609–613, 1998.

Fisk WJ, Mirer AG, Mendell MJ. Quantitative relationship of sick building syndrome symptoms with ventilation rates. *Indoor Air* 19:159–165, 2009.

Fleming DO, Richardson JH, Tulis JJ, et al., eds. *Laboratory Safety: Principles and Practices*, 2nd ed. Washington, DC: American Society for Microbiology, 1995.

Fliermans CB. *Legionella* ecology. In Burge HA, ed. *Bioaerosols*. Boca Raton, FL: CRC/Lewis Publishers, 1995, pp. 49–76.

Foto M, Vrijmoed LLP, Miller JD, et al. A comparison of airborne ergosterol, glucan and Air-O-Cell data in relation to physical assessments of mold damage and some other parameters. *Indoor Air* 15:257–266, 2005.

Fox JG, Lipman NS. Infections transmitted by large and small laboratory animals. *Infect Dis Clin North Am* 5:131–163, 1990.

Franz DR, Jahrling PB, Friedlander AM, et al. Clinical recognition and management of patients exposed to biological warfare agents. *JAMA* 278:399–411, 1997.

Fraser DW. Sources of legionellosis. In Thornsberry C, Balows A, Feeley JC, et al., eds. *Proceedings of the Second International Symposium on* Legionella. Washington, DC: ASM Press, 1984, pp. 277–280.

Freije MR. *Legionellae Control in Health Care Facilities. A Guide for Minimizing Risk.* Indianapolis, IN: HC Information Resources, Inc., 1996.

Frommer W, Ager B, Archer L, et al. Safe biotechnology. III. Safety precautions for handling microorganisms of different risk classes. *Appl Microbiol Biotechnol* 30:541–552, 1989.

Garner JS, Simmons BP. CDC guideline for isolation precautions in hospitals. *Am J Infect Control* 4:245–325, 1983.

Garner JS, Favero MS. Guideline for handwashing and hospital environmental control. *Am J Infect Control* 14:110–126, 1986.

Gear JJS, Cassel GA, Gear AJ, et al. Outbreak of Marburg virus disease in Johannesburg. *Br Med J* 4:489–493, 1975.

Gibson DG, Benders GA, Andrews-Pfannkoch C, et al. Complete chemical synthesis, assembly, and cloning of a Mycoplasma genitalium genome. *Science* 319:1215–1220, 2008.

Gibson DG, Glass J, Lartigue C, et al. Creation of a bacterial cell controlled by a chemically synthesized genome. *Science* 329:52–56, 2010.

Gilchrist M, Fleming D, Hindler J. Laboratory safety management update: Aerosol borne microorganisms. In Eisenberg HD, ed. *Clinical Microbiology Procedures Handbook,* Supplement #1. Washington, DC: American Society for Microbiology, 1994, p. xxix.

Glasgow HB, Burkholder JM, Schmechel DE, et al. Insidious effects of a toxic estuarine dinoflagellate on fish survival and human health. *J Toxicol Environ Health* 46:501–522, 1995.

Glendon A, Litherland D. Safety climate factors, groups differences and safety behaviour in road construction. *Safety Science* 39:157–188, 2001.

Glibert PM, Burkholder JM. The complex relationships between increases in fertilization of the earth, coastal eutrophication and proliferation of harmful algal blooms. In Granéli E and Turner JT, eds. *Ecology of Harmful Algae*. Berlin: Springer-Verlag, 2006, pp. 341–354.

Gobin I, Newton P, Hartland EL, et al. Infections caused by nonpneumophila species of *Legionella. Rev Med Microbiol* 20:1–11, 2009.

Godish T. *Diagnosing problem buildings. Sick Buildings. Definition, Diagnosis and Mitigation.* Boca Raton, FL: Lewis Publishers, 1995, pp. 205–271.

Goldman RH. Medical surveillance in the biotechnology industry. *Occup Med* 6(2):209–225, 1991.

Goldman RH. Medical surveillance program. In Liberman DF, ed., *Biohazard Management Handbook*. New York: Marcel Dekker, 1995, pp. 173–192.

Gordon S, Preece R. Prevention of laboratory animal allergy. *Occupational Medicine* 2003 53:371–377, DOI: 10.1093/occmed/kqg117.

Górny RL, Reponen T, Willeke K, et al. Fungal fragments as indoor air biocontaminants. *Applied Environ Microbiol,* 68:3522–3531, 2002.

Guillemin MP. Occupational hygiene education and status: Global trends and a global future. *Ann Occup Hyg* 50:645–649, 2006.

Gyntelberg F, Suadicani P, Nielsen JW, et al. Dust and the sick building syndrome. *Indoor Air* 4:223–238, 1994.

Hansen VM, Winding A, Madsen AM. Exposure to bio-aerosols during the growth season of tomatoes in an organic greenhouse using Supresivit (*Trichoderma harzianum*) and Mycostop (*Streptomyces griseoviridis*). *Appl Environ Microbiol* 76:5874–5881, 2010.

Hanskaar S, Fosse RT. Allergy to laboratory mice and rats: A review of pathophysiology, epidemiology, and clinical aspects. *Lab Animal* 24:358–374, 1990.

Hardin BD, Robbins CA, Fallah P, et al. The concentration of no toxicologic concern (CoNTC) and airborne mycotoxins. *J Toxicol Environ Health A* 72:585–598, 2009.

Harding AL, Byers KB. Epidemiology of laboratory-associated infections. In Fleming DO, Hunt DL, eds. *Biological Safety: Principles and Practice,* 3rd ed. Washington, DC: American Society for Microbiology, 2000.

Harrington JM, Shannon HS. Incidence of tuberculosis, hepatitis, brucellosis, and shigellosis in British medical workers. *Br Med J* 1:759–762, 1976.

Hatch TF. Distribution and deposition of inhaled particles in the respiratory tract. *Bacteriol Rev* 25:237–240, 1961.

Health Canada. Fungal Contamination in Public Buildings: A Guide to Recognition and Management. Federal-Provincial Committee on Environmental and Occupational Health. Ottawa, Ontario: Environmental Health Directorate, 1995. www.hc-sc.gc.ca/ehp/ehd/catalogue/bch_pubs/fungal.pdf.

Heisler J, Glibert PM, Burkholder JM, et al. Eutrophication and harmful algal blooms: A scientific consensus. *Harmful Algae* 8:3–13, 2008.

Henderson DA, Inglesby TV, Bartlett JG, et al. Smallpox as a biological weapon: Medical and public health management. *JAMA* 281:2127–2137, 1999.

Herwaldt BL, Juranek DD. Protozoa and helminths. In Fleming DO, Richardson JH, Tulis JJ, eds. *Laboratory Safety: Principles and Practices,* 2nd ed. Washington, DC: American Society for Microbiology, 1995.

Heymann DL, ed. *Control of Communicable Diseases Manual,* 19th ed. Washington, DC: American Public Health Association, 2008.

Hill RH, Gaunce JA, Whitehead P. Chemical safety levels (CSLs): A proposal for chemical safety in microbiological and biomedical laboratories. *Chemical Health & Safety* July/Aug:6–14, 1999.

Hintikka E-L, Nikulin M. Airborne mycotoxins in agricultural and indoor environments. *Indoor Air* 4:66–70, 1998.

Hoage CW, Breiman RF. Advances in the epidemiology and control of *Legionella* infections. *Epidemiol Rev* 13:329–339, 1991.

Hodgson MJ. Exposures in indoor air. In Rosenstock L, Cullen MR, eds. Textbook of Clinical Occupational and Environmental Medicine. Philadelphia: WB Saunders, pp. 866–875, 1994.

Hodgson M. Indoor environmental exposures and symptoms. *Environ Health Perspect* 110:663–667, 2002.

Hodgson MJ, Morey P, Leung W-Y, et al. Building-associated pulmonary disease from exposure to *Stachybotrys chartarum* and *Aspergillus versicolor*. *J Occup Environ Med* 40:241–249, 1998.

Holloway HC, Norwood AE, Fullerton CS. The threat of biological weapons: Prophylaxis and mitigation of psychological and social consequences. *JAMA* 278:425–427, 1997.

Holt JG, ed. *Bergey's Manual of Determinative Bacteriology,* 9th ed. Baltimore, MD: Williams & Wilkins, 1994.

Hooper DG, Bolton VE, Guilford FT, et al. Mycotoxin detection in human samples from patients exposed to environmental molds. *Int J Mol Sci* 10:1465–1475, 2009.

Hornei B, Ewig S, Exner M, et al. Legionellosis. In Bartram J, Chartier Y, Lee JV, et al., eds. Legionella *and the Prevention of Legionellosis.* Geneva: World Health Organization, 2007a, pp. 1–27.

Horner WE, Barnes C, Codina R, et al. Guide for interpreting reports from inspections/investigations of indoor mold. *J Allergy Clin Immunol* 121:592–597, 2008.

Horwitz MA, Marston BJ, Broome CV, et al. Prospects for vaccine development. In Barbaree JM, Breiman RF, Dufour AP, eds. Legionella: *Current Status and Emerging Perspectives.* Washington, DC: ASM Press, 1993, pp. 296–297.

Hudnell HK. Chronic biotoxin-associated illness: Multiple-system symptoms, a vision deficit, and effective treatment. *Neurotoxicol Teratol* 27:733–743, 2005.

Hung L-L, Miller JD, Dillon HK, eds. *Field Guide for the Determination of Biological Contaminants in Environmental Samples,* 2nd ed. Fairfax, VA: AIHA, 2005.

Hurst C. Decontamination. In *Textbook of Military Medicine,* Zathuk R, ed. Washington, DC: U.S. Department of Army, Surgeon General, and the Borden Institute, 1997, pp. 351–359.

Hurst CJ, ed. Manual of Environmental Microbiology. Washington, DC: American Society for Microbiology, 1997.

Inglesby TV, Henderson DA, Bartlett JG, et al. Anthrax as a

biological weapon: Medical and public health management. *JAMA* 281:1735–1745, 1999.

Institute of Medicine. *Chemical and Biological Terrorism: Research and Development to Improve Civilian Medical Response.* Washington, DC: National Academies Press, 1999.

Institute of Medicine. Indoor biologic exposures. In *Clearing the Air: Asthma and Indoor Air Exposures.* Washington, DC: National Academies Press, 2000, pp. 105–222.

Institute of Medicine, Committee on Damp Indoor Spaces and Health. *Damp Indoor Spaces and Health.* Washington. DC: National Academies Press, 2004.

International Society of Indoor Air Quality and Climate. *Control of Moisture Problems Affecting Biological Indoor Air Quality.* TFI-1996. Ottawa, Canada: International Society of Indoor Air Quality and Climate, 1996.

Ippolito G, Puro V, Heptonstall J, et al. Occupational human immunodeficiency virus infection in health care workers: Worldwide cases through September 1997. *Clin Infect Dis* 28:365–383, 1999.

Isenberg HD, d'Amato RF. Indigenous and pathogenic microorganisms of humans. In *Manual of Clinical Microbiology,* Balows A, Hausler WJ, Herrmann KL, et al., eds. Washington, DC: American Society for Microbiology, 1991, pp. 2–14.

Jacobs RR. Endotoxins in the environment. *Int J Occup Environ Health* 3:S3–S5, 1997.

Jacobson JT, Orlob RB, Clayton JL. Infections acquired in clinical laboratories in Utah. *J Clin Microbiol* 21:486–489, 1985.

Jarvis BB, Sorenson WG, Hintikka E-L, et al. Study of toxin production by isolates of *Stachybotrys chartarum* and *Memnoniella echinata* isolated during a study of pulmonary hemosiderosis in infants. *Appl Environ Microbiol* 64:3620–3625, 1998.

Johanning E, Biagini R, Hull DL, et al. Health and immunology study following exposure to toxigenic fungi (*Stachybotrys chartarum*) in a water-damaged office environment. *Int Arch Occup Environ Health* 68:207–218, 1996.

Johanning E, Lansbergis P, Gareis M, et al. Clinical experience and results of a sentinel health investigation related to indoor fungal exposure. *Environ Health Perspect* 107(suppl 3):489–494, 1999.

Joly JR. Monitoring for the presence of *Legionella*: Where, when, and how? In Legionella: *Current Status and Emerging Perspectives*, Barbaree JM, Breiman RF, Dufour AP, eds. Washington, DC: ASM Press, 1993, pp. 211–216.

Karunasena E, Larrañaga MD, Simoni JS, et al. Building-associated neurological damage modeled in human cells: A mechanism of neurotoxic effects by exposure to mycotoxins in the indoor environment. *Mycopathologia* 170:377–390, 2010.

Keim M, Kaufmann A. Principles for emergency response to bioterrorism. *Ann Emerg Med* 34:177–182, 1999.

Kelman BJ, Robbins CA, Swenson LJ, et al. Risk from inhaled mycotoxins in indoor office and residential environments. *Int J Toxicol* 23:3–10, 2004.

Kenny MT, Sabel FL. Particle size distributions of *Serratia marcescens* aerosols created during common laboratory procedures and simulated laboratory accidents. *Appl Microbiol* 16:1146–1150, 1968.

Kent PT, Kubica GP. Safety in the laboratory. In *Public Health Mycobacteriology. A Guide for the Level III Laboratory.* Atlanta: Centers for Disease Control (DHHS, PHS), 1985, pp. 5–10.

Klein M, Deforest A. The inactivation of viruses by germicides. *Chem Specialists Manuf Assoc Proc* 49:116–118, 1963.

Kortepeter MG, Parker GW. Potential biological weapons threat. *Emerg Infect Dis* 5:523–527, 1999.

Kreiss, K. Building-related illness. In *Preventing Occupational Disease and Injury,* 2nd ed., Levy BS, Wagner GR, and Rest KM, eds. Washington, DC: American Public Health Association, 2005, pp. 134–141.

Krieger J, Jacobs DE, Ashley PJ, et al. Asthma-related indoor biologic agents: A review of the evidence. *J Public Health Management Practice* 16:S11–S20, 2010.

Kruse RH, Puckett WH, Richardson JH. Biological safety cabinetry. *Clin Microbiol Rev* 4:207–241 (Tables 5–10), 1991.

Kuenzi M, Assi F, Chmiel A, et al. Safe biotechnology: General considerations. A report prepared by the Safety in Biotechnology Working Party of the European Federation of Biotechnology. *Appl Microbiol Biotechnol* 21:1–6, 1985.

Laboratory Centre for Disease Control. *Laboratory Biosafety Guidelines,* 2nd ed. Ottawa, Canada: Health Protection Branch, Health Canada, 1996.

Ladics GS, Selgrade MJK. Identifying food proteins with allergenic potential: Evolution of approaches to safety assessment and research to provide additional tools. *Regulatory Toxicology and Pharmacology* 54(3) (supplement):S2–S6, Aug. 2009.

Larsson L. Use of mass spectrometry for determining microbial toxins in indoor environments. *J Environ Monit* 10:301–304, 2008.

Lee HW, Johnson KM. Laboratory-acquired infections with hantaan virus, the etiologic agent of Korean hemorrhagic fever. *J Infect Dis* 146:645–51, 1982.

Li Y, Leung GM, Tang JW, et al. Role of ventilation in airborne transmission of infectious agents in the built environment: A multidisciplinary systematic review. *Indoor Air* 17:2–18, 2007.

Liebers F, Raulf-Heimsoth M, Brüning T. Health effects due to endotoxin inhalation (review). *Arch Toxicol* 82:203–210, 2008.

Lillibridge SR, Bell AJ, Roman RS. Centers for Disease Control and Prevention bioterrorism preparedness and response. *Am J Infect Control* 27:463–464, 1999.

Lin S, Zhang H, Dubois A. Low abundance distribution of *Pfiesteria piscicida* in Pacific and Western Atlantic as detected by mtDNA-18S rDNA real-time polymerase chain reaction. *J Plankton Res* 28:667–681, 2006.

Lin YE, Stout JE, Yu VL. Controlling *Legionella* in hospital drinking water: An evidence-based review of disinfection methods. *Infect Control Hosp Epidemiol* 32:166–173, 2011.

Lloyd G, Jones N. Infection of laboratory workers with hantavirus acquired from immunocytomas propagated in laboratory rats. *J Infect Dis* 12:117–125, 1986.

Lundberg GD. Editorial: Reducing ongoing transmission of tuberculosis. *JAMA* 280:1702–1703, 2000.

Lupo D. Certification of biosafety cabinets and controlled environments. In Liberman DF, ed. *Biohazards Management Handbook*. New York: Marcel Dekker, 1995, pp. 79–86.

Macher JM. Bioaerosols. In *Air Sampling Instrument Selection Guide: Indoor Air Quality*. Cincinnati, OH: ACGIH, 1998, pp. 33–39.

Macher JM, Rosenberg J. Evaluation and management of exposure to infectious agents. In *Handbook of Occupational Safety and Health*, DiBerardinis LJ, ed. New York: Wiley, 1999, pp. 291–295.

Macher JM, Douwes J, Prezant B, et al. Bioaerosols. In *CRC Aerosols Handbook: Measurement, Dosimetry, and Health Effects*, 2nd ed., Ruzer LS and Harley NH, eds. Boca Raton, FL: CRC Press, 2012.

Macintyre AF, Christopher GW, Eitzen E Jr., et al. Weapons of mass destruction events with contaminated casualties: Effective planning for health care facilities. *JAMA* 283:242–249, 2000.

Mahoney FJ, Stewart K, Hu H, et al. Progress toward the elimination of hepatitis B virus transmission among health care workers in the United States. *Arch Intern Med* 157:2601–2605, 1997.

Malmberg P, Larsson K. Acute exposure to swine dust causes bronchial hyperresponsiveness in healthy subjects. *Eur Respir J* 6:400–404, 1993.

Marmot AF, Eley J, Stafford M, et al. Building health: An epidemiological study of "sick building syndrome" in the Whitehall II study. *Occup Environ Med* 63:283–289, 2006.

Marston BJ, Plouffe JF, Breiman RF, et al. Preliminary findings of a community-based pneumonia incidence study. In Legionella: *Current Status and Emerging Perspectives,* Barbaree JM, Breiman RF, Dufour AP, eds. Washington, DC: ASM Press, 1993, pp. 36–37.

Marston BJ, Lipman HB, Breiman RF. Surveillance for Legionnaires' disease. Risk factors for morbidity and mortality. *Arch Intern Med* 154:2417–2422, 1994.

Marston BJ, Plouffe JF, File TM Jr, et al. Incidence of community-acquired pneumonia requiring hospitalization. Results of a population-based active surveillance study in Ohio. The Community-Based Pneumonia Incidence Study Group. *Arch Intern Med* 157:1709–1718, 1997.

Martini GA, Siegert R, eds. *Marburg Virus Disease.* Berlin: Springer-Verlag, 1971.

Martyny JW, Martinez KF, Morey PR. Source sampling. In Macher JM, Ammann HM, Burge HA, et al., eds. *Bioaerosols: Assessment and Control.* Cincinnati, OH: American Conference of Industrial Hygienists, 1999, pp. 12-1–12-8.

Maryland Department of Health and Mental Hygiene. *Use of personal protective equipment and recommended work practices for reducing* Pfiesteria *and related toxins exposure in estuarine waters.* Baltimore, MD: Maryland Dept. of Health and Mental Hygiene, 1998a.

Maryland Department of Health and Mental Hygiene. *Maryland guidelines for protection of workers who may be exposed to estuarine waters.* Baltimore, MD: Maryland Dept. of Health and Mental Hygiene, 1998b.

Masuda T, Isokawa T. Biohazards in clinical laboratories in Japan. *Kansenshogaku Zasshi* 65(2):209–215, 1991.

Mazur LJ, Kim J. Spectrum of noninfectious health effects from molds. *Pediatrics* 118:e1909–e1926, 2006.

McDade JE, Franz D. Bioterrorism as a public health threat. *Emerg Infect Dis* 4:493–494, 1998.

McMahon BJ, Alward WL, Hall DB, et al. Acute hepatitis B virus infection: Relation of age to the clinical expression of disease and subsequent development of the carrier state. *J Infect Dis* 151:599–603, 1985.

Mendell MJ, Cozen M, Lei-Gomez Q, et al. Indicators of moisture and ventilation system contamination in U.S. office buildings as risk factors for respiratory and mucous membrane symptoms: Analyses of the EPA BASE data. *J Occup Environ Hyg* 3:225–233, 2006.

Mendell MJ, Mirer AG, Cheung K, et al. Respiratory and allergic health effects of dampness, mold, and dampness-related agents: A review of the epidemiologic evidence. *Environ Health Perspect* doi:10.1289/

ehp.1002410, 2011.

Merchant JA. Plant and vegetable exposures. In Rosenstock L, Cullen MR, eds. *Textbook of Clinical Occupational and Environmental Medicine*. Philadelphia: WB Saunders, 1994, pp. 693–699.

Merchant JA, Thorne PS, Reynolds SJ. Animal exposures. In Rosenstock L, Cullen MR, eds. *Textbook of Clinical Occupational and Environmental Medicine*. Philadelphia: WB Saunders, 1994, pp. 688–693.

Merianos A. Surveillance and Response to Disease Emergence. *Current Topics in Microbiology and Immunology* 315:477–509, 2007.

Michel O, Ginanni R, Duchateau J, et al. Domestic endotoxin exposure and clinical severity of asthma. *Clin Exp Allergy* 21:441–448, 1991.

Millar JD, Morris GK, Shelton BG. Legionnaires' disease: Seeking effective prevention. *ASHRAE J* 39:22–29, Jan 1997.

Miller JD. Mycotoxins. In *Organic Dusts: Exposure, Effects, and Prevention,* Rylander R, Jacobs RR, eds. Boca Raton, FL: Lewis Publishers, 1994, pp. 87–92.

Miller JD, Sun M, Gilyan A, et al. Inflammation-associated gene transcription and expression in mouse lungs induced by low molecular weight compounds from fungi from the built environment. *Chem Biol Interact* 183:113–124, 2010.

Milton DK. Bacterial endotoxins: A review of health effects and potential impact in the indoor environment. In *Indoor Air and Human Health*, Gammage RB, Berven BA, ed. Boca Raton, FL: CRC Press,1996, pp. 179–195.

Milton DK. Endotoxin. In *Bioaerosols*, Burge HA, ed. Boca Raton, FL: CRC/Lewis Publishers, 1995, pp. 77–86.

Milton DK. Endotoxin and other bacterial cell-wall components. In *Bioaerosols: Assessment and Control*, Macher JM, Ammann HM, Burge HA, et al., eds. Cincinnati, OH: ACGIH, 1999, pp. 23-1–23-13.

Morey PR. Indoor air quality in nonindustrial occupational environments. In *Handbook of Occupational Safety and Health*, 2nd ed., DiBerardinis LJ, ed. New York: Wiley, 1991, pp. 531–594.

Morris GK, Shelton BG. Technical Bulletin 1.5. Legionella: *Bacteria in Environmental Samples: Hazard Analysis and Suggested Remedial Actions*. Norcross, GA: PathCon Laboratories, 1998.

Morris JG, Grattan LM, Wilson LA, et al. Occupational exposure to *Pfiesteria* species in estuarine waters is not a risk factor for illness. *Environ Health Perspect.* 114:1038–1043, 2006.

Murray PR, Baron MJ, Pfaller MA, et al., eds. *Manual of Clinical Microbiology,* 7th ed. Washington, DC: American Society for Microbiology, 1999.

National Academy of Sciences. PPE specifically for biologic agents. In *Chemical and Biological Terrorism: Research and Development to Improve Civilian Medical Response*. Washington, DC: National Academies Press, 1999, pp. 41–42.

National Antimicrobial Information Network. Lists of EPA registered products.

National Committee for Clinical Laboratory Standards. *Protection of Laboratory Workers from Instrument Biohazards and Infectious Disease Transmitted by Blood, Body Fluids and Tissue—Approved Guideline M 29-A*. NCCLS:17(20), (ISBN 1-56238-339-6). Wayne, PA: NCCLS, 1997.

National Institute for Occupational Safety and Health. Weber AM, Martinez KF. *Martin County Courthouse and Constitutional Office Building, Stuart Florida*. HETA 93-1110-2575. Cincinnati, OH: NIOSH Publications Office, 1993.

National Institute for Occupational Safety and Health. *Preventing Organic Dust Toxic Syndrome*. DHHS (NIOSH) Pub. No. 94–102. Cincinnati, OH: NIOSH, 1994.

National Institute for Occupational Safety and Health. *NIOSH Guide to the Selection and Use of Particulate Respirators Certified Under 42 CFR 84*. DHHS (NIOSH) Pub. No. 96–101, Cincinnati, OH: NIOSH, 1996.

National Institute for Occupational Safety and Health. Mold & Dampness Assessment Sheet–Draft. Cincinnati, OH: NIOSH. www.miaqc.org/Draft NIOSH Moisture Assessment Sheet.pdf

National Institutes of Health. Actions under the guidelines, guidelines for research involving recombinant DNA molecules. *Fed Reg* 56:33174–33183, July 18, 1991.

National Institutes of Health. *Guidelines for research involving recombinant DNA molecules*. Washington, DC: DHHS/NIH, October 2011.

National Institutes of Health Consensus Development Conference Panel Statement. Management of hepatitis C. *Hepatology* 26:2S–10S, 1997.

National Research Council—Committee on the Introduction of Genetically Engineered Organisms into the Environment. Washington, DC: National Academies Press, 1987.

National Research Council—Committee on Hazardous Biological Substances in the Laboratory. *Biosafety in the Laboratory: Prudent Practices for the Handling of Infectious Materials*. Washington, DC: National Academies Press, 1989.

National Sanitation Foundation. Standard 49–Class II (Laminar Flow) Biohazard Cabinetry. Ann Arbor, MI:

The National Sanitation Foundation, 1992.

Nellis BF, Van Houten J. New frontiers in biosafety: The industrial prospective. In Liberman DF, ed., *Biohazards Management Handbook*. New York: Marcel Dekker, 1995, pp. 193–219.

Nettleman MD. Biological warfare and infection control. *Infect Control Hosp Epidemiol* 12(6):368–372, 1991.

New York City Department of Health. Guidelines on Assessment and Remediation of Fungi in Indoor Environments. New York: NYCDOH, Bureau of Environmental & Occupational Disease Epidemiology, 2000. www.ci.nyc.ny.us/html/doh/html/epi/moldrpt1.html

Nguyen TMN, Ilef D, Jarraud S, et al. A community-wide outbreak of Legionnaires Disease linked to industrial cooling towers: How far can contaminated aerosols spread? *J Infect Dis* 193:102–111, 2006.

Nielsen KF, Holm G, Uttrup LP, et al. Mould growth on building materials under low water activities. Influence of humidity and temperature on fungal growth and secondary metabolism. *Int Biodeter Biodegr* 54:325–336, 2004.

Norbäck D. An update on sick building syndrome. *Curr Opin Allergy Clin Immunol* 9:55–59, 2009.

North Carolina Department of Health and Human Services. *Recommended work practices and use of personal protective equipment for reducing algal toxin exposure and human health risk in estuarine waters*. Raleigh, NC: North Carolina Dept. of Health and Human Services, 1998.

Noss I, Wouters IM, Visser M, et al. Evaluation of a low-cost electrostatic dust fall collector for indoor air endotoxin exposure assessment. *Appl Environ Microbiol* 74:5621–5627, 2008.

Occupational Safety and Health Act of 1970, Publ. L. No. 91–596. General Duty Clause, Section 5 (a)(1) (1970).

Occupational Safety and Health Administration. Respiratory Protection. *Code of Federal Regulations* Title 30, Part 11. Washington, DC: Office of the Federal Register, National Archives and Records Administration, 1980, pp. 7–70.

Occupational Safety and Health Administration. Protection from bloodborne pathogens (29 *CFR* Part 1910.1030). *Fed Reg* 56:#235, 64175–64182, Dec. 6, 1991.

Occupational Safety and Health Administration. Enforcement Procedures and Scheduling for Occupational Exposure to Tuberculosis. CPL 2.106. Washington, DC: OSHA, 1996.

Occupational Safety and Health Administration. Occupational Exposure to Tuberculosis: Proposed Rule. *Fed Reg* 62:54159–54309, 1997.

Occupational Safety and Health Administration. Enforcement procedures for the occupational exposure to blood-borne pathogens standard. CPL 2–2.44D. Washington, DC: OSHA, 1999.

Occupational Safety and Health Administration. Indoor air quality investigation. In OSHA Technical Manual. Washington, DC: OSHA, 1999. www.osha.gov/dts/osta/otm/otm_iii/otm_iii_2.html

Occupational Safety and Health Administration. Legionnaires' Disease. In *Technical Manual*. Washington, DC: OSHA, 2003, Section III: Chapter 7. www.osha.gov/dts/osta/otm/legionnaires/pdf.html

Office of Science and Technology Policy. Coordinated framework for the regulation of biotechnology. *Fed Reg* 51:23302–23393, 1986.

Official Journal of the European Communities. Directive 90/679/ EEC on the protection of workers from risks related to exposure to biological agents at work. *Official J Eur Communities* 374:1–12, Dec. 31, 1990.

Oldach DW, Grattan LM, Morris JG. *Pfiesteria piscicida* and human health. In Scheld WM, Craig WA, Hughes JM, eds., *Emerging Infections 3*. Washington, DC: American Society for Microbiology, 1999, pp. 135–151.

Olenchock SA. Airborne endotoxin. In Hurst CJ, ed. *Manual of Environmental Microbiology*. Washington, DC: ASM Press, 1997, pp. 661–665.

O'Neill EO, Humphreys H. Surveillance of hospital water and primary prevention of nosocomial legionellosis: What is the evidence? *J Hosp Infect* 59:273–279, 2005.

Organization for Economic Cooperation and Development. *Recombinant DNA Safety Considerations*. Paris: Organization for Economic Cooperation and Development, 1986.

Otten JA, Burge HA. Bacteria. In *Bioaerosols: Assessment and Control,* Macher JM, Ammann HM, Burge HA, et al., eds. Cincinnati, OH: ACGIH, 1999a, pp. 18-1–18-10.

Otten JA, Burge HA. Amebae. In *Bioaerosols: Assessment and Control,* Macher JM, Ammann HM, Burge HA, et al., eds. Cincinnati, OH: ACGIH, 1999b, pp. 20-1–20-5.

Otten JA, Burge HA. Viruses. In *Bioaerosols: Assessment and Control,* Macher JM, Ammann HM, Burge HA, et al., eds. Cincinnati, OH: ACGIH, 1999c, pp. 21-1–21-6.

Patel R, Moore MR, Fields BS. Legionellosis. In *Bacterial Infections of Humans,* Evans AS and Brachman PS, eds. New York: Springer Science+Business Media, LLC, 2009, pp. 395–413.

Paterson RRM, Lima N. The weaponization of mycotoxins. In *Mycotoxins in Food, Feed and Bioweapons,* Rai M and Varma A, eds. Berlin: Springer-Verlag, 2010, pp. 367–384.

Patterson RM, Noga E, Germolec D. Lack of evidence for

contact sensitization by *Pfiesteria* extract. *Environ Health Perspect* 115:1023–1028, 2007.

Pauli G, Bessot JC. Rare indoor allergens. *Eur Ann Allergy Clin Immunol* 41:99–105, 2009.

Pavlin JA. Epidemiology of bioterrorism. *Emerg Infect Dis* 5:528–530, 1999.

Pearson GS. The complementary role of environmental and security biological control regimes in the 21st century. *JAMA* 278:369–372, 1997.

Peden DB, Boehlecke B. Airborne contaminants and asthma: The effects of ozone, NO_2, SO_2, endotoxin and diesel particulates on normal and asthmatic lungs. In *Asthma: Causes and Mechanisms of an Epidemic Inflammatory Disease,* Platts-Mills T, ed. Boca Raton, FL: CRC Press, 1999, pp. 173–195.

Pernis B, Vigliani EC, Cavagna C, et al. The role of bacterial endotoxins in occupational diseases caused by inhaling vegetable dusts. *Br J Indust Med* 18:120–129, 1961.

Pestka JJ, Yike I, Dearborn DG, et al. *Stachybotrys chartarum*, trichothecene mycotoxins, and damp building-related illness: New insights into a public health enigma. *Toxicol Sci* 104:4–26, 2008.

Peterson JS. *Pfiesteria*. In *Biological Safety: Principles and Practices*, 3rd ed., Fleming DO, Hunt DL, eds. Washington, DC: American Society for Microbiology, 2000.

Pike RM. Past and present hazards of working with infectious agents. *Arch Pathol Lab Med* 102:333–336, 1978.

Pike RM. Laboratory-associated infections: Incidence, fatalities, causes, and prevention. *Ann Rev Microbiol* 33:41–66, 1979.

Poole JA, Dooley GP, Saito R, et al. Muramic acid, endotoxin, 3-hydroxy fatty acids, and ergosterol content explain monocyte and epithelial cell inflammatory responses to agricultural dusts. *J Toxicol Environ Health A* 73:684–700, 2010.

Popendorf W, Donham KJ. Agricultural hygiene. In Clayton GD, Clayton FE, eds., *Patty's Industrial Hygiene and Toxicology 1: Part A-General Principles*. New York: Wiley, pp. 721–759, 1991.

Portnoy JM, Barnes CS, Kennedy K. Sampling for indoor fungi. *J Allergy Clin Immunol* 113:189–198, 2004.

Postgate J. *Microbes and Man.* Cambridge, UK: Cambridge University Press, 1992.

Prezant B, Weekes DM, Miller JD, ds. *Recognition, Evaluation, and Control of Indoor Mold*. Fairfax, VA: AIHA, 2008.

Price DL, Ahearn DG. Sanitation of wallboard colonized with *Stachybotrys chartarum. Current Microbiol* 39:21–26, 1999.

Prusiner SB. Novel proteinaceous infectious particles cause scrapie. *Science* 216:136–144, 1982.

Qian Y, Willeke K, Grinshpun SA, et al. Performance of N95 respirators: Filtration efficiency for airborne microbial and inert particles. *Am Ind Hyg Assoc J* 59:128–132, 1998.

Radon K. The two sides of the "endotoxin coin." *Occup Environ Med* 63:73–78, 2006.

Rand TG, Sun M, Gilyan A. Dectin-1 and inflammation-associated gene transcription and expression in mouse lungs by a toxic (1,3)-beta-D: Glucan. *Arch Toxicol* 84:205–220, 2010.

Rao CY, Burge HA, Chang JCS. Review of quantitative standards and guidelines for fungi in indoor air. *J Air Waste Manage Assoc* 46:899–908, 1996.

Rao CY, Fink RC, Wolfe LB, et al. A study of aflatoxin production by Aspergillus flavus growing on wallboard. *J Am Biol Safety Assoc* 2:36–42, 1997.

Raviglione MG, Snider DE, Kochi A. Global epidemiology of tuberculosis. *JAMA* 273:220–226, 1995.

Reitman M, Wedum AG. Microbiological safety. *Public Health Rep* 71:659–665, 1956.

Ricci ML, Fontana S, Bella A, et al. A preliminary assessment of the occupational risk of acquiring Legionnaires' disease for people working in telephone manholes, a new workplace environment for *Legionella* growth. *Am J Infect Control* 38:540–545, 2010.

Ricketts KD, Joseph CA. Legionnaires' Disease in Europe 2003–2004. *Eurosurveillance* 10:256–259, 2005.

Rietschel ET, Brade H. Bacterial endotoxins. *Scientific American* 267:55–61, 1992.

Rose CS. Antigens. In *Bioaerosols: Assessment and Control*, Macher JM, Ammann HM, Burge HA, et al., eds. Cincinnati, OH: ACGIH, 1999, pp. 25-1–25-11.

Rutala WA. APIC guideline for selection and use of disinfectants. *Am J Infect Control* 24(4):313–342, 1996.

Rylander R. Endotoxin and occupational airway disease. *Curr Opin Allergy Clin Immunol* 6, 62–66, 2006.

Rylander R. Endotoxin in the air: Good or bad for you? *Clin Pulm Med* 14:140–147, 2007.

Rylander R. Endotoxins. In Rylander R, Jacobs RR, eds., *Organic Dusts: Exposure, Effects, and Prevention*. Boca Raton, FL: Lewis Publishers, 1994, pp. 73–79.

Rylander R. Evaluation of the risks of endotoxin exposures. *Int J Occup Env Health* 3:S32–S36, 1997.

Rylander R. Organic dust induced pulmonary disease: The role of mould derived B-glucan. *Ann Agric Environ Med* 17:9–13, 2010.

Rylander R, Sörensen S, Goto H, et al. The importance of endotoxin and glucan for symptoms in sick buildings. In *Present and Future of Indoor Air Quality*, Proceedings of the Brussels Conference. New York: Excerpta Medica, 1989.

Saito R, Cranmer BK, Tessari JD, et al. Recombinant Factor C (rFC) assay and Gas Chromatography/Mass Spectrometry (GC/MS) analysis of endotoxin variability in four agricultural dusts. *Ann Occup Hyg* 7:713–722, 2009.

Salares VR, Hinde CA, Miller JD. Analysis of settled dust in homes and fungal glucan in air particulate collected during HEPA vacuuming. *Indoor Built Environ* 18:485–491, 2009.

Samson RA, Flannigan B, Flannigan ME, et al., eds. Recommendations. In *Health Implications of Fungi in Indoor Environments.* New York: Elsevier, 1994, pp. 531–538.

Schnurrenberger PR, Grigor JK, Walker JF, et al. The zoonosis-prone veterinarian. *J Am Vet Med Assoc* 173:373–376, 1978.

Schreiber GB, Busch MP, Kleinman SH, et al. The risk of transfusion-transmitted viral infections. *N Engl J Med* 334:1685–1690, 1996.

Seeff LB, Buskell-Bales Z, Wright EC, et al. Long-term mortality after transfusion-associated non-A, non-B hepatitis. *N Engl J Med* 327:1906–1911, 1992.

Seppänen O, Fisk WJ, Lei QH. Ventilation and performance in office work. *Indoor Air* 16:28–36, 2006.

Sewell DL. Laboratory-associated infections and biosafety. *Clin Microbiol Rev* 8:389–405, 1995.

Shapiro CN. Occupational risk of infection with hepatitis B and hepatitis C virus. *Surg Clin North America* 75(6):1047–1056, 1995.

Shaughnessy R, Morey PR, Cole EC. Prevention and control of microbial contamination. In *Bioaerosols: Assessment and Control,* Macher JM, Ammann HM, Burge HA, et al., eds. Cincinnati, OH: ACGIH, 1999, pp. 10-1–10-13.

Shaughnessy RJ, Morey PR. Remediation of microbial contamination. In *Bioaerosols: Assessment and Control,* Macher JM, Ammann HM, Burge HA, et al., eds. Cincinnati, OH: ACGIH, 1999, pp. 15-1–15-7.

Sheretz RJ, Hampton AL. Infection control aspects of hospital employee health. In *Preventional Control of Nosocomial Infections,* Werzel RP, ed. Baltimore: Williams & Wilkins, 1986, pp. 175–204.

Shoemaker RD, Lawson W. *Pfiesteria* in estuarine waters: The question of health risks. *Environ Health Perspect* 115:A126–A127, 2007.

Short LJ, Bell DM. Risk of occupational exposure with bloodborne pathogens in operating and delivery room settings. *Am J Infect Control* 21:343–350, 1993.

Simon JD. Biological terrorism: Preparing to meet the threat. *JAMA* 278:428–430, 1997.

Sjöstedt L, Willers S, Ørback P. Laboratory animal allergy: A review. *Indoor Environ* 4:67–79, 1995.

Smit LA, Heederik D, Doekes G, et al. Occupational endotoxin exposure reduces the risk of atopic sensitization but increases the risk of bronchial hyperresponsiveness. *Int Arch Allergy Immunol* 152:151–158, 2010.

Smit LAM, Wouters IM, Hobo MM, et al. Agricultural seed dust as a potential cause of organic dust toxic syndrome. *Occup Environ Med* 63:59–67, 2006.

Smith HO, Hutchison CA III, Pfannkoch C, et al. Generating a synthetic genome by whole genome assembly: phiX174 bacteriophage from synthetic oligonucleotides. *Proc Natl Acad Sci* USA 100:15440–15445, 2003.

Spaan S, Heederik DJJ, Thorne PS, et al. Optimization of airborne endotoxin exposure assessment: Effects of filter type, transport conditions, extraction solutions, and storage of samples and extracts. *Appl Environ Microbiol* 73:6134–6143, 2007.

Spaan S, Schinkel J, Wouters IM, et al. Variability in endotoxin exposure levels and consequences for exposure assessment. *Ann Occup Hyg* 52:303–316, 2008.

Spaan S, Wouter IM, Oosting I, et al. Exposure to inhalable dust and endotoxins in agricultural industries. *J Environ Monit* 8:63–72, 2006.

Stout J. Preventing legionellosis. *ASHRAE Journal* 49:58–62, 2007.

Stout JE, Muder RR, Mietzner S, et al. Role of environmental surveillance in determining the risk of hospital-acquired legionellosis: A national surveillance study with clinical correlations. *Infect Control Hosp Epidemiol* 28:818–824, 2007.

Stratton CW. Topics in clinical microbiology: Tuberculosis, infection control, and the microbiology laboratory. *Infect Control Hosp Epidemiol* 14(6):481–487, 1993.

Sulkin SE, Pike RM. Survey of laboratory-acquired infections. *Am J Public Health* 41:769–780, 1951.

Surman-Lee S, Fields B, Hornei B, et al. Ecology and environmental sources of *Legionella.* In Legionella *and the Prevention of Legionellosis,* Bartram J, Chartier Y, Lee JV, et al., eds. Geneva: World Health Organization, 2007, pp. 29–38.

Tager IB, Lurmann FW, Haight T, et al. Temporal and spatial patterns of ambient endotoxin concentrations in Fresno, California. *Environ Health Perspect* 118:1490–1496, 2010.

Teeuw KB, Vandenbroucke-Grauls CM, Verhoef J. Airborne gram-negative bacteria and endotoxin in sick building syndrome. A study in Dutch governmental office buildings. *Arch Intern Med* 154:2339–2345, 1994.

Thorne PS, Adamcakova-Dodd A, Kelly KM, et al., Metal working fluid with mycobacteria and endotoxin induces hypersensitivity pneumonitis in mice. *Am. J Respir Crit Care Med* 173:759–768, 2006.

Thorne PS, Perry SS, Saito R, et al. Evaluation of the

Limulus amebocyte lysate and recombinant Factor C assays for assessment of airborne endotoxin. *Appl Environ Microbiol* 76:4988–4995, 2010.

Torok, TJ, Tauxe RV, Wise RP, et al. A large community outbreak of salmonellosis caused by intentional contamination of restaurant salad bars. *JAMA* 278:389–395, 1997.

Tronel H, Hartemann P. Overview of diagnostic and detection methods for legionellosis and *Legionella* spp. *Lett Appl Microbiol* 48:653–656, 2009.

Tucker JB. National health and medical services response to incidents of chemical and biological terrorism. *JAMA* 278:362–368, 1997.

Tumpey TM, Basler CF, Aguilar PV, et al. Characterization of the reconstructed 1918 Spanish influenza pandemic virus. *Science* 310:77–80, 2005.

Tuomi T, Rejula K, Johnsson T, et al. Mycotoxins in crude building materials from water-damaged buildings. *Appl Environ Microbiol* 66:1899–1904, 2000.

Ueno Y. Trichothecene mycotoxins: Mycology, chemistry, and toxicology. *Adv Nutr Res* 3:301–353, 1989.

U.S. Department of Health and Human Service/National Institute for Occupational Safety and Health. Respiratory protective devices; tests for permissibility; fees. *Code of Federal Regulations* Title 30, Part 11. Washington, DC: U.S. Government Printing Office, pp. 47–111, 1993.

U.S. Department of Health and Human Service/National Institute for Occupational Safety and Health. Approval of respiratory protective devices. *Code of Federal Regulations* Title 42, Part 84. Washington, DC: U.S. Government Printing Office, pp. 528–593, 1996.

U.S. Department of Transportation. ANPRM Hazardous Materials Regulations. Docket HM-181G. 58 FR 12207, Mar 3, 1993.

U.S. Department of Transportation, Research and Special Programs Administration. Amendment Docket HM181G, No 171–178, 59 FR 48762, Sept 22, 1994.

U.S. Department of Transportation. 49 *CFR* Parts 171–180. Hazardous materials regulations.

U.S. Environmental Protection Agency. *A Standardized EPA Protocol for Characterizing Indoor Air Quality in Large Buildings. Office of Research and Development and Office of Air and Radiation.* Washington, DC: EPA, 1994.

U.S. Environmental Protection Agency. *IAQ Building Education and Assessment Model (I-BEAM).* Washington, DC: EPA, 2002. http://www.epa.gov/iaq/largebldgs/i-beam/index.html, accessed on April 27, 2011.

U.S. Environmental Protection Agency. *Risk Assessment for Noncancer Effects.* On the Air Toxics Website, Technology Transfer Network. Washington, DC: U.S. EPA, 2007. http://www.epa.gov/airtoxics/toxsource/noncarcinogens.html

U.S Environmental Protection Agency. Mold Remediation in Schools and Commercial Buildings: Checklist for Mold Remediation. Washington, DC: EPA, 2011. http://www.epa.gov/mold/checklist.html

U.S. Public Health Service. *National Cancer Institute Safety Standard for Research Involving Oncogenic Viruses—Manual.* Publication No.: (NIH) 75–790. Washington, DC: U.S. Government Printing Office, 1974.

U.S. Public Health Service. Final rule: Additional requirements for facilities transferring or receiving select agents. *Fed Reg* 61 FR 29327, Oct. 24, 1996.

U.S. Public Health Service, Office of Emergency Preparedness. *Metropolitan Medical Strike Team Field Operations Guide.* Rockville, MD: U.S. PHS, 1997.

van Egmond HP. Fungi, mycotoxins and microbial volatile organic compounds in mouldy interiors from water-damaged buildings. *J Environ Monit* 11:1847–1848, 2009.

Vesley D, Hartmann HM. Laboratory-acquired infections and injuries in clinical laboratories: A 1986 survey. *Am J Public Health* 78:1213–1215, 1988.

Vesley D, Lauer JL. Decontamination, sterilization, disinfection, and antisepsis. In *Laboratory Safety: Principles and Practices,* 2nd ed., Fleming DO, Richardson JH, Tulis JJ, et al., eds. Washington, DC: American Society for Microbiology, 1995, pp. 226–227.

Vincent JH. Graduate education in occupational hygiene: A rational framework. *Ann Occup Hyg* 49:649–659, 2005.

Wang H, Reponen T, Lee S-A, et al. Submicron size airborne mist and endotoxin-contanining particles in metalworking fluid environments. *J Occup Environ Hyg* 4:157–165, 2007.

Weber DJ, Rutala WA, Eron J. Management of healthcare workers exposed to hepatitis B virus or hepatitis C virus. *UpToDate* Apr. 7, 2011. http://www.uptodate.com/contents/management-of-healthcare-workers-exposed-to-hepatitis-b-virus-or-hepatitis-c-virus

Wedum AG, Barkley WE, Hellman A. Handling of infectious agents. *J Am Vet Med Assoc* 161:1557–1567, 1972.

Winn WC. *Legionella.* In *Manual of Clinical Microbiology,* 7th ed., Murray PR, Baron EJ, Pfaller MA, et al., eds. Washington, DC: ASM Press, 1999, pp. 572–585.

Wong TM, Chan YC, Yap EH, et al. Serological evidence of hantavirus infection in laboratory rats and personnel. *Int J Epidemiol* 17:887–890, 1988.

World Health Organization. Ebola haemorrhagic fever in Sudan and Zaire, 1976: Report of a WHO/international study team. *Bull World Health Organ* 56:247–293, 1978.

World Health Organization. *Laboratory Biosafety Manual,* 2nd ed. Geneva: World Health Organization, 1993.

World Health Organization. Proposed global action plan and timetable for safe handling and maximum containment of wild poliovirus and potentially infectious materials. In *Global Programme for Vaccines and Immunization.* Geneva: World Health Organization, 1998.

World Health Organization. *Global Action Plan for Laboratory Containment of Wild Poliovirus. Global Programme for Vaccines and Immunization.* Geneva: World Health Organization, 1999.

World Health Organization/International Union Against Tuberculosis and Lung Disease. *Anti-tuberculosis Drug Resistance in the World.* WHO Report No. 2. Geneva: World Health Organization, March 24, 2000.

World Health Organization. Legionella *and the Prevention of Legionellosis.* Bartram J, Chartier Y, Lee JV, et al., eds. Geneva: World Health Organization, 2007.

World Health Organization. *Guidelines for Drinking Water Quality,* 3rd ed., Vol. 1. Recommendations. Geneva: World Health Organization, 2004.

World Health Organization. *Guidelines for Safe Recreational Water Environments.* Vol. 2. Swimming Pools, Spas and Similar Recreational Water Environments. Geneva: World Health Organization, 2006.

World Health Organization. *Guide to Ship Sanitation,* 2nd ed. Geneva: World Health Organization, 2007.

World Health Organization. *WHO Guidelines for Indoor Air Quality: Dampness and Mould.* Copenhagen: World Health Organization Regional Office for Europe, 2009.

Yang CS, Johanning E. Airborne fungi and mycotoxins. In *Manual of Environmental Microbiology,* Hurst CJ, ed. Washington, DC: ASM Press, 1997, pp. 651–660.

Yike I, Distler AM, Ziady AG, et al. Mycotoxin adducts on human serum albumin: Biomarkers of exposure to *Stachybotrys chartarum. Environ Health Perspect* 114:1221–1226, 2006.

Zhiping W, Malmberg P, Larsson B-M, et al. Exposure to bacteria in swine-house dust and acute inflammatory reactions in humans. *Am J Respir Crit Care Med* 154:1261–1266, 1996.

PART IV

Evaluation of Hazards

CHAPTER 15

Evaluation

by Elizabeth R. Gross, CIH
Elise Pechter, CIH

In industrial hygiene, evaluation is the decision-making process that assesses the hazards to workers from exposures to chemical, physical, and biological agents. The actions taken to protect workers are based on a combination of observation, interviews, and measurement of the levels of energy or air contaminants resulting from a process or work operation and the effectiveness of control measures used.

GENERAL PRINCIPLES

The need to evaluate hazards is driven by the acknowledgment that chemical, biological, and physical agents and psychosocial factors can cause injury, disease, and premature death among exposed workers. The U.S. Department of Labor's Bureau of Statistics reported 3.3 million occupational work-related injuries and illnesses in private industry in 2009. The actual number is much larger, because many occupational illnesses are unrecognized, many injuries and illnesses are not reported, and the public sector is not included in this count. For example, Rosenman et al. used capture-recapture statistical methods to estimate the undercount of occupational injury and illness, estimating that 68 percent of Michigan occupational injuries and illnesses were missed using current data collection methods. Boden and Ozonoff analyzed data from workers' compensation and the Bureau of Labor Statistics (BLS) in six states, and found that BLS missed 340,000 job injuries, with 69,000 injuries never reported to either BLS or the workers' compensation system. Given the weaknesses of the data systems, a focus on evaluation of hazards is even more important. This task of evaluating the nature and severity of hazards and prevention of disease, injury, and death relies on judgment based on many factors:

- *Toxicity:* the inherent capacity of an agent to cause harm, the nature of that harm, and target organs affected.
- *Exposure levels or dose:* the amount that workers absorb through all routes of entry during work.
- *Duration of exposure:* longer shifts or more than one job can lead to greater opportunities for exposure.
- *Process or operation analysis:* the awareness of operations, from raw materials through their transformation to products and by-products, that may result in the release of chemicals or energy that could cause harm.
- *Maintenance activities, spills, and accidents:* the knowledge of acute incidents, infrequent events, leaks, and releases that are missed in routine evaluations.
- *Epidemiology and risk assessment:* a literature review of population-based research and case-based surveillance that may provide information about adverse health effects not yet noticed in an individual workplace.
- *Interview:* the information obtained from workers regarding health symptoms, tasks, and changes in conditions, can provide essential details regarding process analysis, health impact, and other stressors on the job. These stressors may be chemical, physical, ergonomic, psychosocial or biological.
- *Unequal distribution of risks:* awareness that some populations of workers are more likely to experience increased risks of diseases and injuries in the workplace. For example, older workers are at greatly increased risk of injury fatality; more partially disabled workers who may require special protection have been able to re-enter the workplace with protection afforded by the ADA; and working teens are at higher risk of injury per working-hour.
- *Variability of response:* the way individuals vary in their susceptibility because of factors such as age, size, respiratory rate, and general health status. Recognition of the nonuniversality of response helps maintain awareness of possible unrecognized hazards and special sensitivities.

The purpose of evaluation is the prevention of hazardous exposures and resulting adverse health effects. Unlike health care providers, whose job is to treat existing conditions, industrial hygienists can prevent illness through recognition and correction of hazards before they cause harm. The industrial hygienist uses many sources of information and methods to evaluate the workplace. The next section describes some of them.

Basic Approach to Hazard Recognition

Almost any work environment has either potential or actual environmental hazards that the health and safety professional must recognize, measure, and monitor. The first step toward recognition of these potential hazards is the consideration of the raw materials being used, including any known impurities, and the potential of those materials to do harm. The next consideration is how these raw materials are modified through intermediate steps. Finally, an evaluation of the finished product or by-products must also be done, both under normal conditions and under anticipated emergency conditions, to determine whether any hazards might exist at this point.

A basic, systematic procedure can be followed in the recognition of occupational health hazards. Hazard recognition methods are similar whether a chemical, physical, or biological agent is involved. Questions should be formulated to organize information:

- What are the raw materials?
- Are there any trace contaminants?
- What is produced?
- What intermediate products are formed in the process?
- What by-products may be released?
- What are the usual cleaning or maintenance procedures at the end of the day, end of a run, or changeover to another product?
- What hazardous waste is produced and how is it disposed?

There is a wealth of health and safety information that should be researched to help anticipate potential hazards in any work setting. Included in this search should be a review of the known hazards associated with industrial processes or job classifications. An inventory can then be made of previously identified hazards by category, and any relevant standards or guidelines can be referenced. Armed with this information, the next step is to study the specific operation or process and consider where air contaminants are released, as well as where and when employees are exposed.

Any job can include physical hazards as well as chemical hazards. Energy uses, electromagnetic fields, noise sources, fire hazards, physically demanding tasks, and material-handling jobs must all be noted. Hazards that could result in acute traumatic injuries also include vehicles and sources of energy. Vehicles include automobiles, forklift trucks, and overhead cranes. Energy sources could be mechanical (pneumatic or hydraulic), electrical, thermal, or chemical. The postures of work may include sitting, standing, pushing, twisting, and the like. Physical hazards could also include vibration, radiation, barometric pressure alterations, and hazardous motions or postures that could cause cumulative trauma disorders. Temperature extremes, lighting levels, and physical surroundings are additional factors to consider in the initial hazard surveillance approach.

Biological hazards include infectious agents (bacteria, viruses, parasites, and fungi), toxins associated with plants or animals, and pharmacoactive substances such as enzymes, hormones, or other biological materials. Infectious agents include tuberculosis in shelters, clinics, hospitals, or offices; bloodborne pathogens for first aid providers; and mold or mildew in a basement office after a flood. In evaluations of agricultural work areas, one may need to consider other agents. In biotechnology or pharmaceutical companies, exotic endotoxins or biologically engineered materials may be employed.

Psychosocial hazards such as high job demands and low control can cause psychological and physical strain and should also be considered. Some factors that can result in emotional strain include

- machine pacing;
- boring, repetitive tasks;
- complex, highly demanding requirements;
- shift work;
- job insecurity;
- physical violence;
- forced overtime;
- harassment or bullying;
- computer monitoring of performance; and
- the absence of social or coworker support.

Review of Literature

Prior to evaluating any workplace, it is useful to know what hazards are anticipated. A literature review of the industry in question or the type of operation being done can facilitate this analysis. Recommended general resources include Burgess (1995), Rose and Cohrssen (2010), the International Labour Organization (ILO), Weeks et al. (1991), and Levy & Wegman (2011).

The National Institute for Occupational Safety and Health (NIOSH) and the Occupational Safety and Health Administration (OSHA) have published very useful pamphlets, criteria documents, reports, and technical bulletins on many subjects related to workplace hazards. Online searches of OSHA (http://www.osha.gov/) and NIOSH (http://www.cdc.gov/niosh/) can provide valuable information about industry sector characteristics and common OSHA violations. Both NIOSH and OSHA maintain mailing lists, e-news, or list serves for regular updates. Other sources to be consulted include technical journals in the fields of industrial hygiene, occupational medicine, environmental analysis (including the Environmental Protection Agency's toxics release inventory information at http://www.epa.gov/triexplorer/), and epidemiology. Some trade associations incorporate health and safety articles into their regular communications with members.

Inventory

A list should be prepared of all chemicals present in the facility. The list should include all raw materials and final products. This chemical inventory is required by OSHA's Hazard Communication Standard, 29 CFR 1910.1200, for the purpose of anticipating possible hazards and ensuring that these risks are communicated to employers and employees before they are encountered in the workplace. The manufacturer or supplier of each chemical must provide a Safety Data Sheet (SDS), formerly Material Safety Data Sheet (MSDS), for every product.

For every chemical, the relevant standards should be looked up. The standards cover many of the most hazardous materials currently in use and often highlight possible chemical exposures that must be controlled. The legal standards are OSHA's permissible exposure limits (PELs), which set the maximum boundaries for allowable worker exposures. There are different types of limits. Time-weighted average (TWA) limits are used to evaluate average sampling results covering a whole shift. Short-term exposure limits (STELs) or ceiling (C) levels are used to evaluate brief exposure times or peak releases.

Although not enforceable by law, other guidelines are often more current and therefore more protective of workers. These include recommended exposure limits (RELs), developed by NIOSH to guide OSHA in promulgating its legal standards, and Threshold Limit Values (TLVs®), offered by the American Conference of Governmental Industrial Hygienists (ACGIH®) annually in a pocket-sized booklet as a guideline for good workplace control. See Appendix B for the 2012 TLVs® and BEIs®. A convenient reference for OSHA and NIOSH limits is the NIOSH Pocket Guide to Chemical Hazards (2010) http://www.cdc.gov/niosh/npg/.

Unfortunately, there are no standards, recommended occupational exposure limits (OELs), or guidelines for most chemicals that reflect current experience or research.

It has been estimated that over 1000 new chemical products are introduced into the workplace every year, resulting in tens of thousands of chemicals in widespread commercial use in the western nations. Of these, the Office of Technology Assessment (OTA) estimated that only 5,000 chemicals have ever been tested for toxicity. Approximately 500 chemicals have specific limits promulgated by OSHA. Maintenance of a complete inventory of chemicals used in the workplace helps to provide oversight and to keep track of any previously unrecognized problems and health effects.

The inventory can be extended to include physical, ergonomic, biological, and psychosocial hazards as well as chemical ones. For example, see Table 15–A for an inventory of potential hazards in a hospital setting. Any inventory should be maintained, updated, and used to develop, manage, and evaluate the appropriate health and safety programs and to ensure awareness of the broad range of hazards that may be present in the workplace.

TABLE 15–A	Categories of Potential Hazards Found in Hospitals	
Hazard Categories	**Definition**	**Examples Found in the Hospital Setting**
Biological	Infectious/biological agents, such as bacteria, viruses, fungi, or parasites that can be transmitted by contact with infectious patients with contaminated body secretions/fluids	Human Immunodeficiency virus (HIV) Hepatitis B or C virus Tuberculosis
Ergonomic	Ergonomics attempts to fit the job to the worker instead of the traditional method of fitting worker to the job. It is the study of human characteristics, both behavioral and biological, for the appropriate design of the living and working environment.	Lifting patients Lifting supplies/ radiation shields Standing for long periods of time Poor lighting Poor workstation design
Chemical	Chemicals that are potentially toxic or irritating to the body, including medications, gases, laboratory reagents, or cleaning products	Ethylene oxide Formaldehyde Glutaraldehyde Waste anesthetic gases Chemotherapy Pentamidine Ribavirin
Psychological	Factors/situations encountered in the workplace that create or potentiate stress, emotional strain, or interpersonal problems	Stress Workplace hierarchy Shiftwork Fear of layoff Fear of violence
Physical	Physical agents that can cause tissue trauma	Radiation Lasers Noise High-voltage equipment Extreme temperatures Needlesticks

DESCRIPTION OF PROCESS OR OPERATION

The inventory provides information about the identity of the hazards present, but it cannot indicate the degree of risk from actual exposure to those materials. It does not quantify the amounts employed in the process, indicate how or where they are used or produced, or detail at what point,

via what route, or for how long employees are potentially exposed. The severity of the hazards present depends on the potential for worker contact as well as the duration and concentration of exposure to the hazardous materials. Therefore, information about the industrial processes and operations is needed to link the hazardous materials to their use in production and to personnel contact. Facility engineering and manufacturing personnel should be consulted regarding usual operations, abnormal operating conditions, and other factors that can affect exposures.

There are numerous industrial operations that should immediately alert the health and safety professional to a potential health hazard. Lists of industrial operations such as the ones shown in Table 15–B are helpful in reviewing processes that might create special risks such as the aerosolization of a hazardous material. After a list of process operations that possibly produce harmful air contaminants has been prepared, certain operations should be selected for closer scrutiny.

Process Flow Sheet

A simple process flow sheet should be drawn that shows in a stepwise fashion how and where each material is introduced and at what point products and by-products are made (Figure 15–1). Process flow sheets and the standard operating procedures (SOPs) that describe the particular operations involved should be obtained and studied. They not only provide a good description of the general operations involved, but also serve as an excellent source for the terminology used in that particular industry. In many industrial operations, many different hazards exist simultaneously. Therefore, it is necessary to carefully examine the overall process so that potentially hazardous conditions are not overlooked.

It is important to identify the air contaminants produced and to pinpoint the location and tasks of personnel that might be exposed to them. Repetitive operations, wherein a worker remains in one location and repeats the same task, can be relatively straightforward to analyze. In operations during which several contaminants are generated, the evaluation process involves identifying the points at which each material is released and the duration of each release, and factoring in the maximum number of times per workshift these exposures occur. This allows prediction of the amount of contaminant potentially released into the environment, and can help target areas for personal or area air sampling. A process flow sheet may be less useful in workplaces where tasks vary from day to day, depending on the products being made, work assignment, and other factors. Individual assessments are necessary in these workplaces.

TABLE 15–B	Common Unit Processes and Associated Hazards by Route of Entry*
Unit Process	**Route of Entry and Hazard**
Abrasive blasting (surface treatment with high velocity sand, steel shot, pecan shells, glass, aluminum oxide, etc.)	Inhalation: silica, metal and paint dust Noise

Acid/alkali treatments
(dipping metal parts in open baths to remove oxides, grease, oil, and dirt)
  Acid pickling (with HCl, HNO_3, H_2SO_4, H_2CrO_4, HNO_3/HF)
  Acid bright dips (with HNO_3/H_2SO_4)
  Molten caustic descaling
  Bath (high temperature)
	Inhalation: acid mist
	Skin contact: burns and corrosion
	Inhalation: NO_2, acid mists
	Inhalation: smoke and vapors
	Skin contact: burns

Blending and mixing (powders and/or liquid are mixed to form products, undergo reactions, etc.)	Inhalation: dusts and mists of toxic materials Skin contact: toxic materials
Crushing and sizing (mechanically reducing the particle size of solids and sorting larger from smaller with screens or cyclones)	Inhalation: dusts, free silica Noise
Degreasing (removing grease, oil, and dirt from metal and plastic with solvents and cleaners) Cold-solvent washing (clean parts with ketones, cellosolves, and aliphatic, aromatic, and stoddard solvents)	Inhalation: vapors Skin contact: dermatitis and absorption Fire and explosion (if flammable) Metabolic: carbon monoxide formed from methylene chloride
Vapor degreasers (with trichloroethylene, methyl chloroform, ethylene dichloride, and certain fluorocarbon compounds)	Inhalation: vapors; thermal degradation may form phosgene, hydrogen chloride, and chlorine gases Skin contact: dermatitis and absorption

Electroplating
(coating metals, plastics and rubber with thin layers of metals)
  Copper
  Chromium
  Cadmium
  Gold
  Silver
	Inhalation: acid mists, HCN, alkali mists, chromium mists
	Skin contact: acids, alkalis
	Ingestion: cyanide compounds

Forging (deforming hot or cold metals by presses or hammering)	Inhalation: hydrocarbons in smokes (hot processes) including polyaromatic hydrocarbons, SO_2, CO, NOx, and other metals sprayed on dies (e.g., lead and molybdenum) Heat stress Noise
Furnace operations (melting and refining metals; boilers for steam generation)	Inhalation: metal fumes, combustion gases, e.g., SO_2 and CO Noise from burners Heat stress Infrared radiation, cataracts in eyes
Grinding, polishing, and buffing (an abrasive is used to remove or shape metal or other material)	Inhalation: toxic dusts from both metals and abrasives Noise
Industrial radiography (x-ray or gamma-ray sources used to examine parts of equipment)	Radiation exposure
Machining (metals, plastics, or wood are worked or shaped with lathes, drills, planers, or milling machines)	Inhalation: airborne particles, cutting oil mists, toxic metals, nitrosamines formed in some water-based cutting oils Skin contact: cutting oils, solvents sharp chips Noise

(continues)

Table 15–B. *(Concluded.)*

Unit Process	*Route of Entry and Hazard*
Materials handling and storage (conveyors, forklift trucks are used to move materials to/from storage)	Inhalation: CO, exhaust particulate, dusts from conveyors, emissions from spills or broken containers
Mining (drilling, blasting, mucking to remove loose material, and material transport)	Inhalation: silica dust, NO_2 from blasting, gases from the mine Heat stress Noise
Painting and spraying (applications of liquids to surfaces, e.g., paints, pesticides, coatings)	Inhalation: solvents and mists and vapors, toxic materials Skin contact: solvents, toxic materials
Soldering (joining metals with molten alloys of lead or silver)	Inhalation: lead and cadmium particulates ("fumes") and flux fumes

Welding and metal cutting
(joining or cutting metals by heating them to molten or semi-molten state)
  Arc welding
  Resistance welding
  Flame cutting and welding
  Brazing
	Inhalation: metal fumes, toxic gases and materials, flux particulates, etc.
	Noise: from burner
	Eye and skin damage from infrared and ultraviolet radiation

*The health hazards may also depend on the toxicity and physical form(s) (gas, liquid, solid, powder, etc.) of the materials used. For further information see Burgess WA. *Recognition of Health Hazards in Industry: A Review of Materials and Processes*, 2nd edition, New York: Wiley, 1995. *(Source: Reprinted with permission from Levy B, Wegman DH.* Occupational Health, Recognizing and Preventing Work-Related Disease, *6th ed. Philadelphia: Lippincott Williams & Wilkins, 2011.)*

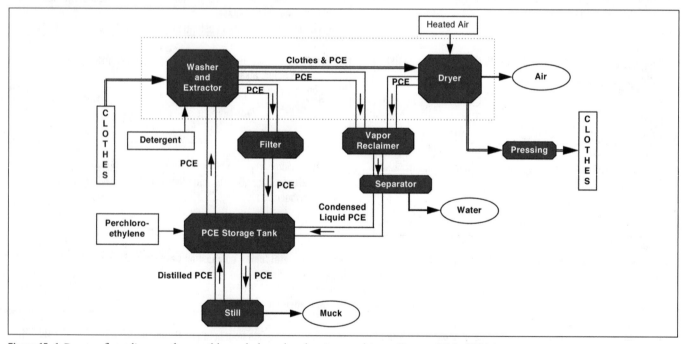

Figure 15–1. Process flow diagram for perchloroethylene dry cleaning machines. *(Source EPA, 1991.)*

Chemical process companies involved with the manufacture of large volumes of chemicals use closed systems. Although chemicals are not routinely released to the atmosphere, exposure to air contaminants in work areas arises from

- leaks from joints, fittings, closures, and other components

that allow release from the otherwise closed system;
- the process of charging the system or preparing and loading the raw materials;
- intentional releases of contaminants from vents, process sampling points, or quality control checkpoints;
- stack gases from combustion processes;

- accidental or unintentional releases resulting from equipment malfunction or failure; and
- maintenance or repair activities or infrequently performed functions without standard operating procedures.

Many valves leak even when they are supposed to be shut, and such leaks can release significant concentrations of chemical air contaminants. Purges, minor overpressures, and system breathing into the atmosphere should be contained by collection, scrubbing, reaction, incineration, or other measures that safely dispose of the products or eliminate their release altogether. Environmental Protection Agency (EPA) emission requirements may require further control measures. Efforts by the environmental movement have influenced state and local legislation to discourage the use of hazardous materials completely. These toxic use reduction (TUR) efforts have emphasized review of chemical operations to eliminate or reduce the use of hazardous chemicals and substitute safer materials wherever possible.

Checklists

A checklist for evaluating environmental hazards that can arise from industrial operations is presented here. It should be modified to fit each organization's particular situation.

Overall Process or Operation

List all hazardous chemical, biological or physical agents used or formed in the process. Carry out the following tasks, answering all of the appropriate questions:

❑ List the conditions necessary for the agent to be released into the workroom atmosphere. Does it usually occur in the process as a dust, mist, gas, fume, vapor, a low-volatile liquid, or a solid (Table 15–C)? What process conditions could cause material to be sprayed or discharged into the air as a liquid aerosol or dust cloud? Have the consequences of the exposure of raw materials or intermediates on people or operations been considered? Are incompatible materials, such as acids and cyanides in plating operations, kept separate from one another?

❑ Review storage of raw materials, finished product, and hazardous waste. Are unstable materials such as methyl ethyl ketone peroxide properly stored? Have chemical incompatibilities been considered? Are containers appropriate? Has flammability been considered?

❑ Consider transport and disposal. Have provisions been made for the safe disposal of toxic materials in compliance with all relevant regulations? Can reactants be removed and disposed of promptly in an emergency? Can spills be quickly and effectively contained?

❑ List the background airborne concentration levels in the workroom that would usually be present as a function of time. List the peak airborne concentrations as a func-

TABLE 15–C	Potentially Hazardous Operations and Air Contaminants	
Process Types	**Contaminant Type**	**Contaminant Examples**
Hot operations Welding Chemical reactions Soldering Melting Molding Burning	Gases (g) Particulates (p) (Dusts, fumes, and mists)	Chromates (p) Zinc and compounds (p) Manganese and compounds (p) Metal oxides (p) Carbon monoxide (g) Ozone (g) Cadmium oxide (p) Fluorides (p) Lead (p) Vinyl chloride (g)
Liquid operations Painting Degreasing Dipping Spraying Brushing Coating Etching Cleaning Dry cleaning Pickling Plating Mixing Galvanizing Chemical reactions	Vapors (v) Gases (g) Mists (m)	Benzene (v) Trichloroethylene (v) Methylene chloride (v) 1,1,1-trichloroethylene (v) Hydrochloric acid (m) Sulfuric acid (m) Hydrogen chloride (g) Cyanide salts (m) Chromic acid (m) Hydrogen cyanide (g) TDI, MDI (v) Hydrogen sulfide (g) Sulfur dioxide (g) Carbon tetrachloride (v)
Solid operations Pouring Mixing Separations Extraction Crushing Conveying Loading Bagging	Dusts (d)	Cement Quartz (free silica) Fibrous glass
Pressurized spraying Cleaning parts Applying pesticides Degreasing Sand blasting Painting	Vapors (v) Dusts (d) Mists (m)	Organic solvents (v) Chlordane (m) Parathion (m) Trichloroethylene (v) 1,1,1-trichloroethylene (v) Methylene chloride (v) Quartz (free silica, d)
Shaping operations Cutting Grinding Filing Milling Molding Sawing Drilling	Dusts (d)	Asbestos Beryllium Uranium Zinc Lead

Note: d = dusts, g = gases, m = mists, p = particulates, v = vapors.

(Source: AIHA. A Strategy Manual for Assessing and Managing Occupational Exposures, 3rd ed. Fairfax, VA: AIHA Press, 2006.)

tion of task duration. List the appropriate PELs, RELs, TLVs, and STELs.

❑ Review fire safety. Are fire extinguishers the correct type and size for the materials present? Are they inspected and recharged on a scheduled basis? Are the extinguishing agents compatible with process materials? Is an evacuation plan prepared and disseminated? Are alarms visible, audible, and understandable? Are employees trained in fire safety? Do they know where emergency equipment is located?

❑ List the levels of those physical agents that are normally present (such as noise, heat, ionizing and nonionizing radiation).

Equipment

Conduct all of the following procedures, listing those pieces of equipment that contain sufficient hazardous material or energy such that a hazard would be produced if their contents were suddenly released to the environment:

❑ List the equipment that could release hazardous levels of physical agents during normal operations or abnormal situations such as power outages; these agents include any source of electrical, mechanical, hydraulic, pneumatic, chemical, thermal, or other energy.

❑ List the equipment that can produce hazardous concentrations of airborne contaminants. For each item, indicate the control measures installed to minimize the hazard. Is the health and safety control measure adequate, fail-safe, and reliable? Is it checked on a routine basis?

❑ List process equipment with components that are likely to fail due to corrosion or to leak hazardous materials such as valves, pump packing, and tank vents. What safeguards have been taken to prevent expected leakage? Is each safeguard adequate, fail-safe, and reliable? Is there a preventive maintenance program in place to ensure routine examination and replacement of these components?

❑ Label all chemical containers, transport vessels, and piping systems in accordance with the OSHA hazard communication standard. Are labels appropriate for the literacy level and language of the work force?

❑ Ensure that all equipment can be correctly locked out and tagged out during necessary procedures. Are emergency disconnect switches properly marked?

Cleaning Methods

Cleaning operations should be noted to identify hazardous materials and processes. The primary cleaning/disinfection methods used in industry include the following:

❑ manual wiping of parts or equipment with a solvent-soaked rag

❑ chemical stripping, degreasing, or removal by dissolving
❑ use of hand-held or mechanical brushes
❑ scraping or sanding
❑ dry sweeping or wet mopping
❑ wet sponging
❑ spraying cleaning products with disinfectants
❑ abrasive blasting
❑ steam cleaning
❑ using compressed air to blow off dust
❑ using vacuum-cleaning devices

The common feature of all these operations is that by some physical and/or chemical action, a contaminant is dislodged from the surface to which it was adhering and could be released into the work environment. In addition, the cleaning agent used to remove a hazardous material might introduce another, equally hazardous, chemical into the workplace.

For example, cleaning chemicals and disinfectants have been associated with work-related asthma. Surveillance of work-related asthma is now funded by NIOSH in five states. Surveillance results indicated that cleaning materials were the fifth most frequently reported cause of asthma cases, including both new-onset asthma and work-aggravated asthma. Cleaning agents and disinfectants may contain strong irritants (e.g., bleach, ammonia) or sensitizers (e.g., benzalkonium chloride, formaldehyde, chlorhexidine). Similarly, rag cleaning with organic solvents results in worker exposure to organic vapors, by inhalation and by skin contact. A brush used to sweep up dusty substances or a scraper used to dislodge built-up cakes of dry substances can disperse dust into the air. The use of compressed air to blow dust from surfaces re-entrains dust that had settled out and will probably produce the greatest concentration of particulate air contaminants. OSHA regulations prohibit the use of compressed air to clean except when the pressure is reduced to 30 psi, and then only if an effective chip guard and personal protective equipment are used. The use of compressed air with asbestos dust is forbidden.

High-pressure water blasting and steam cleaning are essentially wet methods that might initially appear to be designed to suppress the generation of air contaminants. However, hydroblasting equipment to remove a solid can produce substantial concentrations of air contaminants, as can steam cleaning, because of the temperatures and forces involved.

The use of vacuum cleaners, which collect and contain material for removal, appears to be the most satisfactory method of cleaning dry, dusty materials without producing excessive amounts of contaminants. However, a special vacuum with a high-efficiency particulate filter (HEPA) is needed when dealing with certain highly toxic dusts such as asbestos, lead, arsenic, or cadmium. HEPA vacuuming is often accompanied by low pressure, wet methods such as misting or airless spraying to keep levels of airborne toxic dusts to a minimum. There should also be an SOP for changing out the HEPA filter in a contained environment to prevent rerelease of these materials into the work space.

A preferable step is to reduce the dispersal of airborne dusts in the first place. Some power sanders and soldering guns can be specially fitted for dust or fume removal at the point of generation. The need for cleaning can sometimes be further reduced by analysis of the source of the material that must be removed. For example, degreasing is not necessary if oil or coolant is not applied to a part in the first place. A toxic-use-reduction approach would seek to identify and prevent the source of the contamination, if possible, and then use the safest method to remove it; for example, with a water-based cleaner rather than a volatile organic solvent.

Process Safety Management

Inherent in the use or storage of large quantities of highly hazardous or flammable chemicals is the risk of catastrophic releases that would prove injurious or fatal both to employees and to those living in the immediate vicinity of the facility. On December 2, 1984, methyl isocyanate was released from Union Carbide's pesticide plant in Bhopal, India, which caused at least 6,500 deaths and an estimated 20,000 to 50,000 serious injuries. This experience taught the world a tragic lesson about worker and community consequences of an unexpected chemical release and the need for controls and emergency preparedness.

Process safety management is a systematic approach to evaluating an entire process for the purpose of preventing such unwanted releases of hazardous chemicals into locations that could expose employees and others to serious hazards. In 1992, OSHA promulgated a standard for general industry, 29 CFR 1910.119, which mandates process safety management of highly hazardous chemicals for companies that use or store large quantities of flammable or highly hazardous chemicals in one location. It requires them to implement a program that incorporates analyses, written operating procedures, training, inspection and testing, and safety reviews for their own employees and for contractors. OSHA defines process safety management as the proactive identification, evaluation, and mitigation or prevention of chemical releases that could occur as a result of failures in process, procedures, or equipment.

OSHA acknowledges several acceptable methods to evaluate hazards of the process being analyzed:

- what-if scenarios
- checklists
- what-ifs in a checklist format
- hazard and operability studies (HAZOPs)
- failure mode and effects analysis (FMEA)
- fault tree analysis
- other equivalent methods

Employers are required to determine and document the priority order for conducting process-hazard analyses based on a rationale that considers the extent of the process-hazards, the number of potentially affected employees, the age of the processes, and the facility's operating history.

This approach requires the development of expertise, experience, and proactive initiative by a team of concerned individuals. These goals are attained primarily by conducting process-hazard analyses, directed toward evaluating potential causes and consequences of fires, explosions, releases of toxic or flammable chemicals, and major spills of hazardous chemicals. The health and safety professional, with the assistance of process managers, employees, and others, must determine the potential failure points or modes in a process. The focus is on equipment, instrumentation, utilities, human actions (routine and nonroutine), and external factors that might impact the process.

For the health and safety professional, a process-hazard analysis can provide a starting point in an overall hazard evaluation. Such analyses should be performed whenever possible. For those evaluating businesses where quantities of hazardous materials in use fall below the OSHA requirements for a written plan, the guidelines contained in the Process Safety Standard may still serve as a useful tool in the evaluation process.

FIELD SURVEY

Thus far in the evaluation process, most of the research recommended has probably been conducted outside of the workplace. Process diagrams, literature searches, and inventories can be reviewed in the office, but evaluation requires on-site and direct observation, measurement, and interviews, and interpretation of the collected information. It is at this point that the anticipation of hazards must be integrated with actual conditions. Whether the motivation for the evaluation is compliance, insurance, expert testimony, complaint investigation, or development of a comprehensive health and safety plan, direct, on-site involvement on the part of the industrial hygienist is required. This usually begins with a walk-through of the workplace.

The walk-through, or initial field survey, follows the flow of materials into the facility, through all the various processes involved in the operation, to the shipping of finished product, as well as tracking unwanted by-products.

Figure 15–2. Observing dusty operations, patterns of shavings, or powder on the floor, overspray on walls, puddles underneath valves, or wetness around an area not currently in use, alerts the industrial hygienist to problems not considered before. The pattern of wood dust under this saw indicated that the local exhaust ventilation was disconnected. *(Photo by Elise Pechter.)*

It should also include nonproduction areas such as maintenance and other service operations. It should be conducted with the facility or process manager, someone familiar with both the process design and usual operations. The walk-through introduces the industrial hygienist to the language of facility operations, establishes a baseline of current conditions, and allows an initial assessment of hazards or areas that may require further evaluation.

The industrial hygienist can use this opportunity to meet operators of key processes, area supervisors, and other health and safety personnel. Communication with these individuals is essential to understanding the sources and locations of hazards on the job, and for planning future sampling and analyses. A checklist, a sketch of the facility layout, preliminary notes, or a tape recording is useful for documenting initial impressions and serves as a reminder to return to areas that require more thorough inspection.

With the shift to a service economy, the traditional manufacturing facility tour may be conducted less frequently. The field survey will, however, remain a vital tool of the industrial hygienist, with the focus of the initial walk-through being individual operations within a building. It can be invaluable to conduct the initial assessment of the operation with an area supervisor who can help obtain a sketch of the physical operation of interest and familiarize the industrial hygienist with the current problems. The industrial hygienist should also develop a checklist to use in the walk-through itself.

Sensory Perception

Field surveys also allow industrial hygienists to make use of their sensory perceptions (vision, hearing, and sense of smell) to note potential hazards. Observing dusty operations, patterns of shavings or powder on the floor (Figure 15–2), overspray on walls, puddles underneath valves, or wetness around an area not currently in use alerts the industrial hygienist to potential problems. The exact location of processes of concern, such as welding stations, degreasers, flammable storage areas, exits, and break areas can be precisely located and added to the facility layout for later consideration.

The absence or presence of visible dust should not sway initial judgment excessively. Because dust particles of respirable size are not visible to the unaided eye, lack of a visible dust cloud does not guarantee an atmosphere free of respiratory hazards. Timing of dry sweeping and shaking out of dust collection devices should be noted. The need for air sampling for dusts should be determined by the source, processes, identity, toxicity, medical evidence, and health concerns.

Whenever the tour guide must move closer to the industrial hygienist in order to be understood, it is likely that noise levels are excessive and this fact should be noted. Patterns of hearing protector use should also be recorded during the walk-through.

The presence of many vapors and gases is detectable by smell. The odor thresholds for some chemicals are in the parts per billion range, which helps serve as an early warning of exposure. This is especially true for someone entering an area from elsewhere and for certain aromatic or strong-smelling chemicals such as toluene or hydrogen sulfide. The sense of smell fatigues with time and is variable from person to person. Odor thresholds listed in resource tables can vary by a factor of 100 from one person to another. Detecting an odor or experiencing eye or throat irritation should indicate to the occupational health professional that a chemical is present to some degree in the air, and an attempt should be made to identify the process or chemical. These sensory impressions do not necessarily reveal an overexposure, but they can provide important clues to a potentially hazardous source. Also, it is important to note that absence of an odor or irritation does not necessarily mean the absence of a chemical exposure.

Control Measures in Use

During the walk through or initial field survey, the types, locations, and effectiveness of control measures should be appraised. The best ways to avoid very hazardous exposures include substitution of safer chemicals for more hazardous ones, or total isolation of the hazardous materials from the work force. Existing hazards should be controlled by means of local exhaust and general dilution ventilation, shielding, and personal protective equipment such as gloves, respirators, hearing protectors, and safety glasses. Storage of respirators in an area free of contaminants and availability of replacement cartridges are good indicators of a company's oversight of their respirator program.

Ventilation design should be appropriate for the hazard and the process. Homemade ventilation may be inadequate. For example, it might consist of a canopy hood for unheated processes or hoods distant from the source, both of which would provide less than adequate capture velocity. Ventilation and airflow patterns can be visualized with an air current tube or calculated by taking air velocity measurements. The distance between the air collection device and source should be observed, and any turbulence created by portable fans or locations on aisles should be recorded.

Administrative controls such as job rotation, scheduling of particularly hazardous operations during shifts when fewer workers are present, enforcement of lock-out/tag-out, for example, are not always obvious. Questions regarding these types of controls should be included on any questionnaire and asked of the process manager.

Observation and Interview

Observation and interviews with workers can reveal the best information regarding hazard evaluation and adequacy of controls. During the walk-through, or while conducting sampling, the occupational health professional must carefully observe workers performing their jobs and note all opportunities for exposure by inhalation, ingestion, or dermal absorption. This observation must be done without altering the behavior of the workers being observed, if at all possible. Without jeopardizing worker confidentiality, employees should be interviewed regarding the content of their jobs, how they spend their time, exposures of concern, and any health symptoms or concerns, especially as they relate to contact with various chemical products or processes. Identifying particularly hazardous operations may be possible by a review of recent incidents. Documenting variations in production levels, assignments, shifts, seasonal work, and ventilation patterns helps in determining when peak exposures might occur and where sampling would be most useful (Table 15–D). Review of the OSHA 300 log may also provide information about departments or locations where injuries or illnesses have occurred.

MONITORING AND SAMPLING

Rationale

There are a number of reasons why environmental measurements should be taken in the workplace. Of primary concern to the health and safety professional is evaluating the degree of employee exposure to hazardous materials on the job. Other important reasons include identification of the tasks or processes that could be sources of peak exposures, evaluation of the impact of process changes and control measures, and compliance with occupational and environmental regulations. Environmental sampling can be used to clear an area for reoccupancy, decide if a confined space is safe for entry, establish background or usual concentrations, or warn of a peak release of a hazardous product.

Monitoring

Monitoring is a continuous program of observation, measurement, and judgment. It requires an awareness of the presence of potential health hazards as processes undergo change, and constant assessment of the adequacy of the control measures in place.

Monitoring is more than simply sampling the air to which an employee is exposed or examining the medical status of that employee. It is a combination of observation, interview, and measurement that permits a judgment to be made relative to the potential hazards and the adequacy of protection afforded employees. Included in the process are both personal and environmental monitoring, performed during a given operation where hazardous materials may be released, and follow-up biological and medical monitoring of the employees involved in that process.

TABLE 15–D	Checklist for Evaluating Chemical Exposure

A. Evaluate the Potential for Airborne Exposure.

1. **Exposure Sources** (rank high/medium/low):
   a. Types and amounts of chemicals in use or created by combustion or decomposition.
   b. Visible leaks, spills, or emissions from process equipment, vents, stacks, or from containers.
   c. Settled dust, which may be resuspended into the air.
   d. Open containers from which liquids may evaporate.
   e. Heating or drying, which may make a chemical more volatile or dusty.
   f. Odors. Consult an odor threshold table to get an estimate of concentration.
   g. Do air monitoring where the presence of a contaminant is suspected but cannot be verified by sight or smell.
   h. Visualize exposure by taking photographs or videotape.

2. *Job Functions* (estimate hours/day):
   a. Manual handling in general.
   b. Active verb job tasks such as grinding, scraping, sawing, cutting, sanding, drilling, spraying, measuring, mixing, blending, dumping, sweeping, wiping, pouring, crushing, filtering, extracting, packaging.

3. *Control Failures:*
   a. Visible leaks from ventilation hoods, ductwork, collectors.
   b. Hoods that are located too far from the source or are missing or broken.
   c. Ductwork that is clogged, dented or has holes.
   d. Insufficient make-up air to replace exhausted air.
   e. Contamination inside respirators.
   f. Improperly selected, maintained, or used respirator.
   g. Lack of or inadequate housekeeping equipment.
   h. Lack of or inadequate doffing and laundering procedures for clothing contaminated by dust.

B. Evaluate the Potential for Accidental Ingestion.

1. *Exposure Sources* (rank high/medium/low):
   a. Types and amounts of chemicals in use or created by combustion or decomposition. Solids are of primary concern.
   b. Contamination of work surfaces, which may spread to food, beverage, gum, cigarettes, hands or face.
   c. Contamination of hands or face, which may enter mouth.
   d. Do wipe sampling to verify the presence of a contaminant on work surfaces, hands, face, and so forth.

2. *Control Failures:*
   a. Contamination of inside of respirator, which may enter mouth.
   b. Contamination of lunchroom surfaces, which may spread to food, beverage, gum, cigarettes, hands or face.

C. Evaluate the Potential for Skin Contact and Absorption.

1. *Exposure Sources:*
   a. Types and amounts of chemicals in use or created by combustion or decomposition. Check dermal absorption potential. Do not rely on OSHA skin notations. Assume most liquids will penetrate skin.
   b. Consider whether one chemical can act as a carrier for other chemicals.
   c. Visualize dermal exposure by taking photographs or videotape.

2. *Job Functions:*
   a. Dipping hands into material.
   b. Handling of wet objects or rags.

3. *Control Failures:*
   a. Contamination of inside of gloves.
   b. Improperly selected, maintained, or used gloves.
   c. Improperly selected, maintained, or used chemical protective clothing.
   d. Lack of or inadequate facilities for washing of hands and face close to work areas.
   e. Lack of or inadequate shower facilities.

(Source: Reprinted from New Solutions, *Spring 1991, p. 77, P.O. Box 281200, Lakewood, CO 80228-8200.)*

Personal Monitoring

Personal monitoring is the measurement of a particular employee's exposure to airborne contaminants and, in theory, reflects actual exposure to the employee. It is usually done during a specific time period, often an 8-hr shift or a 15-min period, to ensure compliance with OSHA PELs or STELs; it can therefore include times when the employee is at break or involved in activities where the contaminant of interest is not in use. It is because of this variability that it is extremely important to observe individuals being monitored

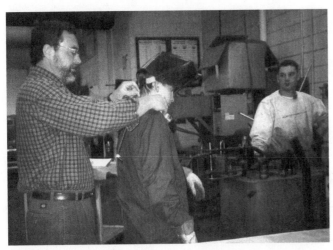

Figure 15–3. In personal monitoring, the measurement device, or dosimeter, is placed as close as possible to the contaminant's route of entry into the body. For example, when monitoring an air contaminant that is toxic if inhaled, the measurement device, or dosimeter, is placed on the employee's lapel or as close to the breathing zone as possible. When monitoring noise, the dosimeter should be placed close to the ear. *(Photo by Elise Pechter.)*

and to interview them about their work, before, during, and after the monitoring is done.

In personal monitoring, the measurement device, or dosimeter, is placed as close as possible to the contaminant's route of entry into the body (Figure 15–3). For example, when monitoring an air contaminant that is toxic if inhaled, the measurement device is placed on the employee's lapel or as close to the breathing zone as possible. When monitoring noise, the dosimeter should be placed close to the ear.

Even with the proper placement of the dosimeter, there is no guarantee that results of personal sampling will reflect actual exposure levels. Some materials are absorbed through the skin or mucous membranes in addition to being inhaled. The release of contaminants is often not uniform, and the side of the employee where the monitor is placed may not be the side closest to the point of release of the contaminant. The results would therefore underestimate the exposure. On the other hand, if the sampling device is placed outside a respirator or face shield, the result might overestimate the true exposure to the worker.

Personal, active sampling relies on portable, battery-operated sampling pumps that the employee wears throughout the sampling. This offers freedom of movement because there is no need to maintain proximity to electrical outlets. The pumps, however, can be noisy and heavy, and employees are sometimes not willing to wear them on a continuous basis. In addition, because the pumps are battery operated, they might have a variable output throughout the day, or might actually stop operating in the middle of sampling. The

effective use of personal sampling pumps relies on proper calibration and maintenance and consistent supervision by well-trained professionals during the monitoring process.

Passive sampling may also be done, using a wide assortment of contaminant-specific dosimeters (badges) worn on the employee's lapel. While often less accurate than active methods, they are easier for the employee to wear. Passive dosimeters are widely used in industrial settings and usually meet the accuracy requirements set by OSHA, so long as manufacturers' expiration dates and instructions are followed.

Area Monitoring

Area sampling is another method used by industrial hygienists to evaluate exposure. Here, however, exposure is measured not in terms of a particular employee, but rather in terms of the ambient air concentration of a particular substance in a given area at a given period of time. The measurement device, which does not have to be battery operated and can be larger and more rugged than those used in personal sampling, is placed adjacent to a worker's normal workstation. Centralized analytical devices can be attached to remote probes so that data can be acquired from several areas simultaneously and monitored from a central location (Figure 15–4). An alarm can be sounded if a preset limit is exceeded (as shown in Figure 15–5). Area sampling is an important technique to determine the need to develop, implement, or improve control measures.

Ideally, area sampling would be so thorough and the pattern of potential exposure to workers so well defined that, in any given work space, knowledge of a worker's activity would be sufficient to estimate that person's exposure, and personal monitoring would not be necessary. If, for instance, vapor concentrations and their duration around equipment were known and could be superimposed on a floor plan, then a worker's exposure could be determined from observing that worker's movements and plotting the frequency and duration spent in each area. The employee's daily exposure could then be found by adding short-term exposures to compute the time-weighted average (TWA) exposure. This in-depth area exposure analysis is not routinely done, however. It requires a tremendous amount of time and monitoring equipment and may still miss crucial contributions to a worker's exposure on any given day.

In most processes, airborne concentrations of materials usually vary over time. The fluctuations may be large, and continue for hours, or they may be brief, sometimes lasting only seconds or minutes. Only extensive, continuous sampling can provide information about such fluctuations in any given location. The data, if collected with a real-time monitor, printed on a strip-chart recorder or done in con-

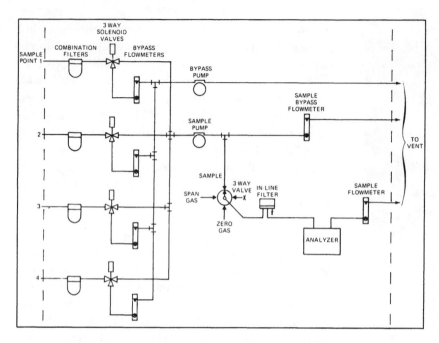

Figure 15–4. Centralized analytical devices can be attached to remote probes so that data can be acquired from several areas simultaneously and monitored from a central location.

junction with real-time video recording, provide valuable clues about the main sources and timing of exposure, and thus a means to design controls that should be used in a process. The computer printout, strip chart, or strip chart/video recording can be used to estimate an individual's exposure and can also serve as a historical record.

Area sampling is also used to establish usual background concentrations for chemicals that are ubiquitous in our environment. An incident that occurred in Boston, Massachusetts, illustrates this rationale. A transformer fire released polychlorinated biphenyls (PCBs) into an office basement and ventilation system in October 1981. In June 1985 a new tenant, prior to occupying the building, performed testing that revealed contamination, including dioxins and dibenzofurans, which required extensive cleaning, even though the building had been thoroughly cleaned after the original incident. Sampling methods were so sensitive, and the chemicals so persistent, that they were detected four years after the incident. Questions about the adequacy of the cleanup and the attendant risk led researchers to consider what normal background concentrations in similar settings might be. In order to establish normal background concentration levels, area air sampling was conducted in similar buildings with no history of PCB release. These results were subsequently used to develop a criterion for re-entry into a previously contaminated area, with assurance that the exposure and risk would be no greater than usual (U.S. Department of Health & Human Services [U.S. DHHS], NIOSH, 1987, 1988). Area sampling for the same purpose is used after asbestos or lead abatement is carried out in commercial or residential settings.

Area sampling has its disadvantages, though. Sampling

equipment can be made rugged and reliable, but often it is not, and leaving it unattended for hours or days at a time without the supervision of a trained technician could result in no reliable data collection during a crucial period in the process. Area sampling may underestimate exposure if the worker works close to a process but the measurement probe or collection device is at a farther distance from the exposure point.

Biological Monitoring and Medical Screening

Biological monitoring is a tool that can be used to assess workers' total exposure to chemicals, or provide information about the impact of workplace hazards on health. Air

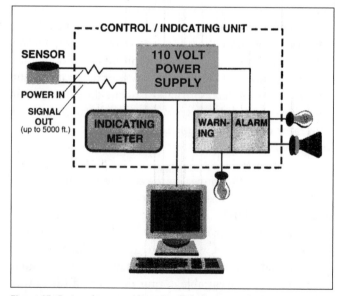

Figure 15–5. An alarm can be sounded if a preset limit is exceeded.

sampling evaluates the inhalation hazard; measurement of an individual's exhaled air, blood, or urine can provide information about absorption of hazardous materials by all routes of exposure and the physiological effect of the total dose.

In general, there are three categories of biological monitoring: measurement of the contaminant itself, measurement of a metabolite of the chemical, and measurement of enzymes or functions that reflect harm caused by a hazardous exposure.

The most direct approach measures the contaminant itself in blood or urine; this method is used with lead, mercury, cadmium, and arsenic. Carbon monoxide may be measured in exhaled air. Often, the hazardous chemical cannot be measured directly, but a metabolite can be. For example, methylene chloride is metabolized to carboxyhemoglobin in the human body, and elevated carboxyhemoglobin levels in the blood could reveal overexposure to methylene chloride. Another example is styrene, for which exposure and absorption can be evaluated by the concentration of mandelic acid in urine at the end of a workshift.

Sometimes the adverse effect of a workplace exposure is only revealed when medical evaluation reveals an unusual laboratory result or abnormal function test. These are usually ordered to help diagnose a health problem. For example, a pulmonary function test on an autobody spray painter with a cough can reveal deficits in forced expiratory volume. Such a reduced ability to exhale may be a marker of occupational asthma caused by contact with the isocyanates in polyurethane paint.

Another medical test result that may indicate occupational injury or disease is a slowed nerve conduction velocity, which may be done to help diagnose numbness and tingling in the hands. Slowed conduction (prolonged time) may indicate trauma, repetitive strain, or peripheral neuropathy. Abnormal liver function enzymes may reflect hepatitis or liver injury from chronic solvent exposure. Such results reveal a disease process or harm but do not necessarily indicate the cause of the harm, which also may be attributable to factors outside the workplace or to unrelated medical conditions. Therefore, the results are nonspecific and require interpretation by a trained occupational physician or occupational health nurse. Unfortunately, many physicians have not been trained to identify the occupational or environmental causes of diseases, and some fail to ask their patients about their work and exposure hazards. For example, abdominal pain, insomnia, infertility, and high blood pressure may never be linked diagnostically to the lead poisoning that caused them.

Interest in biological monitoring has increased recently. The American Industrial Hygiene Association (AIHA) wrote a position statement (1999) calling for the incorporation of requirements for biological monitoring into more OSHA standards. With 800,000 work-related illnesses each year, they reasoned, PELs to limit inhalation exposures have not prevented occupational disease. AIHA calls for biological monitoring as an inexpensive, practical, effective hazard assessment tool, as used in Germany and England. The Social Concerns Committee of AIHA countered that biological monitoring is limited in its usefulness because of issues limiting interpretation of the results, as well as privacy, confidentiality, invasiveness, and worker acceptance issues.

The values measured can be compared to background population values or to reference values such as the ACGIH Biological Exposure Indices (BEI), in the same way air-sampling data are evaluated. If conducted side-by-side with industrial hygiene sampling, then biological results may be correlated with airborne concentrations. This information is useful in etiological research and in demonstrating health effects at concentrations of chemical previously thought to be acceptable.

The test must be reproducible, as well as sensitive and specific, to be sure that true positives (people with an adverse health effect or disease) and negatives (those without disease) are identified. There is a section later in the chapter, "Required Accuracy and Precision," about these same issues in relation to air sampling testing. The laboratories must be proficient and certified and participate in laboratory quality control programs. The interpretation of test results may be difficult. The usefulness of the biological test may be limited by:

- few validated tests
- laboratory reliability
- interindividual variability
- intraindividual variability
- inappropriate timing of testing (Value may reflect a peak exposure or a valley from time away from work or clearance of the chemical from the body. Knowledge of the metabolism and half-life of the chemical is required.)
- wide range of normal values in the population
- elevated background levels for many who are not occupationally exposed (see the ACGIH BEI notation "B")
- nonspecific biological indicator (see the ACGIH BEI notation "Ns")
- ambiguous quantitative interpretation (see ACGIH BEI notations "Nq" and "Sq")
- biological value may indicate exposure and uptake have occurred, but the health consequences are unknown

Biological monitoring may be an important component for evaluating illness and linking symptoms to exposures, but caution should be exercised in its use and interpretation. The significance of results from biological monitoring is open to interpretation; alterations in function or unusual laboratory findings can be viewed as evidence of harm, or they can be viewed as only a marker that exposure has occurred. For example, the indication on chest x-ray films of pleural plaques (small, hard, plate-like surfaces on the pleura), which can exist in the absence of disease is a marker of past asbestos exposure. Interpretation of radiological findings in the lungs is known to be inconsistent; abnormalities are difficult to detect and even more difficult to interpret, so x-ray films should not be the sole determinant in diagnosis of occupational disease (Figure 15–6). There is no simple test to diagnose occupational disease.

Guidelines for biological monitoring must reflect an understanding of the biochemical dynamics of the contaminant in relation to physiological processes. Measurements may represent peak exposures and absorption prior to any significant clearance, or they may reflect equilibrium levels attained only after steady state has been reached. Obtaining information about the relationship between the timing of exposure and biological testing is very important.

For example, lead concentration in blood is used as an index of lead exposure by inhalation and ingestion in the previous days or weeks, whereas zinc protoporphyrin (ZPP) is used as a measure of lead exposure during the previous three or four months. Research shows that bone x-ray fluorescence (XRF) may reveal the total body burden of lead, including that portion stored in the skeleton. These measurements can be used to identify hazardous exposures, dangerous work practices, or inadequacies in ventilation

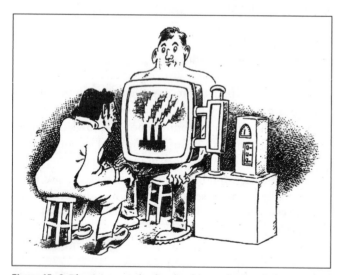

Figure 15–6. Physicians and other health professionals have a vital role in recognizing occupational disease. Contrary to the drawing, there is no simple test. The suspicion and the determination of work-relatedness depend primarily on a careful occupational history. *(Drawing by Nick Thorkelson) (Reprinted with permission from Levy B, Wegman DH. Occupational Health, Recognizing and Preventing Work-Related Disease, 4th ed. Philadelphia: Lippincott Williams & Wilkins, 2000.)*

and personal protective equipment. Differences in blood lead and ZPP concentrations provide information about the timing of exposure and which tasks pose the greatest risk. Blood lead values can be used to identify individuals at risk, who should be removed from any further exposure.

Medical surveillance. Medical surveillance can extend beyond biological monitoring of individuals to incorporate screening of exposed populations for the adverse effects of those exposures. For example, audiometric testing can be used to determine the extent of temporary or permanent shifts in thresholds of hearing acuity caused by noise exposure. Liver enzymes can be measured to assess the effect of solvents suspected of causing hepatitis or other liver injury. The appearance of the lungs on x-ray films can reveal pneumoconiosis, hypersensitivity pneumonitis, or other respiratory diseases. Baseline skin testing, followed by further skin testing after a potential exposure, is essential for those working in health care or other occupations at high risk for exposure to tuberculosis. Positive changes from baseline should lead to further evaluation or medical treatment.

One purpose of medical surveillance is the early detection of disease or conditions for which treatment can prevent further illness. The affected individual should be removed from the hazardous exposure and receive needed medical treatment and supervision. OSHA has incorporated this concept of medical removal protection (MRP) in its standards to protect workers overexposed to lead and cadmium. OSHA requires that if a worker's medical evaluation indicates overexposure or the adverse health effects associated with these substances, the employer must either provide alternative work in an area where there is no risk of exposure or allow the employee to stay home with full compensation during the period of treatment.

Medical screening can also be an invaluable preventive tool in hazard control. For example, regular testing of urine for mercury in an exposed worker population allows identification of individual workstation or work practice as sources of contamination. Routine analysis of the group may allow early detection of subtle increases in mercury absorption that might reflect a breakdown in controls or a weakness in the training program.

OSHA has proposed that medical screening and evaluation be used to measure the effectiveness of its PELs. If workers exhibit adverse health effects, while at the same time air-sampling results show compliance with OSHA's standards, then OSHA will use the results to re-examine the adequacy of the PEL.

Over 30 OSHA standards now have requirements for medical examinations or tests, focusing on either medical screening of individuals or surveillance of an entire exposed group (Table 15–E). The medical evaluation required may involve screening of an exposed employee group for an individual agent, or it may include a more comprehensive examination of employee health in the workplace. The more hazardous the exposure, the more in-depth the health evaluation should be. For example, hazardous waste workers should receive preplacement screening and periodic medical examinations, with testing for specific exposures as necessary. Table 15–F describes a recommended medical program. In work environments where respirator use is necessary, workers should be medically evaluated for fitness to wear a respirator. In most cases, medical surveillance should include a medical and occupational history and a physical examination, with attention paid to the target organs and functions potentially affected. Medical records should be maintained to allow for review of deviations from the baseline of preplacement health status.

Biological exposure indices. The concept of biological monitoring has led the ACGIH to develop a list of Biological Exposure Indices (BEIs®), published annually in their TLV booklet. Similarly, OSHA has incorporated required biological monitoring into several standards (Table 15–E). Several of OSHA's standards (such as those for benzene and ethylene oxide) only require medical surveillance when air sampling has revealed a pattern of exposure above either the action level (AL) or PEL during a specific number of days per year.

NIOSH, in conjunction with state departments of health, has promoted the use of medical screening and biological sampling results to investigate occupational exposure and illnesses. Since 1992, the CDC's state-based Adult Blood Lead Epidemiology and Surveillance (ABLES) program has tracked laboratory reported elevated blood lead levels in U.S. adults. This surveillance can document industries, occupations, and tasks of concern and can be used to target intervention and to develop educational materials for small businesses needing assistance in controlling hazards. Ninety-five percent of those with elevated blood lead levels were work-related; the leading specific industries were manufacturing of storage batteries, mining of lead and zinc ores, and painting. The Massachusetts Occupational Lead Registry found that 70 percent of their registrants with blood lead concentrations greater than 40 micrograms of lead per deciliter of blood worked in painting, deleading, and other construction jobs. This discovery led to efforts to work with the state's highway department to more closely supervise bridge-painting contracts.

Combined effects. At present, very little is known about how the body integrates two different types of stress and the resultant strain, even if both stressors are chemical. The

TABLE 15–E	OSHA Standards Requiring Medical Surveillance
29 CFR	**Standard**
1910.95	Occupational Noise Exposure
1910.156	Fire Brigade
1910.134	Respiratory Protection
1910.120	Hazardous Waste Operations and Emergency Response standard (HAZWOPER)
1910.1001	Asbestos
1910.1003	13 Carcinogens (Exposure during emergency); individual chemicals also listed separately under 1910.1004-1016; medical surveillance referred back to 1910.1003
1910.1017	Vinyl Chloride
1910.1018	Inorganic Arsenic
1910.1025	Lead
1910.1026	Chromium (VI)
1910.1027	Cadmium
1910.1028	Benzene
1910.1029	Coke Oven Emissions
1910.1030	Occupational Exposure to Bloodborne Pathogens
1910.1043	Cotton Dust
1910.1044	1,2-Dibromo-3-chloropropane
1910.1045	Acrylonitrile
1910.1047	Ethylene Oxide
1910.1048	Formaldehyde
1910.1050	Methylenedianiline
1910.1051	1,3-Butadiene
1910.1052	Methylene Chloride
1910.1450	Hazardous Chemicals in Labs
1926: Construction Standards: The requirements applicable to construction work under these sections are identical to those set forth above, under 1910….	
1926.52	Occupational Noise Exposure
1926.62	Lead in Construction
1926.65	HAZWOPER
1926.103	Respiratory Protection
1926.803	Compressed Air Environments
1926.1101	Asbestos
1926.1103	13 Carcinogens (4-Nitrobiphenyl, etc.)
1926.1117	Vinyl Chloride
1926.1118	Inorganic Arsenic
1926.1126	Chromium (VI)
1926.1127	Cadmium
1926.1128	Benzene
1926.1129	Coke Oven Emissions
1926.1144	1,2-Dibromo-3-chloropropane
1926.1145	Acrylonitrile
1926.1147	Ethylene Oxide
1926.1148	Formaldehyde
1926.1151	1,3 Butadiene
1926.1152	Methylene Chloride
1928.1027 Agriculture Standards: The requirements Applicable to agricultural work under this section are identical to those set forth above, under 1910…	Cadmium

TABLE 15–F	Recommended Medical Program	
Component	**Recommended**	**Optional**
Preplacement screening	Medical history Occupational history Physical examination Determination of fitness to work while wearing protective equipment Baseline monitoring for specific exposures	Freezing preplacement serum specimen for later testing (limited to specific situations).
Periodic medical examinations	Yearly update of medical and occupational history; yearly physical examination; testing based on examination results, exposures, and job class and task More frequent testing based on specific exposures	Yearly testing with routine medical tests.
Emergency treatment	Provide emergency first aid on site Develop liaison with local hospital and medical specialists. Arrange for decontamination of victims Arrange in advance for transport of victims Transfer medical records; give details of incident and medical history to next care provider	
Nonemergency treatment	Develop mechanism for nonemergency health care	
Record keeping and review	Maintain and provide access to medical records in accordance with OSHA and state regulations Report and record occupational injuries and illnesses Review site safety plan regularly to determine whether additional testing is needed Review program periodically. Focus on current site hazards, exposures, and industrial hygiene standards.	

usual assumption is that chemicals affecting different organs or tissues should be considered independently, whereas those that affect the same organ or tissue should be considered jointly because they may produce additive or synergistic effects.

Synergism is known to occur with certain exposures. The best-known synergistic effect is that of smoking combined with asbestos exposure. The risk of lung cancer increases greatly, beyond that expected from adding the risks together. Similarly, in vitro studies of organophosphorus pesticides have shown that a combined exposure to malathion and Diazinon (dimpylate) results in cholinesterase inhibition significantly greater than a mere summation of the effects would predict.

Other research has focused on less obvious combined effects. One study looked at the effects of different chemicals on hearing and found that trichloroethylene, arsenic, heavy metals, organo-tin compounds, and manganese all caused some degree of hearing loss or audiometric abnormalities in occupationally exposed workers. Carbon disulfide interacted with noise to cause sensorineural hearing loss; toluene and noise acted synergistically to increase the incidence of hearing loss. Another study, looking at the combined effects of chemicals commonly found at hazardous waste sites, saw both synergistic and antagonistic interactions. Whereas lead tetra-acetate and arsenic trioxide produced antagonistic effects in one assay, tetrachloroethylene and dieldrin produced synergistic effects. The authors of this genotoxicity study cautioned that compounds may behave differently in a mixture than when alone.

The OSHA airborne exposure limits, as well as the RELs and TLVs, have been developed under the assumption that workers are exposed to chemicals one at a time. In fact, exposure to just a single chemical rarely occurs. One method to calculate the alteration in guidelines necessary to evaluate combined exposure is to add concentrations as a fraction of their respective TLVs. If the total equals or exceeds one, then an overexposure has been detected. This is not a conservative approach, because it assumes additive effects and allows excessive exposures if the effects are synergistic or if other stressors are present.

In most workplace exposure assessments, chemical, physical, biological, and psychological hazards are present at the same time. For example, the process of tunneling can involve simultaneous exposures to high atmospheric pressure, dust, noise, heat, high humidity, carbon monoxide, and physical safety hazards. An assessment of strain produced by any one of these stressors would be complicated by the presence of any or all of the others.

Limitations of biological monitoring. Biological monitoring is one way to compare exposure to dose. However, it must be remembered that it measures exposure only after it occurs, and after the containment has affected the body in some way. It must be used properly and in conjunction with other environmental controls and not as the sole control measure, as is sometimes the case when employers want to spare the cost of a more comprehensive, and therefore more expensive, monitoring program. Biological monitoring and medical surveillance are not replacements for environmental or personal sampling but should be used to complement them.

When biological monitoring is required by an OSHA comprehensive standard, the health care provider conducting the monitoring must be given a copy of the requirements. In some cases, the medical personnel will want to tour the workplace to enhance their awareness of potential hazards.

Sampling

Strategy

The preliminary research and initial field survey help identify potential hazards to which workers may be exposed. The next task is to devise a sampling strategy to determine the intensity of exposure, the source of the hazards, and the adequacy of controls in place. Included in the plan must be a consideration of the sources of error, the desired precision and accuracy of measurements, and the degree of confidence needed for interpretation of the results.

If the industrial hygiene sampling is conducted to evaluate a problem, the sampling strategy can be designed to measure the "worst case." An example that occurred in central Massachusetts in 1990 illustrates this approach. Periodic use of a degreaser had resulted in dizziness and headaches in the two operators, as well as complaints from a neighboring department. Because the use of the degreaser was limited to three hours in the morning, it seemed unlikely that the eight-hour TWA exposure exceeded the relevant PEL. However, the health symptoms and complaints indicated a problem with the operation of the degreaser, its cooling coils, or the local exhaust ventilation. Air sampling was planned to capture the particular solvent used during the worst-case exposure, when the smallest parts were being cleaned. Before sampling proceeded for this suspect carcinogen, the industrial hygienist made sure that the work practices and ventilation were exactly the same as they had been the day before, when the complaints had occurred.

Evaluating the worst case first, during the time of greatest exposure, at a location known to have caused problems, offers three advantages. First, this sampling is designed to solve a problem. Measuring the concentration of the chemical believed to have caused health symptoms and concerns helps identify the source, improve the controls, and correct the problem. Second, such results teach employees

valuable lessons about indicators of equipment malfunction, the warning signs of overexposure, and the impact of work practices on airborne solvent levels, such as reducing drag-out of solvent. Finally, the process of evaluating the worst case during the longest exposure time to the highest expected concentration—if lower than the referenced PELs, STELs, TLVs, and RELs—allows assumptions and assurances to be made regarding shorter-term, lower-level exposures.

Another approach to air sampling is to capture "typical" conditions. This is not always as easy as it sounds. Day-to-day variations may make a typical exposure difficult to define and measure. In addition, managers and employees being monitored may take extra precautions when they know they are being observed by health and safety professionals. Concerns about being "sampled" or evaluated may serve to encourage companies to present their best face by adding ventilation or opening doors and windows that are usually closed. Preliminary air sampling is usually done on the day shift, when supervision is better, shipping doors are more likely to be open, and the timer for the ventilation is on the occupied setting.

A good sampling strategy makes use of both worst-case and typical sampling methods, each selected to answer the questions what, where, when, how, and whom to sample.

What and How to Sample

The first, and key, principle to keep in mind is that samples should represent workers' exposures. Decisions about which chemicals to evaluate should be based on such factors as quantities and methods of use; worker reports of adverse experiences; concerns regarding high toxicity, volatility, carcinogenicity, or teratogenicity; and percent representation in mixtures.

For time-weighted average sampling, the NIOSH *Manual of Analytical Methods 2003* can be referred to for the correct sampling technique. There is a wide choice of collection media, from charcoal or silica gel tubes for organic nonpolar vapors or polar vapors, respectively, to cellulose ester or fiberglass filters for fumes and particulate materials. The appropriate medium for a specific reagent is stated in the NIOSH manual if there is an approved method. These are methods that have proved to be reproducible, given certain flow rates and sampling and analytical conditions.

Also available to the industrial hygienist are grab sampling methods, in which a specific release point is monitored at a specific time in the process (Figure 15–7). This is done with colorimetric tubes (such as Draeger or Sensidyne tubes) or by "grabbing" a volume of air in a sampling bag, canister, or other container, which is then analyzed in an

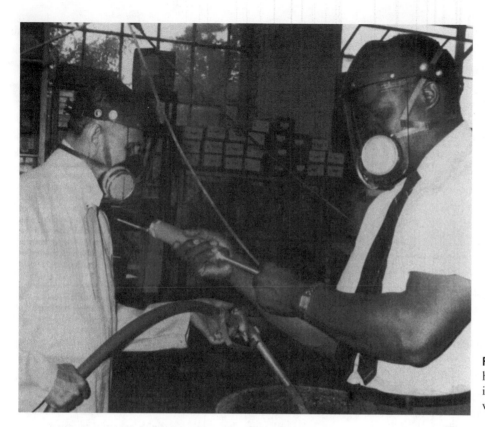

Figure 15–7. The gas detector tubes shown here are useful for obtaining direct readings of gas or vapor contamination in the workplace air.

accredited laboratory. The colorimetric tube method has limitations in its accuracy and should be used only as an initial, rough exposure estimate. The sampling bag method has limitations in collection efficiency and should be performed under the guidance of a laboratory accredited by the American Industrial Hygiene Association (AIHA).

Direct-reading instruments are available for a number of different chemical, physical, and radiation hazards (Figure 15–8). They provide immediate information about current conditions or concentrations, and can therefore be used to locate a source or detect a leak. Given this instant feedback, changes can be made in operating conditions, and the work site can be evaluated for improvement. For example, it might be possible to alter ventilation settings and observe the impact on airborne hazard levels, or turn off a compressor and note a drop in noise levels.

Materials that are not listed in the NIOSH manual are more difficult to evaluate, and an accredited analytical laboratory should be consulted. All samples taken should be sent to an accredited analytical laboratory, and results will be reported back at a later date.

Where to Sample

Personal monitoring is used to evaluate actual exposures to an individual by sampling for specific agents in the worker's immediate vicinity for durations corresponding to the process of concern or the appropriate occupational exposure limit (such as TWA, STEL, or ceiling). The sampling device is attached directly to the employee and is worn throughout the sampling period, reflecting worker movements in relation to the source of contamination, during both work and rest periods. The results from personal monitoring should be used to determine the effectiveness of control measures

Figure 15–8. The portable ambient air analyzer can be used to measure concentrations at the operator's workstation. *(Photo courtesy of Draeger. Used with permission.)*

(engineering, work practices, and administrative) implemented to prevent overexposure.

Area monitoring is used to measure the contaminants found in the work area that is generally occupied by employees. Also called environmental monitoring, it provides information about the amount and type of exposures found in a fixed area of interest. It reflects the effectiveness of engineering controls put into place to control the release of hazardous materials. It only reflects actual employee exposure to the extent that the time period monitored represents the time most employees spend in a given area.

Monitoring conducted for the purpose of measuring employee exposure is normally done with personal sampling. The recommended sampling method or equipment may, however, be inconvenient to use. If the industrial hygienist wishes to determine what air concentrations are in an area where the highest levels of contaminant release are anticipated, or where continuous exposure close to a particular point source may occur, then area monitoring is often useful. If results from these types of "worst-case" exposures are less than the upper regulatory or recommended limits, and if the contaminant in question is released only in that area, then an assumption can usually be made that workers spending their day in this area have exposures below the acceptable upper limit. This type of assumption is frequently made.

Whom to Sample

If the initial determination indicates the possibility of excessive exposure to airborne concentrations of a toxic substance, measurements of the most highly exposed employee should be made. This can be determined by observing the point of release and selecting the employee who is closest to the source of the contaminant in question.

Air movement patterns within a workroom must be considered when evaluating potential exposures to workers. Especially in operations or processes involving heating or combustion, the natural air circulation could be such that the maximum-risk employee might be located at considerable distance from the source. The location of ventilation booths, air supply inlets and outlets, and open doors and windows, and the size and shape of the work area are all factors that affect workroom airflow patterns. These airflow patterns can produce elevated concentrations at locations far removed from the source.

Differences in work habits of individual workers can significantly affect levels of exposure. Even though several workers are performing essentially the same tasks with the same materials, their individual methods of performing their work could affect the contaminant concentration to which each is exposed. Initial monitoring is often limited to a representative sample of the exposed population, usually those considered at greatest risk. Exposure results over the action level or PEL indicate that more extensive sampling is needed.

When to Sample

Another factor that must be considered is when to sample. If temperature varies greatly from season to season, with windows kept open during one season and not another, then sampling should be done during both periods. Or, in this case, because more dilution of the contaminant occurs with windows open, worst-case exposure monitoring should be done with the windows closed. If air conditioning is used, levels of contaminant may be fairly constant throughout the year. However, this is not necessarily the case with variable air volume (VAV) systems that restrict fresh airflow during the coldest and hottest periods of the year. (See Chapter 21, General Ventilation of Nonindustrial Occupancies, for further discussion.) If the facility has more than one workshift, samples should be collected during each shift. Concentrations can vary considerably from time to time during the day because of such factors as differences in production rate, degree of supervision, and ventilation provided during off-peak shifts.

How Long to Sample

The volume of air sampled and the duration of sampling is based on the sensitivity of the analytical procedure or direct-reading instrument, the estimated air concentration, and the OSHA standard or the TLV for that particular agent. Again, the NIOSH *Manual of Analytical Methods* or an accredited analytical laboratory should be consulted.

The duration of the sampling period should represent some identifiable period of time; for example, a complete cycle of an operation or a full shift. The appropriate time period is specified in the regulatory upper limits when looking at a PEL; often a full 8-hour shift of monitoring is called for. For comparison to an OSHA short-term exposure limit (STEL), 15-minute samples during a worst-case exposure scenario are required. Longer workshifts require recalculation of the relevant standard, because the total time exposed is increased. For example, a 10-hour workshift requires that the PEL or TLV be modified to reflect the extra exposure time and be reduced to four-fifths of the original 8-hour standard. To illustrate this point, OSHA's lead standard, in which the 8-hour TWA is 50 µg/m^3, requires employers to calculate the permissible exposure limit for workers exposed to lead for more than eight hours in any workday, using the following formula: Maximum permissible limit (in µg/m^3) = 400/hours worked in a day.

The concentration of contaminant in the workplace is sometimes low. Direct-reading instruments and other devices used to collect samples for subsequent analysis must collect a sufficient quantity of the sample so that the chemist doing the analysis can accurately determine the presence of minute amounts (parts per million or sometimes parts per billion) of the contaminant.

What to Note During Sampling

Accurate record keeping is essential for the correct interpretation of air-sampling results. The fundamental records include total time sampled; pump flow rate, both at the beginning and end of the sampling period; location of the area or identification of the person being monitored; and a description of the process being evaluated. In addition, sampling notes should include the engineering controls present, the location of any local or general exhaust ventilation, any system deficiencies noted at the time of sampling, as well as any measurements of these taken at the time of sampling. If other processes are located close enough to affect the sampling results, they should be described. It is important to write down as many observations noted as possible; there may be a lengthy period of time between sampling and the receipt of results and often these details can be forgotten.

Use of personal protective equipment should be documented. Observations of work practices can help explain differences between results for workers performing the same task. An air-sampling worksheet can be developed to help prompt such notes (Figure 15–9).

How Many Samples to Take

There is no predetermined number of samples that must be taken to adequately evaluate a worker's exposure. The number of samples to be taken depends on the purpose of the sampling, the number of different tasks a worker performs in a given day, and the variability inherent in the contaminant generation process. There are guidelines that can help in this decision-making process, such as the AIHA *Strategy Manual for Assessing and Managing Occupational Exposures.*

When to Stop Monitoring

For the chemicals it regulates, OSHA requires that monitoring be conducted on a routine basis; the frequency depends on the substance and the results from the initial or most recent monitoring. For example, monitoring for formaldehyde can be terminated if results from two consecutive sampling periods, taken at least 7 days apart, show that employee exposure is below both the action level and the STEL. Any change in process or engineering controls requires additional sampling to assess the effects of the change.

If initial sampling results are low, it is not necessary to repeat routine monitoring of employee exposure, as long as

monitoring of other factors crucial to the overall health and safety program continues. Areas of interest should include the adequacy of engineering controls, work practices, the use of personal protective equipment, and training in all of these aspects. Documentation of this oversight should be part of any effective health and safety management program. This continued monitoring also serves to meet the requirements of many OSHA standards, including the Hazard Communication Standard (29 CFR 1910.1200), Occupational Exposure to Hazardous Chemicals in Laboratories (29 CFR 1910.1450), the Respirator Standard (29 CFR 1910.134), and other, more specific ones that may apply to a given workplace.

Who Should Conduct Sampling

Although the concept of air sampling and the use of air-monitoring devices may at first appear to be simple, there are many considerations that must be balanced when devising a sampling strategy and interpreting the results, and it is often previous experiences that allow a final judgment to be made. It is therefore crucial that those conducting the sampling be adequately trained and supervised by a professional industrial hygienist. They must be cognizant of the potential for error and ensure proper calibration, maintenance, and use of sampling equipment. They must be familiar with potential problems and be available to resolve them if they occur. They must be aware of the limitations of sampling alone, know how to integrate observation and interviews with quantitative measurements, and know when it is not necessary to sample. The initial sampling strategy may lead to further questions or contradictions and significantly alter the overall plan. A comprehensive evaluation of the workplace depends on the judgment of the industrial hygienist.

The title Certified Industrial Hygienist (CIH) indicates that the professional has at least five years' experience in the field of industrial hygiene, is currently in active practice, has met certain educational requirements, and has passed the professional exam required by the American Board of Industrial Hygiene (ABIH). Certification rosters are maintained by the ABIH. Membership in other professional organizations, such as the AIHA and ACGIH, indicates active participation in the current field of industrial hygiene but does not guarantee the CIH title. Both the AIHA and ACGIH maintain rosters of their members.

Required Accuracy and Precision

Although the word "sampling" is commonly used, its full implications are not always realized. To "sample" means to measure only part of the environment, and, from the measurements taken, infer conclusions about the whole. In all sampling methods, there are both systematic and ran-

Air Sampling Worksheet

Sample ID	Employee/Job Description	Flow Rate (Start/Stop)	Time (Start/Stop)	Total time (min)

Process Description:

Engineering Controls:

Work Practice Controls:

Ventilation Measurements:

Personal Protective Equipment Used:

Worker Comments:

Figure 15–9. Example of air sampling worksheet. *(Printed with permission from Nancy Comeau, Massachusetts Division Occupational Hygiene.)*

dom errors to consider that can affect the interpretation of results and, therefore, final judgment about the work environment as a whole. Any exposure average calculated from air-sampling measurements is only an estimate of the true exposure. It is important to recognize, preferably in advance, where possible sources of error lie; to eliminate or control them to the degree possible; and to account for them in the interpretation of results.

Accuracy. Accuracy concerns the relationship between a measured value and the true value. For a measurement to be accurate, it must be close to the true value.

Precision. Precision is the degree of agreement among results obtained by repeated measurements under the same conditions and under a given set of parameters. It is possible for a measurement to be precise but not accurate, and vice versa (Figure 15–10).

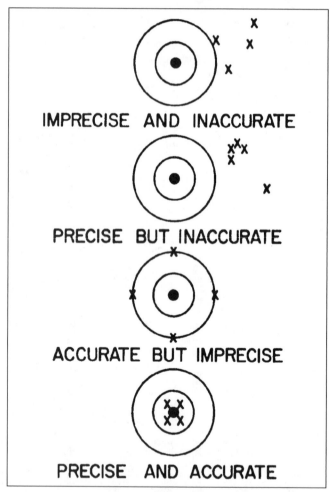

Figure 15–10. It is possible for a measurement to be precise but not accurate, and vice versa. *(Reprinted with permission from Powell CH, Hosey AD, eds.* The Industrial Environment—Its Evaluation and Control, *2nd ed. U.S. Public Health Services Pub No. 614, 1965.*

Accuracy is affected by controllable sources of error. These are called determinate or systematic errors and include method error, personal error, and instrument error. Incorrect calculations, personal carelessness, poorly calibrated equipment, and use of contaminated reagents are examples of systematic error. Systemic errors contribute a consistent bias to the results that render those results inaccurate. Where possible, these errors must be identified before sampling is performed, and eliminated or controlled.

Precision is affected by indeterminate or random errors, which cannot be controlled. These include intra- or interday concentration fluctuations, sampling equipment variations such as random pump flow fluctuations, and analytical method fluctuations such as variation in reagent addition or instrument response. These factors cause variability among the sample results. Statistical techniques are used to account for random error. For example, increasing the number of samples taken minimizes the effect of random error.

In several of the OSHA substance-specific standards, accuracy ranges for the sampling methods are specified for both the PEL and the STEL. For example, the Ethylene Oxide Standard (29 CFR 1910.1047) requires that a sampling method with accuracy to a confidence level of 95 percent (within 25 percent) be obtained for airborne concentrations of ethylene oxide at the 1.0 ppm PEL and within 35 percent at the action level of 0.5 ppm.

To ensure accuracy and precision, the following guidelines should be used:

- Manufacturers' data for direct-reading instruments should be obtained whenever possible, stating the accuracy and precision of their method.
- A calibration schedule should be established and documented for all sampling equipment.
- The NIOSH *Manual of Analytical Methods* should be consulted for accuracy and precision of the methods chosen. When reporting the results of the sampling, cite the NIOSH sampling method that was followed.
- Only laboratories that participate in industrial hygiene quality control programs, such as the one conducted by the AIHA, should be used.

In addition, to ensure compliance or violation, OSHA compliance officers use one-sided confidence limits (upper and lower confidence limits, UCL and LCL) whenever sampling is performed (OSHA Technical Manual, 2008, Section II, Ch.I-XI). This practice recognizes that the sample measured on the employee is rarely the same as the "true" exposure, because of sampling and analytical errors (SAEs). The UCL and LCL incorporate these error factors statistically to obtain the lowest (LCL) and the highest (UCL) value that the true exposure could be, within a 95 percent confidence interval. The UCL and LCL are called one-sided limits because they are used by both OSHA and employers to ensure that the true exposure lies on one side of the OSHA permissible exposure limit (PEL), either above or below it.

For example, if neither the measured results nor its UCL exceed the PEL, then one can be 95 percent confident that the exposure does not exceed the PEL. On the other hand, if both the measured exposure and its LCL exceed the PEL, then one can be 95 percent confident that the exposure exceeds the PEL, and a violation is established. Also listed in Appendix 1–F of the OSHA Technical Manuel are grayer areas of evaluation; for example, when the UCL of an exposure exceeds the PEL but the measured exposure does not. OSHA offers guidance in these instances, including suggesting that further monitoring be conducted.

To compute the UCL and the LCL, the coefficient of variation (CV) for each analytical method must be computed. These can also be found in the NIOSH *Manual of Analytical Methods*.

$$CV = 100\frac{sd}{m} \tag{1}$$

where   sd = standard deviation of the method
m = mean (or analytical result)
100 = factor to convert from fraction to percent

SAEs are often listed in OSHA report forms, but can be derived from the CV_{total}:

$$SAE = 1.645(CV_{total}) \tag{2}$$

Where CV_{total}: The coefficient of variation of the sampling method plus the coefficient of variation of the analytical method.

In general, the formula for the LCL at the 95th percentile level is

$$LCL\ (95\%) = \frac{x_{mean}}{PEL} - 1.645\frac{CV_{total}}{\sqrt{n}} \tag{3}$$

where
LCL (95%) = lower confidence limit at the 95th percentile
x_{mean} = average airborne concentration
CV_{total} = coefficient of variation including sampling error
n = number of data points to determine x mean
1.645 = appropriate factor from large sample statistics

In a similar fashion, the general formula for the UCL at the

$$UCL\ (95\%) = \frac{x_{mean}}{PEL} + 1.645\frac{CV_{total}}{\sqrt{n}} \tag{4}$$

OSHA uses simplified versions of the above formulas and distinguishes between three types of samples: full-period, continuous single samples; full-period consecutive samples; and grab samples. For a complete discussion of the calculations, refer to Appendix 1–F of the OSHA Technical Manual.

Example
A charcoal tube and personal sampling pump were used to sample for xylene for an 8-hour period. The laboratory reported results of 105 ppm of xylene. The PEL for xylene is 100 ppm. The SAE for the sampling and analytical method is 0.10.

Solution
The steps required to calculate the UCL and the LCL for this full-period, single sample are as follows:

Determine the standardized concentration, Y:

$$Y = \frac{X}{PEL} \tag{5}$$

where X is the full-period sampling result. Therefore, for our example,

$$Y = \frac{105}{100} = 1.05 \tag{6}$$

Compute the UCL (95%) and the LCL (95%):

$$UCL\ (95\%) = Y + SAE \tag{7}$$

$$LCL\ (95\%) = Y - SAE \tag{8}$$

Therefore, for our example,
$$UCL = 1.05 + 0.10 = 1.15 \tag{9}$$
$$LCL = 1.05 - 0.10 = 0.95 \tag{10}$$

According to OSHA, when the UCL ≤ 1 a violation does not exist, and when the LCL > 1 a violation exists. If the LCL ≤ 1 and UCL > 1, the result is classified as a possible overexposure. In our example, because the LCL ≤ 1 and the UCL > 1, a possible overexposure exists.

INDUSTRIAL HYGIENE CALCULATIONS

Gases and Vapors
Calculations for gas and vapor concentrations are based on the gas laws. Briefly, these are as follows:

- The volume of gas under constant temperature is inversely proportional to the pressure: $P_1 V_1 = P_2 V_2$
- The volume of gas under constant pressure is directly proportional to the Kelvin temperature, which is based on absolute zero ($0°C = 273°K$). The Rankine temperature scale is also used, where $0°C = 492°R$, or degrees R = degrees F + 460.

$$\frac{V_1}{T_1} = \frac{V_2}{T_2} \qquad (11)$$

- The pressure of a gas of a constant volume is directly proportional to the Kelvin (or Rankine) temperature:

$$\frac{P_1}{T_1} = \frac{P_2}{T_2} \qquad (12)$$

and $PV = nRT$

Thus, when measuring contaminant concentrations, it is necessary to know the atmospheric temperature and pressure under which the samples were taken. At standard temperature ($0°C$) and pressure (760 mmHg) (STP), 1 g-mol of an ideal gas occupies 22.4 liters. If the temperature is increased to $25°C$ (normal room temperature) and the pressure is the same, then 1 g-mol occupies 24.45 liters.

$$(22.4 \text{ liters})\frac{273 + 25}{273} = 24.45 \qquad (13)$$

The concentration of gases and vapors is usually expressed in parts of contaminant per million parts of air, or parts per million (ppm).

$$ppm = \frac{\text{Parts of contaminant}}{\text{Million parts of air}} \qquad (14)$$

This is a volume-to-volume relationship. Equivalent parts per million expressions include

$$\frac{\text{liters}}{10^6 \text{ liters}} = \frac{\text{centimeter}^3}{10^6 \text{ centimeter}^3} = \frac{10^{-3} \text{ L}}{10^3 \text{ L}} =$$

$$\frac{\text{milliliters}}{\text{meter}^3} = \frac{\text{feet}^3}{10^6 \text{ feet}^3} \qquad (15)$$

Sometimes it is necessary to convert milligrams per cubic meter (mg/m^3), a weight-per-unit volume ratio, into a volume-per-volume ratio. To begin, milligrams per cubic meter must be converted to millimoles per cubic meter and to milliliters per cubic meter, or parts per million. It is helpful in making this conversion to use dimensional analysis.

$$\left(\frac{mg_x}{m^3 \text{ air}}\right)\left(\frac{mmol_x}{mg_x}\right)\left(\frac{24.45 \text{ mL}_x}{mmol_x}\right) = \frac{mL_x}{m^3 \text{ air}} = ppm \qquad (16)$$

At room temperature, to convert from ppm to mg/m^3, a similar conversion can be performed:

$$\frac{mg}{m^3} = \frac{\text{molecular weight}}{24.45 \text{ at } 25 \text{ C}} ppm \qquad (17)$$

Another method to predict gas or vapor concentration in parts per million is the partial pressure method. By dividing the vapor pressure of the material in question by the barometric pressure, the resultant percent fraction can then be multiplied by one million (10^6) to give a volume percent in ppm.

$$\frac{\text{vapor pressure of one constituent}}{\text{total barometric pressure}} 10^6 \qquad (18)$$

$$= ppm \text{ of constituent}$$

Example
Given the concentration of a vapor at STP in grams per liter, convert this to parts per million (ppm).

Solution
Given that the gram-molecular volume at STP ($0°C$ and 760 mmHg) is 22.4 L, and that molecular weight is g/mol, the concentration of vapor at STP is

$$\frac{\text{grams of vapor}}{\text{liters of vapor}} = \left(\frac{g}{\text{mole}}\right)\left(\frac{\text{mole}}{L}\right)$$

$$= \frac{\text{molecular wt (g)}}{22.4 (L)} \qquad (19)$$

Rearranging terms,

$$\text{liters of vapor} = \frac{(\text{grams of vapor})(22.4)}{\text{molecular wt}} \qquad (20)$$

$$ppm = \frac{\text{parts of vapor}}{1,000,000 \text{ parts of air}} = \frac{\text{liters of vapor}}{10^6 \text{ L of air}} \qquad (21)$$

Substituting liters of vapor from Equation 21 into Equation 22,

$$ppm = \frac{\dfrac{(\text{grams of vapor})(22.4)}{\text{molecular wt (g)}}}{10^6 \text{ L of air}}$$

$$= \frac{\dfrac{(10^3 \text{ mg of vapor})(22.4)}{\text{molecular wt (g)}}}{10^6 \text{ L}} \qquad (22)$$

Given that $10^6 L = 10^3 m$,

$$\text{ppm} = \frac{(10^3 \text{ mg})(22.4)}{(10^3 \text{ m}^3)(\text{molecular wt of vapor})}$$

$$= \left(\frac{\text{mg}}{\text{m}^3}\right)\frac{22.4}{\text{molecular wt}} \qquad (23)$$

For some chemicals, the analytical method requires the collection of material into a fixed volume of absorbing or reacting solution. The laboratory to which the sample is sent first analyzes the concentration of contaminant in the collection medium, then multiplies the volume of solution by the contaminant concentration and reports the total amount of contaminant collected during the sampling period. This can be converted to air concentration by dividing the total amount of contaminant sampled by the total amount of air collected.

Example

At 25°C and 755 mmHg, 15 L of air is bubbled through 30 mL of a solution that has 100 percent collection efficiency for HCl (molecular weight = 36.5). The analytical laboratory reports the solution concentration as 15 mg/mL. What is the air concentration of HCl in ppm?

Solution

First, the total amount of HCl is

$$\frac{15 \ \mu g}{\text{mL}}(30 \text{mL}) = 450 \ \mu g \qquad (24)$$

Correcting for temperature and pressure in micromoles (μmol), the volume of 1 μmol of HCl is as follows:

$$1 \ \mu\text{mol} \times 22.4 \times \frac{298}{273} \times \frac{760}{755} = 24.6 \ \mu L \qquad (25)$$

Finally, the air concentration sampled in ppm is

$$\frac{450 \ \mu g \ HCl}{15 \ L \text{ of air}} \times \frac{\mu\text{mol } HCl}{36.5 \ \mu g \ HCl} \times \frac{24.6 \ \mu l \ HCl}{\mu\text{mol } HCl}$$

$$= \frac{11{,}070 \ \mu L \ HCl}{547.5 \ L \text{ of air}} = 20.22 \text{ ppm} \qquad (26)$$

Another useful equation to derive is the vapor concentration of a given amount of material in a chamber or a room, given the following:

VT = chamber volume in liters
MW = molecular weight of a substance, in g/mol
T = absolute temperature in degrees Kelvin

$(K = C+273)$
P = pressure in mmHg
ρ = density, in g/mL
V_x = volume of material in chamber or room, in mL
C = concentration, in ppm

To find liters of pure vapor

$$\frac{(V_x \text{mL})(\rho)(22.4 \text{ L/mol})}{\text{molecular wt of material}}\left(\frac{T}{273}\right)\left(\frac{760}{P}\right) \qquad (27)$$

$$C = \left(\frac{\text{liters of pure vapor}}{V_T}\right)10^6 \text{ parts of air}$$

$$= \frac{(V_x)(\rho)\left(\frac{22.4 \text{ L}}{\text{g-mol}}\right)\left(\frac{\text{g-mol}}{\text{MW}}\right)\left(\frac{T}{273}\right)\left(\frac{760}{P}\right)}{V_T 1} \times 10^6$$

$$= \frac{(V_x)(\rho)\left(\frac{22.4}{\text{MW}}\right)\left(\frac{T}{273}\right)\left(\frac{760}{P}\right)}{V_T} \times 10^6 \qquad (28)$$

One can also calculate the volume of liquid necessary to produce a desired concentration in a given volume at room temperature and standard pressure:

$$V_x = \frac{C \times \text{MW} \times 273 \times P \times V_T}{\rho \times 22.4 \times T \times 760 \times 10^6} \qquad (29)$$

Example

How much acetone (MW=58.08 g/mol; density = 0.7899 g/mL) is needed to generate a concentration of 200 ppm in a 20-L container at 25°C and 740 mmHg?

Solution

$$V_x = \frac{(200)(58.08)(273)(740)(20)}{(0.7899)(22.4)(298)(760)} \times \frac{1}{10^6}$$

$$= 0.012 \text{ mL} \qquad (30)$$

Vapor Equivalents

When a liquid is released into a space of known dimensions, it is useful to determine the volume it will occupy when evaluating potential exposures from this release. The following formula is often helpful, because it establishes the amount of pure vapor formed at sea level by the complete evaporation of a known volume or weight of a liquid into an area, based on the following assumptions:

liters/mole of vapor at STP = 22.4

grams/pound = 453.6
liters/cubic foot = 28.32
grams/gram-mole = MW

$$\frac{\text{cubic feet of vapor}}{\text{pound of liquid}} = \left(\frac{\text{ft}^3}{\text{L}}\right)\left(\frac{\text{L}}{\text{mol}}\right)\left(\frac{\text{mol}}{\text{g}}\right)\left(\frac{\text{g}}{\text{lb}}\right)$$

$$= \left(\frac{1\ \text{ft}^3}{28.3\ \text{L}}\right)\left(\frac{22.4\ \text{L}}{\text{mol}}\right)\left(\frac{\text{mol}}{\text{g-MW}}\right)\left(\frac{453.6\ \text{g}}{\text{lb}}\right) = \frac{359}{\text{MW}} \qquad (31)$$

This can be calculated for different temperatures and pressures.

Example
At 70°F, what volume would one pound of toluene (MW = 92) occupy?

$$\frac{\text{cubic feet}}{\text{pound}}\ \text{at 70 F} = \frac{(530\ \text{R})(359)}{(492\ \text{R})(\text{mol wt})}$$

$$= \frac{387}{92} = 4.163\ \text{ft}^3 \qquad (32)$$

Solution
Note that the Rankine scale was used here, and that degrees R = degrees F + 460. Therefore, 70°F = 530°R, and 0°C = 32°F = 492°R. However, it must be noted that quantities of liquids are often stated as volumes, for example in pints or liters, and that, in order to use equation (31), liters or pints must first be converted into pounds.

Example
A 1-pint container of toluene breaks in a room 50 feet by 100 feet by 15 feet. Assuming complete evaporation and no ventilation, what would you expect the concentration of toluene to be in the room, assuming the following:

T = 70°F
mass of water = 1.041 pounds/pint
specific gravity (sp gr) of toluene = 0.866 (the ratio of the mass of toluene to the mass of water at that temperature)

$$\left(\frac{\text{cubic feet}}{\text{pound}}\right)\left(\frac{\text{pound}}{\text{pint}}\right) = \frac{\text{cubic feet}}{\text{pint}} \qquad (33)$$

$$= \frac{(387)(1.041)(\text{sp gr})}{\text{molecular wt}} = \frac{(403)(0.866)}{92} = 3.79\ \text{ft}^3$$

and the room volume is (50 ft)(100 ft)(15 ft) = 75,000 ft³. The concentration is then

$$\frac{3.79\ \text{cubic feet of toluene}}{75,000\ \text{cubic feet air}} \times 10^6 = 50.53\ \text{ppm} \qquad (34)$$

Example
A half-pound cylinder of chlorine fell and broke in a closed room 60 feet by 45 feet by 15 feet. What is the concentration of chlorine in ppm?

Solution
The room volume is

$$(60\ \text{ft})(45\ \text{ft})(15\ \text{ft})\left(\frac{1\ \text{m}^3}{35.31\ \text{ft}^3}\right) = 1{,}147\ \text{m}^3 \qquad (35)$$

Therefore, the concentration of chlorine in the room is

$$(0.5\ \text{lb Cl}_2)\left(453.6\frac{\text{g}}{\text{lb}}\right)\left(\frac{\text{mol}}{71\ \text{g}}\right)\left(\frac{24.45\ \text{L}}{\text{mol}}\right)$$

$$\left(\frac{\text{m}^3}{10^3\ \text{L}}\right)\left(\frac{1}{1{,}147\ \text{m}^3}\right) \times 10^6 = 68.2\ \text{ppm} \qquad (36)$$

Weight-per-Unit Volume

When a contaminant is released into the atmosphere as a solid or liquid and not as a vapor—for example as a dust, mist, or fume—its concentration is usually expressed as a weight per volume. Outdoor air pollutants and stack effluents are usually expressed in grams, milligrams, or micrograms per cubic meter of air (g, mg, or µg/m³), ounces per thousand cubic feet (oz/1,000 ft³), pounds per thousand pounds of air (lb/1,000 lb), or as grains per cubic foot (gcf).

Time-Weighted Average Exposure

The time-weighted average (TWA) exposure evolved as a method to calculate daily or full-shift average exposures, given that employees' job tasks may vary during a day and that facility operating conditions may also vary. In typical work environments, workers may experience several different, short-term exposures to the same material. By taking a time-weighted average of these exposures, the industrial hygienist can estimate or integrate the short-term measurements into an eight-hour exposure estimate and compare this to the relevant health and safety regulations or information. The TWA is determined by the following formula, where

C = concentration of the contaminant
T = time period during which this concentration was measured

$$\text{TWA} = \frac{C_1 T_1 + C_2 T_2 + \ldots C_n T_n}{8\ \text{hrs}} \qquad (37)$$

The TWA is usually expressed in ppm or in mg/m³. Because OSHA's PELs and the ACGIH's® TLVs® are both based on an 8-hour workday, the denominator in this formula is usually eight hours. However, any TWA can be determined, using the following formula:

$$\frac{\sum\limits_{i=1}^{n} (T_i)(C_i)}{T_{total} \text{ work time}} = TWA \tag{38}$$

where i is an increment of time and C is the concentration measured during that time. In this way, sequential incremental measurements can be made, allowing analysis of short-term exposures at the same time as a longer TWA is being computed. The total time covered by the samples should be as close to the total exposure time as possible.

Example

A TWA of a foundry worker's exposure to particulates can be evaluated by the following series of short-term samples:

Sample Number	Time
1	7:00 a.m. to 8:00 a.m.
2	8:00 a.m. to 9:30 a.m.
3	9:30 a.m. to 11:00 a.m.
4	11:00 a.m. to 1:00 p.m. (turned off and covered during 30-min lunch)
5	1:00 p.m. to 3:30 p.m.

The measurement obtained is a full-period consecutive-sample measurement because it covers the entire time period applicable to the PEL or TLV.

In some cases, because of limitations in measurement methodology—for example, direct-reading instruments or charcoal tubes—it is impossible to collect consecutive samples whose total sampling duration equals that of the required time period stated in the relevant standard. In these cases, the grab methods are used for time periods that are felt to be representative of the entire workshift.

Example

It is necessary to use charcoal tubes to estimate an employee's exposure to chloroform. Each charcoal tube is limited to 60 minutes' collection time. Out of the possible eight samples that could have been taken, only six were collected. The following results were obtained:

Sample Number	Results (ppm)
1	55
2	65
3	55
4	60
5	45
6	60

Solution

The six-hour TWA for these exposures is

$$\frac{1}{360 \text{ min}} [(60 \text{ min})(55 \text{ ppm}) + (60)(65)$$

$$+ (60)(55) + (60)(60) + (60)(45) + (60)(60)]$$

$$= 57 \text{ ppm} \tag{39}$$

If there is not much variation in the levels of air contamination measured, and it is certain that the employee's entire workday is spent in one area, then it is probably acceptable to assume that this represents an eight-hour TWA. If there is significant variation, however, resampling should be done for the entire eight-hour day.

Example

An employee spends four hours of an eight-hour shift in an area where measured CO air concentrations remain fairly constant at 50 ppm. For the remaining four hours, the employee works in an area where there is no measurable CO in the air. What is the employee's eight-hour TWA?

Solution

$$\frac{(4 \text{ h})(50 \text{ ppm}) + (4 \text{ h})(0 \text{ ppm})}{8 \text{ h}} = \frac{200 \text{ ppm} \cdot \text{h}}{8 \text{ h}}$$

$$= 25 \text{ ppm} \tag{40}$$

Example

A machinist works from 7:00 a.m. to 4:00 p.m. tending an automatic screw machine. The following levels of oil mist were measured:

Time	Average Level of Oil Mist (mg/m³)	Time	Average Level of Oil Mist (mg/m³)
7:00-8:00	0	11:00-12:00	2.0
8:00-9:00	1.0	12:00-1:00	0.0*
9:00-10:00	1.5	1:00-3:00	4.0
10:00-11:00	1.5	3:00-4:00	5.0

*lunch period, no exposure

Solution

The TWA of the machinist's exposure to oil mist is calculated as follows:

$$\frac{\sum\limits_{i=1}^{i=8} (T_i)(C_i)}{T_{total} = 8 \text{ h}} = \text{TWA} \tag{41}$$

Time (h) x Concentration (mg/m³)		
(1)	(0)	= 0
(1)	(1)	= 1
(1)	(1.5)	= 1.5
(1)	(1.5)	= 1.5
(1)	(2.0)	= 2.0
(1)	(0.0)	= 0.0
(2)	(4.0)	= 8.0
(1)	(5.0)	= 5.0
		19.0 (h)(mg/m³)

$$\frac{\sum\limits_{i=1}^{i=8} (T_i)(C_i) = (19.0 \text{ h})(\text{mg/m}^3)}{8 \text{ h}} = 2.38 \text{ mg/m}^3 \tag{42}$$

Example

An employee is exposed to an average level of 100 ppm of xylene for 10 minutes out of every hour; during the remaining 50 minutes of each hour, there is no exposure to xylene. What is the TWA for xylene for this employee?

Solution

Because there are eight hours in a workday, each of which includes 10 minutes' exposure to 100 ppm and 50 minutes' exposure to 0 ppm, an eight-hour TWA can be calculated as follows:

$$\frac{(8)(10 \text{ min})(100 \text{ ppm}) + (8)(50 \text{ min})(0 \text{ ppm})}{480 \text{ min}}$$

$$= \frac{8,000 \text{ min} \cdot \text{ppm}}{480 \text{ min}} = 16.7 = 17 \text{ ppm} \tag{43}$$

Example

An employee is exposed to the same material at two work locations during an eight-hour shift. Monitoring of this worker's exposure was conducted by taking grab samples at each of the locations. The following results were obtained:

Operation	Duration	Sample	Results (ppm) (5-min sample)
Cleaning room	8:00–11:30 a.m.	A	150
		B	120
		C	190
		D	170
		E	210
Print Shop	12:30–4:30 p.m.	F	90
		G	70
		H	120
		I	110

Solution

The average exposure (C2) in the cleaning room:

$$C_i = \frac{120 + 150 + 170 + 190 + 210}{5} = 168 \text{ ppm} \tag{44}$$

The average exposure in the print shop:

$$C_2 = \frac{70 + 90 + 110 + 120}{4} = 98 \text{ ppm} \tag{45}$$

Thus the TWA exposure for the eight-hour shift, excluding 60 minutes for lunch, is as follows:

$$\text{TWA} = \frac{(168 \text{ ppm})(3.5 \text{ hr}) + (98 \text{ ppm})(4.0 \text{ hr})}{8}$$

$$= 122.5 \text{ ppm} \tag{46}$$

Example

As part of her job, a hospital central supply worker unloads sterilized materials from an ethylene oxide (EtO) sterilizer. She does this four times per eight-hour shift, it takes 15 minutes each time, and she has no other exposure to EtO during the shift. The eight-hour PEL for EtO is 1 ppm; the 15-minute excursion limit is 5 ppm. The following 15-minute sampling results were obtained: 4.8, 3.5, 4.9, and 3.4. None of the results exceeded the 5 ppm excursion limit. What is the eight-hour PEL for this worker?

Solutions

$$\frac{1}{480 \text{ min}}[(15 \text{ min})(4.8 \text{ min}) + (15)(3.5)$$

$$+ (15)(4.9) + (15)(3.4) + (420 \text{ min})(0 \text{ ppm})]$$

$$= 0.52 \text{ ppm} \tag{47}$$

Excursions

TWA concentrations imply fluctuations in the level of airborne contaminant. Excursions above the TLV are permissible if equivalent excursions below the TLV occur. The TLV booklet stipulates that short-term exposures may exceed three times the TLV for no more than a total of 30 minutes during the workday; under no circumstances should exposures exceed five times the TLV. This stipulation is valid if TLV–TWA is not exceeded. In some cases, a specific short-term exposure limit (STEL) has been established, for example, for formaldehyde and ethylene oxide.

INTERPRETATION OF RESULTS

Interpretation of the results obtained from sampling is the next step in evaluating the workplace environment. The chemicals monitored, the sites chosen for the sampling, and the timing of the monitoring all reflect the industrial hygienist's best judgment about which exposures might be significant. Potential sources of error and the limitations of the sampling and analytical methods have been taken into consideration. There are times when the interpretation of results is not a completely straightforward process, and it is always important to keep in mind why the sampling was done. If it was done purely for compliance reasons, then OSHA standards are the guide. If "good practices" and worker protection are the ultimate goals, then ACGIH TLVs, NIOSH RELs, and other recommended occupational and environmental limits should be considered. In either case, it is important to know whether the referenced standard is mandatory or recommended and whether there is evidence for harm at lower concentrations. Appropriate follow-up may depend on this.

Comparison with Standards and Guidelines

The first step in evaluating sampling results is to compare them with the relevant standards and guidelines. The legally enforceable maximum allowed exposures in general industry are the OSHA permissible exposure limits (PELs), which have been determined for approximately 500 air contaminants and are listed in three tables in the Code of Federal Regulations (29 CFR 1910.1000). Thirty-eight comprehensive standards have been promulgated for chemicals that specify additional protections. Sampling results greater than the PEL and its lower confidence limit can result in citations and fines. Most PELs are for eight-hour time-weighted averages; some are short term exposure limits (STELs), usually assessed over 15-minutes or ceilings (C) which should never be exceeded.

Because of the role of sampling results in legal proceedings, they must be analyzed in a cookbook fashion. For example, unless documentation exists that exposure levels are constant, any work time for which no sampling was conducted may be considered as unexposed time, and a zero is factored in any calculation of the time-weighted average. Consider, for example, the sampling results for chloroform presented in equation 39. The time-weighted average calculated for the six hours sampled was 57 ppm. The PEL for chloroform is 50 ppm, ceiling. The ACGIH TLV–TWA is 10 ppm. Clearly, the measured air concentration exceeds both limits; the ceiling level was exceeded in five out of the six hours sampled. NIOSH identifies chloroform as a potential occupational carcinogen, and recommends a STEL of 2 ppm measured over 60 minutes. NIOSH previously recommended that exposure to carcinogens be restricted to the Lowest Feasible Concentration. The new NIOSH policy regarding carcinogens establishes a quantitative REL based on a no-effect exposure or an exposure with identified residual risk. A situation like the one in the example, which would result in such a high concentration of an occupational carcinogen, would require immediate action to prevent continued overexposure.

If the solvent measured had been 2-butoxyethanol, which has a PEL of 50 ppm, and the six-hour TWA had also been 57 ppm, then the interpretation of the results would be different. At first, this might also appear to exceed the eight-hour PEL. However, there is an additional consideration in this case. Two hours of the employee's workday had not been sampled. If there is no documentation to prove that he was similarly exposed during the remaining time, a 0 ppm concentration could be factored into the eight-hour PEL calculation:

$$\frac{(57 \text{ ppm})(360 \text{ min}) + (0 \text{ ppm})(120 \text{ min})}{480 \text{ min}}$$

$$= 43 \text{ ppm} \tag{48}$$

The sampling results remain the same, but the interpretation has changed. This result, 43 ppm, is in compliance with the PEL. Such a result would not lead to a citation for violation of 29 CFR 1910.1000, but it can be interpreted as a significantly high exposure to a solvent, which should be controlled. (The ACGIH TLV–TWA is 20 ppm, the NIOSH REL is 5 ppm.) Such an exposure has the potential to cause irritation to the respiratory system, eyes, and skin, and damage to blood forming capacity. 2-butoxyethanol may be dermally absorbed (OSHA and NIOSH have assigned a Skin designation). If it is possible that the worker is exposed to this chemical at some concentration during the time not sampled, it is possible that the sampling omission and perceived OSHA compliance would allow workers to remain overexposed indefinitely.

The results calculated in the example described in equation 40 can be analyzed in a similar manner. The concentration of carbon monoxide (CO) is in compliance with the OSHA PEL (50 ppm) and the NIOSH REL (35 ppm) for an eight-hour TWA, despite the fact that during four hours of the day the worker is exposed to 50 ppm. The ACGIH TLV for CO is 25 ppm (this guideline has been reduced over the years as the adverse effects of carbon monoxide exposure have been demonstrated at lower levels). At first glance, this result might be considered satisfactory because it does not exceed the OSHA PEL. However, because there is evidence that a lower level is recommended by NIOSH and ACGIH, other questions might be triggered by these results: Are there excursions during the four hours over the STEL? Do results vary from day to day? Would the results be viewed as acceptable if the worker in this example were pregnant? Is it acceptable to leave the hazard in place and simply rotate different employees into the area, so that no single individual is overexposed, but all of them are exposed for part of the day? The best actions in response to these sampling data would be to identify the source of the CO for the four hours of exposure measured, and to reduce exposure to the lowest feasible level.

In another example, a consultant industrial hygienist sampled for acetic acid during a weekly decontamination procedure in a biotechnology firm's clean room, as a result of complaints about eye, nose, and throat irritation from a nonlaboratory neighbor. She looked to both OSHA and NIOSH for required or recommended occupational upper exposure limits. OSHA's PEL (eight-hour) is 10 ppm; NIOSH has a 15-minute, recommended short-term exposure limit (STEL) of 15 ppm. Three 25-minute samples were taken during the procedure of interest; results were 11.7, 9.10, and 19.3 ppm.

If one were to do a PEL calculation, assuming no other exposure to acetic acid during the rest of the day, the result would be 2.1 ppm. This is clearly lower than the OSHA PEL and requires no further action. However, one of the three short term samples exceeds the 15 minute recommended NIOSH limit, and, persists for 25 minutes. While not required by law to reference limits other than OSHA's, most health professionals would cite the NIOSH limit as good practice and make changes in work practices or engineering controls to reduce exposures. It is interesting to note that if only one sample had been collected, and if the

single sample had been collected during the time when the excursions were lower, the exposures would have been seen as compliant with the PEL and the NIOSH REL.

Exposure limits can be compared to speed limits. Traveling one mile per hour less than the posted limit does not guarantee safety. In addition, chemical exposure has a cumulative effect if the time between exposures has not been sufficient to allow clearance of the chemical and its metabolites from the body and recovery from the adverse physiological effects.

Limitations of Standards

Any sampling result that is less than the PEL is considered to be in compliance with the law. This evaluation is often misinterpreted as meaning a clean bill of health. A review of OSHA's sampling results shows that 92 percent of them were in compliance, but OSHA estimates that hundreds of thousands of new cases of occupational illness occur annually. There have been many criticisms of the OSHA standards, including the following:

- They only evaluate inhalation exposures.
- They are out of date—most PELs were based on 1968 ACGIH TLVs.
- They have been based on inadequate research that fails to consider chronic toxicity, including immune or endocrine system function, reproductive toxicity, sensitization, and neurological changes.
- Standards were often adopted based on health and epidemiological data on workers who were mainly white and male, excluding analyses of nonwhite and female employees.
- They allow a level of risk not tolerated for general environmental exposure, such as a risk for cancer of one in a thousand compared to one in a million for environmental exposures.
- They fail to account for multiple exposures that are additive or synergistic.
- They offer limits for less than 10 percent of the chemicals in widespread commercial use.
- Rather than representing a health-based guideline, they represent a political compromise regarding economic feasibility.

Industrial hygienists sometimes analyze sampling results and conclude that compliance with PELs is not sufficient to guarantee health in the workplace. Where NIOSH RELs and ACGIH TLVs differ from PELs, these guidelines provide additional benchmarks that represent conclusions from research designed to further control exposures.

RELs exist for nearly 700 chemicals; NIOSH tends to propose more conservative exposure limits and has criticized several OSHA PELs as being insufficiently protective.

Most RELs were developed in the 1970s, and some have been outdated by more recent findings.

The TLVs have been criticized as well, because of corporate involvement in their development, avowed inability to protect all workers, and limited transparency. Such deficiencies do not necessarily mean that TLVs are wrong. Nor do the deficiencies detract from the contribution to worker health provided by the TLVs. They do, however, limit the conclusions that can be drawn when using them to evaluate air-sampling results. Recently, corporate suits against the TLVs have been unsuccessful, but have required large investments of both time and money on the part of the ACGIH, which might have been used in other endeavors to protect workers.

The task of providing guidance regarding risk in the absence of complete information often leads occupational health specialists to settle for existing data and guidelines without analyzing their adequacy. A minimum standard of care in many responsible industries is the maintenance of airborne chemical concentrations below all existing standards, guidelines, and internally generated standards. In addition, when employee health complaints persist when a standard is not exceeded, further investigation and action are often needed to ensure health. The Industrial Hygiene Code of Ethics (see Chapter 1) requires placing employee health first in all considerations.

Not only do standards and guidelines differ within the United States, but also between regulating bodies worldwide. Given the international reach of chemical manufacture and distribution around the world, the Globally Harmonized System for the Classification and Labeling of Chemicals (GHS) is being promoted. Broader in scope than currently mandated MSDSs and hazard communication requirements, GHS comprises harmonized criteria for classifying chemicals and mixtures according to their health, environmental, and physical hazards; provides criteria for chemical safety communication on labels and safety data sheets; and standardizes words and symbols for representing hazards. GHS draws from OSHA, EPA, and Consumer Protection agencies in the U.S., United Nations' recommendations regarding transport, Canadian worker and consumer standards, and the above referenced European Union standards. (See Chapter 31 for more information on global cooperation and regulation.)

Another system called Registration, Evaluation and Authorization for Chemicals (REACH) are European regulations that derive no-effect levels and predict likely exposures over the life cycle of chemicals. Special attention is paid to persistent, bioaccumulative, and toxic chemicals. It has been suggested that OSHA replace their permissible exposure limits with a program requirement that companies should identify and correct hazards without requiring air sampling; this approach is called "find-it and fix-it."

There are also attempts to address small employers, and to provide "health-conscious" or "safe-sided" protection. These include COSHH Essentials, developed by the UK Health and Safety Executive, and the Chemical Control Toolkit proposed by the International Labor Organization. Both of these systems, collectively known as "control banding" rely on the European Union's (EU) risk phrases (R-phrases) that characterize health hazards.

Comparison of Results with Other Data

Sampling may be conducted to investigate a problem or to measure the impact of changes in production processes or control measures. In these cases current sampling results can be compared to previous results to determine the effectiveness of the new or modified control measure in reducing airborne concentrations. In other cases, when the intent of the sampling is to evaluate the effectiveness of in-place monitors used for regular surveillance, the current data collected should also be compared to previous results to look for trends.

It can also be helpful to review sampling data from various types of workplaces that are available from NIOSH Health Hazard Evaluation reports. This data can be used to evaluate the effectiveness of the current sampling or the health and safety oversight at the worksite in question.

Industrial hygienists are sometimes asked to evaluate the significance of chemical-sampling results for which there are no published standards or guidelines. In these situations, the manufacturer may have developed internal standards for the chemical's use within the company. Lacking any other guidelines, a review of anecdotal reports in the literature, health surveys among those exposed on the job, or a careful consideration of animal toxicology data can be helpful. The LD_{50} (lethal dose for 50 percent of the exposed animal population in question during experiments) can be found in the Registry of Toxic Effects of Chemical Substances (RTECS) database from NIOSH. (See Appendix A, Additional Resources, for more information.) Animal research that establishes a no effect level (NOEL) is especially useful.

While debate continues over the usefulness of standards and guidelines, industrial hygienists still conduct air sampling and analyze results, attempting to make the best use of all that is available to them as evaluation tools, including their skills in measurement, observation, interviewing, interpretation, and communication with employers and employees. The hierarchy of controls, eliminating or substituting safer for more hazardous chemicals forms the backdrop for all these considerations. In addition, they often consult with other professionals in the fields of occupational medicine, infection control, ventilation, architecture, engineering, health physics, and others to ensure a broad and in-depth analysis of an industrial hygiene problem. This networking with other professionals is invaluable in the evaluation process.

SUMMARY

There are many factors to consider in evaluating the workplace. Evaluation is a process that must incorporate new research, advances in production technology, a changing work force, and alterations in air-sampling methodology, with the most fundamental concern being the lives and health of workers. This is at the core of the code of ethics for industrial hygienists and forms the basis for all interactions with other health professionals in the practice of prevention of occupational illness and injury.

BIBLIOGRAPHY

Alarcon WA, Roscoe RJ, Calvert GM, et al. Adult blood lead epidemiology and surveillance—United States, 2005-2007. *MMWR* 58(14):365-369, 2009.

American Conference of Governmental Industrial Hygienists. *Documentation of Threshold Limit Values Including Biological Exposure Indices (BEIs®) and Issue of Supplements*, 7th ed. Cincinnati, OH: ACGHI®, 2011.

American Conference of Governmental Industrial Hygienists Board of Directors. Threshold Limit Values: A more balanced appraisal. *Appl Occup Environ Hygiene* 5:340–344, 1990.

American Industrial Hygiene Association. *A Strategy Manual for Assessing and Managing Occupational exposures*, 3rd edition. Fairfax, VA: AIHA Press, 2006.

Ashford NA, Spadafor CJ, Hattis DB, et al. *Monitoring the Worker for Exposure and Disease: Scientific, Legal, and Ethical Considerations in the Use of Biomarkers.* Baltimore: The Johns Hopkins University Press, 1990.

Boden LI, Ozonoff A. Capture-recapture estimates of non-fatal workplace injuries and illnesses. *Ann Epidemiol* 18(6):500-506, 2008.

Bureau of Labor Statistics, U.S. Department of Labor. *Workplace illness and injury summary, October 2010.* Washington, DC: Bureau of Labor Statistics, 2010. http://www.bls.gov/news.release/osh.nr0.htm, accessed March 12, 2011.

Bureau of National Affairs. OSHA advance notice of proposed rulemaking on a generic standard for exposure monitoring. *Occup Saf Health Rptr* September 1988a:950–959.

Bureau of National Affairs. OSHA advance notice of proposed rulemaking on medical surveillance programs. *Occup Saf Health Rptr* September 1988b:960–963.

Burgess WA. *Recognition of Health Hazards in Industry: A Review of Materials and Processes* 2nd ed. New York: Wiley, 1995.

Castleman BI, Ziem GE. Corporate influence on Threshold Limit Values. *Am J Ind Med* 13:531–559, 1988.

Centers for Disease Control and Prevention. *NIOSH Manual of Analytical Methods*, 3rd Supplement. (DHHS [NIOSH] Publication No. 2003-154) Washington, DC: GPO, 2003. http://www.cdc.gov/niosh/docs/2003-154/

Centers for Disease Control and Prevention, NIOSH. *Pocket Guide to Chemical Hazards.* DHHS (NIOSH) Publication No. 2005-149. Cincinnati, OH: NIOSH, September 2005. http://www.cdc.gov/niosh/npg/default.html

Gerhardsson L, Attewell R, Chettle DR, et al. In vivo measurements of lead in bone in long-term exposed lead smelter workers. *Arch Environ Health* 48:147–156, 1993.

Hathaway GJ, Proctor NH. *Proctor and Hughes' Chemical Hazards of the Workplace*, 5th ed. New York: Wiley, 2004.

Hu H. Bone lead as a new biologic marker of lead dose: Recent findings and implications for public health. *Environ Health Perspectives* 106:961-967.

Hu H, Milder FL, Bulger DE. X-ray fluorescence: Issues surrounding the application of a new tool for measuring burden of lead. *Environ Res* 49:295–317, 1989.

International Labour Organisation. *Encyclopaedia of Occupational Health and Safety*, 4th ed. Geneva, Switzerland: ILO. http://www.ilocis.org/en/contilo.html, accessed online March 12, 2011.

Iyaniwura TI. In vitro toxicology of organophosphorus pesticide combinations. *J Mol Cell Toxicol* 3:37–377, 1990.

Jon RM, Nicas M. Margins of safety provided by COSHH Essentials and the ILO Chemical Control Toolkit. *Ann Occup Hyg* 50(2):149-156, 2006.

Lauwerys RR, Hoet P. Industrial Chemical Exposure, Guidelines for Biological Monitoring, 3rd ed. Boca Raton, FL: Lewis Publishers, 2001.

Leigh JP, Markowitz SB, Fahs M, et al. Occupational injury and illness in the United States. Estimates of costs, morbidity, and mortality. *Arch Intern Med* 157(14):1557-68, 1997.

Levy BS, Wegman DH. *Occupational Health: Recognizing and Preventing Work-Related Disease*, 6th ed. Philadelphia: Lippincott Williams & Wilkins, 2011.

Ma T-H, Sandhu SS, Peng Y, et al. Synergistic and antagonistic effects on genotoxicity of chemicals commonly found in hazardous waste sites. *Mutation Res* 270:71–77, 1992.

Mastromatteo E. On the concept of threshold. *Am Ind Hyg Assoc* 142:763–770, 1981.

Nicas M. Industrial hygiene sampling strategy. *State of the Workplace, Internal Bulletin HESIS* (California Hazard Evaluation System and Information Service) 4:8–11, 1990.

Paul M, ed. *Occupational and Environmental Reproductive Hazards: A Guide for Clinicians.* Baltimore: Williams & Wilkins, 1993.

Roach SA, Rappaport SM. But they are not thresholds: A critical analysis of the documentation of Threshold Limit Values. *Am J Ind Med* 17:727–753, 1990.

Robinson JC, Paxman DG, Rappaport SM. Implications of OSHA's reliance on TLVs in developing the air contaminants standard. *Am J Ind Med* 19:3–13, 1991.

Rose V, Cohrssen B, eds. *Patty's Industrial Hygiene*, 6th ed, vols I–IV. New York: Wiley, 2010.

Rosenman KD, Kalush A, Reilly MJ, et al. How much work-related injury and illness is missed by the current national surveillance system? *JOEM* 48(4):357-365, 2006. https://www.msu.edu/~kalush/projects/JOEMWorkplaceInjuries.pdf, accessed online March 12, 2011.

Ryback LP. Hearing: The effects of chemicals. *Otolaryngol Head Neck Surg* 106:677–85, 1992.

Senn EP. An evaluation of the effectiveness of OSHA's program to control chemical exposures in the workplace. Paper presented at 1992 *American Industrial Hygiene Conference and Exposition*, Boston, June 1992.

Sentes R. OSHA and standard-setting. *Am J Ind Med* 21:759–764, 1992.

Silverstein M. Analysis of medical screening and surveillance in twenty-one OSHA standards: Support for a generic medical surveillance standard. *Am J Ind Med* 26:283–295, 1994.

Tarlau ES. Playing industrial hygiene to win. *New Solutions* 4:72–81, 1991.

Tumpowsky CM, Davis LK, Rabin R. Elevated blood lead levels among adults in Massachusetts: 1991–1995. *Public Health Reports* 115:364-369, 2000.

U.S Congress, Office of Technology Assessment. *Preventing Illness and Injury in the Workplace.* OTA-H-256. Washington, DC: OTA, April 1985.

U.S. Congress, Office of Technology Assessment. *Reproductive Health Hazards in the Workplace.* OTA-BA-266. Washington, DC: OTA, December 1985.

U.S. Department of Health and Human Services, NIOSH. Health Hazard Evaluation, Commercial Office Buildings, Boston, Massachusetts, *HETA 86-472-1832.* Cincinnati, OH: NIOSH, September 1987.

U.S. Department of Health and Human Services, NIOSH. Health Hazard Evaluation, 50 Standiford Street Office Building, Boston, Massachusetts. *HETA 86-092-1870.* Cincinnati, OH: NIOSH, February 1988.

U.S. Department of Health and Human Services, NIOSH. *National Occupational Research Agenda.* DHHS (NIOSH) Publication No. 96-115. Cincinnati, OH: NIOSH April 1996.

U.S. Department of Health and Human Services, NIOSH. *Occupational Safety and Health Guidance Manual for Hazardous Waste Site Activities.* (DHHS [NIOSH] Publication No. 85-115) Washington, DC: GPO, October 1985.

USDOL-OSHA. 29 *Code of Federal Regulations*, Parts 1910 and 1926. Washington, DC: GPO, 1994.

USDOL-OSHA. *Framework for a Comprehensive Health and Safety Program in the Hospital Environment.* Washington, DC: GPO, 1993.

USDOL-OSHA. *OSHA Technical Manual.* Washington, DC: OSHA, 2008. http://www.osha.gov/dts/osta/otm/otm_extended_toc.html

U.S. Department of Labor, Bureau of Labor Statistics. *Occupational Injuries and Illnesses: Counts, Rates and Characteristics*, 1997 Bulletin 2518. Washington, DC: October 1999.

U. S. Environmental Protection Agency. *Sector Notebook Project: Dry Cleaning* (EPA/310-R-95-001). Washington, DC: GPO, 1995.

U.S. Government Accountability Office. *Workplace safety and health: Enhancing OSHA's record audit process could improve the accuracy of worker injury and illness data* (GAO-10-10). Washington, DC: GAO, 2009. http://www.gao.gov/products/GAO-10-10, accessed online March 12, 2011.

Weeks JL, Levy BS, Wagner GR, eds. *Preventing Occupational Disease and Injury.* Washington, DC: American Public Health Association, 1991.

CHAPTER 16

Air Sampling

by Theodore J. Hogan, PhD, CIH

Industrial hygienists are responsible for the evaluation and control of employee exposure to occupational health hazards. For the evaluation and control of inhalation hazards, hygienists typically compare the measured concentration of an airborne chemical to a recognized exposure limit. Standardized methods for the collection of air samples have been developed to ensure that accurate and meaningful information is collected.

This chapter will review the different types of air sampling—personal versus area, grab versus integrated—and when each might be used; the components of a sampling train, including suction pumps and flow-rate meters; the collection devices and methods used to sample gases and vapors; the collection devices and methods used to sample particles; how to select a sampling method; and how to calibrate sampling pumps.

TYPES OF AIR SAMPLING

Air sampling is used to evaluate employee exposure, assist in the design or evaluation of control measures, and document compliance with government regulations. These sampling objectives define the type of air sampling selected.

Personal versus Area Sampling

Personal air sampling is the preferred method of evaluating worker exposure to airborne chemicals and is usually required for compliance sampling. The worker wears a sampling device that collects an air sample. The sampling device is placed as close as possible to the breathing zone of the worker (defined as a hemisphere in front of the shoulders with a radius of 6–9 in.) so the data collected closely approximate the concentration inhaled. Concentration is equal to the mass of the contaminant collected divided by the volume of air passed through the collection device. The sampling device should be placed on the shoulder of the dominant hand, as this is usually closer to the source. Special steps may be required for some tasks. For example, sampling for welding is usually conducted with the sampling device underneath the welding face shield (special holders are available). This best represents the worker exposure, as the sample collects air both when the worker has the shield down and when it is up.

Area air samples can be used to evaluate background concentrations, locate sources of exposure, or evaluate the effectiveness of control measures. The sampling device is strategically placed in a fixed location in the area of interest. For example, if a leak is suspected in a process, several area samples taken at key locations could be used to pinpoint the source. In general, this type of sampling is not used to provide an estimate of worker exposure because conditions at the fixed location may not be the same as those experienced by the worker. Consider the use of direct reading instruments as an alternative to area sampling, as direct reading instruments can provide additional information about the variation of concentrations throughout the workshift.

Grab versus Integrated Sampling

Grab samples are taken to measure the airborne concentration of a substance over a short time period (usually less than five minutes). Personal or area grab samples are used to identify peak or ceiling concentrations. Many chemicals have acute effects that occur at short, high concentrations. For example, grab samples can be used to measure brief exposures to acrolein in wood smoke that produce strong eye and lung irritation. A full-shift sample will not be helpful in identifying these important exposures. Grab samples can also be helpful for evaluating different parts of the work cycle: for example, setups, maintenance, or spills that may result in higher exposures than regular operations. This type of sampling can help pinpoint where to focus control efforts.

Grab samples alone are rarely used to estimate an employee's eight-hour time-weighted average exposure. This is because they do not account for the time between samples. However, they can be used as a screening method to determine whether more extensive sampling is needed. For example, if multiple grab samples and observations throughout the workday indicate that the concentration of a chemical is well below the eight-hour time-weighted average exposure limit, then sampling for the full shift may not be necessary.

Integrated air sampling is used to estimate a worker's eight-hour or 15-minute exposure to a particular substance by collecting one or more personal air samples for the duration of a particular task or workshift. It is called *integrated sampling* because the result integrates all of the various con-

centrations to which the worker has been exposed during the sampling period. The resulting concentration represents an average exposure over the sampling period, also known as a time-weighted average (TWA).

AIR-SAMPLING EQUIPMENT

There are two categories of air-sampling equipment: direct-reading instruments and sample collection devices. Direct-reading instruments provide an immediate measurement of concentration and can be used to show the variation in concentration throughout the day. These devices are covered in Chapter 17, Direct-Reading Instruments for Gases, Vapors, and Particulates. Sample collection devices draw air through media (such as a filter or tube) that is subsequently analyzed or weighed at a laboratory. Sample collection devices are the focus of this chapter.

Sampling Train

Air sample collection devices are typically made of five basic components called the sampling train: an air inlet orifice, a collection device, an airflow meter, a flow-rate control device, and a suction pump (Figure 16–1). Each of these plays an important role in determining how a sample is collected.

Air enters the sampling train through the orifice and the chemical is collected on a collection medium such as a filter. The size, shape, and positioning of the air inlet orifice can greatly affect what is actually collected from the air. This is particularly true when sampling particle exposures.

The suction pump moves air through all of the components of the sampling train. The pump must be able to draw air at the required flow rate for the time required to

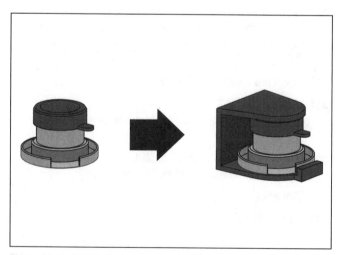

Figure 16–1. Components of a typical air-sampling train used to collect airborne particles. *(Printed with permission of SKC Inc.)*

collect the sample. The airflow rate is set using the rate control valve. Airflows are usually measured in liters per minute or cubic centimeters of air per minute. Most air sampling pumps have built-in flow-rate meters to allow the user to visually gauge the approximate flow rate. However, these cannot be used to determine the actual flow rate. Most pumps have features to maintain a constant airflow throughout a shift, compensating for increased resistance through sampling media such as filters that get loaded up during the shift. Some pumps also correct for the effects of changes in temperature and pressure on volumetric flow rates. Even so, it is still necessary to measure (calibrate) the flow rate through the sampling train before and after sampling to ensure that a valid sample is collected.

Each contaminant sampling method has defined flow rates and minimum/maximum sample times. For example, a flow that is too slow may not collect enough material for laboratory analysis. A flow that is too high can cause contaminants such as gases and vapors to pass through the sample media and not get collected, resulting in an invalid sample. Too high a flow rate may also cause particles to bounce off the media. Too low or too high a flow rate can cause a particle sampler to collect the wrong size particles, rendering the sample invalid for comparison against exposure guidelines.

COLLECTION DEVICES FOR GASES AND VAPORS

Gases and vapors are formless fluids that completely occupy a space or enclosure. A substance is considered a gas if this is its normal physical state under standard temperature and barometric pressure conditions (70°F and 760 mmHg, or 21.1 C and 101.3 kilopascals). Carbon monoxide released by incomplete combustion is an example of a gas. A vapor is the gaseous phase of a substance that under standard conditions exists as a liquid or a solid in equilibrium with its vapor. For example, gasoline is a liquid at room temperature that readily vaporizes, which is evident from its distinctive odor.

Gases and vapors behave similarly. They follow the ideal gas laws in that their volume is affected by changes in temperature and pressure. At typical concentrations found in workplace air, they do not stratify based on their densities. Instead, they diffuse and mix freely with the general atmosphere and form homogeneous mixtures with other gases.

In some cases, a chemical may exist as both a gas or vapor and a solid particle at the same time. Burning wood and other materials generate a mix of vaporous and particulate carcinogenic polyaromatic hydrocarbons (PAHs). In such cases collection devices for both the gaseous and

solid phases must be used to provide an accurate measure of employee exposure.

Grab Sampling

Although direct-reading devices are usually used for grab sampling, the collection of a known volume of air for subsequent laboratory analysis is another method used. Figures 16–2 and 16–3 are examples of the most commonly used collection devices, the evacuated canister and the gas-sampling bag. Depending on selection of flow controllers, these samplers can collect almost instantaneously or collect over many hours.

The advantages of grab sampling are that it is simple to use, and it normally collects 100 percent of the chemical. This may be helpful for sampling a complex mixture or to identify unknown contaminants. The disadvantage is that usually it cannot be used to sample reactive gases such as hydrogen sulfide, nitrogen dioxide, and sulfur dioxide unless the samples are analyzed immediately. It can be impractical for personal monitoring. Reactive gases can react with atmospheric dust particles, other gases, moisture, container sealant compounds, or the container itself, producing erroneous results. Check with the laboratory that is conducting the analysis for specific guidance on what type of specific collection canister or bag to use, and for proper handling procedures.

Figure 16–2. An evacuated container is used to collect air for analysis.

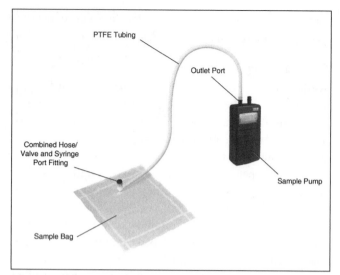

Figure 16–3. Sample bags are filled with air from the environment for further and analytical analysis. *(Printed with permission of SKC Inc.)*

Integrated Air Sampling

Integrated air sampling involves the extraction of a gas or vapor from a sample airstream, followed by laboratory analysis. Two extraction techniques are normally used: absorption and adsorption.

Absorption

In the absorption technique, a gas, vapor, or mixed aerosol is removed from the airstream as it passes through a liquid that captures the contaminant. The gas or vapor may be highly soluble in and nonreactive with the liquid, or the liquid can contain a reactive reagent. Deionized water, for example, is a commonly used absorbing solution for acids because acids are highly soluble in water. A reactive absorbing reagent captures a gas or vapor by quickly reacting with it and creating a more stable compound, which can be analyzed by a laboratory. While impingers can be difficult to use, they may be necessary for collecting some materials that exist in both a vapor and solid state in the workplace.

Absorption devices include gas wash bottles and fritted bubblers (Figure 16–4). The simplest is the gas wash bottle, which forces air through a nozzle into the absorbing solution. The most commonly used gas wash bottle is the midget impinger. Because absorbing solutions do not collect 100 percent of the gas or vapor passing through, sometimes two impingers are used in series. This increases the total amount of vapor or gas collected. The fritted bubbler impinger causes the formation of many tiny bubbles as air is forced through the fritted surface. This increases the surface area of air in contact with the absorbing liquid, increasing

collection efficiency. The fritted bubbler is appropriate for gaseous substances that are only moderately soluble or that react slowly with the absorbing liquid. Acid and caustic liquid absorbents may injure a worker if spilled out of the impinger, and such samples may be better suited for area rather than personal sampling.

During the course of work, the worker may accidentally invert the impinger, causing the absorbing liquid to be drawn into the sampling pump. To avoid this, an empty bottle or impinger is connected to the sampling train to collect spilled liquid. Although this precaution prevents damage to the pump, the recovered liquid is contaminated and cannot be used for an analysis. There are spillproof midget impingers available to help alleviate this problem. Table 16–A lists selected National Institute for Occupational Safety and Health (NIOSH) impinger sampling methods.

Adsorption

Air sampling for insoluble or nonreactive gaseous substances is commonly conducted using tubes filled with a granular sorbent such as activated charcoal or silica gel. The gas or vapor is retained or adsorbed, physically and chemically unchanged, onto the surface of the sorbent for subsequent laboratory extraction and analysis.

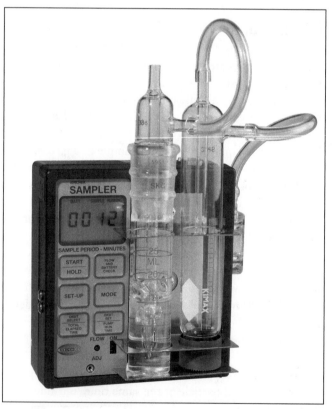

Figure 16–4. Impinger containing liquid absorbent (left), with an empty bottle (right) to prevent solution from being drawn into the pump. *(Printed with permission of SKC Inc.)*

TABLE 16-A	Selected NIOSH Impinger Sampling Methods		
Chemical	*NIOSH Sampling Method No.*	*Impinging Solution*	*Analytical Method*
Aminoethanol compounds II	3509	15 mL of 2 mM hexanesulfonic acid	Ion chromatography
Monomethylaniline	3511	10 mL of 0.05 M sulfuric acid	Gas chromatography
Acetaldehyde	3507	15 mL of Girard T reagent	High-pressure liquid chromatography
Isocyanates, Monomeric	5521	Solution of 1-(2-methoxyphenyl)-piperazine in toluene	High-pressure liquid chromatography

Activated charcoal is the most widely used solid sorbent for adsorbing organic vapors. The charcoal most commonly used is from coconut shells. Coconut shell charcoal provides a large adsorptive surface area and is electrically nonpolar, meaning it preferentially adsorbs organic vapors rather than polar molecules such as water vapor. A standard charcoal tube is 7 cm long and 4 mm wide, and is divided into two sections. The first section contains 100 mg of charcoal and a fiberglass, glass wool, or urethane foam plug; the backup section contains 50 mg of charcoal (Figure 16-5). Different sizes and compositions of charcoal tubes are available, so check with the laboratory to get the right tube for the specific sampling application.

Although activated charcoal has a large adsorptive capacity, some contaminants pass through the first section if the flow rate is too high or if there is a high concentration of the contaminant in the air. The backup section increases collection efficiency by adsorbing some of the material that was initially missed. *Breakthrough* describes the condition where sampled materials pass through the

collection device and are collected on the backup section. Breakthrough is considered significant when the mass of a collected gas or vapor in the backup section is greater than 10 percent of the mass in the front section. This means that a significant quantity of the contaminant may not have been collected. The calculated concentration, therefore, is of questionable validity. It is very important to use the recommended flow rates and sample volumes specified in the sampling methods to prevent breakthrough. Note that high humidity and the presence of other adsorbing compounds in the sampled environment can increase the potential for breakthrough.

Charcoal tubes have a high adsorptive capacity for a large range of organic vapors. They can be used to sample several kinds of vapors at once. The analytical laboratory should be consulted to determine whether there is a limit to the number of organic vapors that can be extracted or whether any of the sampled organic vapors must be collected separately.

Silica gel tubes are used to sample for gases and vapors that cannot be efficiently collected or extracted from activated charcoal. They are constructed in the same manner as charcoal tubes except that an amorphous form of silica is used as the adsorbent material. Silica gel is not as commonly used as activated charcoal because it is electrically polar and tends to attract interfering polar molecules such as water vapor. Silica gel may be treated with chemicals to collect specific gases and vapors.

Many solid sorbent materials with chemical coatings have been developed to sample for reactive gases and vapors that are not efficiently collected by charcoal or silica gel. There are many specialized sampling tubes, including ones containing XAD®-2, Tenax®-GC, Ambersorb®, or Chromosorb® sorbents (Table 16-B).

There is a great variety of apparently similar tube sampling media. But they are not interchangeable. For example, one media supplier provides over 20 different types of silica gel tubes for different applications. Contact the laboratory before sampling to ensure you are collecting the sample in a way that will allow it to be analyzed and provide valid results.

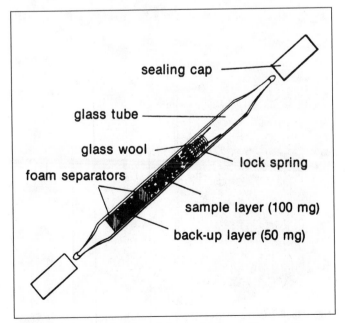

Figure 16-5. Standard activated charcoal tube used in organic vapor sampling.

TABLE 16–B	NIOSH-Recommended Sorbent Tubes		
Chemical	**NIOSH Method No.**	**Tube**	**Analytic Method**
Methanol	2000	Silica gel	Gas chromatograph
Aromatic amines	2002	Silica gel	Gas chromatograph
Halogenated hydrocarbons	1003	Charcoal	Gas chromatograph
Naphthas	1550	Charcoal	Gas chromatograph
Phosphorus	7905	Tenax® GC	Gas chromatograph
Nitroethane	2526	XAD®-2	Gas chromatograph
Methyl ethyl ketone	2500	Beaded carbon	Gas chromatograph
n-Butyl mercaptan	2525	Chromosorb® 104	Gas chromatograph

Diffusion (Passive) Samplers

Diffusion samplers (also called passive samplers) allow personal sampling without the use of sampling pumps. Whereas solid sorbent tubes rely on a sampling pump to draw air through the adsorbing material, diffusion samplers do not require a pump to move the air, but rely on passive diffusion (Figure 16–6). Diffusion is the passage of molecules through a semipermeable barrier. It occurs because molecules tend to move from an area of high concentration to an area of low concentration. If the ambient concentration of a particular gas or vapor is greater than the concentration inside the monitor, then the gas or vapor molecules will diffuse across a barrier into the monitor and be collected by a sorbent material (Figure 16–7). As the sorbent adsorbs the gas or vapor, the concentration inside the monitor becomes less than the concentration outside. This keeps the diffusion process going.

Sampling begins when the device's cover is removed; the time is recorded. The worker wears the monitor in his or her breathing zone. When sampling is complete, the monitor is removed and resealed and the time is recorded. The badge is then sent to the laboratory for analysis.

Diffusion samplers are inexpensive and easy to use. Their accuracy has been studied extensively. Most commercially available monitors meet or exceed NIOSH accuracy requirements (±25% for 95% of samples tested between 0.5 and 2.0 times the exposure limit). As with all sampling methods, care must be taken to use them properly. Factors that can influence the accuracy of passive monitors include temperature extremes and lack of air movement across the badge face. Sampling in painting operations or other processes that can leave a coating on the badge membrane will interfere with the accuracy of the sample collection.

Colorimetric passive monitors are also available for some gases and vapors. They come in a variety of designs, including diffusion tubes that look similar to, but are not the same as, detector tubes (Figure 16–8). The media inside the passive monitor chemically reacts with the contaminant in the air, resulting in a color change. The color change is com-

pared against a guide provided by the manufacturer. Passive monitors are simple to use and provide quick feedback on exposures. These can be used for 15-minute or full-shift sampling, depending on the monitor specifications. Passive monitors can be a screening tool, used as a step along the way to more thorough sampling. Although these can be very useful, some regulatory agencies may not accept them for required compliance monitoring. Like all sampling methods, colorimetric passive monitors are subject to interference from other chemicals in the air, temperature extremes, and other factors (which are usually identified by the monitor manufacturer). These can result in erroneous color changes and incorrect exposure assessment.

Figure 16–6. Passive diffusion monitors are an inexpensive and easy-to-use alternative to solid sorbent tubes. *(Photo courtesy of Assay Technology, Inc., www.assaytech.us.)*

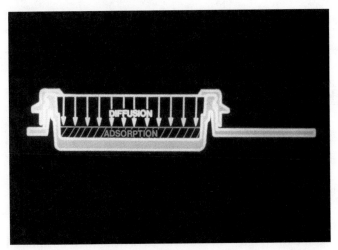

Figure 16–7. Gas or vapor molecules diffuse into a passive diffusion monitor across a permeable barrier and are collected by a sorbent material. *(Courtesy 3M.)*

Figure 16–8. Passive sampling with color diffusion tubes.

COLLECTION DEVICES FOR PARTICLES

Airborne particles can be solid, liquid, or both. Dusts, fumes, smoke, and fibers are dispersed solids; mists and fogs are dispersed liquids. They range in size from visible to microscopic. A number of devices can be used to collect particles, each relying on different mechanisms for particle capture (Table 16–C).

Filters

The filter is the most common collection device for particulate matter. There are several types, including glass fiber (GF), mixed cellulose ester fiber (MCE), and polyvinyl chloride (PVC) filters. They are selected based on their ability to collect the material of interest and their suitability for laboratory analysis. For mineral and nuisance dusts, for example, the total weight of the collected particulate mat-

TABLE 16–C	Sampling Techniques for Collection of Airborne Particles	
Sampling Technique	*Force or Mechanism*	*Examples*
Filters	Combination of inertial impaction, interception, diffusion, electrostatic attraction, and gravitational forces	Various types and sizes of fibrous, membrane, and nucleopore filters with holders
Impactors	Inertial-Impaction on a solid surface	Single- and multijet cascade impactors and single-stage impactors
Impingers	Inertial-impingement and capture in liquid media	Greenburg-Smith and midget impingers
Elutriators	Gravitational separation	Horizontal and vertical elutriators
Electrostatic precipitation	Electrical charging with collection on an electrode of opposite polarity	Tube type, point-to-plane, and plate precipitators
Thermal precipitation	Thermophoresis-Particle movement under the influence of a temperature gradient in the direction of decreasing temperature	Various devices for particulate collection for microscopy analysis
Cyclones	Inertial-Centrifugal separation with collection on a secondary stage	Tangential and axial inlet cyclones in varying sizes
Inhalable sampler	Separation and collection of inhalable particles (100 um and less) onto filters	IOM Criteria Inhalable Sampler, various manufacturers
Thoracic cyclone	Cyclone designed to separate thoracic particles (10 um and less)	Various manufacturers. Note: standard cyclones collect respirable particles
Mini-cascade impactor	Impactor that has multiple impaction plates that separate out particles by size	Various manufacturers

TABLE 16–D		Selected NIOSH-Recommended Filters	
Chemical	**NIOSH Sampling Method No.**	**Filter**	**Analytic Method**
Copper (dust and fume)	7029	MCE	Atomic absorption spectroscopy
Carbon black	5000	PVC	Gravimetric
Mineral oil mist	5026	PVC or MCE	Infrared spectrophotometry
Asbestos	7400	25-mm MCE	Phase contract microscopy
Arsenic trioxide as As	7901	Na_2Co_3-impregnated MCE	Atomic absorption, graphite furnace
(2,4-Dichlorophenoxy) acetic acid	5001	GF	High-pressure liquid chromatography

ter is of concern. In this case, PVC filters are used because they can be easily weighed. For metal dusts, the amount of a particular metal in the sample is of concern, so a chemical analysis must be done. MCE filters are generally used in this case as they usually have low background concentrations of metals. However, it is still important to provide "blank" (unsampled) media to the laboratory so that background levels can be determined. See Table 16–D for a list of some NIOSH-recommended filters.

A typical collection device used for particulate matter sampling is a closed-face filter cassette, 37 mm in diameter, containing a filter supported with a cellulose backup pad (Figure 16–9). Closed face means that the top of the cassette is not removed during the sampling; only the top and bottom caps are removed. The air inlet side of the cassette, opposite the filter, is usually marked so that the filter is not attached backwards.

There are some exceptions to the standard filter setup.

Asbestos, for example, is collected using a 25-mm filter and cassette with an open-face 50-mm conductive extension cowl (Figure 16–10). The cassette is used open faced because an even distribution of fibers on the filter is needed for microscopic analysis. The 25-mm filter improves the sensitivity of the test. The electrically conductive extension cowl reduces the number of asbestos fibers attracted to the sides of the cassette by static electricity.

Chemically treated filters may be required for isocyanates and other highly reactive materials. Some of these filters may have to be kept cold before and after sampling, and they may have to be used within a specified period of time before the media degrade. Contact the laboratory for specific media and storage requirements.

Filter Overloading

It's important to periodically check filters during sampling to ensure they are not overloaded. Loose or excessive material on the filter may become dislodged during sampling and shipping, complicating the analysis and interpretation of the results. Material may also deposit on the interior walls of the filter cassette (including materials not visible to the eyes). Analytical procedures for some materials, such as

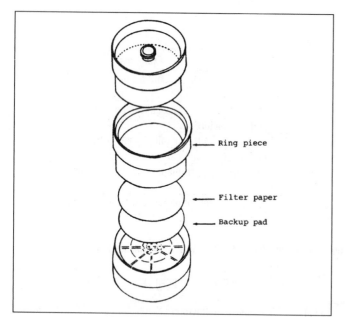

Figure 16–9. Standard filters are 37 mm in diameter and are placed in closed-face cassettes with a backup pad, which prevents contamination. *(Reprinted with permission from OSHA Technical Manual.)*

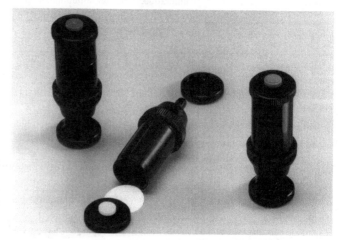

Figure 16–10. Air sampling for asbestos is conducted using a three-piece cassette, a 50-mm black conductive cowl, and a 25-mm filter. *(Courtesy MSA.)*

welding fume and hexavalent chrome, require the laboratory to wipe down the interior of the cassette and include this in the overall analysis.

Particle Sizing

The sizes of the particles to be collected greatly influence the sampling method. Choosing a method without considering particle size may provide an inaccurate exposure assessment. Chapter 8, Particulate Matter, discusses particle sizing and the concept of Aerodynamic Equivalent Diameter. Where particles are deposited in the respiratory tract, and where they cause an adverse effect, is highly dependent on their size.

Three typical size ranges used in industrial hygiene are Inhalable, Thoracic, and Respirable. Choose a particle sizing device that meets the particle size selection efficiency guidelines (Table 16–E) of the American Conference of Governmental Industrial Hygienists (ACGIH®). These guidelines specify how much of each particle size range the device will pass through to the filter. It is critical to use the correct flow rate as this greatly affects a device's particle size selection characteristics.

Total particulate mass (equivalent to OSHA's "Total Dust") is collected with an open- or closed-face filter, as specified by the method. Inhalable particulate mass, such as wood dust (which present a health risk in nasal passages), is collected by the Institute of Occupational Medicine (IOM) sampler, or equivalent (Figure 16–11). The IOM sampler has a 50 percent cut point of 100 um. There are over 80 Threshold Limit Values (TLVs®) that utilize inhalable particulate mass criteria.

Some particles have health effects in the thoracic region (the portion of the respiratory tract below the larynx). Sulfuric acid mist needs to be sampled with a filter and a special thoracic cyclone (Figure 16–12) to accurately measure its hazard. Respirable particles are those that reach the alveoli. Sampling for silica, which causes its damage deep in the lungs, is done with a filter and size-selective cyclone.

Cyclones

A cyclone is used to collect particles of respirable size. Respirable particles are those that are retained in the lung and

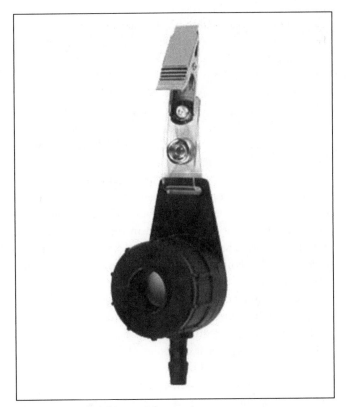

Figure 16–11. Inhalable particle sampler.

Figure 16–12. Thoracic particle sampler.

TABLE 16–E	ACGIH Guidelines for Particle Size Collection	
Size Fraction	**50% cut point***
Inhalable	100 um
Thoracic	10 um
Respirable	4 um

*50% of particles this size are collected. Smaller particles are collected with increasing efficiency up to 100%. Particles larger than cut point are collected with decreasing efficiency as size increases.

are generally considered to be of an aerodynamic size below 10 μm. Cyclones have traditionally been used to sample for mineral dusts containing crystalline silica because of the strong association between the respirable dust fraction and the lung disease silicosis.

Air is drawn into a cyclone tangentially through a small orifice. It is important that the cyclone is operated at the airflow rate for which it was designed (check with the manufacturer of the cyclone). Improper flow rate will result in incorrect particle sizing. The centrifugal motion of the air inside the cyclone forces the larger particles to the periphery of the airstream, where they fall to the bottom of the cyclone. The respirable particles, in the center airstream, are drawn upward onto a preweighed filter. After sampling is completed, the filter is analyzed or weighed to determine how much material has been collected.

Ten-millimeter electrically conductive plastic or aluminum cyclones (Figure 16–13) are used for measuring compliance with OSHA regulations for respirable dust because OSHA uses a 50 percent cut point of 2.5 μm. Some newer cyclones can also meet this criteria by proper flow rate selection. Follow the manufacturer's directions. Older nylon cyclones may not be electrically conductive, which can result in sampling errors.

The science of particle sampling is continually evolving. Check the current manufacturer's instructions for flow-rate settings for particle collection devices, as different flow rates may be needed for compliance with U.S. regulations, international regulations, or outdoor environmental monitoring.

Figure 16–14. Cascade impactor. *(Courtesy Anderson Sampler, Inc.)*

Inertial Impactors

Inertial impactors collect particles by impacting them onto a surface. If an obstacle causes a moving airstream to deviate from a straight course, the particles in the airstream tend to leave the airstream and impact the obstacle. Obstacles include filter paper, glass, stainless steel, and in the case of bioaerosol sampling, nutrient agar. The collection efficiency of this method is affected by the mass of the particles, the size and shape of the obstacle, and the velocity of the air.

Inertial impactors can be used to determine particle size distribution. The mini-cascade impactor (Figure 16–14) is constructed with a series of stages, each of which is calibrated to collect particles of a certain aerodynamic size range.

SUCTION PUMPS

Suction pumps are responsible for the movement of air through the sampling train. To select the type of pump that meets the needs of a particular sampling procedure, one must consider the airflow rate required, the pump's ease of use, and the pump's suitability for use in a potentially hazardous or flammable environment.

Most personal-sampling pumps (Figure 16–15) are lightweight and quiet, use rechargeable batteries, and can be easily attached to the worker's belt. Each has a flow-rate control valve, and some are programmable. They must be listed by Underwriters Laboratories Inc. or its equivalent for use in flammable or explosive atmospheres if they are to be used in such conditions. Most new sample pumps are

Figure 16–13. A cyclone attached to a filter is used to sample for respirable dust. The filter cassette holder can be placed in the worker's breathing zone. *(Printed with permission of SKC Inc.)*

Figure 16–15. Personal sampling pumps must be lightweight and easy to use. (*Courtesy Gillian Instrument Corp.*)

listed as intrinsically safe for use in hazardous locations, but check before use.

Air-sampling pumps are generally available in the following airflow rate ranges: low flow (5–500 mL/min), high flow (0.5–5 and even up to 15 L/min), and dual range (high and low flow). Low-flow pumps are used for solid sorbent tube sampling. High-flow pumps are used for filter, cyclone, and impinger sampling. Special pumps are available when even higher flow rates are needed. The EPA, for example, requires a minimum air volume of 1,200 L for clearance area monitoring after an asbestos abatement project. Using a high-flow air-sampling pump with a typical flow rate of 2 L/min to sample 1,200 L of air would be very time-consuming. In this case, pumps that provide a flow rate of up to 10-15 L/min are used.

The low-power circuitry and sensors, amplifiers and microprocessors, and light plastic cases of the newer pumps have increased their susceptibility to radiofrequency (RF) interference. RF can be generated from facility or communications equipment and may alter the airflow rate or cause the pump to stop. Manufacturers usually incorporate RF shielding in new sampling pumps.

FLOW-RATE METERS

Maintaining a constant flow rate during sampling is critical. Devices that help maintain a constant flow rate include pressure-compensating devices and critical-flow orifices.

Pressure-Compensating Devices

Pressure-compensating devices are designed to overcome the flow-rate variations inherent in many sampling situations. A sampling pump will slow down if the filter becomes loaded with dust or the hose is crimped. Pumps

with pressure-compensating devices have sensors with feedback mechanisms that detect pressure changes and maintain the preset flow rate.

Critical-Flow Orifice

Some pumps use critical or limiting orifices to regulate the airflow rate. A critical orifice is a precisely drilled hole in a metal plate through which the airstream being sampled is directed. When certain parameters are met, the flow rate through the orifice remains constant despite conditions at the inlet (such as a clogged filter). A critical orifice attached to a sampling pump causes the pump to draw air at the desired flow rate.

The principle of the method is to draw air through the orifice under critical-flow conditions and constant upstream pressure. The volume flow rate of a gas through an orifice will increase with a decrease in the ratio of downstream pressure (*p2*) to upstream absolute pressure (*p1*) until the velocity through the opening reaches sonic velocity. The ratio, *p2/p1*, at which acoustic velocity is attained is called the *critical pressure ratio*. The velocity through the orifice will remain constant even if a much lower downstream pressure exists. Therefore, when the pressure ratio is less than critical, the rate of flow through the orifice is dependent only on upstream pressure.

Orifices are calibrated under certain temperature and air pressure conditions. If the air sampling is conducted at a significantly different temperature and pressure, then a correction factor must be used to determine the actual airflow rate. (See the formula under Calibration later in this chapter.)

Most sampling pumps have a mechanism to maintain a constant airflow rate. A device such as a calibrated precision rotameter can also be used to check the airflow rate during the sampling period. (Precision rotameters are discussed later in this chapter.) If the rate changes, it is manually adjusted to the desired rate using the flow-rate control valve.

SELECTING SAMPLING METHODS

The selection of a sampling method depends on a number of factors:

- the sampling objective (documenting exposures, determining compliance, pinpointing sources of exposure)
- the physical and chemical characteristics of the chemical
- the presence of other chemicals that may interfere with the collection or analysis of the chemical
- the required accuracy and precision
- regulatory requirements
- portability and ease of operation

- cost
- reliability
- type of sampling needed (area, personal, grab, integrated)
- duration of sampling

Standardized sampling methods provide the information needed to sample the air for a particular chemical. Procedures are in the NIOSH *Manual of Analytical Methods* and the *OSHA Sampling and Analytical Methods*. They can be found on their respective web sites. OSHA regulations do not usually specify a particular sampling method, but they do require that the method used has a specified and proven degree of accuracy. Some analytical laboratories have developed their own procedures that meet or exceed the OSHA criteria. Note that relatively high or low temperatures can affect the ability of the sampling media to properly collect the contaminant and can invalidate the results. Check with the laboratory before sampling under such conditions to ensure the sampling method can be used.

Role of the Industrial Hygiene Laboratory

The industrial hygiene laboratory analyzes the samples collected in the field. The laboratory can provide support for the sampling process, including the following:

- identifying the sampling method to use (methods are continually evolving)
- defining the flow rate and minimum/maximum sampling time
- providing sampling media
- renting or lending sampling and calibration equipment
- providing chain of custody forms
- guiding the sampler on proper methods for sample shipping and preservation (such as refrigeration)
- calculating the concentrations of the contaminants in the air
- identifying potential problems with the sample (such as overloading and breakthrough)

Laboratories may have sampling guides available via the Internet. Some have step-by-step videos for a large number of specific sampling techniques. These can be accessed via computers or smartphones, and can be quickly reviewed when setting up the sampling train. Most labs will provide technical guidance on proper sample collection via email and phone. Experienced industrial hygienists make it a practice to check with the laboratory to ensure proper sampling parameters as methodologies evolve over time.

Laboratories that analyze industrial hygiene air samples can be accredited by a variety of organizations, including:

- American Industrial Hygiene Association Laboratory Accreditation Programs, LLC, for a wide variety of sample types
- National Voluntary Laboratory Accreditation Program

(NVLAP) from the National Institute of Standards and Technology (NIST), for asbestos fiber analysis
- state agencies, typically for asbestos and lead
- American Association for Laboratory Accreditation (A2LA)
- International Organization for Standards (ISO)

Laboratories may hold multiple accreditations. Accreditation is not an approval of all analyses conducted by a laboratory, but approval of specific methods. For example, a laboratory may be accredited for charcoal tube analyses, but not for diffusive sampler analyses. It's important to determine that the laboratory is accredited for the specific type of analysis needed for the samples collected. State agency–specific accreditation may also be necessary if the sample has been collected to evaluate compliance with a specific state requirement.

An example of a NIOSH sampling procedure is given in Figure 16–16.

This sampling method for acetic acid (NIOSH Method 1603) provides information for both the industrial hygienist and the laboratory. The method requires a coconut shell charcoal tube (100 mg of charcoal with a 50-mg backup section), an airflow rate between 0.01 and 1.0 L/min, and an air sample volume between 20 and 300 L. Precautions include analyzing the samples within seven days and ensuring that the atmosphere being tested does not contain formic acid, which interferes with the analysis.

The recommended air sample volumes are important guidelines to follow. The minimum air sample volume is the minimum amount of air needed to ensure analytical accuracy. It also allows the laboratory to analyze the sample to a concentration well below the exposure limit for that chemical. This is called the sampling method's *lower limit of detection* and is the smallest amount of the chemical that the laboratory can detect.

Sample media may require special handling before, during, and after sampling. Some sample media need to be stored and shipped cold. Others may require that the sampling tube be covered during sampling to prevent degradation of the sample. Some filtering methods, such as for hexavalent chromium, require that the filter be removed from the cassette after sampling and placed into a separate container for shipping back to the laboratory.

Minimum sample volumes can be calculated if the lower limit of detection (LOD) of the analytical method is known. This can be useful if there is no listed minimum air sample volume or if the listed volume is quite large. Published values must assume worst-case conditions are present and have built-in safety factors to ensure that an adequate volume is collected. If the concentration of the contaminant can be estimated, then the following formula can be used:

ACETIC ACID

CH₃COOH   MW: 60.05   CAS: 64-19-7   RTECS: AF1225000

METHOD: 1603, Issue 2   **EVALUATION: FULL**   **Issue 1: 15 May 1989**
Issue 2: 15 August 1994

OSHA : 10 ppm
NIOSH: 10 ppm; STEL 15 ppm
ACGIH: 10 ppm; STEL 15 ppm
(1 ppm = 2.46 mg/m³ @ NTP)

PROPERTIES: liquid; d 1.049 g/mL @ 25 °C;
BP 118 °C; MP 17 °C;
VP 1.5 kPa (11.4 mm Hg) @ 20 °C;
explosive range 5.4 to 16% v/v in air

SYNONYMS: glacial acetic acid; methane carboxylic acid; ethanoic acid

---

SAMPLING	MEASUREMENT
SAMPLER: SOLID SORBENT TUBE (coconut shell charcoal, 100 mg/50 mg)	**TECHNIQUE:** GAS CHROMATOGRAPHY, FID
	ANALYTE: acetic acid
FLOW RATE: 0.01 to 1.0 L/min	**DESORPTION:** 1 mL formic acid; stand 60 min
VOL-MIN: 20 L @ 10 ppm	
-MAX: 300 L	**INJECTION VOLUME:** 5 µL
SHIPMENT: routine	**TEMPERATURE-INJECTION:** 230 °C
	-DETECTOR: 230 °C
	-COLUMN: 130 to 180 °C, 10°/min or 100 °C isothermal
SAMPLE STABILITY: at least 7 days @ 25 °C	**CARRIER GASES:** N₂ or He, 60 mL/min
BLANKS: 2 to 10 field blanks per set	**COLUMN:** 1 m x 4-mm ID glass; Carbopack B 60/80 mesh/3% Carbowax 20M/0.5% H₃PO₄

ACCURACY	
	CALIBRATION: standard solutions of acetic acid in 88 to 95% formic acid
RANGE STUDIED: 12.5 to 50 mg/m³ [1] (173-L samples)	**RANGE:** 0.5 to 10 mg per sample
BIAS: 5.4%	**ESTIMATED LOD:** 0.01 mg per sample [2]
OVERALL PRECISION (Ŝ_rT): 0.058 [1]	
ACCURACY: ± 15.5%	**PRECISION (Ŝ_r):** 0.007 @ 0.3 to 5 mg per sample [1,3]

APPLICABILITY: The working range is 2 to 40 ppm (5 to 100 mg/m³) for a 100-L air sample. High (90% RH) humidity during sampling did not cause breakthrough at 39 mg/m³ for 4.6 hrs [1].

INTERFERENCES: Formic acid contains a small amount of acetic acid which gives a significant blank value. High-purity formic acid must be used to achieve an acceptable detection limit. Alternate columns are 3-m glass, 2-mm ID, 0.3% SP-1000 + 0.3 % H₃PO₄ on Carbopack A and 2.4-m x 2-mm ID glass, 0.3% Carbowax 20M/0.1% H₃PO₄ on Carbopack C.

OTHER METHODS: This revises Method S169 [3].

Figure 16–16. NIOSH Sampling Method 1603 provides for acetic acid sampling. *(Reprinted from NIOSH Manual of Analytical Methods, 1994.)*

ACETIC ACID: METHOD 1603, Issue 2, dated 15 August 1994 - Page 2 of 4

REAGENTS:

1. Formic acid, aqueous 88% to 95%, high-purity (<0.02% acetic acid).*
   NOTE: The acetic acid content varies from lot to lot of formic acid. Test each lot before use.
2. Glacial acetic acid, reagent grade.*
3. Propionic acid, reagent grade.
4. Eluent: Formic acid, 88% to 95%, with 0.1% v/v propionic acid or other suitable internal standard.
5. Nitrogen, purified.
6. Hydrogen, prepurified.
7. Air, filtered.

* See Special Precautions

EQUIPMENT:

1. Sampler: glass tube with plastic caps, 7 cm long, 6-mm OD, 4-mm ID, flame-sealed ends, containing two sections of activated (600 °C) coconut shell charcoal (front = 100 mg; back = 50 mg) separated by a 2-mm urethane foam plug. A silylated glass wool plug precedes the front section and a 3-mm urethane foam plug follows the back section. Pressure drop across the tube at 1 L/min airflow must be less than 3.4 kPa. Tubes are commercially available.
2. Personal sampling pump, 0.01 to 1 L/min, with flexible connecting tubing.
3. Gas chromatograph, flame ionization detector, integrator and column (see page 1603-1).
4. Vials, 2-mL, PTFE-lined caps.
5. Syringes, 10-µL and other convenient sizes for preparing standards, readable to 0.1 µL.
6. Volumetric flasks, 10-mL.

SPECIAL PRECAUTIONS: Care should be taken to avoid skin contact with formic acid and/or acetic acid. These reagents may cause severe burns.

SAMPLING:

1. Calibrate each personal sampling pump with a representative sampler in line.
2. Break the ends of the sampler immediately before sampling. Attach sampler to personal sampling pump with flexible tubing.
3. Sample at an accurately known flow rate between 0.01 and 1 L/min for a total sample size of 20 to 300 L.
4. Cap the samplers and pack securely for shipment.

SAMPLE PREPARATION:

5. Place the front and back sorbent sections of the sampler tube in separate vials. Discard the glass wool and foam plugs.
6. Add 1.0 mL eluent to each vial. Attach crimp cap to each vial.
7. Allow to stand 60 min with occasional agitation.

CALIBRATION AND QUALITY CONTROL:

8. Calibrate daily with at least six working standards over the range 0.01 to 10 mg acetic acid per sample.
   a. Add known amounts of acetic acid to eluent in 10-mL volumetric flasks and dilute to the mark.
   b. Analyze together with samples and blanks (steps 11 and 12).
   c. Prepare calibration graph (ratio of peak area of analyte to peak area of internal standard vs. mg acetic acid).

NIOSH Manual of Analytical Methods (NMAM), Fourth Edition, 8/15/94

Figure 16–16. Continued.

9. Determine desorption efficiency (DE) at least once for each batch of charcoal used for sampling in the calibration range (step 8). Prepare three tubes at each of five levels plus three media blanks.
   a. Remove and discard back sorbent section of a media blank sampler.
   b. Inject a known amount of acetic acid directly onto front sorbent section with a microliter syringe.
   c. Cap the tube. Allow to stand overnight.
   d. Desorb (steps 5 through 7) and analyze together with working standards (steps 11 and 12).
   e. Prepare a graph of DE vs. mg acetic acid recovered.
10. Analyze three quality control blind spikes and three analyst spikes to insure that the calibration graph and DE graph are in control.

MEASUREMENT:

11. Set gas chromatograph according to manufacturer's recommendations and to conditions given on page 1603-1. Inject sample aliquot manually using solvent flush technique or with autosampler.
    NOTE: If peak area is above the linear range of the working standards, dilute with formic acid, reanalyze and apply the appropriate dilution factor in calculations.
12. Measure peak area. Divide the peak area of analyte by the peak area of internal standard on the same chromatogram.

CALCULATIONS:

13. Determine the mass, mg (corrected for DE) of acetic acid found in the sample front (W_f) and back (W_b) sorbent sections, and in the average media blank front (B_f) and back (B_b) sorbent sections.
    NOTE: If $W_b > W_f/10$, report breakthrough and possible sample loss.
14. Calculate concentration, C, of acetic acid in the air volume sampled, V (L):

$$C = \frac{(W_f + W_b - B_f - B_b) \cdot 10^3}{V}, \text{ mg/m}^3.$$

EVALUATION OF METHOD:

Method S169 was issued on May 13, 1977 [3], and validated over the range 12.5 to 50 mg/m^3 at 22 °C and 767 mm Hg using a 173-L sample [1,4]. Overall precision, $\hat{S}_{rT}$, was 0.058 with an average recovery of 105.4%, representing a non-significant bias. The concentration of acetic acid was independently verified by a total hydrogen analyzer. Desorption efficiency was 0.96 in the range 2.1 to 8.4 mg per sample. Breakthrough (5% on back section) was never achieved and testing was discontinued after 4.6 hrs when 10.4 mg of acetic acid was collected without breakthrough for a 269-L sample at 90% RH. A user check gave an estimated LOD of 0.01 mg per sample and a desorption efficiency of 1.01 in the range 0.3 to 5 mg per sample [2].

REFERENCES:

[1]   Backup Data Report for Acetic Acid, prepared under NIOSH Contract No. 210-76-0123, available as "Ten NIOSH Analytical Methods," Order No. PB 275-834 from NTIS, Springfield, VA 22161.
[2]   User check, UBTL, NIOSH Sequence #4213-K (unpublished, January 31, 1984).
[3]   NIOSH Manual of Analytical Methods, 2nd ed., V. 4, S169, U.S. Department of Health, Education, and Welfare, Publ. (NIOSH) 78-175 (1978).

NIOSH Manual of Analytical Methods (NMAM), Fourth Edition, 8/15/94

Figure 16–16. Continued.

---

[4]   NIOSH Research Report-Development and Validation of Methods for Sampling and Analysis of Workplace Toxic Substances, U.S. Department of Health and Human Services, Publ. (NIOSH) 80-133 (1980).

METHOD REVISED BY:

G. David Foley and Y. T. Gagnon, NIOSH/DPSE; S169 originally validated under NIOSH Contract CDC-210-76-0123.

Figure 16–16. Continued.

$$SV = \frac{LOD}{EL \times F} \quad (1)$$

where   SV = Minimum sample volume (L)
     LOD = Lower limit of detection (µg)
       EL = Exposure limit (mg/m³)
        F = Anticipated fraction of TLV in atmosphere (decimal)

The LOD for acetic acid is 0.01 mg (10 µg). If the anticipated concentration is 25 percent of the TLV, then the minimum sample volume is calculated as follows:

$$SV = \frac{10 \ \mu g}{25 \ mg/m^3 \times 0.25}$$
$$= 1.6 \ L \quad (2)$$

Establishing a maximum air sample volume is necessary to prevent breakthrough when sampling for gases and vapors or overloading of the filter when sampling for particles. Breakthrough occurs when a significant quantity of a gas or vapor passes uncollected through a collection device. Breakthrough happens when the device is saturated with the chemical, or there are interfering chemicals, or the airflow rate is too fast. In particle sampling, filter overloading may make the suction pump slow down or quit, or cause loss of some of the loose sample material on the filter as it is being handled in the laboratory, or make the analysis of the filter difficult. The maximum air sample volume is designed to minimize these problems.

Established maximum air sample volumes are designed to handle concentrations up to twice the exposure limit of a single contaminant. If the atmospheric concentration is well above twice the exposure limit or there are other interfering gases and vapors, saturation and breakthrough occur more quickly than anticipated. Maximum air sample volumes in these cases must be adjusted.

The flow rate specified in the air-sampling method ensures that sufficient material is collected for the analysis and that adequate collection efficiency for the chemical being sampled is maintained. For gases and vapors, it means that the analyte will be in contact with the absorbing or adsorbing material long enough to be captured. For particles, as described above, the flow rate determines the sizes of particles collected.

With the recommended flow rate and air sample collection volumes, the industrial hygienist can determine the time necessary to collect a sample. For example, if the recommended flow rate is 0.2 L/min and the minimum sample volume is 10 L, the sample time is at least 50 min. The formula is as follows:

$$\frac{\text{Required sample}}{\text{time (min)}} = \frac{\text{Minimum sample volume (L)}}{\text{Flow rate (L/min)}} \quad (3)$$

$$\text{Required sample time} = \frac{10 \ L}{0.2 \ L/min} = 50 \ min \quad (4)$$

Using the example above, it may be necessary, in this case, to use a series of samples to cover an eight-hour shift.

Laboratories require blanks for each set of samples submitted for analysis. The laboratory specifies the number and type of blanks needed. Two types of blanks may be used: a field blank or a media or lab blank. A field blank is a sample collection device that has been briefly opened and closed and is handled in the field identically to the other samples. The field blank is used to determine whether the air samples have been contaminated during handling. In contrast, a media blank is an unopened collection device used to determine whether the sampling collection tube or filter itself is contaminated. While the laboratory may specify only one or two field blanks, industrial hygienists typically collect field blanks for each day or sampling event, and for each type of sample being collected.

CALIBRATION

The suction pumps used for air sampling must be calibrated to the airflow recommended in the sampling method. Calibration is critical because the determination of air sample volume depends on the flow rate and the elapsed time. There are two categories of calibration devices: primary and secondary. Primary devices provide a direct measurement of airflow. Secondary calibration devices provide indirect measurements of airflow and must be periodically calibrated with a primary calibration device.

Primary Calibration: Soap-Bubble Burette

One primary calibration instrument is the soap-bubble burette. This is an inexpensive alternative to other primary standards. While it is seldom used anymore, it's included here because it helps in visualizing the calibration process. It consists of an inverted volumetric burette connected to the sampling train. The sampling train must contain the type of collection device that will be used to conduct air sampling because each device causes a unique pressure drop. The pressure drop will affect the sampling pump's flow rate and must be accounted for during the calibration.

The general procedure for soap-bubble burette calibration is as follows:

1. Set up the apparatus as shown in Figure 16–17. Wet the inside of the burette with the soap solution or water before setup.
2. Allow the sampling pump to run for five minutes. Check the sampling pump's battery. If the battery is low, recharge the pump. Check the manufacturer's instructions for proper battery testing and recharging procedures.

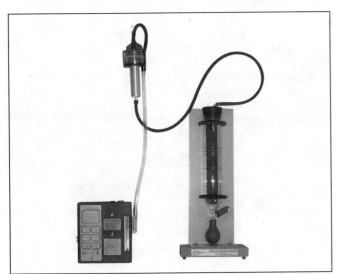

Figure 16–17. Calibration setup for personal sampling pump with filter cassette. *(Printed with permission of SKC Inc.)*

3. Connect the sampling train to the burette.
4. To create a bubble, momentarily submerge the opening of the burette and then draw two or three bubbles up the length of the burette.
5. Adjust the pump to the nominal desired flow rate.
6. Create a soap bubble and, using a stopwatch, measure the time it takes to traverse a convenient calibration volume. For high-volume pumps, a 1,000-mL burette is used and the bubble is timed as it travels from 0 to the 1,000-mL mark. For low-flow pumps, a 100-mL burette is used.
7. Calculate the flow rate. The flow rate is determined by measuring the time required for the bubble to pass between two scale markings. For example, if 30 seconds were required for the bubble to go from the 0-mL to the 1,000 mL mark, then the flow rate is calculated as follows:

$$\frac{1,000 \text{ mL}}{30 \text{ s}} \times \frac{60 \text{ s}}{1 \text{ min}} = 2,000 \text{ mL/min or 2 L/min} \qquad (5)$$

8. If a different flow rate is desired, adjust the pump and repeat the procedure.
9. Repeat the determination at least twice. Calculate the average flow rate.
10. Record the following:
   - volumes measured
   - elapsed times
   - air temperature
   - atmospheric pressure
   - make, model, and serial number of the sampling pump
   - collection device used
   - name and date of person performing calibration

Primary Calibration: Electronic Instruments

Electronic primary calibrators work by drawing air through a fixed-volume cylinder and measuring the time it takes for the air to move through it (Figure 16–18). A *wet* process uses a soap bubble and times the speed of the bubble moving from the bottom to the top of the cylinder. A *dry* process uses a float that fills the diameter of the cylinder, and the instrument times the speed of the float from the bottom to the top of the cylinder. Another type of electronic primary calibrator is a *mass flow* sensor that measures the mass of air per time passing through the calibrator. These types of methods allow calibration in less time and with greater accuracy than the traditional burette method. The accuracy of electronic primary calibrators needs to be recertified as recommended by the manufacturer in order to ensure the integrity of the calibration process, as this affects the accuracy of the whole sampling process.

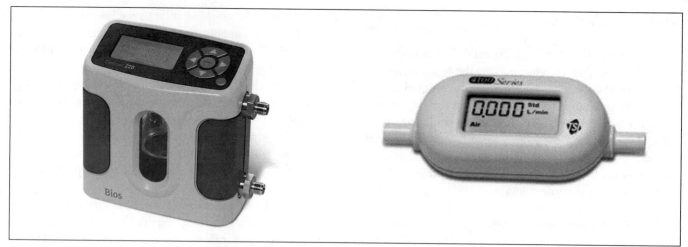

Figure 16–18. Electronic airflow calibrators: dry cylinder (left) and mass flow (right). *(Bios Definer® 220, dry cylinder calibrator, printed with permission of Bio International Corp.; Mass flow calibrator used courtesy of TSI.)*

Secondary Calibration: Precision Rotameter

A rotameter consists of a float, or ball, that is free to move in a vertically tapered tube (Figure 16–19). Air is pulled through the tube so that the ball rises until there is equilibrium between the force of gravity and the force of the air traveling upward. The flow rate is determined by reading the height of the float on an attached numerical scale. Rotameters are frequently used in the field to check pump flow rate periodically during full-shift sampling.

The rotameter's numerical scale has no meaning until it has been calibrated against a primary calibration device. A soap-bubble burette or other primary standard is used as the primary calibration device. First, an air-sampling pump is calibrated with the soap-bubble burette. Then a rotameter is attached to the sampling train (Figure 16–20) to determine what scale marking relates to this flow rate. This is done several times so that a graph (see Figure 16–21 or chart of measured flow rate versus rotameter scale reading can be made. For rotameters used on a regular basis, this process should be repeated monthly. Position the rotameter so that the ball is at eye level, and read the scale at the center of the ball.

Rotameters that are part of an air-sampling pump are not precision rotameters and should not be used for calibration purposes. They provide only an approximate indication of the airflow rate.

Calibration Parameters
Temperature and Pressure

Air volume is directly affected by temperature and pressure. If the conditions during air sampling are significantly different from those during calibration, then a correction

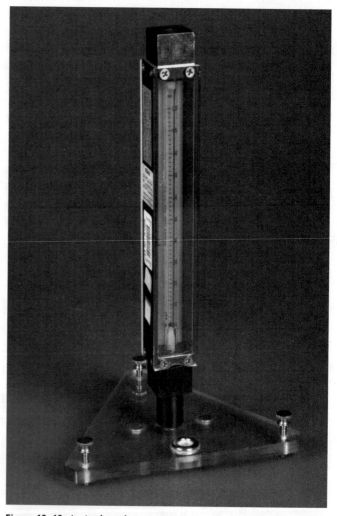

Figure 16–19. A single-column precision rotameter can be used as a secondary calibration device. *(Courtesy Fermilab Visual Media Services Dept.)*

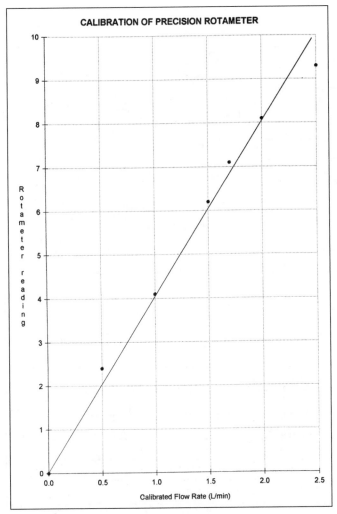

Figure 16–20. A calibration chart is needed when using a precision rotameter. The chart relates the rotameter's scale to a specific flow rate.

factor must be used when calculating the sample air volume (the field volume). This can be done using the following expression:

$$V_{field} = V_{calibration} \times \frac{T_{field}}{T_{calibration}} \times \frac{P_{calibration}}{P_{field}} \quad (6)$$

where

V_{field} = air sample volume in liters obtained during sampling period

$V_{calibration}$ = air sample volume in liters obtained by multiplying the calibrated airflow rate by the elapsed sampling time

T_{field} = absolute temperature during sampling in degrees Kelvin or Rankine

$T_{calibration}$ = temperature during calibration in degrees Kelvin or Rankine

$P_{calibration}$ = atmospheric pressure during calibration in mmHg or inches of water

P_{field} = atmospheric pressure during sampling in mmHg or inches of water

Note that some electronic calibrators automatically provide for temperature and pressure compensation and the sample volume will not need to be adjusted using Equation 6.

Calibration Error

The accuracy of calibration depends on the measuring limits of the equipment used. Each measuring instrument has a margin of error. This information can be obtained from the manufacturer.

Soap-bubble burette calibration, for example, uses a volumetric burette and a stopwatch. The burette may be accurate to within ±5 mL (or 5 percent); when the 1,000-mL mark is read, the true volume could be anywhere between 1,005 and 995 mL. Stopwatches have a similar margin of error.

The margin of error associated with the calibration of airflow rate can be calculated using the error of measurement from each piece of equipment used in the calibration, using the following equation:

$$\text{Error} = [(\text{instrument error})^2 + (\text{instrument error})^2]^{1/2} \quad (7)$$

For the soap-bubble burette, for example, if the accuracy of the burette is 0.5 percent and the accuracy of the stopwatch is 0.5 percent, then the total margin of error is 0.7 percent. A calibrated flow rate of 2 L/min is more accurately reported as 2 L/min ±0.7 percent.

SAMPLING AND ANALYTICAL ERROR

Once the air sample results are received from the analytical laboratory and the time-weighted averages are calculated, there should be a calculated margin of error associated with the results. This is called the sampling and analytical error (SAE), and can be calculated using the following formula:

$$\begin{aligned} \text{SAE} = [(\text{airflow error})^2 + (\text{time error})^2 \\ + (\text{analytical error})^2]^{1/2} \quad (8) \end{aligned}$$

The airflow error is the error of measurement associated with the calibration of the air-sampling pump. The time error is associated with the instrument used to measure the time period over which the sample was collected. The analytical error is the error associated with the analytical methods used by the laboratory.

Air Sampling Worksheet

U. S. Department of Labor
Occupational Safety and Health Administration

1. Reporting ID 5555555	2. Inspection Number 123456789	3. Sampling Number: 497330105	
4. Establishment Name J & N Casting		5. Sampling Date: 06–14–07	6. Shipping Date: 06–15–07
7. Person Performing Sampling (Signature) Signature		8. Print Last Name RIMA	9. CSHO ID Z1234

10. Employee (Name, Address, Telephone Number): (123) 456–7899	14. Exposure Information	a. Number: 2	b. Duration: 3.5 Yrs/ea person
B.J. Albrecht, 850 Lego Road Pixar City, CA 99999	c. Frequency: 6 hr./day		
	15. Weather Conditions: Indoors	16. Photo(s): Y	

11. Job Title: Brass Squeeze Molder Machine Operator – 12 years	12. Occupation Code

13. PPE (Type and effectiveness): Safety glasses and ear plugs, no respirator worn	17. Pump Checks and Adjustment: 7:30 – ok, 8:30 – ok, 9:30 – ok, 10:30 – ok, 11:30 – ok, 12:30 – ok, 1:30 – ok, 2:30 – ok

18. Job Description, Operation, Work Location(s), Ventilation, and Controls

Operates brass squeeze molding machine. Fills and compacts sand into mold. Finished molds placed on pouring lines. There are fans but no exhaust ventilation.

Cont'd

19. Pump Number: 10337   **Sampling Data**

20. Lab Sample Number					
21. Sample Submission Number	ER300				
22. Sample Type	P				
23. Sample Media	MCEF				
24. Filter/Tube Number	ER300				
25. Time On/Off	6:30am	1:00pm			
	12:30pm	2:48pm			
26. Total Time (in minutes)	360	108			
27. Flow Rate ☒ l/min ☐ cc/min	2.13	2.13			
28. Volume (in liters)	766.8	230	= 996.8 Total volume		
29. Net Sample Weight (in mg)					

30. Analyze Samples for:	31. Indicate Which Samples to Induce In TWA, Ceiling, etc. Calculations				
Welding Fume (Lead & Cadmium)	T				

32. Interferences and IH Comments to Lab	33. Supporting Samples	34. Chain of Custody	Initials	Date
	a. Blanks: ER302	a. Seals Intact?	Y N	
		b. Rec'd in Lab		
	b. Bulks	c. Rec'd by Anal.		
		d. Anal. Completed		
		e. Calc. Checked		
		f. Supr. OK'd		

Case File Page ___ of ___

OSHA-91A (Rev. 1/84)

Figure 16–21. Air-sampling worksheet used by OSHA to record all pertinent information related to the collection of an air sample.

Pre-Sampling Calibration Records

P r e	**35.** Pump Mfg. & SN Gilian 10337 **36.** Voltage Checked? ☐ Yes ☐ No **37.** Location/T & Alt. I.H. Lab – Area Office	**38.** Flow Rate Calculations: 2128 2132 2129

39. Flow Rate: 2.13	**40.** Method ☒ Bubble ☐ PR	**41.** Initials: JR	**42.** Date/Time: 06/14/07 – 5:30am

Post-Sampling Calibration Records

P o s t	**43.** Location/T & Alt. I.H. Lab – Area Office	**44.** Flow Rate Calculations: 2129 2131 2133

45. Flow Rate: 2.13	**46.** Initials: JR	**47.** Date/Time: 06/14/07 – 3:35pm

Sample Weight Calculations

48. Filter No.					
49. Final Weight *(mg)*					
50. Initial Weight *(mg)*					
51. Weight Gained *(mg)*					
52. Blank Adjustment					
53. Net Sample Weight *(mg)*					

54. Calculations and Notes:

_____

_____

_____

_____

_____

_____

_____

_____

_____

_____

_____

_____

_____

_____

_____

_____

_____

_____

_____

_____

_____

_____

_____

_____

_____

RECORD KEEPING

Complete and detailed records must be kept on sampling procedures, sampling conditions, and sample results. The hygienist must document that sampling was conducted according to accepted professional standards. Records should include the identity of the equipment and collection devices used, the calibration procedures and results, the identity of the analytical laboratory and related laboratory reports, and the air-sampling calculations.

The conditions under which the sampling was conducted should also be carefully documented to ensure the integrity and usefulness of the results. Anything that might help interpret or explain the final air sample result should be recorded. For example, in a production welding operation, the record should contain the name and location of the welder, the material being welded, the types of welding rods used, the number of pieces welded, the use of personal protective equipment, and the use and location of local exhaust ventilation. An important goal of good documentation is to provide enough information so that someone else can repeat the sample using the same method and under similar work conditions.

Many industrial hygiene programs have developed air-sampling forms to ensure that all the necessary information is collected. OSHA has developed an air-sampling worksheet (Figure 16–21) for its Industrial Hygiene Compliance Officers.

OSHA Standard 29 CFR 1910.20, Access to Employee Exposure and Medical Records

This standard requires that employee exposure records be preserved for at least 30 years. This information must be readily available to employees and their representative(s). Background data such as laboratory reports and field notes need only be retained for one year as long as information on the sampling method, the analytical and mathematical methods, and summary of other background information is retained for the required 30 years. However, it is good practice to retain all sampling-related records.

PREPARING AND SHIPPING SAMPLES TO LABORATORY

Proper packaging and shipping are necessary to ensure sample integrity. Carefully package samples to prevent jostling and breakage. Do not ship air samples and bulk samples in the same package. Timely shipping is also important, as samples can degrade quickly and the analytical results will not accurately reflect exposures. Some samples may need to be kept cold to prevent deterioration.

Bulk Samples

Bulk samples may be needed for metalworking fluids and some solvent analyses. Bulk samples need to be packaged and sent separately from the other samples. Bulk sample shipping may be subject to U.S. Department of Transportation regulations for hazardous materials or International Air Transport Association regulations. There are significant regulatory penalties for persons who improperly package and offer to ship hazardous materials. Contact the shipping company and the laboratory for guidance.

Media and Sample Stability

Sampling media will degrade over time. It's important to promptly ship samples to the laboratory for analysis. Samples can degrade over short periods of time. For example, the OSHA Hexavalent Chromium Method ID-215 states that welding fume samples need to be shipped overnight and analyzed within eight days of sampling to avoid significant sample loss.

SUMMARY

Evaluating and controlling employee exposure to airborne occupational health hazards usually includes a comparison of the measured concentration of an airborne chemical to a recognized exposure limit. The various methods, instruments, and devices used for such air sampling have been described in this chapter.

BIBLIOGRAPHY

American Conference of Governmental Industrial Hygienists. *Air Monitoring for Toxic Exposures,* 2nd ed., HJ McDermott, ed. Cincinnati, OH: ACGIH, 2004.

American Conference of Governmental Industrial Hygienists. *Modern Industrial Hygiene,* Vol 1-3, JL Perkins, ed. Cincinnati, OH: ACGIH, 2012.

American Conference of Governmental Industrial Hygienists. *An Overview of Air Sampling Methodologies: Instrumentation and Analytical Techniques for Evaluation of Atmospheric Contaminants.* A Monograph of the ACGIH® Air Sampling Instruments Committee, Publication #ASI22, Cincinnati, OH: ACGIH, 2009.

American Conference of Governmental Industrial Hygienists. *2012 Threshold Limit Values® for Chemical Substances and Physical Agents and Biological Exposure Indices.* Cincinnati, OH: ACGIH, 2012.

American Industrial Hygiene Association. *Burton*

Field Guide for Industrial Hygiene, DJ Burton, ed. Falls Church, VA: AIHA, 2002.

American Industrial Hygiene Association. *The Occupational Environment: Its Evaluation, Control, and Management,* 3rd ed. (Vol. 1 & 2), DH Anna, ed. Falls Church, VA: AIHA, 2011.

American Industrial Hygiene Association. *A Strategy for Assessing and Managing Occupational Exposures,* 3rd ed., JS Ignacio, WH Bullock, eds. Falls Church, VA: AIHA, 2006.

National Institute for Occupational Safety and Health. *NIOSH Manual of Analytical Methods,* 4th ed. DHHS (NIOSH) Publication No. 94-113, NMAM First Supplement: DHHS (NIOSH) Publication No. 96-135, NMAM Second Supplement: DHHS (NIOSH) Publication No. 98-119, NMAM Third Supplement: DHHS (NIOSH) Publication No. 2003-154. Atlanta: NIOSH, 1994.

Occupational Safety and Health Administration. OSHA Instruction TED 01-00-015 [TED 1-0.15A], Section II: Sampling, Measurement Methods and Instruments, from *OSHA Technical Manual.* Washington, DC: OSHA, 2008.

Rose VE, Cohrssen B, eds. *Patty's Industrial Hygiene,* 6th ed. Hoboken, NJ: Wiley, 2010.

U.S. Army Public Health Command. *Industrial Hygiene Sampling Guide: Technical Guide 141.* Aberdeen Proving Ground, MD: U.S. Army Medical Dept., 2010. http://phc.amedd.army.mil/topics/workplacehealth/ih/Pages/IHTechnicalGuides.aspx

U.S. Navy and Marine Corps Public Health Center. *Industrial Hygiene Field Operations Manual.* Portsmouth, VA: U.S Navy, 2012. http://www.nmcphc.med.navy.mil/occupational_health/industrial_hygiene/ih_fieldops_manual.aspx

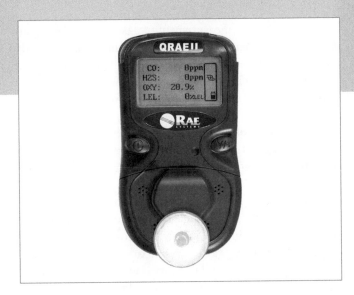

CHAPTER 17

Direct-Reading Instruments for Gases, Vapors, and Particulates

by Philip A. Smith, PhD, CIH
Marc Roe, MS, CIH
Michael Andrew, MS, CIH, CSP
and Ben Kollmeyer, MPH, CIH

Direct-reading instruments for chemical contaminants identify and/or quantify the concentration of many gases, vapors, and particulates in air—in real-time or near real-time. Instruments are designed to give their users information, which when used in the appropriate context is actionable. An appropriately selected direct-reading instrument may be used to quickly establish a safe zone around a chemical spill, and direct-reading instruments are often used to assess the exposure of workers to hazardous chemicals. Understanding an instrument's capabilities and, more importantly, its limitations allows the user to better protect worker and public health. This chapter is designed to give an overview of the various types of commonly encountered instruments, frequently utilized sensing technologies, and associated considerations for their use. The intersection of these issues and how they impact use of a given instrument is covered by example in the discussion of combustible gas monitors early in this chapter. While an effort is made to provide broad coverage to relevant issues, it must be stressed that more instrument-specific knowledge, and in some instances training, is recommended prior to using a given device, especially for important measurements where health and safety risks are present.

INTRODUCTION

While direct-reading instruments are promoted in the marketplace for the detection of specific compounds or for specific applications, their capabilities are ultimately defined by the sensing technologies they incorporate. Field detection instrument sensing technologies can range in complexity

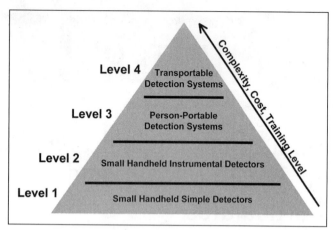

Figure 17–1. A hierarchical approach to categorizing real-time instruments. *(Used with permission of AIHA Press. Copyright 2012.)*

from something as simple as pH paper to complex cart-mounted laboratory systems, such as a gas chromatography–mass spectrometey (GC-MS). Direct-reading instruments can be arranged in a hierarchy with level one instruments at the bottom and level four instruments at the top (Figure 17–1). Generally, ascending the hierarchy brings about increased complexity, cost, training requirements, and decreased portability, but may have the benefit of increased accuracy. Level one instruments include pH paper, colorimetric detector tubes, and even some simple electrochemical sensors. Level two instruments are small electronic handheld devices, which can include most electrochemical sensors, photoionization detectors, and particle detectors. Level three instruments include traditional laboratory technologies that have been miniaturized to be person-portable, such as the Thermo Scientific MIRAN SapphIRe. Level four instruments are traditional laboratory systems that have been made portable, such as a van-mounted GC-MS instrument, or a cart-mounted fourier transform infrared (FTIR) spectrometer.

Proper operation of direct-reading instruments used in hazard evaluation is essential to ensure that the information obtained is accurate enough to provide a useful interpretation. Faulty operation of air-sampling instruments can result in either high or low readings. Low readings could falsely indicate that no hazard is present when dangerous conditions might exist; conversely, high instrument readings could lead to the implementation of unnecessary control measures. It is therefore important to recognize that an understanding of the underlying sensing technologies is crucial for selecting the right instrument and using its data in a contextually appropriate manner.

COMMON TYPES OF INSTRUMENTS

As discussed above, a broad range of sensing technologies

is available for the measurement of gases, vapors, and particulates. In the marketplace, these instruments are variously designed, packaged, and promoted for different applications and end users. This section discusses some of the more common types of instruments found in the marketplace.

General Instrument Types
One way to generally categorize direct-reading instruments is by their capability in measuring one or more compounds as follows:

- *Compound-Specific Monitors.* These are devices that are designed to measure a single compound. Some of the most common types include instruments for measuring hydrogen sulfide (H_2S), carbon monoxide (CO), chlorine gas (Cl_2), oxygen (O_2), and mercury (Hg), although technologies are available for specifically measuring a broad range of compounds. These types of monitors commonly rely upon colorimetric and electrochemical sensing technologies. Although designed to be compound-specific, cross-sensitivities can still exist and users should be cognizant of the limits of a particular device.

- *Nonspecific Monitors.* These devices are not compound-specific nor are they specific for whole classes of compounds, although they may provide a limited degree of selectivity. These are generally of value as leak detectors or in atmospheres that are already known to contain only a single contaminant, as many similar compounds can interfere with readings. Nonspecific instruments used for detection of airborne contaminants include devices that contain catalytic combustible gas sensors, flame ionization, photoionization, and thermal conductivity detectors.

- *Broad-Range Monitors.* These devices are designed to differentiate and specifically measure a broad range of compounds. While they incorporate the most complex and costly sensing technologies, they are also the most powerful in identifying multiple or unknown contaminants. Such devices typically incorporate gas chromatography, or spectrochemical detectors such as a mass spectrometer.

Combustible Gas/Multiple Gas Monitors
Perhaps the most commonly utilized direct reading instrument is a multi-gas or 4-gas monitor. These devices are typically designed for use in confined space entry, containing sensors for combustible gas (LEL), oxygen (O_2), carbon monoxide (CO), and hydrogen sulfide (H_2S). Some manufacturers are combining this typical sensor package along with additional technologies for measuring volatile organic compounds such as a photoionization detector (PID).

Because of their intended application for confined-space entry by field personnel, these devices have evolved to be small, lightweight, and durable with minimal user interface.

They are frequently equipped with visible and audible warning systems when levels of any monitored contaminants reach preset limits. These preset limits may be adjustable (Figure 17–2). However, this simplicity of use also can have the unintended consequence of end users not taking the time to understand the limitations and maintenance requirements of such devices. As a result, additional care should be taken to ensure appropriate device-specific training for all end users.

Specific information regarding the detection methods for O_2, CO, and H_2S is provided in the sensing technologies section below. Because of the potentially life-threatening nature of combustible gases and the widespread use of such detectors, a detailed discussion of this application follows. This discussion incorporates by example many of the considerations users of direct-reading instruments must account for to ensure they are properly utilized.

Explosive (Flammable) Limits

When certain proportions of combustible vapor are mixed with air and a source of ignition is present, a fire or explosion can occur. The range of concentrations over which fire or explosion can occur is called the explosive (or flammable) range. The low end of this range is called the lower explosive (or flammable) limit (LEL), and the high end is called the upper explosive (or flammable) limit (UEL). The explosive range and the lower and upper explosive limits are expressed as volume percents. On the simplest type of combustible gas instrument, only sensitivity for the LEL is provided, usually with readings from 0 to 100 percent of the LEL. Different models of combustible gas meters are supplied with meters that range from 5 percent of the LEL to 100 percent by volume of the combustible gas. While the LEL is typically the most relevant parameter to monitor from a health and safety standpoint, the UEL is also relevant. In an atmosphere that is above the UEL, dilution with fresh air could bring the mixture into the flammable or explosive range, so any atmosphere with a flammable or explosive gas near or above the UEL should be considered a significant explosion hazard as well.

Instrument Design

Combustible gas monitors are based on three different types of detectors. They are the catalytic combustible gas sensor, the metal oxide semiconductor (MOS) detector, and the thermal conductivity detector. These are described in more detail in the sensing technologies section.

Because the heat of combustion, the adsorptive properties of a combustible gas on the surface of an MOS, and thermal conductivity are all compound dependent, instrument response for all these instruments is compound dependent. Similarly, the lower explosive limits of combustible gases are also compound dependent. Thus, a combustible gas meter is typically calibrated with a particular compound (often pentane or hexane) such that the concentration of other combustible gases present would be overestimated by an instrument calibrated with methane. Instrument manufacturers often provide calibration curves or tables for a variety of different combustibles for use in correlating meter readings to the concentration of nonmethane gases and vapors. Figure 17–3 is an example of such a table.

All combustible gas meters that rely on a heated wire or filament—an ignition source—have a flashback arrestor that prevents the combustion in the detector from spreading to the atmosphere outside the instrument. This means that the sensor component is generally intrinsically safe (that is, it can be operated safely in flammable or explosive atmospheres). However, the intrinsic safety designation for the entire instrument needs to include (among other things) the electronics, the display, and the power source. For example, some intrinsically safe devices are rated as such when operating on battery, but not while plugged-in. The manufacturer's instructions for operating a combustible gas meter should be carefully reviewed before the device is used. In general, combustible gas meters require a brief initial warm-up period so that the batteries can heat any components that operate at an elevated temperature.

Air is most commonly drawn through the sampling

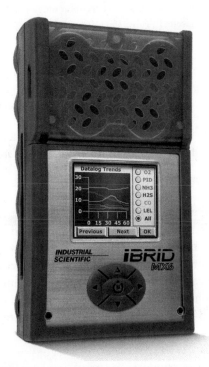

Figure 17–2. A multigas monitor that has an adjustable set point and audible and visible alarms. *(Photo courtesy of Industrial Scientific Corp.)*

CALIBRATION GAS

GAS BEING SAMPLED	Acetone	Butane	Hexane	Hydrogen	Methane	Propane
Benzene	1.1	1.1	0.7	1.9	1.9	1.2
Methane	0.6	0.6	0.4	1.0	1.0	0.6
Methanol	0.6	0.6	0.5	1.1	1.1	0.7
Ethylene	0.8	0.8	0.6	1.4	1.3	0.9
Toluene	1.3	1.2	0.9	2.1	2.1	1.3
Acetone	1.0	1.0	0.7	1.7	1.7	1.1

Example: The instrument has been calibrated on methane and is now reading 10% LEL in a toluene atmosphere. To find the actual percent LEL, multiply by the number found at the intersection of the methane column (calibration gas) and the toluene row (gas being sampled)—in this case, 2.1. Therefore, the actual percent LEL is 21% (10% x 2.1).

Multiplier accuracy is ±25%, subject to change without notice, pending additional testing.

If the sensor is used in atmospheres containing unknown contaminants (silicone, sulfur, lead, or halogen compound vapors) methane is the recommended calibration gas. Periodic comparison of methane and pentane readings is recommended when using this chart. Contact Industrial Scientific for details.

Figure 17–3. A table of correction factors for the catalytic combustion sensor, based on the gas used for calibration. *(Based on a table courtesy of Industrial Scientific Corp.)*

probe and into the detector by means of a small sampling pump. In some cases, air diffuses into the instrument without being actively drawn in. In most work areas, the concentration of combustible gas or vapor fluctuates constantly and so it is necessary to observe the instrument carefully to determine average and peak readings. Some instruments have built-in data-logging features that can store and recall integrated average and peak measurements.

Zero Adjustment
The zero adjustment must be made by taking the instrument to a location that does not contain combustible gases or by passing air into the instrument through an activated carbon filter that removes all combustible vapors and gases (except methane). Because methane is not removed by activated charcoal filters, extra caution is required during zeroing if the presence of methane is suspected. In addition, the charcoal filter should be changed periodically because it becomes inactivated by moisture or hydrocarbon saturation.

Interpretations of Meter Readings
As with all instruments, users of combustible gas meters must be aware of interfering gases and vapors that could create discrepancies in instrument response. All instru-

ments are subject, to some extent, to interferences from noncombustible and nonexplosive gases. For example, the presence of argon, which has a lower thermal conductivity than air, could create a false positive reading in combustion and thermal conductivity detectors. As a precaution, the least-sensitive LEL scale (generally 0–100 percent of the LEL) should be used first to determine whether an explosive atmosphere exists and to prevent overloading of a more sensitive (0–10 percent of LEL) scale. The typical meter responses to methane gas are shown in Figure 17–4 at the LEL, in the explosive range, and above the UEL.

If the indicator of the meter moves above the UEL and remains there, an explosive concentration of gas or vapor is present. However, if the meter climbs rapidly and then falls back to zero, there is either a concentration above the UEL or a gas mixture that lacks sufficient oxygen to support combustion. The instrument may read zero for several different reasons. Assuming that the instrument is functioning properly, the absence of an instrument response can mean that there is little or no combustible gas in the space being tested or that the concentration is significantly above the UEL and combustion cannot occur because of insufficient oxygen.

Great care must be exercised to ensure that a reading above the UEL is not misinterpreted as a true zero reading. Figure 17–5 is a reminder of the importance of proper interpretation of the instrument readings, in this case in the evaluation of the atmosphere in a confined space. A very high concentration of combustible gas can be identified by carefully watching the readout as the probe is moved into and withdrawn from the space being tested. At some point during entry and withdrawal, the instrument will exceed the LEL if a level above the LEL is actually present. These instruments should not be used to measure the concentration of combustible gases in steam or inert atmospheres because of the measurement uncertainties or interferences in nonair atmospheres.

High-Flash Point Solvents

Although it is relatively easy to operate a combustible gas indicator to detect a flammable gas or vapor, these instruments have some limitations. They respond only to combustible vapors drawn into the detector cell. If the vapor pressure of a combustible liquid is relatively low at room temperature, a relatively low concentration will be indicated. If a closed vessel holding a liquid contaminant is later heated (by welding or cutting, for example) the vapor concentrations will increase and the concentration of the substance in the atmosphere of the container may increase and become explosive. Continuous monitoring may be recommended in this situation. When testing the atmosphere in drying ovens, or other places where the temperature is unusually high, there may be some difficulty in measuring solvents with relatively high boiling points (e.g., napthas). This is because the vapors of such compounds may condense in the sampling line, thus giving a false indication of safety. In some instances, condensation can be prevented by heating the sampling line and the instrument to a tem-

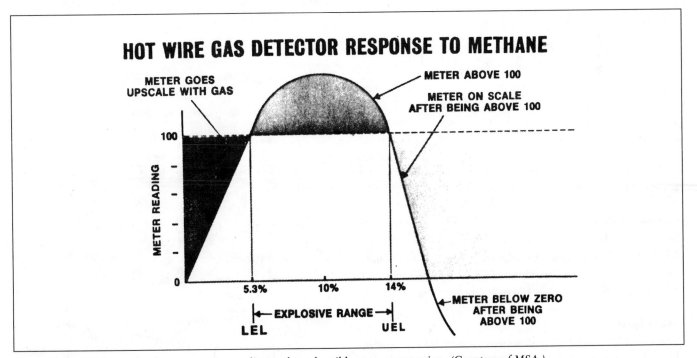

Figure 17–4. The relationship between meter reading and combustible gas concentration. *(Courtesy of MSA.)*

the indications of their presence. Instrument manufacturers' instructions should be followed carefully because high concentrations of chlorinated hydrocarbons (such as trichloroethylene) or acid gases (such as sulfur dioxide) may cause depressed meter readings in combustion-type meters when high concentrations of combustibles are, in fact, present. Trace amounts of these interferences may not affect the readings directly but can corrode the detector elements. High-molecular-weight alcohols in the atmosphere may burn out the filaments, rendering the instrument inoperative. When such limitations are understood, the user can obtain reliable and accurate results.

Indoor Air Quality Monitors

Industrial hygienists are frequently called upon to assess indoor air quality (IAQ) concerns, and instruments have been tailored for this purpose. Typical IAQ monitors incorporate sensors to measure temperature and relative humidity (both discussed in Chapter 21 of this book), as well as carbon dioxide (CO_2). Many devices will have options for including sensors for additional gases of relevance in IAQ investigations, most commonly CO. These sensing technologies are commonly packaged in handheld devices that can be easily placed in various locations around a workplace for long-term data logging (Figure 17–6).

Particle Counters

Rather than measuring for specific chemical compounds, several types of direct-reading monitors are used to measure airborne particulate concentrations. More precisely, these

Figure 17–5. A worker monitors the atmosphere of a confined space prior to entry. *(Photo courtesy of MSA.)*

perature equal to, or above that, of the space to be tested.

Several types of combustible gas monitors have been designed to be calibrated so that specific combustibles can be measured. One variation of the instrument has adjustable calibration controls and can measure five different gases or vapors in the 0–100 percent LEL range for each. Another type has a dual-scale multiple-calibration curve in the 0–10 percent and 0–100 percent range of the LEL.

Catalyst Poisoning

Because minute concentrations of silicone vapors—even 1 or 2 ppm—can rapidly poison the catalytic activity of the platinum filament, a hot-wire combustible gas indicator should not be used in areas where silicone vapors are present.

Interferences

Interfering gases and vapors can seriously affect instrument response, therefore it is important that the user recognize

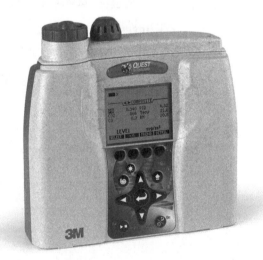

Figure 17–6. An indoor environmental monitor that simultaneously measure particulates (mass concentration), volatile organic compounds (VOCs), toxic gas, carbon dioxide (CO_2), relative humidity, temperature, and air velocity. *(Photo courtesy of 3M Co.)*

devices are generally aerosol monitors in which the aerosol is a solid (dust), liquid (mist), or condensed vapor from a high-temperature process such as combustion or welding (fume).

Most of these devices are based on the light-scattering properties of particulate matter, and are sensitive to the size, shape, and refractive index of the particles (Figure 17–7). The light source could be monochromatic or polychromatic, using either visible or infrared radiation, and the scattered light detector could be a photomultiplier tube, photodiode, or infrared detector. Most instruments have a pump that draws a sample into the sensing volume, but there are some in which convection is relied on to do that. The instrument must be calibrated with particulates of a size and refractive index similar to those to be measured in the ambient air. If this is not done, the results indicated on the instrument could easily be off by an order of magnitude or more.

Another type of particulate monitoring device relies on the behavior of a piezoelectric crystal. The frequency of the crystal's oscillations is changed by the amount of particulate matter deposited on it when it carries an electrostatic charge. After the sampling period is complete, the concentration of dust is displayed and the crystal is automatically cleaned and ready for the next cycle. The instrument measures particles ranging in size from 0.01 to 3.5 μm. An inertial impactor in the device eliminates particles of larger size.

Other devices use condensation-nuclei counting technology. This type of particulate monitor is highly sensitive and is used as a direct-reading instrument for the evaluation of fit factors in air-purifying respirators (Figure 17–8). This device is based on the ability of small concentrations of dust particles to serve as condensation nuclei, that is, solid centers on which supersaturated vapors can condense to form droplets. If particulate matter is drawn into a vapor that is supersaturated with ethanol, these condensation nuclei will form and can be detected through light-scattering measurements. The technique is very sensitive, and thus ambient concentrations of dust, and their reduction on the inside of a respirator worn by a test subject, can serve as a measure of the fit factor of the respirator. This particulate measurement technology has proven to be very useful in doing quantitative fit testing of respirators rather than using the older technology of generating a much higher concentration of aerosol particles in a test chamber and putting the subject to be fit-tested in that chamber.

Formaldehyde Vapor Monitors

There have been a number of instruments developed over the past 20 years that are designed to be specific for formaldehyde, most specify the capability to measure low concentrations at the current Threshold Limit Value (TLV®) ceiling level of 0.3 ppm (v/v). One instrument that claims to measure down to 0.01 ppm of formaldehyde over a five-minute sampling period is based on the principle of fluorescence. In a fluorescence method, the intensity of electromagnetic radiation emitted from the molecules of interest after they have been excited with monochromatic light is measured. This intensity is related to the concentration of the molecules present and allows near real-time measurements to be done.

Mercury Monitors

Portable, battery-operated ultraviolet analyzers are available for mercury vapor. The section on ultraviolet spectrophotometers has more information on the principles of operation of such devices. In this instrument, the wavelengths of ultraviolet light emitted from a mercury vapor lamp are

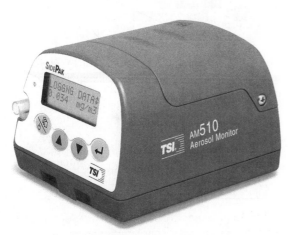

Figure 17–7. A direct-reading aerosol monitor using near-infrared light scattering to detect particles. *(Photo courtesy of TSI Inc.)*

Figure 17–8. A particle counting device using condensation nuclei counting technology for the evaluation of fit factors in respirators. *(Photo courtesy of TSI Inc.)*

Figure 17–9. An instrument for monitoring mercury vapor based on the conductivity of a gold foil. *(Photo courtesy of Arizona Instrument Corp.)*

absorbed by mercury vapor in the ambient air drawn into the instrument. In a dual-beam instrument, the ratio of the intensity of this absorption to that in a reference cell is translated electronically into a concentration of mercury vapor in the air. The specificity of absorption enables the instrument to detect well below 0.05 mg/m³.

Another type of mercury-specific direct-reading instrument (Figure 17–9) relies on the change in electrical conductivity of a gold foil when it comes into contact with mercury vapor to form an amalgam (a solid solution of another metal in mercury). Air containing mercury vapor is drawn into the cell and amalgamates the gold. The conductivity of the amalgam is different from that of the pure gold, and the change in conductivity is related to the concentration of mercury in the air sampled during the fixed sampling periods of 1 or 10 seconds. Periodically, after the conductivity changes are significant, the gold foil is heated by an external power source and the amalgam is destroyed as the mercury vapor is driven off by the high temperature. The foil, thus renewed, is ready for a new series of measurements.

SENSING TECHNOLOGIES

As the previous section illustrates, direct-reading instruments for gases, vapors, and particulates are promoted in the marketplace in a variety of ways, be it the detection of a specific compound, a broad range of compounds, or for specific applications. Regardless of how they are packaged and marketed, their capabilities and limitations in measuring the levels of a given contaminant in the environment are ultimately defined by the sensing technologies they incorporate.

It is therefore critical that users have an understanding of the underlying sensing technologies these instruments utilize in order to select the right instrument and to use the data obtained in a contextually appropriate manner.

Catalytic Combustible Gas Sensor

In the catalytic combustible gas detector, heat is released when a combustible gas or vapor, in contact with the detector, is burned (oxidized). In simple versions of these monitors, the detector element is a heated coil of platinum wire that forms one arm of a Wheatstone bridge circuit (Figure 17–10). The heat released by the burning causes a change in the electrical resistance of the detector filament that is proportional to the combustible gas concentration. The change in resistance produces an imbalance in the bridge circuit that can be measured electrically and is translated into a combustible gas concentration.

More recent versions of the sensors for catalytic combustion devices have a matched-pair of alumina coated filaments. The sensing filament forms one leg of a Wheatstone bridge and burns the combustible gas. The compensating filament forms a second leg of the Wheatstone bridge but does not burn the combustible gas. In all other respects the two filaments behave similarly. This improved catalytic combustible gas sensor allows for significantly improved zero and span stability. It also corrects for thermal conductivity effects related to noncombustible atmospheric impurities.

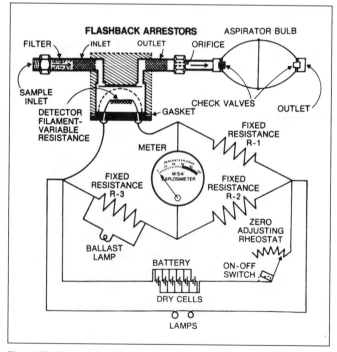

Figure 17–10. A schematic diagram of a typical hot-wire combustible gas monitor. *(Photo courtesy of MSA.)*

Colorimetric

Direct-reading colorimetric devices use the reaction of an airborne contaminant with a color-producing agent to yield a stain length or color intensity, which can be directly read to provide an instantaneous or time-weighted average (TWA) value of the concentration of that contaminant. The colorimetric detector tube and badge are widely used by industrial hygienists and other health professionals. Their simplicity of operation, low initial cost, and the availability of multiple types for the detection of numerous contaminants make these popular devices for field use. Nevertheless, like nearly all direct-reading instruments, these devices are limited in applicability, specificity, and accuracy. The user must be familiar with these critical limitations if proper judgments are to be made about appropriate use and about the results.

Colorimetric detector tubes provide a simple and economical method of measuring the exposure of workers to various hazardous gases and vapors and are by far the most commonly used colorimetric sensing technology. As such, they are discussed below at length followed by a shorter treatment of other colorimetric devices.

Detector Tubes

Detector tubes are generally not specific for a single compound because nearly all have interferences. In atmospheres that are well-characterized for such interferences, they can be useful for estimating concentrations of certain airborne contaminants. The cost of chemical indicator tubes is considerably less than the cost of a chemical analysis of a sorbent tube in the laboratory. However, the sensitivity of the tubes, their lower accuracy, the possible presence of interferences, and the potential lack of appropriate tubes for determining anything more than instantaneous concentrations are all limitations that must be considered when using these devices.

Principles of Operation

The hermetically sealed glass tubes contain an inert granular material impregnated with an agent that develops a color when it reacts with the contaminant (Figure 17–11). Sometimes there is a section in the tube or a separate tube that first causes a reaction to take place before the indicating section. Chemical indicator tubes can be characterized by how the air reaches the active portion of the tube: by active sampling using a hand pump (for short-term measurements) or battery-operated pump (for longer-term measurements) or by passive sampling relying on diffusion. Tubes can be categorized as short-term measurement tubes or longer-term (TWA) measurement tubes.

Active Sampling

In a test using an actively sampled tube, both ends of the indicator tube are broken off and a volume of air is drawn

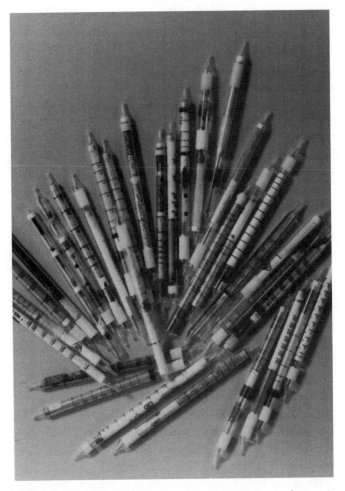

Figure 17–11. Length of stain tubes intended for short sampling periods. *(Photo courtesy of Draeger Safety, Inc.)*

through the tube, using a hand pump or electrically operated pump (Figure 17–12). Most such tubes have an increased sensitivity if larger volumes of air are drawn through the tube. Tubes intended for multiple compound detection may have a linear scale printed on the tube and the relationship of that scale to contaminant concentration is provided separately. The manufacturer prints a calibration curve on the tube and also provides instructions for interpretation of the stain length when multiples of the minimum volume of air (typically 50 or 100 mL) are drawn through the tube. Tubes used with hand pumps are usually designed to determine average concentrations of an airborne contaminant over periods of 0.5–10 min, depending on the total air volume drawn through the tube. See the American Society for Testing and Materials (ASTM) "Standard Practice for Measuring the Concentration of Toxic Gases or Vapors Using Length-of-Stain Dosimeters" (ASTM D4599–03, reapproved 09) for further information.

Tubes designed for use with a battery-operated pump

Figure 17–12. Manual and automatic pumps for short sampling period tubes. *(Photo courtesy of Drägerwerk AG & Co. KGaA, Lubeck. All rights reserved. No portion hereof may be reproduced, saved, or stored in a data processing system, electronically or mechanically copied, or otherwise recorded by any other means without express prior written permission.)*

have been developed for determination of longer-term (1–8 h) (TWA) concentrations. The color development principle on which they are based is often identical to that for short-term tubes. However, the readings on the tube are often given as ppm-hours and the (TWA) concentration of the contaminant is determined by dividing the reading by the sampling time (in hours). One example of using colorimetric tubes with a digital interface is a device that does the actual reading of the stain length and displays the results digitally. This device has 10 capillary tubes in it mounted on a chip, each tube filled with a reagent that develops a color when in contact with the contaminant of interest (Figure 17–13). A pump draws a known quantity of air through a single capillary, and the optics of the instrument read the length of the stain formed in the capillary. A fixed number of measurements can be made before the chip must be replaced.

Flow rates for length-of-stain devices must be maintained in accordance with the manufacturer's operating instructions and the flow rates of the pumps used with length-of-stain devices must be checked periodically. Proper flow rate ensures an appropriate residence time of the air sample in the device and provides sufficient time for the contaminant to react with the chemicals in the detector tube. To obtain meaningful test results, the residence time must be the same as that used to develop the color chart or length-of-stain chart supplied by the manufacturer.

Passive Sampling

Some colorimetric tubes are not designed for use with a sampling pump, although they may closely resemble those that do. These tubes are called passive or diffusional monitors. The driving force moving air into the tube is the difference in contaminant concentration between the ambient

air and inside the tube at the point of reaction (where it is effectively zero). Some passive sampling tubes can be used to sample the atmosphere for several hours, whereas others are intended for only short sampling periods. Passive colorimetric monitors provide concentration information in terms of ppm-hours. The (TWA) concentration during the period the tube is exposed to the air equals the ppm-hours indicated on the tube divided by the number of hours the tube was open. Although most passive tubes function on the same chemical principle as actively pumped tubes, a few passive tubes are calibrated from the closed end of the tube. The air contaminant diffuses into the closed end of the tube

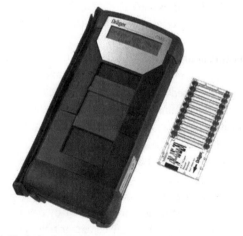

Figure 17–13. A device with automatic reading of capillary colorimetric tubes. *(Photo courtesy of Drägerwerk AG & Co. KGaA, Lubeck. All rights reserved. No portion hereof may be reproduced, saved, or stored in a data processing system, electronically or mechanically copied, or otherwise recorded by any other means without our express prior written permission.)*

and then creates the stain as it rediffuses back toward the open end, chemically modified.

One manufacturer of passively sampling chemical indicator tubes has shown that wind velocities below 0.011–0.022 mph (0.5–1.0 cm/s) result in undersampling of the contaminant, giving a lower reading than the true value. Therefore, these devices should not be used as area samplers where there is little or no air movement. Conversely, they recommend that the devices not be used in situations in which the air velocity past the tube opening exceeds 5.6 mph (250 cm/s), lest the contaminant be oversampled, giving a concentration higher than the true value.

Interpreting the Results

It is important to recognize that some color stains fade or change with time. Thus, readings of stain length should be made as promptly as possible or in accordance with the manufacturer's recommendations. The ability to read color-change detector tubes and badges depends on the color perception of the observer and the lighting conditions. The exposed devices should be examined in an area with daylight or incandescent illumination rather than fluorescent lighting. Mercury vapor lamps should generally be avoided because the color change may not be visible and the end of the color stain may be difficult to perceive.

With most length-of-stain tubes, the stain front may not be sharp, so the exact length of stain cannot be readily determined. It could be helpful to obtain the results of a calibration test performed on known concentrations before using the tubes in the field. The National Institute for Occupational Safety and Health (NIOSH) has recommended that such tubes must yield a concentration value within ±25 percent of the true value, as determined by a reference method, at the occupational exposure limit.

Obviously, performing reliable tests with indicating tubes requires careful use and thorough knowledge of their limitations. Experience has shown that the following measures help to minimize some errors:

- Test each batch of tubes with a known concentration of the air contaminant to be measured.
- Read the length of stain in a well-lighted area.
- Comply with the manufacturer's expiration date and discard outdated tubes.
- Store detector tubes in accordance with the manufacturer's recommendations.
- Refer to the manufacturer's data for a list of interfering materials.

Specificity

Most colorimetric detector tubes, both passive and active, are intended to measure a specific compound (or group of compounds) such as H_2S, Cl_2, mercury vapor, alcohols, or hydrocarbons. Because no colorimetric device is completely specific for the substances of interest, care must be taken to ensure that interferences do not invalidate the sampling results. Specificity is one of the primary considerations in selecting a detector system. In most cases, the manufacturer has identified interfering substances and conditions and has included this information in the instructions enclosed with the tubes. Sometimes a preconditioning section is used in the detector tubes to remove potential contaminants or convert the gas or vapor of interest to a new compound that may be detected and measured by the second section.

Chemical reactions that occur in the detector tubes are temperature-dependent. The tube's instructions give an acceptable temperature range in which it is usable. Drastic differences in the temperature affect the volume of air going through the detector tube, but the uncertainty produced by the effect of temperature on volume is modest compared with other uncertainties in the measurement. Interchanging tubes obtained from various manufacturers may lead to erroneous results because the sampling rates of the various pumps may not be the same, nor will the reaction rates of the chemical reagents in the indicator tubes. Each manufacturer produces, calibrates, and sells equipment as an integral system; tubes produced by one manufacturer and pumps produced by another should not be mixed.

Shelf Life

The shelf life of detector tubes is a critical consideration because the tubes may not be used very often and, therefore, may not be used within the manufacturer's expiration date. While it has been suggested that shelf life can be extended by storage under refrigeration, this practice is generally not advisable. It is better to only use expired tubes for training purposes. Detector tubes should be stored at temperatures below 86°F (30°C) and never in direct sunlight.

Certification of Detector Tubes

Before September 1985, many chemical detector tubes were certified by NIOSH. The NIOSH program was designed to ensure that commercial detector tubes complied with established performance specifications. However, as a result of budget cuts, NIOSH eliminated the certification program for detector tubes. A private organization, the Safety Equipment Institute (SEI) of Arlington, Virginia, filled the void left by NIOSH's departure from the tube certification program. The SEI now certifies detector tube systems through a program similar to that established by the NIOSH, which involves product testing and quality assurance audits conducted by designated, third-party independent laboratories. The SEI offers certification of manufacturers' product models and grants the right to use the SEI certification mark if the testing laboratory has determined that the product models submitted have been tested according to the appropriate standard and the quality assurance auditor has determined that the manufacturer has complied with SEI quality-assurance requirements. The SEI certifies a manufacturer to produce a gas detector tube unit if it meets the minimum requirements set forth, basically ±35 percent accuracy at one half the exposure limit and ±25 percent at one to five times the exposure limit. The quality of future production lots is secured by a quality assurance plan, which the SEI approves as part of the certification process. Adherence to the quality assurance plan is verified by periodic plant inspections and by testing samples obtained from actual inventory.

Other Colorimetric Direct-Reading Devices

Indicator Badges. Both passive and active colorimetric indicator badges rely on the contaminant gas or vapor reacting with an indicating reagent to yield a uniform color change in the reactive portion of the badge. In some devices, the color changes as a function of time as well as concentration, so the user must note the duration of exposure and refer to a plot of color intensity versus time for a given concentration of the contaminant. The color may be compared against a color comparator, which provides a reference color intensity for a given number of ppm-hours. Some badges have the color comparator built into the badge, while others require a separate color-comparing card. Other badges simply show a color change at a specified ppm-hour exposure that is identified on the card. Knowledge of the exposure time, in the latter case, will provide an estimate of (TWA) concentration. In a passively sampled badge, airborne target analyte molecules diffuse to the surface of the badge and react to form the color. In an actively sampled badge, air is drawn though a chemically treated porous paper, with a sampling pump, for a fixed time period and a color appears if the contaminant is present. A color comparator is used to estimate the concentration of the contaminant.

Glove Breakthrough Indicators. Although one would be hard-pressed to call such devices instruments, there are commercially available, direct-reading indicators that are worn underneath chemically resistant gloves to give an indication of when breakthrough of any of a group of compounds has taken place. The indicator contains a microencapsulated (proprietary) detection indicator that changes color when in contact with a significant quantity of the compound of interest. Current indicators are available for the following groups of compounds: aromatic amines, aliphatic amines, aromatic isocyanates, aliphatic isocyanates, acids/bases, hydrazines, polynuclear aromatic hydrocarbons, solvents (including ketones, glycol ethers, and chlorinated hydrocarbons), and heavy metals.

Colorimetric Tape Samplers. Another device that uses the color change resulting from a chemical reaction to measure air contaminants is a colorimetric tape sampler. In modern devices, a chemically treated paper tape is drawn at a constant rate over the sampling orifice; the air contaminant drawn through the tape reacts with the chemical to produce a stain. The intensity of color is directly related to the concentration of the contaminant and is read optically and then displayed on a digital readout. Chemically impregnated paper tape devices have been in use since the early 1950s. The first units were developed to detect hydrogen sulfide (H_2S). A filter paper was impregnated with a lead acetate solution that produced a dark stain (lead sulfide) when exposed to H_2S. The concentration of H_2S was then determined by measuring the transmission of light through the stained paper. Light of equal intensity (from a common source through matched fiber optics) is directed to both the top and bottom track and measured by a set of matched photoelectric detectors mounted at an angle of 45 degrees. The difference in reflected light is then measured. The system thereby compensates for slight tape variations. This is illustrated in Figure 17–14, which schematically illustrates the general principle of operation. This diagram also shows the capstan-driven cassette, which moves the impregnated paper tape past the exposure orifice and readout section of the optical block and gate assembly. The manufacturer of this particular instrument markets different impregnated tapes for compounds ranging from aliphatic amines/ammonia to sulfur dioxide.

Electrochemical

A number of instruments, usually containing multiple sensors, are available for detection of a large number of different compounds (Figures 17–15, 17–16, 17–17).

These instruments are typically based on electrochemical cells, either potentiometric (galvanic) or coulometric, described in the section on oxygen and carbon monoxide monitoring. They almost always have combustible gas and oxygen deficiency sensors in addition to other toxic gas sensors. Common commercially available sensors include, but are not limited to, H_2S, sulfur dioxide (SO_2), Cl_2, nitrogen monoxide (NO), nitrogen dioxide (NO_2), dihydrogen (H_2), hydrogen cyanide (HCN), hydrogen chloride (HCl), and ammonia (NH_3).

All of these sensors are affected by other compounds, which interfere with the measurement of the compound of interest. However, sensor specificity for these compounds can be enhanced by adding filters that remove potential interferences, controlling the voltage in a coulometric cell to mini-

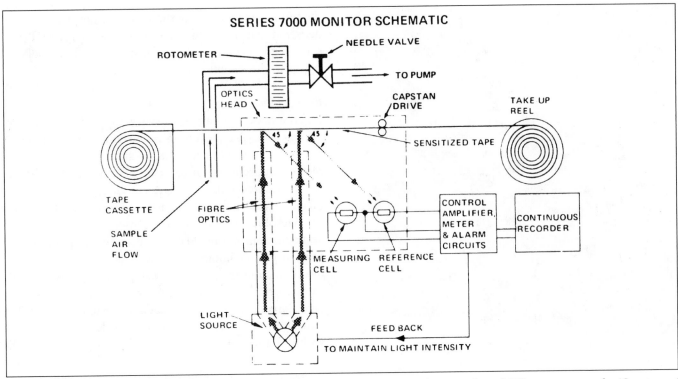

Figure 17–14. A schematic diagram of a colorimetric paper tape area monitor usable for a number of different compounds. *(Courtesy of MDA Scientific, Inc.)*

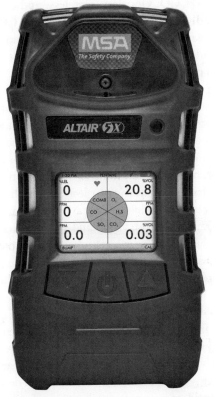

Figure 17–15. A hand-held six-gas detector using electrochemical sensors. *(Photo courtesy of MSA.)*

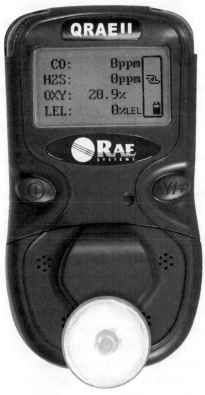

Figure 17–16. A hand-held four-gas detector common for confined space entry. *(Photo courtesy of RAE Systems.)*

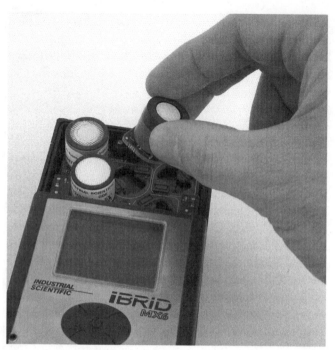

Figure 17–17. An example of user replaceable sensor modules. *(Photo courtesy of Industrial Scientific Corp.)*

mize unwanted oxidation-reduction reactions, choosing an appropriate sensing electrode that selectively catalyzes the oxidation or reduction of the chemical species of interest, or introducing a semipermeable barrier into the cell to minimize the entry of interfering gases. For example, one manufacturer of H_2S sensors provides a list of cross-sensitivities for its device, listing 11 compounds and 2 classes of compounds (saturated and unsaturated hydrocarbons) that may interfere. Among these, only HCN, HCl, Cl_2, and phosgene ($COCl_2$) give positive interferences; NO_2 gives a negative interference. The sensitivity of the sensor to HCN is half that for H_2S, and for the others 0.2 times or less that for H_2S.

At present, multiple-gas monitors are available that can accommodate up to six different detectors at a time. These instruments are typically configured to include combustible gases and vapors, oxygen, and carbon monoxide, all of which are of interest in confined spaces, but could include any compound for which a sensor is available. Some of the more common types of electrochemical sensors are discussed below.

Combustible Gas

In the metallic oxide semiconductor (MOS) combustible gas sensor, a change in the electrical conductivity occurs when a combustible gas is adsorbed on the surface of a semiconductor. This change in electrical conductivity is proportional to the concentration of the combustible gas present and is translated into a combustible gas concentration. Changing

the surface temperature of the sensor by varying the power delivered to its heater alters the sensitivity of the MOS sensor to a given compound. In principle, this allows the MOS sensor to show some compound selectivity.

Hydrogen Sulfide

H_2S is a toxic and flammable gas with a characteristic rotten egg odor. A typical four-gas meter arrangement generally includes a sensor for H_2S; as although it is easily first recognized, sensory fatigue can quickly set in leading to overexposures and death. H_2S can be contained in crude oil and natural gas, and can also be formed as a byproduct of anaerobic digestion. H_2S is denser than air, leading to accumulations in vaulted confined spaces with low ventilation, such as manholes and process tanks. H_2S sensors are most commonly conductivity or amperometric electrochemical sensors. Conductivity sensors are commonly used for detection of corrosive gases that are able to be ionized. The ionized form of the gas decreases the electrical resistance within the sensor in a linear fashion proportional to the atmospheric concentration. The instrument measures the electrical resistance of the sensor and translates the reading into an atmospheric concentration, which is then displayed.

Carbon Monoxide

One of the most insidious toxic gas hazards in an industrial atmosphere is CO. Odorless, tasteless, and colorless, CO can be deadly even in small concentrations. CO can occur in many areas, including gas and utility properties, garages, bus terminals, sewers, vaults, blast furnaces, open-hearth furnaces, and mines. A number of instruments are available for measuring carbon monoxide (Figure 17–18).

The most common instruments use a potentiometric or coulometric cell. The resulting voltage or current is translated into a concentration, with temperature compensation factored in. Samples are introduced to the detector cell through a diffusion barrier. Potentiometer cells rely on a change in voltage difference between two electrodes in the presence of a particular air contaminant. Typical portable carbon monoxide detectors feature both visible and audible alarms that alert the user when the danger level is reached. Typical battery-powered instruments can measure carbon monoxide in the atmosphere in the range of 1–2,000 ppm by volume.

Chlorine

Although fairly ubiquitous throughout industrial settings, chlorine's primary use is in the production of certain plastics, such as polyvinyl chloride (PVC). Highly toxic at low levels, Cl_2 and many of its derivatives are typically detected using amperometric or potentiometric sensors. In amperometric sensors, chlorine, which has diffused across a hydrophobic

Figure 17–18. A direct-reading carbon monoxide monitor. *(Photo courtesy of MSA.)*

membrane, is reduced at the sensor's cathode. This reduction reaction generates a small amount of current within the sensor which is proportional to the chlorine concentration. In theory, amperometric sensors are accurate over a wide measurement range, and have good low-level sensitivity. In potentiometric sensors, chlorine diffuses across the hydrophobic membrane reacting with an electrolyte. The resulting oxidation-reduction reaction causes a change in the electrical potential between the anode and cathode, which is proportional to the gas concentration. Since the reaction activity is temperature-dependant, it is important to note the operating range listed by the manufacturer. While neither the amperometric nor potentiometric sensors are specific for chlorine, selection of the hydrophobic membrane by the sensor manufacturer can result in a certain degree of selectivity.

Oxygen

Although oxygen does not have a specific occupational exposure level, OSHA defines an oxygen-deficient atmosphere as one containing less than 19.5 percent oxygen. Oxygen levels are routinely measured in the workplace, particularly in enclosed areas where combustion or other processes may use up the available oxygen. Excess oxygen from oxyacetylene or oxyhydrogen flame operation should also be monitored to prevent a fire hazard. Air normally contains about 21 percent oxygen by volume. Sixteen percent oxygen is considered the minimum to support life. In some cases, however, air with less than 19.5 percent oxygen may be considered oxygen deficient, such as at high altitudes where atmospheric pressures are lower.

In many locations, such as mines, manholes, tunnels, or other confined spaces, the oxygen content can become low enough to be life-threatening. In such situations, it is necessary to determine the oxygen content of the air. In addition, it is necessary to take a sample to determine whether combustible gases are present in dangerous concentrations. Direct-reading oxygen monitors are small, lightweight, and easy to use. The instruments generally use a coulometric cell to detect oxygen, while a few rely on polarographic detectors. Both types are discussed below:

- *Coulometric detectors* rely on the measurement of current flowing in an electrolyte between two electrodes, maintained at a controlled voltage difference, as a result of an oxidation-reduction reaction in the detector cell. The current flow is translated into an airborne concentration of the contaminant undergoing the oxidation or reduction. The most commonly used detector cell for oxygen is a coulometric cell, which has a semipermeable membrane that selectively allows oxygen to enter the cell. One of the electrodes is consumed during the flow of electrons, thus limiting the lifetime of the cell. The cells are temperature-compensated through the use of an external thermistor. Cells from different manufacturers have different response times, accuracies, and temperature and relative humidity performance ranges.

- *Polarographic detectors* rely on two parameters: the ability of the compound of interest to be chemically oxidized or reduced at an electrode at a given electrode potential, and the rate-determining step of the discharge of ions at a microelectrode that is determined by diffusion. Polarographic detectors are used to measure oxygen and carbon monoxide in ambient air.

Thermal Conductivity Detectors

Thermal conductivity detectors rely on the change in the ability of contaminated air to transmit or conduct thermal energy. Air with the contaminant is passed over one leg of a Wheatstone bridge in which the filaments are heated by a current flowing through them. The change in thermal conductivity of the measurement leg versus the reference leg causes a change in temperature in one leg, inducing an imbalance in the bridge circuit and a resultant measurable electrical voltage that is proportional to the combustible gas concentration. This can then be translated into a concentration for a known contaminant.

Flame Ionization Detectors

Flame ionization detectors (FIDs) burn compounds in a hydrogen flame and thus require a hydrogen fuel source and atmospheric oxygen for operation. They are highly sensitive to compounds that ionize in the presence of an oxyhydrogen flame and are commonly used to detect volatile organic compounds (VOCs) (Figure 17–19). The ions are collected and the electric current generated for the compound of interest (whose response factor has been determined) can be translated into a concentration. FIDs are good at detecting high concentrations (up to approximately 50,000 ppm), but perform poorly in the sub ppm range. Organic compounds that have a large number of carbon–hydrogen (C-H) bonds are detected with great sensitivity with FIDs. However, as the number of C–H bonds decreases, as with chloroform (CHl$_3$), for example, the sensitivity decreases, generally making these devices less useful for detecting inorganic gases.

Since FIDs are sensitive to a broad range of organic gases, caution must be exercised when using readings taken from organic gas mixes. Readings are more reliable when it is known that the environment sampled is dominated by a particular organic compound.

Photoionization Detectors

Photoionization detectors (PIDs) are sensitive to compounds that are ionized by certain wavelengths of ultraviolet light and are used for the detection of VOCs and some inorganic gases as well. The ions produced by the ultraviolet lamp in a PID are collected and this current is translated electronically into a signal that can be read on the instrument (Figure 17–20). Aromatic hydrocarbons are particularly sensitively detected with a PID. There are several different

wavelengths of ultraviolet lamp available for some direct-reading PIDs, which can introduce some selectivity into the detection. However, the instrument must be ordered with a given ultraviolet lamp. Stable air constituents such as oxygen and nitrogen are not ionized by PIDs. Most hydrocarbons (except methane) cause a response on a PID. Water vapor can attenuate the signal of a PID, causing it to under-respond in a more humid environment. Efforts should be made to calibrate and use the instrument under similar humidity conditions to the extent possible.

In comparison to FIDs, PIDs are generally lower cost, more portable, more reliable and easier to use. Since they do not combust the compounds sampled, they function even in low oxygen environments and allow subject gases and vapors to be collected on a suitable sampling medium after passing through the PID. They perform well in the sub-ppm and sub-ppb ranges but do not perform as well as FIDs at high concentrations (limited to approximately 10,000 ppm). Unlike FIDs, PIDs are not responsive to methane.

Spectrochemical Monitors

Spectrochemical monitors are a unique type of light-based sensors by which the chemicals species and concentration

Figure 17–19. An intrinsically safe FID monitor. *(Photo courtesy of Photovac, Inc.)*

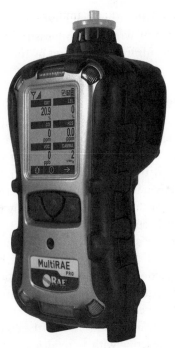

Figure 17–20. A hand-held PID incorporating additional gas sensors. *(Photo courtesy of RAE Systems.)*

may be determined by its interaction with, or generation of, light. They work on the general principle that certain chemicals respond in a predictive way when exposed to specific wavelengths of light, or emit light when chemically reacted. When chemical species are exposed to specific wavelengths of light or chemically reactive conditions, the radiation intensity of the absorbed, scattered, or emitted light is measured. Common spectrochemical monitor types include infrared spectrometers, and ultraviolet and visible light photometers; as well as chemiluminescent detectors, photometric analyzers, and Raman spectrometers. This section will only be covering infrared (IR), visible (VIS) and ultraviolet radiation (UV) analyzers. Ultraviolet and visible light photometers are often combined into a single UV-VIS analyzer.

Infrared and UV-VIS Analyzers

Many gases and vapors, both inorganic and organic, absorb certain characteristic frequencies of infrared (IR), visible (VIS), and ultraviolet (UV) radiation. This property and the resultant spectrum can be used to identify and quantify compounds in the air that absorb in these electromagnetic regions. For infrared analyzers, this includes most organic compounds except the diatomic molecules such as H_2, nitrogen (N_2), and O_2. However, their agents may be detected by UV-VIS photometers.

IR and UV-VIS analyzers have similar basic setups. In

an IR analyzer, an infrared source in the analyzer emits the full frequency range of infrared radiation. The window material in the cell may absorb certain frequencies, and thus limits the frequencies that can be used. In a dispersive instrument, the radiation is separated into its component wavelengths with a prism or grating and the desired wavelengths are directed through the sample and onto a detector. In a nondispersive instrument, the infrared radiation is passed through a filter to limit the frequency of light energy to a narrow band that is specific to the target analyte. It is then passed through an air sample, and onto a detector. The analyzers are noncontact and nondestructive of the sample.

In a double-beam instrument, the infrared energy passes through two cell paths simultaneously. At the opposite end is a detector that measures the energy transmitted through the two cells. One of the cells is the sample cell. The other is a sealed comparison cell with a special mixture inside. If the sample cell contains a gas or vapor that absorbs energy at the selected frequency, then the detector will detect less energy coming through the sample cell than through the comparison cell. The detector emits an electrical signal to alert the user to this imbalance. The same would be true with a single-beam instrument, but the infrared absorption background of uncontaminated air would not be subtracted out of the signal.

One battery-operated portable dispersion instrument can generate an entire infrared spectrum and has a preprogrammed library of compounds in its memory, so that the instrument automatically determines the correct wavelength to monitor for the compound of interest (Figure 17–21).

When a single contaminant is present, identification and measurement are achieved easily. Lightweight instruments

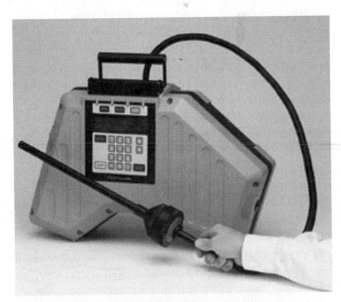

Figure 17–21. A portable, direct-reading instrument with an infrared spectrophotometer. *(Photo courtesy of Thermo Scientific.)*

using filters are available for single, specific compound detection. When a number of absorbing contaminants are present, separation of the contaminants may not be possible, depending on the differences in infrared absorption spectra among the compounds of interest. If the spectra do not overlap significantly, analysis of multiple compounds in the same sample, and thus compound specificity is possible when an instrument with narrow bandwidth resolution is used. The absorbance measured at the detector for a single airborne analyte is correlated to the chemical concentration through a relationship known as Beer's law.

$$A = \varepsilon l c \qquad (1)$$

Where A is the absorbance measured at the detector
ε is the molar absorptivity of the specific wavelength of light by the chemical being measured
l is the path length of the sample
c is the molar concentration of the gas or vapor in the sample cell

Infrared spectrometers measure a chemical's interaction to electromagnetic radiation in the infrared range, wavelengths 770 nanometers (nm) to 1000 micrometers (μm). Visible light photometers measure a chemical's absorptive properties in the wavelength range of 350 nm to 770 nm. Ultraviolet photometers measure the same properties in the wavelengths from 10 nm to 350 nm.

Fourier Transform & Open-Path Infrared Spectroscopy

Fourier-transform and open path infrared analyzers are special types of infrared analyzers. Fourier-transform infrared (FTIR) spectrophotometers are capable of doing a complete scan of a wide range of infrared wavelengths in seconds and may have a much higher resolution than traditional infrared spectrophotometers. These characteristics allow this instrument to quantitate a large number of different chemical compounds in a complex gas sample.

An open path infrared analyzer is capable of airborne monitoring some distance away from the device. In these instruments, there is no gas cell in which the contaminant is measured, but rather the open air is the environment in which the measurement is made. The transmitter and receiver of the infrared radiation may be built into one device, with a remote mirror reflecting the signal back, or else the transmitter and receiver of the infrared radiation may be separated by a considerable distance. This device is intended for the detection of major leaks or spills of combustible or toxic gases within a distance of roughly 200 m. The response time is less than three seconds, making it a truly real-time monitor for major spills. The sensitiv-

ity of the open path infrared analyzer—and thus the maximum distance over which it can measure—depends on the intensity of the infrared absorption by the compound(s) of interest.

Solid State Resistors

Solid-state resistors are a type of conductivity sensor based on a single block semiconductor with no moving or consumable parts. When gas comes in contact with the sensor it is absorbed by the metal oxide top layer. If the gas itself is not conductive, it may be adsorbed by the metal oxide surface, thereby causing the surface coating to be less resistive. If the gas is conductive, it may directly act to reduce the resistance across the sensor. The instrument measures the resistance of the solid-state resistor which responds in a logarithmic function to the gas concentration. As the solid-state resistor's natural resistance is temperature-dependent, a heater is integrated which allows for temperature control and increased surface reaction with the contaminant gas. Since the gas is reacting with an oxidized substance, oxygen in the atmosphere is not required for accurate measurement. These types of sensors are commonly used for NH_3, H_2S, and SO_2, which are corrosive gases.

Gas Chromatographs

When a simple detector is used to measure a complex mixture, assumptions must be made concerning the basis for a quantitative detector response. When several airborne analytes that may cause a detector to respond are simultaneously present, a method to measure the contribution of each analyte to the detector signal is needed. Chromatography is a method that separates the components of complex mixtures to accomplish this. In gas chromatography (GC), the components of a mixture migrate at different rates through a column swept with a carrier gas. Typical GC columns are <1 mm in diameter, and are coated with a thin film of liquid-like stationary phase, or are lined with a high-surface-area adsorbent material. In the commonly used liquid film GC column, organic analytes will partition into the stationary phase to differing degrees, and those analytes with higher partition coefficients for the stationary phase will elute from the column in the carrier gas later than those that partition less into the stationary phase. The gas/liquid partition coefficient for an analyte depends greatly upon temperature, and thus the column temperature must be controlled to reproducibly separate analytes. Historically, this has been done using a small convection to house the GC column.

Most GC analyses occur with temperature programming starting with the initial GC column temperature slightly above ambient conditions. While the more volatile analytes may partition to the gas phase appreciably, less volatile analytes will not unless the column temperature is raised. As analysis proceeds, the GC column temperature is raised in a linear fashion to allow analytes with progressively less volatility to partition to the gas phase and thus move towards the end of the GC column. Temperature program GC allows for analysis of compounds with a wider range of volatilities compared to isothermal analysis, which limits analysis to compounds with similar volatilities.

As analyte molecules elute from the GC column and are detected, a chromatogram is produced that graphically shows the retention time on the x-axis, and the detector response on the y-axis (Figure 17–22). Retention time is the time required for a compound to pass through the chromatographic column. Simple detectors used for portable gas chromatographs are often based on flame ionization, photoionization, electron capture, flame-photometry, or thermal conductivity. Quantitative analysis for a specific component requires separation of the component from other compounds in the sample mixture and quantitation with a calibrated detector. Calibration of the detector requires the introduction of known amounts of the compound into the detector and the determination of the relationship between the amount introduced and the instrument response. The use of retention time alone is a common, though somewhat uncertain, means of analyte identification. However, if the components of a sample mixture being analyzed are well

understood, then the potential for misidentification is lessened when this approach is used.

Several person-portable GC-MS instruments are now available. Mass spectrometry as a stand-alone method is discussed elsewhere in this chapter, but when used with a GC to first separate analytes, the information obtained is much more useful, as *clean* mass spectra and the unique GC retention times for individual compounds can both be used to identify unknown and unexpected chemicals with high certainty. In addition to a chromatogram with similar x- and y-axis components produced by GC with a simple detector, GC-MS data have an additional z-axis component: a mass spectrum associated with each GC peak (Figure 17–23).

While most of the detectors commonly used for GC are discussed as stand-alone instruments in this chapter, a brief discussion is needed for the flame photometric detector. This is used to selectively detect chemiluminescence produced when compounds containing either sulfur or phosphorous atoms are burned in a hydrogen flame. The emission wavelengths used to detect sulfur and phosphorous are 394 and 520 nm respectively, and if a dual channel detector is used, both sulfur and phosphorous compounds may be detected simultaneously as light emitted from the flame is passed through optical filters to generate signals from two photomultipliers, one for each channel. The intensity of the signal is related to the amount of the element in the flame,

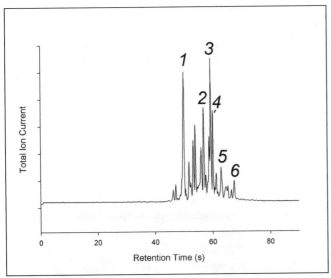

Figure 17–22. A chromatogram from a GC analysis of paint-thinner vapor, illustrating component compounds as peaks. *(Figure from: Smith, Philip A., Roe, Marc T.A., Sadowski, Charles, and Lee, Edgar D. Unknown exposures: Gaps in basic characterization addressed with person-portable gas chromatography-mass spectrometry instrumentation. Journal of Occupational and Environmental Hygiene, 8(3):129-138, first published February 10, 2011. Reprinted with permission of publisher, Taylor & Francis Ltd, www.taylorandfrancis.com.)*

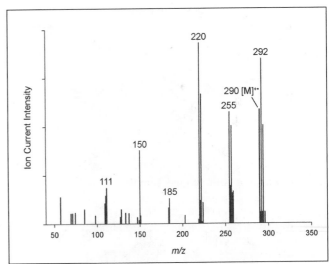

Figure 17–23. A mass spectrum obtained during elution of a specific GC peak, illustrating molecular mass in the x-axis and showing various isotope clusters for the molecular ion. *(Figure from: Smith, Philip A., Roe, Marc T.A., Sadowski, Charles, and Lee, Edgar D. Unknown exposures: Gaps in basic characterization addressed with person-portable gas chromatography-mass spectrometry instrumentation. Journal of Occupational and Environmental Hygiene, 8(3):129-138, first published February 10, 2011. Reprinted with permission of publisher, Taylor & Francis Ltd, www.taylorandfrancis.com.)*

although the detector response for sulfur follows a quadratic curve instead of a straight line. This detector is important for detection of many chemical warfare agent compounds as many of these contain either phosphorous (e.g., the nerve agents such as sarin and tabun), sulfur (e.g., the vesicant sulfur mustard), or both (e.g., the nerve agent VX). For this reason, defensive military detection systems based on GC with flame photometric detection have been developed.

Samples may be introduced into a portable gas chromatograph directly from the air onto a GC column, from thermal desorption of a preconcentrated air sample collected on a sorbent tube, or by using a technique known as solid phase microextraction (SPME). A field-portable GC instrument that has been preprogrammed to recognize the retention time for a given compound and apply a predetermined response factor can provide an airborne concentration for that analyte in the field. Instrument reliability, ease of operation, ease of calibration, and instrument reliability are key considerations when defining the minimum technical skill required to operate the device. A portable gas chromatograph is shown in Figure 17–24.

An important advance for improved performance in field-portable GC systems has been the development of fast GC column-heating methods that use little power. In at least four commercially available GC instruments designed for field-portability, the GC column is heated using wires intertwined with the lightweight GC column. Several wires heat the column assembly resistively with electrical current, while resistance is measured in a separate platinum wire. Sloan

et al. demonstrated this column-heating approach in 2001, showing that the resistance in the temperature-sensing wire could be used to measure the column temperature and control the application of current to the resistive heating wires. To allow battery operation when using traditional convection heating of the GC column in a metal oven, older field-portable GC designs often involved a convection oven for low-temperature GC column-heating programs or isothermal analyses. This limited the usefulness of field-portable GC to the analysis of volatile compounds such as benzene, toluene, hexane, etc. As an example of the expanded volatility range possible with high-temperature analysis conditions (similar to lab GC instruments), low-power resistive GC column heating per Sloan et al. allowed Smith and coworkers to detect heavy polychlorinated biphenyl compounds in 2011 using a person-portable/battery-powered GC, with column heating up to 270°C.

Mass Spectrometers

Mass spectrometers are available as field-deployable stand-alone instruments, but most often are combined with a gas chromatograph to provide a hyphenated GC-MS instrument. Field-portable GC-MS systems may be divided into two broad categories. A person-portable system may be transported and operated by a single individual under battery power using self-contained carrier gas (Figure 17–25). A transportable system may be smaller than a laboratory GC-MS instrument, but must be mounted in a vehicle or other structure due to size, weight, and power requirements.

A mass spectrometer produces mass spectra that represent ionic molecular fragments or intact ionic molecules. In GC-MS, following separation by gas chromatography pure compounds are eluted from the GC column into the high

Figure 17–24. A field-portable GC. *(Photo courtesy of Photovac, Inc.)*

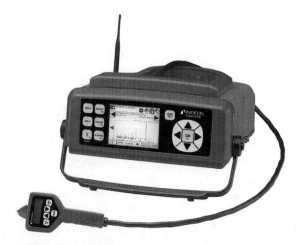

Figure 17–25. A field-portable HAPSITE® gas chromatograph-mass spectrometer. *(Photo courtesy of INFICON Inc.)*

vacuum region of a mass spectrometer. Here some of the molecules are ionized. For most laboratory and field-portable GC-MS systems, ionization of target analytes is produced by a high energy electron source (electron ionization). Following electron ionization, many molecules will fragment, producing smaller ions and neutrals. The relative abundance and mass-to-charge ratio (m/z) of the different ions will be combined graphically as a mass spectrum (Figure 17–23), which may be used to identify the intact molecule that was subjected to the GC-MS process. In order to do this, a mass spectrometer must be able to measure the m/z values of the resulting ions, as well as their abundances. For GC-MS in the laboratory, the most common approach to accomplish this uses a quadrupole design to sort the ions by m/z values with a series of rapid, discrete scans. During a scan, the various positively charged ions are repelled away from the ion source into a quadrupole mass filter. At any instant during a scan, only ions with a specific m/z value will successfully pass through to an electron multiplier detector. The ion current measured by this detector for ions at each specific m/z value is proportional to the relative abundance of these ions in the source region. In another design, ions are briefly stored in an ion trap using a quadrupolar radiofrequency field, followed by a scan to sequentially eject and count ions with specific m/z values. The ion trap design has less stringent vacuum requirements, and thus is used in several field-portable mass spectrometers.

The advent of relatively inexpensive mass spectrometers that could be used as GC-MS detectors occurred at about the same time as the advent of the U.S. Environmental Protection Agency, which eventually led to the widespread use of laboratory-based GC-MS instruments. In determining the identities of unknown organic environmental pollutants, it was clear that "any technique that left ambiguity in the analytical result was likely to lead to continual controversy and litigation" (Heller et al., 1975).

Development of small, high performance GC-MS systems has been catalyzed by the need for defensive military detection of highly dangerous chemicals such as chemical warfare agents. However, the same types of instruments can be used for hazardous waste sites or spills, emergency response monitoring, or the identification of unknown chemicals in occupational settings. The ability to identify unknown and unexpected chemical contaminants using field-portable GC-MS can be followed up by traditional sampling and laboratory-based analysis methods to quantify exposures.

Ion Mobility Spectrometers

In the ion mobility spectrometer, ion-molecule reactions are often initiated by the electrons emitted from a radioactive ^{63}Ni source. The resulting ions created from target analytes are directed towards a collector electrode at the far end of an electric field, separating the ions, which have different arrival times that depend on charge and cross-sectional area, with pressure in the spectrometer close to standard atmospheric conditions. This type of instrument was commercially developed for the rapid detection of chemical warfare agent and explosives vapors, but versions are now available for detection of other gases or vapors in the workplace. An ion mobility spectrometer may be set up to detect a number of compounds, but is often used for toluene diisocyanate (TDI) monitoring because of the ceiling occupational exposure limit for this compound and the rapid response of the ion mobility spectrometer.

Photoacoustic Spectrometers

Photoacoustic spectrometers rely on the absorption of a characteristic band of wavelengths of infrared radiation within the detector cell. The absorption of the infrared radiation causes slight heating, and thus expansion, of the gas contained in the cell. The measurement of the change of pressure in the cell is translated into a concentration of the contaminant present in the cell. The measurement is specific only if no other contaminant that is present absorbs infrared radiation significantly in the same band of wavelengths.

Surface Acoustic Wave Detectors

Surface acoustic wave detectors are relatively simple and rugged. The basic principle is that acoustic waves are transmitted at a resonant frequency into a piezoelectric material. This material can be coated with a variety of different absorptive polymers. The resonant frequency is determined by the mass of the vapors present in the air that are absorbed by the polymer. Changes in that frequency can be measured and translated into a signal that is proportional to the concentration of a particular contaminant in the air.

Electron Capture Detectors

An electron capture detector relies on the ability of the compound of interest to capture primary and secondary electrons from a small radioactive source (typically tritium, ^3H, or ^{63}Ni) and thus attenuate a current flowing from the radioactive source to a collector electrode. The electronegativity of the elements (the most electronegative elements are in the upper-right portion of the periodic table) that make up the compound determines the sensitivity of the electron capture detector to the compound. Thus, halogen-containing compounds, as well as those containing nitrogen or oxygen, are detected with high sensitivity by an electron capture detector. Portable or transportable electron capture detectors are used to evaluate fume hood performance through the release of sulfur hexafluoride (SF_6) at the face of the hood. Sampling points outside the hood draw air samples into the electron capture detector, which indicates the hood's capture efficiency by comparing the external concentration of SF_6 with its internal concentration.

ADDITIONAL CONSIDERATIONS

As discussed in the previous sections, there is a broad array of direct reading instruments available for detecting gases, vapors, and particulates. Likewise, there is a broad array of capabilities, limitations, and use characteristics of the various sensing technologies that require consideration. Beyond the factors discussed above, there are several common dynamics to be considered when using such instruments. These dynamics are covered below.

Calibration

All direct-reading instruments used for sampling and analysis of gases, vapors, or particulates must be calibrated before use and again at intervals recommended by the manufacturer. It is important that the operator thoroughly understand how to operate the instrument, know the instrument's intended use, and know the calibration procedures recommended by the manufacturer. The instrument's limitations and possible sources of error must also be fully understood.

An instrument's response to a concentration of a substance can shift as the result of a variety of factors, such as chemical degradation of sensors, physical damage, drift in electronic components, exposure to extreme environmental conditions, extremely high exposures, or exposure to poisons and inhibitors. It is very important to establish that an instrument accurately responds to the substance it is designed to sample, detect, measure, or analyze. This is generally carried out by performing calibration procedures with standard concentrations of the substance of interest. In the case of particulate monitors, it may require a standard particle size, as well.

The response of some sensors can vary with environmental conditions. Sensor response may be different (lower or higher) depending on these environmental conditions. Therefore, whenever possible, instruments should be calibrated at environmental conditions that are the same as (or similar to) actual field conditions. A permanent record should be maintained of all calibration procedures, data, and results. The information to be kept for this record includes instrument identification, temperature, humidity, trial run results, and final results.

Full Calibration

There are a number of commercially available static-type calibration kits for commonly measured gases and vapors.

These kits generally contain one or more cylinders filled with a known concentration of a specified gas-air mixture, a regulating valve, a pressure gauge for measuring the pressure in the container, and a hose adapter that connects the cylinder to the instrument to be checked. Once the container kit is attached to the instrument, a sample of the gas-air mixture from the container is permitted to flow into the device. The meter reading of the instrument is then compared with the known concentration of the sample to verify the proper response.

A somewhat more difficult way of calibrating gas or particulate detection instruments requires the generation of the desired mixture by adding the desired contaminants in a known quantity to a known quantity of air resulting in a calculated airborne concentration. The rate of airflow and the rate at which the contaminant is added to the sample stream must be carefully controlled to produce a known dilution ratio. Dynamic systems offer a continuous supply of contaminant, allow for rapid and predictable concentration changes, and minimize the effect of wall losses as the test substance comes into equilibrium with the interior surfaces of the system.

Functional/Bump Test

In addition to full calibration, many direct-reading instruments require a functional, or "bump," test. This is especially true for situations where frequent confirmation of the sensor's performance is important because of hazardous conditions. A bump test is performed by briefly exposing the instrument to a concentration of a substance in excess of the lowest alarm set-point for each sensor. The test gas concentration should be high enough to trigger the instrument alarm for each sensor. If the response of the instrument is within an accepted tolerance, then the calibration is verified. Many manufacturers of portable gas detection instruments have automatic and semi-automatic calibration stations, which can bump test, calibrate, charge, and download the instruments use data between uses (Figure 17–26).

Exposure Assessment

Beyond their obvious usefulness in leak testing, emergency response, or as immediately hazardous condition indicators, direct-reading instruments can be useful tools in performing exposure assessments over a variety of time intervals and conditions. These instruments can provide a measurement of concentration quickly and are therefore very useful in measuring concentrations over very short time intervals. For example, they may be useful in assessing whether short-term exposure limits (STEL) or ceiling limits are being exceeded.

Many modern instruments are relatively small and lightweight and include functions for logging of concentration

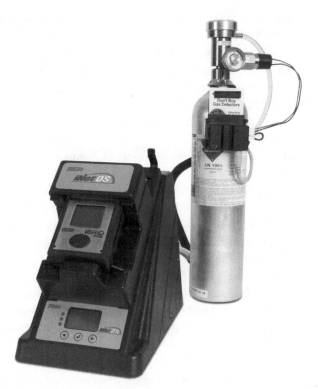

Figure 17–26. A calibration docking station which bump tests, calibrates, downloads data, and charges the instrument. *(Photo courtesy of Industrial Scientific Corp.)*

data over time and even computing TWA concentrations. These instruments can be used for personal sampling over both the short- and long-term time intervals. The logging of concentration measurements over a time period allows for identifying peaks of concentration over the sampling period. Therefore, the data may have the dual use of comparing to both short-term and long-term exposure limits. This data allows for additional analysis of exposure patterns, which can lead to better and more effective controls. Used in conjunction with video monitoring systems, one can assess in great detail how a worker's exposure is influenced by work activity.

As with any exposure assessment, the accuracy of the data, including an assessment of the potential error, must be considered in the judgments of exposure. Considerations for evaluating variability of exposure for an individual worker and between different workers will be similar whether using direct-reading instruments or other methods of measuring gas, vapors, and particulates.

Performance Evaluations & Instrument Specifications

New direct-reading instruments come on the market with some frequency. Knowledge of the performance specifications of a particular instrument is important. Additionally,

knowing that an instrument complies with one or more of the existing standards is also of considerable value. In addition to independent researchers, third-party organizations and government agencies exist that evaluate instruments with regard to their claimed performance specifications and with regard to other instruments that are similar or identical in function. The U.S. National Institute of Occupational Safety and Health (NIOSH) researchers regularly conduct evaluations of direct-reading instruments and publish the results. NIOSH research publications can be searched at their website (http://www2.cdc.gov/nioshtic-2/). For a limited set of commercially available instruments deemed to be homeland-security related, the EPA's Technology Testing and Evaluation Program (TTEP) has conducted third-party performance evaluations.

Various standard developers and publishers such as the Instrument Society of America (ISA), the International Safety Equipment Association (ISEA), and ASTM International, have developed performance requirements for various direct-reading instruments that are approved and available through the American National Standards Institute (ANSI). Standards from these publishers can be found at the ANSI website (http://www.ansi.org).

In Europe, both the International Electrotechnical Commission (IEC) and the European Commission for Electrotechnical Standardization (CENELEC) have established performance standards for direct-reading instruments. Information about CENELEC standards can be obtained from their Web site (http://www.cenelec.eu), while information about IEC standards can be obtained from their Web site (http://www.iec.ch).

Trends

Direct-reading instruments are continuing to advance with "smarter" automatic operations, better sensing technologies, and smaller sizes allowing their use for a broader range of applications. One drawback to the adoption of direct-reading instruments for in-field measurements is that the quality-control and quality-assurance role now lies with the user, whereas for laboratory-analyzed samples, these tasks are completed by highly trained laboratory personnel. One common strategy to help mitigate this issue is to have purchasers request from the manufacturer a standardized specification sheet that allows enhanced understanding and comparison of instruments. A more sound and emergent approach is to require specific training for end users with third-party verification of proficiency.

Another trend in the evolution of direct-reading instruments is the integration of more advanced information technology tools, including powerful proprietary software packages and remote data retrieval. The result is that while some devices have evolved greater simplicity, others have evolved greater complexity, therefore requiring a greater degree of user knowledge on device functionality. These trends further emphasize the need for users of direct-reading instruments to take the time to understand the specific characteristics, capabilities, and limitations of the devices they rely upon for gathering data to use in environmental health and safety decision-making.

BIBLIOGRAPHY

Arthur CL, J Pawliszyn. Solid-phase microextraction with thermal desorption using fused silica optical fibers. *Anal Chem* 62:2145-2148, 1990.

Baron PA. Personal aerosol sampler design: A review. *Appl Occup Environ Hyg* 13:313-320, 1998.

Carner KR, Mainga AM, Zhang X, et al. *Evaluation of Personal Multigas Monitors.* Springfield, VA: National Technical Information Service, 1994.

DiNardi SR, ed. *The Occupational Environment—Its Evaluation and Control.* Fairfax, VA: AIHA, 1997.

Draper WM, Ashley K, Glowacki CR, et al. Industrial hygiene chemistry: Keeping pace with rapid change in the workplace. *Anal Chem* 71(12):33R-42R, 1999; these pages cover monitoring instruments and sensors.

Harris R, ed. *Patty's Industrial Hygiene,* 5th ed. vols I–IV. New York: Wiley, 2000.

Heller SR, McGuire JM, Budde WL. Trace organics by GC/MS. *Environ Sci Technol* 9(3):210-213, 1975.

Hering SV, Cohen BS, eds. *Air Sampling Instruments for Evaluation of Atmospheric Contaminants,* 9th ed. Cincinnati, OH: ACGIH, 2001.

Linch AL. *Evaluation of Ambient Air Quality by Personnel Monitoring,* 2nd ed. Boca Raton, FL: CRC Press, 1981.

Perper JB, Dawson BJ. *Direct Reading Colorimetric Indicator Tubes Manual,* 2nd ed. Fairfax, VA: AIHA, 1993.

Safety Equipment Institute. *Certified Product List, Safety Equipment List: Personal Protective Equipment.* Arlington, VA: Safety Equipment Institute, Oct 1993.

Sloan KM, Mustacich RV, Eckenrode BA: Development and evaluation of a low thermal mass gas chromatograph for rapid forensic GC-MS analyses. *Field Anal Chem Technol* 5:288-301, 2001.

Smith PA, Roe MTA, Sadowski C, et al. Unknown exposures: Gaps in basic characterization addressed with person-portable gas chromatography-mass spectrometry instrumentation. *J Occup Environ Hyg* 8:129-138, 2011.

Smith PA, Sheely MV, Hakspiel SJ, et al. Volatile organic compounds produced during irradiation of mail. *Am Ind Hyg Assoc J* 64:189-195, 2003.

Willard HH, Merritt Jr. LL, Dean JA, et al. *Instrumental Methods of Analysis,* 7th ed. Belmont, CA: Wadsworth, 1988.

Woebkenberg ML, et al. Direct-reading gas and vapor instruments. In *Air Sampling Instruments for Evaluation of Atmospheric Contaminants,* 9th ed. BS Cohen and SV Herring, eds. Cincinnati, OH: ACGIH, 2000.

PART V
Control of Hazards

PART V

CHAPTER 18

Methods of Control

by Susan M. Raterman, CIH

The general principles and methods involved in control- ling occupational health hazards will be discussed in this chapter. In the field of industrial hygiene, the objective of occu- pational health hazard control is to ensure that exposure to harmful chemical stresses and physical agents does not result in occupational illness. The quantities of interest that must be measured are the concentration or intensity of the particular hazard and the duration of exposure.

The types of industrial hygiene control measures to be instituted depend on the nature of the harmful substance or agent and its routes of entry into the body. An employee's exposure to airborne substances is related to the amount of contaminants in the breathing zone and the time interval during which the employee is exposed to this concentration. Reducing the amount of contaminant in the employee's breathing zone or the amount of time that an employee spends in the area will reduce the overall exposure.

With employment in the United States continuing to shift from manufacturing to the service sector, many workplaces today present nontraditional occupational health hazards. Industrial hygienists need to possess the skills to implement control methodology in both traditional industrial settings and workplaces such as laboratories, offices, hospitals, schools, con- struction sites, and environmental hazard remediation projects. This requires an understanding of the toxicology of a broad range of potential hazards, including biological agents, chemi- cals, construction materials, and physical stressors, as well as an understanding of process technologies and work practices. A thorough understanding of the circumstances surrounding an exposure hazard is required in choosing methods that will provide adequate control. To lower exposures, the industrial hygienist must first determine the contaminant source, the path it travels to the worker, and the employee's work pattern

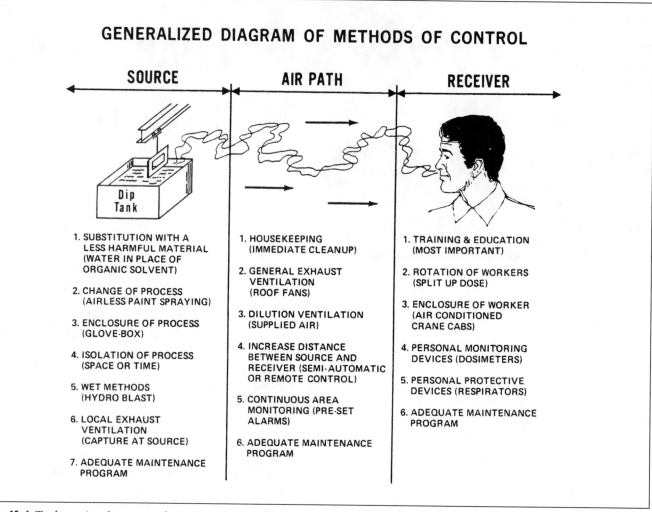

Figure 18–1. To determine the extent of exposure, locate the contaminant source, its path to the employee, and the employee's work pattern and use of protective equipment.

and use of protective equipment (Figure 18–1). The design of exposure controls should also consider bystander exposure to contaminants, for example, in a dusty environment where there are multiple trades working in the same area.

Hazards can change with time, so health hazard control systems require continuous review and updating.

METHODS OF CONTROL

The methods of control of health hazards in the work environment are divided into the following categories:

- Engineering controls, which remove or reduce the hazard either by initial engineering design specifications or by applying methods of substitution, isolation, or ventilation.
- Administrative controls that minimize employees' exposures by scheduling reduced work times in contaminant

areas, good work practices, and employee training. Appropriate training includes hazard recognition and work practices specific to the employee's job that can help reduce exposures.

- Personal protective equipment, which employees wear to protect them from their environment. Personal protective equipment can be used in conjunction with engineering controls and other methods of control.

Engineering controls are to be used as the first line of defense against workplace hazards wherever feasible. Such built-in protection, inherent in the design of a process, is preferable to a method that depends on continual human implementation or intervention. The federal regulations, and their interpretation by the Occupational Safety and Health Review Commission, mandate the use of engineering controls to the extent feasible, and if these are not sufficient to achieve acceptable limits of exposure, the use of personal protective equipment and other corrective measures may be considered.

However, to prevent exposure to highly toxic materials, the OSHA standard for carcinogens (29 CFR 1910.1003) requires implementation of stringent controls that incorporate the use of engineering, administrative, and personal protective equipment exposure controls together. For a number of carcinogens including benzo(a)pyrene, benzidine, and beta-Naphthylamine, the American Conference of Governmental Industrial Hygienists (ACGIH®) indicates that exposure by all routes should be carefully controlled to levels as low as possible. A combination of hazard control methods is generally required to achieve this goal.

Engineering controls include ventilation to minimize dispersion of airborne contaminants, isolation of a hazardous operation or substance by means of barriers, and substitution of a material, equipment, or process to provide control of a hazard. Although administrative control measures can limit the duration of individual exposures, they are not generally favored by employers because they are difficult to implement and maintain because of job training and jurisdictional considerations. Control of health hazards by using respirators and protective clothing is usually considered secondary to the use of engineering control methods because of the additional burden to the employee as well as the employer in terms of training, record keeping, and enforcement.

ENGINEERING CONTROLS AT DESIGN STAGE

The best time to introduce engineering controls is when a facility is in the design phase. At that time, control measures can be integrated more readily into the design than after the facility has been built or the processes are on-line.

The systematic layout of the physical building, processes, and systems should comply with occupational safety and health standards. What is planned must be reconciled with what is permissible by law or advised by consensus standards. In any particular situation, jurisdiction and applicability of standards may become complex. When more than one agency or standard is involved, the more stringent standard can be assumed to be the controlling one. Consideration should be given to specifying design criteria that comply with proposed standards that may take effect after the facility goes on-line.

It is becoming increasingly common for facility and design engineers to consult with the industrial hygienist and environmental health and safety professional at the design phase of a new facility or process. Including industrial hygiene control measures at this point can be less costly than adding them later in the construction process. During the design phase, the proposed facility layout must be characterized with respect to construction type, proposed activities in all areas, and possible health hazards. The influence of one area on another and one work activity on another must be assessed. At this point, ergonomic concerns must be identified and corrected with proper workstation design (see Chapter 13, Ergonomics).

In terms of the building structure, it is important that the design specifications contemplate the control of moisture to minimize the likelihood of microbial growth. Microbial organisms can adversely affect indoor air quality and cause toxic or allergic responses among building occupants. Proper design of the building envelope and control of indoor relative humidity and the accumulation of condensation on HVAC equipment components will limit the availability of moisture necessary for the growth of microorganisms. It is also important to evaluate the finished materials within a facility for their propensity to generate hazardous air contaminants. For example, the installation of new carpets, furniture, flooring materials, adhesives, and paints can generate volatile organic compounds in concentrations that could result in respiratory and eye irritation in the building occupants.

When air contaminants are created, generated, or released in concentrations that can injure the health of workers, ventilation is the usual method of providing protection. However, other methods of protection should be investigated; one example is automatic operations.

Ideally, hazardous operations should be conducted in entirely closed systems, but not all processes lend themselves to this approach. When closed systems are used, raw materials can be brought to the processing site in sealed containers and their contents emptied into storage tanks or containers, minimizing employee contact with the material being processed.

All systems and components should be designed so that airborne contaminants are kept below their acceptable Threshold Limit Values (TLVs®). With respect to carcinogens, components should be designed to control levels as low as possible. Do not permit leaking of toxic chemicals from process equipment, such as pumps, piping, and containers, to cause a condition in which the TLVs® are routinely exceeded in any location where employees may be present. In industrial settings, isolate process equipment and vent to a scrubber, absorber, incinerator, or particle collector, as applicable. If feasible, remotely control the process from a protected control room.

Some work operations, if conducted separately, do not present a serious hazard, but when combined with other job operations can become hazardous in certain situations. Two types of interrelationships can exist.

The first concerns accumulation, as can arise when additional welding stations are provided in a building of fixed general ventilation or when additional noise sources are added to an already noisy work area.

The second type of interrelationship concerns many activities going on in the same area. Activities that by themselves are safe can become hazardous in certain circumstances. For example, vapor degreasing with chlorinated solvents, even when the airborne concentration of the vapors is within permissible limits, may create major hazards when the activity is near work areas where ultraviolet (UV) radiation (from welding arcs, bright sunlight, or molten metal) exists. The decomposition of these solvents caused by the UV radiation can produce phosgene gas—a potent and toxic eye and lung irritant. Merely maintaining the concentration of solvent vapor below the TLV is not satisfactory. The most positive control is to prevent the chlorinated solvent vapors from entering the welding area in any detectable concentrations, for example by using a closed degreaser. If vapors cannot be reduced to a minimum, the UV field should be reduced to a minimum by shielding the welding arc.

The problem of considering safety and health with activity and workstation relationships becomes difficult when more than three or four activities must be considered, as in laying out workstations for new or relocated manufacturing operations where 20 or more activities might require consideration. Decisions should be made to arrive at either an optimum arrangement or a preferred compromise.

Design

Occupational health hazards can best be minimized by workplace design that controls contaminants as much as possible. This requires close cooperation between the industrial hygienist and the design engineer and architect. The ideal situation would have the principles of health hazard protection so thoroughly ingrained in the design professionals that the health and safety professional need only be a passive reviewer. However, the design team needs the help of the health and safety professional during the design process to make sure that a system can be set up that does not pose safety or health hazards to the operator or facility occupants. A chemical process flowsheet should be reviewed from overall material balance, environmental, industrial hygiene, and safety perspectives (Figure 18–2).

Production processes in chemical plants should be designed so that hazardous materials are not released into the environment. It is important to keep the materials and the by-products and wastes within the closed system. Material that becomes airborne and gets into the work environment to cause personnel exposure problems can be an insignificant fraction of the total amount of material that

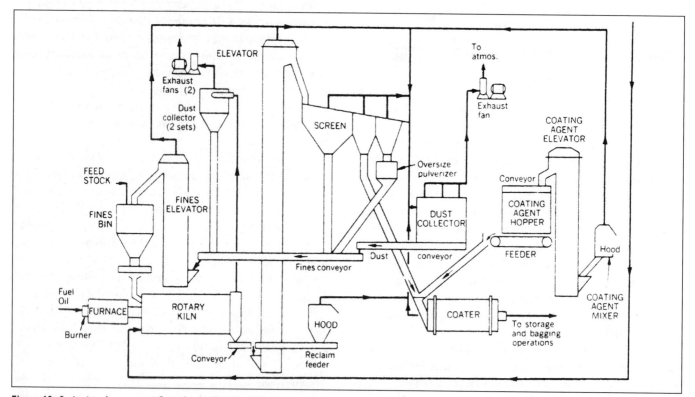

Figure 18–2. A simple process flowsheet showing the stepwise introduction of raw material and the product of each step. The extent of chemical or physical hazards that can occur at any step in the operation should be determined.

is circulated through the system. In a material balance, the quantity of material that is released into the workplace that causes the hazard can be insignificant when compared with the total amount present in the system. Nonetheless, the leak may pose an occupational health hazard.

In processes where toxic, reactive, flammable, or explosive chemicals are involved above specified threshold quantities, OSHA requires that a process hazard analysis be performed to prevent or minimize the consequences of catastrophic releases (29 CFR 1910.119).

Design factors that should be addressed include the following:

- To what degree is it possible to remove hazardous residues from a piece of equipment before it is opened?
- To what extent can a system be designed to be relatively maintenance-free?
- Can the system be designed so that the entire operation can be conducted as a closed system?
- Can the process be conducted automatically without worker involvement?
- Can the system be cleaned automatically without worker involvement?
- What precautions can be taken to prevent and detect unplanned releases?

A design engineer should have extensive knowledge not only of the main aspects of the process being created but also of the finer details, such as health hazard controls and safety devices. Design engineers are usually more familiar with the safety hazards because the effects of their being overlooked (fire, explosion) are much more obvious that those occurring when health hazards are overlooked (chronic health effects).

The same importance should be assigned to minimize contaminant dispersion in other workplace settings such as mixed-use office buildings. The architect and engineer on the design team should address the following factors:

- Has the building been designed to effectively control moisture and prevent microbial growth on construction materials and in the HVAC system?
- Are there any activities taking place in the building that use or generate hazardous materials?
- Is the fresh air intake located away from any contaminant source or air pathway for these contaminant sources?
- Has the HVAC system been designed to deliver an appropriate volume of air to each occupied space in accordance with the standards of the American Society of Heating, Refrigeration and Air Conditioning Engineers (ASHRAE)?
- Is local exhaust ventilation required in any special-use areas, such as printing operations, photo developing, welding, or solvent degreasing?

- Are any special filters required to clean incoming outside air or recirculated air?
- If tobacco smoking is permitted on the premises, is it located away from outside air intakes, doors, and operable windows? (See Chapter 21, General Ventilation of Nonindustrial Occupancies.)

When health professionals are involved early in the design process, it is possible to plan the development of sampling and analytical methods to yield exposure data concurrent with the development of the engineering design. Contaminant monitoring systems can be included as part of the engineering design. Automated leak-detection systems with chemical sensors designed into the process can yield valuable information for evaluating health hazards in the operating unit (Figure 18–3).

Similarly, contaminant monitoring systems can be installed in the ventilation system to alert building engineers of high levels of carbon monoxide or carbon dioxide, which serve as a general indicator of degrading air quality.

Neglect of the health professional-engineer-architect interaction in facility design can lead to major management problems. What could have been an easy solution in the design phase can become an extremely difficult problem later. Changes that might have been readily accomplished during the design phase must now be done as a matter of equipment change and compromise. Worse yet, it may be necessary to shut down production or evacuate employees to correct a hazard that was overlooked. Consequently, management should consider that for certain processes and materials, the initial design of facilities to minimize the health hazards may be a significant and necessary part of the investment.

Figure 18–3. This multipoint area-wide ambient air monitor is capable of detecting several different toxic or combustible gases. A single sensor point is shown. *(Courtesy of MSA-The Safety Company.)*

Maintenance Considerations

It is important to look not only at planned operations but also at the fine details of what is not supposed to be happening. These untoward events may best be described in two general classes.

First, there may be releases of contaminants into the work environment that are relatively continuous, such as flange leaks, exhaust hoods that are not completely effective, pump seals that have weakened, diffusion that occurs along valve stems, or noise emission from leaks in ill-fitting acoustic lagging on a machine. This general class of airborne contaminants or fugitive emissions may have begun as a low-level background that initially was not high enough to be of serious concern. Coupled with this is another kind of episodic exposure. As equipment becomes worn and starts to leak, the general level of ambient emissions may eventually result in significant worker exposures. Much of this leakage can be dealt with by continuous, careful, intensive maintenance; however, much of it might have been avoided in the initial design. The degree to which any possibility of leakage is engineered or designed out of a system depends to a great extent on how much these potential leaks have been anticipated.

The second class of emissions of airborne contaminants arises when a closed system or control process becomes momentarily open or uncontrolled. For instance, the acoustical lagging has to be removed from the compressor to perform some adjustments, or perhaps samples have to be collected or filters replaced. These situations are common in chemical industries. A filter change operation may occur as infrequently as once every six months; however, when problems occur it may have to be done four times a shift. The system has to be designed so that it is possible to clean and purge the filter container so that an employee can perform needed maintenance without hazard.

From time to time, the system as a whole must be shut down for cleaning and purging and afterward opened for maintenance. Under these circumstances, exposures tend to be brief, but exposure levels can be quite high and may be detected only by closely maintained industrial hygiene surveillance on a day-to-day basis.

Knowledge of the hazards that are present and the potential for the exposure that may exist in an operation gives an industrial hygienist an ideal starting point from which to develop the surveillance program. All too often this step is omitted and the industrial hygienist becomes aware of an engineering project only in the advanced stage of development. Waiting to make changes in the design until the system is about to go to construction can dramatically increase cost.

Design Specifications

The design specifications are the drawings and documents that enable the engineers and architects to precisely define the building, systems, and processes. Environmental health and safety professionals should have a clear understanding of where in these specifications health hazards may occur as a result of the process, building materials, or system design.

Review

Before a new operation or process is begun, an engineering review should be carried out that goes over the whole process to ensure that nothing was forgotten and everything will proceed as planned. Although these reviews are very detailed and time-consuming, it is worthwhile for an industrial hygienist and safety professional to be involved. Sometimes, last-minute changes in the process or equipment are made that can significantly increase or decrease the health hazard.

Start-up

The industrial hygiene surveillance begins when a process is put into operation or a facility is brought on-line and should continue for as long as the operation continues.

When a facility is brought on-line, it is recommended that the ventilation system be operated for 48 hours prior to occupancy to purge construction-related contaminants. Air balancing reports for the ventilation system should be reviewed before the building is occupied and processes involving hazardous materials commence. Problems in handling and operating procedures that were not anticipated during the design stage will become apparent when the facility is operational. Prompt correction of these problems is much easier during the early setup phase when procedures and people are still somewhat flexible.

Sample Taking

In many industrial operations, such as steel mills and petrochemical facilities, taking product samples is a common procedure. The design engineer and the industrial hygienist can choose between a product sampling system that does not provide much control and a system that provides almost total control. Each of these choices probably has some cost increment associated with it. The choice should be based on assessment of the severity of the potential health hazard.

Loading Operations

One of the most serious problems in the field of health hazard control is the loading and unloading of tank cars, tank trucks, and barges. Putting a liquid into a space previously occupied by air or vapor quickly saturates that air with vapor. It may become necessary to go to vented systems, enclosed systems, and automatic loading systems that include vapor recovery so that the vapor that is pushed out of the tank will be recovered (Figure 18–4).

Figure 18–4. Loading or unloading of tank trucks can release airborne contaminants.

Episodic exposures are difficult to control from an engineering point of view. Also, for these infrequent emergency or nonroutine events, personal protection can be the appropriate solution. However, design engineers should recognize that these exposure events will happen, that product samples must be taken, that equipment must be maintained, and that filters must be changed. The industrial hygienist working with the designer must consider how these operations can be conducted so that the worker need not be overexposed.

Hazardous Materials

Some materials must be handled carefully because of their toxicity, flammability, reactivity, or corrosivity. The processes and practices to be used must be consistent with the standards applicable to materials with these characteristics.

Stringent controls regulating mutual proximities, ventilation, sources of ignition, and design are imposed on general industry by federal codes. When potentially photochemically reactive solvents are involved, process controls and discharges to the atmosphere are subject to regulation by air-quality regulatory authorities.

Compressed gas and equipment for its use in industry are extensively referenced in the Compressed Gas Association's standards. Methods of marking, hydrostatic testing of cylinders and vessels, labeling, metering, safety devices, and pipework and outlet and inlet valve connecting are thoroughly described in pamphlets issued by the association.

Standards for the design and use of air receivers are promulgated based on the American Society of Mechanical Engineers (ASME) Boiler and Pressure Vessel Codes. The

provision and use of compressed gases in industrial settings must be carefully undertaken; otherwise, catastrophic situations may develop.

INDUSTRIAL HYGIENE CONTROL METHODS

The use of industrial hygiene control methods for reducing or eliminating environmental hazards or stressors has been recorded since 50 AD when Pliny the Elder described the use of animal bladders for protection from zinc and sulfur. In 1556 Agricola described the hazards associated with the mining industry and recommended ventilation and protective masks be used to protect workers. Merewether and Price described the principle methods for controlling dust in asbestos industries in 1930. These are the same industrial hygiene exposure control methods used today and include the following:

- substitution of a less hazardous material for one that is harmful to health
- change or alteration of a process to minimize worker exposure
- isolation or enclosure of a process or work operation to reduce the number of employees exposed, or isolation or enclosure of a worker in a control booth or area
- wet work methods to reduce generation of dust and avoid dry sweeping of dust
- local exhaust ventilation at the point of generation or dispersion of contaminants
- general or dilution ventilation to provide circulation of fresh air without drafts or to control temperature, humidity, or radiant heat load
- personal protective devices, such as special clothing or eye and respiratory protection
- good housekeeping and maintenance, including cleanliness of the workplace and adequate hygiene and eating facilities
- administrative controls, including adjusting work schedules or rotating job assignments so that no employee receives an overexposure
- special control methods for specific hazards, such as shielding, monitoring devices, and continuous sampling with preset alarms
- employee training and education that is specific to the hazards and includes work methods that help reduce contaminant exposure
- emergency response training and education
- waste treatment and disposal

A generalized diagram of these methods is shown in Figure 18–1. Each of these industrial hygiene control methods will be discussed in turn.

PRINCIPLES OF ENGINEERING CONTROLS

Substitution: Changing the Material

An often effective industrial hygiene method of control is the substitution of nontoxic or less toxic materials for highly toxic ones. However, an industrial hygienist must exercise extreme caution when substituting one chemical for another, to ensure that some previously unforeseen hazard does not occur along with the substitution. Examples of this include fire hazards, synergistic interactions between chemical exposures, or previously unknown toxicity problems attributed to the "nontoxic" substitute chemical. The classic examples of substitution as an industrial hygiene control measure include replacement of white lead in paint pigments by zinc, barium, or titanium oxides; the use of phosphorus sesquisulfide instead of white phosphorus in matchmaking; shotblasting instead of sandblasting; and substitution of calcium silicates and mineral wool for asbestos as an insulating material. Recently, new bismuth-containing alloys have replaced lead in the making of brass and bronze alloys. This substitution not only minimizes health concerns due to employee exposures to lead, it reduces the overall cost of OSHA and EPA compliance.

As technology advanced and more toxicity information became available, the substitutions of degreasing solvents progressed from carbon tetrachloride to chlorinated hydrocarbons such as perchloroethylene and trichloroethylene. When studies revealed the possible carcinogenicity of chlorinated solvents, they were replaced with chlorofluorocarbon (CFC) and hydrochlorofluorocarbon (HCFC) solvents. Because CFCs and HCFCs have been identified as ozone-depleting substances, nonflammable, less toxic hydrofluorocarbon-based solvents are being used for industrial degreasing. When substituting solvents, it is always advisable to experiment on a small scale before making the new solvent part of the operation or process. Detergent-and-water cleaning solutions or a steam-cleaning process should be considered for use in place of organic solvents.

Synthetic materials rather than sandstone can be used as grinding wheels and as nonsilica parting compounds in foundry molding operations. Removing beryllium phosphors from formulations for fluorescent lamps eliminated a serious pulmonary hazard to the workers making such lamps.

A change in the physical condition of raw materials received by a facility for further processing may eliminate health hazards. Pelletized or briquette forms of some materials are less dusty and can drastically reduce atmospheric dust contamination in some processes.

However, there are instances when substitution of some toxic materials may be impossible or impractical, as in the manufacture of pesticides, drugs, or solvents, and processes producing ionizing radiation.

Substituting less hazardous materials or process equipment may be the least expensive and most positive method of controlling many occupational health hazards and can often result in substantial savings. Exposure control by substitution is becoming more important from an environmental health and community air pollution perspective as well. Process materials should be selected only after review of their ozone depletion potential and global warming potential.

Substitution: Changing the Process

A change in process offers an ideal chance to concomitantly improve working conditions. Most changes are made to improve quality or reduce the cost of production. However, in some cases, a process can be modified to reduce the dispersion of dust or fume and thus markedly reduce the hazard. For example, in the automotive industry, the amount of lead dust created by grinding solder seams with small, high-speed rotary sanding disks was greatly reduced by changing to low-speed, oscillating-type sanders. More recently, lead solder was replaced with tin solder and silicone materials.

Brush painting or dipping instead of spray painting can minimize the concentration of airborne contaminants. Other examples of process changes are employing arc welding to replace riveting, using vapor degreasing in tanks with adequate ventilation controls to replace hand washing of parts in open containers, using ultrasonic or steam cleaning of parts instead of vapor degreasing, using airless paint-spraying techniques instead of compressed-air spraying to minimize over-spray, and employing machine application of lead oxide to battery grids, which reduces lead exposure to operators making storage batteries.

Using automatic electrostatic paint-spraying instead of manual compressed-air paint-spraying and using mechanical continuous hopper-charging instead of manual batch-charging are additional examples of a change in process to control health hazards.

Isolation

Potentially hazardous operations should be isolated to minimize exposure to employees. The isolation can be a physical barrier, such as acoustic panels used to minimize noise transmission from a whining blower or a screaming ripsaw (Figure 18–5).

The isolation can be in terms of time, such as providing remote control semiautomatic equipment so that an operator does not have to stay near the noisy machine constantly; or the worker may be isolated or enclosed in a soundproof control booth supplied with a clean source of air.

Isolation is particularly useful for jobs requiring rela-

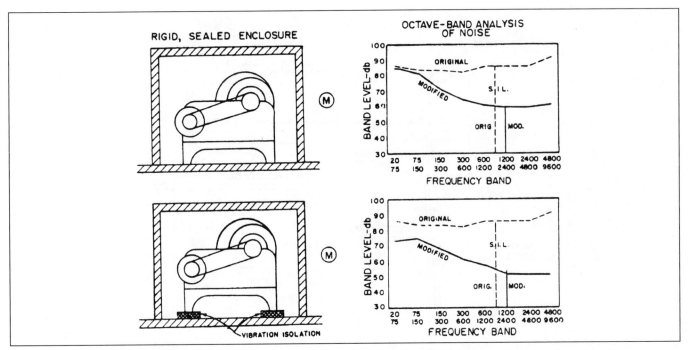

Figure 18–5. Noise can be abated by enclosing an operation (top), and adding vibration isolators reduces sound transmission even more (bottom).

tively few workers and when control of particulates by other methods is difficult or not feasible. The hazardous job can be isolated from the rest of the work operations, thus eliminating exposures for the majority of workers. Additionally, the workers performing tasks at adjacent workstations where contaminants are released should be protected by installing local ventilation systems (Figure 18–6).

In foundries, the shakeout operation may be performed in isolation using a robotic arm/manipulator, which removes the castings from their sand mold. Alternatively, there are fully enclosed vibratory drums and shakeouts with sand reclamation systems to minimize airborne dust.

Exposure to employees and building occupants may likewise be minimized by isolating hazardous materials in place. Exposure to asbestos-containing materials and lead-based paint can be abated in some instances by sealing these materials in airtight enclosures to prevent their disturbance.

It may not be feasible to enclose and exhaust all operations. Abrasive blasting operations, such as those found in shipbuilding and construction, are examples. The sandblasting should be done in a specified location, which is as far away as is practical from other employees. Another way to isolate the sandblasting is to do it when the least number of other employees would be exposed.

Other work that can be scheduled to minimize the number of workers exposed to a hazard includes blasting in mines or quarries, which can be done at the end of or between shifts; and maintenance procedures, such as cleaning tanks

and replacing filters on weekends when few workers are present. In offices, remodeling work and metal maintenance should be performed during off hours when building occupants will not be exposed to construction dust and vapors from paints, adhesives, cleaning solvents, and finishes.

In some operations, other methods of control cannot be relied on to maintain contaminants at desired levels, so these operations (such as asbestos and lead remediation projects) should be isolated. Without the use of proper isolation techniques such as enclosures under negative pressure, remediation projects may generate contaminants in large quantities that disperse throughout a work area or building to expose all workers to a hazard, although only a few of them are actually engaged in the operation.

Equipment isolation can be the easiest method of preventing hazardous physical contact. Insulating a hot water line may not be economical from a strictly heat conservation standpoint but may be necessary if that line is not sufficiently isolated from people.

When very toxic materials are to be processed, automation can be used to allow handling of equipment from a remote location. Robotic techniques can reproduce many industrial procedures, thus eliminating worker exposures. The work area can be viewed by remote-control television cameras or mirrors. The degree of isolation required depends on the toxicity of the contaminant, the amount released, and work patterns around the process. Moving a process to another area is often sufficient. In other cases, a

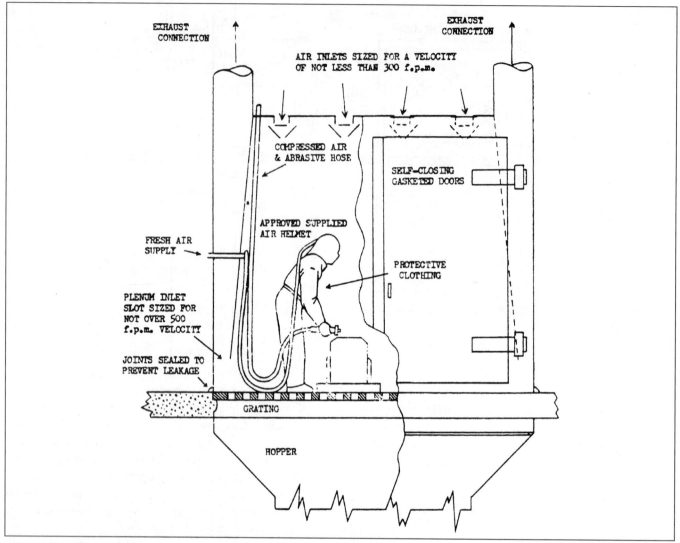

Figure 18–6. Air inlets and exhaust are arranged to sweep contaminated air away from the worker's breathing zone in this enclosed sandblast area. Downdraft averages 80 fpm over the entire floor area. Air should exhaust downward (as shown) or on two sides of the room at the floor line. *(Courtesy Connecticut State Department of Health.)*

control room supplied with fresh air may be needed to isolate the process from employees monitoring the operation.

Many modern chemical facilities have centralized control rooms with automatic sampling and analysis, remote readout of various sensors, and on-line computer processing of the data and operation of the process. Some operations require complete enclosure and remote control so that nobody is exposed, as in many processes involving nuclear radiation (Figure 18–7).

Total enclosure can be accomplished by mechanization or automation to ensure that workers do not come into contact with toxic materials. The crane operators in a large foundry or in a bulk material storage building can be provided with a completely enclosed cab ventilated with filtered air under positive pressure to keep out contaminants. The

same principle can be applied to heavy equipment operators in mines, coal yards, scrap metal recycling facilities, and soil remediation projects. In automatic stone-crushing, grinding, and conveying processes, only periodic or emergency attendance is required by an operator; therefore, small, well-ventilated rooms, supplied with filtered air and strategically located within a large workroom, can be occupied by the workers during the major part of the workshift.

Automated plating tanks, paint-dipping operations, and similar processes can be located in separate rooms. When continuous supervision of such operations by a worker is not necessary, general ventilation may be adequate to prevent buildup of air contamination in the workroom. If necessary, an exposed worker can be given a respirator for protection during the brief periods of exposure.

Figure 18–7. Some operations require complete enclosure.

Segregating a hazardous operation or locating one or more such operations together in a separate enclosure or building not only sharply reduces the number of workers exposed but greatly simplifies the necessary control procedures.

Enclosing the process or equipment is a desirable method of control, because the enclosure prevents or minimizes the escape of contaminants into the workroom atmosphere. Enclosure should be one of the first control measures attempted, after substitution has been considered. Additional precautions must be taken when cleaning enclosed equipment or during start-up or shutdown to avoid exposure to high concentrations of contaminants.

Enclosed equipment is usually tightly sealed and is opened only during cleaning or filling operations. Examples of such equipment include glove boxes (Figure 18–7), air-less-blast or shot blast machines for cleaning castings, and abrasive blasting cabinets.

In the chemical industry, the isolation of hazardous processes in closed systems is a widespread practice. This explains why the initial manufacture of toxic substances is often less hazardous than their subsequent use under less well-controlled conditions at other locations. In other industries, complete enclosure is often the best solution to severe dust or fume hazards, such as those from sandblasting or metal-spraying operations.

All equipment, whether enclosed or automated, requires maintenance and repair, during which control measures may have to be removed. In such circumstances, safety procedures must be specified, including confined space entry and lockout/tagout procedures to work on such maintenance operations. These nonroutine maintenance, repair, and cleaning operations can pose the greatest exposure risks to those performing the task as well as other trade workers in the area and should be carefully reviewed by health and safety professionals.

Isolation can also be provided by appropriate use of distance and time, for example, with respect to radiation and noise exposure. Both radiation and noise exposures decrease with an increase in the distance from the source and a decrease in the exposure time.

Ventilation

Ventilation is a method of controlling the work environment by strategically supplying (adding) or exhausting (removing) air. Ventilation is used to dilute the concentration of contaminants to acceptable levels, to remove contaminants at their source, and to heat or cool the work environment. Ventilation can also serve to control humidity, odor, and other environmental conditions for worker comfort. (See Chapters 19, Local Exhaust Ventilation, Chapter 20, Dilution Ventilation of Industrial Workplaces, and Chapter 21, General Ventilation of Nonindustrial Occupancies for more information.)

General Ventilation

General ventilation systems supply and exhaust large volumes of air from work spaces. They are used for temperature and humidity control or to dilute the concentration of an air contaminant below hazardous levels. This system uses natural convection through open doors or windows, roof ventilators, and chimneys, or air movement produced by mechanical fans or blowers. Exhaust fans mounted in roofs, walls, or windows constitute general ventilation.

With the exception of comfort control, general ventilation should be used only in situations meeting the following criteria:

- when small quantities of air contaminants are being released into the work environment at fairly uniform rates
- when there is sufficient distance between the worker and the contaminant source to allow sufficient air movement to dilute the contaminant to safe levels
- when only contaminants of low toxicity are being used
- when there is no need to collect or filter the contaminants before the exhaust air is discharged into the community environment
- when there is no possibility of corrosion or other damage to equipment from the diluted contaminants in the work environment air

The major disadvantage of general, or dilution, ventilation is that employee exposures can be very difficult to control near the source of the contaminant where sufficient dilution has not yet occurred. For this reason, local exhaust ventilation is most often the proper method to control exposure to toxic contaminants.

When air is exhausted from a work area, consideration must be given to providing makeup, or replacement, air, especially during winter months. Makeup air volumes should be equivalent to the air being removed; the air should be clean and the temperature and humidity regulated as required for comfort.

Care should be taken in selecting the makeup air intake locations so that toxic gases and vapors from discharge stacks, emergency vents, or operations outside of the building that generate hazardous contaminants are not brought back into work areas. When exhaust stacks and air supply inlets are not separated adequately, the exhaust air may be directed into the air inlet and recirculated to work areas. Inadvertent recirculation of exhaust air contaminants is a common problem, which ideally should be addressed in the design phase. It is not uncommon to find the air supply intake for a facility located adjacent to a loading dock or alley where gasoline and diesel engine vehicles idle. This can result in contamination of the fresh air supply and will almost certainly cause exposure or odor problems, or both.

Because equipment for moving, filtering, and tempering air is expensive, some engineers attempt to save money by recirculating some exhaust air into the supply system. Adequate monitoring of the recirculated air is necessary to prevent buildup of harmful contaminants. Recirculation of exhaust air may be forbidden in certain locations, such as smoking lounges. Check state and federal regulations and American Society of Heating, Refrigerating, and Air-Conditioning Engineers (ASHRAE) standards.

Design of the general ventilation system in a nonindustrial or office environment must take into account conditions that affect worker comfort, such as temperature and humidity, odor level, the space provided per occupant, and concentrations of tobacco smoke if permitted in the facility. Construction practices, construction materials, and heightened public awareness have made indoor air quality an important ventilation design issue. ASHRAE Consensus Standard 62–2010 should be referred to for design parameters. (See Chapter 21, General Ventilation of Nonindustrial Occupancies.)

General ventilation should not be used where there are major localized sources of air contamination (especially highly toxic dusts and fumes); local exhaust ventilation is more effective and economical in such cases. More information on general ventilation is presented in Chapter 20, Dilution Ventilation of Industrial Workplaces.

Local Exhaust Ventilation

Local exhaust ventilation is considered the classic method of control. Local exhaust systems capture or contain contaminants at their source before they escape into the work area environment. A typical system consists of one or more hoods, ducts, an air cleaner if needed, and a fan (Figure 18–8).

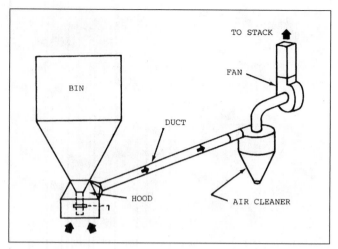

Figure 18–8. A typical local exhaust ventilation system consists of hoods, ducts, air cleaner, fan, and stack. *(Courtesy American Conference of Governmental Industrial Hygienists.)*

Local exhaust systems remove air contaminants rather than just dilute them, but removal of the contaminant is not always 100 percent effective. This method should be used when the contaminant cannot be controlled by substitution, changing the process, isolation, or enclosure. Although a process has been isolated, it still may require a local exhaust system.

A major advantage of local exhaust ventilation systems is that they require less airflow than dilution ventilation systems. The total airflow is important for plants that are heated or cooled, because heating and air-conditioning costs are a significant operating expense. Also, local exhaust systems can be used to conserve or reclaim reusable materials.

Two main principles govern the proper use of local exhaust ventilation to control airborne hazards. First, the process or equipment is enclosed as much as possible; and second, air is withdrawn at a rate sufficient to ensure that the direction of airflow is into the hood and that the airflow rate will entrain the contaminant into the airstream and thus draw it into the hood (Figure 18–9).

The proper design of exhaust ventilation systems depends on many factors, such as the temperature of the process, the physical state of the contaminant (dust, fume, smoke, mist, gas, or vapor), the manner in which it is generated, the velocity and direction with which it is released to the atmosphere, its toxicity, and the location of the worker (Figure 18–10).

Local exhaust systems can be difficult to design. The hoods or pickup points must be properly shaped and located to capture air contaminants and the fan and ducts must be designed to draw the correct amount of air through each hood. Hood selection is based on the characteristics

Figure 18–9. The fumes arising from lead melting operations are controlled by local lateral-slot exhaust ventilation. *(Courtesy of Ford Motor Co.)*

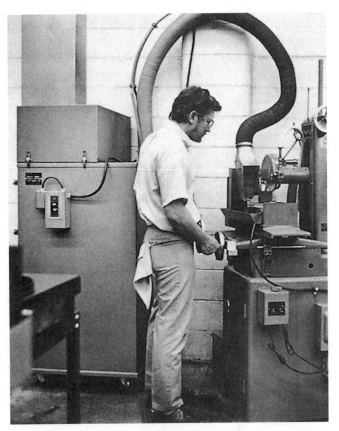

Figure 18–10. A typical local exhaust ventilation system—a dust collector—traps contaminants near their source, so the worker is not exposed to harmful concentrations.

of the contaminants and how they are dispersed. The hood should be located so that the contaminant is moved away from the operator's breathing zone. The use and selection of an air cleaner are dependent on the contaminant, its concentration, and air pollution standards. (See Chapter 19, Local Exhaust Ventilation of Industrial Occupancies, for more details.)

The low-volume, high-velocity exhaust system uses small volumes of air at relatively high velocities to control dust. Control is achieved by exhausting the air directly at the point of dust generation using close-fitting hoods. Capture velocities are relatively high, but the exhaust volume is low. For flexibility, small-diameter, lightweight plastic hoses are used with portable tools, resulting in very high duct velocities. This method allows the application of local exhaust ventilation to portable tools, which otherwise require relatively large air volumes and large ductwork when controlled by conventional exhaust methods.

Portable local exhaust ventilation systems can be useful for facilities where dust- or fume-generating operations are not stationary. These machines capture contaminated air, filter particulate matter, and exhaust cleaned air into the work area. They can be a cost-effective solution for welding stations and enclosed areas where renovation and construction are being performed (Figure 18–10).

After the local exhaust ventilation system is installed and set in operation, its performance should be checked to see that it meets the engineering specifications—correct rates of airflow and duct velocities. Its performance should

be rechecked periodically as a maintenance measure.

Full details on the design and operation of local exhaust ventilation systems are given in Chapter 19, Local Exhaust Ventilation of Industrial Occupancies.

There are some circumstances, such as on construction sites where a fixed local exhaust hood is not a practical solution to control airborne particulates. Dust collection can be achieved on portable tools like sanders, grinders, and saws with a dust extraction vacuum equipped with high efficiency filters.

ADMINISTRATIVE CONTROLS

Engineering controls are to be used as the first line of defense against workplace hazards. Some circumstances require administrative controls, such as in cases when engineering controls are not technologically feasible, or during the installation of engineering controls. Administrative control of occupational hazards, such as work period reduction, job rotation, appropriate work practices, proper maintenance, and personal hygiene, depends on constant employee implementation or intervention, which makes it a less desirable form of control.

However, administrative controls are often useful in supplementing engineering controls to achieve acceptable exposure levels. The majority of the expanded OSHA health standards require administrative control measures including hygienic change rooms, regulated areas, and specific work and hygiene practices.

Reduction of Work Periods

Reduction of work periods is another method of control in limited areas where engineering control methods at the source are not practical. Heat stress can be managed by following a work-rest regimen that prevents excessive fatigue and reduces heart rate. For example, in the job forge, foundry, and construction industries, especially in hot weather, frequent rest periods are used to minimize the effects of exposures to high temperatures, thereby lessening the danger of heat exhaustion or heatstroke.

For workers who must labor in a compressed-air environment, schedules of maximum length of workshift and length of decompression time have been prepared. The higher the pressure, the shorter is the workshift and the longer the decompression time period.

However, job rotation, when used as a way to reduce employee exposure to toxic chemicals or harmful physical agents, must be used with care. Rotation, although it may keep exposure below recommended limits, exposes more workers to the hazard. Job rotation is not permitted by certain OSHA standards for highly toxic material such as asbestos and 1,3-butadiene.

Special considerations need to be made when rotating jobs that require repetitive motion and physical labor. If job rotation is implemented to relieve the strain on one area of the body by using a job that requires another area, careful analysis by an expert trained in ergonomics should be made. This will ensure that some of the same muscles and tendons are not still being used in the new activity.

Wet Methods

Airborne dust hazards can often be minimized or greatly reduced by applying water or other suitable liquid. Wetting of floors before sweeping to keep down the dispersion of harmful dust is advisable when better methods, such as vacuum cleaning, cannot be used.

Wetting down is one of the simplest methods of dust control. Its effectiveness, however, depends on proper wetting of the dust. This may require the addition of a wetting agent (surfactant) to the water and proper disposal of the wetted dust before it dries out and is redispersed.

Significant reductions in airborne dust concentrations

have been achieved by the use of water forced through the drill bits used in rock drilling operations. Many foundries successfully use water under high pressure for cleaning castings in place of sandblasting. Airborne dust concentrations can be kept down if molding sand is kept moist, molds with cooled castings can be moistened before shakeout, and the floors are wetted intermittently.

High-pressure water washing, used in a contained space or enclosure and with proper work practices, can effectively reduce airborne dusts and asbestos in the demolition and construction industry. In some instances it may be necessary to blanket the dust source completely. The particles must be thoroughly wetted by means of high-pressure sprays, wetting agents, deluge sprays, or other procedures while in the containment.

Batch charging of materials that are slightly moistened or that are packaged in paper bags rather than in a dry bulk state may eliminate or reduce the need for dust control in storage bins and batch mixers.

Workers in quarries, construction and demolition projects, road building, and similar outdoor worksites will benefit from the distribution of water on roadways by water tank trucks equipped with spray bars.

Personal Hygiene

Personal hygiene is an important control measure. The worker should be able to wash exposed skin promptly to remove accidental splashes of toxic or irritant materials. If workers are to minimize contact with harmful chemical agents, they must have easy access to hand-washing facilities (Figure 18–11).

Inconveniently located wash stations invite such undesirable practices as washing at workstations with solvents, mineral oils, or industrial detergents, none of which is appropriate or intended for skin cleansing. Many workplace hand cleansers are available as plain soap powders, abrasive soap powders, abrasive soap cakes, liquids, cream soaps, and waterless hand cleaners and sanitizers.

Powdered soaps provide a feeling of removing soils because of stimulation of the nerve endings in the skin by the abrasives. Waterless cleaners have become very popular because they remove most soils, such as greases, grimes, tars, and paint, with relative ease. Be aware, however, that some waterless hand cleaners have solvent bases. Soaps may also contribute to industrial dermatitis. Sensitive persons may require pH-neutral soaps or moisturizing agents. Antibacterial soaps are necessary in workplaces where infectious agents may be present.

The provision of washing facilities, emergency showers, and eyewash fountains is required in areas where hazardous or extremely toxic materials are handled. These should

Figure 18–11. To minimize worker contact with harmful chemical agents, hand-washing facilities must be conveniently located. *(Photo courtesy of the Bradley Corporation. Used with permission.)*

be located in an area convenient to employee workstations in case of accidental exposures. The practice of removing particulates from clothing or disposable coveralls using compressed air should be forbidden. This practice causes the material to become airborne and increases the risk of employee and bystander exposure. In addition to creating a respiratory hazard, compressed air can cause hearing damage and physical injury. Particles can enter the eyes and abrade the skin, and air under pressure can enter the bloodstream through breaks in the skin or through the mouth or nose, causing serious internal damage to the body.

When designated or suspected carcinogens are involved, stringent regulation of work areas and activities must be undertaken. The OSHA carcinogen regulations state that the employer must set aside a regulated area where only the particular carcinogen may be produced or handled. Only authorized and specially trained personnel with proper personal protection may be allowed to enter that area.

The eating, storage, or drinking of foods and liquids in areas where toxic materials are used should be forbidden.

All entrances to the regulated area where biohazards or suspected carcinogens are handled must be properly posted to inform employees of hazards and regular and emergency procedures required. Set aside special areas for employees to change clothing and protective equipment.

Many of the major OSHA health standards, such as asbestos, lead, and coke oven emissions, require hygienic change rooms and showers.

Housekeeping and Maintenance

Good housekeeping plays a key role in the control of occupational health hazards. Good housekeeping is always important, but where there are toxic materials, it is of paramount importance, and often mandated by OSHA regulation. Remove dust on overhead ledges and on the floor before it can become resuspended into the air because of disturbance by traffic, vibration, and random air currents *(reentrainment)*. Reentrainment can result in workers and bystanders being inadvertently exposed to toxic materials.

Immediate cleanup of any spills of toxic materials is a very important control measure. A regular cleanup schedule using vacuum cleaners is an effective method of removing dirt and dust from the work area. Never use compressed air to remove dust from rafters, ledges, and other surfaces.

Good housekeeping is essential where solvents are stored, handled, and used. Immediately remedy leaking containers or spigots by transferring the solvent to sound containers or by repairing the spigots. Clean up spills promptly. Deposit all solvent-soaked rags or absorbents in airtight metal receptacles and remove daily to a safe location for proper disposal.

Maintenance Provisions

If the thermostat or a seal on a vapor degreaser fails or is accidentally broken, excessive concentrations of solvent might quickly build up in the work area unless the equipment is shut down immediately and the necessary repairs made. Abnormal operating conditions can be detected by continuously monitoring airborne contaminants with instrumentation that triggers an alarm when concentrations exceed an established level. The workers or supervisors can then take steps to reduce airborne levels.

Large-scale, periodic equipment and process shutdowns typically result in many crafts working to clean and repair process, transport, and power generation equipment. Exposures of all workers to hazardous or toxic materials from different activities in a given area should be anticipated. Provisions should be made for cleaning the equipment and piping systems by flushing them with water, steam, or a neutralizing agent (depending on the conditions involved) to render them nonhazardous before dismantling. Safety considerations, such as the control of hazardous energy (lockout/tagout) and confined space entry, should be evaluated prior to conducting the maintenance work. Before any equipment is disassembled, a plan for suitable short-term exposure controls such as portable local exhaust ventilation, isolation enclosures, and protective clothing and respirators should be developed. Contaminated equipment, tools, and protective clothing must be decontaminated before they are removed from the work area.

Air monitoring during nonroutine exposure is important in order to develop a database for these types of exposures and select the most effective exposure controls for future maintenance activities. Operations and maintenance programs for hazardous materials or agents such as lead, asbestos, bioaerosols, and noise are important tools in the prevention of employee exposures. These programs are designed to identify and control hazardous conditions by means of periodic inspection, contaminant monitoring, and hazard abatement.

SPECIAL CONTROL METHODS

Many of the general methods mentioned previously (either alone or in combination) can be used for the control of most occupational health hazards. A few special methods, however, deserve particular mention.

Shielding

This is one of the better control measures used to reduce or eliminate exposures to physical stresses such as heat, ionizing radiation, and nonionizing radiation. Lead and concrete are two materials commonly used to shield employees from high-energy ionizing radiation sources, such as particle generators and radioisotopes. Specialized shielding can also be used for protection from electric and magnetic fields (see Chapter 11, Nonionizing Radiation).

Shielding can also be used to protect employees against exposure to radiant heat sources. Furnaces can be shielded with shiny reflective aluminum panels. Nonreflective metal is not effective because it may act as a "black body," which absorbs and then reradiates the heat.

WASTE DISPOSAL

Industrial hygiene controls include the proper disposal of wastes. Management and disposal of hazardous waste are regulated by the complex requirements of several governmental agencies (see Chapter 30, Government Regulations). To develop an appropriate waste management plan, employers must first make the following determinations:

- Are potentially regulated waste materials generated at this site?
- Are the wastes hazardous, special, infectious, or radioactive by regulatory definition? Have they been tested to determine hazardous characteristics?
- Can wastes be treated and rendered innocuous prior to disposal?
- Can wastes be recycled as part of the process?
- Given the quantities of waste generated, is the company a small-quantity or large-quantity generator?
- Is the company a waste generator, transporter, or treatment/storage/disposal facility?

These determinations will provide much of the information necessary to choose treatment and disposal alternatives. These decisions are particularly onerous, as generators of hazardous waste are perpetually responsible for on-site and off-site damages to the environment and worker and community health. This is often referred to as cradle-to-grave responsibility.

Disposal of hazardous materials must be done by highly trained individuals under strict supervision. Procedures should be established in accordance with the EPA's Resource Conservation and Recovery Act (RCRA) and other applicable regulations for the safe disposal of hazardous chemicals, toxic residues, and other contaminated waste, as well as containers of chemicals that are no longer needed and containers whose labels have been lost or obliterated.

A competent chemist can determine the best way to neutralize or detoxify small amounts of chemicals that are no longer needed. In some instances it may be appropriate to perform experimental investigations to determine a means of neutralizing and rendering waste products harmless before full-scale disposal operations are begun. There are a number of methods by which some dangerous chemicals can be rendered safe for disposal.

A number of facilities are available for off-site disposal of hazardous materials. All of them can be expensive and none of them provides a universal means of disposal for all hazardous materials. Landfills, incinerators, and chemical treatment facilities are the most commonly used disposal options for hazardous waste. Before a disposal facility is chosen, a determination should be made that the facility is competently managed, is in regulatory compliance, and has significant financial resources.

PERSONAL PROTECTIVE EQUIPMENT

When it is not feasible to render the work environment free of occupational health hazards, it may be necessary to protect the worker from the environment with personal protective equipment. The use of personal protective equipment should be considered a last resort, when engineering or administrative controls are not possible or when they are not sufficient to achieve acceptable limits of exposure. Personal protective equipment may be appropriate during short exposures to hazardous contaminants, such as during nonroutine equipment maintenance or emergency responses to spills. The primary disadvantage of personal protective devices is that they do not eliminate the hazard from the workplace, and thus their failure results in immediate exposure to the hazard. A protective device may become ineffective without the wearer's knowledge, resulting in serious harm. The integrity and fit of a personal protective device are vital to its effectiveness. (See Chapter 23, Personal Protective Equipment.)

The Occupational Safety and Health Administration (OSHA) requires that employers perform a workplace hazard assessment to determine if the use of personal protective equipment is warranted and to determine the proper selection of protective devices (29 CFR 1910.132). Successful use of any personal protective equipment requires that a program be established and administered. The purpose of the program is to ensure that personal protective equipment is properly chosen, used, and maintained to protect workers. Employee training and record keeping as required by regulation must be part of this program.

Respiratory Protective Devices

Respiratory protective devices are normally restricted for use in intermittent exposures or for operations that are not feasible to control by other methods. Respiratory protection should not be considered a substitute for engineering control methods.

Respiratory protection devices offer emergency or short-term protection. Respirators are a primary protective device for normal operations only when no other method of control is possible (Figure 18–12).

Respirators should be used when it is necessary to enter a highly contaminated atmosphere for rescue or emergency repair work; as a means of escape from a suddenly highly contaminated atmosphere; and for short-term maintenance or repair of equipment located in a contaminated atmosphere. Respirators should be used for normal operation in conjunction with other control measures when the contaminant is so toxic that other control measures, such as ventilation, cannot be relied upon to keep the atmosphere safe from contamination, for example in the case of asbestos and other carcinogens such as benzidene and methyl chloromethyl ether.

An approved respirator must be selected for the particular hazard and environment in which it is to be used (Figure 18–13).

Figure 18–12. Respirators are used when the work operation cannot be controlled by other methods.

The type of air contaminant, its expected maximum concentration, the possibility of oxygen deficiency, the useful life of the respirator, the escape routes available, and other factors must all be considered in selecting the proper type of respirator for emergency use or for standby purposes. When these factors are not known with certainty, the device providing the greatest factor of safety must be used.

There are two general types of respiratory protective devices: air-purified respirators, which remove the contaminant from the breathing air by filtering or chemical absorption, and air-supplied respirators, which provide clean air from an outside source or from a tank. Full details of types of respirators certified by the National Institute of Occupational Safety and Health (NIOSH) should be obtained from the manufacturer. Only NIOSH-certified respirators should be used (42 CFR Part 84). (See Chapter 22, Respiratory Protection, for more details.)

Half-mask cartridge respirators cover the mouth and

Figure 18–13. An approved respirator must be selected for the particular hazard and environment.

nose. Full-facepiece respirators also protect the eyes. For dust protection, there are a large number of respirators that have met the requirements established by NIOSH, which call for high filtering efficiency and low resistance to breathing. Respirators have been certified for protection against metal fumes, mists, radionuclides, ammonia, and pesticide application.

Air-line respirators may be preferred by workers to chemical cartridge or mechanical filter respirators because they are cooler and offer no resistance to breathing; however, they require a proper source of Grade D breathing air (ANSI/Compressed Gas Association Commodity Specification for Air, G–7.1–2004) and a suitable compressor located outside of the contaminated atmosphere.

Self-contained breathing apparatuses, which are mostly used for emergency and rescue work, have face masks attached by hoses to compressed air cylinders. Such apparatuses enable a worker to enter a contaminated or oxygen-

deficient atmosphere, up to certain limits specified in the respirator certifications.

Selection of the proper type of respiratory protective equipment should be based on the following factors:

- identification of the substance or substances for which respiratory protection is necessary and the activities of the workers
- determination of the hazards of each substance and its significant physical and chemical properties, particularly the presence or absence of oil particles
- determination of the maximum levels of air contamination expected, probability of oxygen deficiency, and the condition of exposure
- determination of the period of time for which respiratory protection must be worn
- determination of the capabilities, physical characteristics, and limitations essential to the safe use of the respiratory protective device
- identification of facilities needed for maintenance
- determination of the location of the hazardous work area in relation to the nearest area with respirable-quality air
- occupational exposure limit for substance
- respirator assigned protection factors.

Because wearing a respirator often becomes uncomfortable after extended periods, the worker must fully realize the need for protection or he or she will not wear it. To obtain the worker's cooperation, the following factors are important:

- Prescribe respiratory protective equipment only after every effort has been made to eliminate the hazard.
- Explain the situation fully to the worker.
- Instruct the worker in the proper use and limitations of the respirator.
- Fit the respirator carefully according to OSHA guidelines.
- Provide for maintenance and cleanliness, including sterilization before reissue.

A respirator program is required by OSHA whenever respirators are used. The OSHA requirements for a respiratory protection program are contained in the Code of Federal Regulations for General Industry at 29 CFR 1910.134. The standard also addresses employee use of respirators on a voluntary basis when not required by OSHA or the employer. Certain OSHA standards (such as asbestos and lead standards) have other specific regulations on respirator use. Check the Code of Federal Regulations for this information. (See Chapter 22, Respiratory Protection, for more details.)

Protective Clothing

Chemical-protective clothing is worn as a barrier to a chemical, physical, or biological hazard that may cause injury if it contacts or is absorbed by the skin. Applications of chemical protective clothing include

- emergency response;
- hazardous waste site cleanup and disposal;
- asbestos removal; and
- agricultural application of pesticides.

A broad range of chemical-protective clothing is available to protect the body. Gloves, gauntlets, boots, aprons, and coveralls are available in a number of materials, each designed for protection against specific hazards. Choosing the most appropriate chemical-protective clothing depends on the hazards present and the tasks to be performed. Protective clothing is manufactured from different materials that protect against acids, alkalis, solvents, oils, and other chemical and physical agents. The selection should take into account the performance of the protective clothing in exposure reduction, the physical limitations created by using protective clothing, and site-specific factors. Physical and psychological stress, impaired mobility and vision, and heat stress influence or limit the selection of protective clothing.

The factors that should influence selection of protective clothing are

- clothing design;
- material chemical resistance;
- physical properties;
- ease of decontamination;
- cost; and
- chemical-protective clothing standards.

Chemical-protective clothing is manufactured in a variety of styles and configurations to protect specific parts of the body or the entire body. Selection of the proper equipment should include design considerations such as clothing configuration and construction, sizes, ease of putting on and taking off, accommodation of other selected ensemble equipment, comfort, and restriction of mobility.

The effectiveness of protective clothing against chemical exposure depends on how well the material resists permeation, degradation, and penetration. Permeation is the process by which a chemical moves through a protective clothing material on a molecular level. Degradation occurs when chemical contact causes deterioration of the physical properties of the protective clothing material, resulting in, for example, discoloration, swelling, or loss of physical strength. Penetration is the direct flow of a chemical through closures, seams, pinholes, or other imperfections in the protective clothing material.

No material protects against all chemicals and combinations of chemicals. Protective clothing material recommendations for chemicals based on an evaluation of chemical resistance test data are available in *Quick Selection Guide to Chemical Protective Clothing* (Mansdorf, 2007) and from

vendors. Many vendors and manufacturers supply charts with permeation and degradation test data and material recommendations. Protective garments constructed of rubber, neoprene, nitrile, polyvinyl chloride, and other synthetic fibers and coatings are available. It is important to select the material that protects most effectively against the specific hazard in question (acids, alkalis, oils, fibers, etc.). For mixtures of chemicals, materials having the broadest chemical resistance should be worn.

Chemical-protective materials offer wide ranges of physical qualities in terms of strength, resistance to physical hazards, and operation/effectiveness in extreme environmental conditions. The following parameters should be considered: physical strength; tear, puncture, cut, and abrasion resistance; flexibility to perform needed tasks; flame resistance; and integrity and flexibility under hot and cold extremes.

The difficulty involved in decontaminating protective clothing and the endurance of the material may dictate whether disposable or reusable clothing is selected. The relative cost of replacement and decontamination depend on the garment and the hazard. Limited-use/disposable chemical-protective clothing can be provided to minimize employee exposure to hazardous chemicals at a reasonable cost. These types of garments are not designed to provide high levels of protection and should be used appropriately.

Body protection clothing, ranging from aprons to limited use/disposable coveralls to totally encapsulating chemical-protective suits, is constructed of a flexible plastic or rubber film, sheet, coated plastic, or laminate. In contrast, totally encapsulating chemical-protective (TECP) suits are designed to prevent chemical exposure to the wearer.

For intermittent protection against radiant heat, reflective aluminum clothing is available. These garments need special care to preserve their essential shiny surface. Air-cooled jackets and suits are available to minimize the risk of heat-related illnesses. For protection against ionizing radiation, garments constructed of lead-bearing materials are available.

OSHA requires that employers provide, and require employees to use, appropriate hand protection when there is a risk of absorption of harmful substances; chemical or thermal burns; extreme temperatures; or severe cuts, lacerations, abrasions, or punctures (29 CFR 1910.138).

Gloves are the most common form of chemical-protective clothing. Gloves should be selected for a specific job according to the guidelines above. Manufacturers provide a large selection of gloves made of butyl rubber, natural rubber, neoprene, nitrile rubber, polyvinyl alcohol, polyvinyl chloride, Teflon®, Viton®, and other construction materials. The material that has the highest level of protection should be used. A thicker glove will increase the level of protection but will result in loss of dexterity. Impregnated gloves protect against cuts and abrasions but are not liquid-proof, and they are therefore not chemical resistant. Cotton or leather gloves are useful for protecting the hands against friction and dust.

More information on the subject of protection against skin hazards and the use of barrier creams is presented in Chapter 3, The Skin and Occupational Dermatoses. Also consult applicable OSHA regulations and ANSI standards.

Eye and Face Protection

Eye and face protection includes safety glasses, chemical goggles, and face shields. The correct type of protector is chosen based on the hazard (such as corrosive liquids and vapors, foreign bodies, or ultraviolet radiation). Goggles fit snugly to the face, preventing chemical exposure in the event of a splash, and, depending on the style, may prohibit vapor exposure. Face shields are designed only to prevent direct splash exposures to the face and not to provide complete eye protection. Eye protection from exposure to ultraviolet radiation, such as that produced in welding operations, is accomplished with filter lenses of the correct shade mounted in the welding helmet.

Many chemicals in the workplace can cause significant eye damage and facial scarring from direct chemical contact. It is important that the protective device be worn at all times when the hazard is present. (See Chapter 5, The Eyes, for further information. Also consult applicable OSHA regulations and ANSI standards.)

Hearing Protection

Personal hearing protectors, such as earplugs or earmuffs, can provide adequate protection against noise-induced hearing impairment. The wearer is afforded effective protection only if the hearing protectors are properly selected, fitted, and worn. Like other types of personal protective equipment, these devices should be used as an exposure control alternative when noise exposures cannot feasibly be reduced below the OSHA permissible limit. Hearing protection must be used when the noise level is 85 dBA or higher and/or the employee has suffered a significant threshold shift that is work related or aggravated by occupational noise exposure.

There are primarily two forms of hearing protectors: insert types, which seal against the ear canal walls, and earmuffs, which seal against the head around the ear. Choice of the proper hearing protection should take into account the physiological and anatomical characteristics of the wearer, the noise exposure dose, the work activity, and environmental conditions (e.g., dusty atmosphere, requirement to hear radio communications). (See Chapter 9, Industrial Noise, for more information on hearing conservation.)

EDUCATION AND TRAINING

Proper training and education are critical to supplement engineering controls and ensure the success of exposure controls in the workplace. It is important that all employees be provided the health and safety information and instruction needed to minimize their occupational health risk and that of their coworkers.

In a typical manufacturing plant, the primary responsibility for safe operation and control rests with the line organization of the operations department. This generally would include a first-line supervisor, a shift supervisor, and a facility area manager, all people familiar with every aspect of the day-to-day operation of the facility and the manufacturing process and readily available when critical decisions must be made.

The education of supervisors usually is process and equipment oriented. The aim of the safety and health professional should be to teach them about the safety and health hazards that may be found in their work areas. The supervisors should be told when and under what circumstances to request aid in solving the problems those hazards pose. Supervisors should be knowledgeable and well informed about hazardous processes, operations, and materials for which they are responsible so that they can issue work orders to eliminate the problem.

Short courses on industrial hygiene can be an easy way to transmit a lot of valuable information with a small expenditure of time. Industrial hygiene short courses for managers should identify health hazards in broad areas. The courses should also consider the cost-benefit relationships of controlling health hazards in the work environment.

The worker must know the proper operating procedures that make engineering controls effective. If the worker performs an operation away from an exhaust hood, the purpose of the control measure will be defeated and the work area may become contaminated. Workers can be alerted to safe operating procedures through booklets, instruction signs, labels, safety meetings, and other educational devices.

The safety and health professional, by persuading a worker to position the exhaust hood properly or to change the manner of weighing a toxic material or of handling a scoop or shovel, can do much to minimize unnecessary exposure to air contaminants. For normal facility operations, a prescribed health hazard evaluation routine should be set up. This should include monitoring the exposures of the personnel involved. It can be accomplished by keeping a record of the exposures to chemical and physical agents in work areas.

In addition to the normal operating instructions that each employee is given when starting a new job, employees assigned to areas where exposures to toxic chemicals can occur must, by law, be given a special indoctrination program. Also be sure to give employees training in how to respond to emergencies. Information on when not to respond is also critical. Many deaths have occurred when untrained workers rushed in to save fallen coworkers and were overcome themselves. To minimize operator error, employees should be supplied with a detailed instruction manual outlining procedures for all foreseeable situations and an opportunity to adequately review the information.

Health hazards affect the workers who are exposed and work directly with materials, equipment, and processes. These employees should know about the effects of exposure to the materials and energies they work with through training, Safety Data Sheets, and warning labels so that controls are properly used. An adequately informed worker can often anticipate and take steps to control health hazards before they result in adverse health effects or injuries.

Workers should be given reasons for wearing respirators, protective clothing, and goggles. They also should be informed of the necessity of good housekeeping and maintenance. Because new materials are constantly being marketed and new processes being developed, reeducation and follow-up instruction must also be part of an effective industrial hygiene control program.

Over 100 specific OSHA standards contain training requirements. Some of these standards make it the employer's responsibility to limit certain job assignments to employees who have had special training that defines them as certified, competent, or qualified with respect to a particular hazard.

OSHA has developed Voluntary Training Guidelines to assist employers in determining training needs as well as developing and conducting the training. OSHA encourages employers to follow the model provided in the Voluntary Training Guidelines. The model can be used to develop training programs for a variety of hazards and to assist in compliance with training requirements in specific standards.

The guidelines are as follows:
- Determine whether training is needed.
- Identify training needs.
- Identify goals and objectives.
- Develop learning activities.
- Conduct the training.
- Evaluate program effectiveness.
- Improve the program effectiveness.

OSHA has established a voluntary Outreach Training Program that assists employers in training workers on how to identify, abate, avoid, and prevent occupational hazards. These 10- and 30-hour classes can be used by companies to provide general health and safety training to employees and supervisors.

Additional specific training requirements are set forth by OSHA for general industry in the Hazard Communication, Process Safety Management, Asbestos, Lead, and Bloodborne Pathogens Standards, among others. For example, the Hazard Communication Standard requires a training program that covers the following types of information:
- requirements of the standard
- identification of operations in the workplace where hazardous materials are present
- methods and observations used to detect the presence of hazardous materials in the work area
- physical and health hazards of those materials
- hazards associated with chemicals in unlabeled pipes
- hazards of nonroutine tasks
- measures that employees can take to protect themselves from these hazards
- explanation of the hazardous materials labeling system
- explanation of Safety Data Sheets (SDSs)
- details on the availability and locations of Hazardous Material Inventory, SDSs, and other printed Hazard Communication Program materials.

There are also training requirements in the OSHA construction industry standards such as occupational health and environmental controls, personal protective and life-saving equipment, among others.

The future of state and federal training requirements, led by California's Illness and Injury Prevention Act (Senate Bill 198), focuses on preventing rather than reacting to hazards. Under California's regulation, employers must identify the person responsible for implementing a Written Injury and Illness Prevention Program and provide training in health and safety matters to all employees. This approach is intended to improve efforts to prevent workplace hazards by identifying and evaluating hazards during periodic scheduled inspections.

HEALTH SURVEILLANCE

Health surveillance, although not an occupational exposure control, can be used to prevent health impairments by means of periodic evaluations. A health surveillance program includes preplacement, periodic, special purpose, and hazard-oriented examinations.

Medical surveillance is mandated by specific OSHA; Mine, Safety, and Health Administration; and Environmental Protection Agency (EPA) regulations. Over 30 OSHA standards and proposed standards contain medical surveillance requirements. Among these are the asbestos, lead, formaldehyde, and hazardous waste operations standards.

Hazard-oriented medical surveillance monitors biological indicators of absorption of chemical agents based on analysis of the agent or its metabolite in blood, urine, or expired air. Inorganic lead absorption is measured by blood lead levels, and carbon monoxide absorption is indicated by carboxyhemoglobin levels in blood or carbon monoxide in exhaled air. Refer to Chapter 26, The Occupational Medicine Physician, for a complete discussion of health surveillance.

SUMMARY

Control of occupational exposures to injurious materials or conditions may be accomplished by means of one or more of the following methods:

- proper design engineering
- substitution of less toxic materials or changes in process
- isolation or enclosure of the source or the employee
- local exhaust ventilation at the point of generation or dissemination of the air contaminant
- general ventilation or dilution with uncontaminated air
- maintenance and housekeeping
- personal protective equipment
- employee information and training on health hazards and exposure controls
- proper waste disposal practices

One or a combination of these methods may be necessary to prevent excessive exposures to hazardous materials or physical agents.

Education of workers and periodic workplace inspections are paramount in the prevention of injury and illness. If engineering and administrative controls and the use of personal protective equipment are to be effective in minimizing occupational health risk, workers must be properly trained.

Management is responsible for furnishing the facilities and products required to keep the workplace healthful and safe. The worker also has responsibilities in a health hazard control program, including the following: to heed warnings, to wear protective equipment if it is required, to use the local exhaust ventilation system properly, and to observe all company rules relating to cleanup and disposal of harmful materials.

BIBLIOGRAPHY

Allen RW, Ells MD, Hart AW. *Industrial Hygiene.* Englewood Cliffs, NJ: Prentice Hall, 1976.

American Conference of Governmental Industrial Hygienists, Committee on Industrial Ventilation. *Industrial Ventilation: A Manual of Recommended Practice,* 25th ed. Cincinnati, OH: ACGIH, 2004.

American Industrial Hygiene Association. *Recognition, Evaluation, and Control of Indoor Mold.* Fairfax, VA: AIHA, 2008.

American National Standards Institute. *American National Standard for Respiratory Protection ANSI Z88.2-1992.* New York: ANSI, 1992.

American National Standards Institute. *Compressed Gas Association G-7.1-2004,* 5th ed. Washington, DC: ANSI, 2004.

American Society of Heating, Refrigerating and Air-Conditioning Engineers. ANSI/ASHRAE Standard 62.1-2010: Ventilation for Acceptable Indoor Air Quality. Atlanta: ASHRAE, 2010.

Anna DH. *The Occupational Environment: Its Evaluation, Control, and Management,* 3rd ed. Fairfax, VA: AIHA, 2011.

Beddows NA. Safety and health criteria for plant layout. *National Safety News,* Nov. 1976.

Burgess WA. *Recognition of Health Hazards in Industry: A Review of Materials and Processes,* 2nd ed. New York: Wiley, 1995.

California Illness and Injury Prevention Program, Title 8, Section 3203 Senate Bill 198, 1989.

Cralley LV, Atkins PR. *Industrial Environmental Health: the Worker and the Community.* New York: Academic Press, 1975.

Cralley LV, Cralley LJ, Caplan KJ. *Industrial Hygiene Aspects of Plant Operations,* vols. 1-3. New York: Macmillan, 1985.

Environmental Protection Agency, 42 USC 6901-6992k (1976) as Amended Through P.L. 107-377, Dec 31, 2002.

Grund E. *Lockout/Tagout: The Process of Controlling Hazardous Energy.* Itasca, IL: National Safety Council, 1995.

Harris R, ed. *Patty's Industrial Hygiene,* 5th ed. vols I–IV. New York: Wiley, 2000.

Key MM, Henschel AF, Butler J, et al., eds. *Occupational Diseases: A Guide to Their Recognition,* rev. ed. (DHEW [NIOSH] Publication No. 77-181.) Cincinnati, OH: NIOSH, June 1977.

Lindgren GF. *Managing Industrial Hazardous Waste.* Chelsea, MI: CRC/Lewis, 1989.

Lynch J. *Industrial hygiene input into plant design.* Paper presented at 65th National Safety Congress, Chicago, October 18, 1977.

Macher J, ed. *Bioaerosals: Assessment and Control.* Cincinnati, OH: ACGIH, 1999.

Mansdorf SZ, Forsberg R. *Quick Selection Guide to Chemical Protective Clothing,* 5th ed. New York: Van

Nostrand Reinhold, 2007.

McDermott HJ. *Handbook of Ventilation for Contaminant Control,* 3rd ed. Ann Arbor, MI: Ann Arbor Science Publisher, 2001.

McRae A, Whelchel L, Rowland HS, eds. Toxic Substances Control Sourcebook. Germantown, MD: Aspen Systems Corporation, 1978.

Merewether ERA, Price CW. *Report on Effects of Asbestos Dust on the Lungs and Dust Suppression in the Asbestos Industry.* London: H. M. Stationery Office, 1930 .

National Institute for Occupational Safety and Health. *42 CFR Part 84 Respiratory Protective Devices, Final Rules and Notice.* Washington, DC: NIOSH, June 8, 1995.

National Institute for Occupational Safety and Health. *Engineering Control Research Recommendations.* DHHS (NIOSH) Publication No. 76-180. Cincinnati, OH: NIOSH, Feb. 1976.

National Institute for Occupational Safety and Health. *NIOSH Guide to the Selection and Use of Respirators Certified Under 42 CFR 84.* DHHS (NIOSH) Publication No. 96-101. Washington, DC: NIOSH, 1996.

Occupational Safety and Health Administration. Hazard Communication Standard (50 FR 51852), Dec. 20, 1985 and (61 FR 5507), Feb. 13, 1996. Washington, DC: OSHA, 1985 and 1996.

Occupational Safety and Health Administration. Respiratory Protection Standard (76 FR 33606), June 8, 2011. Washington, DC: OSHA, 2011.

Occupational Safety and Health Administration. Personal Protective Equipment Standard (59 FR 16362), April 6, 1994 and (76 FR 33606) June 8, 2011. Washington, DC: OSHA, 1994 and 2011.

Occupational Safety and Health Administration. Training Requirements in OSHA Standards and Training Guidelines (OSHA 2254). Washington, DC: OSHA, 1998 (revised).

Occupational Safety and Health Reporter. *Hazard Communication Training Programs and Their Evaluations* 31:9701– 9730. Washington, DC: Bureau of National Affairs.

Occupational Safety and Health Reporter. *Special Report: California Employers Face New Compliance Duties as State Moves to Strengthen Safety and Health Enforcement.* 1593–1596. Washington, DC: Bureau of National Affairs, 1991.

Peterson JE. *Industrial Health.* Englewood Cliffs, NJ: Prentice Hall, 1977.

U.S. Department of Labor, OSHA. *Hazardous Waste Operations and Emergency Response,* 51 FR Part 244. Washington, DC: U.S. DOL, Dec. 19, 1986.

CHAPTER 19

Local Exhaust Ventilation

by Henry J. McDermott, CIH, CSP, PE

*T*his chapter describes the following aspects of local exhaust ventilation (LEV) systems: typical components, principles of operation, methods to evaluate performance, and ways to resolve problems. It is designed to give safety and industrial hygiene practitioners sufficient knowledge to determine where LEV is needed, participate with engineers and others during system design, and evaluate and troubleshoot existing systems.

LEV systems are covered in this chapter while dilution ventilation is described in Chapter 20. The bibliography for both chapters appears at the end of Chapter 20, Dilution Ventilation for Industrial Workplaces.

INTRODUCTION

Ventilation is an important method for reducing employee exposures to airborne contaminants. However, ventilation is only one way to reduce exposures and may not be as economical or effective as other control techniques. A couple examples of other control techniques are reducing emissions into the work area by sealing equipment to prevent contaminant release or substituting less toxic or volatile chemicals.

There are two major types of industrial ventilation:

- Dilution systems reduce the concentration of contaminants released into the workroom by mixing with air flowing through the room. Either natural or mechanically induced air movement can be used to dilute contaminants. These systems are discussed in Chapter 20.
- LEV systems capture or contain contaminants at their source before they escape into the workroom environment. The main advantage of local exhaust systems is that they remove contaminants rather than just dilute them. Even with LEV, some airborne contaminants may still be

in the workroom air because of uncontrolled sources or less than 100 percent collection efficiency at the hoods. A second major advantage of local exhaust is that these systems require less airflow than dilution ventilation systems in the same applications. The total airflow is especially important for plants that are heated or cooled since heating and air conditioning costs are an important operating expense.

LOCAL EXHAUST SYSTEM COMPONENTS

A typical local exhaust system consists of the following elements (Figure 19–1):

- Hoods—any point where air is drawn into the ventilation system to capture or control contaminants. Some hoods are designed to fit around existing machinery while others are located next to the contaminant source. Even a plain duct opening is called a "hood" if that is where air enters the system. Different hoods work in different ways: some reach out and capture contaminants; others catch contaminants thrown into the hood; and still others contain contaminants released inside the hood and prevent them from escaping into the workroom. Some hood designs feature a long, narrow slot to distribute the airflow along the length of an open surface tank, welding bench, or laboratory hood.

- Ducts—the network of piping that connects the hoods and other system components.

- Fan—the air-moving device that provides the energy to draw air and contaminants into the exhaust system and through the ducts and other components. It functions by inducing a negative pressure, or suction, in the ducts leading to the hoods and positive pressure in the system after the fan. The fan converts electrical power into pressure and increased air velocity.

- Air cleaner—a device that may be needed to remove airborne materials before the exhaust air is discharged into the community environment. Air cleaners to remove both solid (particulate) and gaseous contaminants are available.

Although not formally part of an LEV system, the arrangement for supplying makeup air to the work area that is being ventilated is also very important. An insufficient quantity of makeup air may cause poor fan operation, inefficient combustion in furnaces, drafts, and problems with slamming doors in the work area.

An LEV system is usually planned to fit existing machinery or industrial processes. A hood shape and location are chosen based upon the source of contamination. The airflow volume into each hood is then determined from reference sources such as the American Conference

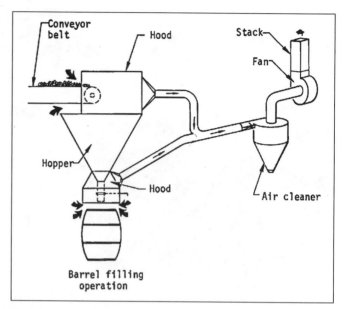

Figure 19–1. Typical local exhaust ventilation system. *(Source: McDermott, ACGIH, 2000. Reprinted with permission.)*

of Government Industrial Hygienists (ACGIH®) *Industrial Ventilation Manual*. Next, the need for an air cleaner is determined, and, if needed, a type and size are selected. With this information the duct layout can be determined and the duct diameters calculated. Finally, the fan type and size needed to draw the required amount of air while overcoming friction and other resistance can be determined. After installation, the system is tested to ensure that it is meeting design criteria. System design is beyond the scope of this chapter; however, the references listed at the end of Chapter 20 describe how to design LEV systems.

Hoods

The hood is the most important part of an LEV system. No local exhaust system will work properly unless the hoods retain or capture enough of the contaminants to reduce the contaminant concentration in the workroom air to below acceptable limits. Both the design and location of the hoods are critical in determining whether a system will work. A poor hood design may prevent the ventilation system from performing adequately, even with high airflow into the hood.

Hood selection is an area where the health and safety professional can make a significant contribution because the keys to good hood selection include the following: knowledge of hood and airflow principles, understanding of the plant processes, and familiarity with employee work patterns around each process. In many plants, the health and safety staff has the best overall understanding of these three areas. Fortunately, once the fundamentals of hood selection are understood, there is a ready reference source for specific

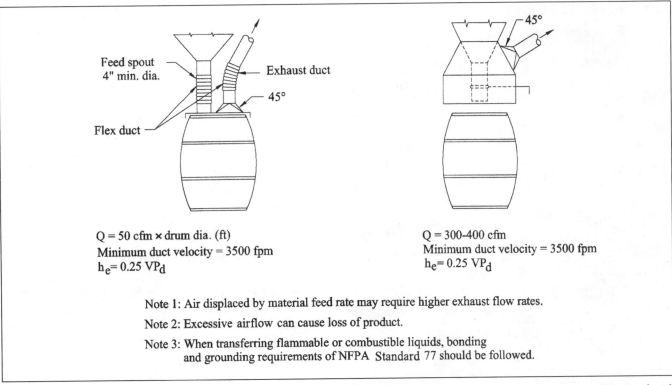

$Q = 50$ cfm × drum dia. (ft)
Minimum duct velocity = 3500 fpm
$h_e = 0.25$ VP$_d$

$Q = 300\text{-}400$ cfm
Minimum duct velocity = 3500 fpm
$h_e = 0.25$ VP$_d$

Note 1: Air displaced by material feed rate may require higher exhaust flow rates.

Note 2: Excessive airflow can cause loss of product.

Note 3: When transferring flammable or combustible liquids, bonding and grounding requirements of NFPA Standard 77 should be followed.

Figure 19–2. Typical hoods for controlling drum-filling operations. *(Source: Industrial Ventilation Manual, ACGIH, 2010. Reprinted with permission.)*

hood designs. The ACGIH *Industrial Ventilation Manual* contains almost 150 design plates (Figure 19–2) showing layout, design parameters, and airflow recommendations for different hoods.

Hood Types

Three different types of hoods are used in local ventilation systems: capturing hoods, enclosures, and receiving hoods. Each works to control contaminants according to one of the following principles:

• Capturing Hoods—hoods that "reach out" to capture contaminants in the workroom air (Figure 19–3). Airflow into the hood is calculated to generate sufficient capture velocity in the air space in front of the hood. The needed capture velocity depends on the amount and motion of contaminants and contaminated air (Table 19–A). This type of hood is widely used since it can be placed alongside the contaminant source rather than surrounding it as with an enclosure. The primary disadvantage is that large air volumes may be needed to generate an adequate capture velocity at the contaminant source. Other disadvantages are that cross drafts in the workroom can severely degrade the capture efficiency of the hood, and the reach of most capturing hoods is limited to about 2 ft from the hood opening.

• Enclosures—hoods that surround the contaminant source as much as possible. Contaminants are kept inside the enclosure by air flowing in through openings in the enclosure (Figure 19–4). Laboratory hoods and paint spray booths are typical examples of this hood type. The quantity of air required for contaminant control is calculated by multiplying the inward air velocity needed to prevent escape by the areas of the openings into the enclosure. The more complete the enclosure, the less airflow is needed for control. Employees generally do not work inside enclosures while contaminants are being generated, although they may reach into the enclosure as long as they do not breathe contaminated air. Because of low exhaust rates, enclosures are often the most economical hoods to install if the open air of the enclosure is not large. Inward face velocities of 100-150 ft/min are typical. Good room conditions are critical for proper enclosure performance, including sufficient replacement air, supply outlets located and designed to avoid drafts, and protection against disruptive air currents from open doors and foot traffic near the hoods. When employees work near the open face of an enclosing hood (e.g., laboratory hood), turbulence caused by their bodies may draw contaminants out of the hood into their breathing zone. The turbulence is generally greater with higher face velocity into the hood.

Figure 19–3. A capturing hood reaches out to draw in contaminants.

• Receiving Hoods—Some processes throw a stream of contaminants in a specific direction. For example, a furnace may emit a hot stream of gases that rises above the unit, while rotating equipment often throws material tangentially from the point of contact between the spinning equipment and workpiece. The ideal hood for this type of process is one that is positioned so it catches the contaminants thrown at it (Figure 19–5). A major limitation to the use of receiving hoods is that gases, vapors, and the very small particles that can be inhaled and retained

in the human respiratory system do not travel very far in air unless carried by moving air. This means that receiving hoods may not be very useful for health protection ventilation systems unless the process emits quantities of hot air or air with sufficient velocity to carry the respirable contaminants into the hood.

In addition to these three major hood classifications, two special hood types are used in LEV systems:

• Slot Hoods—Some capturing hoods and enclosures feature a narrow slot to distribute the inward airflow across the entire hood. By definition, a slot is at least five times as long as it is high. Typical examples are open surface tanks or a long soldering bench; both have limited space for a hood yet have a need for good air distribution over their entire lengths (Figure 19–6). Similarly, a laboratory hood has slots along the back panel to develop more uniform air velocity through the hood opening. One disadvantage of a slot hood is that it creates more energy loss than a hood without a slot. This is due to the turbulence and high air velocity through the narrow slot. Extra suction is needed to move the air through the slot, which requires a larger fan than for a comparable system with no slot hood.

It is important to realize that a high slot velocity does not significantly increase the reach of the hood. The purpose of the slot is solely to distribute the inward velocity evenly along the length of the slot. As a rule-of-thumb, a slot velocity of 2,000 ft/min often gives good air distribution without excessive pressure loss.

• Canopy Hoods—A canopy hood, which is positioned over a source of contaminant release, generally can be used only as a receiving hood over hot processes to collect the gases and vapors rising into the hood. A kitchen range hood is a typical example of a canopy hood; steam from cooking food rises into the hood due to thermal head. Canopies for unheated processes must be designed as capturing hoods since the hood is required to reach out to draw the contaminants into the hood. The large airflow volumes needed to develop adequate capture velocities below the canopy, plus the two-foot limitation on capture distance, often make these hoods impractical. The solution is another type of capturing hood, such as a side draft

TABLE 19–A	Typical Capture Velocities	
Dispersal energy of contaminants	*Typical capture velocity, ft/min*	*Examples*
Very low	50 – 100	Evaporating liquid
Low	100 – 200	Welding
Moderate	200 – 500	Barrel filling
High	500 – 2000	Grinding, abrasive blasting

Figure 19–4. An enclosure-type hood keeps contaminants released inside the hood from escaping into the workroom air.

or slot hood, or an enclosure. However, even over a hot process, a canopy cannot be used when workers must lean over the tank or process because the workers will breathe the contaminated air as the contaminants rise.

Ducts

Ducts carry air between the hoods, air cleaner, fan, and discharge stack. Common duct materials for LEV systems include galvanized steel, aluminum, stainless steel, plastics, and heavy-duty elastomers. Stainless steel and specialty plastics are used where protection against corrosion is needed. Light-weight, wire-wrapped, flexible fabric ducts are usually not recommended for LEV systems because of their tendency to accumulate settled material and sag unless rigidly supported, tendency to collapse under suction, and because of the difficulty in cleaning out settled material.

Selecting duct diameters for a system is often a trade-off between initial and operating cost. Smaller diameter ducts are less expensive to fabricate and install than larger diameter ducts. However, the resulting higher duct velocities in smaller diameter ducts increase pressure losses, thus requiring a larger fan with higher power consumption. Systems carrying particulates generally need to maintain a certain minimum transport velocity to avoid material settling in the ducts. For common dusts, this velocity is often 3,000–4,000 ft/min. For more dense materials, larger particles, or sticky materials, the minimum velocity needed is higher. Although systems handling vapors and gases have no minimum duct velocity criteria, as a general rule, duct velocities of 2,000–3,000 ft/min usually result in a good balance between initial duct construction cost and fan operating cost. Hood design diagrams in the ACGIH *Industrial Ventilation Manual* usu-

ally specify minimum duct velocity criteria for the system.

Air movement is always accompanied by friction where the air meets the duct surface. As a result, the air velocity close to the duct wall is low while at the center of the duct the velocity is higher than the overall average value. Figure 19–7 depicts a very simplified view of the duct velocity profile; any disturbances to smooth airflow such as elbows, branch duct entries, or air cleaners cause an uneven distribution that gradually returns to the typical profile illustrated in the figure.

In addition to friction, turbulence occurs in the ducts because of changes in air velocity and direction. Some loss will occur at every hood, elbow, duct enlargement, or duct junction. Since the fan must be large enough and powerful enough to move the required quantity of air while overcoming the friction and turbulent losses, it is important to avoid duct features that cause unnecessary pressure drop. These include narrow ducts, small radius elbows, and perpendicular junctions where two ducts join.

Another duct consideration is the duct segment just before the fan. The fan can do the greatest amount of beneficial work on incoming air only if the airflow into the fan is straight and uniform. Spinning or nonuniform flow patterns reduce the fan's air volume and/or static pressure output. Major reasons for poor flow patterns are elbows, dampers, duct junctions, or other flow disturbances near the fan. For an existing system, installing flow straighteners in the inlet duct can help to restore straight flow into the fan.

The ACGIH *Industrial Ventilation Manual* contains guidelines for other duct design parameters, such as pressure loss factors, provisions for clean-out ports, and duct wall thickness.

Exhaust Stacks

Every LEV system should have at least a short, straight duct

Figure 19–5. A receiving hood catches contaminants thrown out by the process such as this rotating wire wheel.

Figure 19–6. A slot hood allows for ventilation of a larger work area such as this soldering bench.

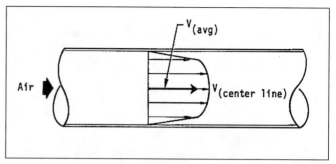

Figure 19–7. Velocity distribution in a duct. The average duct velocity is less than the centerline velocity. *(Source: McDermott, ACGIH®, 2000. Reprinted with permission.)*

or exhaust stack attached to the fan outlet. This helps to change high, uneven velocity patterns at the fan outlet into a uniform flow and results in a phenomenon called *static pressure regain*. This permits the fan to be more efficient in moving air through the system.

Exhaust Discharge Reentry into Buildings

The proper stack height, location, and discharge velocity are important in minimizing reentry of exhausted contaminants into the building and in avoiding problems when the contaminants reach ground level.

Exhaust plume reentry can occur when contaminated air flows on the roof or toward the ground around the building due to either *roof boundary wake* or *crosswind-induced down draft*.

Roof Boundary Wake Reentry

Airflow patterns around buildings are complex, consisting of several discrete air turbulence and recirculating zones. Generally, the air layers near the roof tend to wash across the roof or circulate so they hit the downwind side of the building or the ground behind the building. There is a theoretical distance above the roof where the wind-induced air currents carry contaminants up away from the roof. Ideally, the stack height should be sufficient to discharge the exhaust plume into this zone so it will not contaminate intakes, and where sufficient dilution occurs before the plume reaches the ground or adjacent buildings. A high stack discharge velocity (3,000 ft/min or higher) helps to disperse contami-

nants since the air jet action can increase the effective stack height except under severe wind conditions. Wind velocity also impacts this type of reentry:

- Very low wind speed allows plume to rise because of discharge velocity and any thermal head.
- As wind velocity increases, the first effect will be to decrease plume rise and the resulting dilution.
- Still higher winds will increase turbulence, which increases dilution.

So the worst case often occurs with moderate wind.

For a rectangular building, the discharge should be higher above the roof than the value (H_C) approximated from the dimensions of the building in the direction of the prevailing wind (Figure 19–8):

$$H_C = 0.22[(\text{Dimension}_S)^{0.67} \times (\text{Dimension}_L)^{0.33}] \quad (1)$$

where H_C = Height of roof wake boundary above roof, ft
Dimension_L = Larger of building height or width, ft
Dimension_S = Smaller of building height or width, ft

The stack height should be greater than the calculated "H_C".

Example: For a rectangular building 20' high × 60' wide × 120' long, what is the approximate height to the roof wake boundary (H_c) above the roof when wind direction is blowing toward the 20' × 60' side of building?

Using Equation (1):
$$H_C = 0.22[(\text{Dimension}_S)^{0.67} \times (\text{Dimension}_L)^{0.33}]$$

For this example, D_S = 20 ft and D_L = 60 ft.
$$H_C = 0.22[(20)^{0.67} \times (60)^{0.33}]$$
$$H_C = 0.22[(7.4) \times (3.9)] = 6.3 \text{ ft}$$

So the exhaust stack should terminate at least 6.3 ft above the roof.

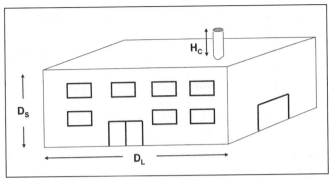

Figure 19–8. The stack height should be greater than H_c to discharge contaminants above the roof boundary layer of recirculating air.

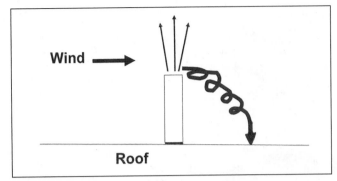

Figure 19–9. Crosswinds can shear the discharge off at the stack outlet and push it down onto the roof.

Crosswind-induced Down Draft Reentry

A strong crosswind can shear the exhaust discharge off at the stack outlet and push it down onto the roof (Figure 19–9). This phenomenon is based on wind velocity and exhaust discharge velocity:

- Normal dispersion (no down draft) occurs when discharge velocity is greater than 150 percent of the wind velocity.
- Slight down draft occurs when exit velocity is approximately equal to wind velocity.
- A significant down draft is likely when exit velocity is 50 percent or less of the wind velocity.

The stack exit velocity for a typical LEV system is about 3000 ft/min (34.1 mph) to keep rain out of the stack. For this discharge velocity: normal dispersion occurs for crosswinds up to 23 mph; slight down draft expected for crosswind speeds of about 35 mph; and, significant down draft may occur for cross winds of 68 mph or higher.

Wind direction is another important factor in minimizing reentry problems. If there is a prevailing wind direction at the site, it should help to locate the stack on the downwind side of the roof. However carefully the stack and air intakes are located, the wind will often blow from other than the prevailing direction. Therefore, the occurrence of some reentry usually cannot be ruled out, so in very sensitive situations, air cleaners on the discharged air or relocation of discharge stack or air intakes may be needed to eliminate problems.

Fans

The fan generates the suction in the system that draws contaminated air into the hoods and through the ducts. A variety of different fans are available, but they all fall into one of two main classes: centrifugal fans or axial flow fans. Centrifugal fans move air by centrifugal action. Blades on a rotating fan wheel throw air outward from the center inlet at a higher velocity or pressure than air entering the fan.

With axial fans, the air travels parallel to the fan shaft and leaves the fan in the same direction as it entered. A screw or propeller action produces airflow.

In LEV systems, centrifugal fans are more widely used than axial fans because they are usually quieter, less expensive to install and operate, and generate higher pressures than axial flow fans of the same airflow capacity. Centrifugal fans can be divided into three categories depending on the shape and setting of the fan wheel blades (Figure 19–10):

- *Radial-blade fans* (Figure 19–10a) have flat blades that extend straight out from the center hub. They are used for dust systems since their flat blades minimize the buildup of dust on the blades. These fans also have large openings between blades and are therefore less likely to clog. They can be built with thick blades to withstand erosion and impact damage from airborne solids. Their major disadvantage is that they are the least efficient fan for local exhaust systems, and so are the noisiest.
- *Forward-curved blade fans* (Figure 19–10b) are useful when large volumes of air must be moved against moderate pressures with low noise levels. These fans have many cup-shaped blades that accelerate the air and discharge it at a higher velocity than the fan wheel tip is moving.
- *Backward-inclined/backward-curved blade fans* have blades that are inclined backward from the direction of fan wheel rotation (Figure 19–10c). The blades are of uniform thickness. If they are straight (flat), the fan is called a backward-inclined blade fan; if the blades are curved back, the fan is called a backward-curved blade fan. Since these fans are more efficient than the forward-curved fan, they are often used for handling large volumes of air containing little dust. Airfoil fans are a modification of the backward-curved blade fan. The blades of airfoil fans are shaped like the cross section of an airplane wing. This shape reduces noise and allows the fan to function smoothly without pulsing airflow through its entire operating range.

(a) RADIAL BLADE FAN

(b) FORWARD CURVED FAN

(c) BACKWARD INCLINED FAN

Figure 19–10. Common types of centrifugal fans. *(Source: McDermott, ACGIH, 2000. Reprinted with permission.)*

Fans perform at their maximum efficiency only when the airflow into the fan is smooth. Any design feature in the system that causes turbulence or spinning air motion at the fan inlet will reduce the fan's ability to move air and generate pressure. The most common cause of inlet problems is a duct elbow too close to the fan inlet. Elbows should be at least five duct diameters from the fan inlet unless turning vanes in the elbow or another method is used to straighten the airflow.

An elbow too close to the fan outlet will also decrease performance because of the high velocity, turbulent flow at the outlet. Elbows should be at least five duct diameters, and preferably ten diameters, away from the fan outlet.

Air-Cleaning Devices

The purpose of this section is to give a broad overview of the types of air cleaners that are available. An important step in system design is the determination of whether an air cleaner is needed to reduce the amount of contaminants discharged to the environment. Local regulations usually are the major factor in this decision.

The ideal air cleaner for a specific application would have these features: low initial and operating cost, high efficiency for the contaminants, no decline in operating efficiency or any service interruptions between scheduled cleaning and maintenance cycles, and provisions for nor-

mal maintenance and cleaning without hazardous employee exposures.

The types of devices to consider depend primarily on the physical state of the contaminants (i.e., whether they are particulates or gases/vapors). For most situations, no single device is highly efficient for both small particulates and for gases/vapors. Scrubbing devices are widely used to collect some particles and gases or vapors in a single unit, but these combination units are generally not highly efficient for fine particles.

Particulate Removal

Typical air cleaners for particulates include the following:

- *Filters* trap particulates as the exhaust gas flows through a porous medium. Filters may be made of woven or felted (pressed) fabric, paper, or woven metal, depending on the application. They are available in a variety of configurations, such as mats, cartridges, bags, and envelopes. Filters have the general advantage of being able to handle varying exhaust gas flow rates and particle loadings. Filter devices fall into two major categories: disposable filters that often use inexpensive materials and are available in different configurations, and reusable filter elements in a housing that is equipped with a cleaning mechanism for periodic removal of trapped material. Selection of disposable or reusable filters is based on the expense of replacing the elements versus the added initial cost of the filter-cleaning mechanism.

- *Electrostatic precipitators* charge particles by means of an electric field that is strong enough to produce ions that adhere to the particles. The charged particles are then collected with a weaker electric field that causes the particles to migrate toward and adhere to the electrode with the opposite charge. Precipitators find greatest use in systems where gas volume is large and high collection efficiency for small particles is needed.

- *Cyclones* impart a circular motion to the exhaust gas that causes particulates to move to the outer part of the airstream where they impact the cyclone walls. Since air velocity is lower at the wall, the particulates drop down the wall into a collection hopper at the bottom. Cyclones may also be operated as wet collectors if a water spray is installed to wet the particles at the inlet. This increases the effective size of small particles, thus increasing collection efficiency.

- *Wet scrubbers* contact particles with water or another liquid and then collect the droplets. To collect extremely fine particles, it is necessary to generate small droplets moving at high speed. Scrubbers can remove particles as small as 0.2 μm; however, the energy required to generate small droplets and cause adequate contact rises exponentially as the particle size decreases. Scrubbers that utilize absorption or chemical reaction as a collection mechanism are also widely used for gas and vapor removal.

The baghouse type air cleaner (Figure 19–11) is a typical example of a particulate air cleaner. It consists of either tubular fabric filters or canister filters arranged in a housing along with the cleaning mechanism, which can be a means of blowing air back through the filter elements from the clean side or, for fabric filter elements, an automatic or manual shaking mechanism. Chunks of the dust cake that are dislodged during the cleaning cycle should be large enough so that they are not re-entrained in the exhaust gas stream, or the section being cleaned should be isolated from the remainder of the bag-house during its cleaning cycle. Baghouses can collect almost all particles greater than 1 μm in diameter as well as a large percentage of submicron particles.

Gas and Vapor Removal

Major removal techniques for gases and vapors are absorption, adsorption, and oxidation:

- *Absorption* is a diffusion process in which molecules are transferred from the exhaust gas to a liquid. The diffusion occurs because there is a gradient between the contaminant concentration in the exhaust gas and the liquid phase. This causes the contaminant to move from the higher level in the gas phase to the lower concentration in the liquid. The laws of mass transfer govern absorption. Mass transfer occurs at the interface between the gas or vapor molecule and the liquid and is enhanced by the following factors:
  - high interfacial area between the exhaust gas and the liquid
  - turbulent contact between the two phases
  - high solubility of the gas or vapor in the liquid phase
  - higher temperature, which affects solubility
- For easily absorbed contaminants, a spray chamber where the liquid scrubber contacts the exhaust gas may work. However, for materials with low solubility or where a chemical reaction occurs between the contaminant and liquid prior to absorption, a packed bed collector may be needed to maximize contact. The packed bed collector contains mesh screens or special ceramic shapes; the scrubbing liquid is introduced so it trickles over the packing as the exhaust gas flows though the bed. Reactive scrubbing is a special case of gas/vapor scrubbing. In reactive scrubbing, the contaminant reacts with the liquid to form a compound that is retained in the liquid.
- *Adsorption* is the process in which a gas or vapor adheres to the surface of a porous solid material. It occurs when the contaminant condenses into very small liquid droplets

Figure 19–11. Typical baghouse air cleaner.

at an ambient temperature higher than its boiling point. This principle is well-known to industrial hygienists through use of activated carbon sampling devices. With activated carbon, the condensation is due to catalyzing effect of active sites on the surface of the carbon granules that causes the contaminant to collect in micropores (Figure 19–12). Since no chemical reaction is involved, adsorption is reversible. The contaminant can be recovered, if warranted, from the adsorbent by heating, steam flushing, air stripping, vacuum treating, or any other method that vaporizes the condensed material. Removing the adsorbate regenerates the adsorbent for further use. In addition to activated carbon, popular adsorbents include silica gel and molecular sieves.

- *Oxidation* or combustion devices can be used when the air contaminants are combustible. They oxidize (burn) the contaminants under a variety of operating conditions. Many are designed for gases and vapors; often these do not work well when the airstream contains particulates. They are very useful for processes that release extremely odorous organic vapors and fumes. The major expense associated with combustion systems is the auxiliary fuel needed to heat incoming exhaust gas and assure complete combustion. Some devices use a catalyst that causes the contaminant to oxidize at a lower temperature than normal to save fuel. Since most LEV systems exhaust room air with very low levels of contaminants, combustion is often not cost-effective. Combustion devices find more application with process vents or similar sources where the contaminant concentration is relatively high.

Makeup Air

Makeup air is air that enters the workroom to replace air exhausted through the ventilation system. A room or plant with insufficient makeup air is said to be *air bound* or *air starved*. A ventilation system will not work properly if there is not enough air in the room to exhaust. This means that if

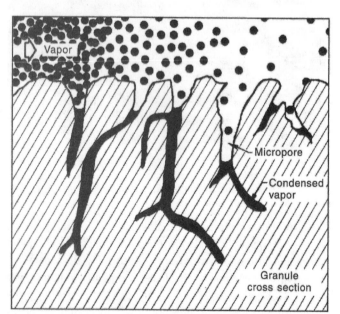

Figure 19–12. Cross-section of activated carbon particle, showing condensation of the contaminant within micropores on the surface of the particle. *(Source: McDermott, ACGIH, 2000. Reprinted with permission.)*

the ambient static pressure within the room becomes slightly negative, the fan may not work properly against this additional resistance.

Makeup air should be supplied through a planned system rather than through random infiltration. The system should have the following features:

- The supply rate should exceed the exhaust rate by about 10 percent. This slight positive pressure in the building helps to keep out drafts and dust. The exception is a situation where no dust or airborne chemicals should travel from the workroom to adjacent offices or other areas. Then a slight negative pressure inside the workroom is preferred.
- The air should flow from cleaner areas of the plant through areas where contaminants may be present and finally to the exhaust system. Flow should also be from normal temperature areas to high heat process areas. The makeup air supply system can be designed to provide some cooling in the summer in hot process areas.
- Makeup air should be introduced into the occupied zone of the plant, generally 8–10 ft from the floor. This gives the workers the benefit of breathing fresh air and, if the air is tempered (heated or cooled), maximizes the comfort provided by the makeup air.
- The air should be heated in winter to a temperature of about 65°F.
- Makeup air inlets outside the building must be located so that no contaminated air from nearby exhaust stacks or chimneys is drawn into the makeup air system.

Combustible Dust Hazards

Many industrial processes generate combustible dusts (e.g., plastic, wood, chemicals, metals). If the concentration is great enough in open air or when confined in an LEV system, a fire or explosion can result under certain conditions. A *combustible dust* is a combustible particulate solid that presents a fire or deflagration hazard when suspended in air or some other oxidizing medium over a range of concentrations, regardless of particle size or shape.

This discussion is limited to combustible dust hazards within LEV systems and dust collectors. Combustion occurs when dust and air mix together in the proper quantities and in the presence of an ignition source. If the event is contained within a duct system or air cleaner, the resulting pressure increase may result in an explosion.

If the process being ventilated can result in a combustible dust hazard, an analysis and mitigation, if needed, must be performed by a qualified engineer. The hazard evaluation begins with an analysis of the dust in the LEV system for combustible properties and includes features such as explosion suppression and explosion venting. If a hazard exists, the systems must be designed and installed with specific features such as grounding and other means to prevent static discharge, proper electrical components based on the hazardous area classification, and explosion prevention and protection measures. There are also detailed training and maintenance requirements for these systems. The National Fire Protection Association (NFPA) has issued standards and other publications related to the prevention of industrial dust explosions; these should be followed during the hazard analysis and mitigation (see the bibliography at the end of Chapter 20).

Note that duct systems and dust collector housings are almost never strong enough to contain an explosion. For this reason the dust collector is installed outdoors if possible, and the cleaner and ducts are equipped with suitable blow-out panels or vents directed to a safe location outdoors. If the dust collector must be installed indoors, a safe vent to the outdoors is needed unless an explosion suppression system (e.g., chemical or water mist) or equipment isolation (e.g., quick-acting dampers and valves) provides adequate personnel protection. There are also requirements to protect the ducts and other LEV components before the dust collector from overpressure due to an explosion.

AIRFLOW AND PRESSURE PRINCIPLES

This section describes the principles that govern LEV system operation. The information is useful in understanding how the components described above function, and how to test and upgrade an installed system. The principles fall into two broad categories: airflow and pressure.

Airflow Principles

The basic airflow concept in ventilation systems is called the *equation of continuity*, which expresses mass balance as air flows through different parts of the system. The equation of continuity is expressed as follows:

$$Q = V \times A \qquad (2)$$

where Q = airflow, ft^3/min
V = air velocity, ft/min
A = area of airflow, ft^2

At each point in a closed system (no additional air entering the duct):

$$Q = V_1 \times A_1 = V_2 \times A_2 \qquad (3)$$

where $_{1 \text{ and } 2}$ = two locations within the closed system

These equations have several important applications, including the following:

- The volumetric airflow (Q) through an opening (doorway, laboratory hood face) or in a duct can be readily determined using Equation (2) by measuring the average air velocity through the duct or opening and the area of the duct or opening.

- After Q is calculated or measured at one location in an LEV system, the velocity at other locations can be calculated from the Q and cross-sectional area at the new location, using Equation (3). This calculation is valid as long as no additional air enters the system through another hood. The calculation is useful to assure that adequate duct velocity is maintained at different parts of the system as duct diameter changes or to select the stack diameter to give a high discharge velocity for dispersion.

Another useful set of equations for capturing hoods describes the relationship between volumetric airflow (Q) into a hood and the capture velocity generated out in front of the hood. These are shown in Figure 19–13 for different capture hood types. The equations can either be used to calculate the Q needed to generate the required capture velocity at X distance in front of the hood or to determine the velocity that will be generated by a given value of Q.

It is important to note that these equations refer only to the centerline velocity, which is the air velocity along a line extending out from the center of the hood or duct, and do not describe the velocity distribution across the hood opening. Also, any distance X may be substituted into the

Hood Type	Airflow into Hood	Hood Entry Loss Factor (F)
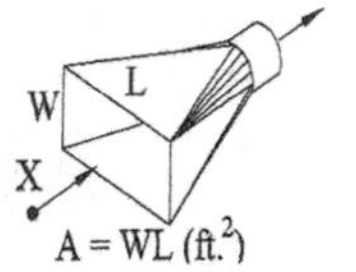 W L X A = WL (ft.^{2}) **Plain Opening**	$Q = V_x(10X^2 + A)$	0.93 VP$_{duct}$
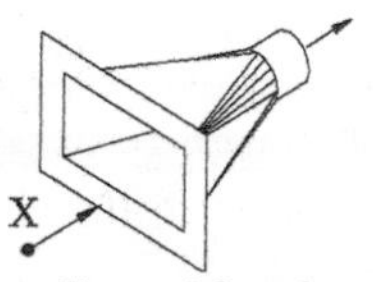 X **Flanged Opening**	$Q = 0.75V_x(10X^2 + A)$	0.49 VP$_{duct}$
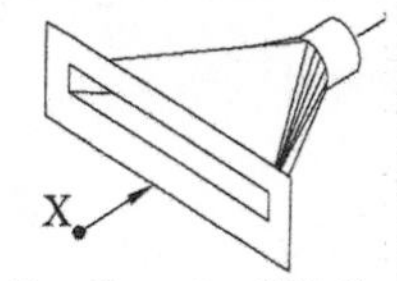 X (L = Length of Slot) **Flanged Slot**	$Q = 2.6\,LVX$	1.78 VP$_{slot}$ + 0.25 VP$_{duct}$

Figure 19–13. Hood data for selected capturing hood types showing the airflow needed to generate a specified velocity, and the hood entry loss factor.

equations to give an answer, but in practice a capturing hood can only reach out about 2 ft to draw in contaminants.

For example, the centerline velocity outside a plain hood (Figure 19–13) is found by using the following equation:

$$Q = V_x(10X^2 + A) \qquad (4)$$

where V_x = air velocity at X distance, ft/min
   Q = airflow into hood, ft³/min
   A = area of hood face, ft²
   X = distance outward from hood along hood axis (i.e., centerline), ft

Figure 19–14 (cross-hatched area) shows the velocity contours in front of this hood type. The contours show that the velocity drops off significantly on either side of the centerline. One reason for this is that the hood draws air from behind the hood outside the contamination zone.

The plain hood can be easily improved by adding a flange or collar to reduce the air drawn from behind the hood as shown in Figure 19–14. This decreases the airflow requirement needed to develop the same V_x by about 25 percent for a flanged hood compared to a plain hood and changes the previous equation to the following:

$$Q = 0.75V_x(10X^2 + A) \qquad (5)$$

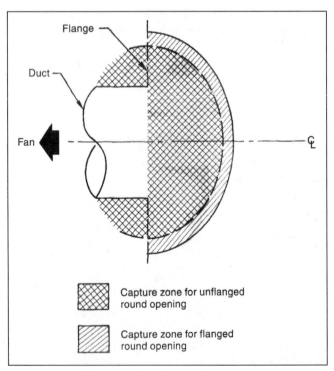

Figure 19–14. A flange increases the size of the capture zone in front of the hood. (*Source: McDermott, ACGIH, 2000. Reprinted with permission.*)

Example: A 4 in. x 8 in. (area = 32 in.² or 0.22 ft²) flanged opening hood is drawing 500 ft³/min of air. What is the velocity 6 in. (0.5 ft) in front of the hood?

Answer:

$$Q = 0.75V_x(10X^2 + A)$$

$$500 \text{ ft}^3/\text{min} =$$
$$(0.75)\ V_x\ [10(0.5)^2 + 0.22] = (0.75)\ V_x\ [10(0.25) + 0.22]$$

$$500 \text{ ft}^3/\text{min} = (0.75)\ V_x\ [2.50 + 0.22] = (0.75)\ V_x\ [2.72]$$

$$V_x = \frac{500 \text{ ft}^3/\text{min}}{(0.75)(2.72)} = 245 \text{ ft/min}$$

When considering airflow into hoods, there may be a tendency to assume that heavier-than-air vapors will tend to settle to the workroom floor and can be collected by a hood located there. In reality, for the small amounts of vapor in contaminated air (1,000 ppm means 1,000 parts of contaminants plus 999,000 parts of air), the resulting density of the mixture is so close to that of air that random air currents disperse the materials throughout the room. The exception to this rule is that a sizable leak of a dense gas or vapor (such as a compressed gas that chills by expansion as it escapes) will form a plume that moves along the ground. In this situation, a floor-level hood might be advantageous, but general room concentrations may still be significant.

Pressure Concepts

Air moves because there is a difference in pressure between two points. In an exhaust system, the fan develops negative pressure (suction) that extends back through the ducts to each hood. There the suction starts room air moving into the hoods and through the system. On the discharge side of the fan, positive pressure pushes the air through any remaining ducts and out the stack.

In ventilation work, pressure is expressed in units of inches of water gauge (in. H₂O). This represents the height of a water column (e.g., the weight of water) that the pressure will support. It is equivalent to more common pressure units, such as pounds per square inch, but is more convenient to use since typical pressures in an LEV system are small. For example, an LEV system may have a maximum static pressure of 5 in. of water, which is equivalent to only 0.2 psi. Pressure in units of in. H₂O can be visualized with a U-tube manometer (Figure 19–15). This simple pressure measuring device consists of a U-shaped glass tube partially filled with water. Plastic tubing is connected to one "leg" of the manometer; when the open end of the plastic tube is held against a hole in a duct under suction, the water in that

Figure 19–15. A U-tube manometer measures pressure directly in units of inches of water gauge.

leg rises while the water level in the other leg drops (Figure 19–16). The difference between the water level in each leg of the manometer is the suction pressure in the duct, expressed in in. H_2O. Although the U-tube manometer illustrates the concept clearly, for actual measurements, devices such as mechanical pressure gauges or digital manometers calibrated in inches of water are more commonly used today (Figure 19–17).

Two Types of Pressure

A local exhaust system has two types of pressure, static pressure and velocity pressure.

- *Static pressure* pulls inward on the ducts before the fan (negative pressure) and pushes outward on the ducts (positive pressure) after the fan. Static pressure in a ventilation system acts to collapse the walls of the ducts on the suction side (inlet) of the fan and to burst the ducts on the discharge side. It acts equally at all locations in the duct (center as well as at the walls). As described above, the easiest way to measure it is by using a manometer to read the bursting force on the duct walls (Figure 19–16), although the same reading will be obtained at any point across the duct at that location. Static pressure can be viewed as potential energy in the system that is available to start air moving and keep it moving by overcoming friction and turbulent losses.

- *Velocity pressure* is the result of air moving through the system, which represents kinetic energy. Velocity pressure is exerted by air in motion and has a positive sign in the direction of airflow. Velocity pressure at any point in the duct is determined by measuring the average velocity across the duct at the point, and using the following equation:

$$VP = \left(\frac{V}{4005}\right)^2 \tag{6}$$

or

$$V = 4{,}005 \sqrt{VP} \tag{7}$$

where VP = velocity pressure, in. H_2O
       V = velocity, ft/min

The equations for velocity pressure assume standard air density, which is 0.075 lb/ft³. Density is affected by the moisture content and temperature of the air as well as altitude relative to sea level. Density corrections are needed to

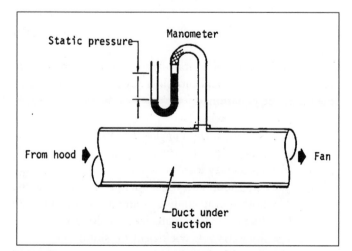

Figure 19–16. A manometer connected to a hole in the duct wall measures the static pressure in the duct at that point. *(Source: McDermott, ACGIH, 2000. Reprinted with permission.)*

Figure 19–17. Mechanical gauges and digital manometers calibrated in units of inches of water gauge are usually used for field pressure measurements.

velocity pressure readings if any of the following separate conditions occur: (1) moisture exceeds about 0.2 pounds of water per pound of air; (2) air temperature is outside the 40°F to 100°F range; or (3) altitude exceeds 1,000 ft relative to sea level. If more than one of these conditions varies significantly from standard conditions, then their combined effect on density should be calculated. The density correction for temperature and atmospheric pressure can be calculated using the following equation:

$$Density_{actual} = \frac{0.075\ lb}{ft^3} \times \frac{530°F}{(460+t)°F} \times \frac{Bar.\ Press.}{29.92} \quad (8)$$

where $Density_{actual}$ = actual air density, lb/ft³
t = temperature, °F
Bar. press = Barometric pressure, inches of mercury

For density corrections caused by elevated moisture, see the ACGIH *Industrial Ventilation Manual*.

With nonstandard air, the velocity pressure equation becomes:

$$VP = \left(\frac{V}{4005}\right)^2 \left(\frac{Density_{actual}}{0.075\ lb/ft^3}\right) \quad (9)$$

The sum of velocity pressure and static pressure at any point in the system equals the total pressure. The concept of total pressure is not very important in most LEV work, but illustrates that static pressure can be changed into velocity pressure and vice versa without an overall loss of pressure (or energy) from the system.

The concept of pressure governs most aspects of ventilation system operation. For example, room air has almost no velocity so its velocity pressure is zero. The LEV system draws that air into a hood and accelerates it up to the duct velocity. At that point the air has a velocity pressure value corresponding to that duct velocity according to Equation (6). For this to occur, the system must give up the same amount of static pressure (i.e., the static pressure is converted into velocity pressure).

Example: What is the acceleration loss to accelerate room air up to 2,500 ft/min duct velocity?

$$VP = \left(\frac{V}{4005}\right)^2$$

$$VP = \left(\frac{2500}{4005}\right)^2 = (0.62)^2 = 0.38\ in.\ H_2O$$

This means that accelerating room air to 2,500 ft/min duct velocity will cause a loss of 0.38 in. H₂O suction from the system.

Hood Entry Loss

In addition to the acceleration loss that occurs at the hood, there is additional loss because turbulence occurs as the air enters the hood and duct. This turbulent loss is called *hood entry loss*, and is separate from acceleration loss.

The energy lost due to turbulence at the hood, expressed in units of "equivalent number of velocity pressures lost," is called the *hood entry loss coefficient (F)* and has been measured experimentally for many hood shapes (Figure 19–13, right column). For a typical hood, the hood entry loss occurs as the air enters the duct at the hood, so the coefficient is referred to as F_d. For hoods with a long, narrow slot to distribute airflow, a loss also occurs at the slot; the coefficient for this loss is called F_s. As shown in the Equation in Figure 19–13, most slot hoods have a total hood entry loss made up of separate slot and duct entry components.

A hood shape that does not cause much turbulence has a lower entry loss coefficient than a hood with close clearances, sharp corners, or other features that produce a lot of turbulence. For example, as shown in Figure 19–13, a plain duct opening has a hood entry loss coefficient of about 93 percent of the duct velocity pressure while a flanged hood reduces the turbulence so that the loss coefficient is just 49 percent of the duct velocity pressure. A narrow slot hood causes such severe turbulence that the slot entry loss coefficient is almost twice the slot velocity pressure.

To calculate the hood entry loss in units of inches of water, multiply the hood entry loss coefficient (F) by the duct or slot velocity pressure. For a hood without a slot, the equation is as follows:

$$h_e = (F_d)\ (VP_d) \quad (10)$$

For a slot hood, the total entry loss is the sum of the h_e value plus the additional entry loss at the slot, calculated by the following equation:

$$h_{e(slot\ hood)} = (F_d)\ (VP_d) + (F_s)\ (VP_s) \quad (11)$$

where h_e = hood entry loss, in. H₂O
$h_{e(slot\ hood)}$ = total hood entry loss for slot hood, including both loss at slot and as air enters duct, in. H₂O
F_d = duct entry loss coefficient for slot hood
F_s = slot entry loss coefficient for slot hood
VP_d = duct velocity pressure, in. H₂O
VP_s = slot velocity pressure, in. H₂O

The hood entry loss coefficients for many different hood shapes can be found in the ACGIH *Industrial Ventilation Manual*.

Hood Static Pressure

For a hood to operate properly, the fan must generate enough suction or static pressure in the duct near the hood to overcome both the acceleration loss and the hood entry loss while drawing the correct amount of air into the hood. This amount of suction is called the *hood static pressure* and is easily measured using a manometer or other pressure sensor (Figure 19–18).

For a hood without a slot, hood static pressure is calculated using the following equation:

$$SP_h = \text{Acceleration Loss} + \text{Hood Entry Loss}$$
$$= (1.0 \times \text{duct velocity press.}) + (F_d \times \text{duct velocity press.})$$
$$= 1.0 VP_d + F_d VP_d$$
$$SP_h = (1.0 + F_d)\, VP_d \qquad (12)$$

where SP_h = hood static pressure (for a hood without a slot), in. H_2O
   F_d = entry loss coefficient for hood
   VP_d = duct velocity pressure, in. H_2O

For a slot hood, the loss caused by the slot must be added in:

$$SP_{h(slot)} = (1.0 + F_d)\, VP_d + F_s\, VP_s \qquad (13)$$

where $SP_{h(slot)}$ = hood static pressure for slot hood, in. H_2O
   F_s = slot entry loss coefficient
   VP_s = slot velocity pressure, in. H_2O

Hood static pressure is important for the following two reasons:

- During system design, the SP_h can be calculated and represents the suction that is needed at the hood for the hood to function properly. Then the fan can be selected to move the required Q while generating sufficient static pressure so the required SP_h will be available at each hood. As a corollary, in an existing system if the fan cannot generate the required SP_h at a hood, then the hood will never function properly.
- Once a ventilation system is installed and operating properly, the hood static pressure can be measured and recorded. Periodic readings can be compared to the original value to determine if the suction available at the hood is still adequate to draw the required amount of air for proper hood operation.

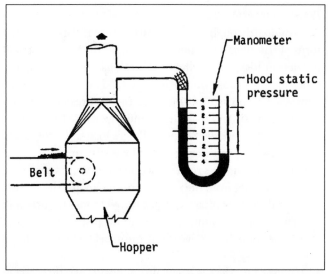

Figure 19–18. Hood static pressure, measured in the duct near the hood, represents the suction or potential energy available to draw air into the hood. *(Source: McDermott, ACGIH®, 2000. Reprinted with permission.)*

Example: The barrel-filling hood in Figure 19–1 has a hood entry loss coefficient (F_d) of 0.25. Measurements show that the hood static pressure is 1.8 in. H_2O in the 4-in. diameter circular duct (area = 0.087 ft²) at the hood. Estimate the airflow into this hood.

Answer: A summary of the data is as follows:

F_d = 0.25
SP_h = 1.8 in. H_2O
Duct Diameter = 4 in. (area = 0.087 ft²)

From Equation (12):
$$SP_h = (1.0 + F_d)\, VP_d$$
$$1.8 \text{ in. } H_2O = (1.0 + 0.25)\, VP_d$$

Solving for VP_d:
$$VP_d = 1.44 \text{ in. } H_2O$$

From Equation (7):
$$V = 4{,}005\, \sqrt{VP}$$

$$V = 4{,}005\, \sqrt{1.44} = 4{,}806 \text{ ft/min}$$

From Equation (2):
$$Q = V \times A$$
$$Q = 4{,}806 \text{ ft/min} \times 0.087 \text{ ft}^2$$
$$Q = 418 \text{ ft}^3/\text{min}$$

Pressure Loss in the Ducts

Air flowing through the ductwork meets resistance in the form of friction and turbulence. Straight duct lengths result in friction loss, while elbows, junctions, air cleaners, and other features cause turbulence losses. These losses can be expressed as pressure drop since they represent pressure lost from the system that the fan must generate to make the system work properly. Because of these losses, the following static pressure profile exists in an LEV system:

- Before the fan, the greatest suction value occurs at the fan inlet. Moving from the fan toward the hoods, the suction value decreases because it has to overcome friction and turbulence losses until, at the hood, just enough static pressure remains to overcome the acceleration and hood entry losses.
- After the fan, the greatest value of positive static pressure is at the fan outlet. The positive static pressure is used to overcome friction loss in any ducts after the fan and the stack, as well as turbulence losses in any elbows. At the stack discharge, any remaining static pressure is used to discharge the air at a higher velocity to aid contaminant dispersion.

Fan Pressure

As described throughout this chapter, the fan generates pressure that causes the air to move through the system. To characterize fan performance, both the volumetric airflow (Q) and the pressure that the fan generates must be specified.

For LEV systems, this fan pressure is called *fan static pressure (FSP)*. It is calculated from an equation used by fan manufacturers as part of a standard test of fan performance:

$$FSP = |SP_{inlet}| + |SP_{outlet}| - VP_{inlet} \qquad (14)$$

where FSP = fan static pressure, in. H_2O
SP = static pressure in. H_2O
VP = velocity pressure, in. H_2O
$_{inlet,\ outlet}$ = fan inlet and outlet

FSP represents the net pressure that the fan adds to the system.

Fan Laws Describe Fan Performance

The following three equations, called *fan laws*, describe the relationship of volumetric airflow, fan static pressure, and brake horsepower to rotating speed for a specific fan:

- Changes in volumetric airflow (ft³/min) vary directly with changes in fan speed. For example, for a given fan, doubling the speed will double the volume output.

$$\frac{Q_1}{Q_2} = \frac{R_1}{R_2} \qquad (15)$$

where R = fan rotating speed, rev/min
Q = airflow, ft³/min

- Changes in static pressure vary directly with the square of changes in fan speed.

$$\frac{FSP_1}{FSP_2} = \left(\frac{R_1}{R_2}\right)^2 \qquad (16)$$

where FSP = fan static pressure, in. H_2O

- Changes in brake horsepower vary directly with the cube of changes in fan speed. Brake horsepower is the energy required to operate the fan, but does not include any drive loss between the fan and motor.

$$\frac{BHP_1}{BHP_2} = \left(\frac{R_1}{R_2}\right)^3 \qquad (17)$$

where BHP = brake horsepower

Since all three of these fan laws act together, any change in fan speed to increase volume output also increases fan static pressure and brake horsepower.

This can be important since a common method of increasing Q in an existing system is to increase the fan rotating speed. This will increase volumetric airflow, but the brake horsepower, which represents electrical power consumption, increases as the third power of increases in fan rotating speed. For example, doubling the fan speed requires eight times more electrical power to run the fan (i.e., $2^3 = 8$). This could make increasing the fan speed a poor economic decision compared to changes in hoods or ducts to improve the performance of the LEV system.

Fan manufacturers specify a maximum safe rotating speed for each fan to prevent mechanical failure. This speed cannot be exceeded when attempting to increase airflow in an LEV system.

Example: A fan is moving 4,000 ft³/min of air. A tachometer reading shows that the rotating speed is 1,650 rev/min. Measurement of electrical consumption shows that the consumption is equivalent to 2.23 brake horsepower. Calculate the effect on rotating speed and horsepower of increasing the airflow to 5,000 ft³/min.

Answer: Since rotating speed and volume output are proportional, use Equation (15) to find the new rotating speed:

$$\frac{Q_1}{Q_2} = \frac{R_1}{R_2}$$

$$\frac{4000}{5000} = \frac{1,650}{R_2}$$

$$R_2 = 2,063 \text{ rev/min}$$

Calculate the new brake horsepower using Equation (17):

$$\frac{2.23}{BHP_2} = \left(\frac{1,650}{2,063}\right)^3$$

$$\frac{2.23}{BHP_2} = (0.80)^3 = 0.51$$

$$BHP_2 = \frac{2.23}{0.51} = 4.4 \text{ horsepower}$$

Whether or not the best solution lies in increasing the fan speed to achieve the desired performance is usually based on an economic evaluation. The cost of the added electrical power can be calculated over the projected life of the fan. For small increases in fan speed, the existing fan motor may be adequate but the fan manufacturer's literature will show whether a higher horsepower motor is needed. Also check the fan specifications to see whether the existing fan is safe at the required rotating speed.

LEV PERFORMANCE EVALUATION AND IMPROVEMENT

This section describes typical tests used to evaluate LEV system performance and, where applicable, simple steps to diagnose and resolve problems.

Smoke Tube Tests

Smoke tubes are glass tubes containing a chemical that produces a chemical fume (smoke) as room air is blown through the tube with a hand-operated bulb. They are useful for the following tests:
- evaluating the capture range of hoods
- identifying drafts and other factors that can interfere with hood performance
- demonstrating the capture distance of hoods to workers so they can position the hood or work item properly

Velocity Measurements

Several devices are available when a quantitative measurement of velocity is required. The main categories include:
- *Thermo-anemometer* works on the principle that the resistance of a heated wire changes with temperature variations (Figure 19–19). Air moving over the heated

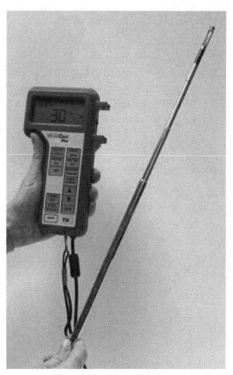

Figure 19–19. Typical thermo-anemometer for measuring air velocity.

wire element changes its temperature depending on the air velocity. The anemometer is calibrated directly in feet per minute. This type of device typically has a narrow probe and so can be inserted into ducts through a small hole to perform duct velocity readings. Very high moisture levels may cause inaccurate readings if the moisture affects the change of resistance in the heated element.
- *Rotating vane anemometer* has a propeller-like velocity sensor connected either to a mechanical or electronic readout unit.
- *Swinging vane velometer* contains a vane or paddle that moves according to the velocity of the air passing through the instrument. The paddle is connected mechanically to a meter that displays the velocity.

Typical applications for these devices are measuring capture velocity outside of capturing hoods, face velocity for enclosures, and slot velocities.

Duct Velocity Traverse

A *traverse* involves measuring the velocity at a number of points across the duct area since velocity distribution is not uniform within the duct. Typically, a velometer with a narrow probe sensor is used for the traverse. The measurement points are selected to give a high probability that the measurements will yield an accurate value for average velocity, according to the following guidelines:
- For round ducts, two traverses at right angles should be

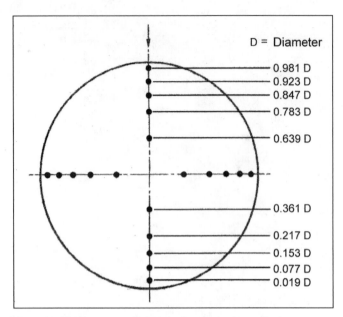

Figure 19–20. Measuring locations for a 10-point velocity traverse in a round duct. Two traverses are performed at 90 degrees to each other.

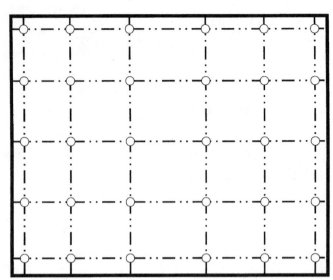

Figure 19–21. Measuring locations for a 30-point velocity traverse in a rectangular duct.

made. For ducts 6 in. in diameter or smaller, make two 6-point traverses. For ducts 6 to 50 in., make at least two 10-point traverses. The locations of the measuring points are selected according to criteria specified to maximize accuracy of the measurement (Figure 19–20 and Table 19–B); they are not equidistant points along the duct diameter. Note that the centerline velocity is not part of the traverse.

• For rectangular ducts, at least 25 measuring points are recommended with no two points more than 8 in. apart. Figure 19–21 and Table 19–C show details of selecting measuring points. Similarly, for large openings, such as laboratory hoods or paint spray booths, a series of velocity readings should be taken and averaged to estimate the average air velocity into the enclosure.

TABLE 19–B	Recommended Traverse Points for Round Ducts								
No. of points	**Traverse position (in fractions of duct diameter from wall)**								
	1	2	3	4	5	6	7	8	9	10
4	0.043	0.290	0.710	0.957						
6	0.032	0.135	0.321	0.679	0.865	0.968				
8	0.021	0.117	0.184	0.345	0.655	0.816	0.883	0.979		
10	0.019	0.077	0.153	0.217	0.361	0.639	0.783	0.847	0.923	0.981

TABLE 19–C	Recommended Traverse Points for Rectangular Ducts					
No. of points	**Traverse position (in fractions of duct diameter from wall)**					
	1	2	3	4	5	6	7
5	0.074	0.288	0.500	0.712	0.926		
6	0.061	0.235	0.437	0.563	0.765	0.939	
7	0.053	0.203	0.366	0.500	0.634	0.797	0.947

Note: Base sampling points on aspect ratio (height:width) of duct; minimum of 25 points needed.

Regardless of duct shape, the best place to perform a traverse is at least 7.5 duct diameters downstream from any major disturbance to smooth airflow, such as dampers or elbows. More specific guidelines for performing velocity traverses and evaluating the validity of the results are contained in the ACGIH® *Industrial Ventilation Manual*.

Example: Find the average velocity and airflow through a 6-in. round duct. Results of two 6-point traverses are recorded below.

Answer:

Point	Measurement point, % of diameter*	Measurement distance	Traverse #1 Velocity (ft/min)	Traverse #2 (perpendicular to #1) Velocity (ft/min)
1	0.032	0.2 in.	3514	3468
2	0.135	0.8 in.	3582	3537
3	0.321	1.9 in.	3821	3800
4	0.679	4.1 in.	3779	3729
5	0.865	5.2 in.	3625	3604
6	0.968	5.8 in.	3468	3422
		Average	3632	3593
			Average Duct Velocity = 3613 ft/min	

* From Table 19–B for a 6-inch diameter duct.

Static Pressure Measurements

Periodic static pressure tests at the hoods and other locations in the LEV system are an excellent way to evaluate performance and diagnose problems. Since static pressure represents the potential energy available to move air in the system, changes in static pressure over time can indicate situations that degrade system performance. The greatest value of static pressure tests is from comparing current results to earlier readings. The LEV system should be balanced and hood velocities measured to assure adequate performance before instituting a static pressure test program.

To measure static pressure in a duct, a small diameter hole ($\frac{1}{16}$ to $\frac{1}{8}$ in.) is drilled through the duct wall. It is important that no burrs around the drilled hole protrude into the flowing airstream; these can be removed by inserting a thin rod with a 90–degree bend into the hole and rotating it to smooth the edges. The holes should be at least 7.5 duct diameters downstream from any disturbance, such as an elbow, damper, or branch duct entry. If this is not possible, then four holes should be drilled 90 degrees apart around the duct and the measured static pressure values averaged. The end of a rubber tube attached to a suitable pressure sensor is pressed against the duct over the hole;

the static pressure is read as inches of water (Figure 19–16). While a short length of metal tubing can be brazed onto the duct around the hole for the static pressure tube connection, simply holding the end of the rubber tubing against the duct will give an accurate reading. The hole does not have to be capped between tests if it is small enough. Permanent installation of a manometer or other pressure gauge is used for LEV systems where continuous measurements are needed.

Hood Static Pressure

The principle of measuring hood static pressure is illustrated in Figure 19–18. The ideal location is about one duct diameter from the throat of a hood with a tapered transition into the duct, and about three duct diameters for plain openings or flanged hoods. This location will avoid measuring hood static pressure within the turbulent zone in the duct near the hood.

In setting up a hood static pressure test program, determine the airflow into hoods using velometer readings or a velocity traverse across the ducts. Adjust airflow to each hood until it meets design criteria, and then measure and record hood static pressure along with volumetric airflow (Q). If subsequent hood static pressure readings show a decrease at a hood, the change in flow rate can be calculated using the following equation:

$$\frac{Q}{Q_o} = \left(\frac{\sqrt{SP_h}}{\sqrt{SP_{h(o)}}} \right) \qquad (18)$$

where Q = current volumetric airflow rate, ft³/min
Q_o = original volumetric airflow rate, ft³/min
SP_h = current hood static pressure, in. H₂O
$SP_{h(o)}$ = original hood static pressure, in. H₂O

This technique is valid for all hood designs, including slot hoods.

Example: The hood static pressure at the conveyor belt discharge hood (i.e., the upper hood) in Figure 19–1 was 1.15 in. H₂O with airflow of 1,050 ft³/min. Recent tests show the hood static pressure is now 0.87 in. H₂O. What is the current airflow into the hood?

Answer: From Equation (18):

$$\frac{Q}{Q_o} = \left(\frac{\sqrt{SP_h}}{\sqrt{SP_{h(o)}}} \right)$$

$$Q = Q_o \frac{\sqrt{SP_h}}{\sqrt{SP_{h(o)}}}$$

$$Q = 1050 \text{ ft}^3/\text{min} \left(\frac{\sqrt{0.87}}{\sqrt{1.15}} \right)$$

$$Q = 1050 \text{ ft}^3/\text{min} \left(\frac{0.93}{1.07} \right) = 913 \text{ ft}^3/\text{min}$$

The decline in airflow could be caused by a loose fan belt, plugged duct, or other problem.

Other Static Pressure Test Locations

Static pressure tests at various other system locations are also valuable in measuring system performance and diagnosing malfunctions. Typical locations (in addition to hoods) to measure static pressure are at entries into main ducts, on each side of air cleaners, on each side of the fan, and at several points along long ducts. Initial and periodic static pressure readings should be recorded on a data sheet.

Differences between readings at the same location that exceed 10 percent should be investigated to determine the reason for the change. Typical reasons include clogged air cleaners, plugged ducts, loose duct joints, and fan problems such as loose drive belts or dirty/damaged fan blades.

SUMMARY

Local exhaust ventilation (LEV) systems are an important technique for controlling employee exposures to airborne contaminants. A sound understanding of system components and the airflow and pressure principles that govern system operation will help the safety and industrial hygiene practitioner apply LEV properly.

A bibliography for this chapter appears at the end of Chapter 20, Dilution Ventilation for Industrial Workplaces.

CHAPTER 20

Dilution Ventilation of Industrial Workplaces

by Henry J. McDermott, CIH, CSP, PE

This chapter describes the principles and practices for using dilution ventilation to remove airborne contaminants from industrial work areas such as shops and factories, and for enclosed or confined spaces. General ventilation to control indoor air quality in offices and similar settings is covered in Chapter 21, General Ventilation of Nonindustrial Workplaces.

INTRODUCTION

As described in Chapter 19, Local Exhaust Ventilation, *local exhaust ventilation* and *dilution ventilation* are both used to control the concentration of air contaminants in the workplace.

Dilution occurs when contaminants released into the workroom mix with air flowing through the room (Figure 20–1). Either natural or mechanically-induced air movement can be used to dilute contaminants. Dilution ventilation is sometimes called *general* ventilation. However, the overall heating, ventilating, and air conditioning (HVAC) system in a building is often referred to as the general ventilation system. To avoid confusion, in this chapter the term *dilution* is used for contaminant control systems.

It is important to realize that with dilution ventilation, the contaminants actually disperse into the workroom air and then are gradually removed. The dilution airflow is not capable of generating air currents that "sweep" the contaminants directly from the source to the wall or roof mounted exhaust fan. Some of the dilution air passes through the zone of contaminant release and dilutes the contaminants to a lower concentration. The dilution continues as the material moves farther from the process until the contaminated air is removed by the exhaust fan. Depending on the

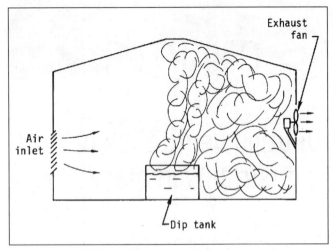

Figure 20–1. Dilution ventilation gradually removes contaminants dispersed in the workroom air. *(Source: McDermott, ACGIH, 2000.)*

location of the air inlet and exhaust fan, and the total airflow through the room, a considerable time period may elapse after the process stops before all contaminants are removed from the room.

Dilution ventilation is used in situations meeting these criteria:

- Small quantities of contaminants are released into the workroom at fairly uniform rates.
- There is sufficient distance from the source to the worker (or source of ignition for fire/explosion hazards) to the contaminant source to allow for dilution to safe levels.
- Contaminants are of relatively low toxicity or fire hazard so that no major problems will result from unanticipated minor employee exposure or concentration exceedances.
- No air-cleaning device is needed to collect contaminants before the exhaust air is discharged into the community environment.
- There is no corrosion or other problems from the diluted contaminants in the workroom air.

The major disadvantage of dilution ventilation is that the inherent uncertainties existing in many of the design parameters require that large safety factors be applied to ensure that exposures are controlled. This is described in detail later in this chapter, but the uncertainties often result in large volumes of air being needed, and may make dilution ventilation less cost-effective than local exhaust ventilation or another exposure control technique.

Dilution ventilation can also be used to control hot temperatures from industrial operations or other sources. Heat can be a health hazard in extreme exposures, so the proper design of dilution systems to control this hazard is important. Heat load occurs both from the radiant heat and convective heat emitted by hot sources (called *sensible* heat), and

from the heat released to the room from condensing steam or water vapor (called *latent* heat). A thorough explanation of the data needed to calculate the required airflow to control heat exposures is beyond the scope of this chapter (see the American Conference of Governmental Industrial Hygienists [ACGIH®] *Industrial Ventilation Manual* for details).

DILUTION VENTILATION SYSTEMS

Natural Ventilation
Natural ventilation is air movement within a work area caused by wind, temperature differences between the exterior and interior of a building, or other factors where no mechanical air mover is used.

Even moderate winds can move large volumes of air through open doors or windows. For example, a 15 mph wind blowing directly at a window with an open area of 36 ft² can move 25,000 ft³/min or more through the window if the air can freely escape from the building through a doorway or other large opening. Unfortunately, the wind speed and direction are usually not reliable, so unless production can be scheduled to coincide with favorable winds, this would not be an adequate exposure control technique. In many regions this large dilution air volume must be heated in winter. This is an important cost factor that can override the apparent savings of a system with no mechanical air mover.

Air movement caused by temperature differences may be more useful than motion caused by wind. Hot processes heat the surrounding air and the rising column of warm air will carry contaminants upward to roof vents. As long as a worker does not have to lean over the heated process and breathe the rising contaminated air, this type of natural ventilation may be adequate. A good supply of replacement air for the building is needed, especially during winter when doors and windows may be closed for thermal comfort.

Mechanical Ventilation
Mechanical systems range from simple wall-mounted exhaust propeller fans or roof-mounted mechanical ventilators to complex designs with engineered supply and exhaust systems that use outdoor air properly distributed in the work area to dilute the contaminants. Propeller fans can provide a constant, reliable flow of air, but a major characteristic is that they are efficient air movers only as long as an adequate supply of replacement or makeup air can *readily* enter the area being exhausted (as described in Chapter 19, Local Exhaust Ventilation). Thus, many dilution systems require a sophisticated air supply system with fans and ducts to reliably control employee exposures. These systems increase the effectiveness of dilution, but the

total installed and operating costs can approach the cost of a local exhaust system.

DILUTION SYSTEM DESIGN CONSIDERATIONS

Safety Factors

The equations for calculating the dilution airflow rate required for either health protection or fire/explosion prevention are straightforward, but there are some limitations that must be understood. The equations are based on the concept that the contaminant is released at a certain rate (*ft³/min*), and so the ventilation system must move the correct airflow (*ft³/min*) to dilute this generated rate of contaminant to an acceptable level. To apply these equations prudently, it is important to understand two factors:

- The theoretical equations assume that complete mixing occurs in the room. This means that all of the dilution air helps to dilute the contaminant to acceptable levels before anyone breathes the air (or, for fire/explosion prevention, before the vapors reach a source of ignition). Complete mixing rarely occurs in real world situations.

- These equations will yield the airflow needed to keep the airborne level precisely at the target concentration selected as a parameter in the dilution equations. So the OSHA Permissible Exposure Limit or ACGIH Threshold Limit Value (TLV®) can never be selected as the target concentration since the theoretical equations will yield the required airflow to keep airborne levels exactly at that level. An adequate safety factor should be applied to keep concentrations well below the acceptable exposure level. It is common to use 10-25 percent of the PEL or TLV as the target concentration.

The dilution equations discussed below adjust for these considerations. The airflow equations for systems designed to protect heath (as contrasted with fire/explosion prevention) contain a *K factor* that increases the theoretical quantity needed to dilute the contaminants. The equations for fire/explosion prevention use a $S_{f\,factor}$ that performs the equivalent function. In both cases it is the designer's responsibility to choose the appropriate value to account for

- the design and layout of the exhaust fan and any air supply system (in relation to the work operation) that impacts how much of the airflow actually works to dilute the contaminants before workers breathe the air or the contaminated air reaches a source of ignition (Table 20–A);

- any significant unknown information or parameters about a new process or operation that could impact the amount of contaminant released or whether the release is constant or irregular; and

- any additional safety factor needed to account for circumstances such as nonroutine work patterns that could bring workers closer than expected to the contaminant source, or other conditions where an added safety factor is warranted.

Even if the appropriate considerations are applied when choosing the *K* factor, there is still a risk that changes in the chemicals used or reductions in the original allowable exposure limits for the chemicals will render the system unacceptable. For example, if the TLV for a chemical was reduced by 50 percent, the calculated dilution airflow would have to be doubled to maintain the same ratio of actual concentration to TLV. There is less risk of this occurring with local exhaust ventilation (LEV) because the design assumption for LEV systems is to prevent contaminant escape to the work environment rather than diluting them to acceptable levels once they are released.

Dilution Ventilation System Layout

Dilution systems work best when the air is supplied from a fan-driven supply arrangement with the air discharged above or behind workers so that fresh air moves past the

TABLE 20–A	Dilution System Configurations Impacting "K" Values	
Air Mixing Conditions	**Typical K-Factor[a]**	**Examples**
Optimal	1 – 2	Dilution air is supplied by fan-driven system from directly behind or above worker; exhaust fan is located so that it draws clean air first past worker then over source of contaminants.
Good	2 – 3	Dilution air supplied by fan-driven system from directly behind or above worker provides most of the dilution effect; exhaust fan in roof or wall removes contaminated air from room.
Fair	3 – 5	Dilution air supplied by fan-driven system provides effective general air circulation in room; exhaust fan in roof or wall removes contaminated air from room.
Poor	6 – 10	Dilution air supplied by fan-driven system provides limited air circulation in room; exhaust fan in roof or wall removes contaminated air from room. There are areas of poor dilution in workroom.

[a] Final "*K*" factor used in calculations also depends on the number of employees and their work pattern in the workroom as well as the source of contaminants and their toxicity.

worker, then over the source of contaminants, and finally toward the exhaust fans that remove the mixed air from the workroom (Figure 20–2). This generates a flushing action so that airborne concentrations around the workers are as low as possible. Note that this type of engineered dilution ventilation system is much more complex than a simple arrangement with an exhaust fan in one wall of a building and an open door or window serving as the sole source of fresh air. Since only the air that passes through the area where contaminants are released is available for immediate dilution of contaminants to safe levels, the *K* factor described in Table 20–A is selected to reflect the mixing conditions in the room. The final *K* factor used in calculations depends on the number of employees and their work pattern in the workroom, and the source of contaminants and their toxicity, as well as the air supply and exhaust configuration.

The air inlet and exhaust fans should be arranged so that air movement is from cleaner to dirtier areas. Locate the processes or locate the fan so that the units that release contaminants are as close as possible to the fan. Also eliminate or provide separate exhaust for areas where contaminants may accumulate and defeat the dilution effect of the airflow from the overall system.

CALCULATING DILUTION AIRFLOW FOR HEALTH PROTECTION

When a chemical is first released at a constant rate into a ventilated workroom, there is a gradual concentration buildup until a steady-state condition is reached. At this concentration, the emission rate and removal rate are in equilibrium so the concentration remains about constant. After chemical release stops, there is a gradual purging of the workplace air until the concentration reaches zero (Figure 20–3).

Dilution Ventilation for Health: Steady-State

When the contaminant is an evaporating liquid, the amount of dilution airflow required depends on the physical properties of the contaminant (molecular weight and specific gravity [compared to water]), rate of contaminant release, the target airborne concentration, and the overall safety factor (*K*) as described above. The equation for calculating the steady-state dilution airflow rate for toxic or irritating contaminants is:

$$Q = \frac{403 \times \text{sp gr} \times W \times K \times 1{,}000{,}000}{M \times L} \quad (1)$$

where Q = dilution airflow, ft³/min
  sp gr = specific gravity of liquid (water = 1.0)

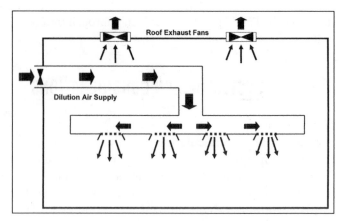

Figure 20–2. An effective dilution system introduces fresh air above or behind workers to create air movement that reduces their exposure to contaminants. For this configuration, $K \approx 2\text{-}3$.

W = amount of liquid used (evaporated), pints/minute

M = molecular weight of contaminant

L = target airborne concentration of contaminant to be maintained in the work environment (usually based on OSHA standards or TLV with an appropriate safety factor), ppm

K = dimensionless safety factor to increase the calculated airflow rate over the minimum, to take nonideal conditions into account. K normally ranges from 3 to 10 depending on the overall effectiveness of the ventilation system and uniformity of contaminant evolution. A higher K value is associated with poor airflow conditions and other unknown conditions or circumstances that could increase exposures to workers (see Table 20–A or the ACGIH *Industrial Ventilation Manual*).

Example: A cleaning operation in an open-bay work area uses methyl ethyl ketone (2-butanone) at the rate of 2 pints/h. The general air distribution is good but the layout of the workroom prevents some of the dilution air from passing directly through the zone of contaminant evolution at the workbench—assume a value of 5 for *K*. Calculate the dilution airflow requirement to maintain the airborne concentration at 20 ppm.

Answer: The amount of chemical released is 2 pints/h, or 0.033 pints/min. The specific gravity of methyl ethyl ketone is 0.81 and its molecular weight is 72. Applying Equation 1:

$$Q = \frac{403 \times \text{sp gr} \times W \times K \times 1{,}000{,}000}{M \times L}$$

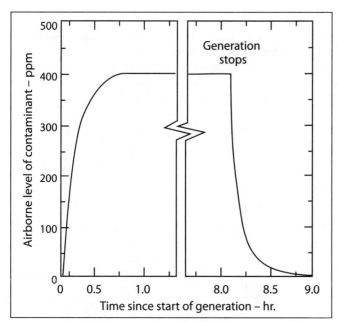

Figure 20–3. Concentration versus time for a workplace ventilated by a dilution system. The overall goal is to maintain the steady-state airborne level at or below the target concentration. *(Source: McDermott, ACGIH®, 2000.)*

$$Q = \frac{403 \times 0.81 \times 0.033 \text{ pints/min} \times 5 \times 1,000,000}{72 \times 20}$$

$$Q = 37,403 \text{ ft}^3/\text{min}$$

Dilution Ventilation for Health: Purging

The purging rate equation can estimate how long it will take the fan to remove the contaminated air from the work environment after the release or generation of contaminant ceases. This is when all residual liquid has been cleaned up or has evaporated into the air, which is when the release of contaminant ceases.

Since these calculations are more complex than Equation (1), it is easier to define a new term that can be used in the purging equation:

$$Q' = \frac{Q}{K} \qquad (2)$$

where Q' = effective ventilation airflow (i.e., the airflow that dilutes the contaminants before they reach the workers' breathing zone), ft³/min
Q = actual ventilation airflow, ft³/min
K = dimensionless safety factor that accounts for any airflow that is not effective in diluting contaminants before they reach an employee's breathing zone, see complete definition under Equation (1)

When further release of generation of contaminant has ceased, the concentration as a function of time can be calculated from:

$$C_t = C_{\text{original}} \left[e^{(-Q't/Vr)}\right] \qquad (3)$$

where C_t = concentration at any time t, ppm
C_{original} = concentration when generation ceased, ppm
t = time since contaminant release ceased, minutes
V_r = room volume, ft³

Because of the mathematical relationship involved, C_t will never reach zero. However, the time to reach very low concentrations (approaching zero) can be estimated. The right portion of Figure 20–3 illustrates concentration as a function of time during purging.

Equation (3) is particularly useful in estimating the airborne concentration versus elapsed time following a spill or release of a chemical in a work area where the dilution ventilation rate is known.

Example: There was a spill of methyl ethyl ketone in the work area described in the previous example. The area was evacuated immediately, and a properly equipped emergency squad responded to clean up the spilled liquid. The airborne levels measured with a direct reading instrument showed 8,000 ppm after the clean-up was completed. How long will it take for the airborne level to return to the target concentration of 20 ppm? The dimensions of the work area are 40 ft × 30 ft × 12 ft high.

Answer: Applying Equation (2):

$$Q' = \frac{Q}{K}$$

$$Q' = \frac{Q}{K} = \frac{37,403 \text{ ft}^3/\text{min}}{5} = 7481 \text{ ft}^3/\text{min}$$

Applying Equation (3) with V_r = 40' × 30' × 12' = 14,400 ft³:

$$C_t = C_{\text{original}} \left[e^{(-Q't/Vr)}\right]$$

$$20 \text{ ppm} = 8,000 \left[e^{(-7481\ t/14,400)}\right]$$

$$\frac{20}{8,000} = \left[e^{(-0.52\ t)}\right]$$

$$0.0025 = \left[e^{(-0.52\ t)}\right]$$

$$\ln(0.0025) = \ln\left[e^{(-0.52\ t)}\right]$$

$$-5.99 = -0.52t$$

$$t = 11.6 \text{ minutes}$$

TABLE 20-B	Time to Purge Workroom Based on Effective Air Exchange Rate	
Effective Air Exchange Rate,[a] Air changes/min	**Approximate time (minutes) to reach stated percent of original concentration after contaminant generation ceases**	
	10 percent of C_o	**1 percent of C_o**
0.02	115	230
0.05	46	92
0.10	23	46
0.15	15	30
0.20	12	24
0.25	9	18
0.30	8	15
0.35	7	13
0.40	6	12
0.45	5	10
0.50	5	9
0.60	4	8

[a] See definition in text.

Table 20–B shows the use of Equation (3) to estimate the approximate elapsed time to reach 10 percent and 1 percent of the original concentration based on the ratio of Q' to room volume:

$$\text{Effective Air Exchange Rate (air changes/min)} = \frac{Q'}{V_r} \qquad (4)$$

Example: For the previous example, estimate the time until the concentration reaches one percent of the original concentration (i.e., 80 ppm).

Answer: Applying Equation (4):

Effective Air Exchange Rate (air changes/min) =

$$\frac{Q'}{V_r} = \frac{7,481 \text{ ft}^3/\text{min}}{14,400 \text{ ft}^3} = 0.52 \text{ air changes/min}$$

From Table 20–B, the closest listed value of Effective Air Exchange Rate is 0.50. With this rate it will take approximately 9 minutes to reach 80 ppm, which is one percent of the original concentration.

Dilution Airflow Design Data

As an option to calculating required dilution airflow, the ACGIH *Industrial Ventilation Manual* contains airflow recommendations for some applications such as general welding (Table 20–C), and use of lift trucks powered by internal combustion engines inside buildings. This type of design information is especially helpful for new facilities where no ambient contaminant measurements can be conducted prior to system design.

TABLE 20-C	Dilution Air Flow for Welding[a]
Welding Rod Diameter, inches	**Airflow, ft³/min per welder**
3/32	1000
3/16	1500
1/4	3500
3/8	4500

or

A. For open areas, where welding fume can rise away from the breathing zone: ft³/min required = 800 × lb/hour rod used.

B. For enclosed areas or positions where fume does not readily escape breathing zone: ft³/min required = 1600 × lb/hour rod used.

[a] Where Local Exhaust Ventilation cannot be used

CALCULATING DILUTION AIRFLOW FOR FIRE AND EXPLOSION PREVENTION

Dilution ventilation is used to reduce concentrations of flammable or explosive gases, vapors, or dust to safe levels well below their lower explosive limit (LEL). The dilution must occur before the contaminated air reaches any source of ignition. The accumulation of flammable or explosive mixtures in basements, pits, and other locations also must be considered in addition to diluting vapors in the general work area. The equation for calculating dilution airflow for flammable or explosive gases or vapors is:

$$Q = \frac{403 \times \text{sp gr} \times W \times S_f \times 100}{M \times LEL \times B} \qquad (5)$$

where Q = dilution airflow, ft³/min

sp gr = specific gravity of liquid (water = 1.0)

W = amount of flammable liquid used or released, pints/min

S_f = dimensionless safety factor that depends on the percentage of LEL acceptable for safe conditions. For some applications the concentration should not exceed 25 percent of the LEL so S_f = 4 (i.e., 100 ÷ 25 = 4); for other situations S_f values of 10 or higher may be more appropriate.

M = molecular weight of contaminant

LEL = lower explosive limit of contaminant, percent

B = constant reflecting that the LEL decreases at elevated temperatures. B = 1 for temperatures up to 250°F, B = 0.7 for temperatures above 250°F.

Equation (5) is based on the assumption that 100 percent of the dilution air is effective in diluting the contaminant before the contaminated air reaches a source of ignition. If this is not the case, the calculated Q must be multiplied by an additional safety factor.

Some operations release peak amounts of contaminants over a short time period. For example, drying ovens evaporate solvents rapidly during the first few minutes after objects are placed in the oven. In these cases the value of W should reflect the peak emission rate rather than the average rate.

When both employee exposure and fire/explosion prevention are considered for the same operation, the dilution flow rate calculated using Equation (1) almost always governs. The allowable airborne levels for breathing are significantly lower than the LELs for almost all, if not all, substances.

Example: As part of a laboratory analytical test, one pint of n-hexane is evaporated per hour in a small evaporation chamber. How much airflow is needed through the chamber to keep the concentration at 5 percent of the LEL? The specific gravity of n-hexane is 0.66, the molecular weight is 86, and the LEL is 1.1 percent.

Answer: Since one pint is evaporated per hour:

$$W = \frac{1 \text{ pint}}{h} \times \frac{(h)}{(60 \text{ min})} = 0.017 \text{ pints/min}$$

Since the temperature is less than 250°F, B = 1. To maintain the concentration at 5 percent of the LEL, S_f = 20 (i.e., 100 ÷ 5 = 20). Applying Equation (5):

$$Q = \frac{403 \times \text{sp gr} \times W \times S_f \times 100}{M \times LEL \times B}$$

$$Q = \frac{403 \times 0.66 \times 0.017 \times 20 \times 100}{86 \times 1.1 \times 1}$$

$$Q = 95.6 \text{ ft}^3/\text{min}$$

Air Density Adjustments Due to High Temperatures

Equations (1) through (5) assume that the dilution air has standard density of 0.075 lb/ft³. This is the density of air at 70°F, 29.92 in. of mercury atmospheric pressure, and 50 percent relative humidity. Factors that affect density are temperature, altitude, and humidity. Density correction calculations are explained in Chapter 19, "Local Exhaust Ventilation." For dilution systems, the most common factor is high temperature within drying ovens or similar enclosures. Density adjustments for high temperatures can be calculated from:

$$Q_{actual} = Q_{calculated} \frac{(460°F + T)}{(530°F)} \tag{6}$$

where Q_{actual} = dilution airflow at actual temperature, ft³/min

$Q_{calculated}$ = dilution airflow calculated from Equations (1) or (5), ft³/min

T = actual dilution air temperature, °F

FANS FOR DILUTION VENTILATION

As explained in Chapter 19, Local Exhaust Ventilation, there are two main categories of fans: centrifugal fans and axial flow fans. Centrifugal fans, most often used in LEV systems, were described in the previous chapter. Dilution systems may use either type of fan. With axial fans the air travels parallel to the fan shaft and leaves the fan in the same direction as it entered. A screw or propeller action produces airflow. There are three different types of axial fans:

- *Propeller fans* feature large blades and are often mounted in the wall of a building. These fans move air where there is no resistance to airflow and there is a ready source of make-up air. Of all the axial fans, the propeller fan exhibits the most severe drop in airflow as resistance increases. They are not used with ducts because they do not produce pressure (either positive pressure or suction).

- *Tubeaxial fans* are special propeller fans mounted inside a short duct section (Figure 20–4). The blades are specially shaped to enable the fan to move air against low resistance. This type of fan can be used as an exhaust fan, and may be used with flexible ducts for temporary dilution set-ups. It is also used for some LEV applications such as paint spray booths.

Figure 20–4. Typical tubeaxial fan used to ventilate temporary work spaces.

- *Vaneaxial fans* are similar to tubeaxial fans but have numerous short blades and vanes mounted in the duct to convert spinning air motion into higher static pressure and to straighten out the moving air. This type of fan is commonly used with flexible ducts in dilution systems for temporary ventilation of tanks, underground vaults, and similar applications. For permanent dilution systems, they can be used as an exhaust fan or the supply fan. These fans are also used in HVAC systems. They are usually noisier than other axial fan designs.

DILUTION VENTILATION OF TEMPORARY WORKSPACES

Dilution is often used as temporary ventilation for: workspaces such as tanks and utility vaults that are usually unoccupied but occasionally require workers to enter for inspection, cleaning, maintenance, or other tasks; and for activities in normally occupied spaces when work that generates contaminants is performed. In these cases ventilation fills the following needs:

- provides adequate outside air to maintain oxygen concentration above 19.5 percent and below 23.5 percent; flammable gas, vapor, or mist at a safe level (e.g., below 10 percent of their lower flammable limits [LFL]); and, combustible dust at a safe concentration
- controls contaminants produced inside the space (welding or cutting fumes, vapors from residues, insulation or coatings, etc.) below their Permissible Exposure Limit (PEL), TLV, or other occupational exposure limit
- achieves compliance with OSHA regulations (involving confined space or hot work as discussed below)
- controls temperature in hot climates, where the sun raises inside temperature excessively, or where operations inside the space (e.g., welding) produce excessive heat

Effective use of dilution in these situations using a mechanical air moving system to maintain an acceptable environment for workers can follow two approaches:

- forced supplied ventilation configured so that fresh air is supplied to the workspace
- general mechanical ventilation using exhaust fans (or other large capacity air movers)

Good air distribution is often easier to achieve if fresh air is blown into the space using a flex duct arrangement rather than using the fan to exhaust the space. A fan throws a jet of air over a greater distance than it can draw air (Figure 20–5). The air can be discharged into the area where people are working, and will flow out available openings. However, this is not a good approach if either: (1) the ventilated space should be maintained at a slight negative pressure to prevent contaminants from migrating into adjacent work areas; or (2) the air jet can stir up loose debris that causes an eye or inhalation hazard for workers.

Make-up or Supply Air Quality

Regardless of the ventilation configuration, the quality of air

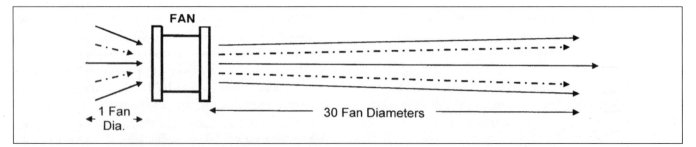

Figure 20–5. The air velocity 30 fan diameters from the fan discharge is nearly equal to the inward velocity 1 fan diameter from the fan inlet. For this reason, blowing air into a temporary workspace often provides better dilution ventilation than an exhaust configuration.

entering the workspace must be high. When air is exhausted from the space, make-up air will enter through any available opening. It is important to ensure that no contaminants will degrade make-up air quality. Examples include carbon monoxide from compressor or vehicle exhausts, contaminants from other nearby work, chemical residues in equipment connected to the space, or H_2S or vapors from sewers connected to the workspace. When make-up air quality is an issue with exhaust ventilation, it may be preferable to use a separate ducted air supply system with the intake located at a safe point.

OSHA Requirements

Work in confined or enclosed spaces presents special hazards including oxygen deficiency, toxic contaminants, risk of engulfment by solid materials, and the risk of being trapped by small passageways. Working safely in these locations where hazards either exist or might develop requires extraordinary care. A safety plan for work in these locations includes features such as preventing unauthorized entry, identifying and controlling the potential hazards, performing air monitoring, providing ventilation, providing rescue equipment and personnel, and training employees. The work may be subject to specific regulations such as the OSHA "Permit-Required Confined Spaces" standard (U.S. OSHA: 29 CFR 1910.146). Other standards may cover specific work tasks, such as welding, and require local exhaust ventilation or specific respiratory protection depending on the materials involved. Generally, the standards fall into these areas:

- General requirement to use engineering controls rather than personal protective equipment (e.g., respirators) to ensure a safe environment (O_2, flammables, toxins, etc.). Exposures to contaminants must be maintained below the PELs.
- Welding and other Hot Work—OSHA's requirements for

this type of work (U.S. OSHA: 29 CFR 1910.252) recognize three main factors that govern welder exposure to contaminants: dimensions of the welding space, especially ceiling height; the number of welders; and possible evolution of hazardous fumes or dust depending on the metals, fluxes, and other materials involved. Other factors, such as weather, the amount of heat generated, and the presence of volatile solvents, also contribute to the need for ventilation or respiratory protective devices. For certain materials, OSHA may allow a choice between control measures or specify which ones are to be used (Table 20–D).

The requirements in all applicable legal and consensus standards must be understood before beginning any work in these locations.

Effective Ventilation of Temporary Workspaces

Effective use of dilution should follow these principles:

- In many enclosed spaces there is a natural air movement due to the solar load or other factors. For example, in a large tank or process vessel located outdoors there is often a *chimney effect* from the sun's heat that causes the air to rise (Figure 20–6). Underground utility vaults may have a natural air movement caused by thermal load on an attached building or other structure. In some spaces the air direction may change over the course of a day because of warming and cooling cycles. Dilution ventilation should be arranged to take advantage of the natural movement. Mechanical dilution fans may not be strong enough to overcome natural air movement if the set-up requires the fan to work against the natural forces such as convection.
- Air distribution inside these spaces must be managed. *Short circuiting* can occur if the air moves from the air inlet to the exhaust fan without diluting contaminants where employees are working. Temporary scaffolding or other internal features may impede good airflow. It may be

TABLE 20–D	Federal OSHA Ventilation Requirements for Confined Space Welding, Cutting, or Brazing		
Material or Process	**General or Local Exhaust Ventilation or Air-Supplied Respirators**[a]	**Local Exhaust Ventilation or Air-Supplied Respirators**[a]	**Local Exhaust Ventilation and Air-Supplied Respirators**[a]
Zinc	●		
Lead – base metal	●		
Lead – other		●	
Cadmium filler	●		
Cadmium – other		●	
Chromium	●		
Mercury		●	
Beryllium			●

[a] Air-supplied respirator use is permissible only when required ventilation is not feasible.

necessary to block off some air inlets or take other steps to assure good air distribution. As mentioned earlier, good air distribution may be easier to achieve if fresh air is blown into the space rather than an exhaust configuration.

- Another type of short circuiting can occur if the exhaust fan or duct is not sealed to the workspace opening. In this case outside air is pulled back through the fan rather than air from the interior of the closed space. Bolts and clamps to hold the fan in place can solve this problem, with a plywood adapter plate between the fan and workspace opening where needed.

Ventilation Equipment for Temporary Dilution Systems

Axial flow fans find wide application in dilution systems for temporary workplaces. The largest of the vaneaxial fans can move up to about 4500 ft³/min through 50 ft of 16" diameter flex duct while tubeaxial fans can move up to 2300 ft³/min through 50 ft of 12" diameter flex duct. "Confined Space Ventilation" packaged units using centrifugal fans are also available that move about 500-1000 ft³/min through 8-12" diameter flex duct.

There are also a variety of special-application ventilators such as hatch-mounted exhausters (for tanks and similar process vessels), and compressed air-driven ventilators. For compressed air-driven equipment, the quantity and pressure of compressed air is critical for proper performance. If the compressed air discharge enters the flowing air, these devices must be configured to exhaust the workspace unless the compressed air is of respirable quality.

Often ventilation systems for temporary installations are offered as packages consisting of the air mover, flex ducts, and other accessories with a specific air flow (Q) listed in the product literature depending on the duct length and other system components. However, it is important to note that the performance of all air movers diminishes with increased resistance to airflow, which may be caused by factors such as insufficient openings to allow free air movement into or out of the workspace. For ducted systems, increased airflow resistance can be caused by excessive duct length, number of elbows or sharp turns in the flex duct, and restricted duct diameter due to the duct not being fully extended or sagging where not supported. The literature descriptions of the "confined space package" equipment may not cover these factors, which can result in the fan moving less than 50 percent the airflow specified in the catalog. To maximize airflow, stretch flex ducts to full length to achieve a full diameter and smooth interior, support duct runs to avoid sag, and avoid sharp bends. As a general rule, it is prudent to select a confined space package with double the calculated required airflow; the actual airflow is verified using field measurements after the equipment is in place.

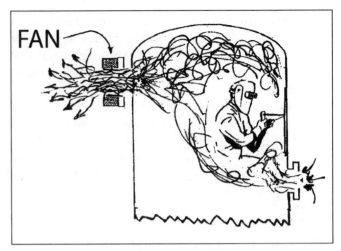

Figure 20–6. Where contaminated air tends to rise due to the "chimney effect," locating the exhaust at the highest point in the work space will enhance dilution ventilation.

Recommended Airflow for Temporary Workspaces

In selecting ventilation equipment, it is necessary to select an airflow (ft³/min) or air exchange rate (air changes per hour [ACH]) for the application. Where contaminants are generated within the workspace (e.g., welding, painting, etc.) the required airflow should be calculated based on the air volume needed to dilute the contaminants to acceptable levels before the air is inhaled by workers. Where there are no contaminants generated inside the space (e.g., inspection, mechanical disassembly, etc.) the airflow should be sufficient to maintain good air quality and thermal comfort. Although ACH is not widely used as a design parameter for ventilation systems, one logical comparison where no contaminants are generated is the suggested ventilation rate for chemical laboratories of 4-12 ACH.

Typical Approach to Ventilating Temporary Workspaces

Because of the factors discussed above, a typical approach to proper dilution ventilation of temporary workspaces follows these criteria:

1. The minimum ventilation rate is determined from the following:
   - General supply or exhaust ventilation has sufficient air changes per hour (ACH) to maintain an acceptable environment within the space, considering contaminants generated within the space and other factors.
   - Local exhaust ventilation, where feasible, is used to control emissions from localized sources (welding, etc.).
   - For welding:
     – The LEV must generate 100 ft/min toward hood through welding zone when the hood is at its most remote point from the point of welding. Depending on the hood configuration and its distance from

the weld point, the airflow to satisfy this velocity is 600–1000 ft³/min per welder.
- Otherwise Federal OSHA requires 2000 ft³/min per welder (when welding with only general ventilation is permitted).

2. Minimum fan capacity must be greater than the quantity determined in Step (1) to compensate for actual field performance of fans and fan/duct systems as compared to higher catalog or nameplate airflow that cannot be achieved under field conditions. A prudent total fan capacity is 1.5 to 2 times the airflow from Step (1).

3. Consider Forced Air Ventilation to improve air distribution except for these situations:
   • The workspace should be kept at a slight negative pressure (e.g., work is in a portion of a building and contaminants should not be allowed to migrate into the remainder of the building).
   • The velocity of the supplied air may stir up debris and cause a potential eye or inhalation hazard.
   • There is a natural airflow resulting from thermal head or other factors that can be used in conjunction with exhaust fans to ventilate the workspace.

4. Workspaces where contaminated air rises as a result of thermal head (especially tank and vertical vessels that are exposed to the sun) are to be exhausted from an opening near the top of the space. If this is not possible, a ducted exhaust blower should be used with the exhaust duct opening located so it draws air from the top of the space. This ensures that the ventilation system does not work against the upward induced air movement due to the chimney effect.

5. Locate fans or make other arrangements to ensure that the general ventilation flushes the entire work zone inside the space to avoid short circuiting that occurs if the air moves from the air inlet to the exhaust fan without diluting contaminants where employees are working. Methods include blocking off some air inlets, or using

a duct that terminates well inside the space to supply or draw air to avoid *stale air zones* (Figure 20–7). Note that exhaust set-ups are more prone to short-circuiting than supply configurations.

6. The fan or duct is to be bolted or clamped tightly to the opening if the set-up is susceptible to recirculation of outside air. Recirculation through the fan can occur if the exhaust fan or duct is not sealed to the workspace opening. Another solution is to use a duct and run it well inside the work space.

7. Measure *differential static pressure* between the space and ambient environment (as described below) when the ventilation is operating. Differential static pressure values greater than 1 inch of water gauge indicate that there are insufficient openings for replacement air to enter the space, which may impair fan performance because of too little replacement air. Correct this deficiency by providing more openings or installing supply fans in available openings.

8. For compressed-air driven fans, a pressure gauge is to be installed in the compressed air line near the blower because proper fan performance depends on adequate air pressure.

MEASURING DILUTION PERFORMANCE

A description of air measuring devices and techniques is in Chapter 19, Local Exhaust Ventilation.

Smoke tubes are useful in identifying the air distribution patterns in the work area, the movement of contaminants from discrete sources, the direction of natural air movement, and problems such as short-circuiting. Typical smoke tube applications include:
• verifying that air flow is in the expected direction (in or out) of openings;
• identifying any stale air zones where general or local

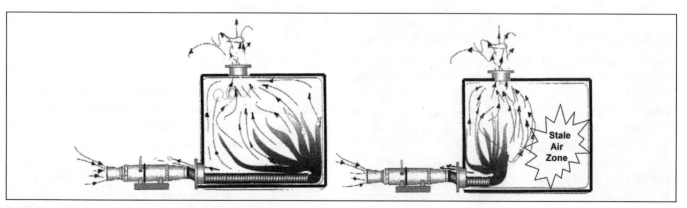

Figure 20–7. Discharging air into a stale air zone can improve dilution ventilation (left). Using too short a duct or too low air flow (right) can result in the ventilation air not penetrating the stale air zone.

forced ventilation is not generating adequate air motion; and

• determining whether the air velocity from a local forced ventilation system is too high and could adversely affect weld quality.

A digital manometer (Figure 20–8) can be used to measure the pressure differential between the inside of the workspace and the ambient environment. This is an important measurement in these applications because the fans generally do not perform well when working against static pressure. This means that the airflow will drop off for an exhauster if the static pressure inside the space becomes negative, and conversely, an air supply blower will not perform properly if the static pressure inside the space is positive. Static pressure will deviate from zero (ambient) inside a ventilated space if openings are not large enough to permit free airflow of replacement air.

To measure whether a work space is at positive or negative pressure, place the manometer inside or outside the space. Leave one "leg" of the manometer exposed to the local atmosphere and run a tube from the other leg to the opposite location. The open end of the tube should be at least three feet from the opening in the workspace, and not impacted by wind. The manometer reading shows the differential pressure between the two locations.

Velometers are used to determine the velocity through openings. For a space that is being exhausted, it may be easier and more accurate to measure the make-up air flowing into the space rather than measure the fan's output directly.

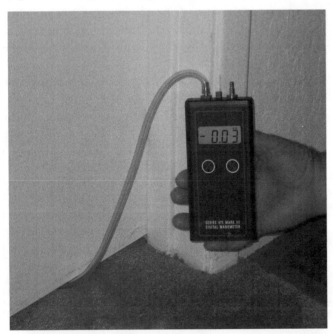

Figure 20–8. A digital manometer is used to measure pressure differential between a workspace and the surrounding environment.

Volumetric airflow is determined from this equation:

$$Q = V \times A \qquad (7)$$

where Q = volumetric airflow, ft³/min
V = velocity, ft/min
A = area of flow, ft²

Where accurate airflow data is needed, follow the instructions for a velocity traverse in Chapter 19, Local Exhaust Ventilation.

SUMMARY

Dilution occurs when contaminants released into the workroom mix with air flowing through the room. It is used in situations where small quantities of relatively low toxicity (or low fire hazard) contaminants are released into the workroom air, and sufficient dilution occurs before workers breathe the contaminated air or a flammable contaminant/air mixture reaches a source of ignition. The major difficulty in designing a dilution ventilation system is that the inherent uncertainties that exist in many of the design parameters require that large safety factors be applied to airflow equations to ensure that safe conditions are maintained. This can result in large air volumes being exhausted from the workplace.

Dilution is also used to ventilate temporary workspaces that are either normally unoccupied but occasionally require workers to enter; and for activities in normally occupied spaces when work that generates contaminants is performed. Work in confined or enclosed spaces presents special hazards, and work in these locations where hazards either exist or might develop requires extraordinary care. Effective use of dilution in these situations requires careful application of the general principles that apply to all work settings plus additional concepts unique to confined or enclosed spaces.

BIBLIOGRAPHY

The following references apply to Chapter 19, Local Exhaust Ventilation, and Chapter 20, Dilution Ventilation of Industrial Workplaces. All copyrighted figures are used with the permission of the copyright holder.

American Conference of Governmental Industrial Hygienists. *Industrial Ventilation – A Manual of Recommended Practice*, 27th Ed. Cincinnati, OH: ACGIH, 2010.
American Conference of Governmental Industrial Hygien-

ists. *TLVs® and BEIs®*. Cincinnati, OH: ACGIH, current edition.

American National Standards Institute/American Industrial Hygiene Association (ANSI/AIHA) Ventilation-related Standards (below). New York: ANSI, current edition:

Z9.1: *Ventilation and Operation of Open Surface Tanks*

Z9.2: *Fundamentals Governing the Design and Operation of Local Exhaust Ventilation Systems*

Z9.3: *Spray Finishing Operations – Design, Construction and Operation*

Z9.4: *Abrasive Blasting Operations – Ventilation and Safe Practices for Fixed Locations*

Z9.5: *Laboratory Ventilation*

Z9.6: *Exhaust Systems for Grinding, Polishing and Buffing*

Z9.7: *Recirculation of Air from Industrial Process Exhaust Systems*

Z9.9: *Portable Ventilation Systems*

American Society of Heating, Refrigerating and Air Conditioning Engineers, Inc. *Handbook of Fundamentals*. Atlanta: ASHRAE, 2009.

Harris MK, Booher LE, Carter S. *Field Guidelines for Temporary Ventilation of Confined Spaces*. Fairfax, VA: AIHA, 1996.

McDermott HJ. *Handbook of Ventilation for Contaminant Control*, 3rd ed. Cincinnati, OH: ACGIH, 2000.

National Fire Protection Association Standard Codes Ventilation-relevant Standards (below). Quincy, MA: NFPA, current edition:

68: *Standard on Explosion Protection by Deflagration Venting*

69: *Standard on Explosion Prevention Systems*

91: *Standard for Exhaust Systems for Air Conveying of Vapors, Gases, Mists, and Noncombustible Particulate Solids*

654: *Standard for the Prevention of Fire and Dust Explosions from the Manufacturing, Processing, and Handling of Combustible Particulate Solids*

National Research Council. *Prudent Practices for Handling Hazardous Chemicals in Laboratories*. Washington, DC: National Academy Press, 1981.

U.S. Occupational Safety and Health Administration. *Permit-required Confined Spaces*. General Industry Safety and Health Regulations, U.S. Code of Federal Regulations, Title 29, Chapter XVIII, Part 1910.146.

U.S. Occupational Safety and Health Administration. *Welding, Cutting and Brazing*. General Industry Safety and Health Regulations, U.S. Code of Federal Regulations, Title 29, Chapter XVIII, Part 1910.252.

CHAPTER 21

General Ventilation of Nonindustrial Occupancies

By Henry J. McDermott, CIH, CSP, PE

Industrial Hygiene practitioners usually get involved with heating, ventilating, and air conditioning (HVAC) systems in response to complaints about Indoor Air Quality (IAQ). To resolve these issues, practitioners must have an understanding of HVAC systems, how they impact the indoor environment, and other factors involved in IAQ episodes.

INTRODUCTION

Heating, ventilating, and air conditioning (HVAC) systems are built to provide adequate amounts of fresh, clean, and tempered air to the occupants of a building. The air supplied by the HVAC system must contain sufficient fresh outdoor air (OA) to provide sufficient oxygen and maintain concentrations of indoor airborne chemicals and odors at acceptable levels. The recommended quantity of fresh air (cubic feet of fresh outside air per minute per person, commonly written as "cfm OA/person") has varied over the years. Figure 21–1 shows the history of OA recommendations from the American Society of Heating, Refrigerating and Air-Conditioning Engineers (ASHRAE), the leading technical organization for IAQ criteria. For nonsmoking commercial occupancies, it is currently 15-20 cfm OA/person depending on specific use.

Many buildings that were constructed or renovated during the 1970s and 1980s sought to minimize HVAC-related energy costs by limiting the amount of outside air brought into the building. Under then-current standards, the OA rates were as low as 5 cfm/person; the result has been under-ventilated buildings from that era leading to occupants' complaints about indoor air quality. Additionally, many new building methods, building materials and furnish-

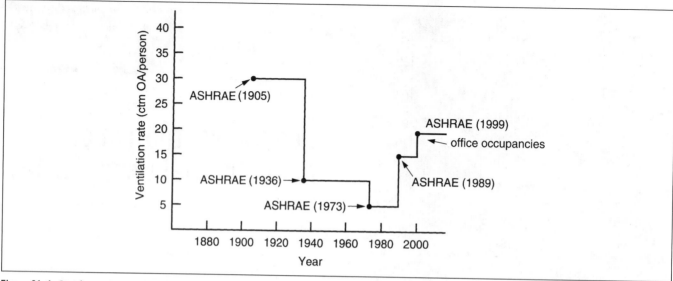

Figure 21–1. Outdoor air consensus standards over the years.

ings, and maintenance products were introduced during that time that released air contaminants inside buildings, which also triggered IAQ complaints.

Since that time period, building and ventilation standards have been revised based on experience and new research. Indoor air quality considerations are now usually a selection criterion for construction materials and furnishings for new and remodeled buildings. Building managers are more aware of the impact of maintenance, landscaping, and other activities on IAQ. The importance of HVAC system preventive maintenance is better understood. The elimination of smoking in many occupancies has also reduced IAQ complaints. Overall, these factors have resulted in more awareness of indoor air quality issues, and the need to deal with complaints or episodes of possible building-related illness promptly and professionally.

Over the past 20 years there has also been more attention paid to the impact of microorganisms, such as molds and the volatile organic compounds they emit, on indoor air quality. Wet surfaces and organic debris in the HVAC system, along with water-damaged building components or furnishings, are a major source of microorganism-related complaints.

In commercial buildings, heating, air conditioning, and ventilation account for about 50 percent of the energy consumed by the building (Figure 21–2) so there is always pressure on HVAC design and operation to minimize energy consumption to conserve resources and save money.

The role of industrial hygienists in ventilation of commercial buildings and other nonindustrial occupancies is usually diagnosing and resolving IAQ issues. Generally, industrial hygienists are not involved in the specialized tasks of system design, commissioning, or periodic testing and balancing.

TERMS

Air-handling unit (AHU) is the ventilation equipment in HVAC systems used to condition and circulate air. The AHU usually consists of the fan (or "blower"), heating and cooling elements, filters, and dampers.

ASHRAE (American Society of Heating, Refrigerating and Air-Conditioning Engineers) is the primary North American consensus standard-setting organization dealing with IAQ issues. It has developed a number of IAQ–related standards.

Acceptable indoor air quality is air in which there are no known contaminants at harmful levels, as determined by appropriate authorities, and air with which 80 percent or more of the people do not express dissatisfaction based on several acceptability criteria (such as temperature, relative humidity, odors, and air movement).

Commissioning is the acceptance process in which an HVAC system's performance is determined, verified against design criteria, and documented to ensure proper operation in accordance with codes, standards, design intentions, and purchase and installation contracts.

Constant air volume (CV) is an HVAC system in which the supply air volume is constant; temperature and humidity are varied at the air-handling unit (AHU).

Exhaust air (EA) is the portion of return air that is discharged outside the building from the HVAC system.

HVAC (heating, ventilating, and air conditioning, pronounced "H-Vac") systems are air-handling systems designed primarily for temperature, humidity, odor, and air-quality control.

Mixed air (MA) is the air drawn into the supply fan. It con-

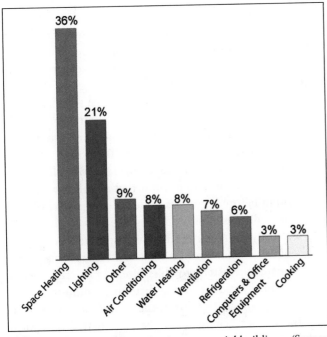

Figure 21–2. Energy consumption in commercial buildings. *(Source: U.S. Energy Administration,* Commercial Building Energy Consumption Survey, *2008)*

sists of outside air plus the portion of return air (RA) not exhausted from the building.

Occupied zone is usually the region within an occupied space between the floor and 72 in. above the floor and more than 2 ft from the walls.

Outdoor air (OA) is "fresh" air drawn into the HVAC system; the OA is mixed with RA to dilute contaminants in the supply air (SA).

Return air (RA) is the air from occupied spaces that is channeled back into the HVAC system to either be exhausted from the building or mixed with OA to be supplied to the building.

Supply air (SA) is the air in the ducts supplying the building areas. The term is used to denote the mixed air (MA) after it has been filtered and the temperature and relative humidity adjusted.

Variable air volume (VAV) refers to HVAC systems in which the air volume supplied to the building is varied by dampers or fan speed controls to maintain the temperature; these systems are usually more energy efficient than CV systems.

HVAC SYSTEMS

The term HVAC implies mechanically ventilating, heating, cooling, humidifying, dehumidifying, and cleaning air for comfort, safety, and health. HVAC systems also provide

odor control and maintain oxygen and carbon dioxide levels at acceptable concentrations. Mechanical air-handling systems (as opposed to natural ventilation, which relies on wind and temperature differences to induce airflow through a building) range from a simple fan to complex, digitally controlled, central air-handling units. The designer (or user) of an HVAC system must choose combinations of volume flow rate, temperature, humidity, and air quality that satisfy the needs of the space.

Zoned Systems

Individual units may be installed in the space they serve, or central units can be installed to serve multiple areas of the building (called *zones*). Figure 21–3 shows zones in a commercial building along with the typical nomenclature used to describe different zones. Most zones are defined by one thermostat so the temperature setting through the zone is the same.

The zone concept is important in achieving thermal comfort because different parts of the building may require varying heating and cooling capacity. For example, south facing offices on a sunny day may need cooling while offices on the northern side with no solar gain need heating. Often in the morning, the entire building may need heating for a morning warm up, while soon after only the perimeter offices need heating and the interior core needs cooling due to occupant- or equipment-generated heat. Because interior zones are not subject to as much solar heating in summer and loss of heat to the outdoors during winter as the exterior (or perimeter) zones, some system designs or operating controls may limit the volumetric air flow to interior zones. Insufficient air flow can cause or exacerbate IAQ complaints. For this reason, air quality investigations need to identify whether problems are associated with a single zone or the whole building.

Testing and troubleshooting HVAC systems with zones requires the participation of a competent HVAC technician or

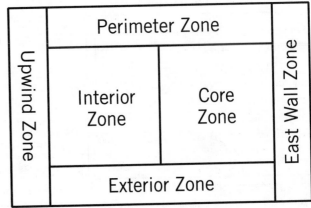

Figure 21–3. Terms used to identify building HVAC zones.

engineer familiar with the sensors and control systems (e.g., dampers and related actuators) in that particular system.

The following paragraphs describe basic systems and how they function.

Constant-Volume Systems

A constant volume (CV) system supplies a fixed air volume to the building when the fan is operating; temperature and humidity in the flowing air is varied to achieve comfort.

The single-zone, constant-volume HVAC system (Figure 21–4) is the simplest in design and operation. Outdoor air (OA) enters the intake drawn by suction from the supply fan; an adjustable damper regulates the amount of OA taken into the system. Intake dampers should have a minimum set point such that an adequate supply of outside air is delivered to building occupants at all times. The OA mixes with the portion of the return air (RA) from the occupied space that is to be reused, forming mixed air (MA). The MA usually passes through a filter; one type is a coarse filter (arrestance filter), which removes insects, leaves, and larger dust particles. If better filtration is needed, a more efficient filter, called a *dust spot filter*, will collect smaller particles. The air then enters the fan.

As the air moves through the fan, it is discharged under positive pressure and is pushed through coils that heat or cool the air depending on air temperature, the season, and the zone being served. A drain pan is located below the coils to collect water that condenses on the cooling coil; provision must be made to drain the condensate pan to avoid standing water that fosters microbial growth. Air leaving the coils may be humidified (or dehumidified) to adjust the relative humidity to the 30- to 60-percent desired range. Typically, the conditioned SA leaves the air handling unit and moves through metal duct-work (sometimes covered on the inside with an insulating lining that must be kept dry and mold-free) at about 1,000–2,000 fpm to a distribution box. From there it travels through smaller ducts to the terminal devices that discharge the air into the building space.

Air leaving the terminal devices has a velocity of 500–1,000 fpm and has a tendency to hug the ceiling and walls due to a phenomenon known as the Coanda effect. Installing louvers on the terminal device directs the air into the occupied space and counteracts the Coanda effect. Once in the room, the air slows to a velocity of 40–50 fpm; as shown on Figure 21–4 this is often called the *terminal velocity*. For comfort reasons, it is important that supply air slows to 40–50 fpm before it reaches building occupants as higher velocities will cause drafts and possible discomfort.

Typically the residence time of supplied air in the room is about five to ten minutes. After that, the air migrates to the return air register, which is often a louvered opening into a return air duct or a return air plenum (the space above the ceiling tiles). From the plenum it moves to the return air duct, where it may be recirculated (RA) or be exhausted to the outdoors (EA). Many buildings are maintained under slight positive pressure so air may exfiltrate anywhere along the building periphery. Except for simple systems, sophisticated controls manage the system and determine how much OA will be introduced, how much RA will be exhausted, and what temperatures and relative humidities will be maintained.

Multiple Zone Constant-Volume System

A CV system will allow temperature control in different rooms or areas served by the system by adding additional zones, each with its own thermostat. Figure 21–5 shows how a single-zone constant-volume (CV) system design can be modified to serve more than one zone. The discharge device in each zone is fitted with a reheat coil or electrical reheater, which is controlled by a thermostat. With this arrangement, air is cooled at the central cooling coil and then reheated if needed at the final distribution point to maintain proper temperature. In practice, some terminal devices may not be equipped with a reheater if that zone only requires cool supply air to maintain thermal comfort.

Another design approach to serve multiple zones from a single CV air handler is the Dual Duct system (Figure 21–6). The air is split into two separate ducts at the AHU before the heating and cooling coils. Dual ducts carry heated and cooled air to final distribution boxes near the zones, where the air is mixed before delivery to the discharge device. Thermostats control dampers that mix the appropriate amounts of air to achieve the desired temperature.

Variable Air Volume Systems

In contrast to the constant-volume system, which varies air

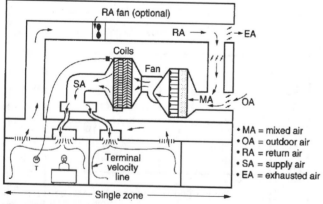

Figure 21–4. Typical single-zone constant volume HVAC system. (*Source: D. Jeff Burton, 2011. Reprinted with permission.*)

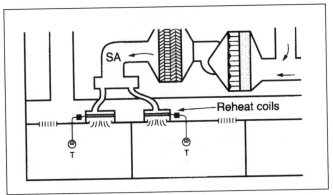

Figure 21–5. Multiple-zone constant volume HVAC system with terminal reheaters. *(Source: D. Jeff Burton, 2011. Reprinted with permission.)*

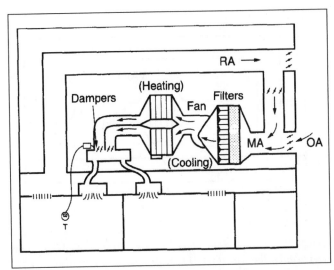

Figure 21–6. Dual-duct constant volume HVAC system. *(Source: D. Jeff Burton, 2011. Reprinted with permission.)*

temperature to maintain temperature, a variable air volume (VAV) system varies the amount of air delivered to the space to maintain temperature. Figure 21–7 shows a single zone VAV system. In this system the fan speed will increase to supply additional cool air if the temperature increases due to thermal load or occupant-generated heat. As the space temperature drops to desired levels, the airflow is reduced. These systems are energy efficient, but they may cause problems if insufficient outside air is provided. For example, in poorly performing or poorly designed VAV systems, the airflow may drop too low to provide enough OA if the space's thermostat is not calling for cool air. In extreme cases the airflow may drop to zero flow. In cases where a minimum volume of air is required, reheat coils may be needed in the terminal device to maintain enough heat for thermal comfort.

The advantages of variable airflow are energy conservation and lower operating costs. In a VAV system the air volume is controlled by adjusting fan speed. As described in the Chapter 19 discussion of fan laws, the air volume moved by the fan is directly related to the fan rotating speed. If the airflow is to be cut in half, then the control system reduces the fan speed to half the original speed. But horsepower and speed are related through a third-power relationship. If the speed is reduced by half, the horsepower and the electrical costs to run the fan are reduced by a factor of eight ($2^3 = 8$). Fan speed controls provide the greatest electrical savings, but another approach used to vary airflow in VAV systems is a fan inlet damper (i.e., adjustable radial vanes or paddles located at the fan inlet) that imparts a spin to the air to reduce the quantity of air moved by the fan.

Multiple Zone Variable Air Volume Systems
VAV systems can serve more than one zone through use of distribution boxes equipped with dampers that modulate the amount of air flowing to each zone based on input from

the thermostat in that zone (Figure 21–8). In this system, a static pressure sensor in the supply duct controls fan speed to maintain sufficient positive pressure in the duct to supply all zones. For example, as the temperature in a zone reaches the thermostat setting, the demand for air decreases. The damper at the distribution box for this zone closes to the minimum airflow setting, which causes the pressure in the supply duct to increase above the normal reading. The pressure sensor, which is connected to the fan speed controller, then triggers a reduction in fan speed, which reduces the amount of supplied air that returns the pressure reading in the duct to within its normal range.

The VAV systems described above are simple designs; in larger or more complex systems the terminal devices may be equipped with reheaters, or a dual duct system may be used. In a dual duct system there are separate cool air and warm air ducts, each with its own adjustable speed supply fan. Both ducts are connected to sophisticated air distribution boxes serving each zone, and dampers modulate the amount of cool and warm air delivered to the zone.

HVAC System Components
Unit Ventilators
Unit ventilators are stand-alone systems that contain all of the components in a single housing. Window-mounted units and small roof units fall into this category. For small roof ventilation systems, the outside air intake is usually a screen-covered opening on the side of the unit. Often there is only one visible duct leaving the unit (e.g., supply air) as the unit is mounted directly over the space being served and is connected to a ceiling grille in the space that serves as the return air duct.

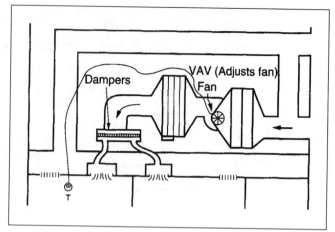

Figure 21–7. Single-zone Variable Air Volume HVAC system. (*Source: D. Jeff Burton, 2011. Reprinted with permission.*)

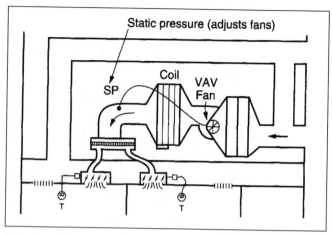

Figure 21–8. Multiple-zone Variable Air Volume HVAC system. (*Source: D. Jeff Burton, 2011. Reprinted with permission.*)

Dampers

Dampers are used in HVAC duct systems (e.g., MA, EA, and OA) to control airflow. Damper positions can be set automatically or manually depending on the type and complexity of the HVAC control system. It is important to note the position of dampers during inspections and it may be necessary to set them to a specific position during IAQ measurements to simulate conditions during complaint periods. For example, in some moderate climates, OA dampers may be closed to minimum flow in the morning to allow the building to heat from occupant activities, then opened fully in midmorning to cool the building, then closed to minimum flow in the afternoon as the outdoor temperature increases. The OA damper may also be closed manually or by a clock timer during scheduled work such as lawn mowing to avoid odors and allergens being brought into the building. Dampers, actuators, and control systems should always be checked and maintained regularly to ensure proper flow of air through the system. Fire dampers are used to restrict the spread of heat and smoke during a fire; a fire damper closes when the temperature at the fusible link that controls the device exceeds the melting point of the link. Fire dampers need to be manually reset after they close.

Terminal Devices

Supply diffusers and grilles, and associated dampers and controls, are used to achieve proper distribution of the supply air. The number, location, and type of terminal devices determine the air distribution in the occupied space. Improper or malfunctioning devices can lower the ventilation effectiveness and create stagnant areas, drafts, odor buildup, uneven temperatures, short-circuiting of the air, and air stratification.

Delivery of adequate airflow to a space from the terminal devices does not guarantee that proper mixing will occur. The Coanda Effect causes air discharged from the

terminal device to adhere to an adjacent ceiling or wall. One function of the discharge device is to direct the flowing air toward the occupied space, and diffuse it so drafts do not occur. Placement of partitions, bookshelves, furniture, windows, and moveable walls changes the movement of air, and can interfere with proper mixing. Insufficient or poorly located discharge devices also impede good mixing.

When mixing in the occupied zone is less than ideal, improvements to the airflow from the HVAC must be made or portable fans provided to overcome the obstacles to mixing. Good mixing can be attained by

- providing and properly positioning an adequate number of supply and return registers;
- locating supply registers so they circulate air to where people are located in the occupied zone; and
- providing free-standing fans for people located in areas of poor mixing.

Thermal comfort is a function of air motion, temperature, and humidity. When air lacks noticeable motion, it may feel up to 2°F warmer than its actual temperature. When evaluating problem situations in which air motion might be the cause or a contributing factor, the following points should be considered:

- Airflow patterns are different for heating and cooling cycles. Ceiling outlets may not perform as well during heating than cooling cycles, since the buoyant warmer air stratifies along the ceiling. Likewise, floor outlets are less effective during cooling cycles.
- Good terminal device performance assumes that there are no obstructions to good room air circulation. Features that add flexibility to the office architecture, such as moveable walls or portable office partitions that extend to the floor, can impede air movement. In extreme cases, carbon dioxide (CO_2) levels can be higher inside office

cubicles than in the space above the partitions.

• In a modern, sealed building the beneficial effect of good air movement is limited if the temperature set point is higher than the range of comfort. For example, almost no diffuser operating at a low volumetric flow rate to conserve energy will be able to maintain enough air motion to minimize discomfort at 78°F for people in business attire. In many settings, complaints will increase when the temperature exceeds 74°F.

Return Air Systems

Return air grilles are usually either attached directly to the return air duct or are installed in the ceiling leading to the open space above the ceiling. In the latter case, a fan in the RA system keeps the space above the ceiling (called the *return plenum*) at a slight negative pressure to draw the air toward the fan, where it is recirculated as shown in Figure 21–4. Where the space above the ceiling is used for returning air, the space should be kept clean and dry to reduce microbial problems, and ceiling tiles and access doors must be kept in place to ensure proper airflow from the occupied space to the return system.

Ducts

Ducts can become both the source and the pathway for dirt, dust, and biological contaminants to spread through the building. ASHRAE 62.1 and other standards specify that efforts be made to keep dirt, moisture, and high humidity from ductwork. Filters must be used and kept in good working order to keep contaminants from collecting in the HVAC system. Duct contaminants may include a variety of organic and inorganic particles, mold, bacteria, leaves, dirt, and paper. These may contribute to IAQ problems if they release odors, support microbial growth, or are blown into the occupied space.

Duct cleaning or replacement is generally only warranted in the following conditions: there is slime growth in the duct; there is permanent water damage; there is debris that restricts airflow; dust or particles are actually seen issuing from supply registers; or offensive odors come from the ductwork. There is no proven beneficial effect from routine duct cleaning.

INDOOR AIR QUALITY ISSUES AND HVAC STANDARDS

The U.S. Environmental Protection Agency (EPA) attributes most IAQ problems in commercial buildings to three main causes: indoor air pollutants; ventilation issues; or unintended, unplanned, or poorly planned uses of the building. These are explained in Table 21–A. Focusing on HVAC aspects, Table 21–B gives more detail on how HVAC systems impact indoor air quality.

HVAC Standards for Maintaining Adequate IAQ

The American Society of Heating, Refrigeration, and Air Conditioning Engineers (ASHRAE) is the primary consensus organization that develops standards regarding HVAC

TABLE 21–A	Common Causes of IAQ Problems
Cause	*Examples*
Indoor air pollution sources	• Organic vapors from building materials, carpets, and other office furnishings • Cleaning materials and activities • Paints, adhesives, copying machines, reprographic equipment, and other chemical-containing products or equipment • Biological contaminants from dirty ventilation systems or water-damaged building components or furnishings • Tobacco smoke • Chemicals from pest management practices
Ventilation system issues	• Inadequate amounts of outdoor air • Inadequate air distribution causing outdoor air to not actually reach the breathing zone of building occupants • Improperly located outdoor air intakes that bring in air contaminated with vehicle exhaust, boiler emissions, fumes from dumpsters, or air exhausted from restrooms • Spread of biological contaminants that have multiplied in cooling towers, humidifiers, dehumidifiers, air conditioners, or the inside surfaces of ventilation duct work
Uses of the building	• Pollutants circulated from portions of the building used for specialized purposes, such as restaurants, reprographic shops, and dry-cleaning stores, into offices in the same building • Carbon monoxide and other components of automobile exhaust drawn in from underground parking garages • Room partitions and other renovations that restrict air recirculation or cause an inadequate supply of outdoor air

Source: EPA, The Inside Story: A Guide to Indoor Air Quality, 1995.

TABLE 21–B	Deficiencies in HVAC Systems and Their Causes	
Deficiency	**Potential Causes/Typical Problems**	**Potential Corrections**
Insufficient total air delivery to occupied space	• Inadequate fan capacity • Worn fan blades • Faulty fan components • Imbalanced air-supply system • Increased number of occupants	• Increase fan speed • Replace/repair wheel • Provide maintenance • Balance air-distribution system • Increase air capacity; redistribute occupants
Insufficient outdoor air (OA) delivered to occupied space	• OA dampers set too low • Imbalanced supply and return systems • OA damper controls inoperative • Temperature-control capacity insufficient to meet space needs	• Increase OA; provide fixed minimum OA delivery • Balance systems • Inspect, calibrate, reset controls • Increase system capacity
Air distribution within space not adequate; improper; insufficient	• Improper supply system balancing • Poorly operating dampers, boxes • Maladjustment of thermostat/controls • Improper location of supply diffuser • Diffusers blocked • Office partitions resting on floor • Diffusers not attached to supply ducts	• Rebalance • Repair, maintain, inspect boxes and control equipment • Calibrate thermostats • Relocate diffusers or occupants • Remove obstructions • Raise or remove partitions • Inspect, reattach connecting ductwork
AHU components not operating properly	• System does not start before arrival of occupants; shuts down before departure • Filters inadequate • Room temperature and humidity controls inoperative	• Reformat controls • Use appropriate filters; install filters in accordance with manufacturer's instructions; change filters on a regular basis • Monitor or calibrate; maintain

Source: D. Jeff Burton, 2011. Reprinted with permission.

systems and indoor air quality. The three most important consensus standards affecting IAQ are ASHRAE 62.1 on Ventilation for IAQ, ASHRAE 55 on Thermal Comfort, and ASHRAE 52.2 on Air Filtration. These standards are updated periodically; always refer to the latest standards for guidance. Typical elements covered by these standards are described in the following paragraphs.

ASHRAE 62.1: Ventilation for Acceptable Air Quality

The scope of this standard is design and operating guidance to achieve satisfactory IAQ:

• Ventilation air shall be supplied throughout the occupied zone. This implies delivery to where people actually are, as opposed to simply delivering air to the building space.
• Where variable air volume systems are used, and when the supply of air is reduced during times a space is occupied, indoor air quality shall be maintained throughout the occupied zone.
• Ventilation systems should be designed to prevent the growth and dissemination of microorganisms.
• Inlets and outlets shall be located to avoid contamination of intake air.

• Where practical, exhaust systems shall remove contaminants at the source.
• Where combustion sources, clothes dryers, or exhaust systems are used, adequate makeup air should be provided.
• Where necessary, particle filters and gas/vapor scrubbers should be sized and used to maintain air quality.
• Relative humidity should be maintained between 30 and 60 percent.
• Air handling unit (AHU) condensate pans shall be designed for self-drainage. Provision for periodic in-situ cleaning of cooling coils and condensate pans shall be provided.
• The AHU shall be easily accessible for inspection and preventive maintenance.
• Steam is preferred for humidification. Standing water used in humidifiers and water sprays should be treated to avoid microbial buildup.
• Special care should be taken to avoid entrainment of moisture drift from cooling towers into makeup air and intake vents.
• Indoor air should not contain contaminants at concentrations known to impair health or cause discomfort.

Outdoor air introduced to the building through the ventilation system should not exceed U.S. EPA National Primary Ambient-Air Quality Standards. If the outdoor air containment levels exceed EPA values, the air should be treated. When confronted with air known to contain contaminants not on the EPA list, one should refer to other references for guidance.

- The standard lists minimum OA requirements for about 100 occupancies, including offices and classrooms. The standard assumes good mixing and distribution of the outdoor air. It also assumes a certain occupant loading. Where these are not the case, additional OA may be required.

ASHRAE 55: Thermal Environmental Conditions for Human Occupancy

The standard specifies conditions in which 80–90 percent or more of the occupants should find the environment thermally acceptable. It does not address other environmental factors such as air quality and contaminants. This standard attempts to predict what conditions of temperature, humidity, activity, clothing, air movement, and radiant heat sources will satisfy 80–90 percent of the people. Satisfaction for any single parameter (such as temperature) should be 90 percent or more, and the satisfaction expressed for all parameters collectively should be 80 percent or more.

Figure 21–9 is a simplified version of the current standard's recommendations for temperature and relative humidity to achieve occupant comfort.

ASHRAE 52.2: Method of Testing General Ventilation Air-Cleaning Devices for Removal Efficiency by Particle Size

The technical content of this standard is of less importance to industrial hygienists than that in ASHRAE 55 and 62.1. The important concept of ASHRAE 52.2 is that it describes the test methods for two types of air filters used in HVAC systems: a roughing or arrestance filter to remove large particles; and a dust spot filter to remove smaller particles. (Activated carbon filters and high efficiency particle filters may be used in rare instances to remove gases, vapors, and very small particles.) The three performance characteristics of greatest importance in selecting an air filter are

- the filter's efficiency in removing particles from the air stream;
- the resistance to airflow through the filter; and
- the time interval between cleaning or replacement.

Filters used in HVAC systems should be labeled that they comply with provisions of ASHRAE 52.2.

Regulatory Standards

All existing buildings should have been built to comply with the local building and fire codes in force at the time of

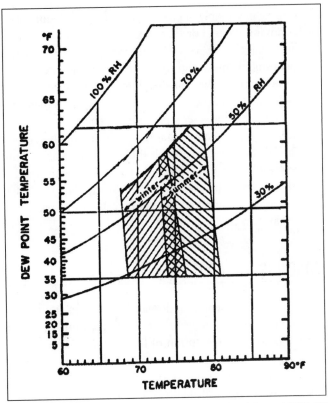

Figure 21–9. Thermal comfort standard. *(Adapted from ASHRAE 55-1992.)*

construction or renovation. Many building code authorities have adopted some version of ASHRAE 62.1 and 55. The building owner or manager should have records of HVAC-related standards that applied as part of building code requirements when the building was constructed or renovated.

Ensuring Proper HVAC System Performance

Most HVAC systems function properly and are never the cause of potential comfort or health concerns. For any HVAC system to operate properly and consistently over its life span, commissioning, testing, and maintenance are required:

- Commissioning is a process in which a new HVAC system's performance is verified and documented to ensure proper operation and compliance with codes, standards, and design calculations and assumptions.
- Testing and balancing is periodically required for all systems. This involves the testing and adjusting of system components (such as dampers) to ensure adequate air distribution to the occupied spaces.
- Maintenance is routinely required for all systems. For simple unit ventilators it may consist of changing filters, checking the fan wheel for debris buildup or damage,

cleaning any visible deposits or moisture, and lubrication of moving parts. For complex systems, it also involves checks that dampers and other system components are operating properly and tests of the control system.

The detailed plan for meeting these requirements to ensure proper operation should be spelled out in the building owner's or manager's procedures and records. Table 21–C lists typical records that should be maintained. These documents need to be available if IAQ concerns arise. Fully understanding them is usually beyond the background of health and safety professionals; for this reason HVAC specialists must be involved in IAQ investigations where the HVAC system can be a factor.

DIAGNOSING IAQ ISSUES

An industrial hygiene practitioner usually gets involved in IAQ and HVAC systems when there are complaints. The investigation and resolution of IAQ complaints requires a step-by-step process to identify possible causes and solutions, both HVAC-related and from other sources. IAQ problems are often difficult to diagnose because of confounding factors:

- IAQ problems arise from complaints about odors, headache, respiratory tract irritation, or similar symptoms. These may affect only a few individuals, especially at early stages.
- Airborne levels of specific contaminants are generally very low as compared to published allowable levels for the occupational setting. Where the level of a specific contaminant is elevated above "background," it may serve

as a marker for the presence of the problem rather than be the cause of the problem itself. For example, slightly elevated carbon monoxide (CO) levels may indicate vehicle exhaust (consisting of numerous irritating or odorous compounds) entering the building even though the CO levels are not hazardous.

- Individual health problems (flu, allergies, etc.), and general stress from work pressures, management-employee relations, and other factors may be involved. Additionally, widespread episodes may be triggered by an accumulation of smaller problems that remain unsolved, which makes it difficult to find the specific cause.

Because of these factors, diagnosis and resolution of IAQ problems should follow well-established protocols. It is often important to document the steps that are planned in advance and share them with concerned occupants and other involved parties. The information gained from each step is used to refine the next steps in the process. These protocols usually consist of the following:

- Employees fill out a questionnaire or are interviewed to determine the type and extent of symptoms and their commonality throughout the building. It is important to identify when symptoms occur (time, day of week, or season), and what other factors employees feel may contribute to the problem in order to reach a final resolution.
- Carry out an initial survey of the building space where the complaints occur. Table 21–D lists the observations during this phase.
- Gather and review relevant records (Table 21–C) for an understanding of the HVAC system, maintenance practices, system changes, and previous IAQ issues.
- Do a walkthrough inspection covering the factors in Table

TABLE 21–C   Building Owner's HVAC Programs and Records
References and Calculations for Required Supply Rate of OA
Methods of measuring/monitoring OA supply
Description of OA control systems
Description of temperature/humidity control systems
Description of filter systems including filter efficiency
Written preventive maintenance program and records
Written Standard Operating Procedures
Plans, drawings, and specifications of building and mechanical systems (as built/as is)
Manufacturer literature for all operating equipment and control systems
Testing, balancing, and monitoring records
Building permits, stack permits, other applicable licenses/permits
History of changes to HVAC systems and building occupancies

Source: D. Jeff Burton, 2011. Reprinted with permission.

TABLE 21-D	Space Characterization
Number of people working in space
Diagram showing doors, windows, supply and return registers, and other relevant features. Draw on floor plan or make a separate sketch
Room dimensions and volume
Prior or current Temperature, Relative Humidity, and Carbon Dioxide readings
Prior or current Terminal (draft) velocity readings or similar existing data
Pressure relationship with hallways or building exterior
Other issues within space: Lighting, Noise, etc.

Source: D. Jeff Burton, 2011. Reprinted with permission.

21-E to identify possible causes of IAQ issues. Devices such as smoke tubes to visualize airflow, a hand-held CO_2 instrument to check for obvious elevated levels, and a digital manometer to measure pressure differentials between the space and adjacent hallways or rooms may be useful. If maintenance, cleaning, or other conditions that are easy to fix are found, they should be corrected immediately. For HVAC system inspection, have a qualified HVAC technician participate in the inspection.

• Take readings of temperature, relative humidity, CO_2, and perhaps some common contaminants, such as carbon monoxide, using direct reading instruments. Hand-held devices can be used with measurements being made periodically through the workday. Recording devices are available that have multiple sensing stations and can store measurements for later analysis. Refer to Figure 21-9 for comfort ranges of temperature and humidity. Low relative humidity can cause particles and vapors in the air to be more irritating than at high levels of humidity, while high humidity aggravates odor problems and fosters mold growth. High humidity also leads to complaints of stuffiness and thermal discomfort.

• If potential mold or bioaerosols issues were identified during the walkthrough inspection, refer to the information in Chapter 14 (Biological Hazards) to determine possible next steps. Note that Volatile Organic Compounds (VOCs) emitted by the bioaerosols may need to be considered as a possible causal factor.

• If indicated by earlier findings or observations, either ventilation system measurements or additional air sampling may need to be done depending on the situation:

  – CO_2 levels in occupied spaces exceeding about 1000 ppm indicate that insufficient outdoor air is being provided to the space. Figure 21-10 illustrates a typical CO_2 profile in a building with insufficient outdoor air. This can be caused by insufficient total airflow, too little outdoor air in the total supplied air, or too many occupants for the amount of air provided to that area

by the HVAC system. With elevated CO_2 levels, either rebalancing of the system, increasing OA, or other ventilation system adjustments may be a logical next step.

  – If the possible cause is an organic vapor from some suspected or unknown source, the next step may be to collect air samples. Generally the typical industrial hygiene compliance air sampling methods that determine contaminant levels at some percent of the Permissible Exposure Limits or Threshold Limit Values

TABLE 21-E	Initial IAQ Walk-Through Survey
Stuffiness due to lack of outside air
Inadequate air distribution
Pressure difference between rooms or interior/exterior of building
Air infiltration at windows or other building components
Detectable odors, especially tobacco smoke
Temperature too warm or too cold
Humidity too high or too low
Poorly vented heating equipment
Poorly located air intakes
Improper exhaust ventilation for bathrooms, showers, cooking areas, contaminant-generating equipment, etc.
Poorly located loading docks or vehicle idling areas
Recent or ongoing renovation or maintenance activities
Visible mold, slime
Visible water or water-damaged furnishings
Cleaning chemicals stored in mechanical (fan) room
Deteriorated insulation
Buildup of debris, especially organic
Evidence of inadequate HVAC maintenance
Outdoor contaminant sources nearby
Predominant wind direction and velocity

Source: D. Jeff Burton, 2011. Reprinted with permission.

are of little value since concentrations are usually far below these levels. Instead consider collecting samples for a GC/MS profile of many organic compounds. For example, air samples collected in an evacuated stainless steel cylinder (Figure 21–11) can be analyzed for 61 compounds at very low parts per billion levels (Table 21–F). Sampling time can be specified from a few hours to 24 hours or more. With any environmental samples it is advisable to collect samples in both problem and non-problem areas of the building, and outside at the HVAC intake and possibly main entrance to the building for later comparison.

– If the possible cause is airborne dust, air sampling designed to identify the makeup of the dust may be indicated. If the dust originates outside the building, size data may be helpful in selecting suitable HVAC filters to remove the dust.

• If complaints are due to smoking, it will probably be difficult to resolve them without separating smoking occupancies from the rest of the occupants. This will involve not recirculating any air from the smoking areas and exhausting the smoking areas separately from the building.

MEASURING BUILDING VENTILATION RATES

HVAC ventilation rates are usually measured to estimate the amount of outdoor air being delivered to each area of the building. This is done by measuring the total airflow to each area, and then determining how much outdoor air is in the total airflow.

Ventilation rates can be determined by measuring airflow directly in the system ducts or outlet registers serving each part of the building, or by use of a tracer technique in which the gradual decline in the concentration of a tracer gas in the building is measured and related to air exchange rates. HVAC settings (airflow, outdoor air damper position,

etc.) must be typical of HVAC performance during the occupied portion of the day or time period of concern for IAQ complaints.

Airflow Measurements

Velocity measurements at hoods or in ducts are often used to evaluate the performance of local exhaust systems. Similar measurements at inlet and return air grilles and at outside air inlets and exhaust air outlets are used for HVAC system evaluation. Because these techniques are explained in Chapter 19, the details are not covered in this chapter.

The most convenient way to measure airflow to each space is by measuring the airflow from each terminal unit (grille) in the area with special flowmeter called a *balometer* (Figure 21–12). These devices, which are used by air balancing technicians, report airflow directly in units of cubic feet per minute. If a balometer is not available, in smaller systems the airflow can be estimated by measuring the average velocity through the open area of each discharge grille with a velometer. Some terminal devices use a jet of supply air or

Figure 21–11. Evacuated canister for extended sampling of volatile organic compounds. *(Source: Galson Laboratories.)*

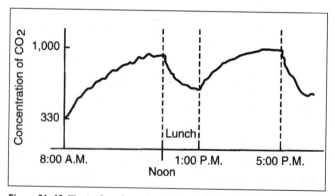

Figure 21–10. Typical carbon dioxide profile in a building with marginal OA supply.

TABLE 21–F		61 Substance Volatile Organic Compound Profile*			
Substance	**LOQ****	**Substance**	**LOQ****	**Substance**	**LOQ****
Acetone	5 ppb	1,1 – Dichloroethene	5 ppb	Propylene	5 ppb
Allyl Chloride	5 ppb	trans – 1,2 – Dichloroethene	5 ppb	Styrene	5 ppb
Benzene	5 ppb	cis – 1,2 – Dichloroethylene	5 ppb	1,1,2,2 – Tetrachloroethane	5 ppb
Benzyl Chloride	5 ppb	1,2 – Dichloropropane	5 ppb	Tetrahydrofuran	5 ppb
Bromodichloromethane	5 ppb	cis – 1,3 – Dichloropropene	5 ppb	Tetrachloroethylene	5 ppb
Bromoform	5 ppb	trans – 1,3 – Dichloropropene	5 ppb	1,1,1 – Trichloroethane	5 ppb
Bromomethane	5 ppb	1,4 – Dioxane	20 ppb	1,1,2 – Trichloroethane	5 ppb
1,3 – Butadiene	5 ppb	Ethyl Acetate	5 ppb	Trichloroethylene	5 ppb
Carbon Disulfide	10 ppb	Ethylbenzene	5 ppb	1,2,4 – Trimethylbenzene	5 ppb
Carbon Tetrachloride	5 ppb	4 – Ethyltoluene	5 ppb	1,3,5 – Trimethylbenzene	5 ppb
Chlorobenzene	5 ppb	Freon – 11	5 ppb	2,2,4 – Trimethylpentane	5 ppb
Chloroethane	5 ppb	Freon – 12	5 ppb	Toluene	5 ppb
Chloroform	5 ppb	Freon – 113	5 ppb	Vinyl Acetate	5 ppb
Chloromethane	5 ppb	Freon – 114	5 ppb	Vinyl Bromide	5 ppb
Cyclohexane	5 ppb	Heptane	5 ppb	Vinyl Chloride	5 ppb
Dibiomochloromethane	5 ppb	Hexane	5 ppb	m,p – Xylene	10 ppb
1,2 – Dibromomethane	5 ppb	Isopropyl Alcohol	5 ppb	o – Xylene	5 ppb
1,2 – Dichlorobenzene	5 ppb	Methyl Butyl Ketone	20 ppb		
1,3 – Dichlorobenzene	5 ppb	Methylene Chloride	5 ppb		
1,4 – Dichlorobenzene	5 ppb	Methyl Ethyl Ketone	5 ppb		
1,1 – Dichloroethane	5 ppb	Methyl Isobutyl Ketone	20 ppb		
1,2 – Dichloroethane	5 ppb	Methyl Tert – Butyl Ether	5 ppb		

* Sample collected in Evacuated Canister over sampling period up to 24 hours (Air volume: 0.4 – 1 L); analyzed by GC/MS according to a modified OSHA PV2120/EPA TO-15 method.

** Limit of quantification

a small fan to draw room air into the terminal device and then discharge it with the supplied air back into the room, which induces extra air circulation in the room. Outlet readings on these units must be adjusted for the quantity of room air being recirculated to avoid overestimating the air supply rates, since a portion of the air being measured is recirculated room air rather than system air.

If a velometer (instead of a balometer) is used, the volumetric airflow can readily be calculated from the air velocity and area of flow:

$$Q = V \times A \qquad (1)$$

where Q = volumetric airflow, ft^3/min
$\quad V$ = velocity, ft/min
$\quad A$ = area of flow (area of inlet or grille, etc.), ft^2

In IAQ investigations, a key parameter is the amount of outside air supplied to each area. This is a percentage of the total airflow to the area, which can be estimated by either the *Temperature method* or the *Carbon Dioxide method*. Both methods involve measuring the relevant parameter (temperature or CO_2 level) at three locations in the system (Figure 21–4): return air, outdoor air, and mixed air.

Using the Temperature method to estimate the amount of outdoor air:

$$\text{Outdoor Air},\% = \frac{T_{\text{return}} - T_{\text{mixed}}}{T_{\text{return}} - T_{\text{outdoor}}} \times 100 \qquad (2)$$

where Outdoor Air,% = percent of outdoor air in total airflow
$\quad T_{\text{return}}$ = temperature in return air, °F
$\quad T_{\text{mixed}}$ = temperature in mixed air, °F
$\quad T_{\text{outdoor}}$ = temperature in outdoor air, °F

Figure 21–12. Balometer used to measure airflow from HVAC discharge and return air registers. *(Source: IHI Environmental)*

Using the Carbon Dioxide method to estimate the amount of outdoor air:

$$\text{Outdoor Air,\%} = \frac{CO_{2(return)} - CO_{2(mixed)}}{CO_{2(return)} - CO_{2(outdoor)}} \times 100 \qquad (3)$$

where Outdoor Air,% = percent of outdoor air in total airflow

$CO_{2(return)}$ = carbon dioxide concentration in return air, ppm

$CO_{2(mixed)}$ = carbon dioxide concentration in mixed air, ppm

$CO_{2(outdoor)}$ = carbon dioxide concentration in outdoor air, ppm

The percent of outdoor air calculated by either of these methods will be more accurate as the differences between the three measured values increase.

Example: Balometer readings at the terminal devices serving one work area show that the total air supplied to the space is 875 ft³/min. CO_2 readings at the 3 specified locations are:

$$CO_{2(return)} = 610 \text{ ppm}$$
$$CO_{2(mixed)} = 465 \text{ ppm}$$
$$CO_{2(outdoor)} = 400 \text{ ppm}$$

If there are 25 people in the work area, calculate the amount of outdoor air per person being supplied to the area.

The percent of outdoor air in the total airflow is calculated from Equation (3):

$$\text{Outdoor Air,\%} = \frac{CO_{2(return)} - CO_{2(mixed)}}{CO_{2(return)} - CO_{2(outdoor)}} \times 100 \qquad (3)$$

$$= \left(\frac{610 - 465}{610 - 400}\right) \times 100 = \frac{145}{210} \times 100$$

$$\text{Outdoor Air,\%} = 69.0\%$$

$$Q_{outdoor} = 875 \text{ ft}^3/\text{min } (0.69) = 604 \text{ ft}^3/\text{min}$$

$$Q_{outdoor} \text{ per person} = \frac{604 \text{ ft}^3/\text{min}}{25 \text{ people}} = 24.2 \text{ ft}^3/\text{min per person}$$

To determine if this value meets current guidelines, refer to the latest version of ASHRAE Standard 62.1, "Ventilation for Acceptable Indoor Air Quality" for the type of occupancy (office, school, etc.). Note that if the building was designed when an earlier version of ASHRAE Standard 62.1 was in effect, you cannot conclude that the system is inadequate simply because the outdoor airflow per person is below current standards. However, if IAQ complaints exist in a building with OA rates lower than are currently recommended, this is a logical factor to consider when trying to resolve the problem.

Tracer Techniques

In some situations it is not feasible to determine the amount of outdoor air using balometer measurements and the equations described above. This includes complex systems, rooms with very high ceilings where balometer measurements are impractical, and buildings where a significant amount of outdoor air infiltrates through doors, windows, or other openings. In these situations, tracer studies are sometimes used in indoor air quality evaluations.

The tracer technique involves use of a stable, nontoxic, easily measured gas, ideally with a density near that of air. The tracer is distributed throughout the work area, and the level measured periodically. The airborne level decreases over time due to dilution with supply air or infiltration of outdoor air through open doors or cracks. The concentration values can be used to calculate an approximate air exchange rate.

Where the occupant density is sufficient to generate increased CO_2 levels, this can be used as a tracer. To be a successful test agent, the occupant-generated CO_2 levels must be higher than ambient levels so that the dilution with outside air can be measured over time (e.g., 1000 ppm). These tracer tests are conducted immediately after workers leave for the day to avoid interference caused by additional CO_2 that is contributed by the occupants during the test.

Where a tracer gas has to be introduced into the area, either CO_2 (from dry ice or a fire extinguisher) or sulfur hexafluoride (SF_6) are often selected. SF_6 has many traits of a good tracer gas (e.g., density similar to air and low toxicity) but it has high global warming potential and so its use may be restricted in some jurisdictions. Tracer studies using a released gas are also conducted when the building is vacant.

To perform a tracer study, obtain the gas, a Safety Data Sheet (formerly a Material Safety Data Sheet) for the gas, a properly calibrated direct reading analytical instrument, and mixing fans. Then follow this general procedure:

- Ensure that the HVAC system controls are set to operate in a manner typical of the time period being evaluated. For example, in studies conducted after the close of business, be certain that automatic setbacks will not reduce airflow rates if the tests are to represent normal daytime operations.
- Set up mixing fans that will circulate air inside the space being tested to keep the concentration of tracer gas nearly constant throughout the space. Also identify the sampling locations inside the space – generally readings are collected at several points and then averaged to estimate the concentration.
- Measure background levels of the tracer gas both indoors and outside.
- Release the gas and, when it is thoroughly mixed, make the initial reading and record it along with the time. Temperature, relative humidity, and system operating parameters should also be recorded so that the factors affecting ventilation rates can be reconstructed later.
- Periodically repeat the concentration measurements and record the level and time until the indoor level of the tracer drops to near the ambient level. At this point, stop the test.
- Calculate the air exchange rate using this equation:

$$A_X = \frac{1}{\Delta t}(ln\, C_o - ln\, C_t) \qquad (4)$$

where A_X = air exchange rate, air changes/hour
   C_o = indoor concentration of tracer gas at start of test (minus any level in outdoor air), ppm
   C_t = indoor concentration at end of test (minus any level in outdoor air), ppm
   Δt = elapsed time of test, hours
   ln = natural logarithm (to base e).

- Convert the air exchange rate (A_X) into volumetric airflow by multiplying A_X by the room volume or, where the ceilings are high and complete mixing of incoming HVAC system air does not occur throughout the whole room, by the occupied volume in the lower part of the room as estimated during the study:

$$Q = A_X \frac{\text{air changes}}{\text{hour}} \times V_r \frac{\text{ft}^3}{\text{air change}} \times \frac{\text{hour}}{60 \text{ min}} \qquad (5)$$

where Q = volumetric airflow rate, ft^3/min
   A_X = air exchange rate from Equation (4), air changes/hour
   V_r = room volume, ft^3/air change (to allow units to cancel).

This value of Q is the total outside air diluting the tracer, and includes infiltration as well as outside air from the ventilation supply system.

Example: A tracer study using released CO_2 (from a fire extinguisher) is to be performed in one large room in an office building. The test will begin after employees leave. CO_2 levels will be measured with an infrared instrument. Room dimensions are 50 ft $\times$ 25 ft $\times$ 10 ft; room occupancy is normally 15 people doing sedentary office work. Outdoor CO_2 level is 425 ppm.

Answer: The following CO_2 levels are measured during the test:

Time (p.m.)	Indoor CO$_2$ level, ppm	Indoor CO$_2$ level – Outdoor level, ppm
6:00	1730	1305
6:30	1375	950
7:00	1120	695
7:30	835	410
8:00	615	190

From these data, the initial and final values as well as the elapsed time are:

C_o = 1305 ppm
C_t = 190 ppm
Δt = 2.0 hours

Using Equation (4):

$$A_X = \frac{1}{\Delta t}(ln\, C_o - ln\, C_t)$$

$$= \frac{1}{2.0}(ln\ 1305 - ln\ 190)$$

$$= \frac{1}{2.0}(7.17 - 5.25)$$

$$A_x = 0.96\ \text{air changes/hour}$$

The room volume is 12,500 ft³ (50' × 25' × 10') so the volumetric airflow can be calculated from Equation (5):

$$Q = A_x\ \frac{\text{air changes}}{\text{hour}} \times V_r\ \frac{\text{ft}^3}{\text{air change}} \times \frac{\text{hour}}{60\ \text{min}}$$

$$Q = 0.96\ \frac{\text{air changes}}{\text{hour}} \times 12{,}500\ \frac{\text{ft}^3}{\text{air change}} \times \frac{\text{hour}}{60\ \text{min}}$$

$$Q = 200\ \text{ft}^3/\text{min}$$

On a per-person basis, this ventilation rate is:

$$\frac{200\ \text{ft}^3/\text{min}}{15\ \text{people}} = 13.3\ \text{ft}^3/\text{min per person}$$

This rate can be compared to the current ASHRAE Standard 62.1 to see if it meets the airflow guidelines for a system being designed today.

Assembling Relevant Information

The information gathered during the diagnosis and measurement phases should give a good picture of IAQ-related factors in the complaint area. However, at this stage it is important to check that no important parameters have been overlooked. Probably the most common reason for incomplete information is that some contaminant-generating situations are very time specific or intermittent, and these have not been occurring during the inspection and measurement steps.

RESOLVING IAQ ISSUES

Once all of the stakeholders agree that the relevant factors are being considered, the findings and observations can be reviewed to identify likely causes of the problem. Refer to the tables throughout this chapter to identify relevant factors. Easy-to-fix maintenance and other issues should have been corrected immediately, so the first step is to decide if these were the primary source of complaints. Unless all issues have been resolved, make a list of possible causes and potential solutions; often it is helpful to rank these by likelihood of being the cause/solution, and also how expensive or difficult the potential solution will be to implement.

Table 21–G lists items for ventilation-related issues. Increasing the airflow in the entire HVAC system is not a preferred first step (due to expense and higher energy consumption) unless the entire building is under ventilated. For localized low flow or poor circulation problems, rebalancing the system or trying pedestal fans may be a better first step.

For possible causes other than HVAC, consider other exposure control approaches:

- Engineering controls: source removal or substitution; source modification, local ventilation or room-specific exhaust discharged outside, etc.
- Administrative controls: changes in procedures or behaviors to mitigate the problems. Examples include restricting use of certain chemical products, prohibiting smoking or vehicles idling near air intakes, etc. The success of administrative controls often depends on education and motivation of employees and contractors on the need to change established practices to improve air quality and conserve energy.

TABLE 21–G	HVAC Typical Problems
Insufficient outdoor air (OA) introduced to the system	
Intake and exhaust dampers inoperative, malfunctioning	
Intake and exhaust at improper location	
Poor roughing filtration—dirt, bugs, pollen in air-delivery system	
Inadequate dust spot filtration	
Poor system maintenance	
Improper balance of distribution system	
Distribution dampers at incorrect positions	
Building under negative pressure	
Terminal diffusers not at correct positions	
VAV systems in non-delivery or low-delivery mode	
Terminal diffusers not attached to delivery system	
Poor distribution or stratification of supply air in occupant space	
Draftiness—too much supply air or improper terminal settings	
Placement of desks or personnel located in high-velocity areas	
Stuffiness—not enough air delivery or not delivered properly	
Improper pressure differences between rooms—doors slam or are difficult to open	
Temperature extremes—too hot or too cold	
Humidity extremes—too dry or too humid	
Energy conservation has higher priority than IAQ	
Settled water in system	
Visual evidence of slime or mold	

Source: D. Jeff Burton, 2011. Reprinted with permission.

SUMMARY

Proper ventilation of commercial buildings and other non-industrial occupancies is important in protecting health and productivity, and conserving energy. HVAC systems have the goal of maintaining the indoor environment at a comfortable temperature and relative humidity with no contaminants above the concentration of concern. Indoor air quality complaints can arise due to many causes – some ventilation-related but also from other causes. Careful diagnosis and measurement can help to identify potential causes and remedies, so that the IAQ issues can be resolved in an economical and energy efficient manner.

BIBLIOGRAPHY

Special acknowledgement is due to D. Jeff Burton, CIH, PE, CSP for use of tables and figures from his books listed below, and for his contribution to this chapter in earlier editions of *Fundamentals of Industrial Hygiene*.

Books

American Conference of Governmental Industrial Hygienists. *Industrial Ventilation – A Manual of Recommended Practice*, 27th ed. Cincinnati, OH: ACGIH, 2010.

American Industrial Hygiene Association. *Recommendations for the Management, Operation, Testing, and Maintenance of HVAC Systems*. Fairfax, VA: AIHA, 2004.

American Society of Heating, Refrigerating and Air Conditioning Engineers. *The Indoor Air Quality Guide – Best Practices for Design, Construction and Commissioning*. Atlanta: ASHRAE, 2009.

Burton DJ. *IAQ and HVAC Workbook*, 4th ed. Bountiful, UT: IVE, Inc., 2011.

Burton DJ. *Industrial Ventilation Workbook*, 6th ed. Bountiful, UT: IVE, Inc., 2010.

McDermott HJ. *Handbook of Ventilation for Contaminant Control*, 3rd ed. Cincinnati, OH: ACGIH, 2000.

Sheet Metal and Air Conditioning Contractors' National Association. *HVAC Systems – Testing, Adjusting, and Balancing*. Chantilly, VA: SMACNA, 2002.

Sheet Metal and Air Conditioning Contractors' National Association. *Duct Cleanliness for New Construction*. Chantilly, VA: SMACNA, 2000.

Standards and Codes

ASHRAE Standard 62.1-2010: *Ventilation for Acceptable Indoor Air Quality*. Atlanta: ASHRAE, 2010.

ASHRAE Standard 52.2-2007: *Method of Testing General Ventilation Air-Cleaning Devices for Removal Efficiency by Particle Size*. Atlanta: ASHRAE, 2007.

ASHRAE Standard 55-2010: *Thermal Environmental Conditions for Human Occupancy*. Atlanta: ASHRAE, 2010.

Agencies and Organizations Involved in IAQ

American Conference of Governmental Industrial Hygienists (ACGIH). Cincinnati, OH. www.acgih.org.

American Industrial Hygiene Association (AIHA). Fairfax, VA. www.aiha.org.

American Society of Heating, Refrigerating and Air Conditioning Engineers (ASHRAE). Atlanta. www.ashrae.org.

National Institute for Occupational Safety and Health (NIOSH). Washington, DC. www.cdc.gov/niosh.

U.S. Department of Energy (DOE). Washington, DC. www.energy.gov.

U.S. Energy Information Administration. Washington, DC. www.eia.gov.

U.S. Environmental Protection Agency (EPA). Washington, DC. www.epa.gov.

CHAPTER 22

Respiratory Protection

by Craig E. Colton, CIH

A *primary objective of industrial hygiene programs in industry is the control of airborne contaminants by accepted engineering and work practice control measures. When effective engineering controls are not feasible, or while they are being instituted, appropriate respirators must be used. The Occupational Safety and Health Administration (OSHA) has established a standard, 29 CFR 1910.134 Respiratory Protection, for regulating the use of respiratory-protective equipment.*

If the environment is still not completely safe after effective engineering and work practice controls have been fully implemented to reduce exposure to the lowest possible level, it will be necessary to use respirators to protect workers from contact with airborne contaminants or oxygen-deficient environments. Respiratory-protective equipment varies in design, specifications, application, and protective capability. Proper selection depends on the contaminant involved, conditions of exposure, human capabilities, and respirator fit.

Respirators are the least satisfactory means of exposure control because they provide good protection only if they are properly selected, fit tested, worn by the employees, and replaced when their service life is over. In addition, some employees may not be able to wear a respirator because of health or physical limitations. Respirators can also be cumbersome to use and hot to wear, and they may reduce vision and interfere with communication.

Despite these difficulties, respirators are the only form of protection available in the following situations: during the installation or implementation of feasible engineering and work practice controls; in work operations such as maintenance and repair activities for which engineering and work practice controls are not yet sufficient to reduce exposure to or below the permissible exposure limit (PEL); and in emergencies. This chapter describes the various classes of respirators and infor-

mation important to their proper selection. This information will assist the reader with proper selection of respirators and the implementation of key elements of the respiratory protection program.

RESPIRATORY PROTECTION PROGRAMS

A written respiratory protection program must be established when respiratory protection is needed. It should include worksite-specific procedures covering the following minimum program elements:

- procedures for selection of proper respiratory-protective equipment, including exposure assessment
- procedures for medical evaluation of respirator wearers
- procedures for fit testing of workers using tight-fitting respirators
- procedures for proper respirator use during routine and reasonably foreseeable emergency situations
- procedures and schedules for cleaning, disinfecting, storing, inspecting, repairing, and discarding respirators
- procedures to ensure adequate air quality, quantity, and flow of breathing air for atmosphere-supplying respirators
- procedures for training workers on respirator use and respiratory hazards
- procedures for regular program evaluation

In addition, a program administrator must be appointed to manage the program.

The OSHA standard (29 CFR 1910.134) requires that these points be addressed This standard applies to General Industry (part 1910), Shipyards (part 1915), Marine Terminals (part 1917), Long-shoring (part 1918), and Construction (part 1926). The American National Standard Institute (ANSI) is a voluntary consensus standard setting organization. They have developed and published several standards related to the use of respirators (*e.g.,* ANSI Z88.2, ANSI Z88.6, ANSI Z88.10). It is highly recommended that these American National Standards be consulted as well as the OSHA regulation.

Worksite-Specific Procedures

Written worksite-specific procedures that cover the entire respiratory protection program need to be developed and implemented as they apply to each employer's own facility. The procedures need to cover all the elements of the program listed above as well as the issuance and purchasing of respirators and any company policies pertaining to respirator use. Each element must be covered in enough detail so it is clear exactly how each element will be accomplished. Restating the OSHA requirements such as, "We will do fit testing annually," does not suffice. The worksite-specific

procedures must spell out exactly how the company intends to implement each program element at each worksite. Who will do the fit testing? Where will the fit testing be done? Which fit-test protocol will be used? Examples of employer policies that may be included are disciplinary action for not using the respirator and policies regarding facial hair. The program should be a tool to enhance worker protection.

In addition, written worksite-specific procedures must be developed for respirator use in emergency and rescue operations. Although every situation cannot be anticipated, many of the needs for emergency and rescue use of respirators can be envisioned. This can be done by considering

- an analysis of the emergency and rescue uses of respirators based on materials, equipment, work area, processes and personnel involved;
- a determination, based on the above analysis, of whether the available respirators can provide adequate protection to allow workers to enter the potentially hazardous environments;
- selection of the appropriate type and numbers of respirators; and
- maintenance of these respirators so that they are readily accessible and operational when needed.

Copies of these procedures must be available for the employees to read. The procedures need to be reviewed and revised as conditions and equipment change.

Exposure Assessment of Respirator Wearers

Exposure assessments are basic to the proper use of respiratory-protective equipment. This information is used not only to identify the need for respirators but also to identify the level of protection required. The information is also needed to establish the required change schedule for chemical cartridge and gas mask respirators used for gases and vapors. The levels of worker exposure are determined by instruments and equipment designed to measure the concentrations of air contaminants and oxygen. Adequate air sampling and analysis should be carried out to determine time-weighted average concentrations and, when appropriate, compliance with ceiling and short-term exposure limits as well. Other chapters in this book should be consulted for more detail.

Selection of Proper Respiratory-Protective Equipment

Selection of the proper respirator is a very important task. The respirator must be approved by the National Institute for Occupational Safety and Health (NIOSH). Respirator selection must be based on an exposure assessment and relevant workplace and user factors. Although it is obvious that the respirator selection must be based on the hazard to which the worker is exposed, there are many points that must be considered. These issues will be discussed later in this chapter.

Medical Evaluations of Respirator Wearers

Respirators can impose several physiological stresses ranging from very mild restriction of breathing to burdens of great weight and effort. The type of effects produced depends on the type of respirator in use, the job, and workplace conditions. For this reason, a physician or other licensed health care professional (PLHCP) must determine whether or not an employee has any medical conditions that would preclude the use of respirators.

To assist the PLHCP, the program administrator must advise them of the types and weights of respirators to be used for either emergency or routine use: typical work activities; expected physical work effort; additional protective clothing and equipment to be worn; environmental conditions, such as high heat; frequency and duration of respirator use; and hazards for which the respiratory-protective equipment will be worn.

Although it is generally agreed that relatively few nondisabling medical conditions make respirator use dangerous, especially for employees who need respirators only briefly or occasionally to perform their tasks, it is important to identify those employees who may experience difficulties. A medical evaluation to determine the worker's ability to use the respirator must be completed before the worker is fit tested or required to use the respirator. This medical evaluation may be performed by either administering a questionnaire or an initial medical examination. A copy of the questionnaire is in Appendix C of the OSHA respiratory protection standard. Depending on the results of the initial medical evaluation, a follow-up medical examination may be required to investigate potential problems with respirator use. The follow-up medical examination must include any medical tests, consultations, or diagnostic procedures deemed necessary to make a final determination regarding ability to wear a respirator. Pulmonary function tests (spirometry) are not specifically required. Pulmonary function testing has not been demonstrated to provide sensitive or specific indicators for respirator tolerance or safety (ANSI Z88.6-2006). The respiratory system's large reserve permits most healthy workers to tolerate the small respiratory impact of many respirators. They may be required during the follow-up medical examination, however, if the physician deemed the tests necessary to make a determination.

Additional medical evaluations are not required annually; however, they must be provided under the following conditions:

- An employee reports medical signs or symptoms that are related to ability to use a respirator.

- A physician or other licensed health care professional, supervisor, or the respirator program administrator informs the employer that an employee needs to be reevaluated.
- Information from the respiratory protection program, including observations made during fit testing and program evaluation, indicates a need for employee reevaluation.
- A change occurs in workplace conditions (for example, physical work effort, protective clothing, and temperature) that may result in a substantial increase in the physiological burden placed on an employee.

A physician may require that additional medical evaluations be based on a specific frequency (for example, annually) or on a frequency based on the age of the worker. For example, a younger worker may receive an additional medical evaluation every three years whereas an older worker may receive one annually, even if not reporting difficulty with respirator use, problems during fit testing, or changes in the workplace.

For further information, consult the *American National Standard for Respiratory Protection-Respirator Use—Physical Qualifications for Personnel* and *Respiratory Protection Guidelines from the American Thoracic Society* (see Bibliography).

Respirator Fit

Each respirator wearer of a tight-fitting respirator (Figure 22–1) must be provided with a respirator that fits. To find the respirator that fits, the worker must be fit tested. Fit-testing procedures will be discussed later in this chapter. In addition, each respirator wearer must be required to check the seal of the respirator by appropriate means before entering a harmful atmosphere. Each respirator manufacturer provides instructions on how to perform these user seal checks. A user seal check is a test conducted by the wearer to determine if the respirator is properly adjusted to the face. The procedures may vary slightly from one respirator to another because of differences in construction and design. In general, the employee is checking either for pressure or flow of air around the sealing surface. User seal checks are not substitutes for qualitative or quantitative fit tests. Care must be taken in conducting user seal checks. Thorough training in carrying out these tests must be given to respirator wearers.

A respirator equipped with a tight-fitting facepiece must not be worn if facial hair comes between the sealing periphery of the facepiece and the face, or if facial hair interferes with valve function. Only respirators equipped with loose-fitting hoods or helmets are acceptable with interfering facial hair (Figure 22–2). If spectacles, goggles,

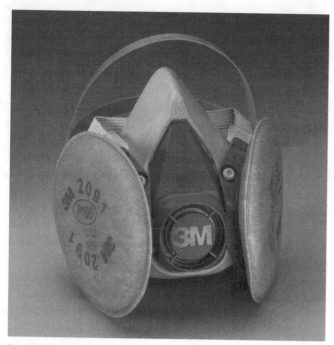

Figure 22–1a

Figure 22–1b

Figure 22–1. The two types of tight-fitting respiratory inlet coverings: a. Half facepiece with P100 particulate filters. b. Full facepiece with cartridges and N95 particulate filters. *(Photos courtesy of 3M.)*

or face shields must be worn with a half- or full-facepiece respirator, they must be worn so as not to adversely affect the seal of the facepiece to the face. Full facepieces come with spectacle kits to enable the user to wear prescription glasses without disturbing the facepiece seal.

Training

For the safe use of any respirator, it is essential that the user be properly instructed in its use. Qualified persons must instruct supervisors as well as the person issuing respirators. Emergency and rescue teams must be given adequate training to ensure proper respirator use. The OSHA standard requires that all employees be trained in the proper use of the device assigned to them. Many companies have their employees sign a document attesting to their having completed a training session with the respiratory-protective equipment. As a minimum, written records of the names of those trained and the dates when the training occurred should be kept. The workers need to be trained upon initial assignment of a respirator and followed up with annual training.

Each respirator wearer must be able to demonstrate knowledge of at least the following:

- why the respirator is necessary and how improper fit, usage, or maintenance can compromise the protective effect of the respirator
- what the limitations and capabilities of the respirator are
- how to use the respirator effectively in emergency situations, including situations in which the respirator malfunctions
- how to inspect, put on and remove, use, and check the seals of the respirator
- what the procedures are for maintenance and storage of the respirator
- how to recognize medical signs and symptoms that may limit or prevent the effective use of respirators
- the general requirements of the OSHA respiratory protection standard

The training must be conducted in a manner that is understandable to the employee and provided prior to requiring the employee to use a respirator in the workplace. In addition to being retrained annually, retraining must be performed when: changes in the workplace or respirator type make the previous training obsolete, inadequacies in the employee's knowledge or use of the respirator indicate that the employee has not retained the required level of understanding or skill, or any other situation arises in which retraining appears necessary to ensure safe respirator use. The training in putting on the respirator must include an opportunity for each wearer to handle the respirator with instructions in the proper fitting of the respirator, including demonstrations and practice in how the respirator must

Figure 22–2a

Figure 22–2b

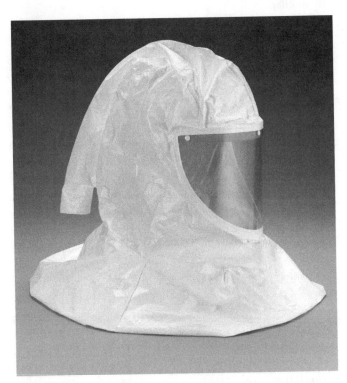

Figure 22–2c

Figure 22–2. The three types of loose-fitting respiratory inlet coverings: a. Loose-fitting facepiece. b. Helmet. c. Hood. Respirators with loose-fitting respirator inlet coverings do not need to be fit tested. The loose-fitting facepiece (a) is not suitable for workers with beards because it forms a partial seal with the face. The loose-fitting helmet (b) and hood (c) are acceptable for workers with beards. *(Photos courtesy 3M.)*

be worn, how to adjust it, and how to determine if it fits properly. Respirator manufacturers can provide training materials that tell and show how the respirator is to be adjusted, put on, and worn. The training session must also allow for time to practice. Hence, simply showing a videotape is not sufficient unless it is followed up with actual hands-on time. Close, frequent supervision can be useful to ensure that the workers continue to use the respirator in the manner they were trained. Supervisory personnel should periodically monitor the use of respirators to insure they are worn properly.

Respirator Maintenance

The respirator maintenance program includes cleaning and disinfecting of respirators where necessary, inspection of the equipment for defects, maintenance and repair of defects found, and proper storage of the respirator. A maintenance schedule should be implemented that ensures each worker is provided with a respirator that is clean, sanitary, and in good operating condition. The manufacturer's instructions should be followed. The precise nature of the program will vary because of such factors as size of the facility and the equipment involved.

Cleaning and Disinfecting

Personally assigned respirators must be cleaned and disinfected regularly. Respirators that may be worn by different individuals must be cleaned and disinfected before being worn by a different individual. Cleaner-disinfectants that

653

effectively clean the respirator and contain a bactericidal agent are commercially available. The bactericidal agent is often a quaternary ammonium compound. For personally assigned respirators, equipment wipes containing these compounds are available. Wipes should not be the only cleaning method in place. Alternatively, respirators can be washed in a mild detergent solution (such as a dishwashing liquid) and then immersed in a disinfecting solution. Commonly recommended disinfecting solutions are an aqueous hypochlorite (bleach) solution and aqueous iodine solution; 50 ppm of chlorine and iodine, respectively. The recommended immersion time is two minutes. Strong cleaning and disinfecting agents and many solvents can damage rubber and elastomeric respirator parts. These substances should be used with caution. It is advisable to check the respirator manufacturer's instructions or contact them if there are questions.

Inspection

The respirator must be inspected by the wearer immediately prior to each use to ensure that it is in proper working order. In addition, emergency and rescue use respirators must be inspected at least monthly. Emergency escape-only respirators must be inspected before being carried into the workplace for use. All respirators that do not pass the inspection must be immediately removed from service and repaired or replaced. The respirators should also be inspected during cleaning to determine if they are in good condition, if parts need to be replaced or repaired, or whether they should be discarded.

Respirator inspection must include a check for tightness of connections, for the condition of the respiratory inlet covering, head harness, valves, connecting tubes, harness assemblies, hoses, filters, cartridges, canisters, end-of-service-life indicator, electrical components, and shelf-life date(s). The inspection should also include a check for proper function of the regulators, alarms, and other warning systems. Compressed gas cylinders on self-contained breathing apparatus (SCBA) must be checked to ensure that they are fully charged. The cylinders must be recharged when the pressure falls to 90 percent of the manufacturer's recommended pressure level.

The inspection of emergency use respirators must be certified by documenting the date the inspection was performed, the name (or signature) of the person who made the inspection, the findings, required remedial action, and a serial number or other means of identifying the inspected respirator. The information should be provided on a tag or label that is attached to the respirator storage compartment, is kept with the respirator, or is included in inspection reports stored as paper or electronic files. It must be kept until it is replaced by a subsequent certification.

Repair

Replacement of all but disposable parts and any repair should be done only by personnel with adequate training in the proper maintenance and assembly of the respirators. Replacement parts, including the air hoses on air-line respirators, must be only those designated for the specific respirator being repaired. Failure to do so may result in malfunction of the respirator. In addition it will void the NIOSH approval (NIOSH, 2007).

Storage

The respirators must be properly stored to protect them from dust, sunlight, excessive heat, extreme cold, excessive moisture, damaging chemicals, and physical damage from things such as vibration and shock. Tool boxes, paint-spray booths, and lockers are not appropriate storage locations unless they are protected from contamination, distortion, and damage. In addition, emergency and rescue use respirators that are located in the work area must be readily accessible. Their location must be clearly marked.

Air Quality

When a program includes atmosphere-supplying respirators, then assurance of breathing air quality must be included. Compressed air, compressed oxygen, liquid air, and liquid oxygen used in atmosphere-supplying respirators must be of high purity. Oxygen must meet the requirements of the United States Pharmacopoeia for medical or breathing oxygen. Compressed gaseous air must meet the requirements for grade D, as specified in the Compressed Gas Association (CGA) Standard, G-7.1-2011, Commodity Specification for Air. The limiting characteristics are listed in Table 22–A. When cylinders of purchased breathing air are used, the employer must have a certificate of analysis from the supplier stating that the breathing air meets the requirements of grade D. The moisture content of the cylinder air must not exceed a dew point of –50°F (–45.6°C) at one atmosphere pressure.

When compressors are used to supply breathing air, the moisture content must be controlled so that the dew

TABLE 22–A	Grade D Breathing Air Requirements
Limiting Characteristics	***Allowable Maxima***
Percent O_2 (balance predominantly N_2)	19.5-23.5%
Water	Variable from very dry to saturated; no liquid water
Oil (condensed)	5 mg/m³
Carbon monoxide	10ppm
Odor	No pronounced odor
Carbon dioxide	1,000 ppm

point at one atmosphere pressure is 10°F (5.56°C) below the ambient temperature. Sorbent beds and filters that are used to ensure the air quality must be maintained and replaced or refurbished periodically following the manufacturer's instructions. A tag maintained at the compressor must contain the most recent change date and signature of the person authorized to perform the change. Additional information for compressed breathing air and systems can be found in the Canadian Standards Association publication (CSA Z180.1-2000).

Program Administration

Responsibility and authority for administration of a respiratory protection program must be assigned to one person who may, and probably will, have assistance from others. Centralizing authority and responsibility ensures that there is coordination and direction for the program. Respiratory protection programs will vary widely from company to company, and depend upon many factors; a program may involve specialists such as safety personnel, industrial hygienists, health physicists, and physicians. In small plants or companies having no formal industrial hygiene, health physics, or safety engineering department, the respiratory protection program should be administered by a qualified person responsible to the facility manager. The administrator must have sufficient knowledge to supervise the program properly. It is important that the administrator keep abreast of current issues, advances in technology, and regulations. In any case, overall responsibility must reside in a single individual if the program is to achieve optimum results.

The program administrator's responsibilities include

- conducting exposure assessments of the work area prior to respirator selection and periodically during respirator use to ensure that the proper respirator is being used;
- selecting the appropriate respirator that will provide adequate protection from all contaminants present or anticipated;
- maintaining records as well as the written procedures in a manner that documents the respirator program and allows for the evaluation of the program's effectiveness; and
- evaluating the program's effectiveness through ongoing surveillance of the program.

In addition to watching the program day to day, program evaluations must be performed periodically (such as yearly) to ensure that the program reflects the worksite specific procedures and complies with current regulations and standards. The program must be periodically reevaluated to determine whether its goals are being met or if changes are needed. It is recommended that the evaluation be conducted by a knowledgeable person not directly associated with the program instead of the respiratory protection program administrator. The outside individual brings a new set of eyes in an attempt to prevent overlooking deficiencies.

At a minimum, records and certifications regarding medical evaluations, fit testing, inspection of emergency use respirators, replacement of filters and sorbents for ensuring good air quality from compressors, air sampling, and objective data used to establish schedules for chemical cartridge changes must be maintained.

A program evaluation checklist covering the entire program should be prepared and updated as required. There must be an effective means for correcting any defects found during the evaluation. A record should be kept of the findings along with plans and target dates for correction of deficiencies or problems, and actual date completed.

HISTORY OF RESPIRATOR REGULATIONS AND APPROVALS

After enactment of the Occupational Safety and Health Act (OSHAct), the National Institute for Occupational Safety and Health (NIOSH), and the U.S. Bureau of Mines (USBM) jointly promulgated 30 CFR Part 11, which prescribed approval procedures, established test requirements, and set fees for obtaining joint approval of respirators. Over the years, government reorganization has resulted in transfer of the approval functions to NIOSH. NIOSH has been named as the testing, approving, and certifying agency for respirators. When NIOSH took over the sole responsibility for respirator approval, the approval requirements were changed and moved to 42 CFR Part 84 (42 CFR 84). The respirator approvals are issued by NIOSH with the exception of self-contained self-rescuers. These devices are used for self-rescue from mines. NIOSH and the Mine Safety and Health Administration (MSHA) jointly approve them.

The NIOSH Testing and Certification Laboratory has the following responsibilities:
- to publish certification requirements
- to test and certify products meeting those requirements
- to publish lists of certified products
- to audit respirator manufacturer's facilities to determine the acceptability of their quality-assurance programs
- to sample products from the open market and test them for continued conformance to certification requirements
- to perform research on the development of new test methods and requirements for product improvement where necessary to ensure worker protection

All NIOSH-approved respiratory protection devices have an approval label similar to that shown in Figure 22–3.

NIOSH — National Institute for Occupational Safety and Health

3M

St. Paul, Minnesota, USA

1-800-243-4630

L Series SG Headgear with V-Series Valves

Type C, Continuous Flow, Supplied-Air Respirator

THESE RESPIRATORS ARE APPROVED ONLY IN THE FOLLOWING CONFIGURATIONS:

RESPIRATOR COMPONENTS

TC-	PROTECTION[1]	MODEL NUMBER	CAUTIONS AND LIMITATIONS[2]
19C-442	SA/CF	L-901SG	ABCDEJMNOS
19C-443	SA/CF	L-905SG	ABCDEJMNOS
19C-444	SA/CF	L-705SG	ABCDEJMNOS
19C-445	SA/CF	L-901SG	ABCDEJMNOS
19C-446	SA/CF	L-905SG	ABCDEJMNOS
19C-447	SA/CF	L-705SG	ABCDEJMNOS

Rev. A: 12-08-08

(Not part of label) 15964_78-8150-0713-9FLa.xls

1. **PROTECTION**
SA - Supplied-Air
CF - Continuous Flow

2. **CAUTIONS AND LIMITATIONS**
A - Not for use in atmospheres containing less than 19.5 percent oxygen.
B - Not for use in atmospheres immediately dangerous to life or health.
C - Do not exceed maximum use concentrations established by regulatory standards.
D - Air-line respirators can be used only when the respirators are supplied with respirable air meeting the requirements of CGA G-7.1 Grade D or higher quality.
E - Use only the pressure ranges and hose lengths specified in the User's Instructions.
J - Failure to properly use and maintain this product could result in injury or death.
M - All approved respirators shall be selected, fitted, used and maintained in accordance with MSHA, OSHA and other applicable regulations.
N - Never substitute, modify, add, or omit parts. Use only exact replacement parts in the configuration as specified by the manufacturer.
O - Refer to User's Instructions, and / or maintenance manuals for information on use and maintenance of these respirators.
S - Special or critical User's Instructions and/or specific use limitations apply. Refer to User's Instructions before donning .

Figure 22–3. A typical approval label that accompanies each NIOSH-approved respiratory. This label is for several air-line respirators. It identifies the major components of each approved respirator and its limitations. The user should make sure the limitations of the device are understood. (*Courtesy 3M.*)

Voiding an Approval

Once a NIOSH-approved respirator has been selected, the user should become acquainted with the limitations of the device as set forth in the approval. The approval will be void if the device is used in conditions beyond the limitations set by NIOSH or those established by the manufacturer. The user should also guard against any alteration being made to the device. All parts, filters, canisters, cartridges, or anything else not specifically intended to be used on the device by NIOSH or the manufacturer will void the existing approval. If there is any question concerning parts, alteration, or limitation of the device, always check with the manufacturer. The employer should take care so as not to knowingly void the approval for a piece of equipment.

NIOSH has the authority to purchase and test respiratory-protective devices on the open market as a continuing check on manufacturers' quality-assurance standards and adherence to approvals. Manufacturers may not institute design changes of the device or its components without obtaining an extension of an existing approval or resubmitting a device for a new approval.

Passage of the OSHAct affected respiratory protection in another way besides leading to NIOSH approvals. Shortly after OSHA was established, OSHA promulgated a standard regulating the use of respiratory-protective devices. In January 1998, OSHA revised its respiratory protection standard. This standard, 29 CFR 1910.134, "Respiratory Protection," established the requirements for a respiratory protection program. These program requirements are essentially identical to those discussed earlier in this chapter. NIOSH and OSHA requirements are interrelated in that OSHA requires approved respirators to be used and NIOSH certification establishes limitations on the use of the respirators; OSHA regulates the use, whereas NIOSH regulates the design and performance of respiratory-protective equipment. OSHA sometimes allows for use of respirators that are different from the NIOSH use limitations. NIOSH, however, sometimes makes recommendations regarding respiratory-protective equipment use that may be different than OSHA requirements. These recommendations do not change or replace OSHA standards.

In addition to 29 CFR 1910.134, OSHA has promulgated other standards that address respiratory protection requirements that may be more specific to certain situations or more stringent. These include the ventilation standard for abrasive blasting respirator use requirements, the standards for hazardous waste operations and emergency response, permit-required confined spaces, and the fire brigade, as well as the various substance-specific standards such as asbestos, lead, benzene, and cadmium. This is not a comprehensive list; OSHA is continually promulgating new substance-specific standards. Consult the appropriate OSHA standards covering the industries or operations in question.

CLASSES OF RESPIRATORS

Respiratory-protective devices can be described based on their capabilities and limitations and placed in three classes: air-purifying, atmosphere-supplying, and combination air-purifying and atmosphere-supplying devices.

Air-Purifying Devices

The air-purifying device cleanses the contaminated atmosphere. Ambient air passes through an air-purifying element that can remove specific gases and vapors, aerosols, or a combination of these contaminants. This type of device is limited in its use to those environments where there is sufficient oxygen to support life and the contaminant's airborne concentration level is within the maximum use concentration of the device. The useful life of an air-purifying device is limited by the concentration of the air contaminants, the breathing rate of the wearer, temperature and humidity levels in the workplace, and the removal capacity of the air-purifying medium.

Aerosol-Removing Respirators

Aerosol removing respirators offer respiratory protection against airborne particulate matter, including dusts, fibers, mists, and fumes, but they do not protect against gases, vapors, or oxygen deficiency. These respirators are equipped with filters to remove aerosols (particles) from the air. The filter may be a replaceable part or a permanent part of the respirator. They consist essentially of a facepiece, half-face (under the chin) (Figure 22–1a) or full-face design (Figure 22–4). Directly attached to the facepiece is one of several types of filters made up of a fibrous material that removes the particles by trapping them as air is inhaled through the filter. Particulate respirators where the filter is a permanent part of the respirator or the entire facepiece is composed of the filtering medium, are sometimes referred to as disposable respirators and more recently as filtering facepiece respirators.

There are many classes of filter respirators specifically designed for airborne particulate matter. Although a single particulate respirator can be made to provide effective protection against all aerosols, in most cases it would be too expensive and perhaps too cumbersome for the great majority of users. There are potentially nine classes of filter respirators allowed by 42 CFR 84. The filter classes are designed for different types of aerosols, use times, and filter efficiency levels. Therefore, proper filter selection depends on knowledge of the particulate contaminant and the work conditions.

Figure 22–4. A full facepiece respirator with replaceable P100 particulate filters. The viewing lens has been adapted to accommodate a welding lens for welding applications. A welding shroud covers the full facepiece and exposed skin for skin protection. *(Photo courtesy of 3M.)*

In these fibrous filters, various filtration mechanisms are at work. These filtration mechanisms include particle interception, sedimentation, impaction, and diffusion. In addition to these mechanical mechanisms, some filters will also use electrostatic attraction. Aerosol removal occurs using all the filtration mechanisms to some degree in every filter, as the filter manufacturer attempts to make an efficient filter with low breathing resistance. The exact contribution of each mechanism depends on flow rate and particle size.

In *interception capture*, the particles do not deviate from their original streamline of air (Figure 22–5). As the airstreams approach a fiber lying perpendicular to their path, they split and compress in order to flow around the fiber. The airstreams rejoin on the other side of the fiber. If the center of a particle in these airstreams comes within one particle radius of the fiber, it contacts the fiber surface and is captured. As particle size increases, the probability of interception increases.

Sedimentation capture is caused by the effect of gravity on the particle; therefore, the flow rate through the filter must be low (Figure 22–6). It is most significant for large particles, for example, larger than 3 μm aerodynamic diameter (AD).

Particles with sufficient inertia cannot change direction enough to avoid the fiber. As the airstreams split and change direction suddenly to go around the fiber, these particles are captured due to *impaction* on the surface of the fiber (Figure 22–7). A particle's size, density, speed, and shape determine its inertia.

Diffusion is particle movement caused by air molecule bombardment and is important only for smaller particles (Figure 22–8). The particles can randomly cross the air-

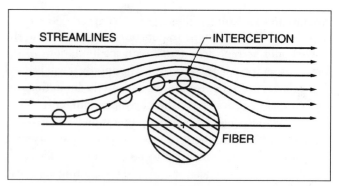

Figure 22–5. Interception capture mechanism.

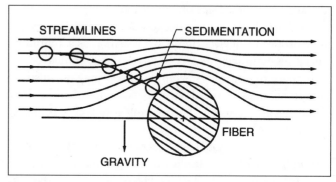

Figure 22–6. Sedimentation capture mechanism.

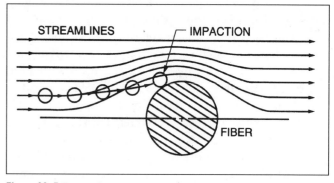

Figure 22–7. Impaction capture mechanism.

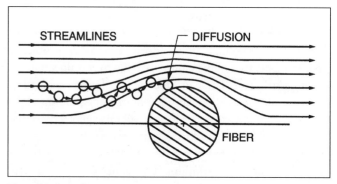

Figure 22–8. Diffusion capture mechanism.

streams and encounter a filter fiber. This random motion is dependent on particle size and temperature. For example, as particle size decreases, diffusive activity of the particle increases. This increases the chance of capture. A lower flow rate through the filter also increases the chance of capture as the particle spends more time in the area of the fiber.

In *electrostatic capture* the charged particles are attracted to filter fibers or regions of the filter fiber having the opposite charge. Uncharged particles may also be attracted depending on the level of charge imparted on the filter fiber. This mechanism aids the other removal mechanisms, especially interception and diffusion. These filter types use electrical charges to enhance their mechanical filtering capabilities. In the past, two types of electrostatic materials were used in respirator filters in the United States, resin wool and electrets. With the revision of the nonpowered particulate respirator approval tests, NIOSH-approved respirators with resin wool filters no longer exist. All electrostatic filters are of the electret type.

Electret fibers are a recent development in filtration technology. Over the last several years, they have undergone many improvements. Electret fibers are plastic fibers that have a strong electrostatic charge more permanently embedded into their surface during processing, unlike resin wool filters. They maintain a positive charge on one side of the fiber and a negative charge of equal magnitude on the opposite side of the fiber (Figure 22–9). Both charged and uncharged particles will be attracted to electret fibers. Charged particles are attracted to the parts of the fiber that have an opposite charge. Uncharged particles have equal internal positive and negative charges. The strong electrostatic forces of the electret fibers polarize these charges, inducing a dipole within the particle, and the particle is then attracted to the fiber by a polarization force. Long-term environmental testing of electret filters using elevated temperatures and humidity indicated they were not affected by exposure to these conditions.

The exact combination of capture mechanisms depends upon several factors. Generally, large heavy particles are removed by impaction and interception; large, light particles are removed by diffusion and interception. Diffusion removes very small particles (Figure 22–10). When the fiber used in the explanation of the capture mechanisms is joined by other fibers to create a filter maze of certain average porosity and thickness, the different filtration mechanisms will combine at different particle sizes to affect total filtration performance and efficiency. The capture mechanisms of sedimentation, interception, and inertial impaction combine effectively to remove nearly all particles sized above 0.6 μm. Additionally the low flow rates through respirator filters of only a few centimeters per second let diffusion play its part very effectively for particles below 0.1 μm.

However, between these two particle size regions (0.1 to 0.6 μm), diffusion and impaction are not as effective, and a minimum filtration efficiency exists as shown in Figure 22–10. The lowest point on this curve is called the *most penetrating particle size* and can be determined empirically in the laboratory. The most penetrating size range can vary with filter design and flow rate. The addition of an electrostatic charge to the fibers improves the filtering ability in

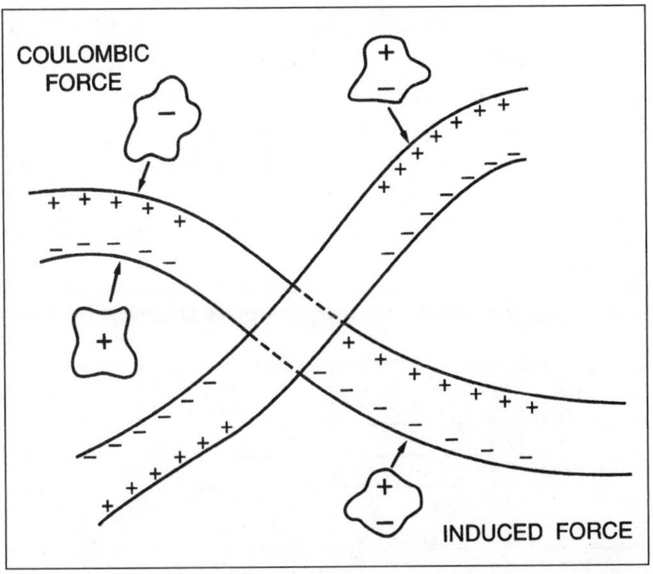

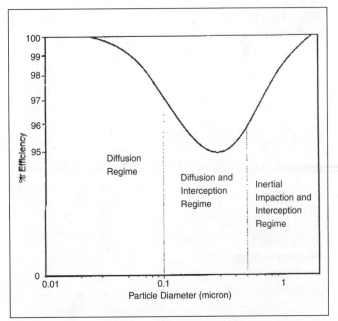

Figure 22–9. Long-range attraction of particles by the permanently charged electret fibers. A Coulombic force attracts the two charged particles on the left, while the polarization force attracts the two uncharged particles on the right.

Figure 22–10. Filter efficiency versus particle size with mechanical filtration mechanisms identified.

this range by increasing the capture efficiency at the most penetrating particle size. Most respirator filters have a most penetrating particle size between 0.2 and 0.4 μm AD. For electret filters, the most penetrating particle size is shifted toward a smaller particle size. Each filter design can have a slightly different most penetrating particle size. This is the basis for the widely used dioctyl phthalate (DOP) test for particulate filters using a 0.3-μm particle. The filter efficiency for good filters will always be much better at any particle size other than the most penetrating particle size. Because a respirator filter has measurable penetration of particles in the most penetrating particle size range, it is easy to forget the fact that anywhere else in the wide range of particle size in the workplace, filtration efficiency is essentially 100 percent. For the filter in Figure 22–10, the penetration at the most penetrating particle size is around five percent, while at 1 μm the penetration is only about one percent. It is the reduction of the entire actual work environment particulate challenge in particle number or mass that is important to protecting the worker. Table 22–B shows overall mass efficiency for a filter with five-percent penetration at the most penetrating size, a class 95 filter. Note that the overall efficiency is much greater than 95 percent for the industrial aerosols shown.

The most desirable compromise must be worked out for each filter classification with respect to filter-surface area, resistance to breathing, efficiency in filtering particles of specific size ranges, and the time to clog the filter. Filters may be made of randomly laid nonwoven fiber materials or fibrous glass that may be loosely packed in a filter container or made into a flat sheet of filter material that is pleated and placed in a filter container. Pleating is a way in which the filter surface area is increased, which can improve filter loading, and lower breathing resistance.

NIOSH certifies nine classes of filters (42 CFR 84). These filters may be either replaceable or an integral part of the respirator. At the end of service the filters are discarded or, in the case where they are a permanent part of the respirator, the entire respirator is discarded. The replaceable filters may be used on either a half-facepiece or full-facepiece respirator. The nine classes of filters are divided into three filter series, N, R, and P. Because some oils and oil-like materials may affect some filter materials so that the filter efficiency (not the filter) is degraded with use, three categories with different degrees of resistance to filter efficiency degradation were established.

Each filter series has three levels of filter efficiency: 95 percent, 99 percent, and 99.97 percent.

- *N-Series Filters.* These filters are restricted to use in atmospheres free of oil aerosols. They may be used for any solid or liquid airborne particulate hazard that does not contain oil. Generally these filters should be used and reused subject only to conditions of hygiene, damage, and increased breathing resistance.
  - N95 Particulate Filter: This N-Series filter is at least 95 percent efficient when tested with ~0.3 μm mass median aerodynamic diameter (MMAD) NaCl aerosol. Many of the so-called filtering facepiece respirators have N95 particulate filter approvals. However, this respirator category is not restricted to filtering facepiece respirator types. These filters may also be approved for use as replaceable filters on half facepieces and full facepieces (Figure 22–11).
  - N99 Particulate Filter: This N-Series filter is at least 99 percent efficient when tested with ~0.3 μm MMAD NaCl aerosol.
  - N100 Particulate Filter: This N-Series filter is at least 99.97 percent efficient when tested with ~0.3 μm MMAD NaCl aerosol (Figure 22–12).
- *R-Series Filters.* A filter intended for the removal of any particle including oil-based liquid aerosol. They may be used for any solid or liquid airborne particulate hazard.

TABLE 22–B	Mass Efficiency for Class 95 Filters by Industry		
Industry	*Size (MMAD)[1]*	*GSD*	*% Efficiency[2]*
Lead smelter, sintering	11	2.4	100
Lead smelter, furnace	3.3	15.7	99.67
Brass foundry, pouring	2.1	10.3	99.65
Brass foundry, grinding	7.2	12.9	99.73
Woodworking, fine	1.3	2.7	99.70
Woodworking, coarse	33.1	2.6	100
Wood model shop	7.2	1.4	100
Spray painting, lacquer	6.4	3.4	99.95
Spray painting, enamel	5.7	2.0	100

[1] MMAD – mass median aerodynamic diameter.
[2] Calculated at a moderate work rate, 30 Lpm.

Source: Adapted from: Hinds WC, Bellin P. Effect of facial-seal leaks on protection provided by half-mask respirators. Appl Ind Hyg 3(5):158-164, 1988.

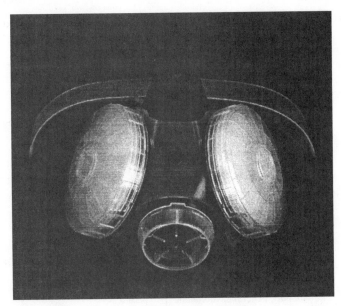

Figure 22–11a

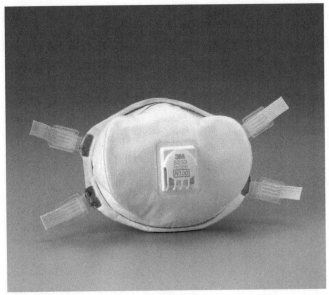

Figure 22–12. Disposable (filtering facepiece) N100 particulate filter respirator. *(Photo courtesy of 3M.)*

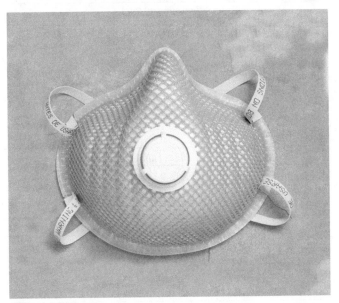

Figure 22–11b

Figure 22–11. a. Half-facepiece respirator with replaceable N95 particulate filters. *(Photo courtesy of 3M.)* b. Disposable half-facepiece N95 particulate filter respirator. Also referred to as a filtering facepiece respirator. *(Photo courtesy of Moldex Metric, Inc.)*

If the atmosphere contains oil, the R-Series filter should be used only for a single shift (or for eight hours of continuous or intermittent use). In the approval tests these filters are loaded with 200 mg of the test aerosol and filter efficiency is then determined. It is not known what happens beyond this loading point, but at 200 mg level the filter efficiency is still equal to or greater than that required for certification at the indicated level.

– R95 Particulate Filter: This R-Series filter is at least 95 percent efficient when tested with ~0.3 μm MMAD DOP (dioctyl phthalate) aerosol (Figure 22–13).
– R99 Particulate Filter: This R-Series filter is at least 99 percent efficient when tested with ~0.3 μm MMAD DOP (dioctyl phthalate) aerosol.
– R100 Particulate Filter: This R-Series filter is at least 99.97 percent efficient when tested with ~0.3 μm MMAD DOP (dioctyl phthalate) aerosol.

• *P-Series Filters.* A filter intended for the removal of any particle including oil-based liquid aerosol. They may be used for any solid or liquid airborne particulate hazard. These filters have been tested to a point where filter efficiency was not degrading. Consequently they have longer use periods than the R-series filters. Because no filter will last forever, NIOSH requires respirator manufacturers to put a time restriction for all P-series filters. Consult the manufacturer's instructions for specific guidance on how long to use the filter before it should be replaced.

– P95 Particulate Filter: This P-Series filter is at least 95 percent efficient when tested with ~0.3 μm MMAD DOP (dioctyl phthalate) aerosol.
– P99 Particulate Filter: This P-Series filter is at least 99 percent efficient when tested with ~0.3 μm MMAD DOP (dioctyl phthalate) aerosol.
– P100 Particulate Filter: This P-Series filter is at least 99.97 percent efficient when tested with ~0.3 μm MMAD DOP (dioctyl phthalate) aerosol. This filter or its container is magenta colored (Figures 22–1a, 22–4).

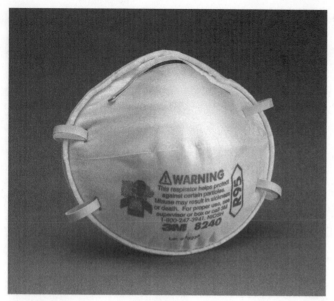

Figure 22–13. Filtering facepiece R95 particulate filter respirator. *(Photo courtesy of 3M.)*

Operation	MMAD, µm	GSD
Mining		
Open pit, general environment	2.5	4.7
Open pit, in cab	1.1	2.4
Coal mine, continuous miner	4.6	2.5
Coal mine, continuous miner	15.0	2.9
Coal mine, continuous miner	17.0	3.1
Coal mine, other operations	11.5	2.8
Oilshale mine	2.8	3.5
Smelting and Foundry		
Lead smelter, sintering	11.0	2.4
Lead smelter, furnace	3.3	15.7
Brass foundry, pouring	2.1	10.3
Brass foundry, grinding	7.2	12.9
Iron foundry, general environment	2.8	5.1
Iron foundry, general environment	16.8	4.4
Be-Cu foundry, furnace	5.0	2.4
Nuclear fuel fabrication	2.1	1.6
Non-mineral Dust		
Bakery	12.1	4.2
Cotton gin	47.1	2.7
Cotton mill	7.6	4.0
Swine confinement building	9.6	4.0
Woodworking, machining, sanding		
fine mode	1.3	2.7
coarse mode	33.1	2.6
Wood model shop	7.2	1.4
Metal Fume		
SMA (stick) welding	0.38	1.8
MIG welding	0.48	2.3
Lead fume (O_2-Nat. gas)	0.37	2.1
Mist and Spray		
Pressroom, ink mist	27.4	4.3
Spray painting, lacquer	6.4	3.4
Spray painting, enamel	5.7	2.0
Aerosol spray products	6.4	1.8
Other		
Forging	5.5	2.0
Refinery, fluid catalytic cracker	6.2	2.4
Cigarette smoke (diluted)	0.4	1.4
Pistol range	2.6	3.8
Diesel exhaust (age = 5-600 s)	0.12	1.4

TABLE 22–C Aerosol Size Distributions for Various Industrial Operations

Source: Adapted from: Hinds WC, Bellin P. Effect of facial-seal leaks on protection provided by half-mask respirators. Appl Ind Hyg 3(5):158-164, 1988.

It is difficult to perceive the difference between aerosol filters visually. Therefore it is important to read the NIOSH-approval label or filter designation to identify against which aerosols (oils or non-oils) the filter should be used. Oil has never been defined by a regulatory agency. The following definition may be helpful, however, in deciding whether the material should be considered an oil.

Oil: Any of numerous mineral, vegetable, and synthetic substances and animal and vegetable fats that are generally slippery, combustible, viscous, liquid, or liquefiable at room temperatures, soluble in various organic solvents such as ether but not in water.

While there are differences in stated filter efficiencies at the most penetrating particle size, it is important to note that industrial aerosols are not predominantly in this size range (Table 22–C). When NIOSH established these filter categories, they stated that all of these filters would be effective against any particle size. Particle size is not a major concern when selecting one of these filters. Generally speaking, however, the higher the filter efficiency the greater the breathing resistance. Breathing resistance can greatly affect the comfort of the wearer and affect the amount of time the worker wears the respirator (see wear time discussion).

Gas/Vapor-Removing Respirators

These air-purifying respirators protect against certain gases and vapors by using various chemical filters to purify the inhaled air (Figure 22–14). They differ from aerosol filters in that they use cartridges or canisters containing sorbents, generally carbon, to remove harmful gases and vapors. The cartridges may be replaceable or the entire respirator may be disposable. Sorbents are granular, porous materials that interact with the gas or vapor molecule to clean the air. In contrast to aerosol filters, which are effective to some degree no matter what the particle, cartridges and canisters are

Figure 22–14. Half-facepiece chemical cartridge respirator with interchangeable cartridges affords protection against light concentrations of organic vapors and certain gases. *(Photo courtesy of 3M.)*

TABLE 22–D	Chemical Cartridge Types and Removal Mechanisms
Chemical Cartridge Type	***Removal Mechanism***
Organic Vapors	Adsorption
Acid Gases[1]	Chemisorption
Organic Vapors/Acid Gases	Adsorption/Chemisorption
Ammonia & Methylamine	Chemisorption
Formaldehyde	Chemisorption
Multiple Gases & Vapors[2]	Organic vapors via adsorption/ others via chemisorption
Mercury Vapors[3]	Chemisorption
Hydrogen Fluoride	Chemisorption and/or chemical reaction

[1] Acid gases includes chlorine dioxide, hydrogen chloride, hydrogen fluoride, hydrogen sulfide, and sulfur dioxide.
[2] May vary with the manufacturer. May include organic vapors, acid gases, ammonia, methylamine, and formaldehyde.
[3] Usually have an end-of-service life indicator.

designed for protection against specific contaminants (such as ammonia gas or mercury vapor) or classes of contaminants (such as organic vapors). Table 22–D identifies the various types of chemical cartridges approved by NIOSH. Activated carbon is commonly used for removal of organic vapors. Activated carbon is a carbon material that has its surface greatly enhanced using heat and steam. The most common starting carbon materials for respirator cartridges are coconut and coal. Activated carbon has an extensive network of internal pores of near molecular dimensions and consequently large internal surface areas. The typical range of surface area is 1,000–2,000 m²/gram of carbon.

Organic vapors are removed by the process of adsorption. Adsorption is the adherence of gas or vapor molecules to the surface of the activated carbon. The attractive force between the activated carbon and the chemical molecule is a relatively small, weak physical force. The strength of the attraction depends in part on the chemical. Generally, organic vapors of molecular weight (MW) greater than 50 or boiling points (BP) greater than 70°C are effectively adsorbed by activated charcoal. For gases and vapors that would otherwise be weakly adsorbed, sorbents can be impregnated with chemical reagents to make them more selective. Examples are activated charcoal impregnated with iodine (to remove mercury vapor), with metal salts like nickel chloride (to remove ammonia gas), or with copper oxides and metal sulfates or salts of sulfamic acid (to remove formaldehyde).

Impregnated activated carbon removes specific gas and vapor molecules by chemisorption. *Chemisorption* is the formation of bonds between molecules of the impregnant and the chemical contaminant. These bonds are much stronger than the attractive forces of physical adsorption. Both removal mechanisms are essentially 100-percent efficient until the sorbent's capacity is exhausted. At this point *breakthrough* occurs as the contaminant passes through the cartridge or canister and into the respirator.

Cartridges and canisters should be changed before breakthrough occurs. To do this, cartridge change schedules must be established based on the expected service lifetime for the particular workplace environment in which the cartridge is being used. When the breakthrough point is reached, the worker should exit to a clean area and replace the cartridges, canister, or respirator. Cartridges are similar to canisters. The basic difference is the volume of sorbent, not the function. Canisters have the larger sorbent volume.

Service life of these respirators depends on the following factors: quality and amount of sorbent; packing uniformity and density; and exposure conditions, including breathing rate of the wearer, relative humidity, temperature, contaminant concentration, the affinity of the gas or vapor for the sorbent, and the presence of other gases and vapors. (Generally, high concentrations, a high breathing rate, and humid conditions adversely affect service life.) Table 22–E shows various chemical cartridge breakthrough times for different organic gases and vapors. Although the organic vapor cartridge is approved by testing against carbon tetrachloride, the cartridge may last a longer (as with butanol) or a much shorter (as with methanol) time period than when compared to the test agent. Hence, an organic vapor cartridge may be recommended for use against butanol, but not for methanol (MW < 50; BP < 70°C), even though both compounds are classified as organic vapors.

TABLE 22–E	Organic Vapor Chemical Cartridge Breakthrough Times for Various Chemicals

Chemical	Time to 1% (10 ppm) Breakthrough (minutes)[1]
Aromatics	
Benzene	73
Toluene	94
Xylene	99
Alcohols	
Mathanol	0.2
Isopropanol	54
Butanol	115
2-Methoxyethanol	116
Chlorinated hydrocarbons	
Methyl chloride	0.05
Vinyl chloride	3.8
Dichloromethane	10
Trichloroethylene	55
Carbon tetrachloride	77
Perchloroethylene	107
Ketones	
Acetone	37
2-Butanone	82

[1]Cartridges challenged with 1000 ppm of the respective chemical. Tested at 50 percent relative humidity, 22°C, and 53.3 L/min.
Source: Adapted from Nelson GE, Harder CA. AIHA Journal 35: 391-410. 1974.

Relative Humidity. Relative humidity (RH) greater than 50 percent (especially greater than 65 percent) can have a dramatic effect on service life of organic vapor chemical cartridges. The effect of relative humidity on service life of organic vapor cartridges will depend on the relative humidity level, the chemical concentration, volatility of the chemical, and the chemical's *miscibility*—ability to dissolve—in water. For chemicals with low volatility, such as styrene, the effect of high relative humidity is small. For more volatile chemicals, the most significant RH effect is at low concentrations. The service life for cartridges using impregnated activated charcoal is not affected by relative humidity like the organic vapor cartridge. In fact, higher RH may actually increase the service life of cartridges with impregnated carbon, especially those for acid gases.

Migration. Since only weak physical forces hold the organic vapors on activated carbon, the process can be reversed. This is called desorption. *Desorption* is the process of an adsorbed material *letting go* from the activated carbon. Desorption can occur naturally during periods of nonuse or by the presence of another more strongly adsorbed substance displacing a less strongly adsorbed chemical (that is, a more volatile chemical). Generally, the more volatile the chemical, the less strongly adsorbed, or the more likely it

will undergo desorption. Desorption during storage or non-use times can result in chemical migration. Migration is the movement of a previously adsorbed chemical through the chemical cartridge, even without air movement. Migration is mainly a concern only for organic vapor cartridges. Variables that appear to impact migration include:

- volatility—the more volatile the chemicals, the greater the concern for migration
- water vapor co-adsorption—co-adsorption (from use in atmospheres with high relative humidity [>50%]) can increase the migration effect
- amount of material adsorbed onto the cartridge in the first use
- storage time
- vapor type

The potential for both desorption and migration makes reuse of organic vapor cartridges a concern. Desorption of very volatile contaminants can occur after a short period (hours) without use (e.g., overnight). Partial use of the chemical cartridge and subsequent reuse could potentially expose the user to the contaminant. This is most significant for the most volatile and poorly retained organic vapors (for example, boiling point < 65°C). These chemicals are often classified as low boiling chemicals. However, a boiling point of 65°C is not a fine line between chemicals that migrate and those that do not. Chemicals with boiling points greater than 65°C can still migrate, but the nonuse period of concern may be longer than above. As the volatility decreases, migration will become less of a concern.

The chemical bonds formed during chemisorption typically result in irreversible binding of the chemical contaminant to the impregnant. Migration is usually not a concern for these cartridges. Thus, reuse of chemical cartridges that work on the principle of chemisorption is not a problem.

Limitations. Chemical cartridges and canisters are limited to use in concentrations that are no greater than the assigned protection factor of the respirator multiplied by the occupational exposure limit. This is called the maximum use concentration (MUC). At one time, maximum use limits (MUL) were included on the cartridge or canister. These have been removed by NIOSH; thus the maximum use concentration limits are dependent upon the respirator's assigned protection factor. This topic will be discussed later in this chapter. *Gas mask* is a term used often for a gas- or vapor-removing respirator that uses a canister (Figure 22–15). Although gas masks are limited by their assigned protection factor, they can be used for escape-only from atmospheres immediately dangerous to life or health (IDLH) that contain adequate oxygen to support life (≥19.5% O_2). They must never be used for entry into an IDLH atmosphere.

Cartridge and Canister Replacement. Cartridges and canisters should be replaced under any one or more of the following conditions:

- if the end of service life indicator (if available) shows the specified color change
- as indicated by the change schedule
- if the cartridge/canister shelf life is exceeded
- if an OSHA regulation specifies a disposal frequency (as with formaldehyde and benzene)

If a person is wearing a cartridge or canister that needs replacement, they should return to fresh air as quickly as possible. In addition, if uncomfortable heat in the inhaled air is detected or the wearer has a feeling of nausea, dizziness, or ill-being, it is imperative they return to fresh air. (A properly operating cartridge or canister may become warm on exposure to certain gases or vapors, but a device that becomes extremely hot indicates that concentrations greater than the device's limits have been reached.)

Combination Aerosol Filter/Gas or Vapor-Removing Respirators

These respirators use aerosol-removing filters with a chemical cartridge or canister for exposure to multiple contaminants or more than one physical form (e.g., mist and vapor) (Figure 22–1b). The filter is generally a permanent part of the canister, but can be either permanent or replaceable on the chemical cartridge. Replaceable filters are sometimes used because the filter and chemical cartridge are not exhausted at the same time (Figure 22–16). This allows for disposing only of the part that is in need of changing. Filters used in combination with cartridges must always be located on the inlet side of the cartridge. This way, any gas or vapor adsorbed onto a filtered particle is captured by the sorbent

Figure 22–15a

Figure 22–15b

Figure 22–15. Gas masks provide longer service life than chemical cartridge respirators for many commonly encountered vapors and gases. a. Chin-style gas mask. b. Belt-mounted gas mask. *(Photo courtesy of MSA – The Safety Company.)*

Figure 22–16. Workers wearing combination chemical cartridge/N95 particulate filter respirator for protection from solvent vapors and mists and glass fibers in a fiberglass operation. *(Photo courtesy of 3M.)*

as it desorbs from the particle. The combination aerosol filter/gas or vapor-removing respirators most often used are for paint spray and pesticides.

Powered Air-Purifying Respirators

The air-purifying element of these respirators may be a filter, chemical cartridge, or canister. They protect against particles or gases and vapors, or particles and gases and vapors. The difference between these and the air-purifying respirators previously discussed is that the powered air-purifying respirator (PAPR) uses a power source (usually a battery) to operate a blower that passes air across the air-cleansing element to supply purified air to a respiratory inlet (mouth and nose) covering. To be certified as a powered air-purifying respirator by NIOSH, the blower must provide at least four cubic feet per minute (cfm) of air to a tight-fitting facepiece (half-face or full facepiece) and at least six cfm to a loose-fitting helmet, hood, or facepiece. Figure 22–17 shows a powered air-purifying respirator with a tight-fitting facepiece and Figure 22–18 shows one with a loose-fitting hood. The great advantage of the powered air-purifying respirator

is that it usually supplies air at positive pressure, reducing inward leakage when compared to the negative-pressure respirators. This is why they have a higher assigned protection factor than their negative-pressure counterpart. It is possible, however, at high work rates to create a negative pressure in the facepiece, thereby increasing facepiece leakage. This can be reduced by fit testing tight-fitting powered air-purifying respirators. When 42 CFR 84 was promulgated, the PAPR filter classifications were not changed. However, all of the 30 CFR 11 PAPR particulate filters were eliminated except for the high efficiency filter. Today the only particulate filter available for PAPRs is the high efficiency filter. This filter is approved for all aerosols. These filters are many times referred to as high efficiency particulate air (HEPA) filters or simply high efficiency filters.

The high efficiency refers to the filter test requirement they must meet (42 CFR 84). HEPA filters must be at least 99.97 percent efficient when tested against 0.3 μm MMAD dioctyl phthalate (DOP) particle. DOP is the test material for the filter. These filters do not undergo loading with the test aerosol. The labels for these filters may also state they

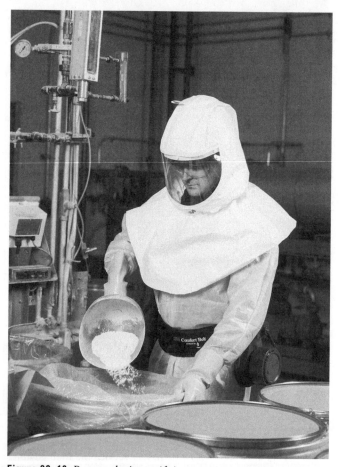

Figure 22–17. A full facepiece powered air-purifying respirator with the motor and blower assembly mounted in the facepiece. *(Photo courtesy of MSA – The Safety Company.)*

Figure 22–18. Powered air-purifying respirators with hoods or helmets can be worn by workers with beards and/or eye glasses. *(Photo courtesy of 3M.)*

can be used for particulate radionuclides. Radionuclides are materials that spontaneously emit ionizing radiation.

Atmosphere-Supplying Respirators

Atmosphere-supplying devices are the class of respirators that provide a respirable atmosphere to the wearer, independent of the ambient air. The breathing atmosphere is supplied from an uncontaminated source. The air source for an atmosphere-supplying respirator must conform to grade D requirements as specified in the Compressed Gas Association Standard, G-7.1-2011, Commodity Specification for Air. Table 22–A lists the air quality requirements for grade D breathing air. Atmosphere-supplying respirators fall into three groups: air-line respirators, self-contained breathing apparatus (SCBA), and combination air-line and SCBA.

Air-Line Respirators

Air-line respirators deliver breathing air through a supply hose connected to the wearer's facepiece or head enclosure. The breathing air is supplied through the hose from either a compressor or compressed air cylinders. If a compressor supplies air, it must be equipped with specific safety devices according to OSHA. Oil-lubricated compressors must have a high-temperature or carbon monoxide alarm, or both, to monitor carbon monoxide levels. If only high-temperature alarms are used, the air supply must be monitored at sufficient intervals to prevent carbon monoxide from exceeding 10 ppm in the breathing air. For compressors that are not oil-lubricated, the employer must ensure that the carbon monoxide level does not exceed 10 ppm in the breathing air. No specific alarms or methods are required. A flow control valve, regulator, or orifice is provided to govern the rate of airflow to the worker. Depending on the certification, up to 300 feet of air supply hose is allowable. Hose supplied by the respirator manufacturer, along with recommended hose lengths and operating pressures, must be used. The maximum permissible inlet pressure is 125 pounds per square inch (psig). The approved pressure range and hose length are noted in the operating instruction manual provided with each approved device (Figure 22–19).

These devices should only be used in non-IDLH atmospheres, or atmospheres in which the wearer can escape without the use of a respirator. This limitation is necessary because the air-line respirator is entirely dependent upon an air supply that is not carried by the wearer of the respirator. If this air supply fails, the wearer may have to remove the respirator to escape from the area. OSHA considers all oxygen-deficient atmospheres to be IDLH. However, OSHA has established an exception. Any air-line respirator may be used in oxygen-deficient atmospheres if the employer can demonstrate that, under all foreseeable conditions, the

Figure 22–19. Continuous flow air-line respirators are used in conjunction with a compressor system. The manifold for connecting to the air source can be seen in the background. *(Photo courtesy of 3M.)*

oxygen concentration can be maintained within the ranges specified in Table 22–F. Another limitation is that the air hose limits the wearer to a fixed distance from the air supply source.

Air-line respirators operate in three modes: demand, pressure demand, and continuous flow. The respirators are equipped with half facepieces, full facepieces, helmets, hoods, or loose-fitting facepieces. Some of these respiratory inlet coverings may provide eye protection.

Demand. Demand air-line respirators are equipped with either half or full facepieces. They deliver airflow only upon inhalation. Due to their design, a negative pressure with respect

	Oxygen-Deficient Atmospheres Where
TABLE 22–F	Atmosphere-Supplying Respirators May Be Used

Altitude (ft)	Percent Oxygen (% O$_2$)
Less than 3,001	16.0-19.5
3,001-4,000	16.4-19.5
4,001-5,000	17.1-19.5
5,001-6,000	17.8-19.5
6,001-7,000	18.5-19.5
7,001-8,000[1]	19.3-19.5

[1]Above 8,000 feet the exception does not apply. Oxygen-enriched breathing air must be supplied above 14,000 feet.
Source: Reprinted from OSHA General Industry Standards, 29 CFR 1910.134.

to the outside of the respirator is created in the facepiece upon inhalation. These respirators are negative-pressure devices. While these respirators can still be found in work-sites, they are not recommended if one is buying new respirators because the pressure-demand type is available. The pressure-demand air-line respirator is much more protective and the cost differential between the two is negligible.

Pressure Demand. Pressure-demand air-line respirators are very similar to the demand type except that because of their design, the pressure inside the respirator is generally positive with respect to the air pressure outside the respirator during both inhalation and exhalation. This positive pressure means that when a leak develops in the face seal due to head movement, for example, the leakage of air would be outward. Thus they provide a higher degree of protection to the user. They are available only with half and full facepieces (Figure 22–20). Such respirators are normally used when the air supply is restricted to high-pressure compressed air cylinders. A suitable pressure regulator is required to make sure the air pressure is reduced to the proper level for breathing.

Continuous flow. A continuous-flow unit has a regulated amount of air delivered to the facepiece or head enclosure and is normally used where there is an ample air supply such as that provided by an air compressor. These devices may be equipped with either tight-fitting or loose-fitting head enclosures. Those equipped with tight-fitting enclosures, a half or full facepiece, must provide at least 4 cfm measured at the facepiece (Figure 22–21). When loose-fitting helmets, hoods, or facepieces are used, the minimum amount of air

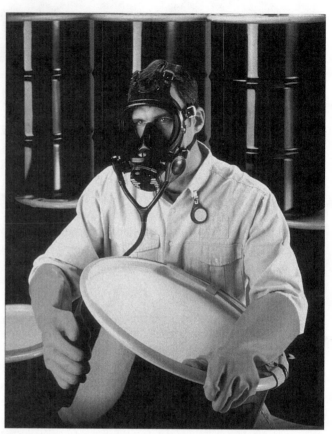

Figure 22–21. A continuous flow air-line respirator with a tight-fitting facepiece. *(Photo courtesy of 3M.)*

to be delivered is 6 cfm. In either case the maximum flow is not to exceed 15 cfm. Versions of these respirators may be designed for welding (Figure 22–22) or abrasive blasting (Figure 22–23). Respiratory-protective equipment designed for abrasive blasting is equipped to protect the wearer from impact of the rebounding abrasive material. A special hood may be used to protect the wearer's head and neck and shielding material may be used to protect the viewing windows of the head enclosures.

Self-Contained Breathing Apparatus

The self-contained breathing apparatus (SCBA) provides respiratory protection against gases, vapors, particles, and oxygen-deficient atmospheres. The wearer is independent of the surrounding atmosphere because the breathing gas is carried by the wearer. SCBA may be used in IDLH and oxygen-deficient atmospheres either as escape-only devices or for entry into and escape from these atmospheres. A full facepiece is most commonly used with SCBA. Half face-pieces, hoods, and mouthpieces are available on some units. There are two major types of SCBAs: closed circuit and open circuit.

Figure 22–20. Pressure demand air-line respirators are used with compressed air supplied by a compressor or a cascade of compressed air cylinders. *(Photo courtesy of MSA – The Safety Company.)*

Figure 22–22. A continuous flow air-line respirator with a helmet with a viewing lens adapter for welding. *(Photo courtesy of 3M.)*

Closed-circuit SCBA. In closed circuit SCBA (Figure 22–24) all or a percentage of the exhaled gas is scrubbed and rebreathed. Closed-circuit units have the advantage of lower weight for the same use duration as open-circuit devices. Units are available with use durations from 15 minutes to 4 hours. Disadvantages include increased complexity (for example, a carbon dioxide scrubber is required in many of the units) and cost. Due to the design of many of the devices, the air supply can become quite warm because of rebreathing of the air. Closed-circuit SCBAs are available as both negative- and positive-pressure devices. They may be designed as a stored-oxygen system or an oxygen-generating system.

Stored-oxygen systems supply oxygen compressed in cylinders or carried as a liquid. Oxygen is admitted to a breathing bag either as a continuous flow or controlled by a regulator governed by the pressure or degree of inflation of the bag. The wearer inhales from the bag and exhales into it. Exhaled breath is scrubbed of carbon dioxide by a chemical bed, usually a caustic such as sodium hydroxide.

Oxygen-generating systems rely on chemical reactions to provide the needed oxygen. Water vapor from the exhaled breath reacts with a solid chemical, usually potassium superoxide, in a canister-size container that releases oxygen. Carbon dioxide is removed from the exhaled breath in the canister also.

Figure 22–23. Abrasive blasting continuous flow air-line respirator. *(Photo courtesy of 3M.)*

Figure 22–24. Closed circuit self-contained breathing apparatus designed for 60 minutes of service. *(Photo Courtesy of Neutronics/ Biomarine, Inc.)*

Open-Circuit SCBA. In an open-circuit SCBA the exhaled breath is released to the surrounding environment rather than being recirculated. The breathing gas is generally compressed air. Typically they are designed to provide 30 to 60 minutes of service and may operate in either the demand or pressure-demand mode (Figure 22–25). According to OSHA regulation 1910.134, only full-facepiece, pressure-demand (positive-pressure) SCBAs can be used in IDLH atmospheres.

Escape SCBA. Some SCBAs are designed for escape only (Figure 22–26). They are similar in design to the types described above, except that the use duration tends to be shorter, typically 5, 7, or 10 minutes. Units approved for escape only may not be used to enter into a hazardous atmosphere. The fact that they are certified for escape only means that assigned protection factors have not been established for this category of respirator.

Combination Self-Contained Breathing Apparatus and Air-Line Respirator

These units are air-line respirators with an auxiliary self-contained air supply combined into a single device (Figure 22–27). An auxiliary SCBA is an air supply that is independent of the one to the air-line respirator allowing a person to evacuate a contaminated area. Because they have escape provisions, these devices are usable in IDLH and oxygen-deficient atmospheres. A worker can switch to the auxiliary air supply in the event the primary air supply fails to operate. This allows the wearer to escape from the IDLH atmosphere.

An advantage of these devices is they can be used in situations requiring extended work periods where the self-contained air supply alone does not provide sufficient time. In this situation, the wearer may connect to an air-line to provide longer service time. The longer service life and smaller SCBA cylinder make these devices particularly convenient for use in confined spaces.

The auxiliary self-contained air supply may be NIOSH-approved in one of two categories: 3-, 5-, or 10-minute service times or for 15 minutes or longer. If the SCBA portion is rated for a service life of 3, 5, or 10 minutes, the wearer must use the air line during entry into a hazardous atmosphere; the SCBA portion is used for emergency egress only. When the SCBA is rated for service of 15 minutes or longer, the SCBA may be used for emergency entry into a hazardous atmosphere (to connect the air line) provided not more than 20 percent of the air supply's rated capacity is used during entry. This allows for enough air for egress when the warning device indicates a low air supply.

The combination SCBA/air-line respirators may operate in demand or pressure-demand mode. These devices use the

Figure 22–25. Pressure demand self-contained breathing apparatus approved for oxygen deficient and immediately dangerous to life or health atmospheres. *(Photo courtesy of MSA – The Safety Company.)*

Figure 22–26. Some self-contained breathing apparatus are designed for escape-only from hazardous atmospheres. *(Photo courtesy of MSA – The Safety Company.)*

same principles as the respective air-line respirator. Pressure-demand mode is required by OSHA for IDLH environments.

Combination Air-Purifying and Atmosphere-Supplying Devices

Another type of respirator is gaining in popularity. It is a combination of an air-line respirator and an auxiliary air-purifying attachment, which provides protection in the event the air supply fails (Figure 22–28). NIOSH has approved

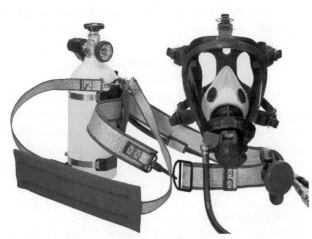

Figure 22–27. Combination self-contained breathing apparatus and air-line respirators can be connected to an external air supply for working in a hazardous atmosphere and still allowing for escape without removing the respirator. *(Photo courtesy of Honeywell Safety Products/Sperian Respiratory Protection USA.)*

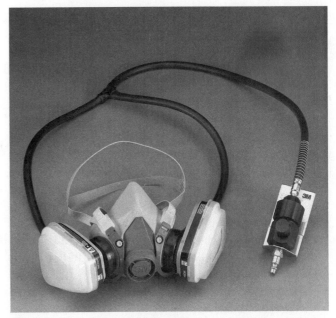

Figure 22–28. Combination air-purifying and air-line respirators provide protection in the event the air supply fails. *(Photo courtesy of 3M.)*

combination air-line and air-purifying respirators with the air line operating in either continuous-flow or pressure-demand. These respirators can be used in either an air-purifying or air-line mode. The most popular versions are ones in which the air-purifying element is a class 100 filter, but devices are available with a complete array of chemical cartridges as well.

These respirators have additional limitations:

- They are not for use in IDLH atmospheres.
- They are not for use in atmospheres containing less than 19.5 percent oxygen.
- They must use only the hose lengths and pressure ranges specified in the operator's manual.
- They can only be used in atmospheres for which the air-purifying element is approved.

The approval label and operator's manual must be consulted for proper use of the respirator in the air-purifying mode. The restrictions can vary from manufacturer to manufacturer depending on the respirator design.

RESPIRATOR SELECTION

Proper selection of respirators must start with an assessment of the inhalation hazards present in the workplace. This assessment must include the following:

- the nature of the hazardous operation or process
- the type of respiratory hazard
- the location of the hazardous area in relation to the nearest respirable air source
- the time period that respirators must be worn
- the workers' activities

Respirators must then be selected for the situation after the physical characteristics and functional capabilities and limitations of the various types of respirators and their assigned protection factors (APFs) have been considered.

Selection Requirements

The OSHA Standard 29 CFR 1910.134 states that respirators shall be selected on the basis of the respiratory hazard(s) in the workplace and relevant workplace and user factors. A NIOSH-approved respirator must be selected. The workplace respiratory hazards must be identified and evaluated; this evaluation includes a reasonable estimate of worker exposures to respiratory hazard(s) and an identification of the contaminant's chemical state and physical form. If the respiratory hazard cannot be identified or the worker exposure estimated, the atmosphere must be considered IDLH. For certain respiratory hazards, specific instructions about respirator use are given in other OSHA regulations (for example, Asbestos, 1910.1001 and 1926.1101; Vinyl Chloride, 1910.1017; and substances regulated after promulgation of vinyl chloride).

When the respiratory hazard concentration has been determined, assigned protection factors (APF) are used to determine what level of protection is needed. The APF is listed in the OSHA respirator standard, 29 CFR 1910.134 except for 1,3-butadiene (29 CFR 1910.1051). To provide additional protection, an employer may select a respirator prescribed for concentrations higher than those found in the workplace. These standards also call for a respiratory protection program as spelled out in the OSHA regulations. The general selection requirements of 29 CFR 1910.134 must be followed.

Respirator selection involves determining the hazard and following a selection logic to choose the correct type or class of respirator that offers adequate protection.

Hazard Determination

The steps for hazard determination are as follows:

1. If the potential for an oxygen-deficient atmosphere exists, measure the oxygen content.
2. Determine what contaminant(s) may be present in the workplace.
3. Determine whether there are Threshold Limit Values® (TLVs), Permissible Exposure Limits (PELs), or any other available exposure limits.
4. Determine if the IDLH concentration for the contaminant(s) is available.
5. Determine if there is a substance-specific health standard (e.g., lead, asbestos) for the contaminant(s). If so, there may be specific respirators required that will influence the selection process.
6. Determine the physical state of the contaminant. Several contaminants have been identified in the TLV booklet with a footnote of IFV (inhalable fraction and vapor). This footnote is used when a material exerts sufficient vapor pressure such that it may be present in both particle and vapor phases, each contributing a significant portion of the dose at the TLV-TWA concentration.
7. Measure or estimate the concentration of the contaminant(s).
8. Determine whether the contaminant(s) can be absorbed through the skin, cause skin sensitization, or be irritating or corrosive to the eyes or skin. Respirators that provide skin or eye protection or supplied -air suits may be required in addition to providing protection from the inhalation hazard.
9. For gases or vapors, determine if a known odor, taste, or irritation threshold exists because these may provide a secondary indication for cartridge breakthrough.

Skin Absorption

Chemical absorption through skin can be a significant route of exposure. Depending on the chemical, this route of exposure may be more significant than absorption through the respiratory system. For example, assuming 100 percent skin absorption, two drops of aniline on the skin would be equivalent to an inhalation exposure at the ACGIH TLV for eight hours. To avoid this possibility, selection of protective clothing may be required. Respirators may provide limited skin protection by a full facepiece or hood that protects the face area from absorption of gaseous contaminants and splashes. For total skin protection, either chemical clothing that encapsulates the respirator and worker or supplied-air suits must be selected. Encapsulation suits are available from several suppliers (Figure 22–29).

Supplied-air suits are usually custom-made for the intended purpose of the user. Generally, they consist of a full body suit and an air line to supply air to the suit. For more information on supplied-air suits, consult the American Industrial Hygiene Associations's *Respiratory Protection: A Manual and Guideline.*

Warning Properties

In the past, warning properties such as odor, eye irritation, and respiratory irritation have been relied on almost completely for indicating when chemical cartridge breakthrough was starting. In fact, organic vapor chemical cartridges were approved by NIOSH only for those organic vapors with good warning properties. However, warning properties rely upon human senses, and those senses are not foolproof. The 1987 NIOSH *Respirator Decision Logic* (updated as the NIOSH *Respirator Selection Logic 2004*) described the typical wide variation of odor threshold in the general population (greater than two orders of magnitude). Other problems exist: shift in odor threshold caused by extended low exposures, shifts due to simple colds and other illnesses, and failure to recognize odor because distractions in the workplace are competing for the worker's attention. Given the variability among people with respect to detection of odors and differences in measuring odor thresholds, a better practice is to establish cartridge change schedules. Because of this fact, when OSHA revised its respiratory protection standard, it prohibited the reliance on warning properties as the primary means for indicating when it was time to change the chemical cartridges. Instead, OSHA requires that a change schedule be established that identifies how long a chemical cartridge can be used in a particular workplace before being replaced. OSHA has indicated that if an effective change schedule can be established for chemicals with poor warning properties, chemical cartridges could also be used for these chemicals as well. NIOSH updated its respirator use policy to be consistent with OSHA by recognizing the use of change schedules and by recommending against reliance on warning properties. The warning properties in these cases should be used as a secondary indicator for cartridge change. Early detection of the material (i.e, before the end of the established change schedule) indicates the change schedule should be reviewed.

Selection Steps

After information is collected in the hazard determination step, proper selection should be made as follows:

Figure 22–29. Totally encapsulating suits can be selected to provide skin protection and accommodate the respirator. *(Photo courtesy of ILC Dover.)*

1. If there is an oxygen-deficient atmosphere (<19.5% O_2) consider the atmosphere IDLH (see next item and Figure 22–25).

2. If the potential contaminants present were unable to be identified, consider the atmosphere IDLH (see next item).

3. If no exposure limit or guideline is available and estimates of toxicity cannot be made, consider the atmosphere IDLH (see next item).

4. If the measured or estimated concentration of the contaminants exceeds the IDLH levels, the atmosphere is IDLH (see next item).

5. Divide the measured or estimated concentration by the exposure limit or guideline to obtain a hazard ratio.

6. If a substance-specific standard exists for the contaminant, consider those guidelines/requirements.

7. If more than one chemical is present, potential additive and synergistic effects of exposure should be considered. If the ACGIH TLV for mixtures is used, a result greater than unity (that is, one) is the hazard ratio. Select a respirator with an assigned protection factor (APF) greater than the value of the hazard ratio. If an air-purifying respirator is selected, go on to the next step.

8. If the contaminant is a particle, a respirator with a particulate filter must be selected. Determine the filter efficiency required. Use a class 100 (99.97% efficiency) filter if a specific regulation or regulatory policy requires it. If no such regulation or policy exists, a class 95 (95% efficiency) filter may be used. Next, determine the filter series needed. If no oil is present, an N-, R-, or P-series filter may be selected for the respirator with the appropriate APF. If oil is present, either an R- or P-series filter must be selected. R-series filters must be changed after eight-hour use or after the respirator is loaded with 200 mg of aerosol. Where oil is suspected, but air samples have not been taken to determine its presence, an R- or P-series filter should be selected.

9. If the contaminant is a gas or vapor, a respirator with a cartridge effective against the contaminant and with an assigned protection factor greater than the hazard ratio must be selected. If there is no chemical cartridge that is effective against the contaminant, an atmosphere-supplying respirator with an appropriate APF must be selected.

10. For gases or vapors, determine if the effective chemical cartridge has an end-of-service-life indicator (ESLI) or if service life data exists to allow for a cartridge change schedule to be established.

11. If a respirator with either a chemical cartridge or canister is selected, establish a change schedule that results in replacing the cartridge or canister before significant breakthrough (concentrations exceeding the exposure limit) occurs.

12. If the contaminant(s) is a particle and gas or vapor, such as with paint spray or pesticides, an air-purifying respirator with both an appropriate chemical cartridge and particulate filter, or an atmosphere-supplying respirator, must be selected. A change schedule for the cartridge or canister must be established.

Immediately Dangerous to Life or Health

Numerous definitions have been presented for immediately dangerous to life or health (IDLH) atmospheres. OSHA defines IDLH as an atmosphere that poses an immediate threat to life, would cause irreversible adverse health effects, or would impair an individual's ability to escape from a dangerous atmosphere. The common theme in all the definitions is that IDLH atmospheres will affect the worker acutely as opposed to chronically. Thus, if the concentration is above the IDLH levels only highly reliable respiratory protective equipment is allowed. The only two devices that meet this requirement and provide escape provisions for the wearer are

- a full-facepiece pressure-demand or other positive-pressure self-contained breathing apparatus (SCBA) certified for a minimum service life of 30 minutes; and

• a combination type, full-facepiece pressure-demand air-line respirator with auxiliary self-contained air supply.

The IDLH limits are conservative, so any approved respirator may be used up to this limit as long as the maximum use concentration for the device has not been exceeded (Figure 22–30). IDLH limits have not been established by OSHA. NIOSH has recommended IDLH values for many chemicals in the NIOSH *Pocket Guide to Chemical Hazards* for the purpose of respirator selection. Two factors have been considered when establishing IDLH concentrations:

• The worker must be able to escape without losing his or her life or suffering permanent health damage within 30 minutes. Thirty minutes is considered by NIOSH as the maximum permissible exposure time for escape.

• The worker must be able to escape without severe eye or respiratory irritation or other reactions that could inhibit escape.

A location is considered IDLH when an atmosphere is known or suspected to have chemical concentrations above the IDLH level or if a confined space contains less than the normal 20.9 percent oxygen, unless the reason for the reduced oxygen level is known. Otherwise, according to OSHA, oxygen levels of less than 19.5 percent are IDLH unless the requirements for the OSHA exception discussed earlier can be met. When there is doubt about the oxygen content, the contaminants present, or their airborne levels, the situation should be treated as IDLH. If an error in respirator selection is made, it should be on the side of safety. Thus in emergency situations, such as a spill, where the chemical or its airborne concentration are unknown, one of the above two respirators must be selected.

Lower Explosive Limit and Fire Fighting

Concentrations in excess of the lower explosive limit (LEL) are considered to be IDLH. Generally, entry into atmospheres exceeding 10 percent of the LEL is not recommended except for life saving rescues. For concentrations at or above the LEL, respirators must provide maximum protection. Such devices include pressure-demand SCBA and combination pressure-demand air-line respirators with egress cylinders.

For interior structural fire fighting and other IDLH environments, the pressure-demand SCBA of at least 30-minute duration must be selected. In addition to being NIOSH-approved, the SCBA used for fire fighting (Figure 22–25) should comply with the most current edition of the National Fire Protection Association (NFPA) standard, NFPA 1981 (last published in 2007). These SCBAs are also required to be approved for chemical, biological, radiological and nuclear (CBRN) hazards by NIOSH.

Assigned Protection Factors

Assigned protection factors (APFs) are a very important part of the selection process. The APF is the expected workplace level of respiratory protection that would be provided by a properly functioning respirator or a class of respirators to properly fitted and trained users when a continuing effective respiratory protection program is implemented. Simply stated, APFs are a measure of the overall effectiveness of a

---

Example of Maximum Use Concentration (MUC) Determination

| Problem: |
| What is the MUC for a half facepiece respirator with N95 particulate filters for copper dust? |

Solution:

| TLV for copper dust: | 1 mg/m^3 |
| APF for half facepiece respirator | 10 |

$$\begin{aligned} \text{MUC} &= \text{TLV} \times \text{APF} \\ &= 1 \text{ mg/m}^3 \times 10 \\ &= 10 \text{ mg/m}^3 \end{aligned}$$

Explanation:

If air sampling indicates an ambient concentration greater than 10 mg/m^3, this respirator does not provide sufficient protection! Note that for half and full facepiece respirators, the filter or chemical cartridge type does not change the APF for the respirator.

Figure 22–30. Assigned protection factors are used in the selection process to determine the maximum use concentration for the respirator. It is determined by multiplying the TLV® by the assigned protection factor (Table 22–G). The assigned protection factors should be used only when the employer has established a respiratory protection program meeting the requirements stated in this chapter and satisfactory fit testing has been performed.

TABLE 22–G OSHA Assigned Protection Factors					
Type of Respirator[1,2]	*Quarter mask*	*Half mask*	*Full Facepiece*	*Helmet/Hood*	*Loose-fitting facepiece*
1. Air-Purifying Respirator	5	[3]10	50	---------	---------
2. Powered Air-Purifying Respirator (PAPR)	---------	50	1000	[4]25/1000	25
3. Supplied-Air Respirator or Air-Line Respirator					
• Demand mode	---------	10	50	---------	---------
• Continuous-flow mode	---------	50	1000	[4]25/1000	25
• Pressure-demand or other positive pressure mode	---------	50	1000		
4. Self-Contained Breathing Apparatus (SCBA)					
• Demand mode	---------	10	50	50	---------
• Pressure-demand or other positive-pressure mode (e.g., open/closed circuit)	---------	---------	10,000	10,000	---------

Note: These APFs do not apply to respirators used solely for escape. For escape respirators used in association with specific substances covered by 29 CFR 1910 subpart Z, employers must refer to the appropriate substance-specific standards in that subpart. Escape respirators for other IDLH atmospheres are specified by 29 CFR 1910.134 (d)(2)(ii).

[1]Employers may select respirators assigned for use in higher workplace concentrations of a hazardous substance for use at lower concentrations of that substance, or when required respirator use is independent of concentration.

[2]The assigned protection factors in this table are only effective when the employer implements a continuing, effective respirator program as required by this section (29 CFR 1910.134), including training, fit testing, maintenance, and use requirements.

[3]This APF category includes filtering facepieces, and half masks with elastomeric facepieces.

[4]The employer must have evidence provided by the respirator manufacturer that testing of these respirators demonstrates performance at a level of protection of 1,000 or greater to receive an APF of 1,000. This level of performance can best be demonstrated by performing a WPF or SWPF study or equivalent testing. Absent such testing, all other PAPRs and SARs with helmets/hoods are to be treated as loose-fitting facepiece respirators, and receive an APF of 25.

respirator used in conjunction with a good respirator program. The APFs established by OSHA (Table 22–G) are based on tests measuring the performance of respirators in the workplace or simulated workplace environments. These studies are sometimes referred to as workplace protection factor studies. In these studies, measurements are taken simultaneously outside and inside the respirator while the worker does their normal job (Figure 22–31). The results of these studies indicate that an APF of 10 for both disposable (filtering facepiece respirators) and elastomeric half-facepiece respirators is appropriate. An APF of 10 means the respirator will reduce the concentration actually breathed in by 10 times compared with the actual airborne concentration.

APFs should be used only when the employer has established an acceptable respiratory protection program meeting the requirements of 29 CFR 1910.134 and satisfactory fit testing of tight-fitting respirators has been performed.

Change Schedules

When a respirator with an end-of-service-life indicator is not available, the only method available for replacing cartridges or canisters before breakthrough is by a cartridge change schedule. The objective data used to set a change schedule must be documented in a written respiratory protection program. It is not necessary to develop a cartridge change schedule for gas and vapor contaminants regulated by OSHA's substance-specific standards, since cartridge change schedules are specified in each regulation. A change schedule is a predetermined interval of time after which a used cartridge is replaced with a new one. To determine an appropriate change schedule, the breakthrough time for the gas or vapor in question must be known or estimated. Breakthrough means that a stated concentration of the chemical can be detected, measured, on the downstream side of the cartridge. The amount of time required to reach breakthrough is sometimes referred to as the service life of the cartridge. An appropriate cartridge change schedule is one that is both convenient and assures that the concentration of the chemical downstream does not exceed the exposure limit.

Figure 22–31. Workplace studies simultaneously measuring air contaminants outside and inside the respirator are being used to establish assigned protection factors for the classes of respirators. *(Photo courtesy of 3M.)*

The service life estimate is the fundamental piece of information to base a change schedule on. In no case should the change schedule exceed the breakthrough time. Several methods can be used to estimate breakthrough times (that is, service life). These vary in cost, complexity, and precision. All methods require professional judgment to establish an appropriate change schedule and all require the same basic information. This information includes the specific respirator and cartridge to be used, airborne concentration of the contaminant(s), temperature and humidity in the workplace, the pattern of respirator use (e.g., hours per shift, shifts per week), and the expected work rate. Each of these can affect cartridge service life. Service life can be estimated using general guidelines, determined by testing cartridges in the laboratory or in the field, or calculated using breakthrough equations.

A few general guidelines for estimating the service life of organic vapor chemical cartridges exist. Basically, high boiling point materials are collected more efficiently than low boiling point materials. Guidelines for estimating change-out for organic vapor cartridges are:

- If the organic vapor's boiling point is greater than 70°C, and its concentration is less than 200 ppm, the organic vapor cartridge should last eight hours at a normal work rate (assuming normal breathing rate).
- Service life is inversely proportional to flow rate.
- If the concentration is reduced by a factor of 10, the service life will only increase by a factor of 5.

There are no general guidelines to follow for the other types of chemical cartridges.

Respirator manufacturers, private testing laboratories, and research scientists have done laboratory testing with some chemicals. Many commercial labs are equipped to run tests for a fee. Laboratory testing involves measuring the actual breakthrough time for a specific cartridge when tested with a specific chemical. The cartridge is mounted in a test apparatus, and a known concentration of the chemical is drawn through it at a specific flow rate, temperature, and humidity. The time it takes to detect a stated concentration of the chemical on the downstream side of the cartridge is measured. Laboratory testing gives an actual measurement of breakthrough time for the test conditions. Because laboratory studies are usually conducted at high concentrations to save time, professional judgment or rules of thumb must be used to apply this information to workplace conditions. It is also possible to conduct a series of tests at different concentrations and humidity levels in order to develop a breakthrough curve to predict the performance of the cartridge at a wide range of conditions. Laboratory testing can be done with mixtures, but problems of generating and controlling a complex test atmosphere must be overcome.

The cost for laboratory testing is rather high, approximately $2,000 for a single chemical.

Much of the breakthrough data published in the literature were collected using cartridges manufactured more than 30 years ago. Table 22–E lists examples of published breakthrough data for several chemicals. Generally this information is for single chemicals, but it is possible to test more than one chemical simultaneously at concentrations and relative humidity that mimic the work environment. When the testing conditions are not representative of the workplace, it is more difficult to extrapolate to the workplace. Because respirator and carbon technology have improved over the years, modern cartridges are likely to perform better than published data indicate.

Field testing determines breakthrough time in the workplace. Air from the workplace is drawn through the cartridge, and the downstream air is monitored to determine when breakthrough occurs. Pumps capable of drawing 20 to 60 liters per minute are required, which typically means that the pump must be in a fixed location. Consequently, the challenge to the cartridge may not accurately represent workers' actual exposures. Field testing overcomes many of the disadvantages of mathematical models and laboratory testing. Relative humidity and the presence of several vapors in the atmosphere are automatically incorporated into the breakthrough measurement. However, field testing has the disadvantage of being relatively equipment- and labor-intensive. In addition, since workplace concentrations of each vapor can vary considerably, samples may need to be collected over several days.

Breakthrough equations or mathematical models have been developed to estimate breakthrough time for organic vapor cartridges and canisters. The calculation of breakthrough time depends on organic vapor contaminant variables, carbon variables, and ambient conditions. Models currently used for organic vapors are limited to liquids. Some may be limited by humidity and restricted to single chemicals. Mathematical models provide estimates of service life based on the physical properties of the chemical and the carbon used in the cartridges. Many respirator manufacturers have developed these models for use with their respirators. Some provide service life estimates for inorganic chemicals. These models can usually be obtained from the respirator manufacturer's website. It is important to use the service life estimate model for the brand of chemical cartridge being used. NIOSH has developed more general software, to be used with any manufacturer's cartridge, for estimating service life on multiple vapors and various relative humidity levels.

To verify that the change schedule is appropriate, an alternate field testing procedure can be used. It determines the remaining service life of cartridges after use in the workplace. This type of test is used to demonstrate that the gas or vapor has not broken through. It is easily accomplished by sampling behind the cartridge near the end of the use period. Any sampling method with sufficient sensitivity to detect the chemical of interest at a concentration below the exposure limit can be used to take the sample. Sampling behind the cartridge has been used for a limited number of materials and exposures. It is a simple method that allows breakthrough to be measured in the workplace at the actual contaminant concentration, environmental conditions, and work rate. It enables verification of service life predictions from mathematical models or change schedules based on limited information. This method is also suitable for atmospheres containing several vapors. Its primary disadvantage is its labor intensity, particularly if no preliminary service life estimate is available.

Setting an appropriate change schedule requires professional judgment to interpret information and apply appropriate safety factors. This is especially true when general guidelines, laboratory data, field data, or mathematical models are used. An acceptable margin of safety between a service life estimate and a change schedule is influenced by:

- toxicity of the chemical
- warning properties
- quality of data and assumptions
- exposure estimate
- service life data
- work rate estimate
- workplace temperature and humidity

Chemical migration through the chemical cartridge must be considered when the change schedule includes nonuse time periods. For organic vapors with a boiling point less than 65°C, it is recommended that the organic vapor cartridge never be used longer than one shift even if the estimated service life is greater than the shift duration and the cartridge is used for only a short time during the shift. For chemicals with boiling points greater than 65°C, nonuse or storage periods of a few days, like over a weekend, may be a concern. The reuse pattern must be carefully evaluated even for these less volatile chemicals. Chemicals with low volatility will give long service lives, but even in these situations, use should probably not extend beyond a week or two even if the service life estimate is longer. For workers that use their respirators intermittently and perhaps in different environments, such as a maintenance worker or inspector, the organic vapor cartridges should probably never be reused.

The user can conduct desorption studies, mimicking the work conditions of use and nonuse, to determine acceptable patterns of reuse.

Health Care Settings

One of the more recent worksites seeing increased respirator usage is health care settings. Respiratory-protective devices are being used to reduce exposure to aerosolized drugs (eg., pentamidine, ribavirin, antineoplastics) and bioaerosols from airborne transmissible diseases (eg., *Mycobacterium tuberculosis* [TB], avian flu, H1N1 flu). This area presents many challenges including unknown safe levels of exposure for these agents or respirator efficacy for bioaerosols. Acceptable airborne levels have not been established for many pharmaceutical drugs or potentially infectious aerosols. NIOSH-approved or certified respirators have not been tested against bioaerosols such as TB-containing droplet nuclei and H1N1-flu-containing aerosol.

This lack of information makes the respirator selection process difficult. Use of a properly selected respirator may reduce the risk caused by exposure to these materials, but cannot guarantee protection. Respirators with high APFs should be expected to reduce risk to a lower level than respirators with lower APFs when used within a respirator program and worn properly and diligently by the worker. On the other hand, respirators with higher APFs are more complex, burdensome to the worker, and costly. The proper balance needs to be achieved. Disposable particulate respirators (filtering facepiece respirators) mentioned earlier have been used in health care settings because of their simplicity, cost, and efficiency, and also because of the ease of disposal if they become contaminated. Reuse of a respirator or its disposal must also be consistent with the operating procedures of the infection-control program of the health care facility. Decontamination procedures prior to reuse for filtering facepiece respirators have not been established.

Nanoparticles

With the rise in the use of engineered nanoparticles in industry, there has been growing concern about their effect on human health. A nanoparticle is an object with all three external dimensions in the size range from ~1 to 100 nm. The effects of their small size, large surface area and other chemical and physical properties on toxicity have generated concern. Even though the development of occupational exposure limits (OEL) are in the early stages (less than a handful of proposed OELs), the use of respiratory protection has become a practice in many workplaces with engineered nanoparticles. Without an OEL, it is impossible to select a respirator by determining the hazard ratio and subsequent identification of an appropriate APF. There are little data at present to determine if respiratory protection is needed and, if so, how to select the appropriate respirator in these workplaces. However, many nanotechnology industries use half facepiece respirators with particulate filters when the potential for exposure to nanoparticles exists. Filter penetration, face seal leakage, and respirator protection factors are frequently cited as the factors for determining the appropriateness of a respirator for nanoparticles.

Filter penetration. The mechanisms describing particle capture were discussed previously. Theory predicts that as the particle gets smaller than the most penetrating particle size, filter efficiency increases. As the particles approach molecular size, however, it is theorized that thermal rebound effects may cause deviations from single-fiber filtration theory. Thermal rebound occurs when the particles bounce through the filter because of their thermal velocity rather than being trapped by collision with a filter fiber. The exact size at which thermal rebound will occur is unclear. The theory has been shown to be true for particles in the 2-60 nm range. A study conducted on NIOSH-approved and CE-approved (approval from EU) filtering facepiece respirators, with particles below the most penetrating particle size, showed a decrease in filter penetration levels with decreasing particle size. This study measured particle penetration down to 4 nm for NIOSH-certified N95 and P100 filters and found no evidence of thermal rebound.

Face seal leakage. Good face fit is critical to the respirator performing properly and is evaluated by fit testing procedures in the OSHA respiratory protection standard (29 CFR 1910.134). A concern has been voiced that nanoparticles are more likely to penetrate face seal leaks because of their small size. So are current fit-test methods adequate for fit-testing respirators used against nanoparticles? It has been suggested that a gaseous fit-test challenge agent (e.g., isoamyl acetate) may be a more critical test than using an aerosol (e.g., saccharin, Bitrex™, ambient aerosols). The results of a study comparing fit factors measured using vapor challenges to those measured using an aerosol challenge suggested that the leakage of submicron particles was similar to that of the vapor challenge. A workplace protection factor (WPF) study showed that the use of a vaporous challenge agent did not result in a higher fifth percentile WPF than WPF tests using aerosol fit tests. A commonly used quantitative fit test method (i.e., TSI PortaCount™) uses ambient particles to measure fit factors. A version of this equipment only measures ambient nanoparticles in the 40-60 nm range, so one is essentially fit testing with nanoparticles. In addition, one study correlated ambient aerosol and generated aerosol fit tests with Freon-113 (gaseous contaminant) exposures. All of the qualitative fit-test methods published in the OSHA respiratory protection standard were validated by comparing qualitative fit-test (QLFT) results to generated aerosol quantitative fit test (QNFT) fit factors. Thus, respirator fit

tests conducted in accordance with the OSHA procedures should provide assurance to users that they are obtaining expected levels of fit regardless of the type of contaminant.

Protection factors. A third issue is the applicability of existing respirator APFs to engineered nanoparticle exposure. Some of this concern is because existing APFs for half facepiece respirators were derived by WPF studies. These WPF studies analyzed contaminant mass. It is thought by some that OELs for nanoparticles should be based on particle count or surface area instead of mass. Based on correlation studies, fit factors generated by mass-based and count-based methods for quantitative fit testing have been used interchangeably. This suggests that the same approach can be used with protection factors for materials with OELs based on other parameters. No WPF studies have been done in engineered nanoparticle environments; however, WPF studies have been conducted on half-mask respirators in welding environments where nanoparticles are generated. These studies indicate the existing APF for half facepieces apply in welding situations. NIOSH has concluded that industrial hygienists and safety professionals should continue to use traditional respirator selection guidance based on OSHA APF values until WPF studies can be performed. Without an OEL for the nanoparticle, it is impossible to select the respirator by calculating a hazard ratio. In addition, organizations have made recommendations based on their professional judgment. The range of recommendations can be viewed in the NIOSH review.

Effective Protection Factor

Another variable that is often overlooked when selecting a respirator is worker acceptability. If the device is not acceptable to the worker, it probably will not be worn. A respirator must be worn to be effective. Not wearing a respirator for even short periods of time while it is needed can have a profound effect on the overall protection that a respirator is capable of providing. If a respirator is not worn, the protection factor it provides is one, that is, the individual is exposed to the ambient contaminant concentration.

The effect of not wearing a respirator can be calculated from the following equation.

$$\text{Effective Protective Factor} = \frac{\text{Work shift time, min}}{(1/\text{APF})(\text{wear time, min}) + (\text{Nonwear time, min})}$$

The exposure during wear time can be reduced by the APF or any assumed level of protection.

For example, if a person removes their respirator for one minute to talk during a task that takes one hour, the wear time is 98 percent. If the person uses a respirator with an APF of 1,000, the effective level of protection (effective protection factor) received is 56 when this one minute of nonwear time is included. In training it is important that people understand the effect of nonwear time on the level of performance that can be achieved. As nonwear time increases for any respirator, the protection level for all respirators approaches one. Where poor wear habits exist, the effective protection levels of an SCBA and a half mask may be identical (Table 22–H).

RESPIRATOR FIT TESTING

After close consideration of all the details pertaining to respirator selection, proper protection will not be provided if the respirator facepiece does not fit the wearer properly. One make and model of respirator should not be expected to fit the entire work force. Because of the great variety in face sizes and shapes encountered in male and female workers, most respirator manufacturers make their models of respirators available in more than one size or make several models of the same respirator type. In addition, the size and shape of each facepiece varies among the different manufacturers. In other words, the medium-size half facepiece of one manufacturer is not the same shape and size as the medium-size half facepiece from another manufacturer. For these reasons, it may be necessary to buy several commercially available respirators to conduct a good respirator fit-testing program. The exact number of respirators to meet this requirement will vary. For a small number of respirator wearers (for example, four) one manufacturers' style and size may suffice. On the other hand, for a larger employer with hundreds of respirator wearers, several manufacturers' respirators in various sizes may be necessary.

All tight-fitting (half- and full-facepiece) respirators, whether negative or positive pressure, must be fit tested. This includes filtering facepiece respirators. This can be achieved by one of two fitting methods: qualitative or quantitative fit testing. In either case, test agents or chemicals are used to detect leaks in the respirator facepiece-to-face seal. Fit testing should be conducted on all tight-fitting respirator wearers at least once every 12 months. The fit test must be repeated when a worker has a new condition that may affect the fit, such as a significant change in weight (plus or minus 10 percent or more), significant scarring in the face seal area, dental changes, or reconstructive or cosmetic surgery.

The fit-test conductor should be able to set up the test equipment, prepare any solutions, and maintain the test respirators. This individual should be familiar with the physical characteristics that may interfere with a face seal (such as beards) and should be able to recognize improper respirator

| TABLE 22–H | Effect of Wear Time on Effective Protection Factor |

Assigned Protection Factor	Effective Protection Factor Percent time worn			
	80%	90%	95%	100%
10 e.g., half face APR[1]	3.6	5.3	6.9	10
25 e.g., PAPR w/LFF[2]	4.3	7.4	11.4	25
50 e.g., PAPR w/HF[3]	4.6	8.5	14.5	50
100 e.g., full face APR	4.8	9.2	16.8	100
1000 e.g., air-line, PD, FF[4]	4.98	9.9	19.6	1000
10,000 e.g., SCBA, PD[5]	4.99	9.99	19.9	10,000

[1] APR – air-purifying respirator
[2] PAPR w/LFF – powered air-purifying respirator with loose fitting facepiece
[3] PAPR w/HF – powered air-purifying respirator with half facepiece
[4] Air-line, PD, FF – pressure demand air-line respirator with full facepiece
[5] SCBA, PD – pressure-demand self-contained breathing apparatus

donning and performance of the user seal checks. The test conductor must also be able to perform the fit test and recognize a good test from an improper fit test. In addition, for quantitative fit testing, the fit tester should be able to perform preventive maintenance on the test equipment, check the system for leaks, and calibrate the equipment or perform the required daily checks and tests for the equipment.

Qualitative Fit Testing

A qualitative fit test relies on the wearer's subjective response. The test agent is a substance that typically can be detected by the wearer, such as isoamyl acetate (banana oil), saccharin, Bitrex™, or irritant smoke. The respirator must be equipped to remove the test agent (Figure 22–32). For example, if using isoamyl acetate, which is an organic chemical that gives off a vapor, an organic-vapor chemical

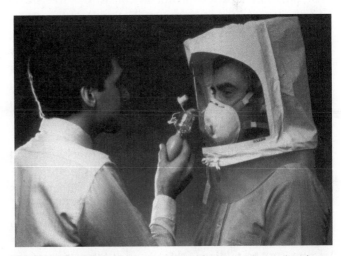

Figure 22–32. The saccharin qualitative fit test can be used with any particulate or gas/vapor respirator equipped with any particulate filter to determine adequacy of fit. *(Photo courtesy of 3M.)*

cartridge must be used. With a respirator in good repair, if the wearer smells isoamyl acetate, the respirator does not fit well. These tests are relatively fast, easily performed, and use inexpensive equipment. Because these tests are based on the respirator wearer's subjective response to a test chemical, it is important that the purpose and importance of this test be thoroughly explained to the worker.

Four qualitative tests are commonly used. Detailed protocols are available in the OSHA Respiratory Protection Standard that must be followed when conducting fit testing. These tests have been shown to identify poor fitting respirators by studies conducted in the laboratory. Three tests have had sufficient testing to be considered validated. An important point for validation is to be able to generate reliably low concentrations of the test agent to test the workers' ability to identify low levels of the test agent inside the respirator. The validated fit-test methods have been designed to assess fit factors of 100 (≤ 1 percent face seal leakage). When qualitative fit tests are used to fit-test negative-pressure respirators, the respirators can be used only in atmospheres up to ten times the occupational exposure limit (OEL). This means that if a full-facepiece negative-pressure respirator is fit tested qualitatively, it can be used only up to ten times the OEL. To use a negative-pressure full-facepiece respirator in concentrations up to its APF (i.e., 50), quantitative fit testing must be performed. The test protocols that have been validated are the isoamyl acetate vapor test and the saccharin and Bitrex mist test. These tests have further been shown to be effective through WPF studies. Where these protocols have been used for fit testing, the results show the workers received adequate protection as indicated by the in-facepiece sampling results.

Qualitative Fit-Test Protocols

The qualitative fit-test protocols consist of three steps: threshold screening, respirator selection, and fit testing. The threshold screening step is performed without wearing a respirator to determine if the subject can detect low levels of the test agent. This level would be similar to the amount inside the respirator if the facepiece-to-face seal had a small leak. During this test, the test subject also learns what to expect if the respirator is leaking.

The purpose of the respirator selection step is to find one that provides the most comfortable fit. Every make and model respirator has a different size and shape. If the respirator is correctly chosen and properly worn and fit as indicated by a fit test, it should provide adequate protection. The respirators used in this step must be equipped with the filter or cartridge appropriate for the test agent. This is necessary to minimize the effects of filter or cartridge penetration so that only facepiece-to-face seal is evaluated. Respirators fit tested using isoamyl acetate must be equipped

with organic vapor cartridges or canisters. Any respirator with a particulate filter can be fit tested with saccharin and Bitrex mist. The saccharin and Bitrex solution aerosol protocols are the only fit-test protocols currently available that are validated and can be used with disposable particulate respirators (filtering facepiece respirators) not equipped with class 100 filters. Respirators must be equipped with class 100 filters to be tested with irritant smoke.

The fit test consists of the test subject's wearing the respirator while exposed to the test agent and performing facial movements (exercises) to test the facepiece-to-face seal. The qualitative fit-test protocols are in Appendix A of 29 CFR 1910.134.

Isoamyl Acetate Protocol

This protocol uses an organic vapor as the test agent, therefore respirators equipped with organic vapor cartridges or canisters must be used. This minimizes the effects of cartridge penetration so only the facepiece-to-face seal is evaluated.

Saccharin and Bitrex Solution Aerosol Protocol

These protocols use a test agent in the form of a fine mist. Therefore, the respirator must be equipped with particulate filters so only face seal leakage is evaluated. Each respirator must be equipped with a particulate filter, that is, N-, R-, or P-95–100 particulate filter. NIOSH has previously recommended against the saccharin fit test because of its classification as a potential carcinogen. However, NIOSH recently re-examined the potential risk to workers that would be posed by saccharin used in fit testing. Finding that the risk to workers from use of saccharin in respirator fit testing is extremely small and may be zero, and in accordance with the new REL (Recommended Exposure Limit) policy, NIOSH recommends both saccharin and Bitrex for use in qualitative respirator fit testing, consistent with OSHA's respiratory protection standard (29 CFR 1910.134).

Irritant Fume Protocol

This protocol uses a particle produced by condensation. This process produces very small particles. Therefore, the respirator must be equipped with a class 100 or HEPA filter so only face-seal leakage is evaluated. It is important to note that there is no threshold screening test as the threshold levels for irritant smoke have not been established. For this reason, respiratory protection experts do not consider the irritant fume protocol as a validated fit-test method. NIOSH reviewed the revised protocol for the irritant smoke test in OSHA's final respiratory protection standard and concluded that a risk exists for overexposure to hydrogen chloride during a facepiece fit test. To check the test subject's sensitivity, they are required to breathe irritant smoke both before and after a successful fit test. Generated concentrations to which test subjects are subjected are not measured in the test protocol. A concentration of 5 ppm is the accepted threshold level at which a response is evoked from most persons. A fit test is a failure when a test subject experiences an involuntary cough or irritation. Retesting requires repeating the sensitivity check. In each case, the responses of coughing and irritation are the adverse health effects for which hydrogen chloride's exposure limits are intended to protect against. Consequently, NIOSH does not recommend the use of irritant smoke as a fit-testing agent. It is acceptable for OSHA compliance, however.

Quantitative Fit Testing

A quantitative fit test measures actual leakage of a test gas, vapor, or aerosol into the facepiece. Instrumentation is used to sample and measure the test atmosphere and the air inside the respirator facepiece. With this information, a quantitative fit factor (or fit factor) is calculated. The fit factor is the ratio of the outside concentration to the concentration inside the respirator facepiece. The advantage of this type of testing is that it does not rely on a subjective response. The disadvantages are cost of instrumentation, need for highly trained personnel to conduct the test, and use of probed respirators (Figures 22–33, 22–34) to sample air from inside the respirator.

Commercially available quantitative fit-testing equipment uses sodium chloride or corn oil mist generating systems (Figure 22–35). These devices use test enclosures to contain the test agent. Another system that measures the penetration of ambient aerosols into the facepiece is very portable (Figure 22–36). No test enclosure is required in this system. Fit testing with either of these systems must use respirators equipped with class 100 filters. Class 100 filters are used to minimize particle penetration through the filters and allow facepiece fit evaluations. Some of these instruments can be fitted with an adapter to allow quantitative fit testing of class 95 respirators.

A third method of quantitative fit testing does not involve aerosol measurement, but rather determines leakage by creating a negative pressure inside the facepiece and measuring the leakage rate of air. This technique is sometimes referred to as the controlled negative-pressure method (Figure 22–37). The respirator does not need a probe, but test adapter manifolds are placed on the respirator in place of filters or cartridges. Only respirators that can be adapted with the manifolds can be tested by this method. These manifolds are specific for the brand of respirator. The manifolds seal the respirator inlets so air cannot enter the respirator. One manifold contains a valve, which allows air to enter the respirator so the subject can breathe. The valve can be closed by squeezing a bulb hooked to this manifold. The sec-

Figure 22–33. A probed respirator is used for qualitative fit testing to measure aerosol inside the facepiece. *(Photo courtesy of 3M.)*

Figure 22–34. A quantitative fit-test adapter that can be placed on the respirator for fit testing and then removed when finished is shown. *(Photo courtesy of 3M.)*

ond manifold contains ports so air can be pumped from the respirator, creating a negative pressure inside the facepiece.

To perform a test, the test subject puts on the properly equipped respirator, takes a deep breath, and holds it. The person conducting the test squeezes the bulb to "seal off"

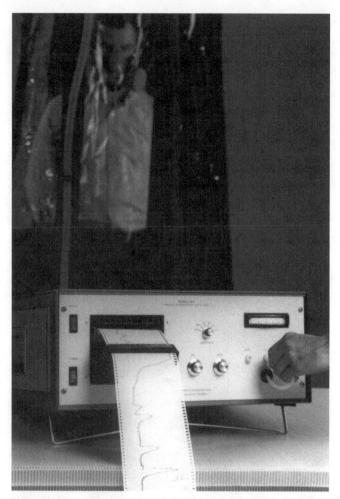

Figure 22–35. A portable corn oil quantitative fit-test system utilizes a test enclosure. *(Photo courtesy of Air Techniques, Inc.)*

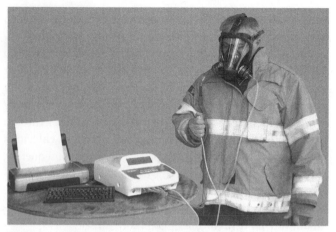

Figure 22–37. This quantitative fit-test equipment determines leakage by creating a negative pressure inside the facepiece similar to normal inspiratory pressures and measuring the leakage rate of air. *(Photo courtesy of Occupational Health Dynamics.)*

the respirator. The only way air can enter the respirator then is through face seal leaks. The instrument, which contains a pump to pull air out of the facepiece, is then started. Air is drawn out of the respirator until a predetermined "challenge pressure" is reached. This negative pressure created inside the facepiece causes air to leak into the facepiece from around the seal. The pump speed is then controlled to maintain the challenge pressure. The amount of air pumped out of the respirator is equal to the air that leaks into the facepiece, thus the leak rate is measured. An equivalent fit factor is then calculated by the instrument comparing the airflow needed to maintain the negative pressure and the leak rate. A single measurement takes about 12 seconds. The OSHA protocol provides instructions on how to perform facial exercises while testing.

Quantitative Fit-Test Protocol

The OSHA standard provides protocols for three methods of quantitative fit testing: generated aerosol, ambient aerosol condensation nuclei counting, and controlled negative-pressure fit testing. These three commercially available methods are schematically represented in Figure 22–38. This figure points out the major differences and similarities of the three quantitative fit-test methods.

If the TSI Portacount® Respirator Fit Tester is used, the worker should not be allowed to smoke within 30 minutes of the fit test. This can result in low fit factors since this instrument counts particles in the air. It is also important that all connections to tubing be tight. The respirator probe must not leak around the outside. These situations can result in low fit factors that do not reflect face seal leakage.

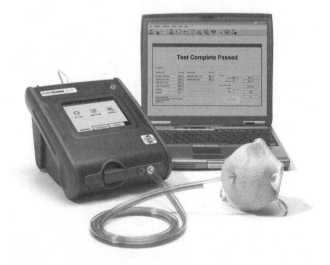

Figure 22–36. The ambient aerosol quantitative fit-test system does not use a test enclosure and must be used with respirators equipped with high-efficiency filters. *(Photo courtesy of TSI.)*

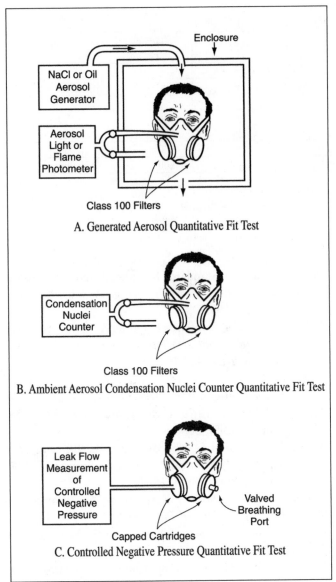

Enclosure

NaCl or Oil Aerosol Generator

Aerosol Light or Flame Photometer

Class 100 Filters

A. Generated Aerosol Quantitative Fit Test

Condensation Nuclei Counter

Class 100 Filters

B. Ambient Aerosol Condensation Nuclei Counter Quantitative Fit Test

Leak Flow Measurement of Controlled Negative Pressure

Valved Breathing Port

Capped Cartridges

C. Controlled Negative Pressure Quantitative Fit Test

Figure 22–38. Schematic representation of commercially available quantitative fit tests. *(Adapted from Han DH, et al. AIHA Journal 58:219-228, 1997.)*

Positive-Pressure Respirators

Tight-fitting positive-pressure respirators must be either qualitatively or quantitatively fit tested in the negative-pressure mode. Qualitative fit testing of these respirators is accomplished by temporarily converting the respirator user's actual facepiece into a negative-pressure respirator with the appropriate filters, or by using an identical negative-pressure air-purifying respirator facepiece with the same sealing surfaces as a surrogate for the atmosphere-supplying or powered air-purifying respirator facepiece. This can be done on tight-fitting powered air-purifying respirators by turning the blower off as long

as the proper air-purifying element is on the respirator. Air-line respirators and SCBAs can be tested by obtaining the air-purifying model with the same facepiece design and size used on the air-line respirator or SCBA. For some manufacturers, only filter or cartridge adapters need to be purchased that attach to the air-line respirator or SCBA facepiece. Combination air-line/air-purifying respirators can be fit tested in the negative-pressure mode by disconnecting from the air supply and placing the proper filter or cartridge on the facepiece. This may require obtaining adaptors from the respirator manufacturer in order to attach the cartridges or filters. Quantitative fit testing of these respirators is done by modifying the converted or surrogate facepiece to allow sampling inside the facepiece in the breathing zone of the user, midway between the nose and mouth. This can be accomplished by installing a permanent sampling probe onto a surrogate facepiece (Figure 22–33), or by using a sampling adapter designed to temporarily provide a means of sampling air from inside the facepiece (Figure 22–34).

Any modifications to the respirator facepiece for fit testing must be completely removed, and the facepiece restored to the NIOSH-approved configuration, before that facepiece is used in the workplace.

The purpose for fit testing the facepiece of a positive-pressure respirator is to eliminate "gross" face seal leakage that might degrade protection or shorten service life for SCBA. Either qualitative or quantitative fit testing may be used for all positive-pressure, tight-fitting atmosphere-supplying respirators and tight-fitting PAPRs. While these respirators are used as positive-pressure respirators in the workplace, they are fit tested in the negative-pressure mode. As a consequence, the minimum acceptable fit factor for a facepiece in the negative-pressure mode is lower than the APF, which is based on use in the positive-pressure mode. Positive-pressure respirators that pass the qualitative fit test or quantitative fit test may be used up to the APFs of these respirators. Only the fitting capability of the facepiece is being evaluated, not the performance of the respirator. Successful completion of the qualitative fit test indicates the respirator fit is acceptable for the positive-pressure respirator. When quantitative fit testing is used, all respirators with a full facepiece must meet or exceed a fit factor of 500, while half-mask respirators must meet or exceed 100. During qualitative fit testing a fit factor is not determined. If the qualitative fit test is passed, the fit is acceptable and the APF can be used. The assigned protection factors from Table 22–G can be issued after successful fit-testing of the respirator. Table 22–I summarizes the fit testing requirements and APFs for tight-fitting positive-pressure respirators.

TABLE 22–I	Acceptable Fit-Testing Methods for Positive Pressure Tight-Fitting Respirators				
Respirator Type	QLFT[1]	QNFT[2]	Minimum Fit Factor	APF[3]
PAPR Half Facepiece	Yes	Yes	100	50
PAPR Full Facepiece	Yes	Yes	500	1000
Air Line Respirators, continuous flow or pressure demand mode				
• Half Facepiece	Yes	Yes	100	50
• Full Facepiece	Yes	Yes	500	1000
SCBA—Full Facepiece, Positive Pressure	Yes	Yes	500	10,000
SCBA/Air Line—Full Facepiece, Positive Pressure	Yes	Yes	500	10,000

[1]QLFT—qualitative fit test
[2]QNFT—quantitative fit test
[3]Assigned Protection Factor from *American National Standard for Respiratory Protection, ANSI Z88.2-1992.*

SUMMARY

The material presented in this chapter is intended for persons concerned with establishing and maintaining a respiratory protection program. It presents certain basic information for guidance purposes. However, it is not intended to be all-inclusive in content or scope.

Simplified interpretations of certain federal regulations pertaining to respiratory protection and monitoring were presented in this chapter. While these interpretations convey background information about the regulations, under no circumstances should they be used as the sole basis of a respiratory protection program. In all cases, the current federal regulations, as published in the Federal Register and later collected in the Code of Federal Regulations, should be carefully studied, and the rules and procedures in those regulations explicitly followed. Only they define the specific requirements that are in force. For additional information the reader should refer to the Bibliography.

BIBLIOGRAPHY

Ackley MW. Degradation of electrostatic filters at elevated temperature and humidity. In World Filtration Congress III. Croydon, England: Uplands Press, 1982. pp. 169-176.

American Conference of Governmental Industrial Hygienists. *2012 TLVs and BEIs, Threshold Limit Values for Chemical Substances and Physical Agents & Biological Exposure Indices.* Cincinnati, OH: ACGIH, 2012.

American Industrial Hygiene Association. *Odor Thresholds for Chemicals with Occupational Health Standards.* Fairfax, VA: AIHA, 1989.

American Industrial Hygiene Association. *Respiratory Protection: A Manual and Guideline,* 3rd ed. Fairfax, VA: AIHA, 2001.

American National Standards Institute. *American National Standard for Respiratory Protection, Z88.2, 1992.* New York: ANSI, 1992.

American National Standards Institute. *American National Standard for Respirator Fit Testing Methods, Z88.10, 2010.* New York: ANSI, 2010.

American National Standards Institute. *American National Standard for Respiratory Protection—Respirator Use—Physical Qualifications for Personnel, Z88.6-2006.* New York: ANSI, 2006.

American National Standards Institute. *Practices for Respiratory Protection for the Fire Service, Z88.5-1981.* New York: ANSI, 1981.

American Thoracic Society. Respiratory protection guidelines. *Am J Respir Crit Care* 154:1153–1165, 1996.

Assigned Protection Factors; Final Rule. 71 Fed. Reg.164 (Aug. 24, 2006) p. 50122.

Canadian Standards Association. *Compressed Breathing Air and Systems CAN/CSA Z180.1-00 (R2010).* Toronto, ON: Canadian Standards Association, 2010.

Code of Federal Regulations, Title 29, Parts 1900-1926. *Labor.* Washington, DC: GPO, 2011.

Code of Federal Regulations, Title 29, part 1910.134. *Respiratory Protection.* Washington, DC: GPO, 2005, pp. 419-444.

Code of Federal Regulations, Title 42, Part 84. *Approval of Respiratory Protective Devices.* Washington, DC: GPO, 2007, pp. 498-561.

Code of Federal Regulations, Title 42, Part 84. *Public Health.* Washington, DC: GPO, 2011.

Coffey CC, Campbell DL, Myers WR, et al. Comparison of six respirator fit-test methods with an actual measurement of exposure in a simulated health care environment: Part II–Method comparison testing. *Am Ind Hyg Assoc* 59:862-870, 1998.

Compressed Gas Association. *Commodity Specification for*

Air. G-7.1, 2011 Arlington, VA: CGA, 2011.

Compressed Gas Association. *Compressed Air for Human Respiration.* G-7, 2008. Arlington, VA: CGA, 2008.

Crutchfield CD, Eroh MP, Van Ert MD. A feasibility study of quantitative respirator fit testing by controlled negative pressure. *AIHA Journal* 52(4):172–176, 1991.

Ernstberger HG, Gall RB, Turok CW. Experiments supporting the use of ambient aerosols for quantitative respirator fit testing. *Am Ind Hyg Assoc J* 49:613-619, 1988.

Fardi B, Liu BYH. Performance of disposable respirators. *Particle & Particle Systems Characterization* 8:308–314, 1991.

Fiserova-Bergerova V. Relevance of occupational skin exposure. *Ann Occup Hyg* 37 (6):673–685, 1985.

Gardner PD, Hofacre KC, Richardson AW. Comparison of simulated respirator fit factors using aerosol and vapor challenges. *J Occup Environ Hyg* 1:29-38, 2004.

Hinds WC, Bellin P. Effect of facial-seal leaks on protection provided by half-mask respirators. *Appl Ind Hyg* 3(5):158–164, 1988.

International Standards Organization. Nanotechnologies—terminology and definitions for nano-objects—Nanoparticles, nanofibre and nanoplate. Geneva, Switzerland: ISO, 2009.

Japuntich DA. Respiratory particulate filtration. *Int Soc Respir Prot* 2:137–169, 1984.

Kim CS, et al. Filtration efficiency of a fibrous filter for nanoparticles. *Journal of Nanoparticle Research* 8(2):215-221, 2006.

Moyer ES. Review of influential factors affecting the performance of organic vapor air-purifying respirator cartridges. *Am Ind Hyg Assoc J* 44(1):46-51, 1983.

Laye R. Evaluation of a miniaturized condensation nucleus counter for measurement of respirator fit factor. *J Int Soc Respir Prot* 5(3):1-7, 1987.

National Fire Protection Association. *Self-Contained Breathing Apparatus for Fire Fighters,* NFPA, 1981. Quincy, MA: NFPA, 2007.

National Institute for Occupational Safety and Health. *A Guide to Industrial Respiratory Protection, No. 87-116.* Cincinnati, OH: NIOSH, 1987.

National Institute for Occupational Safety and Health.

Respirator Information Notice on Chemical Cartridge Respirators. Morgantown, WV: NIOSH, February 26, 1990.

National Institute for Occupational Safety and Health, U.S. Department of Health and Human Services. *NIOSH Pocket Guide to Chemical Hazards.* Washington, DC: NIOSH, 2010. http://www.cdc.gov/niosh/npg/

National Institute for Occupational Safety and Health. NIOSH Respirator Use Policy Workgroup, Aug 4, 1999. Cincinnati, OH: NIOSH, 1999.

National Institute for Occupational Safety and Health. *Respirator Selection Logic 2004, No. 2005-100.* Cincinnati, OH: NIOSH, 2004.

National Institute for Occupational Safety and Health. *Respirator User's Notice: Use of Replacement and Spare Parts.* Pittsburgh, PA: NIOSH, May 4, 2007.

National Institute for Occupational Safety and Health. *MultiVapor Version 2.2.3.* Washington, DC: NIOSH, 2011. http://www.cdc.gov/niosh/npptl/multivapor/multivapor.html

Nelson GE, Harder CA. Respirator cartridge efficiency studies: V. Effect of solvent vapor. *AIHA Journal* 35:391–410, 1974.

Rengasamy S, Eimer BC, Shaffer RE: Comparison of nanoparticle filtration performance of NIOSH-approved and CE-marked particulate filtering facepiece respirators. *Ann Occup Hyg* 53:117-128, 2009.

Rose JC, Oestenstad RK, Rose VE. A comparison of respirator fit factors determined by portable condensation nuclei counting and forward light-scattering photometric methods. *Appl Occup Environ Hyg* 5:792-797, 1990.

Shaffer RE, Rengasamy S. Respiratory protection against airborne nanoparticles: A review. *J Nanopart Res*11:1661-1672, 2009.

Stevens GA, Moyer ES. "Worst case" aerosol testing parameters: I. Sodium chloride and dioctylphthalate aerosol filter efficiency as a function of particle size and flow rate. *AIHA Journal* 50:257–264, 1989.

Weber RA, Mullins HE. Measuring performance of a half-mask respirator in a styrene environment. *AIHA Journal* 61:415-421, 2000.

CHAPTER 23

Personal Protective Equipment

by Bruce Millies, MS, JD

T*he word* personal *in personal protective equipment refers to the fact that articles such as safety glasses, safety boots, hard hats, and chemical-protective clothing are worn on the body by a person and are a form of protection against hazards that have not been removed or sufficiently controlled by some other method. The hazards for which personal protective equipment (PPE) is available—and that are discussed in this chapter—include mechanical agents such as impact, compression, puncture, laceration, and abrasion; physical agents such as heat and optical radiations (infrared [IR], visible, ultraviolet [UV])); radioactive contamination; chemical exposure and contamination; and biological agents (Figure 23–1). This chapter does not cover personal protective equipment for hearing protection (see Chapter 9, Industrial Noise), respiratory protection (see Chapter 22, Respiratory Protection), flotation, or fall protection.*

Because this book covers the basics of industrial hygiene, this chapter generally provides greater emphasis on health topics such as protection from contact with chemicals or exposure to ultraviolet light, as opposed to safety issues such as protection from falling objects. However, the line between health and safety is not always distinct; the industrial hygienist may have safety-related duties, and most importantly, the hygienist must not ignore safety hazards that she or he encounters. Also, many items of PPE are used for protection against both health and safety hazards (for example, a welder's helmet.) Therefore safety PPE cannot be excluded from this discussion.

Personal protective equipment must be selected based upon an analysis of the hazards. Workers and supervisors must understand why PPE is necessary, and know how to use it properly. Personal protective equipment must be inspected and maintained—and replaced when it is worn out or defective. Proper selection, training, use, and maintenance of PPE are best accomplished when the employer has a PPE program.

There are consensus standards and test methods for PPE, which determine its effectiveness and its limitations. OSHA legal standards require hazard analysis, selection of appropriate PPE, and employee training. OSHA standards require that the employer provide and pay for PPE (with certain exceptions). Even in the case of employee-provided PPE, the employer is still responsible for ensuring that it is correctly used and maintained.

Engineering methods are usually the most effective controls for workplace hazards. However, personal protective equipment will often be a necessary supplement to engineering methods. All personal protective equipment must be used according to the manufacturer's specifications and instructions. Modification of PPE by the user is prohibited.

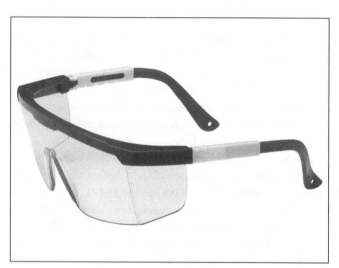

Figure 23–1a.

Figure 23–1b.

THE HIERARCHY OF CONTROLS

A basic concept of industrial hygiene is the *hierarchy of controls*. This concept ranks control measures in the order of their effectiveness and stresses the elimination of the hazard, or the implementation of engineering methods, as preferable to the use of personal protective equipment. PPE is at the bottom of the list of control measures. The concept of a hierarchy of controls is most obviously applicable to respiratory protection, where the goal is usually to minimize the average exposure over the workday. Engineering controls such as local exhaust ventilation are more efficient than relying on each worker to correctly use a respirator. Effective engineering controls can eliminate the need for respirators.

Other types of personal protective equipment—safety glasses, safety boots, hard hats, cut-resistant gloves, and electrical-protective equipment—are worn to protect against sudden events such as impact from flying or falling objects, or electric shock. These are hazards for which a reduction in the average occurrence does not result in sufficient worker protection. For example, proper machine guarding (an engineering control) of a grinding wheel includes a shield to reduce or redirect the flow of particles and sparks. However, a worker must still wear impact-resistant safety glasses and/or a face shield when using this machine. The goal is not merely a reduction in the average number of particles reaching the eyes, but rather the complete prevention of eye impact. As a second example, a properly fitted toeboard can prevent tools or other objects from rolling

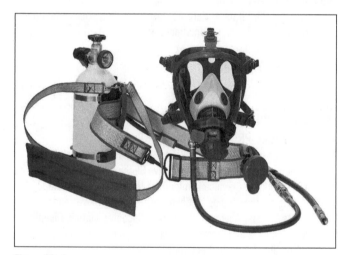

Figure 23–1c.

Figure 23–1. Some examples of the many types of personal protective equipment available. *(Safety glasses photo courtesy of Protective Industrial Products; earmuffs photo courtesy of Howard Leight/ Sperian Hearing Protection, LLC; and respirator photo is courtesy of Honeywell Safety Products/Sperian Respiratory Protection, USA.)*

off a scaffold. Workers below the scaffold must still wear hard hats because there are other ways that objects might drop from above.

Engineering controls are subject to temporary failure or decreased efficiency. A ventilation system might accidentally be turned off, a drive belt might break, or the filter might become overloaded. Assuming that the system is promptly returned to service, the result is an increase in average exposure, which might still be below the permissible exposure limit (PEL). However, in the case of flying or falling objects, or electrical shock, a failure of engineering controls could result in an immediate injury to the worker.

Engineering methods are necessary and important. They are the first line of worker protection; they are at the top of the hierarchy of controls. However, to protect workers from flying objects, cuts, electric shock, and many other hazards that can immediately cause injury, personal protective equipment must often be used in addition to engineering controls.

ROUTES OF ENTRY

Identification of the routes of entry is an industrial hygiene concept that is useful in determining what type of personal protective equipment is necessary. For example, if dermal exposure to solvents is possible during a parts-cleaning task, then chemical-protective gloves can be worn to prevent or limit exposure by that route. This concept is also useful when addressing other, nonchemical hazards. We should consider all parts of the worker's body that a harmful agent can reach, in order to determine whether PPE is necessary and appropriate. For example, if an arc welder wears leather gloves and an appropriately shaded welding mask, the welder's hands, eyes, and face are protected from exposure to ultraviolet radiation. But the employer should also prevent exposure to other exposed skin areas by requiring a long-sleeve shirt or providing gauntlets.

PERSONAL PROTECTIVE EQUIPMENT PROGRAM

If the hazards in the workplace necessitate the use of personal protective equipment, then the employer must ensure that employees have the appropriate PPE for each job task, and that they use the PPE correctly. Employers can best meet their PPE responsibilities by establishing a PPE program through which they can accomplish the following:

- assess the hazards of each task to determine whether PPE is necessary
- select PPE that provides the necessary protection, but

does not unduly interfere with the job task, or create additional hazards
- specify the required PPE in written standard operating procedures that include change-out schedules, if necessary
- ensure that each item of PPE fits the individual who will wear it
- train all employees in the correct use of the PPE that they are required to wear
- ensure that each item of PPE is properly maintained
- pay for most types of PPE
- ensure the adequacy, maintenance, and sanitation of any employee-owned PPE
- establish policies for the voluntary use of PPE
- maintain records related to PPE acquisition, use, and training
- regularly evaluate the PPE program

Each of these items is discussed below. They are not, however, completely separate steps. The implementation of each item must take into account how it affects and is affected by other parts of the PPE program. For example, the hazard assessment must consider how workers actually perform a task, which may be different from the standard operating procedure. The assessment process might lead to a consideration of changes in standard operating procedures, or changes in the training that workers receive. It is beneficial to involve both supervisory and production employees in the creation, evaluation, and updating of the personal protective equipment program. This will help to ensure that the program is workable and relevant to the specific conditions and job tasks for which PPE is required.

The complexity of the program will vary with the size of the organization and the types of hazards. The PPE program should be in writing and will usually be part of the employer's overall safety and health program. OSHA standards do not *explicitly* require a PPE program for protective equipment other than respirators, but the standards do require several of the elements listed above, including hazard assessment, selection of appropriate PPE, and worker training. Establishing a well-thought-out, comprehensive PPE program is the best way to ensure that employees have the PPE they need, and to comply with OSHA standards.

Hazard Assessment
In order to reliably select the appropriate PPE for a job, one must have a comprehensive understanding of the task, how the hazards of that task can affect each worker doing the task, and how the hazards might affect other workers not directly involved in the task (Figure 23–2). A hazard assessment (also called hazard analysis or job task analysis) will include these steps:

- Identify each step of the job task.

- Identify and quantify the hazard(s) that might be created during each step.
- Determine how each hazard might affect the worker doing the task.
- Determine whether each hazard might also affect other workers.
- Determine whether it is feasible to apply engineering controls to control the hazard.
- Determine whether PPE is necessary (either because engineering controls are not feasible, or because in addition to engineering controls, PPE is still necessary to ensure sufficient protection).

It is important to remember that the hazards of a job relate to how the worker actually does the job, not to how it is *supposed* to be done. Ideally, these are the same thing, but in practice they often are not. If workers are unable, or unwilling, to do the task according to the standard operating procedure, this may indicate that the procedure needs to be revised, or that worker training needs to be augmented.

Selection of Appropriate PPE

Based on a careful hazard assessment and an understanding of the available types of PPE and their uses and limitations,

Figure 23–2. A thorough hazard analysis is the basis for selecting appropriate personal protective equipment.

the employer must select PPE that (1) provides the required protection, (2) does not unduly restrict the worker's ability to do the job task, (3) does not create additional hazards—or if it does, control those hazards—and (4) is sufficiently comfortable that the worker will, in fact, use the PPE.

Whether a particular article of PPE provides the necessary protection depends on the nature and magnitude of the hazard, in relation to the manufacturer's specifications for that particular article. This is why in the hazard assessment it was necessary not only to identify but to quantify the hazards—either through direct measurement techniques or by relying on tabulated information. For example, the required shade strength of a welder's protective eyewear depends on the intensity of the optical radiation, which can be measured directly, or derived from tables based on the amperage of the welding arc or size of the flame. Selection procedures for particular types of PPE—for example, the use of manufacturer's breakthrough time and permeation rate charts for selecting chemical-protective gloves—are discussed in the specific PPE sections of this chapter.

In the selection process, it is important to ensure that the PPE does not unduly interfere with the worker's ability to do the job. The word *unduly* is used here to emphasize that PPE often creates some unavoidable interference with the job. For example, chemical-protective gloves affect the worker's dexterity and make it harder to handle small objects. From among the available gloves that provide adequate chemical protection, select the model that allows the greatest dexterity. If this is not sufficient, then the job task must be redesigned; the worker should not remove the gloves to perform the task.

Personal protective equipment can exacerbate hazards or create additional hazards. For example, chemical-protective suits limit the evaporation of sweat, which can increase the risk of heat stress. The job must be planned to allow sufficient rest periods and adequate hydration. It may be possible to do the job during a cooler part of the day, move the job away from heat sources, or provide shade or air-conditioning. Removing, opening, or tearing protective clothing is not an acceptable response.

Human beings will naturally want to remove items that are painful, cause itching, restrict vision or hearing, cause feelings of claustrophobia, require additional exertion, or are otherwise uncomfortable. Worker comfort must be considered in the selection of PPE, even if this results in providing a more expensive model. Again, it might be necessary to redesign the job so that PPE is not required, or so that a more comfortable type of PPE can be used. Training also must ensure that workers understand the hazards and why the PPE provides necessary protection.

Standard Operating Procedures

Written standard operating procedures help to ensure that workers and supervisors perform a job task in the safest possible manner consistent with the hazards identified by the hazard analysis. The written procedure should specify not only how to do the task, but what, if any, personal protective equipment is required, and when during the task it must be worn. The information must be specific, stating, for example, which specific type of chemical-protective glove or which shade of protective lens must be used. The procedure must include a change-out schedule if applicable; for example, it must specify when to replace chemical-protective gloves so that the breakthrough time is not exceeded.

Proper Fit

Personal protective equipment that is too big or too small for the user can be uncomfortable, ineffective, and even hazardous. Pant legs on a chemical-protective suit that are too long pose a tripping hazard. It is not acceptable to attempt to tailor protective clothing with scissors and/or duct tape. Workers will discard gloves that are too small, because they are uncomfortable and restrict movement of the fingers. On the other hand, a glove that is too large may fall off, may unnecessarily reduce dexterity, or may allow the intrusion of solid or liquid materials. Supervisors responsible for safety and health must communicate with the purchasing department to ensure the procurement of models and sizes of protective equipment that fit each individual worker who will use the equipment.

Some personal protective equipment is adjustable. For example, hard hats have an adjustable suspension. Training must ensure that workers know how to operate the adjustment mechanism, and how to tell that the equipment is properly adjusted.

Training

Personal protective equipment only works if the person using it knows when to wear it and how to wear it and understands its limitations. This requires training, even for something as seemingly simple as a hard hat (Figure 23–3). The employee must be able to recognize the hazards that require personal protective equipment, and understand the protection that the equipment provides and the limitations of wearing the equipment. Employees must be familiar with the standard operating procedures that specify the required protective equipment for a particular task. They must be able to inspect the equipment and recognize damage, don (put on) and adjust the equipment, wear it correctly, and doff (take off) the equipment. They must also recognize when the equipment is not functioning properly and know when to replace it in accor-

Figure 23–3. Worker training in the proper use of personal protective equipment. *(Courtesy of J. J. Keller. Copyrighted photo used with permission.)*

dance with an applicable change-out schedule.

Training in the proper use of personal protective equipment must include both knowledge components and hands-on practice. There must be a performance evaluation to ensure that each individual demonstrates the proper use of the equipment. OSHA requires that the training, including the employee's demonstration of proper use, be completed before the employee does the work for which the PPE is required. OSHA requires retraining if there are changes in the workplace that make the prior training obsolete, changes in the type of PPE used, or indications that the worker does not understand how to use the PPE correctly. The employer must maintain records certifying that each individual worker has been properly trained. The standards do not contain a periodic refresher training requirement for PPE other than respirators, nor for workers in general. However, periodic (generally annual) refresher training is a good idea because workers may use several types of PPE, might not use them every day, and, even with regular use, might become lax with regard to proper inspection and use of the PPE.

Maintenance, Inspection, Washing, Storage, and Shelf Life

Nondisposable personal protective equipment must be regularly inspected for wear and damage, and kept clean and sanitary. It may need to be decontaminated, and it must be stored safely in a clean cabinet, locker, or storeroom when not in use. The individual user may be assigned these tasks, but it remains the management's responsibility to see that they are carried out. Especially in a larger establishment, it is often more practical to have designated employees responsible for the inspection, cleaning, maintenance, and storage of all PPE. Employing single-use, disposable protective equipment can reduce the burden of cleaning, sanitizing, and maintaining some types of protective equipment. In addition to periodic inspection, each individual user should always perform a user check of PPE before donning. This applies to all PPE, including brand-new multiuse and single-use items, PPE that has been reissued after periodic inspection and maintenance, and PPE that the user maintains. Each user must also be able to recognize damage or deficiencies as they occur.

Personal protective equipment should be stored in a clean, dry environment. Avoid exposure to sunlight or other sources of ultraviolet light during storage. Some manufacturers specify a shelf life or useful life for some models of PPE. Even if the shelf life is not specified, it is a good practice to rotate stock as new items are acquired. Personal protective equipment that has been taken out of service, whether single-use or multiuse, must be disposed of properly, recognizing that chemically contaminated items might be hazardous waste. It is a good idea to render the equipment unusable (for example, by cutting), if this can be done safely, to prevent possible inappropriate reuse.

Paying for PPE

OSHA standards require the employer to pay for most personal protective equipment, except for certain items. These are the types of PPE the employer can require the employee to pay for, even if the PPE is necessary to do the job safely in compliance with safety standards:

- nonspecialty safety-toe footwear—that is, safety shoes or boots that have standard-compliant steel or composite toe protection, but do not have any additional protective features. If the footwear also provides chemical, electrical, puncture, or metatarsal protection (but see the next item), then the employer pays.
- boots or shoes with metatarsal protection built in, in cases where the employer provides strap-on metatarsal guards, but the employee wants to wear boots or shoes with the metatarsal protection built in
- logging boots, including spiked-sole "corks" or "caulks," chain-saw-cut-resistant boots, and nonspecialty water-resistant or waterproof ankle-supporting logging boots

- everyday clothing such as shirts, pants, and regular shoes
- ordinary weather-protective clothing or equipment such as waterproof or water-resistant boots, raincoats, parkas, jackets, sunglasses, and sunscreen. However, if any of these items has additional required safety features, such as high visibility, retroreflection, or flotation, then the employer must pay for it. Some states have laws that require employers to pay for uniforms. However, this is not a safety and health issue, and is not addressed by OSHA standards.
- replacement PPE after an employee has lost or intentionally damaged an item paid for by the employer

Although not required, it may be in the employer's interest to pay for the excepted items listed above. Employer payment may make it easier to ensure that employees have appropriate PPE that provides adequate protection. Employer payment might also be required by a collective bargaining agreement.

Employee-Owned PPE

OSHA makes the employer responsible for ensuring proper use and maintenance of all personal protective equipment, including employee-owned PPE. To fulfill this responsibility, the employer must monitor the use of employee-provided protective equipment, inspect it regularly, and prohibit the use of PPE that is defective or unsanitary. If the protective equipment is withdrawn from use, then the employee must not continue the task until the proper PPE is available.

Voluntary Use of PPE

There may be situations in which a worker chooses to use personal protective equipment that is not necessary based on the hazard assessment and the standard operating procedures. The employee may have a particular concern or belief, or may simply feel more comfortable using the PPE. Even in this voluntary situation, the employer remains responsible for ensuring that the protective equipment is used correctly, is sanitary, and its use does not create additional hazards.

Record Keeping

OSHA requires employers to certify in writing that employees have received training in the use of required personal protective equipment. Except for this requirement regarding training, there is no general OSHA requirement for PPE record keeping. Several standards for specific chemicals do require records of PPE use by employees exposed to that specific chemical. Some OSHA standards (for example, process safety management) require the employer to develop standard operating procedures that include any required PPE. The OSHA standard on access to employee exposure records requires retention of these records, which, in accord with industrial hygiene practice, would indicate the PPE used by the employee at the time of the sampling, monitoring, or other exposure assessment. OSHA Form 301, Injury and Illness Incident Report, asks for "the tools, equipment or materials the employee was using" just before the incident. This includes personal protective equipment.

Whether or not OSHA standards require employers to keep records related to personal protective equipment, there are legal and practical reasons to do so. Records of PPE selection, acquisition, use, and training serve to document compliance with the standards and with best industry practices. These records may be important in responding to OSHA enforcement actions, workers' compensation claims, and other civil or criminal liability proceedings. Standard operating procedures, whether or not required by OSHA, must specify any required PPE. Records related to PPE can assist the employer in evaluating and updating its safety and health program. Records of PPE acquisition and use will assist the employer in determining which types and models of PPE to order in the future.

Program Evaluation

The personal protective equipment program should be periodically evaluated, at least annually. The program should be revised as necessary, taking into account accident and incident history, supervisor and user experience, changes in the workplace environment, changes in work tasks, new processes and procedures, and the availability of new models of PPE. A review of illness and injury reports will show whether PPE use or nonuse was a factor, and whether the incident suggests the need for additional or different PPE, additional training, or changes to standard operating procedures. Program evaluation is an ideal subject for involvement of the safety and health committee. Whether or not there is a committee, worker input should be sought.

Matters to address in the evaluation include the following: Is the PPE specified in standard operating procedures appropriate—does it provide the necessary protection without interfering with the job? Do employees use PPE correctly, in accord with standard operating procedures? Are there employee suggestions or complaints about PPE? Are all aspects of the PPE program, as described above, functioning properly?

OSHA STANDARDS FOR PERSONAL PROTECTIVE EQUIPMENT

Each of OSHA's principal industry standards (general industry, construction, shipyards, marine terminals, and longshoring) contains a subpart on personal protective equipment that has various sections on head protection, eye and face

protection, and so on. The respiratory protection section is the same for all industries, but the other PPE sections are not identical. The PPE subparts in the various industry standards do not contradict each other, but some contain more specific requirements than others. For example, the general industry PPE standard requires worker training about PPE, while the construction PPE standard does not specifically mention training. However, a general section in the construction industry standard does require the employer to "instruct each employee in the recognition and avoidance of unsafe conditions," which would include the proper use of necessary PPE. Several specific standards (for example, process safety management and asbestos) have provisions related to PPE. The Occupational Safety and Health Act requires, and good practice mandates, that the employer provide a safe and healthy workplace, which would include providing all necessary PPE and ensuring that workers use it correctly.

EYE AND FACE PROTECTION

There are several hazards to the eyes and face for which personal protective equipment is available. These hazards include impact by flying objects; contact with splashed liquids, molten metals, dust, and other air contaminants; and exposure to optical radiations (infrared, visible, and ultraviolet). Personal protective equipment includes various types of glasses, goggles, and face shields designed to offer protection against one or more eye and face hazards. The visor or window of a full-face respirator, which can protect the eyes from contact with air contaminants, is not necessarily designed for protection against impact, optical radiations, or heat hazards.

The OSHA general industry standard (1910.133) requires employers to ensure (1) "that each affected employee uses appropriate eye or face protection"; (2) that protective eyewear "provide side protection if there is a hazard from flying objects"; (3) that an employee who needs prescription eyewear "wears eye protection that incorporates the prescription in its design, or wears eye protection that can be worn over the prescription lenses"; (4) that employees exposed to "injurious" optical radiation wear "filter lenses that have a shade number appropriate to the work performed"; and (5) that eye and face protective equipment be marked to identify the manufacturer. Not all of these requirements are specifically listed in each of the other OSHA industry standards (construction, shipyards, marine terminals, and longshoring,) but all of the standards reference one or more versions of the ANSI Z87.1, *American National Standard for Occupational and Educational Personal Eye and Face Protection Devices,* which contains these requirements.

The OSHA general industry and maritime standards require that protective eyewear comply with any of three recent versions of ANSI Z87.1 or be at least as effective as protective devices that comply with Z87.1. The OSHA construction industry standard continues to specify the 1968 version of Z87.1. OSHA has stated that in the future it will "update the national consensus standards referenced in its PPE standards as new editions become available."

The most recent version of Z87.1 is the 2010 edition. As of the printing of this book, OSHA has not yet incorporated the 2010 version into its standard. ANSI Z87.1-2010 contains specifications for protective eyewear designed to protect eyes and face against impact, chemicals, optical radiations, heat/hot materials, and dust.

Impact Resistance

Impact-resistant eyewear must be worn whenever there is the potential for flying objects in the workplace. Examples include chips and particles from grinding wheels, lathes, drills, routers, planers, sanders, and other powered equipment—and also from hand tools—used to cut or form metal, wood, plastic, stone, or other materials. Larger objects (nuts, bolts, screws, nails, small tools, etc.) can also be eye hazards if they are accidentally thrown by a moving or rotating machine, or as the result of hand tool use (e.g., pulling nails, using a cold chisel.)

ANSI Z87.1-2010 provides for two impact ratings: nonimpact rated and impact rated. Impact-resistant lenses are made of polycarbonate plastic. The frames of protective eyewear will be marked with the manufacturer's monogram and "Z87.1." For impact-rated eyewear, the marking will also include a + sign. Lenses are marked with the manufacturer's monogram, with a + for impact-rated lenses. Spectacles, goggles (both eye-cup and cover types), face shields, hood-style powered air-purifying respirators with face shield, and welding helmets are all available with impact-rated lenses. Impact-rated prescription lenses are available. There are also impact-rated over spectacles that can be worn over normal prescription glasses to provide front and lateral impact protection. Some full-face respirators are advertised as having impact-resistant lenses. However, they are only ANSI Z87.1-2010 impact rated if the lens is marked Z87.1+.

The OSHA general industry standard states that side protection from flying objects may be accomplished with detachable side shields. However, ANSI Z87.1-2010 requires integral lateral coverage that must be part of the design of impact rated + eyewear (Figure 23–4).

Category of Mark	Type of Protection	Mark	Notes
Non impact resistant	Plano lens, nonimpact	Z 87	
	Prescription lens, nonimpact	Z 87-2	
Impact resistant	Plano lens, impact rated	Z 87 +	
	Prescription lens, impact rated	Z87-2 +	
Type of lens	Clear lens	No additional mark	
	IR filter lens	R followed by the scale number	Scale rating from 1.3 through 10. R1.3: highest transmittance. R10: least transmittance.
	Special purpose	V	.
	Welding filter lens	W followed by the shade number	Shade rating from 1.3 through 14. W1.3: least shading. W14: darkest shade.
	UV filter lens	U followed by the scale number	Scale rating from 2 through 6. U2: lowest protection. U6: highest.
	Variable	S	
	Visible light and glare filter lens	L followed by the scale number	Scale rating from 1.3 through 10. L1.3: highest transmittance. L10: least transmittance.
Chemical protection	Slash and droplet protection	D3	
	Dust	D4	
	Fine dust	D5	

Figure 23–4. Markings for protective eyewear. This chart summarizes the marking requirements of ANSI Z87.1. Consult the ANSI standard for complete detailed specifications.

Dust and Chemicals

Spectacles that meet ANSI impact standards for front and lateral coverage do not seal against the face and thus are not protective against chemical splashes or droplets of chemical mists. For protection against chemicals, there are four options: chemical goggles (either eye cup or cover type), a chemical face shield worn over spectacles, a chemical face shield worn over goggles, or a full-face respirator. Chemical goggles seal against the face and have ventilators that are designed with an indirect air path to prevent the entry of splashes and droplets. These goggles are marked D3.

Both eye cup and cover type goggles are available that are designed to limit the entrance of nuisance dusts. There are two ANSI ratings with required markings: dust, D4; and fine dust, D5.

Optical Radiations

Depending on their frequency, optical radiations (infrared, visible, and ultraviolet) can cause erythema and thermal pain, sunburn, photokeratitis, burns to the cornea or retina, cataracts, and skin cancer. Optical radiations are emitted by many different processes and equipment, as well as the sun, fires, and other environmental sources. Radiation exposure may be direct or reflected. Work processes that produce optical radiations include arc or plasma welding and cutting, gas welding and cutting, brazing, soldering, viewing the charge in ovens and furnaces (e.g., metals, glass, boilers), and pouring molten metals.

Filter lenses provide eye and face protection against optical radiations. The intensity of the radiation determines the amount of optical density (shading) required. Shading of welding lenses is measured on a numerical shade scale from 2 to 14. Optical density increases with higher shade numbers. The OSHA general industry standard [1910.133(A)(5)] and ANSI Z87.1 contain tables that indicate the lens shade required for various types of welding, cutting, brazing, and soldering, based on the amperage of the arc or the size of the flame. Amperage and flame size affect the intensity of the emitted radiations. ANSI Z87.1 requires shaded lenses to be marked with a W followed by the shade number. The W comes from the word *welding*.

There are also ANSI numerical scales for ultraviolet, infrared, and visible light. Lenses that provide protection against UV radiation are marked with a U followed by the scale number. Infrared lenses have an R and the appropriate IR scale number. Lenses for bright visible light and glare have an L followed by a scale number.

Heat and Hot Materials

Many operations, including cutting, welding, and grinding, generate hot sparks. Pouring and casting metals can cause molten splashes. Spectacles, goggles, and face shields are available that are designed to protect against sparks and limited contact with molten metals. Examine the written specifications; there is no ANSI marking for spark and molten metal hazards.

Furnaces, ovens, molten metals, and other high-temperature operations release radiant heat. Wear a heat-resistant face shield over spectacles or goggles. There are two types of heat-resistant face shield. One type incorporates a metal screen to dissipate heat and the other has a coating that reflects heat. Work involving high heat may also expose workers to optical radiations requiring eye and face protectors that also incorporate the proper shaded lens.

HEAD PROTECTION

The most common device for occupational head protection is the hard hat, which OSHA standards (1910.135 and 1926.100) require to be worn "when working in areas where there is a potential for injury to the head from falling objects." In addition to falling objects, hard hats can limit the effects of other "struck-by" incidents, including side impact, and can offer electrical protection. The protection provided by a hard hat is not absolute; it is limited to the particular hard hat's design specifications, which are based on ANSI standard Z89.1.2009.

Types of Hard Hats

Hard hats conform to one of two ANSI types for impact and penetration resistance. The conventional Type I hard hat consists of a shell and an interior suspension system and is designed to protect the head from impact or penetration by objects falling from above. The hard hat shell is usually made of high-density polyethylene (HDPE.) Hard hats made of other materials such as fiberglass and aluminum are also available. The shell resists penetration and distributes the energy of top impact to the suspension band, which is attached to the shell at four or six points. The band then distributes the energy to four, six, or eight straps that rest on the head. The Type II hard hat provides additional protection against side, front, or rear impact, and off-center penetration. In a Type II hard hat, the shell distributes the energy of impact to a foam liner. Some Type II hard hats have a chin strap to retain the hat and provide side impact protection if the worker falls and strikes her or his head.

Something that looks like a hard hat, but isn't, is the bump cap. This is a lightweight plastic hat often worn by pest control operators, meter readers, auto mechanics, meat packers, and food processors. The bump cap provides very limited impact and penetration protection from impact and does not meet the requirements of the ANSI standard for hard hats.

Hard Hat Electrical Protection

The ANSI Z89.1 standard provides for three classes of hard hat based on the insulating or conducting properties of the hard hat shell (Figure 23–5). Class G (general) hard hats are electrically tested to 2,200 V. Class E (electrical) hard hats are tested to 20,000 V. These are specification voltages used in the testing laboratory. It cannot be assumed that the hard hat will protect the wearer from contact with live parts at these voltages in a real workplace setting. Good work practice must still include maintaining a safe distance from energized parts.

Class C (conductive) hard hats provide no protection upon contact with live electrical conductors. A Class C hard hat would only be appropriate when there is no foreseeable risk of head contact with live parts, and the prevention of static sparks and the dissipation of static electricity are essential, as in an explosive atmosphere.

Additional Hard Hat Features

Hard hats are also available that are designed to be worn backwards (reverse donning), to provide high visibility (HV), and to accept additional items of PPE such as earmuff-style hearing protectors, face shields, goggles, and headlamps. Models are also available that have been tested at a low temperature (LT) of –30°C (–22°F), or have cooling slots to improve comfort in a hot environment. Some models have heat-resistant shells for working in foundries, steel mills, and other high-heat workplaces. Most hard hats will accept a replaceable cushioned brow pad. To provide protection from the sun, Type I hard hats are available with front brims, full brims, and wide, cowboy-style full brims. Type II hard hats have front brims only. Skullcap liners are available for added protection and comfort in cold weather or in cold storage warehouses. Flame-resistant liners are also available.

Adjustment and Use

To adjust the fit, hard hats have a ratchet at the rear of the suspension band, or a series of holes and pins in the band. The suspension usually has an additional band that fits below the rounded back of the head for better retention. Workers should receive training on how to inspect and adjust the hard hat. An improperly fitted hard hat might provide less shock absorption, and is more likely to fall off.

Wearing a hard hat backwards, if the hat is not designed for reverse donning, does not provide the expected protection, may increase the likelihood of injury from an impact, and is an OSHA violation. Like all personal protective equipment, hard hats must be used according to the manufacturer's instructions.

Painting a hard hat or affixing stickers or decals is generally an unsafe practice for two reasons. First, paint, stickers, and decals hide the shell's surface and make it difficult to properly inspect the shell. Secondly, solvents in the paint

Impact, Penetration, and Electrical Specifications for Hard Hats	
Type and Class	*Specified Tests*
Type I	Top impact resistance: 8-lb steel ball dropped 5 ft; 850 maximum average force transmission to head form. Top penetration resistance: 2.2-lb steel penetrator dropped 8 ft within 3-inch circle on top of helmet; no contact with head form allowed.
Type II	Top impact and penetration resistance: same tests as for Type I, above. Side impact: helmeted head form weighing 11 lb dropped on flat and curved anvils. Off-center penetration resistance: 2.2-lb penetrator dropped 4 ft outside of top circle; no contact with head form allowed.
Class E (Electrical)	Tested at 20,000 V* for 3 minutes. Maximum leakage allowed: 9 mA. Retested at 30,000 V,* no burn-through allowed.
Class G (General)	Tested at 2,200 V* for 3 minutes. Maximum leakage allowed: 3 mA.
Class C (Conductive)	Provides no electrical protection.
An ANSI-compliant hard hat will have both a type and a class specification; for example, "ANSI Type I, Class E."	
* The specified test voltages do not mean that the hard hat will protect the wearer from contact with energized parts at that voltage.	

Figure 23–5. Hard hat specifications for impact, penetration, and electrical protection. OSHA requires hard hats to comply with ANSI Z-89.1. Bump caps may be similar in appearance to hard hats, but they are not included in these specifications and do not meet OSHA requirements for protection against falling objects.

or glue may cause deterioration of the synthetic shell materials. Some manufacturers specify certain parts of the shell surface where decals or stickers may be attached.

Hard Hat Service Life, Inspection, and Cleaning

The ANSI Z89.1 standard does not require manufacturers to specify a service life for hard hats. The actual service life depends upon the conditions of use and storage, including wear and tear, exposure to sunlight and other sources of UV radiation, mechanical damage sustained, and exposure to paints and solvents. Some manufacturers provide service life guidelines and suggest replacing the suspension after a certain number of months (typically 12), and the entire hat after a certain number of years (typically three to five.)

There is no way to field-test the structural or dielectric integrity of a hard hat. This means that a hard hat is designed to protect a worker only once, and should be removed from service and replaced immediately after a forceful impact or contact with a high voltage. The terms *forceful impact* and *high voltage* are admittedly vague; always err on the side of caution. A hard hat can be damaged by falling. A rule of thumb is to replace the hard hat if it sustains a drop of two stories (approximately 20 ft).

Every hard hat should be inspected daily by the wearer before use, and rejected if defects or deterioration are found. Inspect both the suspension and the shell. Carefully look at and touch the suspension straps and clips. Look for cracks, tears, or fraying. Push on the suspension to ensure that it will maintain the shell between 1 in. and 1¼ in. away from the head. Check both the outside and inside of the shell. Look for cracks, perforations, dents, or other signs of damage such as color change, loss of shine, chalking, or flaking. The interior surface of the shell can be inspected without removing the suspension. Color fading, loss of shine, flaking, and chalking indicate damage caused by exposure to sunlight or other sources of ultraviolet (UV) radiation, such as welding arcs, which can deteriorate synthetic resins and weaken the shell. Any hard hat shell exhibiting UV damage must be discarded and replaced immediately. Clean the shell and suspension only with dishwashing liquid or other mild soap and dry with a towel or allow to air dry. Never use solvents or strong detergents; they might damage the shell or the suspension.

FOOT PROTECTION

OSHA standards (General Industry Standard 1910.136 and others) require employers to "ensure that each affected employee uses protective footwear when working in areas where there is a danger of foot injuries due to falling or rolling objects, or objects piercing the sole, and where employees' feet are exposed to electrical hazards." Shoes, boots, and overboots are available that protect against one or more of these hazards. Footwear is also available that is antistatic, chain saw cut resistant, insulated against temperature extremes, and/or protective against chemical exposures. Chemical-protective footwear is discussed below in the section on chemical-protective clothing. OSHA refers to shoes and boots that have toe protection, but none of the other protections listed above as "nonspecialty safety-toe protective footwear." Protective footwear can also be designed to be slip resistant, water resistant, or waterproof.

Design and testing standards for protective footwear come from ASTM, but they were previously the domain of ANSI. OSHA requires protective footwear to comply with the current ASTM standard (ASTM F-2412 and -2413, 2005), or with either of two prior ANSI standards (ANSI Z41-1991 or -1999). All ASTM-compliant protective footwear must have integral impact- and compression-resistant toe caps. The footwear may have additional design features to comply with other ASTM requirements for metatarsal, conductive, electric shock, static-dissipative, sole puncture, chain-saw-cut, and dielectric protection (Figure 23–6).

Falling or Rolling Objects

Protective footwear has permanent, integral toe caps made of steel or a reinforced polymer (e.g., Kevlar®) to provide impact and compression resistance. Add-on toe caps are not ASTM compliant. There are two impact ratings: 50 ft-lbs

Consensus Standards for Protective Footwear	
ASTM F2412-11	Standard Test Methods for Foot Protection
ASTM F2413-11	Standard Specifications for Performance Requirements for Protective (Safety) Toe Cap Footwear
ASTM F1116-03	Standard Test Method for Determining Dielectric Strength of Dielectric Footwear
ASTM F1116-88	Standard Test Method for Determining Dielectric Strength of Overshoe Footwear
ASTM F1117-03	Standard Specification for Dielectric Footwear
ASTM F1117-93	Standard Specification for Dielectric Overshoe Footwear
ASTM F1458-08	Standard Test Method for Measurement of Cut Resistance to Chain Saw Foot Protective Devices
ASTM F1818-04	Standard Specification for Foot Protection for Chain Saw Users
ANSI Z41.1	American National Standard for Personal Protection – Protective Footwear

Figure 23–6. Consensus standards for protective footwear. ANSI Z41.1 has been superseded by ASTM F2412 and F2413. OSHA allows footwear that complies with any of the three most recent consensus standards, which as of the printing of this book includes ANSI Z41.1.

and 75 ft-lbs. An impact rating of I/50 means that the toe cap will retain at least a specified clearance inside of the shoe following impact by a 50-lb weight dropped from 1 ft above. An I/75-rated toe cap will retain the specified clearance following impact by a 50-lb weight dropped from 1.5 ft. The specified clearance is 0.50 in. for men's footwear and 0.468 in. for women's. These ratings can prevent serious injury in the majority of falling-object incidents, which involve boxes, tools, boards, blocks, etc., but they do not necessarily prevent injury from impact by heavy machinery, large rocks, and other very heavy falling objects. There are also two ASTM compression ratings for heavy objects that roll onto the toe without falling: C/50 retains the specified clearance under a weight of 1,750 lbs, and C/75 can withstand 2,500 lbs. Any particular item of ASTM-compliant footwear has either the two lower ratings for impact and compression (I/50, C/50) or the two higher ratings (I/75, C/75); no footwear is certified with a mixture of a high and a low rating.

Safety footwear with metatarsal protection provides additional impact and compression resistance over the top of the foot, between the toes, and at the ankle. An ASTM-compliant steel or polymer metatarsal protector is integral to the shoe or boot. A Class 50 product must retain a specified height in the metatarsal area following an impact of 50 ft-lbs; a Class 75 product is tested at 75 ft-lbs. The minimum height (measured on a wax metatarsal insert) is 1.0 in. for men's shoes and 0.937 in. for women's. OSHA also permits the use of separate metatarsal guards that attach to the outside of the shoe or boot. In either case, a metatarsal guard is designed to extend over the rear edge of the toe cap.

Puncture and Cutting

ASTM-compliant puncture-resistant footwear has (in addition to impact- and compression-resistant toe cups) an integral steel or polymer plate (shank) between the inner and outer soles. The footwear is tested with a pointed steel pin applying a force of 270 lbs. This approximates the effect of a 270-lb worker stepping on an upward-pointing nail. The shank must also meet specifications for corrosion resistance and repeated flexing without cracking. A chain-saw-cut-resistant boot has an inlay of Kevlar® fiber on the top and sides that is designed to snag and stop the chain if it cuts into the boot.

Electrical Hazards

ASTM has four electricity-related specifications for protective footwear: conductive, static dissipative, electrical shock protective, and dielectric. To be compliant with any of these, the footwear must also meet the specifications for impact- and compression-resistant toe cups. Both conductive footwear and static-dissipative footwear reduce the possibility of a static discharge from the worker's body that might detonate explosives or ignite a flammable atmosphere. Conductive footwear has conductive material on the sole and heel, and is designed to provide an electrically conductive path to the ground in order to prevent or minimize the accumulation of static electricity on the worker's body. Because this footwear is conductive, it must never be worn by workers where there is a possibility of contact with live electrical circuits.

Static-dissipative shoes and boots also address the hazard of static buildup on the body, but this footwear has a higher electrical resistance. It is designed to conduct the static charge to the ground, while resisting current flow from incidental contact with a live circuit.

Electric-shock-resistant shoes and boots have non-conductive heels and soles to provide protection against shock *in dry conditions* in case of incidental contact with live electrical circuits and parts. This footwear is tested to 14,000 V *under dry conditions*. The actual electrical resistance if the footwear is worn wet will be greatly reduced. Dielectric footwear consists of waterproof rubbers, boots, and galoshes that are designed to be worn over other shoes or boots to provide additional protection in case the wearer comes in contact with live electrical circuits or parts. This footwear is tested using water inside and outside the footwear as the conductive electrodes. Dielectric footwear is available that has been tested to 20,000 V AC.

HAND PROTECTION

OSHA (General Industry Standard 1910.138 and others) requires employers "to select and require employees to use appropriate hand protection when employees' hands are exposed to hazards such as those from skin absorption of harmful substances; severe cuts or lacerations; severe abrasions; punctures; chemical burns; thermal burns; and harmful temperature extremes." Various types of protective gloves are available that are designed to address each of these hazards, and several others, including vibration, electricity, ultraviolet radiation, and infectious materials. There are also gloves that provide high visibility and reflectivity for traffic control, signaling, and other situations where hand visibility is important.

Protection often comes at the expense of dexterity. Operating procedures must provide a way to do the job without the worker having to remove a glove because it impedes the work. Wearing gloves may be hazardous when working around moving parts of machinery; the glove might be caught, pulling the hand into the machine. Proper machine guarding is essential. A job may create multiple different hazards to the hands, and the worker may need to wear more than one type of glove at the same time. For example, in material handling involving chemicals, the worker might wear a chemical-protective glove inside an abrasion-resistant glove. Chemical-protective gloves are discussed below in the section on chemical-protective clothing.

Common leather and fabric work gloves provide abrasion resistance and limited protection against heat and cold. They do not provide puncture resistance, and have limited cut resistance. They should never be used when chemical exposure is possible, unless an appropriate chemical-protective inner glove is also worn. A leather or fabric glove will absorb liquids and can actually increase the exposure to bare skin underneath.

The new ANSI/ISEA 105-2011, American National Standard for Hand Protection Selection Criteria, published by the International Safety Equipment Association (ISEA), provides a numeric scale method for manufacturers to rate their products against certain contaminants and exposures. With classification based on this scale, users can make decisions on which gloves are suitable for which tasks. Glove performance and pass/fail criteria are included for the following hazardous exposures: cut, puncture, and abrasion resistance; protection from cold; chemical permeation and degradation; detection of holes; and heat and flame resistance. The standard also includes reference information on special considerations such as biological protection, electrical protection, and radiation hazards. Every end use is different, and no single test method can fully replicate the variety of hazards that a worker may encounter. The ISEA suggests that users should contact glove manufacturers for information on the new glove ratings and labeling of their products that meet the standard.

CHEMICAL-PROTECTIVE CLOTHING

Chemical-protective clothing (CPC) serves two important functions: (1) to prevent or minimize skin contact with hazardous chemical, radioactive, or biological materials; and (2) to reduce the spread of contaminants (if the worker removes the protective clothing before leaving the worksite), and thus help to protect co-workers, the community, and the worker's family. Some chemical-protective clothing is also designed to provide protection against injuries such as lacerations and abrasions. OSHA requires the employer to provide and maintain protective clothing for any type of work "whenever it is necessary." There are also chemical-protective clothing requirements in several specific OSHA standards, for example, the HAZWOPER, asbestos, lead, and chromium standards.

Chemical-protective clothing includes numerous types of one-piece suits, jackets, pants, hoods, coveralls, gloves, boots, and accessory garments such as aprons and gauntlets. It is made from a variety of fabrics and materials. The specific types of chemical-protective clothing that a worker needs, and the materials or fabrics from which the clothing is made, must be chosen based upon the job task, the procedure by which the worker does the task, and the chemicals involved. The choice must take into account the possible ergonomic (physical and psychological) stresses that the protective clothing might create, including restricted mobility, impaired vision, claustrophobia, and heat stress. The protective clothing must not cause unnecessary additional hazards, and it must not unnecessarily impede performance of the job. Protective clothing should be selected that provides appropriate protection. Overprotection can also be hazardous.

Workers who need to wear CPC include HAZWOPER workers (those who tackle hazardous waste cleanup; treatment, storage, and disposal; and emergency response), asbestos and lead removal workers, laboratory workers, and pesticide applicators. Any worker who uses or handles hazardous chemical, radiological, or biological materials must wear the appropriate type of protective clothing. A maintenance worker using a cleaning solvent might not need a protective suit, but she or he needs to wear gloves that are rated to protect against skin contact with that particular solvent or solvent solution. Depending on the circumstances, additional protective clothing may be necessary, as well as other protective equipment such as safety glasses and a respirator. It is useful to plan the job and select all necessary personal protective equipment as an ensemble of equipment that works together. This concept is formalized in the levels of protection discussion later in this section.

Workers who wear chemical-protective clothing, as well as those responsible for selecting CPC and for buying it, should be aware of its limitations. Protective clothing wears out; zippers become difficult to operate; fabrics degrade with exposure to sunlight. CPC becomes contaminated, and wearing used CPC that has not been properly decontaminated can increase exposures. CPC is often uncomfortable, and it can reduce dexterity and agility. Most CPC is not heat and flame resistant, and may in fact burn readily. Wearing CPC, even in relatively mild temperatures, can cause heat stress if adequate breaks for rest and hydration are not taken.

Heat Stress
Always consider the potential for heat stress when wearing chemical-protective clothing. Protective clothing materials restrict, and may completely prevent, evaporative cooling of the skin. If the clothing is necessary for chemical protection,

then any resulting heat stress must be relieved by reducing the work load and/or providing more frequent rest breaks. Always ensure that workers drink water in sufficient quantities at regular intervals, even if they do not feel thirsty. A healthy worker can acclimate to working in a hot environment, but no one can acclimate to the inability for sweat to evaporate.

Solids, Liquids, Gases, and the "Skin" Notation

Workers encounter hazardous chemical, radiological, and biological materials as bulk solids or liquids, as solid or liquid particulate air contaminants, or, in the case of chemical and radiological materials, as gas or vapor air contaminants. Most chemical-protective clothing is designed to protect against skin contact with bulk solids and liquids; for example, touching the surface of a liquid or solid, stepping in spilled materials, or being splashed. Most chemical-protective clothing is not designed to protect against skin contact air contaminants (particulates, gases, or vapors.) Air contaminants can pass easily around collars and up sleeves, and can permeate through small openings (stitches, zippers, and buttonholes). Vapors and gases may also be able to diffuse through clothing materials. Therefore, only specially designed fully encapsulating vapor-protective (level A) suits ensure protection against skin contact with air contaminants.

Respiratory protection (via local exhaust ventilation or respirators) is necessary whenever air contaminant levels might approach a designated action level. However, protection against skin contact with air contaminants is only necessary in unusual situations involving very highly hazardous materials, for example, chemical warfare agents or certain pesticides that act through airborne skin contact. There are two reasons why skin contact with air contaminants may not be a significant hazard, even though contact with bulk liquids and solids often is. First, the skin generally presents a more substantial barrier to the absorption of air contaminants than does the interior surface of the lungs. More importantly, the actual amount of skin exposure to an air contaminant is tiny compared to skin exposure to the same material in bulk liquid form. Compare skin exposure to 300 ppm of toluene vapor (150% of the OSHA PEL and six times the ACGIH® TLV®) with skin exposure to liquid toluene. The concentration of pure liquid toluene would be 1 million ppm. Also, liquid toluene is several hundred times more dense than air. Thus the airborne skin exposure, in terms of the number of molecules in contact with the skin, is six orders of magnitude less than the bulk liquid exposure.

In both the ACGIH TLVs, and the OSHA PELs, certain chemicals have a "skin" notation. This means that overexposure may occur from dermal contact, even though the airborne exposure is below the PEL. For example, an auto body worker who uses the correct respirator while mixing and applying paint is protected against inhalation of solvent vapors, and the skin exposure to vapors in the air is small. Nevertheless there will be a significant exposure to solvents by skin contact and absorption if the worker washes the spray equipment in liquid solvent without wearing chemical-protective gloves. The skin notation is a warning, not a quantitative standard specifying the maximum permissible skin exposure.

Effectiveness of Chemical-Protective Clothing Materials

There are limitations to the effectiveness of, and thus the protection provided by, chemical-protective clothing. The effectiveness of chemical-protective clothing depends on several factors, including the materials of which it is made, the manner in which it is made, the chemicals to which it is exposed, the way in which it is used, and the length of time it is exposed. There are several fabrics and materials commonly used to manufacture chemical-protective clothing. No single clothing material or fabric offers protection against all chemicals, and there is probably no material or fabric that provides unlimited protection against any particular chemical (Figure 23–7).

Fabrics and Materials Used for Chemical-Protective Clothing	
Material/Fabric	**Typical Uses**
Barricade™	Suits
Butyl Rubber	Suits, Gloves, Boots
CPF3™	Suits
Natural Rubber (Latex)	Gloves
Neoprene Rubber	Suits, Gloves, Boots
Nitrile Rubber	Suits, Gloves, Boots
Polyethylene (PE)	Suits, Gloves, Boots
Polyethylene / Ethylene Vinyl Alcohol (PE/EVAL)	Gloves
Polyvinyl Alcohol (PVA)	Gloves
Polyvinyl Chloride (PVC)	Suits, Gloves, Boots
Responder™	
Saranex™	Suits
Teflon™	Suits, Gloves, Boots
Trellchem™	Suits
Tychem™	Suits
Tyvek™	Suits
Viton™	Suits, Gloves

Neoprene is a trade name and Teflon™, Barricade™, Tychem™ and Tyvek™ are trademarks of the DuPont Company. Viton™ is a registered trademark of DuPont Dow Elastomers. Saranex is a trade name of the Dow Chemical Company. CPF3™ and Responder™ are trademarks of the Kappler Company. Trellchem™ is a trademark of the Trelleborg Company.

Figure 23–7. Fabrics and materials used for chemical-protective clothing.

Several terms characterize the limitations of chemical-protective clothing when challenged by exposure to chemicals. *Permeation* refers to the passage of a chemical through a protective clothing fabric or material on a molecule-by-molecule basis, often without apparent effect or change in the material or fabric. The challenge chemical is absorbed on one side of the material, defuses through it, and desorbs on the other side. *Degradation* refers to damage caused by a challenge chemical such as burns, holes, cracks, blistering, or embrittlement. Permeation and degradation are generally related to the chemical properties of the material or fabric, and how these properties relate to the challenge chemical. *Penetration* refers to the movement of a chemical—on a nonmolecular basis (e.g., droplets)—through stitches, zippers, buttonholes, or defects. Penetration is generally related to design aspects of the clothing, for example, the type of stitching, and how the seams are sealed.

There are standard methods for determining the *breakthrough detection time* of a particular protective clothing fabric or material when exposed to a particular challenge chemical in a laboratory test. This is the time from when one side of the material is exposed to a chemical until it is detected on the other side. Once breakthrough has occurred, it is possible to measure the *permeation rate* at which the challenge chemical moves from one side of the material or fabric to the other (Figure 23–8). Another parameter that may also be measured is the *cumulative amount permeated in 1 hour*. It is important to remember that the results of these tests depend upon the sensitivity and accuracy of the detection method. Ironically, a less well-equipped or less skilled laboratory could record longer breakthrough times.

Workplace environmental factors may affect the efficacy of protective clothing. For example, heat (ambient temperature and/or the temperature of objects handled) can increase permeation rates, while cold can make protective clothing materials more brittle.

Selection of Appropriate Chemical-Protective Clothing

The selection of appropriate chemical-protective clothing for a particular job task includes two aspects. First, the clothing material or fabric must provide sufficient protection against *all* of the specific chemicals to which it might be exposed during the job. It must resist degradation and penetration, and limit permeation for a useful length of time. Secondly, the clothing must be appropriate in terms of its design.

Safety Data Sheets (SDSs), formerly known as Material Safety Data Sheets (MSDSs), often provide only general statements such as "do not get on skin or clothing," without specifying appropriate protective clothing materials. The NIOSH *Recommendations for Chemical-Protective*

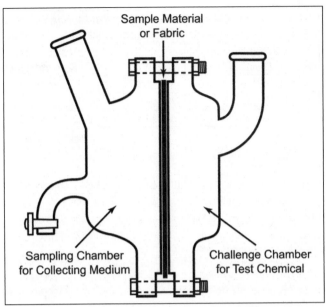

Figure 23–8. Permeation test cell. A piece of the fabric or material to be tested is fastened between the flanges of the two cups. One side of the test cell is then filled with the challenge chemical. The other side contains an appropriate solvent. Samples are withdrawn periodically from the solvent side and analyzed quantitatively for the presence of the challenge chemical. This is a simplified drawing based on ANSI F739-07 Standard Test Method for Permeation of Liquids and Gases through Protective Clothing Materials under Conditions of Continuous Contact. For exact specifications, see ASTM F739-07.

Clothing are available on-line, and suggest personal protective clothing materials for protection against the several hundred chemicals that have OSHA General Industry PELs and/or NIOSH RELs (Figure 23–9).

Manufacturers of chemical-protective clothing publish selection charts that list the breakthrough times and permeation rates of various challenge chemicals through different fabrics and materials. It is important to remember that the data in the selection charts comes from laboratory tests (as does the NIOSH data mentioned above). The listed breakthrough times may be longer (i.e., appear to be better) than what will occur under real workplace conditions. Permeation and breakthrough data may be different among different manufacturers' charts for CPC made of the same material because of differences in thickness or other design properties.

The design of chemical-protective clothing must be practical. CPC must have sufficient strength, be resistant to temperature extremes, and be adequately sized to be worn on the job without impeding job tasks or creating unnecessary additional hazards. In order to ensure proper fit, the employer must order and stock CPC of various sizes. Wearing protective clothing that is too large or too small will make work more difficult and may create safety hazards.

NIOSH Recommendations for Chemical Protective Clothing: A Companion to the NIOSH Pocket Guide to Chemical Hazards: Data Base (Excerpts)			
Chemical	CAS No.	Recommendation for Skin Protection	Recommended Protective Clothing Barriers
Calcium oxide	1305-78-8	Prevent skin contact	Any barrier that will prevent contamination from the dry chemical
Chlorine	7782-50-5	Frostbite	Prevent possible skin freezing from direct liquid contact
Ethyl butyl ketone	106-35-4	Prevent skin contact	Contact the manufacturer for recommendations
Glutaraldehyde	111-30-8	Prevent skin contact	8 hr: Butyl, Viton 4 hr: Natural, Neoprene, Nitrile, PVC
n-Propyl acetate	109-60-4	Prevent skin contact	8 hr: PE / EVAL
Toluene	108-88-3	Prevent skin contact	8 hr: PVA, Teflon, Viton, PE/EVAL, Barricade, CPF3, Responder, Trellchem, Tychem

8 hr = More than 8 hours of resistance to breakthrough >0.1 g/cm^2/min.

4 hr = At least 4 but less than 8 hours of resistance to breakthrough >0.1 g/cm^2/min.

Data on breakthrough times is based on test results using ASTM Method F739-91, *Test Method for Resistance of Protective Clothing Materials to Permeation by Liquids or Gases Under Conditions of Continuous Contact.*

Neoprene is a trade name and Teflon™, Barricade™ and Tychem 10000™ are trademarks of the DuPont Company. Viton™ is a registered trademark of DuPont Dow Elastomers. Saranex is a trade name of the Dow Chemical Company. 4H is a trademark of the Safety 4 Company. Silver Shield is a trademark of the Siebe North Company. CPF3 and Responder are trademarks of the Kappler Company. Trellchem HPS is a trademark of the Trelleborg Company. Recommendations are NOT valid for very thin Natural Rubber, Neoprene, Nitrile, and PVC gloves (0.3 mm or less).

Figure 23-9. NIOSH recommendations for chemical-protective clothing (CPC). This figure shows some typical entries. The entire database is available on the NIOSH web site. Note that multiple different clothing materials are listed for some chemicals, while for other chemicals there are fewer choices. Some clothing materials are rated for only 4 hours. For some chemicals there is no recommendation; the user is advised to contact the manufacturer of the chemical.

Seams and Zippers

Protective suits, pants, and hoods are created from multiple panels of fabric that are connected by seams. Different types of seams provide varying degrees of resistance to chemical penetration. Fabric panels can be connected by stitching, cementing, heating, or ultrasonic welding, or by some combination of these methods.

Stitched seams rely on the pressure of the stitches to seal the fabric panels together and thus minimize penetration by liquids or solids. Stitches can potentially stretch or relax over time, leaving a less secure seal. The nylon, polyester, or other type of stitching thread may also deteriorate over time and with exposure to chemicals or ultraviolet radiation, allowing the seam to open. The holes created by stitches can stretch and enlarge; they are another source of possible chemical penetration. The manufacturer can cover a stitched seam with a special adhesive tape to provide additional protection against penetration. Stitched seams, without additional heating and taping, are not vapor-tight.

Some protective clothing materials, such as synthetic rubbers like neoprene and nitrile, can be cemented together. Cement provides a very good initial seal, but may deteriorate with time. Fabrics made of or coated with thermoplastic materials such as polyvinylchloride, polyethylene, or polypropylene can be heat-sealed, creating a vapor- and liquid-tight seal. Thermoplastic materials can also be joined by ultrasonic welding, which uses pressure and high-frequency vibration to create friction, causing sufficient heat to bond the panels.

Zippers present an obvious path for chemical penetration. For splash resistance to chemicals that are not highly hazardous in general-duty clothing, ordinary zippers with covering "storm" flaps may be all that is necessary. Flaps may be single or double, and may be secured with a hook-and-loop fastening. For greater protection there are special zippers with tight-sealing covers. Some special zippers/covers are rated vapor-protective.

User Taping

Standard procedures for donning chemical-protective clothing often include the use of duct tape at the interface between sleeves and gloves, and pants and boots. Tape may also be applied over the storm flap of a zipper. The function of the tape is to provide a mechanical connection to keep protective clothing components properly aligned. Chemical-resistant tapes are available that have been tested for permeation and breakthrough of the tape fabric. These tapes have not been tested as a unit with the underlying clothing for penetration between the tape and the fabric. Tape—whether duct tape or specialty tape—should not be considered to provide a chemical-proof seal. Nor should tape be considered an adequate means to repair torn clothing or cover holes and punctures. To facilitate removal, the user should always create a tab by folding over one end of the tape.

Chemical-Resistant Gloves and Boots

The hands are often the part of the body most likely to come in contact with chemicals. In some operations, in particular emergency response, the feet are also at risk. The failure to wear protective gloves when handling chemicals can allow skin contact, resulting in irritation, dermatitis, or chemical burns. Absorption through the skin can lead to systemic health effects. Like other chemical-protective clothing, gloves are made of many different materials. Gloves are usually molded without seams, which makes chemical penetration unlikely. However, if the glove material is not appropriate for the chemical(s) being handled, permeation and/or degradation will result in skin exposure. The exposure might be magnified because the chemical becomes trapped under the glove, against the skin. Friction may exacerbate this effect. The hands often sweat inside protective gloves; the wearer might not be able to sense the presence of liquid chemicals that have permeated the glove. An additional potential problem is that an individual may experience a dermatological reaction to the glove material itself, in particular, natural latex, which is discussed below.

Chemical-resistant boots are usually made of upper and lower parts bonded together around the sole. They too must be selected based on the chemical(s) that they might contact. There are chemical-protective boots designed to be worn over normal work boots.

Latex Allergy

Medical workers have traditionally worn gloves made of natural latex because this material provides a contamination barrier for infection control, while also allowing good dexterity. Chemical workers and emergency responders often wear latex inner gloves. Some people become sensitized to natural latex, which contains proteins recognized as foreign by their immune system. This sensitization is called *latex allergy*. Reactions can include skin rash; irritation of the eyes, nose, or sinuses; asthma; and—rarely—anaphylactic shock. Latex gloves are often manufactured with a powder inside (usually cornstarch) to facilitate donning and doffing. Latex protein attaches to this powder. The actual latex exposure results from contact with the latex glove itself, or from contact with, or inhalation of, the latex-infused powder. Persons with latex allergy should not wear latex gloves, and should avoid areas which may be contaminated with latex-infused powder. Many safety and health professionals recommend the use of only powder-free latex gloves, or the substitution of gloves made of synthetic materials. See Chapter 3, The Skin and Occupational Dermatoses, for more information.

Inspection, Decontamination, Cleaning, Maintenance, and Storage

As with any other article of PPE, the wearer should check chemical-protective clothing before donning. Look for tears, holes, cuts, contamination, and damaged zippers, seals, and valves. After use, CPC must be either thoroughly decontaminated or properly disposed of. Decontamination means cleaning, removing, or neutralizing hazardous substances that have adhered to, soaked into, or become embedded in the clothing. The appropriate method of decontamination depends on the type of clothing, the material(s) it is made of, and the nature of the contamination. Decontamination might be as simple as air-drying to allow evaporation of solvents, or it may require mechanical scrubbing, scraping, washing, and rinsing.

Decontamination might also require the use of specific cleaning agents, neutralizers, and equipment. Decontamination frequently generates waste streams that must be properly disposed of. If thorough decontamination is cost-prohibitive or infeasible, proper disposal and replacement with new CPC are required. Decontamination should be done at the worksite according to standardized procedures. If workers take CPC home, their family will be exposed to contaminants on the clothing.

After decontamination, CPC must be cleaned, as with any clothing that has been worn. CPC must be completely dry before it is stored. Moisture will promote biological growth and result in unpleasant odors, or possible pathogens. Store CPC, whether new or decontaminated/washed, in a clean, cool, and dry environment away from sunlight or other sources of UV radiation.

Disposable Clothing

Many forms of disposable clothing are available. Often they provide protection against fewer chemicals, and have less mechanical strength than durable (nondisposable) CPC. Most disposable CPC is made of nonwoven fabrics such as Tyvek®. For job tasks involving dusts and fibers, but not hazardous liquid chemicals, lightweight disposable CPC might be preferable because its greater air and moisture permeability makes it more comfortable. As with other chemical-protective clothing, the design and material specifications of disposable CPC must be compared to the work situation and the chemicals involved.

Levels of Protection

There are two broad categories of chemical-protective suits: (1) liquid-protective suits designed to limit skin contact with chemicals in liquid or solid form; and (2) vapor-protective suits designed to prevent skin contact with gas/vapor and liquid or solid chemicals. Liquid-protective suits are made of a variety of materials and come in several styles, including two-piece (coat and pants), one-piece (overall), with or without an attached hood, with or without attached booties, and totally encapsulating. No liquid-protective suit is designed to be airtight. Contaminated air can enter through zippers, stitches, and open spaces, if any, at the neck, wrists, and ankles. Even a totally encapsulating liquid-protective suit may admit a small quantity of contaminated air through stitches or closures.

A vapor-protective suit is a fully encapsulating suit that has airtight seams, a special zipper— usually with a snap-lock cover—and one-way vents that allow exhaled air to escape, but prevent the intrusion of contaminated ambient air. The significant benefit of a vapor-protective suit is that it prevents skin contact with airborne contaminants. The suit is not worn to keep air contaminants out of the respiratory system; that hazard is addressed by wearing an atmosphere-supplying respirator.

There are two broad categories of respirators: (1) air-purifying respirators, and (2) atmosphere-supplying respirators. It is impossible to use an air-purifying respirator (APR) inside a vapor-protective suit; there is no source of air. This means that there are only three possible combinations (ensembles) of respirator and chemical-protective suit. The three combinations are designated Level A, Level B, and Level C. A fourth possibility, the absence of either a respirator or a chemical-protective suit, or both, is called Level D. Note that Levels A and B share the same type of category of respirator, and Levels B and C share the same category of protective clothing (Figure 23–10).

Persons new to the field of chemical protection often ask, "Wouldn't it be best to always wear Level A since it provides the maximum possible protection?" The answer has three parts. Most importantly, Level A creates the highest risk of heat stress because it creates the greatest barrier to the evaporation of sweat. Second, vapor-protective suits are significantly more expensive than liquid-protec-

tive suits. Third, as discussed previously, except for exposures to certain pesticides, chemical warfare agents, and very highly toxic substances, limited skin contact with air contaminants generally does not pose a significant risk. A vapor-protective suit is only appropriate if the prevention of skin contact with the ambient air is necessary. Wearing a vapor-protective suit when it is not necessary can create a serious heat-stress condition, and unnecessary expense.

The concept of levels of protection originated with chemical emergency responders. It provides a simple way of describing the respirator and protective clothing required in a particular situation. Within each level there are decisions to make, based on the specific environmental conditions. For example, for Levels B and C, there are many different styles and models of liquid-protective suits. For Level C, either a half-face or full-face APR can be used, depending on the identity and concentration of the contaminant(s). Workers in Level A usually wear a self-contained breathing apparatus (SCBA), but there are also vapor-protective suits designed for use with an air-line respirator. Appendix B of the OSHA HAZWOPER standard contains a description of the four levels of protection; lists appropriate accompanying items such as a hard hat, boots, gloves, and inner coveralls; and provides guidance on selecting the appropriate level of protection based on the potential exposures.

Fire Fighters' Bunker Gear

Structural fire fighters wear bunker gear (turnout gear) that provides thermal protection and water resistance. Suits and pants (and overalls) are fashioned of multiple layers of synthetic fabrics with air spaces between, and must be rated to not ignite, melt, or drip when exposed to 500°F for five minutes. A synthetic polymer, Nomex®, provides the thermal resistance. For close approach to fires with intense heat, such as burning aircraft, or oil and gas wellhead fires, or where fire engulfment is a possibility, there are proximity and entry suits that have a heat-reflective aluminized outer layer. Wildland fire fighters engaged in fire suppression generally wear protective clothing made of a lighter, single-layer Nomex® fabric. The fire fighters' bunker gear is primarily designed to protect the wearer from heat, and to offer water, abrasion, tear, and cut resistance. This gear is generally not rated for protection against chemical permeation, penetration, and degradation.

Level	Respirator	Clothing-Protective Suit
A	SCBA or Air line with escape bottle	Fully encapsulating vapor-protective suit
B	SCBA or Air line with escape bottle	Liquid-protective suit
C	APR	Liquid-protective suit
D	None	None
SCBA = Self-contained breathing apparatus		
APR = Air-purifying respirator		

Figure 23–10. Levels of Protection. Note that Levels A and B use the same category of respirator; Levels B and C use the same category of chemical-protective suit. The specific model of respirator and suit, as well as any accessory items such as boots, gloves, and hard hat, will depend on the job task requirements as set forth in the site safety and health plan.

PROTECTIVE CLOTHING FOR RADIOACTIVE MATERIALS AND IONIZING RADIATION

Ionizing radiation is radiation that has sufficient energy to ionize atoms, including atoms in molecules that are part of living cells. There are three sources of exposure to ionizing radiation: radioactive materials, incident radiations from extraterrestrial sources, and electronic machines and equipment that are designed to emit—or that inadvertently emit—ionizing radiation. The types of ionizing radiation most commonly encountered in industrial, commercial, and medical facilities are alpha, beta, gamma, and x-ray radiation. Additionally, neutron radiation may be a hazard at nuclear reactors and accelerators. There are several other forms of ionizing radiation that might be encountered in specialized facilities. Alpha, beta, and neutron radiation are called *particulate radiations* because they consist of atomic or subatomic particles whose ionizing energy comes from their high velocity (a significant fraction of the velocity of light). Note that this use of the word *particles* is unrelated to dusts, fibers, fumes, and other forms for particulate chemical contamination. Gamma and x-ray radiation are considered to be forms of *pure energy;* they are *electromagnetic radiations.* See Chapter 10, Ionizing Radiation, for more information on this subject.

With regard to worker protection, it is essential to understand several commonly confused concepts: radioactive contamination versus radiation exposure; particulate radiation versus electromagnetic radiation; nonpenetrating versus penetrating radiation; and internal versus external radiation exposure. These concepts will be addressed as necessary in the following discussion.

Radioactive Contamination

Radioactive contamination means contamination with a solid or liquid substance that happens to be radioactive. Whether or not the material is a chemical hazard (e.g., toxic, an irritant, corrosive, etc.), the fact that it is radioactive means that it emits ionizing radiation, which is detectable at very low levels and which may cause injury. Because radioactive contamination is a material, the protective clothing worn to keep this material from contacting the worker's body, and to limit the spread of contamination beyond the worksite, is similar to, and in many cases the same as, chemical-protective clothing. Radiological workers' protective clothing is often called anti-contamination clothing, or simply anti-Cs. It is generally worn over regular work clothes and undergarments. Common outfits include coveralls, boot covers, and gloves. If the coveralls do not have an attached hood, then a separate fabric hood is worn. Materials such as cotton and Tyvek® are chosen because they minimize the adhesion of contaminant particles. For liquid exposures, clothing made of PVC, nitrile, or other materials may be required. As in chemical exposure situations, the specific protective clothing items needed, and the fabric or material of which they are made, must be chosen based on a careful hazard analysis of the particular job task and the contaminant materials involved.

Radioactive contamination, since it is a chemical substance, can get into the body by the same routes of entry that other chemical contaminants take (e.g., inhalation, ingestion, skin absorption, and injection). Once inside the body, radioactive contaminants continue to emit radiation, and are considered internal sources of exposure, or internal hazards. Materials that emit alpha, beta, or gamma radiation are all potential internal hazards. The radiation emitted by radioactive contaminants outside of the body can produce harm if it is sufficiently energetic to penetrate the skin or mucous membranes. Thus gamma-emitting material is also an external hazard, since gamma is highly penetrating. Beta sources can be external hazards, but alpha-emitting materials are not external hazards since alpha radiation is so easily stopped by any clothing material or by the outer dead skin layer.

Anti-contamination clothing, by limiting skin contact, protects against skin absorption of radioactive active materials and thus reduces the risk of accumulating internal radiation sources. Anti-contamination clothing is also an essential part of contamination control procedures that limit the spread of radioactive materials beyond the radiologically controlled area. Anti-contamination clothing does not generally protect against external sources of radiation exposure.

Workers need to know how to properly doff (remove) their anti-contamination clothing when leaving the radiologically controlled area, so that they do not contaminate themselves, and do not track or carry radioactive contamination beyond the boundary of the controlled area. The employer must have a step-by-step doffing procedure that employees learn, practice, and use. It is a common practice to display the procedure on a sign at the doffing location (Figure 23–11). The procedure will include a careful examination of the person's entire body—after removing the anti-Cs—using an appropriate radiation detection instrument. If examination indicates that contamination is present on the person after doffing the anti-Cs, then further decontamination will be required. This will include removal and washing or disposal of the clothing worn under the anti-Cs. The worker will also shower. Scrubbing with mild soap will usually be sufficient.

Ionizing Radiation Exposure

Whether or not protective clothing can prevent or significantly reduce exposure to ionizing radiation depends on the ability of the radiation to penetrate the clothing material. Note that, in this context, *penetration* means that the incident radiation passes through the clothing in a manner analogous to light passing through a glass window. Although we use the same word, this discussion is unrelated to penetration by solid, liquid, or gaseous chemical substances through holes in clothing. Radiation penetration is pre-

---

Anti-Contamination Clothing Doffing Procedure

As you remove each item, place it in the proper labeled container or waste receptacle.

1. Remove one outer rubber shoe cover and place that foot on the step-off pad.

2. Remove the other outer rubber shoe cover and put that foot on the step-off pad.

3. Remove tape from wrists and ankles.

4. Remove outer gloves, one at a time: grab at the cuff and pull inside-out.

5. Remove respirator.

6. Remove dosimeter and place it on the table.

7. Open hood and remove it up and to the back.

8. Open coveralls and remove by pulling down over the shoulders.

9. Remove one inner shoe cover and step forward with that foot off of the step-off pad.

10. Remove the other inner shoe cover and step off with that foot.

11. Remove one inner glove liner.

12. With the other hand (wearing glove liner) pick up the dosimeter. Walk forward to the frisking station.

Figure 23–11. Typical doffing procedure for anticontamination clothing worn in radiologically controlled work areas. It is common to post a procedure such as this at the doffing station.

vented or reduced if the energy of the radiation is absorbed by the clothing material. Energy absorption is related to the type of radiation and to the density and thickness of the clothing material. There are practical limits to clothing thickness and density, and to the resulting weight of the clothing. This means that clothing can provide protection only for limited types and energy levels of ionizing radiation exposure. Therefore it is fundamental that radiological procedures make primary use of the three basic means of exposure control: time, distance, and shielding.

With regard to the particulate radiations, alpha radiation is considered to be nonpenetrating. Alpha gives up its energy so readily on contact with any substance or material that it is absorbed (e.g., stopped) by ordinary clothing, and also by human skin. Beta radiation is poorly to moderately penetrating. Common protective clothing materials may absorb lower-energy beta radiation, but not all beta. Beta radiation can penetrate the outer horny layer of skin to reach living cells, and it can also penetrate mucous membranes. Neutron radiation is highly penetrating. It is not readily stopped by ordinary protective clothing materials.

Depending on its energy level, neutron radiation may penetrate up to several inches in living tissue.

Ordinary protective clothing materials are ineffective against pure-energy x-ray and gamma radiations. These electromagnetic radiations are highly penetrating, which is why they are used for industrial and medical imaging. There is protective clothing designed for use in medical and industrial x-ray applications. This includes gloves, gauntlets, aprons, and gowns made of vinyl impregnated with lead or other energy-absorbing materials. These items are rated in terms of an equivalent millimeter thickness of lead. Compare the specifications of the clothing product to the actual energy exposure to determine whether the protective clothing is adequate. For high-energy x-rays and gamma radiation, the required weight of energy-absorbing material generally makes protective clothing infeasible. Several companies market so-called radiation suits. Examine the specifications carefully before relying on these products.

STANDARDS ORGANIZATIONS

North American consensus specification standards and testing standards for personal protective equipment are promulgated by several nonprofit standards organizations, including:

- ANSI, the American National Standards Institute
- ASTM International, formerly known as the American Society for Testing and Materials
- NFPA, the National Fire Protection Association
- CSA, the Canadian Standards Association

The principal European standards organization is CEN, the European Committee for Standardization. National organizations from over 160 countries participate in ISO, the International Organization for Standardization. The trade organization ISEA, the International Safety Equipment Association, represents companies that manufacture personal protective and other safety and health equipment. ISEA is a member of ANSI. Several ANSI standards originated as ISEA projects.

Military standards, MIL-STD, are developed by the U.S. Department of Defense. Military standards for personal protective equipment items are sometimes more stringent than the corresponding civilian consensus standards.

SUMMARY

Personal protective equipment is necessary to protect workers when other forms of hazard control are not available, or are not sufficient to ensure the degree of protection required. Even when primary and secondary controls are in place, such as engineering methods and safe work practices, PPE, as a tertiary control, may still be necessary in case of a failure of the other control methods. Personal protective equipment must be selected to match the hazards, which requires a careful hazard analysis. Both workers and managers must understand why PPE is necessary, how it works, and how to use it properly.

BIBLIOGRAPHY

ANSI/ISEA 101-1996 (R2008). American National Standard for Limited-Use and Disposable Coveralls—Size and Labeling Requirements. International Safety Equipment Association, 2008.

ANSI/ISEA 103-2010. American National Standard for Classification and Performance Requirements for Chemical Protective Clothing. Arlington, VA: International Safety Equipment Association, 2010.

ANSI/ISEA 105-2011. American National Standard for Hand Protection Selection Criteria. Arlington, VA: International Safety Equipment Association, February 2011.

ANSI/ISEA 107-2010. American National Standard for High-Visibility Safety Apparel and Headwear. Arlington, VA: International Safety Equipment Association, January 2010.

ANSI/ISEA Z87.1-2010. American National Standard for Occupational and Educational Eye and Face Protection Devices. Arlington, VA: International Safety Equipment Association, 2010.

ANSI/ISEA Z89.1-2009. American National Standard for Industrial Head Protection. Arlington, VA: International Safety Equipment Association, 2009.

ASTM F2412-05. Standard Test Methods for Foot Protection, 2005. West Conshohocken, PA: American Society for Testing and Materials, 2005.

ASTM F2413-05. Standard Specification for Performance Requirements for Foot Protection. West Conshohocken, PA: American Society for Testing and Materials, 2005.

Forsberg K, Keith L. *Chemical Protective Clothing: Performance Index*, 2nd ed. Hoboken, NJ: John Wiley and Sons, Inc., 1999.

Forsberg K, Mansdorf SZ. *Quick Selection Guide to Chemical Protective Clothing*, 5th ed. Hoboken, NJ: John Wiley and Sons, Inc., 2007.

Mansdorf SZ. *Recommendations for Chemical Protective Clothing: A Companion to the Pocket Guide to Chemical Hazards*, NIOSH on-line database: http://www.cdc.gov/niosh/ncpc/ncpc1.html

National Institute for Occupational Safety and Health. *Attention Emergency Responders: Guidance on Emergency Responder Personal Protective Equipment (PPE) for Response to CBRN Terrorism Incidents*. Publication 2008-132, Cincinnati, OH: NIOSH, 1990.

Occupational Safety and Health Administration. Chemical protective clothing, from *OSHA Technical Manual*. Washington, DC: OSHA, available on-line: http://www.osha.gov/dts/osta/otm/otm_viii/otm_viii_1.html

Occupational Safety and Health Administration. *Personal Protective Equipment*, OSHA Publication 3151. Washington, DC: OSHA, 2003.

Roder MM. *A Guide for Evaluating the Performance of Chemical Protective Clothing (CPC)*. NIOSH Publication 90-109. Cincinnati, OH: NIOSH, 1990.

Schwope PP, Costas JO, Weitzman DJ. *Guidelines for the Selection of Personal Protective Clothing*, 3rd ed. Cincinnati, OH: ACGIH, 1987.

University of California, Berkeley. Technology Transfer Program. Staying Safe in a Hard Hat, Available on-line: http://www.techtransfer.berkeley.edu/newsletter/09-4/hardhat.php

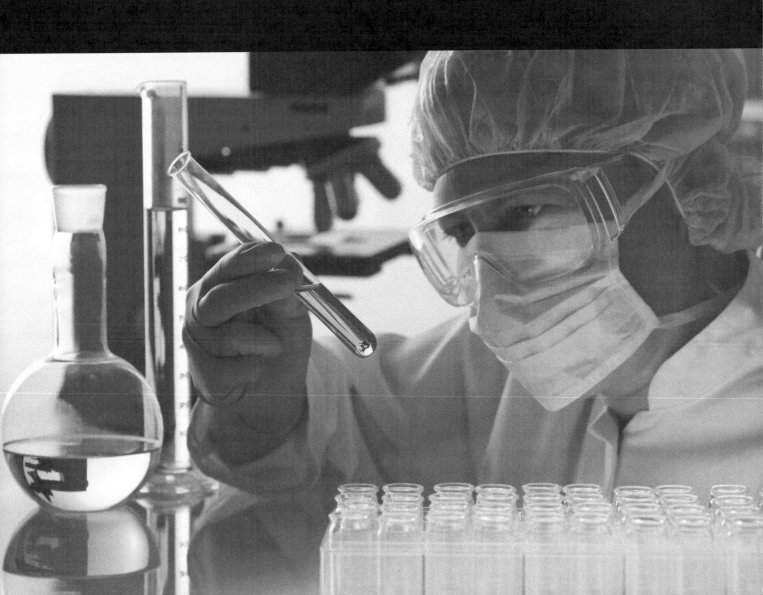

PART VI
Occupational Health and Safety Professions

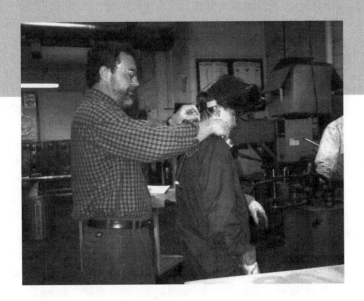

CHAPTER 24

The Industrial Hygienist

revised by Jill Niland, MPH, CIH, CSP

*T*his chapter discusses the background and definition of industrial hygiene, the interrelationship of the industrial hygienist and other occupational groups, occupational settings in which industrial hygienists function, and training programs. The reader will be able to define industrial hygiene, describe the types of jobs and settings in which industrial hygienists work, and identify specific types of educational curricula, resources, and professional organizations that deal with industrial hygiene.

INTRODUCTION

Industrial hygienists are scientists, engineers, and public health professionals committed to protecting the health of people in the workplace and the community. Industrial hygienists must be competent in a variety of scientific fields—principally chemistry, engineering, physics, toxicology, and biology—as well as the fundamentals of occupational medicine. Trained initially in one of these fields, most industrial hygienists acquire knowledge of the other allied disciplines by experience and postgraduate study.

In traditional industrial organizations, industrial hygienists were required to relate to personnel in other functions, including research and development, medical, management, safety, and production. Although the working relationships were close, it was understood that the industrial hygienist was not expected to have expertise in these areas. In today's organization, the industrial hygienist may also act as the safety or environmental professional. Flattened management structures and the use of self-directed work teams have created the need for flexible industrial hygienists who understand not only technical and scientific issues, but also

711

production and research concerns. Hygienists at all levels participate in management of cross-functional projects that draw on the expertise of all team members to develop and maintain a safe and healthful work environment. One of the challenges for this generation of industrial hygienists is maintaining a high level of technical expertise while broadening their roles in the activities just described.

Definition of Industrial Hygiene

The American Industrial Hygiene Association (AIHA) has defined industrial hygiene as

> the science and art devoted to the anticipation, recognition, evaluation, prevention, and control of those environmental factors or stresses arising in or from the workplace which may cause sickness, impaired health and well being, or significant discomfort among workers or among citizens of the community.
>
> Industrial hygienists are scientists and engineers committed to protecting the health and safety of people in the workplace and the community.
>
> While industrial hygiene is considered a "science," it is also an art that involves judgment, creativity, and human interaction. The goal of the industrial hygienist is to keep workers, their families, and the community healthy and safe. Industrial hygienists play a vital part in ensuring that federal, state, and local laws and regulations are followed in the work environment.
>
> Typical roles of the industrial hygienist include:
> - Investigating and examining the workplace for hazards and potential dangers
> - Making recommendations on improving the safety of workers and the surrounding community
> - Conducting scientific research to provide data on possible harmful conditions in the workplace
> - Developing techniques to anticipate and control potentially dangerous situations in the workplace and the community
> - Training and educating the community about job-related risks
> - Advising government officials and participating in the development of regulations to ensure the health and safety of workers and their families
> - Ensuring that workers are properly following health and safety procedures

To develop the depth of knowledge necessary to excel in industrial hygiene, many practitioners specialize in specific subdisciplines, such as toxicology, epidemiology, chemistry, ergonomics, acoustics, ventilation engineering, and statistics, among others. Industrial hygienists often find their work overlapping with that of safety professionals, health physicists, engineers, and others in the fields of air pollution, water pollution, solid waste disposal, and disaster planning.

Industrial hygienists often deal with a variety of health and safety challenges including:
- Indoor air quality (sick building syndrome, second-hand tobacco smoke)
- Evaluating and controlling environmental lead exposure
- Emergency response planning and community right-to-know
- Occupational disease (AIDS in the workplace, tuberculosis, silicosis)
- Potentially hazardous agents such as asbestos, pesticides, and radon gas
- Cumulative Trauma Disorders (repetitive stress injuries, carpal tunnel syndrome)
- Radiation (electromagnetic fields, microwaves)
- Reproductive health hazards in the workplace
- Setting limits on exposure to chemical and physical agents
- Detection and control of potential occupational hazards such as noise, radiation, and illumination
- Hazardous waste management

The industrial hygienist also makes contributions in employee education and training, law and product liability, sales, labeling, and public information. Other health professionals, including physicians, nurses, paramedics, and emergency medical technicians may at times assume some industrial hygiene functions.

Industrial Hygiene Functions

More than 50 years ago, Radcliffe et al. (1959) described the sphere of responsibility of industrial hygienists, which remains relevant today.
- Direct the industrial hygiene program.
- Examine the work environment.
- Study work operations and processes and obtain full details of the nature of the work, materials, and equipment used, products and by-products, number and sex of employees, and hours of work.
- Make appropriate measurements to determine the magnitude of exposure or nuisance to workers and the public, devise methods and select instruments suitable for such measurements, personally (or through others under direct supervision) conduct such measurements, and study and test material associated with the work operations.
- Using chemical and physical means, study the results of tests of biological materials, such as blood and urine, when such examination will aid in determining the extent of exposure.
- Interpret results of the examination of the environment in terms of its ability to impair health, nature of health impairment, workers' efficiency, and community nuisance or damage, and present specific conclusions to appropriate parties such as management, health officials, and

employee representatives.

- Make specific decisions as to the need for or effectiveness of control measures and, when necessary, advise as to the procedures that are suitable and effective for both the work environment and the general environment.
- Prepare rules, regulations, standards, and procedures for the healthful conduct of work and the prevention of nuisance in the community.
- Present expert testimony before courts of law, hearing boards, workers' compensation commissions, regulatory agencies, and legally appointed investigative bodies.
- Prepare appropriate text for labels and precautionary information for materials and products to be used by workers and the public.
- Conduct programs for the education of workers and the public in the prevention of occupational disease and community nuisance.
- Conduct epidemiological studies of workers and industries to discover the presence of occupational disease and establish or improve Threshold Limit Values® or standards for the maintenance of health and efficiency
- Conduct research to advance knowledge concerning the effects of occupation on health and means of preventing occupational health impairment, community air pollution, noise, nuisance, and related problems.

JOB DESCRIPTIONS

The job descriptions and titles of industrial hygiene personnel are often somewhat similar to those of safety personnel. In the recent past, they have evolved to reflect more team-oriented, entrepreneurial, and consultative approaches to safety and health management. However, many job descriptions have common elements that loosely coalesce around the following themes.

The entry-level employee may be called a safety or health technologist or technician. In this function, the employee evaluates hazards and operations using a few instruments, and investigates minor incidents involving occupational health issues.

Occupational Safety and Health Technologist

In 1976 the American Board of Industrial Hygiene (ABIH), in recognition of the growing group of technologists engaged in industrial hygiene activities, established an industrial hygiene technologist certification program. The technologist was recognized as someone who had acquired proficiency in an aspect or phase of industrial hygiene and who performed his or her duties under the supervision of an industrial hygienist. The designation "certified indus-

trial hygiene technologist" was awarded after the applicant passed an examination. In 1985, the ABIH and the Board of Certified Safety Professionals joined to operate this program through a joint committee, and the name was changed to Occupational Health and Safety Technologist (OHST). In 2008, ABIH sold its interest in the OHST certification to the Board of Certified Safety Professionals (BCSP), which became the sole administrator of the certification.

Occupational health and safety technologists, also called industrial hygiene technicians, perform occupational health and safety activities on a full-time or part-time basis as part of their job duties. Such duties may be ancillary to other job functions. Some examples of occupational health and safety activities are as follows: safety inspections; industrial hygiene monitoring; organizing and conducting health and safety training; investigating and maintaining records of occupational accidents, incidents, injuries, and illnesses; and similar functions. Candidates for the OHST need five years of experience in occupational health or safety activities, with those activities comprising at least 35 percent of job duties, must pass the OHST examination, and must complete Certification Maintenance requirements every five years. Candidates may substitute college courses in health and safety or an associate degree or higher in certain disciplines for up to two years of the experience requirement. The OHST examination deals with basic and applied science, laws, regulations and standards, control concepts, investigation (post-event), survey and inspection techniques, data computation and record keeping, education, training, and instruction.

Industrial hygiene technicians and occupational health and safety technologists can function efficiently in their limited technical area. They may take samples and make measurements in the facility or community. Their data and observations can be used to provide information for an industrial hygiene plan or program.

The duties of the technician require thoroughness, dependability, and a concern for the accuracy of the data being collected. They should be given a detailed outline of the duties and have reference information readily available. Technicians must see the relevance and value of their efforts, and their salary and position in the workplace structure should reflect the technician's relevance and value. The technician is part of the team in which the technician and industrial hygienist share responsibility.

Technology changes and adds new problems to the old ones. Rarely are old hazards totally controlled. New problems call for new approaches, new instrumentation, and new ways of recording, compiling, and integrating data. A decade ago, the advent of computerized exposure-monitoring databases accessible through the Internet allowed much quicker sharing of data. Now, fully electronic and computerized monitoring instrumentation can provide real time results for some personal exposures, and provide easily downloadable data that can be used to generate reports quickly.

Industrial Hygienist

An industrial hygienist is a somewhat more experienced and skilled employee than the technician, and functions similarly to the safety engineer. The industrial hygienist carries out more detailed studies of incidents; prepares recommendations and other reports; reviews new processes, machinery, and layouts from a health (or safety) viewpoint; promotes occupational health and safety education; and advises management about health hazards, industrial hygiene practices, procedures, and equipment needs.

The industrial hygiene manager or supervisor has traditionally had duties similar to those of a safety director, and may manage the entire industrial hygiene program. In fact, the last two decades have seen a significant collapsing of functions into an 'SHE' or safety/health/environment function, sometimes with added responsibilities in areas such as facility security, workers' compensation administration, and other aspects of risk management. This has sometimes required that routine activities such as exposure monitoring be delegated to personnel at lower levels.

Many facilities may also have concurrently reduced the size of their safety/health/environmental departments, and instead may rely on outside contractors to provide the personnel and skills necessary for various industrial hygiene projects. Other facilities may put the burden of more technical exposure assessment back on the manager, who again becomes, in some cases, a hands-on hygienist, without the assistance of a staff to support him or her with numerous responsibilities. Because they have the most experience and expertise, managers in these situations are likely to be called on to do the most complicated and advanced industrial hygiene tasks. Such a high degree of responsibility reinforces the need for a recognized level of competence in industrial hygiene personnel, which is provided by the certification mechanism.

Many certified industrial hygienists are also certified safety professionals and vice versa. Proficiency in industrial hygiene, by examination and by experience, follows a route roughly comparable to that of occupational safety. Moreover, the type of organization that employs the industrial hygienist or safety professional often requires similar skills of each. While many industrial hygienists work in private industry, many find positions in other types of organizations that require particular skill sets.

Government industrial hygienists may find that a diplomatic demeanor and well-developed interpersonal skills are among their most important assets. Similarly, consultants must have the flexibility to work with a wide range of clients and demands. Universities require professional capabilities in research, teaching, and program administration. University industrial hygienists need to be well versed in occupational and environmental issues to deal with the many complex problems involving chemical safety, worker safety, student safety, buildings and ground worker safety, building workers, and in those institutions affiliated with medical schools, hospital health, and laboratory biosafety. In such settings there are many opportunities for hands-on industrial hygiene work. Campus health and safety staff, for example, may conduct many laboratory inspections that include field measurements such as hood flow rate and face velocity. They work with contractors doing renovation projects and may need to make air and ventilation measurements. Radiation safety staff also carry out measurement surveys of areas where radiation sources are used.

Labor union industrial hygienists may handle technical inquiries from contractors, union officials, and union members; develop curricula for training and regulatory analyses and testimony; perform job site visits, inspections, and audits; and conduct presentations. Typically they do little actual sampling. Writing and communication skills are essential, as are good interpersonal skills (used in listening to workers and in conflict resolution).

The industrial hygienist should be able to determine whether there are alternative solutions to a problem. Obviously, leadership and management skills are required. Because they have more generalized skills, industrial hygienists should be able to make independent decisions. The industrial hygienist decides what information is available, and how to find the additional facts that are needed. The industrial hygienist must be able to work with other environmental health and safety professionals in the same functional area, and should have the experience, knowledge, and capability to specify corrective procedures to minimize or control environmental health hazards.

Many organizations try to "grow their own industrial hygienist"—that is, taking someone from inside the organization, who has some scientific background and a knowledge of the firm's products, and exposing him or her to a crash program in industrial hygiene. An organization initiating an industrial hygiene effort must recognize that knowledge of the organization alone is not enough for the optimal solution of industrial hygiene problems. The industrial hygienist must have the necessary professional education and expertise.

The capable industrial hygienist who has made the in-house adjustment to the organization's problems should have the versatility and capability to deal with any industrial hygiene problems that arise. In the development of a new product, for example, he or she should be able to meet with research and development personnel and determine the information that is needed. This might include toxicological data, labeling requirements, assistance to customers, and any special engineering control requirements as the research effort progresses through pilot state to commercial production.

With the assistance of an epidemiologist, the industrial hygienist can study an existing (or suspected) environmental health problem through epidemiological and biostatistical approaches, in addition to the usual sampling and measuring procedures. The industrial hygienist should know where to go (for example, personnel, purchasing, or process engineering) for the information he or she needs to investigate and solve a problem. If the industrial hygienist knows of another organization that makes similar products, he or she can exchange information with its EHS professionals and possibly tour each other's sites.

Industrial hygienists must work well with other professionals, such as physicians, nurses, environmental and safety engineers, toxicologists, health physicists, and others, in and out of the organization. They must also communicate and work very closely with employees. Employees have insights into potential health hazards in their work area that only those working with the processes every day can possess. They are a primary source of information and suggestions for the industrial hygienist.

Industrial Hygiene Manager

In an industry setting, the industrial hygiene manager supervises the technical and support staff in an environmental health and safety department; prepares budgets and plans; is familiar with government agencies related to the operation; relates industrial hygiene operations to research and development, production, environmental, and other departments or functions; and prepares appropriate reports. He or she may be called on to assist the corporate legal department when regulatory and worker compensation issues arise. The industrial hygiene manager should be certified by the ABIH (see the description of this organization in the Addendum to this chapter).

Many aspects of industrial hygiene expertise are unique. It makes sense for the industrial hygienist to extend his or her capabilities and sphere of activity by delegating responsibilities to others. This calls for supervisory and planning skills. The industrial hygienist must be able not only to plan, direct, and supervise technicians and assistants, but also to plan, program, and budget the activities of the department and staff. As a manager, he or she must establish priorities and initiate appropriate corrective action.

The industrial hygienist and the industrial hygiene manager must both be effective communicators. Many aspects of their work involve formal or impromptu training of employees, managers, and visitors to a facility. These professionals may also be called on to discuss an organization's health and safety goals and accomplishments with the media and other members of the public, and they must be articulate, knowledgeable, and able to convey technical information in nontechnical language.

Certified Industrial Hygienist (CIH)

The employer, employees, and the public have a right to be reasonably assured that the person to whom their lives are entrusted is professionally capable. One route by which such protection is provided is through licensing, usually by a government agency, a peer review arrangement, or both. Certification by the American Board of Industrial Hygiene (ABIH) provides this assurance. Additionally, industrial hygienists in a number of states have worked to develop various forms of licensing to ensure that only well qualified industrial hygienists are allowed to promote themselves as such.

To be a Certified Industrial Hygienist, an individual must meet rigorous standards of education and experience before proving, by examination, technical knowledge in the comprehensive practice of industrial hygiene. The exams are offered nationwide at commercial testing centers. At the end of 2010, there were over 6600 CIHs in active practice. The designation of certified industrial hygienist by the ABIH indicates that a person has received specific education, and has lengthy experience and proven professional ability in the comprehensive practice of industrial hygiene. Over the years, various sub-specialty exams, including ones in Acoustical Aspects, Air Pollution, Radiological and Toxicological Aspects, and Chemical Practice and Indoor Environmental Quality were offered and later discontinued, primarily due to low interest. There are many industrial hygienists who maintain certification in an aspect or sub-specialty; however certifying examinations in those aspects are no longer offered.

All CIHs must actively work to maintain their certification by earning a specified number of certification maintenance points during a five-year cycle. The certified industrial hygienist is the person most likely to direct an industrial hygiene program capably, to work with other professions and government agencies, and to provide the vision and leadership of an industrial hygiene program to keep occupational hazards at a minimum in a rapidly changing technology and society.

Industrial Hygienist-in-Training (IHIT)

This designation was formerly part of the ABIH's certification program. Historically, the ABIH had issued the IHIT category in 1972 because it then recognized that people with degrees and only one year of work experience wanted to take the core examination before completing the five years of experience in industrial hygiene necessary to take the comprehensive exam.

It was awarded after the candidate passed the core examination, which at that time was the first of two exams taken to become a CIH. The last core exam was given by the ABIH in Fall, 2001. Now the procedure to become a CIH has changed to one in which the candidate takes only one comprehensive examination. The IHIT certification has been phased out.

INDUSTRIAL HYGIENE, CIVIL SERVICE

Training Plan for Entry-Level OSHA Industrial Hygienists

Federally employed industrial hygienists have their own unique training programs that reflect the structure and duties of their positions. TED 01-00-018 instruction, Initial Training Program for OSHA Compliance Personnel issued in August 2008, describes the most recently revised training program for OSHA compliance personnel. TED 01-00-018 supersedes TED 01-00-012, which was issued in July 1992. New stipulations require that each newly hired CSHO complete a minimum of eight courses offered by the OSHA Training Institute (OTI) during the first three years of his/her career as a CSHO.

The OTI training program offers Regional Administrators the opportunity to incorporate up to four additional technical courses into the CSHO's initial three-year training plan. Each CSHO and his/her supervisor are required to track progress throughout the initial three-year period using an Individual Development Plan (IDP) that is updated annually.

The OSHA Training Institute offers formal training for CSHOs with a competency-based approach to curriculum. OSHA notes that competence cannot be achieved through formal training alone. Proficiency requires a mix of experiences over time, personal initiative to develop to the highest level of professionalism possible, and structured on-the-job training, as well as formal training.

OTI's training program provides a flexible program that incorporates technology enabled learning, self-study packages, on-the-job experiences and formal training, and has been developed to accommodate the varying levels of experience and competence during the initial three-year period of a CSHO's career. OTI's safety, health, and construction training paths are designed to reflect basic requirements and competencies applicable to all CSHOs as well as those intending to gain additional expertise. This flexible yet structured approach to curriculum meets the needs of CSHOs with highly diverse academic backgrounds and experiences.

Supervisors and managers are encouraged to incorporate their

office's training priorities into the CSHO's training program. For example, the needs of the Area Office may dictate that new CSHOs receive technical training in industrial noise or machine guarding within their first year. The OTI training program offers Regional Administrators the opportunity to incorporate up to four additional technical courses at any time during the CSHO's initial three-year training plan, provided the CSHO has completed two basic courses. OTI's articulated progression of training requirements for the first three-year period of a CSHO's career supports the pursuit of professional certification and encourages CSHOs to strive for the recognition that such certification provides.

First Three Years of CSHO Training

Organizational Responsibilities:

The National Office supports the training program by providing resources; supplying current information on the status of agency programs, standards, regulations, and directives; ensuring program consistency; and auditing Regional Office training programs.

The Directorate of Administrative Programs ensures that money is budgeted and available to regions for new hires to complete the required training during their first three years as CSHOs.

The Directorate of Training and Education is responsible for providing programs to educate and train OSHA compliance personnel in the skills and knowledge required to perform their duties. Responsibilities include:

1. Planning, developing, and conducting Agency technical and specialized training courses and seminars
2. Conducting needs assessments and gap analyses to identify training needs for compliance personnel
3. Developing classroom and technology-enabled training products designed to support the training and development of CSHOs
4. Maintaining and updating competency-based training information on the OSHA Intranet to assist CSHOs in selecting OSHA Training Institute courses and other training and development opportunities that match his/her Individual Development Plans (IDPs) and other professional development needs
5. Maintaining and updating the technology-enabled OTI course catalog on the OSHA Intranet
6. Conducting evaluations of training courses and programs designed for compliance personnel
7. Keeping CSHO's training records to reflect waived required training and time extensions for required training and alternative training for the #8200 Incident Command System I-200 course

The OSHA Training Institute Director is responsible for the scheduling and delivery of occupational safety and health training. Specific responsibilities include:

1. Overseeing and conducting courses and seminars for federal and State compliance officers, consultants, compliance assistance specialists, regional and national office staff, and other federal agency personnel

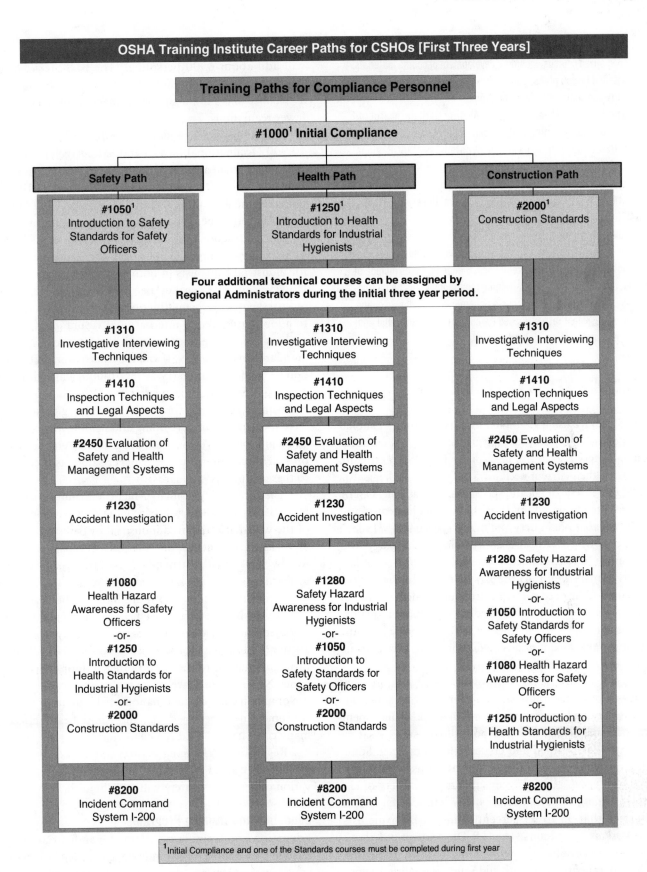

OSHA Training Institute Career Paths for CSHOs [First Three Years]

Training Paths for Compliance Personnel

#1000[1] Initial Compliance

Safety Path	Health Path	Construction Path
#1050[1] Introduction to Safety Standards for Safety Officers	**#1250[1]** Introduction to Health Standards for Industrial Hygienists	**#2000[1]** Construction Standards

Four additional technical courses can be assigned by Regional Administrators during the initial three year period.

#1310 Investigative Interviewing Techniques	**#1310** Investigative Interviewing Techniques	**#1310** Investigative Interviewing Techniques
#1410 Inspection Techniques and Legal Aspects	**#1410** Inspection Techniques and Legal Aspects	**#1410** Inspection Techniques and Legal Aspects
#2450 Evaluation of Safety and Health Management Systems	**#2450** Evaluation of Safety and Health Management Systems	**#2450** Evaluation of Safety and Health Management Systems
#1230 Accident Investigation	**#1230** Accident Investigation	**#1230** Accident Investigation
#1080 Health Hazard Awareness for Safety Officers -or- **#1250** Introduction to Health Standards for Industrial Hygienists -or- **#2000** Construction Standards	**#1280** Safety Hazard Awareness for Industrial Hygienists -or- **#1050** Introduction to Safety Standards for Safety Officers -or- **#2000** Construction Standards	**#1280** Safety Hazard Awareness for Industrial Hygienists -or- **#1050** Introduction to Safety Standards for Safety Officers -or- **#1080** Health Hazard Awareness for Safety Officers -or- **#1250** Introduction to Health Standards for Industrial Hygienists
#8200 Incident Command System I-200	**#8200** Incident Command System I-200	**#8200** Incident Command System I-200

[1]Initial Compliance and one of the Standards courses must be completed during first year

Figure 24–1. OSHA training paths for compliance personnel. *(Source: OSHA Instruction TED 01-00-018, Directorate of Training and Education, 2008.)*

2. Participating in the design and development of technical and specialized courses, including development of course materials, detailed lesson plans, and other educational aids necessary to carry out Institute training programs

The Regional Administrator (RA) directs the execution of the region-wide training and education program in accordance with OSHA policy, through the designated Assistant Regional Administrator (ARA). Specifically, the RA may, at his/her discretion and based on the CSHO's experience level, assign up to four additional technical courses during the initial three-year period of a CSHO's training program.

The Directorate of Training and Education Intranet page offers up-to-date information on course objectives, whether a course is blended, or has specific prerequisites. Blended courses include at least one online, web-based training requirement plus an instructor-led portion. Whenever a course prerequisite includes an online, blended session, that web-based training must be completed prior to attending the instructor-led session.

PERSONNEL NEEDS AND PROBLEMS

In 1975, OSHA, using 1973 NIOSH data, reported a national census of only 500 industrial hygienists, but 15,000 occupational safety and health specialists. The OSHA estimate indicated a then-current need for 5,500 industrial hygienists and 24,000 safety and health specialists. At that time, OSHA also predicted the need for 11,900 industrial hygienists and 62,300 occupational safety and health specialists by 1985.

Cycles of growth and contraction in industry and government have continued to affect the demand for industrial hygienists well into the 21st century. In the 1980s, expansion of the need for hygienists came in nontraditional areas such as environmental remediation, indoor air quality, and a number of areas that many see as temporary trends; asbestos management and remediation projects are prime examples.

In the 1990s, however, downsizing by many corporations resulted in industrial hygienists often functioning as safety and environmental or even risk-management professionals, or delegating responsibilities such as safety training to less trained and credentialed personnel. Some industrial hygienists whose corporate jobs were eliminated now serve as private consultants to a variety of clients, including the corporations they left. Currently it is estimated that 35 to 45 percent of industrial hygienists now work as consultants. The U.S. Department of Labor's Bureau of Labor Statistics reports that in 2008 there were 55,800 "Occupational Health and Safety Specialists," which include not just industrial hygienists but safety professionals and health physicists. The 2008 report also predicted about an 11 percent growth in those professions by 2018, which will add about 6300 personnel. The BLS *Occupational Outlook Handbook* notes that this average growth reflects a "balance of continuing public demand against a desire for fewer regulations."

The Bureau reports additionally that in 2008 there were 10,900 Occupational Health and Safety Technicians, and that a faster than average growth rate of 14 percent should add another 1600 personnel into that field by 2018. They note that the growth in both the "specialist" and "technician" fields may be hampered by off shoring of jobs.

If a contraction of government agencies occurs because of a changing political climate, this may mute the demand for industrial hygienists in both industry and government. However, the last decades also saw a movement by large industry, particularly multinational or "global" employers, to adopt national and international voluntary standards, such as those developed through the American National Standards Institute (ANSI) and the International Organization for Standardization (ISO). ISO 14000, which deals with an organization's management of its relationship to the environment, is such an example. Industrial hygienists clearly have roles to play in developing and helping implement the goals and objectives of these programs to ensure that an organization truly enhances worker safety as it conforms to these voluntary standards.

The outsourcing of many American manufacturing jobs in the 1990s and 2000s to less economically developed parts of the world also required industrial hygienists who work in, or as consultants to, multinational companies to adapt to new work environments, increased travel, and the need to learn international standards and regulations. Today's industrial hygienist is also more likely to be involved in community-based efforts like emergency response planning. Another trend in the last decades has been growth of indoor air quality investigations, which revolved around solving problems related to mold and other indoor air contaminants. New concerns have arisen in the last decade about the use of nanotechnology and nanoparticles in many different consumer and other products, and whose health effects in many cases haven't yet been characterized.

Regardless of changing settings and duties, the need for individuals trained in the prevention of disease and preservation of health and safety will not diminish.

Education and Training Programs
Education and training programs for industrial hygiene include professional school training, graduate curricula, and continuing education (short courses). Professional school curricula in industrial hygiene generally culminate in a Master of Science or a Master of Public Health degree.

Educational Resource Centers

NIOSH's findings of shortages of trained occupational safety and health graduates were cited in successful efforts to expand training grants programs. One part of this expansion was the introduction of multidisciplinary educational resource centers (ERCs). The other part was growth of single-discipline training grants.

Congress authorized creation of up to 20 Educational Resource Centers for occupational safety and health in 1976. Funding increased from $2.9 million in 1977 to $12.9 million in 1980, and in 2011 the ERCs number 17. In 1998, the name of these facilities was changed to Education and Research Centers. These centers provide continuing education to occupational health and safety professionals; combine medical, industrial hygiene, safety, and nursing training so that graduates are better able to work effectively in complex and diverse conditions; conduct research; and conduct regional consultation services. All ERCs are located in universities. The centers are distributed as widely as possible to give regional representation and to meet training needs for all areas of the nation.

About half of the financial support for professional OSH training programs comes from NIOSH. Measured in terms of graduate trainees, for the academic year 2008-2009 there were 689 full-time trainees enrolled in the major OSH disciplines in the ERCs. Of these, 423 (61%) were supported by NIOSH. There were 201 part-time trainees of which 83 (41%) were supported by NIOSH. NIOSH also supports 389 full-time and part-time academic and administrative positions in addition to 201 consultants. Currently there is concern that impending federal budget cuts will force the dismantling of the ERCs, greatly reducing the ability of industrial hygiene and occupational health and safety professionals to receive the education they require.

The ERCs should not be confused with the OSHA Training Institute (OTI) education centers, a program in which designated nonprofit organizations offer the most frequently requested OSHA Training Institute courses for the private sector and other Federal agency personnel.

OTI targets Federal and State compliance officers and State consultation program staff, but also provides training for private sector personnel and Federal personnel from agencies other than OSHA on a space available basis. However, during the 1980s, the number of requests for training from private sector personnel and Federal personnel from agencies other than OSHA increased substantially and the demand eventually exceeded the capacity of the OSHA Training Institute.

In October 1992, the OSHA Training Institute Education Center Program was created when OSHA began partnering with other training and educational institutions to conduct OSHA Training Institute courses. The organizations were selected through a national competitive process and would receive no funding from OSHA; they would be expected to support their OSHA training through their normal tuition and fee structures. Throughout the next decade, the OTI Education Centers Program continued to grow. From four OTI Education Centers in 1992, the Program realized continued growth, expanding to include at least one in each OSHA region. In December 2007, The U.S. Department of Labor announced the selection of eight new OSHA Training Institute (OTI) Education Centers. The annual number of students trained by the OTI Education Centers has steadily increased, with nearly 31,000 students trained and more than 2,000 classes offered by 25 centers in 2009.

Courses currently available through the OTI Education Centers include the most popular ones such as the #500 Trainer Course in Occupational Safety and Health Standards for the Construction Industry and #501 Trainer Course in Occupational Safety and Health Standards for General Industry. These "train the trainer" courses support the OSHA Outreach Training Program, which is the agency's primary way to train workers in the basics of occupational safety and health.

Educational Curricula

Graduate study programs have generally been developed to provide in-depth knowledge of a particular subject area and to develop scholarly research capabilities. The Accrediting Board of Engineering and Technology (ABET) has accredited master's level programs in industrial hygiene since 1985 and currently also accredits baccalaureate level programs. In early 2011, there were 22 accredited master's level programs and accredited baccalaureate level programs. ABET considers industrial hygiene (as well as safety, industrial management, or quality management) to be engineering related fields. The Academy of Industrial Hygiene has been the lead organization responsible for submitting program criteria for industrial hygiene baccalaureate and master's programs to ABET. In the past, these criteria stated specific numbers and types of semester hours of credit that degree candidates needed to complete the degree program. For example, a baccalaureate degree program required 63 or more semester hours of college-level mathematics, including technological courses and a minimum of 21 semester hours in communications, humanities, and social sciences. In the late 1990s, ABET's approach changed to one that asked organizations to state their criteria in terms of outcome measures.

The general criteria for baccalaureate level programs require the institution to evaluate and monitor students to determine if the program is meeting its objectives and that students are meeting program requirements.

Program Criteria for Bachelor's-Level Programs

The program must demonstrate that graduates have necessary knowledge, skills, and attitudes to competently and ethically implement and practice applicable scientific, technical, and regulatory aspects of Industrial Hygiene. To this end, graduates will be prepared to anticipate, recognize, evaluate, and control exposures of workers and others to physical, chemical, biological, ergonomic, and psychosocial factors, agents, and/or stressors that can potentially cause related diseases and/or dysfunctions. More specifically, graduates must be able to:

(a) identify agents, factors, and stressors generated by and/or associated with defined sources, unit operations, and/or processes;

(b) describe qualitative and quantitative aspects of generation of agents, factors, and stressors;

(c) understand physiological and/or toxicological interactions of physical, chemical, biological, and ergonomic agents, factors, and/or stressors with the human body;

(d) assess qualitative and quantitative aspects of exposure assessment, dose-response, and risk characterization based on applicable pathways and modes of entry;

(e) calculate, interpret, and apply statistical and epidemiological data;

(f) recommend and evaluate engineering, administrative, and personal protective equipment controls and/or other interventions to reduce or eliminate hazards;

(g) demonstrate an understanding of applicable business and managerial practices;

(h) interpret and apply applicable occupational and environmental regulations;

(i) understand fundamental aspects of safety and environmental health; and

(j) attain recognized professional certification.

The majority of core Industrial Hygiene and other supporting faculty must hold an earned doctorate. ("core Industrial Hygiene faculty" pertains to those who are teaching industrial hygiene courses and does not include faculty members teaching courses such as epidemiology, statistics, etc.) The majority of core Industrial Hygiene faculty should be Certified Industrial Hygienists; however, a minimum of one core Industrial Hygiene faculty member must be a Certified Industrial Hygienist. Faculty must also demonstrate external professional activity, including, but not limited to, participation on national, regional, state, and/or local committees and advisory boards, professional practice, and/or editorial reviews of professional publications. A full-time faculty member must be identified as administratively in charge of the program.

Program Criteria for Master's-Level Programs

Admitted students must hold an earned baccalaureate that prepares them to apply the basic principles of college-level mathematics, inorganic and organic chemistry, physics, and biology. Exceptions may be admitted with an individually documented plan of study to compensate for any deficiencies.

Master's-level Curriculum Criteria for master's-level programs require the following additions beyond the baccalaureate level: (i) a minimum of one year of study beyond the basic level, consisting of courses with increased depth and rigor; (ii) an applied science project or research activity resulting in a report that demonstrates both mastery of the subject matter and a high level of professional and public communication skills; (iii) an adequate foundation in statistics, applied sciences, and/or related professional practice; and, (iv) advanced qualitative and quantitative problem-solving skills.

Master's-Level Faculty

In addition to the general qualifications specified above for baccalaureate-level faculty, master-level faculty are expected to have demonstrated research activity appropriate to their institution's mission. A full-time faculty member must be identified as administratively in charge of the program.

Continuing Education

A wide variety of opportunities exist for industrial hygienists who want to remain technically current, receive training in previously unfamiliar aspects of industrial hygiene, pursue academic coursework leading to a more advanced degree, or earn certification maintenance points in order to maintain CIH certification.

A number of universities offer coursework leading to degrees. Also available at such universities are usually short courses (a few days or weeks long) on specific industrial hygiene topics. Summer institutes (1–4 weeks long) concentrating on a particular area of industrial hygiene are another opportunity.

Many of the NIOSH ERCs offer courses; most ERCs contain an industrial hygiene component that includes coursework leading to academic degrees and short courses. A number of other not-for-profit and for-profit training organizations provide short courses in industrial hygiene and related topics. These include the National Safety Council and professional industrial hygiene and safety societies as well as consulting firms.

There are also organizations that offer a wide range of self-paced educational activities, including programs that can be delivered over the Internet or in some cases by CD-ROM. Newer technologies also allow courses and seminars to be delivered over the web or via video conference. Large numbers of web sites now address safety, industrial hygiene, and environmental issues. Also available on the Internet are a variety of list-serves on environmental and occupational health that deliver up-to-date information to a computer subscription list.

SUMMARY

The need to control exposures to a rapidly rising number of chemicals and hazardous agents and to comply with and enforce governmental regulations and voluntary guidelines has brought about greater demand for industrial hygienists. This demand exists in private industry, labor unions, government, and academic organizations.

Individuals practicing industrial hygiene routinely work as a team; thus, the physician, the nurse, the safety professional, and the industrial hygienist are quite accustomed to working together. Other professions are included as needed, such as toxicologists, health physicists, epidemiologists, statisticians, professional trainers, and educators. A team approach, using the knowledge and skills of all these professionals, increases the effectiveness of programs to prevent occupational disease and injuries and helps to anticipate future requirements.

The need continues for industrial hygienists to interpret the findings of environmental investigations and to design and implement control measures. The industrial hygienist must, therefore, have the generalist's grasp of varied disciplines in order to interact with divergent groups in developing and maintaining the most effective program.

Educational requirements for industrial hygienists will continue to expand with the increasing need to monitor and control hazardous agents and to comply with more stringent government regulations and voluntary guidelines and standards, such as those promulgated by the American National Standards Institute and ACGIH. The training program for OSHA CSHOs was also discussed.

Personnel from three professional specialties—industrial hygiene, safety, and environmental health—will be working even more closely together in the future, their responsibilities overlapping in many instances. The separation between these professions has become increasingly blurred, and melding may eventually lead to the creation of a single profession whose scope is made up of what is currently recognized today as industrial hygiene and safety.

BIBLIOGRAPHY

Accrediting Board for Engineering and Technology. *Criteria for Accrediting Applied Science Programs.* Baltimore, MD: ABET, 2010. http://www.abet.org

American Board of Industrial Hygiene. Information about Certification for the Practice of Industrial Hygiene. Lansing, MI: ABIH, 2000. http://www.abih.org/certified/index.html.

American Board of Industrial Hygiene website, accessed April 22, 2011, and earlier dates. http:// www.abih.org

American Conference of Governmental Industrial Hygienists website, accessed April 22, 2011, and earlier dates.

http://www.acgih.org

American Industrial Hygiene Association. *About AIHA.* Fairfax, VA: AIHA, accessed April 22, 2011, and previous dates. http://www.aiha.org.

American Industrial Hygiene Association website, accessed April 22, 2011, and earlier dates. http://www.aiha.org/aih/aihindex.html

American Public Health Association. *About Us.* Washington, DC: APHA, accessed April 22, 2011, and earlier dates. http://www.apha.org

Berry CM. What is an industrial hygienist? *National Safety News* 107:69–75, 1973.

Constantin MJ, et al. Status of industrial hygiene graduate education in U.S. institutions. *AIHA Journal* 55:537–545, 1994.

Corn M, Heath ED. OSHA response to occupational health personnel needs and resources. *AIHA Journal* 38:11–17, 1977.

Hermann ER. Education and training of industrial hygienists. *National Safety Congress Trans* 12:64–66, 1975.

Office of Technology Assessment, U.S. Congress. Preventing Injury and Illness in the Workplace (unpublished manuscript). New York: InfoSource, 1985.

Radcliffe JC, Clayton GD, Frederick WG, et al. Industrial hygiene definition, scope, function, and organization. *American Industrial Hygiene Association Journal* 20:429–430, 1959.

U.S. Department of Labor. Occupational Outlook Handbook 2010-2011, edited by Bureau of Labor Statistics. Washington, DC: U.S. DOL, 2010.

ADDENDUM: PROFESSIONAL SOCIETIES AND COURSES OF INTEREST TO INDUSTRIAL HYGIENISTS

American Industrial Hygiene Association

The American Industrial Hygiene Association (AIHA), founded in 1939, is a nonprofit professional society for people practicing industrial hygiene in industry, government, labor, academic institutions, and independent organizations.

AIHA promotes the recognition, evaluation, and control of environmental stresses arising in the workplace and encourages increased knowledge of occupational and environmental health by bringing together specialists in this field. AIHA reported a national membership over 10,000 in early 2011, with 73 local sections. The American Industrial Hygiene Conference and Exposition, cosponsored by AIHA, draws more than 10,000 industrial hygiene professionals each May or June.

AIHA Membership Qualifications and Types

Full membership is for individuals who have worked primarily in industrial hygiene-related activities for at least three years and who hold a baccalaureate degree in industrial hygiene, chemistry, physics, engineering, biology, or other approved discipline. Graduate education may be substituted for some of the experience requirement.

Associate membership is for individuals who have less than three years of experience in the industrial hygiene field. They must hold an associate degree in industrial hygiene, chemistry, physics, engineering, biology, or other discipline, or substitute experience for the educational requirement.

Any person who interacts with occupational and environmental health professionals may become an affiliate member of AIHA. An individual who resides in, and is a citizen of, a country defined by the World Bank as a low-income, lower-middle-income, or upper-middle-income economy, and who is practicing occupational and environmental health and safety can become an international affiliate member.

Individuals enrolled at the college undergraduate or graduate level taking at least one-half the credit hours required for full-time status can join as student members.

Retired membership is reserved for current Full or Associate members who are no longer actively employed (defined as less than 10% of the time) in the practice of industrial hygiene or occupational and environmental health and safety.

Organizational membership is open to organizations having an interest in the industrial hygiene profession.

Local Section Membership

Any person with a professional interest in industrial hygiene may apply for membership in an AIHA local section.

Address: American Industrial Hygiene Association, 2700 Prosperity Ave., Suite 250, Fairfax, VA 22031, (703) 849-8888, www.aiha.org

American Board of Industrial Hygiene

The American Board of Industrial Hygiene (ABIH) was established to improve the practice and educational standards of the profession of industrial hygiene. In 1957, the American Industrial Hygiene Association (AIHA) set out to establish a certification program for qualified industrial hygienists. The American Conference of Governmental Industrial Hygienists joined the effort in 1958. The ABIH was incorporated as an independent organization to develop and administer the certification program. Six members from each sponsoring organization made up the first board; its first annual meeting was held in 1960.

The American Board of Industrial Hygiene issues certificates in the Comprehensive Practice of Industrial Hygiene. In prior years, to achieve certification, each applicant had to pass a two-part examination. In 2001 the first, or Core, examination was eliminated, the ABIH having decided that two full-day examinations were not necessary to identify CIH level practitioners.

The ABIH also administers a certification maintenance program for CIHs. The purpose of this program is to ensure that CIHs continue to develop and enhance their professional industrial hygiene skills for the duration of their careers. The certificate is granted for a period of five years, after which time it expires unless renewed. Certificate holders must provide evidence to the board of their continued professional qualifications in order to renew the certificate. Activities that are accepted as evidence include continuing professional industrial hygiene practice; membership in an approved professional society (other than the Academy of Industrial Hygiene); attendance at approved meetings, seminars, and short courses; participation in technical committees; publishing in peer-reviewed journals; teaching that is not part of the diplomate's primary practice; approved extracurricular professional activities; and reexamination or examination for an additional certification. Points for the approved activities are awarded and publicized by the board, as is a schedule for renewal of certificates.

Besides being entitled to use the CIH designation, people certified in comprehensive practice become members of the Academy of Industrial Hygiene.

Address: American Board of Industrial Hygiene, 6015 West St. Joseph, Suite 102, Lansing, Michigan 48917-3980, (517) 321-4624, www.abih.org

Academy of Industrial Hygiene

The Academy of Industrial Hygiene (AIH) is the organization that represents the interests of Certified Industrial Hygienists who are members of the AIHA or who are Academy Affiliate Members. The Academy is an entity within the AIHA whose purpose is to foster, protect, and advance the recognized competencies of the industrial hygiene practitioner, the professional credentials of the industrial hygiene field, and to ultimately protect the health of workers and the community at large. In 1966, the American Academy of Industrial Hygiene was created as a professional organization. In 1999, AIHA and AAIH voted to merge the Academy into AIHA; the AAIH later became the Academy of Industrial Hygiene.

Activities include establishment of a code of ethics to serve as a guide for professional conduct by industrial hygienists; promotion of the recognition of industrial hygiene as a profession by individuals, employers, and regulatory agencies; advancement of board certification as a basic qualification for employment as an industrial hygienist in both public and private organizations; accreditation of academic programs in industrial hygiene in cooperation with the Accreditation Board of Engineering and Technology; and recruitment of students into academic programs and training through initial education and continuing education for practicing industrial hygienists.

The AIH sponsors the Professional Conference on Industrial Hygiene to provide a forum for exploring professional issues. Continuing education opportunities also are provided. The conference is aimed primarily at issues encountered by the more experienced industrial hygienist, but is not restricted to members of AIH.

See http://www.aiha.org/insideaiha/academy

American Conference of Governmental Industrial Hygienists

The American Conference of Governmental Industrial Hygienists (ACGIH®) was organized in 1938 by a group of government industrial hygienists who desired a medium for the free exchange of ideas and experiences and the promotion of standards and techniques in occupational and environmental hygiene. As of 2011, ACGIH has a membership of approximately 3,000 industrial hygienists. Many hygienists belong to both AIHA and ACGIH.

As an organization devoted to the development of administrative and technical aspects of worker health protection, the ACGIH has contributed substantially to the development and improvement of official occupational health services to industry and labor. ACGIH endeavors to provide opportunities, information, and other resources needed by those who protect worker health and safety. Technical committees, publications, symposia, journals, and other programs work toward this goal. The committees on industrial ventilation and Threshold Limit Values® are recognized throughout the world for their expertise and contributions to industrial hygiene. The ACGIH sets TLVs® as well as Biological Exposure Indices® and annually updates these values.

The mission of the ACGIH is to be an indispensable resource for industrial hygienists and related professionals worldwide. Its purposes are to promote excellence in environmental and occupational health; to provide technical information of the highest quality; to benefit the occupational health and well-being of people worldwide; and to serve the membership and continually improve the organization, including its financial and human resources. It provides a variety of products and services members' needs, including the yearly revision of *Threshold Limit Values® for Chemical Substances and Physical Agents and Biological Exposure Indices*.® This booklet is an indispensable resource that contains quantitative exposure guidelines industrial hygienists use to compare to air and biological sampling results.

ACGIH Membership

ACGIH was originally formed as an organization of industrial hygienists who worked in government. It has recently expanded its scope to offer membership to a broader spectrum of practitioners. Today, anyone who is engaged in the practice of industrial hygiene or occupational and environmental health and safety is eligible for one of five categories of membership.

Regular: An occupational hygiene, occupational health, environmental health, or safety professional whose primary employment is with a government agency or an educational institution.

Associate Member: A person who is engaged in the occupational hygiene, environmental health, occupational health or safety professions, but is not eligible for Regular membership.

Student Member: A person officially enrolled in a full-time course of study in occupational hygiene or a related discipline.

Retired Member: A Regular or Associate member no longer actively employed in occupational hygiene or a related profession. Retirement is defined as employment less than twenty-five percent (25%) of full-time.

Organizational Member: An institution or organization supporting the activities of ACGIH®.

Address: ACGIH, Kemper Meadow Center, 1330 Kemper Meadow Drive, Cincinnati, OH 45240. (513) 742-2020, www.acgih.org

American Public Health Association

The American Public Health Association (APHA), established in 1872, is 50,000 strong in its collective membership, which represents all the disciplines and specialties in the public health spectrum. The APHA is devoted to the protection and promotion of public health. It

- sets standards for alleviating health problems,
- initiates projects designed for improving health, both nationally and internationally,
- researches health problems and offers possible solutions based on that research,
- launches public awareness campaigns about special health dangers,
- publishes materials reflecting the latest findings and developments in public health.

The APHA has over 30 special discipline-based groups that provide places to present papers, share ideas, and get information; these include an occupational health and safety section that includes occupational health physicians and nurses, industrial hygienists, and other allied occupational health professionals

APHA Membership

A number of categories of membership are available:

Regular membership is open to health professionals, other career workers in the health field and any persons interested in public health.

Contributing members are health professionals, other career workers in the health field, and any persons interested in public health.

Special subsidized categories of membership include student member, transitional member (available for one year to those student members who have completed their degree), retired members, consumer members, and special health worker members (those employed in community health with annual salary of less than $40,000 or the equivalent in foreign nations.)

An Agency Member is an organizational membership open to non-profit organizations which requires the approval of the APHA Executive Board.

Address: American Public Health Association, 800 I Street NW, Washington, DC, 20001-3710, (202) 777-APHA, www.apha.org

The Safety Professional

by Peter B. Rice, CIH, CSP

*T*his chapter deals with the role of the safety professional in an effective occupational safety and health program. The duties and functions of safety professionals and how they work with other professionals are briefly discussed, as well as several ways the safety professional can contribute to the success of an occupational safety and health program. As total safety is multidisciplinary, it is critical that the industrial hygienist become familiar with the roles and function of the safety professional.

SCOPE AND FUNCTIONS OF THE SAFETY PROFESSIONAL

Safety is a multidisciplinary profession, drawing its professionals from many different fields such as safety management, industrial hygiene, education, engineering, psychology, medicine, biophysics, chemistry, and labor. Safety professionals identify hazards and evaluate them for the potential to cause injury or illness to people or harm of property and the environment. The safety professional recommends administrative and engineering controls that eliminate or minimize the risk and danger posed by hazards. They work with professionals in other disciplines in many different job settings. They work for companies, government agencies, and private organizations or offer individual professional services. They may engage in design, planning, program management, training, audit, and other aspects of practice. Additionally, they apply hazard recognition, evaluation, and control knowledge and skills in the following areas:
- equipment
- systems
- facilities
- processes

- operations
- manufacturing
- transportation
- construction
- insurance services.

The safety profession today is a sophisticated discipline combining engineering, chemistry, biology, business, behavioral psychology, and a rich knowledge about such topics as systems safety analysis, human factors engineering, biomechanics, and product safety (Figures 25–1, 25–2). In addition, the safety professional must possess a thorough knowledge of an organization's and facility's equipment, property, manufacturing processes, employees, and culture. In many organizations the safety professional must be able to work with management, supervisors, and employees with varying linguistic and cultural backgrounds. The safety professional must display tact, diplomacy, diversity, persuasiveness, persistence, and leadership. In short, today's safety professional must wear many hats and orchestrate many roles.

The safety professional should serve as a counselor to the organization's chief executive. The safety professional must be able to approach the upper management of an organization as an equal. To do this, he or she must understand the basic technology and mission of the organization.

An increasing number of institutions of higher education offer degrees in safety engineering and/or safety management. Such degrees, and the courses leading to them, are essential to the continuing development of safety and health professionals. There are more than 125 colleges and universities that offer degrees in safety management, occupational safety, environmental protection, or a related field. A list of these schools is available from the American Society of Safety Engineers.

In its broadest sense, industrial hygiene has come to mean not only freedom from disease but from injury as well. Because of this, the safety professional has become more closely aligned with the industrial hygienist and the field of occupational medicine. It is rare to find a safety professional who does not also practice some traditional industrial hygiene or vice versa, and even environmental protection in many instances.

There is no question that accidents are painful and costly to the worker, the worker's family, fellow workers,

SCOPE OF A SAFETY PROFESSIONAL

To perform their professional functions, safety professionals must have education, training, and experience in a common body of knowledge. Safety professionals need to have a fundamental knowledge of physics, chemistry, biology, physiology, statistics, mathematics, computer science, engineering mechanics, industrial processes, business, communication, and psychology. Professional safety studies include industrial hygiene and toxicology, design of engineering hazard controls, fire protection, ergonomics, system and process safety, safety and health program management, accident investigation and analysis, product safety, construction safety, education and training methods, measurement of safety performance, human behavior, environmental safety and health, and safety, health, and environmental laws, regulations, and standards. Many safety professionals have backgrounds or advanced study in other disciplines, such as management and business administration, engineering, education, physical and social sciences, and other fields. Others have advanced study in safety. This extends their expertise beyond the basics of the safety profession.

Because safety is an element in all human endeavors, safety professionals perform their functions in a variety of contexts in both public and private sectors, often employing specialized knowledge and skills. Typical settings are manufacturing, insurance, risk management, government, education, consulting, construction, healthcare, engineering and design, waste management, petroleum, facilities management, retail, transportation, and utilities. Within these contexts, safety professionals must adapt their functions to fit the mission, operations, and climate of their employer.

Not only must safety professionals acquire the knowledge and skills to perform their functions effectively in their employment context, through continuous education and training, they stay current with new technologies, changes in laws and regulations, and changes in the workforce, workplace, and world business, political, and social climate.

As part of their positions, safety professionals must plan for and manage resources and funds related to their functions. They may be responsible for supervising a diverse staff of professionals.

By acquiring the knowledge and skills of the profession, developing the mind set and wisdom to act responsibly in the employment context, and keeping up with changes that affect the safety profession, the safety professional is able to perform required safety professional functions with confidence, competence, and respected authority.

Figure 25–1. The scope of the safety professional as defined by the American Society of Safety Engineers. *(Reprinted with permission from the ASSE, www.asse.org.)*

FUNCTIONS OF A SAFETY PROFESSIONAL

The major areas relating to the protection of people, property and the environment are:

1. Anticipate, identify and evaluate hazardous conditions and practices.
2. Develop hazard control designs, methods, procedures and programs.
3. Implement, administer and advise others on hazard control programs.
4. Measure, audit and evaluate the effectiveness of hazard control programs.

Because safety is an element in all human endeavors, safety professionals perform their functions in a variety of contexts in both public and private sectors, often employing specialized knowledge and skills. Typical settings are manufacturing, insurance, risk management, government, education, consulting, construction, healthcare, engineering and design, waste management, petroleum, facilities management, retail, transportation and utilities. Within these contexts, safety professionals must adapt their functions to fit the mission, operations and climate of their employer.

Not only must safety professionals acquire the knowledge and skills to perform their functions effectively in their employment context, through continuing education and training they stay current with new technologies, changes in laws and regulations, and changes in the workforce, workplace, and world business, political and social climate.

As part of their positions, safety professionals must plan for and manage resources and funds related to their functions. They may be responsible for supervising a diverse staff of professionals.

By acquiring the knowledge and skills of the profession, developing the mind set and wisdom to act responsibly in the employment context, and keeping up with changes that affect the safety profession, the safety professional is able to perform required safety professional functions with confidence, competence and respected authority.

Figure 25–2. The functions of the professional safety position as defined by the American Society of Safety Engineers. *(Reprinted with permission from the ASSE website: www.asse.org.)*

the community, and even to society as a whole. (The term *accident* as used here is defined to mean any unexpected event that interrupts the work sequence or process and that may result in injury, illness, or property damage to the extent that it causes loss.) Accidents produce personal, economic, and social loss, impair individual and group productivity, cause inefficiency, upset employee morale and public image, and generally retard progress. Also, in today's world, an organization with a poor safety program often finds it difficult to compete as safety is demanded at nearly all levels by responsible organizations.

Dedicated, motivated, and passionate safety professionals continue to be accident prevention's most valuable asset. The ranks of safety professionals have grown over the years.

On October 11, 1911, a group of 35 safety inspectors formed the United Society of Casualty Inspectors. The group had an office in the Engineering Societies' building in New York City. In 1914, the organization changed its name to American Society of Safety Engineers (ASSE).

In 2011, 100 years after its founding, ASSE has more than 34,000 members who work across all industries around the world protecting people, improving business, and safeguarding the environment. The Society relocated to Chicago in 1924, moved to Park Ridge, IL, in 1967, and has been headquartered in Des Plaines, IL, since 1985. The ASSE has 17 practice specialties, 151 chapters, 28 sections, and 58 student sections.

There are many other qualified safety professionals in addition to the ASSE members, who, together with thousands of specialists and technicians, carry out a limited scope of activities within the occupational safety and health field.

In 1968, the ASSE was instrumental in forming the Board of Certified Safety Professionals (BCSP). Since 1969, over 30,000 individuals have achieved a safety, health, and/or environmental (SH&E) credential. Currently, over 12,000 hold the Certified Safety Professional (CSP) credential and 7,500 retain an Occupational Health and Safety Technologist (OHST), Construction Health and Safety Technologist (CHST), or Safety Trained Supervisor (STS) credential. The value of the safety certification continues to grow. In the United States, numerous laws, regulations, and standards cite it. More importantly, many companies include it in position standards, government agencies rely on it, and contracts for safety services require it.

In 1985, the BCSP and the American Board of Industrial Hygiene (ABIH) began joint sponsorship of the OHST and the CHST certification programs.

There has been an orderly development of safety knowledge, which, when applied with sufficient skill and judgment, has produced significant reductions in occupational disease and in many types of accidents and accidental injuries. However, the tremendous increase in scientific knowledge and technological progress has added to the complexities of safety work.

The focus on the control of industrial disease and accident prevention has oscillated between environmental control or engineering and human factors. Some important trends in the pattern of the safety professional's development have emerged.

- First, increasing emphasis on analyzing the loss potential of the activity with which the safety professional is concerned; such analysis requires greater ability to predict where and how loss- and injury-producing events will occur and to find the means of preventing such events.
- Second, increased development of factual, unbiased, and objective information about loss-producing problems and accident causation, so that those who have ultimate decision-making responsibilities can make sound decisions.
- Third, increasing use of the safety professional's help in developing safe products. The application of the principle of accident causation and control to the product being designed or produced has become more important because of product liability cases; legal aspects in the general field of safety and health, including negligent design; and the obvious impact that a safer product has on the overall safety and health of the environment.

CAREERS IN SAFETY

Protecting America's, and in many cases the international, work force, the general public, and the environment from injury and illness in today's age of technological and scientific advancement has become one of the most challenging and rewarding career fields available. It is here that the safety professional brings to bear technical knowledge, skill, and expertise along with management abilities developed through years of education and practical experience.

There are many career options that one may pursue as a safety professional. The safety professional has the responsibility for studying materials, structures, codes, and operations to find the best way to use resources to control hazards, which can lead to accidents, illness, fires, explosions, etc. Resources may include tools, equipment, machinery, buildings, or any other items that can prevent hazards. Accidents may cause injuries to people or damage to property and the environment as well as other adverse effects.

Safety managers recognize and devise methods to control hazards using the management skills and techniques needed to administer a department or facility. The safety manager may direct the safety program of a large plant, corporation, or a department within local, state, or the federal government.

One very common career within the safety profession is that of a loss control representative for an insurance organization. These professionals help organizations that are insured or seeking to be insured identify risks within their operations and reduce the possibility of accidents, fires, and other losses.

The broad field of safety is concerned with the interaction between people and the physical, chemical, biological, ergonomic, and psychological forces that affect their well-being. It is necessary to realize that all of these forces influence or affect people simultaneously; therefore the safety professional cannot study one area without considering the effects of the others.

The largest employers of safety professionals are manufacturing, service industries, construction, insurance, consulting firms, and the government.

DEFINITION OF A SAFETY PROFESSIONAL

What, then, is a safety professional? The Board of Certified Safety Professionals of the Americas, Inc. has identified a safety professional as a person engaged in the prevention of accidents, incidents, and events that harm people, property, or the environment. In the 21st century, safety professionals confront new challenges not faced a generation or even a decade ago. Today's safety professionals are well-educated, highly motivated and aim to recognize, evaluate, and control risks to people, property, and the environment. They must be able to apply technology and work with top management to minimize risk and ensure that safety, health, and environmental performance are fundamental measures of a business's and/or organization's success.

Professional safety practice today involves aspects of engineering, business, health, education, laws and regulations, human behavior, education and training, and computer and internet technologies. Safety professionals use qualitative and quantitative analysis of simple and complex products, systems, operations, and activities to identify hazards. They evaluate the hazards to identify what events can occur and the likelihood of occurrence, severity of results, risk (a combination of probability and severity), and cost. Safety professionals make recommendations to managers, designers, employers, government agencies, and others. Controls may involve administrative controls (such as plans, policies, procedures, training, etc.), engineering controls (such as safety features and systems, fail-safe features, barriers, and other forms of protection), and personal protective equipment (PPE). Safety professionals may also manage and implement controls.

Besides knowledge of a wide range of hazards, controls, and safety assessment methods, safety professionals must have knowledge of physical, chemical, biological, and behavioral sciences, mathematics, business, training and educational techniques, engineering concepts, and particular kinds of operations (construction, manufacturing, transportation, and other like industries).

Accident Prevention Activities

The basic accident prevention activities (in descending order of effectiveness and preference) are as follows:

- Eliminate the hazard from the machine, method, material, or facility structure.
- Control or contain the hazard by enclosing or guarding it at its source or exhausting an airborne hazard away from the operator.
- Train operating personnel to be aware of the hazard and to follow safe job procedures to avoid it.
- Prescribe personal protective equipment for personnel to

Figure 25–3. Personal protective equipment is commonly used to protect employees from potentially hazardous operations.

shield them from the hazard (Figure 25–3).

It is beyond the scope of this section to describe completely all accident prevention activities of safety professionals at each operation. However, the primary responsibilities are outlined here:

- Provide advisory services on safety and health problems and other matters related to accident prevention.
- Develop a centralized program to control hazards.
- Keep informed of changes in local, state, federal, and in some cases international safety codes, and communicate such information to management.
- Develop and apply safety standards both for production facilities (equipment, tools, work methods, and safeguarding) and for products, based on applicable legal and voluntary codes, rules, and standards.
- Work closely with the engineering, industrial hygiene, medical, and purchasing departments during the development and construction of new equipment and facilities. See that a procedure is established to ensure that only safe tools, equipment, and supplies are purchased; advise the purchasing department on acceptable supplies and materials; and review and approve purchase requisitions for personal protective equipment and safety items.
- Develop, plan, and implement the safety and health inspection program carried out by the operating supervisors and field safety personnel to identify potential hazards, both in the workplace and in the use of the organization's products. Inspect all new equipment in conjunction with engineering, operating, and personnel representatives for adequate safeguards and freedom from major safety and health hazards.
- Guide operating supervision in accident investigations to determine the accident's cause and to prevent recurrence. Review non-disabling-injury accident reports on a sample basis to check the thoroughness of the accident investigation and corrective actions taken.
- Collect and analyze data on injury, illness, and accidents for the purpose of instituting corrective action and to determine accident trends and provide targets for corrective action. Maintain such files as those of inspection records, employee training, OSHA injury and illness logs, a hazard log, and files of complaints and suggestions.
- Ensure education and training of employees in general and specific safety and health principles and techniques (Figure 25–4). Maintain supervisory contacts for new instructions, follow-up, and general safety and health motivation.
- Cooperate with medical personnel on matters of employee health and fitness to work, and with industrial hygiene or environmental quality control personnel on industrial hygiene problems.

Figure 25–4. Construction site daily toolbox safety meeting. Meetings such as this are an important tool for educating employees about the importance of site specific activities, anticipated hazards, safe work practices, and controls.

SAFETY AND HEALTH PROGRAMS

Management usually places administration of the accident prevention or safety and health program in the hands of a safety professional whose title is safety director, manager of safety, or loss control manager.

Full staff responsibility for the safety activities should be assigned to one person. The decision concerning proper placement of responsibility should be based on the size of the organization and the nature of the hazards involved in its operation.

Employment of full-time safety professionals is increasing for the following reasons:

- The passage of the Occupational Safety and Health Act (OSHA) of 1970 requires that certain safety standards be met and maintained.
- A better understanding of the safety professional's services and functions is developing. To administer a safety program effectively, the individual in charge must be highly trained and/or have many years of experience in the safety field.

A safety and health program is not something that is imposed on organization operations as an afterthought. Safety, an integral part of organization operations, must be built into every process or product design and into every operation, activity, and procedure.

The prevention of accidents, illness, and injuries is basically achieved through control of the working environment and control of employees' safety behaviors. The safety professional can assist management to implement such controls.

An organization with an effective health and safety pro-

gram has a working environment in which operations can be conducted safely, economically, and efficiently, with a minimum of employee, customer, and public complaints.

STAFF VERSUS LINE STATUS

In general, the safety and health program is administered by safety professionals or other persons holding line positions in a small company, or staff positions in a large organization. In large organizations, the safety professional(s) and their organization(s) usually have staff status and authority. The exact organizational status of the safety staff is determined by each organization in terms of its own operating policies.

The safety and health program as a staff function should have the following objectives:

- to establish staff credibility and to advise and counsel regarding safety or health matters
- to keep all affected personnel adequately informed regarding safety or health matters
- to ensure that responsibility and accountability for safety are properly assigned with every staff group and operating management
- to program activities that support harmonious supervisor/employee interaction on safety or health matters
- to establish and reinforce consistent attention to preventive practices and actions.

Sometimes the safety professional is delegated authority that is usually reserved for line officials. It is common to find that the safety professional has "Stop Work" authority or authority to order immediate changes to specific equipment, procedures, or operations in the following areas:

- fast-moving and rapidly changing operations
- operations on which delayed action would endanger the lives of workers or others, as in construction and demolition work, fumigation, and chemical processes or processes with other dangerous substances
- emergency work

CODES AND STANDARDS

The safety professional must be familiar with codes and standards applicable to equipment, material, environmental controls, and energy sources. Only by knowing which codes and standards apply can the safety professional give valid advice regarding organization standards for purchasing specifications. The safety professional must know how to meet government agency regulatory requirements (such as those of OSHA, EPA, and the Mine Safety and Health

Administration [MSHA]), but there are also many other guidelines and consensus standards that provide state-of-the-art models. Therefore, the safety professional should be familiar with the following:

- codes and standards approved by the American National Standards Institute (ANSI) and other standards and specifications groups (see Bibliography)
- codes and standards adopted or set by local, state, federal, and in some cases international government or other agencies
- codes, standards, and lists of approved or tested devices published by such recognized authorities as Underwriters Laboratories, Inc., and the National Fire Protection Association
- safety practice recommendations of such organizations as the National Safety Council, American Society of Safety Engineers (ASSE), American Conference of Governmental Industrial Hygienists (ACGIH), American Industrial Hygiene Association (AIHA), insurance carriers or their associations, and trade and industrial organizations.

Policies and Procedures

One of the main tasks confronting the safety professional is the development and implementation of organization safety and health policies and procedures. Policies and procedures are necessary to ensure that OSHA and organization requirements for safety and health are carried out uniformly within an organization. Examples of policies and procedures that many organizations would have in a safety and health program (e.g., Injury and Illness Prevention Program) might include

- management commitment/assignment of responsibilities;
- safety communications system with employees;
- system for assuring employee compliance with safe work practices;
- scheduled inspection/evaluation system;
- accident investigation;
- procedures for correcting unsafe/unhealthy conditions;
- safety and health training and instruction; and
- recordkeeping and documentation.

Additionally, the overall program may include policies and procedures on visitor safety, safety meetings, first aid/CPR training, hazard communication, confined spaces, materials handling and lifting, personal protective equipment, bloodborne pathogens, ergonomics, and fleet/vehicle safety.

Because safety and health policies and procedures often affect a number of departments and have far-ranging effects in terms of operations and costs, they must be reviewed by management as well as the safety professional.

Policies and procedures generally begin with a purpose statement. In other words, what is the policy and procedure intended to accomplish? The purpose statement is often followed by general requirements and a procedure, including designating specific individuals or positions with specific tasks or action steps.

An important duty of the safety professional should be that of checking plans for new or remodeled facilities and new, rebuilt, or rearranged equipment; changes in material used in product or processes and material-storage and handling procedures; and plans for future products (Figure 25–5). Many companies do not permit a drawing or specification to be used until it has been approved by the safety professional. This important function must be done early enough to afford an opportunity to discover health and safety hazards and to correct conditions that might otherwise be built into the facility and its equipment and that would later result in injuries or other casualty losses. There is also the opportunity at this planning stage to build in safety or fire protection features and to provide adequate space for exit aisles, janitor closets, waste-collection equipment, and other commonly overlooked functions.

The safety professional should also make sure that organization policies and applicable standards are followed in purchase specifications for new materials and equipment and for modification of existing equipment. Some companies have arranged for the purchasing department to notify the safety department when new materials or equipment are to be purchased, or when there is a new supplier of safety-related materials. For instance, when a new chemical is requested, the safety department should ensure that any applicable Safety Data Sheet (SDS) (formerly known as the Material Safety Data Sheet) is obtained from the manufacturer.

Figure 25–5. As a production process is being planned, staff from engineering, production, and safety meet to review drawings and plans to incorporate safety and health features.

Engineering

The ultimate objective of an organization's engineering program is to design equipment and processes and to plan work procedures so that the organization can produce the best product with the highest quality at the lowest cost. It is the safety professional's job to see that engineering personnel are acquainted with the particular safety and health hazards involved and to suggest methods of eliminating these hazards.

The goal is to design safe and healthful environments and equipment and to set up job procedures so that employee exposure to the hazards of illness and injury are either eliminated or controlled as completely as possible. This can be accomplished when safety and health are factors incorporated into the design of the equipment or the planning of the process, along with adequate training and supervision.

The most efficient time to engineer safety and health hazards out of the facility, product, process, or job is before building or remodeling, while a product is being designed, before a change in a process is put into effect, or before a job is started. Every effort, therefore, should be made to find and remove potential safety and health hazards at the blueprint or planning stage.

Machine and Equipment Design

The machine manufacturer, like any other business, wants to have satisfied customers. If the machines cause accidents, customers are dissatisfied. If a customer's order for a machine specifies that the machine must meet specific regulations of OSHA (or another organization) and have safety built into it, the manufacturer's designers will regard such a specification as a design requirement that they must meet. If only a general statement such as "must meet OSHA standards" is used, the manufacturer does not know which standards apply, and the equipment may not be properly guarded.

In many instances, guards added to a machine after it has been installed in a facility are easily removed, and often are not replaced. If a guard or enclosure is an aid to production and efficiency rather than a hindrance, however, it is unlikely that the machine would be operated without having the guard in place. Machine safety must be improved without hindering the worker or reducing the efficiency of the equipment. (See Bibliography for more information.)

The best solution lies in a basic guard design that eliminates the safety and health hazard and, if possible, increases efficiency. There can be little prospect for safe operation of a machine unless the idea of building safety and health measures into the machine's function is applied right on the drawing board for the organization that is going to use the equipment.

Purchasing

The safety professional is responsible for generating and documenting safety and health standards to guide the purchasing department. These standards should be set up so that the safety and health hazards associated with a particular kind of equipment or material being purchased are eliminated or, at the very least, substantially reduced.

The purchasing staff, although not directly involved with educational and enforcement activities, is vitally concerned with many phases of engineering activities. They select and purchase the various items of machinery, tools, equipment, and materials used in the organization, and it is to a considerable degree their responsibility to see that safety has received adequate attention in the design, manufacture, and particulars of shipment of these items.

The safety professional should be well prepared to advise the purchasing department when required to do so. The purchasing staff can reasonably expect the safety professional to offer the following:

- specific information about safety and health hazards that can be eliminated by change in design or application of guarding by the manufacturer
- information about equipment, tools, and materials that can cause injuries if misused
- specific information about health and fire hazards at the facility's worksites
- information on federal and state safety and health rules and regulations
- information on accident experience with machines, equipment, or materials that are about to be reordered

Safety and Health Considerations

In purchasing items such as lifting devices and automatic packaging, chemical processing, or storage equipment, safety and health concerns are extremely important. For example, extreme caution must be observed in the purchase of personal protective equipment, including eye protection, respirators, gloves, and the like; of equipment for the movement of suspended loads, such as ropes, chains, slings, and cables; of equipment for the movement and storage of materials; and of miscellaneous substances and fluids for cleaning and other purposes that might constitute or aggravate a fire or health hazard. Adequate labeling that identifies contents and calls attention to safety and health hazards should be specified. This labeling must comply with state, federal, and in some cases international hazard communication (right-to-know) type standards. Because the rules and regulations of federal and state agencies keep changing, the safety professional must keep up to date on both employee and community right-to-know regulations. (See Chapter 31, International Developments in Occupational Safety and Health.

Many commonly unsuspected safety and health hazards must be considered when very ordinary items such as common hand tools, reflectors, tool racks, cleaning rags, and paint for shop walls and machinery are purchased. Among the factors to be considered are maximum load strength; long life without deterioration; sharp, rough, or pointed characteristics of articles; need for frequent adjustment; ease of maintenance; and ergonomic factors that result in excessive fatigue. Where toxic chemicals are involved, disposal of residue, scrap, and shipping containers must be considered. Safety professionals who are in day-to-day contact with the operating problems must give such information to the purchasing agent.

SAFETY AND HEALTH INSPECTIONS

Safety inspections are one of the principal means of locating potential causes of accidents and illness. These inspections also help determine what safeguarding is necessary to protect against safety and health hazards before accidents and personal injuries occur.

Just as the inspection of a process is an important function in quality control, safety and health inspections are important in accident control (Figure 25–6).

Inspections should not be limited to a search for unsafe physical conditions, but should also try to detect unsafe or unhealthful work practices. Finding unsafe conditions and work practices and promptly correcting them is one of the most effective methods of preventing accidents and safeguarding employees. Management can also show employees its interest and sincere effort in accident prevention by immediately correcting unsafe conditions or work practices. Inspections help to "sell" the safety and health program to employees. Each time a safety professional or an inspection committee passes through the work area, management's interest in safety and health is advertised. Regular facility inspections encourage individual employees to inspect their immediate work areas.

In addition, inspections facilitate the safety professional's contact with individual workers, thereby making it easier to obtain their help in eliminating accidents and illnesses. The workers can often point out unsafe conditions and work procedures that might otherwise go unnoticed and uncorrected. When employee suggestions are acted upon, all employees are made to feel that their cooperation is essential and appreciated.

Safety and health inspections should not be conducted primarily to find out how many things are wrong, but rather to determine whether everything is satisfactory. Their purpose should be to discover conditions that, if corrected, will

Figure 25–6. Periodic safety inspections are conducted to recognize and evaluate potential health and safety hazards before an accident occurs.

bring the facility up to accepted and approved safety and health standards and result in making it a safer and more healthful place in which to work. When observed, inspectors should tactfully point out any unsafe work procedures to the employees involved. They should be certain to indicate the hazards. Inspectors may need to recommend new or continuing safety and health training for supervisors and employees.

Inspection of Work Areas

Before the facility walk-through inspection, it is advisable to review reports of all accidents for the previous several years (including noninjury accidents and near misses, if possible), so that special attention can be given to the conditions and locations known to be safety-sensitive.

Most facilities make use of irregularly scheduled inspections, which can include an unannounced inspection of a particular department, job site, piece of equipment, or small work area. Such inspections made by the safety professional tend to keep the supervisory staff alert to find and correct unsafe conditions and operating practices before they are found by the safety inspector.

The need for intermittent inspections is often indicated by accident report analysis. If the analysis shows an unusual number of accidents for a particular department or location or an increase in certain types of injuries, an inspection should be conducted to determine the reasons for the increase and to find out what corrections are necessary. All results of inspections must be discussed with operating supervision if any gain is to be made.

Supervisors should constantly ensure that tools, machines, and other project or department equipment are maintained properly and are safe to use. To do this effectively, they should use systematic inspection procedures and can delegate authority to others in a department.

Inspection programs should be set up for new equipment, materials, procedures, and processes. A process should not be put into regular operation until it has been checked for hazards, additional safeguards have been installed, if necessary, and safety instructions or procedures have been developed. This is also a good time to develop and implement an activity hazard analysis (AHA), job safety analysis (JSA) or equivalent of the operation. It takes less time and effort now than if done later.

Safety Inspectors or Technicians

Inspectors should know how to locate safety and health hazards and should have the authority to act and make recommendations. A good safety inspector must know the organization's accident experience, be familiar with accident potentials, have the ability to make intelligent recommendations for corrective action, and be diplomatic in handling situations and personnel.

Safety inspectors must be equipped with the proper personal protective equipment, protective clothing, and other required equipment to carry out duties. It would be difficult for a safety inspector to persuade an employee to wear eye protection or safety footwear if the inspector does not wear them, or to require workers to use respirators unless the inspector sets the example and uses one in a hazardous environment. It is essential that inspectors practice what they preach.

Safety Professionals

The safety professional has a productive role during safety inspections, coordinating the safety program and teaching by first-hand contact and on-the-spot examples.

The number of safety professionals and inspectors needed for adequate safety inspection activities depends a great deal on the size and complexity of the facility or project and the type of industry involved. Large companies with well-organized safety programs usually employ a staff of full-time safety professionals and inspectors who work directly under a safety director or safety supervisor. Some large companies also have specially designated employees who spend part of their time on inspections, and some have employee inspection committees.

The safety professional should be fully in charge of developing safety inspection activities and should receive the reports of all inspectors. Special departmental inspectors should either make safety inspections personally or supervise the inspectors in their work. Although safety professionals often have a considerable amount of office and/or

administrative work to do, they should get out into the production and maintenance areas as often as possible and make general as well as specific safety inspections. If there is more than one facility involved, there should be a plan to frequently and effectively perform a safety review of each facility.

Third-Party Inspections, or Audits

The value of a third-party inspection of policies, procedures, and practices as well as an inspection of the physical facility and equipment is increasingly evident. The advantages of such audits are as follows:

- Objectivity of the inspecting party is less likely to lead to biased findings in their reporting.
- Results of external audits are usually directed to a higher level of decision-making authority and thus are more likely to be acted on promptly.
- Performance of the audit does not have to depend on the time or convenience of organization staff.
- Professionals contracted for such audits usually have much expertise in a given industry.

Many businesses currently find that a periodic audit and inspection of their facility or facilities to assess the state of their safety, health, and environmental affairs is as important as the traditional financial audit. Results of these third-party audits are often included in the organization's annual report. More information on third-party audit services is often available from insurance carriers, independent safety/health consulting firms, OSHA Consultation Services, or the National Safety Council.

ACCIDENT AND OCCUPATIONAL ILLNESS INVESTIGATIONS

Purpose of Investigations

Investigation and analysis are used by safety professionals to prevent accidents, both those that could result in injury to personnel and those that do not. The investigation and analysis of an accident can produce information that leads to countermeasures to prevent accidents or reduce their frequency and their severity. The more complete the information, the easier it is for the safety professional to design effective control methods. For example, knowing that 40 percent of a facility's accidents involve ladders is useful, but also knowing that 80 percent of employees using ladders had not been effectively trained is perhaps even more so.

An investigation of every disabling injury or illness must be made. Incidents resulting in nondisabling injuries or no injury and "near miss" or "near hit" incidents should also be investigated to evaluate their primary and root causes in relation to injury-producing accidents or breakdowns. This is especially true if there is frequent recurrence of certain types of nondisabling injuries or if the frequency of accidents is high in certain areas of operations.

The consequences of certain types of accidents are so devastating that any hint of conditions that might lead to their occurrence warrants an investigation. In such cases, any divergence from standard safety specifications warrants a thorough investigation.

For purposes of accident prevention, investigations must be fact-finding, not fault-finding; otherwise, they may do more harm than good. However, this is not to say that responsibility should not be fixed when personal failure or negligence has caused injury, or that such persons should be excused from the consequences of their actions.

Types of Investigations

There are several accident investigation and analysis techniques available. Some of these techniques are more complicated than others. The choice of a particular method depends on the purpose and orientation of the investigation.

The accident investigation and analysis procedure focuses primarily on unsafe circumstances surrounding the occurrence of an accident, and it is the most often-used technique. Other similar techniques involve investigation within the framework of defects in man, machine, media, and management (the "four Ms"), or education, enforcement, and engineering (the "three Es of safety") should be analyzed.

Accident investigation techniques involve classifying the data about a group of accidents into different categories for analysis. This is known as the statistical method of analysis. Control methods are designed on the basis of most frequent patterns of occurrence.

Other techniques are discussed later in this chapter under the systems approach to safety. Systems safety stresses an enlarged viewpoint that takes into account the interrelationships between the various events that could lead to an accident. Because accidents rarely have a single cause, the systems approach to safety can lead to the discovery of more than one place in a system where effective controls can be introduced. This allows the safety professional to choose the control methods that best meet criteria for such factors as effectiveness and speed of installment. Systems safety techniques also have the advantage of application before accidents or illnesses occur, and can be applied to new procedures and operations.

Who Conducts the Investigation?

Depending on the nature of the accident and other conditions, the investigation can be conducted by the supervisor, the safety engineer or inspector, the workers' safety and health committee, the general safety committee, the safety professional, or a loss control specialist from the insurance organization or other external source. Also, OSHA requires that fatalities and/or accidents resulting in serious injury be reported to them. Depending on the circumstances surrounding the fatality, serious injury, or illness, an OSHA inspection may result and should be anticipated by the employer. Regardless of who conducts the initial investigation, a representative of the organization's safety department should verify the findings and direct a written report to the proper official or to the general safety committee.

The safety professional's value and ability are best shown in the investigation of an accident. Specialized training and analytical experience enable the professional to search for all the facts, both apparent and hidden, and to submit an unbiased report. The safety professional should have no interest in the investigation other than to get information that can be used to prevent a similar accident.

During an investigation, methods to prevent a recurrence can be identified, but decisions about the specific course to take are best made after all the facts are well-established. There are usually several alternatives; all must be fully understood in order for the most effective decision to be made. The safety professional should present every valid, feasible alternative to operating management for their consideration. At this stage, input from employees can be highly beneficial in determining the best corrective measure.

RECORD KEEPING AND REPORTING

The Williams-Steiger OSHAct of 1970 requires employers to maintain records of work-related employee injuries and illnesses, as well as many inspection reports of high-injury-potential equipment. In addition, many employers are also required to make reports to state compensation authorities.

Safety professionals are faced with two tasks: maintaining those records required by law and by their management, and maintaining records that are useful in an effective safety program. Unfortunately, the two are not always synonymous. A good record-keeping system necessitates more data than those called for in almost all OSHA-required forms. In general, OSHA and related safety records need to be "readily available." How the employer chooses to maintain those records (i.e., paper copy or computerized) is generally a business decision.

Many different safety records must be maintained, and OSHA has established how long many of these records must be maintained by the employer.

Records that must be generated and maintained include records of inspections; accident investigations; general and specific training; medical and exposure monitoring results; the OSHA log of injuries and illnesses; fatality and serious injury and illness reports to OSHA; insurance records such as the employer's and doctor's first reports of injury and illness; and respirator-fit test and other personal protective equipment records addressing the maintenance, use, selection, inspection, and storage of such equipment.

Records of accidents, injuries, and illnesses and the training experience of the people involved are essential to efficient and successful safety programs, just as records of production, costs, sales, and profits and losses are essential to efficient and successful operation of a business. Records supply the information necessary to transform haphazard, costly, and ineffective safety and training efforts into a planned safety and health program that enables control of both conditions and acts that contribute to accidents. Good record keeping is the foundation of a scientific approach to occupational safety.

Uses of Records

A good record-keeping system can help the safety professional in the following ways:

- It provides safety personnel with the means for an objective evaluation of the magnitude of occupational illness and accident problems and with a measurement of the overall progress and effectiveness of the safety and health program.
- It helps identify high-hazard units, facilities, or departments and problem areas so that extra effort can be made in those areas.
- It provides data necessary for an analysis of accidents and illnesses that can point to specific circumstances of occurrence, which can then be attacked by specific countermeasures.
- It can create interest in safety and health among supervisors by furnishing them with information about the accident and illness experience of their own departments.
- It provides supervisors and safety committees with hard facts about their safety and health problems so that corrective efforts can be concentrated.
- It helps in measuring the effectiveness of individual countermeasures and determining whether specific programs are doing the job that they were designed to do.
- It can help establish the need for, and the content of, employee and management training programs that can be tailored to fit the particular needs of that organization or facility.

Accident Reports and Illness Records

To be effective, preventive measures must be based on complete and unbiased knowledge of the causes of accidents and the knowledge of the supervisor and employee about the operation. The primary purpose of an accident report, like the inspection, is to obtain information, not to fix blame. Because the completeness and accuracy of the entire accident record system depend on information in the individual accident reports and the employee training history, it is important that the forms and their purpose are understood by those who must fill them out. Essential training or instruction by the safety professional should be given to those who are responsible for generating the information. Photographs, videotapes, and drawings of the accident or a depiction of the accident can be extremely useful.

The First-Aid Report

Collecting injury or illness data generally begins in the first-aid department or at the clinic. The first-aid attendant fills out a first-aid report for each new case. Copies are sent to the safety department or safety committee, the worker's first-line supervisor, and other departments as management designates.

The first-aid attendant should know enough about accident analysis and illness investigation to be able to record the principal facts about each case. Note that the questioning of the injured or sick person must be complete enough to establish whether the incident is or is not work-related. Current emphasis on chemical air contaminants makes it necessary to include or exclude exposure to known health hazards. First-aid reports can be very helpful to the safety or industrial hygiene personnel. The organization's physician who treats injured employees should be informed of the basic rules for classifying cases because, at times, the physician's opinion of the severity of an injury is necessary to record the case accurately.

The Supervisor's Accident Report Form

This should be completed as soon as possible after an accident occurs, and copies sent to the safety department and to other designated persons. Information concerning unsafe or unhealthful work conditions, behaviors, and improper work practices is important in the prevention of accidents, but information that shows why the unsafe or unhealthful conditions existed can be even more important. This type of information is particularly difficult to get unless it is obtained promptly after the accident occurs. If the information is based on opinion, not on proven facts, it is still important, but should be so identified.

Generally, analyses of accidents are made only periodically and often long after the accidents have occurred. Because it is often impossible to accurately recall the details of an accident, this information must be recorded accurately and completely at once or it may be lost forever.

Injury and Illness Record of an Employee

The first-aid report and the supervisor's report contain information about the agency of injury (type of machine, tool, or material), the type of accident, and other factors that facilitate the use of the reports for accident prevention. Another form must be used to record the injury experience of individual employees.

Much can be learned about accident causes from studying employee injury records. If certain employees or job classifications have frequent injuries or illnesses, a study of the work environment, job training, safety and health training, work practices, and the instructions and supervision given them may reveal more than a study of accident locations, agencies, or other factors.

EDUCATION AND TRAINING

It is critical that safety and health training begins at the time of hiring, before the employee actually starts work on a particular task. Employees who are new to an organization, a task, or use of a material are at greatest risk for injuries and illnesses. An effective safety and health training program includes a carefully prepared and presented introduction to the organization.

New employees immediately begin to learn and form attitudes about the organization and their job, boss, and coworkers, whether or not the employer offers a training program. To encourage a new employee to form positive attitudes, it is important for the employer to provide a sound basis for them, and providing safety and health information is vital. Training about exposure to chemical hazards in the workplace is now mandated by state and federal hazard communication standards (right-to-know laws). (See Chapter 30, Government Regulations, for more information on these and other relevant regulations and standards.) In fact, most new OSHA regulations generally have a training requirement written into the standard.

An effective accident prevention and occupational health hazard control program is based on proper job performance. When people are properly trained to do their jobs, they do them safely. This means that supervisors must know what employee training needs to be given, which means knowing the requirements of the job; know how to train an employee in the safe way of doing a job; and know how to supervise. It also means the safety professional should be familiar with good training techniques. Although the professional is not always directly involved in the training effort, he or she should be able to recognize the elements of a practical training program.

A training program is needed for new employees, when new equipment or processes are introduced, when procedures are revised or updated, when new information must be made available, when employee performance must be improved, when new or unexpected hazards are uncovered, and on a periodic basis to refresh employees' knowledge of the material. Employees with longer tenure also need training so that they have the same information about new equipment, products, or organizational policies that new employees are receiving.

Many supervisors acquired their present positions in organizations where some sort of safety and health program already existed, and their understanding of the program is firmly established. However, a safety professional undertaking the safety training of supervisors almost invariably finds that the first major job is to get supervisors at all levels to understand and accept their role in accident and illness prevention. This job cannot be done in a single meeting or through a single communication.

Simply getting supervisors to agree in theory that responsibility for safety and health is one of their duties is not enough. They must come to understand the many ways in which they can prevent illness and accidents, and they must become interested in improving their safety performance. For a safety and health program to be effective, all levels of management must be firmly committed to the program and express that commitment by action and example. Management is ultimately responsible for the safety and health of the employees. Much of the effort put into an industrial safety and health program by a safety professional is, therefore, directed toward educating and influencing management.

Employee Training

The training of an employee begins the day the employee starts the job. As observed earlier in this chapter, whether or not the firm has a formal safety and health orientation program, the employee starts to learn about the job and to form attitudes about many things—including safety and health—on the first day.

The safety professional assists supervisors in instructing employees in the safe way of doing each job. Accidents can be prevented only when these recommended procedures are based on a thorough analysis of the job and when the procedures are followed. This is why a complete job safety analysis is so valuable (Figure 25–7). It provides a baseline for future comparison, and it details all necessary safety elements of the various job tasks.

The safety professional can provide supervisors with methods for observing all workers in the performance of their tasks to establish the job safety requirements, and should participate in follow-up observations to reinforce the supervisors'

⊕ **National Safety Council** **JOB SAFETY ANALYSIS** *INSTRUCTIONS ON REVERSE SIDE*	JOB TITLE (and number if applicable): Replacing a water bottle	PAGE __1__ OF __2__ JSA NO. __001__	DATE: Today	☒ NEW ☐ REVISED
	TITLE OF PERSON WHO DOES JOB: Maintenance/Janitor	SUPERVISOR: Eric Utney	ANALYSIS BY: Mary Green	
COMPANY/ORGANIZATION: 123 Accounting Corp.	PLANT/LOCATION: General Office	DEPARTMENT: Reception	REVIEWED BY: Bill Camp	
REQUIRED AND/OR RECOMMENDED PERSONAL PROTECTIVE EQUIPMENT: Protective footwear, non-slip gloves			APPROVED BY: Greg Porter	

SEQUENCE OF BASIC JOB STEPS	POTENTIAL HAZARDS	RECOMMENDED ACTION OR PROCEDURE
1. Lift and load the bottle		
2. Transport the bottle and place near the dispenser		
3. Remove empty bottle from dispenser		
4. Position full water bottle on stand		
5. Check system		

Printed in U.S.A

156.15

INSTRUCTIONS FOR COMPLETING THE JOB SAFETY ANALYSIS FORM

Job Safety Analysis (JSA) is an important accident prevention tool that works by finding hazards and eliminating or minimizing them *before* the job is performed, and *before* they have a chance to become accidents. Use JSA for job clarification and hazard awareness, as a guide in new employee training, for periodic contacts and for retraining of senior employees, as a refresher on jobs which run infrequently, as an accident investigation tool, and for informing employees of specific job hazards and protective measures.

Set priorities for doing JSA's: jobs that have a history of many accidents, jobs that have produced disabling injuries, jobs with high potential for disabling injury or death, and new jobs with no accident history.

Select a job to be analyzed. Before filling out this form, consider the following: The purpose of the job—What has to be done? Who has to do it? The activities involved—How is it done? When is it done? Where is it done?

In summary, to complete this form you should consider the purpose of the job, the activities it involves, and the hazards it presents. If you are not familiar with a particular job or operation, interview an employee who is. In addition, observing an employee performing the job, or "walking through" the operation step by step may give additional insight into potential hazards. You may also wish to videotape the job and analyze it.

Here's how to do each of the three parts of a Job Safety Analysis:

SEQUENCE OF BASIC JOB STEPS

Examining a specific job by breaking it down into a series of steps or tasks, will enable you to discover potential hazards employees may encounter.

Each job or operation will consist of a set of steps or tasks. For example, the job might be to move a box from a conveyor in the receiving area to a shelf in the storage area. To determine where a step begins or ends, look for a change of activity, change in direction or movement.

Picking up the box from the conveyor and placing it on a handtruck is one step. The next step might be to push the loaded handtruck to the storage area (a change in activity). Moving the boxes from the truck and placing them on the shelf is another step. The final step might be returning the handtruck to the receiving area.

Be sure to list *all* the steps needed to perform the job. Some steps may not be performed each time; an example could be checking the casters on the handtruck. However, if that step is generally part of the job it should be listed.

POTENTIAL HAZARDS

A hazard is a potential danger. The purpose of the Job Safety Analysis is to identify ALL hazards—both those produced by the environment or conditions and those connected with the job procedure.

To identify hazards, ask yourself these questions about each step:

Is there a danger of the employee striking against, being struck by, or otherwise making injurious contact with an object?

Can the employee be caught in, by, or between objects?

Is there potential for slipping, tripping, or falling?

Could the employee suffer strains from pushing, pulling, lifting, bending, or twisting?

Is the environment hazardous to safety and/or health (toxic gas, vapor, mist, fumes, dust, heat, or radiation)?

Close observation and knowledge of the job is important. Examine each step carefully to find and identify hazards—the actions, conditions, and possibilities that could lead to an accident. Compiling an accurate and complete list of potential hazards will allow you to develop the recommended safe job procedures needed to prevent accidents.

RECOMMENDED ACTION OR PROCEDURE

Using the first two columns as a guide, decide what actions or procedures are necessary to eliminate or minimize the hazards that could lead to an accident, injury, or occupational illness.

Begin by trying to: 1) engineer the hazard out; 2) provide guards, safety devices, etc.; 3) provide personal protective equipment; 4) provide job instruction training; 5) maintain good housekeeping; 6) insure good ergonomics (positioning the person in relation to the machine or other elements in such a way as to improve safety).

List the recommended safe operating procedures. Begin with an action word. Say exactly what needs to be done to correct the hazard, such as, "lift using your leg muscles." Avoid general statements such as, "be careful."

List the required or recommended personal protective equipment necessary to perform each step of the job.

Give a recommended action or procedure for each hazard.

Serious hazards should be corrected immediately. The JSA should then be changed to reflect the new conditions.

Finally, review your input on all three columns for accuracy and completeness. Determine if the recommended actions or procedures have been put in place. Re-evaluate the job safety analysis as necessary.

Figure 25–7. A job safety analysis form is used to record information that will be used as a baseline for future comparison and includes information on all necessary safety elements of the various job tasks. *(Reprinted with permission from the National Safety Council.* Job Safety Analysis: Participant Workbook. *Itasca, IL: NSC Press, 1994.)*

training. In this way, supervisors are informed of any weakness in the organization's safety and health program and will have a common reference point for monitoring these problems.

Training Tips

- Train small groups whenever possible. Employees seem to learn more and are more apt to ask questions and otherwise participate in small training groups.
- Consider providing two levels of training, one for the supervisor and another for the workers. Generally, supervisory training needs to be more comprehensive than that given to workers.
- Consider using outside trainers. Oftentimes employees perceive outside trainers and consultants as having a higher level of credibility.
- Make use of commercially available audiovisual information (web-based training, videotapes, slides, and films). It is important to screen these commercial products, because they are often very generic and must be supplemented with site-specific information and discussions. Many trade associations have produced audiovisual information for their member companies.
- Keep records of employee attendance. Note the date, subjects covered, instructor, and training aids used (such as videos, internet training modules), and make a list of attendees (with their signatures if possible). A copy of any tests given and of the agenda should be kept on file as well.
- With the development and popularity of internet training, it is important to consider that much of this training is very good, however, fairly generic in nature. Employees must be trained and informed in general and specific safety and health measures necessary to do their jobs safely.
- Make the training as participatory as possible. Encourage discussions, use training aids, and practice the use of equipment and procedures discussed in the training.

Maintaining Interest in Safety

A prime objective of a good safety and health program is to maintain interest in safety in order to prevent accidents. It is, however, as difficult to determine the degree of success achieved by an interest-maintaining effort as part of a safety program as it is to isolate the effectiveness of an advertising campaign separate from an entire marketing program. The reason is that companies with sound basic safety and health programs generally have working conditions that are safe, employees who are well trained and safety minded, and high-caliber supervision.

Safety and Health Rule Enforcement

Obeying safety and health rules is actually a matter of education; employees must understand the rules and the importance of following them. In helping an employee understand, the possibility of language barriers should be considered. Language barriers are caused not only by national origins but also, and more often, by the jargon of a particular profession or industry. A considerable amount of confusion can occur when a new employee comes from a different industry or field of work.

Role of the Supervisor

Supervisors are the key people in any program designed to create and maintain interest in safety and health, because they are responsible for translating management's policies into action and for promoting safe and healthful work practices directly among the employees. The supervisors' attitudes toward safety and health are a significant factor in the success of not only specific promotional activities but also the entire safety and health program, because their views will be reflected by the employees in their departments.

How well a supervisor meets this responsibility is determined to a large extent by how well the supervisor has been selected and trained, and training and educating the supervisor in matters of safety and health is oftentimes the responsibility of the safety professional.

Supervisor Training

Supervisors are often responsible for providing safety and health training to employees. They may be the primary safety trainers and have the final responsibility for the effectiveness of training. If the employer chooses to put the responsibility of training on supervisors, the employer must clearly communicate that this is a discrete responsibility. Just as important, the employer must ensure that the supervisor has the time, interest, and training necessary to provide adequate employee training.

Generally speaking, the supervisor needs training at a level equal to or exceeding the training given to labor. Several recent OSHA regulations have been adopted that require employers to provide additional training to supervisors. To illustrate, supervisors who supervise hazardous waste cleanup workers are required (29 CFR 1910.120) to take an additional 8 hours of management/supervisor training covering such topics as the employer's safety and health program, employee training program, personal protective equipment, and health hazard–monitoring procedures and techniques.

Many community colleges, independent training groups, and internet training sites offer supervisory safety and health courses to better prepare supervisors for their safety and health tasks. Also, many organizations offer "train the trainer" courses. Recently the Board of Certified Safety Professionals has developed a Safety Trained Supervisor (STS) certification (www.bcsp.org).

The supervisor who is sincere and enthusiastic about accident prevention can do much to maintain interest because of a direct connection with the worker. Conversely, if the supervisor only pays lip service to the program or ridicules any part of it, this attitude offsets any good that might be accomplished by the safety professional.

Some supervisors may be reluctant to change their mode of operation and slow to accept new ideas. It is the safety professional's task to sell these supervisors on the benefits of accident prevention, and to convince them that promotional activities are not "frills" but rather projects that can help them do their job more easily and prevent illness and injuries. Also, safety has a direct relation to production and quality.

Setting a good example by wearing required personal protective equipment is an excellent way in which supervisors can promote the use of this equipment and demonstrate interest in safety. Teaching safety and health principles to supervisors is an important function of the safety professional; safety posters, a few warning signs, or merely general rules are not enough to do this job.

The safety professional should educate supervisors so that working conditions and work practices are kept as safe and healthful as possible and that the workers consistently follow safe procedures, as a routine part of good job performance. Supervisors are entitled to all of the help the safety professional can give through supplies of educational material for distribution and frequent visits to the job site, as circumstances permit. Supervisors should also receive adequate recognition for independent and original safety activity.

Supervisors can be very effective by giving facts and personal reminders on safety and health to employees as part of their daily work instructions. This procedure is particularly necessary in the transportation and utility industries, where the work crews are on their own.

In any case, supervisors should be encouraged to take every opportunity to exchange ideas on accident prevention with workers, to commend them for their efforts to do the job safely, and to invite them to submit suggestions for better ways to do the job that will prevent injuries or illness.

Job Safety and Health Analysis

Job safety analysis (JSA) (Figures 25–7 and 25–8), sometimes also called job hazard analysis (JHA) or activity hazard analysis (AHA), is a process used by safety professionals and supervisors to review job methods and uncover hazards. Once the safety and health hazards are known, the proper controls can be developed. Some controls are physical changes that control the hazard, such as enclosures to contain an air contaminant or a guard placed over exposed moving machine parts. Others are job procedures that eliminate or minimize the hazard, for example, safe

stacking of materials. Procedure controls require training and supervision.

Benefits of a Job Safety Analysis

The principal benefits that arise from job safety analysis are the establishment of the following practices:

- Individuals are given training in safe, efficient procedures.
- New employees are instructed on safety and health procedures.
- Preparations are made for planned safety and health observations.
- Prejob instructions are given on irregular jobs.
- Job procedures are reviewed after accidents occur.

New employees must be trained in the basic job steps. They must be taught to recognize the safety and health haz-

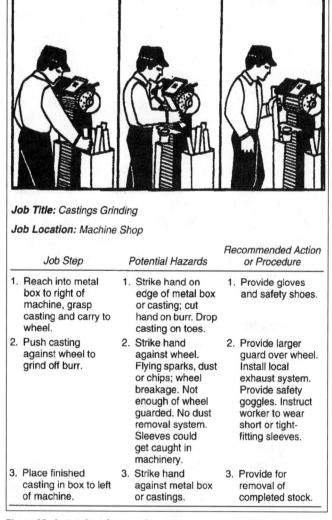

Job Title: *Castings Grinding*

Job Location: *Machine Shop*

Job Step	Potential Hazards	Recommended Action or Procedure
1. Reach into metal box to right of machine, grasp casting and carry to wheel.	1. Strike hand on edge of metal box or casting; cut hand on burr. Drop casting on toes.	1. Provide gloves and safety shoes.
2. Push casting against wheel to grind off burr.	2. Strike hand against wheel. Flying sparks, dust or chips; wheel breakage. Not enough of wheel guarded. No dust removal system. Sleeves could get caught in machinery.	2. Provide larger guard over wheel. Install local exhaust system. Provide safety goggles. Instruct worker to wear short or tight-fitting sleeves.
3. Place finished casting in box to left of machine.	3. Strike hand against metal box or castings.	3. Provide for removal of completed stock.

Figure 25–8. A job safety analysis (JSA), even a simple one, breaks the job into steps and identifies hazards leading to the recommended action or procedure. Here is an employee performing a castings grinding operation.

ards associated with each job step and learn the necessary precautions. There is no better guide for this training than a well-prepared job safety analysis used with the job instruction training method.

All supervisors are concerned with improving job methods to increase safety, reduce costs, and step up production. The job safety analysis is an excellent starting point for questioning the established way of doing a job.

RISK MANAGEMENT

A Five-Step Program

Companies find they must control accidents if they are to continue to do business in a highly competitive market. One large organization uses an approach consisting of five closely related, logically ordered steps for a coordinated program. These steps are hazard identification, hazard elimination, hazard protection, determining the maximum possible loss, and loss retention.

Hazard Identification

To prevent accidents and control losses, first identify all safety and health hazards to determine those areas or activities in an operation where losses can occur. This requires studying processes at the research stage, reviewing design during engineering, checking pilot facility operations and start-up, and regularly monitoring normal production.

Hazard Elimination

Toxic, flammable, or corrosive chemicals can sometimes be replaced by safer materials. Machines can be redesigned to eliminate danger points. Facility layouts can be improved by eliminating such hazards as blind corners and limited-visibility crossings.

Hazard Protection

Hazards that cannot be removed must be protected against. Familiar examples include mechanical guards to keep fingers from pinch points, safety shoes to safeguard toes against dropped objects, and ventilation systems to control the buildup of air contaminants. Industry is concerned with all losses, injury to personnel, damage to products, and destruction of property.

Maximum Possible Loss

This step involves the determination of the maximum loss that could occur if everything went wrong. For example, entire buildings or areas can be lost as the result of a fire or explosion. The amount that an organization could lose under the most adverse conditions can be estimated.

Loss Retention

Having some idea of the amount that could be lost under a combination of unfavorable circumstances, one can then determine what portion of such a loss an organization is willing to bear itself. Industrial companies can afford to retain a portion of each loss. The remaining loss potential is then insured through the organization's insurance carrier. This proves a good incentive for management to institute strong safety and health programs. These activities can be consolidated in one department such as a risk management department, bringing together the safety professional, fire protection manager, security and facility protection manager, occupational physician, occupational health nurse, industrial hygienist, environmental manager, and insurance manager. The administrator of a total loss control program does not need to know all the details of each function, but should be able to develop an atmosphere in which there is harmonious cooperation and mutual understanding. Primary concerns are the control of occupational disease and personnel safety.

Damage Control

There should be a damage control program for investigating all accidents, not just those that produce injuries. This approach of studying accidents instead of injuries recognizes that a so-called no-injury accident, if repeated in the future, could result in personal injury, property damage, or both.

Ferreting out the causes of accidents reveals what unsafe conditions and/or work practices were responsible for the accident.

Three basic steps are successfully used to reduce property damage (and injuries): spot-checking, reporting by repair control centers, and auditing.

Spot-Checking

Spot-checking consists of observing and taking notes to permit damage estimates by comparing total costs for a repair period with those found during sample observations.

Reporting by Repair Control Centers

This step involves developing a system in which the repair or cost control center records property damage. The system should be designed to require the least possible amount of paperwork. No one system works in all companies, because repair cost accounting methods vary greatly from organization to organization, and even from facility to facility within a single organization.

Auditing

An effective reporting program necessitates complete auditing. Safety personnel should receive a copy of every original work order processed through the maintenance, planning, and cost control center. Safety professionals make on-the-spot checks to see if accidental damage was involved.

SYSTEMS SAFETY

Recently, safety professionals have increasingly been exploring systems approaches to industrial accident prevention. Safety professionals are asked to find ways of implementing systems safety techniques. And although complete system safety analysis requires specially trained engineers and rather sophisticated mathematics, safety professionals find that some knowledge of these techniques can directly benefit them when it comes to codifying and directing their safety and health programs.

Through a system analysis, a safety professional can clarify a complex process by devising a chart or model that provides a comprehensive, overall view of the process, showing its principal elements and the ways in which they are interrelated (Figure 25–9).

Having established the concept of a system, the next step is the analysis of systems. Progress in the analysis of complex systems enables safety professionals to solve problems in accident prevention and the control of occupational illness.

Methods of Analysis

There are four principal methods of analysis: failure mode and effect, fault tree, THERP (technique for human error prediction), and cost-effectiveness. Each has variations, and two or more can be combined in a single analysis.

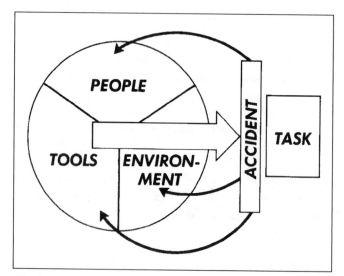

Figure 25–9. A system analysis can show how people, tools, and the environment can combine to produce an accident.

Failure Mode and Effect

In this method the failure or malfunction of each component is considered, including the mode of failure (such as a switch jammed in the on position). The effects of the failure are traced through the system, and the ultimate effect on task performance is evaluated.

Fault Tree

In this method an undesired event is selected, and all the possible occurrences that can contribute to the event are diagrammed in the form of a tree. The branches of the tree are continued until independent events are reached. Probabilities are determined for the independent events, and, after simplifying the tree, both the probability of the undesired event and the most likely chain of events leading up to it can be computed.

THERP

This is a technique for human error prediction, developed by Scandia Corporation, that provides a means for quantitatively evaluating the contribution of human error to the degradation of product quality. It can be used for human components in systems and thus can be combined either with the failure mode and effect or the fault-tree method.

Cost-Effectiveness

In the cost-effectiveness method, the cost of system changes made to increase safety and health measures is compared with either the decreased costs of fewer serious failures or with the increased effectiveness of the system to perform its task to determine the relative value of these changes. Ultimately, all system changes have to be evaluated, and this method makes such cost comparisons explicit. Moreover, cost-effectiveness analysis is often used to help make decisions concerning the choice of one of several systems that can perform the same task.

In all of these analytical methods, the main point is to measure quantitatively the effects of various failures within a system. In each case, probability theory is an important element.

The systems approach to safety can help to change the safety profession from an art to a science by codifying much of safety and health knowledge. It can help change the application of safety measures from piecemeal problem solving (such as putting a pan under a leak) to a safely designed operation (preventing the leak itself).

The safety professional determines what can happen if a component fails, or the effects of malfunction in the various elements of the system, and provides solutions before the accident occurs instead of after the damage has been done.

SAFETY PROFESSIONAL CERTIFICATION

Employers, employees, and the public deserve some assurance that the individuals practicing safety are professionals and are able to provide the safety expertise that, in turn, should provide adequate protection.

Usually, a candidate for professional status must complete a specified course of study, which is followed by practical experience in that field. The applicant must pass an examination to prove mastery of a specific body of knowledge. Finally, a board composed of members of the profession reviews that candidate's qualifications and grants professional certification.

Professional regulation usually results from the need to protect the public from potential harm at the hands of unqualified persons. Clearly, there was a need for professional regulation in the field of industrial safety, and the Board of Certified Safety Professionals was created to fill this need.

The Board of Certified Safety Professionals of the Americas was incorporated in Illinois in 1969 to establish criteria for professional certification, accept applications, evaluate the credentials of candidates, and issue certificates to those who met the requirements.

One method of determining professional abilities is to compare education and experience against a predetermined set of requirements. Once these criteria have been established, each application showing a candidate's education and experience is evaluated against that base. The applicant may be found to be eligible to go to the next step—to take the certification examinations; upon successful completion of the examinations, the candidate is granted certification as a certified safety professional, or CSP.

General Qualifications

To qualify for the Certified Safety Professional title one must
- apply to the Board of Certified Safety Professionals (BCSP);
- meet an academic requirement;
- meet a professional safety experience requirement;
- pass the Safety Fundamentals Examination; and
- pass the Comprehensive Practice Examination.

Applications

Details as to specific requirements, for preparation and application are available at the BCSP web site at www.BCSP.org. The general requirements are identified below.

The Academic Requirement

A CSP candidate must hold either a bachelor's degree or higher in any field or an associate degree in safety, health and environment, or a closely related field. There is no waiver of the academic requirement.

For U.S degrees, BCSP requires the educational institution hold institutional accreditation. There are two organizations that set standards for accrediting bodies. One is the U.S. Department of Education. The other is the Council for Higher Education Accreditation (CHEA). These organizations identify the accrediting organizations that meet their standards.

The Experience Requirement

In addition to the academic requirement, CSP candidates must have professional safety experience. Professional safety experience must meet all of the following criteria to be considered acceptable by BCSP:
- Professional safety must be the primary function of the position. Collateral duties in safety are not considered the primary function.
- The position's primary responsibility must be the prevention of harm to people, property, and the environment, rather than responsibility for responding to harmful events.
- Professional safety functions must be at least 50 percent of the position duties. BCSP defines full-time as at least 35 hours per week. Part-time safety experience is allowed instead of full-time safety experience if the applicant has the equivalent of at least 900 hours of professional safety work during any year (75 hours per month or 18 hours per week) for which experience credit is sought.
- The position must be at the professional level. This is determined by evaluating the degree of responsible charge and reliance of employers or clients on the person's ability to defend analytical approaches used in professional practice. This also encompasses the candidate recommending how to control hazards through engineering and/or administrative approaches.
- The position must have breadth of professional safety duties. This is determined by evaluating the variety of hazards about which the candidate must advise and the range of skills involved in recognizing, evaluating, and controlling hazards. Examples of skills are analysis, synthesis, design, investigating, planning, administration, and communications.

Candidates may substitute advanced degrees and/or the Occupational Health and Safety Technologist (OHST) or Construction Health and Safety Technician (CHST) certifications for part of the experience requirement.

Associate Safety Professional and Examination

The Associate Safety Professional (ASP) designation is the start of the process toward achieving the CSP certification. It is a temporary designation awarded by BCSP. It means that an individual has met the academic requirement and has passed the first of two examinations leading to the CSP credential. Those who receive a waiver of Safety Fundamentals do not receive the ASP designation. Applicants submit only one application for both the ASP designation and CSP certification.

The ASP is not a separate certification and only denotes a CSP candidate who has passed the first exam, Safety Fundamentals.

At the time of application, many candidates have enough points to sit for the Safety Fundamentals examination (48), but do not have the points required for the Comprehensive Practice examination (96). In this instance, BCSP estimates an eligibility date on which candidates will achieve 96 points, assuming they remain employed in a position that meets professional safety practice requirements. Education and other credentials cannot be substituted for work experience. Near that estimated date, candidates must submit a Professional Safety Experience Update form to BCSP.

If the 96 points are not met after the candidate's work experience is updated, BCSP estimates a new eligibility date. Candidates may be dropped from the CSP process if they fail to provide updated information when requested, or have not met eligibility requirements at the end of the third year from the original projected eligibility date.

Comprehensive Practice Examination

All CSP candidates must acquire 96 points and pass the second examination, the Comprehensive Practice Examination. To take this examination, a candidate must meet both the academic and experience requirements and have passed or waived the Safety Fundamentals Examination. The total credit for academic degrees at all levels plus the months of professional safety experience must equal or exceed 96 points. After passing the Comprehensive Practice Examination, a candidate receives the Certified Safety Professional title.

For more information on the Board of Certified Safety Professionals and the certification process, contact them at:

Board of Certified Safety Professionals
2301 W. Bradley Avenue
Champaign, IL 61821
Phone: (217) 359-9623
Fax: (217) 359-0055
Web Site: www.BCSP.org

THE FUTURE OF SAFETY AS A PROFESSION

Problems, both predictable and unpredictable, can be expected to have an impact on the safety professional in the future. Some of these problems will call for reapplication of established safety techniques. Others will call for radical departures and the creation of new methods and new organizational forms. To be able to discriminate between the two solutions will be, perhaps, the safety professional's greatest test.

The field of occupational safety continues to progress and improve, largely through the continued application of techniques and knowledge that have been slowly and painfully acquired over the years. There appears to be no limit to the progress possible through the application of the universally accepted safety techniques of education, engineering, and enforcement.

Large and serious problems remain unsolved. A number of industries still have high accident rates. There are still far too many instances in which management and labor are not working together or have different goals for the safety program.

Resources available to the safety professional have greatly increased, with many resources available on-line. An impressive body of knowledge, a corps of able professional safety professionals, a high level of prestige, and strong organizations for cooperation and exchange of information will fuel the future for the safety profession.

Well-trained workers are in high demand in practically all phases of safety. Growth in the trade and service industries and the expanding safety needs of educational institutions, construction, transportation, insurance, and governmental groups should further accentuate the demand for safety workers.

The ASSE has recently reported that among the fastest-growing areas in the field of safety are those related to computer integrated manufacturing, product safety, software, environmental protection, chemical process safety, and system safety. As more and more organizations turn to automation to streamline their operations, safety professionals will find a greater demand for their abilities to analyze and understand these technologies to ensure safety requirements are met. Similarly, as public awareness of hazard exposures grows and more complicated consumer products enter the market, safety professionals will be called on to help safeguard the users of these products against accidental injury, illness, or damage to the environment.

Obviously, there is a need in safety work for people with varying degrees of education and experience. The range of opportunities extends from what could be considered paraprofessional to the highly trained and skilled professional at the corporate management level, and includes safety educators and government safety inspectors and researchers.

The safety professional will also need diversified education and training to meet the challenges of the future. Growth in the population, the communication and information explosion, problems of urban areas and future transportation systems, and the increasing complexities of everyday life will create many problems and may extend the safety professional's creativity to the maximum to successfully provide the knowledge and leadership needed to conserve life, health, property, and the environment.

Training of the future safety professional can no longer be limited to the on-the-job experience but must include specialized undergraduate-level training leading to a bachelor's or higher degree. Refresher and continuing education is also necessary and will be just as important in the years ahead.

The type of training needed will depend on the individual job requirements. This presents some difficulties for those preparing to enter the safety and health occupations. Some authorities view the safety and health specialist as a behaviorist and therefore would direct training toward the behavioral sciences, for example, psychology. Others see the specialist as a technician able to handle the technical problems of hazard control, and recommend a heavy background in engineering. Still others believe the safety worker's background should include both the engineering and behavioral aspects.

Future application of this knowledge in all aspects of our civilization—whether to industry or transportation, at home or in recreation—makes it imperative that those in this field be trained to use scientific principles and methods to achieve adequate results. The knowledge, skill, and ability to integrate machines, equipment, and environments with humans and their capabilities will be of prime importance.

SUMMARY

The work of the safety professional follows a pattern. Before taking any steps in the containment of injury, illness, or accidents, the safety professional first identifies and appraises all existing safety and health hazards, both immediate and potential. Once having identified the hazards, the necessary accident-prevention procedures are developed and put into operation. However, this is not enough; safety and health information must be communicated to both management and workers. Finally, the safety professional must evaluate the effectiveness of safety and health control measures after they have been put into practice. If conditions warrant, the safety professional can recommend changes in materials or operational procedures or, possibly, that additional enclosures or safety equipment be added to existing machinery.

Accurate records are essential in the search for the cause of an illness or an accident, and can aid in finding the means to prevent future similar incidents. When studying records to determine the cause or causes of accidents, the records

of other companies with similar operations should not be overlooked. Upon determining the cause, the safety professional will have a firm basis on which to propose preventive measures.

Preventive measures are obviously better than corrective measures taken only after an accident has occurred. This means that one of the most valuable functions of the safety professional is to examine the specifications for materials, job procedures, new machinery and equipment, and new structures from the standpoint of safety and health well before installation or construction. In some cases, the safety professional can even help draft the necessary specifications.

As part of the overall safety and health program, the safety professional should recommend policies, codes, safety standards, and procedures that should become part of the operational policies of the organization.

The safety professional draws on specialized knowledge in both the physical and social sciences and applies the principles of measurement and analysis to evaluate safety performance. The safety professional should have a fundamental knowledge of statistics, mathematics, physics, chemistry, industrial hygiene, environmental sciences, and engineering.

The safety professional should be a well-informed specialist who coordinates the safety and health program and supplies the ideas and inspiration while enlisting the wholehearted support of management, supervision, and workers.

BIBLIOGRAPHY

American Society of Safety Engineers. *Scope and Function of the Professional Safety Position.* Des Plaines, IL: ASSE, 2000.

Asfalh CR. *Industrial Safety and Health Management.* Englewood Cliffs, NJ: Prentice-Hall, 1990.

Bird FE, Germain GL. *Practical Loss Control Leadership.* Loganville, GA: International Loss Control Institute, 1990.

Board of Certified Safety Professionals. *The CSP and Speciality Certifications.* Savoy, IL: BCSP, 2000.

Boylston RP. *Managing Safety and Health Programs.* New York: Van Nostrand Reinhold, 1990.

Brauer RL. *Safety and Health for Engineers.* New York: Van Nostrand Reinhold, 1990.

Colvin RJ. *The Guidebook to Successful Safety Programming.* Chelsea, MI: CRC/Lewis Publishers, 1992.

International Labour Office. *Encyclopedia of Occupational Health and Safety,* 4th ed. Geneva, Switzerland: International Labour Office, 1998.

Krause TR, Hidley JH, Hodson SJ. *The Behavior Based Safety Process,* 2nd ed. New York: Van Nostrand Reinhold, 1997.

Manuele FA. *On the Practice of Safety,* 2nd ed. New York: Wiley, 1997.

NSC Press, National Safety Council, various titles, Itasca, IL:

Accident Prevention Manual for Business & Industry:
Administration & Programs, 13th ed., 2009
Engineering & Technology, 13th ed., 2009
Environmental Management, 2nd ed., 2000

Authentic Involvement, 2001

Basics of Safety and Health, rev., 2004

Injury Facts, published annually

Management Safety Policies, Data Sheet. No. 585, R(1995)

Occupational Health & Safety, 3rd ed., 2000

Out in Front: Effective Supervision in the Workplace, 1990

Pocket Guide to Safety Essentials, 2007

Safeguarding Concepts Illustrated, 7th ed., 2002

Supervisors Safety Manual, 10th ed., 2009

U.S. Dept. of Labor, OSHA. *Recordkeeping Requirements Under the Williams-Steiger Occupational Safety and Health Act of 1970.* Washington, DC: OSHA, 1971.

Vincoli JW. *Basic Guide to Accident Investigation and Loss Control.* New York: Van Nostrand Reinhold, 1994.

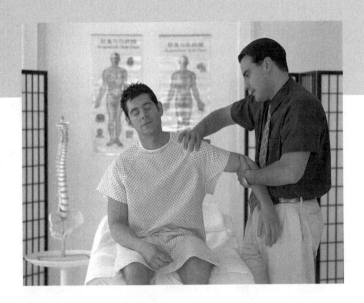

CHAPTER 26

The Occupational and Environmental Medicine Physician

by Linda H. Morse, MD, FACOEM

*T*he field of occupational medicine has changed dramatically over the past 60 years in composition, focus, and scope. Particularly in the past decade, focus has increased dramatically on the environmental aspect of our preventive medicine specialty. New hazards, such as nanotechnology, and new workplaces, such as aerospace and undersea environments, offer continuing challenges. Key to meeting these challenges is a team effort focusing on identification and prevention of workplace hazards, with input from industrial hygienists and occupational health nurses. A partnership must be maintained with government, industry, and labor scientists in the ongoing evaluation of the hazards faced daily in industrial operations, including chemical, biological, physical, stress/shiftwork, safety, and ergonomic hazards. The approach to hazard evaluation needs to include recognizing that what is in the workplace gets into our air, soil, and water—and increasingly into our bodies via food and beverages. Thus, the control of industrial hazards, especially through reduction of hazardous materials and processes, contributes to the ability to control environmental hazards. The occupational physician must also jointly maintain a clear ethical focus in their work. There are strong economic and organizational pressures to look for fiscally productive solutions without always keeping employee and community health and safety as a primary focus.

HISTORY

It is important for the industrial hygienist or safety professional seeking partnership with occupational medicine physicians to have some understanding of the history of the field and its evolution in the United States. Physicians have long noted the importance of occupation in the causation of disease and injury. In a 1713 supplement to his *De Morbis Artificum* (Diseases of Workers), Bernardino Ramazzini turned his attention to the afflictions of scribes and notaries, and his description offers a prescient portrayal of today's upper extremity cumulative trauma disorders:

The maladies that afflict the clerks aforesaid arise from three causes: First, constant sitting; secondly, the incessant movement of the hand and always in the same direction; thirdly, the strain on the mind from the effort not to disfigure the books by errors or cause loss to their employers when they add, subtract or do their sums in arithmetic.... In a word, they lack the benefits of moderate exercise, for even if they wanted to take exercise, they have no time for it; they are working for wages and must stick to their writing all day long. Furthermore, incessant driving of the pen over paper causes intense fatigue of the hand and whole arm because of the continuous and almost tonic strain on the muscles and tendons, which in the course of time results in failure of power in the right hand (Herington & Morse, 1995).

Before 1900, many "doctors" in the United States had no formal training and practiced a variety of healing arts and techniques, few of them based on science. Medical training was not standardized, and licensing of medical professionals was lax. During the late 1800s however, states passed licensing laws requiring doctors to have a degree from a medical school and pass a formal examination. The American Medical Association (AMA), founded in 1846, soon became a powerful force. In 1904 the AMA set up the Council on Medical Education, which began grading medical schools. In 1910 the council issued the Flexner Report, which was harshly critical of the country's 131 medical schools and recommended closing 99 of them; eventually 70 survived.

Many of these changes were spurred by scientific breakthroughs during the late 1800s, among them anesthesia use, aseptic technique, new diagnostic instruments (such as the stethoscope and ophthalmoscope), and tests (such as x-rays and electrocardiograms).Other breakthroughs of this time included identification of the organisms causing diseases, such as cholera and tuberculosis, and the development of vaccines for use against these diseases. Such innovations, combined with standardized population-based tests for vision, height/weight, and IQ, led to the new *scientific practice of medicine*. Hospitals, previously considered dangerous, disease-ridden places where one went to die, became the centers of this new practice of medicine.

As these innovations were evolving, the United States was beginning its evolution from an agricultural society to an industrial one. In the 1860s, railroads and mining companies began to employ physicians, paying them through payroll deductions or putting them on salary. They were hired specifically to treat victims of industrial accidents, keep them working and, it was hoped, prevent lawsuits. Workers' compensation laws did not exist until the early 1900s, when states began adopting laws to set up no-fault compensation systems both to care for injured workers and to confine benefits within a no-fault system, thus preventing legal actions.

In addition to treating injuries, company doctors performed medical examinations and often provided nonindustrial care to workers' families, especially in remote areas. Not only the workers, but also other medical practitioners sometimes viewed these doctors with suspicion. In 1908, a Sears Roebuck Company physician resigned his position because he was excluded from membership in the Chicago Medical Society on the grounds that the reduced-rate services he provided to employees' families constituted "an unethical invasion of private practice."

The American Association of Industrial Physicians was founded in 1916 and later renamed the American Occupational Medicine Association (AOMA). Its members focused primarily on providing physical examinations and dealing with physical trauma. The American Academy of Occupational Medicine (AAOM) was founded in 1946. Its membership was limited to physicians who were devoted full time to the field of occupational medicine, and their primary concern was the prevention of injury and illness, especially from toxic exposures. The American Board of Preventive Medicine (ABPM) was established two years later, and in 1956 it was reorganized into three parts: Public Health, Aviation Medicine (now Aerospace Medicine), and Occupational Medicine. The board provided an avenue for board certification as a specialist in these fields for the first time.

Initially, the AAOM and AOMA (who in 1988 merged into one group, the American College of Occupational Medicine [ACOM]) kept their focus on corporate occupational medicine, and the group's membership was still composed primarily of corporate-based physicians. However, occupational health hazards were increasing as the post-World War II industrial boom brought thousands of new chemicals into existence for which neither human beings nor Earth's ecology had any evolutionary defenses. Even asbestos, silica, lead, and other compounds that occur naturally on our planet were being transformed into new products, resulting in exposures that caused epidemics of disease among workers in mining and production operations. Amid growing public concern about these problems, combined with the civil rights and antiwar activism of the 1960s and 1970s, unions and community organizers formed local Committees on Occupational Health and Safety (COSH) across the country. Many COSH physicians joined the American Public Health Association's (APHA) Occupational Health Section, in part because APHA's political views dovetailed with their own, and in part because APHA was not exclusive to physicians. Membership was open to the entire occupational health team, including nurses, industrial hygienists, and safety personnel.

In 1970 Congress passed the Occupational Safety and Health Act (OSHAct) mandating a safe and healthy workplace for all employees. With passage of this legislation came significant additional resources for industrial hygiene and occupational health nursing programs as well as the development of new physician training programs in occupational medicine, previously limited to a very few corporate and academic centers.

Meanwhile, occupational medicine had grown as a field, soon encompassing environmental issues as well. The ACOM is now known as the American College of Occupational and Environmental Medicine (ACOEM). Over 30 occupational medicine residency programs were developed at major universities across the United States, graduating approximately 75 physicians per year. That number, unfortunately, is barely keeping up with attrition due to retirement or other reasons for leaving the field. Recent fiscal crises in education have compounded the problem, causing the number of programs to drop to 28. Over 4,000 doctors are members of ACOEM; of the approximately 1,500 members who are board-certified as specialists, over half are approaching retirement age.

Like the realm of environmental hazards, the practice of occupational medicine has also changed (and expanded) dramatically since the OSHAct was passed. Corporate downsizing and the practice of contracting work out have led to the demise of the company corporate medical department, although some still exist. At the same time, the rising costs of medical care and the dramatic worsening of U.S. workers' health have triggered a new focus on employee wellness. This new focus has breathed new life into corporate based opportunities for occupational health professionals.

Work with or for unions grew out of the COSH group model of the 1970s and has provided a focus for some in the field. The more recent environmental activism has also attracted full time or volunteer occupational and environmental health physicians. In many large medical group practices, hospitals, and universities, occupational medicine is now its own department or a subspecialty of the medicine or community medicine division. Freestanding occupational health clinics, often combined with urgent-care centers, offer another practice setting, as do private consulting firms and international work—two growing sectors of occupational and environmental medicine practice. The academic, occu-pational, and environmental health departments that are a major development since the 1970s offer clinical, teaching, and research opportunities, which will be discussed in the following sections.

CREDENTIALS AND PROFESSIONAL ASSOCIATIONS

It is important for the industrial hygiene or safety professional working with the occupational medicine physician to understand the background, training, and ethical focus not only of the individual physician, but also the organizational context within which the doctor is working.

Since 1984, medical school graduates who wish to become board certified in occupational medicine have been required to complete a formal occupational medicine residency or fellowship program to become eligible to take the examination. This is a two year program usually taken after, at a minimum, an internship, but preferably after a full residency in another field, such as internal or family medicine. The program includes extensive public health training in toxicology, epidemiology, and statistics, usually leading to a Masters in Public Health (MPH). Training is usually followed by a practicum year of clinical, research, and corporate placements, and public sector agency rotations. Most of the academic occupational medicine residency programs have a very strong focus on toxicology and epidemiology. More recently, increased interest in cumulative trauma disorders has led a number of centers to do research and clinical work on musculoskeletal injuries.

Because many physicians become interested in occupational medicine after having practiced in another field for several years (often having acquired financial and family obligations that would make it difficult to go back to a fellowship salary and schedule), online coursework through the Internet can be a path to an MPH degree. In addition, part time residency programs can be created for the practicum year, thus allowing a qualified physician to make the transition without creating a huge disruption in their personal life. Alternative credentialing for occupational health physicians is also being explored, as the current process is not producing enough qualified practitioners to meet the needs of the country.

The Occupational Medicine Board Examination is a lengthy test offered once a year by the American Board of Preventive Medicine. The 200–300 physicians who take the examination annually must demonstrate proficiency both in preventive medicine and occupational medicine in order to pass. The ABPM also offers credentialing in General Preventive Medicine, Aerospace Medicine, and a new track,

Underseas and Hyperbaric Medicine. In a recent development, all Board Certified OEM specialists are now required to take a recertification examination every 10 years and to maintain documented continuing education in the field.

Professional associations in the field include the American College of Occupational and Environmental Medicine, whose approximately 4,000 members are in the United States, Canada, Mexico, and in a number of smaller countries. Fellowship in ACOEM is conferred only upon those who are board-certified, have worked full time in the field for three years, and are recommended by other fellows as meeting the increasingly rigorous standards set by ACOEM. ACOEM organizes two major educational conferences a year and publishes the monthly *Journal of Occupational and Environmental Medicine*. The American Public Health Association has a very active Occupational Health Section composed of not only physicians but also nurses, industrial hygienists, epidemiologists, and others in the field. The National Association of Occupational Health Professionals was created to provide a venue for occupational health professionals from all fields to develop their skills in marketing, managing clinics, and other difficult administrative challenges.

PRACTICE SETTINGS

Corporate Medical Department

As previously mentioned, the number of corporate medical departments is shrinking as a result of organizational downsizing and the increasing use of outside contractors. However, controversy remains over whether this development is truly cost effective in the long run. Currently, there are few corporate medical directors who oversee a large staff of physicians and nurses providing preplacement and periodic surveillance exams, executive physicals, treatment of acute work-related injury/illnesses, and on-site wellness and nonindustrial acute medical care. Today's corporate medical director is likely to serve as a consultant to the human resources department, helping to provide quality assurance regarding the clinics that are contracted to actually provide the services. Medical directors also provide medical review for difficult workers' compensation cases. Their other duties may include fitness-for-duty evaluations, development of medical surveillance protocols for occupational exposures, and the establishment of wellness programs. In addition to their medical skills, corporate-based OEM physicians or consultants frequently need business and fiscal-management skills and computer skills. Physicians working for multinational corporations also need to become experts in travel medicine, given today's increasing focus on

the issue of international travel and employee exposure to infectious diseases. Corporate medical departments most often require board certification in occupational medicine and, frequently, in another field such as internal medicine.

Multispecialty Group Practice/Hospital-Based Programs

Multispecialty group practices and hospital-based programs have been a growing source of practice opportunities for occupational medicine physicians. The physician may work in a free standing occupational medicine department or as a subspecialist, usually in a division of medicine or family practice, sometimes as part of emergency/urgent care. Usually these positions are primarily clinical and frequently require a heavy patient load of 20 to 30 patients per day. Additional responsibilities may include developing programs to attract local industry (e.g., injury care, preplacement examinations, wellness efforts, and drug testing); performing consults for colleagues from other departments or divisions on environmental exposures or work or disability issues; and helping to ensure that workers' compensation visits are correctly reported and billed. Advertisements for these jobs increasingly request board certification in occupational medicine. Because of the shortage of certified specialists, however, the positions are often filled by physicians certified in other specialties (internal medicine, emergency medicine, family practice) who have transitioned to occupational medicine.

Freestanding Occupational Health Clinics

Freestanding occupational health clinics may be a single entity or part of a chain of clinics located near industry and developed to serve multiple local companies by providing a range of services from preplacement examinations and drug testing to acute care for work-related injuries and illnesses. Sometimes the industrial services are combined with urgent care for nonindustrial problems and even a travel medicine service. These clinics do not usually have the access to specialized services available to hospitals or multispecialty group practice programs. Often practitioners in these clinics are required to see 30-40 patients per day, are not specialists in the field, and focus on injury illness treatment and preplacement and surveillance examinations. Many physicians working in these clinics have little time or the training to deal with complex health and safety issues.

Private Consulting Firms

Many academically trained, board-certified occupational medicine physicians choose to join or set up their own consulting firms. This allows a wide range of practice opportunities, including consulting with companies, local government agencies, and unions; performing medical surveillance and other examinations; acting as expert witnesses; doing epidemiological research; and participating in environmental hazard investigations. These firms frequently have close working relationships with industrial hygienists, epidemiologists, toxicologists, and occupational health nurses.

Academic Occupational Medicine Departments

Occupational medicine departments have been established in all of the universities with occupational medicine residency programs and many others as well, and they are growing in number. Responsibilities in this setting include research and teaching as well as patient care, consulting, and expert witness testimony. Occupational medicine physicians working in academic settings are board-certified, frequently in both occupational medicine and another specialty, and may be allotted additional responsibilities, for example, attending on the Medicine wards, proctoring medical students, etc.

Environmental Agencies and Nongovernmental Organizations

The global environmental crisis has spurred significant growth in activist and scientific environmental organizations that mount legislative campaigns to forestall and/or clean up hazardous sites, and reduce the body burden of industrial chemical contamination through product substitution.

Government Agencies

Policy development and regulatory agencies in the areas of occupational and environmental health and safety often have one or more staff physicians, usually board-certified, who provide scientific oversight and back-up. These physicians are rarely involved in clinical work with patients. Rather, they provide advice regarding epidemiological, toxicological, environmental, and other issues, and often help to perform epidemiological studies in response to public health or regulatory needs. The National Institute for Occupational Safety and Health (NIOSH), federal and state OSHA programs, the Environmental Protection Agency (EPA), and many other federal, state, and local governmental agencies have in-house, well-trained, and credentialed occupational and environmental physicians who can be a significant resource of information for industrial hygiene and safety personnel. All branches of the military also have active occupational medicine programs.

International Occupational & Environmental Health Consulting

International consulting is a growing field that is attracting a number of board-certified occupational medicine physicians. Rapid industrialization in Asia, South America, and parts of Africa has created significant industrial and environmental problems in places that lack the governmental, academic, or private sector infrastructure or expertise to deal with these issues. Occupational health and safety professionals from the United States, Canada, and Europe are finding jobs as consultants, and their duties may range from training local professionals and conducting epidemiological research studies to consulting on governmental policies and legislation and making presentations at international conferences.

Union Occupational Health Physicians

Unions began developing relationships with occupational medicine physicians, industrial hygienists, and epidemiologists in the 1970s. Some unions, such as the Oil, Chemical & Atomic Workers, International Association of Firefighters, and United Auto Workers, have added such personnel to their full time staff. Others have created formal or informal consultant relationships or medical advisory boards. Occupational health and safety has long been an important issue for unions whose members face exposure to significant chemical hazards, and it is a growing issue for newer service sector unions, such as Service Employees International Union, that are concerned about back injuries, cumulative trauma disorders, and protection from violence on the job. Union efforts have been a key factor in spurring legislation mandating stronger workplace health and safety regulations. Professional medical expertise plays a critical role both in creating and supporting such legislation and in a union's efforts to protect the health of its members.

SCOPE OF PRACTICE

It is important that industrial hygiene and safety professionals be aware of the skill and interest level of the particular occupational medicine physician or organization they seek to work with. When considering setting up a professional relationship, careful reading of a clinician's *curriculum vitae* will provide valuable information about their background and level of training, as will an informal meeting, preferably at the clinician's office. Discussing an exposure problem, a case that poses ethical issues, or asking what texts or databases the physician would use to answer a question, can open up productive avenues of discussion.

Physicians who work in the field of occupational medicine should, at a minimum, be familiar with the state and federal workers' compensation systems and be able to evaluate and treat common work-related injuries and illnesses (including determining industrial causation). They should also be able to perform preplacement, Department of Transportation (DOT), and basic medical surveillance examinations for respiratory protection and exposure to toxins, such as asbestos and lead. Most non-board-certified occupational health physicians will not necessarily be competent on issues of toxic chemical exposure, physical hazards, biological hazards (except possibly for bloodborne pathogens), stress/shiftwork issues, difficult ergonomic problems, and/or a company's indoor air quality issues or environmental problems. They should however be familiar with the relevant occupational/environmental medicine resources available in the community and be able to guide the safety/industrial hygiene professional to those who have the expertise to deal with more complicated issues.

Because they are trained in toxicology, epidemiology, and critical review of the medical literature, board-certified occupational and environmental medicine physicians, especially those who are academically trained, should be able to provide expertise and guidance on the more complicated toxic and other workplace hazards, including the difficult issues regarding causation. They should also be familiar with important local and national legislative developments, including employment and health- and safety-related issues, such as the Americans with Disabilities Act, the status of upcoming bills on hot topics such as ergonomics, changes in workers' compensation laws, and legislation about medical surveillance requirements. Protocol and policy development, group medical screenings, presentations to employers and employees, and complicated fitness-for-duty evaluations should also be among their areas of competence. Additionally, they should be able to help in policy development and create medical protocols for surveillance examinations.

Many occupational medicine physicians in the field also have additional specialized credentials as disability evaluators, aviation medical examiners, company wellness program directors, and Medical Review Officers (MROs) for drug screening programs. In cases involving significant environmental hazards, which are usually far more complicated than industrial exposure problems, one should seek out specialty consultant firms and/or physicians working for environmental groups, academic occupational medicine departments, or governmental experts from national, state, or local agencies. These are the professionals who are best able to provide expert-witness testimony and/or create designs for epidemiological studies for either occupational or environmental hazards.

CLINICAL PRACTICE

The Occupational Health History

Because occupational hazards can be a cause of almost any adult disease or injury, a brief occupational health history

should be part of all medical histories. Carpal tunnel syndrome used to be considered a problem of aging women, or was classified as idiopathic—something for which medicine has no explanation. Now we know that a significant percentage of such cases are work related. Coronary artery disease can be caused by exposure to carbon disulfide in rayon manufacturing. Parkinson's disease, a serious neurological disorder, is not only caused by manganese exposure in mining operations but also by some synthetic chemicals used both in industry and in street drugs.

Since most adults spend almost one third of their time at work, consideration of their potentially detrimental work exposures is an important part of modern medicine. Unfortunately, most physicians are still not appropriately trained in how to take a good occupational history. During the four years of medical school, on average just four hours is spent on occupational exposures—in those schools that address the subject at all. This is another reason the safety and health professional must rely on referral to specialists in the field. An excellent, easily reproduced sample occupational history form is included in this chapter (Figure 26–1). Most employees find it easy to fill out. They should be instructed to do so chronologically, either starting with their current job and working backwards, or beginning with work done in grade or high school and working forward to the present. This format allows the employee to be as complete as possible without the burden of being asked dozens of questions about chemicals and processes with which she or he is unfamiliar.

With this history form, for example, a 38-year-old male commercial plumber who was referred for evaluation of acute onset of leukemia, and who had worked in the pipe trades "all my life," was identified as having significant benzene exposure because he noted a six-month stint at a tire manufacturing plant before he became a union apprentice. He did not know what benzene was, and would have answered negatively if questioned only about the chemical.

In addition to past and current occupational history, including exposure and protective equipment notations, the form also covers moonlighting jobs and hobbies, often the source of significant exposures separate from or in addition to those in the full-time occupation. Finally, questions about reproductive history are also an important part of the occupational history, as effects from certain chemicals and other hazards may present first or only in this arena.

Finally, when evaluating a specific job, including questions that focus on three components—the workstation and work tools, work tasks, and the individual's work practices—may be a useful addition to the baseline questions. The answers can provide information indicating corrective measures needed to prevent or resolve

OCCUPATIONAL HISTORY FORM
PART I

Name _____

Please answer the following work history questions. Begin with your first job in school (i.e. paperboy) and list all jobs held in order after that.

**For those in building trades it may be difficult or impossible to remember every job. Please try to list all those where you worked a long time or had toxic exposure or illness. (use back of sheet if necessary)

COMPANY NAME OR SELF-EMPLOYED City, state (include any military service)	DATES From Mo/Yr To Mo/Yr	GIVE JOB TITLE or major activities	LIST POTENTIAL HAZARDS EXPOSED TO			PERSONAL PROTECTIVE EQUIPMENT WORN ON THE JOB (Hard hats, respirators, ear plugs, gloves, aprons, goggles, safety shoes, etc.) List for each job
			Physical (Noise, radiation, vibration, electrical shock, temperature extremes, etc.)	**Chemical** (Mercury, lead, gases, fumes, acids, solvents, caustics, fly ash, dust, etc.)	**Biological** (Viruses, bacteria, parasites, fungus, animal bites, etc.) **Psychological** (Boredom, workshift fatigue, risk of falling or being buried, repetitive tasks, etc.)	

Figure 26–1. Occupational History Form. (Continues)

OCCUPATIONAL HISTORY FORM
PART II

I   If you have had any secondary work such as firefighting, civil defense, farming, gardening, please list.
Type of work   Dates

II   List hobbies and active sports you do (past and present) such as painting, woodworking, welding, hairdressing, scuba diving, etc.

III   Please comment on any work-related experiences you have had that you believe may have been harmful to your health.

IV   Have you or your present or former spouse had any adverse reproductive outcome? If so, please indicate circumstances (e.g., stillborn, deformed, miscarriage, infertility, irregular menses, etc.)

Figure 26–1. Occupational History Form.

injury or illness, especially for problems related to ergonomics or indoor air quality.

Once taken, the occupational history needs to be reviewed by a specialist with a good library and internet search capacity so that specific occupations and exposures can be cross-referenced against the injury or illness of concern.

The Preplacement Examination

Preplacement examinations are an important part of ensuring a safe and healthy workforce because hiring someone who is physically unable to do a job places an added burden and risk of injury on both the worker and their coworkers. Legislative changes and court rulings over recent decades have appropriately limited employers' ability to arbitrarily deny jobs based on criteria unrelated to the actual job requirements.

Preplacement evaluations can range from a simple drug screen and/or a medical history review by a registered nurse to a complete medical exam and occupational history, including a physical examination with functional capacity testing and other tests. A thorough evaluation is appropriate for some occupations. For example, the physical, chemical, and other hazards found in firefighting, hazardous waste work, and certain other job classes warrant complete histories and physicals, with cardiac, pulmonary, and strength and endurance testing.

For most job classifications, however, extensive testing is unwarranted and has not been found to reduce the costs of workers' compensation or absenteeism from nonindustrial illness. If preplacement testing is contemplated, it should be targeted to the job requirements and can also be oriented to provide a baseline for injuries and illnesses that have high compensation costs for the employer. Even without functional capacity testing, a thorough neuromuscular evaluation will identify any preexisting abnormalities of upper trapezius spasm, or a reflex deficit from a prior back disc injury. Jamar dynamometer grip strength testing is advised as part of this process, as it readily identifies individuals whose grip strength is lower than expected and are thus at increased risk of upper extremity injuries from both acute and cumulative trauma. Those found to be deconditioned or lacking flexibility or strength can be counseled and given specific exercises to correct the problem before an injury occurs.

Similarly, in jobs where there is possible exposure to chemical irritants, careful evaluation of the skin, mucous membranes, and eye conjunctivae (for cobblestoning), as well as a lung exam and possibly simple screening spirometry, will establishes a baseline and also allow counseling for those with allergy problems that are not well controlled.

Even simple preplacement medical screens usually involve checking blood pressure and vision and sometimes urinalysis. These can be valuable in detecting nonindustrial diseases such as hypertension and diabetes, which need medical intervention for the health of the employee. Identification of new or uncontrolled problems calls for a referral in writing to the patient's primary-care physician, with a copy of the referral placed in the employee's record. Such efforts not only can result in early diagnosis and treatment, they also increase employees' positive view of the organization's attitude toward their welfare. Wellness counseling, too, should be a big part of any preplacement examination, given the significant shortening of life span and worsening quality of life in the increasing percentage of the population that are either overweight or obese

The examining clinician must take care to avoid making hiring decisions. The purpose of the medical evaluation is to determine "fitness for duty," and the organization, not the clinician, decides whether the job applicant can be accommodated. The clinician gives the employer a simple work slip describing any needed accommodations but without revealing the medical problem requiring them. Even if the employee has signed a release of information form, it is important to avoid revealing confidential personal medical information to nonmedical personnel.

Industrial hygiene, safety, and environmental professionals can help employers identify medical providers who will provide cost-effective and ethical preplacement evaluation services that promote employee wellness.

Fitness for Duty and Return to Work Examinations

Employers should ask the occupational medicine physician to perform fitness for duty (FFD) evaluations only when there are documentable performance problems and documentable reason to believe that the poor performance may have a medical cause. The evaluating physician should insist on a written referral that clearly outlines these issues, accompanied by a detailed functional job description, and should not undertake the examination in the absence of such documentation. Protecting the employee's right to confidentiality is key in such cases, and the employer must understand that the only information the physician will transmit to HR is a brief statement that the employee is either fit for duty, not fit for duty, or fit with accommodations or restrictions. Companies should have clear HR policies and procedures for initiating the FFD examination process, as it has the potential to be misused to terminate an employee for medical reasons rather than go through the appropriate channels of performance counseling and documentation.

Return-to-work evaluations are requested when an employee has been off work for a prolonged period of time due to nonindustrial or work-related injury or illness. The issues and process are similar to the FFD evaluation and usually center on evaluation of potential deconditioning when returning to a job with rigorous physical requirements.

Drug Testing & Medical Review Officer Examinations

Drug testing has become a major focus for many companies concerned about job safety. It is generally required as part of the preplacement screening process, and many companies also require employees to agree to testing in the event of a work injury, or, in sensitive occupations, randomly during the course of a work year. The OEM physician can help employers develop a useful monitoring program and can also provide medical review officer services to evaluate the results of the testing if the physician is MRO certified. This certification requires significant additional training and ongoing accrual of annual continuing education points.

Workers' Compensation Case Evaluation and Treatment

All 50 states require employers to carry workers' compensation insurance, although the laws vary widely from state to state. In addition, there are special laws nationally to cover federal employees who are injured on the job. The maritime, railroad, and long shore industries each have their own nation-wide regulations. The OEM physician practicing in a specific geographic area should familiarize themselves with both the state and national laws relevant to that area.

Most workers who are injured on the job recover and continue working. However, since workers' compensation regulations in general are complicated and difficult to understand, especially because few states send letters and notices to injured workers in any language except English, employees who get caught up in the system often express a significant amount of distrust. This can be magnified if a supervisor or insurer is perceived as exhibiting suspicion about the injury. Psychosocial factors also play a major role in the 15 to 20 percent of cases that involve delayed recovery. In addition to providing evidence-based, cost-effective care that focuses on return to function, the treating OEM physician must also provide compassionate and culturally competent care. This means taking a few extra minutes to encourage patients to bring in letters from the insurance carrier so that the physician can explain them and making sure that translation services are available. It also means understanding that cultural differences can exist; for example using ice versus heat for a certain condition. If not dealt with up front, such differences can interfere with trust in the provider and recovery.

Company or consultant health and safety professionals who are evaluating clinics for referral of workers' compensation injuries should not only examine the credentials of the clinician staff but also of the medical assistants and registered nurses, as administration of breathing, hearing, and drug tests also requires specialized training and certification.

In addition, the ambience at the clinic can be an important factor for the employee. Is it attractive and professional? Are visitors and patients greeted promptly and warmly? Are patient education materials available in the major languages of the community? Does the clinic actively address general wellness issues, discussing smoking cessation and exercise as well as the patient's low back injury?

The past decade has seen an increasing focus on evidence-based medicine. The *ACOEM Practice Guidelines* for evaluation and treatment of work injuries is now in its third edition, which provides an excellent reference for treating clinicians everywhere, and has actually been written into the California Labor Code as the standard by which injuries covered under that state's regulations must be managed.

SUMMARY

Occupational medicine physicians are an essential part of the health, safety, and environmental team, regardless of the setting. Fortunately there is a growing pool of physicians who strive to practice ethical, cost-effective, scientifically based occupational medicine and who recognize the importance of teamwork and the equally essential roles of nursing, industrial hygiene, environmental, and safety professionals.

BIBLIOGRAPHY

Anstadt G. Contracting for occupational health services. *J Occup Med* 36(4):443–461, 1994.

Clever L. Ethical issues in occupational medicine. In *Occupational Injuries: Evaluation, Management and Prevention*, TN Herington, LH Morse, eds. St. Louis, MO: Mosby, 1995, Chapter 7.

Fletcher DJ, Freeman JD. Managing multisite occupational health services. *J Occup Med* 36(4):434–438, 1994.

Goldwater L. *The First Ten Years* (Presentation at the 25th Anniversary Meeting of American Academy of Occupational Medicine), Feb. 8, 1973.

Hathaway JA. Medical programs for multiple domestic sites. *J Occup Med* 36(4):428–433, 1994.

Herington TN, Morse LH. Cumulative trauma/repetitive motion disorders. In *Occupational Injuries: Evaluation Management and Prevention*, TN Herington, LH Morse, eds. St. Louis, MO: Mosby-Year Book, 1995, p. 333.

Kaiser Permanente. *The Evolution of Health Care in the United States*. Oakland, CA: Health Plan Institute, 1995, p. 5–7, 12.

Leone F, Schumann S. Occupational health clinic. In

Occupational Injuries: Evaluation, Management and Prevention, TN Herington, LH Morse, eds. St. Louis, MO: Mosby, 1995, Chapter 3.

McCunney RJ. The academic occupational physician as consultant. *J Occup Med* 36(4):438–442, 1994.

Moore CE. International occupational healthcare. *J Occup Med* 36(4):419–421, 1994.

Welter ES. The role of the primary care physician in occupational medicine: Principles, practical observations and recommendations. In *Occupational Medicine: Principles and Practical Applications*, 2nd ed., C Zenz, ed. Chicago: U.S. Yearbook Medical Publishers, 1988.

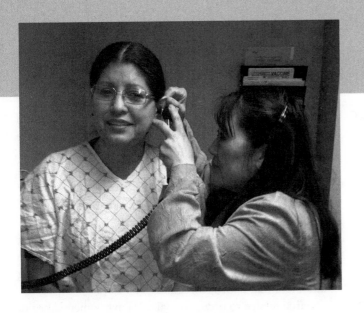

CHAPTER 27

The Occupational Health Nurse

by Barbara J. Burgel, RN, PhD, COHN-S, FAAN

Occupational health nursing has an important historical role in protecting the health of workers. Occupational health nurses have made over 120 years of solid contributions in this public health discipline, and are committed to working with employees and their dependents, employers, and other health and safety team members to attain a safe and healthy workplace.

The occupational health nurse (OHN) manages occupational health and safety prevention-based programs in the worksite and in the community, working in a team relationship with other occupational, environmental, and safety professionals. The OHN provides the critical link between employee health status, the work process, and the determination of employee ability to do the job, protecting the confidentiality of personal health information within a professional ethics-based framework. If there is an injury or exposure, the OHN delivers care, participates in the corrective action process, and supports the injured worker back to work to enhance recovery and minimize disability. Health and safety regulations, workplace hazards, evidence-based practice and direct care skills, counseling/health coaching, teaching, and program management are but a few of the key knowledge areas of the OHN, with strong communication skills of utmost importance. Serving as stewards to protect the environment, and creating new models to provide occupational and environmental health services to small employers and contingent workers present new opportunities for OHNs.

OBJECTIVES

This chapter provides
- an overview of the professional aspects of the OHN role, including standards of practice and certification;
- a model of occupational health nursing, including a dis-

cussion of competencies needed for professional practice activities; and

- examples of primary, secondary, and tertiary prevention programmatic activities by occupational health nurses in the worksite.

OVERVIEW

Definition of the Occupational Health Nurse

As of 2004, an estimated 22,447 registered nurses provide care in occupational health settings (Thompson, 2010) with the goal to prevent work-related injury and illness, prevent disability, and help workers achieve and maintain the highest level of health throughout their lives. Occupational health nurses maintain a focus on the worksite where they deliver quality care, and philosophically support a primary prevention-based practice. If injuries do occur, a case management approach is utilized to return injured employees back to appropriate work in a timely manner. Studying each "case" provides an additional opportunity for worksite prevention. The goal is to provide a safe and healthy workplace for all, and to protect human resources.

Occupational and environmental health nursing is "the specialty practice that provides for and delivers health and safety programs and services to workers, worker populations and community groups" (American Association of Occupational Health Nurses [AAOHN], 2009a, p. 1). The practice of occupational health nursing is grounded in the public health principles of primary, secondary, and tertiary prevention, and is "focused on promotion and the restoration of health, prevention of illness and injury, and protection from work-related and environmental hazards" (AAOHN, 2009a, p. 1).

Scope of Practice

The OHN is licensed as a registered nurse and has both independent and dependent nursing functions, as authorized by the state business and professions code. Advanced practice nursing roles, including nurse practitioner and clinical nurse specialist roles, are also licensed state by state. OHNs use the nursing decision-making process in their encounters with both individuals and organizations, including collecting subjective and objective data, making assessments and plans, and evaluating health care and organizational outcomes. It is the responsibility of OHNs to function within a legal and ethical framework of professional practice, and to maintain competence through ongoing education. Occupational health nursing services include

- clinical and primary care including assessment, diagnosis, management, and documentation of occupational and

nonoccupational illness and injury;
- case management for occupational and nonoccupational illness and injury;
- health hazard assessment and surveillance of employee populations, workplaces, and community groups;
- investigation, monitoring, and analysis of illness and injury episodes and trends, as well as methods to promote and protect employee health and safety;
- compliance with laws, regulations, and standards governing health and safety for employees and the environment;
- management and administration of occupational and environmental health services;
- health promotion and disease prevention strategies using primary, secondary, and tertiary principles;
- counseling, health education, and training programs using adult learning approaches; and
- research related to occupational and environmental health (excerpted from AAOHN, 2004a, p. 3).

Figure 27–1 is one model of occupational health nursing, recognizing environmental forces and internal system inputs impacting the range of OHN services (Rogers, 2005). These environmental forces include dynamic population and health trends, technological factors, economic, and legislative-political factors affecting work. Examples include the aging workforce, the introduction of new technology into a new work process, the amount of resources dedicated to the prevention of work-related injuries, and new OSHA standards or disability regulations. Internal system inputs include organizational factors such as the safety climate at the worksite, and the hazard profile associated with the work process.

STANDARDS OF PRACTICE FOR OCCUPATIONAL AND ENVIRONMENTAL HEALTH NURSING

Standards of Occupational and Environmental Health Nursing Practice, developed by AAOHN (2004), enable the profession to ensure a quality-based practice, and to provide protection to the consumer and the profession alike. A summary of the standards include:

Standard I: Assessment—The occupational and environmental health nurse systematically assesses the health status of the client(s).

Standard II: Diagnosis—The occupational and environmental health nurse analyzes assessment data to formulate diagnoses.

Standard III: Outcome Identification—The occupational and environmental health nurse identifies outcomes specific to the client(s).

Standard IV: Planning—The occupational and environmen-

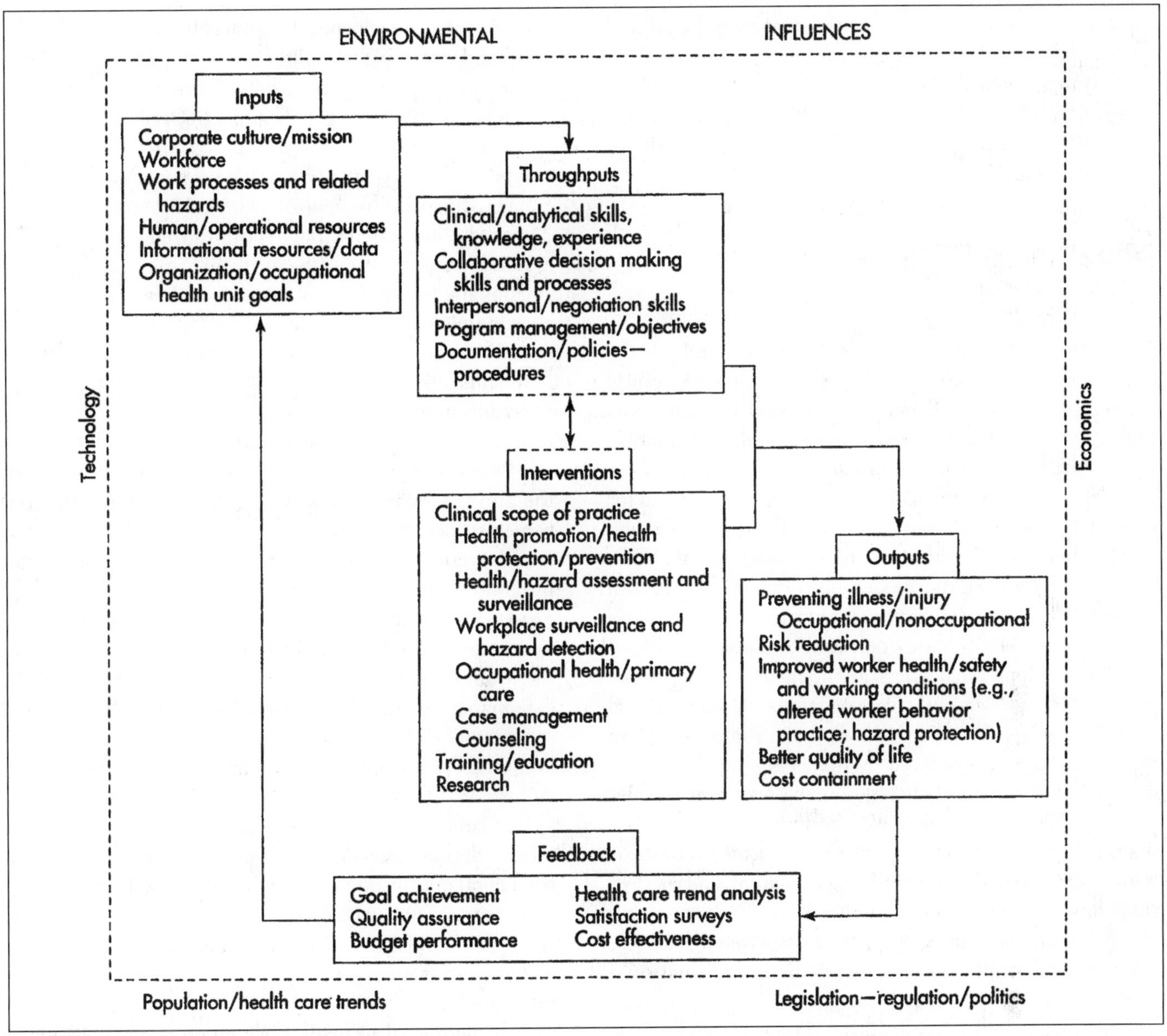

ENVIRONMENTAL   INFLUENCES

Technology

Inputs

Corporate culture/mission
Workforce
Work processes and related
    hazards
Human/operational resources
Informational resources/data
Organization/occupational
    health unit goals

Throughputs

Clinical/analytical skills,
    knowledge, experience
Collaborative decision making
    skills and processes
Interpersonal/negotiation skills
Program management/objectives
Documentation/policies—
    procedures

Interventions

Clinical scope of practice
    Health promotion/health
        protection/prevention
    Health/hazard assessment and
        surveillance
    Workplace surveillance and
        hazard detection
    Occupational health/primary
        care
    Case management
    Counseling
Training/education
Research

Outputs

Preventing illness/injury
    Occupational/nonoccupational
Risk reduction
Improved worker health/safety
    and working conditions (e.g.,
    altered worker behavior
    practice; hazard protection)
Better quality of life
Cost containment

Economics

Feedback

Goal achievement   Health care trend analysis
Quality assurance   Satisfaction surveys
Budget performance   Cost effectiveness

Population/health care trends   Legislation—regulation/politics

Figure 27–1. One model of occupational health nursing, recognizing the environmental influences and the internal system inputs impacting the range of OHN services (*Source: Rogers, Bonnie. Occupational and Environmental Health Nursing: Concepts and Practice, 2nd ed., 2003, page 135.)*

tal health nurse develops a goal-directed plan that is comprehensive and formulates interventions to attain expected outcomes.

Standard V: Implementation—The occupational and environmental health nurse implements interventions to attain desired outcomes identified in the plan.

Standard VI: Evaluation—The occupational and environmental health nurse systematically and continuously evaluates responses to interventions and progress toward the achievement of desired outcomes.

Standard VII: Resource Management—The occupational and environmental health nurse secures and manages

the resources that support occupational health and safety programs and services.

Standard VIII: Professional Development—The occupational and environmental health nurse assumes accountability for professional development to enhance professional growth and maintain competency.

Standard IX: Collaboration—The occupational and environmental health nurse collaborates with clients for the promotion, prevention, and restoration of health within the context of a safe and healthy environment.

Standard X: Research—The occupational and environmental health nurse uses research findings in practice and contributes to the scientific base in occupational and environmental health nursing to improve practice and advance the profession.

Standard XI: Ethics—The occupational and environmental health nurse uses an ethical framework as a guide for decision making in practice (AAOHN, 2004).

PROFESSIONAL MEMBERSHIP AND CERTIFICATION

More than 8,000 OHNs are members of AAOHN, the professional specialty nursing organization. AAOHN established a Code of Ethics and Interpretive Statements (Table 27–A), and a position statement and guidelines on Confidentiality of Health Information (Table 27–B).

Approximately 6,000 OHNs are currently recognized for excellence in occupational health nursing practice through certification by the American Board for Occupational Health Nurses, Inc. (ABOHN). The Certified Occupational Health Nurse (COHN) and the Certified Occupational Health Nurse Specialist (COHN-S) core credentials are awarded based on specific educational preparation, current occupational health work experience, evidence of continuing occupational health and safety education, and successful completion of an examination. For those occupational health nurses already certified in occupational health nursing (as either COHN or COHN-S), additional subspecialty certification in case management or safety management can be achieved by those with evidence of relevant continuing education, and successful completion of an examination.

Additional academic preparation as a manager, nurse practitioner, or clinical nurse specialist in occupational health nursing is available at the graduate level at university-based, NIOSH-funded, educational research centers. Certification for the nurse practitioner role is available through the American Nurses Credentialing Center or the American Academy of Nurse Practitioners. Graduate preparation at the PhD and Doctor of Nursing Practice (DNP) levels is available at NIOSH-funded, educational research centers for OHNs wanting to do research or become educators or consultants in the specialty field of occupational and environmental health nursing.

THE PRACTICE OF OCCUPATIONAL HEALTH NURSING

Models of Occupational Health Services

There are several models for occupational health service delivery, ranging from on-site salaried personnel to off-site contractual arrangements. The scope of occupational health services depends on the following key industry variables:
- company size and demographics of the workforce
- geographic distance to a health care facility in the community
- type of industry (manufacturing versus service)
- hazard profile (review of OSHA 300 log, emergency response needs, potential exposures/trends in claims)
- risk management and health benefit philosophy of the company (eg., percent of insured workforce)
- economic resources
- self-insurance status for workers' compensation and personal health care
- organizational climate, specifically regarding health, hazard communication, and the value of prevention activities

Other team members, depending on an assessment of the above industry variables, may include an industrial hygienist, occupational medicine physician, safety professional, ergonomist, physical therapist, employee assistance program personnel, and rehabilitation counselor.

Depending on the education, expertise, and skills of the nurse, the OHN may take a more involved role in direct care (for example, the nurse practitioner role) (Figure 27–2), case management, employee assistance program activities, ergonomics, safety activities, and environmental monitoring. OHN involvement in creating a healthier workplace culture, in addition to serving as health coaches for individual behavior modification, has gained prominence in the last decade. OHNs are well-positioned to serve as environmental and sustainability stewards at both the industry and community levels. An additional model of OHN care is advocacy and outreach to vulnerable low-wage workers, including immigrant workers, in partnership with community-based organizations.

Occupational health service models vary not only in the type and extent of health service personnel, but also the degree to which they manage work-related and non-work-related health care conditions. Some programs manage only work-related injury and illness, with referral of those health problems not directly related to work to outside resources. Others manage all work-related and a limited number of non-work-related health concerns. A growing number are offering full-service, 24-hour managed care to employees and their dependents, for both work- and non-work-related conditions, using advanced practice OHNs.

Critical to program design is maintaining a focus on a safe and healthy workplace, and recognizing that most work-related injury and illness is preventable. Additionally, the safety and environmental monitoring functions and health functions in an organization need to be administratively linked for a successful and smoothly running program.

TABLE 27–A AAOHN Code of Ethics

CODE OF ETHICS AND INTERPRETATIVE STATEMENTS

Preamble

The American Association of Occupational Health Nurses, Inc. (AAOHN) Code of Ethics has been developed in response to the nursing profession's acceptance of its goals and values and the trust conferred upon it by society to guide the conduct and practices of the profession. As professionals, occupational and environmental health nurses (OHNs) accept the responsibility and inherent obligation to uphold these values.

The Code of Ethics is based on the belief that the goal of occupational and environmental health nurses is to promote the worker, worker population and community health and safety. This specialized practice focuses on promotion and restoration of health, prevention of illness and injury and protection from occupational and environmental hazards. The occupational and environmental nurse has a unique role in protecting the integrity of the workplace and the work environment.

The client can be workers, workers' families/significant others, worker populations, community groups and employers. The purpose of the AAOHN Code of Ethics is to serve as a guide for registered professional nurses to maintain and pursue professionally recognized ethical behavior in providing occupational and environmental health and safety services.

Ethics is synonymous with moral reasoning. Ethics is not law, but a guide for moral action. Professional nurses, when making judgments related to the health and welfare of the client, utilize these significant universal moral principles.

These principles are:
- Right of self-determination
- Confidentiality
- Truth telling
- Doing or producing good
- Avoiding harm
- Fair and nondiscriminatory treatment

Occupational and environmental health nurses recognize that dilemmas may develop that do not have guidelines, data or statutes to assist with problem resolution; thus, occupational and environmental health nurses use problem-solving, collaboration and appropriate resources to resolve dilemmas.

The Code is not intended to establish nor replace standards of care or minimal levels of practice. In summary, the Code of Ethics and Interpretative Statements provide a guiding ethical framework for decision-making and evaluation of nursing actions as occupational and environmental health nurses fulfill their professional responsibilities to society and the profession.

TABLE 27–A	AAOHN Code of Ethics (continued)

1. Occupational and environmental health nurses provide health, wellness, safety and other related services to clients with regard for human dignity and rights, unrestricted by considerations of social or economic status, personal attributes or the nature of the health status.

- Adhere to the obligation to treat clients fairly, respecting their dignity and worth, while recognizing the existence of a vast spectrum of beliefs and values in society.
- Demonstrate respect for these beliefs and values inherent in their clients and themselves by providing services for and with that client accordingly.
- Respect human dignity by recognizing clients' rights, particularly, the right of self-determination.
- Be knowledgeable about clients' rights (as client advocates).
- Avoid abandonment, even in cases when the client refuses care or the nurse's personal convictions prohibit participation.
- Recognize that there are situations in which the rights of individual self-determination may be outweighed or limited by the rights of others. One must weigh the risk of harm or endangerment to self and/or others, particularly in relation to public health.

2. Occupational and environmental health nurses, as licensed health care professionals, accept obligations to society as professional and responsible members of the community.

- Adhere to all laws and statutes (local, state, federal, and international), including those governing occupational and environmental health practice.
- Observe professional codes and uphold practice standards.
- Respect clients' and society's right to know and to receive factual information about potential and actual job and environmental hazards.
- Be knowledgeable of issues and dilemmas affecting the health, safety and welfare of society and take appropriate action.
- Participate, as appropriate, in decision-making processes that pertain to occupational and environmental health and safety.
- Recognize situations in which the interests of management and workers may conflict.
- Demonstrate fairness in conflict resolution.
- Refer and/or delegate to appropriate services.
- Strive to protect clients and the profession from incompetent professionals and individuals who misrepresent themselves and the profession.
- Report to licensing, accrediting and certifying authorities, as may be appropriate, any person or persons who exhibit incompetence or engage in unethical or illegal activities.
- Contribute to the growth of the profession's body of knowledge through development, implementation and evaluation of programs.
- Have moral obligations to self, clients, the profession and society to conduct sound ethical research.
- Seek approval of appropriate bodies, such as institutional review boards, in conducting research activities.
- Communicate and disseminate research findings as appropriate.

3. Occupational and environmental health nurses strive to safeguard clients' rights to privacy by protecting confidential information and releasing information only as required or permitted by law.

- Maintain the confidentiality of health information.
- Adhere to the organizational, local, state, federal and international laws, regulations, guidelines, and policies governing access to confidential information.

TABLE 27–A   AAOHN Code of Ethics (continued)

- Have written policies and procedures to guide the access, release, transmittal, and storage of health information, including electronic records.
- Respect and protect the autonomy, rights and privacy of clients' data and personally identifiable information.
- Respect and protect the autonomy, rights and privacy of research subjects through mechanisms such as voluntary informed consent.

4. Occupational and environmental health nurses promote collaboration with other professionals, community agencies, and stakeholders in order to meet the health, wellness, safety and other related needs of the client.

- Function both interdependently and independently in promoting the welfare of clients.
- Contribute, through an interdisciplinary approach, to interdependent nursing practice by working with members of the health and safety professions, human resources, benefits and other related entities in the provision of services.
- Commit to collaborative planning with members of the health and safety team and other representatives internal and external to the organization in providing services to clients.
- Collaborate by seeking assistance, expertise and resources from other recognized health and safety professionals in the provision of services.
- Function within the scope of nursing practice and delegate responsibility appropriately.
- Adhere to the obligation to promote adequate distribution of health and safety services and nursing resources to meet clients' needs.
- Weigh professional responsibilities and obligations with values/perspective of multiple parties (e.g. employer, management, supervisor, etc.) in protecting the health and safety of workers, worker populations and community groups.

5. Occupational and environmental health nurses maintain individual competence in nursing practice, based on scientific knowledge, and recognize and accept responsibility for individual judgments and actions, while complying with appropriate laws and regulations.

- Strive for excellence and maintain a level of knowledge, judgment, technical skills and professional values necessary for delivering health services.
- Utilize professional and educational activities to improve professional practice.
- Engage in professional, educational and quality improvement activities, and acknowledge the importance of continued and advanced educational activities beyond the basic level of nursing education.
- Maintain competence in practice as a personal and professional responsibility.
- Be accountable for actions and for compliance with nurse practice acts, standards of practice and other laws/regulations governing occupational and environmental health practice.
- Participate in the development of policies to promote competent, ethical, and legal nursing practice.
- Utilize research findings within practice.

AAOHN acknowledges the contributions of the following owners/members in revising the AAOHN Code of Ethics. The AAOHN Code of Ethics Task Force: Phyllis Berryman, Chairman; Kay Campbell, Michelle Kom Gochnour, Kim Gordon, Margie Matsui, Barb Maxwell, Kim Olszewski, Diana Scott, Bill Thomack, Dee Tyler and Janice White.

Revised and approved January 2009

Source: Reprinted with permission of the American Association of Occupational Health Nurses, Inc., Pensacola, FL.

TABLE 27–B   Guidelines for Confidentiality of Employee Health Information

A D V I S O R Y

AAOHN

Confidentiality of Employee Health Information

Importance to Occupational Health

Occupational and environmental health nurses (OHNs) are privy to a great deal of personal health information (PHI), both personal and work related, about employees and their health status. The nurse must clearly understand the legal, ethical, moral and professional obligations and requirements related to confidentiality of this PHI, and establish appropriate policies and procedures to ensure compliance.

The ethical obligation to keep PHI confidential is inherent in the practice of nursing. According to the AAOHN Code of Ethics (2004), OHNs "strive to safeguard employees' rights to privacy by protecting confidential information and releasing information only upon written consent of the employee or as required or permitted by law." The issue is further addressed in the AAOHN Standards of Occupational and Environmental Health Nursing related to assessment, diagnoses and ethical decision-making. The ethical obligation of health care professionals to keep clients' personal health information confidential is well defined. However, in occupational and environmental health settings, there may be no legal protection for this information, and an ethical conflict may arise if the OHN is asked to provide an employer personal health information about an employee without the employee's knowledge or written consent.

Issues to Consider

State: Most legislation protecting health information is enacted at the individual state level. These protections, where they exist, are inconsistent from state to state, leading to disparities and complexities for individuals practicing in multiple states. Most states do not protect communication between occupational health professionals and their clients, since they are acting as agents of employers. In addition, workers' compensation, which may be governed by state law, is an exclusive remedy and individuals filing claims must relinquish some rights to privacy of their records.

Federal: Certain federal laws do protect personal health information in specific circumstances. Occupational Safety and Health Administration (OSHA) Access to Employee Exposure and Medical Records Standard 29CFR1910.1020 requires that the employee or employee's designated representative have access to the employee's exposure and medical records, with the employee's written consent, according to the following guidelines:

· Access must be provided in a reasonable manner and place.
· Records must be provided free of charge, and if possible within 15 working days of the initial request.
· The employer must make provisions for copying of records.

Usually, an employee must give written consent before a designated representative may look at or copy the employee's record, but a recognized or certified collective bargaining agent is automatically considered to be a designated representative for purposes of access to employee exposure records and analyses prepared using exposure or health data.

Americans with Disabilities Act (ADA) protects individuals with disabilities from employment discrimination. The law places limits on an employer's right to collect and use medical information about job applicants and employees. Although the ADA does not require an occupational health professional to be the custodian of employee medical information, it does mandate the health data be kept in separate files and be treated confidentially regardless of whether the data reveal a disability. Specific exceptions to confidentiality under ADA are:

· Supervisors and managers may acquire limited health information if it is needed to make reasonable accommodation. They may also acquire limited health information if a medical determination of "direct threat" by the employee exists.
· First aid and safety personnel may need to be informed of an employee's health status if there is a possibility the employee may need emergency treatment.
· Government officials investigating compliance with the ADA or established health and safety standards (e.g., OSHA) may have access to health information (29CFR 1910.1020).
· State workers' compensation boards or other second injury funding bodies may also access health information. Regulations governing workers' compensation claims supersede the ADA guidelines, provided only information related to the injury is released.

HIPAA: The privacy regulations put forth as a result of the Health Insurance Portability and Accountability Act (HIPAA) restrict access to health information only if the health care provider generating or maintaining the information is a

TABLE 27–B Guidelines for Confidentiality of Employee Health Information (continued)

covered entity under the rule. Many occupational health providers are not covered entities themselves or in the workforce of a covered entity. Even then, because employers are not covered entities, employee records, held in occupational health departments, collected under laws such as OSHA, obtained to assess fitness for duty or related to workers' compensation, are excluded from the definition of protected health information.

EMR: The use of electronic medical/health records (EMR) is becoming the norm for occupational health services as more and more businesses/industries are buying into the age of technology. With the use of the EMR, the OHN has additional issues of security, storage, and access. The OHN should develop written policies and procedures, which address these issues:

· Limit access by use of pass codes, screen savers, workstation placement.
· Restrict access by limiting the number with access.
· Establish and maintain security standards for transmission and storage and destruction of EMR.
· Back up data.

Conclusion

OHNs should be proactive in the development of corporate policies and procedures for protection and disclosure of information before being asked to supply information. Consider the following in developing policies and procedures:

· Develop a written policy for management, access and retention of individual health records. Separate non-occupational and occupational data in the record
· Determine if your state has laws to prevent release of information without the individual's consent. A good resource is www.healthprivacy.org; it has a compilation of state privacy statutes.
· Examine the nurse practice act and any associated rules in your state of practice to determine any specific requirements for protecting confidentiality. Contact the state board of nursing to clarify questions about this information at http://www.ncsbn.org/regulation/boardsofnursing_boards_of_nursing_board.asp
· Consult with corporate legal counsel and/or risk management to clarify your legal responsibilities, if available. If not available, seek counsel through other resources, e.g., manager/director, medical support, state agencies, professional liability, private consult, etc.
· Utilize the Institute for Global Ethics Ethical Fitness TM Model as basis for ethical assessment of information gathered. (AAOHN Journal, January 2002, vol. 50, no.1).

· Determine if you are a covered entity under HIPAA.
· Contact the state workers' compensation board for rules that apply to workers' compensation claims (http://www.workerscompensation.com/).
· Rules of discovery apply to Equal Employment Opportunity Commission (EEOC) claims; check with your company's legal department for information about requirements.
· Examine laws governing the release of information related to HIV/AIDS status, substance abuse, mental health and genetic discrimination. These laws are often separate from more general laws regarding confidentiality of health information. Your corporate attorney will be able to work with you in identifying these laws.
· Subpoenaed information must be released.
· If information in an employee's health record is requested, asking yourself these questions will help you decide what steps to take.
  ◦ For what purpose is the information being sought?
  ◦ Does the employer need access to the entire file, or is there limited specific information, which will meet the employer's needs?
  ◦ Is the requested information work related?
  ◦ Who is requesting the information?
  ◦ Is the requested information aggregate data (which can be anonymous) or individual data?
  ◦ Why was the information gathered?
  ◦ Is the request accompanied by an authorization for release of health records signed by the employee?

RESOURCES

Edgar, P.H., (2002). Resolving Ethical Dilemmas: Applying the Institute for Global Ethics' Ethical Fitness Model to Occupational and Environmental Health Practice Issues. AAOHN Journal, 50 (1), 40-45.

Schuren, W. S, & Livsey, K. (2001). Complying with the Health Insurance Portability and Accountability Act Privacy Standards. AAOHN Journal, 49 (11), 501-507.

The American Association of Occupational Health Nurses. (2004). Code Of Ethics and Interpretive Statements. (Available from the AAOHN marketplace online.)

The American Association of Occupational Health Nurses (2004). AAOHN Standards of Occupational and Environmental Health Nursing. (Available from the AAOHN marketplace online.)

The American Association of Occupational Health Nurses (2001). Core Curriculum for Occupational & Environmental

TABLE 27–B	Guidelines for Confidentiality of Employee Health Information (continued)

Health Nursing, Second Edition. (Available from Publisher: W.B. Saunders, a Harcourt Health Sciences Co., (800) 545-2522, or online at customer.support@mosby.com)

The American With Disabilities Act of 1990, implementing regulations and EEOC compliance manual. (Available at www.eeoc.gov.)

The HIPAA Standards for Privacy of Individually Identifiable Health Information. (Available at http://hhs.gov/ocr/hipaa/.)

Copyright 2004. All rights reserved. Reviewed 2006

Source: Reprinted with permission of the American Association of Occupational Health Nurses, Inc., Pensacola, FL.

OHN Staffing and Outcomes

New health and safety regulations, hazards associated with new work processes (e.g., nanotechnology), new environmental concerns (e.g., *phthalates*), the employment of temporary and contractual workers, musculoskeletal complaints in an aging workforce, the increase in obesity and diabetes in the workforce, and the changing health care insurance system are but a few of the current health issues facing employers. Occupational health nurses are well prepared to manage the complex interactions between health and work, while valuing a prevention agenda. Knowledge of the key

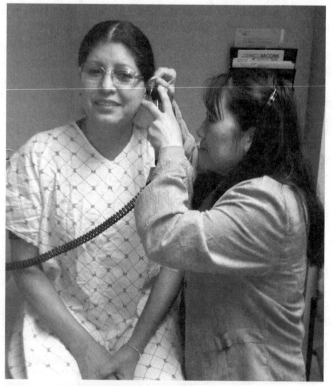

Figure 27–2. OHNs may perform direct care activities, which include post-offer examinations, health surveillance exams, and first aid and urgent care evaluations.

players—the employee, the supervisor, coworkers, the union representative, family members—in addition to knowledge of the work process, allows for worksite interventions to improve the work environment to prevent, for example, a work-related stress claim.

There is very little current data on the supply of and demand for occupational safety and health (OSH) professionals. The majority of OHNs are employed by larger employers in the manufacturing and health care sectors; for smaller employers, the OHN may be the only health care provider on site. The 2000 Institute of Medicine report on the education and training needed to ensure safe work in the 21st century acknowledged that there was a "burden of largely preventable occupational diseases and injuries" and noted "the lack of adequate OSH services in most small and many medium-sized workplaces" (IOM, 2000, p. 208). This report recommended using any new regulatory changes, in addition to using OSHA standards requiring health and safety training, as factors to project future OSH workforce needs. Large employers are aware of the value of OHNs. Hart et al. (2006) explored which competences were most valued by employers of Master's prepared OHNs. In an internet survey of primarily large employers (n=95), those competencies most frequently identified as "very valuable" included: communicating effectively with a variety of stakeholders (e.g., management and labor) (93%); understanding the relationship between occupational exposures and health outcomes (91%); staying current in one's field of practice (89%); functioning effectively on an interdisciplinary team (86%); communicating effectively with other OSH professionals (86%); communicating with senior management on health service program initiatives, outcomes, and cost-effectiveness (86%); and identifying health and safety hazards of worksite processes and operations (85%).

In 2004, ABOHN conducted their periodic role validation study for credentialing purposes. Certified and non-certified occupational health nurse respondents (n=1,223) described their roles, noting the importance and the frequency of specific activities. OHNs spent their time in a wide range of roles including direct care (27%), manager/coordinator (22%), case manager (21%), educator/advisor (14%), and consultant (9%). OHNs additionally estimated percent of time spent in the following activities: safety (17%), ergonomics (15%), infection control (10%), disaster preparedness (7%), industrial hygiene (6%), and travel health programs (6%), amongst others. Forty-one percent of the sample worked as the sole OHN at their place of employment; 20 percent of the sample worked in the health care sector. The top five most significant work tasks were (a) assuring the confidentiality of personal health information, (b) providing treatment of work-related injuries and illnesses, (c) implementing policies and procedures for confidentiality, (d) using and maintaining an employee health record-keeping system, and (e) assessing employees with work restrictions and making accommodations. The top five most frequent work tasks were (a) assuring confidentiality of personal health information, (b) monitoring new developments related to emerging health issues, (c) collaborating to protect and promote worker health and safety, (d) recognizing and responding to ethical issues in practice, and (e) monitoring laws and regulations affecting nursing practice.

A retrospective chart audit of 491 employee records was conducted to explore OHN interventions and outcomes according to standardized nursing taxonomy. These health records were created in an on-site health unit at a small Michigan book manufacturing plant. The audit covers a 7-year time frame where OHN services were provided 4 hours per week. Three nursing diagnoses accounted for the majority of patient encounters: health seeking behaviors (45%), altered health maintenance (27%), and pain (10%). The ten most commonly recorded OHN interventions included health education (19%), risk identification (12%), health screening (12%), teaching disease processes (9%), immunizations (8%), nutritional counsel (6%), exercise promotion (6%), referral (4%), pain management (4%), and health system guidance (3%). This novel study described OHN services provided to individual employees using standardized nursing language. The authors acknowledged that OHN interventions directed at groups of workers and at modifying the work environment were not captured in this study. Use of standardized nursing language to describe the many levels of OHN intervention may prove very helpful in future research.

Studies have documented the quality outcomes and associated cost savings of using advanced practice nursing for primary health care services at the worksite, in addition to the clinical management of worker's compensation cases. In 2004, barriers for nurse practitioner (NP) practice in the Washington State Workers' Compensation system were lifted. Several studies have since documented the positive impact of this change, including quality care by NPs for low back injuries and greater access to care for injured workers in rural areas.

OHN Role and Levels of Prevention

The OHN role requires knowledge, skills, and abilities in the following competencies:

- clinical and primary care
- case management
- work force, workplace, and environmental issues
- regulatory/legislative issues
- management
- health promotion and disease prevention
- occupational and environmental health and safety education/training
- research
- professionalism

The OHN uses all of the above competencies, often in a blended role, to accomplish a wide range of programmatic activities on the worksite. For example, establishment of an ergonomics program requires knowledge, skills, and abilities in

- the diagnosis and treatment evidence for repetitive strain injuries (clinical and primary care);
- program design with policy and procedures (management);
- the ability to educate workers regarding neutral wrist position and postural issues (education/training; health promotion and disease prevention);
- knowledge of ergonomics regulation/guidelines and the Americans with Disabilities Act (ADA) (regulatory/legislative); and
- a team approach to analyze the workstations and institute engineering controls (workforce, workplace, environmental issues; research; and professionalism).

The OHN role includes involvement at each level of prevention: primary, secondary, and tertiary. *Primary prevention* refers to health promotion and health protection measures that prevent the occurrence of disease and injury. Immunizations are a primary preventive measure, as are engineering controls. *Secondary prevention* is the early detection and treatment of disease and injury so that progression is slowed or complications are limited. Screening is a secondary prevention measure to detect asymptomatic disease early in the disease progression. For example, blood lead testing is a secondary preventive measure to detect lead exposure before symptoms of lead toxicity are present. *Tertiary prevention* is the prevention of disability through rehabilitative efforts. Modified duty or transitional work programs are a tertiary disability management strategy, aimed at using the workplace as a part of a rehabilitation plan to improve function and prevent prolonged disability.

The following programmatic components, arranged around levels of prevention, are discussed in more detail:

Primary Prevention
- Preplacement (postoffer) evaluations
- Immunizations
- Employee training
- Wellness programs
- Employee assistance programs

Secondary Prevention
- Assessment and management of health complaints
- Health/medical surveillance

Tertiary Prevention
- Case management
- Modified duty programs

Programs Commonly Managed by OHNs
- Workers' Compensation
- Americans with Disabilities Act
- Recordkeeping
- Bloodborne Pathogens
- Ergonomics

Evaluating Outcomes of OHN Activities

Primary Prevention

Preplacement (Postoffer) Evaluations

Preplacement evaluations are a primary prevention activity, with the goal to place workers in jobs based on physical capabilities, make reasonable accommodations, if needed, and stay in compliance with ADA. Critical to ADA compliance is the need to ensure that all evaluations are job-related and offered to all entering employees within the same job class. Key to the success of a preplacement program is the valuable process of creating a job analysis for each job class. Although time-consuming, this activity involves active dialogue with the supervisor, human resources, representative employees, and the OHN to identify both the physical and emotional requirements of a position. This can provide a powerful opportunity to vary job tasks, remove unrealistic lifting expectations, and push for engineering controls, while discussing possible accommodations that promote healthier job tasks for all.

Another value of the preplacement evaluation is that the OHN can introduce the role of the occupational health service and establish a relationship with the new employee. At this time, an expectation can be set for active participation of the employee in recognizing and reporting potentially hazardous working conditions.

The value of preplacement evaluations is most visible in those positions that are safety sensitive, for example, determining fitness for duty in the transportation indus-

try (e.g., the medical examination for commercial driver fitness determination). However, does the preplacement process prevent later work-related injury, illness, or sickness absence? A Cochrane review was conducted of studies through 2009 to critically evaluate the effectiveness of preemployment screening to prevent injury and illness or sickness absence. After reviewing the seven studies included in the review, the authors concluded there could be a role for a problem-focused health examination, but there is a need for better quality research.

Immunizations

Increasing immunization coverage for both adults and children to prevent vaccine related diseases is a *Healthy People 2020* goal. The vaccination coverage in adults for influenza (2008-09 season), pneumococcal disease, and hepatitis was lower than the Healthy People 2010 targets; however, there has been an overall increase in vaccine coverage in adults over this past decade. In 2008, 25 percent of noninstitutionalized adults aged 18 to 64 years were vaccinated against seasonal influenza, with the goal to increase to 80 percent by 2020. In 2008, 45 percent of health care workers were vaccinated against seasonal influenza, with the goal to increase to 90 percent by 2020. The total economic cost of treating vaccine-preventable diseases among adults, excluding the value of years of life lost, exceeded $10 billion each year.

The worksite is considered an ideal site for immunization delivery; the CDC has a guidance document on how best to design a program for a nontraditional site such as a worksite. OHNs are often engaged in designing worksite immunization programs, which may be mandatory (for example, bloodborne pathogens and hepatitis B vaccination for at-risk employees), or voluntary. In a large cluster, randomized study of 53 industries, Norwalk et al. showed that employers were able to improve influenza vaccination rates with enhanced advertising at intervention sites, a $5.00 incentive gift card for participants, and a choice of influenza vaccine (2010). Drew-Nord outlined a cost-effective policy and procedure to immunize fire department personnel and other first responders with measles, mumps, rubella, and varicella vaccines.

OHNs need to maintain up-to date information from the CDC about changes in immunization schedules. For example, for those OHNs working with health care workers, there is a new recommendation to reimmunize health care workers with Tdap to provide protection against pertussis. Providing immunizations for employees who travel internationally is an additional OHN program.

Employee Training

More than 100 OSHA standards require the employer to train employees in health and safety. Many of the occupational and environmental health and safety objectives in *Healthy People 2020* require training as well; for example, one environmental health objective aims to develop a plan on how to use, label, store, and dispose of hazardous materials. Employee training in one-on-one or group settings encourages workers to engage in safe work practices and stimulates a level of understanding to recognize and report potential hazards to employers.

A key OHN activity in all employee training is the needs assessment phase. One component of a needs assessment is to determine if there is a knowledge, behavior, or skill deficit that would appropriately respond to a training intervention. The needs assessment also includes a walkthrough survey to identify real and potential hazards, and the efficacy of current engineering, administrative, and personal protective controls. Review of the literature will outline possible solutions for any training needs, including learning methods that are culturally sensitive and literacy-level appropriate. The training plan includes ways to evaluate outcomes to determine if the training was successful. Risk communication principles outline ways to make the hazard more real and imaginable to the employee, with a clear understanding of how the hazard can be controlled by taking action (Figure 27–3). Involvement of a task force in the planning of the training will build in success. Pilot testing a risk communication strategy with the task force is recommended prior to full implementation of the training.

OHNs are often involved in the employee training requirement of the Hazard Communication standard. Using a team approach and often involving joint labor-management representatives, the OHN educates employees on potential health effects from potential exposures to hazardous substances, including interpretation of the material safety data sheets. Bouchard, in her review of the literature on literacy and hazard communication, summarized nine studies and identified the following needs: (a) there was a lack of learner involvement to improve the hazard communication process; (b) employers did not routinely assess if employees understood the information provided; and (c) there was no long term assessment of the impact of the training. Examples of other OHN employee training activities include

Figure 27–3. An OHN is engaged in emergency drills to comply with the Toxic Catastrophe Prevention Act in New Jersey.

- education on how best to adjust workstations and the organization of work to streamline tasks and decrease the number of forceful repetitions and help prevent cumulative trauma disorders;

- education on the long-term effects of noise on hearing and the need for hearing protection (Hong et al. evaluated the delivery of a computerized hearing test and tailored health education messages to promote the use of hearing protection in operating engineers. There was a short-term, but not long-term, improvement in hearing protection use with this novel approach, documenting the challenges of changing behavior to consistently use personal protective equipment.);

- education and demonstration of ceiling lifts for safe patient handling, and instituting a hazard awareness campaign through health fairs, posters, paycheck inserts, and e-mails to prevent slips, trips, and falls;

- education about use, care, and maintenance of respirators (Figure 27–4); and

- disaster preparedness and establishment of medical emergency response teams (Figure 27–5).

Wellness Programs

OHNs have long been involved in wellness initiatives in the worksite. In 2009, 52 percent of public sector employees and 25 percent of private sector employees had access to wellness programs at work. The clinical and cost outcomes of "comprehensive, multi-factorial, health promotion, and disease management programs conducted in corporate worksites" have been critically reviewed over

Figure 27–5. OHNs have many diverse roles. For example, at a mining company near Juneau, Alaska, the OHN participates in the Surface Emergency Response Team (SERT). The SERT is trained in firefighting, high angle rope rescue, HAZMAT response both on land and sea, confined space rescue, and emergency medicine. (Photo courtesy of Teresa Cummins, RN, of Hecla Greens Creek Mining Co., Juneau, AK.)

the past twenty years. In *Healthy People 2020*, the goal for occupational health is "to promote the health and safety of people at work through prevention and early intervention." For 2020, there are no specific wellness objectives under "Occupational Health;" however, there are wellness initiatives targeting the worksite in other chapters. For example, in the "Physical Activity" chapter, one objective is to "increase the proportion of employed adults who have access to and participate in employer-based exercise facilities and exercise programs."

There are several *Healthy People 2020* objectives targeting tobacco use in worksites; for example, in 2009, 29 States and the District of Columbia had smoke-free indoor air laws that prohibited smoking in private worksites. The goal is for private employer worksites in 50 states and the District of Columbia to be smoke free by 2020. In recognition of the importance of personal privacy protection, the worksite offers an opportunity to provide individual and group education and coaching to improve one's health, taking advantage of social support and the convenience of the worksite. Opportunities for smoking cessation programs do exist in the workplace: Ott and her colleagues documented an 18 percent prevalence of smoking in two large worksites in the Midwest, with 51 percent of public employees who smoked expressing interest in improving their smoking habits in comparison to 27 percent of employees working for a private employer (p=<0.05). The worksite also provides opportunities for cardiovascular risk reduction education. Diet and physi-

Figure 27–4. OHNs are actively involved in respiratory protection programs, which often includes the review of respiratory questionnaires, performing and reviewing spirometry, fit testing, medical clearance, choice of respirators, and providing education about use, care, and maintenance of respirators.

cal activity interventions successfully reduced serum lipid levels in a 12-week worksite wellness program.

Employee Assistance Programs

Employee Assistance Programs (EAPs) use both primary and secondary prevention methods to recognize, assess, treat, and refer those employees with personal and mental health problems that impact job performance. Approximately 72 percent of workers employed in the public sector and 42 percent of workers employed in the private sector have access to EAP services. Although initially focused on substance abuse, EAPs are now assessing a full range of family and work issues that may affect an employee's ability to be a fully functioning member of a work team. These services may be crisis oriented and in response to changes in work performance, but also be preventive in nature, with an emphasis on communication, conflict resolution, and stress management. The OHN is often the first point of contact, and is able to confidentially counsel and refer employees to an EAP resource.

The appropriate use of psychiatric, chemical dependency, and other services by employees and their dependents is a current case management program in many industries. The OHN manages, implements, and cooperates with the EAP resource at the worksite and, if there is no EAP available to employees, becomes the referral source to mental health care providers in the community. This strong link impacts mental health care in two ways: the employee is educated by the OHN in mental health care options available for themselves or their dependents, and the OHN becomes involved in supporting this individual at the worksite.

Stress at the workplace and at home, workplace violence, drug and alcohol use/abuse, and accommodating employees with psychiatric diagnoses are just a few of the daily challenges facing OHNs. OHNs are often the first resource for the troubled employee, and a common role function is to complete the initial assessment and facilitate referral for long-term treatment.

Secondary Prevention

Assessment and Management of Health Complaints

Most commonly, an employee has an interaction with the OHN for a health complaint. This may be an acute problem, such as wrist pain or an earache, or a visit for a chronic health problem, such as a blood pressure check or a question regarding a medication dose. At all times, the OHN must evaluate any symptom or issue in relationship to the work tasks done by the employee:

- Is there a potential exposure that could cause or aggravate the complaint?
- Was there a change in the work process that could account for this symptom?
- Are other coworkers complaining of similar symptoms?
- Is the employee still capable of performing their work, without threat to self or others? If no, what accommodations are needed?

The OHN needs access to the most recent environmental monitoring data, to be able to fully evaluate the potential work relationships.

The OHN also knows the individual's prior health history, the family system, and the current department work group issues, and therefore can identify if psychosocial issues (both at home and at work) may be influencing this complaint.

The OHN, depending on resources, skills, and expertise, may do the initial evaluation and treat within a first aid/self-care model and refer, if needed, for a more comprehensive medical evaluation. Or the OHN may do the initial evaluation and treat according to medical directives, in collaboration with a physician consultant, and dependent on state regulation of nursing practice. Nurse practitioners may be involved in treating both work- and non-work-related health conditions, on or off site, for employees, their dependents, and/or retirees, as authorized by state regulation of advanced nursing practice. These services are often provided for greater access to health care, with the added benefit in saving employee time during busy work schedules. Cost savings, especially if the employer is self-insured for health care and workers' compensation coverage, can be realized by using a blended team of health care providers who are knowledgeable about the worksite.

If the condition is work related, the OHN is in a pivotal position to conduct a walk-through survey to identify the root cause of the injury and institute preventive measures. The OHN will educate and advocate about the worker's compensation benefit and monitor recovery and return to work in a case management role.

The OHN uses practice guidelines to evaluate the clinical outcomes of medical care, and, if doing case management for a worker compensation carrier, the OHN may use practice guidelines to authorize specific diagnostic or treatment interventions. Practice guidelines are clinical practice recommendations based on a critical review of research and/or evidence. There are numerous practice guidelines, some focused on the diagnosis of a specific health condition, and others focused on the clinical management of a health condition, with the key aim being to standardize care. The website Guideline.gov is a clearinghouse for a wide range of evidence-based practice guidelines. The American College of Occupational and Environmental Medicine (ACOEM) published a set of guidelines primarily for the diagnosis and treatment of work-related musculoskeletal complaints, and an excellent guidance document exploring approaches to prevent needless work disability. Other purposes of clinical practice guidelines include the goal to enhance the translation of current research into practice, to reduce variation in practice across geographic regions and across providers, to improve the quality of health care, and to promote best practices and cost consciousness. Many occupational health settings use practice guidelines as a quality assurance or audit tool to evaluate clinical outcomes of care, and to assist in the disability management process.

Screening

Screening tests aim for early detection of asymptomatic disease with the goal that treatment can render an improved outcome. "Put Prevention into Practice (PPIP)" is a program sponsored by the Agency for Healthcare Research and Quality (AHRQ). PPIP includes health education materials, *The Guide to Clinical Preventive Services*, and other resources that are valuable in worksite screening programs. *The Guide to Clinical Preventive Services, Recommendations of the U.S. Preventive Services Task Force*, 2010-2011, provides the clinician updated, research-based screening recommendations' many of which can be reinforced in wellness initiatives at work. These screening tests can be offered in coordination with the personal health plan to avoid duplication of services. Examples of common screening programs in the worksite are blood pressure screening and blood sugar testing.

Health/Medical Surveillance

Occupational health surveillance is the process of monitoring the health status of worker populations to gather data about the effects of workplace exposures and to use the data to prevent illness or injury.

The goal of health/medical surveillance is early identification of biological markers or endpoints that may signify exposure. Health/medical surveillance, often a requirement of federal health and safety standards, is designed, coordinated, implemented, and evaluated by the OHN.

The OHN may conduct a hearing conservation program, a respiratory protection program, or asbestos surveillance. The health care sector has a range of exposures, and although the focus for health surveillance is on direct care providers, many other "mini-industries" exist within a health care facility with potential exposure to, for example, ethylene oxide.

The OHN reviews the environmental monitoring data, reviews the toxicology of the substance, and in consultation with industrial hygiene and/or occupational medicine, outlines a health surveillance program that is exposure and job specific. Common to OHN practice is the communica-

tion and counseling of test results to the individual employee and to the primary care provider. The OHN develops policies and procedures in anticipation of the potential need for job rotation, job modification, confidentiality, and other potential ethical dilemmas that may arise when an abnormal finding is discovered during health/medical surveillance activities. For example, a laboratory animal allergy surveillance program must clarify, in advance, how any symptoms of sensitization would be managed in terms of job rotation or removal. One-third of laboratory animal workers may develop laboratory animal allergy symptoms, which may take up to three years to express; more than 10 percent of those workers will develop occupational asthma. Good communication skills, used to educate and counsel employees regarding the purpose and use of these test results, are of paramount importance.

Tertiary Prevention
Case Management

Case management is the timely coordination of quality, evidenced-based health services with the goal to decrease fragmentation of care, enhance the client's quality of life, and to contain health care costs (Salazar et al., 1999; Wassel et al., 2006). Case management is a process of care coordination and is the framework for both disease and disability management programs. Case management is a system that aims to provide the right care, at the right time, in the right setting, by the right provider, and at the right cost. The emphasis is on early intervention and coordination of care for those targeted high-risk, high-cost cases.

Frequent and timely communication is an important component of case management. For example, an employee or dependent sustains a spinal cord injury and the OHN recommends early transfer to a spinal cord rehabilitation facility. However, this facility is 100 miles from the family's hometown. Clear OHN communication with the family is needed to explain the anticipated improved outcome in the rehabilitation facility and to gain their support of the transfer.

There are several tools that OHNs use to establish a case management program, including:
- the ability to flag catastrophic and chronic claims, for example, premature births, spinal cord injuries, organ transplants, certain cancers, mental health disorders, and multiple comorbid conditions;
- early identification of workers' compensation cases with high reserves and those injured workers at risk for delayed recovery;
- establishment of a pool of modified duty jobs;
- establishment of a panel of qualified providers who support a sports-medicine approach, with active engagement of the injured worker and support for modified duty;

- access to computerized information systems;
- full knowledge of health benefit packages in the event that alternate benefits need to be negotiated on behalf of the ill employee or dependent, for example, home care with nursing assistance.

Transitional/Modified Duty Programs

Timely return to work, in temporary transitional or modified duty assignments, is a realistic outcome measure for a case management program targeting both non-work- and work-related injuries and illnesses. Advocating for safe transitional work is a major role for the OHN. The OHN not only knows the work process, but also has been very involved in determining the level of care needed for an injured employee. Therefore, the OHN is well positioned to determine readiness to return to work, and to support both the injured employee and his/her supervisor throughout the process. An aggressive sports medicine rehabilitative approach, in addition to modified duty, helps prevent delayed recovery of injured workers.

The establishment of a transitional work program requires a proactive approach with policies and procedures that support placement, based on objective functional capacity, into positions that are meaningful and productive. Communication between all the stakeholders is critical to the success of a modified duty program. Supervisor involvement and support of the transitional work assignment is of prime importance. Shaw et al. conducted a needs assessment of both employees and supervisors to design a training curriculum for supervisors with the goal to improve supervisor response to employee injuries. The goals of the training curriculum were to (a) enhance collaborative problem solving to reduce injury rates, (b) improve supervisor response to injuries to prevent or reduce disability, and (c) improve communication between supervisors and health care providers to prevent or reduce disability. Pilot trainings (4 hours of training using small groups and case simulations) were held with 76 supervisors from two industries. Outcomes included pre- and post-intervention measures of perceived confidence in accommodating an injury and confidence in communicating with injured workers. Both areas demonstrated significant improvement after the training.

Programs Commonly Managed by OHNs
Workers' Compensation

Job-related injuries cost employers billions of dollars per year in direct workers' compensation expenses, which include costs for medical care, temporary and permanent disability, vocational rehabilitation, and medical-legal costs. Additionally, there are indirect costs associated with retraining replacement workers, lost productivity, work-place accommodation, and other preventive efforts. Injured workers may sustain severe economic consequences from workplace injuries, specifically in lost earnings, pain and functional impairment, and decreased quality of life. OHNs are often very involved in the management of the workers' compensation program on-site, or may be in a case management role with the workers' compensation insurance carrier or with the health care provider. The priority is the injured worker and their return to preinjury function as soon as possible. Simultaneously, the OHN must ensure that visible and timely corrective action is done to prevent future injuries. Benefits afforded by the workers' compensation system need to be paid out in a timely fashion as well.

Workers' compensation is a very complex system in many states. Injured workers often do not know how to access these benefits and can become quickly confused and angry if they are attempting to negotiate this system alone. The on-site OHN is often the first contact who is able to explain the full scope of workers' compensation benefits to an injured worker. A case management approach is used by the OHN to determine the appropriate care needed and whether work modifications are required. Close communication with involved parties and monitoring of workers' compensation cases is an important OHN role. If impairment is anticipated that may require a permanent job modification, then an interactive process, as required by the Americans with Disabilities Act, is also often coordinated and documented by the OHN.

Americans with Disabilities Act

Some 43 million Americans have one or more physical or mental disabilities. This population is targeted by the ADA (Public Law No. 101336). The ADA, signed into law in 1991, prohibits discrimination against people with disabilities in employment, transportation, public accommodation, activities of state and local government, and telecommunication relay services.

Employers must not only have nondiscriminatory selection criteria, but must make reasonable accommodation to the known limitations of the qualified applicant unless it causes undue hardship. OHNs advise employers on compliance with the requirements of the ADA, insuring that the preplacement (postoffer) program meets the ADA requirements. In addition, OHNs often recommend reasonable accommodations and counsel employees with physical disabilities. The OHN provides the link between the ADA and other legislative/regulatory benefits, such as the Family Medical Leave Act and the workers' compensation benefit, seeking legal consultation if needed.

OSHA Injury and Illness Recordkeeping Standard

Maintenance of OSHA 300 logs is often an OHN responsibility. The level of care and treatment provided to the injured worker determines if the case is recorded on the OSHA 300 log. First aid cases, as defined by OSHA, are not recorded. Recordable conditions include: every death, every occupational illness and injury which involves medical treatment beyond first aid, lost time, work modification, job transfer, or any loss of consciousness. The OSHA 300 log summary ending December 31 is posted annually the following February 1 through, and no later than, April 30. Reporting requirements for workers' compensation vary from state to state, and these requirements are separate from OSHA record-keeping requirements. The employers' report of occupational injury and illness can be substituted, in many cases, for the supplemental OSHA Form 301.

The OSHA 300 log is one data source for OHN analysis of work-related disease trends. This data helps prioritize walk-through surveys, periodic environmental sampling, health/medical surveillance programs, and employee training schedules.

Access to employee exposure and medical records, as required by OSHA standard, is an additional OHN responsibility. Establishment of a confidential recordkeeping system is a priority from a legal and ethical perspective (Tables 27–A and 27–B). Employees and their designated representatives have access to aggregate exposure records of other employees with past or present job duties that are similar to the employee's. Exposure records include environmental and biological monitoring data. Access need not be provided to voluntary employee assistance records, which are maintained separately from the occupational health medical record.

Bloodborne Pathogens Program

The OSHA Bloodborne Pathogens Standard, adopted in 1992, and revised in 2001, requires employers to establish an exposure control plan for all employees who have occupational exposure to blood or other potentially infectious materials. It mandates the use of universal precautions and the provision of personal protective equipment by the employer, in addition to safe needle disposal containers, self-sheathing needles, and safer medical devices. The standard clarifies the employer's responsibility to provide, at no cost to at-risk employees, the hepatitis B vaccine series. There are specific training requirements, often carried out by the OHN. Postexposure policies and procedures are established by the OHN, as outlined in the OSHA Bloodborne Pathogens Standard and updated by the CDCP.

The management of this bloodborne pathogen standard involves all OHN role competencies. Because of the confidential nature of an exposure, the OHN must use her/his astute communication and counseling skills and strong professional ethics.

Ergonomics

OHNs are often actively involved with ergonomic programs, both in office and manufacturing settings. Often an interdisciplinary activity involving the job design personnel of an industry, the practice of ergonomics involves work station evaluation, job analysis, and training. Work-related musculoskeletal disorders are common in an office, manufacturing, or hospital setting, and are predominant in those positions with the following risk factors: force, repetition, duration, contact stressors, awkward postures, cold temperature, and vibration. An ergonomic program consists of management commitment, worksite analysis, hazard prevention and control, medical management, and training and education. Early intervention with postural education and overall physical fitness is often linked to the ergonomics program. There may be a vendor relationship to staff a fitness center on site; the OHN may additionally bring a physical therapist on site to offer both prevention and treatment services when indicated.

Because of the waxing and waning of symptoms, employees need education and counseling about work-related musculoskeletal disorders, including measures to prevent and also treat the acute flares of this condition. With ergonomic educational programs, there often is an increase in the number of symptomatic employees who present for a health evaluation. However, if engineering controls are introduced and subsequently reinforced on periodic walk-through surveys by the OHN, the severity of symptoms should decrease over time. Program evaluation for ergonomic interventions, therefore, should detail not only the number of cases, but indices of severity as well. Thomas, in her ergonomic intervention program for microscope users in a semiconductor industry, used a total quality management approach to achieve both reductions in fatigue and discomfort or pain associated with microscope use.

Evaluating Outcomes of OHN Activities

Evaluating the effectiveness of OHN activities in the areas of primary health care delivery, case management, ergonomic interventions, and health promotion remains one of the AAOHNs research priorities (Table 27–C). The National Occupational Research Agenda (NORA) priority areas drive research done in the specialty, as was demonstrated in a review of research published in the *AAOHN Journal* from 1990 through 1999, where 88 percent of the studies addressed a NORA priority area.

The OHN plays a critical role in the evaluation of the occupational health services, which often includes collecting health and organizational outcomes data. This evaluation process not only provides for continuous quality improvement, but the data can be used to target activities; establish

TABLE 27–C	AAOHN Research Priorities

1. Effectiveness of primary health care delivery at the worksite.

2. Effectiveness of health promotion nursing intervention strategies.

3. Methods for handling complex ethical issues related to occupational health.

4. Strategies that minimize work-related health outcomes (e.g., respiratory disease).

5. Health effects resulting from chemical exposures in the workplace.

6. Occupational hazards of healthcare workers (e.g., latex allergy, bloodborne pathogens).

7. Factors that influence workers' rehabilitation and return to work.

8. Effectiveness of ergonomic strategies to reduce worker injury and illness.

9. Effectiveness of case management approaches in occupational illness/injury.

10. Evaluation of critical pathways to effectively improve worker health and safety and to enhance maximum recovery and safe return to work.

11. Effects of shift work on worker health and safety.

12. Strategies for increasing compliance with or motivating workers to use personal protective equipment.

Source: Rogers B, Agnew J, Pompeii L. Occupational health nursing research priorities: A changing focus. *American Association of Occupational Health Nurses*, 48(1):9–16, 2000.

short and long term goals; define responsibilities of team members; delineate time frames for action items, expected results, and measurements against goals and benchmarks; and offer rationale and support for additional resources for the occupational health agenda.

Health outcomes are the results or consequences of a process of care. Health outcomes may include satisfaction with care, use of health care resources, and clinical outcomes, such as changes in health status and changes in the length and quality of life as a result of detecting or treating disease. Selected health outcome indicators for clinical care provided to injured workers in an occupational work setting may include:

- *Access to care:* Initial treatment for nonemergency work-related conditions will be delivered within 24 hours after the injury is reported.
- *Patient satisfaction:* On a satisfaction survey, 85 percent of injured workers identified the OHN as very to extremely helpful in answering questions about the workers' compensation system.
- *Primary prevention:* High-risk health care workers will have documentation in their preplacement record of hepatitis B vaccination offer/immunity.
- *Secondary prevention:* Occupational health history is documented in 90 percent of those medical records of employees with occupational injury; or chart documentation of ergonomic evaluation is in place within one week of diagnosis of a work-related upper extremity complaint.
- *Tertiary prevention:* Sustained return to work, without reinjury, for 90 days after release to return to work; or

litigated cases decreased to five percent after OHN case management intervention.

Organizational outcomes include economic indicators in addition to productivity metrics. Selected organizational/economic indicators for occupational health services may include

- injury experience (number of first aid cases and OSHA recordable rates for days away, restricted or job transfer [DART] by department);
- corrective action (For every preventable injury/illness/exposure, a corrective action process will be conducted 100 percent of the time, and completed within 3 months after the date of injury. Claim experiences include average cost per claim, adequacy of reserves, and percent of claims litigated. Cases are closed in less than 6 months.);
- productivity as measured by the Stanford presenteeism scale and/or the Work Limitations Questionnaire;
- sickness absence measures; and
- worker engagement/job satisfaction measures.

SUMMARY

The Occupational Health Nurse, the predominant health provider on site in industry, is key to a comprehensive occupational health and safety program. The OHN has critical relationships, not only with the employee, but also with the supervisor, other coworkers, the union, family members, and the employee's primary care provider. The OHN has knowledge of the work process and potential hazards, and provides the confidential and objective analysis of the interaction between the worker's health status and his/her job. By using primary, secondary, and tertiary prevention strategies, the OHN uses a team approach to prevent work-related injury and illness and maintain the health of the workforce. Case management, which includes coordination of care for the best care at the right cost, is a key strategy used by the OHN in monitoring both work- and non-work-related injury and illness care. New opportunities for OHNs include serving as stewards to protect the environment, and creating new models to provide occupational and environmental health services to small employers and contingent workers. Continued evaluation of the effectiveness of key OHN programmatic activities, including primary health care, case management, ergonomic interventions, and health promotion programs, are future research priority areas in occupational health nursing.

An on-site OHN, either in a full-time or part-time capacity, with the goal to promote and restore health, prevent illness and injury, and provide protection from work-related and environmental hazards, is a valuable asset for both the employer and the employee.

BIBLIOGRAPHY

Acton D, McCauley L. Laboratory animal allergy: An occupational hazard. *AAOHN Journal* 55(6):241–244, 2007.

Aldana SG, Barlow M, Smith R, et al. The diabetes prevention program: A worksite experience. *AAOHN Journal* 53(11):499–507, 2005.

American Association of Occupational Health Nurses. *Standards of Occupational and Environmental Health Nursing.* Pensacola, FL: AAOHN, 2004a. https://www.aaohn.org/for-your-practice-items/standards-of-occupational-and-environmental-health-nursing.html

American Association of Occupational Health Nurses. *Position Statement: Occupational Health Surveillance.* Pensacola, FL: AAOHN, 2004b. https://www.aaohn.org/position-statements/occupational-health-surveillance.html

American Association of Occupational Health Nurses. *Position Statement: Confidentiality of Employee Health Information.* Pensacola, FL: AAOHN, 2004c. https://www.aaohn.org/position-statements/confidentiality-of-employee-health-information.html

American Association of Occupational Health Nurses. *Advisory: Nurse Practitioners in Occupational and Environmental Health.* Pensacola, FL: AAOHN, 2007. https://www.aaohn.org/advisories/nurse-practitioners-in-occupational-and-environmental-health.html

American Association of Occupational Health Nurses. *The Occupational and Environmental Health Nursing Profession.* Pensacola, FL: AAOHN, 2009a. https://www.aaohn.org/dmdocuments/OHN_Profession_2009.pdf

American Association of Occupational Health Nurses. *AAOHN Code of Ethics and Interpretive Statements.* Pensacola, FL: AAOHN, 2009b. https://www.aaohn.org/dmdocuments/Code_of_Ethics_2009.pdf

American Board for Occupational Health Nurses, Inc. Personal communication with Ann Lachat, Executive Director, March 1, 2011.

American College of Occupational and Environmental Medicine. *Occupational Medicine Practice Guidelines: Evaluation and Management of Common Health Problems and Functional Recovery in Workers,* 2nd ed. Elk Grove Village, IL: ACOEM, 2004.

American College of Occupational and Environmental Medicine. *Guidance Statement: Preventing Needless Work Disability by Helping People Stay Employed.* Elk Grove Village, IL: ACOEM, 2006.

Americans with Disabilities Act of 1990. Pub. L. No. 101336 (1990).

Bouchard C. Literacy and hazard communication: Ensuring workers understand the information they receive. *AAOHN Journal* 55(1):18–25, 2007.

Brines J, Salazar MK, Graham KY, et al. Return to work experience of injured workers in a case management program. *AAOHN Journal* 47(8):365–372, 1999.

Burgel BJ. *Innovation at the Worksite: Delivery of Nurse-Managed Primary Health Care Services.* Washington, DC: American Nurses Publishing, 1993.

Burgel BJ, Lashuay N, Israel L, et al. Garment workers in California: Health outcomes of the Asian Immigrant Women Workers Clinic. *AAOHN Journal* 52(11):465–475, 2004.

Burgel BJ. Direct Care in the Occupational Setting. In *AAOHN Core Curriculum for Occupational and Environmental Health Nursing,* 3rd ed., edited by MK Salazar,. St. Louis, MO: Saunders Elsevier, 2006, 295–330.

Centers for Disease Control and Prevention. Adult Immunization Programs in Nontraditional Settings: Quality Standards and Guidance for Program Evaluation. *MMWR* 49(RR01):1–13, March 24, 2000.

Center for Disease Control and Prevention. *ACIP Provisional Recommendations for Health Care Personnel on use of Tetanus Toxoid, Reduced Diphtheria Toxoid and Acellular Pertussis Vaccine (Tdap) and use of Postexposure Antimicrobial Prophylaxis.* 2011. http://www.cdc.gov/vaccines/recs/provisional/downloads/use-of-Tdap-in-hcp.pdf

Center for Disease Control and Prevention. *2009 Adult Vaccination Coverage, The National Health Interview Survey (NHIS).* http://www.cdc.gov/vaccines/stats-surv/nhis/2009-nhis.htm

Chenoweth D, Martin N, Pankowski J, et al. Nurse practitioner services: Three-year impact on health care costs. *Journal of Occupational & Environmental Medicine* 50(11):1293–1298, 2008.

Collins JW, Bell JL, Grönqvist R. Developing evidence-based interventions to address the leading causes of workers' compensation among healthcare workers. *Rehabilitation Nursing* 35(6):225–261, 2010.

Drew-Nord D. Measles, mumps, rubella, and varicella immunization status of first responders: A policy proposal. *AAOHN Journal* 57(5):187–189, 2009.

Gliniecki CM, Burgel BJ. Temporary work restrictions: Guidelines for the primary care provider. *Nurse Practitioner Forum* 6(2):79–89, 1995.

Griffith K, Strasser PB. Integrating primary care with occupational health services: A success story. *AAOHN Journal* 58(12):519–523, 2010.

Hart PA, Olson DK, Fredrickson AL, et al. Competencies most valued by employers—Implications for master's-prepared occupational health nurses. *AAOHN Journal* 54(7):327-335, 2006.

Hau ML. Disaster Planning and Management. In *AAOHN Core Curriculum for Occupational and Environmental Health Nursing*, 3rd ed., edited by MK Salazar. St. Louis, MO: Saunders Elsevier, 2006, 365–407.

Hong O, Ronis DL, Lusk SL, et al. Efficacy of a computer-based hearing test and tailored hearing protection intervention. *International Journal of Behavioral Medicine* 13(4):304–314, 2006.

Hood J, Larrañaga M. Employee health surveillance in the health care industry. *AAOHN Journal* 55(10):426–431, 2007.

Huffman MH. Health Coaching: A fresh approach for improving health outcomes and reducing costs. *AAOHN Journal* 58(6):245–250, 2010.

Institute of Medicine. *Safe Work in the 21st Century. Education and Training Needs for the Next Decade's Occupational Safety and Health Personnel.* Washington DC: National Academy Press, 2000. http://www.nap.edu/openbook.php?isbn=0309070260

Institute of Medicine. *Musculoskeletal disorders and the workplace: Low Back and Upper Extremities.* Washington DC: National Academy Press, 2001. http://www.nap.edu/openbook.php?isbn=0309072840

Knoblauch D, Strasser PB. Legal and Ethical Issues. In *AAOHN Core Curriculum for Occupational and Environmental Health Nursing*, 3rd ed., edited by MK Salazar. St. Louis, MO: Saunders Elsevier, 2006, 71–100.

Lack DM. Presenteeism revisited: A comprehensive review. *AAOHN Journal* 59(2):77–89, 2011.

Mahmud N, Schonstein E, Schaafsma F, et al. Pre-employment examinations for preventing occupational injury and disease in workers. The Cochrane Database of Systematic Reviews 2010, Issue 12, Art. No.: CD008881. DOI: 10.1002/14651858.CD228881.

McCauley LA. Immigrant workers in the United States: Recent trends, vulnerable populations, and challenges for occupational health. *AAOHN Journal* 53(7):313–319, 2005.

McKeown E, Barkauskas V, Quinn A, et al. Occupational nursing service in a small manufacturing plant: Interventions and outcomes. *International Journal of Nursing Terminologies and Classifications* 14(4):125–135, 2003.

McPhaul KM, Lipscomb JA. Incorporating environmental health into practice: The expanded role of the occupational health nurse. *AAOHN Journal* 53(1):31–36, 2005.

National Institute of Occupational Safety and Health. *Costs and benefits of occupational health nursing.* (DHHS-NIOSH Pub. No. 80-140). Cincinnati, OH: U.S. Department of Health and Human Services, 1980.

New FR, Winecoff A. Cost and clinical outcomes of a back injury clinic. *Nursing Economics* 25(2):127–129, 2007.

Nowalk MP, Lin CJ, Toback SL, et al. Improving influenza vaccination rates in the workplace: A randomized trial. *American Journal of Preventive Medicine* 38(3):237–246, 2010.

Ott CH, Plach SK, Beauchamp-Hewitt J, et al. Smoking-related health behaviors of employees and readiness to quit: Basis for health promotion interventions. *AAOHN Journal* 53(6):249–256, 2005.

Papp EM, Miller AS. Screening and surveillance: OSHA's medical surveillance provisions. *AAOHN Journal* 48(2):59–72, 2000.

Pelletier KR. A review and analysis of the clinical and cost-effectiveness studies of comprehensive health promotion and disease management programs at the worksite: Update VII 2004–2008. *Journal of Occupational and Environmental Medicine* 51(7):822–837, 2009.

Redmond MS, Kalina CM. A successful occupational health nurse-driven health promotion program to support corporate sustainability. *AAOHN Journal* 57(12):507–514, 2009.

Rogers B, Agnew J, Pompeii L. Occupational health nursing research priorities: A changing focus. *AAOHN Journal*

48(1):9–16, 2000.

Rogers B. *Occupational and Environmental Health Nursing: Concepts and Practice*, 2nd ed. Philadelphia: WB Saunders, 2003.

Rogers B, Livsey K. Occupational health surveillance, screening and prevention activities in occupational health nursing practice. *AAOHN Journal* 48(2):92–99, 2000.

Rudolph L. A call for quality. *JOEM* 38(4):343–344, 1996.

Rudolph L. Performance measures in occupational medicine: A tool to manage quality. *Occupational Medicine: State of the Art Reviews* 13(4):747–753, 1998.

Salazar MK, Graham K, Lantz B. Evaluating case management services for injured workers: Use of a quality assessment model. *AAOHN Journal* 47(8):348–354, 1999.

Salazar MK, Graham KY. Evaluation of a case management program: Summary and integration of findings. *AAOHN Journal* 47(9):416–423, 1999.

Sears JM, Wickizer TM, Franklin GM, et al. Nurse practitioners as attending providers for workers with uncomplicated back injuries: Using administrative data to evaluate quality and process of care. *JOEM* 49(8):900–908, 2007a.

Sears JM, Wickizer TM, Franklin GM, et al. Nurse practitioners as attending providers for injured workers: Evaluating the effect of role expansion on disability and costs. *Medical Care* 45(12):1154–1161, 2007b.

Sears JM, Wickizer TM, Franklin GM, et al. Expanding the role of nurse practitioners: Effects on rural access to care for injured workers. *The Journal of Rural Health* 24(2):171–178, 2008.

Shaw WS, Robertson MM, Pransky G, et al. Training to optimize the response of supervisors to work injuries—Needs assessment, design, and evaluation. *AAOHN Journal* 54(5):226–235, 2006.

Smith PS, Lusk SL. Occupational health nursing research: An overview from January 1990 to December 1999. *AAOHN Journal* 50(7):315–323, 2002.

Strasser PB. Managing transitional work—Program foundation. *AAOHN Journal* 52(8):323–326, 2004.

Strasser PB, Maher HK, Knuth G, et al. Occupational health nursing: 2004 Practice analysis report. *AAOHN Journal* 54(1):14–23, 2006.

Stoltzfus ER. *Access to Wellness and Employee Assistance Programs in the United States*. Washington, DC: Bureau of Labor Statistics, 2009. http://www.bls.gov/opub/cwc/print/cm20090416ar01p1.htm

Thomas EA. Ergonomic microscope comfort and control: Application of total quality management processes to reduce employee discomfort. *AAOHN Journal* (59)3:119–126, 2011.

Thompson MC. Review of occupational health nurse data from recent national sample surveys of registered nurses—Part I. *AAOHN Journal* 58(1):27–39, 2010.

Tompkins OS, Randolph SA, Ostendorf JS. Frequent flyer business travelers: The role of the occupational health nurse. *AAOHN Journal* 53(3):134–141, 2005.

Twining S. The occupational and environmental health history: Guidelines for the primary care nurse practitioner. *Nurse Practitioner Forum* 6(2):64–71, 1995.

U.S. Department of Health and Human Services. *Assessing Occupational Safety and Health Training: A Literature Review.* (DHHS-NIOSH Pub. No. 98-145) Washington, DC: GPO, 1998. http://www.cdc.gov/niosh/pdfs/98-145.pdf

U.S. Department of Health and Human Services. *Healthy People 2020: Improving the Health of Americans.* Washington, DC: DHHS, 2010, http://www.healthypeople.gov/2020/topicsobjectives2020/default.aspx

U.S. Department of Labor. *Training Requirements in OSHA Standards and Training Guidelines.* OSHA 2254. Washington, DC: OSHA, 1998, rev. http://www.osha.gov/Publications/osha2254.pdf

U.S. Department of Labor. *OSHA Recordkeeping Handbook.* Washington, DC: OSHA, 2005. http://www.osha.gov/recordkeeping/index.html

U.S. Preventive Service Task Force. *Guide to Clinical Preventive Services, 2010-2011,* Washington, DC: AHRQ, 2010. http://www.ahrq.gov/clinic/pocketgd.htm

Wassel ML, Randolph J, Rieth LK. Disability Case Management. In *AAOHN Core Curriculum for Occupational and Environmental Health Nursing*, 3rd ed., edited by MK Salazar. St. Louis, MO: Saunders Elsevier, 2006, 331–364.

Weiss MD. Changing the conversation—The occupational health nurse's role in Integrated HS³™. *AAOHN Journal* 57(7):293–299, 2009.

White K, Jacques PH. Combined diet and exercise intervention in the workplace: Effect on cardiovascular disease risk factors. *AAOHN Journal* 55(3):109–114, 2007.

CHAPTER 28

Environmental Health and Safety

*by James Stewart, PhD, CIH, CSP,
Bryan Connors, MS, CIH, and
Matthew Fragala, MS, CIH*

*S*ince industrial hygienists play a key role in environmental health and safety (EHS), whether in the public or private sector, it is important to have an understanding of what EHS is, what it is composed of, and the different roles that an EHS group may take on in an organization. This chapter is an introduction to EHS operations. The changing expectations of the EHS function within organizations and the trend toward making more of a business case for EHS and measuring the success of initiatives and the recent publication of ISO 26000, an international standard on social responsibility, make EHS an exciting and challenging field.

WHAT IS ENVIRONMENTAL HEALTH AND SAFETY?

When the phrase *environmental health and safety (EHS)* arises, it can mean different things to different people depending on the composition of the audience. For example, when EHS is discussed with a manufacturing worker, the operational aspects of EHS would be different than if EHS were discussed with a student at a major university or a resident of a city or town. The different views of EHS can arise because of diverse expectations of the services but maybe not so much because of the overall mission of EHS. For example, if the mission of EHS is to protect the health and safety of individuals and the environment in which they live and/or work, there may be little or no disagreement between students, town residents, or workers. No formal definition of EHS is found in the literature. In fact, EHS has been defined by the European Union as environmentally harmful subsidies. A website that defines acronyms has 176 different listings that refer to EHS. The highest-probability definition of EHS was extremely hazardous substance (www.all-acronyms.com/EHS, 2011). However, in practice in the United States and many other countries around the world, the phrase environmental health and safety implies the following:

Managing safety, health, and environmental risks to people, property, and the environment to acceptable levels.

This is the definition of EHS that will be used in this chapter, since it applies to EHS functions in most settings. Notice that this functional description does not indicate what management structure will be used to manage EHS risks. The reason for this exclusion is that organizations have different cultures and different means for managing EHS risks. In most, if not all, organizations with employees, managing EHS risks is part of each individual's job. Under this model, each individual is responsible in his or her own day-to-day tasks for ensuring that the EHS requirements for that organization are met. The EHS requirements would be drafted/developed by the EHS function, then approved (or not) by upper management and ultimately implemented by other departments/members of the organization. In addition to these day-to-day challenges, the EHS group/department would participate in strategic planning, policy development, product stewardship, and, in many organizations, auditing and enforcement of the EHS organizational requirements. The EHS role in governmental organizations can range from compliance inspections and accident investigations—for example, the U.S. Occupational Safety and Health Administration (OSHA)—to occupational health and safety research—such as the U.S. National Institute for Occupational Safety and Health (NIOSH). Some government agencies, such as the U.S. Environmental Protection Agency (EPA) have both compliance and research roles. In other public-sector organizations, such as the U.S. Department of Energy or the Department of Defense, EHS has roles similar to those in the private sector. Taiwan, Singapore, and Japan (and other countries) have governmental EHS organizations similar to those described for the United States. In the European Union (EU), the European Agency for Safety and Health at Work (EU-OSHA) has a scientific body with both a policy and regulatory role, while the implementation aspects are left to the member countries. As in the United States, the EU agency responsible for environmental risks is a separate agency called the Directorate General for the Environment.

PEOPLE, PROFIT, AND PLANET

In 1994, the term "Triple Bottom Line" was coined by John Elkington and applied to common EHS issues. This Triple Bottom Line is defined as "People, Profits, and Planet" (often called 3Ps). An example of the 3Ps in the context of the global environment would be global warming and reduction in greenhouse gases. In this situation, industries such as power plants that use fossil fuels may be required to spend money to reduce carbon dioxide emissions. The predicted benefits would accrue to the Planet, the Profits would be impacted in the power generation industry, and the People would experience less intense weather patterns and lower average temperatures (and other predicted benefits). In a macro application of the 3Ps within a company or other organization, the EHS group could

1. reduce risks to employees performing work within the organization (People);
2. accomplish these tasks in a cost-efficient manner (Profit); and
3. reduce emissions or releases to the surrounding environment (Planet).

When thinking about or addressing EHS issues, it is important to think broadly and consider each of the 3Ps. Because EHS issues are complex and often hard to solve and involve allocation of significant resources, it is often difficult to pass new EHS-related regulations because of perceived negative impacts on the economy, business bottom line, and individual freedoms.

ROLE OF THE EHS GROUP/DEPARTMENT WITHIN ORGANIZATIONS

There is no one standard role of the EHS group. Each organization has its own ways of dealing with EHS challenges, or for that matter, any business or operational challenge. The EHS group can be asked to fill the role of a scientific adviser or consultant to the operational personnel who actually take the actions to manage EHS risks. In this supportive role, EHS would develop policies and procedures that would be effective in dealing with the particular EHS challenges of that organization and would provide the training necessary for the operational personnel to perform their functions and for updating, as needed, the policies and procedures. In some organizations, EHS has an added role of auditing/inspecting the operations and enforcing the EHS policies.

In other organizations, EHS is given operational responsibility for various aspects of the program, such as hazardous waste recycling and disposal; radiation licensing, and sourcing, purchasing, and approval of work involving specific high-hazard chemicals and most biological agents. These roles and responsibilities vary based on the type and size of organization that the EHS program covers.

Nearly all EHS programs have a written policy that defines the roles and responsibilities specific to their organization. The mission statement, department divisions, and services are commonly described in EHS program documentation. There are potentially hundreds of roles and responsibilities for EHS departments to manage. Table 28–A provides examples of roles and responsibilities that can be part of a conventional EHS program. Each program area alone is an extensive subject. In fact, entire EHS careers or departments can focus on a specific program area.

Regardless of the variety of subject areas, all EHS departments work closely with their organizations to meet a similar set of general responsibilities that include the following:

- protecting the health and safety of the individuals in their organization
- providing safe and healthy work environments
- facilitating and promoting safety, health, and environmental management
- committing to environmental, health, and safety stewardship

TABLE 28–A	Examples of Environmental Health and Safety Roles and Responsibilities	
Program Area	***Program Subareas***	
Environmental protection	• Air quality • Water quality • Indoor air quality	• Local, state, and federal regulatory compliance • Underground storage tanks • Soil
Fire safety	• Emergency egress • Fire prevention • Fire suppression systems • Hot work permitting	• Alarm and monitoring • Fire safety codes • Permits • Fire drills
Radiation safety	• Radiation surveys • Disposal and transportation • Monitoring • Laser safety • Ionizing radiation	• Nonionizing radiation • ELF radiation • Microwave radiation • Dosimetry
Hazardous materials	• Storage and transportation • Chemical inventory • SDS • Disposal • Waste minimization • Recycling (batteries, electronics)	• Asbestos • Mercury • PCBs • Lead • Compressed gas
Biological safety	• Bloodborne pathogens • Sharps/needles • Mold • Infectious agents	• MRSA/flu/H1N1 • Biological safety cabinets • Medical waste • DNA/viral
Laboratory safety	• Fume hoods • Reactivity hazards • Chemical hygiene	• Animal research • Laboratory waste
Emergency response	• Spill response • Emergency preparedness	• Response coordination
Hazard communication	• Training • Record keeping	• Chemical-specific information • Standard operating procedures
Construction safety	• Heavy equipment (cranes) • Hand and power tools	• Scaffolding • Welding
Health AND safety / occupational safety	• Confined space • Electrical safety • Fall protection • Lockout/Tagout (control of hazardous energy) • Noise hearing conservation • Respiratory protection • PPE • Accident investigation	• Ergonomics • Compressed gas cylinders • Machine guarding • Occupational exposure monitoring • Injury and illness rates • Hazardous chemicals • Hazardous drugs

- maintaining compliance with federal, state, and local environmental, health, and safety laws
- protecting the local community and environment from potential hazards generated by the organization

EHS REGULATORY ENVIRONMENT

Although ensuring compliance with regulations is not the only role EHS plays within an organization, it is often an important one. Numerous regulations exist for such areas as waste chemicals, virus studies, emissions from automobiles (air pollution), and exposure to chemicals in consumer products. The structure of EHS in the U.S. regulatory environment will be used to illustrate how regulations focus on different aspects of EHS, because this philosophy of separate regulations for different aspects of EHS is practiced in most countries around the world.

National and International Regulations

In the United States, OSHA regulates the workplace, the EPA regulates releases of hazardous materials into the environment, the Centers for Disease Control and Prevention (CDC) along with the National Institutes of Health (NIH) and the Department of Homeland Security (DHS) regulate the use of biological agents, and the Nuclear Regulatory Commission (NRC) regulates the use of ionizing radiation inside and outside the workplace. Splitting the regulatory authority is useful for preventing conflicting regulations but presents some challenges to EHS practitioners when the issue they are facing is under the jurisdiction of two or more regulatory bodies. One common example is mixed waste, which is waste that is hazardous according to EPA and has radioactive isotopes in it. This is a common issue in molecular biology research operations.

Organizations of any kind, whether public or private, will have EHS regulations that apply to them. For example, even a financial/accounting firm is impacted by OSHA regulations regarding fire safety, evacuation planning, and developing safe egress routes. The copy machines may emit ozone, which is regulated in the workplace by OSHA. Contrast this to a large manufacturing operation, such as a semiconductor fabrication plant where more than a thousand chemicals may be present, along with ionizing radiation, heavy metals, toxic gases, and so forth. All of these are regulatory challenges that the EHS group will help the company manage. In developing countries, the EHS challenges are more basic: clean water, safe food, control of insect and other disease vectors, poor working conditions, and sometimes uncontrolled emissions from waste disposal sites or manufacturing operations.

Many organizations have taken promising steps to support EHS program growth in developing nations and to increase accountability for EHS risks of multinational companies that operate in the EU. Further EHS regulations and enforcement frameworks are needed in many countries, with particular gaps in many developing nations. Individual countries, quasi-governmental agencies, and the United Nations have worked to develop recommendations, model legislation, and programs to improve EHS within developing nations, which should over time increase the resources allocated to these areas.

The United States and other developed nations have had some success with the implementation of EHS regulations; for example, in 1970 an estimated 14,000 workers were killed on the job. In 2010 there were 4,547, a reduction of approximately 67 percent, while the work force has nearly doubled. Table 28–B lists the major types of regulations by U.S.-based EHS agencies and a partial list of the type of regulations (the list is not meant to be comprehensive).

In addition to governmental agencies that regulate EHS, several quasi-governmental and private groups or associations provide EHS recommendations that impact EHS operations, such as the National Fire Protection Agency (NFPA), the Compressed Gas Association (CGA), the International Organization for Standardization (ISO), and industry associations such as the American Chemical Society (ACS). In addition, NIOSH, often referred to as the research arm of OSHA, which is part of the CDC, researches and develops best-practice approaches to occupational safety and health challenges and makes recommendations to OSHA for new regulations to improve worker safety and health. These groups play an important role as scientific and policy advisers to legislation, provide recommendations to the regulatory agencies, and publish national consensus standards that are sometimes adopted by regulatory agencies and enforced. For example, the National Electrical Code is published by the NFPA (NFPA 70) and has been adopted and enforced in jurisdictions across the United States.

Even with the regulations in place, the dynamic nature of our world's population creates new EHS challenges that are not regulated, such as handling of antineoplastic drugs and ergonomic stressors. Environmental issues such as global climate change are now the subject of new regulations, and EHS is often tasked with leading the efforts to comply.

REACH

In the EU, a significant new set of requirements is being placed on companies that import or manufacture chemicals in the EU. REACH (Registration, Evaluation, Authorisation, and Restriction of Chemical Substances) regulations require manufacturers and importers of chemicals to demonstrate that a

TABLE 28–B	Major U.S.-based EHS Regulations	
Agency	**Types of Regulations**
OSHA	• Hazard communications • Injury and illness tracking • Personal protective equipment • Process safety • "Traditional hazards" (machinery and machine guarding, fall protection, confined space, lockout/tagout, etc.) • Fire protection • Cranes, trenches • Bloodborne pathogens • Hazardous materials (benzene, vinyl chloride, compressed and liquefied gases, asbestos, etc.)
EPA	• Clean Air Act • Clean Water Act • Hazardous waste (Resource Conservation and Recovery Act) • Hazardous materials such as polychlorinated biphenyls (Toxic Substances Control Act) • Hazardous waste sites (i.e., Superfund) • Emergency Planning and Community Right-to-Know Act (EPCRA) • Spill Prevention, Control, and Countermeasure (SPCC) (oil spills) • Toxic Substances Control Act (importing of chemicals, manufacturing of new chemicals)
Department of Transportation	Transportation and shipment of hazardous materials
Nuclear Regulatory Commission	Nuclear reactors, nuclear materials, nuclear waste, and security
Mine Safety and Health Administration	Federal mine safety and health
Coast Guard	Marine protection, maritime spill response and preparedness
Department of Homeland Security	Select biological agents and specific chemicals that could pose a threat to national security
Centers for Disease Control and Prevention and National Institutes of Health	Care and use of biological agents (e.g., bacteria, viruses)

chemical does not have unacceptable health, safety, or environmental risks under conditions of anticipated use. The law went into effect on June 1, 2007, but is being implemented in phases over an 11-year period. This significant piece of EHS legislation will have impacts around the world, not just in the EU. The manufacturer/importer must develop exposure estimates for chemicals in the work environment as well as for consumers. Along with exposure estimates, toxicological testing of the chemicals must be conducted and estimates of risk developed for various exposure scenarios, such as conditions of use and routes of exposure. Other requirements of REACH are labeling, hazard communication, and data sharing between companies. See Chapter 31, International Developments in Occupational Safety and Health, for a full discussion of REACH and the Global Harmonization Standard (GHS) and the new U.S. Department of Labor (DOL) Hazard Communication Standard.

State and Local Regulatory Agencies

In the United States, most states have an agency or group that regulates and enforces environmental regulations, often similar to the federal EPA (such as a Department of Environmental Protection). Twenty-five states plus Puerto Rico and the Virgin Islands operate approved state OSHA plans, which implement OSHA regulations at the state level (plans must be at least as effective as federal programs, and OSHA provides up to 50 percent of the funding). At the local level, fire departments, emergency management agencies, boards of health, and public health commissions play an important role in enforcing EHS at the local level in areas such as hazardous materials, chemical and high-hazard material storage, and biological and radiological substances.

Best-in-class EHS programs not only maintain compliance with the applicable regulatory requirements but also seek to exceed the minimum requirements set by regulation. These EHS programs find ways to continually add value by also addressing issues that regulations do not require them to address, such as indoor air quality and ergonomics. So although regulations provide a powerful framework for developing and managing EHS programs, compliance should be viewed as a minimum requirement.

EHS regulations have been heavily influenced by events outside the technical EHS field, namely societal changes, as when societies change their values such that products are not acceptable and will not be purchased if the environmental costs are too large. This is an example of how the balance between people, profit, and planet has shifted. Companies that produce products notice these value changes and begin to change the way they manufacture and allocate resources, what chemicals they use, and how they are handled and disposed of.

STRUCTURE AND RESOURCES OF EHS GROUPS

The disciplines covered in EHS groups are very broad and are a function of the operations supported by the EHS groups. Few data are available regarding the size, funding levels, and disciplines included in EHS groups. One benchmarking survey of EHS groups in academic settings was conducted in 2009, and the results were published in 2011. Data from this report will be used to demonstrate the size and scope of EHS operations.

Benchmarking data from the Campus Safety, Health and Environmental Management Association (CSHEMA) are the result of a nonrandom sample of 56 colleges and universities across the United States. Although it is a nonrandom sample, it does provide extensive data on EHS operations in academic settings. Of the 56 participants, 45 were classified as research institutions, 2 as large nonresearch institutions, 4 as small colleges, and 5 as medical centers. Data on total research expenditures, EHS expenditures, number of full-time employees (FTEs) in the institution, and the number of FTEs in EHS and estimates of the size of the physical space supported by the EHS group (in ft^2) are examples of the types of data collected. Table 28–C shows some of the characteristics of the institution as well as the budget allocated to EHS.

The Spearman correlation coefficient shows that the strongest correlation of the variables in Table 28–C with EHS expenditures was with institution employees ($\rho = 0.84$), indicating that as the number of employees in the institution increased, there was an increase in EHS resources expended. The next highest correlation found for the EHS budget was laboratory space ($\rho = 0.81$). With our understanding/definition

of EHS, this makes intuitive sense: the more employees the organization has, the higher the demand for basic EHS services. Laboratories in university research settings commonly use many different chemical, radiological, and biological agents. Therefore, as the number of laboratories increases, we expect to see increased demands for specific EHS services. However, the relationship between EHS resources and the number of employees or laboratories (or other locations where EHS services are used) does not have to be linear. As with other business functions/operations, there can be economies of scale, so if the employee head count doubles, creative management may enable the organization to supply high-quality services with less than a doubling of the EHS resources. Remember the 3Ps; there is always going to be balancing of people, profit, and planet when managing EHS risks.

Using the CSHEMA data for research universities only, EHS budget ($) was regressed on laboratory space (ft^2). The following regression equation was the result.

$$\ln(\text{EHS budget}) = 3.33 + 0.84 * \ln(\text{laboratory square feet})$$

$$R^2 = 0.48, p < 0.0001 \tag{1}$$

Note: Because both *EHS budget* and *laboratory square feet* were lognormally distributed, the natural logs of both variables were used in the regression analysis.

What this analysis shows is that a highly statistically significant relationship exists between these variables and that 48 percent of the variance in EHS budget can be explained by a model that contains only one variable (laboratory square feet). The equation can be used to predict (estimate) what the EHS budget would be for research universities with varying amounts of laboratory space. For example, a research university with 100,000 ft^2 of laboratory space would have an estimated EHS budget of \$429,706, while for a research university with 200,000 ft^2 the estimated budget would be \$769,195. Notice that this is a nonlinear relation-

TABLE 28–C   Selected Institutional Characteristics and EHS Budget

Institution Type	Total Institution Employees	Institution Total Budget	Research Budget	Institution Square Feet	Laboratory Space Square Feet	EHS Budget
Research Universities and Medical Centers	9,247	$1,526,964,500	$221,020,000	7,419,712	789,167	$2,240,078
Small College	1,004	$115,167,149	$1,876,832	2,076,271	67,840	$102,350
Medical Center	11,704	$1,338,435,500	$340,690,500	6,073,413	672,287	$2,150,625
Large Nonresearch Institution	1,678	$167,046,578	$6,659,314	1,667,843	173,705	$538,946

Note: All median values from CSHEMA, 2011.

ship. If it were linear, the budget for the 200,000 ft² would be $859,412. This is an interesting but relatively crude analysis because it considers only one predictor variable. However, analyses using statistical tools such as regression analysis on data from EHS operations can be valuable in benchmarking EHS groups/functions and for assessing resource allocation within an organization. Many additional predictor variables could have been evaluated using the CSHEMA data, such as research budget, amount of hazardous waste generated, number of biosafety level 2 and 3 laboratories, injury/illness rates, student enrollment, faculty FTEs, and number of kilograms of hazardous waste per square foot of laboratory space. If a statistical model is used, the choices of predictor variables and output variables determine its interpretability, so it is critically important that the model inputs and outputs be selected carefully, with a clear understanding of what the model is predicting, how the results will be interpreted, and the strengths and limitations of the analysis.

FUNDING OF EHS PROGRAMS (NONGOVERNMENTAL)

Fee-for-Service Model

Funding of EHS services can occur by a variety of means. Differences in source of the funds present different management challenges. This would be true of any function and is not specific to EHS. For example, if the EHS effort charges for a service, such as hazardous waste pickup and disposal, then the generator of the hazardous waste is a "customer" of EHS. Customers are sensitive to price and do not want to overpay for their purchases. EHS would need to work with the customer to arrive at a price that fits the customer's budget and simultaneously meet the organizational goals for properly handling hazardous waste. This is a management challenge that if not dealt with properly could result in the customer looking for other means of getting rid of the waste or storing it beyond statutory limits when the budget is tight. These are manageable issues, but EHS must manage this relationship wisely, meaning it must treat them as if

EHS is a business and the hazardous waste generator is its customer. Under this model, as organizational goals of waste minimization are pursued, the amount of hazardous waste generated could decrease. If the amount of waste decreases, the funding to EHS will decrease. The personnel and other resources within EHS allocated to the waste collection and disposal effort will need to be reduced.

The benefits of this fee-for-service model of funding are that the entity triggering the need for a particular service pays for that service. As the need for the service declines, the entity (customer) saves money. The fee-for-service model would not apply well for services that are generally useful across the organization. For example, if EHS were to charge for calls that come into the office regarding indoor air quality, fire safety, questions on water quality, potential disease clusters, and so forth, then the members of the organization could be discouraged from calling. The problem is that there is no clear single customer for these types of services. Contrast this to the hazardous waste situation where there is a clear source, there usually being a relatively small number of departments that generate hazardous waste. The generator of the hazardous waste pays for its disposal. As you can see in Table 28–D, less than 10 percent of the research universities and medical centers charge back for EHS services, while in small colleges, only 1.5 percent charge back. One possible explanation is that in research and medical institutions, specific services (such as radiation safety, hazardous waste, and respirator protection) can be linked to specific customers, while in small colleges the services provided by EHS (such as indoor air quality) are to the general population.

Centralized Funding Model

Centralized funding means that there are no chargebacks to individual members or departments in an organization. The funds are derived from a central pool usually called overhead (OH). Examples of other centrally funded services are human resources and accounting/finance. These functions provide services across the organization with no real focus on any particular group. From the data in CSHEMA, more than 90 percent of EHS efforts are centrally funded. Using the hazardous waste example, under a central funding model

TABLE 28–D	Percentage of EHS Services Charged Back to Users of the EHS Services		
Institution Type	*Mean*	*Max*	*Min*
Research Universities and Medical Centers	8.2%	49%	0%
Small College	1.5%	9%	0%
Medical Center	9.5%	21%	0%
Large Nonresearch Institution	5.5%	11%	0%

EHS would collect and dispose of whatever wastes are generated, and there would be no fee to the entity generating the waste. The motivation for the generating party to find other methods of disposal has been removed, but there is no budgetary incentive to reduce the generation of hazardous wastes.

Professional Certifications

Professional certifications are offered in many environmental health and safety disciplines. The American Board of Industrial Hygiene (ABIH) and the Board of Certified Safety Professionals (BCSP) are examples of organizations that provide professional certifications for EHS occupations. According to BCSP, "Many professions recognize the need for certification to identify competency in their respective fields. Just as a Certified Public Accountant (CPA) in accounting denotes a measurable standard of competency, the CSP is recognized as having met the professional challenge of illustrating competency through education, experience, and examination." This concept is applicable to many of the professions that make up EHS departments. Professional certifications are present in both the private and public sector and extend through health care, education, private industry, and regulatory agencies.

Certification requirements vary among professional organizations and certification boards, but typically contain requirements in the form of education, coursework, professional work experience, professional references, and a thorough examination.

Requirements to be awarded the Certified Industrial Hygienist (CIH) certification include a bachelor's degree with specific coursework, four years of professional experience, and passing a 250-question full-day examination. The BCSP has similar education requirements, but obtaining the CSP certification is a two-step process involving separate examinations that coincide with the amount of on-the-job experience. After successful completion of the two exams (and associated academic requirements), the certification is awarded.

Table 28–E shows some of the common professional certifications identified among EHS professionals as well as the certification board or professional organization and the website where additional information is available for each certification. Other professional certifications exist for EHS professionals. This table contains the most widely held certifications in EHS disciplines.

TABLE 28–E   Summary of Environmental Health and Safety Professional Certifications

Acronym	Certification	Certification Board or Professional Organization	Information
CIH	Certified Industrial Hygienist	American Board of Industrial Hygiene	www.abih.org
CAIH	Certified Associate Industrial Hygienist	American Board of Industrial Hygiene	www.abih.org
CSP	Certified Safety Professional	Board of Certified Safety Professionals	www.bcsp.org
ASP	Associate Safety Professional	Board of Certified Safety Professionals	www.bcsp.org
GSP	Graduate Safety Practitioner	Board of Certified Safety Professionals	www.bcsp.org
OHST	Occupational Health and Safety Technologist	Board of Certified Safety Professionals	www.bcsp.org
CLCS	Certified Loss Control Specialist	Board of Certified Safety Professionals	www.bcsp.org
CHST	Construction Health and Safety Technician	Board of Certified Safety Professionals	www.bcsp.org
CPE	Certified Professional Ergonomist	Board of Certification in Professional Ergonomics	www.bcpe.org
CHFP	Certified Human Factors Professional	Board of Certification in Professional Ergonomics	www.bcpe.org
RPT	Radiation Protection Technologist	National Registry of Radiation Protection Technologists	www.nrrpt.org
COHN	Certified Occupational Health Nurse	American Board for Occupational Health Nurses	www.abohn.org
OEM	Occupational and Environmental Medicine Physician	American College of Occupational and Environmental Medicine	www.acoem.org
CBSP	Certified Biological Safety Professional	American Biological Safety Association	www.absa.org
RBP	Registered Biosafety Professional	American Biological Safety Association	www.absa.org
ROH	Registered Occupational Hygienist	Canadian Registration Board of Occupational Hygienists	www.crboh.ca
RSP	Registered Safety Professionals	Board of Canadian Registered Safety Professionals	www.bcrsp.ca
CHMM	Certified Hazardous Materials Manager	Institute of Hazardous Materials Management	www.ihmm.org
CHMP	Certified Hazardous Materials Practitioner	Institute of Hazardous Materials Management	www.ihmm.org
CHP	Certified Health Physicists	American Academy of Health Physics	www.hps1.org/aahp

SUMMARY

Environmental health and safety, defined as "managing safety, health, and environmental risks to people, property, and the environment to acceptable levels" is an emerging, challenging field that uses technical skills of a wide range of disciplines, such as industrial hygienists, safety specialists, biosafety specialists, radiation safety specialists, medical personnel, ergonomists, and human factors specialists, to name a few. To be successful, the EHS effort needs to be integrated into the organization's operations and supported. The EHS group needs to be a business partner in developing the organization's strategic plans. Some common principles (people, profit, and planet) drive EHS decision making as well as EHS roles and responsibilities. Although ensuring compliance with regulations is not the only role EHS plays within an organization, it is often an important one. Remember that best-in-class EHS programs seek to not only comply with but to exceed the minimum requirements set by regulations and find ways to continually add business value to whatever organization they are part of.

BIBLIOGRAPHY

Camplin JC. Aligning safety and social responsibility. *Professional Safety* (May):46–55, 2011.

Campus Safety, Health and Environmental Management Association. *2009 Benchmarking Report and Salary Survey*. Bloomington, IN: CSHEMA, 2011.

Elkington J. Towards the sustainable corporation: Win-win-win business strategies for sustainable development. *California Management Review* 36(2):90–101, 1994.

European Agency for Safety and Health at Work. 2011. http://osha.europa.eu/en/about

European Chemicals Agency. 2011. http://www.echa.europa.eu/home_en.asp

European Commission. Environment. 2011. http://ec.europa.eu/environment/chemicals/reach/reach_intro.htm

European Union. 2011. http://europa.eu/about-eu/institutions-bodies/index_en.htm

International Organization of Standardization. *Guidance on Social Responsibility*. ISO/FDIS 26000:2010(E). Geneva: ISO, 2010.

Leeman JE. Delivering business value by linking behavioral EHS competencies to corporate core competencies. *International Journal for Sustainable Business* 12(1):3–11, 2005.

Makower J, Elkington J, Hailes J. *The Green Consumer*. Oakland, CA: Tilden Press, 1993.

Nuwayhid IA. Occupational health research in developing countries: A partner for social justice. *American Journal of Public Health* 94(11):1916–1921, 2004.

Occupational Safety and Health Administration. News Release 2/15/2011. Reference number 11–0225-NAT. Washington, DC: OSHA, 2011.

U.S. Bureau of Labor Statistics. *Number of fatal work injuries, 1992–2010*. Washington, DC: U.S. BLS, 2011. http://stats.bls.gov/iif/oshwc/cfoi/cfch0009.pdf

Veltri A, Ramsay J. Business of safety, economic analysis, make the business case for SH&E. *Professional Safety* (September):22–30, 2009.

CHAPTER 29

The Industrial Hygiene Program

by Victor M. Toy, MPH, CIH, CSP

*T*he industrial hygiene program is the culmination of the understanding of the risks and hazards in the workplace, the processes required to control these risks, and the commitment of resources to provide a safe work environment. The program follows the industrial hygiene mantra of anticipating, recognizing, evaluating, and controlling health hazards. In addition to preventing occupational injury and disease, the program also offers benefits to the organization by reducing costs, increasing productivity, and improving employee morale and brand image.

There are a variety of methods for implementing the industrial hygiene program. Organizations in their infancy may begin by establishing programs to meet prescriptive regulatory requirements. However, as the value of health and safety systems are realized, these organizations may progress to integrating these processes with other parts of the business and establishing best practices for improving health and safety. This chapter provides an introduction into the elements for developing or updating an organization's industrial hygiene program.

It is important to recognize the need for the right level of skills required to establish an effective program. Many aspects to consider in the industrial hygiene program are covered earlier in this book (Part III, IV, and V) and the roles and responsibilities for the professional discipline are covered just prior to this chapter.

It is common to find industrial hygienists with postgraduate training in industrial hygiene or a related degree in science or engineering, along with additional coursework in specific areas of practice such as sampling methodology and analysis, industrial ventilation, radiation safety, hearing conservation, *indoor air quality, toxicology, or ergonomics. These professionals can be staffed internally or by insurance and consulting companies, depending on the size of the organization.*

COMPONENTS OF AN INDUSTRIAL HYGIENE PROGRAM

As mentioned earlier, the industrial hygiene (IH) program can take many different forms. Traditionally, the program begins with a management commitment to employee safety, usually in the form of a policy statement. This is followed by various operational components that include hazard recognition and identification, exposure evaluation and risk assessment, control and mitigation (including employee training and education), and audit or program evaluation. Provisions for management and employee participation are typically included within these elements. Within these components are the relevant aspects applicable to the workplace such as noise, indoor air quality, radiation, ergonomics, and chemical use. Documentation of the industrial hygiene program helps to provide continuity and consistency as well as evidence of conformance to internal and external requirements.

In the last decade, the implementation of industrial hygiene programs has been enhanced through a more systems-oriented approach to help foster continual improvement in health and safety. In 1989, The U.S. Occupational Safety and Health Administration (OSHA) helped promote the use of the systems approach by issuing its Program Management Guidelines, where it leveraged the success of its Voluntary Protection Program. Following suit, the British Standards Institute issued its BS 8800 *Guide to Occupational Health and Safety Management Systems,* followed by the Occupational Health and Safety Series 18001 *Occupational Health and Safety Management Systems,* and the American National Standards Institute/American Industrial Hygiene Association (ANSI/AIHA) Z10 *Occupational Health and Safety Management Systems standard.* These approaches all share a similar design concept by placing the IH program into framework that includes policy development, management and employee participation, planning, implementation, and checking and corrective action.

The format of the program, whether it is traditional or systems oriented, likely depends on a variety of factors. These factors can include the size and type of the organization, its management philosophy, the range of occupational hazards at the facility, and the available health and safety resources. For example, small companies may use the more traditional approach and rely on services and programs provided through their insurance companies or consulting companies. Larger organizations, on the other hand, may have more comprehensive and systems-oriented programs with staff support appropriate for their organization's needs.

BENEFITS OF AN INDUSTRIAL HYGIENE PROGRAM

All organizations benefit from the contributions and productivity of its employees. The industrial hygiene program provides social and economic benefits by sustaining a healthy and fit workforce to help meet company objectives. The following benefits have been cited in well-established programs:

- They provide a place of employment in which employees are protected from known occupational health hazards at the workplace.
- Compensable injuries or illnesses are reduced, thus lowering insurance premiums and associated medical and recordkeeping costs.
- Productivity is increased by improving working conditions, which improves morale and labor relations and reduces lost time from accidents, illnesses, and absenteeism.
- Operating costs are reduced by anticipating and controlling potential occupational health hazards during the design phase of new projects and changes.
- The Occupational Safety and Health Administration (OSHA) and other government regulations concerning industrial hygiene are quickly assessed and implemented.

The introduction of total quality management and the International Organization for Standardization (ISO) 9000 (Quality Management and Quality Assurance) and 14001 (Environmental Management Systems) standards provides the advantage of continuous improvements from instituting management systems for quality and environmental practices. The industrial hygiene program fits under a similar framework in an occupational health and safety management system. These systems align with the plan-do-check-act (PDCA) model developed by W. Edwards Demming in the 1950s, which is well known in large organizations familiar with quality models. It demonstrates how programs, including industrial hygiene, contribute to company objectives by maintaining and improving employee health and safety. Figure 29–1 illustrates the Plan-Do-Check-Act components that serve as the framework for managing the elements of an industrial hygiene program as discussed in the next section. Each of those elements is covered in the implementation of policy, planning, implementation and operation, checking and corrective action, and management review.

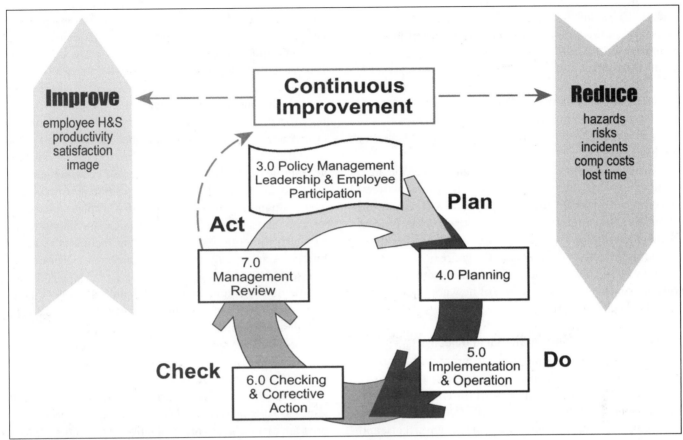

Figure 29–1. An example of an Occupational Health and Safety Management System Cycle, ANSI/AIHA Z10. Numbers 3.0-7.0 correlate to the sections of the Z10 Standard. *(Used with the permission of AIHA®, 2011.)*

ESTABLISHING AN INDUSTRIAL HYGIENE PROGRAM

Elements of an IH Program

The industrial hygiene program can be subdivided into individual programs or processes, each with its own set of requirements and procedures. An example of these programs are listed in Table 29–A. Each program, such as the one for Exposure Assessments, specifies who, what, when, where, and why. In other words, it includes where the requirements apply, what needs to be done, how it should be done, who should be involved, and how often. Parts IV and V of this book provide information that should be considered when developing these programs. Program development should be documented to help convey how these programs are implemented. This information can be used to demonstrate compliance and commitment to employee health and safety during an internal or external audit or inspection. More importantly, written procedures provide measurable performance guidelines for worker protection and help assure continuity from one program owner to another.

TABLE 29-A	Typical Subcategories of an Industrial Hygiene Program

A. Health and Safety Policy
B. Management Commitment and Employee Participation
C. Training & Education (including Hazard Communication)
D. Chemical and Equipment Authorizations
E. Toxic Gases
F. Ergonomics
G. Biohazards
H. Ionizing Radiation
I. Nonionizing Radiation
J. Indoor Air Quality
K. Confined Spaces
L. Exposure Assessment
M. Chemical Safety
N. Process Hazard Reviews
O. Materials Handling Safety
P. Contractor Safety
Q. Hearing Conservation
R. Industrial Ventilation
S. Personal Protective Equipment
T. Emergency Response
U. Safety Inspections and Audits
V. Accident Reporting, Recording, and Investigation
W. Records Retention

The Policy Statement

A policy publicly states a company's commitment to employee health and safety. The industrial hygiene program then aligns itself with the policy provided by the chief administrator, or top management, of the organization. The health and safety policy should be communicated to all employees, state the purpose of the program, and require active participation by all employees. The policy should reflect

- management's commitment and the importance the organization places on the health and safety of its employees;
- compliance with all federal, state, and local regulations and internal company safety and health requirements; and
- the necessity for active leadership, direct participation, and the enthusiastic support of the entire organization.

Often, policies also include a commitment to continuous improvement and the setting of new goals and objectives for health and safety.

Planning Activities: Setting Goals and Objectives

Typically, a young or immature program will focus on reactive activities such as incidents or new legal/regulatory requirements. As a program matures, more time will be spent in the planning phase of the PDCA cycle, focusing on continuous improvement, voluntary commitments, and preventive actions. The establishment of a strategic plan for long- and short-range goals and objectives is vital to the development of an effective industrial hygiene program. These goals and objectives should also be part of the written program. They are often established by a team, such as a joint labor–management health and safety committee.

A goal is a desired outcome, whereas an objective is a specific activity or means of achieving a goal (Table 29–B). Objectives should be realistic and, when possible, measurable. For example, if ergonomics-related injuries are a problem, the goal may be to reduce the number of accidents by 25 percent within a three-year period. The objectives and activities to achieve this goal could include establishing an ergonomics committee, providing training, and modifying the work flow and physical work environment. In all cases, objectives should be directed at fixing the root or underlying cause of an issue. Goals and objectives should not be static—they should be evaluated and updated on a regularly scheduled basis. As conditions change, new issues or improvement opportunities should be prioritized and new goals and objectives set.

Hazard Recognition and Evaluation

Considered one of the first tenets of industrial hygiene, a process must be adopted to anticipate and recognize health hazards in order to identify the potential health and safety risks in the work environment. Workplace stressors include chemical, physical, and biological hazards as well as musculoskeletal and psychosocial issues such as stress. Information is collected during walk-through surveys, inspections, and interviews with employees and management. An assessment is made that includes use of chemicals, equipment, operating procedures, work practices, and available controls. An evaluation, or risk assessment, is then conducted to determine if the real or potential exposures to these hazards are acceptable or if additional engineering or administrative controls or personal protective equipment is necessary. The evaluation includes a review of workplace conditions against applicable regulations, standards, and best practices to which the organization subscribes including those set by OSHA and the American Conference of Governmental Industrial Hygienists.

While professional judgment is indispensable, quantitative techniques are often used to assess health risks. This includes use of direct reading instruments, calibrated sampling equipment, recognized analytical techniques such as the National Institute for Occupational Safety and Health (NIOSH) *Manual of Analytical Methods*, and accredited or certified laboratories for analyzing air, surface, and bulk samples. The results are evaluated in an exposure assessment program that includes both qualitative and quantitative data.

The exposure assessment program is used to determine potential and actual exposures and then use that information to minimize the risks of adverse health effects potentially affecting employees. This program also helps demonstrate compliance with legal and internal company requirements and provides an avenue for employee communication regarding the safety of their work environment.

There are numerous techniques for conducting these assessments. One such method is described in the American Industrial Hygiene Association (AIHA) publication, *A Strategy for Assessing and Managing Occupational Exposures*. Figure 29–2 illustrates the steps in this process. The assessment begins with gathering information on the characteristics of the workplace, workforce, and the chemical, physical, and biological agents. The following information is collected during the initial steps of this process:

- *Workplace characterization*. A description of the processes and operations in the workplace detailing areas with potential exposure to an environmental hazard (Figure 29–3).
- *Work force characterization groups.* Identification of employees with similar work duties or job classifications (Figure 29–4).
- *Agent characterization*: Construction of an inventory of environmental agents including a description of their

TABLE 29–B	Summary of Criteria and Activities for an Industrial Hygiene Program		
Program Element Activity	*Activity*	*Measurement Criteria*	*Goal*
Policy	Write, prepare/present for management acceptance	Is policy complete? Is policy understood and supported by management/employees? Does policy carry authority needed for implementation?	An accepted and working policy that clearly states the scope, responsibilities, and authority of the program
Education	New employee orientation Periodic information and education sessions Written safety and health guidelines Posting of dangerous areas Labeling of materials handled by employees	No. of educational materials produced and distributed Increase in employee knowledge of safety and health issues Employee avoidance of hazards	Increased employee awareness of health and safety in the workplace
Health hazard recognition	Plant survey Chemical inventory Process and equipment review Health hazard review procedures Process change review procedures	No. of surveys Completion and procedure update Procedures and staff in place for review, etc.	Identify all present and potential hazards in the workplace
Health hazard evaluation	Environmental monitoring (area, personal) Sample analysis Statistical analysis of data Biological monitoring Records of data Establishment of criteria	No. of samples collected No. of analyses performed Statistical significance of sample data Well-documented recordkeeping system Established criteria for each stress	Measure and quantitatively evaluate stresses and hazards, determine their impact upon the work environment
Health hazard control	Design and/or recommend administrative and engineering controls Procedural mechanisms for implementing controls Procedural mechanism for including controls as part of planning for new processes and changes in existing processes Administrative review of rejected procedures	Controls implemented and working Administrative procedures in place	Control or reduce to the lowest level all potential workplace hazards
OSHA compliance	Review all present and future regulations, standards Determine level of compliance obtained via compliance inspections	No violations present Program positioned to comply with regulations	Complete compliance with all laws, regulations, standards, etc

Source: Toca FM. Program evaluation: Industrial Hygiene. *AIHAJ* 42:213-216, 1981. Reprinted by permission of Taylor & Francis Ltd, http://www.tandfonline.com.

potential adverse health effects, how they are used, how much is used, and their chemical, physical, or biological properties.

Once the environment is characterized, the evaluation step begins. This usually starts with grouping employees into similar exposure groups, or SEGs. Creating exposure groups is done to apply monitoring data to employees who were not directly monitored, but who might be represented by the samples collected. Workers in SEGs are those who can be expected to have the same or similar exposure profiles to an

environmental agent based on the information gathered during the workplace, work force, and agent characterizations.

The evaluation of each hazard listed for a homogeneous group involves two stages. First, a subjective determination is made as to whether the exposure to each environmental agent listed for a homogeneous exposure group is low, moderate, high, or very high relative to an exposure limit. This determination is based on such factors as the frequency and duration of the exposure, estimated exposure level if known, and the severity of the health effects resulting from

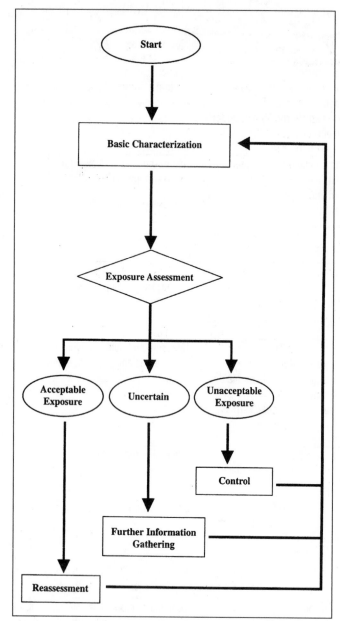

Figure 29–2. A strategy for assessing and managing occupational exposures. *(Reprinted with permission from Ignacio JS, Bullock WH, eds., 2006.)*

on sampling methodologies (Chapter 16), calibration, field use and maintenance of the equipment, quality control, use of approved or accredited laboratories, and the chain of custody to ensure proper handling. In addition, procedures should be developed to ensure that employees receive copies of the monitoring results and are afforded the opportunity to observe monitoring.

Exposure assessments are repeated periodically to check if conditions and related exposures have changed significantly. The frequency and scope of the reevaluation depend on the severity of the hazards. A new assessment should be done whenever a new process, equipment, or hazardous agent is introduced into the workplace.

Hazard Control

Measures must be taken to eliminate or reduce exposures whenever there is unacceptable risk based on standards and professional judgment. Controls range from notification and use of personal protective equipment to more sophisticated engineering controls. In any case, there is a preferred hierarchy of these controls beginning with substitution or elimination, engineering, administrative, and finally the use of personal protective equipment. Substitution, elimination, and engineering controls are typically the best methods and often the most cost effective because they control potential exposures at the source. Personal protective equipment should be the last choice because of the increased attention required for proper use and maintenance. In many instances, a combination of controls may be required.

Controls and performance specifications, such as with local exhaust ventilation requirements, should be specified in the industrial hygiene program or in operating procedures accessible to employees, engineers, and maintenance workers. These controls should be periodically checked and reevaluated during routine maintenance, exposure assessments programs, and industrial hygiene surveys. An effective program is one that considers the use of appropriate control measures during the design of new and modified processes or equipment before use in production. This may include chemical and equipment purchases, building plan reviews, process changes, and facilities maintenance plans. Controls should also be assessed in emergency response plans along with other potential nonroutine exposure situations. The maintenance of operational controls should be documented along with clearly assigned responsibilities and training provided to employees.

Employee Training and Education

An important element of administrative controls is the awareness and knowledge of the potential hazards, health risks, and the work practices required to ensure employee

the exposure. Second, the exposures are monitored and the results compared against established exposure limits. In the first phase, the potential exposures that are rated very high are monitored first, and those rated low are monitored last. Sampling plans should specify the number and duration of samples to be taken to ensure true representation of employee exposures. More information on evaluation and air sampling processes can be found in Chapters 15 and 16).

A written procedure is necessary to ensure that samples are collected in a proper, consistent, and professionally accepted manner. Procedures should include information

---

Sodium Chloride Production Plant

Process Description

Chlorine gas is received directly by pipeline from an adjacent vendor plant; the gas arrives at a line pressure of 200 psig, passes through a pressure letdown valve, and enters T-1 column at 20 psig. 25% hydrogen peroxide is received in tank cars and is diluted with process water to 19% before being pumped to T-2 column. In Columns T-1 and T-2, chlorine and hydrogen peroxide go through a counterflow reaction to produce a 29% aqueous hydrochloric acid (HCl) solution; trace amounts of chlorine are vented to the atmosphere at T-2 column.

A 50% sodium hydroxide solution is received by pipeline from an adjacent vendor plant and is stored in S-2 tank before being pumped to R-1 reactor. From T-2 column, the HCl solution is pumped to R-1 reactor to react with the caustic and produce a 35% sodium chloride solution (brine). The brine is contacted with heated air in F-1 fluid bed dryer to make sodium chloride granules with a size range of 100 to 200 microns. The finished product is transferred to storage hopper H-1.

The industrial grade sodium chloride is packaged in 50-pound bags and palletized in 1,000-pound loads. Each pallet is film-wrapped in an automatic shrink-film apparatus. A tow motor is used to move pallets from the bagging station to the shrink-film station and then to the warehouse. At the warehouse, the tow motor is also used to load the wrapped pallets into truck trailers.

The plant is currently producing about 50 million pounds per year of industrial grade sodium chloride; the plant operates about 300 days per year with the remaining time used for scheduled maintenance work. On a daily basis, the plant receives about 53 tons of chlorine gas, 120 tons of caustic solution, and 306 tons of hydrogen peroxide solution.

Figure 29–3. Process description developed for an example of an exposure assessment strategy at a hypothetical sodium chloride production facility. Development of such a workplace description is fundamental to completing the workplace characterization portion of the basic characterization step of the strategy. *(Reprinted with permission from the American Industrial Hygiene Association, A Strategy for Occupational Exposure Assessment, Fairfax, VA: AIHA, 1991.)*

safety. Proper education must be provided relevant to the roles and responsibilities each worker has in the process. This includes training for those who design the process as well as the employees and managers involved in operations and maintenance. The degree of safety training should be customized for the work situation. New employee orientation should be given to all employees so that they can be actively involved in protecting their safety and those around them. Additional training must be provided for work with specific hazards. Activities such as office work may require general awareness of the importance of safety, incident reporting, general hazard communication, and emergency response procedures. Specific topics, such as ergonomics and chemical safety, should be included for those employees encountering these types of risks. A schedule for refresher training should be developed to ensure such knowledge is current. Employee training and education can be one of the most effective control measures because it provides employees with a real understanding of the potential hazards in their work area and the corrective actions to be taken to prevent adverse effects.

Training has become a standard part of most OSHA regulations. For many of the topics (e.g., hearing conservation) listed in Table 29–A, there is an element of training, education, and awareness ranging from labels and postings to classes and certifications. The method (e.g., labeling versus classroom training) chosen for employee education depends on the type and degree of the hazard, which should be part of the assessment and recommendation provided by the industrial hygienist. The following summary was taken from *Training Requirements in OSHA Standards and Training Guidelines* (OSHA, 1998) and provides guidance for establishing training.

Determine if Training is Needed. This involves an assessment of what controls are most appropriate for solving a problem. Training is most effective where there is a lack of knowledge of a work process, familiarity with equipment or the proper execution of a task.

Sodium Chloride Production Plant

Job Descriptions

Operations Personnel

Superintendent: Spends about 10% of time in general process areas observing operations, checking equipment conditions, and supervising maintenance work; remaining time spent in office environments on administrative, supervisory, and planning activities.

Engineer: Spends about 35% of time in general process areas troubleshooting process problems, supervising maintenance work, and collecting industrial hygiene samples; remaining time spent on training, computer program development, and other office activities.

Shift Supervisor: Spends about 5% of time in general process areas checking on operations and investigating possible process problems; remaining time spent in control room areas overseeing operation of the acid, reactor, and dryer systems.

Relief Operator: Spends about 20% of time covering each of the shift supervisor, acid system operator, reactor system operator, and assistant operator job classifications; remaining time spent on various maintenance activities.

Operator, Acid System: Spends about 40% of time in the HCl production areas checking equipment, adjusting flows, and preparing equipment for maintenance; about 10% of time is spent collecting process samples and another 25% is spent in lab running analyses on all process samples; remaining time is spent in control room areas.

Operator, Reactor System: Spends about 60% of time in the reactor and fluid bed dryer areas checking equipment, adjusting flows, and preparing equipment for maintenance. About 10% of time is spent collecting process samples; remaining time is spent in control room areas.

Assistant Operator: Spends about 50% of time at bagging station loading product into 50-pound bags; another 25% of time is spent using tow motor to move pallets to and from the warehouse and to load product into truck trailers; about 5% of time is spent loading product directly from storage into hopper cars; remaining time is spent in control room areas.

Electrical/Instrument Technician: Spends about 5% of time in the HCl production areas maintaining and calibrating in-line chlorine analyzer; approximately 25% of time is spent in general process areas and switchgear room maintaining electrical equipment; about 50% of time is spent in control room or maintenance shop repairing or modifying process control instruments; remaining time is spent on office activities.

Figure 29–4. Sample job description for operations personnel at a hypothetical sodium chloride production facility. The descriptions were developed to fulfill the workforce characterization requirements of the basic characterization step of the strategy and to be used as an approach for determining homogenous exposure groups. *(Reprinted with permission from the American Industrial Hygiene Association,* A Strategy for Occupational Exposure Assessment, *Fairfax, VA: AIHA, 1991.)*

Identify Training Needs. Proper understanding of the work activity, such as the information obtained through a job analysis, provides insight into the tasks employees are asked to complete. Specific hazards can then be identified and the proper training designed to help employees conduct their work safely. Incident, near miss reports and employee input can also help target training needs.

Identify Goals and Objectives. Learning objectives help you identify performance and improvement outcomes. This helps determine whether the training is effective and informs the employee what is expected at completion of the educational activity. The objectives should describe the level of knowledge, skills development or practices desired.

Develop Learning Activities. Learning activities enable employees to acquire the desired skills and knowledge. There are various methods of delivery available including classroom and on the job training. Regardless of the method, the learning situation should be transferable to the work activity and simulate the actual job as closely as possible.

Conduct Training. Proper course organization and delivery is critical to training effectiveness. Training must reinforce training

Pipe Fitter/Welder: Spends about 30% of time in maintenance shop on welding work associated with process piping and equipment repairs; about 40% of time is spent in general process areas removing or replacing piping and process equipment; remaining time is spent in shop office or control room.

Utility Mechanic: Spends approximately 20% of time helping process operators with preparation of equipment for maintenance; about 50% of time is spent repairing equipment in shop; another 10% of time is spent in general process areas making minor repairs to process equipment; remaining time is spent in shop office or in control room.

Personnel Roster

Name	Company ID No.	Job Classification	Job Code
J. R. Smith	20066	Superintendent	0062
M. C. Jones	10081	Engineer	0085
	10018	Shift Supervisor	0105
	10025	Shift Supervisor	0105
	10038	Shift Supervisor	0105
	10040	Shift Supervisor	0105
	10019	Relief Operator	0121
	10050	Relief Operator	0121
	10029	Operator, Acid System	0123A
	10042	Operator, Acid System	0123A
	10066	Operator, Acid System	0123A
	10071	Operator, Acid System	0123A
	10021	Operator, Reactor	0123R
	10048	Operator, Reactor	0123R
	10052	Operator, Reactor	0123R
	10065	Operator, Reactor	0123R
	10088	Assistant Operator	0129
	10096	Assistant Operator	0129
	10099	Assistant Operator	0129
	10100	Assistant Operator	0129
	10044	Elec/Instr Technician	0210
	10030	Pipe Fitter/Welder	0230
	10061	Utility Mechanic	0255
	10078	Utility Mechanic	0255

Figure 29–4. (Continued.)

goals and objectives and be presented in a manner relevant to the employee and their work. An effective program allows employees to participate in the training process and to practice their skills or knowledge.

Evaluate Program Effectiveness. To make sure that the program is accomplishing educational goals, an evaluation of the training is necessary. Methods of evaluation include student opinions surveys, supervisor's observations, student tests and workplace improvements such as reductions in injury and incidents.

Improving the Program. If, after the evaluation, training did not give the employees the necessary level of knowledge and skills, then the training program must be revised and or repeated. It may be necessary to repeat the steps in the training process.

Employee training records should be kept updated to show how training needs have been met and to serve as a source of information where additional training may be targeted. Records should include attendance records, course outlines or lesson plans, student exams, and handout materials.

Employee Involvement

No program is complete without opportunities for employee participation in the processes affecting their health and safety. This is an important component of management commitment. Possible activities include participation in job reviews, inspections, committee meetings, and training. Selection of the activity should consider the culture of the company and/or location to ensure effective participation. Mechanisms for expressing timely suggestions and concerns should be made available without fear of reprisal. At a minimum, employees should be encouraged to participate by reporting unsafe work conditions and signs or symptoms related to work with hazardous agents so that proper evaluations are conducted and corrective actions taken as necessary.

Documentation/Recordkeeping

Good industrial hygiene practice includes proper documentation that describes how the program is implemented, what is done, and who does it. It helps ensure continuity for those who manage the program and provides proof of compliance with requirements. Records are generated as a result of an activity specified in the industrial hygiene program such as training or testing. Both records and documents must be maintained and kept current. Often, the length of time a record must be maintained is specified in regulatory requirements. For example, OSHA 29 CFR 1910.20 requires exposure records to be kept at least 30 years. In addition to demonstrating compliance, records are also a good source for program evaluation, which can provide input into planning new goals and objectives. Typically, programs such as those listed in Table 29-A are documented and communicated to the affected individuals. Documents may include procedures, IH surveys, reports, forms, planning objectives, audits, and inspections. When completed, these records can be maintained in paper copy or electronic format. Organizations should identify what records are kept and for how long.

Program Evaluation and Program Audit

Methods must be developed to periodically evaluate the effectiveness of the industrial hygiene program. Audits are an effective means for assessing the performance of an IH program. It helps determine whether the elements of the program have been implemented in accordance with established procedures, and whether these procedures are effective in achieving their goal. Audits can be conducted as a targeted program review or as a broader assessment within a certification review of an occupational health and safety management system.

Typically, the review is done by a health and safety specialist or a team of specialists from outside the facility being audited. This ensures the objectivity of the auditor and also provides fresh insight into the program. The audit team is usually from the corporate or headquarters staff, but in some cases an independent third party, such as an insurance loss control representative or independent consultant, is used. Self-audits, though not independent, can nonetheless be a useful evaluation tool.

The scope of an audit depends on the objectives and the allocated time and resources. For a small facility, a comprehensive audit of all industrial hygiene program components can be easily accomplished, whereas a large facility may require more time, more resources, or a limited scope.

Auditors prepare by researching requirements and obtaining documentation of the program to establish a plan for the review. Audit checklists are often developed to guide and focus the collection of information. Extensive lists are usually developed for each program component. In the interest of time, these are often sent in advance to the facility. This gives the organization the opportunity to collect the necessary documentation, schedule interviews with key personnel, and if necessary, ensure that certain processes or tasks of concern can be observed during the audit.

There are generally five phases to an audit:

1. Opening conference with the management of the facility, during which the purpose, scope, and schedule of the audit is discussed.
2. Information is gathered.
3. Information is analyzed, key facts confirmed, and contradictions resolved. During this phase, the auditor can usually generalize from specific situations to underlying program or system deficiencies.
4. Auditors present their findings to management during a closing conference, at which time any remaining concerns can be discussed.
5. A report of findings is issued.

Much of the value of the audit is lost if there is no established mechanism for follow-up. This can be accomplished though follow-up audits and/or by requiring the facility to develop written action plans and submit periodic progress reports. Finally, the findings from the audit are considered during planning activities when new goals and objectives are determined.

ORGANIZATIONAL RESPONSIBILITIES

In a management system for occupational health and safety, all parts of the organization work together to ensure the success of the health and safety program. The industrial hygiene program is a part of this system. Therefore, roles and responsibilities must be clearly defined, communicated, and accepted. Figure 29–5 provides an illustration of an industrial hygiene process and how that process links with functional groups in the organization. Health and safety is a shared responsibility from management to employees and includes the following functional groups.

Safety

Safety professionals and industrial hygienists are typically in the same department and share the same goal for maintaining a safe and healthful work environment. Safety professionals tend to focus on physical hazards that may cause injury, such as electrical, mechanical, and fire/life safety. However, there is often cross over between both disciplines and the same individual may be charged with responsibilities in both fields of practice.

Industrial Hygiene Process

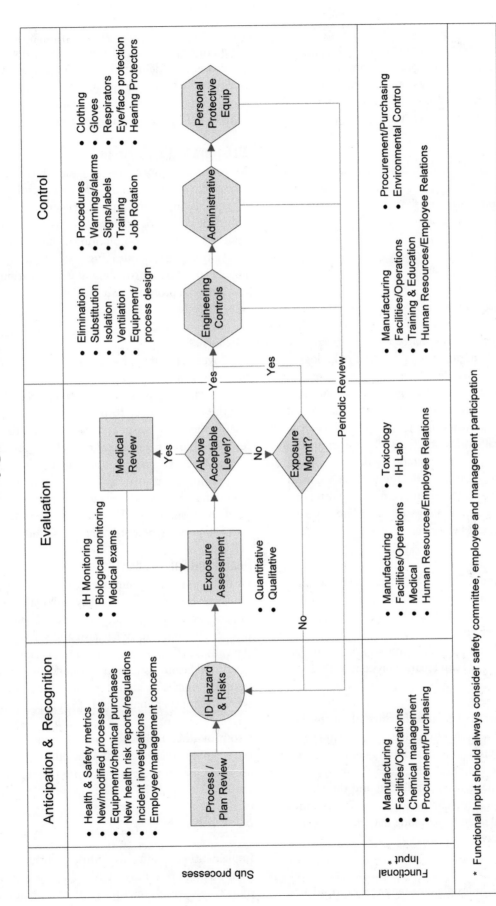

Figure 29–5. Basic illustration of the industrial hygiene process with examples of subprocesses and participants providing functional input.

Medical

Occupational health services include programs designed to promote the health of the work force and prevent occupational and nonoccupational disease and injury. A large corporation may have a full-time staff of occupational health physicians and nurses, equipped with a clinic. Smaller employers, on the other hand, may use a nearby occupational health clinic.

The following activities may be covered under the medical program:

- health examinations
- medical or biological monitoring
- diagnosis and treatment
- medical case management
- health education and counseling
- wellness activities
- medical recordkeeping

Industrial hygiene provides the medical department with information on exposures related to the work environment. This includes work practices and the use of biological, chemical, and physical agents. This information is used to administer medical exams (e.g., biological monitoring, audiometry, and respirator clearance), assess work relatedness of an injury or illness, and, working with the industrial hygienist, determine medical work restrictions where warranted to prevent further exposure. It is common for the medical staff to conduct joint surveys, such as an ergonomic assessment, with industrial hygiene. Maintenance of medical records associated with all medical examinations and findings is the responsibility of medical personnel.

Engineering

Engineers are involved with the design and modification of equipment, manufacturing, and facilities. New or modified processes potentially introduce health and safety hazards and risks into the work environment. To control these risks, engineers work with industrial hygienists to design proper engineering controls and maintenance procedures.

Purchasing

Purchasing is important because they are often the first department to see new orders for materials and equipment. Prior to ordering and receipt, industrial hygiene should provide safety criteria to the purchasing department to ensure the proper reviews have been conducted and the materials and equipment ordered can be used in a safe manner. Requirements should include obtaining material safety data sheets and other safety information.

Top Management

Top management includes general managers, presidents, chief executive officers, and vice presidents who have the ultimate responsibility for employee safety, including the provision for adequate health and safety resources. They must ensure that their organizations comply with applicable corporate policies and government regulations and may look to industrial hygienists to provide advice and counsel.

Managers and Supervisors

Managers and supervisors provide direct oversight over the day-to-day activities and typically control work schedules. They serve an important role ensuring the use and availability of safe work practices and working conditions. This includes ensuring completion of the required health and safety training, encouraging awareness and reporting of unsafe situations, providing and monitoring use of safety and personal protective equipment, and conducting periodic self-inspections.

Employees

Employees can often provide great insight into the safety of their work environment because they work directly with the potential hazards present in the workplace. Every employee has the responsibility to perform work in a manner that ensures their own personal safety as well as the safety of their fellow employees. Employee responsibilities include following the health and safety rules, properly using and maintaining personal protective equipment and other safety devices, maintaining their work area in a neat and clean manner, and notifying their supervisor when observing hazardous work conditions, work practices, accidents, and near misses.

Health and Safety Committee

Health and safety committees are a good way to maintain focus on workplace safety. They provide a forum for securing cooperation, coordination, and the exchange of ideas to maintain and improve health and safety. The committee typically has three major functions: (1) examining company safety and health issues and recommending changes in practices or policies to management, (2) conducting periodic workplace inspections, and (3) evaluating and promoting interest in the program. The health and safety committee also provides a means for involving employees in the program. Joint management-labor health and safety committees are often used if the employees are represented by a union.

SUMMARY

Implementing an effective industrial hygiene program supports an organization's commitment to the health and safety of its employees. It requires participation at all levels of the organization, beginning with its policy statement. The industrial hygiene program includes elements of planning, hazard recognition and evaluation, hazard control, employee training and education, employee involvement, documentation, and program evaluation. As an organization matures, these programs are implemented within an occupational health and safety management system to integrate with other business systems to ensure quality, efficiency, and effectiveness.

BIBLIOGRAPHY

American Conference of Governmental Industrial Hygienists. *2011 TLVs® and BEIs®*. Cincinnati, OH: ACGIH, 2011.

American National Standards Institute/American Industrial Hygiene Association. *ANSI/AIHA Z10-2005 Occupational Health and Safety Management Systems*. Fairfax, VA: AIHA, 2005.

Bridge DP. Developing and implementing an industrial hygiene and safety program in industry. *AIHA Journal* 40:255–263, 1979.

Cralley LJ, Cralley LV, Garrett JT, eds. *Industrial Hygiene Management*. New York: John Wiley & Sons, Inc., 1988.

DiBerardinis LJ, ed. *Handbook of Occupational Safety and Health*. Hoboken, NJ: John Wiley & Sons, Inc., 1998.

DiNardi SR, ed. *The Occupational Environment—Its Evaluation and Control*. Fairfax, VA: AIHA, 2003.

Hollebeck C, ed. *Industrial Hygiene & Safety Auditing—A Manual for Practice*, 2nd ed. Fairfax, VA: AIHA, 2007.

Ignacio JS, Bullock WH, eds. *A Strategy for Assessing and Managing Occupational Exposures*, 3rd ed. Fairfax, VA: AIHA, 2006.

Manuele FA. *Advanced Safety Management Focusing on Z10 and Serious Injury Prevention*. Hoboken, NJ: John Wiley & Sons, Inc., 2008.

Nelson TJ, Holmes RS, Gordon T, et al. Workplace exposure assessment workshop: An integrated approach for the '90s. *AIHA Journal* 54:633–637, 1993.

Occupational Safety and Health Administration. *Training Requirements in OSHA Standards and Training Guidelines*, OSHA 2254. Washington, DC: GPO, 1998 (revised).

Toca FM. Program evaluation: Industrial hygiene. *AIHA Journal* 42:213–216, 1981.

U.S. Department of Health and Human Services. *NIOSH Manual of Analytical Methods (NMAM®)*, 4th ed., DHHS (NIOSH) Publication. Washington, DC: GPO, 1994.

PART VII

Governmental Regulations and Their Impact

CHAPTER 30

Government Regulations

Dorothy Dougherty, MS, Director,
OSHA Directorate of Standards and Guidance,
Amanda Edens, MSPH, Deputy Director,
OSHA Directorate of Standards and Guidance,
William Perry, MS, CIH, Deputy Director,
OSHA Directorate of Standards and Guidance, and
Andrew Levinson, MPH, Director, Office of Biological
Hazards, OSHA Directorate of Standards and Guidance

The OSHA that exists today is the product of a long evolution from a 19th century economy in which occupational safety and health was not the priority it is today. Massachusetts passed the nation's first safety and health legislation in 1877, requiring the guarding of belts, shafts, and gears, protection on elevators, and adequate fire exits in factories. By 1890, nine states provided for factory inspectors, 13 required machine guarding, and 21 made limited provision for health hazards.

In 1903, the U.S. Bureau of Labor began publishing graphically detailed studies of occupational fatalities and illnesses in the dusty trades, as well as other safety and health topics. Dr. Alice Hamilton, considered the founder of industrial medicine in America, worked as a special investigator for the Bureau of Labor until 1921. Hamilton traveled around the country visiting lead smelters, storage battery plants, and other types of workplaces. In 1911, she published a study of the white lead industry that was the first of a series of Bureau of Labor reports known as the "Federal Survey." Hamilton's work led Illinois to establish laws requiring job-related safety measures. By the late 1930s, all states had such laws.

The bill establishing the Department of Labor as a new cabinet-level department was signed on March 4, 1913, by President William Howard Taft. In 1933, President Franklin D. Roosevelt selected Frances Perkins to be the new Secretary of Labor; she became the first woman to serve as a member of the cabinet. Perkins brought to the Labor Department extensive experience in occupational safety and health with the State of New York. To help ensure that workplaces would be "as safe as science and law can make them," Perkins created the Bureau of Labor Standards in 1934. This was the first permanent federal agency established primarily to promote safety and health for working men and women. The bureau also helped state govern-

ments improve their administration of workplace safety and health laws and raise the level of their protective legislation. The Department of Labor's activities related to occupational safety and health would later move from the responsibility of the Bureau of Labor Standards to a newly created agency, OSHA.

The Occupational Safety and Health Act was signed into law on December 29, 1970, by President Richard M. Nixon, culminating nearly a century of endeavors by the states and the federal government to mitigate the vulnerabilities of employees exposed to hazards of the industrial age. Enactment of the Williams-Steiger Occupational Safety and Health Act (OSHAct) was preceded by vigorous debate among government, business, and organized labor over the extent to which federal authority would set and enforce workplace safety and health standards. The Act became effective on April 28, 1971, now the official birthday of the Occupational Safety and Health Administration, the Review Commission, and NIOSH.

THE OCCUPATIONAL SAFETY AND HEALTH ADMINISTRATION

The Occupational Safety and Health Act of 1970 (OSHAct) created the Occupational Safety and Health Administration (OSHA) and was passed to prevent workers from being killed or seriously harmed at work. OSHA's mission is to ensure safe and healthful workplaces. Under the OSHAct, employers are responsible for providing a safe and healthful workplace. OSHA uses three basic strategies, authorized by the Occupational Safety and Health Act, to help employers and employees reduce injuries, illnesses, and deaths on the job:

1. Strong, fair, and effective enforcement of standards
2. Education, training, and compliance assistance
3. Partnerships, alliances, and other cooperative and voluntary programs

Major Authorities, Functional Areas, and Responsibilities

The OSHAct grants the Secretary of Labor the authority to promulgate, modify, and revoke safety and health standards; to conduct inspections and investigations and to issue citations, including proposed penalties; to require employers to keep records of safety and health data; to petition the courts to restrain imminent danger situations; and to approve or reject plans from states proposing to assume jurisdiction from federal OSHA over their private sector industries and state and local governments.

Under Executive Order 12196, the Secretary must ensure that all federal agencies comply with OSHA's standards. The Secretary of Labor's authority regarding federal agencies includes the right to inspect agency worksites based on compensation data and to issue notices of violation when

appropriate. Annual reports are filed with the respective agency heads, citing the deficiencies and positive elements of the agency's program.

Pursuant to the Act, the Secretary of Labor is granted the authority to train personnel in the duties related to their responsibilities under the Act and, in consultation with the U.S. Department of Health and Human Services (HHS), to provide training and education to employers and employees. The section 20 provision of the law directs HHS to delegate its statutory functions to the National Institute for Occupational Safety and Health (NIOSH), an agency within HHS, whenever feasible. The National Institute for Environmental Health Sciences (NIEHS), also in HHS, funds grants to organizations interested in training employees and others on health hazards, primarily in hazardous waste handling.

The Secretary and his or her designees are authorized to consult with employers, employees, and organizations regarding prevention of injuries and illnesses. Under the law, federal OSHA cannot conduct on-site consultation. Only those with whom it contracts under section 7(c) or the state OSHA agencies can consult. The Secretary of Labor, after consulting with the Secretary of HHS, may grant funds to the states to identify program needs and plan development, experiments, demonstrations, administration, and operation of programs. In conjunction with the Secretary of HHS, the Secretary of Labor is charged with developing and maintaining a statistics program for occupational safety and health.

Major Duties Delegated by the Secretary of Labor

In establishing the Occupational Safety and Health Administration, the Secretary of Labor delegated to the Assistant Secretary for Occupational Safety and Health the authority and responsibility for safety and health programs and activities of the Department of Labor, including responsibilities derived from the following legislation:

- Occupational Safety and Health Act of 1970
- Walsh-Healey Public Contracts Act of 1936, as amended
- Service Contract Act of 1965
- Public Law 91-54 of 1969 (Construction Safety Amendments)
- Public Law 85-742 of 1958 (Maritime Safety Act)
- National Foundation on the Arts and Humanities Act of 1965

The delegated authority includes responsibility for organizational changes, for coordination with other officials and agencies with responsibilities in the occupational safety and health area, and for contracting.

At the same time, the commissioner of the Bureau of Labor Statistics was delegated the authority and given the responsibility for developing and maintaining an effective program for collection, compilation, and analysis of occupational safety and health statistics, providing grants to the states to assist in developing and administering the statistics programs, and coordinating functions with the Assistant Secretary for Occupational Safety and Health. The Solicitor of Labor is assigned responsibility for providing legal advice and assistance to the Secretary and all officers of the Department of Labor in the administration of statutes and executive orders relating to occupational safety and health. In enforcing the Act's requirements, the Solicitor of Labor also has the responsibility for representing the Secretary in litigation before the Occupational Safety and Health Review Commission and, subject to the control and direction of the attorney general, before the federal courts.

The Department of Labor regulations dealing with OSHA are published in Title 29 of the Code of Federal Regulations (CFR), as shown in Table 30–A.

General Duties and Obligations Under the OSHAct

The OSHAct sets out two duties for employers and one for employees. The general duty provisions are as follows:

- Each employer shall furnish to each employee a place of employment free from recognized hazards that cause or are likely to cause death or serious physical harm to the employee.
- Each employer shall comply with occupational safety and health standards under the Act.
- Each employee shall comply with occupational safety and health standards and all rules, regulations, and orders issued pursuant to the Act that are applicable to his or her own actions and conduct.

The significance of the General Duty Provision (section 5 (a)(1)) is that it authorizes the enforcement of a recognized industry safety or health standard when identified hazards are not covered by an existing OSHA standard. Only violations viewed as serious may be cited under the general duty clause. This interpretation of the general duty clause for providing a safe and healthful working environment adds new dimensions to the protection of employee health.

TABLE 30–A	Title 29 of the Code of Federal Regulations Dealing with OSHA
29 CFR Part 1902 to 1908	Enforcement and Consultation Regulations
29 CFR Part 1910	General Industry Standards
29 CFR Part 1911–1925	Miscellaneous Regulations
29 CFR Part 1915	Shipyard Standards
29 CFR Part 1917	Marine Terminal Standards
29 CFR Part 1918	Longshoring Standards
29 CFR Part 1926	Construction Standards
29 CFR Part 1928	Agriculture Standards

Key Provisions of the OSHAct

Some of the key provisions of the Act are:

- Ensure, insofar as possible, that every employee has safe and healthful working conditions.
- Require employers to maintain accurate records of exposures to potentially toxic materials or harmful physical agents that are required, under the various safety and health standards, to be monitored or measured, and inform employees of the monitoring results.
- Provide for employee walk-around or interview of employees during the inspection process.
- Provide procedures for investigating alleged violations at the request of any employee or employee representative, issuing citations, and assessing monetary penalties against employers.
- Empower the Secretary of Labor (through the Occupational Safety and Health Administration) to issue safety and health regulations and standards that have the force and effect of law.
- Provide for establishment of new rules and regulations for new or anticipated hazards to health and safety (section 6(b) of OSHAct).
- Establish a National Institute for Occupational Safety and Health (NIOSH), with the same right of entry as OSHA representatives, to undertake health studies of alleged hazardous conditions and to develop criteria to support revisions of health standards or recommendations to OSHA for new health standards.
- Provide up to 50/50 funding with states that wish to establish state programs that are at least as effective as the federal program in providing safe and healthful employment (section 18 of OSHAct).
- Provide funds under section 7(c) to state governments and other entities for the purpose of authorizing and enabling them to conduct on-site consultations for employers upon request.

OSHA JURISDICTION

Section 4 of the OSHAct grants OSHA jurisdiction over workplace safety in the United States and its territories. However, when Congress passed the Act, a few groups were given an exemption from OSHA coverage.

Private Sector Workers

OSHA covers most private sector employers and workers in all 50 states, the District of Columbia, and other U.S. jurisdictions either directly through federal OSHA or through an OSHA-approved state program. State-run programs must be at least as effective as the federal OSHA program.

State and Local Government Workers

State and local government workers are not covered by federal OSHA, but they do have protections in states that operate their own programs. The states and U.S. territories listed in Table 30–B have approved state programs.

Federal Government Workers

OSHA's protection applies to all federal agencies. Although OSHA does not fine federal agencies, it does monitor federal agencies and responds to workers' complaints and can cite federal agencies for failure to follow OSHA standards.

Not Covered by the OSHAct

Self-employed workers and workers whose hazards are regulated by another federal agency (for example, the Mine Safety and Health Administration, Federal Aviation Administration, and Coast Guard) are not covered by the OSHAct.

State Plans

Section 18 of the OSHAct encourages states to develop and operate their own job safety and health programs. OSHA approves and monitors state plans and provides up to 50 percent of an approved plan's operating costs. After the state plan is approved by OSHA, the administering agency must promulgate standards that are at least as effective as the federal standards, not only at the time of approval but on a continuing basis. Although most states adopt the federal standards verbatim, some modify and expand the federal standards to make them more applicable to the state's industries. States have the option to promulgate standards covering hazards not addressed by federal standards.

A state must conduct inspections to enforce its standards, cover public (state and local government) employees, and operate occupational safety and health training and education programs. In addition, most states provide free on-site consultation to help employers identify and correct workplace hazards. Such consultation may be provided either under the plan or through a special agreement under section 21(d) of the Act.

Federal OSHA officers submit periodic written reports to the Assistant Secretary of Labor addressing the quality of state performance as measured by established criteria. The data are gathered and analyzed on an ongoing basis, dialogue is carried on, and meetings are held routinely with state representatives to gather data and resolve problems identified by the measures. To ensure that the level of protection across states is consistent with the intent of the OSHAct, anyone finding inadequacies or other problems in the administration of a state's program may file a complaint about state program administration (CASPA) with the appropriate OSHA regional administrator as well. The

TABLE 30–B	U.S. States and Territories with OSHA-Approved State Worker Protection Programs
Alaska	New Mexico
Arizona	New York
California	North Carolina
Connecticut	Oregon
Hawaii	Puerto Rico
Illinois	South Carolina
Indiana	Tennessee
Iowa	Utah
Kentucky	Vermont
Maryland	Virgin Islands
Michigan	Virginia
Minnesota	Washington
Nevada	Wyoming
New Jersey	

NOTE: The Connecticut, Illinois, New Jersey, New York, and Virgin Islands plans cover public sector (state & local government) employment only. Federal OSHA covers private sector workers in these jurisdictions.

complainant's name is kept confidential. OSHA investigates all such complaints, and where complaints are found to be valid, requires appropriate corrective action on the part of the state.

OSHA STANDARDS

OSHA is granted the authority to promulgate standards that prescribe the methods employers are legally required to follow to protect their workers from hazards. Before OSHA can issue a standard, it must go through a very extensive and lengthy process that includes substantial public engagement, notice, and comment. The agency must show that a significant risk to workers exists and that there are feasible measures employers can take to protect their workers.

Construction, General Industry, Maritime, and Agriculture standards protect workers from a wide range of serious hazards. These standards limit the amount of hazardous chemicals workers can be exposed to, require the use of certain safe practices and equipment, and require employers to monitor certain workplace hazards. Examples of OSHA standards include requirements to provide fall protection, prevent trenching cave-ins, prevent exposure to some infectious diseases, ensure the safety of workers who enter confined spaces, prevent exposure to harmful substances such as asbestos and lead, put guards on machines, provide respirators or other safety equipment, and provide training for certain dangerous jobs. Employers must also comply with the General Duty Clause of the OSHAct. This clause requires employers to keep their workplaces free of serious recognized hazards and is generally cited when no specific OSHA standard applies to the hazard.

In thinking about how OSHA develops and applies standards to different hazards and industry sectors, it is useful to think about some broad categorical distinctions.

Design/specification standards vs. performance standards. A design or specification standard clearly lists the minimum engineering or construction criteria or other explicit elements deemed necessary to protect workers from a particular hazard. Examples of this type of standard are the detailed ventilation system design criteria contained in the ventilation standard (29 CFR 1910.94). Alternatively, a performance standard will more broadly articulate an objective (e.g., reduce or eliminate a worker's exposure to a particular hazard) and allow employers flexibility in how they accomplish that goal, provided that the goal is met. Examples of performance standards include the permissible exposure limits contained in the air contaminants standard (29 CFR 1910.1000).

Vertical standards vs. horizontal standards. A vertical standard applies only to a particular industry, with specifications that relate to individual operations. For example, 29 CFR 1910.261 (subpart R) applies only to pulp, paper, and paperboard mills. Alternatively, a horizontal standard applies to all workplaces in any industry where the particular hazard exists. These standards typically relate to broad hazards, such as Sanitation (29 CFR 1910.141) or Walking and Working Surfaces (29 CFR 1910 subpart D) or Bloodborne Pathogens (29 CFR 1910.1030).

Legal Requirements for OSHA Standards

Section 3(8) of the OSHAct defines an "occupational safety and health standard" as "a standard which requires conditions, or the adoption or use of one or more practices, means, methods, operations, or processes, reasonably necessary or appropriate to provide safe or healthful employment and places of employment." Section 6(b) of the Act authorizes the Secretary of Labor to "promulgate, modify, or revoke any occupational safety or health standard," provides procedures for doing so, and establishes criteria for those standards. Section 6(f) sets forth the standard of review of OSHA standards by federal courts of appeals. Read together, and as interpreted by a number of court decisions, these provisions establish the following legal requirements for OSHA standards:

1. Each standard must substantially reduce a significant risk of material harm.
2. Compliance must be technologically feasible in the sense that the protective measures being required already exist, can be brought into existence with avail-

able technology, or can be created with technology that can reasonably be developed.
3. Compliance must be economically feasible in the sense that the standard will not threaten the industry's long-term profitability or substantially alter its competitive structure.
4. Health standards must eliminate significant risk or reduce a significant risk to the extent feasible and safety standards must be highly protective.
5. Standards must employ the most cost-effective protective measures capable of reducing or eliminating significant risk.
6. Standards must be supported by substantial evidence in the rulemaking record and be consistent with prior agency practice or supported by some justification for departing from that practice.

The Rulemaking Roadmap

Step 1: Pre-Rulemaking Activities

Initiating events. There are many ways that a potentially significant health and safety concern can come to the attention of OSHA and be considered for a rulemaking action. Examples of events that can trigger the Agency to begin evaluating the nature and severity of a hazard are:

- agency initiatives (enforcement data, review of scientific data or new technologies, significant accidents, required reviews of existing regulations);
- the occurrence of a catastrophic national or international event with wide public attention;
- court decisions;
- petition by an interested party, such as a labor union or industry association;
- recommendation by another agency or advisory board, such as: NIOSH, the Environmental Protection Agency (EPA), under the Toxic Substances Control Act; and the Chemical Safety and Hazard Investigation Board (CSB); and
- recommendation by a committee, such as the National Advisory Committee on Occupational Safety and Health (NACOSH), Advisory Committee on Construction Safety and Health (ACCSH), and Maritime Advisory Committee for Occupational Safety and Health (MACOSH).

Determining whether a rule is needed. At this stage, the Agency reviews published scientific research; collects and reviews any additional available data (e.g., OSHA enforcement data); and conducts a preliminary assessment of the occupational hazard. The Agency preliminarily decides whether to pursue rulemaking or use another tool such as guidance or a change in enforcement policy that may be appropriate to effectively manage the hazard.

Preliminary rulemaking projects are announced to the public by listing them on the semiannual Unified Agenda that is published in the *Federal Register* in the spring and fall each year. The Agency then establishes a public rulemaking docket at www.regulations.gov, creating a single, accessible location for all public materials related to a particular rulemaking topic.

The Agency may develop either a Request for Information (RFI), to solicit information from the public on the topic under consideration for rulemaking, or an Advanced Notice of Proposed Rulemaking (ANPRM), which requests information needed to determine whether or not the Agency should develop a proposed rule. In either case, the document will be published in the *Federal Register* and the public usually has 60 to 90 days to submit comments. All comments received during this process become part of the rulemaking docket. Sometimes, the Agency may also hold a stakeholder meeting to gather more information and input during this stage of the rulemaking process. The purpose of this process is to allow the Agency to make a preliminary assessment of whether or not there is sufficient evidence to meet the legal requirements for an OSHA standard (e.g., significant risk, technological feasibility, etc.).

These publications and meetings do not necessarily imply that OSHA will pursue further rulemaking actions because a rulemaking action can be withdrawn at any time during the rulemaking process. The Agency may also determine that alternate approaches, such as new guidance, training, or a change in enforcement policy, may be sufficient to address the hazard.

Step 2: Development of the Proposed Rule

When the Agency determines that a rulemaking action is the best approach to control an occupational hazard, it will begin developing a Notice of Proposed Rulemaking (NPRM). In such cases, the Agency continues to gather information by conducting research activities, collecting and analyzing data, reviewing scientific literature, collaborating with topic experts, and examining similar standards and consensus standards. During this stage, the Agency also consults with internal OSHA directorates and with state and regional OSHA offices. OSHA encourages the public to participate in this stage through meetings with associations and unions, stakeholder meetings, and worksite visits, which employers can volunteer to host for the rulemaking team.

Because the OSHAct requires the Agency to establish the significance of risk, demonstrate standards are economically and technologically feasible, and demonstrate safety standards are reasonably necessary, the Agency conducts several separate analyses that often occur simultaneously. These analyses exchange relevant information throughout the process and entail a great deal of internal and external analysis, which may include consulting with experts. The five types of analyses are:

- *Risk Analysis:* The Agency conducts a risk assessment to preliminarily determine the "significance of risk" caused by the hazard. This analysis must demonstrate that the workplace hazard poses a significant risk and that a standard will substantially reduce that risk.

- *Health Effects Analysis:* For health-related rulemaking, an assessment of health effects is necessary to preliminarily establish that the hazard creates a "material impairment of health" for the workers exposed to the hazard. As stated in section 6(b)(5) of the OSHAct, the Agency must ensure that "no employee will suffer material impairment of health or functional capacity even if such employee has regular exposure to the hazard dealt with by such standard for the period of his working life."

- *Economic Analysis:*
  - OSHA is required to estimate economic costs and benefits of proposed and final rules, as included in Executive Orders 12866 and 13563.
  - The Regulatory Flexibility Act requires the Agency to assess the impact of standards on small entities. If a proposed or final rule may have a "significant impact on a substantial number of small entities," the Agency conducts a Small Business Advocacy Review Panel, in accordance with the Small Business Regulatory Enforcement Fairness Act (SBREFA). This panel is comprised of OSHA, the Small Business Administration, and the White House Office of Management and Budget. The panel solicits feedback from small business representatives to obtain information on the likely impact of a hazard regulation on their businesses. The Agency prepares a Preliminary Initial Regulatory Flexibility Analysis for the panel. A similar analysis (Initial Regulatory Flexibility Analysis) accompanies the proposed rule and a final analysis accompanies a final rule.

- *Technological Feasibility Analysis:* The OSHAct requires OSHA to promulgate standards to the extent feasible. Case law has defined how the Agency conducts a technological feasibility analysis for health standards. Generally, this analysis relies on information from a wide variety of published and unpublished sources to determine the extent to which workers are exposed to the hazard, current practices used by employers to control hazards, and the effectiveness of different approaches for hazard control. The Agency also uses information obtained from voluntary worksite visits in the development of the technological feasibility analysis.

- *Information Collection Analysis:* The Paperwork Reduction Act requires the Agency to prepare an

Information Collection Request (ICR) paperwork package if the proposed rule requires collection of information by employers. First, this analysis identifies actions employers must take to achieve compliance with collecting information under the proposed rule and reasons for collecting such information. Second, the analysis determines which of those actions constitute a paperwork burden by estimating burden hours and costs for employers. The public is given an opportunity to comment on the ICR when the proposed rule is published in Stage 3 of the rulemaking process.

These analyses assist OSHA by:

- establishing the need for a standard (i.e., demonstrating the hazard poses a significant risk and that a standard will substantially reduce that risk);
- identifying affected employers and employees;
- assessing current practices and procedures;
- determining the circumstances under which workers are exposed to a hazard;
- identifying cost-effective methods to reduce or eliminate worker exposure to the hazard;
- analyzing these methods to assess their technological and economic feasibility;
- developing regulatory alternatives; and
- evaluating the benefits (including estimating the reduction in the number of deaths, injuries, or illnesses that may occur) of each approach.

Peer review panels may be convened for the economic analyses, preliminary health effects analysis, and quantitative risk assessment. Compiling all of this information, the Agency drafts the regulatory text and preamble for the proposed rule in preparation for publication of the Notice of Proposed Rulemaking in the *Federal Register*.

As an alternative to the traditional methods of developing a proposed rule, the Agency may conduct negotiated rulemaking. Negotiated rulemaking is a process by which a proposed rule is developed by public committee members representing all interests that will be significantly affected by the rule; the committee also includes OSHA representatives. In order to aid identification of affected parties, the Agency publishes a *Federal Register* notice, requesting public comment on the preliminary list of interested parties. Through a trained mediator, the committee makes decisions by consensus, which generally requires unanimous concurrence among the interests represented. The Agency then uses the committee consensus as the basis for its proposed rule. Other participants and interested parties retain their rights of notice and comment, participation in an informal hearing (if requested), and judicial review. OSHA expects, however, that the preproposal consensus built by the committee will effectively narrow the issues in the rulemaking to only those that truly remain in controversy.

OMB Review of Proposed Rule. In accordance with Executive Order 12866, the Agency must submit all "significant regulatory actions" to the White House Office of Management and Budget (OMB), which has 90 days to review and comment on the proposed rule.

Step 3: Publication of the Proposed Rule

A Notice of Proposed Rulemaking (NPRM) proposes to create, change, or remove a regulation and contains a request for public comments. Once the NPRM is approved, it is published in the *Federal Register* and the public is usually given 60 to 90 days to comment. Once this written comment period is closed, public hearings may be held to solicit informal public feedback in the presence of an administrative law judge. Dates, location, and requirements for parties requesting time to testify at the hearing are all announced in the *Federal Register*. The post-hearing comment period, usually lasting from 60 to 90 days, is allowed for hearing participants to submit post-hearing comments and briefs, followed by formal closing of the record. The administrative law judge presiding over the public hearing establishes the post-hearing comment period and may extend these deadlines based on the circumstances.

As an alternative to publishing a traditional NPRM with a comment period, in rare cases, the Agency may instead choose to publish a direct final rule (DFR) with a companion NPRM. This option is chosen only when OSHA does not expect to receive significant adverse comments on the proposed rule within 30 days of publication. If no adverse comments are received, the final rule becomes effective. If any significant adverse comment or notice of intent to file an adverse comment is received, the DFR is withdrawn and the Agency continues the rulemaking as a "Notice and Comment" rulemaking through the NPRM.

Step 4: Analysis of the Rulemaking Record

This rulemaking stage is largely an internal process. Comments and exhibits submitted in response to the NPRM, as well as public hearing transcripts and post-hearing comments and evidence, which are all available in the public docket, are reviewed. The Agency responds to any significant comments and explains to the party its rationale for agreement or disagreement. A summary and analysis of the rulemaking record is prepared.

Step 5: Development of the Final Rule

A final rule creates, changes, removes, or affirms a regulation.

Preparation of final rule. To develop the final rule, OSHA's decision making relies upon substantial evidence in the rulemaking record. All information gathered during the pre-proposal and proposal stages is included in the public docket for review. Components of the technological and economic feasibility, paperwork, risk assessment, and, if relevant, health effects analyses are updated in response to any relevant data and comments received on the proposed rule. OSHA also uses this information, as necessary, to develop the final regulatory text and prepares the preamble to the final rule that explains the differences between the proposed rule and the final rule. Stakeholder comments are also taken into account and addressed in the preamble of the final rule.

OMB Review of Final Rule. Once received, the OMB has 90 days to review and comment on the final rule if it is determined to be a "significant regulatory action," in accordance with Executive Order 12866. Under this executive order, OMB also solicits comments from other agencies that may be affected by the final rule.

Step 6: Publication of Final Rule

Once the final rule is approved by OMB, it is published in the *Federal Register*. Once published, and in order for the final rule to become effective, it must also be filed with Congress and the Government Accountability Office (GAO), in accordance with the Congressional Review Act (CRA). If the Office of Management and Budget considers the rule to be "major" (e.g., to have a $100 million impact on the economy), OSHA must delay its effective date by 60 days after the publication date in the *Federal Register* or submission to Congress and GAO, whichever is later.

During this 60-day time period, GAO provides Congress with a brief report on OSHA's compliance with the procedural steps required by the various acts and executive orders governing the rulemaking process. The CRA also allows Congress to review every new federal regulation. Within 60 legislative days of publication, a member of Congress can introduce a resolution of disapproval that, if adopted by both Houses and signed by the president, can nullify the Agency's rule.

Section 6(f) of the OSHAct allows for a petition for judicial review. This allows any person who may be adversely affected by a standard a 59-day opportunity to challenge the final rule in the U.S. Court of Appeals.

Upon completion of the filing period, or judicial review, the standard is then published in the *Code of Federal Regulations (CFR)*.

Post-Promulgation Activities. Examples of post-promulgation activities include outreach with developed guidance materials, presentations on the regulation, news releases, compliance directives, and letters of interpretation.

ENFORCEMENT OF THE OSHACT

In accordance with Section 8 (Inspections, Investigations and Recordkeeping), Section 9 (Citations), and Section 10 (Procedures for Enforcement) of the OSHAct, OSHA is authorized to conduct inspections and, when alleged violations of safety and health standards are found, to issue citations and, when necessary, to assess penalties. Upon presenting appropriate credentials to the owner, operator, or agent in charge, OSHA is authorized to

1. Enter without delay and at reasonable times any factory, plant, establishment, construction site, or other area, workplace or environment where work is performed by an employee of an employer; and
2. Inspect and investigate during regular working hours and at other reasonable times, and within reasonable limits and in a reasonable manner, any such place of employment and all pertinent conditions, structures, machines, apparatus, devices, equipment, and materials therein, and to question privately any such employer, owner, operator, agent, or employee.

In conducting inspections and investigations, OSHA may require the attendance and testimony of witnesses and the production of evidence under oath. If necessary, OSHA can get a court order compelling an employer to comply with the OSHAct.

Workplace inspections and investigations are conducted by OSHA compliance safety and health officers who are safety and health professionals trained in the disciplines of safety and industrial hygiene. Inspections are always conducted without advance notice. There are, however, special circumstances under which OSHA may give notice to the employer, but such a notice will normally be less than 24 hours. These circumstances include the following:

- imminent danger situations that require correction as soon as possible
- accident investigations where the employer has notified the agency of a fatality or catastrophe
- inspections that must take place after regular business hours or that require special preparation
- cases where notice is required to ensure that the employer and employee representative or other personnel will be present
- cases where an inspection must be delayed for more than five working days when there is good cause
- situations in which the OSHA Area Director determines that advance notice would produce a more thorough or effective inspection

Employers who receive advance notice of an inspection must inform their employees' representative or arrange for OSHA to do so.

Enforcement Program Scheduling

OSHA has some discretion in setting the priorities and scheduling for enforcement activity. Accordingly, the Agency has established a priority system for conducting inspections. The system is designed to allocate available OSHA resources as effectively as possible to ensure that maximum feasible protection is provided to working men and women. Enforcement activity generally falls into two categories: programmed activity (e.g., planned or scheduled) and unprogrammed activity (e.g., activity as a result of unforeseen events).

Unprogrammed Activity:

- *Imminent Danger:* An imminent danger is any condition where there is reasonable certainty that a danger exists that can be expected to cause death or serious physical harm immediately or before the danger can be eliminated through normal enforcement procedures.
- *Fatality/Catastrophe:* Fatalities and accidents resulting in a death or hospitalization of three or more employees must be reported by the employer to OSHA within eight hours. OSHA investigates to determine the cause of these accidents and whether existing OSHA standards were violated.
- *Emergency Response:* OSHA may respond to significant natural and man-made disasters.
- *Complaint/Referral Processing:* The OSHAct gives each employee the right to request an OSHA inspection when the employee believes he or she is in imminent danger from a hazard or when he or she thinks that there is a violation of an OSHA standard that threatens physical harm. OSHA will maintain confidentiality if requested, inform the employee of any action it takes regarding complaints, and, if requested, hold an informal review of any decision not to inspect.
- *Whistleblower Complaints:* OSHA investigates all complaints of retaliation against employees who exercise their rights under one of the many laws that the Agency administers. These are OSHA's whistleblower protection provisions.
- *Follow-ups and Monitoring:* A follow-up inspection determines if the employer has corrected previously cited violations. If an employer has failed to abate a violation, the compliance officer informs the employer that he or she is subject to "Failure to Abate" alleged violations. This involves proposed additional daily penalties until the employer corrects the violation.

Programmed Inspections:

- *Site-Specific Targeting (SST) Program:* To achieve OSHA's goal of reducing the number of injuries and illnesses that occur at individual worksites, the Site-Specific Targeting (SST) program directs enforcement resources to those worksites where the highest rate of injuries and illness have occurred. The SST is OSHA's primary programmed inspection plan for nonconstruction worksites that have 40 or more employees. The SST Program is based on the data collected by the OSHA Data Initiative (ODI). The ODI collects injury and illness data from approximately 80,000 employers.
- *Construction Inspections:* Due to the mobility of the construction industry, the transitory nature of construction worksites, and the fact that construction worksites frequently involve more than one employer, inspections are scheduled from a list of active construction worksites rather than construction employers.
- *Special Emphasis Programs (SEPs):* Special Emphasis Programs provide for programmed inspections of establishments in industries with potentially high injury or illness rates that are not covered by other programmed inspection scheduling systems or, if covered, where the potentially high injury or illness rates are not addressed to the extent considered adequate under the specific circumstances. SEPs are also based on potential exposure to health hazards. Special emphasis programs may also be used to develop and implement alternative scheduling procedures or other departures from national procedures. Special emphasis programs can include National Emphasis Programs, Regional Emphasis Programs, and Local Emphasis Programs. OSHA develops National Emphasis Programs to focus outreach efforts and inspections on specific hazards in a workplace. Local Emphasis Programs (LEPs) and Regional Emphasis Programs (REPs) are types of special emphasis program in which one or more area offices of a region participate. LEPs and REPs are generally based on knowledge of local industry hazards or local industry injury and illness experience. The description of the particular Special Emphasis Program is identified by one or more of the following: a specific industry, trade/craft, substance or other hazard, type of workplace operation, or the type/kind of equipment.
- *Severe Violator Enforcement Program (SVEP):* This program concentrates Agency resources on inspecting employers who have demonstrated indifference to their OSHAct obligations by committing willful, repeated, or failure-to-abate violations. Enforcement actions for severe violator cases include mandatory follow-up inspections, increased company/corporate awareness of OSHA enforcement, corporate-wide agreements, where appropriate, enhanced settlement provisions, and federal court enforcement under Section 11(b) of the OSHAct.

Generally, priority of accomplishment and of assigning staff resources for inspection categories is:

Priority	Category
First	Imminent Danger
Second	Fatality/Catastrophe
Third	Complaints/Referrals
Fourth	Programmed Inspections

Enforcement Documents

OSHA uses a number of publicly available documents to guide the actions of its compliance officers and establish Agency policy (all documents are available on the OSHA website at: www.osha.gov). The Field Operations Manual (FOM) contains detailed instructions and policies on how to conduct field compliance operations, including: inspection procedures, policies for issuing violations, case file preparation and documentation, and policies for penalties and debt collection. The OSHA Technical Manual provides technical information and guidance on occupational safety and health topics. The content is based on currently available research publications, OSHA standards, and consensus standards. The purpose of the manual is to assist OSHA compliance officers in hazard recognition and to provide guidance in accident prevention. It also serves as a source of advice for compliance officers on safety and health issues. OSHA also issues compliance directives for each specific standard. The compliance directive establishes policies and provides clarifications to ensure uniform inspection procedures are followed when conducting inspections to enforce a particular standard.

Enforcement Responsibilities

The national OSHA office, through its technical and analytical units, coordinates the technical aspects of health and safety programming among the regions. Each regional office covers several states and is responsible for coordinating the technical aspects of the health program within the region. This responsibility includes, but is not limited to, providing guidelines for inspections, evaluating and assisting in contested cases, and guidance in using technical equipment in accordance with criteria provided by the national office. Regional offices also provide oversight for state plan states. The Area Director is the official who administers the field compliance program in the designated geographic area (e.g., a state or part of a state).

In state plan states, area directors and staffs are involved in monitoring the activities of the state staffs using performance measures for significant state plan activities. Simultaneously, the staffs in those offices enforce federal standards in workplaces not covered by the state plan, such as the maritime industry and military bases. All workers are covered in state plan states, including public sector, state, and local employees not covered in federal jurisdiction states.

Inspections are conducted in industries in accordance with priorities outlined earlier. An inspection can be either a complete survey of a particular workplace for all hazards, or a special survey, such as an accident investigation. Some inspections require a team effort because they involve more than one specialty. In such cases, the area director designates a team leader to coordinate the efforts.

Inspection Scope

Inspections, either programmed or unprogrammed, fall into one of two categories depending on the scope of the inspection:

- *Comprehensive:* A comprehensive inspection is a substantially complete and thorough inspection of all potentially hazardous areas of the establishment. An inspection may be deemed comprehensive even though, as a result of professional judgment, not all potentially hazardous conditions or practices within those areas are inspected.
- *Partial:* A partial inspection is one whose focus is limited to certain potentially hazardous areas, operations, conditions, or practices at the establishment.

Conduct of the Inspection

Pre-Inspection Preparation

Before the inspection, the compliance officer will become familiar with as many relevant facts as possible about the workplace, such as its inspection history, the nature of the business, and the particular standards that might apply. This preparation provides the compliance officer with knowledge of the potential hazards and industrial processes that he or she may encounter and aids in selecting appropriate personal protective equipment for use against these hazards during the inspection.

Presentation of the Compliance Officer's Credentials

When the OSHA compliance officer arrives at the establishment, he or she displays official credentials and asks to meet an appropriate employer representative. Employers should always ask to see the compliance officer's credentials. Employers may verify the OSHA federal or state compliance officer credentials by calling the nearest federal or state OSHA office. Compliance officers may not collect a penalty at the time of the inspection or promote the sale of a product or service at any time; anyone who attempts to do so is impersonating a government compliance officer and the employer should contact the FBI or local law enforcement officials immediately.

The Opening Conference

In the opening conference, the compliance officer explains how the establishment was selected and what the likely scope of the inspection will be. The compliance officer also will ascertain whether an OSHA-funded consultation visit is in progress or whether the facility is pursuing or has received an inspection exemption through the consultation program; if so, the inspection may be limited or terminated. The compliance officer will explain the purpose of the visit, the scope of the inspection, and the standards that apply. The compliance officer will give the employer information on how to get a copy of applicable safety and health standards as well as a copy of any employee complaint that may be involved (with the employee's name deleted, if the employee requests anonymity). The compliance officer will ask the employer to select an employer representative to accompany the compliance officer during the inspection. The compliance officer also gives an authorized employee representative the opportunity to attend the opening conference and accompany the compliance officer during the inspection.

At the beginning of inspection, the compliance officer usually requests a complete process flow diagram or facility layout or, if no layout chart is available, he or she can ask that a sketch be made to identify the operations, distribution of equipment including engineering controls, and approximate layout of the facility.

Review of Records

At the start of each inspection, the compliance officer will review the employer's injury and illness records for three prior calendar years. The compliance officer will use these data to calculate the Days Away, Restricted, or Transferred (DART) rate and to observe trends, potential hazards, types of operations, and work-related injuries. Additional records and information will also be requested, including: the OSHA-300 Logs, the total hours worked and the average number of employees for each year, and a roster of current employees. If there is a question regarding a specific case on the log, the officer may also request the OSHA-301s or equivalent form for that case. The compliance officer will also check if the establishment has an on-site medical facility and/or the location of the nearest emergency room where employees may be treated.

The compliance officer may also request a copy of the employer's Hazard Communication Program. Under OSHA's Hazard Communication Standard, employers must establish a written, comprehensive communication program that includes provisions for container labeling, Safety Data Sheets (SDSs), formerly Material Safety Data Sheets (MSDSs), and an employee training program. The program must contain a list of the hazardous chemicals in each work area and the means the employer will use to inform employees of the hazards associated with these chemicals. Where records of employee exposure to toxic substances and harmful physical agents are required, the compliance officer will examine them for compliance with the record-keeping requirements.

The Walk-through

After the opening conference, the compliance officer and accompanying representatives proceed through the establishment to inspect work areas for safety and health hazards. The compliance officer determines the route and duration of the inspection. While talking with employees, the compliance officer will make every effort to minimize any work interruptions. The compliance officer observes safety and health conditions and practices; consults with employees privately, if necessary; takes photos, videotapes, and instrument readings; examines records; collects air samples; measures noise levels; surveys existing engineering controls; and monitors employee exposure to toxic fumes, gases, and dusts. Summaries of the results are provided on request to the appropriate employees, including those exposed or likely to be exposed to a hazard, employer representatives, and employee representatives.

The compliance officer may consult employees during the inspection tour. He or she may stop and question workers, in private, about safety and health conditions and practices in their workplaces. Each employee is protected under the Act from discrimination by the employer for exercising his or her safety and health rights. An inspection tour may cover part or all of an establishment, even if the inspection resulted from a specific complaint, fatality, or catastrophe. If the compliance officer finds a violation in open view, he or she may ask permission to expand the inspection. The compliance officer keeps all trade secrets observed confidential.

During the course of the inspection, the compliance officer will point out to the employer any unsafe or unhealthful working conditions observed. At the same time, the compliance officer will discuss possible corrective action if the employer so desires. Some apparent violations detected by the compliance officer can be corrected immediately. When the employer corrects them on the spot, the compliance officer records such corrections to help in judging the employer's good faith in compliance. Although corrected, the apparent violations will serve as the basis for a citation and, if appropriate, a notice of proposed penalty. OSHA may reduce the penalties for some types of violations if they are corrected immediately.

Evaluating the Employer's Occupational Safety and Health System

The compliance officer will request and evaluate information on the following aspects of the employer's occupational safety and health system as it relates to the scope of the inspection.

Monitoring. The employer's system for monitoring safety and health hazards in the establishment should include a program for self-inspection. The inspection will address the employer's maintenance schedules and inspection records. Additional information shall be obtained concerning activities such as sampling and calibration procedures, ventilation measurements, preventive maintenance procedures for engineering controls, and laboratory services. Compliance with the monitoring requirements of any applicable substance-specific health standards shall be determined.

Medical. The compliance officer will determine whether the employer provides the employees with preplacement and periodic medical examinations. The medical examination protocol will be requested from the employer to determine the extent of the medical examinations and, if applicable, compliance with the medical surveillance requirements of any applicable substance-specific health standards.

Records program. The inspection will evaluate the extent of the employer's records program, such as whether records pertaining to employee exposure and medical records are being maintained in accordance with 29 CFR 1910.1020.

Engineering controls. The compliance officer will identify any engineering controls present, including substitution, isolation, general dilution and local exhaust ventilation, and equipment modification.

Work practice and administrative controls. The inspection will address any control techniques, including personal hygiene, housekeeping practices, employee job rotation, employee training, and education.

Personal protective equipment. An effective personal protective equipment program should exist in the plant. A detailed evaluation of the program will be documented to determine compliance with specific standards.

Regulated areas. The compliance officer will investigate adherence with the requirements for regulated areas as specified by certain standards. Regulated areas must be clearly identified and known to all appropriate employees. The regulated area designation must be maintained according to the prescribed criteria of the applicable standard.

Emergency action plan. The inspection will evaluate the employer's emergency action plan when such a plan is required by a specific standard. The compliance officer will evaluate if potential emergency conditions are included in the written plan, emergency conditions are explained to employees, and there is a training program for the protection of affected employees, including use and maintenance of personal protective equipment.

The Closing Conference

At the conclusion of the inspection, the compliance officer conducts a closing conference with the employer, employees, and/or the employees' representative. The compliance officer gives the employer and all other parties involved a copy of *Employer Rights and Responsibilities Following an OSHA Inspection* (publication OSHA 3000) for their review and discussion. The compliance officer discusses with the employer all unsafe or unhealthful conditions observed during the inspection and indicates all apparent violations for which he or she may issue or recommend a citation, and a proposed penalty. The compliance officer will not indicate any specific proposed penalties but will inform the employer of appeal rights.

During the closing conference, the employer may wish to produce records to show compliance efforts and provide information that can help OSHA determine how much time may be needed to abate an alleged violation. When appropriate, the compliance officer may hold more than one closing conference. This is usually necessary when the inspection includes an evaluation of health hazards, after a review of additional laboratory reports, or after the compliance officer obtains additional factual evidence while concluding an accident investigation. If an employee representative does not participate in either the opening or the closing conference held with the employer, the compliance officer holds a separate discussion with the employee representative, if requested, to discuss matters of direct interest to employees.

Results of an Inspection

After the compliance officer reports findings, the Area Director determines whether he or she will issue citations and/or propose penalties.

Citations. Citations inform the employer and employees of the regulations and standards alleged to have been violated and of the proposed length of time set to correct alleged hazards. The employer will receive citations and notices of proposed penalties by certified mail. The employer must post a copy of each citation at or near the place a violation occurred for three days or until the violation is abated, whichever is longer.

Penalties. These are the types of violations that may be cited and the penalties that may be proposed:

- *Other-Than-Serious Violation:* A violation that has a direct relationship to job safety and health, but probably would not cause death or serious physical harm. The agency may adjust the penalty for an other-than-serious violation downward by as much as 95 percent, depending on the employer's good faith (demonstrated efforts to comply with the Act), history of previous violations, and size of business.

- *Serious Violation:* A violation where there is a substantial probability that death or serious physical harm could result. OSHA may adjust a penalty for a serious violation downward based on the employer's good faith, history of previous violations, and size of business.

- *Willful Violation:* A violation that the employer intentionally and knowingly commits. The employer is aware that a hazardous condition exists, knows that the condition violates a standard or other obligation of the Act, and makes no reasonable effort to eliminate it. An employer who is convicted in a criminal proceeding of a willful violation of a standard that has resulted in the death of an employee may be fined or imprisoned up to six months, or both. A second conviction doubles the possible term of imprisonment.

- *Repeated Violation:* A violation of any standard, regulation, rule, or order where, upon reinspection, a substantially similar violation is found and the original citation has become a final order. Violations can bring fines for each such violation within the previous three years. To calculate repeated violations, OSHA adjusts the initial penalty for the size and then multiplies by a factor of 2, 5, or 10 depending on the size of the business.

- *Failure-to-Abate:* Failure to correct a prior violation may increase a civil penalty for each day that the violation continues beyond the prescribed abatement date.

- De Minimis *Conditions: De minimis* conditions are those where an employer has implemented a measure different than one specified in a standard that has no direct or immediate relationship to safety or health.

Citations and penalty procedures may differ somewhat in states with their own occupational safety and health programs.

Citations issued under the general duty requirements. Section 5(a)(1) of the Act requires that "Each employer shall furnish to each of his employees employment and a place of employment which are free from recognized hazards that are causing or are likely to cause death or serious physical harm to his employees." In evaluating whether an employer may be cited under the general duty requirements, the Review Commission and court precedent have established that the following elements are necessary to prove a violation of the general duty clause:

- The employer failed to keep the workplace free of a hazard to which employees of that employer were exposed.

- The hazard was recognized.
- The hazard was causing or was likely to cause death or serious physical harm.
- There was a feasible and useful method to correct the hazard.

A general duty citation must involve both the presence of a serious hazard and exposure of the cited employer's own employees.

Appealing OSHA Citations
Appeals by Employees
If an employee complaint initiates an inspection, the employee or authorized employee representative may request an informal review of any decision not to issue a citation. Employees may not contest citations, amendments to citations, proposed penalties, or lack of penalties. They may, however, contest the time allowed for abatement of a hazardous condition. They also may contest an employer's "Petition for Modification of Abatement," which requests an extension of the proposed abatement period. Employees must contest the petition within 10 working days of its posting or within 10 working days after an authorized employee representative receives a copy. Employees may request an informal conference with OSHA to discuss any issues raised by an inspection, citation, notice of proposed penalty, or employer's notice of intention to contest.

Appeals by Employers
Within 15 working days of receiving a citation, an employer who wishes to contest must submit a written objection to OSHA. The OSHA Area Director forwards the objection to the Occupational Safety and Health Review Commission (OSHRC), which operates independently of OSHA. When issued a citation and notice of proposed penalty, an employer may request an informal meeting with OSHA's Area Director to discuss the case. OSHA encourages employers to have informal conferences with the Area Director if the employer has issues arising from the inspection that he or she wishes to discuss or provide additional information. The Area Director is authorized to enter into settlement agreements that revise citations and penalties to avoid prolonged legal disputes and result in speedier hazard abatement. (Alleged violations contested before OSHRC do not need to be corrected until the contest is ruled upon by OSHRC.)

Petition for Modification of Abatement
After receiving a citation, the employer must correct the cited hazard by the abatement date unless he or she contests the citation or abatement date. Factors beyond the employer's control, however, may prevent the completion of corrections by that date. In such a situation, the employer

who has made a good-faith effort to comply may file a petition to modify the abatement date. The written petition must specify the steps taken to achieve compliance, the additional time needed to comply, the reasons additional time is needed, and interim steps taken to safeguard employees against the cited hazard during the intervening period. The employer must certify that he or she posted a copy of the petition in a conspicuous place at or near each place where a violation occurred and that the employee representative received a copy of the petition.

Notice of Contest

If the employer decides to contest the citation, the abatement period, or the proposed penalty, they have 15 working days from the time the citation and proposed penalty are received to notify the OSHA Area Director in writing. Failure to do so results in the citation and proposed penalty becoming a final order of the OSHRC without further appeal. An orally expressed disagreement will not suffice. This written notification is called a "Notice of Contest." Although there is no specific format for the Notice of Contest, it must clearly identify the employer's basis for filing— the citation, notice of proposed penalty, abatement period, or notification of failure to correct violations. The employer must give a copy of the Notice of Contest to the employees' authorized representative. If any affected employees are not represented by a recognized bargaining agent, the employer must post a copy of the notice in a prominent location in the workplace or give it personally to each unrepresented employee.

Review Procedure

If the employer files a written Notice of Contest within the required 15 working days, the OSHA Area Director forwards the case to OSHRC. The commission is an independent agency not associated with OSHA or the Department of Labor. The commission assigns the case to an administrative law judge. OSHRC may schedule a hearing at a public place near the employer's workplace. The employer and the employee have the right to participate in the hearing; the OSHRC does not require them to be represented by attorneys. Once the administrative law judge has ruled, any party to the case may request a further review by OSHRC. Any of the three OSHRC commissioners also may, at their own motion, bring a case before the commission for review. Employers and other parties may appeal commission rulings to the appropriate U.S. Court of Appeals.

Appeals in States and Territories with OSHA-Approved Plans

States with their own occupational safety and health programs have a state system for review and appeal of citations,

penalties, and abatement periods. The procedures are generally similar to federal OSHA's, but a state review board or equivalent authority hears cases.

EMPLOYER RESPONSIBILITIES

Employers must

- find and correct safety and health hazards and follow all relevant OSHA standards;
- inform employees about chemical hazards through training, labels, alarms, color-coded systems, chemical information sheets, and other methods;
- notify OSHA within eight hours of a workplace fatality or when three or more workers are hospitalized;
- provide required personal protective equipment at no cost to workers (with certain very limited exceptions);
- keep accurate records of work-related injuries and illnesses;
- post OSHA citations, injury and illness summary data, and the OSHA "Job Safety and Health—It's The Law" poster in the workplace where workers will see them; and
- not discriminate or retaliate against any worker for using their rights under the law.

Employer Reporting Requirements

All employers must report to OSHA within eight hours of learning about

- the death of any employee from a work-related incident; and
- the inpatient hospitalization of three or more employees as a result of a work-related incident.

All work-related amputations must be reported within 24 hours. Amputations include loss of a limb or other external body part, including a fingertip. For an injury to be classified as an amputation, bone must be lost.

In addition, employers must report all fatal heart attacks that occur at work. Deaths from motor vehicle accidents on public streets (except those in a construction work zone) and in accidents on commercial airplanes, trains, subways, or buses do not need to be reported. These reports may be made by telephone or in person to the nearest OSHA area office listed at www.osha.gov or by calling OSHA's toll-free number, (800) 321-OSHA (6742). Employers may be subject to other reporting requirements in other OSHA standards as well.

Employer Record-Keeping Requirements

The Occupational Safety and Health Act of 1970 (OSHAct) requires covered employers to prepare and maintain records of occupational injuries and illnesses. OSHA is responsible for administering the record-keeping system established by the Act. The OSHAct and record-keeping regulations provide specific recording and reporting requirements, which comprise the framework for the nationwide occupational safety and health recording system.

Under this system, it is essential that data recorded by employers be uniform and accurate to ensure the consistency and validity of the statistical data that is used by OSHA for many purposes, including inspection targeting, performance measurement, standards development, resource allocation, Voluntary Protection Program (VPP) and Safety and Health Recognition Program (SHARP) eligibility, and "low-hazard" industry exemptions. The data will also aid employers, employees, compliance officers, and consultants in analyzing the safety and health environment at the employer's establishment.

EMPLOYEE RIGHTS

Workers are entitled to working conditions that do not pose a risk of serious harm. To help ensure a safe and healthful workplace, OSHA also provides workers with the right to
* ask OSHA to inspect their workplace;
* use their rights under the law without retaliation and discrimination;
* receive information and training about hazards, methods to prevent harm, and the OSHA standards that apply to their workplace (training must be in a language employees can understand);
* get copies of test results done to find hazards in the workplace;
* review records of work-related injuries and illnesses; and
* get copies of their medical records.

The OSHA Whistleblower Program
OSHA administers the whistleblower protection provisions of 21 whistleblower protection statutes, including Section 11(c) of the Occupational Safety and Health Act (OSHAct), which prohibits any person from discharging or in any manner retaliating against any employee because the employee has exercised rights under the OSHAct. Rights afforded by the OSHAct include employee participation in safety and health activities, such as complaining to OSHA and seeking an OSHA inspection, participating in an OSHA inspection, participating or testifying in any proceeding related to an OSHA inspection, and reporting a work-related injury, illness, or fatality. The 20 other whistleblower protection statutes administered by OSHA protect employees who report violations of various airline, commercial motor carrier, consumer product, environmental, financial reform, food safety, health care reform, nuclear, pipeline, public transportation agency, railroad, maritime, and securities laws.

A complaint of retaliation filed with OSHA must

allege that the complainant engaged in protected activity, the respondent knew about that activity, the respondent subjected the complainant to an adverse action, and the protected activity motivated or contributed to the adverse action. Adverse action is generally defined as any action that would dissuade a reasonable employee from engaging in protected activity. Depending upon the circumstances of the case, adverse action can include the following:
* firing or laying off
* blacklisting
* demoting
* denying overtime or promotion
* disciplining
* denial of benefits
* failure to hire or rehire
* intimidation

TABLE 30-C	21 Whistleblower Protection Statutes Enforced by OSHA
29 U.S.C. §660	Section 11(c) of the Occupational Safety and Health Act
49 U.S.C. §31105	Surface Transportation Assistance Act (STAA)
15 U.S.C. §2651	Asbestos Hazard Emergency Response Act (AHERA)
46 U.S.C. §80507	International Safe Container Act (ISCA)
42 U.S.C. §300j-9(i)	Safe Drinking Water Act (SDWA)
33 U.S.C. §1367	Federal Water Pollution Control Act (FWPCA)
15 U.S.C. §2622	Toxic Substances Control Act (TSCA)
42 U.S.C. §6971	Solid Waste Disposal Act (SWDA)
42 U.S.C. §7622	Clean Air Act (CAA)
42 U.S.C. §9610	Comprehensive Environmental Response, Compensation and Liability Act (CERCLA)
42 U.S.C. §5851	Energy Reorganization Act (ERA)
49 U.S.C. §42121	Wendell H. Ford Aviation Investment and Reform Act for the 21st Century (AIR21)
18 U.S.C.A. §1514	Sarbanes-Oxley Act (SOX) Amendments to SOX, enacted July 21, 2010 – Sections 922 and 929A of the Dodd-Frank Act (DFA)
49 U.S.C. §60129	Pipeline Safety Improvement Act (PSIA)
49 U.S.C. §20109	Federal Railroad Safety Act (FRSA)
6 U.S.C. §1142	National Transit Systems Security Act (NTSSA)
15 U.S.C. §2087	Consumer Product Safety Improvement Act (CPSIA)
P.L. 111-148	Section 1558 of the Affordable Care Act (ACA)
12 U.S.C.A. §5567	Section 1057 of the Dodd-Frank Wall Street Reform and Consumer Protection Act of 2010
46 U.S.C. §2114 (SPA)	Seaman's Protection Act, as amended by Section 611 of the Coast Guard Authorization Act of 2010, P.L. 111-281
P.L. 111-353	Section 402 of the FDA Food Safety Modernization Act (FSMA)

- making threats
- reassignment affecting prospects for promotion
- reducing pay or hours

The 21 statutes enforced by OSHA are listed in Table 30–C.

OUTREACH, EDUCATION AND TRAINING, AND COMPLIANCE ASSISTANCE

OSHA's web site provides extensive information about the Agency as well as standards, interpretations, directives, technical advisers, compliance assistance, and additional information. The site also includes electronic assistance tools, such as eTools and interactive Expert Advisors, information on specific health and safety topics, videos, and other information for employers and employees. The OSHA website address is www.osha.gov. In addition, OSHA's website includes several special features:

- Spanish-language pages that provide workplace safety and health information in Spanish
- a Small Business page, designed to increase awareness among small business owners about their responsibilities under the OSHAct, and resources to help them at www.osha.gov/smallbusines;
- a Compliance Assistance page that provides a portal to OSHA's compliance assistance resources and information on OSHA's cooperative programs
- a Workers page that explains employees' rights and responsibilities under the OSHAct
- a Teen Workers page that addresses safety and health issues for employees under the age of 18
- an OSHA Training Institute Education Centers page that provides information such as course listings, events, FAQs, and a list of all the Education Centers in each OSHA region

These and other web-based resources are available at www.osha.gov.

OSHA Training and Education

OSHA's Training Institute in Arlington Heights, IL, provides basic and advanced courses in safety and health for federal and state compliance officers, state consultants, federal agency personnel, and private sector employers, employees, and their representatives. The OSHA Training Institute also has established OSHA Training Institute Education Centers (not funded by OSHA) to address the increased demand for its courses from the private sector and from other federal agencies. These centers are nonprofit colleges, universities, and other organizations that have been selected after a competition for participation in the program.

The education centers help administer OSHA's Outreach Training Program—the agency's primary way to train workers in the basics of occupational safety and health. Those who complete a one-week OSHA training course are authorized to teach 10-hour or 30-hour courses in construction or general industry safety and health standards. These individuals go on to train thousands more students each year.

OSHA also provides funds to nonprofit organizations, through grants, to conduct workplace training and education in subjects where OSHA believes there is a lack of workplace training. Grants are awarded annually. Grant recipients are expected to contribute 20 percent of the total grant cost.

Compliance Assistance Materials

OSHA's Compliance Assistance Specialists provide general information about OSHA standards and compliance assistance resources. They respond to requests for help from a variety of groups, including small businesses, trade associations, union locals, and community and faith-based groups. There is one Compliance Assistance Specialist in each OSHA Area Office in states under federal jurisdiction.

OSHA Publications

OSHA has an extensive publications program that produces booklets, fact sheets, and cards detailing various facets of OSHA policy and regulations. Many publications are now available in Spanish as well as English to ensure that Spanish-speaking employees also have access to important workplace safety and health information. All OSHA publications can be downloaded at no cost from the agency's website at www.osha.gov. In addition, most are available in hard-copy form, some at no cost from OSHA and others for purchase from the U.S. Government Printing Office.

OSHA and Emergency Response

As part of the National Response Framework (NRF), OSHA is the lead agency for the Worker Safety and Health Support Annex. The Annex provides federal support to federal, state, tribal, and local response and recovery organizations in ensuring response and recovery worker safety and health during incidents requiring a coordinated federal response. During these types of emergency responses, OSHA helps ensure that controls are in place and workers have the necessary equipment and training to protect their safety and health. Tasks can include the following:

- providing occupational safety and health technical advice and support
- identifying and assessing health and safety hazards and analysis of the incident environment, including response and recovery worker safety monitoring, as necessary

- assessing response and recovery worker safety and health resource needs and identifying sources for those assets
- providing technical assistance to include industrial hygiene expertise, occupational safety and health expertise, engineering expertise, and occupational medicine
- managing the development and implementation of a site-specific health and safety plan
- managing, monitoring, and providing support and assistance in the monitoring of response and recovery worker safety and health hazards
- managing, monitoring, and/or providing technical advice and support in developing, implementing, and/or monitoring a personal protective equipment (PPE) program for the incident, including the selection, use, and decontamination of PPE
- providing technical assistance and support in coordinating the collection and management of data such as response and recovery worker exposure data, or OSHA 300 (or equivalent) accident/injury documentation data to identify trends and facilitate data-sharing among response organizations
- coordinating and providing incident-specific response and recovery worker training
- communicating worker safety and health information to response and recovery workers, labor unions, employers, contractors, and other organizations, especially those providing skilled support
- providing technical assistance and support in the development and distribution of materials for the prevention, awareness, and abatement of safety and health hazards

OSHA Services for Employers

OSHA offers free confidential advice. Several programs and services help employers identify and correct job hazards as well as improve their injury and illness prevention programs.

Free On-Site Consultation

OSHA provides a free on-site consultation service for small businesses with fewer than 250 workers at a site (and no more than 500 employees nationwide). On-site consultation services are separate from enforcement and do not result in penalties or citations. Each year, OSHA makes more than 30,000 consultation visits to small businesses to provide free compliance assistance. By working with the OSHA Consultation Program, certain exemplary employers may request participation in OSHA's Safety and Health Recognition Program, SHARP.

Compliance Assistance

OSHA has Compliance Assistance Specialists throughout the nation who can provide general information about OSHA standards and compliance assistance resources. More information is available at local OSHA offices.

Cooperative Programs

OSHA offers cooperative programs to help prevent fatalities, injuries, and illnesses in the workplace.

- *Alliance Program:* OSHA works with groups committed to worker safety and health to develop compliance assistance resources and to educate workers and employers.
- *Challenge Program:* This program helps employers and workers improve their safety and health management systems and implement an effective system to prevent fatalities, injuries, and illnesses.
- *OSHA Strategic Partnership Program (OSPP):* Partnerships are formalized through tailored agreements designed to encourage, assist, and recognize partner efforts to eliminate serious hazards and achieve model workplace safety and health practices.
- *Voluntary Protection Programs (VPP):* The VPP recognize employers and workers in private industry and federal agencies who have implemented effective safety and health management systems and maintain injury and illness rates below national Bureau of Labor Statistics averages for their respective industries. In VPP, management, labor, and OSHA work cooperatively and proactively to prevent fatalities, injuries, and illnesses.

NATIONAL INSTITUTE FOR OCCUPATIONAL SAFETY AND HEALTH

The mission of the National Institute for Occupational Safety and Health (NIOSH) is to generate new knowledge in the field of occupational safety and health and to transfer that knowledge into practice for the betterment of workers. To accomplish this mission, NIOSH conducts scientific research, develops guidance and authoritative recommendations, disseminates information, and responds to requests for workplace health hazard evaluations. NIOSH is the principal federal agency engaged in research to eliminate on-the-job hazards to the health and safety of American workers. It was established within the Department of Health, Education, and Welfare (now the Department of Health and Human Services) under the Occupational Safety and Health Act of 1970. Additionally, the Federal Mine Safety and Health Amendments Act of 1977 delegated further authority to NIOSH for coal mine health research. Administratively, NIOSH is located within the Centers for Disease Control and Prevention.

NIOSH is responsible for identifying occupational safety and health hazards and for recommending changes in the regulations limiting them. NIOSH has a professionally diverse staff of scientists from the fields of epidemiology, medicine, industrial hygiene, safety, psychology, engineering, chemistry, statistics, economics, and administration. In addition to the research NIOSH conducts in its own laboratories, NIOSH also serves as the major support for occupational safety and health research in academic centers in the United States. NIOSH headquarters are in Washington, DC, and Atlanta, Georgia, with staff in Anchorage, Alaska; Cincinnati, Ohio; Denver, Colorado; Morgantown, West Virginia; Pittsburgh, Pennsylvania; and Spokane, Washington.

National Occupational Research Agenda

In 1996, NIOSH launched the National Occupational Research Agenda (NORA), an innovative public-private partnership to establish priorities for occupational safety and health research both at NIOSH and throughout the country. During its first decade, NORA advanced safety and health knowledge in 21 scientific areas by emphasizing priority-driven research. In 2006, NORA began its second decade by focusing national research on the problems of highest relevance to workers, employers, and occupational safety and health practitioners in the major industrial sectors of agriculture, construction, health care, manufacturing, mining, services, trade, and transportation. NIOSH serves as the steward of NORA and facilitates the work of stakeholder-driven NORA Sector Councils, which have developed roadmaps to direct research and service activities in each sector. It is NIOSH's job to ensure that NORA research activities are relevant to the problems of today's workplaces, conducted using the highest quality science, and having a measurable impact on improving the lives of workers.

Moving Research into Practice

To ensure that NORA research has impact on the lives of workers and their families, NIOSH uses a research-to-practice focus for all its intramural and extramural activities. Through its Research-to-Practice (r2p) Initiative, NIOSH works closely with partners to transfer and translate research findings, technologies, and information into highly effective prevention practices and products that can be adopted immediately in the workplace.

Prevention through Design

Many workplace fatalities and injuries are caused by poor design of equipment and processes, yet design standards for occupational safety and health are few. In 2007, NIOSH began a national initiative called Prevention through Design (PtD) to eliminate hazards from the workplace that result from design flaws. PtD helps engineers and architects, employers, owners, and others to recognize design issues that affect worker safety and to incorporate safe design, equipment, and work practices early in the design process and as new facilities are built or existing ones are renovated.

Total Worker Health™

(Formerly the WorkLife Initiative): A comprehensive organizational strategy that integrates traditional occupational safety and health protection efforts with health promotion and other workplace activities to prevent illness and injury, regardless of cause, so that all workers have opportunities to achieve optimal levels of health and well-being. NIOSH funded and partnered with three national WorkLife Centers of Excellence to further explore and research these concepts (http://www.cdc.gov/niosh/TWH/centers.html). NIOSH will begin building an intramural research program focused on evolving the WorkLife program concept for integration of health and safety protection and health and wellness promotion into a comprehensive intramural program for Total Worker Health™.

Health Hazard Evaluation Program

The Health Hazard Evaluation (HHE) Program is at the front line of NIOSH research and service. In response to requests from workers (or their representatives), employers, and other government agencies, HHE scientists conduct workplace assessments to determine if workers are exposed to hazardous materials or harmful conditions and whether these exposures are affecting worker health. NIOSH evaluates the workplace environment and the health of employees by reviewing records and conducting on-site environmental sampling, epidemiologic surveys, and medical testing.

Training

NIOSH funds programs to support occupational safety and health research and education through 17 regional university-based Education and Research Centers; eight Centers for Agricultural Disease and Injury Research, Education, and Prevention; and 31 Training Project grants that train occupational health professionals and researchers to help meet the increasing demand for occupational physicians, occupational nurses, industrial hygienists, and safety professionals. The NIOSH-supported centers also conduct research and prevention projects to address the nation's occupational health and safety problems.

NIOSH Recommendations

Acting under the authority of the Occupational Safety and Health Act of 1970 and the Federal Mine Safety and Health Act of 1977, NIOSH develops and periodically revises recommended exposure limits (RELs) for hazardous substances or conditions in the workplace. NIOSH also recommends appropriate preventive measures to reduce or eliminate the adverse health and safety effects of these hazards. To formulate these recommendations, NIOSH evaluates all known and available medical, biological, engineering, chemical, trade, and other information relevant to the hazard. These recommendations are then published and transmitted to OSHA and the Mine Safety and Health Administration (MSHA) for use in promulgating legal standards.

NIOSH recommendations are published in a variety of documents. The following criteria documents recommend workplace exposure limits and appropriate preventive measures to reduce or eliminate adverse health effects and accidental injuries.

- *Current Intelligence Bulletins (CIBs)* are issued to disseminate new scientific information about occupational hazards. A CIB may draw attention to a formerly unrecognized hazard, report new data on a known hazard, or present information on hazard control.
- *Alerts, Special Hazard Reviews, Occupational Hazard Assessments, and Technical Guidelines* support and complement the other standards development activities of the Institute. Their purpose is to assess the safety and health problems associated with a given agent or hazard (e.g., the potential for injury or for carcinogenic, mutagenic, or teratogenic effects) and to recommend appropriate control and surveillance methods. Although these documents are not intended to supplant the more comprehensive criteria documents, they are prepared to assist OSHA and MSHA in the formulation of regulations.
- *The NIOSH Pocket Guide to Chemical Hazards* is intended as a source of general industrial hygiene information for workers, employers, and occupational health professionals. The *Pocket Guide* presents key information and data in abbreviated tabular form for 677 chemicals or substance groupings (e.g., manganese compounds, tellurium compounds, inorganic tin compounds, etc.) that are found in the work environment. The industrial hygiene information found in the *Pocket Guide* should help users recognize and control occupational chemical hazards.

In addition to these publications, NIOSH periodically presents testimony before various congressional committees and at OSHA and MSHA rulemaking hearings.

Respirator Certification

NIOSH specifies minimum approval requirements for respiratory protective devices in Title 42 Code of Federal Regulations (CFR) Part 84. NIOSH reviews respirator approval applications, which contain technical specifications, drawings, and other related information. NIOSH also inspects, examines and tests the respirators to determine that the applicable requirements are met to ensure that the respirator is capable of providing the expected level of protection for workers. The use of NIOSH-approved respirators is required in OSHA's respiratory protection standard (29 CFR 1910.134). NIOSH also maintains an extensive respirator research portfolio to ensure that the development of new personal protective equipment keeps pace with employer and worker needs as work settings and worker populations change and new technologies emerge.

OTHER U.S. GOVERNMENT REGULATORY AGENCIES

In addition to OSHA and NIOSH, there are other federal government regulatory agencies and commissions.

Mine Safety and Health Administration

The Federal Mine Safety and Health Amendments Act of 1977 (Mine Act) provides that MSHA inspectors shall inspect each surface mine at least two times a year and each underground mine at least four times a year (seasonal or intermittent operations are inspected less frequently) to determine whether there is compliance with health and safety standards or with any citation, order, or decision issued under the Mine Act and whether an imminent danger exists. If violations of safety or health standards are found, inspectors will issue citations to the mine operators.

MSHA performs other important mandatory activities under the Mine Act. These include, but are not limited to

- investigating mine accidents, complaints of retaliatory discrimination filed by miners, hazardous condition complaints, knowing or willful (criminal) violations committed by agents of mine operators, and petitions for modification of mandatory safety standards;
- developing improved mandatory safety and health standards;
- assessing and collecting civil monetary penalties for violations of mine safety and health standards; and
- reviewing for approval mine operators' mining plans and education and training programs.

Other activities that support the mandates of the Mine Act include

- maintaining the National Mine Health and Safety Academy to train inspectors, technical support personnel, and mining industry personnel;
- approving and certifying certain mining products for use in underground coal, gassy metal, and nonmetal mines to ensure they do not cause a fire or explosion;
- providing technical assistance to mine operators in meeting the requirements of the Mine Act;
- providing assistance to mine operators in improving their

education and training programs;

- cooperating with states in the development of mine safety and health programs;
- making grants to states in which mining takes place; and
- overseeing rescue and recovery operations.

MSHA's inspection presence does not, by itself, result in violation-free mines. MSHA therefore encourages voluntary compliance with the Mine Act through training, technical assistance, and other nonenforcement activities.

Federal Mine Safety and Health Review Commission

The Federal Mine Safety and Health Review Commission is an independent adjudicative agency that provides administrative trial and appellate review of legal disputes arising under the Federal Mine Safety and Health Amendments Act of 1977 (Mine Act). Under the Mine Act, the Department of Labor issues regulations covering health and safety in the nation's mines. Federal mine inspectors employed by the Department's Mine Safety and Health Administration (MSHA) enforce these regulations by issuing citations and orders to mine operators. The Commission is concerned solely with the adjudication of disputes under the Mine Act, including the determination of appropriate penalties. It does not regulate mining or enforce the Mine Act. The Commission was established as an independent agency to ensure its impartiality.

Most cases deal with civil penalties assessed against mine operators and address whether the alleged safety and health violations occurred as well as the appropriateness of proposed penalties. Other types of cases include orders to close a mine, miners' charges of safety-related discrimination, and miners' requests for compensation after the mine is idled by a closure order.

Environmental Protection Agency
The Toxic Substances Control Act

In 1976, Congress enacted the Toxic Substances Control Act (TSCA), PL 94–469. The act provides the Environmental Protection Agency (EPA) with the authority to require testing of chemical substances entering the environment and to regulate them when necessary. The regulatory actions include toxicity testing and environmental monitoring. This authority supplements and closes the loop of already existing hazardous substance laws in the EPA and other federal agencies. Title I of TSCA also included a provision requiring the EPA to take specific steps to control the risk for polychlorinated biphenyls (PCBs). Three titles have been added to TSCA to address concerns about other specific toxic substances, including asbestos (Title II), radon (Title III), and lead (Title IV).

Title II of TSCA, the Asbestos Hazard Emergency Response Act (PL 99–519), was enacted in 1986 and amended in July 1988. It required the EPA to set standards for responding to the presence of asbestos in schools. The standard set responses based on the physical condition of asbestos, and schools were required to inspect for asbestos-containing material and develop a management plan for such material. The title also requires asbestos contractors and analytical laboratories to be certified and requires schools to use certified people for asbestos work. The title was later amended to extend training and accreditation requirements to include inspectors, contractors, and workers performing asbestos abatement work in all public and commercial buildings. However, the mandate for inspecting buildings for asbestos was not extended to nonschool buildings.

In 1988, Title III, Indoor Radon Abatement (PL 100–551), was added to TSCA. The basic purpose of the amendment is to provide financial and technical assistance to states that support radon monitoring and control; however, neither monitoring nor abatement is required by the act. The title required the EPA to update its pamphlet on radon, develop model constructions standards and techniques for controlling radon levels in new buildings, and provide technical assistance to the states.

Title IV of TSCA, the Residential Lead-Based Paint Hazard Reduction Act (PS 102–550), was enacted in 1992. The purpose of this title is to reduce the risks to young children who are exposed to lead-based paint in their homes. The law aims to stimulate development of lead inspection and hazard abatement services in the private sector. The EPA is directed to develop definitions of lead-contaminated dust, lead-contaminated soil, and lead-based paints hazards; requirements for accreditation of training programs for lead abatement work; criteria to evaluate the effectiveness of commercial products used to detect or reduce risks associated with lead-based paint; protocols for laboratory analysis of lead in paint soils, films, and dust; and certification requirements for laboratories performing such analyses. Also, the EPA is directed to conduct a study of lead hazards resulting from renovation and remodeling activities that may disturb lead-based paint. It must also promulgate guidelines for the renovation and remodeling of buildings or other structures when these activities might create a hazard.

The Resource Conservation and Recovery Act

The Resource Conservation and Recovery Act (RCRA) of 1976 established the federal program regulating solid and hazardous waste management. RCRA actually amends earlier legislation (the Solid Waste Disposal Act of 1965), but the amendments were so comprehensive that the act is commonly called RCRA rather than its official title. The act greatly expanded the federal government's role in solid waste disposal management, with emphasis on hazardous waste disposal.

RCRA continued the federal facilities guidelines under the program established by the 1970 Solid Waste Disposal Act, created a major hazardous waste regulatory program, and prohibited the practice of open dumping. The act provides for extensive federal aid through grants to state and regional agencies for solid waste planning and information programs.

In the cradle-to-grave program of control established by RCRA, custody and responsibility move with a waste material from the generator and transporter to its final disposal site. However, the generator never loses liability for the waste created. Although the original RCRA regulations (1980–1984) exempted small-quantity generators if they produced less than 1,000 kg of hazardous waste per calendar month, the 1984 amendments to RCRA require generators producing between 100 and 1,000 kg per month to meet certain procedural standards.

Since 1980, general waste management requirements of RCRA have included proper notification and recording of hazardous waste activities, along with adequate packaging, labeling, and manifesting of wastes for shipment off site. An RCRA permit is required for treatment, storage, and disposal (TSD) of hazardous waste on site or off site. Standards for TSD facilities include rigorous facility management plans, preparedness and prevention of emergencies and releases, contingency plans, operating records and reports, groundwater protection for land disposal facilities, and closure and postclosure plans with financial responsibility assurance.

The new RCRA requirements, following the amendments of 1984, make TSD facilities responsible for assessing human exposure to current and past waste management operations and for corrective action needed to remedy releases of hazardous constituents to the environment. The RCRA regulations also require worker training, development of safe handling procedures, and emergency response measures. Documentation of training is required and inspectors may require a review of the documentation.

The 1984 amendments required that land disposal of specified highly hazardous wastes be phased out over the period 1986–1990. The EPA was directed to review all wastes that it has defined as hazardous and to determine the appropriateness of land disposal for them. Minimal technological standards were set for new landfills, generally requiring double liners, a leachate collection system, and groundwater monitoring. Under the new amendments, states were encouraged to assume the EPA's hazardous waste program.

The third major amendment to RCRA, the Federal Facility Compliance Act, was passed in 1992. This act allows the states, the EPA, and the Department of Justice to enforce the provisions of RCRA against federal facilities; federal departments and agencies can be subjected to injunction, administrative orders, or penalties for noncompliance.

The act also contains special provisions applicable to mixtures of radioactive and hazardous waste at Department of Energy facilities and to munitions, military ships, and military sewage treatment facilities handling hazardous wastes.

The Comprehensive Environmental Response, Compensation and Liability Act

In 1980, Congress enacted the Comprehensive Environmental Response, Compensation and Liability Act (CERCLA), PL 96-510. This act established the Superfund Program to handle emergencies at uncontrolled waste sites, to clean up the sites, and to deal with related problems. In 1986, CERCLA was reauthorized by Congress as the Superfund Amendment and Reauthorization Act (SARA) of 1986, PL 99-499. The purpose of the amendments was to provide additional funding and additional provisions. The new authorities and programs included in this reauthorization include underground storage tanks, emergency planning, risk assessment, community right-to-know, research, development, demonstrations, and training. In 1990, the Superfund Extension Act authorized appropriations for SARA through 1995.

These regulations include requirements that owner-operators of leaking underground storage tanks undertake corrective action to protect human health and the environment. SARA also established a comprehensive federal program to promote various research, development, demonstration, and training activities, including the following:

- techniques to detect, assess, and evaluate health effects of hazardous substances
- methods to assess human health risks
- methods and technologies to detect hazardous substances and to reduce volume and toxicity

CERCLA created the Agency for Toxic Substances and Disease Registry (ATSDR) in the Public Health Service to carry out the health-related authorities in the Act. In 1986, SARA created new duties for ATSDR. The agency and EPA are to prepare a list of at least 275 of the hazardous substances most commonly found at National Priority List (NPL) sites. The agency is to prepare toxicological profiles of these substances. Where there is insufficient information on a substance, ATSDR is to conduct research. In addition, ATSDR is required to perform a health assessment at each facility on the NPL list. Finally, ATSDR is to provide consultations to the EPA and state and local officials on health issues related to hazardous substances.

With the RCRA amendments and the requirements for cleanup under the CERCLA legislation, the time of total accountability for current and past waste management practices has arrived. Quantitative liabilities for waste management practices are directly proportionate to how much a facility is affected by these requirements and remedial actions. The 1986 law added a provision limiting the amount of coverage specified in the policy. SARA also authorized companies to form risk retention groups as a means of insuring themselves.

Companies covered under the OSHA Hazard Communication standard are also subject to the EPA Hazardous Chemical Reporting Rules under Title III of Superfund. Covered facilities are required to submit either copies of the SDSs they prepare for OSHA compliance or a list of all chemicals for which SDSs are required to the state emergency response commission, the local emergency planning committee, and the local fire department. Covered facilities must also submit emergency and hazardous chemical inventory forms to the same state and local authorities. Information on the maximum daily amounts and chemical locations (designated Tier I information) submittal date was March 1, 1988, and annually thereafter. The more detailed Tier II information would be submitted on request.

Pesticide Safety

EPA's Worker Protection Standard (WPS) for Agricultural Pesticides (40 CFR Part 170) is a federal regulation designed to protect employees on farms, forests, nurseries, and greenhouses from occupational exposures to agricultural pesticides. The WPS offers protections to agricultural workers and pesticide handlers (people who mix, load, or apply pesticides). The WPS contains requirements for

- pesticide safety training;
- notification of pesticide applications;
- use of personal protective equipment;
- restricted entry intervals following pesticide application;
- decontamination supplies; and
- emergency medical assistance.

All agricultural employers, owners, and managers, as well as labor contractors, are required to comply with the WPS when pesticides with labeling that refers to the WPS have been used on an agricultural establishment. Most WPS requirements apply to agricultural workers or pesticide handlers, but there are some requirements that apply to all persons and some that only apply to certain persons such as those who handle pesticide application equipment or clean pesticide-contaminated personal protective equipment.

Indoor Air Quality

Indoor pollution sources that release gases or particles into the air are the primary cause of indoor air quality problems in buildings. Inadequate ventilation can increase indoor pollutant levels by not bringing in enough outdoor air to dilute emissions from indoor sources and by not carrying indoor air pollutants out of the building. High temperature and humidity levels can also increase concentrations of some pollutants. The EPA's Indoor Environments Division (IED) is responsible for conducting research and educating the public about indoor environmental issues, including health risks and the means by which human exposures can be reduced. IED educates the public about health risks associated with a variety of indoor environmental pollutants and sources of pollution, including radon, mold and moisture, secondhand smoke, indoor wood smoke, and environmental asthma triggers.

SUMMARY

This chapter provides an overview of the national, regional, and state government agencies and regulations concerned with occupational health, safety, and environmental issues.

BIBLIOGRAPHY

Congressional Research Service. *Summaries of Environmental Laws Administered by the Environmental Protection Agency,* 93-53 ENR. Washington, DC: Library of Congress, January 14, 1993.

Federal Mine Safety & Health Act of 1977. Pub. L. No. 91-173 [1977]. http://www.msha.gov/REGS/ACT/ACTTC.HTM

Occupational Safety and Health Act of 1970, U.S. Congress (91st) S2193. Pub. L. No. 91-596, U.S. Congress (91st) S2193 [1970]. https://www.osha.gov

Occupational Safety and Health Administration. *Field Operations Manual.* OSHA Instruction CPL 02-00-150. Washington, DC: OSHA, effective date: 04/22/2011. http://www.osha.gov/OshDoc/Directive_pdf/CPL_02-00-150.pdf

Occupational Safety and Health Administration. *OSHA Technical Manual.* OSHA Instruction #TED 01-00-015. Washington, DC: OSHA, effective date: 1/20/1999. https://www.osha.gov/dts/osta/otm/otm_toc.html

CHAPTER 31

International Developments in Occupational Safety and Health

by Jennifer C. Silk, BS
and Paul W. Brigandi, BS

Occupational safety and health typically has been addressed primarily from a domestic perspective, rather than involving multiple countries and regions in developing approaches to common issues of concern. Historically, the exception to this has been global initiatives developed by the United Nations' International Labor Organization (ILO). While important in encouraging countries to address occupational safety and health, these ILO initiatives have generally not been ratified in countries such as the United States, although the United States has actively participated in the development of these documents. Of 189 conventions adopted by the ILO, the United States has ratified 14.

With the broad availability of information about occupational safety and health initiatives on the Internet, the development of a global economy, and multinational companies operating in many different countries and regions, safety and health issues are no longer just a domestic concern. Not only is information about approaches to safety and health issues more widely available, there is increasing recognition that sharing such information can leverage limited resources in all countries, as well as lead to novel approaches in addressing issues of mutual concern. Hopefully, the outcome of these shared resources and experiences will be more effective approaches to safety and health around the world.

Many of the international activities in occupational safety and health involve chemicals and ensuring the safe use of them. The widespread use of chemicals around the world means that one country's management of chemical use can affect protections in other countries. This fact has led to programs designed to reduce the occurrence of adverse effects resulting from chemical use. The Strategic Approach to International Chemicals Management (SAICM) is an international policy framework that was developed to provide a forum where countries, international organizations, and stakeholders can work together to address the sound management of chemicals around the world. SAICM is implementing a global plan for action, with many commitments by participating countries to work together in various areas. The goal of the SAICM is to help ensure that "... by the year 2020, chemicals are produced and used in ways that minimize significant adverse impacts on the environment and human health." (United Nations Environment Programme, 2006.) While not specific to workplace protections, there are many aspects of the SAICM action plan that deal with issues related to chemicals in the workplace. This chapter will address two areas included in the SAICM action plan.

The first is the Globally Harmonized System of Classification and Labeling of Chemicals (GHS). The GHS establishes internationally harmonized classification criteria for the physical, health, and environmental hazards of a chemical. In addition, the GHS specifies the label elements to be used to convey these hazards to chemical users, and the information to be provided on Safety Data Sheets (formerly Material Safety Data Sheets). Implementation of the GHS around the world will help ensure that all workers receive necessary information about the chemicals they work with, and will also provide the informational infrastructure needed to establish programs for the sound management of chemicals.

Most workplaces in the United States—as well as in the rest of the world—do not have industrial or occupational hygienists on their staffs, nor do they have access to such expertise. Many small- to medium-sized businesses lack specific expertise in developing workplace protection programs, but are nevertheless responsible for ensuring their workers have a safe and healthful work environment. Chemical exposures are a particular area of concern given the potential for significant adverse impacts. The challenge is to find a user-friendly way to make industrial hygiene expertise more broadly available, and thus improve protections in such workplaces. Control banding may be the answer in many situations. It is a guidance system that allows employers to input basic information about their workplaces (e.g., the name of the chemical, physical form, amount present, and the label hazard warnings), and obtain recommended control measures for common work operations (e.g., bagging). This chapter will describe the general approach to control banding and how it may be used.

The Member States of the European Union (EU) have adopted a new approach to chemical regulation through the implementation of REACH (Registration, Evaluation, and Control of Chemicals). This chemical regulatory system addresses the use of chemicals from cradle to grave, and makes the manufacturer of the product responsible for developing and disseminating appropriate information about potential hazards, exposures, and appropriate control measures. Given the great extent of chemical trade between European countries and other countries such as the United States, implementation of REACH will have an impact far beyond the borders of Europe. The particular impacts of REACH on the practice of occupational safety and health will be addressed,

In addition to these initiatives involving chemicals, an international approach to occupational health and safety management systems has also been developed. Similar to approaches in the United States such as the Occupational Safety and Health Administration's (OSHA) Voluntary Protection Program, these provisions seek to provide guidance to companies that need to establish an effective workplace protection program, based on such concepts as the need for management commitment and employee involvement.

GLOBALLY HARMONIZED SYSTEM OF CLASSIFICATION AND LABELING OF CHEMICALS

In the United States, workers are provided information about chemicals they are exposed to under the requirements of the Occupational Safety and Health Administration's (OSHA) Hazard Communication Standard (HCS)(29 CFR 1910.1200). Early in OSHA's history, they recognized that the sheer number of chemicals in American workplaces would preclude having specific standards to cover the handling of each one. However, in order for employers to provide appropriate protections, they needed information about the chemicals they purchased for their workplaces. When the standard was first promulgated in 1983, many chemical manufacturers and importers provided limited information to their customers regarding the hazards of their products, or the appropriate ways to handle them. The HCS was promulgated to remedy this situation, and help to ensure that employers and employees would have necessary information about the chemicals in their workplaces. The standard included definitions of health and physical hazards, as well as requirements to provide information about these hazards through labels on containers, Safety Data Sheets (SDSs), formerly known as Material Safety Data Sheets (MSDSs), and worker training.

The pre-2012 HCS was a performance-oriented standard. This meant that OSHA had indicated what employers needed to do to comply, but did not specify exactly how compliance was to be achieved. For example, the standard required labels to include an identity and appropriate hazard warnings for the chemical, but did not indicate what words were to be used to express the warnings.

Other countries have also recognized that information transmittal standards are one way to address issues regarding workplace exposures to chemicals. For example, both Canada and the countries in the European Union have existing systems that provide information to chemical users through labels and safety data sheets. However, their definitions of hazards are slightly different than those in use in the United States. A chemical may be flammable in one country, and not in another. Or it could be considered a carcinogen in one country, but not in another. The differences in the findings of hazard are based on differences in the criteria used to assess hazards. Another significant difference is that many countries, such as those in the EU, specify how to provide the warning information, rather than allowing the chemical manufacturer or importer to determine how to do it as was permitted under OSHA's previous version of the HCS.

The result of the inconsistent approaches in various countries around the world is that labels and Safety Data Sheets for the same chemical convey different information about both the hazardous effects and the appropriate protective measures. Given the extensive global trade in chemicals, this inconsistency results in a compliance burden for companies trying to ensure they follow the requirements of the different countries to which they ship, as well as creating confusion for exposed workers where labels from multiple suppliers are present in their workplaces. In addition, there are many countries that do not have the resources to develop and maintain such a system, and thus can't provide protection to exposed workers and other chemical users in the country. Without a requirement for information about hazardous chemicals, a country would have a difficult time achieving sound management of chemicals.

In recognition of the benefits of having an internationally harmonized approach to classifying and labeling chemicals, a mandate was adopted in 1992 at the United Nations Conference on Environment and Development (UNCED), often referred to as the Earth Summit. The mandate recognized that unlike some other issues, the way a country addresses chemicals can impact another country's ability to protect their citizens. Chemicals can easily cross borders when uncontrolled, or can be shipped without appropriate information if not required by the exporting country. When considering these factors, as well as the burdens of complying with multiple, different hazard classification and labeling requirements, the rationale for a global approach was clearly established.

Adoption of a mandate for action initiated a complicated, lengthy, and difficult process to design an internationally agreed approach through consideration of existing systems. The systems in use in Europe, Canada, and the United States, along with the already harmonized international transport system (United Nations Recommendations for the Transport of Dangerous Goods [TDG]) formed the basis for the work. The process took many years to complete, and involved numerous countries, international organizations, and stakeholder representatives. The GHS became available for implementation in 2003. It was the first time that an international effort of such magnitude was under-

taken to harmonize the approaches of different countries or regions on an occupational safety and health issue of concern to all nations. Many countries are now in various stages of implementing the GHS. The GHS is published by the United Nations, and is also available on the UN web page. The 4th edition became available in 2011. The GHS is commonly referred to as "The Purple Book."

The United States supported the concept of harmonization prior to the adoption of the international mandate to proceed, and actively participated in the development of the GHS. Since completion of the system, the United States has also participated in the international group responsible for maintaining the system, and overseeing its implementation around the world, the United Nations Subcommittee on the Globally Harmonized System of Classification and Labeling of Chemicals (UNSCEGHS). (See Department of Labor, OSHA, 2009, for a detailed description of the history of the GHS and U.S. involvement.)

In terms of U.S. implementation of the GHS, the U.S. Department of Transportation (DOT) has updated provisions regarding the transport of dangerous goods to reflect GHS criteria for hazard classification. In addition, OSHA has modified its HCS to align with the provisions of GHS. The final rule was published in the Federal Register on March 26, 2012 (77 FR 17574). Compliance will be phased in over several years. All labels and SDSs must be changed by June 1, 2015. Both the Environmental Protection Agency (EPA), which regulates classification and labeling of pesticides, and the Consumer Product Safety Commission (CPSC), which regulates chemicals in consumer products, participated actively in development of the GHS. If both agencies ultimately adopt the GHS requirements for classification and labeling of chemicals under their purview, the U.S. agencies will be domestically, as well as internationally, harmonized. This would produce greater benefits than would be achieved if only some of the U.S. federal authorities adopt the GHS.

Provisions of the GHS
Scope

The GHS is intended to cover all types of chemicals, in all varieties of use settings. There are no exemptions for a particular type of use (e.g., pesticides), or for any class of chemicals. The GHS addresses chemicals throughout their life cycle. It is expected that countries will be able to apply the GHS to all the major sectors where chemicals are used, including transport, industrial/workplace, consumer products, and agriculture/pesticides.

The GHS also recognizes that authorities need to have the flexibility to vary the type of coverage applied in these different sectors. For example, the transport sector addresses the physical hazards of chemicals, as well as certain acute health effects and some environmental concerns. In this sector, the exposures are expected to occur in the event of an accident or incident that causes otherwise packaged chemicals to be released, and its provisions are designed for that purpose.

On the other hand, workplace exposures are generally encountered on a daily basis, often over a long period of time. Physical hazards are a concern as in transport, but both the acute and chronic health effects are also important to address in a workplace protection program. Thus, authorities in a country are likely to need all of the GHS health and physical hazard criteria in the parts of their system dealing with workplace protection.

This flexibility or variability in coverage is referred to in the GHS as the *building block* approach. The GHS is designed to provide the building blocks that a country would need for any part of its regulatory system to address hazard classification and labeling of chemicals. The building blocks chosen may be different in each sector. However, where the sectors cover the same aspect of the GHS (e.g., flammability), they would be drawn from the same building blocks, and where coverage is the same, the same criteria would be used. Therefore, in transport, a GHS-consistent country could choose not to cover chronic health effects, and still be considered harmonized.

The GHS is based on assessing the hazards of the chemicals addressed. It is not intended to be a risk-based approach. For purposes of understanding the GHS, a hazard is considered to be an intrinsic property of the chemical. Providing information to users of the product based on the hazards will allow them to factor in the particular use and exposure situations in their workplaces, and make decisions regarding the degree and type of protections needed. In other words, the user is factoring in exposure and establishing the level of risk in the workplace, rather than having the producer make assumptions about risks downstream, and limit the information provided accordingly.

The GHS allows countries to use risk when determining the warnings to give regarding the chronic effects of consumer products. In this situation—unlike in the workplace—the label may be the only information the user receives. Some countries allow presumptions about exposure under normal conditions of use for consumer products, and want to continue this approach when adopting the GHS. Warnings based on presumption of risk cannot be used for workplace chemicals that may cause chronic health effects.

The GHS also recognizes that some types of chemicals may be regulated by hazard in some parts of the life cycle of the product (and thus covered by the GHS at that point), but not in other parts, where existing national requirements may cover a product based on risk. For example, many countries have regulatory requirements for pharmaceuticals prescribed for use by consumers. These requirements are based on risk since the consumer has an ailment or condition that may be alleviated by the pharmaceutical, and a specific dose to address the condition is specified. In this case, the pharmaceutical would not be covered by GHS hazard requirements in terms of labeling for consumers. The label on the container for consumer use would be that prescribed by the authority regulating the risk of pharmaceutical use (e.g., the Food and Drug Administration in the United States).

The pharmaceutical would nonetheless be covered at other stages of the life cycle. For example, the workers involved in making the pharmaceutical would need information about the hazards and protective measures needed to address their exposures. This is of particular concern since the workers do not have the health condition the pharmaceutical addresses, and their exposures are not prescribed. In some cases, such materials have significant adverse health effects for exposed employees—both in the manufacturing process and when exposures occur to health professionals providing medical services to patients. Countries should ensure that exposures occurring in these stages of the life cycle are appropriately covered (e.g., with safety data sheets based on hazard and worker training). Similarly, the transport of such chemicals should also be considered.

Authorities in countries implementing the GHS are thus able to make sure that the scope is adjusted to account for other parts of their regulatory structure that already address aspects of some chemical use. In terms of OSHA's HCS, the current rule already includes scope and application provisions that address such issues, and the provisions of the GHS are quite complementary to the approach taken by OSHA.

Hazard Classification

The GHS includes criteria to define physical, health, and environmental hazards posed by chemicals (see the lists of hazards covered in Table 31–A). The physical hazard criteria are based on the internationally harmonized system for the transport of dangerous goods (United Nations Recommendations for the Transport of Dangerous Goods). Using these existing criteria serves a dual purpose. First, it minimizes the work required to develop criteria for these types of hazards, and takes advantage of the many years of experience and expertise the transport sector has in this area. Secondly, use of the existing criteria also harmonizes the transport sector with other sectors to help ensure the broadest coverage of the GHS. Some modifications were made to the existing transport criteria to adapt them to the needs of other sectors, for example, additional coverage of flammable liquids. The health and environmental hazard criteria were negotiated by national experts based on the criteria in existing systems, as well as the latest scientific information related to the hazard under consideration.

The GHS describes the hazard classification process as follows (United Nations, 2011, GHS paragraph 1.3.2.2.2):

- Identification of relevant data regarding the specific hazard of the substance or mixture.
- Subsequent review and quality check of those data to ascertain the hazards associated with the substance or mixture.
- A decision on whether the substance or mixture will be classified as a hazardous substance or mixture, and the degree of hazard, where appropriate, by comparison of the data with agreed hazard classification criteria.

Each type of hazard covered by the GHS is referred to as a *hazard class*. For example, carcinogenicity would be

a hazard class. In addition to the hazard class, each type of hazard is further broken down into one or more *hazard categories* based on the severity of the effect. As can be seen in Table 31–B, the GHS hazard class for carcinogenicity is separated into two hazard categories based on the weight of the available evidence, and whether it is human or animal evidence. Other hazard classes are divided into hazard categories using quantitative cut-offs, such as flashpoints for flammable liquids.

The GHS is based on the concept that the chemical manufacturer or importer of a substance, or mixture of substances, is responsible for evaluating its hazards according to the criteria. Users of such chemicals will receive information about the hazards and appropriate protective measures through labels and safety data sheets. The user will not be responsible for hazard classification.

The hazard classification process of the GHS, as well as existing systems in the United States and other countries,

TABLE 31–A	Hazard Classes in the GHS	
Physical Hazard Classes	*Health Hazard Classes*	*Environmental Hazard Classes*
Explosives	Acute Toxicity	Hazardous to the Aquatic Environment
Flammable Gases (including chemically unstable gases)	Skin Corrosion/Irritation	Hazardous to the Ozone Layer
Aerosols	Serious Eye Damage/Eye Irritation	
Oxidizing Gases	Respiratory or Skin Sensitization	
Gases under Pressure	Germ Cell Mutagenicity	
Flammable Liquids	Carcinogenicity	
Flammable Solids	Reproductive Toxicity	
Self-Reactive Substances and Mixtures	Specific Target Organ Toxicity—Single Exposure	
Pyrophoric Liquids	Specific Target Organ Toxicity—Repeated Exposure	
Pyrophoric Solids	Aspiration Hazards	
Self-Heating Substances and Mixtures		
Substances and Mixtures which, in contact with water, emit Flammable Gases		
Oxidizing Liquids		
Oxidizing Solids		
Organic Peroxides		
Corrosive to Metals		

TABLE 31–B	GHS Hazard Categories for Carcinogens
CATEGORY 1:	**Known or presumed human carcinogens** The placing of a substance in Category 1 is done on the basis of epidemiological and/or animal data. An individual substance may be further distinguished:
Category 1A:	**Known to have carcinogenic potential for humans; the placing of a substance is largely based on human evidence.**
Category 1B:	**Presumed to have carcinogenic potential for humans; the placing of a substance is largely based on animal evidence.** Based on strength of evidence together with additional considerations, such evidence may be derived from human studies that establish a causal relationship between human exposure to a substance and the development of cancer (known human carcinogen). Alternatively, evidence may be derived from animal experiments for which there is sufficient evidence to demonstrate animal carcinogenicity (presumed human carcinogen). In addition, on a case by case basis, scientific judgement may warrant a decision of presumed human carcinogenicity derived from studies showing limited evidence of carcinogenicity in humans together with limited evidence of carcinogenicity in experimental animals. **Classification**: Category 1 (A and B) Carcinogen
CATEGORY 2:	**Suspected human carcinogens** The placing of a substance in Category 2 is done on the basis of evidence obtained from human and/or animal studies, but which is not sufficiently convincing to place the substance in Category 1. Based on strength of evidence together with additional considerations, such evidence may be from either limited evidence of carcinogenicity in human studies or from limited evidence of carcinogenicity in animal studies. **Classification**: Category 2 Carcinogen

Source: United Nations, 2011. Figure 3.6.1 of the GHS.

involves considerable professional judgment in order to be appropriately accomplished. While some hazard classes require a simple comparison between a numerical test result and the criteria (e.g., acute toxicity), others involve a complicated analysis of the validity of the data, and the weight of the evidence supporting a finding of hazard (e.g., carcinogenicity). Such evaluations should be undertaken by experts in the relevant fields. The availability of internationally agreed-upon criteria for characterizing the hazards of chemicals should lead to more consistent information being available in workplaces than under the diverse existing systems that use different criteria.

Labels

The GHS specifies the information to be provided on a label for a chemical that poses a given hazard. Once the hazard classification for a chemical has been completed, the GHS provides the label elements that apply to the hazard class and category into which the chemical falls. The label elements required for a GHS label are defined as follows (United Nations, 2011):

- *Pictogram:* A graphical composition that may include a symbol plus other graphic elements, such as a border, background pattern or color that is intended to convey specific information.
- *Signal word:* A word used to indicate the relative level of severity of hazard and alert the reader to a potential hazard on the label. The GHS uses *Danger* and *Warning*

as signal words.

- *Hazard statement:* A statement assigned to a hazard class and category that describes the nature of the hazards of a hazardous product, including, where appropriate, the degree of hazard.
- *Precautionary statements:* A phrase (and/or pictogram) that describes recommended measures that should be taken to minimize or prevent adverse effects resulting from exposure to a hazardous product, or improper storage or handling of a hazardous product.

The GHS has harmonized the pictograms, signal words, and hazard statements, and assigned them to each hazard class and hazard category. Figure 31–1 illustrates how the GHS presents the assigned label elements for a hazard class, and its associated hazard categories.

The pictograms in the GHS are black symbols on a white background, surrounded by a red, diamond-shaped border. There are nine pictograms in the GHS, and some of them are used for more than one type of hazard. Pictograms were not widely used in the U.S. hazard classification and labeling laws until now, but they are used frequently in other existing systems (e.g., the EU and Canada). They attract the attention of anyone reading the label and can convey information without words—which is useful where the target audience may not be literate or may not understand the language on the label. Figure 31–2 includes all of the pictograms in the GHS, with the hazards to which they are applied.

The signal words in the GHS are also intended to attract

FLAMMABLE LIQUIDS				
Category 1	*Category 2*	*Category 3*	*Category 4*	*Note*
Danger	 Danger	 Warning	No pictogram	Under the *UN Recommendations on the Transport of Dangerous Goods, Model Regulations*, the symbol, number, and border line may be shown in black instead of white. The background color stays red in both cases.
Extremely flammable liquid and vapour	Highly flammable liquid and vapour	Flammable liquid and vapour	Warning Combustible liquid	
			Not required under the *UN Recommendations on the Transport of Dangerous Goods Model Regulations*	

Figure 31–1. GHS allocation of label elements by hazard class and categories. *(Source: United Nations, 2011. Annex 1, Allocation of Label Elements.)*

attention to the existence of hazards for the product, as well as to convey information about the degree of severity of the effect. *Danger* is used for the more severe hazards, while *warning* is assigned to less severe hazard categories. In the United States, people may also be familiar with the signal word *caution*, which is used for some products. A review of the literature related to comprehensibility indicated that label readers had difficulty differentiating between *warning* and *caution*, so the GHS developers decided to only use one of those terms to convey the less severe hazards.

The hazard statements in the GHS provide the substantive information about the effects associated with the product of concern. Hazard statements are assigned to each hazard category in a hazard class, and vary with the degree of severity of the effect. For example, the most severe hazard category for flammable liquids has the following hazard statement: *Extremely flammable liquid and vapor*. The least severe category for flammable liquids, on the other hand, has this hazard statement: *Combustible liquid*. The hazard statements have been codified in the GHS, which means that they are numbered for easy reference (e.g., H227 is the codification for the hazard statement *Combustible liquid*).

Precautionary statements in the GHS provide important information for safe handling of the substance or mixture. Precautionary statements have been developed and assigned to each hazard category. However, they are not yet considered to be harmonized. Implementing countries thus have the choice to either use the statements in the GHS or to have statements of their own in their GHS-aligned requirements. It is anticipated that the statements will eventually be considered part of the harmonized label elements. An example of a precautionary statement under the GHS is: Keep away from heat/sparks/open flames/hot surfaces. No smoking.

Precautionary statements have been divided into five subject areas: 1) general, 2) prevention, 3) response, 4) storage, and 5) disposal. In codifying these statements, the first number of the code represents the area to which the statement belongs. For example, the statement mentioned above is P210—which indicates it is intended to address prevention.

In addition to the label elements that address the hazards and preventive measures, the GHS label must include a product identifier and the contact information for the supplier. Other information is permitted on the labels. However, the required label elements should be located in close proximity to each other, and any additional information may not detract from the required label elements.

Safety Data Sheets (formerly Material Safety Data Sheets)

The GHS includes specifications for a 16-section Safety Data Sheet (SDS). The 16-section approach was originally developed in the United States as an American National Standards Institute (ANSI) voluntary industry consensus standard, and was later adopted in the EU, as well as by the International

GHS Pictograms and Hazard Classes They Represent

- Oxidizers

- Flammables
- Self-reactives
- Pyrophorics
- Self-heating
- Emits flammable gas
- Organic peroxides

- Explosives (1.1-1.4)
- Self-reactives
- Organic peroxides

- Acute toxicity (severe)

- Corrosive to metals
- Skin corrosion
- Serious eye damage

- Gases under pressure

- Carcinogenicity
- Respiratory sensitization
- Toxic to reproduction
- Specific target organ toxicity (repeated)
- Germ cell mutagenicity
- Aspiration hazard

- Aquatic toxicity (acute)
- Aquatic toxicity (chronic)

- Acute toxicity (harmful)
- Skin/eye irritation
- Skin sensitization
- Specific target organ toxicity (single)
- Hazardous to the ozone layer

Figure 31–2. GHS pictograms and the hazard classes they represent.

Organization for Standardization (ISO). When the GHS was being prepared, the developers decided that using this already widely available format would help to encourage and expedite adoption of the GHS requirements addressing SDSs. Table 31–C lists the 16 sections in a GHS-compliant SDS. The GHS also indicates information that should be included under each of the sections, and provides additional guidance for the preparation of SDSs in Annex 4 of the GHS.

While the GHS applies to many different sectors, the SDS is intended primarily for use in the industrial or workplace sector. As such, its advice and recommendations are generally related to preventing or reducing worker exposures to the substances or mixtures, and to ensuring that downstream users have all the necessary information to do so. Like the SDSs in the United States, some of the information is more technical, and thus intended for use by professionals providing services to employers and exposed employees (e.g., toxicological information). Other information, particularly in the initial sections of the SDS, is to be written for a broader audience to use (e.g., hazard identification). The SDS concept originated in the United States, but has evolved into an international approach to providing customers and users with extensive information about a substance or mixture, its properties, and recommendations for its safe use and handling. Having a common format among countries will help make the information more accessible when chemicals are shipped across borders, as well as ensuring that those who will handle the material will always have the information needed to manage its use.

TABLE 31–C GHS Safety Data Sheet Sections
1. Identification
2. Hazard(s) identification
3. Composition/information on ingredients
4. First-aid measures
5. Fire-fighting measures
6. Accidental release measures
7. Handling and storage
8. Exposure controls/personal protection
9. Physical and chemical properties
10. Stability and reactivity
11. Toxicological information
12. Ecological information
13. Disposal considerations
14. Transport information
15. Regulatory information
16. Other information

Training

The GHS does not include harmonized provisions for training, but it does recognize that training is necessary for appropriate implementation of the system. Unlike labels and SDSs that cross borders—and thus create potential trade barriers—training requirements do not. The major existing systems with hazard communication requirements currently have training requirements for workers exposed to chemicals. Training requirements help ensure that workers know and understand the hazards of the materials in their workplaces. In addition, it is likely that countries can anticipate that training for employers will be needed as national systems are revised to adopt the GHS.

Implementation of the GHS in U.S. Workplaces

As noted above, OSHA published a final rule to modify the HCS to align its provisions with the GHS on March 26, 2012 (referred to as HazCom 2012). The rule went into effect May 25, 2012, but the provisions are being phased in over a four-year compliance period. In order to align its provisions with the GHS approach, significant modifications have been made to the OSHA standard. The revised standard, like the GHS, is specification oriented, rather than taking the performance-oriented approach of the former rule. To accomplish harmonization, national and regional requirements need to follow the same provisions. A flexible, performance-oriented approach would not result in harmonization. Therefore, OSHA has changed the HCS as follows:

- The HCS currently includes definitions for health and physical hazards covered by the rule. These definitions are relatively general in nature, and are supplemented by a requirement to report as a hazard any health effects found in one toxicological study. HazCom 2012 adopts the detailed and specific physical and health hazard classification criteria in the GHS. Many of the hazard classes are further subdivided into hazard categories that reflect the severity of the effect. This additional information helps employers and employees determine the relative risk of exposure to hazards in the workplace.

- The HCS currently requires labels on shipped containers and on containers in workplaces. However, the shipped-container requirements are performance oriented, requiring minimal information, with no specifics on how to present that information on a label. To be consistent with the GHS, OSHA has adopted the GHS approach of specified label elements, assigned to each hazard class and hazard category determined during the hazard classification process. Thus HazCom 2012 has a cookbook approach to labeling on shipped containers. Once the detailed hazard classification criteria have been applied, and the hazard categories relevant to the substance or mixture have been identified, chemical manufacturers and importers are required to allocate the GHS label elements to each identified hazard category. Label elements include signal words, pictograms, hazard statements, and precautionary statements. For workplace containers, OSHA allows employers to use either the shipped container label or an alternative approach.

- SDSs prepared to comply with the original HCS may present the required information in any format chosen by the supplier. Under the GHS, a 16-section SDS is specified. HazCom 2012 includes provisions to provide SDS information in the order dictated by the GHS, and addresses what information needs to be in each section.

- Many other aspects of the HCS remain essentially the same as they are not affected by adoption of the GHS. These include scope and application provisions, written hazard communication program requirements, worker training provisions, and the approach to identifying and maintaining trade secret information.

All employers must train workers potentially exposed to chemicals on the new approach to labels and SDSs by December 1, 2013. Labels and SDSs must be prepared in accordance with HazCom 2012 by June 1, 2015. All requirements are to be implemented by June 1, 2016.

Conclusions on the GHS

Development and adoption of the GHS has been a significant contribution to the tools available for countries to address the hazards of the hundreds of thousands of chemical substances and mixtures used in workplaces around the world. Its benefits include increased protections for exposed workers, as well as improved information for safety and health professionals, and facilitation of international trade in chemicals. Implementation in U.S. workplaces has begun, and it is also taking place in other parts of the world (such as the EU). In countries like the United States that have existing requirements to address hazard communication, implementation of the GHS is an opportunity to improve the protective aspects of those requirements based on experiences both in the United States and in other countries, as well as having important trade benefits for employers.

CONTROL BANDING

The GHS addresses the global provision of consistent and comprehensive information to users through application of agreed hazard classification criteria, and the preparation and dissemination of labels and Safety Data Sheets. Once the information is available, the question is what steps need to be taken to prevent the adverse effects of chemicals from occurring in workplaces. Industrialized countries such as the United States, and Member States of the European Union (EU), have traditionally addressed exposure to chemicals through the establishment of occupational exposure limits (OELs). The processes for setting these limits vary, as do the limits themselves, the chemicals addressed, and the use of the limits in workplaces. While establishment and enforcement of OELs have resulted in the successful control of a number of chemical hazards, there is no way that any country or region could address the majority of chemicals in workplaces through such rules. Most countries that follow this approach have several hundred exposure limits, while the chemicals produced by manufacturers around the world number in the tens of thousands. For example, the European Chemicals Agency (ECHA) has received notifications of classification and labeling for 107,067 distinct substances as of January 2011. Clearly, there will never be OELs for that many substances.

The situation is complicated by the fact that many businesses, particularly those that are small- or medium-sized enterprises, have no professional occupational safety and health staff. While consultants may be used for purposes of assessing workplaces and designing control measures, there are many workplaces that do not have the resources for such assistance. While this is true in developed countries such as the United States, it is an even more pressing issue in many economies in transition. The challenge has been to find a way to improve protections in such workplaces through guidance that utilizes information available to the employer, in conjunction with a tool that can take that information, apply known approaches and solutions, and provide simplified, user-friendly assistance to employers to select appropriate control measures.

Many international organizations, researchers, occupational safety and health professionals, governments, and multinational companies have been involved in finding and refining a method that could be used to improve controls for chemical exposures, as well as other workplace risks. A common approach has evolved from these various sources and is generally referred to as *control banding*. Unlike the strategy based on quantitative approaches that involve measuring specific exposures, comparing them to an established OEL, and selecting control measures based on what is needed to achieve exposure at or below the OEL, control banding is a qualitative approach to assessing the risks and selecting appropriate controls. There are some variations in the approach depending on the source, but there are common aspects to of all of them.

While the pharmaceutical industry is generally credited with initially developing the overall control-banding approach, perhaps the best known and most available system for control banding is part of the United Kingdom's (UK) Health and Safety Executive's (HSE) Control of Substances

Hazardous to Health (COSHH) Essentials. The International Labor Organization (ILO) and World Health Organization (WHO) have also used the HSE approach and other information to develop an international risk management toolkit.

Under requirements of a European framework directive for workplaces in the European Union, Member States have regulations for employers to perform risk assessments of their workplaces to identify, and subsequently control, risks to exposed workers. Many employers are not able to properly assess the risks or select appropriate control measures. In order to address this issue, the UK COSHH program provides guidance that includes a control-banding strategy to help businesses meet the requirements of the UK regulations. Other European countries (e.g., Germany) have also been involved in further developing such an approach, and using it to help employers perform required risk assessments in workplaces and improve control of exposures.

The system implements a generic risk assessment process that is based on the hazard of the chemical or product, as well as the potential for exposure to the chemical or product. Figure 31–3 illustrates the process. The health hazard of the material is represented in this generic risk assessment by the standardized phrases assigned to the chemical during the hazard classification. Initially, the HSE approach used the R-phrases that were included in the European classification and labeling approach. However, as described above, the internationally harmonized GHS also includes harmonized hazard statements. These have been codified as H-statements, with a number assigned to each one. The control-banding approach may also be implemented using the GHS phrases, rather than the original R-phrases in Europe. The R-phrases are being phased out since the EU has adopted the GHS.

The practical implication of this in the United States is that adoption of the GHS by OSHA will also result in the standardized hazard statements being made available on labels and safety data sheets. Under the current HCS performance-oriented approach, there are no standardized phrases. Thus, applying a control-banding approach without such information on the HCS labels and SDSs required some interpretation of available data to be able to use a package such as the one developed by HSE. With OSHA's adoption of the GHS, the opportunity to use control banding in U.S. workplaces will be enhanced.

The determination of exposure potential is accomplished by using the physical properties of the substances, and the amount of the substances used in the process or operation under consideration. The approach covers solids and liquids, but not gases or liquids used above their boiling points. It also includes consideration of dustiness for solids, as well as volatility for liquids.

The risk assessment in this generic, qualitative approach combines information on the health hazards with the exposure potential, and determines the degree of control needed for the process or operation. A control approach can then be identified. The scheme defines what is considered to be adequate control for different hazards in the exposure ranges. Then, it characterizes exposure ranges that are associated with different control approaches and links these two aspects in the workplace.

The basic premise of this approach is that while there are many chemicals in the workplace, the range of control options is fairly limited, and often well known to occupational safety and health professionals. In these situations, the decision logic built into the system can use the information provided by the employer to estimate exposures, and recommend an effective control based on the exposure range. More stringent controls are recommended for chemicals with high levels of exposures and severe effects than for low levels of exposure and mild effects. It is also recognized that expert advice is needed in situations where the health effect is very significant (e.g., a reproductive hazard), and specific controls will not be recommended in those situations.

These are the types of evaluations that are generally made by professionals assessing workplace operations to determine control measures. However, in situations where such professionals are not available, the necessary expertise and advice has essentially been made accessible through a user-friendly system that can be implemented by the employer on site. The potential to positively impact the degree of chemical control in small- to medium-sized work-

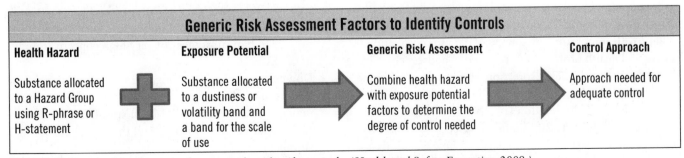

Generic Risk Assessment Factors to Identify Controls

Health Hazard	Exposure Potential	Generic Risk Assessment	Control Approach
Substance allocated to a Hazard Group using R-phrase or H-statement	Substance allocated to a dustiness or volatility band and a band for the scale of use	Combine health hazard with exposure potential factors to determine the degree of control needed	Approach needed for adequate control

Figure 31–3. Generic risk assessment factors used to identify controls. (*Health and Safety Executive, 2009.*)

places through broad implementation of such an approach is significant.

While control banding has been used successfully in a number of situations, work to validate the method continues in many different venues. This research will help both to refine the method as used for chemicals, and expand the approach to other types of work operations that need a systematic approach for determining controls. Work has already been undertaken to apply control-banding approaches to nanotechnology operations, as well as to physical hazards. With the implementation of the GHS in the United States, more of these efforts can be expected to take place and ultimately to provide important resources to smaller U.S. employers to help them identify appropriate controls in an efficient and cost-effective way.

REACH

The Member States of the European Union (EU) are in the process of implementing a new, comprehensive approach to the regulation of chemicals in their region. Commonly referred to as REACH, this regulation addresses the Registration, Evaluation, Authorization and Restriction of Chemicals throughout their life cycle.

The EU, as well as other industrialized countries, has long had regulations that address various aspects of handling chemicals safely. This new approach recognizes that a more integrated, complete approach to all chemicals is needed to help ensure that these materials can be handled appropriately and controlled in all types of use settings. While these requirements are being implemented in European countries, they have broad impact in the rest of the world due to the great extent of European chemical trade. Chemical manufacturers in other countries exporting to European countries will have to comply with the REACH requirements to sell their products in Europe.

In addition to these compliance burdens for U.S. employers, however, REACH is expected to result in the development and assembly of extensive information on each substance addressed. This information ultimately will be available in public databases, and thus accessible globally. Public availability of this extensive information on chemicals will provide important new sources of data for occupational safety and health professionals required to address chemical hazards in workplaces. Protection of workers worldwide will be facilitated by access to such information.

The REACH Regulation (EC) No 1907/2006 entered into force on June 1, 2007, and is based on the premise that industry is best suited to understand how chemicals are used and to ensure that chemicals do not adversely affect human health or the environment. The REACH regulation established the European Chemicals Agency (ECHA) to coordinate implementation. REACH also streamlined the legislative framework on chemical management in the EU by repealing many existing chemical regulations and directives, and incorporating their scope into REACH. REACH establishes processes for the Registration, Evaluation, Authorization and Restriction of Chemicals for new and existing substances registered on the European Inventory of Existing Commercial Substances (EINECS). The intent of the REACH regulation is to provide users of dangerous substances with specific advice to control human and environmental exposures to appropriate levels in order to prevent adverse effects.

Key Provisions
Some of the key provisions of the REACH regulation are as follows:
- There is a general obligation to submit a registration for substances on their own, in mixtures, or in articles that are manufactured/imported (M/I) into the EU, in quantities of one ton or more per year.
- When there is an indication that a substance may pose a risk to man or the environment, ECHA can select specific substances for a detailed evaluation by a Member State. The evaluation may lead to conclusions that a chemical manufacturer must address, such as action to be taken under the restriction or authorization procedures of REACH, or giving information to other authorities to take appropriate action under other legislation.
- The existing restrictions set out in the Marketing and Use Directive (76/769/EEC) were incorporated into REACH. Additionally, going forward, REACH provides the competent authorities with a regulatory process to impose restrictions or prohibit the use of dangerous substances when unacceptable risks to humans or the environment have been identified.
- For substances of very high concern (e.g., carcinogens, mutagens, reproductive toxins, persistent bioaccumulative and toxic [PBT]/very persistent or very bioaccumulative [vPvB]), a process to require authorization for specific uses of a substance may be initiated by ECHA. REACH also provides competent authorities with a regulatory process to ban substances of very high concern from use in the EU.
- Downstream users are obligated to implement the conditions of use (i.e., operational conditions [OC] and risk management measures [RMM]) specified in the exposure scenarios (described below) they receive from their suppliers.

REACH applies to all chemical substances as such, in

mixtures and in articles over the life cycle of the substance, except for those substances specifically exempted in Article 2. Radioactive substances, the transport of dangerous substances, dangerous substances in dangerous mixtures and wastes, are covered under other EU legislation and are therefore exempt from REACH. Article 2 also exempts substances, on their own, in mixtures, or in articles subject to customs supervision under specified conditions, and non-isolated intermediates.

Specific obligations under REACH depend on the activities associated with the use of a substance. Because the requirements under REACH relate to individual substances, a user of chemicals is likely to have more than one defined role, and will need to determine their obligations for each substance they use. In fact, a user of chemicals may have more than one role per substance. The major roles and associated responsibilities under REACH are as follows:

- The manufacturer or importer (M/I) is responsible for the registration of substances.
- Downstream users (DU) in general are responsible for using a substance, as is, in mixtures, or in articles, in compliance with the conditions of use recommended by their suppliers. Downstream users' responsibilities vary based on the type of DU. For example, a formulator is responsible for implementing the exposure scenario conditions of use provided to them from their suppliers when preparing mixtures. The formulator is also responsible for communicating safe use information on their mixtures to their customers. An industrial user is responsible for checking that their use is compliant with any exposure scenarios they receive from their suppliers.
- Distributors are responsible for passing along information on the products they distribute both up and down the supply chain (i.e., from suppliers to customers and from customers to suppliers).

A good resource for understanding the roles and responsibilities defined under REACH is provided in the ECHA publication *Guidance for Downstream Users.*

Registration of Substances

Effective June 1, 2007, REACH was immediately binding for all new substances introduced into the EU. The requirement to register substances is placed on manufacturers and importers. All substances previously registered under the EU's existing requirements in their Dangerous Substances Directive were immediately considered as registered under REACH. Given the scope of the effort to register all existing substances grandfathered under the EINECS inventory, REACH provides a phase-in approach that considers the tonnage and classification of substances as follows:

- December 1, 2010:

  - substances that are carcinogenic, mutagenic, or toxic to reproduction in quantities of ≥ 1 ton
  - substances classified as very toxic to aquatic organisms that may cause long-term adverse effects in quantities of ≥ 100 tons
  - substances in quantities of ≥ 1,000 tons
- June 1, 2013:
  - substances in quantities of ≥ 100 tons
- June 1, 2018:
  - substances in quantities of ≥ 1 ton

Technical Dossier

A technical dossier is required for all substances manufactured/imported in quantities of ≥ 1 ton. It provides basic information, including: the identity of the M/I and substance, information on manufacture and use(s), classification and labeling, guidance on safe use, and study summaries of physical/chemical, toxicological, and ecotoxicological test data.

Chemical Safety Assessment

A Chemical Safety Assessment (CSA) is required for all substances manufactured/imported in quantities of ≥ 10 tons. It will always include the following four hazard assessment steps:

1. Human health hazards
- To determine substance classification and labeling and derived no effect levels (DNELs) or derived minimal effect levels (DMEL) when it is not possible to derive the DNEL. The DNEL is the level of exposure above which humans should not be exposed.
2. Physicochemical hazards
- To determine the classification and labeling of the substance.
3. Environmental hazards
- To determine the classification and labeling and predicted no effect concentrations (PNEC) of the substance. The PNEC is the concentration below which adverse effects in an environmental compartment are not expected to occur.
4. Persistent, bioaccumulative, and toxic (PBT) and very persistent and very bioaccumulative (vPvB) hazards
- To determine if the data on the substance meet the PTB/vPvB criteria provided in REACH Annex XIII.

For dangerous or PBT/vPvB substances manufactured or imported in quantities greater than 10 tons, the CSA must also include two additional steps, taking into consideration the entire life cycle of the substance, including its use as is, in mixtures, and articles:

5. Exposure assessment
- To identify all relevant uses throughout the life cycle of the substance, and to generate exposure scenarios

(ES) documenting the conditions of use that will result in a safe use.

- The need to systematically evaluate the exposure concentration of substances across each life cycle stage has led to the development of broad based exposure estimation models in the EU. An initial assessment using these conservative exposure estimation models (i.e., Tier 1 models) can be used to comply with the REACH requirement to systematically complete substance exposure assessments for all dangerous substances manufactured or imported in quantities greater than 10 tons. If safe use cannot be demonstrated using the Tier 1 models, then Tier 2 models maybe helpful in demonstrating safe use.

- The creation of ES will be an iterative process in which the operational conditions and/or risk management measures may require refinement after an initial exposure assessment using modeling tools (i.e., Tier 1 assessments). After each adjustment to the OC and/or RMM, a subsequent exposure assessment will be needed to determine if the exposure is below the appropriate DNEL or PNEC. The exposure assessment process may also include the use of other (higher tier) tools or the use of exposure monitoring data.

6. Risk characterization

- To determine if the potential risks resulting from the use of a substance are adequately controlled. It consists of a comparison of the derived no effect levels (DNELs) and predicted no effect concentrations (PNECs) with the estimated or measured exposure concentrations, documented in the exposure assessment step, to humans and the environment, respectively.

Derived No Effect Levels

DNELs are established based on all available hazard information for specific populations (e.g., workers, consum-

ers), specific route(s) of exposure (e.g., inhalation, dermal, and ingestion for consumers), duration of exposure (e.g., acute, long-term), and type of effect (e.g., local, systemic). In those cases where minimal hazard data are available, the calculated DNEL involves considerable uncertainty, and may require the use of default assessment factors for multiple steps in the calculation process resulting in conservative exposure levels. As further toxicological information becomes available, a more robust estimation becomes possible, and it is expected that when more data on substances is developed under REACH, many DNELs will be updated.

Expected exposure patterns can be taken into consideration so all combinations of populations, routes, exposure duration, and effect types, as listed in Table 31–D, need not be calculated.

DNELs are used via the risk characterization process to support the decision to require operational conditions and/or risk management measures that keep the exposure concentration of a substance below the DNEL. They do not replace occupational exposure limits, and downstream users are not required to monitor exposures to maintain a level below a DNEL.

Predicted No Effect Concentrations

PNECs are based on all available hazard information for all endpoints; however, the endpoints most frequently used are mortality, growth, and reproduction. PNECs are calculated for specific compartments of the environment because the types of organisms inhabiting the different environments (i.e., water, soil, air) and compartments (e.g., water, sediment) are not the same. Additionally, the bioavailability of a substance can vary in different compartments. Similar to the derivation of DNELs, conservative assessments factors resulting in conservative no-effect concentration limits are applied in those cases with minimal hazard data. As further ecotoxicological information becomes available,

TABLE 31–D	DN(M)ELS that May Be Derived		
Exposure pattern	***DNEL/DMEL***		
	Workers	***General Population***	
Acute – Inhalation, Systemic effects	✔	✔	
Acute – Dermal, Local effects	✔	✔	
Acute – Inhalation, Local effects	✔	✔	
Long-term – Dermal, Systemic effects	✔	✔	
Long-term – Inhalation, Systemic effects	✔	✔	
Long-term – Oral, Systemic effects	Not Relevant	✔	
Long-term – Dermal, Local effects	✔	✔	
Long-term – Inhalation, Local effects	✔	✔	

Source: European Chemicals Agency. *Guidance on information requirements and chemical safety assessment.* Chapter R8: Characterization of dose [concentration]-response for human health. December 2010.

a more robust estimation becomes possible. It is expected as more data on substances are developed under REACH, many PNECS will be updated.

Table 31–E lists common examples of the different target organisms and compartment and their relationship to the PNECs derived under REACH. PNECs are used via the risk characterization process to support the decision to require operational conditions and/or risk management measures that keep the exposure concentration of a substance below the PNEC.

Exposure Scenarios

An exposure scenario (ES) is the main output of the exposure assessment process, which documents a set of operational conditions and risk management measures for a specific use. In a quantitative exposure scenario, the conditions of use ensure that expected exposure resulting from the use of the substance will be below the appropriate DNEL or PNEC. ECHA's recommended four-section ES format for communication in the supply chain contains the following section headers and information:

- Section 1: Title of Exposure Scenario.
  - Provides information on the specific use(s) covered by the exposure scenario. Under REACH, use is systematically communicated via the application of a use descriptor system based on five types of codes. The combinations of use descriptor codes form a brief description of a use. The five types of codes used in the system are as follows.
    - *Sector of Use* describes the sector of the economy where the substance is used (e.g., manufacture, industrial use, consumer use).
    - *Product Category* describes the type of mixture the substance is contained in on end use (e.g., adhesives, sealants, coatings, and paints).
    - *Process Category* describes the technical process or application of the substance in an occupational setting (e.g., industrial spraying, roller or brushing application).
    - *Environmental Release Category* describes the broad conditions of use from the environmental perspective (e.g., manufacture of substances, formulation of mixtures).
    - *Article Category* describes the type of article into which the substance has been processed (e.g., wood and wood furniture, toys, scented toys).
- Section 2: Conditions of use affecting exposure.
  - Contains the conditions of use that affect the level of exposure (e.g. Operating Conditions and Risk Management Measures) for the specific use(s) covered by the exposure scenario. The types of information included are:
    - Operational Conditions (OC)
      - the physical form in which the substance is manufactured, processed, and/or used; and
      - the description of activities in terms of the duration and frequency of exposure, specification of room size, temperature, the concentration of the substance if used in a mixture, and the amount used.
    - Risk Management Measures (RMM)
      - description of risk management measures, such as engineering controls or personal protective equipment to reduce or avoid exposure of workers and the environment; and
      - the waste management measures to reduce or avoid exposure of humans or the environment during waste disposal and recycling.
- Section 3: Exposure estimation and reference to its source.
  - The estimated level of exposure to a substance and the corresponding risk characterization ratios are provided demonstrating that the exposure assessment process has resulted in a safe use to man and the environment.
- Section 4: Guidance to downstream users to evaluate if they work inside the boundaries set by the ES.
  - This section provides information to the downstream users so they can evaluate if the exposure scenario covers their use when not all of their conditions of use are identical to those provided by the supplier.

TABLE 31–E Relationship Between Target Organisms/Compartments for Target Environmental Exposure Assessments

Target	Medium of Exposure	PNEC
Aquatic organisms	Surface water	PNEC (freshwater)
	Seawater	PNEC (marine water)
Benthic organisms	Sediment	PNEC (freshwater sediment)
	Marine sediment	PNEC (marine sediment)
Microorganisms	STP aeration tank	PNEC (sewage treatment plant)
Terrestrial organisms	Agricultural soil	PNEC (soil)
Fish-eating predators	Marine fish	PNEC (oral predators)

Source: European Chemicals Agency. *Guidance on Information Requirements and Chemical Safety Assessment.* Chapter R10: Characterization of dose [concentration]-response for environment, May 2008.

Risk Characterization

Where possible, the exposure-based assessment should be quantitative. In a quantitative assessment the estimated or measured exposure must be compared against the DNEL or PNEC. For the purpose of REACH, an exposure is considered safe when the estimated or measured exposure concentration of the substance for a specific use is less than the corresponding safe use concentration. In REACH this is expressed as the risk characterization ratio (RCR), which is calculated by dividing the estimated or measured exposure concentration by the DNEL or PNEC. If the RCR is < 1, then the use described in the exposure is considered safe. If the RCR is > 1, then the conditions of use must be modified to reduce the exposure (e.g., reduce the duration or frequency of tasks, and/or require additional risk management measures).

Chemical Safety Report

The Chemical Safety Report (CSR) provides comprehensive documentation of physical/chemical properties, uses, hazard information, classification, and labeling, and, if appropriate, exposure-based assessment information for a single substance. A CSR is required for all substances manufactured or imported in quantities of greater than 10 tons a year. The Exposure Assessment and Risk Characterization chapters need only be completed when a substance is classified as dangerous and/or it meets the REACH PBT/vPvB criteria. Table 31–F lists the contents of a CSR.

Part A of the CSR provides a summary of the risk management measures for all the registered uses of a substance. The preparer of the CSR must also certify that they have implemented the recommended risk management measures

TABLE 31–F	Chemical Safety Report (CSR) Format
Part A	
1. Summary of Risk Management Measures	
2. Declaration that RMM are Implemented	
3. Declaration that RMM are Communicated	
Part B	
1. Identity of the Substance and Physical Chemical Properties	
2. Manufacture and Uses	
3. Classification and Labeling	
4. Environmental Fate Properties	
5. Human Health Assessment	
6. Human Health Assessment of Physicochemical Properties	
7. Environmental Hazard Assessment	
8. PBT and vPvB Assessment	
9. Exposure Assessment	
10. Risk Characterization	

Source: Corrigendum to Regulation (EC) No 1907/2006 of the European Parliament and of the Council of 18 December 2006 concerning the Registration, Evaluation, Authorization and Restriction of Chemicals (REACH), establishing a European Chemicals Agency. *Official Journal of the European Union* L 396, 30 December 2006.

for their own uses(s), and that they have communicated the exposure scenario information to distributors and downstream users in applicable Safety Data Sheets.

Part B of the CSR provides the detailed data used during the chemical safety assessment and provides justifications for the decisions taken during the hazard and exposure assessment processes. Manufacturers and importers have an obligation to ensure that the information provided in a safety data sheet is consistent with the information submitted in the CSR.

Information in the Supply Chain
Safety Data Sheet

The Safety Data Sheet (SDS) is the primary tool for transmitting REACH-required information down the supply chain. The SDS with the REACH information is referred to as an extended SDS. The legal requirements to supply an SDS are detailed in the articles of REACH, and a detailed guide to the compilation of SDSs is provided in Annex II of REACH. A summary of the exposure scenarios documented in the CSR must be attached at the end of the SDS to provide downstream users with the conditions of use that will adequately control the risks associated with a dangerous and/or PBT/vPvB substance.

Downstream Users

Downstream users (DU) are obligated to apply the recommended conditions of use (e.g., operating conditions and risk management measures) documented in the SDS and/or exposure scenarios they receive from their suppliers. The key steps in meeting this obligation are as follows.

- Read the description of use in part 1 of the exposure scenario to determine if your use is consistent with the use being described.
- Compare your use of the substance or mixture to determine if it might lead to a higher exposure. For example, you may use it in a smaller room, at higher temperatures, for longer durations, or more frequently, or in larger amounts. If your operational conditions suggest that your use may result in a higher exposure, then you may not be in compliance with the exposure scenario.
- If the supplier specifies risk management measures in the exposure scenario, compare them to your current practices when using the substance. You'll need to determine if your RMM are just as, or more, efficient as those recommended by your supplier. If during your evaluation of the RMM you believe the supplier's recommended RMM are inadequate, then you are obligated to inform your supplier that their recommendations are inappropriate.
- If you determine that your use is not described, or that your operational conditions and/or RMM would result

in a higher exposure, then you may want to contact your supplier. Your options are to provide sufficient information for your supplier to update their substance registration to include your use, register the use yourself or look for less hazardous alternate substances or mixtures.

Summary on REACH

Over time, the amount of hazard data for chemicals under REACH will increase as a result of the need to register substances previously grandfathered on the EINECS inventory. As these existing substances are registered, and data gaps are identified, more toxicological information will become available to better assess the hazards of chemicals—which will lead to improved exposure controls for previously unclassified chemicals. Additionally, there are requirements to systematically evaluate the exposure to dangerous or PTB and vPvB substances, manufactured or imported in quantities of greater than 10 tons, for the life cycle of a substance. These evaluations are expected to result in additional exposure control recommendations for these substances leading to a reduction in health effects associated with occupational exposure to chemicals. Increased information on chemicals found in workplaces should help to facilitate industrial hygienists devising protective programs for workers exposed to chemicals.

OCCUPATIONAL HEALTH AND SAFETY MANAGEMENT SYSTEMS

It has been long recognized by occupational safety and health professionals that a comprehensive, systematic approach to a safety and health program is likely to achieve the best results in terms of employee protections. In the United States, there are no general mandatory requirements for such an approach at the federal level of OSHA standards. However, there are federal OSHA requirements in the construction industry and for federal workplaces. A number of OSHA state plans also have either voluntary provisions or mandatory requirements for safety and health programs in workplaces in their states. OSHA has long encouraged the adoption of such programs through their Voluntary Protection Program (VPP). Companies in the VPP have been recognized by OSHA as having exemplary programs to protect their workers.

OSHA has voluntary guidelines regarding the provision of effective and comprehensive safety and health programs. The major elements of such programs include:
- management commitment and employee involvement;
- worksite analysis;
- hazard prevention and control; and
- safety and health training.

In addition to these voluntary OSHA provisions, there is a national voluntary industry consensus standard that addresses occupational safety and health programs. Adopted by the American National Standards Institute (ANSI), ANSI Z10, Occupational Health and Safety Management Systems, provides industry with guidance on how to establish an effective program.

Similar initiatives have been developed in other countries. In particular, the British Standards Institute (BSI) developed a standard for occupational health and safety management systems, and the ILO developed Guidelines on OSH Management Systems. While varying in scope and detail, these standards all have a similar approach as that described in the OSHA guidelines.

Some stakeholders have argued for an international voluntary consensus standard to address occupational health and safety management systems through the International Organization for Standardization (ISO). The ISO previously adopted ISO 9000, a group of related standards that address quality management systems and include a certification process for facilities meeting the standards. In addition, the ISO also adopted ISO 14000, an environmental management system that also allows facilities to be certified as meeting the standards. Having an ISO standard for occupational health and safety management was seen as being complementary to these two approaches, and would also allow facilities to have their health and safety programs certified.

In the absence of an ISO standard in this area, a group of these stakeholders, led by the BSI, developed standards that are referred to as Occupational Health and Safety Assessment Series (OHSAS) 18000, which provides standards for occupational health and safety management, along with the opportunity to be certified. OHSAS 18001 is the source of the specified provisions to which a facility is certified, while OHSAS 18002 provides guidelines for the implementation of OHSAS 18001. The OHSAS developers indicate that at such time as a similar international standard to address occupational health and safety management systems is adopted (for example, by the ISO), these provisions developed by an ad hoc group of interested parties (the OHSAS Project Group) will be withdrawn. In the meantime, a number of facilities have been certified to these provisions. There has not been widespread application of the approach in the United States.

Any of the documents mentioned can provide a template for employers wishing to establish an occupational health and safety management system in their facility. Establishing a systematic approach to evaluating hazards in a workplace and identifying control measures has been shown by companies implementing such a system to be an effective way to handle safety and health issues. It helps to ensure that all issues are addressed, and that both managers and employees are invested in ensuring that the system is effective. While there are minimal mandatory requirements in the United States regarding such programs, their utility is undeniable. Implementing such a systematic approach would be useful in all types of workplaces.

SUMMARY

This chapter provides a brief overview of several international initiatives to address occupational safety and health issues. Such issues are faced in all workplaces around the world. While the conditions may vary, the general approaches are the same. There is increasing recognition that exchanging information on approaches to identifying, evaluating, and controlling workplace hazards will leverage limited resources and provide a forum where novel and creative ideas can be shared. Safety and health professionals can learn from both the successes and the mistakes of their counterparts in other countries. Practitioners of occupational safety and health should seek to learn more about international initiatives, as well as take the opportunity to participate in such endeavors where possible. Hopefully, the result will be increased protections for workers around the world, which will lead to fewer illnesses and injuries from workplace conditions.

BIBLIOGRAPHY

American National Standards Institute. Z400.1/Z129.1-2010, *Hazardous Workplace Chemicals – Hazard Evaluation and Safety Data Sheet and Precautionary Labeling Preparation*. Washington, DC: ANSI, 2010.

American National Standards Institute. Z10, *Occupational Health and Safety Management Systems*. Washington, DC: ANSI, 2005.

Commission of the European Communities. Council Directive 89/391/EEC of 12 June 1989 on the introduction of measures to encourage improvements in the safety and health of workers at work. OJ L 183, 29.6.1989, 1–8.

Department of Labor, Occupational Safety and Health Administration. *Hazard Communication*: Proposed Rule. Federal Register, 74 FR 50280-50549. Washington, DC. September 29, 2009.

European Agency for Safety and Health at Work. *Dangerous Substances: Occupational Exposure Limits*. Bilbao, Spain: EU-OSHA 2011. http://osha.europa.eu/en/topics/ds/oel/index.stm

European Chemicals Agency. *Exposure Scenario for Chemical Safety Report and Communication. Example: Consumer Use of a Substance in Cleaning Products*. Helsinki, Finland: ECHA, August 2011. http://echa.europa.eu/documents/10162/17234/es_for_consumer_20110829_en.pdf

European Chemicals Agency. *Exposure Scenario for Chemical Safety Report and Communication. Example: Professional Use of a Substance in Floor Coatings*. Helsinki, Finland: ECHA, August 2011. http://echa.europa.eu/documents/10162/17235/es_professional_use_20110829.pdf

European Chemicals Agency. *Guidance for downstream users*. Helsinki, Finland: ECHA, January 2008. http://guidance.echa.europa.eu/docs/guidance_document/du_en.pdf?vers=29_01_08h

European Chemicals Agency. *Guidance on Information Requirements and Chemical Safety Assessment*. Chapter R.10: Characterisation of dose [concentration]-response for environment. Helsinki, Finland: ECHA, May 2008. http://echa.europa.eu/documents/10162/17224/information_requirements_r10_en.pdf

European Chemicals Agency. *Guidance on Information Requirements and Chemical Safety Assessment*. Exposure Scenario Format in Part D: Exposure scenario building and Part F: CSR Format. Helsinki, Finland: ECHA, May 2010. http://echa.europa.eu/documents/10162/17224/information_requirements_esformat_en.pdf

European Chemicals Agency. *Guidance on Information Requirements and Chemical Safety Assessment*. Chapter R.8: Characterisation of dose [concentration]-response for human health. Helsinki, Finland: ECHA, December 2010. http://echa.europa.eu/documents/10162/17224/information_requirements_r8_en.pdf

European Chemicals Agency. *Guidance on Information Requirements and Chemical Safety Assessment*. Part B: Hazard assessment. Helsinki, Finland: ECHA, August 2011. http://echa.europa.eu/documents/10162/17235/information_requirements_part_b_en.pdf

European Chemicals Agency. Press Release: ECHA Received 3.1 Million Classification and Labeling Notifications, ECHAPR/11/01. Helsinki, Finland. January 4, 2011. http://echa.europa.eu/documents/10162/17096/pr_11_01_clp_deadline_20110104_en.pdf

European Union. Corrigendum to Regulation (EC) No 1907/2006 of the European Parliament and of the Council of 18 December 2006 concerning the Registration, Evaluation, Authorization and Restriction of Chemicals (REACH), establishing a European Chemicals Agency, amending Directive 1999/45/EC and repealing Council Regulation (EEC) No 793/93 and Commission Regulation (EC) No 1488/94 as well as Council Directive 76/769/EEC and Commission Directives 91/155/EEC, 93/67/EEC, 93/105/EC and 2000/21/EC. *Official Journal of the European Union* L 396, 30 December 2006.

European Union. Regulation (EC) No 1272/2008 of the European Parliament and of the Council of 16 December 2008 on classification, labeling and packaging of substances and mixtures, amending and repealing Directives 67/548/EEC and 1999/45/EC, and amending Regulation (EC) No 1907/2006. *Official Journal of the European Union* L 353, 31 December 2008.

European Union. Regulation (EC) No 1272/2008 of the European Parliament and of the Council of 16 December 2008 on classification, labeling and packaging of substances and mixtures, amending and repealing Directives 67/548/EEC and 1999/45/EC, and amending Regulation (EC) No 1907/2006. *Official Journal of the European Union* L 353, 31 December 2008.

Health and Safety Executive. I. London: HSE, September 2009. http://www.coshh-essentials.org.uk/assets/live/CETB.pdf

International Labor Organization. *Chemical Control Toolkit.* Geneva: ILO, 2011. http://www.ilo.org/legacy/english/protection/safework/ctrl_banding/toolkit/icct/index.htm

International Labor Organization. *Guidelines on Occupational Safety and Health Management Systems, ILO-OSH 2001.* Geneva: ILO, January 2001. http://www.ilo.org/safework/areasofwork/occupational-safety-and-health-management-systems/lang--en/index.htm

International Labor Organization. *List of Ratifications of International Labor Conventions—United States.* Geneva: ILO, 2011. http://webfusion.ilo.org/public/applis/appl-byCtry.cfm?lang=EN&CTYCHOICE=0610

International Labor Organization. *Programme on Safety and Health at Work and the Environment (SafeWork), Guidelines on Occupational Safety and Health Management Systems.* Geneva: ILO, 2001. http://www.ilo.org/safework/areasofwork/occupational-safety-and-health-management-systems/lang--en/index.htm

International Labor Organization. *Programme on Safety and Health at Work and the Environment (SafeWork): ILO Instruments on OSH.* Geneva: ILO, 2011. http://www.ilo.org/safework/normative/lang--en/index.htm

OHSAS Project Group. *Occupational Health and Safety Assessment Series (OHSAS) 18001.* Cheshire, England: The Occupational Health and Safety Group, 2007.

Occupational Safety and Health Administration. *Safety and Health Program Management Guidelines; Issuance of Voluntary Guidelines.* Washington, DC. OSHA/DOL, 1989. http://www.osha.gov/pls/oshaweb/owadisp.show_document?p_id=12909&p_table=FEDERAL_REGISTER

United Nations. *Globally Harmonised System of Classification and Labelling of Chemicals (GHS),* 4th ed. New York and Geneva: United Nations, 2011. http://www.unece.org/trans/danger/publi/ghs/ghs_rev04/04files_e.html

United Nations Environment Programme. *Strategic Approach to International Chemicals Management,* from SAICM Texts and Resolutions of the International Conference on Chemicals Management. Geneva: United Nations, March 2006. http://www.saicm.org/documents/saicm%20texts/SAICM_publication_ENG.pdf

Zalk DM, *Control Banding, A Simplified, Qualitative Strategy for the Assessment of Occupational Risks and Selection of Solutions.* Delft, Netherlands: TU Delft publisher, 2010.

Zalk DM, Nelson DI. History and Evolution of Control Banding: A Review. *J Occup Environ Hyg* 5:5, 330-346, 2008.

APPENDICES

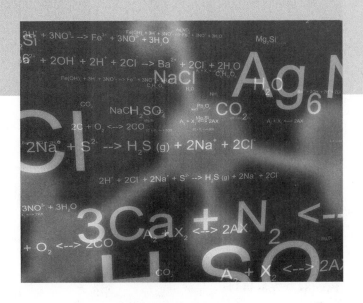

Additional Resources

by Karen Andrews, MLS

The 40 years since the passage of the Occupational Safety and Health Act have seen an almost explosive broadening in the practice of industrial hygiene. Industrial hygiene practice may now include such diverse issues as the control of airborne chemical contaminants, noise, ionizing and nonionizing radiations, ergonomics, environmental pollution, infectious and communicable diseases, safety, and indoor air quality.

It is almost impossible for any one professional to be an expert on every aspect of industrial hygiene practice. Fortunately, there are many organizations that the industrial hygienist or safety professional can turn to for help, including: professional organizations

- *scientific and service organizations*
- *governmental agencies*
- *occupational health clinics*
- *Council for Occupational Safety and Health (COSH) and other community groups*
- *industry organizations*
- *labor unions and other employee organizations*
- *university based research and training programs*

The first part of this chapter includes some information about those types of organizations. The second part of this chapter includes information about on-line sources of information, including the Internet.

PROFESSIONAL ORGANIZATIONS

American Association of Occupational Health Nurses (AAOHN)
7794 Grow Dr.
Pensacola, FL 32514
(800) 241-8014 or (850) 474-6963; Fax (850) 484-8762;
www.aaohn.org

American Biological Safety Association
1200 Allanson Rd.
Mundelein, IL 60060-3808
(866) 425-1385 or (847) 949-1517
Fax (847) 566-4580
www.absa.org.
Certifies biosafety professionals. Many areas have affiliates.

American Board of Industrial Hygiene
6015 West St. Joseph, Suite 102
Lansing, MI 48917-3980
(517) 321-2638
Fax (517) 321-4624
www.abih.org
ABIH is the certifying body for the Certified Industrial Hygienist (CIH) and Certified Associate Industrial Hygienist (CAIH).

American Conference of Governmental Industrial
Hygienists (ACGIH)
Kemper Woods Center
1330 Kemper Meadow Dr.
Cincinnati, OH 45240
(513) 742-2020
Fax (513) 742-3355
www.acgih.org
The ACGIH annually publishes Threshold Limit Values for air contaminants, and other consensus standards, and publishes and distributes a wide range of manuals and other materials regarding industrial hygiene practice.

American Industrial Hygiene Association (AIHA)
3141 Fairview Park Dr., Suite 777
Falls Church, VA 22042
(703) 849-8888
Fax (703) 207-3561
www.aiha.org
The AIHA provides continuing education programs and opportunities for industrial hygienists to meet and exchange ideas. It also maintains a laboratory certification program.

American Public Health Association (APHA)
800 I St. NW
Washington, DC 20001-3710
(202) 777-2742
TTY (202) 777-2500
Fax (202) 777-2534
www.apha.org
The Occupational Health Section of the APHA works to promote safe and healthy jobs by organizing around current issues; contributes to occupational health and safety policy development.

American Society of Heating, Refrigerating, and Air
Conditioning Engineers (ASHRAE)
1791 Tullie Circle, NE
Atlanta, GA 30329
(800) 527-4723 or (404) 636-8400
Fax (404) 321-5478
www.ashrae.org
ASHRAE publishes consensus standards regarding the performance of building ventilation systems and other indoor air quality issues.

American Society of Safety Engineers
1800 E. Oakton St.
Des Plaines, IL 60018
(847) 699-2929
Fax (847) 768-3434
www.asse.org

Board of Certified Safety Professionals
2301 W. Bradley Ave.
Champaign, IL 61821
(217) 359-9263
Fax (217) 359-0055
www.bcsp.org
The Board of Certified Safety Professionals certifies practitioners in the safety profession.

Health Physics Society
1313 Dolley Madison Blvd., Suite 402
McLean, VA 22101
(703) 790-1745
Fax (703) 790-2672
www.hps.org

Human Factors and Ergonomics Society
P.O. Box 1369
Santa Monica, CA 90406-1369
(310) 394-1811
Fax (310) 394-2410
www.hfes.org

Illuminating Engineering Society
120 Wall St. Floor 17
New York, NY 10005-4001
(212) 248-5000
Fax (212) 248-5017 or (212) 248-5018
www.ies.org

Society of Manufacturing Engineers
One SME Dr.
Dearborn, MI 48121

(800) 733-4763 or (313) 425-3000

Fax (313) 425-3400

www.sme.org

Society of Toxicology
1821 Michael Faraday Dr., Suite 300
Reston, VA 20190
(703) 438-3115
Fax (703) 438-3113
www.toxicology.org

SCIENTIFIC AND SERVICE ORGANIZATIONS

American National Standards Institute (ANSI)
1899 L St., NW, 11th Floor
Washington, DC 20036
(202) 293-8020
Fax (202) 293-9287
www.ansi.org
Publishes consensus standards on a variety of health and safety issues; standards available for purchase on-line.

National Council on Radiation Protection
and Measurements
7910 Woodmont Ave., Suite 400
Bethesda, MD 20814-3095
(301) 657-2652
Fax (301) 907-8768
www.ncrponline.org

National Fire Protection Association
1 Batterymarch Park
Quincy, MA, 02169-7471
(800) 344-3555 or (617) 770-3000
Fax (617) 770-0700
www.nfpa.org
Publishes national consensus fire code and interpretive handbooks.

National Safety Council
1121 Spring Lake Dr.
Itasca, IL 60143-3201
(800) 621-7615 or (630) 285-1121
Fax (630) 285-1315
www.nsc.org

Underwriters Laboratories Inc.
2600 N.W. Lake Rd.
Camas, WA 98607-8542
(877) 854-3577

Fax (360) 817-6278
www.ul.com
Website includes a list of testing laboratories.

U.S. GOVERNMENT AGENCIES

NIOSH

The National Institute for Occupational Safety and Health (NIOSH) was established by the Occupational Safety and Health Act of 1970. The OSHAct made NIOSH responsible for conducting research to make the nation's work places healthier and safer.

To identify hazards, NIOSH conducts inspections, laboratory and epidemiological research, publishes its findings, and makes recommendations for improved working conditions to regulatory agencies such as the Occupational Safety and Health Administration and the Mine Safety and Health Administration.

NIOSH works with groups and individuals who share its concern for protecting the health of all American workers. It plays a vital role training occupational health and safety experts and communicating the latest results to those most concerned.

All NIOSH Services can be accessed through a toll-free number: (800) CDC-INFO (232-4636). NIOSH can also be reached at http://www.cdc.gov/niosh/.

Key NIOSH Services
Health Hazard Evaluations
Employers, employees, or their representatives who suspect a health problem in the workplace can request a NIOSH Health Hazard Evaluation (HHE) to assess the problem.

Mine Safety
Inspectors from the Mine Safety and Health Administration (MSHA) check surface mines at least twice a year and underground mines at least four times a year. They also conduct investigations of accidents and complaints.

Fatal Accident Investigations
NIOSH identifies risk factors for work-related fatalities and injuries through its Fatal Accident Circumstances and Epidemiology project (FACE).

Extramural Grants
NIOSH sponsors extramural research in priority areas and coordinates this with its intramural and contract research and that of other Health and Human Services (HHS) and U.S. departments.

Databases

NIOSH maintains extensive databases of occupational safety and health information from around the world.

Respirators

NIOSH tests and certifies respirators to assure their compliance with federal requirements.

Educational Research Centers

NIOSH supports Education and Research Centers (ERCs) at U.S. universities to help assure an adequate supply of trained occupational safety and health professionals (see listing below).

Publications

NIOSH publishes and distributes a variety of publications related to occupational safety and health. Most publications are available on-line.

In addition to NIOSH, many state health departments maintain their own occupational health and safety divisions. Contact them for more information specific state regulations.

OSHA

The Occupational Safety and Health Administration (OSHA) was created under the Occupational Safety and Health Act (OSHAct) of 1970, within the Department of Labor "... *to assure so far as possible every working man and woman in the Nation safe and healthful working conditions and to preserve our human resources.*"

U.S. Department of Labor
Occupational Safety and Health Administration (OSHA)
200 Constitution Ave. NW
Washington, DC 20210
(800) 321-OSHA (6742) to report an emergency, file a complaint, or for information
TTY (877) 889-5627
www.osha.gov

Regional Offices

(Please Note: In addition to OSHA, many states maintain their own federally approved occupational safety and health plans. States that do so are indicated with *).

Region I
(CT*, MA, ME, NH, RI, VT*)
JFK Federal Building, Room E340
Boston, MA 02203
(617) 565-9860
Fax (617) 565-9827

Region II
(NJ*, NY*, PR*, VI*)
201 Varick St.
Room 670
New York, NY 10014
(212) 337-2378
Fax (212) 337-2371

Region III
(DC, DE, MD*, PA, VA*, WV)
U.S. Department of Labor / OSHA
The Curtis Center 170 S. Independence Mall West
Suite 740 West
Philadelphia, PA 19106-3309
(215) 861-4900
Fax (215) 861-4904

Region IV
(AL*, FL, GA, KY*, MS, NC*, SC*, TN*)
61 Forsyth St., SW Room 6T50
Atlanta, GA 30303
(678) 237-0400
Fax (678) 237-0447

Region V
(IL*, IN*, MI*, MN*, OH, WI)
230 S. Dearborn St.
Room 3244
Chicago, IL 60604
(312) 353-2220
Fax (312) 353-7774

Region VI
(AR, LA, NM*, OK, TX)
525 Griffin St.
Suite 602
Dallas, TX 75202
(972) 850-4145
Fax (972) 850-4149
FSO Fax (972) 850-4150

Region VII
(IA*, KS, MO, NE)
Two Pershing Square Building
2300 Main St., Suite 1010
Kansas City, MO 64108-2416
(816) 283-8745
Voice (816) 283-0545
Fax (816) 283-0547

Region VIII
(CO, MT, ND, SD, UT*, WY*)
1999 Broadway, Suite 1690
Denver, CO 80202
(720) 264-6550
Fax (720) 264-6585

Region IX
(American Samoa, AZ*, CA*, Guam, HI*, NV*)
90 7th St., Suite 18100
San Francisco, CA 94103
(415) 625-2547 (Main Public - 8:00 AM - 4:30 PM Pacific)
Fax (415) 625-2534

Region X
(AK*, ID, OR*, WA*)
1111 Third Ave., Suite 715
Seattle, WA 98101-3212
(206) 553-5930
Fax (206) 553-6499

* These states and territories operate their own OSHA-approved job safety and health programs (the Connecticut and New York plans cover public employees only). States with approved programs must have a standard that is identical to, or at least as effective as, the federal standard.

ASSOCIATION OF OCCUPATIONAL AND ENVIRONMENTAL CLINICS

The Association of Occupational and Environmental Clinics (AOEC) is a network of over 60 clinics in the United States and Canada. Their purpose is to evaluate and treat patients with occupational and environmental exposures. Further information on all of the following clinics may be accessed via the Internet at www.aoec.org.

California
Occupational and Environmental Health Clinic
University of California at San Francisco
2330 Post St., Suite 460
San Francisco, CA 94115
(415) 885-7580
Fax (415) 771-4472
Patricia Quinlan, MPH, CIH
Alt. Contact: Robert Harrison, MD, MPH

Occupational and Environmental Health Clinic
Employee Health Services

University of California, Davis Medical Center
Cypress Building Suite A
2221 Stockton Blvd.
Sacramento, CA 95817
(530) 754-7635
Fax (530)752-3239
Stephen McCurdy, MD, MPH

Occupational and Environmental Health Clinic
University of California at Irvine
5201 California Ave., Suite 100
Irvine, CA 92617
(949) 824-8641
Fax (949) 824-2345
Dean Baker, MD, MPH

Colorado
Division of Environmental and Occupational Health Sciences
National Jewish Medical Research Center
1400 Jackson St.
Denver, CO 80206
(303) 398-1520
Appts (303) 398-1733
Fax (303) 398-1452
Peggy Mroz, MSPH
Alt. Contact: Cecile Rose, MD, MPH

Denver Health Center for Occupational Safety and Health
605 Bannock St., 4th Floor
Denver, CO 80204-4507
(303) 436-7155
Fax (303) 436-5113
Karen Mulloy, DO, MSCH

Denver Health Clinic at DIA
Main Terminal-6th Level DIA Airport
8400 Pena Blvd.
Denver, CO 80249
(303) 317-0607
Fax (303) 342-8479

Connecticut
Yale University Occupational and
Environmental Medicine Program
135 College St., 3rd Floor
New Haven, CT 06510
(203) 785-4197
Fax (203) 785-7391
Carrie Redlich, MD
Alt. Contact: Peter M. Rabinowitz, MD, MPH

University of Connecticut-Farmington
Occupational and Environmental Medicine Program
263 Farmington Ave.
Farmington, CT 06030
(860) 679-2893-6210
Fax (860) 679-1349
Oluremi Aliyu, MD, MPH

District of Columbia

Mid-Atlantic Center for Children's Health and the
Environment
2233 Wisconsin Ave., NW #317
Washington, DC 20007
(202) 471-4829
Fax (202) 471-4806
Jerome Paulson, MD

Florida

Comprehensive Occupational Medicine for
Business and Industry (COMBI)
9210 Florida Palm Dr.
Tampa, FL 33619
(813) 246-4277
Fax (813) 246-4654
Bruce K. Bohnker, MD, MPH

Georgia

Georgia Occupational & Environmental Toxicology Clinic
Grady Memorial Hospital
80 Jesse Hill Jr. Dr.
12th Floor, C Wing
Atlanta, GA 30303
(404) 616-3409
Fax (404) 616-2961
Brent W. Morgan, MD

Illinois

John H. Stroger, Jr. Hospital of Cook County
Occupational and Environmental Medicine
1900 West Polk, Room 918
Chicago, IL 60612
(312) 864-5520
Fax (312) 864-9701
Anne Krantz, MD, MPH
Peter Orris, MD, MPH
Ann Naughton, RN, MPH, COHN

University of Illinois-Chicago
Occupational & Environmental Medicine Program
835 South Wolcott, M/C 684

Chicago, IL 60612
(312) 996-7420
Fax (312) 413-8485
Susan Buchanan, MD, MPH

Iowa

University of Iowa College of Medicine
Occupational Medicine Clinic
Department Internal Medicine
200 Hawkins Dr., C33-GH
Iowa City, IA 52242
(319) 353-7072
Appts (319) 356-8486
Fax (319) 353-6406
Patrick G. Hartley, MB, BCh, MPH

Kansas

University of Kansas Medical Center
Environmental & Occupational Health
3901 Rainbow Blvd., G572 KU Hospital
Kansas City, KS 66160-7371
(913) 588-6152
Fax (913) 588-2715
H. William Barkman, MD, MSPH

Kentucky

University of Kentucky Occupational Medicine Program
2400 Greatstone Point
Lexington, KY 40504
(859) 257-5150
Fax (859) 257-8982
Scott Prince, MD, MSPH

Maryland

Johns Hopkins University
Center for Occupational Health (Pulmonary only)
5501 Hopkins Bayview Circle
Baltimore, MD 21224
(410) 550-5864
Fax (410) 955-1811
Virginia M. Weaver, MD, MPH

Occupational Health Program
University of Maryland School of Medicine
405 W. Redwood St., 2nd Floor
Baltimore, MD 21201
(410) 706-7464
Fax (410) 706-4078
Melissa McDiarmid, MD, MPH
Carrie Dorsey, MD, MPH

Massachusetts

Cambridge Health Alliance
Occupational and Environmental Health Center
1493 Cambridge St.
Cambridge, MA 02139
(617) 665-1580
Fax (617) 665-1671
Rose Goldman, MD, MPH

Caritas Good Samaritan Occupational Health Services
Merchants Building
75 Stockwell Dr.
Avon, MA 02332
(508) 427-3900
Fax (508) 427-3905
Robert Naparstek, MD

Boston University
Occupational Health Center
930 Commonwealth Ave., West
Boston, MA 02215
(617) 353-6630
Fax (617) 353-6848
Cheryl S. Barbanel, MD, MBA, MPH

Children's Hospital
Pediatric Environmental Health Center
300 Longwood Ave., 5th Floor
Boston, MA 02115
(617) 355-8177
Fax (617) 738-0049
Alan Woolf, MD, MPH

Occupational and Environmental Health Network, Inc.
5 Mount Royal Ave.
Marlborough, MA 01752
(508) 251-7260
Fax (508) 251-7265
Thomas Winters, MD, FACOEM, FACPM, Chief, OEM

Michigan

Michigan State University
Department of Medicine
117 West Fee
East Lansing, MI 48824-1316
(517) 353-1846
Appts (517) 353-4941
Fax (517) 432-3606
Kenneth Rosenman, MD

Center for Occupational and Environmental Medicine, P.C.
118 North Washington Ave.
Royal Oak, MI 48067
(248) 547-9100
Fax (248) 547-9336
Laura Harbut, EMT, MBA

Occupational Health Service
St. Lawrence Hospital Work and Health Institute
1210 W. Saginaw
Lansing, MI 48915
(517) 377-0309
Fax (517) 377-0310
R. Michael Kelly, MD, MPH

University Physician Group
Occupational and Environmental Health Clinic
3750 Woodward Ave., Suite 200C
Detroit, MI 48201
(313) 577-2644
Fax (313) 577-2744
Bengt Arnetz, MD, PhD, MPH

Minnesota

Health Partners- St. Paul Clinic
Occupational and Environmental Medicine
205 South Wabasha St.
St. Paul, MN 55107
(651) 293-8269
Fax (651) 293-8195
Paula Geiger, Program Assistant

HealthPartners-Riverside Clinic
Occupational & Environmental Medicine
2220 Riverside Avenue South
Minneapolis, MN 55454
(612) 373-4144
Fax (612) 373-4173

HealthPartners-St. Louis Park Clinic
Occupational & Environmental Medicine
5100 Gamble Dr., #100
St. Louis Park, MN 55416
(952) 591-7855
Fax (952) 951-7856

Montana

St. Patrick Hospital
Occupational Health Services
500 West Broadway, 3rd Floor

Missoula, MT 59802
(406) 329-5746
Fax (406) 329-5697
Dana Headapohl, MD, MPH

New Jersey
UMDNJ - Robert Wood Johnson Medical School
Environmental and Occupational Health Clinic Ctr
Environmental and Occupational Health Sciences
170 Frelinghuysen Rd.
Piscataway, NJ 08854
(732) 445-0123
Fax (732) 445-0127
Howard Kipen, MD, MPH

New Mexico
University of New Mexico
Occupational & Environmental Medicine Clinic
EOHS, Family Practice Center Room 232
MSC 10-5550
Albuquerque, NM 87131
(505) 272-8034
Appts (505) 272-8043
Fax (505) 272-8044
Denece Kesler, MD, MPH

New York
Occupational & Environmental Health Center of
Eastern New York
1873 Western Ave.
Albany, NY 12203
(518) 690-4420 or (800) 419-1230
Fax (518) 690-4427
Jean McMahon, MD

Long Island Occupational &
Environmental Health Center
1741 B North Ocean Ave.
Medford, NY 11764
(631) 289-1405
Fax (631) 289-1428
Linda Cocchiarella, MD, MSc

Mount Sinai-Irving J. Seilikoff Center for
Occupational & Environmental Medicine
1212 Fifth Avenue, Suite 1A
New York, NY 10029
(212) 241-5555 or (212) 241-0176
Fax (212) 996-0407
Stephen Levin, MD

New York University, Bellevue Hospital
Occupational & Environmental Medicine Clinic
Bellevue Hospital, Room CD349
462 First Ave.
New York, NY 10016
(212) 562-4572
Fax (212) 562-4574
George Friedman-Jimenez, MD

Comprehensive Occupational Medical Services
51 Webster St.
North Tonawanda, NY 14120
(716) 692-6541
Fax (716) 692-7091
Gordon C. Steinagle, DO, MPH

Finger Lakes Occupational Health Services
2180 South Clinton Ave., Suite D
Rochester, NY 14618
(585) 244-4771 or (800) 925-8615
Fax (585) 256-2271
Rathin Vora, MD, MPH

Central New York Occupational Health
Clinical Center
6712 Brooklawn Parkway, Suite 204
Syracuse, NY 13211-2195
(315) 432-8899
Fax (315) 431-9528
Michael B. Lax, MD, MPH

Long Island Occupational and Environmental Health Center
1741 B North Ocean Ave.
Medford, NY 11764
(631) 289-1405
Fax (631) 289-1428
Linda Cocchiarella, MD, MSC

North Carolina
Duke University Medical Center
Division of Occupational and Environmental Medicine
Box 3834
Durham, NC 27710
(919) 286-3232
Fax (919) 286-1021
Dennis J. Darcey, MD, MSPH

Ohio
Cincinnati Children's Hospital
Medical Center Pediatric Environmental Health and
Lead Clinic

Div. of General and Community Pediatrics
3333 Burnet Ave., MLC 7035
Cincinnati, OH 45229-3039
(800) 672-3113
Fax (513) 636-4402
Nicholas Newman, D.O., FAAP

University of Cincinnati
Center for Occupational Health
OH Respiratory Disorder Center
3223 Eden Ave, Kettering Bldg.
Cincinnati, OH 45267-0056
(513) 558-0030
Fax (513) 558-6272
James E. Lockey, MD, MS

Oregon

Northwest Occupational Health Associates
9370 SW Greenberg Rd., Suite 101
Portland, OR 97223
(503) 246-7030
Fax (503) 246-0429
James Harris, MD, MSPH

Pennsylvania

University of Pennsylvania School of
Medicine, Occupational Medicine Clinic
Silverstein Pavilion, 3400 Spruce St.
Philadelphia, PA 19104-4283
(215) 349-5708
Fax (215) 614-0666
Edward A. Emmett, MD

Consulting Toxicologists, LLC
110 West Lancaster Ave., Suite 230
Wayne, PA   19087
(610) 688-6700
Fax (610) 964-9003
Michael I. Greenberg, MD, MPH
Clinic Director

Rhode Island

Occupational & Environmental Health Center of
Rhode Island
410 South Main St.
Providence, RI 02903
(401) 621-2228
Fax (401) 621-2229
Mary Ellen DiMaio, Clinic Administrator

Texas

University of Texas Health Services
P.O. Box 203487
Houston, TX 77216
(713) 500-3267
Fax (713) 500-3263
Thomas Mackey, PhD, APRN

Univ. of Texas Health Science Center, Tyler Texas Inst. of
Occupational Safety & Health
11937 U.S. Highway 271
Tyler, TX 75708-3154
(903) 877-5609
Fax (903) 877-5864
Aman Dhillon, MD, MS

Utah

University of Utah
Family & Preventive Medicine Program
Rocky Mountain Center for OEM
391 Chippewa Way, Suite C
Salt Lake City, UT   84108
(801) 581-5056
Fax (801) 585-3759
Eric Wood, MD, MPH, Clinic Director

Virginia

Roanoke Community Hospital
Carilion Occupational Medicine
Fralin Center, 101 Elm Ave.
Roanoke, VA 24013
(540) 985-8552
Appts (540) 985-8521
Fax (540) 985-8118
Elaine Gill, Administrative Director
Hetzal Hartley, MD, MPH, Medical Director

Washington

University of Washington, Occupational &
Environmental Medicine Program
Harborview Medical Center
325 9th Ave., #359739
Seattle, WA 98104-2499
(206) 744-9382
Fax (206) 744-9936
Jordan A. Firestone, MD, PhD, MPH

West Virginia

Marshall University School of Medicine
Department Family & Community Medicine
Occupational & Environmental Health

1600 Medical Center
Huntington, WV 25755
(304) 691-1178
Fax (304) 691-1153
Chris McGuffin, MSCH, MSOSH

West Virginia University School of Medicine
Institute of Occupational and Environmental Health
3801 Robert F. Byrd Health Sci Ctr, South
Morgantown, WV 26506-9190
(304) 293-3693
Fax (304) 293-2629
Chris Martin, MD, MSc, Director

CANADA

Alberta

University of Alberta
Department of Medicine
Occupational & Environmental Medicine Clinic
13-103 Clinical Sciences Building
Edmonton, AB T6G 2G3
Canada
(780) 492-6291
Fax (780) 492-9677
Jeremy Beach, MD, FFOM, FRCP
Nicola Cherry, MD, PhD, FRCP(C), FFOM

Ontario

Occupational Health Clinics for
Ontario Workers (OHCOW)
848 Main St. East
Hamilton, ON L8M 1L9
Canada
(905) 549-2552 or (800) 263-2129
Fax (905) 549-7993
Leah Casselman, Exec. Dir.

Occupational Health Clinics for
Ontario Workers (OHCOW)
171 Kendall St.
Point Edward, ON N7V 4G6
Canada
(519) 337-4627
Fax (519) 337-9442
Jim Brophy, Exec. Dir.

Occupational Health Clinics for
Ontario Workers (OHCOW)
84 Cedar St., Suite 4

Sudbury, ON P3E 1A5
Canada
(705) 523-2330 or (800) 461-7120
Fax (705) 523-2606
Donna Campbell, Exec. Dir.

Occupational Health Clinics for
Ontario Workers (OHCOW)
970 Lawrence Ave. West, Suite 110
Toronto, ON M6A 3B6
Canada
Clinic (416) 449-0009
Admin. (416) 443-7669 or (888) 596-3800
Fax (416) 449-7772
Leslie Piekarz, MLIS Exec. Dir.

Occupational Health Clinics for Ontario Workers, Inc.-
Windsor (OHCOW)
3129 Marentette Ave., Unit 1
Windsor, ON N8X 4G1
Canada
(519) 973-4800 (ext. 211) or (800) 565-3185
Fax (519) 973-1906
Mark Parent, Exec. Dir.

GERMANY

University of Munich
Institute and Outpatient Clinic for
Occupational, Social and Environmental Medicine
Ziemssenstr. 1
D-80336 Munchen,
Germany
+49-89-5160-2301
Fax +49-89-5160-4445
Dennis Nowak, MD, PhD

COMMUNITY ORGANIZATIONS

Committees for Occupational Safety and Health (COSH) and similar organizations are comprised of rank-and-file workers, labor leaders, occupational safety and health professionals, medical professionals, and community activists. They are an excellent source of current information. Many of them maintain libraries and have professionals on staff who can provide technical assistance.

Alaska
Alaska Health Project

218 E. 4th Ave.
Anchorage, AK 99501
(907) 276-2864
Fax (907) 279-3089

Arkansas
Arkansas Coalition on Safety and Health
2801 S. University Ave.
Little Rock, AR 72204
(501) 569-8477
Fax (501) 569-8538
email: scopley438@aol.com (Steve Copley) or
nmstepp@ualr.edu (Meredith Stepp)

California
SoCalCOSH - Southern California Coalition for
Occupational Safety & Health
Pete Greyshock, Coordinator
1000 N Alameda St. Suite 240
Los Angeles, CA 90012
(213) 346-3277
Fax (213) 808-1009
email: socalcosh@gmail.com

Worksafe
55 Harrison St., Suite 400,
Oakland, CA 94607
(510) 302-1027 or (510) 302-1021
email: snoero@worksafe.org or rskelley@worksafe.org

Connecticut
ConnectiCOSH
683 North Mountain Rd.
Newington, CT 06111
(860) 953-COSH (2674)
email: Connecticosh@snet.net

Illinois
CACOSH
Chicago Area Committee on Occupational
Safety and Health
1636 W. Van Buren St.
Chicago, IL 60612
Director: Emmanual Blackwell
(312) 666-1611 or (708) 359-3303
email: cacosh@sbcglobal.net or emanuelblck@aol.com

Louisiana
Safety Council
(225) 766-0955 or (877) 345-1253

Locations:
7640 LA Highway One South
Addis, LA 70710
(225) 282-3271 or (225) 282-3272

2612 South Ruby Rd.
Gonzales, LA 70737
(225) 647-8161

7166 Siegen Lane
Baton Rouge, LA 70810
(225) 282-3269

Maine
Maine Labor Group on Health, Inc.
283 Water St.
Second Floor, Suite 203
Augusta, ME 04330
Mailing Address:
P.O. Box 5197
Augusta, ME 04332
(207) 622-7823 or (207) 622-3483
mlgh@gwi.net

Massachusetts
MassCOSH
1532B Dorchester Ave.
Dorchester, MA 02122
(617) 825-SAFE (7233)
Fax (617) 506-0542

Western MassCOSH
640 Page Blvd.
Suite 104
Springfield, MA 01104
(413) 734-6520
http://wmasscosh.org/contact

Michigan
SEMCOSH
1550 Howard St.
Detroit, MI 48216
(313) 961-3345
Fax (313) 961-3588
semcosh@mich.com

New Hampshire
NH Coalition for Occupational Safety and Health
161 Londonderry Turnpike
Hooksett, NH 03106
(603) 232-4406

Fax (603) 232-4461
http://www.nhcosh.org/contact.asp

New Jersey
New Jersey Work Environment Council
142 West State St., 3rd Floor
Trenton, NJ 08608
(609) 695-7100
email: info@njwec.org

New York
NYCOSH
New York City
116 John St., Suite 604
New York, NY 10038
(212) 227-6440
Fax (212) 227-9854

Long Island
150 Motor Parkway - Suite 306
Hauppauge, NY 11788
(631) 435-1857 (ext. 1865)
Fax (631_ 435-1893
email: nycosh@nycosh.org

CNYCOSH
615 W. Genesee St.
Syracuse, NY
(315) 471-6187
Fax (315) 471-6193
email: cnycosh@cnymail.com

WNYCOSH
Tri-Main Building
2495 Main St. Suite 438
Buffalo, NY 14214
(716) 833-5416
Fax (716) 833-7507
email: GermainHarnden@wnycosh.org

North Carolina
NCOSH
1214 Grove St.
Greensboro, NC 27403
email: marilynb@ncosh-project.org

Pennsylvania
PhilaPOSH
3001 Walnut St., 5th Floor
Philadelphia, PA 19104
(215) 386-7000

Fax (215) 386-3529
email: philaposh@aol.com

Rhode Island
RICOSH
741 Westminster St.
Providence, RI 02903
(401) 751-2015
Fax (401) 751-7520
email: jobhealth@juno.com

Wisconsin
WisCOSH
1535 W. Mitchell St.
Milwaukee, WI 53204
(414) 933-2338
(888) WISCOSH (947-2674)
email: wiscosh@wiscosh.org

Other Community Groups
California
Asian Immigrant Women Advocates
310 8th St.
Oakland, CA 94607
(510) 268-0192
Fax (510) 268-0194

1010 Ruff Dr.
San Jose, CA 95110
(408) 289-8983
Fax (408) 289-8883
email: info@aiwa.org
http://www.aiwa.org/index.php

Labor Occupational Health Program (Bay Area)
2223 Fulton St., 4th Floor
Berkeley, CA 94720-5120
(510) 642-5507
Fax (510) 643-5698
email: info@lohp.org
http://www.lohp.org/

UCLA-LOSH Program
A subunit of UCLA's Institute for Research on Labor and
Employment (IRLE) and the Center for Occupational and
Environmental Health (COEH)
10945 Le Conte Ave.
Suite 2107
Box 951478
Los Angeles, CA 90095
(310) 794-5964

Fax (310) 794-6403
email: loshinfo@ucla.edu
http://www.losh.ucla.edu/

New Jersey
New Jersey Work Environment Council
142 West State St., 3rd Floor
Trenton, NJ 08608
(609) 695-7100
email: info@njwec.org
http://www.njwec.org/

New York
Midstate Central Labor Council
302 Van Ostrand Rd.
Newfield, NY 14867
607-564-3508

Ohio
Greater Cincinnati Occupational Health Center
125 East Court St., Suite 210
Cincinnati, OH 45202
(513) 531-7101
Fax (513) 531-7102
email: gcohc@fuse.net
http://www.gcohc.com/

West Virginia
West Virginia University
Extension Service
Room 709 Knapp Hall
PO Box 6031
Morgantown, WV 26506-6031
(304) 293-3323
Fax (304) 293- 3395
http://www.laborstudiesandresearch.ext.wvu.edu/

Canada
Windsor Occupational Health Information Service
3129 Marentette Ave.
Windsor, ON
N8X 4G1
Canada
(519) 254-5157
Fax (519) 254-4192
email: jham@wohis.org
http://www.wohis.org/

United Kingdom
London Hazards Centre
Hampstead Town Hall Centre

213 Haverstock Hill
London NW3 4QP
UK
+44 20 7794 5999
Fax +44 20 7794 4702
email: mail@lhc.org.uk
http://www.lhc.org.uk/

HAZARDS Magazine
PO Box 4042
Sheffield, S8 2DG
England
+44 114 201 4265
http://www.hazards.org/

INDUSTRY ORGANIZATIONS

Industry and trade associations allow their members to share information and work to promote the interests of the industry as a whole. Many of these associations actively participate in the development of regulations, and some sponsor research into the health and safety issues in their industry. These associations can also be a source of information regarding current practices in the industry. A few of the organizations that are active in health and safety issues are listed below. Most public libraries carry directories of these organizations, such as the annual National Trade and Professional Associations of the United States, which cross-indexes organizations by subject.

American Hospital Association
155 N. Wacker Dr.
Chicago, IL 60606
(312) 422-3000

325 7th St., NW
Washington, DC 20004-2802
(202) 638-1100
www.aha.org

American Iron and Steel Institute
1140 Connecticut Ave., NW Suite 705
Washington, DC 20036
(202) 452-7100

2000 Town Center Suite 320
Southfield, MI 48075
(248) 945-4777

680 Andersen Dr.
Pittsburgh, PA 15220

(412) 922-2772
www.steel.org

American Petroleum Institute
1220 L St. NW
Washington, DC 20005- 4070
(202) 682-8000
www.api.org

American Welding Society
550 NW LeJeune Rd.
Miami, FL 33126
(800) 443-9353
Intl. (305) 443-9353
www.aws.org

American Chemical Council
1300 Wilson Blvd.
Arlington, VA 22209
(703) 741-5000
www.cmahq.com

Compressed Gas Association
4221 Walney Rd., 5th Floor
Chantilly VA 20151-2923
(703) 788-2700
Fax (703) 961-1831
email: cga@cganet.com
www.cganet.com

Electric Power Research Institute
3412 Hillview Ave.
Palo Alto, CA 94304
(800)313-3774 or (650)855- 2121
email: askepri@epri.com
www.epri.com

International Safety Equipment Association (ISEA)
1901 N. Moore St., Suite 808
Arlington, VA 22209 -1762
(703) 525-1695
Fax (703) 528-2148
http://www.safetyequipment.org/

Semiconductor Industry Association
1101 K St., NW, Suite 450
Washington, DC 20005
(866) 756-0715 or (202) 446-1700
Fax (202) 216-9745
http://www.sia-online.org/

Society of Plastics Engineers, Inc.
PO Box 403
Brookfield, CT 06804-0403
(203) 775-0471
Fax (203) 775-8490
email: info@4spe.org
www.4spe.org

Labor Unions

Many labor unions maintain health and safety departments and are active in promoting and developing health and safety regulations. All of the labor organizations listed below have websites with health and safety pages. The health and safety departments of these unions can often provide information about the hazards in specific industries. The AFL-CIO web-site provides a page of links to affiliated unions.

American Federation of Labor - Congress of Industrial Organizations (AFL-CIO)
815 16th St., NW
Washington, DC 20006
(202) 637-5000
Fax (202) 637-5058
www.aflcio.org

Change to Win
1900 L St., NW, Suite 900
Washington, DC 20036
(202) 721-0660
Fax (202) 721-0661
e-mail: info@changetowin.org
http://www.changetowin.org/

American Federation of State, County and Municipal Employees (AFSCME)
1625 L St., NW
Washington, DC 20036-5687
(202) 429-1000
TTY (202) 659-0446
Fax (202) 429-1293
www.afscme.org

International Association of Machinists and Aerospace Workers (IAM)
9000 Machinists Place
Upper Marlboro, MD 20722-2687
(301) 967-4500
www.iamaw.org

International Brotherhood of Teamsters
25 Louisiana Ave., NW
Washington, DC 20001
(202) 624-6800
www.teamster.org

Union of Needle Trades, Industrial and Textile Employees
(UNITE HERE)
275 7th Ave.
New York, NY 10001-6708
(212) 265-7000
www.uniteunion.org

International Longshoremen's and Warehousemen's Union
(ILWU)
1188 Franklin St.
San Francisco, CA 94109-6800
(415) 775-0533
Fax (415) 775-1302
www.ilwu.org

Laborers' International Union of North America
905 16th St., NW
Washington, DC 20006
(202) 737-8320
Fax (202) 737-2754
www.liuna.org

Service Employees' International Union (SEIU)
1800 Massachusetts Ave., NW
Washington, DC 20036
(800) 424-8592
TDD (202) 730-7481
www.seiu.org

United Auto Workers (UAW)
8000 E. Jefferson Ave.
Detroit, MI 48214
(313) 926-5000
www.uaw.org

United Farmworkers of America (UFW)
PO Box 62
29700 Woodford-Tehachapi Rd.
Keene, CA 93531
(661) 823-6151
www.ufw.org

United Food and Commercial Workers International Union
(UFCW)
1775 K St., NW

Washington, DC 20006
(202) 223-3111
www.ufcw.org

United Mine Workers of America (UMWA)
18354 Quantico Gateway Dr., Suite 200
Triangle, VA 22172-1179
(703) 291-2400
www.umwa.org

United Steel Workers of America
Five Gateway Center
Pittsburgh, PA 15222
(412) 562-2400
www.usw.org/

University-Based Research and Training Programs
NIOSH Education and Research Center Grants (ERCS)

NIOSH has developed a program to establish centers of learning for occupational safety and health throughout the United States. These Educational Research Centers, known by the acronym ERC, are located within 27 universities serving all 10 Department of Health and Human Services (DHHS) Regions.

Alabama Education and Research Center
University of Alabama at Birmingham
School of Public Health
1665 University Blvd.
Birmingham, AL 35294-0022
(205) 934-6208
Fax (205) 975-6341
R. Kent Oestenstad, PhD, Director
email: oestk@uab.edu

California Education and Research Center - Northern
University of California at Berkeley
Center for Occupational and Environmental Health
50 University Hall #7360
Berkeley, CA 94720-7360
Fax (510) 642-5815
John R. Balmes, MD, Director
email: john.balmes@ucsf.edu
(510) 642-8365

California Education and Research Center - Southern
University of Southern California
School of Public Health
650 Charles E. Young Dr. South
Los Angeles, CA 90095-1772
(310) 825-2079

Fax (310) 794-9317
Niklas Krause, MD, MPH, PhD , SCERC Director
email: niklaskrause@ucla.edu

Cincinnati Education and Research Center
University of Cincinnati
Department of Environmental Health ML. Box 670056
3223 Eden Ave.
Cincinnati, OH 45267-0056
(513) 558-1751
Fax (513) 558-2772
Carol Rice, PhD, CIH, Director
email: alerdilr@ucmail.uc.edu

Colorado Education and Research Center
University of Colorado School of Public Health
13001 E. 17th Place, B-119
Aurora, CO 80045
(303) 315-0880
Fax (303) 315-7642
Lee S. Newman, MD, MA, FCCP, FACOEM, Director
email: lee.newman@uchsc.edu

Harvard Education and Research Center
Harvard School of Public Health
Department of Environmental Health
665 Huntington Ave.
Bldg. 1, Rm. 1407
Boston, MA 02115
(617) 432-3323
Fax (617) 432-3441
David C. Christiani, MD, Director
email: dchris@hohp.harvard.edu

Illinois Education and Research Center
University of Illinois at Chicago
School of Public Health
2121 W. Taylor St.
Chicago, IL 60612
(312) 996-7469
Fax (312) 413-9898
Lorraine M. Conroy, ScD, CIH, Director
email: lconroy@uic.edu

Iowa Education and Research Center
University of Iowa
College of Public Health
Department of Occupational and Environmental Health
100 Oakdale Campus – 126 IREH
Iowa City, IA 52242-5000

(319) 335-4428
Fax (319) 335-4225
Craig Zwerling, MD, PhD, MPH, Director
email: craig-zwerling@uiowa.edu

Johns Hopkins Education and Research Center
Johns Hopkins University
Bloomberg School of Public Health
615 North Wolfe St., Room 7503
Baltimore, MD 21205
(410) 955-4037
Fax (410) 614-4986
Jacqueline Agnew, PhD, Director
email: jagnew@jhsph.edu

Michigan Education and Research Center
University of Michigan
School of Public Health
1420 Washington Heights
Ann Arbor, MI 48109-2029
(734) 936-0757
Fax (734) 763-8095
Thomas G. Robins, MD, Director
email: trobins@umich.edu

Minnesota Education and Research Center
University of Minnesota
Prevention Research Training Program Division of
Environmental Health Sciences School of Public Health
Minnesota Mayo Mail Code 807
420 Delaware St., SE
Minneapolis, MN 55455
(612) 625-5934
Fax (612) 626-0650
Susan G. Gerberich, PhD, MSPH, Director
email: gerbe001@umn.edu

New York / New Jersey Education and Research Center
Mount Sinai School of Medicine
Department of Community and Preventive Medicine
PO Box 1057
One Gustave L. Levy Place
New York, NY 10029-6574
(212) 824-7018
Fax (212) 996-0407
Philip J. Landrigan, MD, MSc, Interim Director
email: phil.landrigan@mssm.edu

North Carolina Education and Research Center
University of North Carolina at Chapel Hill

School of Public Health
1700 Airport Rd., CB 7502
Chapel Hill, NC 27599-7502
(919) 966-1765
Fax (919) 966-8999
Bonnie Rogers, DrPH, COHN-S, FAAN, LNCC, Director
email: rogersb@email.unc.edu

South Florida Education and Research Center
University of South Florida
College of Public Health
13201 Bruce B. Downs Blvd., MDC 56
Tampa, FL 33612-3805
(813) 974-6629
Fax (813) 974-4718
Thomas E. Bernard, PhD, Director
email: tbernard@ health.usf.edu

Texas Education and Research Center
University of Texas Health Science Center at Houston
School of Public Health
PO Box 20186
Houston, TX 77225-0186
(713) 500-9464
Fax (713) 500-9442
Sarah A. Felknor, PhD, Director
email: sarah.a.felknor@uth.tmc.edu

Utah Education and Research Center
University of Utah
Rocky Mountain Center for Occupational and
Environmental Health
391 Chipeta Way, Suite C
Salt Lake City, UT 84108
(801) 581-4800
Fax (801) 581-7224
Kurt Hegmann, MD, MPH, Director
email: kurt.hegmann@hsc.utah.edu

Washington Education and Research Center
University of Washington
Department of Environmental Health and
Occupational Health Sciences
P O Box 354695
Seattle, WA 98105
(206) 685-7189
Fax (206) 616-6240
Noah S. Seixas, PhD, Director
email: nseixas@u.washington.edu

REFERENCE MATERIALS

Internet Resources

In the eleven years since the last edition of this book, the Internet has continued to change and shape the way we find and access information.

Google

www.google.com

While Google has emerged as the dominant search engine, there are other portals to searching for relevant information on the Web.

Finding Information on the Internet

www.lib.berkeley.edu/TeachingLib/Guides/Internet/FindInfo.html

This site links to a comparison chart of search engines, suggests specialized databases for your subject area, and suggests ways to plan your Web search strategy.

IPL2

www.ipl.org/

Library and information science professionals and students from across the nation have helped to build this collection of selected websites. You can search by keyword or subject. IPL2 merges the collections of resources from the Internet Public Library (IPL) and the Librarians' Internet Index (LII) websites.

Sheldon Margen Public Health Library at UC Berkeley

www.lib.berkeley.edu/PUBL/internet.html

Search here by topic or for databases of interest selected by UC Berkeley librarians.

A word of caution: Anyone can say anything on the Internet. It is an unedited morass of jewels and garbage. To be able to trust your Internet sources it is best to stick to web sites that are administered by a credible entity. Web addresses ending in .gov are government entities and are usually excellent sources of accurate information. Likewise web addresses ending in the suffix .edu, which indicates educational facilities, usually universities, are good sources of accurate information. If you search a university's online library catalog and you find something useful, it is most likely to be reliable since the materials in libraries are carefully selected by librarians. Remember to use common sense and proceed with caution.

Following are some very useful websites.

Agency for Toxic Substances and Disease Registry (ATSDR)

www.atsdr.cdc.gov/

Search for chemical structure and limited health and safety info by chemical name, Chemical Abstracts Service (CAS) number, or chemical structure.

Centers for Disease Control and Prevention
www.cdc.gov/
Provides on-line access to Morbidity and Mortality Weekly Reports and Emerging Infectious Diseases.

Department of Energy
http://www.doe.gov

EPA
http://www.epa.gov

Integrated Risk Information System (IRIS)
The IRIS database contains information on human health effects of hundreds of chemicals.
- EPA access
  www.epa.gov/iris/index.html
- U.S. National Library of Medicine access
  toxnet.nlm.nih.gov/cgi-bin/sis/htmlgen?IRIS.htm

National Institute for Occupational Safety and Health (NIOSH)
Search the NIOSH website by keyword, topic, or A to Z index.
www.cdc.gov/niosh/
- NIOSH Manual of Analytical Methods
  www.cdc.gov/niosh/docs/2003-154/
- NIOSH Workplace Survey Reports
  http://www.cdc.gov/niosh/surveyreports/
- National Ag Safety Database (NASD)
  http://nasdonline.org/

National Library of Medicine, National Institutes of Health
- Household Products Database
  http://householdproducts.nlm.nih.gov/index.htm
- PubMed
  http://www.ncbi.nlm.nih.gov/pubmed/
- TOXNET
  http://toxnet.nlm.nih.gov/

National Toxicology Program (NTP)
http://ntp.niehs.nih.gov/

OSHA
http://www.osha.gov
- OSHA Inspection Data
  http://www.osha.gov/oshstats/index.html
- OSHA Sampling and Analytical Methods home page
  http://www.osha.gov/dts/sltc/methods/index.html
- OSHA Index of Sampling and Analytical Methods
  http://www.osha.gov/dts/sltc/methods/toc.html
- OSHA Standards Interpretations
  http://www.osha.gov/pls/oshaweb/owasrch.search_

form?p_doc_type=INTERPRETATIONS&p_toc_level=0
- OSHA Technical Manual
  http://www.osha.gov/dts/osta/otm/otm_toc.html

American Biological Safety Association
http://www.absa.org/index.html

American Chemical Society
http://www.acs.org/

California Department of Pesticide Regulation Ingredients Search
http://www.cdpr.ca.gov/docs/chemical/monster.htm

Canadian Centre for Occupational Safety and Health
http://www.ccohs.ca/
Check out "OSH Answers" for information on common occupational and workplace hazards.

Cornell University Office of Environmental Health and Safety
Links to sites with Material Safety Data Sheets
http://www.med.cornell.edu/ehs/msds.htm

ChemBioFinder.com
http://chemfinder.camsoft.com/chembiofinder/Forms/Home/ContentArea/Home.aspx

Hardin MD: Medical Information + Pictures
http://hardinmd.lib.uiowa.edu/
Provides many links to information on toxicology and occupational medicine.

International Labour Organization (ILO)
http://www.ilo.org

International Health Care Worker Safety Center.
http://www.healthsystem.virginia.edu/internet/epinet/
Includes safety device list and information on the EPINET database among other resources.

OSU Safety Manuals
http://www.ehs.okstate.edu/manuals/index.htm
Includes confined spaces, laboratory, trenching and shore, and lock-out/tag-out manuals.

Training for Development of Innovative Control Technologies
http://www.tdict.org/
Contains much information on engineering controls to prevent needlesticks and other sharps injuries to health care workers. Includes recommendations for device evaluation criteria.

TWI Job Knowledge for Welders
http://www.twi.co.uk/services/technical-information/job-knowledge/?locale=en Includes good information about welding processes.

Emergency Response Guidebook
http://www.phe.gov/emergency/responseguide/Pages/default.aspx

JOURNALS, MAGAZINES, NEWSLETTERS, AND REPORTS

American Journal of Epidemiology
Johns Hopkins Bloomberg School of Public Health
http://aje.oxfordjournals.org/

American Journal of Industrial Medicine
Malden, MA: John Wiley & Sons Inc.
Steven B. Markowitz, editor
Queens College, Flushing, NY
http://onlinelibrary.wiley.com/journal/10.1002/(ISSN)1097-0274

American Journal of Public Health
Washington, DC: American Public Health Association
http://ajph.aphapublications.org/

Annals of Occupational Hygiene
Oxford, UK: Oxford University Press for the British Occupational Hygiene Society
http://annhyg.oxfordjournals.org/

Annual Review of Public Health
Palo Alto, CA: Annual Reviews
http://www.annualreviews.org/journal/publhealth

ASHRAE Journal
Atlanta: American Society of Heating, Refrigerating and Air Conditioning Engineers
http://www.ashrae.org/publications/page/540

CTD News
Horsham, PA: LRP Publications
http://www.shoplrp.com/product/p-31026.html

EHS Today
The Magazine for Environment, Health and Safety Leaders
Cleveland: Penton, Media Inc.
http://ehstoday.com/

Environmental Health Perspectives
Research Triangle Park, NC: National Institute of Environmental Health Sciences
http://ehp03.niehs.nih.gov/home.action

Epidemiology
Philadelphia: Lippincott Williams & Wilkins
http://journals.lww.com/epidem/pages/default.aspx

Ergonomics
London: Taylor & Francis
http://www.tandf.co.uk/journals/terg

Hazards Magazine
Sheffield, UK: Rory O'Neill, ed. Independently owned.
http://www.hazards.org/

International Archives of Occupational and Environmental Health
New York: Springer
Hans Drexler, editor
http://www.springer.com/environment/environmental+health+-+public+health/journal/420

International Journal of Epidemiology
Oxford, UK: Oxford University Press
http://ije.oxfordjournals.org/

Journal of the American Medical Association
Chicago: American Medical Association
http://jama.ama-assn.org/

Journal of Occupational and Environmental Hygiene
Cincinnati, OH: Taylor and Francis, Inc. for the American Conference of Governmental Industrial Hygienists and the American Industrial Hygiene Association
http://www.tandf.co.uk/journals/uoeh

Journal of Occupational and Environmental Medicine
Philadelphia, PA: Wolters Kluwer/Lippincott Williams & Wilkins
Official Journal of the American College of Occupational and Environmental Medicine,
Paul W. Brandt-Rauf, MD, ScD, DrPH, editor-in-chief
http://journals.lww.com/joem/pages/default.aspx

Journal of Toxicology and Environmental Health
Philadelphia: Taylor & Francis
Part A: Current Issues – http://www.tandf.co.uk/journals/titles/15287394.html

Part B: Critical Reviews – http://www.tandf.co.uk/journals/titles/10937404.asp

Monthly Labor Review
Washington, DC: Bureau of Labor Statistics, U.S. Department of Labor.
http://www.bls.gov/mlr/

New England Journal of Medicine
Waltham, MA: Massachusetts Medical Society
http://www.nejm.org/

New Solutions: A Journal of Environmental and Occupational Health Policy
Amityville, NY: Baywood Publishing Company, Inc.
http://www.baywood.com/journals/previewjournals.asp?id=1048-2911

Noise Control Engineering Journal
Indianapolis, IN: Institute of Noise Control Engineering
http://www.inceusa.org/publications/ncej

Occupational and Environmental Medicine
London, UK: BMJ Publishing Group
http://oem.bmj.com/

Occupational Health & Safety
Chatsworth, CA: 1105 Media Inc.
http://ohsonline.com/issues/issue-archive.aspx

Occupational Medicine
Oxford: Oxford University Press for the Society of Occupational Medicine
http://occmed.oxfordjournals.org/

Occupational Safety & Health Reporter
Arlington, VA: Bureau of National Affairs, Inc.
http://www.bna.com/occupational-safety--p4900/

Professional Safety
Des Plaines, IL: American Society of Safety Engineers
http://www.asse.org/professionalsafety/

Public Health Reports
Washington, DC: Association of Schools of Public Health
http://www.publichealthreports.org/

Safety + Health
Itasca, IL: National Safety Council
http://www.nsc.org/news_resources/nsc_publications/Pages/NSC_publications.aspx

Scandinavian Journal of Work, Environment & Health
Helsinki, Finland: Finnish Institute of Occupational Health
http://www.sjweh.fi/

Sound & Vibration
Bay Village, OH: Acoustical Publications, Inc.
http://www.sandv.com/home.htm

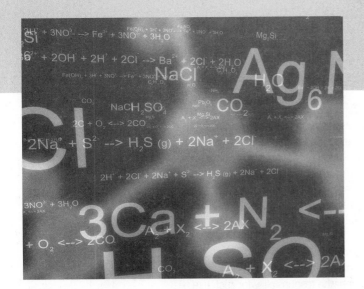

APPENDIX B

ACGIH® Threshold Limit Values (TLVs®) and Biological Exposure Indices (BEIs®)

This appendix gives the Threshold Limit Values (TLVs®) for Chemical Substances and Physical Agents and the Biological Exposure Indices (BEIs®) that were adopted in 2012 by the American Conference of Governmental Industrial Hygienists (ACGIH®). The content is reprinted directly from the ACGIH®, 2012 TLVs® and BEIs® Book. Copyright 2012. Reprinted with permission.

POLICY STATEMENT ON THE USES OF TLVs® AND BEIs®

The Threshold Limit Values (TLVs®) and Biological Exposure Indices (BEIs®) are developed as guidelines to assist in the control of health hazards. These recommendations or guidelines are intended for use in the practice of industrial hygiene, to be interpreted and applied only by a person trained in this discipline. They are not developed for use as legal standards and ACGIH® does not advocate their use as such. However, it is recognized that in certain circumstances individuals or organizations may wish to make use of these recommendations or guidelines as a supplement to their occupational safety and health program. ACGIH® will not oppose their use in this manner, if the use of TLVs® and BEIs® in these instances will contribute to the overall improvement in worker protection. However, the user must recognize the constraints and limitations subject to their proper use and bear the responsibility for such use.

The Introductions to the TLV®/BEI® Book and the TLV®/BEI® *Documentation* provide the philosophical and practical bases for the uses and limitations of the TLVs® and BEIs®. To extend those uses of the TLVs® and BEIs® to include other applications, such as use without the judgment of an industrial hygienist, application to a different population, development of new exposure/recovery time models, or new effect endpoints, stretches the reliability and even viability of the database for the TLV® or BEI® as evidenced by the individual *Documentation*.

It is not appropriate for individuals or organizations to impose on the TLVs® or the BEIs® their concepts of what the TLVs® or BEIs® should be or how they should be applied or to transfer regulatory standards requirements to the TLVs® or BEIs®.

Approved by the ACGIH® Board of Directors on March 1, 1988.

Special Note to User

The values listed in this book are intended for use in the practice of industrial hygiene as guidelines or recommendations to assist in the control of potential workplace health hazards and for no other use. These values are *not* fine lines between safe and dangerous concentrations and *should not* be used by anyone untrained in the discipline of industrial hygiene. **It is imperative that the user of this book read the Introduction to each section and be familiar with the *Documentation* of the TLVs® and BEIs® before applying the recommendations contained herein.** ACGIH® disclaims liability with respect to the use of the TLVs® and BEIs®.

2012

TLVs® and BEIs®

Based on the Documentation of the

Threshold Limit
Values

for Chemical Substances
and Physical Agents

&

Biological Exposure
Indices

Defining the Science of
Occupational and Environmental Health®

Signature Publications

ISBN: 978-1-607260-48-6

Printed in the United States.

ACGIH® is a member-based organization that advances occupational and environmental health. The organization has contributed substantially to the development and improvement of worker health protection. The organization is a professional society, not a government agency.

The *Documentation of the Threshold Limit Values and Biological Exposure Indices* is the source publication for the TLVs® and BEIs® issued by ACGIH®. That publication gives the pertinent scientific information and data with reference to literature sources that were used to base each TLV® or BEI®. For better understanding of the TLVs® and BEIs®, it is essential that the *Documentation* be consulted when the TLVs® or BEIs® are being used. For further information, contact The Science Group, ACGIH®. The most up-to-date list of substances and agents under study by the Committees is available at www.acgih.org/TLV/Studies.htm.

Comments, suggestions, and requests for interpretations or technical information should be directed to The Science Group at the address below or to the following E-mail address: science@acgih.org. To place an order, visit our website at www.acgih.org/store, contact Customer Service at the address or phone number below, or use the following E-mail address: customerservice@acgih.org.

> *Help ensure the continued development of TLVs® and BEIs®. Make a tax deductible donation to the FOHS Sustainable TLV®/BEI® Fund today!*
>
> **http://www.fohs.org/SusTLV-BEIPrgm.htm**

ACGIH®
1330 Kemper Meadow Drive
Cincinnati, OH 45240-4148
Telephone: 513-742-2020; Fax: 513-742-3355
www.acgih.org

> **In the event significant errata are required, they will be listed on the ACGIH® website at http://www.acgih.org/TLV/.**

TABLE OF CONTENTS

Chemical Substances

iv — Contents

STATEMENT OF POSITION REGARDING THE TLVs® AND BEIs®

The American Conference of Governmental Industrial Hygienists (ACGIH®) is a private, not-for-profit, nongovernmental corporation whose members are industrial hygienists or other occupational health and safety professionals dedicated to promoting health and safety within the workplace. ACGIH® is a scientific association. ACGIH® is not a standards-setting body. As a scientific organization, it has established committees that review the existing published, peer-reviewed scientific literature. ACGIH® publishes guidelines known as Threshold Limit Values (TLVs®) and Biological Exposure Indices (BEIs®) for use by industrial hygienists in making decisions regarding safe levels of exposure to various chemical and physical agents found in the workplace. In using these guidelines, industrial hygienists are cautioned that the TLVs® and BEIs® are only one of multiple factors to be considered in evaluating specific workplace situations and conditions.

Each year, ACGIH® publishes its TLVs® and BEIs® in a book. In the introduction to the book, ACGIH® states that the TLVs® and BEIs® are guidelines to be used by professionals trained in the practice of industrial hygiene. The TLVs® and BEIs® are not designed to be used as standards. Nevertheless, ACGIH® is aware that in certain instances the TLVs® and the BEIs® are used as standards by national, state, or local governments.

Governmental bodies establish public health standards based on statutory and legal frameworks that include definitions and criteria concerning the approach to be used in assessing and managing risk. In most instances, governmental bodies that set workplace health and safety standards are required to evaluate health effects, economic and technical feasibility, and the availability of acceptable methods to determine compliance.

ACGIH® TLVs® and BEIs® are not consensus standards. Voluntary consensus standards are developed or adopted by voluntary consensus standards bodies. The consensus standards process involves canvassing the opinions, views, and positions of all interested parties and then developing a consensus position that is acceptable to these parties. While the process used to develop a TLV® or BEI® includes public notice and requests for all available and relevant scientific data, the TLV® or BEI® does not represent a consensus position that addresses all issues raised by all interested parties (e.g., issues of technical or economic feasibility). The TLVs® and BEIs® represent a scientific opinion based on a review of existing peer-reviewed scientific literature by committees of experts in public health and related sciences.

ACGIH® TLVs® and BEIs® are health-based values. ACGIH® TLVs® and BEIs® are established by committees that review existing published and peer-reviewed literature in various scientific disciplines (e.g., industrial hygiene, toxicology, occupational medicine, and epidemiology). Based on the available information, ACGIH® formulates a conclusion on the level of exposure that the typical worker can experience without adverse health effects. The TLVs® and BEIs® represent conditions under which ACGIH® believes that nearly all workers may be repeatedly exposed without adverse health effects. They are not

vi — Statement of Position

fine lines between safe and dangerous exposures, nor are they a relative index of toxicology. The TLVs® and BEIs® are not quantitative estimates of risk at different exposure levels or by different routes of exposure.

Since ACGIH® TLVs® and BEIs® are based solely on health factors, there is no consideration given to economic or technical feasibility. Regulatory agencies should not assume that it is economically or technically feasible for an industry or employer to meet TLVs® or BEIs®. Similarly, although there are usually valid methods to measure workplace exposures at the TLVs® and BEIs®, there can be instances where such reliable test methods have not yet been validated. Obviously, such a situation can create major enforcement difficulties if a TLV® or BEI® was adopted as a standard.

ACGIH® does not believe that TLVs® and BEIs® should be adopted as standards without full compliance with applicable regulatory procedures, including an analysis of other factors necessary to make appropriate risk management decisions. However, ACGIH® does believe that regulatory bodies should consider TLVs® or BEIs® as valuable input into the risk characterization process (hazard identification, dose-response relationships, and exposure assessment). Regulatory bodies should view TLVs® and BEIs® as an expression of scientific opinion.

ACGIH® is proud of the scientists and the many members who volunteer their time to work on the TLV® and BEI® Committees. These experts develop written *Documentation* that includes an expression of scientific opinion and a description of the basis, rationale, and limitations of the conclusions reached by ACGIH®. The *Documentation* provides a comprehensive list and analysis of all the major published peer-reviewed studies that ACGIH® relied upon in formulating its scientific opinion. Regulatory agencies dealing with hazards addressed by a TLV® or BEI® should obtain a copy of the full written *Documentation* for the TLV® or BEI®. Any use of a TLV® or BEI® in a regulatory context should include a careful evaluation of the information in the written *Documentation* and consideration of all other factors as required by the statutes which govern the regulatory process of the governmental body involved.

- *ACGIH® is a not-for-profit scientific association.*

- *ACGIH® proposes guidelines known as TLVs® and BEIs® for use by industrial hygienists in making decisions regarding safe levels of exposure to various hazards found in the workplace.*

- *ACGIH® is not a standard-setting body.*

- *Regulatory bodies should view TLVs® and BEIs® as an expression of scientific opinion.*

- *TLVs® and BEIs® are not consensus standards.*

- *ACGIH® TLVs® and BEIs® are based solely on health factors; there is no consideration given to economic or technical feasibility. Regulatory agencies should not assume that it is economically or technically feasible to meet established TLVs® or BEIs®.*

- *ACGIH® believes that TLVs® and BEIs® should NOT be adopted as standards without an analysis of other factors necessary to make appropriate risk management decisions.*

- *TLVs® and BEIs® can provide valuable input into the risk characterization process. Regulatory agencies dealing with hazards addressed by a TLV® or BEI® should review the full written Documentation for the numerical TLV® or BEI®.*

ACGIH® is publishing this Statement in order to assist ACGIH® members, government regulators, and industry groups in understanding the basis and limitations of the TLVs® and BEIs® when used in a regulatory context. This Statement was adopted by the ACGIH® Board of Directors on March 1, 2002.

TLV®/BEI® DEVELOPMENT PROCESS: AN OVERVIEW

Provided below is an overview of the ACGIH® TLV® and BEI® development process. Additional information is available on the ACGIH® website (www.acgih.org). Please also refer to the attached Process Flowchart (Figure 1).

1. **Under Study:** Each committee determines its own selection of chemical substances or physical agents for its Under Study list. A variety of factors is used in this selection process, including prevalence, use, number of workers exposed, availability of scientific data, existence/absence of a TLV® or BEI®, age of TLV® or BEI®, input from the public, etc. The public may offer input to any TLV® or BEI® committee by e-mail to science@acgih.org.

   When a substance or agent is selected for the development of a TLV® or BEI® or for review of an adopted value, the appropriate Committee places it on its Under Study list. This list is published each year by February 1 on the ACGIH® website (www.acgih.org/TLV/Studies.htm), in the ACGIH® Annual Reports, and later in the annual TLVs® and BEIs® book. In addition, the Under Study list is updated by July 31 into a two-tier list.

   - Tier 1 entries indicate which chemical substances and physical agents **may** move forward as an NIC or NIE in the upcoming year, based on their status in the development process.

   - Tier 2 consists of those chemical substances and physical agents that **will not** move forward, but will either remain on or be removed from the Under Study list for the next year.

   This updated list will remain in two-tiers for the balance of the year. ACGIH® will continue this practice of updating the Under Study list by February 1 and establishing the two-tier list by July 31 each year.

   The Under Study lists published in the ACGIH® Annual Reports and the annual TLVs® and BEIs® book are current as of January 1. All updates to the Under Study lists and publication of the two-tier lists are posted on the ACGIH® website (http://www.acgih.org/TLV/Studies.htm).

   The Under Study list serves as a notification and invitation to interested parties to submit substantive data and comments to assist the Committee in its deliberations. Each Committee considers only those comments and data that address the health science, not economic or technical feasibility. Comments must be accompanied by copies of substantiating data, preferably in the form of peer-reviewed literature. Should the data be from unpublished studies, ACGIH® requires written authorization from the owner of the studies granting ACGIH® permission to (1) use, (2) cite within the Documentation, and (3) upon request from a third party, release the information. All three permissions must be stated/covered in the written authorization. (See endnote for a sample permission statement.) Electronic submission of all information to the ACGIH® Science Group at science@acgih.org greatly increases the ease and efficiency with which the Committee can consider the comments or data.

2. **Draft *Documentation*:** One or more members of the appropriate Committee are assigned the task of collecting information and data from the scientific literature, reviewing results of unpublished studies submitted for review, and developing a draft TLV® or BEI® *Documentation*. The draft *Documentation* is a critical evaluation of the scientific literature relevant to recommending a TLV® or BEI®; however, it is not an exhaustive or broad-based critical review of the scientific literature. Particular emphasis is given to papers that address minimal or no adverse health effect levels in exposed animals or workers, that deal with the reversibility of such effects, or in the case of a BEI®, that assess chemical uptake and provide applicable determinant(s) as an index of uptake. Human data, when available, are given special emphasis. This draft *Documentation*, with its proposed TLV® or BEI®, is then reviewed and critiqued by additional Committee members, and eventually by the full Committee. This often results in several revisions to the draft *Documentation* before the full Committee accepts the proposed TLV® or BEI® and *Documentation*. The draft *Documentation* is not available to the public through this stage of the development process and is not released until it is at the Notice of Intended Changes (NIC) stage. Authorship of the *Documentation* is not disclosed.

3. **Notice of Intended Changes (NIC):**

   *[**Notice of Intent to Establish (NIE):** The physical agents section of the TLVs® and BEIs® book also uses the term Notice of Intent to Establish (NIE) in addition to NIC. An NIE follows the same development process as an NIC. For purposes of this process overview, only the term NIC is used.]*

   When the full Committee accepts the draft *Documentation* and its proposed TLV® or BEI®, the *Documentation* and proposed values are then recommended to the ACGIH® Board of Directors for ratification as an NIC. If ratified, each proposed TLV® or BEI® is published as an NIC in the *Annual Reports of Committees on TLVs® and BEIs®*, which is published in the ACGIH® member newsletter, *Today! Online* and is also available online for purchase at http://www.acgih.org/store. At the same time, the draft *Documentation* is made available through ACGIH® Customer Service or online at http://www.acgih.org/store. All information contained in the Annual Reports is integrated into the annual *TLVs® and BEIs®* book, which is usually available to the general public in February or March of each year. The proposed TLV® or BEI® is considered a trial limit by ACGIH® for approximately one year following the NIC ratification by the ACGIH® Board of Directors. Interested parties, as well as ACGIH® members, are invited to provide data and substantive comments, preferably in the form of peer-reviewed literature, on the proposed TLVs® or BEIs® contained in the NIC. Should the data be from unpublished studies, ACGIH® requires written authorization from the owner of the studies granting ACGIH® permission to (1) <u>use</u>, (2) <u>cite</u> within the *Documentation*, and (3) upon request from a third party, <u>release</u> the information. All three permissions must be stated/covered in the written authorization. (*See* endnote for a sample permission statement.) The most effective and helpful comments are those that address

x — Development Process

specific points within the draft *Documentation*. Changes or updates are made to the draft *Documentation* as necessary. If the Committee finds or receives substantive data that change its scientific opinion regarding an NIC TLV® or BEI®, and possibly change its proposed TLV® or BEI® values or notations, the Committee may revise the proposal(s) and recommend to the ACGIH® Board of Directors that it be retained on the NIC.

Important Notice: The comment period for an NIC or NIE draft *Documentation* and its respective TLV(s)®, notation(s), or BEI(s)® is limited to a firm 6-month period, running from February 1 to July 31 of each year. ACGIH® restructured the comment period effective January 1, 2007 to ensure all comments are received by ACGIH® in time for full consideration by the appropriate Committee before its fall meeting. Because of the time required to review, evaluate, and consider comments during the fall meetings, any comments received after the July 31 deadline will not be considered in that year's committee deliberations regarding the outcome for possible adoption of an NIC or NIE. As general practice, ACGIH® reviews all comments regarding chemical substances and physical agents on the Under Study list, as well as NICs or NIEs, or currently adopted TLV(s)® or BEI(s)®. All comments received after July 31 will be fully considered in the following year. Draft *Documentation* will be available for review during the full 6-month period.

When submitting comments, ACGIH® requires that the submission be limited to 10 pages in length, including an executive summary. The submission may include appendices of citable material not included as part of the 10-page limit. It would be very beneficial to structure comments as follows:

A. ***Executive Summary*** *– Provide an executive summary with a limit of 250 words.*

B. ***List of Recommendations/Actions*** *– Identify, in a vertical list, specific recommendations/actions that are being requested.*

C. ***Rationale*** *– Provide specific rationale to justify each recommendation/action requested.*

D. ***Citable Material*** *– Provide citable material to substantiate the rationale.*

The above italicized procedure is requested to permit ACGIH® to more efficiently and productively review comments.

4. **TLV®/BEI® and Adopted *Documentation*:** If the Committee neither finds nor receives any substantive data that change its scientific opinion regarding an NIC TLV® or BEI®, the Committee may then approve its recommendation to the ACGIH® Board of Directors for adoption. Once approved by the Committee and subsequently ratified by the Board, the TLV® or BEI® is published as adopted in the *Annual Reports of the Committees on TLVs® and BEIs®* and in the annual *TLVs® and BEIs®* book, and the draft TLV® or BEI® *Documentation* is finalized for formal publication.

5. **Withdraw from Consideration:** At any point in the process, the Committee may determine not to proceed with the development of a TLV® or BEI® and withdraw it from further consideration. Substances or physical agents that have been withdrawn from consideration can be reconsidered by placement on the Under Study List (step 1 above).

Development Process — xi

There are *several important points* to consider throughout the above process:

i. The appropriate method for an interested party to contribute to the TLV® and BEI® process is through the submission of literature that is peer-reviewed and public. ACGIH® strongly encourages interested parties to publish their studies, and not to rely on unpublished studies as their input to the TLV® and BEI® process. Also, the best time to submit comments to ACGIH® is in the early stages of the TLV® and BEI® development process, preferably while the substance or agent is on the Under Study list.

ii. An additional venue for presentation of new data is an ACGIH®-sponsored symposium or workshop that provides a platform for public discussion and scientific interpretation. ACGIH® encourages input from external parties for suggestions on symposium topics, including suggestions about sponsors, speakers and format. ACGIH® employs several criteria to determine the appropriateness of a symposium. A key criterion is that the symposium must be the most efficient format to present the Committee with information that will assist in the scientific judgment used for writing the *Documentation* and in setting the respective TLVs® or BEIs®. A symposium topic should be suggested while the substance/agent is Under Study, as symposia require considerable time, commitment, and resources to develop. Symposium topic suggestions submitted while a substance is on the NIC will be considered, but this is usually too late in the decision-making process. A symposium topic will not be favorably considered if its purpose is to provide a forum for voicing opinions about existing data. Rather, there must be ongoing research, scientific uncertainty about currently available data, or another scientific reason for the symposium. Symposium topic suggestions should be sent to the ACGIH® Science Group (science@acgih.org).

iii. ACGIH® periodically receives requests from external parties to make a presentation to a committee about specific substances or issues. It is *strictly by exception* that such requests are granted. While there are various reasons for this position, the underlying fact is that the Committee focuses on data that have been peer-reviewed and published and not on data presented in a private forum. A committee may grant a request when the data is significantly new, has received peer review, is the best vehicle for receipt of the information, and is essential to the committee's deliberations. The presentation is not a forum to voice opinions about existing data. In order for a committee to evaluate such a request, the external party must submit a request in writing that, at a minimum, addresses the following elements: (a) a detailed description of the presentation; (b) a clear demonstration of why the information is important to the Committee's deliberations; and (c) a clear demonstration of why a meeting is the necessary method of delivery. This request must be sent to the ACGIH® Science Group (science@acgih.org).

Also, the Committee may initiate contact with outside experts (a) to meet with the Committee to discuss specific issues or to obtain additional knowledge on the subject, and (b) to provide written input or review of a *Documentation*. This is only done on an as needed basis, and not as a routine practice.

xii — Development Process

iv. ACGIH® does *not* commit to deferring consideration of a new or revised TLV® or BEI® pending the outcome of proposed or ongoing research.

Important dates to consider throughout each calendar year of the TLV®/BEI® Development Process:

First Quarter:

- The TLV®/BEI® Annual Reports and the *TLVs® and BEIs®* book are published.

Year Round:

- Public comments are accepted.*

- Committees meet.

* Note: It is recommended that comments be submitted as early as practical, and preferably no later than July 31st to allow sufficient time for their proper consideration/review. This is essential for an NIC or NIE TLV®/BEI®.

Important Notice: The comment period for an NIC or NIE draft *Documentation* and its respective TLV(s)®, notation(s), or BEI(s)®, is limited to a firm 6-month period, running from February 1 to July 31 of each year. ACGIH® restructured the comment period effective January 1, 2007 to ensure all comments are received by ACGIH® in time for full consideration by the appropriate Committee before its fall meeting.

Third Quarter:

- Two-tier Under Study list published on website (http://www.acgih.org/TLV/Studies.htm).

Fourth Quarter: **

- TLV®/BEI® Committees vote on proposed TLVs®/BEIs® for NIC or final adoption.

- ACGIH® Board of Directors ratifies TLV®/BEI® Committee recommendations.

** Note: These actions typically occur early in the fourth quarter, but may occur during other periods of the quarter or year.

Endnote: Sample permission statement granting ACGIH® authorization to use, cite, and release unpublished studies:

[Name], [author or sponsor of the study*] grants permission to ACGIH® to use and cite the documents listed below, and to fully disclose them to parties outside of ACGIH® upon request.

Development Process — xiii

Permission to disclose the documents includes permission to make copies as needed.

Example: Joseph D. Doe, PhD, co-author of the study, grants permission to ACGIH® to use and cite the document listed below, and to fully disclose this document to parties outside of ACGIH®. Permission to disclose the document includes permission to make copies as needed.

"Effects of Quartz Status on Pharmacokinetics of Intratracheally Instilled Cristobalite in Rats, March 21, 2003."

*This statement must be signed by an individual authorized to give this permission, and should include contact information such as title and address.

Last Revised January 31, 2008

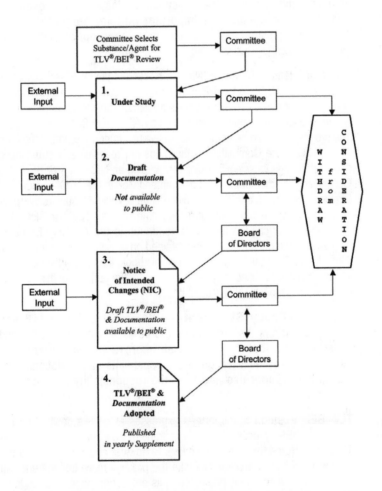

FIGURE 1. The TLV®/BEI® Development Process Flow Chart.

December 20, 2004

ONLINE TLV® AND BEI® RESOURCES

In an effort to make the threshold limit values (TLVs®) and biological expo-sures indices (BEIs®) guideline establishment process more transparent, and to assist ACGIH® members, government regulators, and industry groups in under-standing the basis and limitations of the TLVs® and BEIs®, ACGIH® has an online TLV®/BEI® Resources Section on its website at www.acgih.org/TLV/.

The TLV®/BEI® Resources Section is divided into eight categories, each containing clear and concise information. The categories are:

- **Conflict of Interest Policy** — applies to the Board of Directors, Committee Chairs, and Committee members (including con-sultant members), and safeguards the integrity and credibility of ACGIH® programs and activities. The Policy, as well as ACGIH®'s oversight and review, each play an important part in the protection of ACGIH®'s programs and activities from inappropriate influences (www.acgih.org/TLV/COIPolicy.htm).

- **Notice of Intended Changes (NIC)** — a listing of the proposed actions of the TLV®-CS, TLV®-PA, and BEI® Committees. This Notice provides an opportunity for public comment. Values remain on the NIC for approximate-ly one year after they have been ratified by ACGIH®'s Board of Directors. The proposals should be considered trial values during the period they are on the NIC. If the Committee neither finds nor receives any substantive data that change its scientific opinion regarding an NIC TLV® or BEI®, the Committee may then approve its recommendation to the ACGIH® Board of Directors for adoption. If the Committee finds or receives substantive data that change its scientific opinion regarding an NIC TLV® or BEI®, the Committee may change its recommendation to the ACGIH® Board of Directors for the matter to be either retained on or withdrawn from the NIC. [Note: In the Physical Agents section of this book, the term Notice of Intent to Establish (NIE) is used in addition to NIC. For the purpose of this process overview, only the term NIC is used.]

- **TLV®/BEI® Policy Statement** — states what the TLVs® and BEIs® are and how they are intended to be used. While the TLVs® and BEIs® do contribute to the overall improvement in worker pro-tection, the user must recognize the constraints and limitations sub-ject to their proper use and bear the responsibility for such use (www.acgih.org/TLV/PolicyStmt.htm).

- **TLV®/BEI® Position Statement** — expresses ACGIH®'s position on the TLVs® and BEIs® process. ACGIH® is proud of the positive impact that the TLVs® and BEIs® have had on workers worldwide, and stands behind the hard work of its Committees to make the process more transparent and accessible. This section is presented in its entirety on pages v through vii (www.acgih.org/TLV/PosStmt.htm).

- **TLV®/BEI® Development Process** — gives an overview of the process the Committees go through when establishing a TLV® or BEI®. This section is presented in its entirety on pages viii through xiii (www.acgih.org/TLV/DevProcess.htm).

- **Committee Operations Manuals** — portable data files (PDF) of the Threshold Limit Values for Chemical Substances, the Threshold Limit Values for Physical Agents, and the Biological Exposure Indices Committees' Operations Manuals. Each Manual covers such areas as the Committee's mission, membership in the Committee, Committee make-up, internal and external communications with the Committee, flow of information, procedures for development of symposia and workshops, etc. (www.acgih.org/TLV/OpsManual.htm).

- **TLV®/BEI® Process Presentations** — stand-alone PowerPoint presentations from the annual American Industrial Hygiene Conference and Exposition (AIHce) are offered. These forums are open to all AIHce registrants and focus on the process used by ACGIH® and its TLV®, BEI®, and Bioaerosols Committees. These presentations are posted on the ACGIH® website (www.acgih.org/TLV/TLVPresentation.htm).

- **Under Study List** — contains substances, agents, and issues that are being considered by the Committees. Each Committee solicits data, comments, and suggestions that may assist in their deliberations about substances, agents, and issues on the Under Study list (www.acgih.org/TLV/Studies.htm). Further, each Committee solicits recommendations for additional chemical substances, physical agents, and issues of concern to the industrial hygiene and occupational health communities.

REVISIONS OR ADDITIONS
FOR 2012

All pertinent endnotes, abbreviations, and definitions relating to the materials in this publication appear on the inside back cover.

Chemical Substances Section

- Proposed TLVs® that appeared on the 2011 NIC are adopted for the following substances:

Allyl bromide	Nitrogen dioxide
Carbonyl sulfide	Nonane
Diacetyl	o-Phthalodinitrile
Ethyl formate	Piperazine and salts

- *Documentation* and adopted TLV® are withdrawn for the following substances [*see* also Appendix G]:

Nonane, all isomers	Piperazine dihydrochloride

- The following chemical substances and proposed TLVs® new to this section are placed on the NIC:

N,N-Diethylhydroxylamine (DEHA)	Peracetic acid

- Revisions to adopted TLVs® are proposed for the following substances and placed on the NIC:

Butane, all isomers	Methyl isoamyl ketone
Clopidol	Tributyl phosphate
2,4-D	Trichloroacetic acid
1-Methoxy-2-propanol	1,2,3-Trichloropropane

- *Documentation* and adopted TLV® for the following substance is proposed to be withdrawn:

  Aliphatic hydrocarbon gases, Alkanes [C_1–C_4]

- The following substances are retained on the NIC with revised TLV® recommendations or notations:

Acetaldehyde	Ethyl tert-butyl ether
1-Bromopropane	Naphthalene
Diethylene glycol monobutyl ether	

- The following substances are retained on the NIC without revised TLV® recommendations or notations:

  Acetone   Toluene-2,4- or 2,6-
                             diisocyanate (or as a
                             mixture)

- The following substance is retained on the NIC to withdraw *Documentation* and adopted TLV®:

  Glycerin mist

- Previously proposed TLV® for the following substance is retained on the NIC with revised TLV® recommendations or notations:

  Manganese, elemental and inorganic compounds, as Mn

- *Documentation* was updated for the following without change to the recommended TLV®. *See* the 2012 Supplement to the *Documentation* of the TLVs® and BEIs®, 7th ed.:

  Wood dusts

Definitions and Notations Section

- The definition for Sensitization to include Dermal Sensitization (DSEN) and Respiratory Sensitization (RSEN) notations that appeared on the 2011 NIC is adopted.

Biological Exposure Indices (BEIs®) Section

- Proposed BEI® that appeared on the 2011 NIC is adopted for the following substance:

  Fluorides

- First-time BEIs® are recommended for the following substances:

  Naphthalene   Toluene diisocyanate

- Revisions to the BEIs® for the following are proposed and placed on the NIC:

  Ethyl benzene   Methyl ethyl ketone
  Mercury   Pentachlorophenol

- *Documentation* was updated for the following without change to the recommended BEI®. *See* the 2012 Supplement to the *Documentation* of the TLVs® and BEIs®, 7th ed.:

  Xylenes

xviii — Revisions/Additions

Physical Agents Section

- The following agents that appeared on the 2011 NIC with revisions/additions are adopted:

Ionizing Radiation   Lasers

Biologically Derived Airborne Contaminants Section

No new information for 2012.

2012

Threshold Limit Values for Chemical Substances in the Work Environment

Adopted by ACGIH®
with Intended Changes

Contents

2 — Members

2011 TLV® CHEMICAL SUBSTANCES COMMITTEE

TLV®–CS

Terry Gordon, PhD — Chair
Robert Spirtas, DrPH — Vice Chair
Jeremy R. Beach, MD
William S. Beckett, MD, MPH
Philip L. Bigelow, PhD, CIH, ROH
James V. Bruckner, PhD, MS
Dennis M. Casserly, PhD, CIH
B. Dwight Culver, MD
Laura Deakin, PhD, MPH
Alison C. Elder, PhD
Deborah C. Glass, PhD, MA, MSc
Ian A. Greaves, MD
Gregory L. Kedderis, PhD
Gerald L. Kennedy, Jr., DABT
David A. Macys, MS, DABT
David C. May, ScD, CIH, PE
James N. McDougal, PhD, ATS
Bruce D. Naumann, PhD, DABT
Rachel Rubin, MD, MPH
Edward V. Sargent, PhD, MPH, DABT
Darius D. Sivin, PhD

ACGIH® also appreciates the contributions of the following individual:

Jessica Ramsey — ACGIH® Bloomfield Awardee

INTRODUCTION TO THE CHEMICAL SUBSTANCES

General Information

The TLVs® are guidelines to be used by professional industrial hygienists. The values presented in this book are intended for use only as guidelines or recommendations to assist in the evaluation and control of potential workplace health hazards and for no other use (e.g., neither for evaluating or controlling community air pollution; nor for estimating the toxic potential of continuous, uninterrupted exposures or other extended work periods; nor for proving or disproving an existing disease or physical condition in an individual). Further, these values are not fine lines between safe and dangerous conditions and should not be used by anyone who is not trained in the discipline of industrial hygiene. TLVs® are not regulatory or consensus standards.

Editor's note: The approximate year that the current *Documentation* was last substantially reviewed and, where necessary, updated may be found following the CAS number for each of the adopted entries in the alphabetical listing, e.g., Aldrin [309-00-2] (2006). The reader is advised to refer to the "TLV® Chronology" section in each *Documentation* for a brief history of the TLV® recommendations and notations.

Definition of the TLVs®

Threshold Limit Values (TLVs®) refer to airborne concentrations of chemical substances and represent conditions under which it is believed that *nearly all* workers may be repeatedly exposed, day after day, over a working lifetime, without adverse health effects.

Those who use the TLVs® **MUST** consult the latest *Documentation* to ensure that they understand the basis for the TLV® and the information used in its development. The amount and quality of the information that is available for each chemical substance varies over time.

Chemical substances with equivalent TLVs® (i.e., same numerical values) cannot be assumed to have similar toxicologic effects or similar biologic potency. In this book, there are columns listing the TLVs® for each chemical substance (that is, airborne concentrations in parts per million [ppm] or milligrams per cubic meter [mg/m³]) and critical effects produced by the chemical substance. These critical effects form the basis of the TLV®.

ACGIH® recognizes that there will be considerable variation in the level of biological response to a particular chemical substance, regardless of the airborne concentration. Indeed, TLVs® do not represent a fine line between a healthy versus an unhealthy work environment or the point at which material impairment of health will occur. TLVs® will not adequately protect all workers. Some individuals may experience discomfort or even more serious adverse health effects when exposed to a chemical substance at the TLV® or even at concentrations below the TLV®. There are numerous possible reasons for increased susceptibility to a chemical substance, including age, gender, ethnicity, genetic factors (predisposition), lifestyle choices (e.g., diet, smoking, abuse of alcohol and other drugs), medications, and pre-existing medical conditions (e.g., aggravation of asthma or cardiovascular disease). Some individu-

4 — Introduction

als may become more responsive to one or more chemical substances following previous exposures (e.g., sensitized workers). Susceptibility to the effects of chemical substances may be altered during different periods of fetal development and throughout an individual's reproductive lifetime. Some changes in susceptibility may also occur at different work levels (e.g., light versus heavy work) or at exercise — situations in which there is increased cardiopulmonary demand. Additionally, variations in temperature (e.g., extreme heat or cold) and relative humidity may alter an individual's response to a toxicant. The *Documentation* for any given TLV® must be reviewed, keeping in mind that other factors may modify biological responses.

Although TLVs® refer to airborne levels of chemical exposure, dermal exposures may possibly occur in the workplace (*see* "Skin" on page 72 of the ***Definitions and Notations*** section).

Three categories of TLVs® are specified: time-weighted average (TWA); short-term exposure limit (STEL); and a ceiling (C). For most substances, a TWA alone or with a STEL is relevant. For some substances (e.g., irritant gases), only the TLV–C is applicable. If any of these TLV® types are exceeded, a potential hazard from that substance is presumed to exist.

Threshold Limit Value–Time-Weighted Average (TLV–TWA): The TWA concentration for a conventional 8-hour workday and a 40-hour workweek, to which it is believed that nearly all workers may be repeatedly exposed, day after day, for a working lifetime without adverse effect. Although calculating the average concentration for a workweek, rather than a workday, may be appropriate in some instances, ACGIH® does not offer guidance regarding such exposures.

Threshold Limit Value–Short-Term Exposure Limit (TLV–STEL): A 15-minute TWA exposure that should not be exceeded at any time during a workday, even if the 8-hour TWA is within the TLV–TWA. The TLV–STEL is the concentration to which it is believed that workers can be exposed continuously for a short period of time without suffering from 1) irritation, 2) chronic or irreversible tissue damage, 3) dose-rate-dependent toxic effects, or 4) narcosis of sufficient degree to increase the likelihood of accidental injury, impaired self-rescue, or materially reduced work efficiency. The TLV–STEL will not necessarily protect against these effects if the daily TLV–TWA is exceeded. The TLV–STEL usually supplements the TLV–TWA where there are recognized acute effects from a substance whose toxic effects are primarily of a chronic nature; however, the TLV–STEL may be a separate, independent exposure guideline. Exposures above the TLV–TWA up to the TLV–STEL should be less than 15 minutes, should occur no more than four times per day, and there should be at least 60 minutes between successive exposures in this range. An averaging period other than 15 minutes may be recommended when this is warranted by observed biological effects.

Threshold Limit Value–Ceiling (TLV–C): The concentration that should not be exceeded during any part of the working exposure. If instantaneous measurements are not available, sampling should be conducted for the minimum period of time sufficient to detect exposures at or above the ceiling value. ACGIH® believes that TLVs® based on physical irritation should be considered no less binding than those based on physical impairment. There is increasing evidence that physical irritation may initiate, promote, or accelerate adverse health effects through interaction with other chemical or biologic agents or through other mechanisms.

Excursion Limits

For many substances with a TLV–TWA, there is no TLV–STEL. Nevertheless, excursions above the TLV–TWA should be controlled, even where the 8-hour TLV–TWA is within recommended limits. Excursion limits apply to those TLV–TWAs that do not have TLV–STELs.

> Excursions in worker exposure levels may exceed 3 times the TLV–TWA for no more than a total of 30 minutes during a work-day, and under no circumstances should they exceed 5 times the TLV–TWA, provided that the TLV–TWA is not exceeded.

The approach here is that the maximum recommended excursion should be related to the variability generally observed in actual industrial processes. In reviewing large numbers of industrial hygiene surveys conducted by the U.S. National Institute for Occupational Safety and Health, Leidel et al. (1975) found that short-term exposure measurements were generally lognormally distributed.

While a complete discussion of the theory and properties of the lognormal distribution is beyond the scope of this section, a brief description of some important terms is presented. The measure of central tendency in a lognormal distribution is the antilog of the mean logarithm of the sample values. The distribution is skewed, and the geometric mean (m_g) is always smaller than the arithmetic mean by an amount that depends on the geometric standard deviation. In the lognormal distribution, the geometric standard deviation (sd_g) is the antilog of the standard deviation of the sample value logarithms, and 68.26% of all values lie between m_g/sd_g and $m_g \times sd_g$.

If the short-term exposure values in a given situation have a geometric standard deviation of 2.0, 5% of all values will exceed 3.13 times the geometric mean. If a process displays variability greater than this, it is not under good control, and efforts should be made to restore control.

The approach is a considerable simplification of the lognormal concentration distribution concept but is considered more convenient. If exposure excursions are maintained within the recommended limits, the geometric standard deviation of the concentration measurements will be near 2.0, and the goal of the recommendations will be accomplished. It is recognized that the geometric standard deviations of some common workplace exposures may exceed 2.0 (Buringh and Lanting, 1991). If such distributions are known and workers are not at increased risk of adverse health effects, recommended excursion limits should be modified based upon workplace-specific data. When the toxicologic data for a specific substance are available to establish a TLV–STEL or a TLV–C, these values take precedence over the excursion limit.

TWA and STEL versus Ceiling (C)

A substance may have certain toxicological properties that require the use of a TLV–C rather than a TLV–TWA excursion limit or a TLV–STEL. The

6 — Introduction

amount by which the TLVs® may be exceeded for short periods without injury to health depends upon a number of factors such as the nature of the contaminant, whether very high concentrations — even for short periods — produce acute poisoning, whether the effects are cumulative, the frequency with which high concentrations occur, and the duration of such periods. All factors must be taken into consideration in arriving at a decision as to whether a hazardous condition exists.

Although the TWA concentration provides the most satisfactory, practical way of monitoring airborne agents for compliance with the TLVs®, there are certain substances for which it is inappropriate. In the latter group are substances that are predominantly fast-acting and whose TLV® is more appropriately based on this particular response. Substances with this type of response are best controlled by a TLV–C that should not be exceeded. It is implicit in these definitions that the manner of sampling to determine noncompliance with the TLVs® for each group must differ. Consequently, a single, brief sample that is applicable to a TLV–C is not appropriate to the TLV–TWA; here, a sufficient number of samples are needed to permit determination of a TWA concentration throughout a complete cycle of operation or throughout the workshift.

Whereas the TLV–C places a definite boundary that exposure concentrations should not be permitted to exceed, the TLV–TWA requires an explicit limit to the excursions which are acceptable above the recommended TLV–TWAs.

Mixtures

Special consideration should also be given to the application of the TLVs® in assessing the health hazards that may be associated with exposure to a mixture of two or more substances. A brief discussion of basic considerations involved in developing TLVs® for mixtures and methods for their development, amplified by specific examples, is given in Appendix E.

Deviations in Work Conditions and Work Schedules

Application of TLVs® to Unusual Ambient Conditions

When workers are exposed to air contaminants at temperatures and pressures substantially different than those at normal temperature and pressure (NTP) conditions (25°C and 760 torr), care should be taken in comparing sampling results to the applicable TLVs®. For aerosols, the TWA exposure concentration (calculated using sample volumes not adjusted to NTP conditions) should be compared directly to the applicable TLVs® published in the *TLVs® and BEIs®* book. For gases and vapors, there are a number of options for comparing air-sampling results to the TLV®, and these are discussed in detail by Stephenson and Lillquist (2001). One method that is simple in its conceptual approach is 1) to determine the exposure concentration, expressed in terms of mass per volume, at the sampling site using the sample volume not adjusted to NTP conditions, 2) if required, to convert the TLV® to mg/m^3 (or other mass per volume measure) using a molar volume of 24.4 L/mole, and 3) to compare the exposure concentration to the TLV®, both in units of mass per volume.

A number of assumptions are made when comparing sampling results obtained under unusual atmospheric conditions to the TLVs®. One such assumption is that the volume of air inspired by the worker per workday is not appreciably different under moderate conditions of temperature and pressure as compared to NTP (Stephenson and Lillquist, 2001). An additional assumption for gases and vapors is that absorbed dose is correlated to the partial pressure of the inhaled compound. Sampling results obtained under unusual conditions cannot easily be compared to the published TLVs®, and extreme care should be exercised if workers are exposed to very high or low ambient pressures.

Unusual Work Schedules

Application of TLVs® to work schedules markedly different from the conventional 8-hour day, 40-hour workweek requires particular judgment to provide protection for these workers equal to that provided to workers on conventional work shifts. Short workweeks can allow workers to have more than one job, perhaps with similar exposures, and may result in overexposure, even if neither job by itself entails overexposure.

Numerous mathematical models to adjust for unusual work schedules have been described. In terms of toxicologic principles, their general objective is to identify a dose that ensures that the daily peak body burden or weekly peak body burden does not exceed that which occurs during a normal 8-hour/day, 5-day/week shift. A comprehensive review of the approaches to adjusting occupational exposure limits for unusual work schedules is provided in *Patty's Industrial Hygiene* (Paustenbach, 2000). Other selected readings on this topic include Lapare et al. (2003), Brodeur et al. (2001), Caldwell et al. (2001), Eide (2000), Verma (2000), Roach (1978), and Hickey and Reist (1977).

Another model that addresses unusual work schedules is the Brief and Scala model (1986), which is explained in detail in *Patty's Industrial Hygiene* (Paustenbach, 2000). This model reduces the TLV® proportionately for both increased exposure time and reduced recovery (i.e., non-exposure) time, and is generally intended to apply to work schedules longer than 8 hours/day or 40 hours/week. The model should not be used to justify very high exposures as "allowable" where the exposure periods are short (e.g., exposure to 8 times the TLV–TWA for 1 hour and zero exposure during the remainder of the shift). In this respect, the general limitations on TLV–TWA excursions and TLV–STELs should be applied to avoid inappropriate use of the model with very short exposure periods or shifts.

The Brief and Scala model is easier to use than some of the more complex models based on pharmacokinetic actions. The application of such models usually requires knowledge of the biological half-life of each substance, and some models require additional data. Another model developed by the University of Montreal and the Institute de Recherche en Sante et en Securite du Travail (IRSST) uses the Haber method to calculate adjusted exposure limits (Brodeur et al., 2001). This method generates values close to those obtained from physiologically based pharmacokinetic (PBPK) models.

Because adjusted TLVs® do not have the benefit of historical use and long-time observation, medical supervision during initial use of adjusted TLVs® is advised. Unnecessary exposure of workers should be avoided, even if a model shows such exposures to be "allowable." Mathematical models should not be used to justify higher-than-necessary exposures.

TLV-CS

TLV® Units

TLVs® are expressed in ppm or mg/m³. An inhaled chemical substance may exist as a gas, vapor, or aerosol.

- A gas is a chemical substance whose molecules are moving freely within a space in which they are confined (e.g., cylinder/tank) at normal temperature and pressure (NTP). Gases assume no shape or volume.
- A vapor is the gaseous phase of a chemical substance that exists as a liquid or a solid at NTP. The amount of vapor given off by a chemical substance is expressed as the vapor pressure and is a function of temperature and pressure.
- An aerosol is a suspension of solid particles or liquid droplets in a gaseous medium. Other terms used to describe an aerosol include dust, mist, fume, fog, fiber, smoke, and smog. Aerosols may be characterized by their aerodynamic behavior and the site(s) of deposition in the human respiratory tract.

TLVs® for aerosols are usually established in terms of mass of the chemical substance in air by volume. These TLVs® are expressed in mg/m³.

TLVs® for gases and vapors are established in terms of parts of vapor or gas per million parts of contaminated air by volume (ppm), but may also be expressed in mg/m³. For convenience to the user, these TLVs® also reference molecular weights. Where 24.45 = molar volume of air in liters at NTP conditions (25°C and 760 torr), the conversion equations for gases and vapors [ppm ↔ mg/m³] are as follows:

$$\text{TLV in ppm} = \frac{(\text{TLV in mg/m}^3)\,(24.45)}{(\text{gram molecular weight of substance})}$$

OR

$$\text{TLV in mg/m}^3 = \frac{(\text{TLV in ppm})\,(\text{gram molecular weight of substance})}{24.45}$$

When converting values expressed as an element (e.g., as Fe, as Ni), the molecular weight of the element should be used, not that of the entire compound.

In making conversions for substances with variable molecular weights, appropriate molecular weights should be estimated or assumed (*see* the TLV® *Documentation*).

User Information

Each TLV® is supported by a comprehensive *Documentation*. It is imperative to consult the latest *Documentation* when applying the TLV®.

Additional copies of the *TLVs® and BEIs®* book and the multi-volume *Documentation of the Threshold Limit Values and Biological Exposure Indices*, upon which this book is based, are available from ACGIH®. *Documentation* of individual TLVs® is also available. Consult the ACGIH® website (www.acgih.org/store) for additional information and availability concerning these publications.

> **ACGIH® disclaims liability with respect to the use of TLVs®.**

References and Selected Readings

Brief RS; Scala RA: Occupational health aspects of unusual work schedules: a review of Exxon's experiences. Am Ind Hyg Assoc J 47(4):199–202 (1986).

Brodeur J; Vyskocil A; Tardif R; et al.: Adjustment of permissible exposure values to unusual work schedules. Am Ind Hyg Assoc J 62:584–594 (2001).

Buringh E; Lanting R: Exposure variability in the workplace: its implications for the assessment of compliance. Am Ind Hyg Assoc J 52:6–13 (1991).

Caldwell DJ; Armstrong TW; Barone NJ; et al.: Lessons learned while compiling a quantitative exposure database from the published literature. Appl Occup Environ Hyg 16(2):174–177 (2001).

Eide I: The application of 8-hour occupational exposure limits to non-standard work schedules offshore. Ann Occup Hyg 34(1):13–17 (1990).

Hickey JL; Reist PC: Application of occupational exposure limits to unusual work schedules. Am Ind Hyg Assoc J 38(11):613–621 (1977).

Lapare S; Brodeur J; Tardif R: Contribution of toxicokinetic modeling to the adjustment of exposure limits to unusual work schedules. Am Ind Hyg Assoc J 64(1):17–23 (2003).

Leidel NA; Busch KA; Crouse WE: Exposure measurement action level and occupational environmental variability. DHEW (NIOSH) Pub. No. 76-131; NTIS Pub. No. PB- 267-509. U.S. National Technical Information Service, Springfield, VA (December 1975).

Paustenbach DJ: Pharmacokinetics and Unusual Work Schedules. In: Patty's Industrial Hygiene, 5th ed., Vol. 3, Part VI, Law, Regulation, and Management, Chap. 40, pp. 1787–1901. RL Harris, Ed. John Wiley & Sons, Inc., New York (2000).

Roach SA: Threshold limit values for extraordinary work schedules. Am Ind Hyg Assoc J 39(4):345–348 (1978).

Stephenson DJ; Lillquist DR: The effects of temperature and pressure on airborne exposure concentrations when performing compliance evaluations using ACGIH TLVs and OSHA PELs. Appl Occup Environ Hyg 16(4):482–486 (2001).

Verma DK: Adjustment of occupational exposure limits for unusual work schedules. Am Ind Hyg Assoc J 61(3):367–374 (2000).

TLV®–CS

> All pertinent notes relating to the material in the Chemical Substances section of this book appear in the appendices for this section or on the inside back cover.

10 — Adopted Values

TLV®–CS

Substance [CAS No.] (*Documentation date*)	ADOPTED VALUES			MW	TLV® Basis
	TWA	STEL	Notations		
‡ Acetaldehyde [75-07-0] (1992)	—	(C 25 ppm)	A3	44.05	Eye & URT irr
Acetic acid [64-19-7] (2003)	10 ppm	15 ppm	—	60.00	URT & eye irr; pulm func
Acetic anhydride [108-24-7] (2010)	1 ppm	3 ppm	A4	102.09	Eye & URT irr
‡ Acetone [67-64-1] (1996)	(500 ppm)	(750 ppm)	(A4); BEI	58.05	(URT & eye irr; CNS impair; hematologic eff)
Acetone cyanohydrin [75-86-5], as CN (1991)	—	C 5 mg/m³	Skin	85.10	URT irr; headache; hypoxia/cyanosis
Acetonitrile [75-05-8] (1996)	20 ppm	—	Skin; A4	41.05	LRT irr
Acetophenone [98-86-2] (2008)	10 ppm	—	—	120.15	URT irr; CNS impair; pregnancy loss
Acetylene [74-86-2] (1990)	Simple asphyxiant (D)			26.02	Asphyxia
Acetylsalicylic acid (Aspirin) [50-78-2] (1977)	5 mg/m³	—	—	180.15	Skin & eye irr
Acrolein [107-02-8] (1995)	—	C 0.1 ppm	Skin; A4	56.06	Eye & URT irr; pulm edema; pulm emphysema
Acrylamide [79-06-1] (2004)	0.03 mg/m³ (IFV)	—	Skin; A3	71.08	CNS impair
Acrylic acid [79-10-7] (1986)	2 ppm	—	Skin; A4	72.06	URT irr
Acrylonitrile [107-13-1] (1997)	2 ppm	—	Skin; A3	53.05	CNS impair; LRT irr
Adipic acid [124-04-9] (1990)	5 mg/m³	—	—	146.14	URT irr; ANS impair

Adopted Values — 11

TLV®–CS

ADOPTED VALUES

Substance [CAS No.] (Documentation date)	TWA	STEL	Notations	MW	TLV® Basis
Adiponitrile [111-69-3] (1990)	2 ppm	—	Skin	108.10	URT & LRT irr
Alachlor [15972-60-8] (2006)	1 mg/m³ (IFV)	—	SEN; A3	269.8	Hemosiderosis
Aldrin [309-00-2] (2006)	0.05 mg/m³ (IFV)	—	Skin; A3	364.93	CNS impair; liver & kidney dam
‡ (Aliphatic hydrocarbon gases Alkanes [C₁–C₄] (2001)	(1000 ppm)	(—)	(—)	(Varies)	(Card sens; CNS impair)
Allyl alcohol [107-18-6] (1996)	0.5 ppm	—	Skin; A4	58.08	Eye & URT irr
* Allyl bromide [106-95-6] (2011)	0.1 ppm	0.2 ppm	Skin; A4	120.99	Eye & URT irr
Allyl chloride [107-05-1] (2010)	1 ppm	2 ppm	Skin; A3	76.50	Eye & URT irr; liver & kidney dam
Allyl glycidyl ether (AGE) [106-92-3] (1995)	1 ppm	—	A4	114.14	URT irr, dermatitis; eye & skin irr
Allyl propyl disulfide [2179-59-1] (2001)	0.5 ppm	—	SEN	148.16	URT & eye irr
Aluminum metal [7429-90-5] and insoluble compounds (2007)	1 mg/m³ (R)	—	A4	26.98 Varies	Pneumoconiosis; LRT irr; neurotoxicity
4-Aminodiphenyl [92-67-1] (1968)	— (L)	—	Skin; A1	169.23	Bladder & liver cancer
2-Aminopyridine [504-29-0] (1966)	0.5 ppm	—	—	94.12	Headache; nausea; CNS impair; dizziness
Amitrole [61-82-5] (1983)	0.2 mg/m³	—	A3	84.08	Thyroid eff

901

12 — Adopted Values

TLV®–CS

ADOPTED VALUES

Substance [CAS No.] (*Documentation date*)	TWA	STEL	Notations	MW	TLV® Basis
Ammonia [7664-41-7] (1970)	25 ppm	35 ppm	—	17.03	Eye dam; URT irr
Ammonium chloride fume [12125-02-9] (1970)	10 mg/m³	20 mg/m³	—	53.50	Eye & URT irr
Ammonium perfluorooctanoate [3825-26-1] (1992)	0.01 mg/m³	—	Skin; A3	431.00	Liver dam
Ammonium sulfamate [7773-06-0] (1956)	10 mg/m³	—	—	114.13	
tert-Amyl methyl ether (TAME) [994-05-8] (1999)	20 ppm	—	—	102.2	CNS impair, embryo/fetal dam
Aniline [62-53-3] (1979)	2 ppm	—	Skin; A3; BEI	93.12	MeHb-emia
o-Anisidine [90-04-0] (1979)	0.5 mg/m³	—	Skin; A3; BEI$_M$	123.15	MeHb-emia
p-Anisidine [104-94-9] (1979)	0.5 mg/m³	—	Skin; A4; BEI$_M$	123.15	MeHb-emia
Antimony [7440-36-0] and compounds, as Sb (1979)	0.5 mg/m³	—	—	121.75	Skin & URT irr
Antimony hydride [7803-52-3] (1990)	0.1 ppm	—	—	124.78	Hemolysis; kidney dam; LRT irr
Antimony trioxide [1309-64-4], production (1977)	—(L)	—	A2	291.5	Lung cancer; pneumoconiosis
ANTU [86-88-4] (1990)	0.3 mg/m³	—	A4; Skin	202.27	Thyroid eff; nausea
Argon [7440-37-1] (1990)	Simple asphyxiant (D)			39.95	Asphyxia
Arsenic [7440-38-2] and inorganic compounds, as As (1990)	0.01 mg/m³	—	A1; BEI	74.92 Varies	Lung cancer

Adopted Values — 13

Substance [CAS No.] (*Documentation date*)	TWA	STEL	Notations	MW	TLV® Basis
			ADOPTED VALUES		
Arsine [7784-42-1] (2006)	0.005 ppm	—	—	77.95	PNS & vascular system impair; kidney & liver impair
Asbestos [1332-21-4], all forms (1994)	0.1 f/cc (F)	—	A1	—	Pneumoconiosis; lung cancer; mesothelioma
Asphalt (Bitumen) fume [8052-42-4], as benzene-soluble aerosol (1999)	0.5 mg/m³ (I)	—	A4; BEI$_P$	—	URT & eye irr
Atrazine [1912-24-9] (and related symmetrical triazines) (1985)	5 mg/m³	—	A4	215.69	CNS convul
Azinphos-methyl [86-50-0] (1999)	0.2 mg/m³ (IFV)	—	Skin; SEN; A4; BEI$_A$	317.34	Cholinesterase inhib
Barium [7440-39-3] and soluble compounds, as Ba (1990)	0.5 mg/m³	—	A4	137.30	Eye, skin, & GI irr; muscular stim
Barium sulfate [7727-43-7] (1983)	10 mg/m³	—	—	233.43	Pneumoconiosis
Benomyl [17804-35-2] (2007)	1 mg/m³ (I)	—	SEN; A3	290.32	URT irr; male repro & testicular dam; embryo/fetal dam
Benz[a]anthracene [56-55-3] (1990)	—(L)	—	A2; BEI$_P$	228.30	Skin cancer
Benzene [71-43-2] (1996)	0.5 ppm	2.5 ppm	Skin; A1; BEI	78.11	Leukemia
Benzidine [92-87-5] (1979)	—(L)	—	Skin; A1	184.23	Bladder cancer

TLV®–CS

14 — Adopted Values

TLV®–CS

ADOPTED VALUES

Substance [CAS No.] (Documentation date)	TWA	STEL	Notations	MW	TLV® Basis
Benzo[b]fluoranthene [205-99-2] (1990)	—(L)	—	A2; BEI$_P$	252.30	Cancer
Benzo[a]pyrene [50-32-8] (1990)	—(L)	—	A2; BEI$_P$	252.30	Cancer
Benzotrichloride [98-07-7] (1994)	—	C 0.1 ppm	Skin; A2	195.50	Eye, skin, & URT irr
Benzoyl chloride [98-88-4] (1992)	—	C 0.5 ppm	A4	140.57	URT & eye irr
Benzoyl peroxide [94-36-0] (1990)	5 mg/m³	—	A4	242.22	URT & skin irr
Benzyl acetate [140-11-4] (1990)	10 ppm	—	A4	150.18	URT irr
Benzyl chloride [100-44-7] (1990)	1 ppm	—	A3	126.58	Eye, skin, & URT irr
Beryllium [7440-41-7] and compounds, as Be (2008)	0.00005 mg/m³ (I)	—	Skin; SEN; A1	9.01	Beryllium sens; chronic beryllium disease (berylliosis)
Biphenyl [92-52-4] (1979)	0.2 ppm	—	—	154.20	Pulm func
Bismuth telluride [1304-82-1] (1970) Undoped, as Bi$_2$Te$_3$ Se-doped, as Bi$_2$Te$_3$	10 mg/m³ 5 mg/m³	— —	A4 A4	800.83	Lung dam
Borate compounds, inorganic [1330-43-4; 1303-96-4; 10043-35-3; 12179-04-3] (2004)	2 mg/m³ (I)	6 mg/m³ (I)	A4	Varies	URT irr
Boron oxide [1303-86-2] (1985)	10 mg/m³	—	—	69.64	Eye & URT irr

Adopted Values — 15

ADOPTED VALUES

Substance [CAS No.] (*Documentation date*)	TWA	STEL	Notations	MW	TLV® Basis
Boron tribromide [10294-33-4] (1990)	—	C 1 ppm	—	250.57	URT irr
Boron trifluoride [7637-07-2] (1962)	—	C 1 ppm	—	67.82	LRT irr, pneumonitis
Bromacil [314-40-9] (1976)	10 mg/m³	—	A3	261.11	Thyroid eff
Bromine [7726-95-6] (1991)	0.1 ppm	0.2 ppm	—	159.81	URT & LRT irr; lung dam
Bromine pentafluoride [7789-30-2] (1979)	0.1 ppm	—	—	174.92	Eye, skin, & URT irr
Bromoform [75-25-2] (2008)	0.5 ppm	—	A3	252.73	Liver dam; URT & eye irr
‡ 1-Bromopropane [106-94-5] (2003)	(10 ppm)	—	(—)	122.99	(Liver & embryo/fetal dam; neurotoxicity)
1,3-Butadiene [106-99-0] (1994)	2 ppm	—	A2	54.09	Cancer
‡ Butane, all isomers [106-97-8; 75-28-5]		(See Aliphatic hydrocarbon gases: Alkanes [C₁–C₄])			
n-Butanol [71-36-3] (1998)	20 ppm	—	—	74.12	Eye & URT irr
sec-Butanol [78-92-2] (2001)	100 ppm	—	—	74.12	URT irr; CNS impair
tert-Butanol [75-65-0] (1992)	100 ppm	—	A4	74.12	CNS impair
Butenes, all isomers [106-98-9; 107-01-7; 590-18-1; 624-64-6; 25167-67-3]	250 ppm	—	—	56.11	Body weight eff
Isobutene [115-11-7] (2007)	250 ppm	—	A4	—	URT irr; body weight eff

TLV®–CS

16 — Adopted Values

TLV®–CS

ADOPTED VALUES

Substance [CAS No.] (*Documentation date*)	TWA	STEL	Notations	MW	TLV® Basis
2-Butoxyethanol (EGBE) [111-76-2] (1996)	20 ppm	—	A3; BEI	118.17	Eye & URT irr
2-Butoxyethyl acetate (EGBEA) [112-07-2] (2000)	20 ppm	—	A3	160.2	Hemolysis
n-Butyl acetate [123-86-4] (1995)	150 ppm	200 ppm	—	116.16	Eye & URT irr
sec-Butyl acetate [105-46-4] (1965)	200 ppm	—	—	116.16	Eye & URT irr
tert-Butyl acetate [540-88-5] (1965)	200 ppm	—	—	116.16	Eye & URT irr
n-Butyl acrylate [141-32-2] (1996)	2 ppm	—	SEN; A4	128.17	Skin, eye, & URT irr
n-Butylamine [109-73-9] (1985)	—	C 5 ppm	Skin	73.14	Headache; URT & eye irr
Butylated hydroxytoluene (BHT) [128-37-0] (2001)	2 mg/m³ (IFV)	—	A4	220.34	URT irr
tert-Butyl chromate, as CrO₃ [1189-85-1] (1960)	—	C 0.1 mg/m³	Skin	230.22	LRT & skin irr
n-Butyl glycidyl ether (BGE) [2426-08-6] (2002)	3 ppm	—	Skin; SEN	130.21	Repro dam
n-Butyl lactate [138-22-7] (1973)	5 ppm	—	—	146.19	Headache; URT irr
n-Butyl mercaptan [109-79-5] (1968)	0.5 ppm	—	—	90.19	URT irr
o-sec-Butylphenol [89-72-5] (1977)	5 ppm	—	Skin	150.22	URT, eye, & skin irr
p-tert-Butyl toluene [98-51-1] (1990)	1 ppm	—	—	148.18	Eye & URT irr, nausea

Adopted Values — 17

TLV®–CS

ADOPTED VALUES

Substance [CAS No.] (Documentation date)	TWA	STEL	Notations	MW	TLV® Basis
Cadmium [7440-43-9] and compounds, as Cd (1990)	0.01 mg/m^3 0.002 mg/m^3 (R)	— —	A2; BEI A2; BEI	112.40 Varies	Kidney dam
Calcium chromate [13765-19-0], as Cr (1988)	0.001 mg/m^3	—	A2	156.09	Lung cancer
Calcium cyanamide [156-62-7] (1973)	0.5 mg/m^3	—	A4	80.11	Eye & URT irr
Calcium hydroxide [1305-62-0] (1979)	5 mg/m^3	—	—	74.10	Eye, URT, & skin irr
Calcium oxide [1305-78-8] (1990)	2 mg/m^3	—	—	56.08	URT irr
Calcium silicate, synthetic nonfibrous [1344-95-2] (1988)	10 mg/m^3 (E)	—	A4	—	URT irr
Calcium sulfate [7778-18-9; 10034-76-1; 10101-41-4; 13397-24-5] (2005)	10 mg/m^3 (I)	—	—	136.14	Nasal symptoms
Camphor, synthetic [76-22-2] (1990)	2 ppm	3 ppm	A4	152.23	Eye & URT irr; anosmia
Caprolactam [105-60-2] (1997)	5 mg/m^3 (IFV)	—	A5	113.16	URT irr
Captafol [2425-06-1] (1990)	0.1 mg/m^3	—	Skin; A4	349.06	Skin irr
Captan [133-06-2] (1999)	5 mg/m^3 (I)	—	SEN; A3	300.60	Skin irr
Carbaryl [63-25-2] (2007)	0.5 mg/m^3 (IFV)	—	Skin; A4; BEI$_A$	201.20	Cholinesterase inhib; male repro dam; embryo dam
Carbofuran [1563-66-2] (2001)	0.1 mg/m^3 (IFV)	—	A4; BEI$_A$	221.30	Cholinesterase inhib

18 — Adopted Values

TLV®–CS

Substance [CAS No.] [Documentation date]	TWA	STEL	Notations	MW	TLV® Basis
Carbon black [1333-86-4] (2010)	3 mg/m³ (I)	—	A3	—	Bronchitis
Carbon dioxide [124-38-9] (1983)	5000 ppm	30,000 ppm	—	44.01	Asphyxia
Carbon disulfide [75-15-0] (2005)	1 ppm	—	Skin; A4; BEI	76.14	PNS impair
Carbon monoxide [630-08-0] (1989)	25 ppm	—	BEI	28.01	COHb-emia
Carbon tetrabromide [558-13-4] (1972)	0.1 ppm	0.3 ppm	—	331.65	Liver dam; eye, URT, & skin irr
Carbon tetrachloride [56-23-5] (1990)	5 ppm	10 ppm	Skin; A2	153.84	Liver dam
Carbonyl fluoride [353-50-4] (1990)	2 ppm	5 ppm	—	66.01	LRT irr; bone dam
* Carbonyl sulfide [463-58-1] (2011)	5 ppm	—	—	60.08	CNS impair
Catechol [120-80-9] (1985)	5 ppm	—	Skin; A3	110.11	Eye & URT irr; dermatitis
Cellulose [9004-34-6] (1985)	10 mg/m³	—	—	NA	URT irr
Cesium hydroxide [21351-79-1] (1990)	2 mg/m³	—	—	149.92	URT, skin, & eye irr
Chlordane [57-74-9] (1985)	0.5 mg/m³	—	Skin; A3	409.80	Liver dam
Chlorinated camphene [8001-35-2] (1990)	0.5 mg/m³	1 mg/m³	Skin; A3	414.00	CNS convul; liver dam
o-Chlorinated diphenyl oxide [31242-93-0] (1979)	0.5 mg/m³	—	—	377.00	Chloracne; liver dam
Chlorine [7782-50-5] (1986)	0.5 ppm	1 ppm	A4	70.91	URT & eye irr

Adopted Values — 19

TLV®–CS

| Substance [CAS No.] (*Documentation date*) | ADOPTED VALUES | | | | | |
	TWA	STEL	Notations	MW	TLV® Basis
Chlorine dioxide [10049-04-4] (1991)	0.1 ppm	0.3 ppm	—	67.46	LRT irr; bronchitis
Chlorine trifluoride [7790-91-2] (1979)	—	C 0.1 ppm	—	92.46	Eye & URT irr; lung dam
Chloroacetaldehyde [107-20-0] (1990)	—	C 1 ppm	—	78.50	URT & eye irr
Chloroacetone [78-95-5] (1986)	—	C 1 ppm	Skin	92.53	Eye & URT irr
2-Chloroacetophenone [532-27-4] (1990)	0.05 ppm	—	A4	154.59	Eye, URT, & skin irr
Chloroacetyl chloride [79-04-9] (1988)	0.05 ppm	0.15 ppm	Skin	112.95	URT irr
Chlorobenzene [108-90-7] (1988)	10 ppm	—	A3; BEI	112.56	Liver dam
o-Chlorobenzylidene malononitrile [2698-41-1] (1990)	—	C 0.05 ppm	Skin; A4	188.62	URT irr; skin sens
Chlorobromomethane [74-97-5] (2008)	200 ppm	—	—	129.39	CNS impair; liver dam
Chlorodifluoromethane [75-45-6] (1990)	1000 ppm	—	A4	86.47	CNS impair; asphyxia; card sens
Chlorodiphenyl (42% chlorine) [53469-21-9] (1979)	1 mg/m³	—	Skin	266.50	Liver dam; eye irr; chloracne
Chlorodiphenyl (54% chlorine) [11097-69-1] (1990)	0.5 mg/m³	—	Skin; A3	328.40	URT irr; liver dam; chloracne
Chloroform [67-66-3] (1990)	10 ppm	—	A3	119.38	Liver dam; embryo/fetal dam; CNS impair

20 — Adopted Values

TLV®–CS

Substance [CAS No.] (*Documentation* date)	ADOPTED VALUES				
	TWA	STEL	Notations	MW	TLV® Basis
bis(Chloromethyl) ether [542-88-1] (1979)	0.001 ppm	—	A1	114.96	Lung cancer
Chloromethyl methyl ether [107-30-2] (1979)	—(L)	—	A2	80.50	Lung cancer
1-Chloro-1-nitropropane [600-25-9] (1971)	2 ppm	—	—	123.54	Eye irr; pulm edema
Chloropentafluoroethane [76-15-3] (1978)	1000 ppm	—	—	154.47	Card sens
Chloropicrin [76-06-2] (1990)	0.1 ppm	—	A4	164.39	Eye irr; pulm edema
1-Chloro-2-propanol [127-00-4] and 2-Chloro-1-propanol [78-89-7] (1999)	1 ppm	—	Skin; A4	94.54	Liver dam
β-Chloroprene [126-99-8] (1990)	10 ppm	—	Skin	88.54	URT & eye irr
2-Chloropropionic acid [598-78-7] (1988)	0.1 ppm	—	Skin	108.53	Male repro dam
o-Chlorostyrene [2039-87-4] (1972)	50 ppm	75 ppm	—	138.60	CNS impair; peripheral neuropathy
o-Chlorotoluene [95-49-8] (1971)	50 ppm	—	—	126.59	URT, eye, & skin irr
Chlorpyrifos [2921-88-2] (2000)	0.1 mg/m³ (IFV)	—	Skin; A4; BEI$_A$	350.57	Cholinesterase inhib
Chromite ore processing (Chromate), as Cr	0.05 mg/m³	—	A1	—	Lung cancer

Adopted Values — 21

TLV®–CS

ADOPTED VALUES

Substance [CAS No.] (Documentation date)	TWA	STEL	Notations	MW	TLV® Basis
Chromium, [7440-47-3] and inorganic compounds, as Cr (1991)					
Metal and Cr III compounds	0.5 mg/m³	—	A4	Varies	URT & skin irr
Water-soluble Cr VI compounds	0.05 mg/m³	—	A1; BEI	Varies	URT irr; cancer
Insoluble Cr VI compounds	0.01 mg/m³	—	A1	Varies	Lung cancer
Chromyl chloride [14977-61-8] (1990)	0.025 ppm	—	—	154.92	URT & skin irr
Chrysene [218-01-9] (1990)	—(L)	—	A3; BEI$_P$	228.30	Cancer
Citral [5392-40-5] (2009)	5 ppm (IFV)	—	Skin; SEN; A4	152.24	Body weight eff; URT irr; eye dam
‡ Clopidol [2971-90-6] (1972)	(10 mg/m³)	—	A4	192.06	(URT irr)
Coal dust (1995)					
Anthracite	0.4 mg/m³ (R)	—	A4	—	Lung dam; pulm fibrosis
Bituminous or Lignite	0.9 mg/m³ (R)	—	A4	—	Lung dam; pulm fibrosis
Coal tar pitch volatiles [65996-93-2], as benzene soluble aerosol (1984)	0.2 mg/m³	—	A1; BEI$_P$	—	Cancer
Cobalt [7440-48-4] and inorganic compounds, as Co (1993)	0.02 mg/m³	—	A3; BEI	58.93 / Varies	Asthma; pulm func; myocardial eff
Cobalt carbonyl [10210-68-1], as Co (1980)	0.1 mg/m³	—	—	341.94	Pulm edema; spleen dam

22 — Adopted Values

TLV®–CS

Substance [CAS No.] (*Documentation date*)	ADOPTED VALUES		Notations	MW	TLV® Basis
	TWA	STEL			
Cobalt hydrocarbonyl [16842-03-8], as Co (1980)	0.1 mg/m³	—	—	171.98	Pulm edema; lung dam
Copper [7440-50-8] (1990)				63.55	Irr, GI; metal fume fever
Fume, as Cu	0.2 mg/m³	—	—		
Dusts and mists, as Cu	1 mg/m³	—	—		
Cotton dust, raw, untreated (2009)	0.1 mg/m³ (T)	—	A4	—	Byssinosis; bronchitis; pulm func
Coumaphos [56-72-4] (2005)	0.05 mg/m³ (IFV)	—	Skin; A4; BEI_A	362.8	Cholinesterase inhib
Cresol, all isomers (2009) [1319-77-3; 95-48-7; 108-39-4; 106-44-5]	20 mg/m³ (IFV)	—	Skin; A4	108.14	URT irr
Crotonaldehyde [4170-30-3] (1995)	—	C 0.3 ppm	Skin; A3	70.09	Eye & URT irr
Crufomate [299-86-5] (1971)	5 mg/m³	—	A4; BEI_A	291.71	Cholinesterase inhib
Cumene [98-82-8] (1997)	50 ppm	—	—	120.19	Eye, skin, & URT irr; CNS impair
Cyanamide [420-04-2] (1974)	2 mg/m³	—	—	42.04	Skin & eye irr
Cyanogen [460-19-5] (1966)	10 ppm	—	—	52.04	LRT & eye irr
Cyanogen chloride [506-77-4] (1977)	—	C 0.3 ppm	—	61.48	Pulm edema; eye, skin, & URT irr
Cyclohexane [110-82-7] (1964)	100 ppm	—	—	84.16	CNS impair
Cyclohexanol [108-93-0] (1979)	50 ppm	—	Skin	100.16	Eye irr; CNS impair

Adopted Values — 23

TLV®–CS

ADOPTED VALUES

Substance [CAS No.] (Documentation date)	TWA	STEL	Notations	MW	TLV® Basis
Cyclohexanone [108-94-1] (1990)	20 ppm	50 ppm	Skin; A3	98.14	Eye & URT irr
Cyclohexene [110-83-8] (1964)	300 ppm	—	—	82.14	URT & eye irr
Cyclohexylamine [108-91-8] (1990)	10 ppm	—	A4	99.17	URT & eye irr
Cyclonite [121-82-4] (1994)	0.5 mg/m³	—	Skin; A4	222.26	Liver dam
Cyclopentadiene [542-92-7] (1963)	75 ppm	—	—	66.10	URT & eye irr
Cyclopentane [287-92-3] (1978)	600 ppm	—	—	70.13	URT, eye, & skin irr; CNS impair
Cyhexatin [13121-70-5] (1990)	5 mg/m³	—	A4	385.16	URT irr; body weight eff; kidney dam
‡ 2,4-D [94-75-7] (1990)	(10 mg/m³)	—	( ); A4	221.04	(URT & skin irr)
DDT [50-29-3] (1979)	1 mg/m³	—	A3	354.50	Liver dam
Decaborane [17702-41-9] (1979)	0.05 ppm	0.15 ppm	Skin	122.31	CNS convul; cognitive decrement
Demeton [8065-48-3] (1998)	0.05 mg/m³ (IFV)	—	Skin; BEI_A	258.34	Cholinesterase inhib
Demeton-S-methyl [919-86-8] (1998)	0.05 mg/m³ (IFV)	—	Skin; SEN; A4; BEI_A	230.3	Cholinesterase inhib
Diacetone alcohol [123-42-2] (1979)	50 ppm	—	—	116.16	URT & eye irr
* Diacetyl [431-03-8] (2011)	0.01 ppm	0.02 ppm	A4	86.10	Lung dam (Bronchiolitis obliterans-like illness)

24 — Adopted Values

TLV®–CS

Substance [CAS No.] (*Documentation date*)	ADOPTED VALUES		Notations	MW	TLV® Basis
	TWA	STEL			
Diazinon [333-41-5] (2000)	0.01 mg/m³ (IFV)	—	Skin; A4; BEI$_A$	304.36	Cholinesterase inhib
Diazomethane [334-88-3] (1970)	0.2 ppm	—	A2	42.04	URT & eye irr
Diborane [19287-45-7] (1990)	0.1 ppm	—	—	27.69	URT irr; headache
2-N-Dibutylaminoethanol [102-81-8] (1980)	0.5 ppm	—	Skin; BEI$_A$	173.29	Eye & URT irr
Dibutyl phenyl phosphate [2528-36-1] (1987)	0.3 ppm	—	Skin; BEI$_A$	286.26	Cholinesterase inhib; URT irr
Dibutyl phosphate [107-66-4] (2008)	5 mg/m³ (IFV)	—	Skin	210.21	Bladder, eye & URT irr
Dibutyl phthalate [84-74-2] (1990)	5 mg/m³	—	—	278.34	Testicular dam; eye & URT irr
Dichloroacetic acid [79-43-6] (2002)	0.5 ppm	—	Skin; A3	128.95	URT & eye irr, testicular dam
Dichloroacetylene [7572-29-4] (1992)	—	C 0.1 ppm	A3	94.93	Nausea; PNS impair
o-Dichlorobenzene [95-50-1] (1990)	25 ppm	50 ppm	A4	147.01	URT & eye irr, liver dam
p-Dichlorobenzene [106-46-7] (1990)	10 ppm	—	A3	147.01	Eye irr, kidney dam
3,3'-Dichlorobenzidine [91-94-1] (1990)	—(L)	—	Skin; A3	253.13	Bladder cancer, eye irr
1,4-Dichloro-2-butene [764-41-0] (1990)	0.005 ppm	—	Skin; A2	124.99	URT & eye irr
Dichlorodifluoromethane [75-71-8] (1979)	1000 ppm	—	A4	120.91	Card sens
1,3-Dichloro-5,5-dimethyl hydantoin [118-52-5] (1979)	0.2 mg/m³	0.4 mg/m³	—	197.03	URT irr

TLV®–CS

ADOPTED VALUES

Adopted Values — 25

Substance [CAS No.] (*Documentation date*)	TWA	STEL	Notations	MW	TLV® Basis
1,1-Dichloroethane [75-34-3] (1990)	100 ppm	—	A4	98.97	URT & eye irr; liver & kidney dam
1,2-Dichloroethylene, all isomers [540-59-0; 156-59-2; 156-60-5] (1990)	200 ppm	—	—	96.95	CNS impair; eye irr
Dichloroethyl ether [111-44-4] (1985)	5 ppm	10 ppm	Skin; A4	143.02	URT & eye irr; nausea
Dichlorofluoromethane [75-43-4] (1977)	10 ppm	—	—	102.92	Liver dam
Dichloromethane [75-09-2] (1997)	50 ppm	—	A3; BEI	84.93	COHb-emia; CNS impair
1,1-Dichloro-1-nitroethane [594-72-9] (1978)	2 ppm	—	—	143.96	URT irr
1,3-Dichloropropene [542-75-6] (2003)	1 ppm	—	Skin; A3	110.98	Kidney dam
2,2-Dichloropropionic acid [75-99-0] (1997)	5 mg/m³ (I)	—	A4	143.00	Eye & URT irr
Dichlorotetrafluoroethane [76-14-2] (1979)	1000 ppm	—	A4	170.93	Pulm func
Dichlorvos (DDVP) [62-73-7] (1998)	0.1 mg/m³ (IFV)	—	Skin; SEN; A4; BEI_A	220.98	Cholinesterase inhib
Dicrotophos [141-66-2] (1998)	0.05 mg/m³ (IFV)	—	Skin; A4; BEI_A	237.21	Cholinesterase inhib
Dicyclopentadiene [77-73-6] (1973)	5 ppm	—	—	132.21	URT, LRT, & eye irr
Dicyclopentadienyl iron, as Fe [102-54-5] (1990)	10 mg/m³	—	—	186.03	Liver dam
Dieldrin [60-57-1] (2009)	0.1 mg/m³ (IFV)	—	Skin; A3	380.93	Liver dam; repro eff; CNS impair

26 — Adopted Values

TLV®-CS

| Substance [CAS No.] (Documentation date) | ADOPTED VALUES | | | MW | TLV® Basis |
	TWA	STEL	Notations		
Diesel fuel [68334-30-5; 68476-30-2; 68476-31-3; 68476-34-6; 77650-28-3], as total hydrocarbons (2007)	100 mg/m³ (IFV)	—	Skin; A3	Varies	Dermatitis
Diethanolamine [111-42-2] (2008)	1 mg/m³ (IFV)	—	Skin; A3	105.14	Liver & kidney dam
Diethylamine [109-89-7] (1992)	5 ppm	15 ppm	Skin; A4	73.14	URT & eye irr
2-Diethylaminoethanol [100-37-8] (1991)	2 ppm	—	Skin	117.19	URT irr; CNS convul
Diethylene triamine [111-40-0] (1985)	1 ppm	—	Skin	103.17	URT & eye irr
Di(2-ethylhexyl)phthalate (DEHP) [117-81-7] (1996)	5 mg/m³	—	A3	390.54	LRT irr
Diethyl ketone [96-22-0] (1995)	200 ppm	300 ppm	—	86.13	URT irr; CNS impair
Diethyl phthalate [84-66-2] (1996)	5 mg/m³	—	A4	222.23	URT irr
Difluorodibromomethane [75-61-6] (1962)	100 ppm	—	—	209.83	URT irr; CNS impair; liver dam
Diglycidyl ether (DGE) [2238-07-5] (2006)	0.01 ppm	—	A4	130.14	Eye & skin irr; male repro dam
Diisobutyl ketone [108-83-8] (1979)	25 ppm	—	—	142.23	URT & eye irr
Diisopropylamine [108-18-9] (1979)	5 ppm	—	Skin	101.19	URT irr; eye dam
N,N-Dimethyl acetamide [127-19-5] (1990)	10 ppm	—	Skin; A4; BEI	87.12	Liver dam; embryo/fetal dam
Dimethylamine [124-40-3] (1989)	5 ppm	15 ppm	A4	45.08	URT irr; GI dam

Adopted Values — 27

TLV®–CS

| Substance [CAS No.] [*Documentation date*] | ADOPTED VALUES | | | MW | TLV® Basis |
	TWA	STEL	Notations		
bis(2-Dimethylaminoethyl)ether (DMAEE) [3033-62-3] (1997)	0.05 ppm	0.15 ppm	Skin	160.26	URT, eye, & skin irr
Dimethylaniline [121-69-7] (1990)	5 ppm	10 ppm	Skin; A4; BEI$_M$	121.18	MeHb-emia
Dimethyl carbamoyl chloride [79-44-7] (2006)	0.005 ppm	—	Skin; A2	107.54	Nasal cancer; URT irr
Dimethyl disulfide [624-92-0] (2006)	0.5 ppm	—	Skin	94.2	URT irr, CNS impair
Dimethylethoxysilane [14857-34-2] (1991)	0.5 ppm	1.5 ppm	—	104.20	URT & eye irr, headache
Dimethylformamide [68-12-2] (1979)	10 ppm	—	Skin; A4; BEI	73.09	Liver dam
1,1-Dimethylhydrazine [57-14-7] (1993)	0.01 ppm	—	Skin; A3	60.12	URT irr; nasal cancer
Dimethyl phthalate [131-11-3] (2005)	5 mg/m³	—	—	194.19	Eye & URT irr
Dimethyl sulfate [77-78-1] (1985)	0.1 ppm	—	Skin; A3	126.10	Eye & skin irr
Dimethyl sulfide [75-18-3] (2001)	10 ppm	—	—	62.14	URT irr
Dinitrobenzene, all isomers [528-29-0; 99-65-0; 100-25-4; 25154-54-5] (1979)	0.15 ppm	—	Skin; BEI$_M$	168.11	MeHb-emia; eye dam
Dinitro-o-cresol [534-52-1] (1979)	0.2 mg/m³	—	Skin	198.13	Basal metab
3,5-Dinitro-o-toluamide [148-01-6] (2006)	1 mg/m³	—	A4	225.16	Liver dam

28 — Adopted Values

TLV®–CS

ADOPTED VALUES

Substance [CAS No.] (Documentation date)	TWA	STEL	Notations	MW	TLV® Basis
Dinitrotoluene [25321-14-6] (1993)	0.2 mg/m³	—	Skin; A3; BEI$_M$	182.15	Card impair; repro eff
1,4-Dioxane [123-91-1] (1996)	20 ppm	—	Skin; A3	88.10	Liver dam
Dioxathion [78-34-2] (2001)	0.1 mg/m³ (IFV)	—	Skin; A4; BEI$_A$	456.54	Cholinesterase inhib
1,3-Dioxolane [646-06-0] (1997)	20 ppm	—	—	74.08	Hematologic eff
Diphenylamine [122-39-4] (1990)	10 mg/m³	—	A4	169.24	Liver & kidney dam; hematologic eff
Dipropyl ketone [123-19-3] (1978)	50 ppm	—	—	114.80	URT irr
Diquat [2764-72-9; 85-00-7; 6385-62-2] (1990)	0.5 mg/m³ (I) / 0.1 mg/m³ (R)	— / —	Skin; A4 / Skin; A4	Varies	LRT irr, cataract / LRT irr, cataract
Disulfiram [97-77-8] (1979)	2 mg/m³	—	A4	296.54	Vasodilation; nausea
Disulfoton [298-04-4] (2000)	0.05 mg/m³ (IFV)	—	Skin; A4; BEI$_A$	274.38	Cholinesterase inhib
Diuron [330-54-1] (1974)	10 mg/m³	—	A4	233.10	URT irr
Divinyl benzene [1321-74-0] (1990)	10 ppm	—	—	130.19	URT irr
Dodecyl mercaptan [112-55-0] (2001)	0.1 ppm	—	SEN	202.4	URT irr
Endosulfan [115-29-7] (2008)	0.1 mg/m³ (IFV)	—	Skin; A4	406.95	LRT irr; liver & kidney dam
Endrin [72-20-8] (1979)	0.1 mg/m³	—	Skin; A4	380.93	Liver dam; CNS impair; headache
Enflurane [13838-16-9] (1979)	75 ppm	—	A4	184.50	CNS impair; card impair

918

Adopted Values — 29

TLV®–CS

| Substance [CAS No.] [Documentation date] | ADOPTED VALUES | | | MW | TLV® Basis |
	TWA	STEL	Notations		
Epichlorohydrin [106-89-8] (1994)	0.5 ppm	—	Skin; A3	92.53	URT irr; male repro
EPN [2104-64-5] (2000)	0.1 mg/m³ (I)	—	Skin; A4; BEI_A	323.31	Cholinesterase inhib
(Ethane [74-84-0])	(See Aliphatic hydrocarbon gases: Alkanes [C_1–C_4])				
Ethanol [64-17-5] (2008)	—	1000 ppm	A3	46.07	URT irr
Ethanolamine [141-43-5] (1985)	3 ppm	6 ppm	—	61.08	Eye & skin irr
Ethion [563-12-2] (2000)	0.05 mg/m³ (IFV)	—	Skin; A4; BEI_A	384.48	Cholinesterase inhib
2-Ethoxyethanol (EGEE) [110-80-5] (1981)	5 ppm	—	Skin; BEI	90.12	Male repro dam; embryo/fetal dam
2-Ethoxyethyl acetate (EGEEA) [111-15-9] (1981)	5 ppm	—	Skin; BEI	132.16	Male repro dam
Ethyl acetate [141-78-6] (1979)	400 ppm	—	—	88.10	URT & eye irr
Ethyl acrylate [140-88-5] (1986)	5 ppm	15 ppm	A4	100.11	URT, eye, & GI irr; CNS impair; skin sens
Ethylamine [75-04-7] (1991)	5 ppm	15 ppm	Skin	45.08	Eye & skin irr; eye dam
Ethyl amyl ketone [541-85-5] (2006)	10 ppm	—	—	128.21	Neurotoxicity
Ethyl benzene [100-41-4] (2010)	20 ppm	—	A3; BEI	106.16	URT irr; kidney dam (nephropathy); cochlear impair

919

TLV®–CS

30 — Adopted Values

ADOPTED VALUES

Substance [CAS No.] (*Documentation date*)	TWA	STEL	Notations	MW	TLV® Basis
Ethyl bromide [74-96-4] (1990)	5 ppm	—	Skin; A3	108.98	Liver dam; CNS impair
‡ Ethyl tert-butyl ether (ETBE) [637-92-3] (1997)	(5 ppm)	—	(—)	102.18	(Pulm func; testicular dam)
Ethyl butyl ketone [106-35-4] (1995)	50 ppm	75 ppm	—	114.19	CNS impair; eye & skin irr
Ethyl chloride [75-00-3] (1992)	100 ppm	—	Skin; A3	64.52	Liver dam
Ethyl cyanoacrylate [7085-85-0] (1995)	0.2 ppm	—	—	125.12	URT & skin irr
Ethylene [74-85-1] (2001)	200 ppm	—	A4	28.05	Asphyxia
Ethylene chlorohydrin [107-07-3] (1985)	—	C 1 ppm	Skin; A4	80.52	CNS impair; liver & kidney dam
Ethylenediamine [107-15-3] (1990)	10 ppm	—	Skin; A4	60.10	
Ethylene dibromide [106-93-4] (1980)	—	—	Skin; A3	187.88	
Ethylene dichloride [107-06-2] (1977)	10 ppm	—	A4	98.96	Liver dam; nausea
Ethylene glycol [107-21-1] (1992)	—	C 100 mg/m^3 (H)	A4	62.07	URT & eye irr
Ethylene glycol dinitrate (EGDN) [628-96-6] (1980)	0.05 ppm	—	Skin	152.06	Vasodilation; headache
Ethylene oxide [75-21-8] (1990)	1 ppm	—	A2	44.05	Cancer; CNS impair
Ethyleneimine [151-56-4] (2008)	0.05 ppm	0.1 ppm	Skin; A3	43.08	URT irr; liver & kidney dam
Ethyl ether [60-29-7] (1966)	400 ppm	500 ppm	—	74.12	CNS impair; URT irr

Adopted Values — 31

TLV®–CS

ADOPTED VALUES

Substance [CAS No.] (*Documentation date*)	TWA	STEL	Notations	MW	TLV® Basis
* Ethyl formate [109-94-4] (2011)	—	100 ppm	A4	74.08	URT irr
2-Ethylhexanoic acid [149-57-5] (2006)	5 mg/m³ (IFV)	—	—	144.24	Teratogenic eff
Ethylidene norbornene [16219-75-3] (1971)	—	C 5 ppm	—	120.19	URT & eye irr
Ethyl mercaptan [75-08-1] (2003)	0.5 ppm	—	—	62.13	URT irr; CNS impair
N-Ethylmorpholine [100-74-3] (1985)	5 ppm	—	Skin	115.18	URT irr; eye dam
Ethyl silicate [78-10-4] (1979)	10 ppm	—	—	208.30	URT & eye irr; kidney dam
Fenamiphos [22224-92-6] (2005)	0.05 mg/m³ (IFV)	—	Skin; A4; BEI$_A$	303.40	Cholinesterase inhib
Fensulfothion [115-90-2] (2004)	0.01 mg/m³ (IFV)	—	Skin; A4; BEI$_A$	308.35	Cholinesterase inhib
Fenthion [55-38-9] (2005)	0.05 mg/m³ (IFV)	—	Skin; A4; BEI$_A$	278.34	Cholinesterase inhib
Ferbam [14484-64-1] (2008)	5 mg/m³ (I)	—	A4	416.50	CNS impair; body weight eff; spleen dam
Ferrovanadium dust [12604-58-9] (1990)	1 mg/m³	3 mg/m³	—	—	Eye, URT, & LRT irr
Flour dust (2001)	0.5 mg/m³ (I)	—	SEN	—	Asthma; URT irr; bronchitis
Fluorides, as F (1979)	2.5 mg/m³	—	A4; BEI	Varies	Bone dam; fluorosis
Fluorine [7782-41-4] (1970)	1 ppm	2 ppm	—	38.00	URT, eye, & skin irr

32 — Adopted Values

TLV®–CS

Substance [CAS No.] (*Documentation* date)	ADOPTED VALUES					
	TWA	STEL	Notations	MW	TLV® Basis
Fonofos [944-22-9] (2005)	0.1 mg/m³ (IFV)	—	Skin; A4; BEI_A	246.32	Cholinesterase inhib
Formaldehyde [50-00-0] (1987)	—	C 0.3 ppm	SEN; A2	30.03	URT & eye irr
Formamide [75-12-7] (1985)	10 ppm	—	Skin	45.04	Eye & skin irr, kidney & liver dam
Formic acid [64-18-6] (1965)	5 ppm	10 ppm	—	46.02	URT, eye, & skin irr
Furfural [98-01-1] (1978)	2 ppm	—	Skin; A3; BEI	96.08	URT & eye irr
Furfuryl alcohol [98-00-0] (1979)	10 ppm	15 ppm	Skin	98.10	URT & eye irr
Gallium arsenide [1303-00-0] (2004)	0.0003 mg/m³ (R)	—	A3	144.64	LRT irr
Gasoline [86290-81-5] (1990)	300 ppm	500 ppm	A3	Varies	URT & eye irr, CNS impair
Germanium tetrahydride [7782-65-2] (1970)	0.2 ppm	—	—	76.63	Hematologic eff
Glutaraldehyde [111-30-8], activated or inactivated (1998)	—	C 0.05 ppm	SEN; A4	100.11	URT, skin, & eye irr; CNS impair
‡ (Glycerin mist [56-81-5] (1990))	(10 mg/m³)	(—)	(—)	(92.09)	(URT irr)
Glycidol [556-52-5] (1993)	2 ppm	—	A3	74.08	URT, eye, & skin irr
Glyoxal [107-22-2] (1999)	0.1 mg/m³ (IFV)	—	SEN; A4	58.04	URT irr; larynx metaplasia
Grain dust (oat, wheat, barley) (1985)	4 mg/m³	—	—	NA	Bronchitis; URT irr; pulm func

Adopted Values — 33

| Substance [CAS No.] (*Documentation date*) | ADOPTED VALUES | | Notations | MW | TLV® Basis |
	TWA	STEL			
Graphite (all forms except graphite fibers) [7782-42-5] (1988)	2 mg/m³ (R)	—	—	—	Pneumoconiosis
Hafnium [7440-58-6] and compounds, as Hf (1990)	0.5 mg/m³	—	—	178.49	URT & eye irr; liver dam
Halothane [151-67-7] (1979)	50 ppm	—	A4	197.39	Liver dam; CNS impair; vasodilation
Helium [7440-59-7] (1990)	Simple asphyxiant (D)			4.00	Asphyxia
Heptachlor [76-44-8] and Heptachlor epoxide [1024-57-3] (1990)	0.05 mg/m³	—	Skin; A3	373.32 389.40	Liver dam
Heptane, all isomers [142-82-5; 590-35-2; 565-59-3; 108-08-7; 591-76-4; 589-34-4] (1979)	400 ppm	500 ppm	—	100.20	CNS impair; URT irr
Hexachlorobenzene [118-74-1] (1994)	0.002 mg/m³	—	Skin; A3	284.78	Porphyrin eff; skin dam; CNS impair
Hexachlorobutadiene [87-68-3] (1979)	0.02 ppm	—	Skin; A3	260.76	Kidney dam
Hexachlorocyclopentadiene [77-47-4] (1990)	0.01 ppm	—	A4	272.75	URT irr
Hexachloroethane [67-72-1] (1990)	1 ppm	—	Skin; A3	236.74	Liver & kidney dam
Hexachloronaphthalene [1335-87-1] (1965)	0.2 mg/m³	—	Skin	334.74	Liver dam; chloracne
Hexafluoroacetone [684-16-2] (1986)	0.1 ppm	—	Skin	166.02	Testicular dam; kidney dam
Hexafluoropropylene [116-15-4] (2009)	0.1 ppm	—	—	150.02	Kidney dam

TLV®–CS

923

34 — Adopted Values

TLV®–CS

ADOPTED VALUES

Substance [CAS No.] (Documentation date)	TWA	STEL	Notations	MW	TLV® Basis
Hexahydrophthalic anhydride, all isomers [85-42-7; 13149-00-3; 14166-21-3] (2002)	—	C 0.005 mg/m³ (IFV)	SEN	154.17	Resp sens; eye, skin, & URT irr
Hexamethylene diisocyanate [822-06-0] (1985)	0.005 ppm	—	—	168.22	URT irr; resp sens
Hexamethyl phosphoramide [680-31-9] (1990)	—	—	Skin; A3	179.20	URT cancer
n-Hexane [110-54-3] (1996)	50 ppm	—	Skin; BEI	86.18	CNS impair; peripheral neuropathy; eye irr
Hexane isomers, other than n-Hexane [75-83-2; 79-29-8; 107-83-5; 96-14-0] (1979)	500 ppm	1000 ppm	—	86.17	CNS impair; URT & eye irr
1,6-Hexanediamine [124-09-4] (1990)	0.5 ppm	—	—	116.21	URT & skin irr
1-Hexene [592-41-6] (1999)	50 ppm	—	—	84.16	CNS impair
sec-Hexyl acetate [108-84-9] (1963)	50 ppm	—	—	144.21	Eye & URT irr
Hexylene glycol [107-41-5] (1974)	—	C 25 ppm	—	118.17	Eye & URT irr
Hydrazine [302-01-2] (1988)	0.01 ppm	—	Skin; A3	32.05	URT cancer
Hydrogen [1333-74-0] (1990)	Simple asphyxiant (D)			1.01	Asphyxia
Hydrogenated terphenyls (nonirradiated) [61788-32-7] (1990)	0.5 ppm	—	—	241.00	Liver dam

Adopted Values — 35

TLV®–CS

ADOPTED VALUES

Substance [CAS No.] [*Documentation date*]	TWA	STEL	Notations	MW	TLV® Basis
Hydrogen bromide [10035-10-6] (2001)	—	C 2 ppm	—	80.92	URT irr
Hydrogen chloride [7647-01-0] (2000)	—	C 2 ppm	A4	36.47	URT irr
Hydrogen cyanide and cyanide salts, as CN (1991)					URT irr; headache; nausea; thyroid eff
Hydrogen cyanide [74-90-8]	—	C 4.7 ppm	Skin	27.03	
Cyanide salts [592-01-8; 151-50-8; 143-33-9]	—	C 5 mg/m^3	Skin	Varies	
Hydrogen fluoride [7664-39-3], as F (2004)	0.5 ppm	C 2 ppm	Skin; BEI	20.01	URT, LRT, skin, & eye irr; fluorosis
Hydrogen peroxide [7722-84-1] (1990)	1 ppm	—	A3	34.02	Eye, URT, & skin irr
Hydrogen selenide [7783-07-5], as Se (1990)	0.05 ppm	—	—	80.98	URT & eye irr; nausea
Hydrogen sulfide [7783-06-4] (2009)	1 ppm	5 ppm	—	34.08	URT irr; CNS impair
Hydroquinone [123-31-9] (2007)	1 mg/m^3	—	SEN; A3	110.11	Eye irr; eye dam
2-Hydroxypropyl acrylate [999-61-1] (1997)	0.5 ppm	—	Skin; SEN	130.14	Eye & URT irr
Indene [95-13-6] (2007)	5 ppm	—	—	116.15	Liver dam
Indium [7440-74-6] and compounds, as In (1990)	0.1 mg/m^3	—	—	114.82	Pulm edema; pneumonitis; dental erosion; malaise

36 — Adopted Values

TLV®–CS

ADOPTED VALUES

Substance [CAS No.] (Documentation date)	TWA	STEL	Notations	MW	TLV® Basis
Iodine and iodides (2007)					
Iodine [7553-56-2]	0.01 ppm (IFV)	0.1 ppm (V)	A4	126.91	Hypothyroidism; URT irr
Iodides	0.01 ppm (IFV)	—	A4	Varies	Hypothyroidism; URT irr
Iodoform [75-47-8] (1979)	0.6 ppm	—	—	393.78	CNS impair
Iron oxide (Fe$_2$O$_3$) [1309-37-1] (2005)	5 mg/m^3 (R)	—	A4	159.70	Pneumoconiosis
Iron pentacarbonyl [13463-40-6], as Fe (1979)	0.1 ppm	0.2 ppm	—	195.90	Pulm edema; CNS impair
Iron salts, soluble, as Fe (1990)	1 mg/m^3	—	—	Varies	URT & skin irr
Isoamyl alcohol [123-51-3] (1990)	100 ppm	125 ppm	—	88.15	Eye & URT irr
Isobutanol [78-83-1] (1973)	50 ppm	—	—	74.12	Skin & eye irr
Isobutyl acetate [110-19-0] (1966)	150 ppm	—	—	116.16	Eye & URT irr
Isobutyl nitrite [542-56-3] (2000)	—	C 1 ppm (IFV)	A3; BEI$_M$	103.12	Vasodilation; MeHb-emia
Isooctyl alcohol [26952-21-6] (1990)	50 ppm	—	Skin	130.23	URT irr
Isophorone [78-59-1] (1992)	—	C 5 ppm	A3	138.21	Eye & URT irr; CNS impair; malaise; fatigue
Isophorone diisocyanate [4098-71-9] (1985)	0.005 ppm	—	—	222.30	Resp sens
2-Isopropoxyethanol [109-59-1] (1990)	25 ppm	—	Skin	104.15	Hematologic eff

TLV®–CS

Adopted Values — 37

Substance [CAS No.] (*Documentation date*)	TWA	STEL	Notations	MW	TLV® Basis
ADOPTED VALUES					
Isopropyl acetate [108-21-4] (2001)	100 ppm	200 ppm	—	102.13	Eye & URT irr; CNS impair
Isopropylamine [75-31-0] (1962)	5 ppm	10 ppm	—	59.08	URT irr, eye dam
N-Isopropylaniline [768-52-5] (1990)	2 ppm	—	Skin; BEI$_M$	135.21	MeHb-emia
Isopropyl ether [108-20-3] (1979)	250 ppm	310 ppm	—	102.17	Eye & URT irr
Isopropyl glycidyl ether (IGE) [4016-14-2] (1979)	50 ppm	75 ppm	—	116.18	URT & eye irr, dermatitis
Kaolin [1332-58-7] (1990)	2 mg/m³ (E,R)	—	A4	—	Pneumoconiosis
Kerosene [8008-20-6; 64742-81-0]/Jet fuels, as total hydrocarbon vapor (2003)	200 mg/m³ (P)	—	Skin; A3	Varies	Skin & URT irr; CNS impair
Ketene [463-51-4] (1962)	0.5 ppm	1.5 ppm	—	42.04	URT irr, pulm edema
Lead [7439-92-1] and inorganic compounds, as Pb (1991)	0.05 mg/m³	—	A3; BEI	207.20 Varies	CNS & PNS impair; hematologic eff
Lead chromate [7758-97-6], as Pb (1990) as Cr	0.05 mg/m³ 0.012 mg/m³	— —	A2; BEI A2	323.22	Male repro dam; teratogenic eff; vasoconstriction
Lindane [58-89-9] (1990)	0.5 mg/m³	—	Skin; A3	290.85	Liver dam; CNS impair
Lithium hydride [7580-67-8] (1990)	0.025 mg/m³	—	—	7.95	Skin, eye, & URT irr
(L.P.G. (Liquefied petroleum gas) [68476-85-7])	(See Aliphatic hydrocarbon gases: Alkanes [C₁–C₄])				

927

38 — Adopted Values

TLV®–CS

ADOPTED VALUES

Substance [CAS No.] (Documentation date)	TWA	STEL	Notations	MW	TLV® Basis
Magnesium oxide [1309-48-4] (2000)	10 mg/m³ (I)	—	A4	40.32	
Malathion [121-75-5] (2000)	1 mg/m³ (IFV)	—	Skin; A4; BEI$_A$	330.36	Cholinesterase inhib
Maleic anhydride [108-31-6] (2010)	0.01 mg/m³ (IFV)	—	SEN; A4	98.06	Resp sens
‡ (Manganese [7439-96-5] and inorganic compounds, as Mn) (1992)	(0.2 mg/m³)	—	(—)	54.94 Varies	CNS impair
Manganese cyclopentadienyl tricarbonyl [12079-65-1], as Mn (1992)	0.1 mg/m³	—	Skin	204.10	Skin irr; CNS impair
Mercury [7439-97-6], alkyl compounds, as Hg (1992)	0.01 mg/m³	0.03 mg/m³	Skin	Varies	CNS & PNS impair; kidney dam
Mercury [7439-97-6], all forms except alkyl, as Hg (1991)				200.59	
Aryl compounds	0.1 mg/m³	—	Skin	Varies	CNS impair; kidney dam
Elemental and inorganic forms	0.025 mg/m³	—	Skin; A4; BEI	Varies	CNS impair; kidney dam
Mesityl oxide [141-79-7] (1992)	15 ppm	25 ppm	—	98.14	Eye & URT irr; CNS impair
Methacrylic acid [79-41-4] (1992)	20 ppm	—	—	86.09	Skin & eye irr
(Methane [74-82-8])	(See Aliphatic hydrocarbon gases: Alkanes [C$_1$–C$_4$])				
Methanol [67-56-1] (2008)	200 ppm	250 ppm	Skin; BEI	32.04	Headache; eye dam; dizziness; nausea
Methomyl [16752-77-5] (1992)	2.5 mg/m³	—	A4; BEI$_A$	162.20	Cholinesterase inhib

TLV®–CS

ADOPTED VALUES

Substance [CAS No.] (*Documentation date*)	TWA	STEL	Notations	MW	TLV® Basis
Methoxychlor [72-43-5] (1992)	10 mg/m³	—	A4	345.65	Liver dam; CNS impair
2-Methoxyethanol (EGME) [109-86-4] (2005)	0.1 ppm	—	Skin; BEI	76.09	Hematologic eff, repro eff
2-Methoxyethyl acetate (EGMEA) [110-49-6] (2005)	0.1 ppm	—	Skin; BEI	118.13	Hematologic eff, repro eff
(2-Methoxymethylethoxy)propanol (DPGME) [34590-94-8] (1979)	100 ppm	150 ppm	Skin	148.20	Eye & URT irr, CNS impair
4-Methoxyphenol [150-76-5] (1992)	5 mg/m³	—	—	124.15	Eye irr, skin dam
‡ 1-Methoxy-2-propanol [107-98-2] (1992)	(100 ppm)	(150 ppm)	(—)	90.12	(Eye irr; CNS impair)
Methyl acetate [79-20-9] (1992)	200 ppm	250 ppm	—	74.08	Headache; eye & URT irr; ocular nerve dam
Methyl acetylene [74-99-7] (1956)	1000 ppm	—	—	40.07	CNS impair
Methyl acetylene-propadiene mixture (MAPP) [59355-75-8] (1964)	1000 ppm	1250 ppm	—	40.07	CNS impair
Methyl acrylate [96-33-3] (1997)	2 ppm	—	Skin; SEN; A4	86.09	Eye, skin, & URT irr; eye dam
Methylacrylonitrile [126-98-7] (2010)	1 ppm	—	Skin; A4	67.09	CNS impair; eye & skin irr
Methylal [109-87-5] (1970)	1000 ppm	—	—	76.10	Eye irr; CNS impair
Methylamine [74-89-5] (1990)	5 ppm	15 ppm	—	31.06	Eye, skin, & URT irr

40 — Adopted Values

TLV®–CS

ADOPTED VALUES

Substance [CAS No.] (Documentation date)	TWA	STEL	Notations	MW	TLV® Basis
Methyl n-amyl ketone [110-43-0] (1978)	50 ppm	—	—	114.18	Eye & skin irr
N-Methyl aniline [100-61-8] (1992)	0.5 ppm	—	Skin; BEI_M	107.15	MeHb-emia; CNS impair
Methyl bromide [74-83-9] (1994)	1 ppm	—	Skin; A4	94.95	URT & skin irr
Methyl tert-butyl ether (MTBE) [1634-04-4] (1999)	50 ppm	—	A3	88.17	URT irr; kidney dam
Methyl n-butyl ketone [591-78-6] (1995)	5 ppm	10 ppm	Skin; BEI	100.16	Peripheral neuropathy; testicular dam
Methyl chloride [74-87-3] (1992)	50 ppm	100 ppm	Skin; A4	50.49	CNS impair; liver & kidney dam; testicular dam; teratogenic eff
Methyl chloroform [71-55-6] (1992)	350 ppm	450 ppm	A4; BEI	133.42	CNS impair; liver dam
Methyl 2-cyanoacrylate [137-05-3] (1995)	0.2 ppm	—	—	111.10	URT & eye irr
Methyl cyclohexane [108-87-2] (1962)	400 ppm	—	—	98.19	URT irr; CNS impair; liver & kidney dam
Methylcyclohexanol [25639-42-3] (2005)	50 ppm	—	—	114.19	URT & eye irr
o-Methylcyclohexanone [583-60-8] (1970)	50 ppm	75 ppm	Skin	112.17	URT & eye irr; CNS impair
2-Methylcyclopentadienyl manganese tricarbonyl [12108-13-3], as Mn (1970)	0.2 mg/m³	—	Skin	218.10	CNS impair; lung, liver, & kidney dam
Methyl demeton [8022-00-2] (2006)	0.05 mg/m³ (IFV)	—	Skin; BEI_A	230.30	Cholinesterase inhib

Adopted Values — 41

TLV®–CS

| Substance [CAS No.] (Documentation date) | ADOPTED VALUES | | Notations | MW | TLV® Basis |
	TWA	STEL			
Methylene bisphenyl isocyanate (MDI) [101-68-8] (1985)	0.005 ppm	—	—	250.26	Resp sens
4,4'-Methylene bis(2-chloroaniline) (MBOCA) [101-14-4] (1991)	0.01 ppm	—	Skin; A2; BEI	267.17	Bladder cancer; MeHb-emia
Methylene bis(4-cyclohexylisocyanate) [5124-30-1] (1985)	0.005 ppm	—	—	262.35	Resp sens; LRT irr
4,4'-Methylene dianiline [101-77-9] (1992)	0.1 ppm	—	Skin; A3	198.26	Liver dam
Methyl ethyl ketone (MEK) [78-93-3] (1992)	200 ppm	300 ppm	BEI	72.10	URT irr, CNS & PNS impair
Methyl ethyl ketone peroxide [1338-23-4] (1992)	—	C 0.2 ppm	—	176.24	Eye & skin irr; liver & kidney dam
Methyl formate [107-31-3] (1962)	100 ppm	150 ppm	—	60.05	URT, LRT, & eye irr
Methyl hydrazine [60-34-4] (1991)	0.01 ppm	—	Skin; A3	46.07	URT & eye irr; lung cancer; liver dam
Methyl iodide [74-88-4] (1978)	2 ppm	—	Skin	141.95	Eye dam; CNS impair
‡ Methyl isoamyl ketone [110-12-3] (1979)	(50 ppm)	(—)	—	114.20	(URT & eye irr; kidney & liver dam; CNS impair)
Methyl isobutyl carbinol [108-11-2] (1966)	25 ppm	40 ppm	Skin	102.18	URT & eye irr, CNS impair
Methyl isobutyl ketone [108-10-1] (2009)	20 ppm	75 ppm	A3; BEI	100.16	URT irr, dizziness; headache
Methyl isocyanate [624-83-9] (1986)	0.02 ppm	—	Skin	57.05	URT irr

42 — Adopted Values

TLV®–CS

ADOPTED VALUES

Substance [CAS No.] (Documentation date)	TWA	STEL	Notations	MW	TLV® Basis
Methyl isopropyl ketone [563-80-4] (2010)	20 ppm	—	—	86.14	Embryo/fetal dam; neonatal toxicity
Methyl mercaptan [74-93-1] (2003)	0.5 ppm	—	—	48.11	Liver dam
Methyl methacrylate [80-62-6] (1992)	50 ppm	100 ppm	SEN; A4	100.13	URT & eye irr; body weight eff; pulm edema
1-Methyl naphthalene [90-12-0] and 2-Methyl naphthalene [91-57-6] (2006)	0.5 ppm	—	Skin; A4	142.2	LRT irr; lung dam
Methyl parathion [298-00-0] (2008)	0.02 mg/m³ (IFV)	—	Skin; A4; BEI$_A$	263.2	Cholinesterase inhib
Methyl propyl ketone [107-87-9] (2006)	—	150 ppm	—	86.17	Pulm func; eye irr
Methyl silicate [681-84-5] (1978)	1 ppm	—	—	152.22	URT irr; eye dam
α-Methyl styrene [98-83-9] (2009)	10 ppm	—	A3	118.18	URT irr; kidney dam; female repro dam
Methyl vinyl ketone [78-94-4] (1994)	—	C 0.2 ppm	Skin; SEN	70.10	URT & eye irr; CNS impair
Metribuzin [21087-64-9] (1981)	5 mg/m³	—	A4	214.28	Liver dam; hematologic eff
Mevinphos [7786-34-7] (1998)	0.01 mg/m³ (IFV)	—	Skin; A4; BEI$_A$	224.16	Cholinesterase inhib
Mica [12001-26-2] (1962)	3 mg/m³ (R)	—	—	—	Pneumoconiosis

Adopted Values — 43

ADOPTED VALUES

Substance [CAS No.] (Documentation date)	TWA	STEL	Notations	MW	TLV® Basis
Mineral oil, excluding metal working fluids (2009)				Varies	URT irr
Pure, highly and severely refined	5 mg/m³ (I)	—	A4		
Poorly and mildly refined	— (L)	—	A2		
Molybdenum [7439-98-7], as Mo (1999)				95.95	
Soluble compounds	0.5 mg/m³ (R)	—	A3		LRT irr
Metal and insoluble compounds	10 mg/m³ (I)	—	—		
	3 mg/m³ (R)	—	—		
Monochloroacetic acid [79-11-8] (2005)	0.5 ppm (IFV)	—	Skin; A4	94.5	URT irr
Monocrotophos [6923-22-4] (2002)	0.05 mg/m³ (IFV)	—	Skin; A4; BEI$_A$	223.16	Cholinesterase inhib
Morpholine [110-91-8] (1992)	20 ppm	—	Skin; A4	87.12	Eye dam; URT irr
Naled [300-76-5] (2002)	0.1 mg/m³ (IFV)	—	Skin; SEN; A4; BEI$_A$	380.79	Cholinesterase inhib
‡ Naphthalene [91-20-3] (1992)	(10 ppm)	(15 ppm)	Skin; (A4)	128.19	(Hematologic eff; URT & eye irr; eye dam)
β-Naphthylamine [91-59-8] (1979)	— (L)	—	A1	143.18	Bladder cancer
(Natural gas [8006-14-2])	(See Aliphatic hydrocarbon gases: Alkanes [C$_1$–C$_4$])				
Natural rubber latex [9006-04-6], as inhalable allergenic proteins (2007)	0.0001 mg/m³ (I)	—	Skin; SEN	Varies	Resp sens

TLV®–CS

44 — Adopted Values

TLV®–CS

ADOPTED VALUES

Substance [CAS No.] (Documentation date)	TWA	STEL	Notations	MW	TLV® Basis
Neon [7440-01-9] (1992)	Simple asphyxiant (D)			20.18	Asphyxia
Nickel, as Ni (1996)					
Elemental [7440-02-0]	1.5 mg/m³ (I)	—	A5	58.71	Dermatitis; pneumoconiosis
Soluble inorganic compounds (NOS)	0.1 mg/m³ (I)	—	A4	Varies	Lung dam; nasal cancer
Insoluble inorganic compounds (NOS)	0.2 mg/m³ (I)	—	A1	Varies	Lung cancer
Nickel subsulfide [12035-72-2], as Ni	0.1 mg/m³ (I)	—	A1	240.19	Lung cancer
Nickel carbonyl [13463-39-3], as Ni (1980)	0.05 ppm	—	—	170.73	Chemical pneumonitis
Nicotine [54-11-5] (1992)	0.5 mg/m³	—	Skin	162.23	GI dam; CNS impair; card impair
Nitrapyrin [1929-82-4] (1992)	10 mg/m³	20 mg/m³	A4	230.93	Liver dam
Nitric acid [7697-37-2] (1992)	2 ppm	4 ppm	—	63.02	URT & eye irr; dental erosion
Nitric oxide [10102-43-9] (1992)	25 ppm	—	BEI_M	30.01	Hypoxia/cyanosis; nitrosyl-Hb form; URT irr
p-Nitroaniline [100-01-6] (1992)	3 mg/m³	—	Skin; A4; BEI_M	138.12	MeHb-emia; liver dam; eye irr
Nitrobenzene [98-95-3] (1992)	1 ppm	—	Skin; A3; BEI	123.11	MeHb-emia
p-Nitrochlorobenzene [100-00-5] (1985)	0.1 ppm	—	Skin; A3; BEI_M	157.56	MeHb-emia
4-Nitrodiphenyl [92-93-3] (1992)	—(L)	—	Skin; A2	199.20	Bladder cancer

Adopted Values — 45

TLV®–CS

ADOPTED VALUES

Substance [CAS No.] (Documentation date)	TWA	STEL	Notations	MW	TLV® Basis
Nitroethane [79-24-3] (1979)	100 ppm	—	—	75.07	URT irr; CNS impair; liver dam
Nitrogen [7727-37-9] (1992)		Simple asphyxiant (D)		14.01	Asphyxia
* Nitrogen dioxide [10102-44-0] (2011)	0.2 ppm	—	A4	46.01	LRT irr
Nitrogen trifluoride [7783-54-2] (1992)	10 ppm	—	BEI_M	71.00	MeHb-emia; liver & kidney dam
Nitroglycerin (NG) [55-63-0] (1980)	0.05 ppm	—	Skin	227.09	Vasodilation
Nitromethane [75-52-5] (1997)	20 ppm	—	A3	61.04	Thyroid eff; URT irr; lung dam
1-Nitropropane [108-03-2] (1992)	25 ppm	—	A4	89.09	URT & eye irr; liver dam
2-Nitropropane [79-46-9] (1992)	10 ppm	—	A3	89.09	Liver dam; liver cancer
N-Nitrosodimethylamine [62-75-9] (1992)	— (L)	—	Skin; A3	74.08	Liver & kidney cancer; liver dam
Nitrotoluene, all isomers (1992) [88-72-2; 99-08-1; 99-99-0]	2 ppm	—	Skin; BEI_M	137.13	MeHb-emia
5-Nitro-o-toluidine [99-55-8] (2006)	1 mg/m³ (I)	—	A3	152.16	Liver dam
Nitrous oxide [10024-97-2] (1986)	50 ppm	—	A4	44.02	CNS impair; hematologic eff; embryo/fetal dam
* Nonane [111-84-2] (2011)	200 ppm	—	—	128.26	CNS impair

46 — Adopted Values

TLV®–CS

ADOPTED VALUES

Substance [CAS No.] (Documentation date)	TWA	STEL	Notations	MW	TLV® Basis
Octachloronaphthalene [2234-13-1] (1970)	0.1 mg/m³	0.3 mg/m³	Skin	403.74	Liver dam
Octane [111-65-9], all isomers (1979)	300 ppm	—	—	114.22	URT irr
Osmium tetroxide [20816-12-0], as Os (1979)	0.0002 ppm	0.0006 ppm	—	254.20	Eye, URT, & skin irr
Oxalic acid [144-62-7] (1992)	1 mg/m³	2 mg/m³	—	90.04	URT, eye, & skin irr
p,p′-Oxybis(benzenesulfonyl hydrazide) [80-51-3] (1997)	0.1 mg/m³ (I)	—	—	358.40	Teratogenic eff
Oxygen difluoride [7783-41-7] (1983)	—	C 0.05 ppm	—	54.00	Headache; pulm edema; URT irr
Ozone [10028-15-6] (1995)				48.00	Pulm func
Heavy work	0.05 ppm	—	A4		
Moderate work	0.08 ppm	—	A4		
Light work	0.10 ppm	—	A4		
Heavy, moderate, or light workloads (≤ 2 hours)	0.20 ppm	—	A4		
Paraffin wax fume [8002-74-2] (1972)	2 mg/m³	—	—	—	URT irr, nausea
Paraquat [4685-14-7], as the cation (1979)	0.5 mg/m³	—	—	257.18	Lung dam
	0.1 mg/m³ (R)	—	—		
Parathion [56-38-2] (2000)	0.05 mg/m³ (IFV)	—	Skin; A4; BEI	291.27	Cholinesterase inhib
Particles (insoluble or poorly soluble) not otherwise specified	See Appendix B				

Adopted Values — 47

TLV®–CS

ADOPTED VALUES

Substance [CAS No.] (Documentation date)	TWA	STEL	Notations	MW	TLV® Basis
Pentaborane [19624-22-7] (1970)	0.005 ppm	0.015 ppm	—	63.17	CNS convul & impair
Pentachloronaphthalene [1321-64-8] (1970)	0.5 mg/m³	—	Skin	300.40	Liver dam; chloracne
Pentachloronitrobenzene [82-68-8] (1988)	0.5 mg/m³	—	A4	295.36	Liver dam
Pentachlorophenol [87-86-5] (1992)	0.5 mg/m³	—	Skin; A3; BEI	266.35	URT & eye irr; CNS & card impair
Pentaerythritol [115-77-5] (1970)	10 mg/m³	—	—	136.15	Eye & URT irr
Pentane, all isomers [78-78-4; 109-66-0; 463-82-1] (1989)	600 ppm	—	—	72.15	Peripheral neuropathy
2,4-Pentanedione [123-54-6] (2010)	25 ppm	—	Skin	100.12	Neurotoxicity; CNS impair
Pentyl acetate, all isomers [628-63-7; 626-38-0; 123-92-2; 625-16-1; 624-41-9; 620-11-1] (1997)	50 ppm	100 ppm	—	130.20	URT irr
Perchloromethyl mercaptan [594-42-3] (1988)	0.1 ppm	—	—	185.87	Eye & URT irr
Perchloryl fluoride [7616-94-6] (1962)	3 ppm	6 ppm	—	102.46	LRT & URT irr; MeHb-emia; fluorosis
Perfluorobutyl ethylene [19430-93-4] (2001)	100 ppm	—	—	246.1	Hematologic eff
Perfluoroisobutylene [382-21-8] (1989)	—	C 0.01 ppm	—	200.04	URT irr; hematologic eff
Persulfates, as persulfate (1993)	0.1 mg/m³	—	—	Varies	Skin irr
Phenol [108-95-2] (1992)	5 ppm	—	Skin; A4; BEI	94.11	URT irr; lung dam; CNS impair

937

48 — Adopted Values

TLV®–CS

Substance [CAS No.] (Documentation date)	ADOPTED VALUES				MW	TLV® Basis
	TWA	STEL	Notations			
Phenothiazine [92-84-2] (1968)	5 mg/m³	—	Skin		199.26	Eye photosens; skin irr
N-Phenyl-β-naphthylamine [135-88-6] (1992)	— (L)	—	A4		219.29	Cancer
o-Phenylenediamine [95-54-5] (1988)	0.1 mg/m³	—	A3		108.05	Anemia
m-Phenylenediamine [108-45-2] (1988)	0.1 mg/m³	—	A4		108.05	Liver dam; skin irr
p-Phenylenediamine [106-50-3] (1988)	0.1 mg/m³	—	A4		108.05	URT irr, skin sens
Phenyl ether [101-84-8], vapor (1979)	1 ppm	2 ppm	—		170.20	URT & eye irr, nausea
Phenyl glycidyl ether (PGE) [122-60-1] (1992)	0.1 ppm	—	Skin; SEN; A3		150.17	Testicular dam
Phenylhydrazine [100-63-0] (1988)	0.1 ppm	—	Skin; A3		108.14	Anemia; URT & skin irr
Phenyl mercaptan [108-98-5] (2001)	0.1 ppm	—	Skin		110.18	CNS impair; eye & skin irr
Phenylphosphine [638-21-1] (1992)	—	C 0.05 ppm	—		110.10	Dermatitis; hematologic eff, testicular dam
Phorate [298-02-2] (2002)	0.05 mg/m³ (IFV)	—	Skin; A4; BEI_A		260.40	Cholinesterase inhib
Phosgene [75-44-5] (1992)	0.1 ppm	—	—		98.92	URT irr, pulm edema; pulm emphysema
Phosphine [7803-51-2] (1992)	0.3 ppm	1 ppm	—		34.00	URT & GI irr; headache; CNS impair
Phosphoric acid [7664-38-2] (1992)	1 mg/m³	3 mg/m³	—		98.00	URT, eye, & skin irr

Adopted Values — 49

TLV®–CS

Substance [CAS No.] (Documentation date)	ADOPTED VALUES TWA	STEL	Notations	MW	TLV® Basis
Phosphorus (yellow) [12185-10-3] (1992)	0.1 mg/m³	—	—	123.92	LRT, URT, & GI irr, liver dam
Phosphorus oxychloride [10025-87-3] (1979)	0.1 ppm	—	—	153.35	URT irr
Phosphorus pentachloride [10026-13-8] (1985)	0.1 ppm	—	—	208.24	URT & eye irr
Phosphorus pentasulfide [1314-80-3] (1992)	1 mg/m³	3 mg/m³	—	222.29	URT irr
Phosphorus trichloride [7719-12-2] (1992)	0.2 ppm	0.5 ppm	—	137.35	URT, eye, & skin irr
Phthalic anhydride [85-44-9] (1992)	1 ppm	—	SEN; A4	148.11	URT, eye, & skin irr
m-Phthalodinitrile [626-17-5] (2008)	5 mg/m³ (IFV)	—	—	128.14	Eye & URT irr
* o-Phthalodinitrile [91-15-6] (2011)	1 mg/m³ (IFV)	—	—	128.13	CNS convul; body weight eff
Picloram [1918-02-1] (1992)	10 mg/m³	—	A4	241.48	Liver & kidney dam
Picric acid [88-89-1] (1992)	0.1 mg/m³	—	—	229.11	Skin sens; dermatitis; eye irr
Pindone [83-26-1] (1992)	0.1 mg/m³	—	—	230.25	Coagulation
* Piperazine and salts [110-85-0], as piperazine (2011)	0.03 ppm (IFV)	—	SEN; A4	86.14	Resp sens; asthma
Platinum [7440-06-4], and soluble salts (1979) Metal	1 mg/m³	—	—	195.09	Asthma; URT irr
Soluble salts, as Pt	0.002 mg/m³	—	—	Varies	Asthma; URT irr

50 — Adopted Values

TLV®–CS

| Substance [CAS No.] (*Documentation date*) | ADOPTED VALUES | | | MW | TLV® Basis |
	TWA	STEL	Notations		
Polyvinyl chloride (PVC) [9002-86-2] (2007)	1 mg/m³ (R)	—	A4	Varies	Pneumoconiosis; LRT irr; pulm func changes
Portland cement [65997-15-1] (2009)	1 mg/m³ (E,R)	—	A4	—	Pulm func; resp symptoms; asthma
Potassium hydroxide [1310-58-3] (1992)	—	C 2 mg/m³	—	56.10	URT, eye, & skin irr
(Propane [74-98-6])	(See Aliphatic hydrocarbon gases: Alkanes [C₁–C₄])				
Propane sultone [1120-71-4] (1976)	— (L)	—	A3	122.14	Cancer
n-Propanol (n-Propyl alcohol) [71-23-8] (2006)	100 ppm	—	A4	60.09	Eye & URT irr
2-Propanol [67-63-0] (2001)	200 ppm	400 ppm	A4; BEI	60.09	Eye & URT irr; CNS impair
Propargyl alcohol [107-19-7] (1992)	1 ppm	—	Skin	56.06	Eye irr, liver & kidney dam
β-Propiolactone [57-57-8] (1992)	0.5 ppm	—	A3	72.06	Skin cancer; URT irr
Propionaldehyde [123-38-6] (1998)	20 ppm	—	—	58.1	URT irr
Propionic acid [79-09-4] (1977)	10 ppm	—	—	74.08	Eye, skin, & URT irr
Propoxur [114-26-1] (1992)	0.5 mg/m³	—	A3; BEI_A	209.24	Cholinesterase inhib
n-Propyl acetate [109-60-4] (1962)	200 ppm	250 ppm	—	102.13	Eye & URT irr
Propylene [115-07-1] (2005)	500 ppm	—	A4	42.08	Asphyxia; URT irr
Propylene dichloride [78-87-5] (2005)	10 ppm	—	SEN; A4	112.99	URT irr; body weight eff

Adopted Values — 51

TLV®–CS

ADOPTED VALUES

Substance [CAS No.] (*Documentation date*)	TWA	STEL	Notations	MW	TLV® Basis
Propylene glycol dinitrate [6423-43-4] (1980)	0.05 ppm	—	Skin; BEI$_M$	166.09	Headache; CNS impair
Propylene oxide [75-56-9] (2000)	2 ppm	—	SEN; A3	58.08	Eye & URT irr
Propyleneimine [75-55-8] (2008)	0.2 ppm	0.4 ppm	Skin; A3	57.09	URT irr; kidney dam
n-Propyl nitrate [627-13-4] (1962)	25 ppm	40 ppm	BEI$_M$	105.09	Nausea; headache
Pyrethrum [8003-34-7] (1992)	5 mg/m^3	—	A4	345 (avg.)	Liver dam; LRT irr
Pyridine [110-86-1] (1992)	1 ppm	—	A3	79.10	Skin irr; liver & kidney dam
Quinone [106-51-4] (1970)	0.1 ppm	—	—	108.09	Eye irr; skin dam
Resorcinol [108-46-3] (1992)	10 ppm	20 ppm	A4	110.11	Eye & skin irr
Rhodium [7440-16-6], as Rh (1981)				102.91	
Metal and Insoluble compounds	1 mg/m^3	—	A4	Varies	Metal = URT irr; Insoluble = LRT irr
Soluble compounds	0.01 mg/m^3	—	A4	Varies	Asthma
Ronnel [299-84-3] (2005)	5 mg/m^3 (IFV)	—	A4; BEI$_A$	321.57	Cholinesterase inhib
Rosin core solder thermal decomposition products (colophony) [8050-09-7] (1992)	— (L)	—	SEN	NA	Skin sens; dermatitis; asthma
Rotenone (commercial) [83-79-4] (1992)	5 mg/m^3	—	A4	391.41	URT & eye irr; CNS impair
Selenium [7782-49-2] and compounds, as Se (1992)	0.2 mg/m^3	—	—	78.96	Eye & URT irr

52 — Adopted Values

TLV®–CS

ADOPTED VALUES

Substance [CAS No.] (*Documentation date*)	TWA	STEL	Notations	MW	TLV® Basis
Selenium hexafluoride [7783-79-1], as Se (1992)	0.05 ppm	—	—	192.96	Pulm edema
Sesone [136-78-7] (1992)	10 mg/m³	—	A4	309.13	GI irr
Silica, crystalline — α-quartz [14808-60-7; 1317-95-9] and cristobalite [14464-46-1] (2009)	0.025 mg/m³ (R)	—	A2	60.09	Pulm fibrosis; lung cancer
Silicon carbide [409-21-2] (2002)				40.10	
Nonfibrous	10 mg/m³ (I,E)	—	—		URT irr
	3 mg/m³ (R,E)	—	—		URT irr
Fibrous (including whiskers)	0.1 f/cc (F)	—	A2		Mesothelioma; cancer
Silicon tetrahydride [7803-62-5] (1992)	5 ppm	—	—	32.12	URT & skin irr
Silver [7440-22-4], and compounds (1992)				107.87	Argyria
Metal, dust and fume	0.1 mg/m³	—	—	Varies	
Soluble compounds, as Ag	0.01 mg/m³	—	—		
Sodium azide [26628-22-8] (1992)				65.02	Card impair; lung dam
as Sodium azide	—	C 0.29 mg/m³	A4		
as Hydrazoic acid vapor	—	C 0.11 ppm	A4		
Sodium bisulfite [7631-90-5] (1992)	5 mg/m³	—	A4	104.07	Skin, eye, & URT irr
Sodium fluoroacetate [62-74-8] (1992)	0.05 mg/m³	—	Skin	100.02	CNS impair; card impair; nausea
Sodium hydroxide [1310-73-2] (1992)	—	C 2 mg/m³	—	40.01	URT, eye, & skin irr

Adopted Values — 53

Substance [CAS No.] (Documentation date)	ADOPTED VALUES		Notations	MW	TLV® Basis
	TWA	STEL			
Sodium metabisulfite [7681-57-4] (1992)	5 mg/m³	—	A4	190.13	URT irr
Starch [9005-25-8] (1992)	10 mg/m³	—	A4	—	Dermatitis
Stearates[J] (1985)	10 mg/m³	—	A4	Varies	Eye, skin, & URT irr
Stoddard solvent [8052-41-3] (1980)	100 ppm	—	—	140.00	Eye, skin, & kidney dam; nausea; CNS impair
Strontium chromate [7789-06-2], as Cr (1989)	0.0005 mg/m³	—	A2	203.61	Cancer
Strychnine [57-24-9] (1992)	0.15 mg/m³	—	—	334.40	CNS impair
Styrene, monomer [100-42-5] (1996)	20 ppm	40 ppm	A4; BEI	104.16	CNS impair; URT irr; peripheral neuropathy
Subtilisins [1395-21-7; 9014-01-1], as 100% crystalline active pure enzyme (1972)	—	C 0.00006 mg/m³	—	—	Asthma; skin, URT, & LRT irr
Sucrose [57-50-1] (1992)	10 mg/m³	—	A4	342.30	Dental erosion
Sulfometuron methyl [74222-97-2] (1991)	5 mg/m³	—	A4	364.38	Hematologic eff
Sulfotepp (TEDP) [3689-24-5] (1993)	0.1 mg/m³ (IFV)	—	Skin; A4; BEI$_A$	322.30	Cholinesterase inhib
Sulfur dioxide [7446-09-5] (2008)	—	0.25 ppm	A4	64.07	Pulm func; LRT irr
Sulfur hexafluoride [2551-62-4] (1985)	1000 ppm	—	—	146.07	Asphyxia

TLV®–CS

943

54 — Adopted Values

TLV®–CS

ADOPTED VALUES

Substance [CAS No.] (*Documentation* date)	TWA	STEL	Notations	MW	TLV® Basis
Sulfuric acid [7664-93-9] (2000)	0.2 mg/m3 (T)	—	A2 (M)	98.08	Pulm func
Sulfur monochloride [10025-67-9] (1986)	—	C 1 ppm	—	135.03	Eye, skin, & URT irr
Sulfur pentafluoride [5714-22-7] (1962)	—	C 0.01 ppm	—	254.11	URT irr, lung dam
Sulfur tetrafluoride [7783-60-0] (1992)	—	C 0.1 ppm	—	108.07	Eye & URT irr, lung dam
Sulfuryl fluoride [2699-79-8] (1992)	5 ppm	10 ppm	—	102.07	CNS impair
Sulprofos [35400-43-2] (2008)	0.1 mg/m3 (IFV)	—	Skin; A4; BEI_A	322.43	Cholinesterase inhib
Synthetic vitreous fibers (1999)					
Continuous filament glass fibers	1 f/cc (F)	—	A4	—	URT irr
Continuous filament glass fibers	5 mg/m3 (I)	—	A4	—	URT irr
Glass wool fibers	1 f/cc (F)	—	A3	—	
Rock wool fibers	1 f/cc (F)	—	A3	—	
Slag wool fibers	1 f/cc (F)	—	A3	—	
Special purpose glass fibers	1 f/cc (F)	—	A3	—	
Refractory ceramic fibers	0.2 f/cc (F)	—	A2	—	Pulm fibrosis; pulm func
2,4,5-T [93-76-5] (1992)	10 mg/m3	—	A4	255.49	PNS impair
Talc [14807-96-6] (2009)					
Containing no asbestos fibers	2 mg/m3 (E,R)	—	A4	—	Pulm fibrosis; pulm func
Containing asbestos fibers	Use Asbestos TLV® (K)	—	A1	—	

Adopted Values — 55

TLV®–CS

Substance [CAS No.] (*Documentation date*)	ADOPTED VALUES			MW	TLV® Basis
	TWA	STEL	Notations		
Tellurium [13494-80-9] and compounds (NOS), as Te, excluding hydrogen telluride (1992)	0.1 mg/m³	—	—	127.60	Halitosis
Tellurium hexafluoride [7783-80-4], as Te (1992)	0.02 ppm	—	—	241.61	LRT irr
Temephos [3383-96-8] (2002)	1 mg/m³ (IFV)	—	Skin; A4; BEI$_A$	466.46	Cholinesterase inhib
Terbufos [13071-79-9] (1999)	0.01 mg/m³ (IFV)	—	Skin; A4; BEI$_A$	288.45	Cholinesterase inhib
Terephthalic acid [100-21-0] (1990)	10 mg/m³	—	—	166.13	—
Terphenyls [26140-60-3] (1977)	—	C 5 mg/m³	—	230.31	URT & eye irr
1,1,2,2-Tetrabromoethane [79-27-6] (2005)	0.1 ppm (IFV)	—	—	345.70	Eye & URT irr, pulm edema; liver dam
1,1,1,2-Tetrachloro-2,2-difluoroethane [76-11-9] (2007)	100 ppm	—	—	203.83	Liver & kidney dam; CNS impair
1,1,2,2-Tetrachloro-1,2-difluoroethane [76-12-0] (2007)	50 ppm	—	—	203.83	Liver & kidney dam; CNS impair
1,1,2,2-Tetrachloroethane [79-34-5] (1995)	1 ppm	—	Skin; A3	167.86	Liver dam
Tetrachloroethylene [127-18-4] (1990)	25 ppm	100 ppm	A3; BEI	165.80	CNS impair
Tetrachloronaphthalene [1335-88-2] (1992)	2 mg/m³	—	—	265.96	Liver dam
Tetraethyl lead [78-00-2], as Pb (1992)	0.1 mg/m³	—	Skin; A4	323.45	CNS impair
Tetraethyl pyrophosphate (TEPP) [107-49-3] (2006)	0.01 mg/m³ (IFV)	—	Skin; BEI$_A$	290.20	Cholinesterase inhib

56 — Adopted Values

TLV®–CS

| Substance [CAS No.] [*Documentation date*] | ADOPTED VALUES | | | | MW | TLV® Basis |
	TWA	STEL	Notations			
Tetrafluoroethylene [116-14-3] (1997)	2 ppm	—	A3		100.20	Kidney & liver dam; liver & kidney cancer
Tetrahydrofuran [109-99-9] (2002)	50 ppm	100 ppm	Skin; A3		72.10	URT irr; CNS impair; kidney dam
Tetrakis (hydroxymethyl) phosphonium salts (2002)						Body weight; CNS; hepatic
Tetrakis (hydroxymethyl) phosphonium chloride [124-64-1]	2 mg/m³	—	A4		190.56	
Tetrakis (hydroxymethyl) phosphonium sulfate [55566-30-8]	2 mg/m³	—	SEN; A4		406.26	
Tetramethyl lead [75-74-1], as Pb (1992)	0.15 mg/m³	—	Skin		267.33	CNS impair
Tetramethyl succinonitrile [3333-52-6] (1992)	0.5 ppm	—	Skin		136.20	Headache; nausea; CNS convul
Tetranitromethane [509-14-8] (1992)	0.005 ppm	—	A3		196.04	Eye & URT irr; URT cancer
Tetryl [479-45-8] (1984)	1.5 mg/m³	—	—		287.15	URT irr
Thallium [7440-28-0] and compounds, as Tl (2009)	0.02 mg/m³ (I)	—	Skin		204.37 Varies	GI dam; peripheral neuropathy
4,4'-Thiobis(6-tert-butyl-m-cresol) [96-69-5] (2010)	1 mg/m³ (I)	—	A4		358.52	URT irr
Thioglycolic acid [68-11-1] (1992)	1 ppm	—	Skin		92.12	Eye & skin irr
Thionyl chloride [7719-09-7] (2009)	—	C 0.2 ppm	—		118.98	URT irr

Adopted Values — 57

ADOPTED VALUES

Substance [CAS No.] (*Documentation date*)	TWA	STEL	Notations	MW	TLV® Basis
Thiram [7440-31-5] (2007)	0.05 mg/m³ (IFV)	—	SEN; A4	240.44	Body weight & hematologic eff
Tin [7440-31-5], and inorganic compounds, excluding Tin hydride, as Sn (1992)					
Metal	2 mg/m³	—	—	118.69	Pneumoconiosis (or Stannosis)
Oxide and inorganic compounds	2 mg/m³	—	—	Varies	
Tin [7440-31-5], organic compounds, as Sn	0.1 mg/m³	0.2 mg/m³	Skin; A4	Varies	Eye & URT irr; headache; nausea; CNS & immune eff
Titanium dioxide [13463-67-7] (1992)	10 mg/m³	—	A4	79.90	LRT irr
o-Tolidine [119-93-7] (1992)	—	—	Skin; A3	212.28	Eye, bladder, & kidney irr; bladder cancer; MeHb-emia
Toluene [108-88-3] (2006)	20 ppm	—	A4; BEI	92.13	Visual impair; female repro; pregnancy loss
‡ Toluene-2,4- or 2,6-diisocyanate (or as a mixture) [584-84-9; 91-08-7] (1992)	(0.005 ppm)	(0.02 ppm)	( ); SEN; (A4)	174.15	(Resp sens)
o-Toluidine [95-53-4] (1984)	2 ppm	—	Skin; A3; BEI_M	107.15	
m-Toluidine [108-44-1] (1984)	2 ppm	—	Skin; A4; BEI_M	107.15	Eye, bladder, & kidney irr; MeHb-emia
p-Toluidine [106-49-0] (1984)	2 ppm	—	Skin; A3; BEI_M	107.15	MeHb-emia

TLV®—CS

58 — Adopted Values

TLV®–CS

| Substance [CAS No.] [Documentation date] | ADOPTED VALUES | | | Notations | MW | TLV® Basis |
	TWA	STEL				
‡ Tributyl phosphate [126-73-8] (1992)	(0.2 ppm)	—		(); BEI_A	266.32	(Nausea; headache; eye & URT irr)
‡ Trichloroacetic acid [76-03-9] (1992)	(1 ppm)	—		A3	163.39	Eye & URT irr
1,2,4-Trichlorobenzene [120-82-1] (1975)	—	C 5 ppm		—	181.46	Eye & URT irr
1,1,2-Trichloroethane [79-00-5] (1992)	10 ppm	—		Skin; A3	133.41	CNS impair; liver dam
Trichloroethylene [79-01-6] (2006)	10 ppm	25 ppm		A2; BEI	131.40	CNS impair; cognitive decrements; renal toxicity
Trichlorofluoromethane [75-69-4] (1992)	—	C 1000 ppm		A4	137.38	Card sens
Trichloronaphthalene [1321-65-9] (1970)	5 mg/m³	—		Skin	231.51	Liver dam; chloracne
‡ 1,2,3-Trichloropropane [96-18-4] (1992)	(10 ppm)	—		(Skin; A3)	147.43	(Liver & kidney dam; eye & URT irr)
1,1,2-Trichloro-1,2,2-trifluoroethane [76-13-1] (1992)	1000 ppm	1250 ppm		A4	187.40	CNS impair
Trichlorphon [52-68-6] (1998)	1 mg/m³ (I)	—		A4; BEI_A	257.60	Cholinesterase inhib
Triethanolamine [102-71-6] (1990)	5 mg/m³	—		Skin; A4	149.22	Eye & skin irr
Triethylamine [121-44-8] (1991)	1 ppm	3 ppm		Skin; A4	101.19	Visual impair
Trifluorobromomethane [75-63-8] (1979)	1000 ppm	—		—	148.92	CNS & card impair
1,3,5-Triglycidyl-s-triazinetrione [2451-62-9] (1994)	0.05 mg/m³	—		—	297.25	Male repro dam
Trimellitic anhydride [552-30-7] (2007)	0.0005 mg/m³ (IFV)	0.002 mg/m³ (IFV)		Skin; SEN	192.12	Resp sens

Adopted Values — 59

TLV®–CS

Substance [CAS No.] (*Documentation date*)	ADOPTED VALUES			MW	TLV® Basis
	TWA	STEL	Notations		
Trimethylamine [75-50-3] (1990)	5 ppm	15 ppm	—	59.11	URT irr
Trimethyl benzene (mixed isomers) [25551-13-7] (1970)	25 ppm	—	—	120.19	CNS impair; asthma; hematologic eff
Trimethyl phosphite [121-45-9] (1980)	2 ppm	—	—	124.08	Eye irr, cholinesterase inhib
2,4,6-Trinitrotoluene (TNT) [118-96-7] (1984)	0.1 mg/m³	—	Skin; BEI$_M$	227.13	MeHb-emia; liver dam; cataract
Triorthocresyl phosphate [78-30-8] (1992)	0.1 mg/m³	—	Skin; A4; BEI$_A$	368.37	Cholinesterase inhib
Triphenyl phosphate [115-86-6] (1992)	3 mg/m³	—	A4	326.28	Cholinesterase inhib
Tungsten [7440-33-7], as W (1979)				183.85	
Metal and insoluble compounds	5 mg/m³	10 mg/m³	—	Varies	LRT irr
Soluble compounds	1 mg/m³	3 mg/m³	—	Varies	CNS impair, pulm fibrosis
Turpentine [8006-64-2] and selected monoterpenes [80-56-8; 127-91-3; 13466-78-9] (2001)	20 ppm	—	SEN; A4	136.00	URT & skin irr; CNS impair; lung dam
Uranium (natural) [7440-61-1] (1992) Soluble and insoluble compounds, as U	0.2 mg/m³	0.6 mg/m³	A1; BEI	238.03 Varies	Kidney dam
n-Valeraldehyde [110-62-3] (1984)	50 ppm	—	—	86.13	Eye, skin, & URT irr
Vanadium pentoxide [1314-62-1], as V (2008)	0.05 mg/m³ (I)	—	A3	181.88	URT & LRT irr
Vinyl acetate [108-05-4] (1992)	10 ppm	15 ppm	A3	86.09	URT, eye, & skin irr; CNS impair

60 — Adopted Values

TLV®–CS

ADOPTED VALUES

Substance [CAS No.] (*Documentation* date)	TWA	STEL	Notations	MW	TLV® Basis
Vinyl bromide [593-60-2] (1996)	0.5 ppm	—	A2	106.96	Liver cancer
Vinyl chloride [75-01-4] (1997)	1 ppm	—	A1	62.50	Lung cancer; liver dam
4-Vinyl cyclohexene [100-40-3] (1994)	0.1 ppm	—	A3	108.18	Female & male repro dam
Vinyl cyclohexene dioxide [106-87-6] (1994)	0.1 ppm	—	Skin; A3	140.18	Female & male repro dam
Vinyl fluoride [75-02-5] (1996)	1 ppm	—	A2	46.05	Liver cancer; liver dam
N-Vinyl-2-pyrrolidone [88-12-0] (2000)	0.05 ppm	—	A3	111.16	Liver dam
Vinylidene chloride [75-35-4] (1992)	5 ppm	—	A4	96.95	Liver & kidney dam
Vinylidene fluoride [75-38-7] (1996)	500 ppm	—	A4	64.04	Liver dam
Vinyl toluene [25013-15-4] (1992)	50 ppm	100 ppm	A4	118.18	URT & eye irr
Warfarin [81-81-2] (1992)	0.1 mg/m³	—	—	308.32	Coagulation
Wood dusts (2011)				NA	
Western red cedar	0.5 mg/m³ (I)	—	SEN; A4		Asthma
All other species	1 mg/m³ (I)	—	—		Pulm func
Carcinogenicity					
Oak and beech	—	—	A1		
Birch, mahogany, teak, walnut	—	—	A2		
All other wood dusts	—	—	A4		

Adopted Values — 61

TLV®–CS

Substance [CAS No.] (*Documentation date*)	ADOPTED VALUES		Notations	MW	TLV® Basis—Critical Effect(s)
	TWA	STEL			
Xylene [1330-20-7] [o, m & p isomers] [95-47-6; 108-38-3; 106-42-3] (1992)	100 ppm	150 ppm	A4; BEI	106.16	URT & eye irr; CNS impair
m-Xylene α,α'-diamine [1477-55-0] (1992)	—	C 0.1 mg/m³	Skin	136.20	Eye, skin, & GI irr
Xylidine (mixed isomers) [1300-73-8] (1999)	0.5 ppm $^{(IFV)}$	—	Skin; A3; BEI$_M$	121.18	Liver dam; MeHb-emia
Yttrium [7440-65-5] and compounds, as Y (1986)	1 mg/m³	—	—	88.91	Pulm fibrosis
Zinc chloride fume [7646-85-7] (1992)	1 mg/m³	2 mg/m³	—	136.29	LRT & URT irr
Zinc chromates [13530-65-9; 11103-86-9; 37300-23-5], as Cr (1992)	0.01 mg/m³	—	A1	Varies	Nasal cancer
Zinc oxide [1314-13-2] (2001)	2 mg/m³ (R)	10 mg/m³ (R)	—	81.37	Metal fume fever
Zirconium [7440-67-7] and compounds, as Zr (1992)	5 mg/m³	10 mg/m³	A4	91.22	

TLV®–CS

2012 NOTICE OF INTENDED CHANGES

These substances, with their corresponding values and notations, comprise those for which (1) a limit is proposed for the first time, (2) a change in the Adopted value is proposed, (3) retention as an NIC is proposed, or (4) withdrawal of the *Documentation* and adopted TLV® is proposed. In each case, the proposals should be considered trial values during the period they are on the NIC. These proposals were ratified by the ACGIH® Board of Directors and will remain on the NIC for approximately one year following this ratification. If the Committee neither finds nor receives any substantive data that change its scientific opinion regarding an NIC TLV®, the Committee may then approve its recommendation to the ACGIH® Board of Directors for adoption. If the Committee finds or receives substantive data that change its scientific opinion regarding an NIC TLV®, the Committee may change its recommendation to the ACGIH® Board of Directors for the matter to be either retained on or withdrawn from the NIC.

Documentation is available for each of these substances and their proposed values.

This notice provides an opportunity for comment on these proposals. Comments or suggestions should be accompanied by substantiating evidence in the form of peer-reviewed literature and forwarded in electronic format to The Science Group, ACGIH®, at science@acgih.org. Please refer to the ACGIH® TLV®/BEI® Development Process on the ACGIH® website (http://www.acgih.org/TLV/DevProcess.htm) for a detailed discussion covering this procedure, methods for input to ACGIH®, and deadline date for receiving comments.

2012 NOTICE OF INTENDED CHANGES

Substance [CAS No.]	TWA	STEL	Notations	MW	TLV® Basis
† Acetaldehyde [75-07-0]	—	25 ppm	A3	44.05	Eye & URT irr
Acetone [67-64-1]	200 ppm	500 ppm	BEI	58.05	CNS impair; URT irr
† Aliphatic hydrocarbon gases, Alkanes [C1–C4]	WIITHDRAW ADOPTED *DOCUMENTATION* AND TLV®. METHANE, ETHANE, PROPANE, LIQUEFIED PETROLEUM GAS (LPG) AND NATURAL GAS — REFER TO NIC ENTRY FOR BUTANE, ALL ISOMERS.				
	REFER TO APPENDIX F: MINIMAL OXYGEN CONTENT. BUTANE AND ISOBUTANE — REFER TO NIC ENTRY FOR BUTANE, ALL ISOMERS.				

NIC — 63

TLV®–CS

2012 NOTICE OF INTENDED CHANGES

Substance [CAS No.]	TWA	STEL	Notations	MW	TLV® Basis
† 1-Bromopropane [106-94-5]	0.1 ppm	—	A3	122.99	CNS impair; peripheral neuropathy; hematological eff; male & female repro toxicity; developmental toxicity
† Butane, all isomers [106-97-8; 75-28-5]	—	1000 ppm	—	58.12	CNS impair
† Clopidol [2971-90-6]	3 mg/m³ (IFV)	—	A4	192.06	Mutagenic eff; male repro system dam
† 2,4-D [94-75-7]	10 mg/m³ (I)	—	Skin; A4	221.04	Thyroid eff; kidney tubular dam
† Diethylene glycol monobutyl ether [112-34-5]	10 ppm (IFV)	—	—	162.23	Hematologic, liver, & kidney eff
† N,N-Diethylhydroxylamine (DEHA) [3710-84-7]	2 ppm	—	—	89.14	URT irr
† Ethyl tert-butyl ether [637-92-3]	25 ppm	—	A4	102.18	URT & LRT irr; CNS impair
Glycerin mist [56-81-5]	*WITHDRAW ADOPTED DOCUMENTATION AND TLV®*				
† Manganese [7439-96-5], elemental and inorganic compounds, as Mn	0.02 mg/m³ (R) 0.1 mg/m³ (I)	— —	A4	54.94 varies	CNS impair
† 1-Methoxy-2-propanol [107-98-2]	50 ppm	100 ppm	A4	90.12	Eye & URT irr
† Methyl isoamyl ketone [110-12-3]	20 ppm	50 ppm	—	114.20	CNS impair; URT irr
† Naphthalene [91-20-3]	5 ppm	—	Skin; A3	128.19	URT irr

64 — NIC

TLV®–CS

2012 NOTICE OF INTENDED CHANGES

Substance [CAS No.]	TWA	STEL	Notations	MW	TLV® Basis
† Peracetic acid [79-21-0]	—	0.2 ppm	A4	76.051	URT, eye, & skin irr
Toluene-2,4- or 2,6-diisocyanate (or as a mixture) [584-84-9; 91-08-7]	0.001 ppm (IFV)	0.003 ppm (IFV)	Skin; SEN; A3	174.15	Asthma
† Tributyl phosphate [126-73-8]	5 mg/m³ (IFV)	—	A3; BEI$_A$	266.32	Bladder, eye, & URT irr
† Trichloroacetic acid [76-03-9]	0.5 ppm	—	A3	163.39	Eye & URT irr
† 1,2,3-Trichloropropane [96-18-4]	0.05 ppm	—	A2	147.43	Cancer; eye & URT irr; liver dam

CHEMICAL SUBSTANCES AND OTHER ISSUES UNDER STUDY

The TLV® Chemical Substances Committee solicits information, especially data, which may assist in its deliberations regarding the following substances and issues. Comments and suggestions, accompanied by substantiating evidence in the form of peer-reviewed literature, should be forwarded in electronic format to The Science Group, ACGIH® at science@acgih.org. In addition, the Committee solicits recommendations for additional substances and issues of concern to the industrial hygiene and occupational health communities. Please refer to the ACGIH® TLV®/BEI® Development Process found on the ACGIH® website for a detailed discussion covering this procedure and methods for input to ACGIH® (http://www.acgih.org/ TLV/DevProcess.htm).

The Under Study list is published each year by February 1 on the ACGIH® website (www.acgih.org/TLV/Studies.htm), in the ACGIH® Annual Reports, and later in the annual *TLVs® and BEIs®* book. In addition, the Under Study list is updated by July 31 into a two-tier list.

- Tier 1 entries indicate which chemical substances and physical agents **may** move forward as an NIC or NIE in the upcoming year, based on their status in the development process.

- Tier 2 consists of those chemical substances and physical agents that **will not** move forward, but will either remain on, or be removed from, the Under Study list for the next year.

This updated list will remain in two tiers for the balance of the year. ACGIH® will continue this practice of updating the Under Study list by February 1 and establishing the two-tier list by July 31 each year.

The substances and issues listed below are as of January 1, 2012. *After this date, please refer to the ACGIH® website (http://www.acgih.org/TLV/ Studies.htm) for the up-to-date list.*

TLV®–CS

Chemical Substances

Acetylene
Acrylonitrile
Antimony and compounds, as Sb
Antimony hydride
Antimony trioxide, production
Argon
Atrazine (and related symmetrical triazines)
Barium sulfate
Benz[a]anthracene
Benzidine
Benzo[b]fluoranthene
Benzophenone
Benzo[a]pyrene
Borate compounds, inorganic
Boron tribromide
Boron trifluoride

Bromodichloromethane
sec-Butyl acetate
tert-Butyl acetate
tert-Butyl hydroperoxide
n-Butyl isocyanate
Butylated hydroxytoluene (BHT)
Calcium silicate, naturally occurring as wollastonite
Calcium silicate, synthetic nonfibrous
Chlorine
Chromite ore processing (Chromate), as Cr
Chromium and inorganic compounds, as Cr
Chromyl chloride
Chrysene

66 — Under Study

TLV®–CS

Coal tar pitch volatiles, as benzene
  soluble aerosol
Cobalt and inorganic compounds,
  as Co
Cobalt carbonyl
Cobalt hydrocarbonyl
Creosote
Cyanogen
Cyanogen bromide
Cyanogen chloride
Dibutyl phthalate
3,3'-Dichlorobenzidine
1,3-Dichloro-5,5-dimethyl hydantoin
Dicyclopentadiene
Diethyl phthalate
Diethylamine
Di(2-ethylhexyl)phthalate (DEHP)
N,N-Dimethyl acetamide
Dimethyl carbamoyl chloride
Dimethyl phthalate
Dimethylamine
Dimethylformamide
Dipropyl ketone
1-Ethoxy-2-propylene
Ethyl cyanoacrylate
Ethyl isocyanate
Ethylamine
Ethylene norbornene
Ethylidene norbornene
Fluorides, as F
Fluorine
Gasoline, all formulations
Hard metals, Cobalt and Tungsten
  carbide
Helium
Hexamethylene diisocyanate
Hydrogen
Iodoform
Isophorone diisocyanate
Lead and inorganic compounds,
  as Pb
Lithium hydride
Mercury, alkyl compounds
Methanol
Methomyl
Methyl acetate
Methyl acetylene

Methyl formate
Methyl isocyanate
Methyl mercaptan
Methyl vinyl ketone
Methylamine
Methylene bis(4-cyclohexyliso-
  cyanate)
Methylene bisphenyl isocyanate
  (MDI)
1-Naphthylamine
2-Naphthylamine
Neon
Nickel and inorganic compounds,
  including Nickel subsulfide
Nickel carbonyl
Nitric acid
Nitrogen
Paraquat
Pentachlorophenol
Pentaerythritol
Pentane, all isomers
2,3-Pentanedione
Phenyl isocyanate
Phosphine
o-Phthalaldehyde
Phthalic anhydride
Polycyclic aromatic hydrocarbons
  (PAHs)
Polymeric MDI
Propoxur
Silicon tetrahydride
Simazine
Stearates
Stoddard solvent
Terephthalic acid
Tetramethyl succinonitrile
Thiacloprid
Thioglycolic acid
Titanium dioxide
Triethanolamine
Triethylamine
Trimethylamine
Tungsten and compounds, as W
Tungsten carbide
Vinyl acetate
5-Vinyl-2-norbornene

Chemical Substances as Vapor and Aerosol (V) – Review for Update to Inhalable Fraction and Vapor (IFV)

Iodine and iodides
Phenyl ether, vapor
Phosphorous (yellow)
Tetramethyl lead, as Pb

Trichloronaphthalene
Warfarin
m-Xylene α,α′-diamine

Chemical Substances Designated as Sensitizers (SEN) – Review for Update to Respiratory Sensitization (RSEN) and/or Dermal Sensitization (DSEN)

Alachlor
Allyl propyl disulfide
Azinphos-methyl
Benomyl
Beryllium and compounds, as Be
n-Butyl acrylate
n-Butyl glycidyl ether (BGE)
Captan
Citral
Demeton-S-methyl
Dichlorvos (DDVP)
Dodecyl mercaptan
Flour dust
Formaldehyde
Glutaraldehyde, activated or inactivated
Glyoxal
Hexahydrophthalic anhydride, all isomers
Hydroquinone
2-Hydroxypropyl acrylate
Maleic anhydride

Methyl acrylate
Methyl methacrylate
Methyl vinyl ketone
Naled
Natural rubber latex, as inhalable allergenic proteins
Phenyl glycidyl ether (PGE)
Phthalic anhydride
Piperazine and salts
Propylene dichloride
Propylene oxide
Rosin core solder thermal decomposition products (colophony)
Tetrakis (hydroxymethyl) phosphonium sulfate
Thiram
Toluene-2,4- or 2,6-diisocyanate (or as a mixture)
Trimellitic anhydride
Turpentine and selected monoterpenes
Wood dusts (Western red cedar)

Other Issues Under Study

1. Appendix A: Carcinogenicity

2. Appendix H: Reciprocal Calculation Method for Certain Refined Hydrocarbon Solvent Vapor Mixtures

3. Excursion limits

4. Explosion hazard endnote

5. Sensitization (SEN) notation and definition

6. Simple asphyxiants and endnote (D)

7. TLV®/BEI® Development Process

8. Vapor and aerosol endnote (V)

DEFINITIONS AND NOTATIONS

Definitions

Documentation

The source publication that provides the critical evaluation of the pertinent scientific information and data with reference to literature sources upon which each TLV® or BEI® is based. See the discussion under "TLV®/BEI® Development Process: An Overview" found at the beginning of this book. The general outline used when preparing the *Documentation* may be found in the Operations Manual of the Threshold Limit Values for Chemical Substances (TLV®-CS) Committee, accessible online at: www.acgih.org/TLV/OPSManual.pdf.

Minimal Oxygen Content

An oxygen (O_2)-deficient atmosphere is defined as one with an ambient ρO_2 less than 132 torr (NIOSH, 1980). The minimum requirement of 19.5% oxygen at sea level (148 torr O_2, dry air) provides an adequate amount of oxygen for most work assignments and includes a margin of safety (NIOSH, 1987; McManus, 1999). Studies of pulmonary physiology suggest that the above requirements provide an adequate level of oxygen pressure in the lungs (alveolar ρO_2 of 60 torr) (Silverthorn, 2001; Guyton, 1991; NIOSH, 1976).

Some gases and vapors, when present in high concentrations in air, act primarily as simple asphyxiants, without other significant physiologic effects. A simple asphyxiant may not be assigned a TLV® because the limiting factor is the available oxygen. Atmospheres deficient in O_2 do not provide adequate warning and most simple asphyxiants are odorless. Account should be taken of this factor in limiting the concentration of the asphyxiant particularly at elevations greater than 5000 feet where the ρO_2 of the atmosphere is less than 120 torr. Several simple asphyxiants present an explosion hazard. Consult the *Documentation* for further information on specific simple asphyxiants. *See* page 83 for adopted Appendix F: Minimal Oxygen Content.

Notation

A notation is a designation that appears as a component of the TLV® in which specific information is listed in the column devoted to Notations.

Notice of Intended Change (NIC)

The NIC is a list of actions proposed by the TLV®-CS Committee for the coming year. This Notice provides an opportunity for public comment. Values remain on the NIC for approximately one year after they have been ratified by the ACGIH® Board of Directors. The proposals should be considered trial values during the period they are on the NIC. If the Committee neither finds nor receives any substantive data that change its scientific opinion regarding an NIC TLV®, the Committee may then approve its recommendation to the ACGIH® Board of Directors for adoption. If the Committee finds or receives substantive data that change its scientific opinion regarding an NIC TLV®, the Committee may change its recommendation to the ACGIH® Board of Directors for the matter to be either retained on or withdrawn from the NIC.

Values appearing in parentheses in the Adopted TLV® section are to be used during the period in which a proposed change for that value or notation appears on the NIC.

Particulate Matter/Particle Size

For solid and liquid particulate matter, TLVs® are expressed in terms of "total" particulate matter, except where the terms inhalable, thoracic, or respirable particulate mass are used. The intent of ACGIH® is to replace all "total" particulate TLVs® with inhalable, thoracic, or respirable particulate mass TLVs®. Side-by-side sampling using "total" and inhalable, thoracic, or respirable sampling techniques is encouraged to aid in the replacement of current "total" particulate TLVs®. *See* Appendix C: Particle Size-Selective Sampling Criteria for Airborne Particulate Matter, for the definitions of inhalable, thoracic, and respirable particulate mass.

Particles (insoluble or poorly soluble) Not Otherwise Specified (PNOS)

There are many insoluble particles of low toxicity for which no TLV® has been established. ACGIH® believes that even biologically inert, insoluble, or poorly soluble particles may have adverse effects and suggests that airborne concentrations should be kept below 3 mg/m^3, respirable particles, and 10 mg/m^3, inhalable particles, until such time as a TLV® is set for a particular substance. A description of the rationale for this recommendation and the criteria for substances to which it pertains are provided in Appendix B.

TLV® Basis

TLVs® are derived from publicly available information summarized in their respective *Documentation*. Although adherence to the TLV® may prevent several adverse health effects, it is not possible to list all of them in this book. The basis on which the values are established will differ from agent to agent (e.g., protection against impairment of health may be a guiding factor for some, whereas reasonable freedom from irritation, narcosis, nuisance, or other forms of stress may form the basis for others). Health impairments considered include those that shorten life expectancy, adversely affect reproductive function or developmental processes, compromise organ or tissue function, or impair the capability for resisting other toxic substances or disease processes.

The TLV® Basis represents the adverse effect(s) upon which the TLV® is based. The TLV® Basis column in this book is intended to provide a field reference for symptoms of overexposure and as a guide for determining whether components of a mixed exposure should be considered as acting independently or additively. Use of the TLV® Basis column is not a substitute for reading the *Documentation*. Each *Documentation* is a critical component for proper use of the TLV(s)® and to understand the TLV® basis. A complete list of the TLV® bases used by the Threshold Limit Values for Chemical Substances Committee may be found in their Operations Manual online at: (http://www.acgih.org/TLV/Approved_Revised_TLV-CS_Comm_Ops_Manual-final.pdf).

959

Abbreviations used:

card – cardiac	*impair* – impairment
CNS – central nervous system	*inhib* – inhibition
COHb-emia – carboxyhemoglo-binemia	*irr* – irritation
	LRT – lower respiratory tract
convul – convulsion	*MeHb-emia* – methemoglobinemia
dam – damage	*PNS* – peripheral nervous system
eff – effects	*pulm* – pulmonary
form – formation	*repro* – reproductive
func – function	*resp* – respiratory
GI – gastrointestinal	*sens* – sensitization
Hb – hemoglobin	*URT* – upper respiratory tract

Notations/Endnotes

Biological Exposure Indices (BEIs®)

The notation "BEI" is listed in the "Notations" column when a BEI® (or BEIs®) is (are) also recommended for the substance. Three subcategories to the "BEI" notation have been added to help the user identify those substances that would use only the BEI® for Acetylcholinesterase Inhibiting Pesticides or Methemoglobin Inducers. They are as follows:

BEI_A = *See* the BEI® for Acetylcholinesterase inhibiting pesticide

BEI_M = *See* the BEI® for Methemoglobin inducers

BEI_P = *See* the BEI® for Polycyclic aromatic hydrocarbons (PAHs)

Biological monitoring should be instituted for such substances to evaluate the total exposure from all sources, including dermal, ingestion, or nonoccupational. See the BEI® section in this book and the *Documentation* of the TLVs® and BEIs® for these substances.

Carcinogenicity

A carcinogen is an agent capable of inducing benign or malignant neoplasms. Evidence of carcinogenicity comes from epidemiology, toxicology, and mechanistic studies. Specific notations (i.e., A1, A2, A3, A4, and A5) are used by ACGIH® to define the categories for carcinogenicity and are listed in the Notations column. *See* Appendix A for these categories and definitions and their relevance to humans in occupational settings.

Inhalable Fraction and Vapor (IFV)

The Inhalable Fraction and Vapor (IFV) endnote is used when a material exerts sufficient vapor pressure such that it may be present in both particle and vapor phases, with each contributing a significant portion of the dose at the TLV–TWA concentration. The ratio of the Saturated Vapor Concentration (SVC) to the TLV–TWA is considered when assigning the IFV endnote. The IFV endnote is typically used for substances with an SVC/TLV® ratio between 0.1 and 10.

The industrial hygienist should also consider both particle and vapor phases to assess exposures from spraying operations, from processes involving

TLV®–CS

temperature changes that may affect the physical state of matter, when a significant fraction of the vapor is dissolved into or adsorbed onto particles of another substance, such as water-soluble compounds in high humidity environments (Perez and Soderholm, 1991).

Sensitization

The designations, "DSEN" and/or "RSEN", in the "Notations" column in the *TLVs® and BEIs®* book refers to the potential for an agent to produce dermal and/or respiratory sensitization. RSEN and DSEN are used in place of the SEN notation when specific evidence of sensitization by that route is confirmed by human or animal data. The DSEN and RSEN notations do not imply that sensitization is the critical effect on which the TLV® is based, nor does it imply that this effect is the sole basis for that agent's TLV®. If sensitization data exist, they are carefully considered when recommending the TLV® for the agent. TLVs® that are based upon sensitization are meant to protect workers from induction of this effect. These TLVs® are not intended to protect those workers who have already become sensitized.

In the workplace, respiratory or dermal exposures to sensitizing agents may occur. Similarly, sensitizers may evoke respiratory or dermal reactions. The notation does not distinguish between sensitization involving any of these tissues. The absence of a DSEN or RSEN notation does not signify that the agent lacks the ability to produce sensitization but may reflect the paucity or inconclusiveness of scientific evidence.

Sensitization often occurs via an immunologic mechanism and should not be confused with hyperreactivity, susceptibility, or sensitivity. Initially, there may be little or no response to a sensitizing agent. However, after a person is sensitized, subsequent exposure may cause intense responses, even at low exposure concentrations (well below the TLV®). These reactions may be life-threatening and may have an immediate or delayed onset. Workers who have become sensitized to a particular agent may also exhibit cross-reactivity to other agents that have similar chemical structures. A reduction in exposure to the sensitizer and its structural analogs generally reduces the frequency or severity of reactions among sensitized individuals. For some sensitized individuals, complete avoidance of exposure to the sensitizer and structural analogs provides the only means to prevent the specific immune response.

Agents that are potent sensitizers present special problems in the workplace. Respiratory and dermal exposures should be significantly reduced or eliminated through process control measures and personal protective equipment. Education and training (e.g., review of potential health effects, safe handling procedures, emergency information) are also necessary for those who work with known sensitizing agents.

For additional information regarding the sensitization potential of a particular agent, refer to the TLV® *Documentation* for the specific agent.

Skin

The designation "Skin" in the "Notations" column refers to the potential significant contribution to the overall exposure by the cutaneous route, including mucous membranes and the eyes, by contact with vapors, liquids, and solids.

72 — Definitions/Notations

TLV®–CS

Where dermal application studies have shown absorption that could cause systemic effects following exposure, a Skin notation would be considered. The Skin notation also alerts the industrial hygienist that overexposure may occur following dermal contact with liquid and aerosols, even when airborne exposures are at or below the TLV®.

A Skin notation is not applied to chemicals that may cause dermal irritation. However, it may accompany a SEN notation for substances that cause respiratory sensitization following dermal exposure. Although not considered when assigning a Skin notation, the industrial hygienist should be aware that there are several factors that may significantly enhance potential skin absorption of a substance that otherwise has low potential for the cutaneous route of entry. Certain vehicles can act as carriers, and when pretreated on the skin or mixed with a substance can promote the transfer of the substance into the skin. In addition, the existence of some dermatologic conditions can also significantly affect the entry of substances through the skin or wound.

While relatively limited quantitative data currently exist with regard to skin absorption of gases, vapors, and liquids by workers, ACGIH® recommends that the integration of data from acute dermal studies and repeated-dose dermal studies in animals and humans, along with the ability of the chemical to be absorbed, be used in deciding on the appropriateness of the Skin notation. In general, available data which suggest that the potential for absorption via the hands and forearms during the workday could be significant, especially for chemicals with lower TLVs®, could justify a Skin notation. From acute animal toxicity data, materials having a relatively low dermal LD_{50} (i.e., 1000 mg/kg of body weight or less) would be given a Skin notation. When chemicals penetrate the skin easily (i.e., higher octanol–water partition coefficients) and where extrapolations of systemic effects from other routes of exposure suggest dermal absorption may be important in the expressed toxicity, a Skin notation would be considered. A Skin notation is not applied to chemicals that cause irritation or corrosive effects in the absence of systemic toxicity.

Substances having a Skin notation and a low TLV® may present special problems for operations involving high airborne concentrations of the material, particularly under conditions where significant areas of the skin are exposed for a long period. Under these conditions, special precautions to significantly reduce or preclude skin contact may be required.

Biological monitoring should be considered to determine the relative contribution to the total dose from exposure via the dermal route. ACGIH® recommends a number of adopted Biological Exposure Indices (BEIs®) that provide an additional tool when assessing the total worker exposure to selected materials. For additional information, refer to *Dermal Absorption* in the "Introduction to the Biological Exposure Indices," *Documentation of the Biological Exposure Indices* (2001), and to Leung and Paustenbach (1994). Other selected readings on skin absorption and the skin notation include Sartorelli (2000), Schneider et al. (2000), Wester and Maibach (2000), Kennedy et al. (1993), Fiserova-Bergerova et al. (1990), and Scansetti et al. (1988).

The use of a Skin notation is intended to alert the reader that air sampling alone is insufficient to quantify exposure accurately and that measures to prevent significant cutaneous absorption may be required.

TLV®–CS

References and Selected Reading

American Conference of Governmental Industrial Hygienists: Dermal absorption. In: Documentation of the Biological Exposure Indices, 7th ed., pp. 21–26. ACGIH®, Cincinnati, OH (2001).

Fiserova-Bergerova V; Pierce JT; Droz PO: Dermal absorption potential of industrial chemicals: Criteria for skin notation. Am J Ind Med 17(5):617–635 (1990).

Guyton AC: Textbook of Medical Physiology, 8th ed. W.B. Sanders Co., Philadelphia, PA (1991).

Kennedy Jr GL; Brock WJ; Banerjee AK: Assignment of skin notation for threshold limit values chemicals based on acute dermal toxicity. Appl Occup Environ Hyg 8(1):26–30 (1993).

Leung H; Paustenbach DJ: Techniques for estimating the percutaneous absorption of chemicals due to occupational and environmental exposure. Appl Occup Environ Hyg 9(3):187–197 (1994).

McManus N: Safety and Health in Confined Spaces. Lewis Publishers, Boca Raton, FL (1999).

NIOSH U.S. National Institute for Occupational Safety and Health: A Guide to Industrial Respiratory Protection, DHEW (NIOSH) Pub. No. 76–198. NIOSH, Cincinnati, OH (1976).

NIOSH U.S. National Institute for Occupational Safety and Health: Working in Confined Spaces. DHHS (NIOSH) Pub. No. 80–106. NIOSH, Cincinnati, OH (1980).

NIOSH U.S. National Institute for Occupational Safety and Health: NIOSH Respirator Decision Logic. DHHS (NIOSH) Pub. No. 87–108. NIOSH, Cincinnati, OH (1987).

Perez C; Soderholm SC: Some chemicals requiring special consideration when deciding whether to sample the particle, vapor, or both phases of an atmosphere. Appl Occup Environ Hyg 6:859–864 (1991).

Sartorelli P: Dermal risk assessment in occupational medicine. Med Lav 91(3):183–191 (2000).

Scansetti G; Piolatto G; Rubino GF: Skin notation in the context of workplace exposure standards. Am J Ind Med 14(6):725–732 (1988).

Schneider T; Cherrie JW; Vermeulen R; Kromhout H: Dermal exposure assessment. Ann Occup Hyg 44(7):493–499 (2000).

Silverthorn DE: Human Physiology: An Integrated Approach, 2nd ed. Prentice-Hall, New Jersey (2001).

Wester RC; Maibach HI: Understanding percutaneous absorption for occupational health and safety. Int J Occup Environ Health 6(2):86–92 (2000).

> **All pertinent notes relating to the material in the Chemical Substances section of this book appear in the appendices for this section or on the inside back cover.**

74 — Notes

NOTES

ADOPTED APPENDICES

APPENDIX A: Carcinogenicity

ACGIH® has been aware of the increasing public concern over chemicals or industrial processes that cause or contribute to increased risk of cancer in workers. More sophisticated methods of bioassay, as well as the use of sophisticated mathematical models that extrapolate the levels of risk among workers, have led to differing interpretations as to which chemicals or processes should be categorized as human carcinogens and what the maximum exposure levels should be. The categories for carcinogenicity are:

A1 — *Confirmed Human Carcinogen:* The agent is carcinogenic to humans based on the weight of evidence from epidemiologic studies.

A2 — *Suspected Human Carcinogen:* Human data are accepted as adequate in quality but are conflicting or insufficient to classify the agent as a confirmed human carcinogen; OR, the agent is carcinogenic in experimental animals at dose(s), by route(s) of exposure, at site(s), of histologic type(s), or by mechanism(s) considered relevant to worker exposure. The A2 is used primarily when there is limited evidence of carcinogenicity in humans and sufficient evidence of carcinogenicity in experimental animals with relevance to humans.

A3 — *Confirmed Animal Carcinogen with Unknown Relevance to Humans:* The agent is carcinogenic in experimental animals at a relatively high dose, by route(s) of administration, at site(s), of histologic type(s), or by mechanism(s) that may not be relevant to worker exposure. Available epidemiologic studies do not confirm an increased risk of cancer in exposed humans. Available evidence does not suggest that the agent is likely to cause cancer in humans except under uncommon or unlikely routes or levels of exposure.

A4 — *Not Classifiable as a Human Carcinogen:* Agents which cause concern that they could be carcinogenic for humans but which cannot be assessed conclusively because of a lack of data. *In vitro* or animal studies do not provide indications of carcinogenicity which are sufficient to classify the agent into one of the other categories.

A5 — *Not Suspected as a Human Carcinogen:* The agent is not suspected to be a human carcinogen on the basis of properly conducted epidemiologic studies in humans. These studies have sufficiently long follow-up, reliable exposure histories, sufficiently high dose, and adequate statistical power to conclude that exposure to the agent does not convey a significant risk of cancer to humans; OR, the evidence suggesting a lack of carcinogenicity in experimental animals is supported by mechanistic data.

Substances for which no human or experimental animal carcinogenic data have been reported are assigned no carcinogenicity designation.

Exposures to carcinogens must be kept to a minimum. Workers exposed to A1 carcinogens without a TLV® should be properly equipped to eliminate to the fullest extent possible all exposure to the carcinogen. For A1 carcinogens with a TLV® and for A2 and A3 carcinogens, worker exposure by all routes should be carefully controlled to levels as low as possible below the TLV®.

TLV®–CS

76 — Appendices

Refer to the "Guidelines for the Classification of Occupational Carcinogens" in the Introduction to the Chemical Substances in the *Documentation of the Threshold Limit Values and Biological Exposure Indices* for a complete description and derivation of these designations.

APPENDIX B: Particles (insoluble or poorly soluble) Not Otherwise Specified (PNOS)

The goal of the TLV®-CS Committee is to recommend TLVs® for all substances for which there is evidence of health effects at airborne concentrations encountered in the workplace. When a sufficient body of evidence exists for a particular substance, a TLV® is established. Thus, by definition the substances covered by this recommendation are those for which little data exist. The recommendation at the end of this Appendix is supplied as a guideline rather than a TLV® because it is not possible to meet the standard level of evidence used to assign a TLV®. In addition, the PNOS TLV® and its predecessors have been misused in the past and applied to any unlisted particles rather than those meeting the criteria listed below. The recommendations in this Appendix apply to particles that:

• Do not have an applicable TLV®;

• Are insoluble or poorly soluble in water (or, preferably, in aqueous lung fluid if data are available); and

• Have low toxicity (i.e., are not cytotoxic, genotoxic, or otherwise chemically reactive with lung tissue, and do not emit ionizing radiation, cause immune sensitization, or cause toxic effects other than by inflammation or the mechanism of "lung overload").

ACGIH® believes that even biologically inert, insoluble, or poorly soluble particles may have adverse effects and recommends that airborne concentrations should be kept below 3 mg/m^3, respirable particles, and 10 mg/m^3, inhalable particles, until such time as a TLV® is set for a particular substance.

APPENDIX C: Particle Size-Selective Sampling Criteria for Airborne Particulate Matter

For chemical substances present in inhaled air as suspensions of solid particles or droplets, the potential hazard depends on particle size as well as mass concentration because of 1) effects of particle size on the deposition site within the respiratory tract and 2) the tendency for many occupational diseases to be associated with material deposited in particular regions of the respiratory tract.

ACGIH® has recommended particle size-selective TLVs® for crystalline silica for many years in recognition of the well-established association between silicosis and respirable mass concentrations. The TLV®-CS Committee is now re-examining other chemical substances encountered in particle form in occu-

TLV®–CS

pational environments with the objective of defining: 1) the size-fraction most closely associated for each substance with the health effect of concern and 2) the mass concentration within that size fraction which should represent the TLV®.

The Particle Size-Selective TLVs® (PSS–TLVs) are expressed in three forms:

1. *Inhalable Particulate Matter TLVs®* (IPM–TLVs) for those materials that are hazardous when deposited anywhere in the respiratory tract.
2. *Thoracic Particulate Matter TLVs®* (TPM–TLVs) for those materials that are hazardous when deposited anywhere within the lung airways and the gas-exchange region.
3. *Respirable Particulate Matter TLVs®* (RPM–TLVs) for those materials that are hazardous when deposited in the gas-exchange region.

The three particulate matter fractions described above are defined in quantitative terms in accordance with the following equations:[1–3]

A. IPM fraction consists of those particles that are captured according to the following collection efficiency regardless of sampler orientation with respect to wind direction:

$$IPM\ (d_{ae}) = 0.5\ [1 + \exp(–0.06\ d_{ae})]$$
$$\text{for } 0 < d_{ae} \le 100\ \mu m$$

where: $IPM\ (d_{ae})$ = the collection efficiency
d_{ae} = aerodynamic diameter of particle in μm

B. TPM fraction consists of those particles that are captured according to the following collection efficiency:

$$TPM\ (d_{ae}) = IPM\ (d_{ae})\ [1 – F(x)]$$

where: $F(x)$ = cumulative probability function of the standardized normal variable, x

$$x = \frac{\ln(d_{ae}/\Gamma)}{\ln(\Sigma)}$$

$\ln$ = natural logarithm
Γ = 11.64 μm
Σ = 1.5

C. RPM fraction consists of those particles that are captured according to the following collection efficiency:

$$RPM\ (d_{ae}) = IPM\ (d_{ae})\ [1 – F(x)]$$

where $F(x)$ = same as above, but with Γ = 4.25 μm and Σ = 1.5

The most significant difference from previous definitions is the increase in the median cut point for a respirable particulate matter sampler from 3.5 μm to 4.0 μm; this is in accord with the International Organization for Standardization/ European Standardization Committee (ISO/CEN) protocol.[4,5] At this time, no change is recommended for the measurement of respirable particles using a

78 — Appendices

TLV®–CS

10-mm nylon cyclone at a flow rate of 1.7 liters per minute. Two analyses of available data indicate that the flow rate of 1.7 liters per minute allows the 10-mm nylon cyclone to approximate the particulate matter concentration which would be measured by an ideal respirable particulate sampler as defined herein.[6,7]

Collection efficiencies representative of several sizes of particles in each of the respective mass fractions are shown in Tables 1, 2, and 3. *Documentation* for the respective algorithms representative of the three mass fractions is found in the literature.[2–4]

TABLE 1. Inhalable Fraction

Particle Aerodynamic Diameter (μm)	Inhalable Particulate Matter (IPM) Fraction Collected (%)
0	100
1	97
2	94
5	87
10	77
20	65
30	58
40	54.5
50	52.5
100	50

TABLE 2. Thoracic Fraction

Particle Aerodynamic Diameter (μm)	Thoracic Particulate Matter (TPM) Fraction Collected (%)
0	100
2	94
4	89
6	80.5
8	67
10	50
12	35
14	23
16	15
18	9.5
20	6
25	2

TABLE 3. Respirable Fraction

Particle Aerodynamic Diameter (µm)	Respirable Particulate Matter (RPM) Fraction Collected (%)
0	100
1	97
2	91
3	74
4	50
5	30
6	17
7	9
8	5
10	1

TLV®–CS

References

1. American Conference of Governmental Industrial Hygienists: Particle Size-Selective Sampling in the Workplace. ACGIH®, Cincinnati, OH (1985).
2. American Conference of Governmental Industrial Hygienists: Particle Size-Selective Sampling for Particulate Air Contaminants. JH Vincent, Ed. ACGIH®, Cincinnati, OH (1999).
3. Soderholm, SC: Proposed International Conventions for Particle Size-Selective Sampling. Ann. Occup. Hyg. 33:301–320 (1989).
4. International Organization for Standardization (ISO): Air Quality—Particle Size Fraction Definitions for Health-Related Sampling. ISO 7708:1995. ISO, Geneva (1995).
5. European Standardization Committee (CEN): Size Fraction Definitions for Measurement of Airborne Particles. CEN EN481:1993. CEN, Brussels (1993).
6. Bartley, DL: Letter to J. Doull, TLV® Committee, July 9, 1991.
7. Lidén, G; Kenny, LC: Optimization of the Performance of Existing Respirable Dust Samplers. Appl. Occup. Environ. Hyg. 8(4):386–391 (1993).

APPENDIX D: Commercially Important Tree Species Suspected of Inducing Sensitization

Common	Latin
SOFTWOODS	
California redwood	Sequoia sempervirens
Eastern white cedar	Thuja occidentalis
Pine	Pinus
Western red cedar	Thuja plicata
HARDWOODS	
Ash	Fraxinus spp.
Aspen/Poplar/Cottonwood	Populus
Beech	Fagus
Oak	Quercus

TLV®–CS

TROPICAL WOODS

Abirucana	*Pouteria*
African zebra	*Microberlinia*
Antiaris	*Antiaris africana, Antiaris toxicara*
Cabreuva	*Myrocarpus fastigiatus*
Cedar of Lebanon	*Cedra libani*
Central American walnut	*Juglans olanchana*
Cocabolla	*Dalbergia retusa*
African ebony	*Diospryos crassiflora*
Fernam bouc	*Caesalpinia*
Honduras rosewood	*Dalbergia stevensonii*
Iroko or kambala	*Chlorophora excelsa*
Kejaat	*Pterocarpus angolensis*
Kotibe	*Nesorgordonia papaverifera*
Limba	*Terminalia superba*
Mahogany (African)	*Khaya spp.*
Makore	*Tieghemella heckelii*
Mansonia/Beté	*Mansonia altissima*
Nara	*Pterocarpus indicus*
Obeche/African maple/Samba	*Triplochiton scleroxylon*
Okume	*Aucoumea klaineana*
Palisander/Brazilian rosewood/ Tulip wood/Jakaranda	*Dalbergia nigra*
Pau marfim	*Balfourodendron riedelianum*
Ramin	*Gonystylus bancanus*
Soapbark dust	*Quillaja saponaria*
Spindle tree wood	*Euonymus europaeus*
Tanganyike aningre	

APPENDIX E: Threshold Limit Values for Mixtures

Most threshold limit values are developed for a single chemical substance. However, the work environment is often composed of multiple chemical exposures both simultaneously and sequentially. It is recommended that multiple exposures that comprise such work environments be examined to assure that workers do not experience harmful effects.

There are several possible modes of chemical mixture interaction. Additivity occurs when the combined biological effect of the components is equal to the sum of each of the agents given alone. Synergy occurs where the combined effect is greater than the sum of each agent. Antagonism occurs when the combined effect is less.

The general ACGIH® mixture formula applies to the additive model. It is utilized when additional protection is needed to account for this combined effect.

> **The guidance contained in this Appendix does not apply to substances in mixed phases.**

Application of the Additive Mixture Formula

The "TLV® Basis" column found in the table of Adopted Values lists the adverse effect(s) upon which the TLV® is based. This column is a resource that may help alert the reader to the additive possibilities in a chemical mixture and the need to reduce the combined TLV® of the individual components. Note that the column does not list the deleterious effects of the agent, but rather, lists only the adverse effect(s) upon which the threshold limit was based. The current *Documentation of the TLVs® and BEIs®* should be consulted for toxic effects information, which may be of use when assessing mixture exposures.

When two or more hazardous substances have a similar toxicological effect on the same target organ or system, their combined effect, rather than that of either individually, should be given primary consideration. In the absence of information to the contrary, different substances should be considered as additive where the health effect and target organ or system is the same.

That is, if the sum of

$$\frac{C_1}{T_1} + \frac{C_2}{T_2} + \dots \frac{C_n}{T_n}$$

exceeds unity, the threshold limit of the mixture should be considered as being exceeded (where C_1 indicates the observed atmospheric concentration and T_1 is the corresponding threshold limit; see example). It is essential that the atmosphere is analyzed both qualitatively and quantitatively for each component present in order to evaluate the threshold limit of the mixture.

The additive formula applies to simultaneous exposure for hazardous agents with TWA, STEL, and Ceiling values. The threshold limit value time interval base (TWA, STEL, and Ceiling) should be consistent where possible. When agents with the same toxicological effect do not have a corresponding TLV® type, use of mixed threshold limit value types may be warranted. Table E-1 lists possible combinations of threshold limits for the additive mixture formula. Multiple calculations may be necessary.

Where a substance with a STEL or Ceiling limit is mixed with a substance with a TLV–TWA but no STEL, comparison of the short-term limit with the applicable excursion limit may be appropriate. Excursion limits are defined as a value five times the TLV–TWA limit. The amended formula would be:

TABLE E-1. Possible Combinations of Threshold Limits When Applying the Additive Mixture Formula

Full Shift or Short Term	Agent A	Agent B
Full Shift	TLV–TWA	TLV–TWA
Full Shift	TLV–TWA	TLV–Ceiling
Short Term	TLV–STEL	TLV–STEL
Short Term	TLV–Ceiling	TLV–Ceiling
Short Term	Excursion limits where there is no STEL (5 times TLV–TWA value)	TLV–Ceiling or TLV–STEL
Short Term	TLV–STEL	TLV–Ceiling

$$\frac{C_1}{T_{1STEL}} + \frac{C_2}{(T_2)(5)} \leq 1$$

where: T_{1STEL} = the TLV–STEL
T_2 = the TLV–TWA of the agent with no STEL.

The additive model also applies to consecutive exposures of agents that occur during a single work shift. Those substances that have TLV–TWAs (and STELs or excursion limits) should generally be handled the same as if they were the same substance, including attention to the recovery periods for STELs and excursion limits as indicated in the "Introduction to Chemical Substances." The formula does not apply to consecutive exposures of TLV–Ceilings.

Limitations and Special Cases

Exceptions to the above rule may be made when there is a good reason to believe that the chief effects of the different harmful agents are not additive. This can occur when neither the toxicological effect is similar nor the target organ is the same for the components. This can also occur when the mixture interaction causes inhibition of the toxic effect. In such cases, the threshold limit ordinarily is exceeded only when at least one member of the series (C_1/T_1 or C_2/T_2, etc.) itself has a value exceeding unity.

Another exception occurs when mixtures are suspected to have a synergistic effect. The use of the general additive formula may not provide sufficient protection. Such cases at present must be determined individually. Potentiating effects of exposure to such agents by routes other than that of inhalation are also possible. Potentiation is characteristically exhibited at high concentrations, less probably at low. For situations involving synergistic effects, it may be possible to use a modified additive formula that provides additional protection by incorporating a synergy factor. Such treatment of the TLVs® should be used with caution, as the quantitative information concerning synergistic effects is sparse.

Care must be considered for mixtures containing carcinogens in categories A1, A2, or A3. Regardless of application of the mixture formula, exposure to mixtures containing carcinogens should be avoided or maintained as low as possible. *See* Appendix A.

The additive formula applies to mixtures with a reasonable number of agents. It is not applicable to complex mixtures with many components (e.g., gasoline, diesel exhaust, thermal decomposition products, fly ash, etc.).

Example

A worker's airborne exposure to solvents was monitored for a full shift as well as one short-term exposure. The results are presented in Table E-2.

TLV®–CS

TABLE E-2. Example Results

Agent	Full-Shift Results (*TLV–TWA*)	Short-Term Results (*TLV–STEL)*
1) Acetone	160 ppm (*500 ppm*)	490 ppm (*750 ppm*)
2) sec-Butyl acetate	20 ppm (*200 ppm*)	150 ppm (N/A)
3) Methyl ethyl ketone	90 ppm (*200 ppm*)	220 ppm (*300 ppm*)

According to the *Documentation of the TLVs® and BEIs®*, all three substances indicate irritation effects on the respiratory system and thus would be considered additive. Acetone and methyl ethyl ketone exhibit central nervous system effects.

Full shift analysis would utilize the formula:

$$\frac{C_1}{T_1} + \frac{C_2}{T_2} + \frac{C_3}{T_3} \leq 1$$

thus,

$$\frac{160}{500} + \frac{20}{200} + \frac{90}{200} = 0.32 + 0.10 + 0.45 = 0.87$$

The full-shift mixture limit is not exceeded.

Short-term analysis would utilize the formula:

$$\frac{C_1}{T_{1STEL}} + \frac{C_2}{(T_2)(5)} + \frac{C_3}{T_{3STEL}} \leq 1$$

thus,

$$\frac{490}{750} + \frac{150}{1000} + \frac{220}{300} = 0.65 + 0.15 + 0.73 = 1.53$$

The short-term mixture limit is exceeded.

APPENDIX F: Minimal Oxygen Content

Adequate oxygen delivery to the tissues is necessary for sustaining life and depends on 1) the level of oxygen in inspired air, 2) the presence or absence of lung disease, 3) the level of hemoglobin in the blood, 4) the kinetics of oxygen binding to hemoglobin (oxy-hemoglobin dissociation curve), 5) the cardiac output, and 6) local tissue blood flow. For the purpose of the present discussion, only the effects of decreasing the amount of oxygen in inspired air is considered.

The brain and myocardium are the most sensitive tissues to oxygen deficiency. The initial symptoms of oxygen deficiency are increased ventilation, increased cardiac output, and fatigue. Other symptoms that may develop

TLV®–CS

include headache, impaired attention and thought processes, decreased coordination, impaired vision, nausea, unconsciousness, seizures, and death. However, there may be no apparent symptoms prior to unconsciousness. The onset and severity of symptoms depend on many factors such as the magnitude of the oxygen deficiency, duration of exposure, work rate, breathing rate, temperature, health status, age, and pulmonary acclimatization. The initial symptoms of increased breathing and increased heart rate become evident when hemoglobin oxygen saturation is reduced below 90%. At hemoglobin oxygen saturations between 80% and 90%, physiological adjustments occur in healthy adults to resist hypoxia, but in compromised individuals, such as emphysema patients, oxygen therapy would be prescribed for hemoglobin oxygen saturations below 90%. As long as the partial pressure of oxygen (pO_2) in pulmonary capillaries stays above 60 torr, hemoglobin will be more than 90% saturated and normal levels of oxygen transport will be maintained in healthy adults. The alveolar pO_2 level of 60 torr corresponds to 120 torr pO_2 in the ambient air, due to anatomic dead space, carbon dioxide, and water vapor. For additional information on gas exchange and pulmonary physiology see Silverthorn[1] and Guyton.[2]

The U.S. National Institute for Occupational Safety and Health[3] used 60 torr alveolar pO_2 as the physiological limit that establishes an oxygen-deficient atmosphere and has defined an oxygen-deficient atmosphere as one with an ambient pO_2 less than 132 torr.[4] The minimum requirement of 19.5% oxygen at sea level (148 torr pO_2, dry air) provides an adequate amount of oxygen for most work assignments and includes a margin of safety.[5] However, the margin of safety significantly diminishes as the O_2 partial pressure of the atmosphere decreases with increasing altitude, decreases with the passage of low pressure weather events, and decreases with increasing water vapor,[6] such that, at 5000 feet, the pO_2 of the atmosphere may approach 120 torr because of water vapor and the passage of fronts and at elevations greater than 8000 feet, the pO_2 of the atmosphere may be expected to be less than 120 torr.

The physiological effects of oxygen deficiency and oxygen partial pressure variation with altitude for dry air containing 20.948% oxygen are given in Table F-1. No physiological effects due to oxygen deficiency are expected in healthy adults at oxygen partial pressures greater than 132 torr or at elevations less than 5000 feet. Some loss of dark adaptation is reported to occur at elevations greater than 5000 feet. At oxygen partial pressures less than 120 torr (equivalent to an elevation of about 7000 feet or about 5000 feet accounting for water vapor and the passage of low pressure weather events) symptoms in unacclimatized workers include increased pulmonary ventilation and cardiac output, incoordination, and impaired attention and thinking. These symptoms are recognized as being incompatible with safe performance of duties.

Accordingly, ACGIH® recommends a minimal ambient oxygen partial pressure of 132 torr, which is protective against inert oxygen-displacing gases and oxygen-consuming processes for altitudes up to 5000 feet. Figure F-1 is a plot of pO_2 with increasing altitude, showing the recommended minimal value of 132 torr. If the partial pressure of oxygen is less than 132 torr or if it is less than the expected value for that altitude, given in Table F-1, then additional work practices are recommended such as thorough evaluation of the confined space to identify the cause of the low oxygen concentration; use of continuous monitors integrated with warning devices; acclimating workers to the altitude of

TLV®–CS

the work, as adaptation to altitude can increase an individuals work capacity by 70%; use of rest–work cycles with reduced work rates and increased rest periods; training, observation, and monitoring of workers; and easy, rapid access to oxygen-supplying respirators that are properly maintained.

Oxygen-displacing gases may have flammable properties or may produce physiological effects, so that their identity and source should be thoroughly investigated. Some gases and vapors, when present in high concentrations in air, act primarily as simple asphyxiants without other significant physiologic effects. A TLV® may not be recommended for each simple asphyxiant because the limiting factor is the available oxygen. Atmospheres deficient in O_2 do not provide adequate warning and most simple asphyxiants are odorless. Account should be taken of this factor in limiting the concentration of the asphyxiant particularly at elevations greater than 5000 feet where the ρO_2 of the atmosphere may be less than 120 torr.

References

1. Silverthorn DE: Human Physiology: An Integrated Approach, 2nd ed. Prentice-Hall, New Jersey (2001).
2. Guyton AC: Textbook of Medical Physiology, 8th ed. W.B. Saunders Co., Philadelphia (1991).
3. U.S. National Institute for Occupational Safety and Health: A Guide to Industrial Respiratory Protection, DHEW (NIOSH) Pub. No. 76-198. NIOSH, Cincinnati, OH (1976).
4. U.S. National Institute for Occupational Safety and Health: Working in Confined Spaces. DHHS (NIOSH) Pub. No. 80-106. NIOSH, Cincinnati, OH (1979).
5. NIOSH U.S. National Institute for Occupational Safety and Health: NIOSH Respirator Decision Logic. DHHS Pub. No. 87-108. NIOSH, Cincinnati, OH (1987).
6. McManus N: Safety and Health in Confined Spaces. Lewis Publishers, Boca Raton, FL (1999).

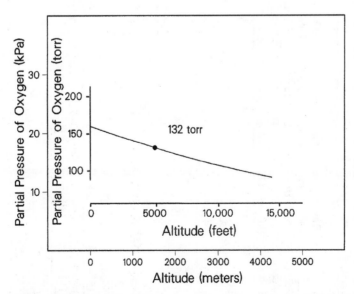

FIGURE F-1. Plot of oxygen partial pressure (ρO_2) (expressed in torr and kPa) with increasing altitude (expressed in feet and meters), showing the recommended oxygen partial pressure of 132 torr.

TLV®–CS

TABLE F-1. Barometric Pressure, Oxygen Partial Pressure, and Percent Oxygen Concentration Variation with Altitude and Physiological Effect [adapted from McManus[6]]

Altitude Feet (meters)	Barometric Pressure torr, Dry Air[A] (kilopascals)	pO₂ Equivalent, torr dry air at 20.948% O₂[B] (kilopascals)	%O₂ Equivalent, Dry Air at Sea Level[C] (percent)	Physiological Effect of pO₂ Levels[D]
0 (0)	760 (101)	159 (21.2)	20.9	
1000 (305)	731 (97.4)	153 (20.4)	20.1	
2000 (610)	704 (93.8)	147 (19.6)	19.3	
3000 (914)	677 (90.3)	142 (18.9)	18.7	
4000 (1219)	652 (86.9)	137 (18.3)	18.0	
5000 (1524)	627 (83.6)	131 (17.5)	17.2	None in healthy adults
6000 (1829)	603 (80.4)	126 (16.8)	16.6	Loss of dark adaptation can occur at elevations above 5000 feet
7000 (2134)	580 (77.3)	121 (16.1)	16.0	Increased pulmonary ventilation and cardiac output, incoordination, and impaired attention and thinking

TLV®–CS

Altitude ft (m)				Physiological effect
8000 (2438)	559 (74.5)	117 (15.6)	15.4	Rapid exposure to altitudes over 8000 feet may cause high altitude sickness (respiratory alkalosis, headache, nausea, and vomiting) in unacclimatized individuals. Rapid ascent increases the risk of high altitude pulmonary edema and cerebral edema
9000 (2743)	537 (71.6)	112 (14.9)	14.7	
10000 (3048)	517 (68.9)	108 (14.4)	14.2	
11000 (3353)	498 (66.4)	104 (13.9)	13.7	Abnormal fatigue on exertion, faulty coordination, impaired judgment, emotional upset
12000 (3658)	479 (63.8)	100 (13.3)	13.2	
13000 (3962)	461 (61.5)	98 (12.9)	12.8	
14000 (4267)	443 (59.1)	93 (12.4)	12.2	Impaired respiration, very poor judgment and coordination, tunnel vision

[A] Calculated from $P_{re:\ sea\ level} = 760 \times e^{-(altitude\ in\ feet/25970)}$

[B] Calculated from $pO_2 = 0.20948 \times 760 \times e^{-(altitude\ in\ feet/25970)}$

[C] Calculated from: $P_{\%O_2} = 20.948 \times e^{-(altitude\ in\ feet/25970)}$

[D] The approximate physiological effect in healthy adults is influenced by duration of the oxygen deficiency, work rate, breathing rate, temperature, health status, age and pulmonary acclimatization.

TLV®–CS

APPENDIX G: Substances Whose Adopted *Documentation* and TLVs® Were Withdrawn For a Variety of Reasons, Including Insufficient Data, Regrouping, Etc.

[Individual entries will remain for a 10-year period, commencing with the year of withdrawal]

Substance [CRN]	Year Withdrawn	Reason
Acetylene tetrabromide	2006	Withdrawn in favor of its IUPAC name; *see* 1,1,2,2-Tetrabromoethane
Aluminum [7429-90-5] and compounds, as Al	2008	Combined into Aluminum metal and insoluble compounds
Aluminum oxide [1344-28-1]	2008	Combined into Aluminum metal and insoluble compounds
Aluminum welding fumes	2004	TLV® withdrawn as a result of Substances of Variable Composition Appendix removal
APPENDIX B: Substances of Variable Composition	2004	Appendix withdrawn, insufficient data
B1: Polytetrafluoroethylene decomposition products		B1: *Documentation* withdrawn as a result of Appendix removal
B2: Welding fumes (not otherwise specified)		B2: *Documentation* and TLV® withdrawn as a result of Appendix removal
Borates, tetra, sodium salts	2005	Combined into Borate compounds, inorganic
Butane [106-97-8]	2004	Presently covered by Aliphatic hydrocarbon gases: Alkanes [C$_1$–C$_4$]
Calcium carbonate [471-34-1]	2007	Insufficient data
Dinitolmide	2007	Withdrawn in favor of its synonym 3,5-Dinitro-o-toluamide
Emery [1302-74-5]	2008	Combined into Aluminum metal and insoluble compounds
Ethane [74-84-0]	2004	Presently covered by Aliphatic hydrocarbon gases: Alkanes [C$_1$–C$_4$]
Iron oxide (Fe$_2$O$_3$) dust and fume, as Fe	2006	Combined into Iron oxide

TLV®–CS

APPENDIX G: Substances Whose Adopted *Documentation* and TLVs® Were Withdrawn For a Variety of Reasons, Including Insufficient Data, Regrouping, Etc.

[Individual entries will remain for a 10-year period, commencing with the year of withdrawal] (Con't.)

Substance [CRN]	Year Withdrawn	Reason
Isopropanol	2006	Withdrawn in favor of its IUPAC name, 2-Propanol
Lead arsenate [3687-31-8], as $Pb_3(AsO_4)_2$	2009	Insufficient data
Liquefied petroleum gas (LPG) [68476-85-7]	2004	Presently covered by Aliphatic hydrocarbon gases: Alkanes [C_1–C_4]
Magnesite [546-93-0]	2006	Insufficient data
Methane [74-82-8]	2004	Presently covered by Aliphatic hydrocarbon gases: Alkanes [C_1–C_4]
Nonane [111-84-2], all isomers	2012	Refer to Nonane
Oil mist, mineral	2010	Refer to Mineral oil, excluding metal working fluids
Particulates (Insoluble) not otherwise specified	2003	Insufficient data; see Appendix B
Perlite [93763-70-3]	2006	Insufficient data
Piperazine dihydrochloride [142-64-3]	2012	Refer to Piperazine and salts
Propane [74-98-6]	2004	Presently covered by Aliphatic hydrocarbon gases: Alkanes [C_1–C_4]
Rouge	2006	Combined into Iron oxide
Rubber solvent (Naphtha) [8030-30-6]	2009	Refer to Appendix H: Reciprocal Calculation Method for Certain Refined Hydrocarbon Solvent Vapor Mixtures

90 — Appendices

TLV®–CS

APPENDIX G: Substances Whose Adopted *Documentation* and TLVs® Were Withdrawn For a Variety of Reasons, Including Insufficient Data, Regrouping, Etc.

[Individual entries will remain for a 10-year period, commencing with the year of withdrawal] (Con't.)

Substance [CRN]	Year Withdrawn	Reason
Silica, amorphous — diatomaceous earth [61790-53-2]	2006	Insufficient data on single-substance exposure, most are co-exposures with crystalline silica
Silica, amorphous — fume [69012-64-2]	2006	Insufficient data
Silica, amorphous — fused [60676-86-0]	2006	Insufficient data
Silica amorphous — precipitated silica and silica gel [112926-00-8]	2006	Insufficient data
Silica, crystalline — cristobalite [14464-46-1]	2006	Combined into one TLV® and *Documentation*, i.e., Silica, crystalline
Silica, crystalline — quartz [14808-60-7]	2006	Combined into one TLV® and *Documentation*, i.e., Silica, crystalline
Silica, crystalline — tridymite [15468-32-3]	2005	Insufficient data
Silica, crystalline — tripoli [1317-95-9]	2006	Insufficient data and unlikely single-substance exposure. Combined into one TLV® and *Documentation*, i.e., Silica, crystalline
Silicon [7440-21-3]	2006	Insufficient data
Soapstone	2011	Refer to Talc
Tantalum [7440-25-7] and Tantalum oxide [1314-61-0] dusts, as Ta	2010	Insufficient data
Tetrasodium pyrophosphate [7722-88-5]	2006	Insufficient data

TLV®–CS

APPENDIX G: Substances Whose Adopted *Documentation* and TLVs® Were Withdrawn For a Variety of Reasons, Including Insufficient Data, Regrouping, Etc.
[Individual entries will remain for a 10-year period, commencing with the year of withdrawal] (Con't.)

Substance [CRN]	Year Withdrawn	Reason
Triphenyl amine [603-34-9]	2008	Insufficient data
Vegetable oil mist	2006	Insufficient data
VM & P naphtha [8032-32-4]	2009	Refer to Appendix H: Reciprocal Calculation Method for Certain Refined Hydrocarbon Solvent Vapor Mixtures

APPENDIX H: Reciprocal Calculation Method for Certain Refined Hydrocarbon Solvent Vapor Mixtures

TLV®–CS

The goal of the TLV®-CS Committee is to recommend TLVs® for all substances and mixtures where there is evidence of health effects at airborne concentrations encountered in the workplace. When a sufficient body of evidence exists for a particular substance or mixture, a TLV® is established. However, hydrocarbon solvents are often complex and variable in composition. The use of the mixture formula, found in Appendix E: Threshold Limit Values for Mixtures, is difficult in such cases because these petroleum mixtures contain a large number of unique compounds, many of which do not have a TLV® recommendation.

The reciprocal calculation procedure (RCP) is a method for deriving occupational exposure limits (OEL) for refined hydrocarbon solvents. Refined hydrocarbon solvents often are found as mixtures created by distillation of petroleum oil over a particular boiling range. These mixtures may consist of up to 200 components consisting of aliphatic (alkane), cycloaliphatic (cycloalkane) and aromatic hydrocarbons ranging from 5 to 15 carbons.

There are two aspects of the RCP— the methodology and the group guidance values (GGVs). The methodology is based on the special case formula found in pre-2004 versions of the Mixture Appendix in *TLVs® and BEIs® Based on the Documentation of the Threshold Limit Values for Chemical Substances and Physical Agents and Biological Exposure Indices*. The RCP formula calculates a unique OEL based on the mass composition of the mixture, the GGVs and where applicable, substance-specific TLVs®.

Group guidance values are categorized based on similar chemical and toxicological concerns. Several entities (both trade groups and regulatory authorities) have adopted group guidance values to utilize with the reciprocal mixture formula (RMF) (Farmer, 1995; UK HSE, 2000; McKee et al., 2005). Two examples of published GGVs are found in Table 1. A mixture-specific time-weighted-average limit (GGV-TWA$_{mixture}$) is calculated based on the mass percent make-up of the designated groups utilizing the reciprocal mixture formula and the GGVs from column *B* or *C* and TLV® values in column *D* found in Table 1.

ACGIH® considers this method to be applicable for mixtures if the toxic effects of individual constituents are additive (i.e., similar toxicological effect on the same target organ or system). The principal toxicological effects of hydrocarbon solvent constituents are acute central nervous system (CNS) depression (characterised by effects ranging from dizziness and drowsiness to anaesthesia) and eye and respiratory tract irritation (McKee et al., 2005; ECETOC, 1997).

Application

The RCP is a special use application. It applies only to hydrocarbon solvents containing saturated aliphatics (normal, iso-alkanes and cycloalkanes) and aromatics predominantly consisting of carbon numbers ranging from C_5 to C_{15} derived from petroleum and boiling in the approximate range of 35–320°C. It does not apply to petroleum derived fuels, lubricating oils, or solvent mixtures for which there exists a unique TLV®. It does not apply to hydrocarbons with a toxicity that is significantly greater than the mixture at large, such as benzene (*see* Limitations below).

Where the mixture is comprised entirely of compounds with unique TLVs®, the mixture should be handled according to Appendix E. When the mixture contains an appreciable amount of a component for which there is a TLV® (i.e., when the use of the TLV® results in a lower GGV-TWA$_{mixture}$), those specific values should be entered into the RCP (*see* column *D*, Table 1). When the mixture itself has been assigned a unique TLV®, that value should be utilized rather than the procedures found in this appendix.

Exposure excursions above the calculated GGV-TWA$_{mixture}$ should be handled according to the procedures found in the Introduction to the TLVs® *(see Excursion Limits)*.

The reciprocal calculation mixture formula is:

$$GGV_{mixture} = \frac{1}{\dfrac{F_a}{GGV_a} + ... + \dfrac{F_n}{GGV_n}}$$

where:

GGV$_{mixture}$ = the calculated 8-hour TWA–OEL for the mixture

GGV$_a$ = the guidance value (or TLV®) for group (or component) *a*

F$_a$ = the liquid mass fraction of group (or component) *a* in the hydrocarbon mixture (value between 0–1)

GGV$_n$ = the guidance value (or TLV®) for the nth group (or component)

F$_n$ = the liquid mass fraction of the nth group (or component) in the hydrocarbon mixture (value between 0–1)

The resulting GGV$_{mixture}$ should identify the source of GGVs used in the calculation (i.e., column *B* or *C*).

The resulting calculated GGV$_{mixture}$ value should follow established recommendations regarding rounding. For calculated values < 100 mg/m^3, round to the nearest 25. For calculated values between 100 and 600 mg/m^3, round to the nearest 50, and for calculated values > 600 mg/m^3, round to the nearest 200 mg/m^3.

Limitations

1. The reciprocal formula requires that the composition of the mixture be characterized at least to the detail of mass percent of the groups found in Table 1.

2. The reciprocal formula does not apply to solvents containing benzene, or n-hexane, or methylnaphthalene, which have individual TLVs® significantly less than the GGV to which they would belong and have unique toxicological properties. Whenever present in the mixture, these components should be measured individually and evaluated using the methodology found in Appendix E, i.e., independent treatment or use of the additive formula depending on the TLV® basis.

3. Care in the use of GGV/RMF should be observed where the mixture in question is known to have significant toxicokinetic interactions of components that are manifested at or below GGV levels.

TLV®–CS

TABLE 1. Group Guidance Values

A Hydrocarbon Group	B McKee et al. (mg/m³)	C UK-HSE 40/2000 (mg/m³)	D ACGIH® Unique TLVs® (mg/m³)
C_5–C_6 Alkanes	1500	1800	Pentane, all isomers (1770) Hexane isomers (1760)
C_7–C_8 Alkanes	1500	1200	Heptane, all isomers (1640) Octane, all isomers (1401)
C_5–C_6 Cycloalkanes	1500	1800	Cyclopentane (1720) Cyclohexane (350)
C_7–C_8 Cycloalkanes	1500	800	Methyl cyclohexane (1610)
C_7–C_8 Aromatics	200	500	Toluene (75) Xylene, all isomers (434) Ethyl benzene (434)
C_9–C_{15} Alkanes	1200	1200	Nonane (1050)
C_9–C_{15} Cycloalkanes	1200	800	
C_9–C_{15} Aromatics*	100	500	Trimethyl benzene, isomers (123) Naphthalene (52) Cumen (246)

*n-Hexane (TLV®-176 mg/m³) and methylnaphthalenes (TLV®-3 mg/m³) are significantly below the recommended GGV. Whenever present in the mixture, these components should be measured individually and evaluated using the methodology found in Appendix E, i.e., independent treatment or use of the additive formula depending on the critical effect.

TLV®–CS

4. The use of the reciprocal formula should be restricted to applications where the boiling points of the solvents in the mixture are relatively narrow, within a range of less than 45°C (i.e., vapor pressure within approximately one order of magnitude). The procedure should not be used in situations where the liquid composition is significantly different from the vapor composition. If these conditions cannot be met, the reciprocal formula can be utilized by substituting $F_{(n)}$ in the equation with the vapor mass fraction for each group (n) in the hydrocarbon mixture, based on situation-specific airborne concentration measurements.

5. The group guidance values apply only to vapors and do not apply to mists or aerosols. The GGV/RMF procedure does not apply to mixtures containing olefins or other unsaturated compounds or polycyclic aromatic hydrocarbons (PAHs).

Example

A solvent containing the following mass composition is matched with the appropriate group guidance value:

Component	Percent by weight	Group Guidance Value (mg/m³)
C_7–C_8 alkanes cycloalkanes	45%	1500
C_9–C_{10} alkanes cycloalkanes	40%	1200
C_7–C_8 aromatics	9%	200
Toluene	6%	75
Benzene	< 1%	-NA-

Based on Column B, Table 1 (McKee et al., 2005), the $GGV_{mixture}$ would be:

$$GGV_{mixture} = \cfrac{1}{\cfrac{.45}{1500} + \cfrac{.40}{1200} + \cfrac{.09}{200} + \cfrac{.06}{75}} = \frac{1}{.001884}$$

$$= 531 \text{ (rounded to 550 mg/m}^3)$$

Toluene (part of the aromatic $C_{7,8}$ fraction) is added as a TLV® rather than a GGV since it makes a difference in the resulting $GGV_{mixture}$. Benzene would be evaluated separately at the current TLV® for benzene.

References

European Centre for Ecotoxicology and Toxicology of Chemicals (ECETOC). Occupational exposure limits for hydrocarbon solvents. Special Report No. 13. Brussels, Belgium (1997).

Farmer TH: Occupational hygiene limits for hydrocarbon solvents. Annals of Occupational Hygiene 40: 237–242 (1995).

McKee RH; Medeiros AM; Daughtrey WC: A proposed methodology for setting occupational exposure limits for hydrocarbon solvents. J of Occ and Env Hygiene 2: 524–542 (2005).

UK Health and Safety Executive (UKHSE) EH40/2000. Occupational Exposure Limits (2000).

96 — Notes

NOTES

2012
Biological Exposure Indices

Adopted by ACGIH®
with Intended Changes

BEIs®

Contents

2011 BIOLOGICAL EXPOSURE INDICES COMMITTEE

Larry K. Lowry, PhD — Chair
Glenn Talaska, PhD, CIH — Vice Chair
Michael Bader, PD Dr
Lee M. Blum, PhD, DABT
John Cocker, PhD
Jean Grassman, PhD, MS
Heiko U. Kaefferlein, PhD
Leena A. Nylander-French, PhD, CIH
Gary J. Spies, MPH, CIH, CSP
Claude Viau, MS, ScD

CONSULTANT

John F. Haynes, Jr., MD

Help ensure the continued development of
TLVs® and BEIs®. Make a tax deductible donation to
the FOHS Sustainable TLV®/BEI® Fund today!

http://www.fohs.org/SusTLV-BEIPrgm.htm

INTRODUCTION TO THE
BIOLOGICAL EXPOSURE INDICES

Biological monitoring provides one means to assess exposure and health risk to workers. It entails measurement of the concentration of a chemical determinant in the biological media of those exposed and is an indicator of the uptake of a substance. Biological Exposure Indices (BEIs®) are guidance values for assessing biological monitoring results. BEIs® represent the levels of determinants that are most likely to be observed in specimens collected from healthy workers who have been exposed to chemicals to the same extent as workers with inhalation exposure at the Threshold Limit Value (TLV®). The exceptions are the BEIs® for chemicals for which the TLVs® are based on protection against nonsystemic effects (e.g., irritation or respiratory impairment) where biological monitoring is desirable because of the potential for significant absorption via an additional route of entry (usually the skin). Biological monitoring indirectly reflects the dose to a worker from exposure to the chemical of interest. The BEI® generally indicates a concentration below which nearly all workers should not experience adverse health effects. The BEI® determinant can be the chemical itself; one or more metabolites; or a characteristic, reversible biochemical change induced by the chemical. In most cases, the specimen used for biological monitoring is urine, blood, or exhaled air. The BEIs® are not intended for use as a measure of adverse effects or for diagnosis of occupational illness.

Biological monitoring can assist the occupational health professional detect and determine absorption via the skin or gastrointestinal system, in addition to that by inhalation; assess body burden; reconstruct past exposure in the absence of other exposure measurements; detect nonoccupational exposure among workers; test the efficacy of personal protective equipment and engineering controls; and monitor work practices.

Biological monitoring serves as a complement to exposure assessment by air sampling. The existence of a BEI® does not indicate a need to conduct biological monitoring. Conducting, designing, and interpreting biological monitoring protocols and the application of the BEI® requires professional experience in occupational health and reference to the current edition of the *Documentation of the Threshold Limit Values and Biological Exposure Indices* (ACGIH®).

Documentation

BEIs® are developed by Committee consensus through an analysis and evaluation process. The detailed scientific criteria and justification for each BEI® can be found in the *Documentation of the Threshold Limit Values and Biological Exposure Indices*. The principal material evaluated by the BEI® Committee includes peer-reviewed published data taken from the workplace (i.e., field studies), data from controlled exposure studies, and from appropriate pharmacokinetic modeling when available. The results of animal research are also considered when relevant. The *Documentation* provides essential background information and the scientific reasoning used in establishing each

BEI®. Other information given includes the analytical methods, possible potential for confounding exposures, specimen collection recommendations, limitations, and other pertinent information.

In recommending a BEI®, ACGIH® considers whether published data are of reasonable quality and quantity, and may also consider unpublished data if verified. There are numerous instances when analytical techniques are available for the measurement of a biological determinant, but published information is unavailable or unsuitable for determining a BEI®. In those instances, occupational health professionals are encouraged to accumulate and report biological monitoring data together with exposure and health data.

Relationship of BEIs® to TLVs®

BEI® determinants are an index of an individual's "uptake" of a chemical(s). Air monitoring to determine the TLV® indicates the potential inhalation "exposure" of an individual or group. The uptake within a workgroup may be different for each individual for a variety of reasons, some of which are indicated below. Most BEIs® are based on a direct correlation with the TLV® (i.e., the concentration of the determinant that can be expected when the airborne concentration is at the TLV®). Some of the BEIs® (e.g., lead) are not derived from the TLV®, but directly relate to the development of an adverse health effect. The basis of each BEI® is provided in the *Documentation*.

Inconsistencies may be observed between the information obtained from air monitoring and biological monitoring for a variety of reasons, including, but not limited to, work-related and methodological factors. Examples are listed below:

- Physiological makeup and health status of the worker, such as body build, diet (water and fat intake), metabolism, body fluid composition, age, gender, pregnancy, medication, and disease state.
- Occupational exposure factors, such as the work-rate intensity and duration, skin exposure, temperature and humidity, co-exposure to other chemicals, and other work habits.
- Nonoccupational exposure factors, such as community and home air pollutants, water and food components, personal hygiene, smoking, alcohol and drug intake, exposure to household products, or exposure to chemicals from hobbies or from another workplace.
- Methodological factors, which include specimen contamination or deterioration during collection and storage and bias of the selected analytical method.
- Location of the air monitoring device in relation to the worker's breathing zone.
- Particle size distribution and bioavailability.
- Variable effectiveness of personal protective devices.

Specimen Collection

Because the concentration of some determinants can change rapidly, the specimen collection time (sampling time) is very important and must be observed and recorded carefully. The sampling time is specified in the BEI® and is determined by the duration of retention of the determinant. Substances and determinants that accumulate may not require a specific sampling time. An explanation of the BEI® sampling time is as follows:

Sampling Time	**Recommended Collection**
1. Prior to shift	16 hours after exposure ceases
2. During shift	Anytime after two hours of exposure
3. End of shift	As soon as possible after exposure ceases
4. End of the workweek	After four or five consecutive working days with exposure
5. Discretionary	At any time

Urine Specimen Acceptability

Urine specimens that are highly dilute or highly concentrated are generally not suitable for monitoring. The World Health Organization has adopted guidelines for acceptable limits on urine specimens as follows:

Creatinine concentration:	> 0.3 g/L and < 3.0 g/L
or	
Specific gravity:	> 1.010 and < 1.030

Specimens falling outside either of these ranges should be discarded and another specimen should be collected. Workers who provide consistently unacceptable urine specimens should be referred for medical evaluation.

Some BEIs® for determinants whose concentration is dependent on urine output are expressed relative to creatinine concentration. For other determinants such as those excreted by diffusion, correction for urine output is not appropriate. In general, the best correction method is chemical-specific, but research data sufficient to identify the best method may not be available. When the field data are only available as adjusted for creatinine, the BEI® will continue to be expressed relative to creatinine; in other circumstances, no correction is recommended, and the BEI® will be expressed as concentration in urine.

Quality Assurance

Each aspect of biological monitoring should be conducted within an effective quality assurance (QA) program. The appropriate specimen must be collected, at the proper time, without contamination or loss, and with use of a suitable container. Donor identification, time of exposure, source of exposure, and the sampling time must be recorded. The analytical method used by the laboratory must have the accuracy, sensitivity, and specificity needed to produce results consistent with the BEI®. Appropriate quality control specimens should be included in the analysis, and the laboratory must follow routine quality control rules. The laboratory should participate in an external proficiency program.

The occupational health professional should provide known blind challenges to the laboratory along with worker specimens (e.g., blanks, purchased or spiked specimens containing the determinant, or split specimens). These blind challenges will enable the occupational health professional to assess the ability of the laboratory to process, analyze, and report results properly, and to

BEIs®

102 — Introduction

have confidence in the laboratory's ability to accurately measure the worker's BEI®. When blind challenges are used, the spiked determinant should be in the same chemical form and matrix as that being analyzed by the laboratory.

Notations

"B" = Background

The determinant may be present in biological specimens collected from subjects who have not been occupationally exposed, at a concentration which could affect interpretation of the result. Such background concentrations are incorporated in the BEI® value.

"Nq" = Nonquantitative

Biological monitoring should be considered for this compound based on the review; however, a specific BEI® could not be determined due to insufficient data.

"Ns" = Nonspecific

The determinant is nonspecific, since it is also observed after exposure to other chemicals.

"Sq" = Semi-quantitative

The biological determinant is an indicator of exposure to the chemical, but the quantitative interpretation of the measurement is ambiguous. These determinants should be used as a screening test if a quantitative test is not practical, or as a confirmatory test if the quantitative test is not specific and the origin of the determinant is in question.

Note:

It is essential to consult the specific BEI® *Documentation* before designing biological monitoring protocols and interpreting BEIs®. In addition, each BEI® *Documentation* now provides a chronology that traces all BEI® recommended actions for the chemical substance in question.

Application of BEIs®

BEIs® are intended as guidelines to be used in the evaluation of potential health hazards in the practice of occupational hygiene. BEIs® do not indicate a sharp distinction between hazardous and nonhazardous exposures. For example, it is possible for an individual's determinant concentration to exceed the BEI® without incurring an increased health risk. If measurements in specimens obtained from a worker on different occasions persistently exceed the BEI®, the cause of the excessive value should be investigated and action taken to reduce the exposure. An investigation is also warranted if the majority of the measurements in specimens obtained from a group of workers at the same workplace and workshift exceed the BEI®. It is desirable that relevant information on related operations in the workplace be recorded.

Due to the variable nature of concentrations in biological specimens, dependence should not be placed on the results of one single specimen. Administrative action should not be normally based on a single isolated measurement, but on measurements of multiple sampling, or an analysis of a repeat specimen. It may be appropriate to remove the worker from exposure following a single high result if there is reason to believe that significant exposure may have occurred. Conversely, observations below the BEI® do not necessarily indicate a lack of health risk.

BEIs® apply to 8-hour exposures, 5 days per week. Although modified work schedules are sometimes used in various occupations, the BEI® Committee does not recommend that any adjustment or correction factor be applied to the BEIs® (i.e., the BEIs® should be used as listed, regardless of the work schedule).

Use of the BEI® should be applied by a knowledgeable occupational health professional. Toxicokinetic and toxicodynamic information is taken into account when establishing the BEI®; thus, some knowledge of the metabolism, distribution, accumulation, excretion, and effect(s) is helpful in using the BEI® effectively. The BEI® is a guideline for the control of potential health hazards to the worker and should not be used for other purposes. The values are inappropriate to use for the general population or for nonoccupational exposures. The BEI® values are neither rigid lines between safe and dangerous concentrations nor are they an index of toxicity.

BEIs®

104 — Adopted Biological Exposure Determinants

BEIs®

ADOPTED BIOLOGICAL EXPOSURE DETERMINANTS

Chemical [CAS No.] *Determinant*	*Sampling Time*	*BEI®*	*Notation*
ACETONE [67-64-1]			
Acetone in urine	End of shift	50 mg/L	Ns
ACETYLCHOLINESTERASE INHIBITING PESTICIDES			
Cholinesterase activity in red blood cells	Discretionary	70% of individual's baseline	Ns
ANILINE [62-53-3]			
Aniline in urine★	End of shift	—	Nq
Aniline released from hemoglobin in blood	End of shift	—	Nq
p-Aminophenol in urine★	End of shift	50 mg/L	B, Ns, Sq
ARSENIC, ELEMENTAL [7440-38-2] AND SOLUBLE INORGANIC COMPOUNDS (excludes gallium arsenide and arsine)			
Inorganic arsenic plus methylated metabolites in urine	End of workweek	35 µg As/L	B
BENZENE [71-43-2]			
S-Phenylmercapturic acid in urine	End of shift	25 µg/g creatinine	B
t,t-Muconic acid in urine	End of shift	500 µg/g creatinine	B
1,3-BUTADIENE [106-99-0]			
1,2 Dihydroxy-4-(N-acetylcysteinyl)-butane in urine	End of shift	2.5 mg/L	B, Sq
Mixture of N-1- and N-2-(hydroxybutenyl)valine hemoglobin (Hb) adducts in blood	Not critical	2.5 pmol/g Hb	Sq

Adopted Biological Exposure Determinants — 105

ADOPTED BIOLOGICAL EXPOSURE DETERMINANTS

Chemical [CAS No.] Determinant	Sampling Time	BEI®	Notation
2-BUTOXYETHANOL [111-76-2]			
Butoxyacetic acid (BAA) in urine★	End of shift	200 mg/g creatinine	—
CADMIUM [7440-43-9] AND INORGANIC COMPOUNDS			
Cadmium in urine	Not critical	5 µg/g creatinine	B
Cadmium in blood	Not critical	5 µg/L	B
CARBON DISULFIDE [75-15-0]			
2-Thioxothiazolidine-4-carboxylic acid (TTCA) in urine	End of shift	0.5 mg/g creatinine	B, Ns
CARBON MONOXIDE [630-08-0]			
Carboxyhemoglobin in blood	End of shift	3.5% of hemoglobin	B, Ns
Carbon monoxide in end-exhaled air	End of shift	20 ppm	B, Ns
CHLOROBENZENE [108-90-7]			
4-Chlorocatechol in urine★	End of shift at end of workweek	100 mg/g creatinine	Ns
p-Chlorophenol in urine★	End of shift at end of workweek	20 mg/g creatinine	Ns
CHROMIUM (VI), Water-soluble fume			
Total chromium in urine	End of shift at end of workweek	25 µg/L	—
Total chromium in urine	Increase during shift	10 µg/L	—

BEIs®

995

BEIs®

106 — Adopted Biological Exposure Determinants

ADOPTED BIOLOGICAL EXPOSURE DETERMINANTS

Chemical [CAS No.] Determinant	Sampling Time	BEI®	Notation
COBALT [7440-48-4]			
Cobalt in urine	End of shift at end of workweek	15 µg/L	B
Cobalt in blood	End of shift at end of workweek	1 µg/L	B, Sq
CYCLOHEXANOL [108-93-0]			
1,2-Cyclohexanediol in urine★	End of shift at end of workweek	—	Nq, Ns
Cyclohexanol in urine★	End of shift	—	Nq, Ns
CYCLOHEXANONE [108-94-1]			
1,2-Cyclohexanediol in urine★	End of shift at end of workweek	80 mg/L	Ns, Sq
Cyclohexanol in urine★	End of shift	8 mg/L	Ns, Sq
DICHLOROMETHANE [75-09-2]			
Dichloromethane in urine	End of shift	0.3 mg/L	Sq
N,N-DIMETHYLACETAMIDE [127-19-5]			
N-Methylacetamide in urine	End of shift at end of workweek	30 mg/g creatinine	—
N,N-DIMETHYLFORMAMIDE (DMF) [68-12-2]			
N-Methylformamide in urine	End of shift	15 mg/L	—
N-Acetyl-S-(N-methylcarbamoyl) cysteine in urine	Prior to last shift of workweek	40 mg/L	Sq
2-ETHOXYETHANOL (EGEE) [110-80-5] and **2-ETHOXYETHYL ACETATE (EGEEA) [111-15-9]**			
2-Ethoxyacetic acid in urine	End of shift at end of workweek	100 mg/g creatinine	—

Adopted Biological Exposure Determinants — 107

ADOPTED BIOLOGICAL EXPOSURE DETERMINANTS

Chemical [CAS No.] Determinant	Sampling Time	BEI®	Notation
‡ ETHYL BENZENE [100-41-4]			
Sum of mandelic acid and phenylglyoxylic acid in urine	End of shift at end of workweek	(0.7 g/g creatinine)	Ns (Sq)
(Ethyl benzene in end-exhaled air)	(Not critical)	(—)	(Sq)
* FLUORIDES [109-86-4]			
Fluoride in urine	Prior to shift	2 mg/L	B, Ns
Fluoride in urine	End of shift	3 mg/L	B, Ns
FURFURAL [98-01-1]			
Furoic acid in urine★	End of shift	200 mg/L	Ns
n-HEXANE [110-54-3]			
2,5-Hexanedion in urine☆	End of shift at end of workweek	0.4 mg/L	—
LEAD [7439-92-1] [See Note below]			
Lead in blood	Not critical	30 µg/100 ml	—

Note: Women of child bearing potential, whose blood Pb exceeds 10 µg/dl, are at risk of delivering a child with a blood Pb over the current Centers for Disease Control guideline of 10 µg/dl. If the blood Pb of such children remains elevated, they may be at increased risk of cognitive deficits. The blood Pb of these children should be closely monitored and appropriate steps should be taken to minimize the child's exposure to environmental lead. (CDC: Preventing Lead Poisoning in Young Children, October 1991; See BEI® and TLV® *Documentation* for Lead).

Chemical [CAS No.] Determinant	Sampling Time	BEI®	Notation
‡ MERCURY			
(Total inorganic mercury in urine)	Prior to shift	(35 µg/g creatinine)	(B)
(Total inorganic mercury in blood)	(End of shift at end of workweek)	(15 µg/L)	(B)

BEIs®

997

BEIs®

108 — Adopted Biological Exposure Determinants

ADOPTED BIOLOGICAL EXPOSURE DETERMINANTS

Chemical [CAS No.] Determinant	Sampling Time	BEI®	Notation
METHANOL [67-56-1] Methanol in urine	End of shift	15 mg/L	B, Ns
METHEMOGLOBIN INDUCERS Methemoglobin in blood	During or end of shift	1.5% of hemoglobin	B, Ns, Sq
2-METHOXYETHANOL (EGME) [109-86-4] and **2-METHOXYETHYL ACETATE (EGMEA) [110-49-6]** 2-Methoxyacetic acid in urine	End of shift at end of workweek	1 mg/g creatinine	—
METHYL n-BUTYL KETONE [591-78-6] 2,5-Hexanedione in urine ✰	End of shift at end of workweek	0.4 mg/L	—
METHYL CHLOROFORM [71-55-6] Methyl chloroform in end-exhaled air	Prior to last shift of workweek	40 ppm	—
Trichloroacetic acid in urine	End of workweek	10 mg/L	Ns, Sq
Total trichloroethanol in urine	End of shift at end of workweek	30 mg/L	Ns, Sq
Total trichloroethanol in blood	End of shift at end of workweek	1 mg/L	Ns
4,4'-METHYLENE BIS(2-CHLOROANILINE) **(MBOCA) [101-14-4]** Total MBOCA in urine	End of shift	—	Nq
‡ METHYL ETHYL KETONE (MEK) [78-93-3] MEK in urine	End of shift	2 mg/L	(—)

Adopted Biological Exposure Determinants — 109

ADOPTED BIOLOGICAL EXPOSURE DETERMINANTS

Chemical [CAS No.] Determinant	Sampling Time	BEI®	Notation
METHYL ISOBUTYL KETONE (MIBK) [108-10-1]			
MIBK in urine	End of shift	1 mg/L	—
N-METHYL-2-PYRROLIDONE [872-50-4]			
5-Hydroxy-N-methyl-2-pyrrolidone in urine	End of shift	100 mg/L	—
NITROBENZENE [98-95-3]			
Total p-nitrophenol in urine	End of shift at end of workweek	5 mg/g creatinine	Ns
Methemoglobin in blood	End of shift	1.5% of hemoglobin	B, Ns, Sq
PARATHION [56-38-2]			
Total p-nitrophenol in urine	End of shift	0.5 mg/g creatinine	Ns
Cholinesterase activity in red cells	Discretionary	70% of individual's baseline	B, Ns, Sq
‡ PENTACHLOROPHENOL (PCP) [87-86-5]			
(Total PCP in urine)	(Prior to last shift of workweek)	(2 mg/g creatinine)	(B)
(Free PCP in plasma)	(End of shift)	(5 mg/L)	(B)
PHENOL [108-95-2]			
Phenol in urine★	End of shift	250 mg/g creatinine	B, Ns
POLYCYCLIC AROMATIC HYDROCARBONS (PAHs)			
1-Hydroxypyrene (1-HP) in urine★	End of shift at end of workweek	—	Nq

BEIs®

110 — Adopted Biological Exposure Determinants

BEIs®

ADOPTED BIOLOGICAL EXPOSURE DETERMINANTS

Chemical [CAS No.] Determinant	Sampling Time	BEI®	Notation
2-PROPANOL [67-63-0]			
Acetone in urine	End of shift at end of workweek	40 mg/L	B, Ns
STYRENE [100-42-5]			
Mandelic acid plus phenylglyoxylic acid in urine	End of shift	400 mg/g creatinine	Ns
Styrene in venous blood	End of shift	0.2 mg/L	Sq
TETRACHLOROETHYLENE [127-18-4]			
Tetrachloroethylene in end-exhaled air	Prior to shift	3 ppm	—
Tetrachloroethylene in blood	Prior to shift	0.5 mg/L	—
TETRAHYDROFURAN [109-99-9]			
Tetrahydrofuran in urine	End of shift	2 mg/L	—
TOLUENE [108-88-3]			
Toluene in blood	Prior to last shift of workweek	0.02 mg/L	—
Toluene in urine	End of shift	0.03 mg/L	—
o-Cresol in urine★	End of shift	0.3 mg/g creatinine	B
TRICHLOROETHYLENE [79-01-6]			
Trichloroacetic acid in urine	End of shift at end of workweek	15 mg/L	Ns
Trichloroethanol in blood☆	End of shift at end of workweek	0.5 mg/L	Ns
Trichloroethylene in blood	End of shift at end of workweek	—	Sq
Trichloroethylene in end-exhaled air	End of shift at end of workweek	—	Sq

ADOPTED BIOLOGICAL EXPOSURE DETERMINANTS

Chemical [CAS No.] Determinant	Sampling Time	BEI®	Notation
URANIUM [7440-61-1]) Uranium in urine	End of shift	200 µg/L	—
XYLENES [95-47-6; 108-38-3; 106-42-3; 1330-20-7] (technical or commercial grade) Methylhippuric acids in urine	End of shift	1.5 g/g creatinine	—

★ With hydrolysis.
☆ Without hydrolysis; n-hexane, methyl n-butyl ketone and trichloroethylene.

BEIs®

112 — NIC

2012 NOTICE OF INTENDED CHANGES

These substances, with their corresponding indices, comprise those for which (1) a BEI® is proposed for the first time, (2) a change in the Adopted index is proposed, (3) retention as an NIC is proposed, or (4) withdrawal of the *Documentation* and adopted BEI® is proposed. In each case, the proposals should be considered trial indices during the period they are on the NIC. These proposals were ratified by the ACGIH® Board of Directors and will remain on the NIC for approximately one year following this ratification. If the Committee neither finds nor receives any substantive data that change its scientific opinion regarding an NIC BEI®, the Committee may then approve its recommendation to the ACGIH® Board of Directors for adoption. If the Committee finds or receives substantive data that change its scientific opinion regarding an NIC BEI®, the Committee may change its recommendation to the ACGIH® Board of Directors for the matter to be either retained on or withdrawn from the NIC.

Documentation is available for each of these substances and their proposed values.

This notice provides an opportunity for comment on these proposals. Comments or suggestions should be accompanied by substantiating evidence in the form of peer-reviewed literature and forwarded in electronic format to The Science Group, ACGIH®, at science@acgih.org. Please refer to the ACGIH® TLV®/BEI® Development Process on the ACGIH® website (http://www.acgih.org/TLV/DevProcess.htm) for a detailed discussion covering this procedure, methods for input to ACGIH®, and deadline date for receiving comments.

2012 NOTICE OF INTENDED CHANGES

Chemical [CAS No.] Determinant	Sampling Time	BEI®	Notation
† ETHYL BENZENE [100-41-4] Sum of Mandelic and Phenylglyoxylic acids in urine	End of shift at end of workweek	0.15 g/g creatinine	Ns
† MERCURY Mercury in urine	Prior to shift	20 µg Hg/g creatinine	—

NIC — 113

BEIs®

2012 NOTICE OF INTENDED CHANGES

Chemical [CAS No.] *Determinant*	*Sampling Time*	*BEI®*	*Notation*
† METHYL ETHYL KETONE [78-93-3]			
Methyl ethyl ketone in urine	End of shift	2 mg/L	Ns
† NAPHTHALENE [91-20-3]			
1-Naphthol★ + 2-Naphthol★	End of shift	—	Nq, Ns
† PENTACHLOROPHENOL [87-86-5]			
Pentachlorophenol in urine★	Discretionary	—	Nq
† TOLUENE DIISOCYANATE [584-84-9; 91-08-7]			
Toluene diamine in urine★, **	End of shift	5 µg/g creatinine	Ns

† = 2012 Revision or Addition to the Notice of Intended Changes

★ With hydrolysis

** Sum of 2,4- and 2,6-isomers

114 — Notes

NOTES

CHEMICAL SUBSTANCES AND OTHER ISSUES
UNDER STUDY

The BEI® Committee solicits information, especially data, which may assist it in its deliberations regarding the following substances and issues. Comments and suggestions, accompanied by substantiating evidence in the form of peer-reviewed literature, should be forwarded in electronic format to The Science Group, ACGIH® (science@acgih.org). In addition, the Committee solicits recommendations for additional substances and issues of concern to the industrial hygiene and occupational health communities. Please refer to the ACGIH® TLV®/BEI® Development Process found on the ACGIH® website for a detailed discussion covering this procedure and methods for input to ACGIH® (http://www.acgih.org/TLV/DevProcess.htm).

The Under Study list is published each year by February 1 on the ACGIH® website (www.acgih.org/TLV/Studies.htm), in the ACGIH® Annual Reports, and later in the annual *TLVs® and BEIs®* book. In addition, the Under Study list is updated by July 31 into a two-tier list.

- Tier 1 entries indicate which chemical substances and physical agents **may** move forward as an NIC or NIE in the upcoming year, based on their status in the development process.
- Tier 2 consists of those chemical substances and physical agents that **will not** move forward, but will either remain on, or be removed from, the Under Study list for the next year.

This updated list will remain in two tiers for the balance of the year. ACGIH® will continue this practice of updating the Under Study list by February 1 and establishing the two-tier list by July 31 each year.

The substances and issues listed below are as of January 1, 2012. *After this date, please refer to the ACGIH® website* (http://www.acgih.org/TLV/Studies.htm) *for the up-to-date list.*

Chemical Substances

Acetone
Acrylamide
Cadmium and inorganic
   compounds
Carbon monoxide
Cobalt
3,3'-Dichlorobenzidine
Ethylene oxide
Hexamethylene diisocyanate
Lead

Manganese
Methyl chloroform
4,4'-Methylene bis(2-chloroaniline)
   (MBOCA)
Nickel
Nitrobenzene
Parathion
Polycyclic aromatic hydrocarbons
   (PAHs)
Styrene

Other Issues Under Study

1. Creatinine normalization

116 — Under Study

2. Metabolic polymorphisms
3. Consistency of BEI® *Documentation*
4. BEI® sampling strategies/frequency of sampling
5. Introduction to the BEI® *Documentation*
6. Sq notation

Feasibility Assessments

For the substances listed below, the BEI® Committee has determined that developing a BEI® is not currently feasible owing to inadequate scientific data. However, the Committee believes that these substances may pose important risks to the health of workers, and therefore, it encourages the submission of new data. Field or experimental studies on the relationship between biological indicators and either health risk or environmental exposure are needed for these agents. A brief summary of the current negative feasibility assessment, including data needs, for each of the listed substances is available from The Science Group, ACGIH®.

Substance	Date of Feasibility Assessment
Acrylonitrile	March 1994
Alachlor	September 2009
Aluminum	September 2007
Antimony	November 1996
Beryllium	November 2010
Chlorpyrifos	October 1996
1,4-Dichlorobenzene	March 1994
2,4-Dichlorophenoxy-acetic acid	March 1994
2-Ethyl hexanoic acid	September 2001
Hydrazines	March 1994
Inorganic borates	October 1995
Manganese	April 1995
Methyl tert-butyl ether	October 1993
Methyl n-butyl ketone	October 1995
Methyl formate	September 2005
α-Methyl styrene	November 2010
Nickel	November 1996
Perfluorooctanoic acid (PFOA)	April 2007
Selenium	October 1995
Thallium	November 2010
Trimethylbenzene	August 1999
Vanadium pentoxide	September 2009
Vinyl chloride	August 2002

2012
Threshold Limit Values for Physical Agents in the Work Environment

Adopted by ACGIH® with Intended Changes

Contents

TLV®–PA

2011 TLV® PHYSICAL AGENTS COMMITTEE

Mary S. Lopez, PhD, CPE — Chair
Thomas J. Armstrong, PhD, CIH
Thomas E. Bernard, PhD, CIH
Martin G. Cherniack, MPH, MD
Anthony P. Cullen, OD, PhD, DSc
Harry Mahar, PhD, CIH
David M. Rempel, MD, MPH
David H. Sliney, PhD
Thomas S. Tenforde, PhD

TLV®–PA

*Help ensure the continued development of
TLVs® and BEIs®. Make a tax deductible donation to
the FOHS Sustainable TLV®/BEI® Fund today!*

http://www.fohs.org/SusTLV-BEIPrgm.htm

INTRODUCTION TO THE PHYSICAL AGENTS

This section presents Threshold Limit Values (TLVs®) for occupational exposure to physical agents of acoustic, electromagnetic, ergonomic, mechanical, and thermal nature. As with other TLVs®, those for physical agents provide guidance on the levels of exposure and conditions under which it is believed that nearly all healthy workers may be repeatedly exposed, day after day, without adverse health effects.

The target organs and health effects of these physical agents vary greatly with their nature; thus, TLVs® are not single numbers, but rather integrations of the measured parameters of the agent, its effects on workers, or both. Due to the many types of physical agents, a variety of scientific disciplines, detection techniques, and instrumentation are applied. Therefore, it is especially important that the physical agents TLVs® be applied only by individuals adequately trained and experienced in the corresponding measurement and evaluation techniques. Given the unavoidable complexity of some of these TLVs®, the most current *Documentation* of the TLVs® for Physical Agents must be consulted when they are applied.

Because of wide variations in individual susceptibility, exposure of an individual at, or even below, the TLV® may result in annoyance, aggravation of a pre-existing condition, or occasionally even physiological damage. Certain individuals may also be hypersusceptible or otherwise unusually responsive to some physical agents at the workplace because of a variety of factors such as genetic predisposition, body mass, age, personal habits (e.g., smoking, alcohol, or other drugs), medication, or previous or concurrent exposures. Such workers may not be adequately protected from adverse health effects from exposures to certain physical agents at or below the TLVs®. An occupational physician should evaluate the extent to which such workers require additional protection.

TLVs® are based on available information from industrial experience, from experimental human and animal studies, and when possible, from a combination of the three, as cited in their *Documentation*.

Like all TLVs®, these limits are intended for use in the practice of occupational hygiene and should be interpreted and applied only by a person trained in this discipline. They are not intended for use, or for modification for use, 1) in the evaluation or control of the levels of physical agents in the community or 2) as proof or disproof of an existing physical disability.

These values are reviewed annually by ACGIH® for revision or additions as further information becomes available. ACGIH® regularly examines the data related to mutagenicity, cancer, adverse reproductive effects, and other health effects of physical agents. Comments, accompanied by substantive documentation in the form of peer-reviewed literature, are solicited and should be forwarded in electronic format to The Science Group, ACGIH® (science@acgih.org).

TLV®–PA

ACGIH® disclaims liability with respect to the use of TLVs®.

Notice of Intended Changes

Each year, proposed actions for the forthcoming year are issued in the form of a "Notice of Intended Changes" (NIC). These physical agents, with their corresponding values, comprise those for which (1) a limit is proposed for the first time (i.e., NIE), (2) a change in the Adopted Values are proposed, or (3) retention as an NIC is proposed, or (4) withdrawal of the *Documentation* and adopted TLV® is proposed. In each case, the proposals should be considered trial values during the period they are on the NIC/NIE. These proposals are ratified by the ACGIH® Board of Directors and will remain as NICs/NIEs for approximately one year following this ratification. If the Committee neither finds nor receives any substantive data that change its scientific opinion regarding the TLVs® for a NIC/NIE physical agent, the Committee may then approve its recommendation to the ACGIH® Board of Directors for adoption. If the Committee finds or receives substantive data that change its scientific opinion regarding an NIC/NIE TLV®, the Committee may change its recommendation to the ACGIH® Board of Directors for the matter to be either retained on or withdrawn from the NIC.

Documentation is available for each of these physical agents and their proposed values.

This notice provides an opportunity for comment on these proposals. Comments or suggestions should be accompanied by substantiating evidence in the form of peer-reviewed literature and forwarded in electronic format to The Science Group, ACGIH®, at science@acgih.org. Please refer to the ACGIH® TLV®/BEI® Development Process on the ACGIH® website (http://www.acgih.org/TLV/DevProcess.htm) for a detailed discussion covering this procedure, methods for input to ACGIH®, and deadline date for receiving comments.

Definitions

TLV® categories used in this section include the following:
a) Threshold Limit Value–Time Weighted Average (TLV–TWA). The time-weighted average exposure for an 8-hour workday and 40-hour workweek.
b) Threshold Limit Value–Ceiling (TLV–C). Exposure limit that should not be exceeded even instantaneously.

Carcinogenicity

The Threshold Limit Values for Physical Agents (TLV®-PA) Committee will apply, as necessary, the carcinogenicity designations developed by the Threshold Limit Values for Chemical Substances (TLV®-CS) Committee. Refer to Appendix A in the Chemical Substances section of this *TLVs® and BEIs®* book for these classifications.

Physical and Chemical Factors

Combinations of physical factors such as heat, ultraviolet and ionizing radiation, humidity, abnormal pressure (altitude), and the like, as well as the interaction of physical factors with chemical substances in the workplace, may place added stress on the body so that the effects from exposure at a TLV®

TLV®-PA

may be altered. This stress may act adversely to increase the toxic response to a foreign substance. Although most TLVs® have built-in uncertainty factors to guard against adverse health effects when there are moderate deviations from normal environments, the uncertainty factors for most exposures are not of such a magnitude as to compensate for gross deviations. In such instances, informed professional judgment must be exercised in the proper adjustment of the TLVs®.

TLV®–PA

ACOUSTIC

INFRASOUND AND LOW-FREQUENCY SOUND

These limits represent sound exposures to which it is believed nearly all workers may be repeatedly exposed without adverse effects that do not involve hearing.

Except for impulsive sound with durations of less than 2 seconds, one-third octave band[1] levels for frequencies between 1 and 80 Hz should not exceed a sound pressure level (SPL) ceiling limit of 145 dB. In addition, the overall unweighted SPL should not exceed a ceiling limit of 150 dB.

There are no time limits for these exposures. However, application of the TLVs® for Noise and Ultrasound, recommended to prevent noise-induced hearing loss, may provide a reduced acceptable level with time. This reduction will depend upon the amount of attenuation allowed for hearing protection.

An alternative but slightly more constrictive criterion, where the peak SPL measured with the linear or unweighted frequency response of a Sound Level Meter does not exceed 145 dB for nonimpulsive events, may be used. When using this criterion, the measurement instrument should conform to ANSI Standard S1.4 and the linear or unweighted response should extend down to at least 2 Hz.

Note: Low frequency sounds in the chest resonance range from about 50 Hz to 60 Hz can cause whole-body vibration. Such an effect may cause annoyance and discomfort. The SPL of such sound may need to be reduced to a level where the problem disappears.

TLV®–PA

References

1. American National Standards Institute: Specification for Octave-Band and Fractional-Octave Band Analog and Digital Filters S1.11-1986 (R1998). ANSI, New York (1998).

NOISE

These TLVs® refer to sound pressure levels and durations of exposure that represent conditions under which it is believed that nearly all workers may be repeatedly exposed without adverse effect on their ability to hear and understand normal speech. Prior to 1979, the medical profession had defined hearing impairment as an average hearing threshold level in excess of 25 decibels (ANSI S3.6-1996)[1] at 500, 1000, and 2000 hertz (Hz). The limits that are given here have been established to prevent a hearing loss at higher frequencies, such as 3000 Hz and 4000 Hz. The values should be used as guides in the control of noise exposure and, due to individual susceptibility, should not be regarded as fine lines between safe and dangerous levels.

It should be recognized that the application of the TLVs® for noise will not protect all workers from the adverse effects of noise exposure. The TLVs® should protect the median of the population against a noise-induced hearing loss exceeding 2 dB after 40 years of occupational exposure for the average of 0.5, 1, 2, and 3 kHz. A hearing conservation program with all its elements, including audiometric testing, is necessary when workers are exposed to noise at or above the TLVs®.

Continuous or Intermittent Noise

The sound pressure level should be determined by a sound level meter or dosimeter conforming, as a minimum, to the requirements of the American National Standards Institute (ANSI) Specification for Sound Level Meters, S1.4-1983, Type S2A,[2] or ANSI S1.25-1991 Specification for Personal Noise Dosimeters.[3] The measurement device should be set to use the A-weighted network with slow meter response. The duration of exposure should not exceed that shown in Table 1. These values apply to total duration of exposure per working day regardless of whether this is one continuous exposure or a number of short-term exposures.

When the daily noise exposure is composed of two or more periods of noise exposure of different levels, their combined effect should be considered rather than the individual effect of each. If the sum of the following fractions:

$$\frac{C_1}{T_1} + \frac{C_2}{T_2} + \cdots \frac{C_n}{T_n}$$

exceeds unity, then the mixed exposure should be considered to exceed the TLV®. C_1 indicates the total duration of exposure at a specific noise level, and T_1 indicates the total duration of exposure permitted at that level. All on-the-job noise exposures of 80 dBA or greater should be used in the above calculations. With sound level meters, this formula should be used for sounds with steady levels of at least 3 seconds. For sounds in which this condition is not met, a dosimeter or an integrating sound level meter must be used. The TLV® is exceeded when the dose is more than 100% as indicated on a dosimeter set with a 3 dB exchange rate and an 8-hour criteria level of 85 dBA.

The TLV® is exceeded on an integrating sound level meter when the average sound level exceeds the values of Table 1.

TLV®-PA

124 — Acoustic

Impulsive or Impact Noise

By using the instrumentation specified by ANSI S1.4,[2] S1.25,[3] or IEC 804,[4] impulsive or impact noise is automatically included in the noise measurement. The only requirement is a measurement range between 80 and 140 dBA and the pulse range must be at least 63 dB. No exposures of an unprotected ear in excess of a C-weighted peak sound pressure level of 140 dB should be permitted. If instrumentation is not available to measure a C-weighted peak, an unweighted peak measurement below 140 dB may be used to imply that the C-weighted peak is below 140 dB.

TABLE 1 . TLVs® for Noise[A]

	Duration per Day	Sound Level dBA[B]
Hours	24	80
	16	82
	8	85
	4	88
	2	91
	1	94
Minutes	30	97
	15	100
	7.50[C]	103
	3.75[C]	106
	1.88[C]	109
	0.94[C]	112
Seconds[C]	28.12	115
	14.06	118
	7.03	121
	3.52	124
	1.76	127
	0.88	130
	0.44	133
	0.22	136
	0.11	139

[A] No exposure to continuous, intermittent, or impact noise in excess of a peak C-weighted level of 140 dB.

[B] Sound level in decibels are measured on a sound level meter, conforming as a minimum to the requirements of the American National Standards Institute Specification for Sound Level Meters, S1.4 (1983)[2] Type S2A, and set to use the A-weighted network with slow meter response.

[C] Limited by the noise source—not by administrative control. It is also recommended that a dosimeter or integrating sound level meter be used for sounds above 120 dB.

TLV®-PA

Notes:

1. For impulses above a C-weighted peak of 140 dB, hearing protection should be worn. The MIL-STD-1474C[5] provides guidance for those situations in which single protection (plugs or muffs) or double protection (both muffs and plugs) should be worn.

2. Exposure to certain chemicals may also result in hearing loss. In settings where there may be exposures to noise and to carbon monoxide, lead, manganese, styrene, toluene, or xylene, periodic audiograms are advised and should be carefully reviewed. Other substances under investigation for ototoxic effects include arsenic, carbon disulfide, mercury, and trichloroethylene.

3. There is evidence to suggest that noise exposure in excess of a C-weighted, 8-hour TWA of 115 dBC or a peak exposure of 155 dBC to the abdomen of pregnant workers beyond the fifth month of pregnancy may cause hearing loss in the fetus.

4. The sum of the fractions of any one day may exceed unity, provided that the sum of the fractions over a 7-day period is 5 or less and no daily fraction is more than 3.

5. Table 1 is based on daily exposures in which there will be time away from the workplace in which to relax and sleep. This time away from the workplace will allow any small change to the worker's hearing to recover. When the worker, for times greater than 24 hours, is restricted to a space or series of spaces that serve as both a workplace and a place to relax and sleep, then the background level of the spaces used for relaxation and sleep should be 70 dBA or below.

TLV®–PA

References

1. American National Standards Institute: Specification for Audiometers. ANSI S3.6- 1996. ANSI, New York (1996).
2. American National Standards Institute: Specification for Sound Level Meters. ANSI S1.4-1983 (R1997). ANSI, New York (1997).
3. American National Standards Institute: Specification for Personal Noise Dosimeters. ANSI S1.25-1991. ANSI, New York (1991).
4. International Electrotechnical Commission: Integrating-Averaging Sound Level Meters. IEC 804. IEC, New York (1985).
5. U.S. Department of Defense: Noise Limits for Military Materiel (Metric). MIL-STD-1474C. U.S. DOD, Washington, DC (1991).

126 — Acoustic

ULTRASOUND

These TLVs® represent conditions under which it is believed that nearly all workers may be repeatedly exposed without adverse effect on their ability to hear and understand normal speech. Previous TLVs® for the frequencies 10 kilohertz (kHz) to 20 kHz, set to prevent subjective effects, are referenced in a cautionary note to Table 1. The 8-hour TWA values are an extension of the TLV® for Noise, which is an 8-hour TWA of 85 dBA. The ceiling values may be verified by using a sound level meter with slow detection and $^1/_3$ octave bands. The TWA values may be verified by using an integrating sound level meter with $^1/_3$ octave bands. All instrumentation should have adequate frequency response and should meet the specifications of ANSI S1.4-1983 (R1997)[1] and IEC 804.[2]

TABLE 1. TLVs® for Ultrasound

| | One-third Octave-Band Level[3] | | |
| | Measured in Air in dB re: 20 µPa; Head in Air | | Measured in Water in dB re: 1 µPa; Head in Water |
Mid-Frequency of Third-Octave Band (kHz)	Ceiling Values	8-Hour TWA	Ceiling Values
10	105A	88A	167
12.5	105A	89A	167
16	105A	92A	167
20	105A	94A	167
25	110B	—	172
31.5	115B	—	177
40	115B	—	177
50	115B	—	177
63	115B	—	177
80	115B	—	177
100	115B	—	177

A Subjective annoyance and discomfort may occur in some individuals at levels between 75 and 105 dB for the frequencies from 10 kHz to 20 kHz especially if they are tonal in nature. Hearing protection or engineering controls may be needed to prevent subjective effects. Tonal sounds in frequencies below 10 kHz might also need to be reduced to 80 dB.

B These values assume that human coupling with water or other substrate exists. These thresholds may be raised by 30 dB when there is no possibility that the ultrasound can couple with the body by touching water or some other medium. [When the ultrasound source directly contacts the body, the values in the table do not apply. The vibration level at the mastoid bone must be used.] Acceleration Values 15 dB above the reference of 1 g rms should be avoided by reduction of exposure or isolation of the body from the coupling source. (g = acceleration due to the force of gravity, 9.80665 meters/second^2; rms = root-mean-square).

TLV®–PA

References

1. American National Standards Institute: Specification for Sound Level Meters. ANSI S1.4-1983 (R1997). ANSI, New York (1997).
2. International Electrotechnical Commission: Integrating-Averaging Sound Level Meters. IEC 804. IEC, New York (1985).
3. American National Standards Institute: Specification for Octave-Band and Fractional-Octave-Band Analog and Digital Filters S1.11-1986 (R1998). ANSI, New York (1998).

TLV®–PA

128 — Electromagnetic Radiation and Fields

TLV®–PA

ELECTROMAGNETIC RADIATION SPECTRUM AND RELATED TLVs®

Region*	Non-ionizing Radiation						Ionizing Radiation
Waveband	Sub-Radiofrequency — ELF	Radiofrequency	Microwave	Infrared (IR-C, IR-B, IR-A)	Light	Ultraviolet (UV-A, UV-B, UV-C)	X-ray
Wavelength	1000 km, 10 km		1 m	1 mm, 3 µm, 1.4 µm	760 nm	400 nm, 315 nm, 280 nm, 180 nm	100 nm
Frequency	300 Hz, 30 kHz		300 MHz	300 GHz			
Applicable TLV®	Sub-Radiofrequency	Radiofrequency and Microwave		Light and Near Infrared		Ultraviolet	Ionizing Radiation
				Lasers			

*The boundaries between regions are set by convention and should not be regarded as absolute dividing lines.

ELECTROMAGNETIC RADIATION AND FIELDS

STATIC MAGNETIC FIELDS

These TLVs® refer to static magnetic field flux densities to which it is believed that nearly all workers may be repeatedly exposed day after day without adverse health effects. These values should be used as guides in the control of exposure to static magnetic fields and should not be regarded as fine lines between safe and dangerous levels.

Routine occupational exposures should not exceed 2 tesla (T) in the general workplace environment, but can have ceiling values of 8 T for workers with special training and operating in a controlled workplace environment. Special training involves making workers aware of transient sensory effects that can result from rapid motion in static magnetic fields with flux densities greater than 2 T. A controlled workplace environment is one in which forces exerted by static magnetic fields on metallic objects do not create potentially hazardous projectiles. Exposure of the limbs of workers in the general workplace environment should not exceed 20 T. Workers with implanted ferromagnetic or electronic medical devices should not be exposed to static magnetic fields exceeding 0.5 mT.

These TLVs® are summarized in Table 1.

TABLE 1. TLVs® for Static Magnetic Fields

Exposure	Ceiling Value
Whole body (general workplace)	2 T
Whole body (special worker training and controlled workplace environment)	8 T
Limbs	20 T
Medical device wearers	0.5 mT

TLV®–PA

130 — Electromagnetic Radiation and Fields

SUB-RADIOFREQUENCY (30 kHz and below) MAGNETIC FIELDS

These TLVs® refer to the amplitude of the magnetic flux density (B) of sub-radiofrequency (sub-RF) magnetic fields in the frequency range of 30 kilohertz (kHz) and below to which it is believed that nearly all workers may be exposed repeatedly without adverse health effects. The magnetic field strengths in these TLVs® are root-mean-square (rms) values. These values should be used as guides in the control of exposure to sub-radiofrequency magnetic fields and should not be regarded as fine lines between safe and dangerous levels.

Occupational exposures in the extremely-low-frequency (ELF) range from 1 to 300 hertz (Hz) should not exceed the ceiling value given by the equation:

$$B_{TLV} = \frac{60}{f}$$

where: f = the frequency in Hz

B_{TLV} = the magnetic flux density in millitesla (mT).

For frequencies in the range of 300 Hz to 30 kHz (which includes the voice frequency [VF] band from 300 Hz to 3 kHz and the very-low-frequency [VLF] band from 3 to 30 kHz), occupational exposures should not exceed the ceiling value of 0.2 mT.

These ceiling values for frequencies of 300 Hz to 30 kHz are intended for both partial-body and whole-body exposures. For frequencies below 300 Hz, the TLV® for exposure of the extremities can be increased by a factor of 10 for the hands and feet and by a factor of 5 for the arms and legs.

The magnetic flux density of 60 mT/f at 60 Hz corresponds to a maximum permissible flux density of 1 mT. At 30 kHz, the TLV® is 0.2 mT, which corresponds to a magnetic field intensity of 160 amperes per meter (A/m).

Contact currents from touching ungrounded objects that have acquired an induced electrical charge in a strong sub-RF magnetic field should not exceed the following point contact levels to avoid startle responses or severe electrical shocks:

A. 1.0 milliampere (mA) at frequencies from 1 Hz to 2.5 kHz;

B. 0.4 f mA at frequencies from 2.5 to 30 kHz, where f is the frequency expressed in kHz.

Notes:

1. These TLVs® are based on an assessment of available data from laboratory research and human exposure studies. Modifications of the TLVs® will be made if warranted by new information. At this time, there is insufficient information on human responses and possible health effects of magnetic fields in the frequency range of 1 Hz to 30 kHz to permit the establishment of a TLV® for time-weighted average exposures.

TLV®–PA

2. For workers wearing cardiac pacemakers, the TLV® may not protect against electromagnetic interference with pacemaker function. Some models of cardiac pacemakers have been shown to be susceptible to interference by power-frequency (50/60 Hz) magnetic flux densities as low as 0.1 mT. It is recommended that, lacking specific information on electromagnetic interference from the manufacturer, the exposure of persons wearing cardiac pace-makers or similar medical electronic devices be maintained at or below 0.1 mT at power frequencies.

TABLE 1. TLVs® for Sub-Radiofrequency(30 kHz and below) Magnetic Fields

Frequency Range	TLV®
1 to 300 Hz	Whole-body exposure: $\dfrac{60}{f^*}$ ceiling value in mT
1 to 300 Hz	Arms and legs: $\dfrac{300}{f^*}$ ceiling value in mT
1 to 300 Hz	Hands and feet: $\dfrac{600}{f^*}$ ceiling value in mT
	* where: f = frequency in Hz
300 Hz to 30 kHz	Whole-body and partial-body ceiling value: 0.2 mT
1 Hz to 2.5 kHz	Point contact current limit: 1.0 mA
2.5 to 30 kHz	Point contact current limit: 0.4 f mA where: f = frequency in kHz

TLV®–PA

132 — Electromagnetic Radiation and Fields

SUB-RADIOFREQUENCY (30 kHz and below) AND STATIC ELECTRIC FIELDS

These TLVs® refer to the maximum unprotected workplace field strengths of sub-radiofrequency electric fields (30 kHz and below) and static electric fields that represent conditions under which it is believed that nearly all workers may be exposed repeatedly without adverse health effects. The electric field intensities in these TLVs® are root-mean-square (rms) values. The values should be used as guides in the control of exposure and, due to individual susceptibility, should not be regarded as a fine line between safe and dangerous levels. The electric field strengths stated in these TLVs® refer to the field levels present in air, away from the surfaces of conductors (where spark discharges and contact currents may pose significant hazards).

Occupational exposures should not exceed a field strength of 25 kilovolts per meter (kV/m) from 0 hertz (Hz) (direct current [DC]) to 220 Hz. For frequencies in the range of 220 Hz to 3 kilohertz (kHz), the ceiling value is given by:

$$E_{TLV} = 5.525 \times 10^6 / f$$

where: f = the frequency in Hz
E_{TLV} = the rms electric field strength in V/m

A rms value of 1842 V/m is the ceiling value for frequencies from 3 to 30 kHz. These ceiling values are intended for both partial-body and whole-body exposures.

Notes:

1. These TLVs® are based on limiting currents on the body surface and induced internal currents to levels below those that are believed to produce adverse health effects. Certain biological effects have been demonstrated in laboratory studies at electric field strengths below those permitted in the TLV®; however, there is no convincing evidence at the present time that occupational exposure to these field levels leads to adverse health effects.

   Modifications of the TLVs® will be made if warranted by new information. At this time, there is insufficient information on human responses and possible health effects of electric fields in the frequency range of 0 to 30 kHz to permit the establishment of a TLV® for time-weighted average exposures.

2. Field strengths greater than approximately 5 to 7 kV/m can produce a wide range of safety hazards such as startle reactions associated with spark discharges and contact currents from ungrounded conductors within the field. In addition, safety hazards associated with combustion, ignition of flammable materials, and electro-explosive devices may exist

Sub-Radiofrequency and Static Electric Fields — 133

when a high-intensity electric field is present. Care should be taken to eliminate ungrounded objects, to ground such objects, or to use insulated gloves when ungrounded objects must be handled. Prudence dictates the use of protective devices (e.g., suits, gloves, and insulation) in all fields exceeding 15 kV/m.

3. For workers with cardiac pacemakers, the TLV® may not protect against electromagnetic interference with pacemaker function. Some models of cardiac pacemakers have been shown to be susceptible to interference by power-frequency (50/60 Hz) electric fields as low as 2 kV/m. It is recommended that, lacking specific information on electromagnetic interference from the manufacturer, the exposure of pacemaker and medical electronic device wearers should be maintained at or below 1 kV/m.

TLV®–PA

RADIOFREQUENCY AND MICROWAVE RADIATION

These TLVs® refer to radiofrequency (RF) and microwave radiation in the frequency range of 30 kilohertz (kHz) to 300 gigahertz (GHz) and represent conditions under which it is believed nearly all workers may be repeatedly exposed without adverse health effects. The TLVs®, in terms of root-mean-square (rms), electric (E), and magnetic (H) field strengths, the equivalent plane-wave free-space power densities (S), and induced currents (I) in the body that can be associated with exposure to such fields, are given in Table 1 as a function of frequency, f, in megahertz (MHz).

A. The TLVs® in Table 1, Part A, refer to exposure values obtained by spatially averaging over an area equivalent to the vertical cross-section of the human body (projected area). In the case of partial body exposure, the TLVs® can be relaxed. In nonuniform fields, spatial peak values of field strength may exceed the TLVs® if the spatially averaged value remains within the specified limits. The TLVs® may also be relaxed by reference to specific absorption rate (SAR) limits by appropriate calculations or measurements.

B. Access should be restricted to limit the rms RF body current and potential for RF electrostimulation ("shock", below 0.1 MHz) or perceptible heating (at or above 0.1 MHz) as follows (*see* Table 1, Part B):

1. For freestanding individuals (no contact with metallic objects), RF current induced in the human body, as measured through either foot, should not exceed the following values:

I = 1000 f mA for (0.03 < f < 0.1 MHz) averaged over 0.2 s, where mA = milliampere; and

I = 100 mA for (0.1 < f < 100 MHz) averaged over 6 min.

TABLE 1. Radiofrequency and Microwave TLVs®

Part A—Electromagnetic Fields[A] (f = frequency in MHz)

Frequency	Power Density, S (W/m^2)	Electric Field Strength, E (V/m)	Magnetic Field Strength, H (A/m)	Averaging Time E^2, H^2, or S (min)
30 kHz–100 kHz		1842	163	6
100 kHz–1 MHz		1842	16.3/f	6
1 MHz–30 MHz		1842/f	16.3/f	6
30 MHz–100 MHz		61.4	16.3/f	6
100 MHz–300 MHz	10	61.4	0.163	6
300 MHz–3 GHz	f/30			6
3 GHz–30 GHz	100			$33{,}878.2/f^{1.079}$
30 GHz–300 GHz	100			$67.62/f^{0.476}$

[A]The exposure values in terms of electric and magnetic field strengths are obtained by spatially averaging over an area equivalent to the vertical cross-section of the human body (projected area). At frequencies above 30 GHz, the power density TLV® is the limit over any contiguous 0.01 m² of body surface.

TLV®–PA

Radiofrequency and Microwave Radiation — 135

Part B—Induced and Contact Radiofrequency Currents[B]
Maximum Current (mA)

Frequency	Through Both Feet	Through Either Foot	Grasping	Averaging Time
30 kHz–100 kHz	2000 f	1000 f	1000 f	0.2 s[c]
100 kHz–100 MHz	200	100	100	6 min[D]

[B] It should be noted that the current limits given above may not adequately protect against startle reactions and burns caused by transient discharges when contacting an energized object. Maximum touch current is limited to 50% of the maximum grasping current. The ceiling value for induced and contact currents is 500 mA.

[C] **I** is averaged over a 0.2 s period.

[D] **I** is averaged over a 6-min period (e.g., for either foot or hand contact, i.e., **I** t ≤ 60,000 mA²-min).

2. For conditions of possible contact with metallic bodies, maximum RF current through an impedance equivalent to that of the human body for conditions of grasping contact as measured with a contact current meter should not exceed the following values:

   I = 1000 f mA for (0.03 < f < 0.1 MHz) averaged over 0.2 s; and

   I = 100 mA for (0.1 < f < 100 MHz) averaged over 6 min.

3. For touch contact with conductive objects, the maximum RF current should not exceed more than one-half the maximum RF current for grasping contact. The means of compliance with these current limits can be determined by the user of the TLVs® as appropriate. The use of protective gloves, the avoidance of touch contact with conductive objects, the prohibition of metallic objects, or training of personnel may be sufficient to ensure compliance with these TLVs®. Evaluation of the magnitude of the induced currents will normally require a direct measurement. However, induced and contact current measurements are not required if the spatially averaged electric field strength does not exceed the TLV® given in Table 1, Part A at frequencies between 0.1 and 100 MHz, as shown graphically in Figure 2.

C. For near-field exposures at frequencies less than 300 MHz, the applicable TLV® is given in terms of rms electric and magnetic field strength, as shown in Table 1, Part A. Equivalent plane-wave power density, S (in W/m²) can be calculated from field strength measurement data as follows:

$$S = \frac{E^2}{377}$$

where: E^2 is in volts squared (V²) per meter squared (m²); and

$$S = 377 \, H^2$$

where: H^2 is in amperes squared (A²) per meter squared (m²).

136 — Electromagnetic Radiation and Fields

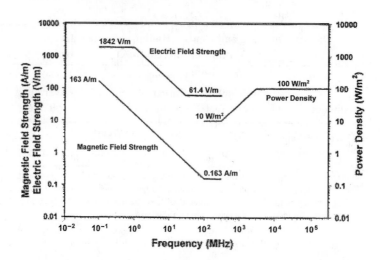

FIGURE 1. Threshold Limit Values (TLVs®) for Radio-frequency/Microwave Radiation in the workplace (for whole-body specific absorption rate [SAR] < 0.4 W/kg. Reprinted with permission of IEEE from Std. C95.1 – 2005.

TLV®–PA

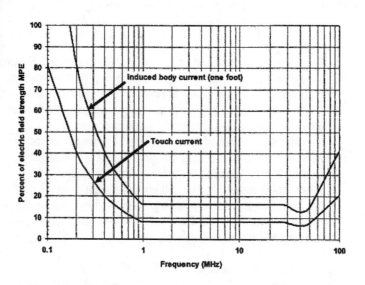

FIGURE 2. Percent of electric field strength TLVs® below which induced and contact current limits are *not* required from 0.1 to 100 MHz. Reprinted with permission of IEEE from Std. C95.1 – 2005.

Radiofrequency and Microwave Radiation — 137

Figure 3 can assist the user of the TLV® in making E, H, and current measurements in the correct order of precedence.

D. For exposures to pulsed fields of pulse duration less than 100 milliseconds (ms) at frequencies in the range 0.1 MHz to 300 GHz, the maximum value of the instantaneous E field is 100 kV/m. The total incident energy density during any 100 ms period within the averaging time (see Table 1, Part A) shall not exceed 20% of the total specific energy absorption (SA) permitted during the entire averaging time for a continuous field, i.e., $0.2 \times 144 = 28.8$ J/kg. For pulse durations greater than 100 ms, normal time-averaging calculations apply.

The TLV® values in Table 1 should be used as guides in the evaluation and control of exposure to radiofrequency and microwave radiation and should not be regarded as fine lines between safe and dangerous levels. The values of E, H and S given in Table 1, Part A are shown graphically as a function of frequency in Figure 1. Figure 2 depicts the maximum permissible current values given in Table 1, Part B through one foot or touch current as a function of the maximum permissible electric field strength TLV® over the frequency range 0.1 to 100 MHz.

Notes:

1. It is believed that workers may be exposed repeatedly to fields up to these TLVs® without adverse health effects. Nevertheless, personnel should not needlessly be exposed to higher levels of RF radiation, approaching the TLVs®, when simple measures can prevent it.

2. For mixed or broadband fields at a number of frequencies for which there are different values of the TLV®, the fraction of the TLV® (in terms of E^2, H^2, or S) incurred within each frequency interval should be determined and the sum of all such fractions should not exceed unity.

3. The TLVs® refer to values averaged over any 6-min (0.1-h) period for frequencies less than 3 GHz, and over shorter periods for higher frequencies down to 10 seconds at 300 GHz, as indicated in Table 1, Part A.

4. At frequencies between 0.1 and 3 GHz, the TLVs® for electromagnetic field strengths may be exceeded if:
   a) the exposure conditions can be shown by appropriate techniques to produce SARs below 0.4 W/kg, as averaged over the whole body;
   b) the induced currents in the body conform with the TLVs® in Table 1, Part B; and
   c) spatial peak SAR values do not exceed 10 W/kg, as averaged over any cubic volume with 10 g of tissue, except for the hands, wrists, feet, ankles, and pinnae, where the spatial peak SAR exposure should not exceed 20 W/kg averaged over any cubic volume of tissue containing 10 g. The SARs are to be averaged over 6 min. Recognition should be given to regions of the body where a 10 cm^3 volume may have a mass significantly less than 10 g because of enclosed voids containing air. In these regions the absorbed power should be divided by the actual mass to determine spatial peak SARs.

5. Above 3 GHz, relaxation of the TLV® conditions may be permissible under partial body exposure conditions.

TLV®–PA

138 — Electromagnetic Radiation and Fields

6. The measurement of RF field strength depends upon several factors, including probe dimensions and distance of the source from the probe. Measurement procedures should follow the recommendations given in IEEE C95.3-2002 (IEEE, 2002) and Report No. 119 of the National Council on Radiation Protection and Measurements (NCRP, 1993).

7. All exposures should be limited to a maximum (peak) electric field intensity of 100 kV/m.

8. Ultrawideband (UWB) radiation is a relatively new modality used for imaging, wireless communications (voice, data, and video), identification tags, security systems, and other applications. UWB signals consist of short pulses (usually < 10 nanoseconds [ns]) and fast rise time (< 200 picoseconds [ps]) that result in a very wide bandwidth. For practical purposes, UWB can be considered as a signal that has a bandwidth greater than the central frequency. The following is a set of guidelines for human exposure to UWB radiation that follows the recommendations of the Tri-Service Electromagnetic Radiation Panel approved in May 1996. For a UWB pulse, the specific absorption rate (SAR) expressed in W/kg of tissue is given by:

$$SAR = S \times PW \times PRF \times 0.025$$

where:

S = equivalent plane-wave power density (W/m^2);
PW = effective pulse width (s), including the ring-down time;
PRF = pulse repetition frequency (s^{-1}); and
0.025 = maximum normalized SAR (W/kg) per W/m^2 in the human body exposed to a 70-MHz RF field.

Exposure limitations are considered for two conditions: (*A*) UWB exposure > 6 min and (*B*) UWB exposure < 6 min with an SAR > 0.4 W/kg, the whole-body limit allowed by the IEEE C95.1 standard for RF radiation issued in 1991 and revised in 1999 and 2005.

Condition A: For exposures > 6 min, the SAR is limited to 0.4 W/kg, averaged over any 6 min period, corresponding to an SA value of 144 J/kg for 6 min. The permitted PRF for a UWB pulse is given by the following:

$$PRF(s^{-1}) = \frac{144 \text{ J/kg}}{(SA \text{ in J/kg per pulse})(360 \text{ s})}$$

Condition B: The conservative assumption is made that the permissible exposure time (ET) is inversely proportional to the square of the SAR in W^2/kg^2. ET is then given by the following equation:

$$ET(s) = \frac{(0.4 \text{ W/kg} \times 144 \text{ J/kg})}{(SAR)^2} = \frac{57.6}{(SAR)^2}$$

9. Many devices used in medicine, manufacturing, telecommunications, and transportation are highly sensitive to interference by exposure to radiofrequency fields (RFI). This problem has increased as a result of the rapid growth in the use of wireless communication devices, such as cellular telephones, handheld transceivers, and vehicle-mounted transceivers. The U.S. Food and Drug Administration's Center for Devices and Radiological Health has made a major effort to inform manufacturers of the need to

Radiofrequency and Microwave Radiation — 139

make medical devices immune to RFI effects to the maximum extent possible. However, RFI problems continue to be identified and can adversely affect the operation of cardiac pacemakers, defibrillators, drug infusion pumps, apnea monitors, and a variety of other medical devices such as electrically powered wheel-chairs. For these devices, the TLVs® may not protect against RFI. The use of sensitive medical equipment or the entry of individuals wearing medical electronic devices subject to RFI should be restricted to locations where the levels of RF-microwave fields at frequencies up to 3 GHz are not expected to interfere with operation of medical devices based on manufacturers' specifications (typically field levels below 3 to 10 V/m that meet compliance requirements for immunity to RFI).

References

Institute of Electrical and Electronic Engineers (IEEE): IEEE Recommended Practice for Measurements and Computations of Radiofrequency Electromagnetic Fields with Respect to Human Exposure to Such Fields, 100 kHz – 300 GHz. IEEE C95.3-2002. IEEE, New York (2002).

National Council on Radiation Protection and Measurements: A Practical Guide to the Determination of Human Exposures to Radiofrequency Fields. Report No 119. NCRP, Bethesda, MD (1993).

Tri-Service Electromagnetic Radiation Panel: Ultra-wideband (UWB) Interim Guidance. Approved May 1996. Available from Brooks Air Force Base, San Antonio, Texas.

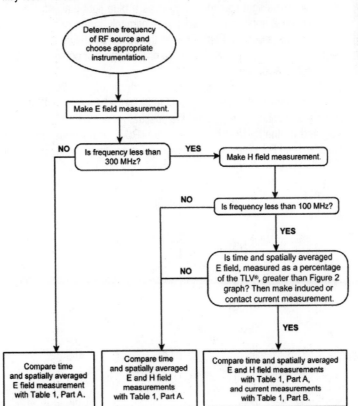

FIGURE 3. Flowchart for making E, H, and current measurements in the correct order of precedence.

LIGHT AND NEAR-INFRARED RADIATION

These TLVs® refer to values for incoherent (non-laser) visible and near-infrared radiation in the wavelength region of 305 to 3000 nm that nearly all workers may be exposed without adverse health effects. The values are based on the best available information from experimental studies. They should be used only as guides in the control of exposures to light and should not be regarded as fine lines between safe and dangerous levels. For purposes of specifying these TLVs®, the optical radiation spectrum is divided into the regions shown in the figure "The Electromagnetic Radiation Spectrum and Related TLVs®" found on page 128.

Recommended Values

The TLVs® for occupational exposure of the eyes to broadband light and near-infrared radiation apply to exposures in any 8-hour workday. Figure 1 is a guide to the application of the TLVs® for visible and near infrared sources.

The first step is to determine if there is a broadband source including the visible light spectrum of sufficient luminance to consider the visible light contributions. If the luminance is greater than 1 candela per square centimeter (cd/cm^2), then the TLVs® in Sections 1 and 2 apply. With a low luminance and no special sources involved, there may not be a significant risk. If the source has a high blue light component such as a blue light-emitting diode (LED), then Section 2 applies. If the source is primarily in the near infrared range because it uses special filters or is in the range by nature (e.g., LED), then Sections 3 and 4 apply. The TLVs® are divided into four potential health effects and spectral regions as follows:

Section 1. *To protect against retinal thermal injury from a visible light source:* Determine the effective spectral radiance of the lamp (L_R) in W/(cm^2 sr) [sr = steradian] by integrating the spectral radiance (L_λ) in W/(cm^2 sr nm) weighted by the thermal hazard function $R(\lambda)$, using Equation 1 or a light meter with an $R(\lambda)$ filter. $R(\lambda)$ is shown in Figure 2 and values are provided in Table 1.

TLV®-PA

Light and Near-Infrared Radiation — 141

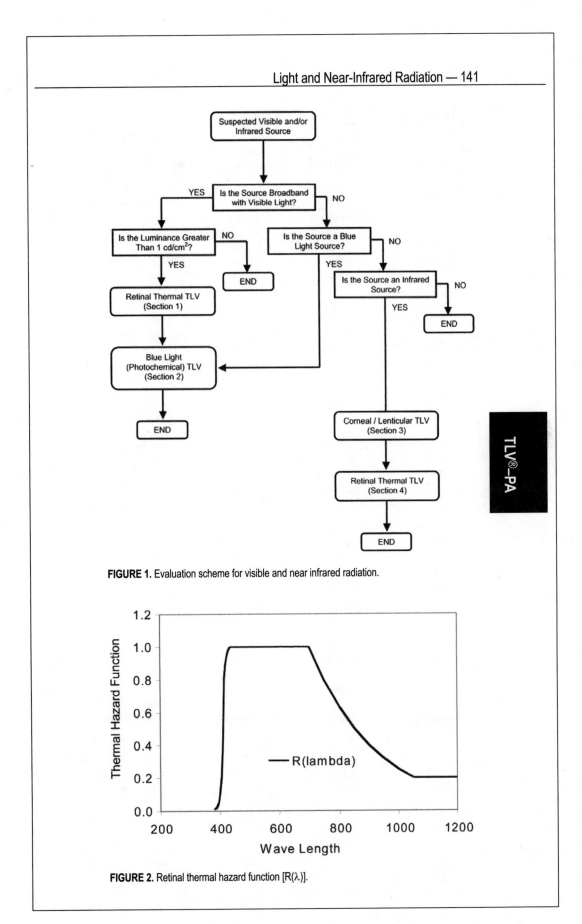

FIGURE 1. Evaluation scheme for visible and near infrared radiation.

FIGURE 2. Retinal thermal hazard function [R(λ)].

142 — Electromagnetic Radiation and Fields

TABLE 1. Retinal and UVR Hazard Spectral Weighting Functions

Wavelength (nm)	Aphakic Hazard Function A(λ)	Blue-Light Hazard Function B(λ)	Retinal Thermal Hazard Function R(λ)
305–335	6.00	0.01	—
340	5.88	0.01	—
345	5.71	0.01	—
350	5.46	0.01	—
355	5.22	0.01	—
360	4.62	0.01	—
365	4.29	0.01	—
370	3.75	0.01	—
375	3.56	0.01	—
380	3.19	0.01	0.01
385	2.31	0.0125	0.0125
390	1.88	0.025	0.025
395	1.58	0.050	0.050
400	1.43	0.100	0.100
405	1.30	0.200	0.200
410	1.25	0.400	0.400
415	1.20	0.800	0.800
420	1.15	0.900	0.900
425	1.11	0.950	0.950
430	1.07	0.980	0.980
435	1.03	1.000	1.00
440	1.000	1.000	1.00
445	0.970	0.970	1.00
450	0.940	0.940	1.00
455	0.900	0.900	1.00
460	0.800	0.800	1.00
465	0.700	0.700	1.00
470	0.620	0.620	1.00
475	0.550	0.550	1.00
480	0.450	0.450	1.00
485	0.400	0.400	1.00
490	0.220	0.220	1.00
495	0.160	0.160	1.00
500	0.100	0.100	1.00
505	0.079	0.079	1.00
510	0.063	0.063	1.00
515	0.050	0.050	1.00
520	0.040	0.040	1.00
525	0.032	0.032	1.00
530	0.025	0.025	1.00
535	0.020	0.020	1.00
540	0.016	0.016	1.00
545	0.013	0.013	1.00
550	0.010	0.010	1.00
555	0.008	0.008	1.00
560	0.006	0.006	1.00
565	0.005	0.005	1.00
570	0.004	0.004	1.00
575	0.003	0.003	1.0

TLV®–PA

TABLE 1 (con't.). Retinal and UVR Hazard Spectral Weighting Functions

Wavelength (nm)	Aphakic Hazard Function A(λ)	Blue-Light Hazard Function B(λ)	Retinal Thermal Hazard Function R(λ)
580	0.002	0.002	1.0
585	0.002	0.002	1.0
590	0.001	0.001	1.0
595	0.001	0.001	1.0
600–700	0.001	0.001	1.0
700–1050	—	—	$10^{[(700-\lambda)/500]}$
1050–1400	—	—	0.2

$$L_R \text{ [W/(cm}^2\text{ sr)]} = \sum_{380}^{1400} L_\lambda \cdot R(\lambda) \cdot \Delta\lambda \tag{1}$$

Some meters provide a total energy emitted in units of J/(cm² sr) over the sampling period, which is the time integral of L_R over the sampling period. Therefore, an alternative expression of the retinal thermal injury TLV® is a dose limit (called DL_R in this TLV®).

Determine the angular subtense (α) of the source in radians (rad). For circular lamps, α is the lamp diameter divided by the viewing distance. If the lamp is oblong, α is estimated from the mean of the shortest and longest dimension that can be viewed divided by the viewing distance, which is according to Equation 2.

$$\alpha \text{ [rad]} = \frac{(l + w)}{2r} \tag{2}$$

For instance, at a viewing distance r = 100 cm from a 0.8-cm diameter tubular flash lamp of length l = 5 cm, the viewing angle α is 0.029 rad.

Large sources are those with an angular subtense (α) greater than 0.1 rad. For large sources, Equations 3a through 3c define the TLV® for protection against retinal thermal injury depending on the exposure duration (t) in seconds [s]. These limits also serve as a useful screening step.

For viewing durations (t) from 1 µs (10^{-6} s) through 0.00063 s, an acceptable exposure is present when Equation 3a is true. For pulse durations less than 1 µs, the TLV® is the same as that for 1 µs. Since the retinal thermal hazard TLVs® for pulsed sources assume a 7-mm, dark-adapted pupil, this exposure limit may be modified for daylight conditions.

$$L_R \text{ [W/(cm}^2\text{ sr)]} \leq \frac{640}{t^{1/4}} \quad \text{OR}$$

$$DL_R \text{ [J/(cm}^2\text{ sr)]} \leq 640 \cdot t^{0.75} \tag{3a}\blacklozenge$$

For viewing durations between 0.63 ms (0.00063 s) and 0.25 s, an acceptable exposure is present when Equation 3b is true.

144 — Electromagnetic Radiation and Fields

$$L_R \, [W/(cm^2 \, sr)] \leq \frac{16}{t^{0.75}} \quad \text{OR}$$

$$DL_R \, [J/(cm^2 \, sr)] \leq 16 \cdot t^{1/4} \tag{3b}\blacklozenge$$

For viewing durations greater than 0.25 s, an acceptable exposure is present when Equation 3c is true. This is a rate-, rather than dose-, limited threshold.

$$L_R \, [W/(cm^2 \, sr)] \leq 45 \tag{3c}\blacklozenge$$

Small sources have an angular subtense (α) less than 0.1 rad. For small sources, the retinal thermal injury risk depends on both the exposure duration (t) and α. The interaction is a maximum value for α (α_{max}) as a function of viewing duration (t [s]).

For viewing durations from 1 μs (10^{-6} s) through 0.00063 s, an acceptable exposure is present when Equation 3a above is true. For pulse durations less than 1 μs, the TLV® is the same as that for 1 μs. Since the retinal thermal hazard TLVs® for pulsed sources assume a 7-mm, dark-adapted pupil, this exposure limit may be modified for daylight conditions.

For viewing durations from 0.00063 to 0.25 s, an acceptable exposure is present when Equation 4a is true.

With $\alpha < \alpha_{max} = 0.2 \cdot t^{0.5}$ rad,

$$L_R \, [W/(cm^2 \, sr)] \leq \frac{3.2}{\alpha \cdot t^{1/4}} \quad \text{OR}$$

$$DL_R \, [J/(cm^2 \, sr)] \leq \frac{3.2 \cdot t^{0.75}}{\alpha} \tag{4a}\blacklozenge$$

For viewing durations greater than 0.25 s, an acceptable exposure is present when Equation 4b is true. This is a rate-limited exposure and a dose limit does not apply.

With $\alpha < \alpha_{MAX} = 0.1$ rad,

$$L_R \, [W/(cm^2 \, sr)] \leq \frac{4.5}{\alpha} \tag{4b}\blacklozenge$$

Note: There may be special individual circumstances where the pupil remains dilated (tonic) and exposures extend beyond 0.25 s. Under these conditions, Equation 4c is the limiting exposure.

With $\alpha < \alpha_{MAX} = 0.1$ rad,

$$L_R \, [W/(cm^2 \, sr)] \leq \frac{3.2}{\alpha \cdot t^{1/4}} \tag{4c}\blacklozenge$$

Section 2. *To protect against retinal photochemical injury from chronic blue-light (305 < λ < 700 nm) exposure:* Determine the integrated effective spectral radiance of the light source (L_B) in W/(cm^2 sr) by integrating the spectral radiance (L_λ) in W/(cm^2 sr nm) weighted by the blue-light hazard function $B(\lambda)$ using Equation 5 or a light meter with a $B(\lambda)$ filter. $B(\lambda)$ is shown in Figure 3 and values are provided in Table 1.

$$L_B \, [\text{W/(cm}^2\,\text{sr)}] = \sum_{305}^{700} L_\lambda \cdot B(\lambda) \cdot \Delta\lambda \tag{5}$$

Some meters provide a total energy emitted in units of J/(cm^2 sr) over the sampling period, which is the time integral of L_B over the sampling period. L_B is the total energy divided by the sample period.

For viewing durations (t) less than 10^4 s (167 min or ~ 2.8 h) in a day, an acceptable exposure is present when:

$$L_B \leq \frac{100 \, [\text{J/(cm}^2\,\text{sr)}]}{t\,[\text{s}]} \tag{6a}$$

Alternatively, when L_B exceeds 0.01 W/(cm^2 sr), the maximum acceptable exposure duration t_{max} in seconds is:

$$t_{max} \, [\text{s}] = \frac{100 \, [\text{J/(cm}^2\,\text{sr)}]}{L_B} \tag{6b}$$

For viewing durations greater than 10^4 s (167 min) in a day, an acceptable exposure is present when:

$$L_B \, [\text{W/(cm}^2\,\text{sr)}] \leq 10^{-2} \tag{6c}$$

Note for blue light hazard: The L_B limits are greater than the maximum permissible exposure limits for 440 nm laser radiation (*see* Laser TLV®) because of the need for caution related to narrow-band spectral effects of lasers.

SPECIAL CASE FOR SMALL-SOURCE ANGLES: For a light source subtending an angle less than 0.011 radian, the above limits are relaxed. Determine the spectral irradiance (E_λ) weighted by the blue-light hazard function $B(\lambda)$:

$$E_B \, [\text{W/cm}^2] = \sum_{305}^{700} E_\lambda \cdot B(\lambda) \cdot \Delta\lambda \tag{7}$$

For durations less than 100 s (1 min, 40 s) in a day, an acceptable exposure is present when:

$$E_B \leq \frac{0.01 \, [\text{J/cm}^2]}{t\,[\text{s}]} \tag{8a}$$

Alternatively, for a source where the blue-light-weighted irradiance E_B exceeds 10^{-4} W/cm^2, the maximum acceptable exposure duration, t_{max}, in seconds is:

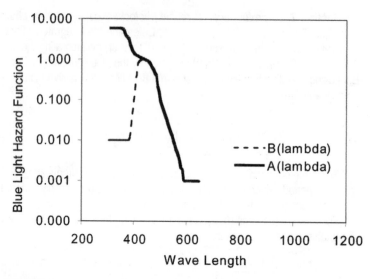

FIGURE 3. Blue light (retinal photochemical) hazard function for normal eyes [B(λ)] and the aphakic hazard function [A(λ)].

$$t_{max} [s] = \frac{0.01 \ [J/cm^2]}{E_B} \tag{8b}$$

For viewing durations greater than 10^2 s (1 min, 40 s) in a day, an acceptable exposure is present when:

$$E_B \leq 10^{-4} \ [W/cm^2] \tag{8c}$$

Special Case: To protect the worker having a lens removed (cataract surgery) against retinal photochemical injury from chronic exposure: Unless an ultraviolet (UV)-absorbing intra-ocular lens has been surgically inserted into the eye, the Aphakic Hazard Function, A(λ), should be used for L_B and E_B, as shown in Equations 9a and 9b.

$$L_B \ [W/(cm^2 \ sr)] = \sum_{305}^{700} L_\lambda \cdot A(\lambda) \cdot \Delta\lambda \tag{9a}$$

$$E_B \ [W/(cm^2 \ sr)] = \sum_{305}^{700} E_\lambda \cdot A(\lambda) \cdot \Delta\lambda \tag{9b}$$

The value for L_B is used in Equation 6 and the value for E_B is used in Equation 8.

Section 3. *To protect against thermal injury to the cornea and lens from infrared (IR) radiation:* To avoid thermal injury of the cornea and possible delayed effects on the lens of the eye (cataractogenesis), the total infrared irradiance in hot environments is calculated as

$$E_{IR-only} [W/cm^2] = \sum_{770}^{3000} E_\lambda \cdot \Delta\lambda \tag{10}$$

For exposure durations (t) less than 10^3 sec (17 min), an acceptable exposure is present when:

$$E_{IR-only} [W/cm^2] \leq \frac{1.8}{t^{0.75}} \tag{11a}$$

For exposure durations greater than 10^3 sec (17 min), an acceptable exposure is present when:

$$E_{IR-only} [W/cm^2] \leq 0.01 \tag{11b}$$

Section 4. *To protect against retinal thermal injury from near infrared (NIR) radiation:* For a near infrared source associated with an infrared heat lamp or any NIR source where a strong visual stimulus is absent (luminance less than 10^{-2} cd/cm²), the total effective radiance (L_{NIR}) as viewed by the eye is the spectral radiance (L_λ) weighted by the thermal hazard function, $R(\lambda)$.

$$L_{NIR} [W/(cm^2 sr)] = \sum_{770}^{1400} L_\lambda \cdot R(\lambda) \cdot \Delta\lambda \tag{12}$$

For exposures less than 810 s, an acceptable exposure is present when:

$$L_{NIR} [W/(cm^2 sr)] < \frac{3.2}{\alpha \cdot t^{1/4}} \tag{13a}\blacklozenge$$

This limit is based upon a 7-mm pupil diameter (since the aversion response may not exist due to an absence of light) and a detector field-of-view of 0.011 rad.

For exposures greater than 810 s in a day, an acceptable exposure is present when:

$$L_{NIR} [W/(cm^2 sr)] \leq \frac{0.6}{\alpha} \tag{13b}\blacklozenge$$

♦ Equations 3, 4, and 13 are empirical and are not, strictly speaking, dimensionally correct. To make the equations dimensionally correct, one would have to insert dimensional correction factors in the right-hand numerator in each equation.

TLV®–PA

148 — Electromagnetic Radiation and Fields

ULTRAVIOLET RADIATION

These TLVs® refer to incoherent ultraviolet (UV) radiation with wavelengths between 180 and 400 nm and represent conditions under which it is believed that nearly all healthy workers may be repeatedly exposed without acute adverse health effects such as erythema and photokeratitis. Some UV sources covered by this TLV® are welding and carbon arcs, gas and vapor discharges, fluorescent, incandescent and germicidal lamps, and solar radiation. Coherent UV radiation from lasers is covered in the TLV® for Lasers. The TLV® values apply to continuous sources for exposure durations equal to or greater than 0.1 second. The sources may subtend an angle less than 80 degrees at the detector and for those sources that subtend a greater angle need to be measured over an angle of 80 degrees.

The values do not apply to UV radiation exposure of photosensitive individuals or of individuals concomitantly exposed to photo-sensitizing agents (*see* Note 3). The values for the eye do not apply to aphakes (persons who have had the lens of the eye removed in cataract surgery), for which case, see Light and Near-Infrared Radiation TLVs®.

The TLVs® should be used as guides in the control of exposure to UV sources and should not be regarded as fine lines between safe and dangerous levels.

Threshold Limit Values

The TLVs® for occupational exposure to UV radiation incident upon the skin or the eye follow. The flow chart in Figure 1 provides a map of the UV TLV®.

Broadband UV Sources (180 to 400 nm) — Corneal Hazard

The first step in evaluating broadband UV sources is to determine the effective irradiance (E_{eff}). To determine E_{eff} for a broadband source weighted against the peak of the spectral effectiveness curve (270 nm), Equation 1 should be used.

$$E_{eff} = \sum_{180}^{400} E_\lambda \bullet S(\lambda) \bullet \Delta\lambda \qquad (1)$$

where: E_{eff} = effective irradiance relative to a monochromatic source at 270 nm [W/cm^2]

E_λ = spectral irradiance at a center wavelength [W/(cm^2 • nm)]

$S(\lambda)$ = relative spectral effectiveness at the center wavelength [unitless]

$\Delta\lambda$ = bandwidth around the center wavelength [nm]

TLV®–PA

More practically, E_{eff} can be measured directly with a UV radiometer having a built-in spectral response that mimics the relative spectral effectiveness values in Table 1 and Figure 2.

The daily exposure (t_{exp}) based on E_{eff} is dose limited to 0.003 J/cm². That is,

$$0.003[J/cm^2] \geq E_{eff}[W/cm^2] \bullet t_{exp}[s] \tag{2}$$

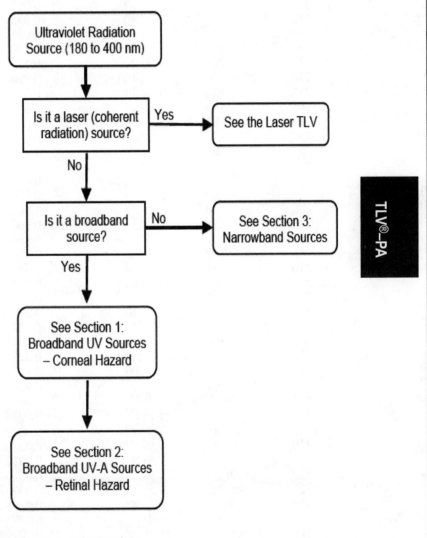

FIGURE 1. Flow chart for UV TLV®.

150 — Electromagnetic Radiation and Fields

TABLE 1. Ultraviolet Radiation TLV® and Relative Spectral Effectiveness

Wavelength[A] (nm)	TLV® (J/m^2)[B]	TLV® (mJ/cm^2)[B]	Relative Spectral Effectiveness, $S(\lambda)$
180	2500	250	0.012
190	1600	160	0.019
200	1000	100	0.030
205	590	29	0.051
210	400	40	0.075
215	320	32	0.095
220	250	25	0.120
225	200	20	0.150
230	160	16	0.190
235	130	13	0.240
240	100	10	0.300
245	83	8.3	0.360
250	70	7.0	0.430
254[C]	60	6.0	0.500
255	58	5.8	0.520
260	46	4.6	0.650
265	37	3.7	0.810
270	30	3.0	1.00
275	31	3.1	0.960
280[C]	34	3.4	0.880
285	39	3.9	0.770
290	47	4.7	0.640
295	56	5.6	0.540
297[C]	65	6.5	0.460
300	100	10	0.300
303[C]	250	25	0.120
305	500	50	0.060
308	1200	120	0.026
310	2000	200	0.015
313[C]	5000	500	0.006
315	1.0×10^4	1.0×10^3	0.003
316	1.3×10^4	1.3×10^3	0.0024
317	1.5×10^4	1.5×10^3	0.0020
318	1.9×10^4	1.9×10^3	0.0016
319	2.5×10^4	2.5×10^3	0.0012
320	2.9×10^4	2.9×10^3	0.0010
322	4.5×10^4	4.5×10^3	0.00067
323	5.6×10^4	5.6×10^3	0.00054
325	6.0×10^4	6.0×10^3	0.00050
328	6.8×10^4	6.8×10^3	0.00044
330	7.3×10^4	7.3×10^3	0.00041
333	8.1×10^4	8.1×10^3	0.00037
335	8.8×10^4	8.8×10^3	0.00034
340	1.1×10^5	1.1×10^4	0.00028
345	1.3×10^5	1.3×10^4	0.00024
350	1.5×10^5	1.5×10^4	0.00020

TABLE 1 (con't.). Ultraviolet Radiation TLV® and Relative Spectral Effectiveness

Wavelength[A] (nm)	TLV® (J/m²)[B]	TLV® (mJ/cm²)[B]	Relative Spectral Effectiveness, S(λ)
355	1.9×10^5	1.9×10^4	0.00016
360	2.3×10^5	2.3×10^4	0.00013
365[C]	2.7×10^5	2.7×10^4	0.00011
370	3.2×10^5	3.2×10^4	0.000093
375	3.9×10^5	3.9×10^4	0.000077
380	4.7×10^5	4.7×10^4	0.000064
385	5.7×10^5	5.7×10^4	0.000053
390	6.8×10^5	6.8×10^4	0.000044
395	8.3×10^5	8.3×10^4	0.000036
400	1.0×10^6	1.0×10^5	0.000030

[A] Wavelengths chosen are representative; other values should be interpolated at intermediate wavelengths.
[B] 1 mJ/cm² = 10 J/m²
[C] Emission lines of a mercury discharge spectrum.

Table 2 gives TLV® values for the effective irradiance for different daily exposure durations. In general, the maximum exposure time (t_{max}) [s] for a broadband UV source can be determined from Equation 3.

$$t_{max}[s] = \frac{0.003\,[J/cm^2]}{E_{eff}[W/cm^2]} \tag{3}$$

TLV®–PA

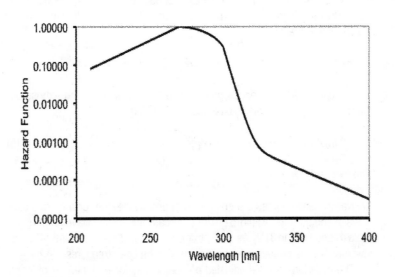

FIGURE 2. Hazard function (relative spectral effectiveness, S(λ)) for UV.

TABLE 2. Exposure Durations for Given Actinic UV Radiation Effective Irradiances

Duration of Exposure Per Day	Effective Irradiance, E_{eff} (mW/cm²)
8 hours	0.0001
4 hours	0.0002
2 hours	0.0004
1 hour	0.0008
30 minutes	0.0017
15 minutes	0.0033
10 minutes	0.005
5 minutes	0.01
1 minute	0.05
30 seconds	0.1
10 seconds	0.3
1 second	3
0.5 second	6
0.1 second	30

TLV®–PA

Broadband UV-A Sources (315 to 400 nm) — Lens and Retinal Hazard

The irradiance, E_{UV-A} [mW/cm²], can be measured with an unfiltered meter that is sensitive to UV-A radiation. For daily exposure periods (t_{exp}) less than 1000 s (17 min), the exposure is dose limited to 1000 mJ/cm² as described in Equation 4.

$$1000 \, [mJ/cm^2] \geq E_{UV-A} \, [mW/cm^2] \bullet t_{exp}[s] \tag{4}$$

For daily exposure periods greater than 1000 s (17 min), the exposure is rate limited to 1.0 mW/cm² as described in Equation 5.

$$1.0 \, [mW/cm^2] \geq E_{UV-A} \, [mW/cm^2] \tag{5}$$

Narrowband Sources

Narrowband sources are comprised of one wavelength or a narrow band of wavelengths (e.g., within 5–10 nm). Locate the center wavelength (λ) in Table 1, and find the TLV_λ as an 8-hour dose limit in J/m² or mJ/cm². The narrowband TLV® is protective for both corneal and retinal exposures.

The dose limit may be adjusted proportionately for work periods of longer or shorter duration. The TLV® dose limit of a daily exposure period (t_{exp}) for a narrowband source can be expressed as Equation 6 using the Spectral Sensitivity (S_λ) from Table 1 and unfiltered irradiance (E_λ) [W/m² or mW/cm²].

Ultraviolet Radiation — 153

$$30 \; [J/m^2] \geq E_\lambda \; [W/m^2] \bullet S(\lambda) \bullet t_{exp}[s] \qquad\qquad (6a)$$

$$3.0 \; [mJ/cm^2] \geq E_\lambda \; [mW/cm^2] \bullet S(\lambda) \bullet t_{exp}[s] \qquad (6b)$$

The maximum exposure time (t_{max}) [s] for a narrowband source can be determined from Equation 7 using the TLV_λ and the unfiltered irradiance (E_λ) [W/m² or mW/cm²]. (Note: The energy and surface area units must match.)

$$t_{max}[s] = \frac{TLV_\lambda}{E_\lambda} \qquad\qquad\qquad (7)$$

Notes:

1. The probability of developing skin cancer depends on a variety of factors such as skin pigmentation, a history of blistering sunburns, and the accumulated UV dose. It also depends on genetic susceptibility and factors such as skin and eye color. Individuals who have a familial history of melanoma, or numerous nevi over their body, for example, may be at higher risk of developing malignant melanoma. The risks for developing melanoma and non-melanoma cancers may differ from each other and depend on the UV exposure history.
2. Outdoor workers in latitudes within 40 degrees of the equator can be exposed outdoors to levels above the TLVs® in as little as five minutes around noontime during the summer.
3. Exposure to ultraviolet radiation concurrently with topical or systemic exposure to a variety of chemicals, including some prescription drugs, can result in skin erythema at sub-TLV® exposures. Hypersensitivity should be suspected if workers present skin reactions when exposed to sub-TLV® doses or when exposed to levels (generally UV-A) that did not cause a noticeable erythema in the same individual in the past. Among the hundreds of agents that can cause hypersensitivity to UV radiation are certain plants and chemicals such as some antibiotics (e.g., tetracycline and sulphathiazole), some antidepressants (e.g., imipramine and sinequan), as well as some diuretics, cosmetics, antipsychotic drugs, coal tar distillates, some dyes, or lime oil.
4. Ozone is produced in air by sources emitting UV radiation at wavelengths below 250 nm. Refer to the latest version of the Chemical Substances TLV® for ozone.

TLV®–PA

154 — Electromagnetic Radiation and Fields

* LASERS

These TLVs® are for exposure to laser radiation under conditions to which it is believed nearly all workers may be repeatedly exposed without adverse health effects. The TLVs® should be used as guides in the control of exposures and should not be re-garded as fine lines between safe and dangerous levels. They are based on the best available inform-ation from experimental studies. In practice, hazards to the eye and skin can be controlled by application of control measures appropriate to the classification of the laser.

Classification of Lasers

Most lasers have a label affixed to them by the manufacturer that describes their hazard class. Normally, it is not necessary to determine laser irradiances or radiant exposures for comparison with the TLVs®. The potential for hazardous exposures can be minimized by the application of control measures that are appropriate to the hazard class of the laser. Control measures are applicable to all classes of lasers except for Class 1. Such meas-ures, and other laser safety information, may be found in the ACGIH® publication, *A Guide for Control of Laser Hazards*, and the ANSI Z136 series published by the Laser Institute of America.

Limiting Apertures

For comparison with the TLVs® in this section, laser beam irradiance or radiant exposure is aver-aged over the limiting aperture appropriate to the spectral region and exposure duration. If the laser beam diameter is less than that of the limiting aperture, the effective laser beam irradiance or radiant exposure may be calculated by dividing the laser beam power or energy by the area of the limiting aperture. Limiting apertures are listed in Table 1.

Source Size and Correction Factor C_E

The following considerations apply only at wavelengths in the retinal haz-ard region, 400–1400 nanometers (nm). Normally, a laser is a small source, which approximates a "point" source and subtends an angle less than α_{min}, which is 1.5 mrad for all values of t. However, any source which subtends an angle, α, greater than α_{min}, and is measured from the viewer's eye, is treated as an "intermediate source" ($\alpha_{min} < \alpha \leq \alpha_{max}$) or a "large, extended source" ($\alpha > \alpha_{max}$). For exposure duration "t", the angle α_{max} is defined as:

α_{max} = 5 mrad for t $\leq$ to 0.625 ms

α_{max} = 200 • $t^{0.5}$ mrad for 0.625 ms < t ⟨ 0.25 s

α_{max} = 100 mrad for t $\geq$ 0.25 s, and

α_{min} = 1.5 mrad

Figure 1 illustrates the time dependence of α_{max}. If the source is oblong, alpha is determined from the arithmetic average of the longest and shortest viewable dimensions.

For intermediate and large sources, the TLVs® in Table 2 are modified by a correction factor C_E, as detailed in the Notes for Table 2.

TABLE 1. Limiting Apertures Applicable to Laser TLVs®

Spectral Region	Duration	Eye	Skin
180 nm to 400 nm	1 ns to 0.25 s	1 mm	3.5 mm
180 nm to 400 nm	0.25 s to 30 ks	3.5 mm	3.5 mm
400 nm to 1400 nm	10^{-4} ns to 0.25 s	7 mm	3.5 mm
400 nm to 1400 nm	0.25 s to 30 ks	7 mm	3.5 mm
1400 nm to 0.1 mm	10^{-5} ns to 0.25 s	1 mm	3.5 mm
1400 nm to 0.1 mm	0.25 s to 30 ks	3.5 mm	3.5 mm
0.1 mm to 1.0 mm	10^{-5} ns to 30 ks	11 mm	11 mm

Correction Factors A, B, C (C_A, C_B, C_C)

The TLVs® for ocular exposures in Table 2 are to be used as given for all wavelength ranges. The TLVs® for wavelengths between 700 and 1049 nm are to be increased by the factor C_A (to account for reduced absorption of melanin) as given in Figure 2. For certain exposure times at wavelengths between 400 and 600 nm, a correction factor C_B (to account for reduced photochemical sensitivity for retinal injury) is applied. The correction factor C_C is applied from 1150 to 1400 nm to account for pre-retinal absorption of the ocular media.

The TLVs® for skin exposure are given in Table 4. The TLVs® are to be increased by a factor C_A, as shown in Figure 2, for wavelengths between 700 nm and 1400 nm. To aid in the determination for exposure durations requiring calculations of fractional powers, Figures 3a, 3b, 4a, and 4b may be used.

Repetitively Pulsed Exposures

Scanned, continuous-wave (CW) lasers or repe-titively pulsed lasers can both produce repetitively pulsed exposure conditions. The TLV® for intrabeam viewing, which is applicable to wavelengths be-tween 400 and 1400 nm and a single-pulse exposure (of exposure duration t > t_{min}), is modified in this instance by a correction factor determined by the number of pulses in the exposure. First, calculate the number of pulses (n) in an expected exposure situation; this is the pulse repetition frequency (PRF in Hz) multiplied by the duration of the exposure. Normally, realistic exposures may range from 0.25 second (s) for a bright visible source to 10 s for an infrared source. The corrected TLV® on a per-pulse basis is:

$$\text{TLV} = (CP)(\text{TLV for Single-pulse}) \tag{1}$$

where C_P = 1.0 for t < t_{min} (i.e., 5 μs for 400–1050 nm and 13 μs for 1050–1400 nm) and for t > t_{min} C_P = 1.0 for α < 5.0 milliradians, which applies to all cases of intrabeam viewing. However, for larger, intermediate extended sources where α > 5 mrad, C_P = $n^{-0.25}$ for the following numbers of pulses: for n < 40 pulses. Otherwise, C_P = 0.4 whenever α < α_{max}. For n < 625, C_P = 0.2 and for greater n, C_P = 0.2 only for α > 0.1 radian. This approach applies only to thermal injury conditions, i.e., all exposures at wavelengths > 700 nm and for many exposures at shorter wavelengths. For wavelengths ≤ 700 nm, the corrected TLV® from Equation 1 applies if the average irradiance does not exceed the TLV® for con-

156 — Electromagnetic Radiation and Fields

tinuous exposure. The average irradiance (i.e., the total accumulated exposure for *nt* s) shall not exceed the radiant exposure given in Table 2 for exposure durations of 10 s to T_1. Some thermal additivity can occur for larger image sizes, and for pulse-repetition frequencies (PRFs) between 150 Hz and 250 Hz where α > 5 mrad and the pulse duration is between 1 ms and 100 ms, the single-pulse TLV® applied should be reduced by a further correction factor, C_P = 0.5. It is recommended that the user of the TLVs® for laser radiation consult *A Guide for Control of Laser Hazards*, 4th Edition, 1990, published by ACGIH®, for additional information.

Lasers — 157

TABLE 2. TLVs® for Direct Ocular Exposures (Intrabeam "Point Source" Viewing) from a Laser Beam

Spectral Region	Wavelength	Exposure, (t) Seconds	TLV®
UVC	180 nm to 280 nm*	10^{-9} to 3×10^4	3 mJ/cm²
UVB	280 nm to 302 nm	"	3 mJ/cm²
	303 nm	"	4 mJ/cm²
	304 nm	"	6 mJ/cm²
	305 nm	"	10 mJ/cm²
	306 nm	"	16 mJ/cm²
	307 nm	"	25 mJ/cm²
	308 nm	"	40 mJ/cm²
	309 nm	"	63 mJ/cm²
	310 nm	"	100 mJ/cm²
	311 nm	"	160 mJ/cm²
	312 nm	"	250 mJ/cm²
	313 nm	"	400 mJ/cm²
	314 nm	"	630 mJ/cm²
UVA	315 nm to 400 nm	10^{-9} to 10	$0.56\ t^{1/4}$ J/cm²
	315 nm to 400 nm	10 to 10^3	1.0 J/cm²
	315 nm to 400 nm	10^3 to 3×10^4	1.0 mW/cm²

Not to exceed (NTE) $0.56\ t^{1/4}$ J/cm² for $t \leq 10$ s

TLV®–PA

158 — Electromagnetic Radiation and Fields

TABLE 2 (continued). TLVs® for Direct Ocular Exposures (Intrabeam "Point Source" Viewing) from a Laser Beam

Spectral Region	Wavelength	Exposure, (t) Seconds	TLV®
Light	400 to 700 nm	10^{-13} to 10^{-11}	1×10^{-7} J/cm^2
	400 to 700 nm	10^{-11} to 5×10^{-6}	2×10^{-7} J/cm^2
	400 to 700 nm	5×10^{-6} to 10	$1.8\ t^{3/4} \times 10^{-3}$ mJ/cm^2
	400 to 450 nm	10 to 100	10 mJ/cm^2
	450 to 500 nm	10 to T_1	1 mW/cm^2
	450 to 500 nm	T_1 to 100	10 C$_B$ mJ/cm^2
	400 to 500 nm	100 to 3×10^4	0.1 C$_B$ mW/cm^2
	500 to 700 nm	10 to 3×10^4	1.0 mW/cm^2
IRA	700 to 1050 nm	10^{-13} to 10^{-11}	1.0×10^{-7} J/cm^2
	700 to 1050 nm	10^{-11} to 5×10^{-6}	$2.0\ C_A \times 10^{-7}$ J/cm^2
	700 to 1050 nm	5×10^{-6} to 10	$1.8\ C_A \times t^{0.75} \times 10^{-3}$ J/cm^2
	700 to 1050 nm	10 to 3×10^4	$C_A \times 10^{-3}$ W/cm^2
	1050 to 1400 nm	10^{-13} to 10^{-11}	$C_C \times 10^{-7}$ J/cm^2
	1050 to 1400 nm	10^{-11} to 1.3×10^{-5}	$2\ C_C \times 10^{-6}$ J/cm^2
	1050 to 1400 nm	1.3×10^{-5} to 10	$9.0\ C_C\ t^{0.75} \times 10^{-3}$ J/cm^2
	1050 to 1400 nm	10 to 3×10^4	$5.0\ C_C \times 10^{-3}$ W/cm^2

TLV®–PA

TABLE 2 (continued). TLVs® for Direct Ocular Exposures (Intrabeam "Point Source" Viewing) from a Laser Beam

Spectral Region	Wavelength	Exposure, (t) Seconds	TLV®
IRB & IRC	1.401 to 1.5 μm	10^{-13} to 10^{-3}	0.3 J/cm²
	1.401 to 1.5 μm	10^{-3} to 4.0	$0.56\ t^{0.25} + 0.2$ J/cm²
	1.401 to 1.5 μm	4.0 to 10	1.0 J/cm²
	1.501 to 1.8 μm	10^{-13} to 10	1.0 J/cm²
	1.801 to 2.6 μm	10^{-13} to 10^{-3}	0.1 J/cm²
	1.801 to 2.6 μm	10^{-3} to 10	$0.56\ t^{1/4}$ J/cm²
	2.601 to 10^3 μm	10^{-13} to 10^{-7}	10 mJ/cm²
	2.601 to 10^3 μm	10^{-7} to 10	$0.56\ t^{1/4}$ J/cm²
	1.400 to 10^3 μm	10 to 3×10^4	100 mW/cm²

*Ozone (O₃) is produced in air by sources emitting ultraviolet (UV) radiation at wavelengths below 250 nm. Refer to Chemical Substances TLV® for ozone.

TLV®–PA

160 — Electromagnetic Radiation and Fields

TLV®–PA

Notes for Table 2

C_A = Fig. 2; C_B = 1 for λ = 400 to ≤ 450 nm; $C_B = 10^{0.02(\lambda - 450)}$ for λ = 450 to 600 nm; C_C = 1.0 for wavelengths less than or equal to 1150 nm; $C_C = 10^{[0.018(\lambda - 1150)]}$ for wavelengths greater than 1150 nm and less than 1200 nm; C_C = 8.0 + $10^{[0.04(\lambda - 1150)]}$ from 1250 to 1400 nm.

T_1 = 10 s for λ = 400 to 450 nm; $T_1 = 10 \times 10^{[0.02(\lambda - 550)]}$ for λ = 450 to 500 nm; and T_1 = 10 s for λ = 500 to 700.

For intermediate or large sources (e.g., laser diode arrays) at wavelengths between 400 nm and 1400 nm, the intrabeam viewing TLVs® can be increased by correction factor C_E (use Table 3) provided that the angular subtense α of the source (measured at the viewer's eye) is greater than α_{min}. C_E depends on α as follows:

Angular Subtense	Source Size Designation	Correction Factor C_E
$\alpha \leq \alpha_{min}$	Small	C_E = 1
$\alpha_{min} < \alpha \leq \alpha_{max}$	Intermediate	$C_E = \alpha/\alpha_{min}$
$\alpha > \alpha_{max}$	Large	$C_E = \alpha_{max}/\alpha_{min}$ = 3.33 for t ≤ 0.625 ms; $C_E = 133.33\ t^{1/2}$ for 0.625 ms < t < 0.25 s C_E = 66.7 for t ≥ 0.25 s

The angle referred to as α_{max} corresponds to the point where the TLVs® may be expressed as a constant radiance and the last equation can be rewritten in terms of radiance L.

$L_{TLV} = (3.81 \times 10^5) \times (TLV_{pt\ source})$ J/(cm² sr) for t < 0.625 μs for 400 < λ < 700 nm

$L_{TLV} = 7.6\ t^{1/4}$ J/(cm² sr) for 0.625 ms < t < 0.25 s for 400 < λ < 700 nm

L_{TLV} = 4.8 W/(cm² sr) for t > 100 s for 400 < λ < 700 nm

Figure 5 illustrates these TLVs® for large sources expressed in terms of radiance. The measurement aperture should be placed at a distance of 100 mm or greater from the source. For large area irradiation, the reduced TLV® for skin exposure applies as noted in the footnote to "IRB & C," Table 4.

TABLE 3. TLVs® for Extended Source Laser Viewing Conditions

Spectral Region	Wavelength	Exposure, (t) Seconds	TLV®
Light	400 to 700 nm	10^{-13} to 10^{-11}	$C_E \times 10^{-7}$ J/cm^2
	400 to 700 nm	10^{-11} to 5 $\times$ 10^{-6}	2 $C_E \times 10^{-7}$ J/cm^2
	400 to 700 nm	5 $\times$ 10^{-6} to 10	1.8 $C_E\, t^{-0.75} \times 10^{-3}$ J/cm^2
	400 to 700 nm	18 $\times$ 10^{-6} to 0.7	1.8 $C_E\, t^{0.75} \times 10^{-3}$ J/cm^2
		Dual Limits for 400 to 600 nm visible laser exposure for t > 0.7 s	
	Photochemical		
	For $\alpha \leq 11$ mrad, the MPE is expressed as irradiance and radiant exposure*		
	400 to 600 nm	0.7 to 100	$C_B \times 10^{-2}$ J/cm^2
	400 to 600 nm	100 to 3 $\times$ 10^4	$C_B \times 10^{-4}$ W/cm^2
	For $\alpha > 11$ mrad, the MPE is expressed as radiance and integrated radiance*		
	400 to 600 nm	0.7 to 1 $\times$ 10^4	100 C_B J/(cm^2 sr)
	400 to 600 nm	1 $\times$ 10^4 to 3 $\times$ 10^4	$C_B \times 10^{-2}$ W/(cm^2 sr)
			and
	Thermal		
	400 to 700 nm	0.7 to T$_2$	1.8 $C_E\, t^{0.75} \times 10^{-3}$ J/cm^2
	400 to 700 nm	T$_2$ to 3 $\times$ 10^4	1.8 $C_E\, T_2^{-0.25} \times 10^{-3}$ W/cm^2

TLV®–PA

162 — Electromagnetic Radiation and Fields

TLV®–PA

TABLE 3 (continued). TLVs® for Extended Source Laser Viewing Conditions

Spectral Region	Wavelength	Exposure, (t) Seconds	TLV®
IRA	700 to 1050 nm	10^{-13} to 10^{-11}	$C_E \times 10^{-7}$ J/cm^2
	700 to 1050 nm	10^{-11} to 5×10^{-6}	$5 \, C_A \, C_E \times 10^{-7}$ J/cm^2
	700 to 1050 nm	5×10^{-6} to T_2	$1.8 \, C_A \, C_E \, t^{0.75} \times 10^{-3}$ J/cm^2
	700 to 1050 nm	T_2 to 3×10^4	$1.8 \, C_A \, C_E \, T_2^{-0.25} \times 10^{-3}$ W/cm^2
	1050 to 1400 nm	10^{-13} to 10^{-11}	$C_C \, C_E \times 10^{-7}$ J/cm^2
	1050 to 1400 nm	10^{-11} to 1.3×10^{-5}	$2 \, C_C \, C_E \times 10^{-6}$ J/cm^2
	1050 to 1400 nm	50×10^{-6} to T_2	$9.0 \, C_C \, C_E \, T^{0.75} \times 10^{-3}$ J/cm^2
	1050 to 1400 nm	T_2 to 3×10^4	$9.0 \, C_C \, C_E \, T_2^{-0.25} \times 10^{-3}$ W/cm^2

* For sources subtending an angle greater than 11 mrad, the limit may also be expressed as an integrated radiance.

$L_p = 100 \, C_B$ J/(cm^2 sr) for 0.7 s $\leq$ t $< 10^4$ s and $L_e = C_B \times 10^{-2}$ W/(cm^2 sr) for t $\geq 10^4$ s as measured through a limiting cone angle γ.

TABLE 3 (continued). TLVs® for Extended Source Laser Viewing Conditions

Spectral Region	Wavelength	Exposure, (t) Seconds	TLV®

These correspond to values of J/cm^2 for $10\ s \leq t < 100\ s$ and W/cm^2 for $t \geq 100\ s$ as measured through a limiting cone angle γ.

γ = 11 mrad for $0.7\ s \leq t < 100\ s$

γ = $1.1 \times t^{0.5}$ mrad for $100\ s \leq t < 10^4\ s$

γ = 110 mrad for $10^4\ s \leq t < 3 \times 10^4\ s$

$T_2 = 10 \times 10^{(\alpha - 1.5)/98.5}$ for α expressed in mrad for λ = 400 to 1400 nm.

For exposure duration "t", the angle α_{max} is defined as:

α_{max} = 5 mrad for $t \leq$ to 0.625 ms

α_{max} = $200\ t^{0.5}$ mrad for $0.625\ ms < t < 0.25\ s$, and

α_{max} = 100 mrad for $t \geq 0.25\ s$

α_{min} = 1.5 mrad

TLV®–PA

164 — Electromagnetic Radiation and Fields

TLV®–PA

Notes for Tables 2 and 3

"NTE": To protect the cornea and lens: Change the 1 J/cm² to this set of dual limits for wavelengths between 400 nm and 1.5 μm. The lower of the TLVs® from Table 2 or Table 3 and the following apply:

Wavelength	NTE (Second of Dual Limits)†
10^{-9} to 10^{-7}	$6\,C_A \times 10^{-2}$ J/cm²
10^{-7} to 10	$3.3\,C_A\,t^{1/4}$ J/cm²
10 to 3×10^4	$0.6\,C_A$ W/cm²
10^{-9} to 10^{-3}	$10^{0.01(1400-\lambda)}$ J/cm²
10^{-3} to 4.0	$0.3 \times 10^{0.01(1400-\lambda)} + 0.56\,t^{0.25} - 0.1$ J/cm²
4.0 to 10	$0.3 \times 10^{0.01(1400-\lambda)} + 0.7$ J/cm²
10 to 3×10^4	$0.3 \times 10^{0.01(1400-\lambda)} + 0.1\,t - 0.3$ W/cm²

Wavelength column (first of table):
400 to 1200 nm
400 to 1200 nm
400 to 1200 nm
1200 to 1400 nm
1200 to 1400 nm
1200 to 1400 nm
1200 to 1500 nm

†These dual limits will rarely apply except for exposures of very large angular subtense α – at least for wavelengths less than 1200 nm.

Lasers — 165

TABLE 4. TLVs® for Skin Exposure from a Laser Beam

Spectral Region	Wavelength	Exposure, (t) Seconds	TLV®
UVA[A]	180 nm to 400 nm	10^{-9} to 10^4	Same as Table 2
Light & IRA	400 nm to 1400 nm	10^{-9} to 10^{-7}	$2\,C_A \times 10^{-2}$ J/cm^2
	" "	10^{-7} to 10	$1.1\,C_A\ ^4\sqrt{t}$ J/cm^2
	" "	10 to 3×10^4	$0.2\,C_A$ W/cm^2
IRB & C[B]	1.401 to 10^3 μm	10^{-14} to 3×10^4	Same as Table 2

[A] Ozone (O$_3$) is produced in air by sources emitting ultraviolet (UV) radiation at wavelengths below 250 nm. Refer to Chemical Substances TLV® for ozone.

$C_A = 1.0$ for $\lambda = 400 - 700$ nm; *see* Figure 2 for $\lambda = 700$ to 1400 nm

[B] At wavelengths greater than 1400 nm, for beam cross-sectional areas exceeding 100 cm^2, the TLV® for exposure durations exceeding 10 seconds is:

$$TLV = (10{,}000/A_s)\ \text{mW/cm}^2$$

where A_s is the irradiated skin area for 100 to 1000 cm^2, and the TLV® is 10 mW/cm^2 for irradiated skin areas exceeding 1000 cm^2 and is 100 mW/cm^2 for irradiated skin areas less than 100 cm^2.

TLV®–PA

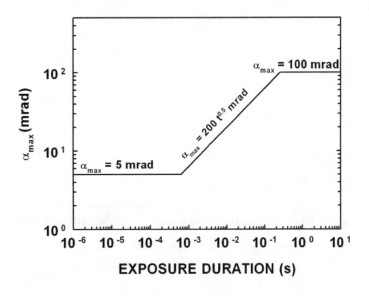

FIGURE 1. Variation of α_{max} with exposure duration.

166 — Electromagnetic Radiation and Fields

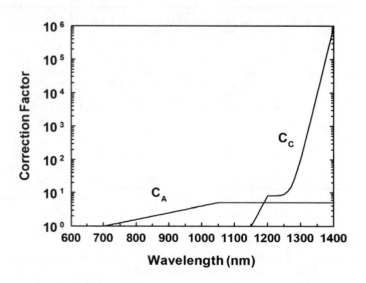

FIGURE 2. TLV® correction factors for λ = 700–1400 nm*
*For λ = 700–1049 nm, C_A = $10^{[0.002(\lambda - 700)]}$; for λ = 1050–1400 nm, C_A = 5; for $\lambda \leq$ 1150 nm, C_C = 1; for λ = 1150–1200 nm, C_C = $10^{[0.018(\lambda - 1150)]}$; and for λ = 1200–1399 nm, C_C = 8 + $10^{[0.04(\lambda - 1250)]}$.

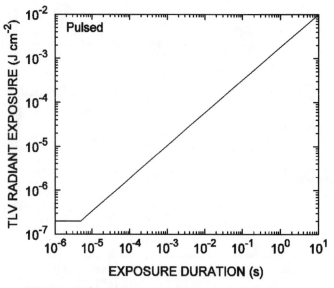

FIGURE 3a. TLV® for intrabeam viewing of laser beam (400–700 nm).

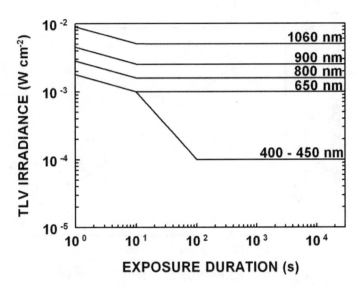

FIGURE 3b. TLV® for intrabeam (direct) viewing of CW laser beam (400–1400 nm).

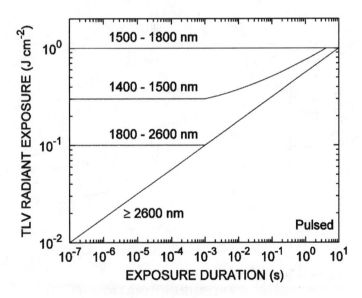

FIGURE 4a. TLV® for laser exposure of skin and eyes for far-infrared radiation (wavelengths greater than 1400 nm).

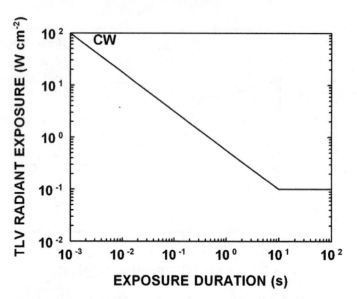

FIGURE 4b. TLV® for CW laser exposure of skin and eyes for far-infrared radiation (wavelengths greater than 1.4 µm).

TLV®–PA

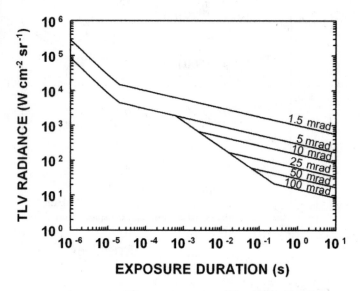

FIGURE 5. TLVs® in terms of radiance for exposures to extended-source lasers in the wavelength range of 400 to 700 nm.

* IONIZING RADIATION

ACGIH® has adopted as a TLV® for occupational exposure to ionizing radiation the guidelines recommended by the International Commission on Radiation Protection (ICRP, 2007) and the National Council on Radiation Protection and Measurements (NCRP, 1993). Ionizing radiation includes particulate radiation (α particles and β particles emitted from radioactive materials, and neutrons, protons and heavier charged particles produced in nuclear reactors and accelerators) and electromagnetic radiation (gamma rays emitted from radioactive materials and X-rays from electron accelerators and X-ray machines) with energy > 12.4 electron volts (eV) corresponding to wavelengths less than approximately 100 nanometers (nm).

The guiding principles of ionizing radiation protection are:

- *Justification:* No practice involving exposure to ionizing radiation should be adopted unless it produces sufficient benefit to an exposed individual or society to offset the detriment it causes.

- *Optimization:* All radiation exposures must be kept as low as reasonably achievable (ALARA), economic and social factors being taken into account.

- *Limitation:* The radiation dose from all occupationally relevant sources should not produce a level of risk of greater than about 10-3 per year of inducing fatal cancer during the lifetime of the exposed individual.*

The TLV® guidelines are the dose limits shown in Table 1. Application of ALARA principles are recommended for all workers to keep radiation exposures as far below the guidelines as practicable.

TLV®–PA

* This level of risk is based on the ICRP (2007) and NCRP (1993) estimate of a 5% lifetime risk of fatal cancer for an exposure of one Sv and an annual occupational exposure of 20 mSv averaged over five years.

TABLE 1. Guidelines for Exposure to Ionizing Radiation[A]

Type of Exposure	Guideline for Annual Exposure
Effective Dose:	
a) in any single year	50 mSv (millisievert)[B]
b) averaged over 5 years	20 mSv per year
Annual Equivalent Dose[C] to:	
a) lens of the eye	150 mSv
b) skin, hands and feet	500 mSv
Cumulative Effective Dose:	10 mSv × age in years
Embryo/Fetus Monthly Equivalent Dose[C]:	0.5 mSv
Radon and Radon Daughters:	4 Working Level Months (WLM)[D]

170 — Electromagnetic Radiation and Fields

A Doses are the effective doses from combined external and internal sources (excluding background radiation from radon, terrestrial, cosmic and internal body sources). The effective dose is that defined by ICRP and NCRP, where the effective dose is $H_T = \sum w_T \sum w_R D_{T,R}$, in which $D_{T,R}$ is the average absorbed dose in each tissue or organ, w_T is the tissue weighting factor representing the proportionate detriment (stochastic cancer risk), and w_R is the radiation weighting factor for the types of radiation(s) impinging on the body or, in the case of internal emitters, the radiation emitted by the source(s). The values of w_R and w_T to be used are those recommended by ICRP (2007).

B 10 mSv = 1 rem.

C The equivalent dose is the sum of external and internal absorbed doses multiplied by the appropriate radiation weighting factors.

D One WLM = 3.5×10^3 Jh/m³. The upper value for the individual worker annual dose is 10 mSv, which corresponds to an upper activity reference level of 1500 becquerels per m³ for radon and radon progeny in equilibrium, where a becquerel is a reciprocal second (ICRP, 1993, 2007).

References

International Commission on Radiological Protection (ICRP): ICRP Publication 103, The 2007 Recommendations of the International Commission on Radiological Protection. Ann ICRP Vol 37(2–4) (2007).

National Council on Radiation Protection and Measurements (NCRP): Limitations of Exposure to Ionizing Radiation, NCRP Report No 116. NCRP, Bethesda, MD (1993).

TLV®–PA

ERGONOMICS

Ergonomics is the term applied to the field that studies and designs the human–machine interface to prevent illness and injury and to improve work performance. It attempts to ensure that jobs and work tasks are designed to be compatible with the capabilities of the workers. ACGIH® recognizes that some physical agents play an important role in ergonomics. Force and acceleration are addressed, in part, in the Hand–Arm Vibration (HAV) and Whole-Body Vibration (WBV) TLVs®. Thermal factors are addressed, in part, in the TLVs® for Thermal Stress. Force is also an important causal agent in injuries from lifting. Other important ergonomic considerations include work duration, repetition, contact stresses, postures, and psychosocial issues.

STATEMENT ON WORK-RELATED MUSCULOSKELETAL DISORDERS

ACGIH® recognizes work-related musculoskeletal disorders (MSDs) as an important occupational health problem that can be managed using an ergonomics health and safety program. The term musculoskeletal disorders refers to chronic muscle, tendon, and nerve disorders caused by repetitive exertions, rapid motions, high forces, contact stresses, extreme postures, vibration, and/or low temperatures. Other commonly used terms for work-related musculoskeletal disorders include cumulative trauma disorders (CTDs), repetitive motion illnesses (RMIs), and repetitive strain injuries (RSIs). Some of these disorders fit established diagnostic criteria such as carpal tunnel syndrome or tendinitis. Other musculoskeletal disorders may be manifested by nonspecific pain. Some transient discomfort is a normal consequence of work and is unavoidable, but discomfort that persists from day to day or interferes with activities of work or daily living should not be considered an acceptable outcome of work.

Control Strategies

The incidence and severity of MSDs are best controlled by an integrated ergonomics program. Major program elements include:

- Recognition of the problem,
- Evaluation of suspected jobs for possible risk factors,
- Identification and evaluation of causative factors,
- Involvement of workers as fully informed active participants, and
- Appropriate health care for workers who have developed musculoskeletal disorders.

General programmatic controls should be implemented when risk of MSDs is recognized. These include:

- Education of workers, supervisors, engineers, and managers;
- Early reporting of symptoms by workers; and
- Ongoing surveillance and evaluation of injury, health and medical data.

TLV®–PA

172 — Ergonomics

Job-specific controls are directed to individual jobs associated with MSDs. These include engineering controls and administrative controls. Personal protection may be appropriate under some limited circumstances.

Among engineering controls to eliminate or reduce risk factors from the job, the following may be considered:

- Using work methods engineering, e.g., time study, motion analysis, to eliminate unnecessary motions and exertions.
- Using mechanical assists to eliminate or reduce exertions required to hold tools and work objects.
- Selecting or designing tools that reduce force requirements, reduce holding time, and improve postures.
- Providing user-adjustable workstations that reduce reaching and improve postures.
- Implementing quality control and maintenance programs that reduce unnecessary forces and exertions, especially associated with nonvalue-added work.

Administrative controls reduce risk through reduction of exposure time and sharing the exposure among a larger group of workers. Examples include:

- Implementing work standards that permit workers to pause or stretch as necessary but at least once per hour.
- Re-allocating work assignments (e.g., using worker rotation or work enlargement) so that a worker does not spend an entire work shift performing high-demand tasks.

Due to the complex nature of musculoskeletal disorders, there is no "one size fits all" approach to reducing the incidence and severity of cases. The following principles apply to selecting actions:

- Appropriate engineering and administrative controls will vary from industry to industry and company to company.
- Informed professional judgment is required to select the appropriate control measures.
- Work-related MSDs typically require periods of weeks to months for recovery. Control measures should be evaluated accordingly to determine their effectiveness.

Nonoccupational Factors

It is not possible to eliminate all musculoskeletal disorders via engineering and administrative controls. There are individual and organizational factors that may influence the likelihood that an individual will experience musculoskeletal disorders. Some cases may be associated with nonoccupational factors such as:

- Rheumatoid arthritis
- Endocrinological disorders
- Acute trauma
- Obesity
- Pregnancy
- Age
- Gender

TLV®–PA

Statement on Work-Related Musculoskeletal Disorders — 173

- Level of physical condition
- Previous injuries
- Diabetes
- Recreational/leisure activities

The recommended TLV® may not provide protection for people with these conditions and/or exposures. Engineering and administrative actions can help eliminate ergonomic barriers for persons with predisposing conditions and thus help to minimize disability.

Chronology of the Statement

1995: *Proposed* "Lifting Statement"
1996: Adopted with name change to "Musculoskeletal Statement"
2000: Editorial changes
2004: Editorial changes

TLV®–PA

174 — Ergonomics

HAND ACTIVITY LEVEL

Although work-related musculoskeletal disorders can occur in a number of body regions (including the shoulders, neck, low back, and lower extremities), the focus of this TLV® is on the hand, wrist, and forearm.

The TLV® shown in Figure 1 is based on epidemiological, psychophysical, and biomechanical studies and is intended for "mono-task" jobs performed for four or more hours per day. A mono-task job involves performing a similar set of motions or exertions repeatedly, such as working on an assembly line or using a keyboard and mouse. The TLV® specifically considers average hand activity level or "HAL" and peak hand force and represents conditions to which it is believed nearly all workers may be repeatedly exposed without adverse health effects.

HAL is based on the frequency of hand exertions and the duty cycle (distribution of work and recovery periods). HAL can be determined by trained observers based on exertion frequency, rest pauses and speed of motion using the rating scale shown in Figure 2. HAL also can be calculated from an analysis of the work method, force, and posture using information on hand exertion frequency and on duty cycle (work time/(work + rest time)) x 100% as described in Table 1 and in the *Documentation*.

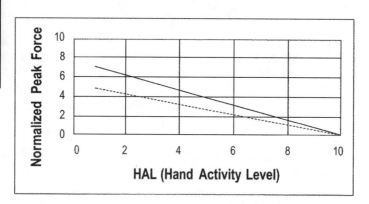

FIGURE 1. The TLV® for reduction of work-related musculoskeletal disorders based on "hand activity" or "HAL" and peak hand force. The top line depicts the TLV®. The bottom line is an Action Limit for which general controls are recommended.

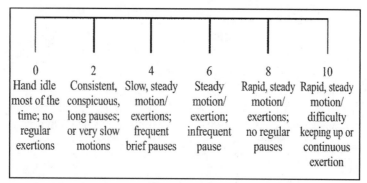

FIGURE 2. Hand Activity Level (0 to 10) can be rated using the above guidelines.

TABLE 1. Hand Activity Level (0 to 10) is Related to Exertion Frequency and Duty Cycle (% of work cycle where force is greater than 5% of maximum)

Frequency (exertion/s)	Period (s/exertion)	Duty Cycle (%)				
		0–20	20–40	40–60	60–80	80–100
0.125	8.0	1	1	—	—	—
0.25	4.0	2	2	3	—	—
0.5	2.0	3	4	5	5	6
1.0	1.0	4	5	5	6	7
2.0	0.5	—	5	6	7	8

Notes:

1. Round HAL values to the nearest whole number.
2. Use Figure 2 to obtain HAL values outside those listed in the table.

TLV®–PA

Peak hand force is the peak force exerted by the hand during each regular work cycle. Peak force can be determined with ratings by a trained observer, rated by workers using a Borg-like scale (*see* TLV® *Documentation* for definition), or measured using instrumentation, e.g., strain gauges or electromyography. In some cases, it can be calculated using biomechanical methods. These methods are intended to measure recurring peak forces; random force peaks associated with noise that occur less than 10% of the time are disregarded. Peak hand force is normalized on a scale of 0 to 10, which corresponds to 0% to 100% of the posture specific strength for the applicable population (males, females, young, old, office workers, factory workers, etc.):

Normalized Peak Force = (Peak force / Posture specific referent strength) $\times$ 10

The solid line in Figure 1 represents those combinations of force and hand activity level associated with a significantly elevated prevalence of musculoskeletal disorders. Appropriate control measures should be utilized so that the force for a given level of hand activity is below the upper solid line in Figure 1. It is not possible to specify a TLV® that protects all workers in all situations without profoundly affecting work rates. Therefore, an action limit is prescribed at which point general controls, including surveillance, are recommended.

176 — Ergonomics

Examples

1. Select a period of the job that represents an average activity. The selected period should include several complete work cycles. Videotapes may be used for documentation purposes and to facilitate rating of the job by others.
2. Rate the Hand Activity Level using the scale shown in Figure 2. Independent rating of jobs and discussion of results by three or more people can help produce a more precise rating than individual ratings.
3. Observe the job to identify forceful exertions and corresponding postures. Evaluate postures and forces using observer ratings, worker ratings, biomechanical analysis, or instrumentation. Normalized peak force is the required peak force divided by the representative maximum force for the posture multiplied by 10.

Consideration of Other Factors

Professional judgment should be used to reduce exposures below the action limits recommended in the HAL TLVs® if one or more of the following factors are present:

- sustained nonneutral postures such as wrist flexion, extension, wrist deviation, or forearm rotation;
- contact stresses;
- low temperatures; or
- vibration.

Employ appropriate control measures any time the TLV® is exceeded or an elevated incidence of work-related musculoskeletal disorders is detected.

LIFTING

These TLVs® recommend workplace lifting conditions under which it is believed nearly all workers may be repeatedly exposed, day after day, without developing work-related low back and shoulder disorders associated with repetitive lifting tasks. There are individual and organizational risk factors that may influence the likelihood that an individual will experience low back and shoulder disorders.

Lifting TLVs®

The TLVs® consist of three tables with weight limits, in kilograms (kg), for two-handed, mono-lifting tasks within 30 degrees of the sagittal [neutral] plane. A mono-lifting task is one in which the loads are similar and the starting and destination points are repeated, and this is the only lifting task performed during the day. Other manual material-handling tasks such as carrying, pushing, and pulling are not accounted for in the TLV®, and care must be exercised in applying the TLVs® under these circumstances.

These TLVs® (Tables 1 through 3) are presented for lifting tasks defined by their durations, either less than or greater than 2 hours per day, and by their frequency, expressed in number of lifts per hour, as qualified in the *Notes* to each table.

In the presence of any factor(s) or working condition(s) listed below, professional judgment should be used to reduce weight limits below those recommended in the TLVs®:

- High-frequency lifting: > 360 lifts per hour.
- Extended work shifts: lifting performed for longer than 8 hours per day.
- High asymmetry: lifting more than 30 degrees away from the sagittal plane.
- Rapid lifting motions and motions with twisting (e.g., from side to side).
- One-handed lifting.
- Constrained lower body posture, such as lifting while seated or kneeling.
- High heat and humidity (*see* Heat Stress and Heat Strain TLVs®).
- Lifting unstable objects (e.g., liquids with shifting center of mass or lack of coordination or equal sharing in multi-person lifts).
- Poor hand coupling: lack of handles, cut-outs, or other grasping points.
- Unstable footing (e.g., inability to support the body with both feet while standing).
- During or immediately after exposure to whole-body vibration at or above the TLV® for Whole-Body Vibration (*see* the current *TLV® Documentation* for Whole-Body Vibration).

Instructions for Users

1. **Read the *Documentation* for the Lifting TLVs®** so you understand the basis for these TLVs® and their limitations.
2. **Classify task duration** as less than or equal to a cumulative 2 hours per day or greater than a cumulative 2 hours per day. Task duration is the total length of time that a worker performs the task in 1 day.

TLV®–PA

178 — Ergonomics

TABLE 1. TLVs® for Lifting Tasks:
≤ 2 Hours per Day with ≤ 60 Lifts per Hour
OR
> 2 Hours per Day with ≤ 12 Lifts per Hour

Vertical Zone	Horizontal Zone[A]		
	Close: < 30 cm	Inter- mediate: 30 to 60 cm	Extended:[B] > 60 to 80 cm
Reach limit[C] or 30 cm above shoulder to 8 cm below shoulder height	16 kg	7 kg	No known safe limit for repetitive lifting[D]
Knuckle height[E] to below shoulder	32 kg	16 kg	9 kg
Middle shin to knuckle height[E]	18 kg	14 kg	7 kg
Floor to middle shin height	14 kg	No known safe limit for repetitive lifting[D]	No known safe limit for repetitive lifting[D]

Footnotes for Tables 1 through 3:

A. Distance from midpoint between inner ankle bones and the load.
B. Lifting tasks should not start or end at a horizontal reach distance more than 80 cm from the midpoint between the inner ankle bones (Figure 1).
C. Routine lifting tasks should not start or end at heights that are greater than 30 cm above the shoulder or more than 180 cm above floor level (Figure 1).
D. Routine lifting tasks should not be performed for shaded table entries marked "No known safe limit for repetitive lifting." While the available evidence does not permit identification of safe weight limits in the shaded regions, professional judgment may be used to determine if infrequent lifts of light weights may be safe.
E. Anatomical landmark for knuckle height assumes the worker is standing erect with arms hanging at the sides.

TLV®–PA

TABLE 2. TLVs® for Lifting Tasks
> 2 Hours per Day with > 12 and ≤ 30 Lifts per Hour
OR
≤ 2 Hours per Day with > 60 and ≤ 360 Lifts per Hour

Vertical Zone	Horizontal Zone[A]		
	Close: < 30 cm	Inter-mediate: 30 to 60 cm	Extended:[B] > 60 to 80 cm
Reach limit[C] or 30 cm above shoulder to 8 cm below shoulder height	14 kg	5 kg	No known safe limit for repetitive lifting[D]
Knuckle height[E] to below shoulder	27 kg	14 kg	7 kg
Middle shin to knuckle height[E]	16 kg	11 kg	5 kg
Floor to middle shin height	9 kg	No known safe limit for repetitive lifting[D]	No known safe limit for repetitive lifting[D]

See Notes in Table 1.

TABLE 3. TLVs® for Lifting Tasks
> 2 Hours per Day with > 30 and ≤ 360 Lifts per Hour

Vertical Zone	Horizontal Zone[A]		
	Close: < 30 cm	Inter-mediate: 30 to 60 cm	Extended:[B] > 60 to 80 cm
Reach limit[C] from 30 cm above to 8 cm below shoulder height	11 kg	No known safe limit for repetitive lifting[D]	No known safe limit for repetitive lifting[D]
Knuckle height[E] to below shoulder	14 kg	9 kg	5 kg
Middle shin to knuckle height[E]	9 kg	7 kg	2 kg
Floor to middle shin height	No known safe limit for repetitive lifting[D]	No known safe limit for repetitive lifting[D]	No known safe limit for repetitive lifting[D]

See Notes in Table 1.

TLV®–PA

180 — Ergonomics

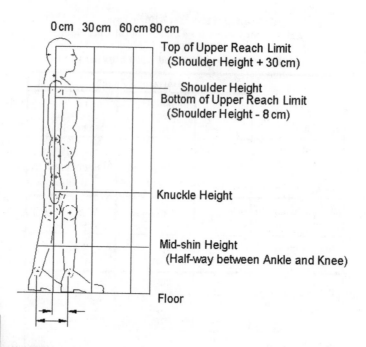

FIGURE 1. Graphic representation of hand location.

3. **Determine the lifting frequency** as the number of lifts a worker performs per hour.
4. **Use the TLV® table that corresponds to the duration and lifting frequency of the task**.
5. **Determine the vertical zone** (Figure 1) based on the location of the hands at the start of the lift.
6. **Determine the horizontal zone of the lift** (Figure 1) by measuring the horizontal distance from the midpoint between the inner ankle bones to the midpoint between the hands at the start of the lift.
7. **Determine the TLV®** in kilograms for the lifting task, as displayed in the table cell that corresponds to the vertical and horizontal zones in the appropriate table, based upon frequency and duration.
8. **Consider load control at destination.** If the load is placed at the destination in a controlled fashion (i.e., slowly or deliberately placed), repeat Steps 5 through 7 using the destination point instead of the start. The TLV® is represented by the lower of the two limits.

HAND–ARM (SEGMENTAL) VIBRATION

The TLVs® in Table 1 refer to component acceleration levels and durations of exposure that represent conditions under which it is believed that nearly all workers may be exposed repeatedly without progressing beyond Stage 1 of the Stockholm Workshop Classification System for Vibration-induced White Finger (VWF), also known as Raynaud's Phenomenon of Occupational Origin (Table 2). Since there is a paucity of dose–response relationships for VWF, these recommendations have been derived from epidemiological data from forestry, mining, and metal working. These values should be used as guides in the control of hand–arm vibration exposure; because of individual susceptibility, they should not be regarded as defining a boundary between safe and dangerous levels.

It should be recognized that control of hand–arm vibration syndrome (HAVS) from the workplace cannot occur simply by specifying and adhering to a given TLV®. The use of 1) antivibration tools, 2) antivibration gloves, 3) proper work practices that keep the worker's hands and remaining body warm and also minimize the vibration coupling between the worker and the vibration tool are necessary to minimize vibration exposure, and 4) a conscientiously applied medical surveillance program are ALL necessary to rid HAVS from the workplace.

TABLE 1. TLVs® for Exposure of the Hand to Vibration in Either X_h, Y_h, or Z_h Directions

Total Daily Exposure Duration ☆	Values of the Dominant,★ Frequency-Weighted, rms, Component Acceleration Which Shall not be Exceeded $a_K,(a_{K_{eq}})$	
	m/s²	g△
4 hours and less than 8	4	0.40
2 hours and less than 4	6	0.61
1 hour and less than 2	8	0.81
less than 1 hour	12	1.22

☆The total time vibration enters the hand per day, whether continuously or intermittently.

★Usually one axis of vibration is dominant over the remaining two axes. If one or more vibration axes exceeds the Total Daily Exposure, then the TLV® has been exceeded.

g△ = 9.81 m/s².

Notes for Table 1:

1. The weighting network provided in Figure 1 is considered the best available to frequency weight acceleration components. However, studies suggest that the frequency weighting at higher frequencies (above 16 Hz) may not incorporate a sufficient safety factor, and CAUTION must be applied when tools with high-frequency components are used.

2. Acute exposures to frequency-weighted, root-mean-square (rms), component accelerations in excess of the TLVs® for infrequent periods of time (e.g., 1 day per week or several days over a 2-week period) are not necessarily more harmful.

3. Acute exposures to frequency-weighted, rms, component accelerations of three times the magnitude of the TLVs® are expected to result in the same health effects after 5 to 6 years of exposure.

TLV®–PA

182 — Ergonomics

4. To moderate the adverse effects of vibration exposure, workers should be advised to avoid continuous vibration exposure by cessation of vibration exposure for approximately 10 minutes per continuous vibration hour.

5. Good work practices should be used and should include instructing workers to employ a minimum hand grip force consistent with safe operation of the power tool or process, to keep their body and hands warm and dry, to avoid smoking, and to use antivibration tools and gloves when possible. As a general rule, gloves are more effective for damping vibration at high frequencies.

6. A vibration measurement transducer, together with its device for attachment to the vibration source, should weigh less than 15 grams and should possess a cross-axis sensitivity of less than 10%.

7. The measurement by many (mechanically underdamped) piezoelectric accelerometers of repetitive, large displacement, impulsive vibrations, such as those produced by percussive pneumatic tools, is subject to error. The insertion of a suitable, low-pass, mechanical filter between the accelerometer and the source of vibration with a cut-off frequency of 1500 Hz or greater (and cross-axis sensitivity of less than 10%) can help eliminate incorrect readings.

8. The manufacturer and type number of all apparatus used to measure vibration should be reported, as well as the value of the dominant direction and frequency-weighted, rms, component acceleration.

TLV®–PA

TABLE 2. Stockholm Workshop HAVS Classification System for Cold-induced Peripheral Vascular and Sensorineural Symptoms

Vascular Assessment		
Stage	**Grade**	**Description**
0	——	No attacks
1	Mild	Occasional attacks affecting only the tips of one or more fingers
2	Moderate	Occasional attacks affecting distal and middle (rarely also proximal) phalanges of one or more fingers
3	Severe	Frequent attacks affecting ALL phalanges of most fingers
4	Very Severe	As in Stage 3, with trophic skin changes in the finger tips

Note: Separate staging is made for each hand, e.g., 2L(2)/1R(1) = stage 2 on left hand in two fingers: stage 1 on right hand in one finger.

Sensorineural Assessment	
Stage	**Symptoms**
0SN	Exposed to vibration but no symptoms
1SN	Intermittent numbness, with or without tingling
2SN	Intermittent or persistent numbness, reducing sensory perception
3SN	Intermittent or persistent numbness, reducing tactile discrimination and/or manipulative dexterity

Note: Separate staging is made for each hand.

Continuous, Intermittent, Impulsive, or Impact Hand–Arm Vibration

The measurement of vibration should be performed in accordance with the procedures and instrumentation specified by ISO 5349 (1986)[1] or ANSI S3.34-1986[2] and summarized below.

The acceleration of a vibration handle or work piece should be determined in three mutually orthogonal directions at a point close to where vibration enters the hand. The directions should preferably be those forming the biodynamic coordinate system but may be a closely related basicentric system with its origin at the interface between the hand and the vibrating surface (Figure 2) to accommodate different handle or work piece configurations. A small and lightweight transducer should be mounted so as to record accurately one or more orthogonal components of the source vibration in the frequency range from 5 to 1500 Hz. Each component should be frequency-weighted by a filter network with gain characteristics specified for human-response vibration measuring instrumentation, to account for the change in vibration hazard with frequency (Figure 1).

Assessment of vibration exposure should be made for EACH applicable direction (X_h, Y_h, Z_h) since vibration is a vector quantity (magnitude and direction). In each direction, the magnitude of the vibration during normal operation of the power tool, machine, or work piece should be expressed by the root-mean-square (rms) value of the frequency-weighted component accelerations, in units of meters per second squared (m/s²), or gravitational units (g), the largest of which, a_K, forms the basis for exposure assessment.

For each direction being measured, linear integration should be employed for vibrations that are of extremely short duration or vary substantially in time. If the total daily vibration exposure in a given direction is

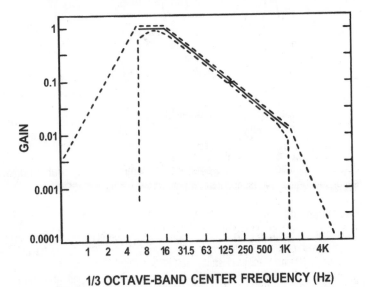

FIGURE 1. Gain characteristics on the filter network used to frequency-weight acceleration components (continuous line). The filter tolerances (dashed lines) are those contained in ISO 5349 and ANSI S3.34-1986.

184 — Ergonomics

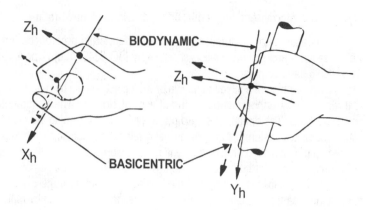

FIGURE 2. Biodynamic and basicentric coordinate systems for the hand, showing the directions of the acceleration components (ISO 5349[1] and ANSI S3.34–1986[2]).

composed of several exposures at different rms accelerations, then the equivalent, frequency-weighted component acceleration in that direction should be determined in accordance with the following equation:

$$
\left(a_{K_{eq}}\right) = \left[\frac{1}{T} \sum_{i=1}^{n} \left(a_{K_i}\right)^2 T_i\right]^{1/2}
$$

$$
= \sqrt{\left(a_{K_1}\right)^2 \frac{T_1}{T} + \left(a_{K_2}\right)^2 \frac{T_2}{T} + \ldots \left(a_{K_n}\right)^2 \frac{T_n}{T}}
$$

where: $T = \sum_{i=1}^{n} T_i$

$T =$ total daily exposure duration

$a_{K_i} =$ *ith* frequency-weighted, rms acceleration component with duration T_i

These computations may be performed by commercially available human-response vibration measuring instruments.

References

1. International Standards Organization: ISO 5349 (1986): Guide for the Measurement and the Assessment of Human Exposure to Hand Transmitted Vibration. ISO, Geneva (1986).
2. American National Standards Institute: ANSI S3.34-1986: Guide for the Measurement and Evaluation of Human Exposure to Vibration Transmitted to the Hand. ANSI, New York (1986).

WHOLE–BODY VIBRATION

The TLVs® in Figures 1 and 2 (tabulated in Tables 1 and 2) refer to mechanically induced whole-body vibration (WBV) acceleration component root-mean-square (rms) magnitudes and durations under which it is believed that nearly all workers may be exposed repeatedly with minimum risk of back pain, adverse health effects to the back, and inability to operate a land-based vehicle properly. The biodynamic coordinate system to which they apply is displayed in Figure 3. These values should be used as guides in the control of WBV exposure, but because of individual susceptibility, they should not be regarded as defining a boundary between safe and dangerous levels.

Notes:

1. Vibration acceleration is a vector with magnitude expressed in units of m/s^2. The gravitational acceleration, g, equals 9.81 m/s^2.

2. Figures 1 and 2 each show a family of daily exposure time–dependent curves. They indicate that human vibration resonance occurs in the 4 to 8 Hz frequency range for the z axis and in the 1 to 2 Hz frequency range for the x and y axes, where the axes are defined in Figure 3.

3. WBV measurements and equivalent exposure time calculations for interrupted exposures, where the rms acceleration levels vary appreciably over time, should be made according to ISO 2631 or ANSI S3.18-1979.[1,2]

4. The TLV® is valid for vibration crest factors of 6 or less. Crest factor is defined as the ratio of peak to rms acceleration, measured in the same direction, over a period of 1 minute for any of the orthogonal x, y, and z axes. The TLV® will underestimate the effects of WBV and must be used with caution when the crest factor exceeds 6.

5. The TLV® is not intended for use in fixed buildings (see ANSI S3.29-1983),[3] in off-shore structures, or in ships.

6. A summary of WBV measurement and data analysis procedures follows:[4]

    a. At each measurement point, three orthogonal, continuous, rms acceleration measurements are simultaneously made and recorded for at least 1 minute along the biodynamic coordinates shown in Figure 3.

    b. Three very light-weight accelerometers, each with a cross-axis sensitivity of less than 10%, are perpendicularly mounted to a light-weight metal cube and placed in the center of a hard rubber disc (per SAE, J1013).[5] The total weight of the disc, cube, accelerometers, and cables should not exceed 10% of the total weight of the object to be measured. Measurements are made by placing the instrumented rubber disc on the top of the driver's seat, under the driver's buttocks, as the vehicle is operated.

    c. For each axis, a $1/3$ octave band (1 to 80 Hz), separate Fourier spectrum analysis is required for comparison to Figure 1 or Figure 2, as appropriate.

TLV®–PA

186 — Ergonomics

TLV®–PA

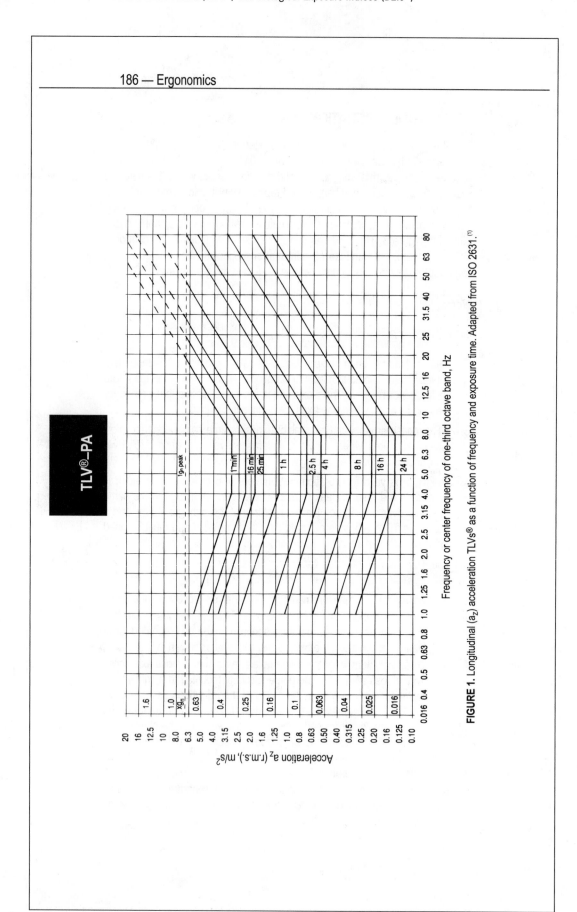

FIGURE 1. Longitudinal (a$_Z$) acceleration TLVs® as a function of frequency and exposure time. Adapted from ISO 2631.[1]

Whole-Body Vibration — 187

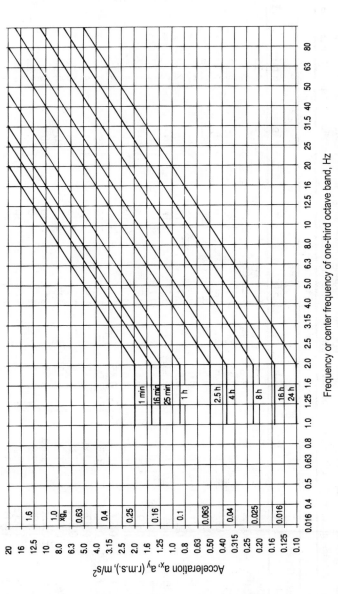

FIGURE 2. Transverse (a_x, a_y) acceleration TLVs® as a function of frequency and exposure time. Adapted from ISO 2631.[1]

TLV®–PA

188 — Ergonomics

TLV®–PA

TABLE 1. Numerical values for vibration acceleration in the longitudinal, a_z, direction [foot-to-head direction] [see Figure 1]. Values define the TLV® in terms of rms value of pure (sinusoidal) single-frequency vibration or of rms value in one-third-octave band for distributed vibration. (Adapted from ISO 2631)

Acceleration, m/s^2

Frequency Hz	Exposure times 24 h	16 h	8 h	4 h	2.5 h	1 h	25 min	16 min	1 min
1.0	0.280	0.383	0.63	1.06	1.40	2.36	3.55	4.25	5.60
1.25	0.250	0.338	0.56	0.95	1.26	2.12	3.15	3.75	5.00
1.6	0.224	0.302	0.50	0.85	1.12	1.90	2.80	3.35	4.50
2.0	0.200	0.270	0.45	0.75	1.00	1.70	2.50	3.00	4.00
2.5	0.180	0.239	0.40	0.67	0.90	1.50	2.24	2.65	3.55
3.15	0.160	0.212	0.355	0.60	0.80	1.32	2.00	2.35	3.15
4.0	0.140	0.192	0.315	0.53	0.71	1.18	1.80	2.12	2.80
5.0	0.140	0.192	0.315	0.53	0.71	1.18	1.80	2.12	2.80
6.3	0.140	0.192	0.315	0.53	0.71	1.18	1.80	2.12	2.80
8.0	0.140	0.192	0.315	0.53	0.71	1.18	1.80	2.12	2.80
10.0	0.180	0.239	0.40	0.67	0.90	1.50	2.24	2.65	3.55
12.5	0.224	0.302	0.50	0.85	1.12	1.90	2.80	3.35	4.50
16.0	0.280	0.383	0.63	1.06	1.40	2.36	3.55	4.25	5.60
20.0	0.355	0.477	0.80	1.32	1.80	3.00	4.50	5.30	7.10
25.0	0.450	0.605	1.0	1.70	2.24	3.75	5.60	6.70	9.00
31.5	0.560	0.765	1.25	2.12	2.80	4.75	7.10	8.50	11.2
40.0	0.710	0.955	1.60	2.65	3.55	6.00	9.00	10.6	14.0
50.0	0.900	1.19	2.0	3.35	4.50	7.50	11.2	13.2	18.0
63.0	1.120	1.53	2.5	4.25	5.60	9.50	14.0	17.0	22.4
80.0	1.400	1.91	3.15	5.30	7.10	11.8	18.0	21.2	28.0

Whole-Body Vibration — 189

TABLE 2. Numerical values for vibration acceleration in the transverse, a_x or a_y, direction [back-to-chest or side-to-side] [*see* Figure 2]. Values define the TLV® in terms of rms value of pure (sinusoidal) single-frequency vibration or of rms value in one-third-octave band for distributed vibration. (Adapted from ISO 2631)

Acceleration, m/s²

Frequency Hz	Exposure times								
	24 h	16 h	8 h	4 h	2.5 h	1 h	25 min	16 min	1 min
1.0	0.100	0.135	0.224	0.355	0.50	0.85	1.25	1.50	2.0
1.25	0.100	0.135	0.224	0.355	0.50	0.85	1.25	1.50	2.0
1.6	0.100	0.135	0.224	0.355	0.50	0.85	1.25	1.50	2.0
2.0	0.100	0.135	0.224	0.355	0.50	0.85	1.25	1.50	2.0
2.5	0.125	0.171	0.280	0.450	0.63	1.06	1.6	1.9	2.5
3.15	0.160	0.212	0.355	0.560	0.8	1.32	2.0	2.36	3.15
4.0	0.200	0.270	0.450	0.710	1.0	1.70	2.5	3.0	4.0
5.0	0.250	0.338	0.560	0.900	1.25	2.12	3.15	3.75	5.0
6.3	0.315	0.428	0.710	1.12	1.6	2.65	4.0	4.75	6.3
8.0	0.40	0.54	0.900	1.40	2.0	3.35	5.0	6.0	8.0
10.0	0.50	0.675	1.12	1.80	2.5	4.25	6.3	7.5	10.0
12.5	0.63	0.855	1.40	2.24	3.15	5.30	8.0	9.5	12.5
16.0	0.80	1.06	1.80	2.80	4.0	6.70	10.0	11.8	16.0
20.0	1.00	1.35	2.24	3.55	5.0	8.5	12.5	15.0	20.0
25.0	1.25	1.71	2.80	4.50	6.3	10.6	15.0	19.0	25.0
31.5	1.60	2.12	3.55	5.60	8.0	13.2	20.0	23.6	31.5
40.0	2.00	2.70	4.50	7.10	10.0	17.0	25.0	30.0	40.0
50.0	2.50	3.38	5.60	9.00	12.5	21.2	31.5	37.5	50.0
63.0	3.15	4.28	7.10	11.2	16.0	26.5	40.0	45.7	63.0
80.0	4.00	5.4	9.00	14.0	20.0	33.5	50.0	60.0	80.0

TLV®–PA

190 — Ergonomics

d. If the rms acceleration of any of the spectral peaks equals or exceeds the values shown in Figure 1 or Figure 2 for the relevant time periods, then the TLV® is exceeded for that exposure time. The axis with the highest spectral peak intersecting the curve with the shortest exposure time dominates and determines the permissible exposure.

7. The total-weighted rms acceleration for each axis can be calculated using Equation 1 with the appropriate axis weighting factors taken from Table 3. For the x axis (analogous equations and definitions apply to the y and z axes), the equation is:

$$A_{wx} = \sqrt{\sum (W_{fx} A_{fx})^2} \tag{1}$$

where: A_{wx} = total weighted rms acceleration for the x axis
          W_{fx} = weighting factor for the x axis at each $^1/_3$ octave
                    band frequency from 1 to 80 Hz (Table 3)
          A_{fx} = rms acceleration value for the x axis spectrum at
                    each $^1/_3$ octave band frequency from 1 to 80 Hz

8. If the vibration axes have similar acceleration magnitudes as determined by Equation 1, the combined motion of all three axes could be greater than any one component and could possibly affect vehicle operator performance.[1,2] Each of the component results determined by Equation 1 may be

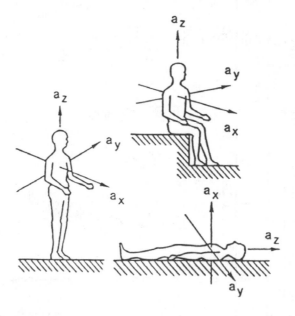

FIGURE 3. Biodynamic coordinate system acceleration measurements (adapted from ISO 2631). a_x, a_y, a_z = acceleration in the direction of the x, y, and z axes; x axis = back-to-chest; y axis = right-to-left; z axis = foot-to-head.

used in Equation 2 to find the resultant, which is the overall weighted total rms acceleration, A_{wt}:

$$A_{wt} = \sqrt{(1.4\,A_{wx})^2 + (1.4\,A_{wy})^2 + (A_{wz})^2} \qquad (2)$$

The factor of 1.4 multiplying the x and y total, weighted rms acceleration values is the ratio of the values of the longitudinal and transverse curves of equal response in the most sensitive human response ranges.

The Commission of the European Communities now recommends 0.5 m/s^2 as an action level for an 8 hour per day overall weighted total rms acceleration. This may be compared with the results of Equation 2.

9. Short-duration, high-amplitude, multiple-vibration shocks may occur with crest factors greater than 6 during the workday, in which cases the TLV® may not be protective (Note 4). Other methods of calculation that include the "4th power concept" may be desirable in these instances.[6]

TABLE 3. Weighting Factors Relative to the Frequency Range of Maximum Acceleration Sensitivity[A] **for the Response Curves of Figures 1 and 2 (Adapted from ISO 2631)**

	Weighting factor for	
Frequency Hz	Longitudinal z Vibrations [Figure 1]	Transverse x, y Vibrations [Figure 2]
1.0	0.50	1.00
1.25	0.56	1.00
1.6	0.63	1.00
2.0	0.71	1.00
2.5	0.80	0.80
3.15	0.90	0.63
4.0	1.00	0.5
5.0	1.00	0.4
6.3	1.00	0.315
8.0	1.00	0.25
10.0	0.80	0.2
12.5	0.63	0.16
16.0	0.50	0.125
20.0	0.40	0.1
25.0	0.315	0.08
31.5	0.25	0.063
40.0	0.20	0.05
50.0	0.16	0.04
63.0	0.125	0.0315
80.0	0.10	0.025

[A] 4 to 8 Hz in the case of $\pm\,a_z$ resonance vibration.
1 to 2 Hz in the case of $\pm\,a_y$ or a_x resonance vibration.

192 — Ergonomics

10. WBV controls may include the use of "air-ride" suspended seats, suspended cabs, maintenance of vehicle suspension systems, proper tire inflation, and remote control of vibrating processes. Seats with arm rests, lumbar support, an adjustable seat back, and an adjustable seat pan are also useful.

11. The following good work practices may also be useful for workers operating vehicles:[7,8]

    a. Avoid lifting or bending immediately following exposure.

    b. Use simple motions, with minimum rotation or twisting, when exiting a vehicle.

References

1. International Standards Organization: ISO 2631/1: Evaluation of Human Exposure to Whole-Body Vibration. ISO, Geneva (1985).
2. American National Standards Institute: ANSI S3.18: Guide for the Evaluation of Human Exposure to Whole-Body Vibration. ANSI, New York (1979).
3. American National Standards Institute: ANSI S3.29: Guide for the Evaluation of Human Exposure to Whole-Body Vibration in Buildings. ANSI, New York (1983).
4. Wasserman, D: Human Aspects of Occupational Vibration. Elsevier Publishers, Amsterdam (1987).
5. Society of Automotive Engineers. SAE J1013: Measurement of Whole Body Vibration of the Seated Operator of Off Highway Work Machines. SAE, Warrendale, PA (August 1992).
6. Griffin, M: Handbook of Human Vibration. Academic Press, London (1990).
7. Wilder, D: The Biomechanics of Vibration and Low Back Pain. Am. J. Ind. Med. 23:577–588 (1993).
8. Wilder, D; Pope, M; Frymoyer, J: The Biomechanics of Lumbar Disc Herniation and the Effect of Overload and Instability. J. Spinal Disorders 1:16–32 (1988).

TLV®–PA

THERMAL STRESS

COLD STRESS

The cold stress TLVs® are intended to protect workers from the severest effects of cold stress (hypothermia) and cold injury and to describe exposures to cold working conditions under which it is believed nearly all workers can be repeatedly exposed without adverse health effects. The TLV® objective is to prevent the deep body temperature from falling below 36°C (96.8°F) and to prevent cold injury to body extremities (deep body temperature is the core temperature of the body determined by conventional methods for rectal temperature measurements). For a single, occasional exposure to a cold environment, a drop in core temperature to no lower that 35°C (95°F) should be permitted. In addition to provisions for total body protection, the TLV® objective is to protect all parts of the body with emphasis on hands, feet, and head from cold injury.

Introduction

Fatal exposures to cold among workers have almost always resulted from accidental exposures involving failure to escape from low environmental air temperatures or from immersion in low temperature water. The single most important aspect of life-threatening hypothermia is the fall in the deep core temperature of the body. The clinical presentations of victims of hypothermia are shown in Table 1. Workers should be protected from exposure to cold so that the deep core temperature does not fall below 36°C (96.8°F); lower body temperatures will very likely result in reduced mental alertness, reduction in rational decision making, or loss of consciousness with the threat of fatal consequences.

Pain in the extremities may be the first early warning of danger to cold stress. During exposure to cold, maximum severe shivering develops when the body temperature has fallen to 35°C (95°F). This must be taken as a sign of danger to the workers and exposure to cold should be immediately terminated for any workers when severe shivering becomes evident. Useful physical or mental work is limited when severe shivering occurs.

Since prolonged exposure to cold air, or to immersion in cold water, at temperatures well above freezing can lead to dangerous hypothermia, whole body protection must be provided.

1. Adequate insulating dry clothing to maintain core temperatures above 36°C (96.8°F) must be provided to workers if work is performed in air temperatures below 4°C (40°F). Wind chill cooling rate and the cooling power of air are critical factors. [Wind chill cooling rate is defined as heat loss from a body expressed in watts per meter squared which is a function of the air temperature and wind velocity upon the exposed body.] The higher the wind speed and the lower the temperature in the work area, the greater the insulation value of the protective clothing required. An equivalent chill temperature chart relating the actual dry bulb air temperature and the wind velocity is presented in Table 2. The equivalent chill temperature should beused when estimating the combined cooling effect of wind and low air temperatures on exposed skin or when determining clothing insulation requirements to maintain the deep body core temperature.

TLV®–PA

194 — Thermal Stress

TABLE 1. Progressive Clinical Presentations of Hypothermia ☆

Core Temperature		
°C	°F	Clinical Signs
37.6	99.6	"Normal" rectal temperature
37	98.6	"Normal" oral temperature
36	96.8	Metabolic rate increases in an attempt to compensate for heat loss
35	95.0	Maximum shivering
34	93.2	Victim conscious and responsive, with normal blood pressure
33	91.4	Severe hypothermia below this temperature
32 } 31 }	89.6 } 87.8 }	Consciousness clouded; blood pressure becomes difficult to obtain; pupils dilated but react to light; shivering ceases
30 } 29 }	86.0 } 84.2 }	Progressive loss of consciousness; muscular rigidity increases; pulse and blood pressure difficult to obtain; respiratory rate decreases
28	82.4	Ventricular fibrillation possible with myocardial irritability
27	80.6	Voluntary motion ceases; pupils nonreactive to light; deep tendon and superficial reflexes absent
26	78.8	Victim seldom conscious
25	77.0	Ventricular fibrillation may occur spontaneously
24	75.2	Pulmonary edema
22 } 21 }	71.6 } 69.8 }	Maximum risk of ventricular fibrillation
20	68.0	Cardiac standstill
18	64.4	Lowest accidental hypothermia victim to recover
1 7	62.6	Isoelectric electroencephalogram
9	48.2	Lowest artificially cooled hypothermia patient to recover

☆Presentations approximately related to core temperature. Reprinted from the January 1982 issue of *American Family Physician,* published by the American Academy of Family Physicians.

2. Unless there are unusual or extenuating circumstances, cold injury to other than hands, feet, and head is not likely to occur without the development of the initial signs of hypothermia. Older workers or workers with circulatory problems require special precautionary protection against cold injury. The use of extra insulating clothing and/or a reduction in the duration of the exposure period are among the special precautions which should be considered. The precautionary actions to be taken will depend upon the physical condition of the worker and should be determined with the advice of a physician with knowledge of the cold stress factors and the medical condition of the worker.

Cold Stress — 195

TABLE 2. Cooling Power of Wind on Exposed Flesh Expressed as Equivalent Temperature (under calm conditions) ★

Estimated Wind Speed (in mph)	Actual Temperature Reading (°F)											
	50	40	30	20	10	0	-10	-20	-30	-40	-50	-60
	Equivalent Chill Temperature (°F)											
calm	50	40	30	20	10	0	-10	-20	-30	-40	-50	-60
5	48	37	27	16	6	-5	-15	-26	-36	-47	-57	-68
10	40	28	16	4	-9	-24	-33	-46	-58	-70	-83	-95
15	36	22	9	-5	-18	-32	-45	-58	-72	-85	-99	-112
20	32	18	4	-10	-25	-39	-53	-67	-82	-96	-110	-121
25	30	16	0	-15	-29	-44	-59	-74	-88	-104	-118	-133
30	28	13	-2	-18	-33	-48	-63	-79	-94	-109	-125	-140
35	27	11	-4	-20	-35	-51	-67	-82	-98	-113	-129	-145
40	26	10	-6	-21	-37	-53	-69	-85	-100	-116	-132	-148

(Wind speeds greater than 40 mph have little additional effect.)

LITTLE DANGER
In < hr with dry skin. Maximum danger of false sense of security.

INCREASING DANGER
Danger from freezing of exposed flesh within one minute.

GREAT DANGER
Flesh may freeze within 30 seconds.

Trenchfoot and immersion foot may occur at any point on this chart.

★ Developed by U.S. Army Research Institute of Environmental Medicine, Natick, MA.

★ Equivalent chill temperature requiring dry clothing to maintain core body temperature above 36°C (96.8°F) per cold stress TLV®.

TLV®–PA

1085

196 — Thermal Stress

Evaluation and Control

For exposed skin, continuous exposure should not be permitted when the air speed and temperature results in an equivalent chill temperature of –32°C (–25.6°F). Superficial or deep local tissue freezing will occur only at temperatures below –1°C (30.2°F) regardless of wind speed.

At air temperatures of 2°C (35.6°F) or less, it is imperative that workers who become immersed in water or whose clothing becomes wet be immediately provided a change of clothing and be treated for hypothermia.

TLVs® recommended for properly clothed workers for periods of work at temperatures below freezing are shown in Table 3.

Special protection of the hands is required to maintain manual dexterity for the prevention of accidents:

1. If fine work is to be performed with bare hands for more than 10 to 20 minutes in an environment below 16°C (60.8°F), special provisions should be established for keeping the workers' hands warm. For this purpose, warm air jets, radiant heaters (fuel burner or electric radiator), or contact warm plates may be utilized. Metal handles of tools and control bars should be covered by thermal insulating material at temperatures below –1°C (30.2°F).

2. If the air temperature falls below 16°C (60.8°F) for sedentary, 4°C (39.2°F) for light, –7°C (19.4°F) for moderate work, and fine manual dexterity is not required, then gloves should be used by the workers.

To prevent contact frostbite, the workers should wear anticontact gloves.

1. When cold surfaces below –7°C (19.4°F) are within reach, a warning should be given to each worker to prevent inadvertent contact by bare skin.

2. If the air temperature is –17.5°C (0°F) or less, the hands should be protected by mittens. Machine controls and tools for use in cold conditions should be designed so that they can be handled without removing the mittens.

Provisions for additional total body protection are required if work is performed in an environment at or below 4°C (39.2°F). The workers should wear cold protective clothing appropriate for the level of cold and physical activity:

1. If the air velocity at the job site is increased by wind, draft, or artificial ventilating equipment, the cooling effect of the wind should be reduced by shielding the work area or by wearing an easily removable windbreak garment.

2. If only light work is involved and if the clothing on the worker may become wet on the job site, the outer layer of the clothing in use may be of a type impermeable to water. With more severe work under such conditions, the outer layer should be water repellent, and the outerwear should be changed as it becomes wetted. The outer garments should include provisions for easy ventilation in order to prevent wetting of inner layers by sweat. If work is done at normal temperatures or in a hot environment

TLV®–PA

before entering the cold area, the employee should make sure that clothing is not wet as a consequence of sweating. If clothing is wet, the employee should change into dry clothes before entering the cold area. The workers should change socks and any removable felt insoles at regular daily intervals or use vapor barrier boots. The optimal frequency of change should be determined empirically and will vary individually and according to the type of shoe worn and how much the individual's feet sweat.

3. If exposed areas of the body cannot be protected sufficiently to prevent sensation of excessive cold or frostbite, protective items should be supplied in auxiliary heated versions.

4. If the available clothing does not give adequate protection to prevent hypothermia or frostbite, work should be modified or suspended until adequate clothing is made available or until weather conditions improve.

5. Workers handling evaporative liquid (gasoline, alcohol or cleaning fluids) at air temperatures below 4°C (39.2°F) should take special precautions to avoid soaking of clothing or gloves with the liquids because of the added danger of cold injury due to evaporative cooling. Special note should be taken of the particularly acute effects of splashes of "cryogenic fluids" or those liquids with a boiling point that is just above ambient temperature.

Work–Warming Regimen

If work is performed continuously in the cold at an equivalent chill temperature (ECT) or below –7°C (19.4°F), heated warming shelters (tents, cabins, rest rooms, etc.) should be made available nearby. The workers should be encouraged to use these shelters at regular intervals, the frequency depending on the severity of the environmental exposure. The onset of heavy shivering, minor frostbite (frostnip), the feeling of excessive fatigue, drowsiness, irritability, or euphoria are indications for immediate return to the shelter. When entering the heated shelter, the outer layer of clothing should be removed and the remainder of the clothing loosened to permit sweat evaporation or a change of dry work clothing provided. A change of dry work clothing should be provided as necessary to prevent workers from returning to work with wet clothing. Dehydration, or the loss of body fluids, occurs insidiously in the cold environment and may increase the susceptibility of the worker to cold injury due to a significant change in blood flow to the extremities. Warm sweet drinks and soups should be provided at the work site to provide caloric intake and fluid volume. The intake of coffee should be limited because of the diuretic and circulatory effects. For work practices at or below –12°C (10.4°F) ECT, the following should apply:

1. The worker should be under constant protective observation (buddy system or supervision).

2. The work rate should not be so high as to cause heavy sweating that will result in wet clothing; if heavy work must be done, rest periods should be taken in heated shelters and opportunity for changing into dry clothing should be provided.

TLV®–PA

198 — Thermal Stress

TLV®–PA

TABLE 3. TLVs® Work/Warm-up Schedule for a 4-Hour Shift ☆

Air Temperature—Sunny Sky		No Noticeable Wind		5 mph Wind		10 mph Wind		15 mph Wind		20 mph Wind	
°C (approx.)	°F (approx.)	Max. Work Period	No. of Breaks	Max. Work Period	No. of Breaks	Max. Work Period	No. of Breaks	Max. Work Period	No. of Breaks	Max. Work Period	No. of Breaks
−26° to −28°	−15° to −19°	(Norm. Breaks)	1	(Norm. Breaks)	1	75 min	2	55 min	3	40 min	4
−29° to −31°	−20° to −24°	(Norm. Breaks)	1	75 min	2	55 min	3	40 min	4	30 min	5
−32° to −34°	−25° to −29°	75 min	2	55 min	3	40 min	4	30 min	5	Non-emergency work should cease	
−35° to −37°	−30° to −34°	55 min	3	40 min	4	30 min	5	Non-emergency work should cease			
−38° to −39°	−35° to −39°	40 min	4	30 min	5	Non-emergency work should cease					
−40° to −42°	−40° to −44°	30 min	5	Non-emergency work should cease							
−43° & below	−45° & below	Non-emergency work should cease									

see next page for NOTES

Cold Stress — 199

NOTES for Table 3:

1. Schedule applies to any 4-hour work period with moderate to heavy work activity, with warm-up periods of ten (10) minutes in a warm location and with an extended break (e.g., lunch) at the end of the 4-hour work period in a warm location. For Light-to-Moderate Work (limited physical movement): apply the schedule one step lower. For example, at −35°C (−30°F) with no noticeable wind (Step 4), a worker at a job with little physical movement should have a maximum work period of 40 minutes with 4 breaks in a 4-hour period (Step 5).

2. The following is suggested as a guide for estimating wind velocity if accurate information is not available:
   5 mph: light flag moves; 10 mph: light flag fully extended; 15 mph: raises newspaper sheet; 20 mph: blowing and drifting snow.

3. If only the wind chill cooling rate is available, a rough rule of thumb for applying it rather than the temperature and wind velocity factors given above would be: 1) special warm-up breaks should be initiated at a wind chill cooling rate of about 1750 W/m²; 2) all non-emergency work should have ceased at or before a wind chill of 2250 W/m². In general, the warmup schedule provided above slightly under-compensates for the wind at the warmer temperatures, assuming acclimatization and clothing appropriate for winter work. On the other hand, the chart slightly over-compensates for the actual temperatures in the colder ranges because windy conditions rarely prevail at extremely low temperatures.

4. TLVs® apply only for workers in dry clothing.

☆ Adapted from Occupational Health & Safety Division, Saskatchewan Department of Labour.

TLV®–PA

200 — Thermal Stress

3. New employees should not be required to work fulltime in the cold during the first days of employment until they become accustomed to the working conditions and required protective clothing.

4. The weight and bulkiness of clothing should be included in estimating the required work performance and weights to be lifted by the worker.

5. The work should be arranged in such a way that sitting still or standing still for long periods is minimized. Unprotected metal chair seats should not be used. The worker should be protected from drafts to the greatest extent possible.

6. The workers should be instructed in safety and health procedures. The training program should include as a minimum instruction in:

    a. Proper rewarming procedures and appropriate first aid treatment.

    b. Proper clothing practices.

    c. Proper eating and drinking habits.

    d. Recognition of impending frostbite.

    e. Recognition of signs and symptoms of impending hypothermia or excessive cooling of the body even when shivering does not occur.

    f. Safe work practices.

Special Workplace Recommendations

Special design requirements for refrigerator rooms include the following:

1. In refrigerator rooms, the air velocity should be minimized as much as possible and should not exceed 1 meter/sec (200 fpm) at the job site. This can be achieved by properly designed air distribution systems.

2. Special wind protective clothing should be provided based upon existing air velocities to which workers are exposed.

Special caution should be exercised when working with toxic substances and when workers are exposed to vibration. Cold exposure may require reduced exposure limits.

Eye protection for workers employed out-of-doors in a snow and/or ice-covered terrain should be supplied. Special safety goggles to protect against ultraviolet light and glare (which can produce temporary conjunctivitis and/or temporary loss of vision) and blowing ice crystals should be required when there is an expanse of snow coverage causing a potential eye exposure hazard.

Workplace monitoring is required as follows:

1. Suitable thermometry should be arranged at any workplace where the environmental temperature is below 16°C (60.8°F) so that overall compliance with the requirements of the TLV® can be maintained.

2. Whenever the air temperature at a workplace falls below –1°C (30.2°F), the dry bulb temperature should be measured and recorded at least every 4 hours.

TLV®–PA

Cold Stress — 201

3. In indoor workplaces, the wind speed should also be recorded at least every 4 hours whenever the rate of air movement exceeds 2 meters per second (5 mph).

4. In outdoor work situations, the wind speed should be measured and recorded together with the air temperature whenever the air temperature is below –1°C (30.2°F).

5. The equivalent chill temperature should be obtained from Table 2 in all cases where air movement measurements are required; it should be recorded with the other data whenever the equivalent chill temperature is below –7°C (19.4°F).

Employees should be excluded from work in cold at –1°C (30.2°F) or below if they are suffering from diseases or taking medication which interferes with normal body temperature regulation or reduces tolerance to work in cold environments. Workers who are routinely exposed to temperatures below –24°C (–11.2°F) with wind speeds less than five miles per hour, or air temperatures below –18°C (0°F) with wind speeds above five miles per hour, should be medically certified as suitable for such exposures.

Trauma sustained in freezing or subzero conditions requires special attention because an injured worker is predisposed to cold injury. Special provisions should be made to prevent hypothermia and freezing of damaged tissues in addition to providing for first aid treatment.

TLV®–PA

202 — Thermal Stress

HEAT STRESS AND HEAT STRAIN

The goal of this TLV® is to maintain body core temperature within + 1°C of normal (37°C). This core body temperature range can be exceeded under certain circumstances with selected populations, environmental and physiologic monitoring, and other controls.

More than any other physical agent, the potential health hazards from work in hot environments depends strongly on physiological factors that lead to a range of susceptibilities depending on the level of acclimatization. Therefore, professional judgment is of particular importance in assessing the level of heat stress and physiological heat strain to adequately provide guidance for protecting nearly all healthy workers with due consideration of individual factors and the type of work. Assessment of both heat stress and heat strain can be used for evaluating the risk to worker safety and health. A decision making process is suggested in Figure 1. The exposure guidance provided in Figures 1 and 2 and in the associated *Documentation* of the TLV® represents conditions under which it is believed that nearly all heat acclimatized, adequately hydrated, unmedicated, healthy workers may be repeatedly exposed without adverse health effects. The Action Limit (AL) is similarly protective of unacclimatized workers and represents conditions for which a heat stress management program should be considered. While not part of the TLV®, elements of a heat stress management program are offered. The exposure guidance is not a fine line between safe and dangerous levels.

Heat Stress is the net heat load to which a worker may be exposed from the combined contributions of metabolic heat, environmental factors, (i.e., air temperature, humidity, air movement, and radiant heat), and clothing requirements. A mild or moderate heat stress may cause discomfort and may adversely affect performance and safety, but it is not harmful to health. As the heat stress approaches human tolerance limits, the risk of heat-related disorders increases.

Heat Strain is the overall physiological response resulting from heat stress. The physiological responses are dedicated to dissipating excess heat from the body.

Acclimatization is a gradual physiological adaptation that improves an individual's ability to tolerate heat stress. Acclimatization requires physical activity under heat-stress conditions similar to those anticipated for the work. With a recent history of heat-stress exposures of at least two continuous hours (e.g., 5 of the last 7 days to 10 of 14 days), a worker can be considered acclimatized for the purposes of the TLV®. Its loss begins when the activity under those heat stress conditions is discontinued, and a noticeable loss occurs after four days and may be completely lost in three to four weeks. Because acclimatization is to the level of the heat stress exposure, a person will not be fully acclimatized to a sudden higher level; such as during a heat wave.

The decision process illustrated in Figure 1, should be started if (1) a qualitative exposure assessment indicates the possibility of heat stress, (2) there are reports of discomfort due to heat stress, or (3) professional judgment indicates heat stress conditions.

Section 1: *Clothing.* Ideally, free movement of cool, dry air over the skin's surface maximizes heat removal by both evaporation and convection.

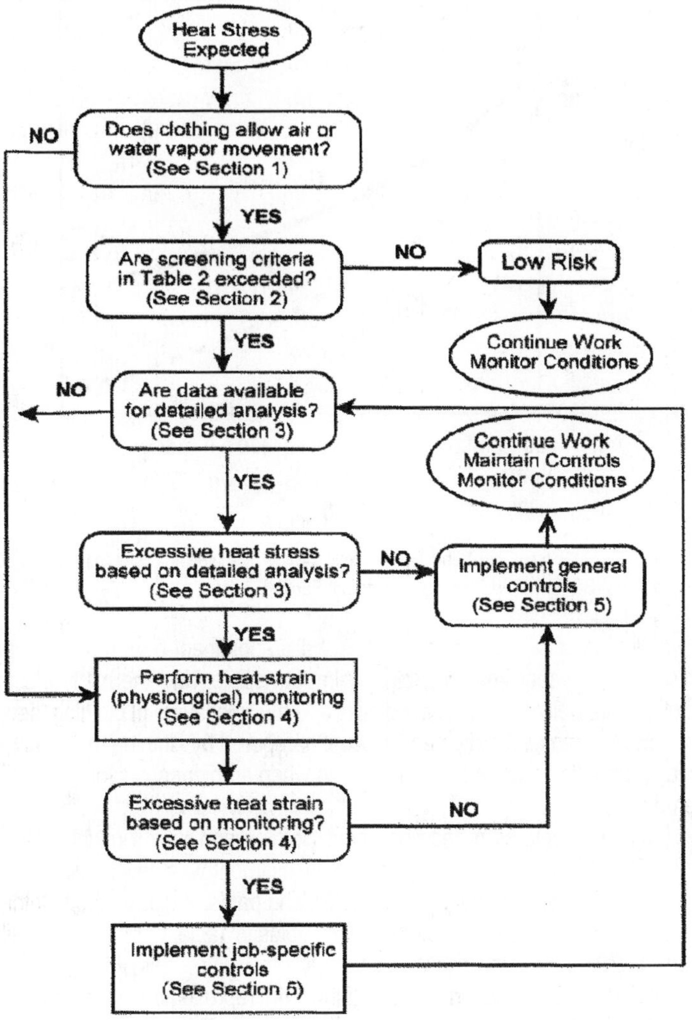

FIGURE 1. Evaluating heat stress and strain.

204 — Thermal Stress

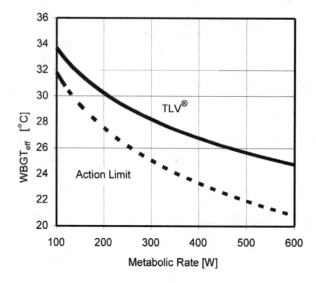

FIGURE 2. TLV® (solid line) and Action Limit (broken line) for heat stress. WBGT$_{eff}$ is the measured WBGT plus the Clothing-Adjustment Factor.

Evaporation of sweat from the skin is the predominant heat removal mechanism. Water-vapor-impermeable, air-impermeable, and thermally insulating clothing, as well as encapsulating suits and multiple layers of clothing, severely restrict heat removal. With heat removal hampered by clothing, metabolic heat may produce excessive heat strain even when ambient conditions are considered cool.

Figure 1 requires a decision about clothing and how it might affect heat loss. The WBGT-based heat exposure assessment was developed for a traditional work uniform of a long-sleeve shirt and pants. If the required clothing is adequately described by one of the ensembles in Table 1 or by other available data, then the "YES" branch is selected.

If workers are required to wear clothing not represented by an ensemble in Table 1, then the "NO" branch should be taken. This decision is especially applicable for clothing ensembles that are 1) totally encapsulating suits or 2) multiple layers where no data are available for adjustments. For these kinds of ensembles, Table 2 is not a useful screening method to determine a threshold for heat-stress management actions and some risk must be assumed. Unless a detailed analysis method appropriate to the clothing requirements is available, physiological and signs/symptoms monitoring described in Section 4 and Table 4 should be followed to assess the exposure.

Section 2: *Screening Threshold Based on Wet-Bulb Globe Temperature (WBGT).* The WBGT offers a useful first order index of the environmental contribution to heat stress. It is influenced by air temperature, radiant heat, air movement, and humidity. As an approximation, it does not fully account for all the interactions between a person and the environment and cannot account for special conditions such as heating from a radiofrequency/microwave source.

Heat Stress and Heat Strain — 205

TABLE 1. Clothing-Adjustment Factors for Some Clothing Ensembles*

Clothing Type	Addition to WBGT [°C]
Work clothes (long sleeve shirt and pants)	0
Cloth (woven material) coveralls	0
Double-layer woven clothing	3
SMS polypropylene coveralls	0.5
Polyolefin coveralls	1
Limited-use vapor-barrier coveralls	11

*These values must not be used for completely encapsulating suits, often called Level A. Clothing Adjustment Factors cannot be added for multiple layers. The coveralls assume that only modesty clothing is worn underneath, not a second layer of clothing.

WBGT values are calculated using one of the following equations:

With direct exposure to sunlight:

$$WBGT_{out} = 0.7\ T_{nwb} + 0.2\ T_g + 0.1\ T_{db}$$

Without direct exposure to the sun:

$$WBGT_{in} = 0.7\ T_{nwb} + 0.3\ T_g$$

where:

T_{nwb} = natural wet-bulb temperature (sometimes called NWB)
T_g = globe temperature (sometimes called GT)
T_{db} = dry-bulb (air) temperature (sometimes called DB)

Because WBGT is only an index of the environment, the screening criteria are adjusted for the contributions of work demands and clothing. Table 2 provides WBGT criteria suitable for screening purposes. For clothing ensembles listed in Table 1, Table 2 can be used when the clothing adjustment factors are added to the environmental WBGT.

To determine the degree of heat stress exposure, the work pattern and demands must be considered. If the work (and rest) is distributed over more than one location, then a time-weighted average WBGT should be used for comparison to Table 2 limits.

As metabolic rate increases (i.e., work demands increase), the criteria values in the table decrease to ensure that most workers will not have a core body temperature above 38°C. Correct assessment of work rate is of equal importance to environmental assessment in evaluating heat stress. Table 3 provides broad guidance for selecting the work rate category to be used in Table 2. Often there are natural or prescribed rest breaks within an hour of work, and Table 2 provides the screening criteria for three allocations of work and rest.

Based on metabolic rate category for the work and the approximate proportion of work within an hour, a WBGT criterion can be found in Table 2 for

TLV®–PA

206 — Thermal Stress

TLV®-PA

TABLE 2. Screening Criteria for TLV® and Action Limit for Heat Stress Exposure

Allocation of Work in a Cycle of Work and Recovery	TLV® (WBGT values in °C)				Action Limit (WBGT values in °C)			
	Light	Moderate	Heavy	Very Heavy	Light	Moderate	Heavy	Very Heavy
75 to 100%	31.0	28.0	–	–	28.0	25.0	–	–
50 to 75%	31.0	29.0	27.5	–	28.5	26.0	24.0	–
25 to 50%	32.0	30.0	29.0	28.0	29.5	27.0	25.5	24.5
0 to 25%	32.5	31.5	30.5	30.0	30.0	29.0	28.0	27.0

Notes:

- See Table 3 and the *Documentation* for work demand categories.
- WBGT values are expressed to the nearest 0.5°C.
- The thresholds are computed as a TWA-Metabolic Rate where the metabolic rate for rest is taken as 115 W and work is the representative (mid-range) value of Table 3. The time base is taken as the proportion of work at the upper limit of the percent work range (e.g., 50% for the range of 25 to 50%).
- If work and rest environments are different, hourly time-weighted averages (TWA) WBGT should be calculated and used. TWAs for work rates should also be used when the work demands vary within the hour, but note that the metabolic rate for rest is already factored into the screening limit.
- Values in the table are applied by reference to the "Work-Rest Regimen" section of the *Documentation* and assume 8-hour workdays in a 5-day workweek with conventional breaks as discussed in the *Documentation*. When workdays are extended, consult the "Application of the TLV®" section of the *Documentation*.
- Because of the physiological strain associated with Heavy and Very Heavy work among less fit workers regardless of WBGT, criteria values are not provided for continuous work and for up to 25% rest in an hour for Very Heavy. The screening criteria are not recommended, and a detailed analysis and/or physiological monitoring should be used.
- Table 2 is intended as an initial screening tool to evaluate whether a heat stress situation may exist (according to Figure 1) and thus, the table is more protective than the TLV® or Action Limit (Figure 2). Because the values are more protective, they are not intended to prescribe work and recovery periods.

Heat Stress and Heat Strain — 207

TABLE 3. Metabolic Rate Categories and the Representative Metabolic Rate with Example Activities

Category	Metabolic Rate [W] *	Examples
Rest	115	Sitting
Light	180	Sitting with light manual work with hands or hands and arms, and driving. Standing with some light arm work and occasional walking.
Moderate	300	Sustained moderate hand and arm work, moderate arm and leg work, moderate arm and trunk work, or light pushing and pulling. Normal walking.
Heavy	415	Intense arm and trunk work, carrying, shoveling, manual sawing; pushing and pulling heavy loads; and walking at a fast pace.
Very Heavy	520	Very intense activity at fast to maximum pace.

* The effect of body weight on the estimated metabolic rate can be accounted for by multiplying the estimated rate by the ratio of actual body weight divided by 70 kg (154 lb).

TLV®–PA

the TLV® and for the Action Limit. If the measured time-weighted average WBGT adjusted for clothing is less than the table value for the Action Limit, the NO branch in Figure 1 is taken, and there is little risk of excessive exposures to heat stress. If the conditions are above the Action Limit, but below the TLV®, then consider general controls described in Table 5. If there are reports of the symptoms of heat-related disorders such as fatigue, nausea, dizziness, and lightheadedness, then the analysis should be reconsidered.

If the work conditions are above the TLV® screening criteria in Table 2, then a further analysis is required following the YES branch.

Section 3: *Detailed Analysis.* Table 2 is intended to be used as a screening step. It is possible that a condition may be above the TLV® or Action Limit criteria provided in Table 2 and still not represent an exposure above the TLV® or the Action Limit. To make this determination, a detailed analysis is required. Methods are fully described in the *Documentation*, in industrial hygiene and safety books, and in other sources.

Provided that there is adequate information on the heat stress effects of the required clothing, the first level of detailed analysis is a task analysis that includes a time-weighted average of the Effective WBGT (environmental WBGT plus clothing adjustment factor) and the metabolic rate. Some clothing adjustment factors have been suggested in Table 1. Factors for other clothing ensembles appearing in the literature can be used in similar fashion following good professional judgment. The TLV® and Action Limit are shown in Figure 2.

The second level of detailed analysis would follow a rational model of heat stress, such as the International Standards Organization (ISO) Predicted Heat Strain (ISO 7933 2004; Malchaire et al., 2001). While a rational method (versus the empirically derived WBGT thresholds) is computationally more difficult, it permits a better understanding of the sources of the heat stress and is a means to appreciate the benefits of proposed modifications in the exposure. Guidance to the ISO method and other rational methods is described in the literature.

The screening criteria require the minimal set of data to make a determination. Detailed analyses require more data about the exposures. Following Figure 1, the next question asks about the availability of data for a detailed analysis. If these data are not available, the NO branch takes the evaluation to physiological monitoring to assess the degree of heat strain.

If the data for a detailed analysis are available, the next step in Figure 1 is the detailed analysis. If the exposure does not exceed the criteria for the Action Limit (or unacclimatized workers) for the appropriate detailed analysis (e.g., WBGT analysis, another empirical method, or a rational method), then the NO branch can be taken. If the Action Limit criteria are exceeded but the criteria for the TLV® (or acclimatized workers) in the detailed analysis are not exceeded, then implement general controls and continue to monitor the conditions. General controls include training for workers and supervisors, heat stress hygiene practices, and medical surveillance. If the exposure exceeds the limits for acclimatized workers in the detailed analysis, the YES branch leads to physiological monitoring as the only alternative to demonstrate that adequate protection is provided.

Section 4: *Heat Strain.* The risk and severity of excessive heat strain will vary widely among people, even under identical heat stress conditions. The normal physiological responses to heat stress provide an opportunity to monitor heat strain among workers and to use this information to assess the level of heat strain present in the workforce, to control exposures, and to assess the effectiveness of implemented controls. Table 4 provides guidance for acceptable limits of heat strain.

Following good industrial hygiene sampling practice, which considers likely extremes and the less tolerant workers, the absence of any of these limiting observations indicates acceptable management of the heat stress exposures. With acceptable levels of heat strain, the NO branch in Figure 1 is taken. Nevertheless, if the heat strain among workers is considered acceptable at the time, consideration of the general controls is recommended. In addition, periodic physiological monitoring should be continued to ensure acceptable levels of heat strain.

If limiting heat strain is found during the physiological assessments, then the YES branch is taken. This means that suitable job-specific controls should be implemented to a sufficient extent to control heat strain. The job-specific controls include engineering controls, administrative controls, and personal protection.

After implementation of the job-specific controls, it is necessary to assess their effectiveness and to adjust them as needed.

TLV®–PA

Heat Stress and Heat Strain — 209

TABLE 4. Guidelines for Limiting Heat Strain

Monitoring heat strain and signs and symptoms of heat-related disorders is sound industrial hygiene practice, especially when clothing may significantly reduce heat loss. For surveillance purposes, a pattern of workers exceeding the heat strain limits is indicative of a need to control the exposures. On an individual basis, the limits represent a time to cease an exposure and allow for recovery.

One or more of the following measures may mark excessive heat strain, and an individual's exposure to heat stress should be discontinued when any of the following occur:

- Sustained (several minutes) heart rate is in excess of 180 bpm (beats per minute) minus the individual's age in years (e.g., 180 – age), for individuals with assessed normal cardiac performance; or
- Body core temperature is greater than 38.5°C (101.3°F) for medically selected and acclimatized personnel; or greater than 38°C (100.4°F) in unselected, unacclimatized workers; or
- Recovery heart rate at one minute after a peak work effort is greater than 120 bpm; or
- There are symptoms of sudden and severe fatigue, nausea, dizziness, or lightheadedness.

An individual may be at greater risk of heat-related disorders if:
- Profuse sweating is sustained over hours; or
- Weight loss over a shift is greater than 1.5% of body weight; or
- 24-hour urinary sodium excretion is less than 50 mmoles

EMERGENCY RESPONSE: If a worker appears to be disoriented or confused, suffers inexplicable irritability, malaise, or chills, the worker should be removed for rest in a cool location with rapidly circulating air and kept under skilled observation. Absent medical advice to the contrary, treat this as an emergency with immediate transport to a hospital. An emergency response plan is necessary.

— **NEVER ignore anyone's signs or symptoms of heat-related disorders** —

Section 5: *Heat Stress Management and Controls.* The elements of a heat stress management program including general and job-specific controls should be considered in the light of local conditions and the judgment of the industrial hygienist. The recommendation to initiate a heat stress management program is marked by 1) heat stress levels that exceed the Action Limit or 2) work in clothing ensembles that limit heat loss. In either case, general controls should be considered (Table 5).

Heat stress hygiene practices are particularly important because they reduce the risk that an individual may suffer a heat-related disorder. The key elements are fluid replacement, self-determination of exposures, health status monitoring, maintenance of a healthy lifestyle, and adjustment of expectations based on acclimatization state. The hygiene practices require the full cooperation of supervision and workers.

TLV®–PA

210 — Thermal Stress

TABLE 5. Elements to Consider in Establishing a Heat Stress Management Program

Monitor heat stress (e.g., WBGT Screening Criteria in Table 2) and heat strain (Table 4) to confirm adequate control

General Controls

- Provide accurate verbal and written instructions, annual training programs, and other information about heat stress and strain
- Encourage drinking small volumes (approximately 1 cup) of cool, palatable water (or other acceptable fluid replacement drink) about every 20 minutes
- Encourage employees to report symptoms of heat-related disorders to a supervisor
- Encourage self-limitation of exposures when a supervisor is not present
- Encourage co-worker observation to detect signs and symptoms of heat strain in others
- Counsel and monitor those who take medications that may compromise normal cardiovascular, blood pressure, body temperature regulation, renal, or sweat gland functions; and those who abuse or are recovering from the abuse of alcohol or other intoxicants
- Encourage healthy lifestyles, ideal body weight and electrolyte balance
- Adjust expectations of those returning to work after absence from hot exposure situations and encourage consumption of salty foods (with approval of physician if on a salt-restricted diet)
- Consider pre-placement medical screening to identify those susceptible to systemic heat injury
- Monitor the heat stress conditions and reports of heat-related disorders

Job-Specific Controls

- Consider engineering controls that reduce the metabolic rate, provide general air movement, reduce process heat and water vapor release, and shield radiant heat sources, among others
- Consider administrative controls that set acceptable exposure times, allow sufficient recovery, and limit physiological strain
- Consider personal protection that is demonstrated effective for the specific work practices and conditions at the location

— **NEVER ignore anyone's signs or symptoms of heat-related disorders** —

TLV®–PA

Heat Stress and Heat Strain — 211

In addition to general controls, appropriate job-specific controls are often required to provide adequate protection. During the consideration of job-specific controls, Table 2 and Figure 2, along with Tables 1 and 3, provide a framework to appreciate the interactions among acclimatization state, metabolic rate, work-rest cycles, and clothing. Among administrative controls, Table 4 provides acceptable physiological and signs/symptoms limits. The mix of job-specific controls can be selected and implemented only after a review of the demands and constraints of any particular situation. Once implemented, their effectiveness must be confirmed and the controls maintained.

The prime objective of heat stress management is the prevention of heat stroke, which is life-threatening and the most serious of the heat-related disorders. The heat stroke victim is often manic, disoriented, confused, delirious, or unconscious. The victim's body core temperature is greater than 40°C (104°F). If signs of heat stroke appear, aggressive cooling should be started immediately, and emergency care and hospitalization are essential. The prompt treatment of other heat-related disorders generally results in full recovery, but medical advice should be sought for treatment and return-to-work protocols. It is worth noting that the possibility of accidents and injury increases with the level of heat stress.

Prolonged increases in deep body temperatures and chronic exposures to high levels of heat stress are associated with other disorders such as temporary infertility (male and female), elevated heart rate, sleep disturbance, fatigue, and irritability. During the first trimester of pregnancy, a sustained core temperature greater than 39°C may endanger the fetus.

TLV®–PA

References

1. International Organization for Standardization (ISO): Ergonomics of the thermal environment – Analytical determination and interpretation of heat stress using calculation of the predicted heat strain. ISO 7933:2004. ISO, Geneva (2004).
2. Malchaire J; Piette A; Kampmann B; et al.: Development and validation of the predicted heat strain model. Ann Occup Hyg. 45(2):123–135 (2001).

2012 PHYSICAL AGENTS UNDER STUDY

The TLV® Physical Agents Committee solicits information, especially data, which may assist it in its deliberations regarding the following agents and issues. Comments and suggestions, accompanied by substantiating evidence in the form of peer-reviewed literature, should be forwarded in electronic format to The Science Group, ACGIH® (science@acgih.org). In addition, ACGIH® solicits recommendations for additional agents and issues of concern to the industrial hygiene and occupational health communities. Please refer to the ACGIH® TLV®/BEI® Development Process found on the ACGIH® website for a detailed discussion covering this procedure and methods for input to ACGIH® (http://www.acgih.org/TLV/DevProcess.htm).

The Under Study list is published each year by February 1 on the ACGIH® website (www.acgih.org/TLV/Studies.htm), in the ACGIH® Annual Reports, and later in the annual *TLVs® and BEIs®* book. In addition, the Under Study list is updated by July 31 into a two-tier list.

- Tier 1 entries indicate which chemical substances and physical agents **may** move forward as an NIC or NIE in the upcoming year, based on their status in the development process.
- Tier 2 consists of those chemical substances and physical agents that **will not** move forward, but will either remain on or be removed from, the Under Study list for the next year.

This updated list will remain in two-tiers for the balance of the year. ACGIH® will continue this practice of updating the Under Study list by February 1 and establishing the two-tier list by July 31 each year.

The substances and issues listed below are as of January 1, 2012. *After this date, please refer to the ACGIH® website (http://www.acgih.org/TLV/Studies.htm) for the up-to-date list.*

1. Acoustic
     - Noise/Impulse noise
2. Electromagnetic Radiation and Fields
     - Light and near-infrared radiation
     - Sub-Radiofrequency and magnetic fields
     - Static magnetic fields
3. Ergonomics
     - Hand-arm vibration
     - Localized fatigue
     - Whole-body vibration
4. Thermal Stress
     - Cold stress
     - Heat stress

Other Issues Under Study

1. Contact ultrasound
2. Hypobaric pressure
3. Neuroendocrine effects of light
4. Whole body fatigue

TLV®–PA

2012
Biologically Derived
Airborne Contaminants

Contents

BDAC

214 — Members

2011 BIOAEROSOLS COMMITTEE

Joseph Torey Nalbone, MS, PhD, CIH — Chair
Paula H. Vance, SM(ASCP), SM(NRM) — Vice Chair
Francis (Bud) J. Offermann, CIH, PE
Carol Y. Rao, ScD, MS, CIH

INTRODUCTION TO THE BIOLOGICALLY DERIVED AIRBORNE CONTAMINANTS

Biologically derived airborne contaminants include bioaerosols (airborne particles composed of or derived from living organisms) and volatile organic compounds that organisms release. Bioaerosols include microorganisms (i.e., culturable, nonculturable, and dead microorganisms) and fragments, toxins, and particulate waste products from all varieties of living things. Biologically derived contaminants are ubiquitous in nature and may be modified by human activity. Humans are repeatedly exposed, day after day, to a wide variety of such materials.

TLVs® exist for certain substances of biological origin, including cellulose; some wood, cotton, flour and grain dusts; nicotine; pyrethrum; starch; subtilisins (proteolytic enzymes); sucrose; vegetable oil mist; and volatile compounds produced by living organisms (e.g., ammonia, carbon dioxide, ethanol, and hydrogen sulfide). However, for the reasons identified below, there are no TLVs® against which to compare environmental air concentrations of most materials of biological origin.

ACGIH® has developed and separately published guidance on the assessment, control, remediation, and prevention of biologically derived contamination of indoor environments.[1] Indoor biological contamination is defined as the presence of a) biologically derived aerosols, gases, and vapors of a kind and concentration likely to cause disease or predispose humans to disease; b) inappropriate concentrations of outdoor bioaerosols, especially in buildings designed to prevent their entry; or c) indoor microbial growth and remnants of biological growth that may become aerosolized and to which humans may be exposed. The term "biological agent" refers to a substance of biological origin that is capable of producing an adverse effect, e.g., an infection or a hypersensitivity, irritant, inflammatory, or other response.

The ACGIH®-recommended approach to assessing and controlling bioaerosol exposures relies on visually inspecting buildings, assessing occupant symptoms, evaluating building performance, monitoring potential environmental sources, and applying professional judgment. The published guidance provides background information on the major groups of bioaerosols, including their sources and health effects, and describes methods to collect, analyze, and interpret bioaerosol samples from potential environmental sources. Occasionally, environmental monitoring detects a single or predominating biological contaminant. More commonly, monitoring reveals a mixture of many biologically derived materials, reflecting the diverse and interactive nature of indoor microenvironments. Therefore, environmental sampling for bioaerosols should be conducted only following careful formulation of testable hypotheses about potential bioaerosol sources and mechanisms by which workers may be exposed to bioaerosols from these sources. Even when investigators work from testable hypotheses and well-formulated sampling plans, results from environmental bioaerosol monitoring may be inconclusive and occasionally misleading.

There are no TLVs® for interpreting environmental measurements of a) total culturable or countable bioaerosols (e.g., total bacteria or fungi); b) specific culturable or countable bioaerosols (e.g., *Aspergillus fumigatus*); c) infectious agents (e.g., *Legionella pneumophila* or *Mycobacterium tuberculosis*); or d) assayable biological contaminants (e.g., endotoxin, mycotoxin, antigens, or microbial volatile organic compounds) for the following reasons.

BDAC

216 — Introduction

A. Total culturable or countable bioaerosols. Culturable bioaerosols are those bacteria and fungi that can be grown in laboratory culture. Such results are reported as the number of colony-forming units (CFU). Countable bioaerosols are those pollen grains, fungal spores, bacterial cells, and other material that can be identified and counted by microscope. A general TLV® for culturable or countable bioaerosol concentrations is not scientifically supportable because of the following:

1. Culturable microorganisms and countable biological particles do not comprise a single entity, i.e., bioaerosols in occupational settings are generally complex mixtures of many different microbial, animal, and plant particles.

2. Human responses to bioaerosols range from innocuous effects to serious, even fatal, diseases, depending on the specific material involved and workers' susceptibility to it. Therefore, an appropriate exposure limit for one bioaerosol may be entirely inappropriate for another.

3. It is not possible to collect and evaluate all bioaerosol components using a single sampling method. Many reliable methods are available to collect and analyze bioaerosol materials. However, different methods of sample collection and analysis may result in different estimates of culturable and countable bioaerosol concentrations.

4. At present, information relating culturable or countable bioaerosol concentrations to health effects is generally insufficient to describe exposure–response relationships.

B. Specific culturable or countable bioaerosols other than infectious agents. Specific TLVs® for individual culturable or countable bioaerosols have not been established to prevent hypersensitivity, irritant, or toxic responses. At present, information relating culturable or countable bioaerosol concentrations to health effects consists largely of case reports and qualitative exposure assessments. The data available are generally insufficient to describe exposure–response relationships. Reasons for the absence of good epidemiologic data on such relationships include the following:

1. Most data on concentrations of specific bioaerosols are derived from indicator measurements rather than from measurements of actual effector agents. For example, investigators use the air concentration of culturable fungi to represent exposure to airborne fungal antigens. In addition, most measurements are from either area or source samples. These monitoring approaches are less likely to reflect human exposure accurately than would personal sampling for actual effector agents.

2. Bioaerosol components and concentrations vary widely within and among different occupational and environmental settings. Unfortunately, replicate sampling is uncommon in bioaerosol assessments. Further, the most commonly used air-sampling devices for indoor monitoring are designed to collect "grab" samples over relatively short time intervals. Measurements from single, short-term grab samples may be orders of magnitude higher or lower than long-term average concentrations and are unlikely to represent workplace exposures accurately. Some organisms and sources release aerosols as "concentration bursts," which may only rarely be detected by limited grab sampling. Nevertheless, such episodic bioaerosol releases may produce significant health effects.

BDAC

3. In studies of single workplaces, the number of persons affected by exposure to biological agents may be small if contamination is localized, thereby affecting only a fraction of the building occupants. However, data from different studies can seldom be combined to reach meaningful numbers of test subjects because the specific types of biological agents responsible for bioaerosol-related illnesses are diverse and often differ from study to study. These factors contribute to the low statistical power common in evaluations of cause–effect relationships between exposures to specific biological agents and building-related health complaints.

C. **Infectious agents.** Human dose–response data are available for only a few infectious bioaerosols. At present, air-sampling protocols for infectious agents are limited and suitable primarily for research endeavors. In most routine exposure settings, public health measures, such as immunization, active case finding, and medical treatment, remain the primary defenses against infectious bioaerosols. Facilities associated with increased risks for transmission of airborne infectious diseases (e.g., microbiology laboratories, animal-handling facilities, and health-care settings) should employ engineering controls to minimize air concentrations of infectious agents. Further, such facilities should consider the need for administrative controls and personal protective equipment to prevent the exposure of workers to these bioaerosols.

D. **Assayable biological contaminants.** Assayable, biologically derived contaminants (e.g., endotoxin, mycotoxins, antigens, and volatile organic compounds) are microbial, animal, or plant substances that can be detected using chemical, immunological, or biological assays. Evidence does not yet support TLVs® for any of these substances. However, assay methods for certain common airborne antigens and endotoxin are steadily improving, and field validation of these assays is also progressing. Dose–response relationships for some assayable bioaerosols have been observed in experimental studies and occasionally in epidemiologic surveys. Therefore, exposure limits for certain assayable, biologically derived, airborne contaminants may be appropriate in the future. In addition, innovative molecular techniques are becoming available for specific bioaerosols currently detectable only by culture or counting.

ACGIH® actively solicits information, comments, and data in the form of peer-reviewed literature on health effects associated with bioaerosol exposures in occupational and related environments that may help the Bioaerosols Committee evaluate the potential for proposing exposure guidelines for selected biologically derived airborne contaminants. Such information should be sent, preferably in electronic format, to The Science Group, ACGIH® (science@acgih.org).

Reference

1. ACGIH®: Bioaerosols: Assessment and Control. JM Macher, Ed; HM Ammann, HA Burge, DK Milton, and PR Morey, Asst. Eds. ACGIH®, Cincinnati, OH (1999).

BDAC

218 — Under Study

BIOLOGICALLY DERIVED AGENTS UNDER STUDY

The Bioaerosols Committee solicits information, especially data, which may assist it in the establishment of TLVs® for biologically derived airborne contaminants. Comments and suggestions, accompanied by substantiating evidence in the form of peer-reviewed literature, should be forwarded in electronic format to The Science Group, ACGIH® (science@acgih.org).

The substances and issues listed below are as of January 1, 2012. *After this date, please refer to the ACGIH® website (http://www.acgih.org/TLV/Studies.htm) for the up-to-date list.*

Agents

gram negative bacterial endotoxin
(1-3) beta, D-glucan

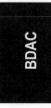

CAS NUMBER INDEX

CAS

CAS NUMBER INDEX

CAS NUMBER INDEX

CAS

CAS NUMBER INDEX

CAS

CAS NUMBER INDEX

CAS

CAS

CAS NUMBER INDEX

CAS

226 — CAS

CAS NUMBER INDEX

CAS

CAS NUMBER INDEX

CAS

228 — CAS

CAS NUMBER INDEX

CAS

CAS NUMBER INDEX

CAS

230 — CAS

CAS NUMBER INDEX

CAS

CAS NUMBER INDEX

CAS

CAS NUMBER INDEX

CAS

CAS NUMBER INDEX

CAS

234 — CAS

CAS NUMBER INDEX

CAS

CAS NUMBER INDEX

CAS

236 — CAS

CAS NUMBER INDEX

CAS

NOTES

238 — Notes

NOTES

Endnotes and Abbreviations

*	2012 Adoption.
‡	See Notice of Intended Changes (NIC).
( )	Adopted values or notations enclosed are those for which changes are proposed in the NIC.
†	2012 Revision or Addition to the Notice of Intended Changes.
A	Refers to Appendix A: Carcinogenicity.
C	Ceiling limit; *see* definition in the "Introduction to the Chemical Substances."
(D)	Simple asphyxiant; *see* discussion covering *Minimal Oxygen Content* found in the "Definitions and Notations" section following the NIC tables.
(E)	The value is for particulate matter containing no asbestos and < 1% crystalline silica.
(F)	Respirable fibers: length > 5 μm; aspect ratio $\geq$ 3:1, as determined by the membrane filter method at 400–450X magnification (4-mm objective), using phase-contrast illumination.
(G)	As measured by the vertical elutriator, cotton-dust sampler; *see* the TLV® *Documentation*.
(H)	Aerosol only.
(I)	Inhalable fraction; *see* Appendix C, paragraph A.
(IFV)	Inhalable fraction and vapor; *see* Notations/Endnotes section, p. 70.
(J)	Does not include stearates of toxic metals.
(K)	Should not exceed 2 mg/m^3 respirable particulate mass.
(L)	Exposure by all routes should be carefully controlled to levels as low as possible.
(M)	Classification refers to sulfuric acid contained in strong inorganic acid mists.
(O)	Sampled by method that does not collect vapor.
(P)	Application restricted to conditions in which there are negligible aerosol exposures.
(R)	Respirable fraction; *see* Appendix C, paragraph C.
(T)	Thoracic fraction; *see* Appendix C, paragraph B.
(V)	Vapor and aerosol.

B	= Background; *see* BEI Intro.
BEI	= Substances for which there is a Biological Exposure Index or Indices (*see* BEI® section).
	BEI_A: *see* BEI® for Acetylcholinesterase Inhibiting Pesticides
	BEI_M: *see* BEI® for Methemoglobin Inducers
	BEI_P: *see* BEI® for Polycyclic Aromatic Hydrocarbons (PAHs)
DSEN	= Dermal Sensitization; *see* definition in the "Definitions and Notations" section.
MW	= Molecular weight.
NOS	= Not otherwise specified.
Nq	= Nonquantitative; *see* BEI Intro.
Ns	= Nonspecific; *see* BEI Intro.
RSEN	= Respiratory Sensitization; *see* definition in the "Definitions and Notations" section.
SEN	= Sensitization; *see* definition in the "Definitions and Notations" section.
Skin	= Danger of cutaneous absorption; *see* discussion under Skin in the "Definitions and Notations" section.
Sq	= Semi-quantitative; *see* BEI Intro.
STEL	= Short-term exposure limit; *see* definition in the "Introduction to the Chemical Substances."
TWA	= 8-hour, time-weighted average; *see* definition in the "Introduction to the Chemical Substances."
ppm	= Parts of vapor or gas per million parts of contaminated air by volume at NTP conditions (25°C; 760 torr).
mg/m^3	= Milligrams of substance per cubic meter of air.

TLV®

BEI®

1330 Kemper Meadow Drive
Cincinnati, Ohio 45240-4148
Phone: (513)742-2020; Fax: (513)742-3355
www.acgih.org

ISBN: 978-1-607260-48-6 © 2012

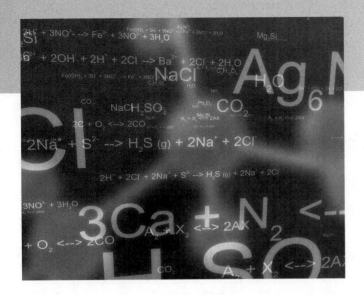

APPENDIX C

Conversion of Units

All physical units of measurement can be reduced to one or more of three dimensions: mass, length, and time. Reducing units to basic dimensions simplifies problem solving and makes comparison between operations, or operations and standards, easier and more accurate.

For example, three airflows could be measured: the first in liters per second, the second in cubic meters per second, and the third in cubic feet per minute. Then the total volume of air in each of the three samplings could be converted to cubic meters or cubic feet, and the airflows could be compared. In another situation, the results of atmospheric pollution studies and stack sampling surveys are often reported as grains per cubic foot, grams per cubic foot, or pounds per cubic foot. The degree of contamination is usually reported in the standard unit of parts of contaminant per million parts of air.

If physical measurements are made or reported in different units, they must be converted to the standard units if any comparisons are to be meaningful.

In order to achieve a uniform system of measurement, governments representing 98 percent of the world's population have committed to using the Système International d'Unités *(SI)* version of the metric system (McQueen MJ. *Conversion to SI units: The Canadian experience.* JAMA 256:3001–3002, 1986.) In 1975, Congress passed the Metric Conversion Act, which endorsed a voluntary conversion to SI, but the English system is still in popular use in the United States. The SI system, however, is the standard for the international scientific community.

FUNDAMENTAL UNITS

Because of the need to conserve time and space when reporting data, universally accepted abbreviations are often used in place of unit names. This appendix shows the abbreviations used throughout this book and those generally agreed on by industrial hygiene practitioners. Conversion factors are provided when data are reported in nonstandard units.

Each measurement unit, such as length, area, and flow, has a table of conversion factors. To use the table to find the numerical value of the quantity desired, locate the unit to be converted in the first column. Then multiply this value by the number appearing at the intersection of the row and the column containing the desired unit. The answer will be the numerical value in the desired unit. Various English system and metric system units are given for your convenience.

An explanation of the SI system and official conversion factors are given to a 6- or 7-place accuracy in ASTM standard E380-76 (ANSI Z210.1-1976). (This standard is available, although not listed in the ANSI Catalog.)

TABLE C–B	Units Derived from Combinations of Base Units	
Derived Unit	**Name and Symbol**	**Expressed as SI Base Derived Unit**
Area	Square meter	m^2
Volume	Cubic meter	m^3
Force	Newton (N)	$kg \cdot m \cdot s^{-2} (kg \cdot m/s^2)$
Frequency	Hertz (Hz)	s^{-1}
Work, energy, heat	Joule (J)	$N \cdot m$
Power	Watt (W)	$J \cdot s^{-1} (J/S)$
Pressure	Pascal (Pa)	$kg \cdot m^{-1} \cdot s^{-2} (N/m^2)$
Electric potential	Volt (V)	$W \cdot A^{-1} (W/A)$
Electric charge	Coulomb (C)	$A \cdot s$
Electric capacitance	Farad (F)	$A \cdot sV^{-1} (A\ s/V\ or\ C/N)$
Inductance	Henry (H)	$V \cdot s \cdot A^{-1} (V \cdot s/A)$

TABLE C–C	Multiples and Submultiples of SI Units	
Factor	**Prefix**	**Symbol**
10^{12}	tetra	T
10^{9}	giga	G
10^{6}	mega	M
10^{3}	kilo	k
10^{-3}	milli	m
10^{-6}	micro	μ
10^{-9}	nano	n
10^{-1}	pico	P
10^{-15}	femto	f
10^{-18}	atto	a

Source: Tables C–A through C–C are reprinted with permission from *JAMA* 256(21) Dec. 5, 1986, pp. 3001–3002, _1986, American Medical Association.

TABLE C–A	Base Système International (SI) Units	
Physical Quantity	**Base Units**	**SI Symbol**
Length	Meter	m
Mass	Kilogram	kg
Time	Second	s
Amount of substance	Mole	mol
Thermodynamic temperature	Kelvin	K
Electric current	Ampere	A
Luminous intensity	Candela	cd

TABLE C–D	Area					
To Obtain		**Square Meter (m²)**	**Square Inch (in.²)**	**Square Foot (ft²)**	**Square Centimeter (cm²)**	**Square Millimeter (mm²)**
Multiply Number of	**by**					
Square meter		1	1,550	10.76	10,000	10^6
Square inch		6.452×10^{-3}	1	6.94×10^{-3}	6.452	645.2
Square foot		0.0929	144	1	929.0	92,903
Square centimeter		0.0001	0.115	0.001	1	100
Square millimeter		10–6	0.00155	0.00001	0.01	1

TABLE C–E   Length

To Obtain		Meter (m)	Centimeter (cm)	Millimeter (mm)	Micron (μ) or Micrometer	Angstrom Unit (Å)	Inch (in.)	Foot (ft)
Multiply Number of	by							
Meter		1	100	1,000	10^6	10^{10}	39.37	3.28
Centimeter		0.01	1	10	10^4	10^8	0.394	0.0328
Millimeter		0.001	0.1	1	10^3	10^7	0.0394	0.00328
Micron		10^{-6}	10^{-4}	10^{-3}	1	10^4	3.94×10^{-5}	3.28×10^{-6}
Angstrom		10^{-10}	10^{-8}	10^{-7}	10^{-4}	1	3.94×10^{-9}	3.28×10^{-10}
Inch		0.0254	2.540	25.40	2.54×10^4	2.54×10^8	1	0.0833
Foot		0.305	30.48	304.8	304,800	3.048×10^9	12	1

TABLE C–F   Density

To Obtain		gm/cm³	lb/ft³	lb/gal
Multiply Number of	by			
Gram/cubic centimeter		1	62.43	8.345
Pound/cubic foot		0.01602	1	0.1337
Pound/gallon (U.S.)		0.1198	7.481	1

Note: 1 grain/ft³ = 2.28 mg/m³

TABLE C–G   Force

To Obtain		Dyne	Newton (N)	Kilogram-Force	Pound-Force (lbf)
Multiply Number of	by				
Dyne		1	1.0×10^{-5}	1.02×10^4	2.248×10^4
Newton		1.0×10^5	1	0.1020	0.2248
Kilogram-force		9.807×10^{-5}	9.807	1	2.205
Pound-force		4.448×10^{-5}	4.448	0.4536	1

TABLE C–H   Mass

To Obtain		Gram (gm)	Kilogram (kg)	Grains (gr)	Ounce (avoir) (oz)	Pound (avoir) (lb)
Multiply Number of	by					
Gram		1	0.001	15.432	0.03527	0.00220
Kilogram		1,000	1	15,432	35.27	2.205
Grain		0.0648	6.480×10^{-5}	1	2.286×10^{-3}	1.429×10^{-4}
Ounce		28.35	0.02835	437.5	1	0.0625
Pound		453.59	0.4536	7,000	16	1

TABLE C-I	Volume				
To Obtain		**ft³**	**Gallon (U.S. Liquid)**	**Liters**	**cm³**	**m³**
Multiply Number of	**by**					

To Obtain / **Multiply Number of**	**by**	**ft³**	**Gallon (U.S. Liquid)**	**Liters**	**cm³**	**m³**
Cubic foot		1	7.481	28.32	28,320	0.0283
Gallon (U.S. liquid)		0.1337	1	3.785	3,785	3.79×10^{-3}
Liter		0.03531	0.2642	1	1,000	1×10^{-3}
Cubic centimeters		3.531×10^{-5}	2.64×10^{-4}	0.001	1	10^{-6}
Cubic meters		35.31	264.2	1,000	10^{6}	1

TABLE C-J	Velocity					
To Obtain / **Multiply Number of**	**by**	**cm/s**	**m/s**	**km/hr**	**ft/s**	**ft/min**	**mph**
---	---	---	---	---	---	---	---
Centimeter/second		1	0.01	0.036	0.0328	1.968	0.02237
Meter/second		100	1	3.6	3.281	196.85	2.237
Kilometer/hour		27.78	0.2778	1	0.9113	54.68	0.6214
Foot /second		30.48	0.3048	18.29	1	60	0.6818
Foot /minute		0.5080	0.00508	0.0183	0.0166	1	0.01136
Mile per hour		44.70	0.4470	1.609	1.467	88	1

TABLE C-K	Flow Rates					
To Obtain / **Multiply Number of**	**by**	**L/min**	**m³/s**	**m³/hr**	**gal/min**	**ft³/min**	**ft³/s**
---	---	---	---	---	---	---	---
Liter/minute		1	1.67×10^{-5}	0.06	0.2640	0.0353	5.89×10^{-4}
Cubic meters/second		4.63×10^{-3}	1	2.77×10^{-4}	1.22×10^{-3}	1.63×10^{-4}	2.7×10^{-6}
Cubic meter/hour		16.67	2.78×10^{-4}	1	4.4	0.588	9.89×10^{-3}
Gallon (U.S.)/minute		3.78	6.3×10^{-5}	0.227	1	0.1338	2.23×10^{-3}
Cubic foot /minute		28.32	4.71×10^{-4}	1.699	7.50	1	0.01667
Cubic foot /second		1.69×10^{3}	2.83×10^{-3}	1.02×10^{2}	448.8	60	1

TABLE C-L	Heat, Energy, or Work						
To Obtain / **Multiply Number of**	**by**	**Joule**	**ft-lb**	**kwh**	**hp-hour**	**kcal**	**cal**	**Btu**
---	---	---	---	---	---	---	---	---
Joules		1	0.737	2.773×10^{-7}	3.725×10^{-7}	2.39×10^{-4}	0.2390	9.478×10^{-4}
Foot-pound		1,356	1	3.766×10^{-7}	5.05×10^{-7}	3.24×10^{-4}	0.3241	1.285×10^{-3}
Kilowatt-hour		3.6×10^{6}	2.66×10^{6}	1	1.341	860.57	860,565	3,412
Hp-hour		2.68×10^{6}	1.98×10^{6}	0.7455	1	641.62	641,615	2,545
Kilocalorie		4,184	3,086	1.162×10^{-3}	1.558×10^{-3}	1	1,000	3.9657
Calorie		4,184	3,086	1.162×10^{-6}	1.558×10^{-6}	0.001	1	0.00397
British thermal unit		1,055	778.16	2.930×10^{-4}	3.93×10^{-4}	0.252	252	1

TABLE C–M Emission Rates

To Obtain		gm/s	gm/min	kg/hr	kg/day	lb/min	lb/hr	lb/day
Multiply								
Number of	by							
Gram/second		1	60	3.6	86.40	0.13228	7.9367	190.48
Gram/minute		0.016667	1	0.06	1.4400	2.2046×10^{-3}	0.13228	3.1747
Kilogram/hour		0.27778	16.667	1	24	0.036744	2.2046	52.911
Kilogram/day		0.011574	0.69444	0.041667	1	1.5310×10^{-3}	9.1860×10^{-2}	2.2046
Pound/minute		7.5598	453.59	27.215	653.17	1	60	1440
Pound/hour		0.12600	7.5598	0.45359	10.886	1.6667×10^{-2}	1	24
Pound/day		5.2499×10^{-3}	0.31499	1.8900×10^{-2}	0.45359	6.9444×10^{-4}	4.1667×10^{-2}	1

TABLE C–N Pressure

To Obtain		lb/in.² (psi)	atm	in. (Hg) 32°F 0°C	mm (Hg) 32°F 0°C	k Pa (k N/m²)	ft (H₂0) 60°F 15°C	in. (H₂O)	lb/ft²
Multiply									
Number of	by								
Pound/square inch		1	0.068	2.036	51.71	6.895	2.309	27.71	144
Atmospheres		14.696	1	29.92	760	101.32	33.93	407.2	2,116
Inch (Hg)		0.4912	0.033	1	25.40	3.386	1.134	13.61	70.73
Millimeter (Hg)		0.01934	0.0013	0.039	1	0.1333	0.04464	0.5357	2.785
Kilopascals		0.1450	9.87×10^{-3}	0.2953	7.502	1	0.3460*	4.019	20.89
Foot (H₂0)(15°C)		0.4332	0.0294	0.8819	22.40	2.989*	1	12	62.37
Inch (H₂0)		0.03609	0.0024	0.073	1.867	0.2488	0.0833	1	5.197
Pound/square foot		0.0069	4.72×10^{-4}	0.014	0.359	0.04788	0.016	0.193	1

* at 4°C

TABLE C–O Radiant Energy Units

To Obtain		Erg	Joule (J)	W-s	µW-s	g-cal
Multiply	by					
Erg		1	10^{-7}	10^{-7}	0.1	2.39×10^{-8}
Joule		10^7	1	1	10^6	0.239
Watt-second		10^7	1	1	10^6	0.239
Microwatt-second		10	10^{-6}	10^{-6}	1	2.39×10^{-7}
Gram-calorie		4.19×10^7	4.19	4.19	4.19×10^6	1

TABLE C–P Energy/Unit Area (Dose Limits)

To Obtain		erg/cm²	J/cm²	W-s/cm²	µW-s/cm²	g-cal/m²
Multiply	by					
Erg/square centimeter		1	10^{-7}	10^{-7}	0.1	2.39×10^{-8}
Joule/square centimeter		10^7	1	1	10^6	0.239
Watt-second/square centimeter		10^7	1	1	10^6	0.239
Microwatt-second/square centimeter		10	10^{-6}	10^{-6}	1	2.39×10^{-7}
Gram-calorie/square centimeter		4.19×10^7	4.19	4.19	4.19×10^6	1

SIGNIFICANT FIGURES

Measurements often result in what are called *approximate numbers,* in contrast to *discrete counts*. For example, the dimensions of a table can be reported as 29.6 in. (75.2 cm) by 50.2 in. (127.5 cm). This implies that the measurement is to the nearest tenth of an inch (or centimeter) and that the table is less than 50.25 in. (127.6 cm) and more than 50.15 in. (127.4 cm) in length. One can show the same thing for the width, using the following symbolic notations:

75.0 cm (29.55 in.) < width < 75.3 cm (29.65 in.)

If, on the other hand, one knows the degree of precision of the measurement (say, 0.03 cm or ± 0.08 cm), one may write:

50.2 ± 0.3 or 50.2 ± 0.8

to indicate the degree of accuracy of the measurement of the length.

In reporting results, the number of significant digits that can be recorded is determined by the precision of the instruments used.

Rules
- In any approximate number, the *significant digits* include the digit that determines the degree of precision of the number and all digits to the left of it, except for zeros used to place the decimal.
- All digits from 1 to 9 are significant.
- All zeros between significant digits are significant.
- Final zeros of decimal numbers are significant. For example:

Number	Number of Significant Digits
0.0702	3
0.07020	4
70.20	4
7,002	4
7,020	3

Scientific Notation

One case where it is difficult to determine the number of significant digits is the figure 7,000. In general, it is considered to have only one significant digit. It is better to use scientific notation.

In standard scientific notation, the number is written as a number between 1 and 10, in which only the significant digits are shown, multiplied by an exponential number to the base 10. For example:

Number	Number of Significant Digits
$5,320,000 = 5.32 \times 10^6$	3
$= 5.320 \times 10^6$	4
$= 5.3200 \times 10^6$	5
$0.00000532 = 5.32 \times 10^{-6}$	3

Addition and Subtraction

The result must not have more decimal places than the number with the fewest decimal places. For example:

21.262	should be	21.3
23.74	should be	23.7
139.6	should be	139.6
184.602	should be	184.6

Multiplication and Division

The result must not have more significant places than are possessed by the number with the fewest significant digits. For example:

$$(50.20)(29.6) = 1485.92$$
$$= 1490$$
$$= 1.49 \times 10^3$$

LOGARITHMS

Logarithms are exponents. The logarithm of any number is the power to which a selected base must be raised to produce the number. The laws of exponents apply to logarithms.

The following two equations:

$$a^x = y$$

and

$$x = \log_a y$$

are two ways of expressing the same thing, that is, the exponent applied to a to give y is equal to x. The value a is called the base of the system of logarithms.

Although any positive number greater than 1 can be used as the base of some system of logarithms, there are two systems in general use. These are the *common* (or Briggs') system and the *natural* (or Napierian) system. In the common system, the base is 10; in the natural system, the base is the irrational number e = 2.71828 . . .

Common Logarithms

Common logarithms use the base 10 and are identified by the notation *log*. The common logarithm of a number consists of a characteristic, which locates the decimal point in the number, and a mantissa, which defines the numerical arrangement of the number.

A bar over a characteristic indicates a negative characteristic and a positive mantissa. The log may be written $\overline{4}.7$ or 6.7 – 10 or –3.3. The form –3.3 does not contain a characteristic and mantissa.

The integral part of a logarithm is called the *characteristic* and the decimal part is called the *mantissa*. In log 824, the characteristic is 2 and the mantissa is 0.9162. For convenience in constructing tables, it is desirable to select the mantissa as positive even if the logarithm is a negative number. For example, log 1/2 = –0.3010; but because –0.3010 = 9.6990 – 10, this may be written log 1/2 = 9.6990 – 10 with a positive mantissa. This is also the log of 0.5, which we could have looked up in the first place. The following illustration shows the method of writing the characteristic and mantissa:

log	8245	= 3.9162
log	824.5	= 2.9162
log	82.45	= 1.9162
log	8.245	= 0.9162
log	0.8245	= 9.9162–10
log	0.08245	= 8.9162–10

By using scientific notation, we can easily find logarithm characteristics, as shown in the table in the next section.

How to Use Logarithms

If the laws of exponents are rewritten in terms of logarithms, they become the *laws of logarithms:*

$$\log_a(x^n) = n \log_a x$$
$$\log_a(xy) = \log_a(x) + \log_a(y)$$
$$\log_a(x^a) = n \log_a x$$

Logarithms derive their main usefulness in computation from these laws because they allow multiplication, division, and exponentiation to be replaced by the simpler operations of addition, subtraction, and multiplication, respectively.

Number	Exponential Form	Common Logarithmic Form		
		Characteristic	Mantissa	Complete Log
0.0005	5×10^{-4}	−4	0.7	$\overline{4}.7$
0.05	5×10^{-2}	−2	0.7	$\overline{2}.7$
5.0	5×10^{0}	0	0.7	0.7
500.0	5×10^{2}	2	0.7	2.7
50,000.0	5×10^{4}	4	0.7	4.7

How to Use Logarithm Tables

At the end of this appendix is a four-place table of logarithms. In this table, the mantissas of the logarithms of all integers from 1 to 99 are recorded correct to four decimal places, which is all one needs to work with decibels, which have three significant digits at most.

To find the logarithm of a given number, use the table as follows: To find the logarithm of 63.5, glance down the column headed *N* for the first two significant digits (63), and then along the top of the table for the third figure (5). In the row across from 63 and in the column under 5 is found 8028. This is the mantissa. Adding the proper characteristic 1, the logarithm (or log) of 63.5 is 1.8028.

Conversely, one can find the number that corresponds to a given logarithm (the antilogarithm). For example, find the number whose logarithm is 1.6355. The mantissa 6355 corresponds to the number in the table that is in the column below 2 and in the row across from 43. Thus, the mantissa corresponds to the number 432. Because the characteristic is 1, the number whose logarithm is 1.6355 is 43.2.

Because in measuring sound we are concerned only with three significant digits, the number whose logarithm is 1.6360 would also be 43.2. The number whose logarithm is 1.6361 would be 43.3.

Decibel Notation

Again, using the measurement of sound as an example, if two sound intensities P_1 and P_2 are to be compared according to the ability of the ear to detect intensity differences, we may determine the number of decibels that expresses the relative value of the two intensities by

$$N_{dB} = 10 \log_{10} \frac{P_1}{P_2}$$

where P_1 is greater than P_2.

The factor 10 comes into this picture because the original unit devised was the *bel*, which is the logarithm of 10 to the base 10 and represents 10 times as many decibels in

any expression involving the relation between two sound intensities as there are bels.

The decibel is a logarithmic unit. Each time the amount of power is increased by a factor of 10, we have added 10 decibels (abbreviated dB).

To determine the number of decibels by which two powers differ, we must *first determine the ratio of the two powers;* we look up this ratio in a table of logarithms to the base 10 and then we multiply the figure obtained by a factor of 10.

If we want to find the relative loudness of 10,000 people who can shout louder than 100 people can, we use the following reasoning.

The logarithm (to the base 10) of any number is merely the number of times 10 must be multiplied by itself to be equal to the number. In the example here, 100 represents 10 multiplied by itself, and the logarithm of 100 to the base 10, therefore, is 2. For example, the number of decibels expressing the relative loudness of 10,000 people shouting compared with 100 is

$$\begin{aligned} N_{dB} &= 10 \log_{10}(10,000 / 100) \\ &= 10 \log_{10}100 \\ &= 10 \times 2.0 \\ &= 20 \end{aligned}$$

Now let us see what happens if we double the number of people to 20,000.

$$\begin{aligned} N_{dB} &= 10 \log_{10}(20,000 / 100) \\ &= 10 \log_{10}200 \\ &= 10 \times 2.3010 \\ &= 23 \text{ (rounded to significant digits)} \end{aligned}$$

It can be seen, therefore, that decibels are logarithm ratios. In their use in sound measurement, *P* (the usual reference level) is 20 micropascals or 0.0002 dynes/square centimeter, which approximates the threshold of hearing, the sound that can just be heard by a young person with excellent hearing.

NORMAL AND LOGNORMAL FREQUENCY DISTRIBUTIONS

The statistical methods discussed here assume that measured concentrations of random occupational environmental samples are lognormally and independently distributed within one 8-hour period and over many daily exposure averages.

Before sample data can be statistically analyzed, we must have knowledge of the frequency distribution of the measurements or some assumptions must be made. Most community air pollution environmental data can be described by a lognormal distribution. That is, the logarithms (either base e or base 10) of the data are approximately normally distributed.

What are the differences between normally and lognormally distributed data? A normal distribution is completely determined by the the arithmetic mean and the standard deviation of the distribution. A lognormal distribution is completely determined by the median or geometric mean (GM) and the geometric standard deviation (GSD). For lognormally distributed data, a logarithmic transformation of the original data is normally distributed. The GM and GSD of the lognormal distribution are the antilogs of the mean and standard deviation of the logarithmic transformation. Normally distributed data have a symmetrical distribution curve whereas lognormally distributed environmental data are generally positively skewed (long "tail" to the right indicating a larger probability of very large concentrations than for normally distributed data.)

Variability

The variability of occupational environmental data (differences between repeated measurements at the same site) can usually be broken into three major components: random errors of the sampling method, random errors of the analytical method, and variability of the environment with time. The first two components of the variability are known in advance and are approximately normally distributed. However, the environmental fluctuations of a contaminant in a facility usually greatly exceed the variability of known instruments (often by factors of 10 or 20).

When several samples are taken in a facility to determine the average concentration of the contaminant to estimate the average exposure of an employee, then the lognormal distribution should be assumed. However, the normal distribution may be used in the special cases of taking a sample to check compliance with a ceiling standard, and when a sample (or samples) is taken for the entire time period for which the standard is defined (be it 15 minutes or 8 hours). In these cases, the entire time interval of interest is represented in the sample, and only sampling and analytical errors are present.

Coefficient of Variation

The relative variability of a normal distribution (such as the random errors of the sampling and analytical procedures) is commonly measured by the coefficient of variation (CV). The CV is also known as the *relative standard deviation*. The CV is a useful index of dispersion in that limits consist-

ing of the true mean of a set of data plus or minus twice the CV will contain about 95 percent of the data measurements.

Thus, if an analytical procedure with a CV of 10 percent is used to repeatedly measure some nonvarying physical property (as the concentration of a chemical in a beaker of solution), then about 95 percent of the measurements will fall within plus or minus 20 percent (two times the CV) of the true concentration.

EXPOSURE CONCENTRATION

Unfortunately, the property we are trying to measure, the employee's exposure concentration, is not a fixed, nonvarying physical property. The exposure concentrations are fluctuating in a lognormal manner. First, the exposure concentrations are fluctuating over the eight-hour period of the time-weighted average (TWA) exposure measurement. Breathing zone grab samples (samples of less than about 30 minutes' duration, typically only a few minutes) tend to reflect this intraday environmental variability so that grab sample results have relatively high variability.

Intraday variability in the sample results can be eliminated from measurement variability by going to a full-period sampling strategy. The day-to-day (interday) variability of the true 8-hour TWA exposures is also lognormally distributed. This interday variability creates a need for an action level where only one day's exposure measurement is used to draw conclusions regarding compliance on unmeasured days.

GEOMETRIC STANDARD DEVIATION

The parameter often used to express either the intraday or interday environmental variability is the *geometric standard deviation* (GSD). A GSD of 1.0 represents absolutely no variability in the environment. GSDs of 2.0 and above represent relatively high variability.

The shape of lognormal distributions with low variabilities, such as those with GSDs less than about 1.4, roughly approximate normal distribution shapes. For this range of GSDs, there is a rough equivalence between the GSD and CV as follows:

GSD	*Approximate CV*	
1.40	35	percent
1.30	27	percent
1.20	18	percent
1.10	9.6	percent
1.05	4.9	percent

COMMON LOGARITHMS

N	0	1	2	3	4	5	6	7	8	9
0	.....	0000	3010	4771	6021	6990	7782	8451	9031	9542
1	0000	0414	0792	1139	1461	1761	2041	2304	2553	2788
2	3010	3222	3424	3617	3802	3979	4150	4314	4472	4624
3	4771	4914	5051	5185	5315	5441	5563	5682	5798	5911
4	6021	6128	6232	6335	6435	6532	6628	6721	6812	6902
5	6990	7076	7160	7243	7324	7404	7482	7559	7634	7709
6	7782	7853	7924	7993	8062	8129	8195	8261	8325	8388
7	8451	8513	8573	8633	8692	8751	8808	8865	8921	8976
8	9031	9085	9138	9191	9243	9294	9345	9395	9445	9494
9	9542	9590	9638	9685	9731	9777	9823	9868	9912	9956
10	0000	0043	0086	0128	0170	0212	0253	0294	0334	0374
11	0414	0453	0492	0531	0569	0607	0645	0682	0719	0755
12	0792	0828	0864	0899	0934	0969	1004	1038	1072	1106
13	1139	1173	1206	1239	1271	1303	1335	1367	1399	1430
14	1461	1492	1523	1553	1584	1614	1644	1673	1703	1732
15	1761	1790	1818	1847	1875	1903	1931	1959	1987	2014
16	2041	2068	2095	2122	2148	2175	2201	2227	2253	2279
17	2304	2330	2355	2380	2405	2430	2455	2480	2504	2529
18	2553	2577	2601	2625	2648	2672	2695	2718	2742	2765
19	2788	2810	2833	2856	2878	2900	2923	2945	2967	2989
20	3010	3032	3054	3075	3096	3118	3139	3160	3181	3201
21	3222	3243	3263	3284	3304	3324	3345	3365	3385	3404
22	3424	3444	3464	3483	3502	3522	3541	3560	3579	3598
23	3617	3636	3655	3674	3692	3711	3729	3747	3766	3784
24	3802	3820	3838	3856	3874	3892	3909	3927	3945	3962
25	3979	3997	4014	4031	4048	4065	4082	4099	4116	4133
26	4150	4166	4183	4200	4216	4232	4249	4265	4281	4298
27	4314	4330	4346	4362	4378	4393	4409	4425	4440	4456
28	4472	4487	4502	4518	4533	4548	4564	4579	4594	4609
29	4624	4639	4654	4669	4683	4698	4713	4728	4742	4757
30	4771	4786	4800	4814	4829	4843	4857	4871	4886	4900
31	4914	4928	4942	4955	4969	4983	4997	5011	5024	5038
32	5051	5065	5079	5092	5105	5119	5132	5145	5159	5172
33	5185	5198	5211	5224	5237	5250	5263	5276	5289	5302
34	5315	5328	5340	5353	5366	5378	5391	5403	5416	5428
35	5441	5453	5465	5478	5490	5502	5514	5527	5539	5551
36	5563	5575	5587	5599	5611	5623	5635	5647	5658	5670
37	5682	5694	5705	5717	5729	5740	5752	5763	5775	5786
38	5798	5809	5821	5832	5843	5855	5866	5877	5888	5899
39	5911	5922	5933	5944	5955	5966	5977	5988	5999	6010
40	6021	6031	6042	6053	6064	6075	6085	6096	6107	6117
41	6128	6138	6149	6160	6170	6180	6191	6201	6212	6222
42	6232	6243	6253	6263	6274	6284	6294	6304	6314	6325
43	6335	6345	6355	6365	6375	6385	6395	6405	6415	6425
44	6435	6444	6454	6464	6474	6484	6493	6503	6513	6522
45	6532	6542	6551	6561	6571	6580	6590	6599	6609	6618
46	6628	6637	6646	6656	6665	6675	6684	6693	6702	6712
47	6721	6730	6739	6749	6758	6767	6776	6785	6794	6803
48	6812	6821	6830	6839	6848	6857	6866	6875	6884	6893
49	6902	6911	6920	6928	6937	6946	6955	6964	6972	6981
50	6990	6998	7007	7016	7024	7033	7042	7050	7059	7067
N	0	1	2	3	4	5	6	7	8	9

N	0	1	2	3	4	5	6	7	8	9
50	6990	6998	7007	7016	7024	7033	7042	7050	7059	7067
51	7076	7084	7093	7101	7110	7118	7126	7135	7143	7152
52	7160	7168	7177	7185	7193	7202	7210	7218	7226	7235
53	7243	7251	7259	7267	7275	7284	7292	7300	7308	7316
54	7324	7332	7340	7348	7356	7364	7372	7380	7388	7396
55	7404	7412	7419	7427	7435	7443	7451	7459	7466	7474
56	7482	7490	7497	7505	7513	7520	7528	7536	7543	7551
57	7559	7566	7574	7582	7589	7597	7604	7612	7619	7627
58	7634	7642	7649	7657	7664	7672	7679	7686	7694	7701
59	7709	7716	7723	7731	7738	7745	7752	7760	7767	7774
60	7782	7789	7796	7803	7810	7818	7825	7832	7839	7846
61	7853	7860	7868	7875	7882	7889	7896	7903	7910	7917
62	7924	7931	7938	7945	7952	7959	7966	7973	7980	7987
63	7993	8000	8007	8014	8021	8028	8035	8041	8048	8055
64	8062	8069	8075	8082	8089	8096	8102	8109	8116	8122
65	8129	8136	8142	8149	8156	8162	8169	8176	8182	8189
66	8195	8202	8209	8215	8222	8228	8235	8241	8248	8254
67	8261	8267	8274	8280	8287	8293	8299	8306	8312	8319
68	8325	8331	8338	8344	8351	8357	8363	8370	8376	8382
69	8388	8395	8401	8407	8414	8420	8426	8432	8439	8445
70	8451	8457	8463	8470	8476	8482	8488	8494	8500	8506
71	8513	8519	8525	8531	8537	8543	8549	8555	8561	8567
72	8573	8579	8585	8591	8597	8603	8609	8615	8621	8627
73	8633	8639	8645	8651	8657	8663	8669	8675	8681	8686
74	8692	8698	8704	8710	8716	8722	8727	8733	8739	8745
75	8751	8756	8762	8768	8774	8779	8785	8791	8797	8802
76	8808	8814	8820	8825	8831	8837	8842	8848	8854	8859
77	8865	8871	8876	8882	8887	8893	8899	8904	8910	8915
78	8921	8927	8932	8938	8943	8949	8954	8960	8965	8971
79	8976	8982	8987	8993	8998	9004	9009	9015	9020	9025
80	9031	9036	9042	9047	9053	9058	9063	9069	9074	9079
81	9085	9090	9096	9101	9106	9112	9117	9122	9128	9133
82	9138	9143	9149	9154	9159	9165	9170	9175	9180	9186
83	9191	9196	9201	9206	9212	9217	9222	9227	9232	9238
84	9243	9248	9253	9258	9263	9269	9274	9279	9284	9289
85	9294	9299	9304	9309	9315	9320	9325	9330	9335	9340
86	9345	9350	9355	9360	9365	9370	9375	9380	9385	9390
87	9395	9400	9405	9410	9415	9420	9425	9430	9435	9440
88	9445	9450	9455	9460	9465	9469	9474	9479	9484	9489
89	9494	9499	9504	9509	9513	9518	9523	9528	9533	9538
90	9542	9547	9552	9557	9562	9566	9571	9576	9581	9586
91	9590	9595	9600	9605	9609	9614	9619	9624	9628	9633
92	9638	9643	9647	9652	9657	9661	9666	9671	9675	9680
93	9685	9689	9694	9699	9703	9708	9713	9717	9722	9727
94	9731	9736	9741	9745	9750	9754	9759	9763	9768	9773
95	9777	9782	9786	9791	9795	9800	9805	9809	9814	9818
96	9823	9827	9832	9836	9841	9845	9850	9854	9859	9863
97	9868	9872	9877	9881	9886	9890	9894	9899	9903	9908
98	9912	9917	9921	9926	9930	9934	9939	9943	9948	9952
99	9956	9961	9965	9969	9974	9978	9983	9987	9991	9996
100	0000	0004	0009	0013	0017	0022	0026	0030	0035	0039
N	0	1	2	3	4	5	6	7	8	9

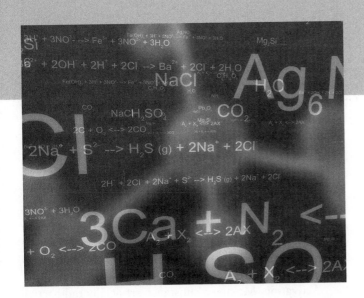

APPENDIX E

Glossary

by Michael Horowitz, MS, CIH

Every industry has its own terminology. The health and safety professional must be aware of the precise meanings of certain words commonly used in industrial hygiene, occupational health, and chemistry to communicate effectively with other professionals in these areas.

A fume respirator, for instance, is worthless as protection against gases or vapors. Too often, these terms are used interchangeably; each term has a definite meaning and describes a certain state of matter that can be achieved only by certain physical changes to the given substance.

This glossary defines words and terms, some of which are peculiar to a single industry and others common to many industries. Many of the definitions in this glossary have been retained from the earliest editions of Fundamentals of Industrial Hygiene *(1971, 1979, 1988). These definitions and terms of oldest vintage were taken or adapted from the then latest editions of* The Chemical Industry Facts Book, *published by the Manufacturing Chemists Association, Washington, DC;* Occupational Diseases and Industrial Medicine, *by RT Johnstone and SE Miller, published by WB Saunders, Philadelphia;* Guide for Industrial Audiometric Technicians, *published by the Safety and Health Services, Employers Insurance of Wausau, WI; American National Standards S1.1:* Acoustical Terminology *and Z88.2:* Respiratory Protection; 101 Atomic Terms and What They Mean, *by the Esso Research and Engineering Company, Linden, NJ;* Paramedical Dictionary, *by JE Schmidt, published by Charles C. Thomas, Springfield, IL;* The Condensed Chemical Dictionary, *published by Van Nostrand Reinhold Publishing, New York;* Stedman's Medical Dictionary, *26th ed., published by W. B. Saunders Company, Philadelphia; and* Dictionary of Scientific and Technical Terms, *4th ed., edited by S Parker, published by McGraw-Hill. Definitions that have been added to the latest two editions of* Fundamentals of Industrial Hygiene *are derived primarily from the context and the usage of the terms given by the authors of the chapters in which the terms are found, with occasional supplementation from general common usage of these terms in the industrial hygiene field. No claim is made about the etymological purity or authoritativeness of the definitions most recently added to this glossary.*

A

A-, an- (prefix). Absent, lacking, deficient, without. Anemia: deficient in blood.

AAOHN. American Association of Occupational Health Nurses.

ABIH. American Board of Industrial Hygiene.

Abrasive blasting. A process for cleaning surfaces by means of such materials as sand, alumina, or steel grit in a stream of high-pressure air.

Absorption. In air sampling, the capture of a gas or vapor accomplished by passing an airstream containing the gas or vapor through a liquid.

Absorption coefficient. See Sound absorption coefficient.

AC. See Alternating current.

Accelerator. A device for imparting very high velocity to charged particles such as electrons or protons. Also, a chemical additive that increases the speed of a chemical reaction.

Acclimation. The process of becoming accustomed to new conditions (such as heat).

Accommodation. The ability of the eye to adjust focus for various distances.

Accuracy (instrument). Often used incorrectly as precision (see Precision). Accuracy is the agreement of a reading or observation obtained from an instrument or a technique with the true value.

ACGIH. American Conference of Governmental Industrial Hygienists. An association whose membership is open to anyone who is engaged in the practice of industrial hygiene or occupational and environmental health and safety.

Acid. A proton donor.

Acid pickling. A bath treatment to remove scale and other impurities from metal surfaces before plating or other surface treatment. Sulfuric acid is commonly used.

Acne. See Oil dermatitis.

Acoustic, acoustical. Containing, producing, arising from, actuated by, related to, or associated with sound.

Acoustic trauma. Hearing loss caused by sudden loud noise in one ear or by a sudden blow to the head. In most cases, hearing loss is temporary, although there may be some permanent loss.

Acro- (prefix). Topmost; outer end. An extremity of the body. Acro-osteolysis is degeneration of the terminal or distal end of bone tissue.

Acrylic. A family of synthetic resins made by polymerizing esters of acrylic acids.

Action level. A term used by OSHA and NIOSH (see entries) to express the level of toxicant that requires medical surveillance, usually one half of the permissible exposure limit.

Activated charcoal. Charcoal is an amorphous form of carbon formed by burning wood, nutshells, animal bones, and other carbonaceous materials. Charcoal becomes activated by heating it with steam to 800–900°C. During this treatment, an aporous, submicroscopic internal structure is formed that gives it an extensive internal surface area. Activated charcoal is commonly used as a gas or vapor adsorbent in air-purifying respirators and as a solid sorbent in air sampling.

Activation. Making a substance artificially radioactive in an accelerator or by bombarding it with protons or neutrons in a reactor.

Activity. Often used as a shortened form of radioactivity; refers to the radiating power of a radioactive substance. Activity may be given in terms of atoms disintegrating per second.

Acuity. This sense pertains to the sensitivity of receptors used in hearing or vision.

Acute. Health effects that show up a short length of time after exposure. An acute exposure runs a comparatively short course.

ADA. Americans with Disabilities Act: a 1991 federal law prohibiting discrimination against people with disabilities in most public activities, including the workplace.

Additives. An inclusive name for a wide range of chemical substances that are added in low percentage to stabilize certain end products, such as antioxidants in rubber.

Aden- (prefix). Pertaining to a gland. Adenoma is a tumor of gland-like tissue.

Adenoma. An epithelial tumor, usually benign, with a gland-like structure (the cells lining gland-like depressions or cavities in the stroma).

Adhesion. The ability of one substance to stick to another. There are two types of adhesion: mechanical, which depends on the penetration of the surface, and molecular or polar adhesion, in which adhesion to a smooth surface is obtained because of polar groups such as carboxyl groups.

Administrative controls. Methods of controlling employee exposures by job rotation, work assignment, time periods away from the hazard, or training in specific work practices designed to reduce the exposure.

Adsorption. The condensation of gases, liquids, or dissolved substances on the surfaces of solids.

AEC. Atomic Energy Commission. Now called Nuclear Regulatory Commission in the U.S. Department of Energy.

Aerobe. Microorganisms that require the presence of oxygen.

Aerodynamic equivalent diameter. In the consideration of particulates the diameter of a theoretical unit density sphere having the same settling velocity as a particle of a given shape and density. Also termed *equivalent aerodynamic diameter (EAD)*.

Aerodynamic forces. The forces exerted on a particle in suspension by either the movement of air or gases around the particle or the resistance of the gas or air to movement of the particle through the medium.

Aerosols. Liquid droplets or solid particles dispersed in air that are of fine enough particle size (0.01–100 μm) to remain so dispersed for a period of time.

Agglomeration. Implies consolidation of solid particles into larger shapes by means of agitation alone, that is, without application of mechanical pressure in molds, between rolls, or through dies. Industrial agglomeration is usually implemented in balling devices such as rotating discs, drums, or cones, but it can occur in a simple mixer. Agglomeration has also been used to describe the entire field of particulate consolidation.

AIDS. Acquired Immunodeficiency Syndrome.

AIHA. American Industrial Hygiene Association.

Air. The mixture of gases that surrounds the earth; its major components are as follows: 78.08 percent nitrogen, 20.95 percent oxygen, 0.03 percent carbon dioxide, and 0.93 percent argon. Water vapor (humidity) varies. See Standard air.

Air bone gap. The difference in decibels between the hearing levels for a particular frequency as determined by air conduction and bone conduction.

Airborne microorganisms. Biologically active contaminants suspended in air either as free-floating particles surrounded by a film or organic or inorganic material, or attached to the surface of other suspended particulates.

Air cleaner. A device designed to remove atmospheric airborne impurities, such as dusts, gases, vapors, fumes, and smokes.

Air conditioning. The process of treating air to control its temperature, humidity, cleanliness, and distribution to meet requirements of the conditioned space.

Air conduction. The process by which sound is conducted to the inner ear through air in the outer ear canal.

Air filter. An air-cleaning device to remove light particulate matter from normal atmospheric air.

Air hammer. A percussion-type pneumatic tool fitted with a handle at one end of the shank and a tool chuck at the other, into which a variety of tools may be inserted.

Air horsepower. The theoretical horsepower required to drive a fan if there are no losses in the fan, that is, if it is 100 percent efficient.

Air monitoring. The sampling for and measuring of pollutants in the atmosphere.

Air mover. Any device that is capable of causing air to be moved from one space to another. Such devices are generally used to exhaust, force, or draw gases through specific assemblies.

Air-purifying respirator. Respirators that use filters or sorbents to remove harmful substances from the air.

Air quality criteria. The amounts of pollution and lengths of exposure at which specific adverse effects to health and welfare take place.

Air-regulating valve. An adjustable valve used to regulate airflow to the facepiece, helmet, or hood of an air-line respirator.

Air, standard. See Standard air.

Air-supplied respirator. Respirator that provides a supply of breathable air from a clean source outside of the contaminated work area.

Albumin. A protein material found in animal and vegetable fluids, characterized by being soluble in water.

Albuminuria. The presence of albumin or other protein substance, such as serum globulin, in the urine.

-algia (suffix). Pain. A prefix such as *neur*-tells where the pain is (*neuralgia*, for example).

Algorithm. A precisely stated procedure or set of instructions that can be applied stepwise to solve a problem.

Aliphatic. (Derived from the Greek word for *oil*.) Pertaining to an open-chain carbon compound. Usually applied to petroleum products derived from a paraffin base and having a straight or branched chain, saturated or unsaturated molecular structure. Substances such as methane and ethane, are typical aliphatic hydrocarbons. See Aromatic.

Alkali. A compound that has the ability to neutralize an acid and form a salt. Sodium hydroxide, known as caustic soda or lye, is an example. Used in soap manufacture and many other applications. Turns litmus paper blue. See Base.

Alkaline earths. Usually considered to be the oxides of alkaline earth metals: barium, calcium, strontium, beryllium, and radium. Some authorities also include magnesium oxide.

Alkyd. A synthetic resin that is the condensed product of a polybasic acid such as phthalic, a polyhydric alcohol such as glycerin, and an oil fatty acid.

Alkylation. The process of introducing one or more alkyl radicals by addition or substitution into an organic compound.

Allergy. An abnormal response of a hypersensitive person to chemical or physical stimuli. Allergic manifestations of major importance occur in about 10 percent of the population.

Alloy. A mixture of metals (and sometimes a nonmetal), as in brass.

Alpha-emitter. A radioactive substance that gives off alpha particles.

Alpha-particle (alpha-ray, alpha-radiation). A small, positively charged particle made up of two neutrons and two protons and of very high velocity, thrown off by many radioactive materials, including uranium and radium.

Alternating current (AC). Electric current that reverses direction. Ordinary house current in the United States reverses direction 60 times per second.

Aluminosis. A form of pneumoconiosis due to the presence of aluminum-bearing dust in the lungs, especially that of alum, bauxite, or clay.

Alveoli. Tiny air sacs of the lungs, formed at the ends of bronchioles; through the thin walls of the alveoli, the blood takes in oxygen and gives up carbon dioxide in respiration.

Alveolus. A general term used in anatomical nomenclature to designate a small sac-like dilation.

Amalgamation. The process of alloying metals with mercury. This is one process used in extracting gold and silver from their ores.

Ambient noise. The all-encompassing noise associated with a given environment; usually a composite of sounds from many sources.

Amorphous. Noncrystalline.

Anaerobe. A microorganism that grows without oxygen. Facultative anaerobes are able to grow with or without oxygen; obligate anaerobes grow only in the absence of oxygen.

Anaerobic bacteria. Any bacteria that can survive in a partial or complete absence of air.

Anaphylaxis. Hypersensitivity resulting from sensitization following prior contact with a chemical or protein.

Andro- (prefix). Man, male. An androgen is an agent that produces masculinizing effects.

Anechoic room (free-field room). One whose boundaries effectively absorb all the sound incident therein, thereby affording essentially free-field conditions.

Anemia. Deficiency in the hemoglobin and erythrocyte content of the blood. Term refers to a number of pathological states that may be attributed to a large variety of causes and appear in many different forms.

Anemometer. A device to measure air speed.

Anesthesia. Loss of sensation; in particular, the temporary loss of feeling induced by certain chemical agents.

Angi-, angio- (prefix). Blood or lymph vessel. Angiitis is the inflammation of a blood vessel.

Angle of abduction. Angle between the longitudinal axis of a limb and a sagittal plane.

Angstrom (Å). Unit of measure of wavelength equal to 1010 m or 0.1 nm.

Anneal. To treat by heat with subsequent cooling for drawing the temper of metals, that is, to soften and render them less brittle. See Temper.

Anode. The positive electrode.

Anorexia. Lack or loss of the appetite for food.

ANSI. American National Standards Institute: a voluntary membership organization (run with private funding) that develops consensus standards nationally for a wide variety of devices and procedures.

Antagonist. A muscle opposing the action of another muscle. An active antagonist is essential for control and stability of action by a prime mover.

Antagonistic interaction. Interaction of two chemicals in which the resultant toxic effect is lower than the chemicals' individual actions.

Anthracosilicosis. A complex form of pneumoconiosis; a chronic disease caused by breathing air containing dust that has free silica as one of its components and that is generated in the various processes in mining and preparing anthracite (hard) coal, and, to a lesser degree, bituminous coal.

Anthracosis. A disease of the lungs caused by prolonged inhalation of dust that contains particles of carbon and coal.

Anthrax. A highly virulent bacterial infection picked up from infected animals and animal products.

Anthropometry. The part of anthropology having to do with measurement of the human body to determine differences in individuals or groups of individuals.

Anti- (prefix). Against. An antibiotic is "against life" in the case of a drug—against the life of disease-causing germs.

Antibiotic. A substance produced by a microorganism that in dilute solutions kills other organisms, or retards or completely represses their growth, normally in doses that do not harm higher orders of life.

Antibody. Any of the body globulins that combine specifically with antigens to neutralize toxins, agglutinate bacteria or cells, and precipitate soluble antigens. It is found naturally in the body or produced by the body in response to the introduction into its tissues of a foreign substance.

Antigen. A substance that when introduced into the body stimulates antibody production.

Antioxidant. A compound that retards deterioration by oxidation. Antioxidants for human food and animal feeds, sometimes referred to as freshness preservers, retard rancidity of fats and lessen loss of fat-soluble vitamins (A, D, E, K). Antioxidants also are added to rubber, motor lubricants, and other materials to inhibit deterioration.

Antiparticle. A particle that interacts with its counterpart of the same mass but opposite electric charge and magnetic properties (e.g., proton and antiproton), with complete annihilation of both and production of an equivalent amount of radiation energy. The positron and its antiparticle, the electron, annihilate each other upon interaction and produce gamma-rays.

Antiseptic. A substance that prevents or inhibits the growth of microorganisms; a substance used to kill microorganisms on animate surfaces, such as skin.

Aplastic anemia. A condition in which the bone marrow fails to produce an adequate number of red blood corpuscles.

Approved. Tested and listed as satisfactory by an authority having jurisdiction, such as U.S. Department of HHS, NIOSH-MSHA; or U.S. Department of Agriculture.

Aqueous humor. Fluid in the anterior chamber of the eye (between the cornea and the lens).

Arc welding. A form of electrical welding using either uncoated or coated rods.

Arc-welding electrode. A component of the welding circuit through which current is conducted between the electrode holder and the arc.

Area monitoring. Collection of and later analysis of airborne contaminants in a given work environment. As the sampling pump and collection media are not attached to a worker, the concentrations found represent average concentrations in that area but may not be representative of the actual exposure of the worker. See personal monitoring.

Argyria. A slate-gray or bluish discoloration of the skin and deep tissues caused by the deposit of insoluble albuminate of silver, occurring after the medicinal administration for a long period of a soluble silver salt; formerly fairly common after the use of insufflations of silver-containing materials into the nose and sinuses. Also seen with occupational exposure to silver-containing chemicals.

Aromatic. Applied to a group of hydrocarbons and their derivatives characterized by the presence of the benzene nucleus (molecular ring structure). See Aliphatic.

Arthr- (prefix). Joint. Arthropathy is a disease affecting a joint.

Artificial abrasive. Materials such as carborundum or emery substituted for natural abrasive such as sandstone.

Artificial radioactivity. That produced by bombardment of a target element with nuclear particles. Iodine-131 is an artificially produced radioactive substance.

Asbestos. A hydrated magnesium silicate in fibrous form.

Asbestosis. A disease of the lungs caused by inhalation of fine airborne asbestos fibers.

Asepsis. The state of being clean and free of microorganisms.

Aseptic technique. A procedure or operation that prevents the introduction of septic material.

ASHRAE. American Society of Heating, Refrigeration, and Air Conditioning Engineers.

Aspect ratio. Length to width ratio.

Asphyxia. Suffocation from lack of oxygen. Chemical asphyxia is produced by a substance such as carbon monoxide that combines with hemoglobin to reduce the blood's capacity to transport oxygen. Simple asphyxia is the result of exposure to a substance, such as methane, that displaces oxygen.

Asphyxiant. A gas whose primary or most acute health effect is asphyxiation. There are two classes of asphyxiant: Simple asphyxiants, such as nitrogen or methane, which act by replacing oxygen; and chemical asphyxiants, such as carbon monoxide, which cause asphyxiation by preventing oxygen uptake at the cellular level.

ASSE. American Society of Safety Engineers.

Assigned Protection Factor (APF). The level of respiratory protection expected from a respirator that is properly functioning, has been properly fitted, and is worn by a worker trained in its use. APFs can be used to help provide an estimate of the maximum concentrations of a contaminant in which a particular respirator can be used.

Asthma. Constriction of the bronchial tubes in response to irritation, allergy, or other stimulus.

Astigmatism. A type of blurry vision caused by irregular curvature of the cornea.

Ataxia. Lack of muscular coordination caused by any of several nervous system diseases.

Atmospheric pressure. The pressure exerted in all directions by the atmosphere. At sea level, mean atmospheric pressure is 29.92 in. Hg, 14.7 psi, or 407 in. wg.

Atmospheric tank. A storage tank designed to operate at pressures from atmospheric through 0.5 psig (3.5 kPa).

Atom. All materials are made of atoms. The elements, such as iron, lead, and sulfur, differ from each other because their atomic structures are different. The word atom comes from the Greek word meaning indivisible. We now know it can be split and consists of an inner core (nucleus) surrounded by electrons that rotate around the nucleus. As a chemical unit, it remains unchanged during any chemical reaction, yet may undergo nuclear transmutations to other atoms, as in atomic fission.

Atom smasher. Accelerator that speeds up atomic and subatomic particles so that they can be used as projectiles to literally blast apart the nuclei of other atoms.

Atomic energy. Energy released in nuclear reactions. Of particular interest is the energy released when a neutron splits an atom's nucleus into smaller pieces (fission) or when two nuclei are joined together under millions of degrees of heat (fusion). *Atomic energy* is a popular misnomer; it is more correctly called nuclear energy.

Atomic hydrogen welding. A shielded gas-electric welding process using hydrogen as the reducing atmosphere.

Atomic number. The number of protons found in the nucleus of an atom. All elements have different atomic numbers. The atomic number of hydrogen is 1, that of oxygen 8, iron 26, lead 82, uranium 92. The atomic number is also called charge number and is usually denoted by Z.

Atomic power. The name given to the production of thermal power in a nuclear reactor or power facility.

Atomic waste. The radioactive ash produced by the splitting of uranium fuel, as in a nuclear reactor. It may include products made radioactive in such a device.

Atomic weight. The atomic weight is approximately the sum of the number of protons and neutrons found in the nucleus of an atom. This sum is also called mass number. The atomic weight of oxygen is approximately 16, with most oxygen atoms containing 8 neutrons and 8 protons. Aluminum is 27; it contains 14 neutrons and 13 protons.

Atrophy. Arrested development or wasting away of cells and tissue.

Attenuate. To reduce in amount. Usually refers to noise or ionizing radiation.

Attenuation. The reduction of intensity at a designated first location as compared with intensity at a second location, which is farther from the source.

Attenuation block. A block or stack, having dimensions 20 cm by 20 cm by 3.8 cm, of Type 1100 aluminum alloy or aluminum alloy having equivalent attenuation.

Audible range. The frequency range across which normal ears hear: approximately 20 Hz to 20,000 Hz. Above the range of 20,000 Hz, the term ultrasonic is used. Below 20 Hz, the term subsonic is used.

Audible sound. Sound containing frequency components lying between 20 and 20,000 Hz.

Audiogram. A record of hearing loss or hearing level measured at several different frequencies—usually 500 to 6,000 Hz. The audiogram may be presented graphically or numerically. Hearing level is shown as a function of frequency.

Audiologist. A person with graduate training in the specialized problems of hearing and deafness.

Audiometer. A signal generator or instrument for measuring objectively the sensitivity of hearing. Pure-tone audiometers are standard instruments for industrial use for audiometric testing.

Audiometric technician. A person who is trained and qualified to administer audiometric examinations.

Audiometric zero. The threshold of hearing: 0.0002 microbars of sound pressure. See Decibel.

Auditory. Pertaining to or involving the sense or organs of hearing.

Auricle. Part of the ear that projects from the head; medically, the pinna. Also, one of the two upper chambers of the heart.

Autoclave. An apparatus using pressurized steam for sterilization.

Autoignition temperature. The lowest temperature at which a flammable gas-air or vapor-air mixture ignites from its own heat source or a contacted heated surface without necessity of spark or flame. Vapors and gases spontaneously ignite at a lower temperature in oxygen than in air, and their autoignition temperature may be influenced by the presence of catalytic substances.

Avogadro's number. The number of molecules in a mole of any substance; it equals $6.02217\,3 \times 10^{23}$. At 0°C and 29.92 in. Hg, 1 mole of any gas occupies 22.414 liters of volume.

Axial-flow fan. A propeller-type fan useful for moving large volumes of air against little resistance.

Axis of rotation. The true line about which angular motion takes place at any instant. Not necessarily identical with anatomical axis of symmetry of a limb, nor necessarily fixed. Thus, the forearm rotates about an axis that extends obliquely from the lateral side of the elbow to a point between the little finger and ring finger. The elbow joint has a fixed axis maintained by circular joint surfaces, but the knee has a moving axis as its cam-shaped surfaces articulate. Axis of rotation of tools should be aligned with true limb axis of rotation. System of rotation of tools should be aligned with true limb axis of rotation. Systems of predetermined motion times often specify such an axis incorrectly.

Axis of thrust. The line along which thrust can be transmitted safely. In the forearm, it coincides with the longitudinal axis of the radius. Tools should be designed to align with this axis.

B

Babbitt. An alloy of tin, antimony, copper, and lead used as a bearing metal.

Babbitting. The process of applying babbitt to a bearing.

Bacillus. A rod-shaped bacterium.

Background radiation. The radiation coming from sources other than the radioactive material to be measured. This background is primarily because of cosmic rays that constantly bombard the earth from outer space.

Background noise. Noise coming from sources other than the particular noise source being monitored.

Bacteria. Microscopic organisms living in soil, water, organic matter, or the bodies of plants and animals characterized by lack of a distinct nucleus and lack of ability to photosynthesize. Singular: Bacterium.

Bactericide. Any agent that destroys bacteria.

Bacteriophage. Viruses that infect bacteria and lyse the bacterial cell.

Bacteriostat. An agent that stops the growth and multiplication of bacteria but does not necessarily kill them. Usually growth resumes when the bacteriostat is removed.

Bag house. Many different trade meanings. Commonly connotes the housing containing bag filters for recovery of fumes of arsenic, lead, sulfur, and others from the flues of smelters.

Bagasse. Sugar cane pulp residues.

Bagassosis. Respiratory disorder believed to be caused by breathing fungi found in bagasse.

Balancing by dampers. Method for designing local exhaust system ducts using adjustable dampers to distribute airflow after installation.

Balancing by static pressure. Method for designing local exhaust system ducts by selecting the duct diameters that generate static pressure to distribute airflow without dampers.

Ball mill. A grinding device using balls usually made of steel or stone in a revolving container.

Banbury mixer. A mixing machine that permits control over the temperature of the batch; commonly used in the rubber industry.

Band-pass filter. A wave filter that has a single transmission band extending from a lower cutoff frequency greater than zero to a finite upper cutoff frequency.

Band-pressure level. Band-pressure level of a sound for a specified frequency band is the sound-pressure level for the sound contained within the restricted band. The reference pressure must be specified.

Bandwidth. When applied to a band-pass filter, bandwidth is determined by the interval of transmitted waves between the low and high cutoff frequencies.

Baritosis. An inert pneumoconiosis produced by the inhalation of insoluble barium compounds.

Barotrauma. An injury to the ear caused by a sudden alteration in barometric (atmospheric) pressure; aerotitis.

Basal metabolism. A measure of the amount of energy required by the body at rest.

Base. A compound that reacts with an acid to form a salt; another term for alkali. It turns litmus paper blue.

Basilar. Of, relating to, or situated at the base.

Bauxite. Impure mixture of aluminum oxides and hydroxides; the principal source of aluminum.

Bauxite pneumoconiosis. Shaver's disease. Found in workers exposed to fumes containing aluminum oxide and minute silica particles arising from smelting bauxite in the manufacture of corundum.

BCSP. Board of Certified Safety Professionals.

Beam axis. A line from the source through the centers of the x-ray fields.

Beam divergence. Angle of beam spread measured in mrad (1 mrad = 3.4 min of arc).

Beam-limiting device. A device that provides a means to restrict the dimensions of an x-ray field.

Beat elbow. Bursitis of the elbow; occurs from use of heavy vibrating tools.

Beat knee. Bursitis of the knee joints caused by friction or vibration; common in mining.

Becquerel (Bq). One disintegration per second; a measure of the rate of radioactive disintegration. There are 37 billion Bqs per curie.

Beehive kiln. A kiln shaped like a large beehive usually used for calcining ceramics.

BEI. See Biological exposure indices.

Bel. A unit of sound level based on a logarithmic scale.

Belding-Hatch index. (See also Heat stress index.) Estimate of the body heat stress of a standard man for various degrees of activity; also relates to sweating capacity.

Benign. Not malignant. A benign tumor is one that does not metastasize or invade tissue. Benign tumors may still be lethal because of pressure on vital organs.

Benzene, CH. A major organic intermediate and solvent derived from coal or petroleum. The simplest member of the aromatic series of hydrocarbons.

Beryl. A silicate of beryllium and aluminum.

Berylliosis. Chronic beryllium intoxication.

Beta decay. The process whereby some radioactive emitters give off a beta particle. Also called beta disintegration.

Beta particle (beta-radiation). A small electrically charged particle thrown off by many radioactive materials; identical to the electron. Beta particles emerge from radioactive material at high speeds.

Betatron. A large doughnut-shaped accelerator in which electrons (beta particles) are whirled through a changing magnetic field gaining speed with each trip and emerging with high energies. Energies of the order of 100 million electron volts have been achieved. The betatron produces artificial beta radiation.

Biceps brachii muscle. The large muscle in the front of the upper arm. Supinates the forearm.

Bicipital tuberosity. A protuberance on the medial surface of the radius to which the biceps brachii attaches.

Billet. A piece of semifinished iron or steel, nearly square in section, made by rolling and cutting an ingot.

Binder. The nonvolatile portion of a coating vehicle that is the film-forming ingredient used to bind the paint pigment particles together.

Binding energy. The energy that holds the neutrons and protons of an atomic nucleus together. Represents the difference between the mass of an atom and the sum of the masses of protons and neutrons that make up its nucleus.

Bioaerosol. Airborne particles of biological origin (living or dead) including microorganisms and their fragments, toxins, and particulate waste products from all varieties of living things.

Biohazard. An abbreviation of *biological hazard.* Organisms or products of organisms that present a risk to humans.

Biohazard area. Any area (a complete operating complex, a single facility, a room within a facility, and so on) in which work has been or is being performed with biohazardous agents or materials.

Biohazard control. Any set of equipment and procedures used to prevent or minimize the exposure of humans and their environment to biohazardous agents or materials.

Biological Exposure Indices (BEI®). Advisory biological limit values adopted by the ACGIH for some substances. Indices are based on urine, blood, or expired air samples. A BEI may be a value for the substance itself or it may refer to a level of a metabolite. BEIs represent the value of the biological determinant that is most likely to be the value of that determinant obtained from a worker exposed at the 8-hour TLV-TWA for the substance in question.

Biological half-life. The time required to reduce the amount of an exogenous substance in the body by half.

Biological monitoring. Collection and analysis for chemical contaminants or their metabolites of expelled biological material such as blood or urine from which estimates of worker exposure to the chemical can be made.

Biological oxygen demand (BOD). Quantity of oxygen required for the biological and chemical oxidation of waterborne substances under test conditions.

Biomechanics. The study of the human body as a system operating under two sets of laws: the laws of Newtonian mechanics and the biological laws of life.

Biopsy. Careful removal of small bits of living tissue from the body for further study and examination, usually under the microscope.

Black liquor. A liquor composed of alkaline and organic matter resulting from digestion of wood pulp and cooking acid during the manufacture of paper.

Bleaching bath. Chemical solution used to bleach colors from a garment preparatory to dyeing it; a solution of chlorine or sodium hypochlorite is commonly used.

Bleph- (prefix). Pertaining to the eyelid.

Blind spot. Normal defect in the visual field due to the position at which the optic nerve enters the eye.

Bloodborne pathogen program. A 1992 OSHA standard mandates exposure control plans and the use of universal precautions for places of employment where there is risk of employee exposure to blood or other potentially infectious material. Hepatitis B and HIV are the most often-discussed pathogens, but the program is not limited to these two areas.

Blood count. A count of the number of corpuscles per cubic millimeter of blood. Separate counts may be made for red and white corpuscles (blood cells).

BLS. Bureau of Labor Statistics.

Body burden. The amount of noxious material in the body at a given time.

Body burden, maximum permissible. The body burden of a radionuclide that if maintained at a constant level would produce the maximum permissible dose equivalent in the critical organ.

Boiling point. The temperature at which the vapor pressure of a liquid equals atmospheric pressure.

Bombardment. Shooting neutrons, alpha particles, and other high-energy particles at atomic nuclei, usually in an attempt to split the nucleus or to form a new element.

Bone conduction test. A special test conducted by placing an oscillator on the mastoid process to determine the nerve-carrying capacity of the cochlea and the eighth cranial (auditory) nerve.

Bone marrow. A soft tissue that constitutes the central filling of many bones and that produces blood corpuscles.

Bone-seeker. Any element or radioactive species that lodges in the bone when introduced into the body.

Brachialis muscle. Short, strong muscles originating at the lower end of the humerus and inserting into the ulna. Powerful flexor of forearm; employed when lifting.

Brady- (prefix). Slow. Bradycardia is slow heartbeat.

Bradycardia. Abnormal slowness of the heartbeat, as evidenced by slowing of the pulse rate to 50 or less.

Brake horsepower. The horsepower required to drive a unit; it includes the energy losses in the unit and can be determined only by actual test. It does not include drive losses between the motor and unit.

Branch (or path) of greatest resistance. The path from a hood to the fan and exhaust stack in a ventilation system that causes the most pressure loss.

Brass. An alloy of copper and zinc that may contain a small amount of lead.

Brattice. A partition constructed in underground passageways to control ventilation in mines.

Braze. To solder with any relatively infusible alloy.

Brazing furnace. Used for heating metals to be joined by brazing. Requires a high temperature.

Breathing tube. A tube through which air or oxygen flows to the facepiece, helmet, or hood.

Breathing zone. Imaginary globe of two foot radius surrounding the head.

Breathing zone sample. An air-sample collected in the breathing zone of workers to assess their exposure to airborne contaminants.

Bremsstrahlung. Secondary x-radiation produced when

a beta particle is slowed down or stopped by a high-density surface.

Briquette. Coal or ore dust pressed into oval or brick-shaped blocks.

Broach. A cutting tool for cutting non-round holes.

Bronch-, broncho- (prefix). Pertaining to the air tubes of the lung.

Bronchial tubes. Branches or subdivisions of the trachea (windpipe). A bronchiole is a branch of a bronchus, which is a branch of the windpipe.

Bronchiectasis. A chronic dilation of the bronchi or bronchioles marked by fetid breath and paroxysmal coughing, with the expectoration of mucopurulent matter. It may affect the tube uniformly, or may occur in irregular pockets, or the dilated tubes may have terminal bulbous enlargements.

Bronchiole. The slenderest of the many tubes that carry air into and out of the lungs.

Bronchiolitis. See Bronchopneumonia.

Bronchitis. Inflammation of the bronchi or bronchial tubes.

Bronchoalveolitis. Bronchopneumonia.

Bronchopneumonia. A name given to an inflammation of the lungs that usually begins in the terminal bronchioles. These become clogged with a mucopurulent exudate forming consolidated patches in adjacent lobules. The disease is essentially secondary in character, following infections of the upper respiratory tract, specific infectious fevers, and debilitating diseases.

Bronzing. Act or art of imparting a bronze appearance with powders, painting, or chemical processes.

Brownian motion. The irregular movement of particles suspended in a fluid as a result of bombardment by atoms and molecules.

Brucella. A genus of short, rod-shaped to coccoid, encapsulated, gram-negative, parasitic, pathogenic bacteria.

Brucellosis. A group of diseases caused by an organism of the *Brucella* genus. Undulant fever. One source is unpasteurized milk from cows suffering from Bang's disease (infectious abortion).

Bubble chamber. A chamber containing a liquefied gas such as liquid hydrogen, under conditions such that a charged particle passing through the liquid forms bubbles that make its path visible.

Bubble tube. A device used to calibrate air-sampling pumps.

Buckyball. A nearly spherical fullerene composed of geometrically arranged carbon atoms. The appellation was selected in recognition of Buckminster Fuller, American philosopher/inventor who popularized the geodesic dome. Buckyballs, discovered in 1985, represented a previously unknown allotrope of carbon. Although initially discovered when produced in the lab, buckyballs have since been found to exist in nature.

Buffer. Any substance in a fluid that tends to resist the change in pH when acid or alkali is added.

Bulk facility. That portion of a property where flammable or combustible liquids are received by tank vessel, pipeline, tank car, or tank vehicle, and are sorted or blended in bulk for the purpose of distributing such liquids.

Burn-up. The extent to which the nuclear fuel in a fuel element has been consumed by fission, as in a nuclear reactor.

Burns. Result of the application of too much heat to the skin. First degree burns show redness of the unbroken skin; second degree, skin blisters and some breaking of the skin; third degree, skin blisters and destruction of the skin and underlying tissues, which can include charring and blackening.

Burr. The thin rough edges of a machined piece of metal.

Bursa. A synovial lined sac that facilitates the motion of tendons; usually near a joint.

Bursitis. Inflammation of a bursa.

Byssinosis. Disease occurring to those who experience prolonged exposure to heavy air concentrations of cotton or flax dust.

C

Calcination. The heat treatment of solid material to bring about thermal decomposition, to lose moisture or other volatile material, or to oxidize or reduce.

Calender. An assembly of rollers for producing a desired finish on paper, rubber, artificial leather, plastic, or other sheet material.

Caulking. The process or material used to fill seams of boats, cracks in tile, etc.

Calorimeter. A device for measuring the total amount of energy absorbed from a source of electromagnetic radiation.

Cancer. A cellular tumor the natural course of which is fatal and usually associated with formation of secondary tumors.

Capitulum of humerus. A smooth hemispherical protuberance at the distal end of the humerus articulating with the head of the radius. Irritation caused by pressure between the capitulum and head of the radius may be a cause of tennis elbow.

Capture velocity. Air velocity at any point in front of the hood necessary to overcome opposing air currents and to capture the contaminated air by causing it to flow into the exhaust hood.

Carbohydrate. An abundant class of organic compounds, serving as food reserves or structural elements for plants and animals. Compounded primarily of carbon, hydrogen, and oxygen, they constitute about two thirds of the average daily adult caloric intake. Sugar, starches, and plant components (cellulose) are all carbohydrates.

Carbon black. Essentially a pure carbon, best known as common soot. Commercial carbon black is produced by making soot under controlled conditions. It is sometimes called furnace black, acetylene black, or thermal black.

Carbon monoxide. A colorless, odorless, toxic gas produced by any process that involves the incomplete combustion of carbon-containing substances. It is emitted through the exhaust of gasoline-powered vehicles.

Carbonizing. The immersion in sulfuric acid of semi-processed felt to remove any vegetable matter present.

Carborundum. A trade name for silicon carbide, widely used as an abrasive.

Carboy. A large glass bottle, usually protected by a crate.

Carboxyhemoglobin. The reversible combination of carbon monoxide with hemoglobin.

Carcinogenic. Cancer-producing.

Carcinoma. Malignant tumors derived from epithelial tissues, that is, the outer skin, the membranes lining the body cavities, and certain glands.

Cardi-, cardio- (prefix). Denoting the heart.

Cardiac. (1) Pertaining to the heart; (2) a cordial or restorative medicine; (3) a person with heart disorder.

Carding. The process of combing or untangling wool, cotton, and so on.

Carding machine. A textile industry machine that prepares wool, cotton, or other fibers for spinning.

Cardiovascular. Relating to the heart and to the blood vessels or circulation.

Carp- (prefix). The wrist.

Carpal tunnel. A passage in the wrist through which the median nerve and many tendons pass to the hand from the forearm.

Carpal tunnel syndrome. A common affliction caused by compression of the median nerve in the carpal tunnel. Often associated with tingling, pain, or numbness in the thumb and first three fingers—may be job-related.

Carrier. A person in apparent good health who harbors a pathogenic microorganism.

Carrier gas. A mixture of gases that contains and moves a contaminant material. Components of the carrier gas are not considered to cause air pollution or react with the contaminant material.

CAS number. Identifies a particular chemical by the Chemical Abstract Service, a service of the American Chemical Society that indexes and compiles abstracts of worldwide chemical literature called Chemical Abstracts.

Case-hardening. A process of surface-hardening metals by raising the carbon or nitrogen content of the outer surface.

Cask (or coffin). A thick-walled container (usually lead) used for transporting radioactive materials.

Casting. Pouring a molten material into a mold and permitting it to solidify to a desired shape.

Catalyst. A substance that changes the speed of a chemical reaction but that undergoes no permanent change itself. In respirator use, a substance that converts a toxic gas (or vapor) into a less toxic gas (or vapor). Usually catalysts greatly increase the reaction rate, as in conversion of petroleum to gasoline by cracking. In paint manufacture, catalysts, which hasten film-forming, sometimes become part of the final product. In most uses, however, they do not, and can often be used over again.

Cataract. Opacity in the lens of the eye that may obscure vision.

Cathode. The negative electrode.

Catwalk. A narrow suspended footway usually used for inspection or maintenance purposes.

Caustic. Something that strongly irritates, burns, corrodes, or destroys living tissue. See Alkali.

Ceiling limit (C). An airborne concentration of a toxic substance in the work environment that should never be exceeded.

Cell. A structural unit of which tissues are made. There are many types: nerve cells, muscle cells, blood cells, connective tissues cells, fat cells, and others. Each has a special form to serve a particular function.

Cellulose. A carbohydrate that makes up the structural material of vegetable tissues and fibers. Its purest forms are chemical cotton and chemical pulp; it is the basis of rayon, acetate, and cellophane.

Celsius (C). The Celsius temperature scale is a designation of the scale previously known as the centigrade scale.

-cele (suffix). Swelling or herniation of a part, as in *rectocele* (prolapse of the rectum).

Cement, portland. Portland cement commonly consists of hydraulic calcium silicates to which the addition of certain materials in limited amounts is permitted. Ordinarily, the mixture consists of calcareous materials such as limestone, chalk, shells, marl, clay, shale, blast furnace slag, and so on. In some specifications, iron ore and limestone are added. The mixture is fused by calcining at temperatures usually up to 1,500 C.

Centrifugal fan. Wheel-type fan useful where static pressure is medium to high.

Centrifuge. An apparatus that uses centrifugal force to separate or remove particulate matter suspended in a liquid.

Cephal- (prefix). Pertaining to the head. *Encephal-*, "within the head," pertains to the brain.

Ceramic. A term applied to pottery, brick, and tile products molded from clay and subsequently calcined.

Cerumen. Earwax.

Cervi- (prefix). Neck.

CFR. See *Code of Federal Regulations*.

Chain reaction. When a fissionable nucleus is split by a neutron it releases energy and one or more neutrons. These neutrons split other fissionable nuclei releasing more energy and more neutrons, making the reaction self-sustaining for as long as there are enough fissionable nuclei present.

Charged particles. A particle that possesses at least a unit electrical charge and that does not disintegrate upon a loss of charge. Charged particles are characterized by particle size, number, and sign of unit charges and mobility. See also Ion.

Chelating agent or chelate. (Derived from Greek word *kelos* for claw.) Any compound that inactivates a metallic ion with the formation of an inner ring structure in the molecule, the metal ion becoming a member of the ring. The original ion, thus chelated, is effectively out of action.

Chemical cartridge. The type of absorption unit used with a respirator for removal of low concentrations of specific vapors and gases.

Chemical engineering. That branch of engineering concerned with the development and application of manufacturing processes in which chemical or certain physical changes of materials are involved. These processes usually may be resolved into a coordinated series of unit physical operations and unit chemical processes. The work of the chemical engineer is concerned primarily with the design, construction, and operation of equipment and facilities in which these unit operations and processes are applied.

Chemical burns. Generally similar to those caused by heat. After emergency first aid, their treatment is the same as that for thermal burns. In certain instances, such as with hydrofluoric acid, special treatment is required.

Chemical hygiene plan. Required by OSHA to protect laboratory employees from hazardous chemicals.

Chemical reaction. A change in the arrangement of atoms or molecules to yield substances of different composition and properties. Common types of reactions are combination, decomposition, double decomposition, replacement, and double replacement.

Chemotherapy. Use of chemicals of particular molecular structure in the treatment of specific disorders on the assumption that known structures exhibit an affinity for certain parts of malignant cells or infectious organisms, and thereby tend to destroy or inactivate them.

Chert. A microcrystalline form of silica. An impure form of flint used in abrasives.

Cheyne-Stokes respiration. The peculiar kind of breathing usually observed with unconscious or sleeping individuals who seem to stop breathing altogether for 540 seconds, then start up again with gradually increasing intensity, stop breathing once more, and then repeat the performance. Common in healthy infants.

Chloracne. Caused by chlorinated naphthalenes and polyphenyls acting on sebaceous glands.

Chol-, chole- (prefix). Relating to bile. Cholesterol is a substance found in bile.

Chon-, chondro- (prefix). Cartilage.

Chromatograph. An instrument that separates and analyzes mixtures of chemical substances.

Chromosome. Important rod-shaped constituent of all cells. Chromosomes contain the genes and are made up of deoxyribonucleic acids (DNA).

Chronic. Persistent, prolonged, repeated.

Cilia. Tiny hairlike whips in the bronchi and other respiratory passages that aid in the removal of dust trapped on these moist surfaces.

Ciliary. Pertaining to the cilium (pl. cilia), a minute vibratile hairlike process attached to the free surface of a cell.

Clays. A great variety of aluminum-silicate-bearing rocks that are plastic when wet and hard when dry. Used in pottery, stoneware, tile, bricks, cements, fillers, and abrasives. Kaolin is one type of clay. Some clay deposits may include appreciable quartz. Commercial grades of clays may contain up to 20 percent quartz.

Clostridium botulinum. Human pathogenic bacteria that produce an exotoxin, botulin, which causes botulism.

Cloud chamber. A glass-domed chamber filled with moist vapor. When certain types of atomic particles pass through the chamber they leave a cloud-like track much like the vapor trail of a jet plane. This permits scientists to see these particles and study their motion. The cloud chamber and bubble chamber serve the same purpose.

CNS. Central nervous system.

Coagulase. An enzyme produced by pathogenic staphylococci; causes coagulation of blood plasma.

Coagulation. Formation of a clot or gelatinous mass.

Coalesce. To unite into a whole; to fuse; to grow together.

Coated welding rods. The coatings of welding rods vary. For the welding of iron and most steel, the rods contain manganese, titanium, and a silicate.

Coccidiomycosis. A fungal disease (also known as valley fever or San Joaquin Valley fever) that can affect agricultural, horticultural, construction, and any workers who disturb soil containing spores. Although most often a respiratory disease, in rare cases it can be systemic and fatal. It is transmitted by inhalation of dust containing spores of *Coccidioides immitis*.

Coccus. A spherical bacterium. Plural: cocci.

Cochlea. The auditory part of the internal ear, shaped like a snail shell. It contains the basilar membrane on which the end organs of the auditory nerve are distributed.

Code of Federal Regulations. The rules promulgated under U.S. law, published in the *Federal Register,* and actually enforced at the end of a calendar year are incorporated in this code (CFR).

Coefficient of discharge. A factor used in figuring flow through an orifice. The coefficient takes into account the facts that a fluid flowing through an orifice contracts to a cross-sectional area that is smaller than that of the orifice, and there is some dissipation of energy caused by turbulence.

Coefficient of entry. The actual rate of flow caused by a given hood static pressure compared to the theoretical flow that would result if the static pressure could be converted to velocity pressure with 100 percent efficiency; it is the ratio of actual to theoretical flow.

Coefficient of variation. The ratio of the standard deviation to the mean value of a population of observations.

Coffin. A thick-walled container (usually lead) used for transporting radioactive materials.

Cohesion. Molecular forces of attraction between particles of like compositions.

Colic. A severe cramping, gripping pain in or around the abdomen.

Collagen. An albuminoid, the main supportive protein of skin, tendon, bone, cartilage, and connective tissue.

Collection efficiency. The percentage of a specific substance removed and retained from air by an air cleaning or sampling device. A measure of the cleaner or sampler performance.

Collimated beam. A beam of light with parallel waves.

Colloid. Generally a liquid mixture or suspension in which the particles of suspended liquid or solid are very finely divided. Colloids do not appreciably settle out of suspension.

Colloid mill. A machine that grinds materials into a very fine state of suspension, often simultaneously placing this suspension in a liquid.

Colorimetry (colorimetric). The term applied to all chemical analysis techniques involving reactions in which a color is developed when a particular contaminant is present in the sample and reacts with the collection medium. The resultant color intensity is measured to determine the contaminant concentration.

Coma. A level of unconsciousness from which a patient cannot be aroused.

Combustible liquids. Combustible liquids are those having a flash point at or above 100°F (37.8°C).

Comedones. Blackheads. Blackened, oily masses of dead epithelial matter clogging the openings of oil glands and hair follicles.

Comfort ventilation. Airflow intended to maintain comfort of room occupants (heat, humidity, and odor).

Comfort zone. The range of effective temperatures over which the majority of adults feels comfortable.

Communicable. A disease whose causative agent is readily transferred from one person to another.

Compaction. The consolidation of solid particles between rolls or by tamp, piston, screw, or other means of applying mechanical pressure.

Compound. A substance composed of two or more elements joined according to the laws of chemical combination. Each compound has its own characteristic properties different from those of its constituent elements.

Compressible flow. Flow of high-pressure gas or air that undergoes a pressure drop resulting in a significant reduction of its density.

Compton effect, or Compton scattering. The glancing collision of a high energy photon (gamma-ray or x-ray) with an electron. The photon gives up part of its energy to the electron, which is ejected from its orbit, while the now lower energy photon is scattered in a new direction.

Concentration. The amount of a given substance in a stated unit of measure. Common methods of stating concentration are percent by weight or by volume, weight per unit volume, normality, and so on.

Conchae. See Turbinates.

Condensate. The liquid resulting from the process of condensation. In sampling, the term is generally applied to the material that is removed from a gas sample by means of cooling.

Condensation. Act or process of reducing from one form to another denser form such as steam to water.

Condensoid. A dispersoid consisting of liquid or solid particles formed by the process of condensation. The dispersoid is commonly referred to as a condensation aerosol.

Conductive hearing loss. Type of hearing loss; not caused by noise exposure, but by any disorder in the middle or external ear that prevents sound from reaching the inner ear.

Confined space. Any enclosed area not designed for human occupancy that has a limited means of entry and egress and in which existing ventilation is not sufficient to ensure that the space is free of a hazardous atmosphere, oxygen deficiency, or other known or potential hazards. Examples are storage tanks, boilers, sewers, and tank cars. A permit-required confined space, as defined by the OSHA standard, is one that requires a permit process and implementation of a comprehensive confined space entry program prior to entry.

Congenital. Some problem that originates before birth.

Conjunctiva. The delicate mucous membrane that lines the eyelids and covers the exposed surface of the eyeball.

Conjunctivitis. Inflammation of the conjunctiva.

Contact dermatitis. Dermatitis caused by contact with a substance—gaseous, liquid, or solid. May be caused by primary irritation or an allergy.

Control banding. A qualitative approach to assessing the risks of exposures to chemicals and selecting appropriate controls for these exposures based upon that risk assessment.

Control rod. A rod (containing an element such as boron) used to control the power of a nuclear reactor. The control rod absorbs neutrons that would normally split the fuel nuclei. Pushing the rod in reduces the release of atomic power; pulling out the rod increases it.

Controlled areas. A specified area in which exposure of personnel to radiation or radioactive material is controlled and that is under the supervision of a person who knows appropriate radiation protection practices, including pertinent regulations, and who is responsible for applying them.

Convection. The motions in fluids resulting from differences in density and the action of gravity.

Converter. A nuclear reactor that uses one kind of fuel and produces another. For example, a converter charged with uranium isotopes might consume uranium-235 and produce plutonium from uranium-238. A breeder reactor produces more atomic fuel than it consumes; a converter does not.

Coolants. Transfer agents used in a flow system to convey heat from its source.

Copolymers. Mixed polymers or heteropolymers. Products of the polymerization of two or more substances at the same time.

Core. (1) The heart of a nuclear reactor where the nuclei of the fuel fission (split) and release energy. The core is usually surrounded by a reflecting material that bounces stray neutrons back to the fuel. It is usually made up of fuel elements and a moderator. (2) A shaped, hard-baked cake of sand with suitable compounds that is placed within a mold, forming a cavity in the casting when it solidifies. (3) The vital centers of the body—heart, viscera, brain—as opposed to the shell—the limbs and integument.

Corium. The deeper skin layer containing the fine endings of the nerves and the finest divisions of the blood vessels, the capillaries. Also called the derma.

Cornea. Transparent membrane covering the anterior portion of the eye.

Corpuscle. A red or white blood cell.

Corrected effective temperature (CET). An index of thermal stress similar to the effective temperature index except that globe temperature is used instead of dry-bulb temperature.

Corrective lens. A lens ground to the wearer's individual prescription.

Corrosion. Physical change, usually deterioration or destruction, brought about through chemical or electrochemical action, as contrasted with erosion, caused by mechanical action.

Corrosive. A substance that causes visible destruction or permanent changes in human skin tissue at the site of contact.

Corundum. An impure form of aluminum oxide.

Cosmic rays. High-energy rays that bombard the earth from outer space. Some penetrate to the earth's surface and others may go deep into the ground. Although each ray is energetic, the number bombarding the planet is so small that the total energy reaching the earth is about the same as that from starlight.

Costo- (prefix), **costal.** Pertaining to the ribs.

Cottrell precipitator. A device for dust collection using high-voltage electrodes.

Coulometry. Measurement of the number of electrons that are transferred across an electrode solution interface when a reaction in the solution is created and carried to completion. The reaction is usually caused by a contaminant in a sample gas that is drawn through or onto the surface of the solution. The number of electrons transferred in terms of coulombs is an indication of the contaminant concentrations.

Count. A click in a Geiger counter or the numerical value for the activity of a radioactive specimen.

Counter. A device for counting. See Geiger counter and Scintillation counter.

Count median size. The size of the particle in a sample of particulate matter containing equal numbers of particles larger and smaller than the stated size.

Covered electrode. A composite filler metal electrode consisting of a core of bare electrode or metal-cored electrode to which a covering (sufficient to provide a slag layer on the weld metal) has been applied. The covering may contain materials providing such functions as shielding from the atmosphere, deoxidation, and arc stabilization and can serve as a source of metallic additions to the weld.

Cps. Cycles per second, now called "hertz."

Cracking. Used almost exclusively in the petroleum industry, cracking is thermal or catalytic decomposition of organic compounds, usually for the manufacture of gasoline. Petroleum constituents are also cracked for the purpose of manufacturing chemicals.

Cramps. Painful muscular contractions that may affect almost any voluntary or involuntary muscle.

Cranio- (prefix). Skull. As in *craniotomy*, incision through a skull bone.

Cristobalite. A crystalline form of free silica, extremely hard and inert chemically, and very resistant to heat. Quartz in refractory bricks and amorphous silica in diatomaceous earth are altered to cristobalite when exposed to high temperatures (calcined).

Critical mass. The amount of nuclear fuel necessary to sustain a chain reaction. If too little fuel is present, too many neutrons will stray, and the reaction will die out.

Critical pressure. The pressure under which a substance may exist as a gas in equilibrium with the liquid at the critical temperature.

Critical temperature. The temperature above which a gas cannot be liquefied by pressure alone.

Crucible. A heat-resistant barrel-shaped pot used to hold metal during melting in a furnace or in other applications.

Crude petroleum. Hydrocarbon mixtures that have a flash point below 150°F (65.6°C) and that have not been processed in a refinery.

Cry-, cryo- (prefix). Very cold.

Cryogenics. The field of science dealing with the behavior of matter at very low temperatures.

CTD. See Cumulative trauma disorder.

Cubic centimeter (cm³). A volumetric measurement that is equal to one milliliter (mL). Also noted as cc.

Cubic meter (m³). A measure of volume in the metric system.

Culture (biology). A population of microorganisms or tissue cells cultivated in a medium.

Culture medium. Any substance or preparation suitable for the growth of cultures and cultivation of microorganisms. Selective medium, a medium composed of nutrients designed to allow growth of a particular type of microorganism; broth medium, a liquid medium; agar medium, solid culture medium.

Cumulative trauma disorder (CTD). A disorder of a musculoskeletal or nervous system component caused or aggravated by repeated and/or forceful movements of the same musculoskeletal systems.

Curie (Ci). A measure of the rate at which a radioactive material decays. The radioactivity of one gram of radium is a curie. It is named for Pierre and Marie Curie, pioneers in radioactivity and discoverers of the elements radium, radon, and polonium. One curie corresponds to 37 billion disintegrations per second. See also Becquerel.

Cutaneous. Pertaining to or affecting the skin.

Cuticle. The superficial scarfskin or upper strata of skin.

Cutie-pie. A portable instrument equipped with a direct-reading meter used to determine the level of ionizing radiation in an area.

Cutting fluids (oils). The cutting fluids used in industry today are usually an oil or an oil-water emulsion used to cool and lubricate a cutting tool. Cutting oils are usually light or heavy petroleum fractions.

CW laser. Continuous wave laser.

Cyan- (prefix). Blue.

Cyanide (as CN). Cyanides inhibit tissue oxidation upon inhalation or ingestion and cause death.

Cyanosis. Blue appearance of the skin, especially on the face and extremities, indicating a lack of sufficient oxygen in the arterial blood.

Cyclone separator. A dust-collecting device that has the ability to separate particles by size. Typically used to collect respirable dust samples.

Cyclotron. A particle accelerator. In this atomic "merry-go-round," atomic particles are whirled around in a spiral between the ends of a huge magnet, gaining speed with each rotation in preparation for their assault on the target material.

Cyst- (prefix). Pertaining to a bladder or sac, normal or abnormal, filled with gas, liquid, or semisolid material. The term appears in many words concerning the urinary bladder (cystocele, cystitis).

Cyto- (prefix). Cell.

Cytoplasm. Cell plasma (protoplasm) that does not include the cell's nucleus.

Cytotoxin. A substance, developed in the blood serum, having a toxic effect upon cells.

D

Damage risk criterion. The suggested baseline of noise tolerance, which, if not exceeded, should result in no hearing loss due to noise. A damage risk criterion may include in its statement a specification of such factors as time of exposure, noise level, frequency, amount of hearing loss considered significant, percentage of the population to be protected, and method of measuring the noise.

Damp. A harmful gas or mixture of gases occurring in coal mining.

Dampers. Adjustable sources of airflow resistance used to distribute airflow in a ventilation system.

Dangerous to life or health, immediately (IDLH). Used to describe very hazardous atmospheres where employee exposure can cause serious injury or death within a short time or serious delayed effects.

Daughter. As used in radioactivity, this refers to the product nucleus or atom resulting from decay of the precursor or parent.

dBA. Sound level in decibels read on the A scale of a sound-level meter. The A scale discriminates against very low frequencies (as does the human ear) and is therefore better for measuring general sound levels. See also Decibel.

dBC. Sound level in decibels read on the C scale of a sound-level meter. The C scale discriminates very little against very low frequencies. See also Decibel.

DC. See Direct current.

Decay. When a radioactive atom disintegrates, it is said to decay. What remains is a different element. An atom of polonium decays to form lead, ejecting an alpha particle in the process.

Decibel (dB). A unit used to express sound-power level (L_W) and sound-pressure level (L_p). Sound power is the total acoustic output of a sound source in watts (W). By definition, sound-power level, in decibels, is: $L_W = 10 \log W/W_0$, where W is the sound power of the source and W_0 is the reference sound power of 10^{-12}. Because the decibel is also used to describe other physical quantities, such as electrical current and electrical voltage, the correct reference quantity must be specified.

Decomposition. The breakdown of a chemical or substance into different parts or simpler compounds. Decomposition can occur because of heat, chemical reaction, decay, etc.

Decontaminate. To make safe by eliminating poisonous or otherwise harmful substances, such as noxious chemicals or radioactive material.

Deltoid muscle. The muscle of the shoulder responsible for abducting the arm sideways and for swinging the arm at the shoulder. Overuse of the deltoid muscle may cause fatigue and pain in the shoulder.

Density. The ratio of mass to volume.

Dent-, dento- (prefix). Pertaining to a tooth or teeth, from Latin.

Derma. The dermis. The corium or true skin.

Dermatitis. Inflammation of the skin from any cause.

Dermatology. Branch of medicine concerned with the diagnosis and treatment, including surgery and prevention, of diseases of the skin, hair, and nails.

Dermatophytosis. Athlete's foot.

Dermatosis. A broader term than dermatitis, it includes any cutaneous abnormality. Thus it encompasses folliculitis, acne, pigmentary changes, and nodules and tumors.

Desiccant. Material that absorbs moisture.

Deuterium. Heavy hydrogen. The nucleus of heavy hydrogen is a deuteron. It is called heavy hydrogen because it weighs twice as much as ordinary hydrogen.

Deuteron. The nucleus of an atom of heavy hydrogen containing one proton and one neutron. Deuterons are often used for the bombardment of other nuclei.

Diagnostic x-ray system. An x-ray system designed for irradiation of any part of the human body for the purpose of diagnosis or visualization.

Diaphragm. (1) The musculomembranous partition separating the abdominal and thoracic cavities. (2) Any separating membrane or structure. (3) A disk with one or more openings, or with an adjustable opening, mounted in relation to a lens, by which part of the light may be excluded from the area.

Diatomaceous earth. A soft, gritty amorphous silica composed of minute siliceous skeletons of small aquatic plants. Used in filtration and decolorization of liquids, insulation, filler in dynamite, wax, textiles, plastics, paint, and rubber. Calcined and flux-calcined diatomaceous earth contains appreciable amounts of cristobalite, and dust levels should be controlled the same as for cristobalite.

Die. A hard metal or plastic form used to shape material to a particular contour or section.

Differential pressure. The difference in static pressure between two locations.

Diffuse sound field. One in which the time average of the mean-square sound pressure is everywhere the same and the flow of energy in all directions is equally probable.

Diffusion, molecular. A process of spontaneous intermixing of different substances attributable to molecular motion and tending to produce uniformity of concentration.

Diffusion rate. A measure of the tendency of one gas or vapor to disperse into or mix with another gas or vapor. This rate depends on the density of the vapor or gas as compared with that of air, which is given a value of 1.

Diluent. A liquid blended with a mixture to reduce concentration of the active agents.

Dilution. The process of increasing the proportion of solvent or diluent (liquid) to solute or particulate matter (solid).

Dilution ventilation. See General ventilation.

Diopters. A measure of the power of a lens or prism, equal to the reciprocal of its focal length in meters.

Direct current (DC). Electric current flowing in one direction only.

Direct-reading instrumentation. Instruments that give an immediate indication of the concentration of aerosols, gases, or vapors or magnitude of physical hazard by some means such as a dial or meter.

Disease. A departure from a state of health, usually recognized by a sequence of signs and symptoms.

Disinfectant. An agent that frees from infection by killing the vegetative cells of microorganisms.

Disintegration. A nuclear transformation or decay process that results in the release of energy in the form of radiation.

Dispersion. The general term describing systems consisting of particulate matter suspended in air or other fluid; also, the mixing and dilution of contaminant in the ambient environment.

Distal. Away from the central axis of the body.

Distal phalanx. The last bony segment of a toe or finger.

Distillery. A facility or that portion of a facility where flammable or combustible liquids produced by fermentation are concentrated and where the concentrated products may also be mixed, stored, or packaged.

Diuretic. Anything that promotes excretion of urine.

DNA. Deoxyribonucleic acid. The genetic material within the cell.

DOP. Dioctyl phthalate, a powdered chemical that can be aerosolized to an extremely uniform size, i.e., 0.3 μm for a major portion of any sample.

Dose. (1) Used to express the amount of a chemical or of ionizing radiation energy absorbed in a unit volume or an organ or individual. Dose rate is the dose delivered per unit of time. (See also Roentgen, Rad, Rem.) (2) Used to express amount of exposure to a chemical substance.

Dose, absorbed. The energy imparted to matter in a volume element by ionizing radiation divided by the mass of irradiated material in that volume element.

Dose equivalent. The product of absorbed dose, quality factor, and other modifying factors necessary to express on a common scale, for all ionizing radiations, the irradiation incurred by exposed persons.

Dose equivalent, maximum permissible (MPD). The largest dose equivalent received within a specified period that is permitted by a regulatory agency or other authoritative group on the assumption that receipt of such a dose equivalent creates no appreciable somatic or genetic injury. Different levels of MPD may be set for different groups within a population. (In popular usage, "dose, maximum permissible" is an accepted synonym.)

Dose-response relationship. Correlation between the amount of exposure to an agent or toxic chemical and the resulting effect on the body.

Dosimeter (dose meter). An instrument used to determine the full-shift exposure a person has received to a physical hazard, such as radiation or noise.

DOT. Department of Transportation.

Drier. Any catalytic material that, when added to a drying oil, accelerates drying or hardening of the film.

Drop forge. To forge between dies using a drop hammer or drop press.

Droplet. A liquid particle suspended in a gas. The liquid particle is generally of such size and density that it settles rapidly and remains airborne for an appreciable length of time only in a turbulent atmosphere.

Dross. The scum that forms on the surface of molten metals, consisting largely of oxides and impurities.

Dry-bulb thermometer. An ordinary thermometer, especially one with an unmoistened bulb, not dependent on atmospheric humidity. The reading is the dry-bulb temperature.

Duct. A conduit used for conveying air at low pressures.

Duct velocity. Air velocity through the duct cross section. When solid particulate material is present in the airstream, the duct velocity must exceed the minimum transport velocity.

Ductile. Capable of being molded or worked, as metals.

Dust collector. An air-cleaning device to remove heavy particulate loadings from exhaust systems before discharge to outdoors; usual range is loadings of 0.003 g/ft³ (0.007 mg/m³) and higher.

Dusts. Solid particles generated by handling, crushing, grinding, rapid impact, detonation, and decrepitation of organic or inorganic materials, such as rock, ore, metal, coal, wood, and grain. Dusts do not tend to flocculate, except under electrostatic forces; they do not diffuse in air but settle under the influence of gravity.

Dynometer. Apparatus for measuring force or work output external to a subject. Often used to compare external output with associated physiological phenomena to assess physiological work efficiency.

Dys- (prefix). Difficult, bad. This prefix occurs in a large number of medical words because it is attachable to a term for any organ or process that is not functioning as well as it should.

Dysfunction. Disturbance, impairment, or abnormality of the functioning of an organ.

Dyspnea. Shortness of breath, difficult or labored breathing. More strictly, the sensation of shortness of breath.

Dysuria. Difficulty or pain in urination.

E

EAP. Employee Assistance Program.

Ear. The entire hearing apparatus, consisting of three parts: external ear, the middle ear or tympanic cavity, and the inner ear or labyrinth. Sometimes the pinna is called the ear.

Ecology. The science of the relationships between living organisms and their environments.

-ectomy (suffix). A cutting out; surgical removal. Denotes any operation in which all or part of a named organ is cut out of the body.

Eczema. A skin disease or disorder. Dermatitis.

Edema. A swelling of body tissues as a result of being waterlogged with fluid.

Effective temperature (ET). An arbitrary index that combines into a single value the effects of temperature, humidity, and air movement on the sensation of warmth and cold on the human body.

Effective temperature index. An empirically determined index of the degree of warmth perceived on exposure to different combinations of temperature, humidity, and air movement. The determination of effective temperature requires simultaneous determinations of dry-bulb and wet-bulb temperatures.

Efficiency, fractional. The percentage of particles of a specified size that are removed and retained by a particular type of collector or sampler. A plot of fractional efficiency values versus the respective sized particles yields a fractional efficiency curve that may be related to the total collecting efficiency of air-cleaning or air-sampling equipment.

Efflorescence. A phenomenon whereby a whitish crust of fine crystals forms on a surface. These are usually sodium salts that diffuse from the substrate.

Effluent. Generally something that flows out or forth, like a stream flowing out into a lake. In terms of pollution, an outflow of a sewer, storage tank, canal, or other channel.

Ejector. An air mover consisting of a two-flow system wherein a primary source of compressed gas is passed through a Venturi and the vacuum developed at the throat of the Venturi is used to create a secondary flow of fluid. In the case of air movers for sampling applications, the secondary flow is the sample gas.

Elastomer. In a chemical industry sense, a synthetic polymer with rubber-like characteristics; a synthetic or natural rubber or a soft, rubbery plastic with some degree of elasticity at room temperature.

Electrical precipitators. A device that removes particles from an airstream by charging the particles and collecting the charged particles on a suitable surface.

Electrolysis. The process of conduction of an electric current by means of a chemical solution.

Electromagnetic radiation. The propagation of varying electric and magnetic fields through space at the speed of light, exhibiting the characteristics of wave motion.

Electron. A minute atomic particle possessing a negative electric charge. In an atom the electrons rotate around a small nucleus. The weight of an electron is so infinitesimal that it would take 500 octillion (500 followed by 27 zeros) of them to make a pound. It is only about a two-thousandth of the mass of a proton or neutron.

Electron volt (eV). A small unit of energy. An electron gains this much energy when it is acted upon by one volt. Energies of radioactive materials may be millions of electron volts (MeV), whereas particle accelerators generate energies of billions of electron volts (BeV).

Electroplate. To cover with a metal coating (plate) by means of electrolysis.

Element. Solid, liquid, or gaseous matter that cannot be further decomposed into simpler substances by chemical means. The atoms of an element may differ physically but do not differ chemically. All atoms of an element contain a definite number of protons and thus have the same atomic number.

ELF. Extremely low frequency electromagnetic field.

Elutriator. A device used to separate particles according to mass and aerodynamic size by maintaining a laminar flow system at a rate that permits the particles of greatest mass to settle rapidly while the smaller particles are kept airborne by the resistance force of the flowing air for longer times and distances. The various times and distances of deposit may be used to determine representative fractions of particle mass and size.

Embryo. The name for the early stage of development of an organism. In humans, the period from conception to the end of the second month.

Emergent beam diameter. Diameter of the laser beam at the exit aperture of the system.

Emery. Aluminum oxide, natural and synthetic abrasive.

Emission factor. Statistical average of the amount of a specific pollutant emitted from each type of polluting source in relation to a unit quality of material handled, processed, or burned.

Emission inventory. A list of primary air pollutants emitted into a given community's atmosphere, in amounts per day, by type of source.

Emission standards. The maximum amount of pollutant permitted to be discharged from a single polluting source.

Emmetropia. A state of perfect vision.

Emphysema. A lung disease in which the walls of the air sacs (alveoli) have been stretched too thin and have broken down.

Emulsifier or emulsifying agent. A chemical that holds one insoluble liquid in suspension in another. Casein, for example, is a natural emulsifier in milk, keeping butterfat droplets dispersed.

Emulsion. A suspension, each in the other, of two or more unlike liquids that usually do not dissolve in each other.

Enamel. A paint-like oily substance that produces a glossy finish to a surface to which it is applied, often containing various synthetic resins. It is lead free, in contrast to the ceramic enamel, that is, porcelain enamel, which contains lead.

Endemic. (1) Present in a community or among a group of people; usually refers to a disease prevailing continually in a region. (2) The continuing prevalence of a disease, as distinguished from an epidemic.

Endo- (prefix). Within, inside of, internal. The endometrium is the lining membrane of the uterus.

Endocrine. Secreting without the means of a duct or tube. The term is applied to certain glands that produce secretions that enter the bloodstream or the lymph directly and are then carried to the particular gland or tissue whose function they regulate.

Endothermic. Characterized by or formed with absorption of heat.

Endotoxin. A toxin that is part of the wall of a microorganism and is released when that organism dies.

Energy density. The intensity of electromagnetic radiation per unit area per pulse expressed in joules per square centimeter.

Engineered nanoparticles. See Nanoparticle.

Engineering controls. Methods of controlling employee exposures by modifying the source or reducing the quantity of contaminants released into the work environment.

Enteric. Intestinal.

Entero- (prefix). Pertaining to the intestines.

Enterotoxin. A toxin specific for cells of the intestine; gives rise to symptoms of food poisoning.

Entrainment velocity. The gas flow velocity, which tends to keep particles suspended and cause deposited particles to become airborne.

Entrance loss. The loss in static pressure of a fluid that flows from an area into and through a hood or duct opening. The loss in static pressure is caused by friction and turbulence resulting from the increased gas velocity and configuration of the entrance area.

Entry loss. Loss in pressure caused by air flowing into a duct or hood.

Environmental Health and Safety. The profession, art and practice of managing safety, health and environmental risks to people, property and the environment to acceptable levels

Enzymes. Delicate chemical substances, mostly proteins, that enter into and bring about chemical reactions in living organisms.

EPA. Environmental Protection Agency.

EPA number. The number assigned to chemicals regulated by the Environmental Protection Agency.

Epicondylitis. Inflammation of certain bony prominences in the area of the elbow, for example, tennis elbow.

Epidemiology. The study of disease in human populations.

Epidermis. The superficial scarfskin or upper (outer) layer of skin.

Epilation. Temporary or permanent loss of body hair.

Epithelioma. Carcinoma of the epithelial cells of the skin and other epithelial surfaces.

Epithelium. The purely cellular, avascular layer covering all the free surfaces—cutaneous, mucous, and serous—including the glands and other structures derived therefrom; for example, the epidermis.

Equivalent chill temperature (ECT). Also known as wind chill index. A temperature index used to account for heat loss from skin exposed to the combined effects of cold temperatures and air speed.

Erg. The force of one dyne acting through a distance of one centimeter. It would be equivalent to the work done by a June bug climbing over a stone 0.5 in. (1 cm) high, or the energy required to ionize about 20 billion molecules of air.

Ergonomics. (1) A multidisciplinary activity dealing with interactions between humans and their total working environment plus stresses related to such environmental elements as atmosphere, heat, light, and sound as well as all tools and equipment of the workplace. (2) The scientific study of or design of equipment and work tasks and their relation to or fit with the operator.

Erysipeloid. A bacterial infection affecting slaughterhouse workers and fish handlers.

Eryth-, erythro- (prefix). Redness. Erythema is indicated by redness of the skin (including a deep blush). An erythrocyte is a red blood cell.

Erythema. Reddening of the skin.

Erythemal region. Ultraviolet light radiation between 2,800 and 3,200 angstroms (280–320 millimicrons); it is absorbed by the cornea of the eye.

Erythrocyte. A type of red blood corpuscle.

Eschar. The crust formed after injury by a caustic chemical or heat.

Essential oil. Any of a class of volatile, odoriferous oils found in plants and imparting to the plants odor and often other characteristic properties. Used in essence, perfumery, etc.

Esters. Organic compounds that may be formed by interaction between an alcohol and an acid, or by other means. Esters are nonionic compounds, including solvents and natural fats.

Etch. To cut or eat away material with acid or another corrosive substance.

Ethylene oxide. A carcinogenic hospital sterilant regulated by OSHA. Ethylene oxide is also a reproductive hazard.

Etiologic agent. Refers to organisms, substances, or objects associated with the cause of disease or injury.

Etiology. The study or knowledge of the causes of disease.

Eu- (prefix). Well and good. A euthyroid person has a thyroid gland that couldn't be working better. A euphoric person has a tremendous sense of well-being.

Eukaryote. An organism whose cells contain mitochondria and a nuclear membrane. Describes organisms from yeasts to humans.

Eustachian tube. A structure about 2.5 in. (6 cm) long leading from the back of the nasal cavity to the middle ear. It equalizes the pressure of air in the middle ear with that outside the eardrum.

Evaporation. The process by which a liquid is changed to the vapor state.

Evaporation rate. The ratio of the time required to evaporate a measured volume of a liquid to the time required to evaporate the same volume of a reference liquid (ethyl ether) under ideal test conditions. The higher the ratio, the slower the evaporation rate.

Exhalation valve. A device that allows exhaled air to leave a respirator and prevents outside air from entering through the valve.

Exhaust ventilation. The removal of air, usually by mechanical means, from any space. The flow of air between two points is because of a pressure difference between the two points. This pressure difference causes air to flow from the high-pressure to the low-pressure zone.

Exothermic, exothermal. Characterized by or formed with evolution of heat.

Exotoxin. A toxin excreted by a microorganism into the surrounding medium.

Explosive limit. See Flammable limit.

Exposure. Contact with a chemical, biological, or physical hazard.

Extension. Movement whereby the angle between the bones connected by a joint is increased. Motions of this type are produced by contraction of extensor muscles.

Extensor muscles. A muscle that, when active, increases the angle between limb segments, for example, the muscles that straighten the knee or elbow, open the hand, or straighten the back.

Extensor tendon. Connecting structure between an extensor muscle and the bone into which it inserts. Examples are the hard, longitudinal tendons found on the back of the hand when the fingers are fully extended.

External mechanical environment. The synthetic physical environment, for example, equipment, tools, machine controls, clothing. Antonym: internal (bio)mechanical environment.

Extravasate. To exude a substance from the body's vessels into tissues.

Extrusion. The forcing of raw material through a die or a form in either a hot or cold state, in a solid state, or in partial solution. Long used with metals and clays, it is now extensively used in the plastic industry.

Eyepiece. Gas-tight, transparent window in a full facepiece through which the wearer may see.

F

Face velocity. Average air velocity into the exhaust system measured at the opening into the hood or booth.

Facepiece. That portion of a respirator that covers the wearer's nose and mouth in a half-mask facepiece, or the nose, mouth, and eyes in a full facepiece. It is designed to make a gas-tight or dust-tight fit with the face and includes the headbands, exhalation valves, and connections for air-purifying device, or respirable gas source, or both.

Facing. In foundry work, the final touch-up work of the mold surface to come in contact with metal is called the facing operation, and the fine powdered material used is called the facing.

Fainting. Technically called syncope, a temporary loss of consciousness as a result of a diminished supply of blood to the brain.

Fallout. Dust particles that contain radioactive fission products resulting from a nuclear explosion. The wind can carry fallout particles many miles.

Fan laws. Statements and equations that describe the relationship between fan volume, pressure, brake horsepower, size, and rotating speed.

Fan rating curve or table. Data that describe the volumetric output of a fan at different static pressures.

Fan static pressure. The pressure added to the system by the fan. It equals the sum of pressure losses in the system minus the velocity pressure in the air at the fan inlet.

Far field (free field). In noise measurement, this refers to the distance from the noise source where the sound-pressure level decreases 6 dBA for each doubling of distance (inverse square law).

Farmer's lung. Fungus infection and ensuing hypersensitivity from grain dust.

Federal Register. Publication of U.S. government documents officially promulgated under the law, documents whose validity depends upon such publication. It is published on each day following a government working day. It is, in effect, the daily supplement to the *Code of Federal Regulations (CFR)*.

Feral animal. A wild animal, or a domestic animal that has reverted to the wild state.

Fertilizer. Plant food usually sold in a mixed formula containing basic plant nutrients: compounds of nitrogen, potassium, phosphorus, sulfur, and sometimes other minerals.

Fetus. The term used to describe the developing organism (human) from the third month after conception to birth.

FEV. Forced expiratory volume.

Fever. A condition in which the body temperature is above its regular or normal level.

Fibrillation. Very rapid irregular contractions of the muscle fibers of the heart resulting in a lack of synchronism of the heartbeat.

Fibrosis. A condition marked by an increase of interstitial fibrous tissue. Exposures to contaminants via inhalation can lead to fibrosis or scarring of the lung, a particular concern in industrial hygiene.

Film badge. A piece of masked photographic film worn by nuclear workers. It is darkened by nuclear radiation, and radiation exposure can be checked by inspecting the film.

Filter. (1) A device for separating components of a signal on the basis of its frequency. It allows components in one or more frequency bands to pass relatively unattenuated, and it greatly attenuates components in other frequency bands. (2) A fibrous medium used in respirators to remove solid or liquid particles from the airstream entering the respirator. (3) A sheet of material that is interposed between patient and the source of x rays to absorb a selective part of the x rays. (4) A fibrous or membrane medium used to collect dust, fume, or mist air samples.

Filter efficiency. The efficiency of various filters can be established on the basis of entrapped particles (that is, collection efficiency), or on the basis of particles passed through the filter (that is, penetration efficiency).

Filter, HEPA. High-efficiency particulate air filter, one that is at least 99.97 percent efficient in removing thermally generated monodisperse dioctyl phthalate smoke particles with a diameter of 0.3 μm.

Firebrick. A special clay that is capable of resisting high temperatures without melting or crumbling.

Fire damp. In mining, the accumulation of an explosive gas, chiefly methane gas. Miners call all dangerous underground gases "damps."

Fire point. The lowest temperature at which a material can evolve vapors to support continuous combustion.

Fission. The splitting of an atomic nucleus into two parts accompanied by the release of a large amount of radioactivity and heat. Fission reactions occur only with heavy isotopes, such as uranium-233, uranium-235, and plutonium-239.

Fissionable. A nucleus that undergoes fission under the influence of neutrons, even very slow neutrons.

Fission product. The highly radioactive nuclei into which a fissionable nucleus splits (fissions) under the influence of neutron bombardment.

Flagellum. A flexible, whip-like appendage on cells used as an organ of locomotion.

Flame ionization detector (FID). A direct-reading monitoring device that ionizes gases and vapors with an oxyhydrogen flame and measures the differing electrical currents thus generated.

Flameproofing material. Chemicals that catalytically control the decomposition of cellulose material at flaming temperature. Substances used as fire retardants are borax-boric acid, borax-boric acid diammonium phosphate, ammonium bromide, stannic acid, antimony oxide, and combinations containing formaldehyde.

Flame propagation. See Propagation of flame.

Flammable aerosol. An aerosol that is required to be labeled *Flammable* under the Federal Hazardous Substances Labeling Act (15 USC 1261).

Flammable limits. Flammables have a minimum concentration below which propagation of flame does not occur on contact with a source of ignition. This is known as the lower flammable explosive limit (LEL). There is also a maximum concentration of vapor or gas in air above which propagation of flame does not occur. This is known as the upper flammable explosive limit (UEL). These units are expressed in percent of gas or vapor in air by volume.

Flammable liquid. Any liquid having a flash point below 100°F (37.8°C).

Flammable range. The difference between the lower and upper flammable limits, expressed in terms of percentage of vapor or gas in air by volume, also often called the explosive range.

Flange. A rim or edge added to a hood to reduce the quantity of air entering from behind the hood.

Flash blindness. Temporary visual disturbance resulting from viewing an intense light source.

Flash point. The lowest temperature at which a liquid gives off enough vapor to form an ignitable mixture with air and produce a flame when a source of ignition is present. Two tests are used: open cup and closed cup.

Flask. In foundry work, the assembly of the cope and the drag constitutes the flask. It is the wooden or iron frame containing sand into which molten metal is poured. Some flasks may have three or four parts.

Flexion. Movement whereby the angle between two bones connected by a joint is reduced. Motions of this type are produced by contraction of flexor muscles.

Flexor muscles. A muscle that, when contracting, decreases the angle between limb segments. The principal flexor of the elbow is the brachialis muscle. Flexors of the fingers and the wrist are the large muscles of the forearm originating at the elbow. See Extensor muscles.

Flocculation. The process of forming a very fluffy mass of material held together by weak forces of adhesion.

Flocculator. A device for aggregating fine particles.

Flora, microflora. Microorganisms present in a given situation (such as intestinal flora, soil flora).

Flotation. A method of ore concentration in which the mineral is caused to float due to chemical frothing agents while the impurities sink.

Flotation reagent. Chemical used in flotation separation of minerals. Added to a pulverized mixture of solids and water and oil, it causes preferential nonwetting by water of certain solid particles, making possible the flotation and separation of nonwet particles.

Flow coefficient. A correction factor used for figuring the volume flow rate of a fluid through an orifice. This factor includes the effects of contraction and turbulence loss (covered by the coefficient of discharge), plus the compressibility effect and the effect of an upstream velocity other than zero. Because the latter two effects are negligible in many instances, the flow coefficient is often equal to the coefficient of discharge (see Coefficient of discharge).

Flow meter. An instrument for measuring the rate of flow of a fluid or gas.

Flow, turbulent. Fluid flow in which the fluid moves transversely as well as in the direction of the tube or pipe axis, as opposed to streamline or viscous flow.

Fluid. A substance tending to flow or conform to the outline of its container. It may be liquid, vapor, gas, or solid (such as raw rubber).

Fluorescence. Emission of light from a crystal, after the absorption of energy.

Fluorescent screen. A screen coated with a fluorescent substance so that it emits light when irradiated with x rays.

Fluoroscope. A fluorescent screen mounted in front of an x-ray tube so that internal organs may be examined through their shadow cast by x rays. It may also be used for inspection of inanimate objects.

Fluoroscopy. The practice of examining through the use of an x-ray fluoroscope.

Flux. Usually refers to a substance used to clean surfaces and promote fusion in soldering. However, fluxes of varying chemical nature are used in the smelting of ores, in the ceramic industry, in assaying silver and gold ores, and in other endeavors. The most common fluxes are silica, various silicates, lime, sodium and potassium carbonate, and litharge and red lead in the ceramic industry. See also Soldering, Galvanizing, and Luminous flux.

Fly ash. Finely divided particles of ash entrained in flue gases arising from the combustion of fuel.

Focus (pl. foci). A center or site of a disease process.

Follicle. A small anatomical cavity or deep, narrow-mouthed depression; a small lymph node.

Folliculitis. Infection of a hair follicle, often caused by obstruction by natural or industrial oils.

Fomites. Clothing or other substances that can absorb and transmit contaminants, as in the case of poison ivy.

Footcandle. A unit of illumination. The illumination at a point on a surface that is one foot from, and perpendicular to, a uniform point source of one candle.

Foot-pounds of torque. A measurement of the physiological stress exerted upon any joint during the performance of a task. The product of the force exerted and the distance from the point of application to the point of stress. Physiologically, torque that does not produce motion nonetheless causes work stress, the severity of which depends on the duration and magnitude of the torque. In lifting an object or holding it elevated, torque is exerted and applied to the lumbar vertebrae.

Force. That which changes the state of rest or motion in matter. The SI (International System) unit of measurement is the newton (N).

Fovea. A depression or pit in the center of the macula of the eye; it is the area of clearest vision.

Fractionation. Separation of a mixture into different portions or fractions, usually by distillation.

Free sound field (free field). A field in a homogeneous, isotropic medium free from boundaries. In practice, it is a field in which the effects of the boundaries are negligible over the region of interest. See Far field.

Frequency (in Hz). Rate at which pressure oscillations are produced. One hertz is equivalent to one cycle per second. A subjective characteristic of sound related to frequency is pitch.

Friction factor. A factor used in calculating loss of pressure due to friction of a fluid flowing through a pipe or duct.

Friction loss. The pressure loss caused by friction.

Fullerene. A nanoscale molecule or structure composed of a geometric arrangement of atoms usually entirely of one element, generally, but not exclusively, carbon.

Fuller's earth. A hydrated silica-alumina compound associated with ferric oxide. Used as a filter medium and as a catalyst and catalyst carrier and in cosmetics and insecticides.

Fume. Airborne particulate formed by the condensation of solid particles from the gaseous state. Usually, fumes are generated after initial volatilization from a combustion process, or from a melting process (such as metal fume emitted during welding). Usually less than 1 μm in diameter.

Fume fever. Metal fume fever is an acute condition caused by a brief high exposure to the freshly generated fumes of metals, such as zinc or magnesium, or their oxides.

Functional anatomy. Study of the body and its component parts, taking into account structural features directly related to physiological function.

Fundamental frequency. The lowest component frequency of a periodic quantity.

Fundus. The interior surface of a hollow organ, such as the retina of the eye.

Fungus (pl. fungi). Any of a major group of lower plants that lack chlorophyll and live on dead or other living organisms. Fungi include molds, rusts, mildews, smuts, and mushrooms.

Fusion. (1) The joining of atomic nuclei to form a heavier nucleus, accomplished under conditions of extreme heat (millions of degrees). If two nuclei of light atoms fuse, the fusion is accompanied by the release of a great deal of energy. The energy of the sun is believed to be derived from the fusion of hydrogen atoms to form helium. (2) In welding, the melting together of filler metal and base metal (substrate), or of base metal only, which results in coalescence.

FVC. Forced vital capacity.

G

Gage pressure. Pressure measured with respect to atmospheric pressure.

Galvanizing. An old but still used method of providing a protective coating for metals by dipping them in a bath of molten zinc.

Gamete. A mature germ cell. An unfertilized ovum or spermatozoon.

Gamma-rays (gamma radiation). The most penetrating of all radiation. Gamma-rays are very high-energy photons.

Ganglion (pl. ganglia). A knot or knot-like mass; used as a general term to designate a group of nerve cell bodies located outside of the central nervous system. The term is also applied to certain nuclear groups within the brain or spinal cord.

Gangue. In mining or quarrying, useless chipped rock.

Gas. A state of matter in which the material has very low density and viscosity, can expand and contract greatly in response to changes in temperature and pressure, easily diffuses into other gases, and readily and uniformly distributes itself throughout any container. A gas can be changed to the liquid or solid state only by the combined effect of increased pressure and decreased temperature (below the critical temperature).

Gas chromatography. A gaseous detection technique that involves the separation of mixtures by passing them through a column that enables the components to be held up for varying periods of time before they are detected and recorded.

Gas metal arc-welding (GMAW). An arc-welding process that produces coalescence of metals by heating them with an arc between a continuous filler metal (consumable) electrode and the work; shielding is obtained entirely from an external supplied gas or gas mixture. Some methods of this process are called MIG or CO_2 welding.

Gas tungsten arc-welding (GTAW). An arc-welding process that produces coalescence of metals by heating them with an arc between a tungsten (nonconsumable) electrode and the work; shielding is obtained from a gas or gas mixture. Pressure may or may not be used, and filler metal may or may not be used. This process has sometimes been called TIG welding.

Gastr-, gastro- (prefix). Pertaining to the stomach.

Gastritis. Inflammation of the stomach.

Gate. A groove in a mold to act as a passage for molten metal.

Geiger counter. A gas-filled electrical device that counts the presence of an atomic particle or ray by detecting the ions produced. Sometimes called a Geiger-Müller counter.

General ventilation. System of ventilation consisting of either natural or mechanically induced fresh air movements to mix with and dilute contaminants in the workroom air. This is not the recommended type of ventilation to control contaminants that are toxic.

Genes. The ultimate biological units of heredity.

Genetic effects. Mutations or other changes produced by irradiation of the germ plasm.

Genetically significant dose (GSD). The dose that, if received by every member of the population, would be expected to produce the same total genetic injury to the population as the actual doses received by the various individuals.

Germ. A microorganism; a microbe usually thought of as a pathogenic organism.

Germicide. An agent capable of killing germs.

GI. Gastrointestinal.

Gingival. Pertaining to the gingivae (gums), the mucous membrane, with the supporting fibrous tissue, that overlies the crowns of unerupted teeth and encircles the necks of those that have erupted.

Gingivitis. Inflammation of the gums.

Gland. Any body organ that manufactures some liquid product and secretes it from its cells.

GHS. Globally Harmonized System of Classification and Labeling of Chemicals. A concept adopted by the UN in 2003 for establishing unified, world-wide criteria for classifying health, physical and environmental characteristics of chemicals as well as the format in which this information is to be conveyed. GHS is in various stages of implementation in about 67 countries, including the United States, in which jurisdiction over GHS components are shared among OSHA, EPA and DOT.

Globe thermometer. A thermometer set in the center of a metal sphere that has been painted black in order to measure radiant heat.

Globulin. General name for a group of proteins that are soluble in saline solutions but not in pure water.

Glossa- (prefix). Pertaining to the tongue.

Glove box. A sealed enclosure in which all handling of items inside the box is carried out through long, impervious gloves sealed to ports in the walls of the enclosure.

Gob. Gob pile is waste mineral material, such as from coal mines, that contains sufficient coal that gob fires may arise from spontaneous combustion.

Gonads. The male (testes) and female (ovaries) sex glands.

Grab sample. A sample taken within a very short time period to determine the constituents at a specific time.

Gram (g). A metric unit of weight. One ounce equals

28.4 grams. Grams per kilogram (g/kg). This indicates the dose of a substance given to test animals in toxicity studies.

Granuloma. A mass or nodule of chronically inflamed tissue with granulations; usually associated with an infective process.

Graticule. See Reticle.

Gravimetric. Pertaining to measurement by weight.

Gravimetric method. A procedure dependent upon the formation or use of a precipitate or residue, which is weighed to determine the concentration of a specific contaminant in a previously collected sample.

Gravitation. The universal attraction existing between all material bodies. The gravitational attraction of the earth's mass for bodies at or near its surface is called gravity.

Gravity, specific. The ratio of the mass of a unit volume of a substance to the mass of the same volume of a standard substance at a standard temperature. Water at 39.2°F (4°C) is the standard substance usually referred to. For gases, dry air, at the same temperature and pressure as the gas, is often taken as the standard substance.

Gravity, standard. A gravitational force that produces an acceleration equal to 32.17 ft (9.8 m) per second. The actual force of gravity varies slightly with altitude and latitude. The standard was arbitrarily established as that at sea level and 45-degree latitude.

Gray (Gy). Unit of absorbed radiation dose equal to one joule of absorbed energy per kilogram of matter; also equal to 100 rad.

Gray iron. The same as cast iron; in general, any iron with high carbon content.

Grooving. Designing a tool with grooves on the handle to accommodate the fingers of the user—a bad practice because of the great variation in the size of workers' hands. Grooving interferes with sensory feedback. Intense pain may be caused by the grooves to the arthritic hand.

Gyn-, gyne- (prefix). Woman, female.

Gynecology. The medical specialty concerned with diseases of women.

Gyratory crusher. A device for crushing rock by means of a heavy steel pestle rotating in a steel cone, with the rock being fed in at the top and passing out of the bottom.

H

Half-life, radioactive. For a single radioactive decay process, the time required for the activity to decrease to half its value by that process. The time it takes for half of the unstable nucleus of a radioisotope to decay to a different isotope.

Half-thickness. The thickness of a specified absorbing material that reduces the dose rate to one half its original value.

Half-value layer (HVL). The thickness of a substance necessary to reduce the intensity of a beam of gamma or x rays to half its original value. Also known as half-thickness.

Halogenated hydrocarbon. A chemical material that has carbon plus one or more of these elements: chlorine, fluorine, bromine, and iodine.

Hammer mill. A machine for reducing the size of stone or other bulk material by means of hammers usually placed on a rotating axle inside a steel cylinder.

Hardness. A relative term to describe the penetrating quality of radiation. The higher the energy of the radiation, the more penetrating (harder) is the radiation.

Hardness of water. A degree of hardness is the equivalent of one grain of calcium carbonate, $CaCO_3$, in one gallon of water.

Hazardous material. Any substance or compound that has the capability of producing adverse effects on the health and safety of humans.

Hazwoper. Hazardous waste operations and emergency response—an OSHA standard intended to protect workers engaged in hazardous waste operations.

Heading. In mining, a horizontal passage or drift of a tunnel, also the end of a drift or gallery. In tanning, a layer of ground bark over the tanning liquor.

Health physicist. A professional person specially trained in radiation physics and concerned with problems of radiation damage and protection.

Hearing conservation. The prevention or minimizing of noise-induced deafness through the use of hearing protection devices, the control of noise through engineering methods, annual audiometric tests, and employee training.

Hearing level. The deviation in decibels of an individual's threshold from the zero reference of the audiometer.

Heat cramps. Painful muscle spasms as a result of exposure to excess heat.

Heat exhaustion. A condition usually caused by loss of body water because of exposure to excess heat. Symptoms include headache, tiredness, nausea, and sometimes fainting.

Heat, latent. The quantity of heat absorbed or given off per unit weight of material during a change of state, such as ice to water or water to steam.

Heat of fusion. The heat given off by a liquid freezing to a solid or gained by a solid melting to a liquid, without a change in temperature.

Heat of vaporization. The heat given off by a vapor condensing to a liquid or gained by a liquid evaporating to a vapor, without a change in temperature.

Heat rash. Itchy rash caused by sweating and inadequate hygiene practices.

Heat, sensible. Heat associated with a change in temperature; specific heat exchange with environment, in contrast to a heat interchange in which only a change of state (phase) occurs.

Heat, specific. The ratio of the quantity of heat required to raise the temperature of a given mass of any substance one degree to the quantity required to raise the temperature of an equal mass of a standard substance (usually water at 59°F [15°C]) one degree.

Heat stress. Relative amount of thermal strain from the environment.

Heat stress index (HSI). Also known as the Belding-Hatch heat stress index, this index combines the environmental heat and metabolic heat into an expression of stress in terms of requirement for evaporation of sweat.

Heatstroke. A serious disorder resulting from exposure to excess heat. It results from sweat suppression and increased storage of body heat. Symptoms include hot dry skin, high temperature, mental confusion, convulsions, and coma. Heatstroke is fatal if not treated promptly.

Heat syncope. A heat-related disorder characterized by symptoms of blurred vision and brief fainting spells, heat syncope is caused by pooling of blood in the legs or skin during prolonged static postures in a hot environment.

Heat treatment. Any of several processes of metal modification, such as annealing.

Heavy hydrogen. Same as deuterium.

Heavy metals. Metallic elements with high molecular weights.

Heavy water. Water containing heavy hydrogen (deuterium) instead of ordinary hydrogen. It is widely used in reactors to slow down neutrons.

Helmet. A device that shields the eyes, face, neck, and other parts of the head.

Hem-, Hemato-, -em- (prefix). Pertaining to blood. *Hematuria* means blood in the urine. When the roots occur internally in a word, the *h* is often dropped for the sake of pronunciation, leaving *em* to denote blood, as in anoxemia (deficiency of oxygen in the blood).

Hematology. Study of the blood and the blood-forming organs.

Hematuria. Blood in the urine.

Hemi- (prefix). Half. The prefix is straightforward enough in *hemiplegia*, "half paralysis," affecting one side of the body. It is not so plain in *migraine* (one-sided headache), a word that shows how language changes through the centuries. The original word was *hemicrania*, "half-head."

Hemoglobin. The red coloring matter of the blood that carries the oxygen.

Hemolysis. Breakdown of red blood cells with liberation of hemoglobin.

Hemoptysis. Bleeding from the lungs, spitting blood, or blood-stained sputum.

Hemorrhage. Bleeding; especially profuse bleeding, as from a ruptured or cut blood vessel (artery or vein).

Hemorrhagic. Pertaining to or characterized by hemorrhage.

HEPA filter. High efficiency particulate air filter. A disposable, extended-medium, dry-type filter with a particle removal efficiency of no less than 99.97 percent for 0.3 μm particles.

Hepatitis. Inflammation of the liver.

Hepatitis B. A virus causing hepatitis. The virus may also cause liver cancer in some of those infected by it. The virus is bloodborne and as such is one of the agents targeted by OSHA's bloodborne pathogen standard.

Hepatotoxin. Chemicals that produce liver damage.

Herpes. An acute inflammation of the skin or mucous membranes, characterized by the development of groups of vesicles on an inflammatory base.

Hertz. The frequency measured in cycles per second. 1 cps = 1 Hz.

High frequency loss. Refers to a hearing deficit starting with 2000 Hz and beyond.

HIV. Human immunodeficiency virus. Held to be the initiating cause of acquired immunodeficiency syndrome (AIDS).

Homeotherm. Uniform body temperature, or a warm-blooded creature remaining so regardless of environment.

Homogenizer. A machine that forces liquids under high pressure through a perforated shield against a hard surface to blend or emulsify the mixture.

Homoiotherm. See Homeotherm.

Hood. (1) Enclosure, part of a local exhaust system. (2) A device that completely covers the head, neck, and portions of the shoulders.

Hood entry loss. The pressure loss from turbulence and friction as air enters the ventilation system.

Hood, slot. A hood consisting of a narrow slot leading into a plenum chamber under suction to distribute air velocity along the length of the slot.

Hood static pressure. The suction or static pressure in a duct near a hood. It represents the suction that is available to draw air into the hood.

Hormones. Chemical substances secreted by the endocrine glands, exerting influence over practically all body activities.

Horsepower. A unit of power, equivalent to 33,000 foot-pounds per minute (746 W). See Brake horsepower.

Host. A plant or animal harboring another as a parasite or as an infectious agent.

Hot. In addition to meaning having a relatively high

temperature, this is a colloquial term meaning highly radio-active.

HSI. See Heat stress index.

Human-equipment interface. Areas of physical or perceptual contact between person and equipment. The design characteristics of the human-equipment interface determine the quality of information. Poorly designed interfaces may lead to excessive fatigue or localized trauma, e.g., calluses.

Humerus. The bone of the upper arm that starts at the shoulder joint and ends at the elbow. Muscles that move the upper arm, forearm, and hand are attached to this bone.

Humidify. To add water vapor to the atmosphere; to add water vapor or moisture to any material.

Humidity. (1) Absolute humidity is the weight of water vapor per unit volume: pounds per cubic foot or grams per cubic centimeter. (2) Relative humidity is the ratio of the actual partial vapor pressure of the water vapor in a space to the saturation pressure of pure water at the same temperature.

Humidity, specific. The weight of water vapor per unit weight of dry air.

HVAC system. Heating, ventilating, and air conditioning system.

Hyalinization. Conversion into a substance resembling glass.

Hydration. The process of converting raw material into pulp by prolonged beating in water; to combine with water or the elements of water.

Hydrocarbons. Organic compounds composed solely of carbon and hydrogen. Several hundred thousand molecular combinations of C and H are known to exist. Basic building blocks of all organic chemicals. Main chemical industry sources of hydrocarbons are petroleum, natural gas, and coal.

Hydrogenation. A reaction of molecular hydrogen with numerous organic compounds. An example is the hydrogenation of olefins to paraffins or of the aromatics to the naphthenes or the reduction of aldehydes and ketones to alcohols.

Hydrolysis. The interaction of water with a material resulting in decomposition.

Hydrometallurgy. Science of metal recovery by a process involving treatment of ores in an aqueous medium, such as acid or cyanide solution.

Hydrophobic. Repelled by water, or water-hating.

Hygroscopic. Readily absorbing or retaining moisture.

Hyper- (prefix). Over, above, increased. The usual implication is overactivity or excessive production, as in hyperthyroidism.

Hyperkeratosis. Hypertrophy of the horny layer of the skin.

Hypertension. Abnormally high tension; especially high blood pressure.

Hypertrophy. Increase in cell size causing an increase in the size of the organ or tissue.

Hypnotic. Anything that induces sleep or that produces the effects ascribed to hypnotism.

Hypo- (prefix). Under, below; less, decreased. The two different meanings of this common prefix can be tricky. *Hypodermic* might reasonably be interpreted to mean that an unfortunate patient has too little skin. The actual meaning is "under or beneath the skin," a proper site for an injection. The majority of *hypo-* words, however, denote an insufficiency, lessening, or reduction from the norm, as in *hypoglycemia*, meaning too little glucose in the blood.

Hypothermia. A systemic effect of cold stress; condition of reduced body temperature.

Hysteresis. A retardation of the effect when the forces acting upon a body are changed (as if from viscosity or internal friction). Specifically, the magnetization of a sample of iron or steel actually lags behind the magnetic field that induced it, when the field varies.

I

IAQ. Indoor air quality.

IARC. International Agency for Research on Cancer.

Iatro- (prefix). Pertaining to a doctor. A related root, *-atrist,* denotes a specialist, as in *psychiatrist.*

Iatrogenic. Caused by the doctor.

ICC. Interstate Commerce Commission.

ICRP. International Commission on Radiological Protection and Measurements.

Idio- (prefix). Peculiar to, private, or distinctive, as in *idiosyncrasy.*

Idiopathic. Disease that originates in itself.

Idiosyncrasy. A special susceptibility to a particular substance introduced into the body.

IDLH. Immediately dangerous to life or health.

IES. Illumination Engineering Society.

Iliac crest. The upper rounded border of the hip bone. No muscles cross the iliac crest, which lies immediately below the skin. It is an important anatomical reference point because it can be felt through the skin. Seat backrests should clear the iliac crest.

Image. The fluorescent picture produced by x rays hitting a fluoroscopic screen.

Image receptor. Any device, such as a fluorescent screen or radiographic film, that transforms incident x-ray photons either into a visible image or into another form that can be made into a visible image by further transformations.

Immiscible. Not miscible. Any liquid that does not mix

with another liquid, in which case the result is two separate layers or cloudiness or turbidity.

Immune. Resistant to disease.

Immunity. The power of the body to successfully resist infection and the effects of toxins. This resistance results from the possession by the body of certain "fighting substances," or antibodies. To immunize is to confer immunity. Immunization is the process of acquiring or conferring immunity.

Impaction. The forcible contact of particles of matter; a term often used synonymously with impingement, but generally reserved for the case where particles are contacting a dry surface.

Impingement. As used in air sampling, impingement refers to a process for the collection of particulate matter in which a particle-containing gas is directed against a wetted glass plate and the particles are retained by the liquid.

Impinger. A device containing an absorbing liquid used in air sampling for the collection of gaseous or particulate constituents of an airstream directed by the device through the liquid. The impinger draws air at high velocity through a glass nozzle or jet. A commonly used type is called the midget impinger.

Inches of mercury column. A unit used in measuring pressures. One inch of mercury column equals a pressure of 0.491 lb/in.^{2} (1.66 kPa).

Inches of water column. A unit used in measuring pressures. One inch of water column equals a pressure of 0.036 lb/in.^{2} (0.25 kPa).

Incompatible. A term applied to liquid and solid systems to indicate that one material cannot be mixed with another specified material without the possibility of a dangerous reaction.

Incubation. Holding cultures of microorganisms under conditions favorable to their growth.

Incubation time. The elapsed time between exposure to infection and the appearance of disease symptoms, or the time period during which microorganisms inoculated into a medium are allowed to grow.

Inductively coupled plasma (ICP). Radiofrequency induced high temperature plasma utilized for analysis of metals either by atomic emission spectrometry or mass spectrophotometry.

Induration. Heat hardening that may involve little more than thermal dehydration.

Inert (chemical). Not having active properties.

Inert gas. A gas that does not normally combine chemically with the base metal or filler metal.

Inert gas welding. An electric welding operation using an inert gas such as helium to flush away the air to prevent oxidation of the metal being welded.

Inertial moment. As related to biomechanics, that moment of force-time caused by sudden accelerations or decelerations. Whiplash of the neck is caused by an inertial moment. In an industrial setting, sidestepping causes application of a lateral inertial moment on the lumbosacral joint, which may cause trauma, pain, and in any case lowers performance efficiency. The inertial moment is one of the seven elements of a lifting task.

Infection. Entrance into the body or its tissues of disease-causing organisms with the effect of damage to the body as a whole or to tissues or organs. It also refers to the entrance into the body of parasites, like certain worms. On the other hand, parasites such as mites and ticks that attack the surface of the body are said to infest, not infect.

Infectious. Capable of invading a susceptible host, replicating and causing an altered host reaction, commonly referred to as a disease.

Infestation. Invasion of the body surface by parasites. See Infection.

Inflammation. The reaction of body tissue to injury, whether by infection or trauma. The inflamed area is red, swollen, hot, and usually painful.

Infrared. Wavelengths of the electromagnetic spectrum longer than those of visible light and shorter than radio waves, 10^{-4}–10^{-1} cm wavelength.

Infrared radiation. Electromagnetic energy with wavelengths from 770 nm to 100,000 nm.

Ingestion. (1) The process of taking substances into the stomach, such as food, drink, or medicine. (2) With regard to certain cells, the act of engulfing or taking up bacteria and other foreign matter.

Ingot. A block of iron or steel cast in a mold for ease in handling before processing.

Inguinal region. The abdominal area on each side of the body occurring as a depression between the abdomen and the thigh; the groin.

Inhalation valve. A device that allows respirable air to enter the facepiece and prevents exhaled air from leaving the facepiece through the intake opening.

Inhibition. Prevention of growth or multiplication of microorganisms.

Inhibitor. An agent that arrests or slows chemical action or a material used to prevent or retard rust or corrosion.

Injury. Damage or harm to the body, as the result of violence, infection, or anything else that produces a lesion.

Innocuous. Harmless.

Inoculation. The artificial introduction of microorganisms into a system.

Inorganic. Used to designate compounds that generally do not contain carbon, whose source is matter other than vegetable or animal. Examples are sulfuric acid and salt.

Exceptions are carbon monoxide and carbon dioxide.

Insomnia. Inability to sleep; abnormal wakefulness.

Instantaneous radiation. The radiation emitted during the fission process. These instantaneous radiations are often called prompt gamma-rays or prompt neutrons. Most fission products continue to emit radiation after the fission process.

Inter- (prefix). Between.

Intermediate. A chemical formed as a middle step in a series of chemical reactions, especially in the manufacture of organic dyes and pigments. In many cases, it may be isolated and used to form a variety of desired products. In other cases, the intermediate may be unstable or used up at once.

Internal biomechanical environment. The muscles, bones and tissues of the body, all of which are subject to the same Newtonian force as external objects in their interaction with other bodies and natural forces. When designing for the body, one must consider the forces that the internal biomechanical environment must withstand.

Interphalangeal joints. The finger or toe joints. The thumb has one interphalangeal joint; the fingers have two interphalangeal joints each.

Interstitial. (1) Pertaining to the small spaces between cells or structures. (2) Occupying the interstices of a tissue or organ. (3) Designating connective tissue occupying spaces between the functional units of an organ or a structure.

Intoxication. Either drunkenness or poisoning.

Intra- (prefix). Within.

Intraperitoneal. Inside the space formed by the membrane that lines the interior wall of the abdomen and covers the abdominal organs.

Intravenous. Into or inside the vein.

Intrinsically safe. Said of an instrument that is designed and certified to be operated safely in flammable or explosive atmospheres.

Inverse square law. The propagation of energy through space is inversely proportional to the square of the distance it must travel. An object 3 m away from an energy source receives one-ninth as much energy as an object 1 m away.

Inversion. Phenomenon of a layer of cool air trapped by a layer of warmer air above it so that the bottom layer cannot rise. This is a special problem in polluted areas because the contaminating substances cannot be dispersed.

Investment casting. There are numerous types of investment casting, and the materials include fire clay, silicon dioxide, silica flour, stillimanite, cristobalite, aluminum oxide, zirconium oxide, and others. The Mercast process uses mercury poured into a steel die. A ceramic shell mold is built around the pattern, and then it is frozen. The mercury is subsequently recovered at room tempera-ture. The potential harm from exposure to mercury often is unrecognized.

Ion. An electrically charged atom. An atom that has lost one or more of its electrons is left with a positive electrical charge. Those that have gained one or more extra electrons are left with a negative charge.

Ion-exchange resin. Synthetic resins containing active groups that give the resin the property of combining with or exchanging ions between the resin and a solution.

Ionization. The process whereby one or more electrons is removed from a neutral atom by the action of radiation. Specific ionization is the number of ion pairs per unit distance in matter, usually air.

Ionization chamber. A device roughly similar to a Geiger counter and used to measure radioactivity.

Ionizing radiation. Radiation energetic enough to create ions by knocking electrons out of the gas, solid, or liquid through which it is passing. Ionizing radiation may be electrically charged or neutral particles, or electromagnetic radiation. There are five major types: alpha, beta, x- (or x-ray), gamma, and neutrons.

Ion pair. A positively charged atom (ion) and an electron formed by the action of radiation on a neutral atom.

Irradiation. The exposure of something to radiation.

Irritant. A substance that produces an irritating effect when it contacts skin, eyes, nose, or respiratory system.

Ischemia. Loss of blood supply to a particular part of the body.

Ischial tuberosity. A rounded projection on the ischium. It is a point of attachment for several muscles involved in moving the femur and the knee. It can be affected by improper chair design and by situations involving trauma to the pelvic region. When seated, pressure is borne at the site of the ischial tuberosities. Chair design should provide support to the pressure projection of the ischial tuberosity through the skin of the buttocks.

Isometric work. Refers to a state of muscular contraction without movement. Although no work in the "physics" sense is done, physiological work (energy use and heat production) occurs. In isometric exercise, muscles are tightened against immovable objects. In work measurements, isometric muscular contractions must be considered as a major factor of task severity.

Isotope. One of two or more atomic species of an element differing in atomic weight but having the same atomic number. Each contains the same number of protons but a different number of neutrons. Uranium-238 contains 92 protons and 146 neutrons; the isotope U-235 contains 92 protons and 143 neutrons. Thus the atomic weight (atomic mass) of U-238 is 3 higher than that of U-235. See also Radioisotope.

Isotropic. Exhibiting properties with the same values when measured along axes in all directions.

-itis (suffix). Inflammation.

J

Jaundice. Icterus. A serious symptom of disease that causes the skin, the whites of the eyes, and even the mucous membranes to turn yellow.

Jigs and fixtures. Often used interchangeably; precisely, a jig holds work in position and guides the tools acting on the work, whereas a fixture holds but does not guide.

Joint. Articulation between two bones that may permit motion in one or more planes. They may become the sites for work-induced trauma (such as tennis elbow or arthritis) or other disorders.

Joule. Unit of energy used in describing a single pulsed output of a laser. It is equal to one watt-second or 0.239 calories. It equals 1×10^7 ergs.

Joule/cm² (J/cm²). Unit of energy density used in measuring the amount of energy per area of absorbing surface or per area of a laser beam. It is a unit for predicting the damage potential of a laser beam.

K

Kaolin. A type of clay composed of mixed silicates and used for refractories, ceramics, tile, and stoneware. In some deposits, free silica may be present as an impurity.

Kaolinosis. A condition induced by inhalation of the dust released in the grinding and handling of kaolin (china clay).

Kelvin scale. The fundamental temperature scale, also called the absolute or thermodynamic scale, in which the temperature measure is based on the average kinetic energy per molecule of a perfect gas. The zero of the Kelvin scale is −273.18 degrees Celsius.

Keratin. Sulfur-containing proteins that form the chemical basis for epidermis tissues; found in nails, hair, and feathers.

Keratinocyte. An epidermal cell that produces keratin.

Keratitis. Inflammation of the cornea.

Kev. A unit of energy equal to 1,000 electron volts.

Kilocurie. 1,000 curies. A unit of radioactivity.

Kilogram (kg). A unit of weight in the metric system equal to 2.2 lb.

Kinesiology. The study of human movement in terms of functional anatomy.

Kinetic energy. Energy due to motion. See Work.

Kyphosis. Abnormal curvature of the spine of the upper back in the anteroposterior plane.

L

Laboratory-acquired infection. Any infection resulting from exposure to biohazardous materials in a laboratory environment. Exposure may be the result of a specific accident or inadequate biohazard control procedure or equipment.

Lacquer. A colloidal dispersion or solution of nitrocellulose or similar film-forming compounds, resins, and plasticizers in solvents and diluents used as a protective and decorative coating for various surfaces.

Laminar airflow. Streamlined airflow in which the entire body of air within a designated space moves with uniform velocity in one direction along parallel flow lines.

LAN. Local area network. A network of computers linked electronically and by software. Located geographically locally, usually in one office or office building.

Lapping. The operation of polishing or sanding surfaces such as metal or glass to a precise dimension.

Laryngitis. Inflammation of the larynx.

Larynx. The organ by which the voice is produced. It is situated at the upper part of the trachea.

Laser. Light amplification by stimulated emission of radiation. Lasers may operate in either pulsed or continuous mode.

Laser light region. A portion of the electromagnetic spectrum including ultraviolet, visible, and infrared light.

Laser system. An assembly of electrical, mechanical, and optical components that includes a laser.

Latent period. The time that elapses between exposure and the first manifestation of damage.

Latex. Originally, a milky extract from the rubber tree, containing about 35 percent rubber hydrocarbon, with the remainder being water, proteins, and sugars. Also applied to water emulsions of synthetic rubbers or resins. In emulsion paints, the film-forming resin is in the form of latex.

Lathe. A machine tool used to perform cutting operations on wood or metal by the rotation of the workpiece.

Latissimus dorsi. A large, flat muscle of the back that originates in the lower back and inserts into the humerus near the armpit. It adducts the upper arm, and when the elbow is abducted, it rotates the arm medially. It is actively used in operating equipment such as the drill press, where a downward pull by the arm is required.

LC$_{50}$. Lethal concentration that kills 50 percent of the test animals within a specified time. See LD$_{50}$.

LD$_{50}$. The dose required to produce the death in 50 percent of the exposed population within a specified time.

Leakage radiation. Radiation emanating from the diagnostic source assembly, except for the useful beam and radiation, produced when the exposure switch or timer is not activated.

Lens, crystalline. Lens of the eye—a transparent biconvex body situated between the anterior chamber (aqueous) and the posterior chamber (vitreous) through which the light rays are further focused on the retina. The cornea provides most of the refractive power of the eye.

Lesion. Injury, damage, or abnormal change in a tissue or organ.

Lethal. Capable of causing death.

Leuk-, leuko- (prefix). White.

Leukemia. A group of malignant blood diseases distinguished by overproduction of white blood cells.

Leukemogenic. Having the ability to cause leukemia.

Leukocyte. White blood cell.

Leukocytosis. An abnormal increase in the number of white blood cells.

Leukopenia. A serious reduction in the number of white blood cells.

Lig- (prefix). Binding. A ligament ties two or more bones together.

Linear accelerator. A machine for speeding up charged particles such as protons. It differs from other accelerators in that the particles move in a straight line at all times instead of in circles or spirals.

Line-voltage regulation. The difference between the no-load and the load-line potentials expressed as a percent of the load-line potential.

Lipo- (prefix). Fat, fatty.

Liquefied petroleum gas. A compressed or liquefied gas usually composed of propane, some butane, and lesser quantities of other light hydrocarbons and impurities; obtained as a by-product in petroleum refining. Used chiefly as a fuel and in chemical synthesis.

Liquid. A state of matter in which the substance is a formless fluid that flows in accord with the law of gravity.

Liter (L). A measure of capacity; one quart equals 0.9 L.

Liver. The largest gland or organ in the body, situated on the right side of the upper part of the abdomen. It has many important functions, including regulating the amino acids in the blood; storing iron and copper for the body; forming and secreting bile, which aids in absorption and digestion of fats; transforming glucose into glycogen; and detoxifying exogenous substances.

Live room. A reverberant room that is characterized by an unusually small amount of sound absorption.

Local exhaust ventilation. A ventilation system that captures and removes the contaminants at the point at which they are being produced before they escape into the workroom air.

Localized. Restricted to one spot or area in the body, and not spread all through it; contrasted with systemic.

Lockout/tagout. A basic safety concept and OSHA standard requiring implementation of practices and procedures to prevent the release of potentially hazardous energy from machines or parts of machines and equipment while maintenance, servicing, or alteration activity is performed. The energy in question may be electrical, mechanical, chemical, or any other form. Also called lockout/tagout/blockout.

Lordosis. The curvature of the lower back in the anteroposterior plane.

Loudness. The intensive attribute of an auditory sensation, in terms of which sounds may be ordered on a scale extending from soft to loud. Loudness depends primarily upon the sound pressure of the stimulus, but it also depends upon the frequency and wave form of the stimulus.

Louver. A slanted panel.

Low-pressure tank. A storage tank designed to operate at pressures between 0.5 and 15 psig (3.5 to 103 kPa).

Lower confidence limit (LCL). In analyzing sampling data, a statistical procedure used to estimate the likelihood that the true value of the sampled quantity is lower than that obtained.

Lower explosive limit (LEL). The lower limit of flammability of a gas or vapor at ordinary ambient temperatures expressed by a percentage of the gas or vapor in air by volume. This limit is assumed constant for temperatures up to 250°F (120°C); above this, it should be decreased by a factor of 0.7, because explosibility increases with higher temperatures.

LP gas. See Liquefied petroleum gas.

Lumbar spine. The section of the lower spinal column or vertebral column immediately above the sacrum. Located in the small of the back and consisting of five large lumbar vertebrae, it is a highly stressed area in work situations and in supporting the body structure.

Lumbosacral joint. The joint between the fifth lumbar vertebrae and the sacrum. Often the site of spinal trauma from lifting tasks.

Lumen. The flux on one square foot of a sphere—one foot in radius—with a light source of one candle at the center that radiates uniformly in all directions.

Luminous flux. The rate of light flow measured in lumens.

Lux. A unit of illumination equal to 10 footcandles.

Lyme disease. A disease transmitted to humans by the deer tick.

Lymph. A pale, coagulable fluid consisting of a liquid portion resembling blood plasma and containing white blood cells (lymphocytes).

Lymph node. Small oval bodies with a gland-like structure scattered throughout the body in the course of the lymph vessels. Also known as lymphatic nodes, lymph glands, and lymphatic glands.

Lymphoid. Resembling lymph.

Lyophilized. Freeze-dried, as in freeze-dried bacterial cultures.

Lysis. The distribution or breaking up of cells by internal or external means.

M

MAC. Maximum allowable concentration.

Maceration. Softening of the skin by action of a liquid.

Macrophage. Immune system cell whose normal function is to engulf and remove foreign matter from the body's tissues.

Macroscopic. Visible without the aid of a microscope.

Macula. An oval area in the center of the retina devoid of blood vessels; the area most responsible for color vision.

Magnification. The number of times the apparent size of an object has been increased by the lens system of a microscope.

Makeup air. Clean, tempered outdoor air supplied to a work space to replace air removed by exhaust ventilation or by some industrial process.

Malaise. A vague feeling of bodily discomfort.

Malignant. As applied to a tumor, cancerous and capable of undergoing metastasis (invasion of surrounding tissue).

Manometer. Instrument for measuring pressure; essentially a U-tube partially filled with a liquid (usually water, mercury, or a light oil) and constructed in such a way that the amount of displacement of the liquid indicates the pressure being exerted on the instrument.

Maser. Microwave amplification by stimulated emission of radiation. When used in the term *optical maser,* it is often interpreted as molecular amplification by stimulated emission of radiation.

Masking. The stimulation of a person's ear with controlled noise to prevent that person from hearing with one ear the tone or signal given to the other ear. This procedure is used when there is at least a 15- to 20-dBA difference in the hearing level between ears.

Mass. Quantity of matter; measured in grams or pounds.

Material safety data sheet (MSDS). See Safety Data Sheets.

Matter. Anything that has mass or occupies space.

Maximum evaporative capacity. The maximum amount of evaporating sweat from a person that an environment can accept.

Maximum line current. The rms current in the supply line of an x-ray machine operating at its maximum rating.

Maximum permissible concentration (MPC). Concentrations set by the National Committee on Radiation Protection (NCRP); recommended maximum average concentrations of radionuclides to which a worker may be exposed assuming that he or she works eight hours a day, five days a week, and 50 weeks a year.

Maximum permissible dose (MPD). A dose of ionizing radiation not expected to cause appreciable bodily injury to a person at any time during his or her life.

Maximum Permissible Exposure (MPE). Analogous to OSHA chemical PELs, MPEs designate maximum exposures for radiofrequency/microwave exposure and laser exposure.

Maximum permissible power or energy density. The intensity of laser radiation not expected to cause detectable bodily injury to a person at any time during his or her life.

Maximum use concentration (MUC). The product of the protection factor of the respiratory protection equipment and the permissible exposure limit (PEL).

Mechanical efficiency curve. A graphical representation of a fan's relative efficiency in moving air at different airflow rates and static pressures.

Mechanotactic stress. Stress caused by contact with a mechanical environment.

Mechanotaxis. Contact with a mechanical environment consisting of forces (pressure, moment), vibration, and so on; one of the ecological stress vectors. Improper design of the mechanotactic interface may lead to instantaneous trauma, cumulative pathogenesis, or death.

Median nerve. A major nerve controlling the flexor muscles of the wrist and hand. Tool handles and other grasped objects should make solid contact with the sensory feedback area of this nerve, located in the palmar surface of the thumb, index finger, middle finger, and part of the ring finger.

Medium. See Culture medium.

Medulla. The part of the brain that controls breathing.

Mega. One million. For example, a megacurie = one million curies.

Mega-, megalo- (prefix). Large, huge. The prefix *macro-* has the same meaning.

Meiosis. The process whereby chromosome pairs undergo nuclear division as the germ cell matures.

Melanoderma. Abnormal darkening of the skin.

Melanocyte. An epidermal cell containing dark pigments.

Melt. In the glass industry, the total batch of ingredients that may be introduced into pots or furnaces.

Melting point. The transition point between the solid and liquid states. Expressed as the temperature at which this change occurs.

Membrane. A thin, pliable layer of animal tissue that covers a surface, lines the interior of a cavity or organ, or divides a space.

Membrane filter. A filter medium made from various polymeric materials such as cellulose, polyethylene, and tetrapolyethylene. These usually exhibit narrow ranges of effective pore diameters and are therefore useful in collecting and sizing microscopic and submicroscopic particles and in sterilizing liquids.

Men-, meno-(prefix). Pertaining to menstruation; from a Greek word for *month*.

Ménière's disease. Of unknown cause, the disease is characterized by episodes of dizziness, nausea, vomiting, tinnitis, and fluctuating hearing loss.

Meson. A particle that weighs more than an electron but generally less than a proton. Mesons can be produced artificially or by cosmic radiation (natural radiation from outer space). Mesons are not stable and disintegrate in a fraction of a second.

Mesothelioma. Cancer of the membranes that line the chest and abdomen.

Metabolism. The flow of energy and the associated physical and chemical changes constantly taking place in the billions of cells that make up the body.

Metal fume fever. A flu-like condition caused by inhaling heated metal fumes.

Metallizing. Melting wire in a special device that sprays the atomized metal onto a surface. The metal can be steel, lead, or another metal or alloy.

Metastasis. Transfer of the causal agent (cell or microorganism) of a disease from a primary focus to a distant one through the blood or lymphatic vessels. Also, spread of malignancy from a site of primary cancer to secondary sites.

Methemoglobinemia. The presence of methemoglobin in the blood. (Methemoglobin is a compound formed when the iron moiety of hemoglobin is oxidized from the ferrous to the ferric state.) This protein inactivates the hemoglobin as an oxygen carrier.

Mev. Million electron volts.

Mica. A large group of silicates of varying composition that are similar in physical properties. All have excellent cleavage and can be split into very thin sheets. Used in electrical insulation.

Microbar. A unit of pressure commonly used in acoustics; equals one dyne/cm². A reference point for the decibel, which is accepted as 0.0002 dyne/cm².

Microbe. A microscopic organism.

Microcurie (μc). One-millionth of a curie. A still smaller unit is the micromicrocurie (μc).

Micron (micrometer). A unit of length equal to 10^{-4}cm, approximately 1/25,000 in.

Microorganism. A minute organism—microbes, bacteria, cocci, viruses, and molds, among others.

Microphone. An electroacoustic transducer that responds to sound waves and delivers essentially equivalent electric waves.

Microscale. Very small, generally involving matter with at least one dimension less than a millimeter.

Midsagittal plane. A reference plane formed by bisecting the human anatomy into a right and left aspect. Human motor function can be described in terms of movement relative to the midsagittal plane.

Miliary. Characterized or accompanied by seedlike blisters or inflamed raised portions of tissue.

Milligram (mg). A unit of weight in the metric system. One thousand milligrams equal one gram.

Milligrams per cubic meter (mg/m³). Unit used to measure air concentrations of dusts, gases, mists, and fumes.

Milliliter (mL). A metric unit used to measure volume. One milliliter equals one cubic centimeter.

Millimeter of mercury (mmHg). The unit of pressure equal to the pressure exerted by liquid mercury one-millimeter-high column at a standard temperature.

Milliroentgen. One one-thousandth of a roentgen.

Millwright. A mechanic engaged in the erection and maintenance of machinery.

Mineral pitch. Tar from petroleum or coal as opposed to wood tar.

Mineral spirits. A petroleum fraction with a boiling range between 300 and 400°F (149 and 240°C).

Miosis. Excessive smallness or contraction of the pupil of the eye.

Mists. Suspended liquid droplets generated by condensation from the gaseous to the liquid state or by breaking up a liquid into a dispersed state, such as by splashing, foaming, or atomizing. Formed when a finely divided liquid is suspended in air.

Mitosis. Nuclear cell division in which resulting nuclei have the same number and kinds of chromosomes as the original cell.

Mixture. A combination of two or more substances that may be separated by mechanical means. The components may not be uniformly dispersed. See also Solution.

Moderator. A material used to slow neutrons in a reactor. These slow neutrons are particularly effective in causing fission. Neutrons are slowed when they collide with atoms of light elements such as hydrogen, deuterium, and carbon—three common moderators.

Mold. (1) A growth of fungi forming a furry patch, as on stale bread or cheese. See Spore. (2) A hollow form or matrix into which molten material is poured to produce a cast.

Molecule. A chemical unit composed of one or more atoms.

Moment. Magnitude of force times distance of application.

Moment concept. A concept based on theoretical and experimental bases that lifting stress depends on the bending moment exerted at susceptible points of the vertebral column rather than depending on weight alone.

Monaural hearing. Hearing with one ear only.

Monochromatic. Single fixed wavelength.

Monomer. A compound of relatively low molecular weight that, under certain conditions, either alone or with another monomer, forms various types and lengths of molecular chains called polymers or copolymers of high molecular weight. Styrene, for example, is a monomer that polymerizes readily to form polystyrene. See Polymer.

Morphology. The branch of biological science that deals with the study of the structure and form of living organisms.

Motile. Capable of spontaneous movement.

MMVF. Manmade vitreous fibers, such as fiber glass.

MOS. Metal oxide semiconductor. A type of detector used in some direct-reading instruments.

MPE. Maximum Permissible Exposure.

MPL. May be either maximum permissible level, limit, or dose; refers to the tolerable dose rate for humans exposed to nuclear radiation.

Mppcf. Million particles per cubic foot.

mrem. Millirem.

mR. Milliroentgen.

MSHA. The Mine Safety and Health Administration; a federal agency that regulates safety and health in the mining industry.

MSDS. Material safety data sheet. See Safety Data Sheet.

Mucous membranes. Lining of the hollow organs of the body, notably the nose, mouth, stomach, intestines, bronchial tubes, and urinary tract.

Musculoskeletal system. The combined system of muscles and bones that comprise the internal biomechanical environment.

Mutagen. Anything that can cause a change (mutation) in the genetic material of a living cell.

Mutation. A transformation of the gene that may result in the alteration of characteristics of offspring.

MWD. Megawatt days, usually per ton. The amount of energy obtained from one megawatt power in one day, normally used to measure the extent of nuclear fuel burnup. 10,000 MWD per ton is about 1 percent burnup.

My-, myo- (prefix). Pertaining to muscle. Myocardium is the heart muscle.

Myelo- (prefix). Pertaining to marrow.

N

Nanomaterial. An engineered substance with at least one dimension in the nanoscale

Nanometer. A unit of length equal to 10^{-7} cm.

Nanoparticles. Particles with at least one dimension between 1 and 100 nanometers. Engineered nanoparticles (ENP) are intentionally created, as opposed to particles that naturally occur in this size range; generally novel, as opposed to well-known particles (such as carbon black particles in the nanoscale), ENP usually have at least two dimensions between 1 and 100 nanometers; ENP are free of or only loosely bound to larger substrates.

Nanoscale. Of the size range of 100 billionths of a meter or less.

Nanotechnology. Production, study and manipulation of human engineered matter with particles at a near atomic scale. These engineered particles are generally conceived as having at least one dimension between one and one hundred nanometers, or billionths of a meter.

Nanotube. An engineered tube, usually only a few nanometers in diameter, but with a length that may reach millimeters or centimeters. (Carbon nanotubes also occur naturally as a result of some combustion processes, but generally at very low concentrations not of direct health concern. Non-engineered naturally occurring biological tubular structures of nanoscale have also been discovered in cell biology. While these protein structures also have been called "nanotubes," they are not the nanotubes of concern in industrial hygiene.)

Naphthas. Hydrocarbons of the petroleum type that contain substantial portions of paraffins and naphthalenes.

Narcosis. Stupor or unconsciousness produced by chemical substances.

Narcotics. Chemical agents that completely or partially induce sleep.

Narrow band. Applies to a narrow band of transmitted waves, with neither the critical or cutoff frequencies of the filter being zero or infinite.

Nasal septum. Narrow partition that divides the nose into right and left nasal cavities.

Nascent. Just forming, as from a chemical or biological reaction.

Nasopharynx. Upper extension of the throat.

Natural gas. A combustible gas composed largely of methane and other hydrocarbons with variable amounts of nitrogen and noncombustible gases; obtained from natural earth fissures or from driven wells. Used as a fuel in the manufacture of carbon black and in chemical synthesis of many products. Major source of hydrogen for the manufacture of ammonia.

Natural radioactivity. The radioactive background or, more properly, the radioactivity that is associated with the heavy naturally occurring elements.

Natural uranium. Purified from the naturally occurring

ore, as opposed to uranium enriched in fissionable content by processing at separation facilities.

Nausea. An unpleasant sensation, vaguely referred to the epigastrium and abdomen. Often precedes vomiting.

NCRP. National Committee on Radiation Protection; an advisory group of scientists and professionals that makes recommendations for radiation protection in the United States.

Near field. In noise measurement, refers to a field in the immediate vicinity of the noise source where the sound-pressure level does not follow the inverse square law.

Necro- (prefix). Dead.

Necrosis. Death of body tissue.

Neoplasm. A cellular outgrowth characterized by rapid cell multiplication; may be benign (semicontrolled and restricted) or malignant.

Nephr-, nephro- (prefix). From the Greek for *kidney*. See also Ren-.

Nephrotoxins. Chemicals that produce kidney damage.

Nephritis. Inflammation of the kidneys.

Neur-, neuro- (prefix). Pertaining to the nerves.

Neural loss. Hearing loss. See also Sensorineural.

Neuritis. Inflammation of a nerve.

Neurological (neurology). The branch of medical science dealing with the nervous system.

Neurotoxin. Chemicals that produce their primary effect on the nervous system.

Neutrino. A particle, resulting from nuclear reactions, that carries energy away from the system but has no mass or charge and is absorbed only with extreme difficulty.

Neutron. A constituent of the atomic nucleus. A neutron weighs about as much as a proton, and has no electric charge. Neutrons make effective atomic projectiles for the bombardment of nuclei.

NFPA. The National Fire Protection Association; a voluntary membership organization whose aim is to promote and improve fire protection and prevention. The NFPA publishes the National Fire Codes.

NIOSH. The National Institute for Occupational Safety and Health; a federal agency that conducts research on health and safety concerns, tests and certifies respirators, and trains occupational health and safety professionals.

Nitrogen fixation. Chemical combination or fixation of atmospheric nitrogen with hydrogen, as in the synthesis of ammonia. Bacteria fixates nitrogen in soil. Provides an industrial and agricultural source of nitrogen.

Node. (1) A point, line, or surface in a standing wave where some characteristic of the wave field has essentially zero amplitude. (2) A small, round, or oval mass of tissue; a collection of cells. (3) One of several constrictions occurring at regular intervals in a structure.

Nodule. A small mass of rounded or irregularly shaped cells or tissue; a small node.

Nodulizing. Simultaneous sintering and drum balling, usually in a rotary kiln.

NOEL. See No observable effect level.

Noise. Any unwanted sound.

Noise-induced hearing loss. Slowly progressive inner-ear hearing loss resulting from exposure to continuous noise over a long period of time, as contrasted to acoustic trauma or physical injury to the ear.

Nonauditory effects of noise. Refers to stress, fatigue, health, work efficiency, and performance effects of loud, continuous noise.

Nonferrous metal. Metal such as nickel, brass, or bronze that does not include any appreciable amount of iron.

Nonionizing radiation. Electromagnetic radiation that does not cause ionization. Includes ultraviolet, laser, infrared, microwave, and radiofrequency radiation.

Nonpolar solvents. The aromatic and petroleum hydrocarbon groups characterized by low dielectric constants.

Nonvolatile matter. The portion of a material that does not evaporate at ordinary temperatures.

No Observable Effect Level (NOEL). In toxicology, the concentration of a substance at (and below) which exposure produces no evidence of injury or impairment.

Normal pulse (conventional pulse). Heartbeat; also, a single output event whose pulse duration is between 200 microseconds and one millisecond.

Nosocomial. (1) Pertaining to a hospital. (2) Disease caused or aggravated by hospital life.

NRC. Nuclear Regulatory Commission of the U.S. Department of Energy.

NTP. National Toxicology Program.

Nuclear battery. A device in which the energy emitted by decay of a radioisotope is first converted to heat and then directly to electricity.

Nuclear bombardment. The shooting of atomic projectiles at nuclei, usually in an attempt to split the atom or to form a new element.

Nuclear energy. The energy released in a nuclear reaction such as fission or fusion. Nuclear energy is popularly, though mistakenly, called atomic energy.

Nuclear explosion. The rapid fissioning of a large amount of fissionable material; creates intense heat, a light flash, a heavy blast, and a large amount of radioactive fission products. These may be attached to dust and debris forming fallout. Nuclear explosions also result from nuclear fusion, which does not produce radioactive fission products.

Nuclear reaction. Result of the bombardment of a nucleus with atomic or subatomic particles or very high energy radiation. Possible reactions are emission of other particles, fission, fusion, and the decay of radioactive material.

Nuclear reactor. A machine for producing a controlled chain reaction in fissionable material. It is the heart of nuclear power facilities, where it serves as a heat source. See Reactor.

Nucleonics. The application of nuclear science and techniques in physics, chemistry, astronomy, biology, industry, and other fields.

Nucleus. The inner core of the atom; consists of neutrons and protons tightly locked together.

Nuclide. A type of atom characterized by its mass number, atomic number, and energy state of the nucleus, provided that the mean life in that state is long enough to be observable.

Nuisance dust. Dust with a long history of little adverse effect on the lungs; does not produce significant organic disease or toxic effect when exposures are kept at reasonable levels.

Null point. The distance from a contaminant source at which the initial energy or velocity of the contaminants is dissipated, allowing the material to be captured by a hood.

N-unit (or n-unit). A measure of radiation dose caused by fast neutrons.

Nutrient. A substance that can be used for food.

Nystagmus. Involuntary movement of the eyeballs.

O

Occupational health nursing (OHN). Specialized nursing practice providing health care service to workers and worker populations.

Occupational Safety and Health Review Commission (OSHRC). An independent body established to review actions of federal OSHA that are contested by employers, employees, or their representatives.

Octave. The interval between two sounds having a basic frequency ratio of two.

Octave band. An arbitrary spread of frequencies. The top frequency in an octave band is always twice the bottom one. The octave band may be referred to by a center frequency.

Ocul-, oculo-, ophthalmo- (prefixes). Refer to the eye; *ophth-* words refer more often to eye diseases.

Odor. That property of a substance that affects the sense of smell.

Odor threshold. The minimum concentration of a substance at which a majority of test subjects can detect and identify the characteristic odor of a substance.

Ohm. The unit of electrical resistance.

Ohm's Law. Voltage in a circuit is equal to the current times the resistance.

Oil dermatitis. Blackheads and acne caused by oils and waxes that plug the hair follicles and sweat ducts.

Olecranon fossa. A depression in the back of the lower end of the humerus in which the ulna bone rests when the arm is straight.

Olefins. A class of unsaturated hydrocarbons characterized by relatively great chemical activity. Obtained from petroleum and natural gas. Examples are butene, ethylene, and propylene. Generalized formula: C_nH_{2n}.

Olfactory. Pertaining to the sense of smell.

Olig-, oligo- (prefix). Scanty, few, little. *Oliguria* means scanty urination.

Oncogenic. Tumor-generating.

Oncology. Study of causes, development, characteristics, and treatment of tumors.

Opacity. The condition of being nontransparent; a cataract.

Ophthalmologist. A physician who specializes in the structure, function, and diseases of the eye.

Optical density (OD). A logarithmic expression of the attenuation afforded by a filter.

Optically pumped laser. A type of laser that derives its energy from a noncoherent light source, such as a xenon flash lamp; usually pulsed and commonly called a solid-state laser.

Organ. An organized collection of tissues that have a special and recognized function.

Organ of Corti. The heart of the hearing mechanism; an aggregation of nerve cells in the ear lying on the basilar membrane that picks up vibrations and converts them to electrical energy, which is sent to the brain and interpreted as sound.

Organic. Chemicals that contain carbon. To date, nearly one million organic compounds have been synthesized or isolated. See also Inorganic.

Organic disease. Disease in which some change in the structure of body tissue could either be visualized or positively inferred from indirect evidence.

Organic matter. Compounds containing carbon.

Organism. A living thing, such as a human being, animal, germ, plant, and so on, especially one consisting of several parts, each specializing in a particular function.

Orifice. (1) The opening that serves as an entrance and/or outlet of a body cavity or organ, especially the opening of a canal or a passage. (2) A small hole in a tube or duct. A critical, or limiting, orifice is used to control rate of flow of a gas in rotometers and other air-sampling equipment.

Orifice meter. A flow meter, employing as the measure of flow rate the difference between pressures measured on the upstream and downstream sides of a restriction within a pipe or duct.

Ortho- (prefix). Straight, correct, normal. *Orthopsychiatry* is the specialty concerned with "straightening out" behavioral disorders.

Orthoaxis. The true anatomical axis about which a limb rotates, as opposed to the assumed axis. The assumed axis is usually the most obvious or geometric one; the orthoaxis is less evident and can only be found by the use of anatomical landmarks.

Os-, oste-, osteo- (prefix). Pertaining to bone. The Latin os-is most often associated with anatomical structures, whereas the Greek osteo-usually refers to conditions involving bone. *Osteogenesis* means formation of bone.

Oscillation. The variation, usually with time, of the magnitude of a quantity with respect to a specified reference when the magnitude is alternately greater and smaller than the reference.

OSHA. U.S. Occupational Safety and Health Administration.

OSHA 300 Log. Record keeping of employee injuries and illnesses is required by OSHA standard; OSHA 300 Log is a format that contains the necessary required details. It may be used by employers and is available from OSHA.

Osmosis. The passage of fluid through a semipermeable membrane as a result of osmotic pressure.

Osseous. Pertaining to bone.

Ossicle. Any member of a chain of three small bones from the outer membrane of the tympanum (eardrum) to the membrane covering the oval window of the inner ear.

ot-, oto- (prefix). Pertaining to the ear. *Otorrhea* means ear discharge.

Otitis media. An inflammation and infection of the middle ear.

Otologist. A physician specializing in surgery and diseases of the ear.

Otosclerosis. A condition of the ear caused by a growth of body tissue about the foot plate of the stapes and oval window of the inner ear; results in a gradual loss of hearing.

Output power and output energy. Power is used primarily to rate CW lasers, because the energy delivered per unit time remains relatively constant (output measured in watts). In contrast, pulsed lasers deliver their energy output in pulses and their effects may be best categorized by energy output per pulse. The output power of CW lasers is usually expressed in milliwatts or watts, pulsed lasers in kilowatts, and q-switch pulsed lasers in megawatts or gigawatts. Pulsed energy output is usually expressed as joules per pulse.

Overexposure. Exposure beyond the specified limits.

Oxidation. Process of combining oxygen with some other substance; technically, a chemical change in which an atom loses one or more electrons. Opposite of reduction.

P

PAH. Polynuclear aromatic hydrocarbons are a subset of the particles created during combustion of diesel fuel and are thought to be associated with possible health effects. PAHs are also found in materials other than diesel fuel.

Pair production. The conversion of a gamma ray into a pair of particles: an electron and a positron. This is an example of direct conversion of energy into matter according to Einstein's famous formula, $E = mc^2$: energy = mass × velocity of light squared.

Palmar arch. Blood vessels in the palm of the hand from which the arteries supplying blood to the fingers are branched. Pressure against the palmar arch by poorly designed tool handles may cause ischemia of the fingers and loss of tactile sensation and precision of movement.

Palpitation. Rapid heartbeat of which a person is acutely aware.

Papilloma. A small growth or tumor of the skin or mucous membrane; warts and polyps, for example.

Papule. A small, solid, usually conical elevation of the skin.

Papulovesicular. Characterized by the presence of papules and vesicles.

Para- (prefix). Alongside, near, abnormal; as in *paraproctitis,* inflammation of tissues near the rectum. A Latin suffix with the same spelling, *-para,* denotes bearing or giving birth, as in *multipara,* a woman who has given birth to two or more children.

Paraffins, paraffin series. (From *parum affinis*—small affinity.) Straight- or branched-chain hydrocarbon components of crude oil and natural gas whose molecules are saturated (that is, carbon atoms attached to each other by single bonds) and therefore very stable. Examples are methane and ethane. Generalized formula: C_nH2_{n+2}.

Parasite. An organism that derives its nourishment from a living plant or animal host. Does not necessarily cause disease.

Parenchyma. The distinguishing or specific (working) tissue of a bodily gland or organ, contained in and supported by the connective tissue framework, or stroma.

Parent. Precursor; the name given to a radioactive nucleus that disintegrates to form a radioactive product or daughter.

Partial barrier. An enclosure constructed so that sound transmission between its interior and its surroundings is minimized.

Particle. A small discrete mass of solid or liquid matter.

Particle concentration. Concentration expressed in terms of number of particles per unit volume of air or other gas. When expressing particle concentrations, the method of determining the concentration should be stated.

Particle size. The measured dimension of liquid or solid particles, usually in microns.

Particle size distribution. The statistical distribution of the sizes or ranges of size of a population of particles.

Particle size fraction. One of three particle size mass fractions by convention used for health-related sampling based upon the fact that smaller particles penetrate deeper into the respiratory system: inhalable, thoracic and respirable fractions, respectively, in order of depth of penetration.

Particulate. A particle of solid or liquid matter.

Particulate matter. A suspension of fine solid or liquid particles in air, such as dust, fog, fume, mist, smoke, or sprays. Particulate matter suspended in air is commonly known as an aerosol.

Particulates Not Otherwise Classified (PNOC). A recent designation replacing the older term "nuisance dusts" for various particulates for which no specific toxicity-related Permissible Exposure Limit exists. The OSHA PEL for all PNOC's is 10 mg/m³. Also may be represented as Particulates Not Otherwise Regulated (PNOR).

Pascal. A unit used in measuring sound pressure. See also *microbar* and *decibel*.

Path-, patho- (prefix), **-pathy** (suffix). Feeling, suffering, disease. *Pathogenic* means producing disease; *enteropathy* means disease of the intestines; pathology is the medical specialty concerned with all aspects of disease. The root appears in the everyday word *sympathy* (feeling with).

Pathogen. Any microorganism capable of causing disease.

Pathogenesis. Describes how a disease takes hold on the body and spreads.

Pathogenic. Producing or capable of producing disease.

Pathognomonic. Distinctive or characteristic of a specific disease or pathological condition; a sign or symptom from which a diagnosis can be made.

Pathological. Abnormal or diseased.

Pathology. The study of disease processes.

PCM. See Phase Contrast Microscopy.

PEL. See Permissible Exposure Limit.

Pelleting. In various industries, powdered material may be made into pellets or briquettes for convenience. The pellet is a distinctly small briquette. See Pelletizing.

Pelletizing. Refers primarily to extrusion by pellet mills; also refers to other small extrusions and to some balled products. Generally regarded as being larger than grains and smaller than briquettes.

Percent impairment of hearing (percent hearing loss). An estimate of a person's ability to hear correctly; usually determined by the pure tone audiogram. The specific rule for calculating this quantity varies from state to state according to law.

Percutaneous. Performed through the unbroken skin, as by absorption of an ointment through the skin.

Peri- (prefix). Around, about, surrounding. *Periodontium* is tissue that surrounds and supports the teeth.

Periodic table. Systematic classification of the elements according to atomic numbers (nearly the same order as by atomic weights) and by physical and chemical properties.

Peripheral neuropathy. Deterioration of peripheral nerve function; affects the hands, arms, feet, and legs. Certain hydrocarbon solvents are known to cause peripheral neuropathies in overexposed individuals.

Permeation. Process by which a chemical moves through a protective clothing material on a molecular level.

Permissible dose. See MPC, MPL.

Permissible Exposure Limit (PEL). An exposure limit published and enforced by OSHA as a legal standard. Most PELs are expressed as eight hour average airborne concentrations of substances to which it is believed most workers may be exposed for a working lifetime without developing serious illness.

Personal monitoring. Measurement of an employee's exposure to airborne contaminants through collection of air samples near the employee's breathing zone and subsequent analysis of the collected sample.

Personal protective equipment. Devices worn by the worker to protect against hazards in the environment. Respirators, gloves, and hearing protectors are examples.

Pesticides. General term for chemicals used to kill such pests as rats, insects, fungi, bacteria, weeds, and so on, that prey on humans or agricultural products. Among these are insecticides, herbicides, fungicides, rodenticides, miticides, fumigants, and repellents.

Petrochemical. A term applied to chemical substances produced from petroleum products and natural gas.

Phase-Contrast Microscopy (PCM). Light microscopy method used to analyze air samples for concentrations of asbestos in fibers per cubic centimeter. Required method in the OSHA asbestos standard.

Pink noise. Noise that has been weighted, especially at the low end of the spectrum, so that the energy per band (usually octave band) is approximately constant over the spectrum.

pH. The degree of acidity or alkalinity of a solution, with neutrality indicated as 7.

Phagocyte. A cell in the body that engulfs foreign material and consumes debris and foreign bodies.

Phalanx (pl. phalanges). Any of the bones of the fingers or toes. Often used as anatomical reference points in ergonomic work analysis.

Pharmaceuticals. Drugs and related chemicals reaching the public primarily through drug suppliers. In government reports, this category includes not only such medicinals as aspirin and antibiotics but also such nutriments as vitamins and amino acids for both human and animal use.

Pharyngeal. Pertaining to the pharynx (the musculo-membranous sac between the mouth, nares, and esophagus).

Phenol. C_6H_5OH. Popularly known as carbolic acid. Important chemical intermediate and base for plastics, pharmaceuticals, explosives, antiseptics, and many other end products.

Phenolic resins. A class of resins produced as the condensation product of phenol or substituted phenol and formaldehyde or other aldehydes.

Phosphors. Fluorescent or luminescent materials.

Photochemical process. Chemical changes brought about by radiant energy acting upon various chemical substances. See Photosynthesis.

Photoelectric effect. Occurs when an electron is thrown out of an atom by a light ray or gamma-ray. This effect is used in an "electric eye;" light falls on a sensitive surface throwing out electrons that can then be detected.

Photoionization detector (PID). A direct-reading monitoring instrument that operates by detecting and distinguishing between ions of vapors and gases following ionization by the instrument's ultraviolet light source.

Photomultiplier tube. A vacuum tube that multiplies electron input.

Photon. A bundle (quantum) of radiation. Constitutes, for example, x rays, gamma-rays, and light.

Photophobia. Abnormal sensitivity to light.

Photosynthesis. The process by which plants produce carbohydrates and oxygen from carbon dioxide and water.

Physiology. The study of the functions or actions of living organisms.

Physiopathology. The science of functions in disease or modified by a disease.

Pig. (1) A container (usually lead) used to ship or store radioactive materials. The thick walls protect workers from radiation. (2) In metal refining, a small ingot from the casting of blast furnace metal.

Pigment. A finely divided, insoluble substance that imparts color to a material.

Pilot facility. Small scale operation preliminary to major enterprises. Common in the chemical industry.

Pinna. Ear flap; the part of the ear that projects from the head. Also known as the auricle.

Pitch. The attribute of auditory sensation in terms of which sounds may be ordered on a scale extending from low to high. Pitch depends primarily on the frequency of the sound stimulus, but also on the sound pressure and wave form of the stimulus.

Pitot tube. A device consisting of two concentric tubes, one serving to measure the total or impact pressure existing in the airstream, the other to measure the static pressure only. When the annular space between the tubes and the interior of the center tube are connected across a pressure-measuring device, the pressure difference automatically nullifies the static pressure, and the velocity pressure alone is registered.

Plasma. (1) The fluid part of the blood in which the blood cells are suspended. Also called protoplasm. (2) A gas that has been heated to a partially or completely ionized condition, enabling it to conduct an electric current.

Plasma arc welding (PAW). A process that produces coalescence of metals by heating them with a constricted arc between an electrode and the workpiece (transferred arc) or between the electrode and the constricting nozzle (nontransferred arc). Shielding is obtained by the hot, ionized gas issuing from the orifice, which may be supplemented by an auxiliary source of shielding gas. Shielding gas can be an inert gas or a mixture of gases. Pressure may or may not be used, and filler metal may or may not be supplied.

Plastics. Any one of a large group of materials that contains as an essential ingredient an organic substance of large molecular weight. Two basic types are thermosetting (irreversibly rigid) and thermoplastic (reversibly rigid). Before compounding and processing, plastics often are referred to as (synthetic) resins. Final form may be a film, sheet, solid, or foam-flexible or rigid.

Plasticizers. Organic chemicals used in modifying plastics, synthetic rubber, and similar materials to facilitate compounding and processing, and to impart flexibility to the end product.

Plenum. Pressure-equalizing chamber.

Plenum chamber. An air compartment connected to one or more ducts or connected to a slot in a hood; used for air distribution.

Pleura. The thin membrane investing the lungs and lining the thoracic cavity, completely enclosing a potential space known as the pleural cavity. There are two pleurae, right and left, entirely distinct from each other. The pleura is moistened with a secretion that facilitates the movements of the lungs in the chest.

Pleurisy. Caused when the outer lung lining (visceral pleura) and the chest cavity's inner lining (parietal pleura) lose their lubricating properties; the resultant friction causes irritation and pain.

PLM. See Polarized Light Microscopy.

Plumbism. One name for lead intoxication.

Plume trap. An exhaust ventilation hood designed to capture and remove the plume given off the target on impact of a laser beam.

Plutonium. A heavy element that undergoes fission under the impact of neutrons. It is a useful fuel in nuclear reactors. Plutonium cannot be found in nature, but can be produced and "burned" in reactors.

PNA. See PAH.

Pneumo- (Greek), **pulmo-** (Latin) (prefix). Pertaining to the lungs.

Pneumoconiosis. Literally "Dusty lungs;" a result of the continued inhalation of various kinds of dust or other particulates; the tissue reaction resulting from the accumulation of such dusts in the lungs.

Pneumoconiosis-producing dust. Dust, which when inhaled, deposited, and retained in the lungs, may produce signs, symptoms, and findings of pulmonary disease.

Pneumonitis. Inflammation of the lungs.

PNOC. See Particulates Not Otherwise Classified.

Poison. (1) A material introduced into the reactor core to absorb neutrons. (2) Any substance that, when taken into the body, is injurious to health.

Polarized Light Microscopy (PLM). Method used to analyze for the presence of asbestos in bulk samples of material. Required method in the OSHA asbestos standard

Polarography. A physical analysis method for determining certain atmospheric pollutants that are electroreducible or electro-oxidizable and are in true solution and stable for the duration of the measurement.

Polar solvents. Solvents (such as alcohols and ketones) that contain oxygen and that have high dielectric constants.

Pollution. Synthetic contamination of soil, water, or atmosphere beyond that which is natural.

Poly-(prefix). Many.

Polycythemia. A condition marked by an excess in the number of red corpuscles in the blood.

Polymer. A high molecular-weight material formed by the joining together of many simple molecules (monomers). There may be hundreds or even thousands of the original molecules linked end to end and often cross-linked. Rubber and cellulose are naturally occurring polymers. Most resins are chemically produced polymers.

Polymerization. A chemical reaction in which two or more small molecules combine to form larger molecules (polymers) that contain repeating structural units of the original molecules. A hazardous polymerization is one with an uncontrolled release of energy.

Polystyrene resins. Synthetic resins formed by polymerization of styrene.

Popliteal clearance. Distance between the front of the seating surface and the popliteal crease. This should be about 5 in. in good seat design to prevent pressure on the popliteal artery.

Popliteal crease (or line). The crease in the hollow of the knee when the lower leg is flexed. Important anatomical reference point for ergonomic considerations.

Popliteal height of chair. The height of the highest part of the seating surface above the floor.

Popliteal height of individual. The distance between the crease in the hollow of the knee and the floor.

Porphyrin. One of a group of complex chemical substances that forms the basis of the respiratory pigments of animals and plants; hemoglobin and chlorophyll are other examples.

Portal. Place of entrance.

Portland cement. See Cement, portland.

Positive displacement pump. Any type of air mover pump in which leakage is negligible, so that the pump delivers a constant volume of fluid, building up to any pressure necessary to deliver that volume.

Positron. A particle that has the same weight and charge as an electron but is electrically positive rather than negative. The positron's existence was predicted in theory years before it was actually detected. It is not stable in matter because it reacts readily with an electron to give two gamma-rays.

Potential energy. Energy due to position of one body with respect to another or to the relative parts of the same body.

Power. Rate at which work is done; measured in watts (one joule per second) and horsepower (33,000 foot-pounds per minute). One horsepower equals 746 watts.

Power density. The intensity of electromagnetic radiation per unit area, expressed as watts/cm.

Power level. 10 times the logarithm to the base 10 of the ratio of a given power to a reference power; measured in decibels.

ppb. Parts per billion.

ppm. Parts per million parts of air by volume of vapor or gas or other contaminant.

PPE. See Personal protective equipment.

Precision. The degree of agreement (expressed in terms of distribution of test results about the mean result) of repeated measurements of the same property, obtained by repetitive testing of a homogeneous sample under specified conditions. The precision of a method is expressed quantitatively as the standard deviation, computed from the results of a series of controlled determinations.

Presby-(prefix). Old. As in *presbyopia*—eye changes associated with aging.

Presbycusis. Hearing loss caused by age.

Pressure. Force applied to or distributed over a surface; measured as force per unit area. See Absolute pressure, Atmospheric pressure, Gage pressure, Standard temperature and pressure, Static pressure, Total pressure, Vapor pressure, and Velocity pressure.

Pressure drop. The difference in static pressure measured at two locations in a ventilation system; caused by friction or turbulence.

Pressure loss. Energy lost from a pipe or duct system through friction or turbulence.

Pressure, static. The normal force per unit area that would be exerted by a moving fluid on a small body immersed in it if the body were carried along with the fluid. Practically, it is the normal force per unit area at a small hole in a wall of the duct through which the fluid flows or on the surface of a stationary tube at a point where the disturbances, created by inserting the tube, cancel. The potential pressure exerted in all directions by a fluid at rest. It is the tendency to either burst or collapse the pipe, usually expressed in inches of water gauge (in. wg) when dealing with air.

Pressure, total. In the theory of the flow of fluids, the sum of the static pressure and the velocity pressure at the point of measurement. Also called dynamic pressure.

Pressure, vapor. The pressure exerted by a vapor. If a vapor is kept in confinement at a constant temperature over its liquid so that it can accumulate above the liquid, the vapor pressure approaches a fixed limit called the maximum, or saturated, vapor pressure, dependent only on the temperature and the liquid.

Pressure vessel. A storage tank or vessel designed to operate at pressures greater than 15 psig (103 kPa).

PRF laser. A pulsed recurrence frequency laser, which is a pulsed-typed laser with properties similar to a CW laser when the frequency is very high.

Probe. A tube used for sampling or for measuring pressures at a distance from the actual collection or measuring apparatus; commonly used for reaching inside stacks or ducts.

Process Safety Management (PSM). Systematic evaluation of an entire process for the purpose of preventing unwanted release of chemicals into the work environment. Required by OSHA for certain chemicals when trigger quantities have been reached. In PSM, each step of a chemical process is analyzed for potential hazards.

Prokaryote. Single-celled organism lacking mitochondria and a defined nucleus. Usually has a cell wall. Describes primarily bacterial organisms.

Proliferation. The reproduction or multiplication of similar forms, especially of cells and morbid cysts.

Pronation. Rotation of the forearm in a direction to face the palm downward when the forearm is horizontal, and backward when the forearm is in a vertical position.

Propagation of flame. The spread of flame through the entire volume of a flammable vapor-air mixture from a single source of ignition. A vapor-air mixture below the lower flammable limit may burn at the point of ignition without propagating from the ignition source.

Prophylactic. Preventive treatment for protection against disease.

Protection factor (PF). In respiratory protective equipment, the ratio of the ambient airborne concentration of the contaminant to the concentration inside the facepiece.

Protective atmosphere. A gas envelope surrounding an element to be brazed, welded, or thermal-sprayed, with the gas composition controlled with respect to chemical composition, dew point, pressure, flow rate, and so on.

Protective coating. A thin layer of metal or organic material, applied as paint to a surface to protect it from oxidation, weathering, and corrosion.

Proteins. Large molecules found in the cells of all animal and vegetable matter containing carbon, hydrogen, nitrogen, and oxygen, and sometimes sulfur and phosphorus. The fundamental structural units of proteins are amino acids.

Proteolytic. Capable of splitting or digesting proteins into simpler compounds.

Proton. A fundamental unit of matter having a positive charge and a mass number of one.

Protoplasm. The basic material from which all living tissue is made. Physically it is a viscous, translucent, semifluid colloid, composed mainly of proteins, carbohydrates, fats, salts, and water.

Protozoa. Single-celled microorganisms belonging to the animal kingdom.

Proximal. The part of a limb that is closest to the point of attachment. The elbow is proximal to the wrist, which is proximal to the fingers.

Psittacosis. Parrot fever. An infectious disease of birds to which poultry handlers and other workers exposed to dried bird feces are at risk. Caused by *Chlamydia psittaci*. The most noted symptom of the disease among humans is fever.

Psych-, psycho- (prefix). Pertaining to the mind, from the Greek word for *soul*.

Psychogenic deafness. Loss originating in or produced by the mental reaction of an individual to their physical or social environment. It is sometimes called functional deafness or feigned deafness.

Psychrometer. An instrument consisting of wet- and dry-bulb thermometers for measuring relative humidity.

Psychrometric chart. A graphical representation of the thermodynamic properties of moist air.

Pterygium. A growth of the conjunctiva caused by a degenerative process brought on by long, continued irritation (as from exposure to wind, dust, and possibly to ultraviolet radiation).

Pulmonary. Pertaining to the lungs.

Pulse length. Duration of a pulsed laser flash; may be measured in milliseconds, microseconds, or nanoseconds.

Pulsed laser. A class of laser characterized by operation in a pulsed mode; that is, emission occurs in one or more flashes of short duration (pulse length).

Pumice. A natural silicate from volcanic ash or lava. Used as an abrasive.

Pupil. The variable aperture in the iris through which light travels toward the interior regions of the eye. The pupil size varies from 2 mm to 8 mm.

Pur-, pus- (Latin), pyo- (Greek) (prefixes). Indicates pus, as in *purulent, suppurative, pustulant,* and *pyoderma.*

Pure tone. A sound wave characterized by its singleness of frequency.

Purpura. Extensive hemorrhage into the skin or mucous membrane.

Push-pull hood. A hood consisting of an air supply system on one side of the contaminant source blowing across the source and into an exhaust hood on the other side.

Putrefaction. Decomposition of proteins by microorganisms, producing disagreeable odors.

Pyloric stenosis. Obstruction of the pyloric opening of the stomach caused by hypertrophy of the pyloric sphincter.

Pylorus. The orifice of the stomach leading to the small intestine.

Pyel-, pyelo- (prefix). Pertaining to the urine-collecting chamber of the kidney.

Pyr-, pyret- (prefix). Fever.

Pyrethrum. A pesticide obtained from the dried, powdered flowers of the plant of the same name; mixed with petroleum distillates, it is used as an insecticide.

Pyrolysis. The breaking apart of complex molecules into simpler units by the use of heat, as in the pyrolysis of heavy oil into gasoline.

Q

QF. See Quality factor.

Q fever. Disease caused by a rickettsial organism that infects meat and livestock handlers; similar but not identical to tick fever.

Q-switched laser. (Also known as Q-spoiled). A pulsed laser capable of extremely high peak powers for very short durations (pulse length of several nanoseconds).

Qualitative fit testing. A method of assessing the effectiveness of a particular size and brand of respirator based on an individual's subjective response to a test atmosphere. The most common test agents are isoamyl acetate (banana oil), irritant smoke, sodium saccharin, and Bitrex®. Proper respirator fit is indicated by the individual reporting no indication of the test agent inside the facepiece during the performance of a full range of facial movements.

Quality. A term used to describe the penetrating power of x rays or gamma-rays.

Quality factor. A linear energy transfer-dependent factor by which absorbed radiation doses are to be multiplied to obtain the dose equivalent.

Quantitative fit testing. A method of assessing the effectiveness of a particular size and brand of respirator on an individual. Instrumentation is used to measure both the test atmosphere (a gas, vapor or aerosol, such as DOP) and the concentration of the test contaminant inside the facepiece of the respirator. The quantitative fit factor thus obtained is used to determine if a suitable fit has been obtained by referring to a table or to the software of the instrumentation. Quantitative fit factors obtained in this way do not correlate well with Assigned Protection Factors, which are based on actual measurements of levels of contaminant inside the facepiece during actual work.

Quantum. "Bundle of energy;" discrete particle of radiation. Pl. quanta.

Quantum nanodot. Crystalline assemblages of a few hundred to a few million atoms of semiconductor and metallic elements that are of small enough size to demonstrate the quantum confinement effect on electrons in the crystal and the consequent property of photon release (fluorescence) at wavelengths related to the size and elemental makeup of the crystal. Quantum dots are generally less than ten nanometers in size, but may be larger.

Quartz. Vitreous, hard, chemically resistant, free silica, the most common form in nature. The main constituent in sandstone, igneous rocks, and common sands.

Quenching. A heat-treating operation in which metal raised to the desired temperature is quickly cooled by immersion in an oil bath.

R

Rabbit. A capsule that carries samples in and out of an atomic reactor through a pneumatic tube in order to permit study of the effect of intense radiation on various materials.

Rad. Roentgen absorbed dose or radiation absorbed dose; a standard unit of absorbed ionizing radiation dose equal to 100 ergs absorbed per gram.

Radial deviation. Flexion of the hand that decreases the angle between its longitudinal axis and radius. Tool design should minimize radial deviation. Strength of grasp is diminished in radial deviation.

Radian. An arc of a circle equal in length to the radius.

Radiant temperature. The temperature resulting from a body absorbing radiant energy.

Radiation (nuclear). The emission of atomic particles or electromagnetic radiation from the nucleus of an atom.

Radiation protection guide (RPG). The radiation dose that should not be exceeded without careful consideration of the reasons for doing so; every effort should be made to encourage the maintenance of radiation doses as far below this guide as practicable.

Radiation (radioactivity). See Ionizing radiation.

Radiation source. An apparatus or material emitting or capable of emitting ionizing radiation.

Radiation (thermal). The transmission of energy by means of electromagnetic waves longer than visible light. Radiant energy of any wavelength may, when absorbed, become thermal energy and result in an increase in the temperature of the absorbing body.

Radiator. That which is capable of emitting energy in wave form.

Radioactive. The property of an isotope or element that is characterized by spontaneous decay to emit radiation.

Radioactivity. Emission of energy in the form of alpha-, beta-, or gamma-radiation from the nucleus of an atom. Always involves change of one kind of atom into a different kind. A few elements, such as radium, are naturally radioactive. Other radioactive forms are induced. See Radioisotope.

Radioactivity concentration guide (RCG). The concentration of radioactivity in the environment that is determined to result in organ doses equal to the radiation protection guide (RPG).

Radiochemical. Any compound or mixture containing a sufficient portion of radioactive elements to be detected by a Geiger counter.

Radiochemistry. The branch of chemistry concerned with the properties and behavior of radioactive materials.

Radiodiagnosis. A method of diagnosis that involves x-ray examination.

Radiohumeral joint. Part of the elbow. Not truly a joint, but a thrust bearing.

Radioisotope. A radioactive isotope of an element. A radioisotope can be produced by placing material in a nuclear reactor and bombarding it with neutrons. Many of the fission products are radioisotopes. Sometimes used as tracers, as energy sources for chemical processing or food pasteurization, or as heat sources for nuclear batteries. Radioisotopes are at present the most widely used outgrowth of atomic research and are one of the most important peacetime contributions of nuclear energy.

Radionuclide. A radioactive nuclide; one that has the capability of spontaneously emitting radiation.

Radioresistant. Relatively invulnerable to the effects of radiation.

Radiosensitive. Tissues that are more easily damaged by radiation.

Radiotherapy. Treatment of human ailments with the application of relatively high roentgen dosages.

Radium. One of the earliest-known naturally radioactive elements. It is far more radioactive than uranium and is found in the same ores.

Radius. The long bone of the forearm in line with the thumb; the active element in the forearm during pronation (inward rotation) and supination (outward rotation). Also provides the forearm connection to the wrist joint.

Radon progeny. Radioactive decay products of radon. See *daughter*.

Rale. Any abnormal sound or noise in the lungs.

Random noise. A sound or electrical wave whose instantaneous amplitudes occur as a function of time, according to a normal (Gaussian) distribution curve. Random noise is an oscillation whose instantaneous magnitude is not specified for any given instant of time. The instantaneous magnitudes of a random noise are specified only by probability functions giving the fraction of the total time that the magnitude, or some sequence of the magnitudes, lies within a specific range.

Rare earths. Originally, the elements in the periodic table with atomic numbers 57 through 71. Often included are numbers 39 and, less often, 21 and 90. Emerging uses include the manufacture of special steels and glasses.

Rash. Abnormal reddish coloring or blotch on some part of the skin.

Rated-line voltage. The range of potentials, in volts, of the supply line specified by the manufacturer at which an x-ray machine is designed to operate.

Rated output current. The maximum allowable lead current of an x-ray high-voltage generator.

Rated output voltage. The allowable peak potential, in volts, at the output terminals of an x-ray high-voltage generator.

Raynaud's syndrome or phenomenon. Abnormal constriction of the blood vessels of the fingers on exposure to cold temperature.

RBE. Relative biological effectiveness; the relative effectiveness of the same absorbed dose of two ionizing radiations in producing a measurable biological response.

REACH. A comprehensive European Union system of chemical regulation covering all production and use, including occupational and environmental safety and health, of chemicals. The acronym stands for **R**egistration, **E**valuation, **A**uthorization and **R**estriction of **C**hemicals

Reactivity (chemical). A substance's susceptibility to undergo a chemical reaction or change that may result in dangerous side effects, such as an explosion, burning, and corrosive or toxic emissions.

Reactor. An atomic "furnace" or nuclear reactor. In a reactor, nuclei of the fuel undergo controlled fission under the influence of neutrons. The fission produces new neutrons in a chain reaction that releases large amounts of energy. This energy is removed as heat that can be used to make steam. The moderator for the first reactor was piled-up blocks of graphite. Thus, a nuclear reactor was formerly referred to as a pile. Reactors are usually classified now as research, test, process heat, and power, depending on their principal function. No workable design for a controlled fusion reactor has yet been devised.

Reagent. Any substance used in a chemical reaction to produce, measure, examine, or detect another substance.

REL. Recommended exposure limit. An exposure limit, generally a time-weighted average, to a substance; developed by NIOSH based on toxicological and industrial hygiene data.

Recoil energy. The energy emitted and shared by the reaction products when a nucleus undergoes a nuclear reaction such as fission or radioactive decay.

Reduction. Addition of one or more electrons to an atom through chemical change.

Refractories. A material exceptionally resistant to the action of heat and hence used for lining furnaces; examples are fire clay, magnesite, graphite, and silica.

Regenerative process. Replacement of damaged cells by new cells.

Regimen. A regulation of the mode of living, diet, sleep, exercise, and so on for a hygienic or therapeutic purpose; sometimes mistakenly called regime.

Reid method. Method of determining the vapor pressure of a volatile hydrocarbon by the *Standard Method of Test for Vapor Pressure of Petroleum Products, ASTM D323.*

Relative humidity. The ratio of the quantity of water vapor present in the air to the quantity that would saturate it at any specific temperature.

Reliability. The degree to which an instrument, component, or system retains its performance characteristics over a period of time.

Rem. Roentgen equivalent man; a radiation dose unit that equals the dose in rads multiplied by the appropriate value of relative biological effect or Quality Factor for the particular radiation.

Renal. Having to do with the kidneys.

Replication. A fold or folding back; the act or process of duplicating or reproducing something.

Resin. A solid or semisolid amorphous (noncrystalline) organic compound or mixture of such compounds with no definite melting point and no tendency to crystallize. May be of vegetable (gum arabic), animal (shellac), or synthetic (celluloid) origin. Some resins may be molded, cast, or extruded. Others are used as adhesives, in the treatment of textiles and paper, or as protective coatings.

Resistance. (1) Opposition to the flow of air, as through a canister, cartridge, particulate filter, or orifice. (2) A property of conductors, depending on their dimensions, material, and temperature, that determines the current produced by a given difference in electrical potential.

Resonance. Each object or volume of air resonates or strengthens a sound at one or more particular frequencies. The frequency depends on the size and construction of the object or air volume.

Respirable-size particulates. Particulates in a size range that permits them to penetrate deep into the lungs upon inhalation.

Respirator. A device to protect the wearer from inhalation of harmful contaminants.

Respiratory system. Consists of the nose, mouth, nasal passages, nasal pharynx, pharynx, larynx, trachea, bronchi, bronchioles, air sacs (alveoli) of the lungs, and muscles of respiration.

Reticle. A scale or grid or other pattern located in the focus of the eyepiece of a microscope.

Retina. The light-sensitive inner surface of the eye that receives and transmits images formed by the lens.

Retro- (prefix). Backward or behind.

Reverberatory furnace. A furnace in which heat is supplied by burning fuel in a space between the charge and the low roof.

Rheumatoid. Resembling rheumatism, a disease marked by inflammation of the connective tissue structures of the body, especially the membranous linings of the joints, and by pain in these parts; eventually the joints become stiff and deformed.

Rhin-, rhino- (prefix). Pertaining to the nose.

Rhinitis. Inflammation of the mucous membrane lining in the nasal passages.

Rickettsia. Rod-shaped microorganisms characterized by growing within the cells of animals. These human pathogens are often carried by arthropods.

Riser. In metal casting, a channel in a mold to permit escape of gases.

Roasting of ores. A refining operation in which ore is heated to a high temperature, sometimes with catalytic agents, to drive off certain impurities; an example is the roasting of copper ore to remove sulfur.

Roentgen (R). A unit of radioactive dose or exposure. See Rad.

Roentgenogram. A film produced by exposing x-ray film to x rays.

Roentgenography. Photography by means of roentgen rays. Special techniques for roentgenography of different areas of the body have been given specific names.

Route of entry. A path by which chemicals can enter the body. There are three main routes of entry: inhalation, ingestion, and skin absorption.

Rosin. Specifically applies to the resin of the pine tree and chiefly derives from the manufacture of turpentine. Widely used in the manufacture of soap and flux.

Rotameter. A flow meter consisting of a precision-bored, tapered, transparent tube with a solid float inside.

Rotary kiln. Any of several types of kilns used to heat material, as in the portland cement industry.

Rouge. A finely powdered form of iron oxide used as a polishing agent.

RTECS. Registry of Toxic Effects of Chemical Substances.

S

SAE. Sampling and analytical error. The reason a particular sampling result may vary from the true value. Quantitative estimates of SAE are often used to develop a clear picture of the potential range of a given exposure.

Safety can. An approved container of not more than 5 gal (19 L) capacity having a spring-closing lid and spout cover and designed to safely relieve internal pressure when subjected to fire exposure.

Safety Data Sheet (SDS). Formerly known as the Material Safety Data Sheet. As part of hazard communication standards (right-to-know laws), federal and state OSHA programs require manufacturers and importers of chemicals to prepare compendia of information on their products. Categories of information that must be provided on SDSs include physical properties, recommended exposure limits, personal protective equipment, spill-handling procedures, first aid, health effects, and toxicological data.

Sagittal plane. A plane from back to front vertically dividing the body into the right and left portions. Important in anthropometric definitions. Midsagittal plane is a sagittal plane symmetrically dividing the body.

Salamander. A small furnace, usually cylindrical in shape, without grates.

Salivation. An excessive discharge of saliva; ptyalism.

Salmonella. A genus of gram-negative, rod-shaped pathogenic bacteria.

Salt. A product of the reaction between an acid and a base. Table salt, for example, is a compound of sodium and chlorine. It can be made by reacting sodium hydroxide with hydrochloric acid.

Sampling. The withdrawal or isolation of a fractional part of a whole. In air analysis, the separation of a portion of an ambient atmosphere with subsequent analysis to determine concentration.

Sandblasting. A process for cleaning metal castings and other surfaces with sand by a high-pressure airstream.

Sandhog. Any worker doing tunneling work requiring atmospheric pressure control.

Sanitize. To reduce the microbial flora in or on articles such as eating utensils to levels judged safe by public health authorities.

Saprophyte. An organism living on dead organic matter.

SAR. Specific absorption rate.

Sarcoma. Malignant tumors that arise in connective tissue.

Scattered radiation. Radiation that is scattered by interaction with objects or within tissue.

Scintillation counter. A device for counting atomic particles by means of the tiny flashes of light (scintillations) that particles produce when they strike certain crystals or liquids.

Scler- (prefix). Hard, tough.

Sclera. The tough white outer coat of the eyeball.

Scleroderma. Hardening of the skin.

Sebum. Oily lubricating secretion of the sebaceous glands.

Scotoma. A blind or partially blind area in the visual field.

SDS. Safety Data Sheet. Chemical information format under GHS that will replace the term Material Safety Sheet as it has existed for decades in the United States under the OSHA hazard communication standard.

Sealed source. A radioactive source sealed in a container or having a bonded cover, in which the container or cover has sufficient mechanical strength to prevent contact with and dispersion of the radioactive material.

Sebaceous. Of, related to, or being fatty material.

Seborrhea. An oily skin condition caused by an excess output of sebum from the sebaceous glands of the skin.

SCBA. Self-contained breathing apparatus.

Semicircular canals. The special organs of balance closely associated with the hearing mechanism and the eighth cranial nerve.

Semiconductor or junction laser. A class of laser that normally produces relatively low CW power outputs; can be tuned in wavelength and has the greatest efficiency.

Sensation. The translation into consciousness of the effects of a stimulus exciting a sense organ.

Sensible. Capable of being perceived by the sense organs.

Sensitivity. The minimum amount of contaminant that can repeatedly be detected by an instrument.

Sensitization. The process of rendering an individual sensitive to the action of a chemical.

Sensitizer. A material that can cause an allergic reaction of the skin or respiratory system.

Sensorineural. Type of hearing loss that affects millions of people. If the inner ear is damaged, the hearing loss is sensory; if the fibers of the eighth nerve are affected, it is a neural hearing loss. Because the pattern of hearing loss is the same in either case, the term sensorineural is used.

Sensory end organs. Receptor organs of the sensory nerves located in the skin. Each end organ can sense only a specific type of stimulus. Primary stimuli are heat, cold, or pressure, each requiring different end organs.

Sensory feedback. Use of external signals perceived by sense organs to indicate quality or level of performance of an event triggered by voluntary action. On the basis of sensory feedback information, decisions may be made; for instance, permitting or not permitting an event to run its course or enhancing or decreasing activity levels.

Septum. A dividing wall or partition; used as a general term in anatomical nomenclature.

Septicemia. Blood poisoning; growth of infectious organisms in the blood.

Sequestrants. Chelates used to deactivate undesirable properties of metal ions without removing these ions from solution. Sequestrants have many uses, including application as antigumming agents in gasoline, antioxidants in rubber, and rancidity retardants in edible fats and oils.

Serum. (1) The clear fluid that separates from the blood during clotting. (2) Blood serum—containing antibodies.

Shakeout. In the foundry industry, the separation of the solid—but still not cold—casting from its molding sand.

Shale. Many meanings in industry, but in geology, a common fossil rock formed from clay, mud, or silt; somewhat stratified but without characteristic cleavage.

Shale oil. Tarry oil distilled from bituminous shale.

Shaver's disease. Bauxite pneumoconiosis.

Shell. The electrons around the nucleus of an atom are arranged in shells—spheres centered on the nucleus. The innermost shell is called K-shell, the next is called the L-shell, and so on to the Q-shell. The nucleus itself may also have a shell-type structure.

Shield, shielding. Interposed material (such as a wall) that protects workers from harmful radiations released by radioactive materials.

Shielded-metal arc welding (SMAW). An arc-welding process that produces coalescence of metals by heating them with an arc between a covered metal electrode and the work. Shielding is obtained from decomposition of the electrode covering. Pressure is not used and filler metal is obtained from the electrode.

Shock. Primarily, the rapid fall in blood pressure following injury, operation, or the administration of anesthesia.

Short Term Exposure Limit (STEL). An airborne concentration of a substance to which workers are permitted to be exposed for a short duration, usually 15 minutes. The STEL is higher concentration than that allowed by an 8 hour exposure limit. Like PELs, STELs are published and enforced by OSHA.

Shotblasting. A process for cleaning metal castings or other surfaces by small steel shot in a high-pressure airstream; a substitute for sandblasting to avoid silicosis.

SI. The *Système International d'Unités* (International System of Units), the metric system that is being adopted throughout the world. It is a modern version of the MKSA (meter, kilogram, second, ampere) system, whose details are published and controlled by an international treaty organization financed by member states of the Metre Convention, including the United States.

Siderosis. The deposition of iron pigments in the lung—can be associated with disease.

Sievert. Unit of absorbed radiation dose in Gray times the Quality Factor of the radiation in comparison to gamma-radiation. A Sievert equals 100 rem.

Silica gel. A regenerative absorbent consisting of amorphous silica manufactured by the action of HCl on sodium silicate. Hard, glossy, quartz-like in appearance. Used in dehydrating and drying and as a catalyst carrier.

Silicates. Compounds of silicon, oxygen, and one or more metals with or without hydrogen. These dusts cause nonspecific dust reactions, but generally do not interfere with pulmonary function or result in disability.

Silicon. A nonmetallic element being, next to oxygen, the chief elementary constituent of the earth's crust.

Silicones. Unique group of compounds made by molecular combination of silicon (or certain silicon compounds) with organic chemicals. Produced in a variety of forms, including silicone fluids, resins, and rubber. Silicones have special properties, such as water repellency, wide temperature resistance, high durability, and great dielectric strength.

Silicosis. A disease of the lungs caused by the inhalation of silica dust.

Silver solder. A solder of varying components but usually containing an appreciable amount of cadmium.

Simple tone (pure tone). (1) A sound wave whose instantaneous sound pressure is a simple sinusoidal function of time. (2) A sound sensation characterized by its singularity of pitch.

Sintering. Process of making coherent powder of earthy substances by heating without melting.

Skin dose. A special instance of tissue dose referring to the dose immediately on the surface of the skin.

Slag. The dross of flux and impurities that rise to the surface of molten metal during melting and refining.

Slot velocity. Linear flow rate through the opening in a slot-type hood (plating, degreasing operations, and so on).

Short-term exposure limit (STEL). ACGIH-recommended exposure limit. Maximum concentration to which workers can be exposed for a short period of time (15 min) only four times throughout the day with at least 1 h between exposures.

Sludge. Any muddy or slushy mass. Specifically, mud from a drill hole in boring, muddy sediment in the steam boiler, or precipitated solid matter arising from sewage treatment processes.

Slug. A fuel element for a nuclear reactor; a piece of fissionable material. Slugs in large reactors consist of uranium coated with aluminum to prevent corrosion.

Slurry. A thick, creamy liquid resulting from the mixing and grinding of limestone, clay, water, and other raw materials.

SMACNA. Sheet Metal and Air Conditioning National Association.

Smog. Irritating haze resulting from the sun's effect on certain pollutants in the air, notably automobile and industrial exhaust.

Smoke. An air suspension (aerosol) of particles originating from combustion or sublimation; generally contains droplets as well as dry particles. Tobacco, for instance, produces a wet smoke composed of minute tarry droplets.

Soap. Ordinarily a metal salt of a fatty acid, usually sodium stearate, sodium oleate, sodium palmitate, or some combination of these.

Soapstone. Complex silicate of varied composition, similar to some talcs, with wide industrial application, including rubber manufacture.

Solder. A material used for joining metal surfaces together by filling a joint or covering a junction. The most commonly used solder contains lead and tin; silver solder may contain cadmium. Zinc chloride and fluorides are commonly used as fluxes to clean the soldered surfaces.

Solid-state laser. A type of laser that uses a solid crystal such as ruby or glass; commonly used in pulsed lasers.

Solution. Mixture in which the components lose their individual properties and are uniformly dispersed. All solutions are composed of a solvent (water or other fluid) and a solute (the dissolved substance). A true solution is homogeneous, as salt in water.

Solvent. A substance that dissolves another substance. Usually refers to organic solvents.

Soma. Body, as distinct from psyche (mind).

Somatic. Pertaining to all tissue other than reproductive cells.

Somatype. Somatotype. In anthropometry, a class of body build.

Somnolence. Sleepiness; also unnatural drowsiness.

Soot. Agglomerations of carbon particles impregnated with tar; formed in the incomplete combustion of carbonaceous material.

Sorbent. (1) A material that removes toxic gases and vapors from air inhaled through a canister or cartridge. (2) Material used to collect gases and vapors during air-sampling.

Sound. An oscillation in pressure, stress, particle displacement, particle velocity, and so on, propagated in an elastic material, in a medium with internal forces (elastic or viscous, for example); or, the superposition of such propagated oscillations. Also the sensation produced through the organs of hearing usually by vibrations transmitted in a material medium, commonly air.

Sound absorption. The change of sound energy into some other form, usually heat, on passing through a medium or striking a surface. Also, the property possessed by materials and objects, including air, of absorbing sound energy.

Sound absorption coefficient. The ratio of the sound energy absorbed by the surface of a medium (or material) exposed to a sound field (or to sound radiation) to the sound energy incident on that surface.

Sound analyzer. A device for measuring the band-pressure level or pressure-spectrum level of a sound as a function of frequency.

Sound level. A weighted sound-pressure level obtained by the use of metering characteristics and the weighting A, B, or C specified in ANSI S1.4.

Sound-level meter and octave-band analyzer. Instruments for measuring sound-pressure levels in decibels referenced to 0.0002 microbars. Readings can also be made in specific octave bands, usually beginning at 75 Hz and continuing through 10,000 Hz.

Sound-pressure level (SPL). The level, in decibels, of a sound is 20 times the logarithm to the base 10 of the ratio of the pressure of this sound to the reference pressure, which must be explicitly stated.

Sound transmission. The word *sound* usually means sound waves traveling in air. However, sound waves also travel in solids and liquids. These sound waves may be transmitted to air to make sound we can hear.

Sound transmission loss. A barrier's ability to block transmission; measured in decibels.

Sour gas. Slang for either natural gas or a gasoline contaminated with odor-causing sulfur compounds. In natural gas, the contaminant is usually hydrogen sulfide; in gasoline, usually mercaptans.

Source. Any substance that emits radiation. Usually refers to a piece of radioactive material conveniently packaged for scientific or industrial use.

Spasm. Tightening or contraction of any set of muscles.

Specific Absorption (SA). Quantity of radiofrequency energy in joules per kilogram.

Specific Absorption Rate. Radiofrequency dosage term (rate at which energy is transferred to tissue) expressed as watts of power per kilogram of tissue.

Specific gravity. The ratio of the mass of a unit volume of a substance to the mass of the same volume of a standard substance at a standard temperature. Water at 39.2°F (4°C) is usually the standard for liquids; for gases, dry air (at the same temperature and pressure as the gas) is often taken as the standard substance. See Density.

Specific ionization. See Ionization.

Specific volume. The volume occupied by a unit mass of a substance under specified conditions of temperature and pressure.

Specific weight. The weight per unit volume of a substance; same as density.

Specificity. The degree to which an instrument or detection method is capable of accurately detecting or measuring the concentration of a single contaminant in the presence of other contaminants.

Spectrography—spectral emission. An instrumental method for detecting trace contaminants using a spectrum formed by exciting the subject contaminants by various means, causing characteristic radiation to be formed, which is dispersed by a grating or prism and photographed.

Spectrophotometer. A direct-reading instrument used for comparing the relative intensities of corresponding electromagnetic wavelengths produced by absorption of ultraviolet, visible, or infrared radiation from a vapor or gas.

Spectroscopy. Observation of the wavelength and intensity of light or other electromagnetic waves absorbed or emitted by various materials. When excited by an arc or spark, each element emits light of certain well-defined wavelengths.

Spectrum. The frequency distribution of the magnitudes (and sometimes phases) of the components of the wave. Also used to signify a continuous range of frequencies, usually wide in extent, within which waves have some specified common characteristics. Also, the pattern of red-to-blue light observed when a beam of sunlight passes through a prism and then projects upon a surface.

Specular reflections. Mirrorlike reflections that are important to minimize in laser work.

Speech interference level (SIL). The average, in decibels, of the sound-pressure levels of a noise in the three octave bands of frequency: 600–1,200, 1,200–2,400, and 2,400–4,800 Hz.

Speech perception test. A measurement of hearing acuity by the administration of a carefully controlled list of words. The identification of correct responses is evaluated in terms of norms established by the average performance of normal listeners.

Speech reading. Lip reading or visual hearing.

Sphincter. A muscle that surrounds an orifice and functions to close it.

Sphygmomanometer. Apparatus for measuring blood pressure (and a good word for testing spelling ability).

Spore. A resistant body formed by certain microorganisms; resistant resting cells. Mold spores: unicellular reproductive bodies.

Spot size. Cross-sectional area of laser beam at the target.

Spot welding. One form of electrical-resistance welding in which the current and pressure are restricted to the spots of metal surfaces directly in contact.

Spray coating painting. The result of the application of a spray in painting as a substitute for brush painting or dipping.

Squamous. Covered with or consisting of scales.

Stain. A dye used to color microorganisms as an aid to visual inspection.

Stamping. A term with many different usages in industry; a common one is the crushing of ores by pulverizing.

Standard air. Air at standard temperature and pressure. The most common values are 70°F (21.1°C) and 29.92 in. Hg (101.3 kPa). Also, air with a density of 0.075 lb/ft^3 (1.2 kg/m^3) is substantially equivalent to dry air at 70°F and 29.92 in. Hg.

Standard air density. The density of air—0.075 lb/ft^3 (1.2 kg/m^3), at standard conditions. Standard conditions. In industrial ventilation, 70°F (21.1°C), 50 percent relative humidity, and 29.92 in. Hg (101.3 kPa) atmospheric pressure.

Standard gravity. Standard accepted value for the force of gravity. It is equal to the force that produces an acceleration of 32.17 ft/s (9.8 m/s).

Standard Industrial Classification (SIC) Code. Classification system for places of employment according to major type of activity.

Standard temperature and pressure. See Standard air.

Standard Threshold Shift (STS). An average loss of hearing acuity in either ear of 10 dB as averaged over the 2,000-, 3,000- and 4,000-hertz frequencies.

Standing wave. A periodic wave having a fixed distribution in space that is the result of interference of progressive waves of the same frequency and kind. Such waves are characterized by the existence of nodes or partial nodes and antinodes that are fixed in space.

Stannosis. A form of pneumoconiosis caused by the inhalation of tin-bearing dusts.

Static pressure. The potential pressure exerted in all directions by a fluid at rest. For a fluid in motion, it is measured in a direction normal (at right angles) to the direction of flow; thus it shows the tendency to burst or collapse the pipe. When added to velocity pressure, it gives total pressure.

Static pressure curve. A graphical representation of the volumetric output and fan static pressure relationship for a fan operating at a specific rotating speed.

Static pressure regain. The increase in static pressure in a system as air velocity decreases and velocity pressure is converted into static pressure according to Bernoulli's theorem.

STEL. See Short Term Exposure Limit.

Sterile. Free of living microorganisms.

Sterility. Inability to reproduce.

Sterilization. The process of making sterile; the killing of all forms of life.

Sterilize. To perform any act that results in the absence of all life on or in an object.

Sternomastoid muscles. A pair of muscles connecting the breastbone and lower skull behind the ears, which flex or rotate the head.

Stink damp. In mining, hydrogen sulfide.

Stp flow rate. The rate of flow of fluid, by volume, corrected to standard temperature and pressure.

Stp volume. The volume that a quantity of gas or air would occupy at standard temperature and pressure.

Stress. A physical, chemical, or emotional factor that causes bodily or mental tension and may be a factor in disease causation or fatigue.

Stressor. Any agent or thing causing a condition of stress.

Strip mine. A mine in which coal or ore is extracted from the earth's surface after removal of overlayers of soil, clay, and rock.

Stupor. Partial unconsciousness or nearly complete unconsciousness.

Sublimation. A process in which a material passes directly from a solid to a gaseous state and condenses to form solid crystals, without liquefying.

Sulcus (pl. sulci). A groove, trench, or furrow; used in anatomical nomenclature as a general term to designate such a depression, especially on the surface of the brain, separating the gyri; also, a linear depression in the surface of a tooth, the sloping sides of which meet at an angle.

Supination. Rotation of the forearm about its own longitudinal axis. Supination turns the palm upward when the forearm is horizontal, and forward when the body is in anatomical position. Supination is an important element of available motions inventory for industrial appli-cation, particularly where tools such as screwdrivers are used. Efficiency in supination depends on arm position. Workplace design should provide for elbow flexion at 90 degrees.

Supra- (prefix). Above, on.

Surface-active agent; surfactant. Any of a group of compounds added to a liquid to modify surface or interfacial tension. In synthetic detergents, which is the best known use of surface-active agents, reduction of interfacial tension provides cleansing action.

Surface coating. Paint, lacquer, varnish, or other chemical composition used for protecting and/or decorating surfaces. See Protective coating.

Suspect carcinogen. A material believed to be capable of causing cancer, based on limited scientific evidence.

Sweating. (1) Visible perspiration. (2) The process of uniting metal parts by heating solder so that it runs between the parts.

Swing grinder. A large power-driven grinding wheel mounted on a counterbalanced swivel-supported arm guided by two handles.

Symptom. Any bit of evidence from a patient indicating illness; the subjective feelings of the patient.

Syncope. Fainting spell.

Syndrome. A collection, constellation, or concurrence of signs and symptoms, usually of disease.

Synergism. Cooperative action of substances whose total effect is greater than the sum of their separate effects.

Synergistic. Pertaining to an action of two or more substances, organs, or organisms to achieve an effect greater than the additive effects of the separate elements.

Synonym. Another name by which a chemical may be known.

Synthesis. The reaction or series of reactions by which a complex compound is obtained from simpler compounds or elements.

Synthetic. (From the Greek word *synthetikos*, "that which is put together.") "Man-made 'synthetic' should not be thought of as a substitute for the natural," according *to Encyclopedia of the Chemical Process Industries*, which adds: "Synthetic chemicals are frequently more pure and uniform than those obtained naturally." A classic example is synthetic indigo.

Synthetic detergents. Chemically tailored cleaning agents soluble in water or other solvents. Originally developed as soap substitutes; because they do not form insoluble precipitates, they are especially valuable in hard water. They may be composed of surface-active agents alone, but generally are combinations of surface-active agents and other substances, such as complex phosphates, to enhance detergency.

Synthetic rubber. Artificial polymer with rubber-like

properties. Types have varying composition and properties. Major types are designated as S-type, butyl, neoprene (chloroprene polymers), and N-type. Several synthetics duplicate the chemical structure of natural rubber.

Systemic. Spread throughout the body; affecting all body systems and organs, not localized in one spot or area.

T

Tachy- (prefix). Indicates fast or speedy, as in *tachycardia,* abnormally rapid heartbeat.

Tailings. In mining or metal recovery processes, the gangue rock residue after all or most of the metal has been extracted.

Talc. A hydrous magnesium silicate used in ceramics, cosmetics, paint, and pharmaceuticals, and as a filler in soap, putty, and plaster.

Tall oil. (Derived from the Swedish word *tallolja*; a material first investigated in Sweden—not synonymous with U.S. pine oil.) Natural mixture of rosin acids, fatty acids, sterols, high-molecular weight alcohols, and other materials, derived primarily from waste liquors of sulfate wood pulp manufacture. Dark brown, viscous, oily liquid often called liquid rosin.

Tar. A loose term embracing wood, coal, or petroleum exudations. In general represents complex mixture of chemicals of top fractional distillation systems.

Tar crude. Organic raw material derived from distillation of coal tar and used for chemicals.

Tare. A deduction of weight, made in allowance for the weight of a container or medium. The initial weight of a filter, for example.

Target. The material into which the laser beam is fired or at which electrons are fired in an x-ray tube.

TEM. See Transmission Electron Microscopy.

Temper. To relieve the internal stresses in metal or glass and to increase ductility by heating the material to a point below its critical temperature and cooling slowly. See Anneal.

Temperature. The condition of a body that determines the transfer of heat to or from other bodies. Specifically, it is a manifestation of the average translational kinetic energy of the molecules of a substance caused by heat agitation. See Celsius and Kelvin scale.

Temperature, dry-bulb. The temperature of a gas or mixture of gases indicated by an accurate thermometer after correction for radiation.

Temperature, effective. An arbitrary index that combines into a single value the effect of temperature, humidity, and air movement on the sensation of warmth or cold felt by the human body. The numerical value is the temperature of still, saturated air that would induce an identical sensation.

Temperature, mean radiant (MRT). The temperature of a uniform black enclosure in which a solid body or occupant would exchange the same amount of radiant heat as in the existing nonuniform environment.

Temperature, wet-bulb. Thermodynamic wet-bulb temperature is the temperature at which liquid or solid water, by evaporating into air, can bring the air to saturation adiabatically at the same temperature. Wet-bulb temperature (without qualification) is the temperature indicated by a wet-bulb psychrometer.

Tempering. The process of heating or cooling makeup air to the proper temperature.

Temporary threshold shift (TTS). The hearing loss suffered as the result of noise exposure, all or part of which is recovered during an arbitrary period of time when one is removed from the noise. It accounts for the necessity of checking hearing acuity at least 16 hours after a noise exposure.

Tendon. Fibrous component of a muscle. It often attaches to bone at the area of application of tensile force. When its cross section is small, stresses in the tendon are high, particularly because the total force of many muscle fibers is applied at the single terminal tendon. See Tenosynovitis.

Tennis elbow. Sometimes called lateral epicondylitis, an inflammatory reaction of tissues in the lateral elbow region.

Tenosynovitis. Inflammation of the connective tissue sheath of a tendon.

Teratogen. An agent or substance that may cause physical defects in the developing embryo or fetus when a pregnant female is exposed to that substance.

Terminal velocity. The terminal rate of fall of a particle through a fluid as induced by gravity or other external force; the rate at which frictional drag balances the accelerating force (or the external force).

Tetanus. A disease of sudden onset caused by the toxin of the bacterium called *Clostridium tetani*. It is characterized by muscle spasms. Also called lockjaw.

Therm. A quantity of heat equivalent to 100,000 Btu.

Thermal pollution. Discharge of heat into bodies of water to the point that the increased warmth activates all sewage, depletes the oxygen the water must have to cleanse itself, and eventually destroys some of the fish and other organisms in the water. Eventually, thermal pollution makes the water smell and taste bad.

Thermonuclear reaction. A fusion reaction, that is, a reaction in which two light nuclei combine to form a heavier atom, releasing a large amount of energy. This is believed to be the sun's source of energy. It is called thermonuclear because it occurs only at a very high temperature.

Thermoplastic. Capable of being repeatedly softened by heat.

Thermoplastic plastics. Plastics that can repeatedly melt or that soften with heat and harden on cooling. Examples: vinyls, acrylics, and polyethylene.

Thermosetting. Capable of undergoing a chemical change from a soft to a hardened substance when heated.

Thermosetting plastics. Plastics that are heat-set in their final processing to a permanently hard state. Examples are phenolics, ureas, and melamines.

Thermostable. Resistant to changes by heat.

Thinner. A liquid used to increase the fluidity of paints, varnishes, and shellac.

Threshold. The level where the first effects occur; also, the point at which a person begins to notice a tone becoming audible.

Thromb- (prefix). Pertaining to a blood clot.

Time-weighted average concentration (TWA). Refers to concentrations of airborne toxic materials weighted for a certain time duration, usually eight hours.

Tinning. Any work with tin such as tin roofing; in particular, in soldering, the primary coating with solder of the two surfaces to be united.

Tinnitus. A perception of sound arising in the head. Most often perceived as a ringing or hissing sound in the ears. Can be the result of high frequency hearing loss.

Tissue. A large group of similar cells bound together to form a structural component. An organ is composed of several kinds of tissue, and in this respect it differs from a tissue as a machine differs from its parts.

TLV®. Threshold Limit Value. A time-weighted average concentration under which most people can work consistently for eight hours a day, day after day, with no harmful effects. A table of these values and accompanying precautions is published annually by the American Conference of Governmental Industrial Hygienists. See Appendix B.

Tolerance. (1) The ability of the living organism to resist the usually anticipated stress. (2) The limits of permissible inaccuracy in the fabrication of an article above and below its design specifications.

Tolerance dose. See Maximum permissible concentration and MPL.

Toluene, $C_6H_5CH_3$. Hydrocarbon derived mainly from petroleum but also from coal. Source of TNT, lacquers, saccharin, and many other chemicals.

Tone deafness. The inability to discriminate between fundamental tones close together in pitch.

Tonometer. Ophthalmic device used to measure eyeball pressure.

Topography. Configuration of a surface, including its relief and the position of its natural and man-made features.

Total pressure. The algebraic sum of the velocity pressure and the static pressure (with due regard to sign).

Toxemia. Poisoning by the way of the bloodstream.

Toxicant. A poison or poisonous agent.

Toxin. A poisonous substance derived from an organism.

Tracer. A radioisotope mixed with a stable material. The radioisotope enables scientists to trace the material as it undergoes chemical and physical changes. Tracers are used widely in science, industry, and agriculture today. When radioactive phosphorus, for example, is mixed with a chemical fertilizer, the radioactive substance can be traced through the plant as it grows.

Trachea. The windpipe, or tube that conducts air to and from the lungs. It extends between the larynx above and the point where it divides into two bronchi below.

Trade name. The commercial name or trademark by which a chemical is known. One chemical may have a variety of trade names depending on the manufacturing or distributors involved.

Transducer. Any device or element that converts an input signal into an output signal of a different form; examples include the microphone, phonograph pickup, loudspeaker, barometer, photoelectric cell, automobile horn, doorbell, and underwater sound transducer.

Transmission Electron Microscopy (TEM). A method of analyzing and quantifying samples for the presence of asbestos. Unlike light microscopy, TEM can definitively distinguish between asbestos fibers and other types of fibers. TEM also has a far higher resolution than light microscopy methods. However, since with TEM asbestos is quantified as number of structures rather than fibers per cubic centimeter, TEM results cannot be directly compared to the Permissible Exposure Limit of 0.1 fiber/cc.

Transmission loss. The ratio, expressed in decibels, of the sound energy incident on a structure to the sound energy that is transmitted. The term is applied both to building structures (walls, floors, etc.) and to air passages (muffler, ducts, etc.).

Transmutation. Any nuclear process that involves a change in energy or identity of the nucleus.

Transport (conveying) velocity. Minimum air velocity required to move the suspended particulates in the airstream.

Trauma. An injury or wound brought about by an outside force.

Tremor. Involuntary shaking, trembling, or quivering.

Triceps. The large muscle at the back of the upper arm that extends the forearm when contracted.

Tridymite. Vitreous, colorless form of free silica formed when quartz is heated to 1,598°F (870°C).

Trigger finger. Also known as snapping finger, a condition of partial obstruction in flexion or extension of a finger. Once past the point of obstruction, movement is eased. Caused by constriction of the tendon sheath.

Tripoli. Rottenstone. A porous, siliceous rock resulting from the decomposition of chert or siliceous limestone. Used as a base in soap and scouring powders, in metal polishing, as a filtering agent, and in wood and paint fillers. A cryptocrystalline form of free silica.

Tritium. Often called hydrogen-3, extra-heavy hydrogen whose nucleus contains two neutrons and one proton. It is three times as heavy as ordinary hydrogen and is radioactive.

Tuberculosis. A contagious disease caused by infection with the bacterium *Mycobacterium tuberculosis*. It usually affects the lung, but bone, lymph glands, and other tissues may be affected.

Tularemia. A bacterial infection of wild rodents, such as rabbits. It may be generalized or localized in the eyes, skin, lymph nodes, or respiratory tract. It can be transmitted to humans.

Tumbling. An industrial process, as in founding, in which small castings are cleaned by friction in a revolving drum (tumbling mill, tumbling barrel), which may contain sand, sawdust, stone, etc.

Turbid. Cloudy.

Turbidity. Cloudiness; disturbances of solids (sediment) in a solution, so that it is not clear.

Turbinates. A series of scroll-like bones in the nasal cavity that serves to increase the amount of tissue surface exposed in the nose, permitting incoming air to be moistened and warmed prior to reaching the lungs. Also called conchae.

Turbulence loss. The pressure or energy lost from a ventilation system through air turbulence.

Turning vanes. Curved pieces added to elbows or fan inlet boxes to direct air and so reduce turbulence losses.

TWA. Time-weighted average.

Tympanic cavity. Another name for the chamber of the middle ear.

U

UCL. Upper confidence limit.

Ulcer. The destruction of an area of skin or mucous membrane.

Ulceration. The formation or development of an ulcer.

Ulna. One of the two bones of the forearm. It forms the hinge joint at the elbow and does not rotate about its longitudinal axis. It terminates at the wrist on the same side as the little finger. Task design should not impose thrust loads through the ulna.

Ulnar deviation. A position of the hand in which the angle on the little finger side of the hand with the corresponding side of the forearm is decreased. Ulnar deviation is a poor working position for the hand and may cause nerve and tendon damage.

Ultrafines. Naturally occurring or manufactured particles in the nanoscale size range.

Ultrasonics. The technology of sound at frequencies above the audio range.

Ultraviolet. Wavelengths of the electromagnetic spectrum that are shorter than those of visible light and longer than x rays, 10^{-5} cm to 10^{-6} cm wavelength.

Unstable. Refers to all radioactive elements, because they emit particles and decay to form other elements.

Unstable (reactive) liquid. A liquid that in the pure state or as commercially produced or transported, vigorously polymerizes, decomposes, condenses, or becomes self-reactive under conditions of shocks, pressure, or temperature.

Upper confidence limit (UCL). In sampling analysis, a statistical procedure used to estimate the likelihood that a particular value is above the obtained value.

Upper explosive limit (UEL). The highest concentration (expressed as the percentage of vapor or gas in the air by volume) of a substance that will burn or explode when an ignition source is present.

Uranium. A heavy metal. The two principal isotopes of natural uranium are U-235 and U-238. U-235 has the only readily fissionable nucleus, which occurs in appreciable quantities in nature—hence its importance as nuclear fuel. Only one part in 140 of natural uranium is U-235. Highly toxic and a radiation hazard that requires special consideration.

Urethr-, urethro- (prefix). Relating to the urethra, the canal leading from the bladder for discharge of urine.

Urticaria. Hives.

USC. United States Code. The official compilation of federal statutes. New editions are issued approximately every 6 years. Cumulative supplements are issued annually.

V

Vaccine. A suspension of disease-producing microorganisms modified by killing or attenuation so that it does not cause disease and can facilitate the formation of antibodies upon inoculation into humans or animals.

Valence. A number indicating the capacity of an atom and certain groups of atoms to hold others in combination. The term also is used in more complex senses.

Valve (air oxygen). A device that controls the direction of air or fluid flow or the rate and pressure at which air or fluid is delivered, or both.

Vapor pressure. Pressure (measured in pounds per square inch absolute-psia) exerted by a vapor. If a vapor is kept in confinement over its liquid so that the vapor can accumulate above the liquid (the temperature being held constant), the vapor pressure approaches a fixed limit called the maximum (or saturated) vapor pressure, dependent only on the temperature and the liquid.

Vapors. The gaseous form of substances that are normally in the solid or liquid state (at room temperature and pressure). The vapor can be changed back to the solid or liquid state either by increasing the pressure or decreasing the temperature alone. Vapors also diffuse. Evaporation is the process by which a liquid is changed to the vapor state and mixed with the surrounding air. Solvents with low boiling points volatilize readily.

Vapor volume. The number of cubic feet of pure solvent vapor formed by the evaporation of one gallon of liquid at 75°F (24°C).

Vasoconstriction. Decrease in the cross-sectional area of blood vessels. This may result from contraction of a muscle layer within the walls of the vessels or may be the result of mechanical pressure. Reduction in blood flow results.

Vat dyes. Water-insoluble, complex coal tar dyes that can be chemically reduced in a heated solution to a soluble form that can impregnate fibers. Subsequent oxidation then produces insoluble color dyestuffs that are remarkably fast to washing, light, and chemicals.

Vector. (1) Term applied to an insect or any living carrier that transports a pathogenic microorganism from the sick to the well, inoculating the latter; the organism may or may not pass through any developmental cycle. (2) Any quantity (for example, velocity, mechanical force, electromotive force) having magnitude, direction, and sense that can be represented by a straight line of appropriate length and direction.

Velocity. A vector that specifies the time rate of change of displacement with respect to a reference.

Velocity, capture. The air velocity required to draw contaminants into the hood.

Velocity, face. The inward air velocity in the plane of openings into an enclosure.

Velocity pressure. The kinetic pressure in the direction of flow necessary to cause a fluid at rest to flow at a given velocity. When added to static pressure, it gives total pressure.

Velometer. A device for measuring air velocity.

Vena contracta. The reduction in the diameter of a flowing airstream at hood entries and other locations.

Veni-, veno- (prefix). Relating to the veins.

Ventilation. One of the principal methods to control health hazards, may be defined as causing fresh air to circu-

late to replace foul air simultaneously removed.

Ventilation, dilution. Airflow designed to dilute contaminants to acceptable levels. Also called general ventilation.

Ventilation, local exhaust. Ventilation near the point of generation of a contaminant.

Ventilation, mechanical. Air movement caused by a fan or other air-moving device.

Ventilation, natural. Air movement caused by wind, temperature difference, or other nonmechanical factors.

Vermiculite. An expanded mica (hydrated magnesium-aluminum-iron silicate) used in lightweight aggregates, insulation, fertilizer, and soil conditioners; as a filler in rubber and paints; and as a catalyst carrier.

Vertigo. Dizziness; more exactly, the sensation that the environment is revolving around you.

Vesicant. Anything that produces blisters on the skin.

Vesicle. A small blister on the skin.

Vestibular. Relating to the cavity at the entrance to the semicircular canals of the inner ears.

Viable. Living.

Vibration. An oscillation motion about an equilibrium position produced by a disturbing force.

Vinyl. A general term applied to a class of resins such as polyvinyl chloride, acetate, butyryl, etc.

Virulence. The capacity of a microorganism to produce disease.

Virulent. Extremely poisonous or venomous; capable of overcoming bodily defensive mechanisms.

Viruses. A group of pathogens consisting mostly of nucleic acids and lacking cellular structure.

Viscera. Internal organs of the abdomen.

Viscose. Term applied to viscous liquid composed of cellulose xanthate.

Viscose rayon. The type of rayon produced from the reaction of carbon disulfide with cellulose and the hardening of the resulting viscous fluid by passing it through dilute sulfuric acid, this final operation causing the evolution of hydrogen sulfide gas.

Viscosity. The property of a fluid that resists internal flow by releasing counteracting forces.

Viscosity, absolute. A measure of a fluid's tendency to resist flow, without regard to density. The product of a fluid's kinematic viscosity times its density, expressed in dyne-seconds per centimeter or poises (or pascal-seconds).

Viscosity, kinematic. The relative tendency of a fluid to resist flow. The value of the kinematic viscosity is equal to the absolute viscosity of the fluid divided by the fluid density and is expressed in units of stoke (or square meters per second).

Visible radiation. The wavelengths of the electromagnetic spectrum between 10^{-4} cm and 10^{-5} cm.

Vision, photopic. Vision attributed to cone function characterized by the ability to discriminate colors and small details; daylight vision.

Vision, scotopic. Vision attributed to rod function characterized by the lack of ability to discriminate colors and small details and effective primarily in the detection of movement and low luminous intensities; night vision.

Visual acuity. Ability of the eye to sharply perceive the shapes of objects in the direct line of vision.

Vitreous humor. Jellylike fluid behind the lens of the eye.

Volatility. The tendency or ability of a liquid to vaporize. Such liquids as alcohol and gasoline, because of their well-known tendency to evaporate rapidly, are called volatile liquids.

Volume flow rate. The quantity (measured in units of volume) of a fluid flowing per unit of time, such as cubic feet per minute, gallons per hour, or cubic meters per second.

Volume, specific. The volume occupied by one pound of a substance under specified conditions of temperature and pressure.

Volumetric analysis. A statement of the various components of a substance (usually applied to gases only), expressed in percentages by volume.

Vulcanization. The process of combining rubber (natural, synthetic, or latex) with sulfur and accelerators in the presence of zinc oxide under heat and usually pressure in order to change the material permanently, from a thermoplastic to a thermosetting composition, or from a plastic to an elastic condition. Strength, elasticity, and abrasion resistance also are improved.

Vulcanizer. A machine in which raw rubber that has been mixed with chemicals is cured by heat and pressure to render it less plastic and more durable.

W

WAN. Wide-area network of linked computers or LANs, whose elements are usually geographically distant.

Wart. A characteristic growth on the skin, appearing most often on the fingers; generally regarded as a result of a virus infection. Synonym: verruca.

Water column. A unit used in measuring pressure. See also Inches of water column.

Water curtain or waterfall booth. A term with many different meanings in industry; but in spray painting, a stream of water running down a wall into which the excess paint spray is drawn or blown by fans, and which carries the paint downward to a collecting point.

Waterproofing agents. Usually formulations of three distinct materials: a coating material, a solvent, and a plasticizer. Among the materials used in waterproofing are cellulose esters and ether, polyvinyl chloride resins or acetates, and variations of vinyl chloride-vinylidine chloride polymers.

Watt (W). A unit of power equal to one joule per second. See Erg.

Watts/cm^2. A unit of power density used in measuring the amount of power per area of absorbing surface, or per area of a CW laser beam.

Wavelength. The distance in the line of advance of a wave from any point to a like point on the next wave. It is usually measured in angstroms, microns, or nanometers.

Weight. The force with which a body is attracted toward the earth. Although the weight of a body varies with its location, the weights of various standards of mass are often used as units of force. See Force.

Weighting network (sound). Electrical networks (A, B, C) associated with sound level meters. The C network provides a flat response over the frequency range 20–10,000 Hz; the B and A networks selectively discriminate against low (less than 1 kHz) frequencies.

Weld. A localized coalescence of metals or nonmetals produced either by heating the materials to suitable temperatures, with or without the application of pressure, or by the application of pressure alone, and with or without the use of filler material.

Welding. The several types of welding are electric arc-welding, oxyacetylene welding, spot welding, and inert or shielded gas welding using helium or argon. The hazards involved in welding stem from the fumes from the weld metal such as lead or cadmium metal, the gases created by the process, and the fumes or gases arising from the flux.

Welding rod. A rod or heavy wire that is melted and fused to metals in arc-welding.

Wet-bulb globe temperature (WBGT) index. An index of the heat stress in humans when work is being performed in a hot environment.

Wet-bulb temperature. Temperature as determined by the wet-bulb thermometer or a standard sling psychrometer or its equivalent. This temperature is influenced by the evaporation rate of the water, which in turn depends on the humidity (amount of water vapor) in the air.

Wet-bulb thermometer. A thermometer having the bulb covered with a cloth saturated with water.

Wheatstone bridge. A type of electrical circuit used in one type of combustible gas monitor. Combustion of small quantities of the ambient gas are detected as changes in electrical resistivity by this circuitry.

White damp. In mining, carbon monoxide.

White noise. A noise whose spectrum density (or spectrum level) is substantially independent of frequency over a specified range.

Wide band. Applied to a wide band of transmitted waves, with neither of the critical or cutoff frequencies of the filter being zero or infinite.

Work. When a force acts against resistance to produce motion in a body, the force is said to do work. Work is measured by the product of the force acting and the distance moved against the resistance. The units of measurement are the erg (a joule is 1×10^7 ergs) and the foot-pound.

Work hardening. The property of metal to become harder and more brittle on being worked (bent repeatedly or drawn).

Work strain. The natural physiological response of the body to the application of work stress. The locus of the reaction may be remote from the point of application of work stress. Work strain is not necessarily traumatic but may appear as trauma when excessive, either directly or cumulatively, and must be considered by the industrial engineer in equipment and task design.

Work stress. Biomechanically, any external force acting on the body during the performance of a task. It always produces work strain. Application of work stress to the human body is the inevitable consequence of performance of any task, and is therefore synonymous with stressful work conditions only when excessive. Work stress analysis is an integral part of task design.

Working level (WL). Any combination of radon daughters in one liter of air that result in the ultimate emission of 1.3×10^5 MeV of alpha energy.

X

Xanth- (prefix). Yellow.

Xero- (prefix). Indicated dryness, as in *xerostomia,* dryness of the mouth.

Xeroderma. Dry skin; may be rough as well as dry.

X rays. Highly penetrating radiation similar to gamma-rays. Unlike gamma-rays, x rays do not come from the nucleus of the atom but from the surrounding electrons. They are produced by electron bombardment. When these rays pass through an object, they give a shadow picture of the denser portions.

X-ray diffraction. Because all crystals act as three-dimensional gratings for x rays, the pattern of diffracted rays is characteristic for each crystalline material. This method is of particular value in determining the presence or absence of crystalline silica in an industrial dust.

X-ray tube. Any electron tube designed for the conversion of electrical energy into x-ray energy.

Z

Z. Symbol for atomic number. An element's atomic number is the same as the number of protons found in one of its nuclei. All isotopes of a given element have the same Z number.

Zinc protoporphyrin (ZPP). Hematopoietic enzyme used as a measure of recent lead exposure.

Zoonoses. Diseases biologically adapted to and normally found in lower animals, but that under some conditions also infect humans.

Zygote. Cell produced by the joining of two gametes (sex or germ cells).

INDEX

Notes

Notes

Notes